Skills in
Mathematics for
**JEE Main &
Advanced**

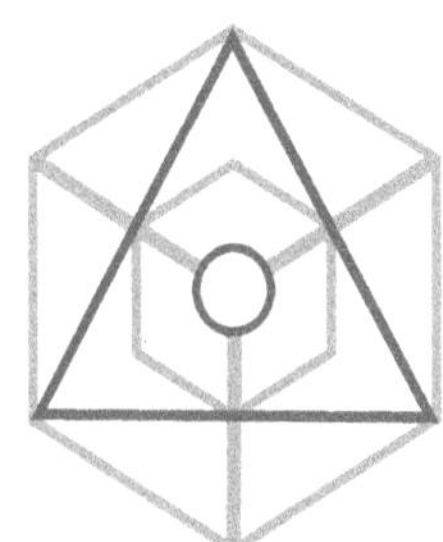

Coordinate Geometry

With Sessionwise Theory & Exercises...

Skills in Mathematics for
JEE Main & Advanced

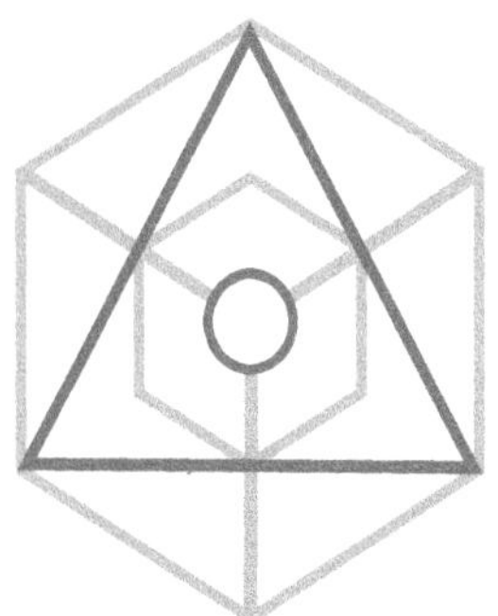

Coordinate Geometry

With Sessionwise Theory & Exercises...

Dr. SK Goyal

ARIHANT PRAKASHAN (Series), MEERUT

ARIHANT PRAKASHAN (Series), MEERUT

卐 Administrative & Production Offices

Regd. Office

'Ramchhaya' 4577/15, Agarwal Road, Darya Ganj, New Delhi -110002
Tele: 011- 47630600, 43518550

卐 Head Office

Kalindi, TP Nagar, Meerut (UP) - 250002 Tel: 0121-7156203, 7156204

卐 Sales & Support Offices

Agra, Ahmedabad, Bengaluru, Bareilly, Chennai, Delhi, Guwahati, Hyderabad, Jaipur, Jhansi, Kolkata, Lucknow, Nagpur & Pune.

卐 ISBN : 978-93-26191-61-6

卐 PRICE : ₹565.00

PO No : TXT-XX-XXXXXXX-X-XX

Published by Arihant Publications (India) Ltd.

For further information about the books published by Arihant, log on to www.arihantbooks.com or e-mail at info@arihantbooks.com

Follow us on   

PREFACE

IF YOU CONTINUOUSLY PUT YOUR EFFORTS ON AN ASPECT, YOU HAVE VERY GOOD CHANCE TO GET POSITIVE OUTCOME i.e. ***SUCCESS***

It is a matter of great pride and honour for me to have received such an overwhelming response to the previous editions of this book from the readers. In a way, this has inspired me to revise this book thoroughly as per the changed pattern of JEE Main & Advanced. I have tried to make the contents more relevant as per the needs of students, many topics have been re-written, a lot of new problems of new types have been added in etcetc. All possible efforts are made to remove all the printing errors that had crept in previous editions. The book is now in such a shape that the students would feel at ease while going through the problems, which will in turn clear their concepts too.

A Summary of changes that have been made in Revised & Enlarged Edition

- Theory has been completely updated so as to accommodate all the changes made in JEE Syllabus & Pattern in recent years.
- The most important point about this new edition is, now the whole text matter of each chapter has been divided into small sessions with exercise in each session. In this way the reader will be able to go through the whole chapter in a systematic way.
- Just after completion of theory, Solved Examples of all JEE types have been given, providing the students a complete understanding of all the formats of JEE questions & the level of difficulty of questions generally asked in JEE.
- Along with exercises given with each session, a complete cumulative exercises have been given at the end of each chapter so as to give the students complete practice for JEE along with the assessment of knowledge that they have gained with the study of the chapter.
- Previous Years questions asked in JEE Main & Adv, IIT-JEE & AIEEE have been covered in all the chapters.

However I have made the best efforts and put my all Coordinate Geometry teaching experience in revising this book. Still I am looking forward to get the valuable suggestions and criticism from my own fraternity i.e. the fraternity of JEE teachers.

I would also like to motivate the students to send their suggestions or the changes that they want to be incorporated in this book. All the suggestions given by you all will be kept in prime focus at the time of next revision of the book.

Dr. SK Goyal

CONTENTS

SYLLABUS

JEE MAIN

Cartesian system of rectangular coordinates in a plane, distance formula, section formula, locus and its equation, translation of axes, slope of a line, parallel and perpendicular lines, intercepts of a line on the coordinate axes.

Straight Lines

Various forms of equations of a line, intersection of lines, angles between two lines, conditions for concurrence of three lines, distance of a point from a line, equations of internal and external bisectors of angles between two lines, coordinates of centroid, orthocentre and circumcentre of a triangle, equation of family of lines passing through the point of intersection of two lines.

Circles, Conic Sections

Standard form of equation of a circle, general form of the equation of a circle, its radius and centre, equation of a circle when the end points of a diameter are given, points of intersection of a line and a circle with the centre at the origin and condition for a line to be tangent to a circle, equation of the tangent. Sections of cones, equations of conic sections (parabola, ellipse and hyperbola) in standard forms, condition for $y=mx+c$ to be a tangent and point (s) of tangency.

JEE ADVANCED

Coordinate Geometry

Cartesian coordinates, distance between two points, section formulae, shift of origin.
Equation of a straight line in various forms, angle between two lines, distance of a point from a line; Lines through the point of intersection of two given lines, equation of the bisector of the angle between two lines, concurrency of lines; Centroid, orthocentre, incentre and circumcentre of a triangle.
Equation of a circle in various forms, equations of tangent, normal and chord. Parametric equations of a circle, intersection of a circle with a straight line or a circle, equation of a circle through the points of intersection of two circles and those of a circle and a straight line.
Equations of a parabola, ellipse and hyperbola in standard form, their foci, directrices and eccentricity, parametric equations, equations of tangent and normal.
Locus problems.

CHAPTER

01

Coordinate System and Coordinates

Learning Part

Session 1

- Introduction
- Coordinate Axes
- Rectangular Cartesian Coordinates of a Point
- Polar Coordinates of a Point
- Relation between the Polar and Cartesian Coordinates

Session 2

- Distance between Two Points
- Choice of Axes
- Distance between Two Points in Polar Coordinates

Session 3

- Section formulae
- Centroid of a Triangle
- Incentre
- Some Standard Results
- Area of Triangle

Session 4

- Locus and Its Equation
- Change of Axes or the Transformations of Axes
- Removal of the Term xy from $F(x, y) = ax^2 + 2hxy + by^2$ without Changing the Origin
- Position of a Point Which Lies Inside a Triangle

Practice Part

- JEE Type Examples
- Chapter Exercises

Arihant on Your Mobile !

Exercises with the symbol can be practised on your mobile. See inside cover page to activate for free.

Session 1

Introduction, Coordinate Axes, Rectangular Cartesian Coordinates of a Point, Polar Coordinates of a Point, Relation between the Polar and Cartesian Coordinates

Introduction

The great philospher and mathematician of France **Rane Descartes** (1596-1665) published a book 'La Geometric' in 1637.

Descartes gave a new idea i.e. each point in a plane is expressed by an ordered pair of algebraic real numbers like $(x, y), (r, \theta)$ etc., called coordinates of the point.

The point (x, y) is called cartesian coordinates and (r, θ) is called polar coordinates of the point. Then represents different forms of equations which are developed for all types of straight lines and curves.

Thus the Coordinate Geometry (or Analytical Geometry) is that branch of mathematics in which geometrical problems are solved with the help of Algebra.

Coordinate Axes

The position of a point in a plane is determined with reference to two intersecting straight lines called the **coordinate axes** and their point of intersection is called the **origin** of coordinates.

If these two axes of reference (generally we call them x and y axes) cut each other at right angle, they are called **rectangular axes** otherwise they are called **oblique axes**. The axes divide the coordinate plane in four quadrants.

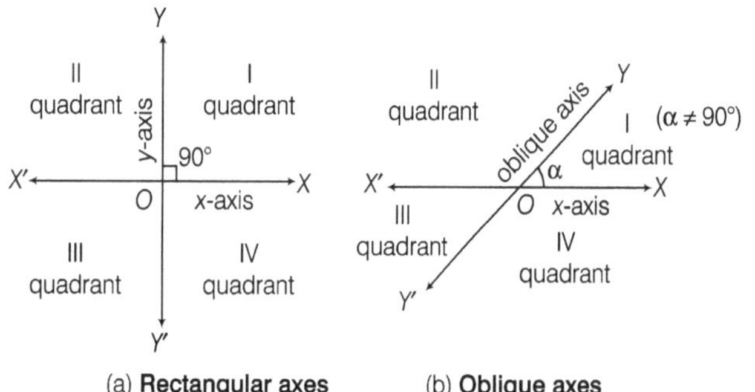

(a) **Rectangular axes** (b) **Oblique axes**

Rectangular Cartesian Coordinates of a Point

Let $X'OX$ and $Y'OY$ be two perpendicular axes in the plane of paper intersecting at O. Let P be any point in the plane of the paper. Draw PM perpendicular to OX. Then the lengths OM and PM are called the rectangular cartesian coordinates or briefly the coordinates of P.

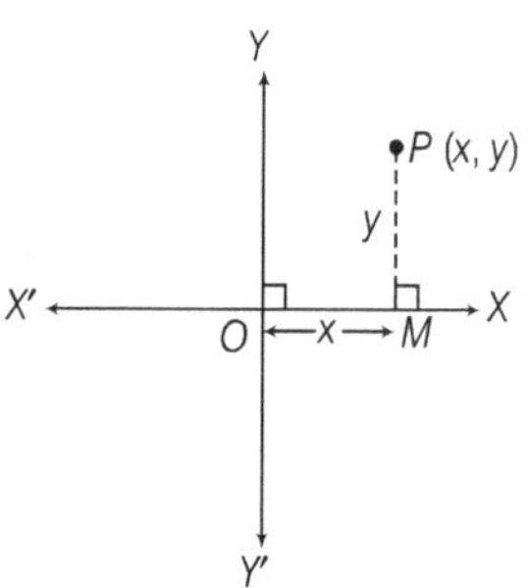

Let $OM = x$ and $MP = y$

Then, the position of the point P in the plane with respect to the coordinate axes is represented by the ordered pair (x, y). The ordered pair (x, y) is called the coordinates of point P.

i.e. $OM = x$-coordinate or abscissa of the point P

and $MP = y$-coordinate or ordinate of the point P.

Remarks

1. The ordinate of every point on X-axis is 0.
2. The abscissa of every point on Y-axis is 0.
3. The abscissa and ordinate of the origin $O(0, 0)$ are both zero.
4. The abscissa and ordinate of a point are at perpendicular distance from Y-axis and X-axis respectively.
5. Table for conversion sign of coordinates :

Quadrants	XOY (I)	$X'OY$ (II)	$X'OY'$ (III)	XOY' (IV)
Sign of x coordinates	+	−	−	+
Sign of y coordinates	+	+	−	−
Sign of (x, y)	$(+, +)$	$(-, +)$	$(-, -)$	$(+, -)$

6. Equation of X-axis, $y = 0$ and equation of Y-axis, $x = 0$.

Polar Coordinates of a Point

If $\qquad OP = r \qquad$ (radius vector)

and $\qquad \angle XOP = \theta \qquad$ (vectorial angle)

Then, the ordered pair of real numbers (r, θ) called the polar coordinates of the point P.

Remarks

1. r may be positive or negative according as θ is measured in anticlockwise or clockwise direction. θ lies between $-\pi$ to π i.e. $-\pi < \theta \le \pi$. If it is greater than π, then we subtract 2π from it and if it is less than $-\pi$, then we add 2π, to it. It is also known as principal value of P.
2. Always taken θ in radian.

Example 1. Draw the polar coordinates $\left(2, \frac{\pi}{3}\right), \left(-2, \frac{\pi}{3}\right), \left(-2, -\frac{\pi}{3}\right)$ and $\left(2, -\frac{\pi}{3}\right)$ on the plane.

Sol.

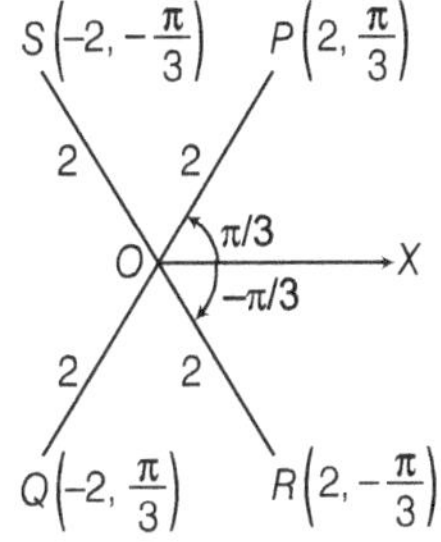

Example 2. Draw the polar coordinate $\left(3, \frac{5\pi}{4}\right)$ on the plane.

Sol. Here, $\qquad \theta = \frac{5\pi}{4} > \pi$

then, $\qquad \theta - 2\pi = \frac{5\pi}{4} - 2\pi = -\frac{3\pi}{4}$

$\therefore \left(3, \frac{5\pi}{4}\right)$ is same $\left(3, -\frac{3\pi}{4}\right)$

Relation between the Polar and Cartesian Coordinates

Let $P(x, y)$ be the cartesian coordinates with respect to axes OX and OY and (r, θ) be its polar coordinates with respect to pole O and initial line OX.

It is clear from figure

$$OM = x = r\cos\theta \qquad \text{...(i)}$$

and

$$MP = y = r\sin\theta \qquad \text{...(ii)}$$

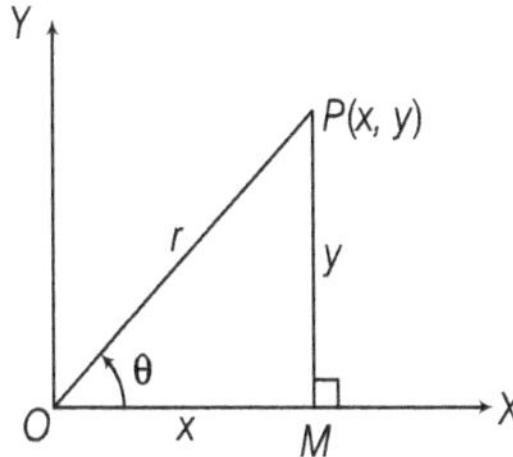

Squaring and adding Eqs. (i) and (ii), we get

$$x^2 + y^2 = r^2 \quad \text{or} \quad r = \sqrt{(x^2 + y^2)}$$

Dividing Eqs. (ii) by (i), then

$$\tan\theta = \left(\frac{y}{x}\right) \quad \text{or} \quad \theta = \tan^{-1}\left(\frac{y}{x}\right)$$

i.e. $\qquad (r\cos\theta, r\sin\theta) \Rightarrow (x, y) \qquad$ ...(iii)

and $\qquad \left(\sqrt{(x^2 + y^2)}, \tan^{-1}\left(\frac{y}{x}\right)\right) \Rightarrow (r, \theta) \qquad$ ...(iv)

If r and θ are known then we can find (x, y) from Eq. (iii) and if x and y are known then we can find (r, θ) from Eq. (iv).

$\because \qquad \theta = \tan^{-1}\left(\frac{y}{x}\right)$

If $\qquad \alpha = \tan^{-1}\left|\frac{y}{x}\right|$

Then, values of θ in four quadrants

Quadrant	I	II	III	IV
θ	α	$\pi - \alpha$	$-\pi + \alpha$	$-\alpha$

Example 3. Find the cartesian coordinates of the points whose polar coordinates are

(i) $\left(5, \pi - \tan^{-1}\left(\frac{4}{3}\right)\right)$ $\qquad$ (ii) $\left(5\sqrt{2}, \frac{\pi}{4}\right)$

Sol. (i) Given, $r = 5, \theta = \pi - \tan^{-1}\left(\frac{4}{3}\right)$

Now, $x = r\cos\theta = 5\cos\left(\pi - \tan^{-1}\left(\frac{4}{3}\right)\right)$

$= -5\cos\left(\tan^{-1}\left(\frac{4}{3}\right)\right)$

$= -5\cos\left(\cos^{-1}\left(\frac{3}{5}\right)\right) = -5\times\frac{3}{5} = -3$

and $y = r\sin\theta = 5\sin\left(\pi - \tan^{-1}\left(\frac{4}{3}\right)\right)$

$= 5\sin\left(\tan^{-1}\left(\frac{4}{3}\right)\right)$

$= 5\sin\left(\sin^{-1}\left(\frac{4}{5}\right)\right) = 5\times\frac{4}{5} = 4$

Hence, cartesian coordinates of the given point will be $(-3, 4)$.

(ii) Given, $r = 5\sqrt{2}, \theta = \frac{\pi}{4}$

Now, $x = r\cos\theta = 5\sqrt{2}\cos\left(\frac{\pi}{4}\right) = 5\sqrt{2}\times\frac{1}{\sqrt{2}} = 5$

and $y = r\sin\theta = 5\sqrt{2}\sin\left(\frac{\pi}{4}\right) = 5\sqrt{2}\times\frac{1}{\sqrt{2}} = 5$

Hence, cartesian coordinates of the given point, will be $(5, 5)$.

Example 4. Find the polar coordinates of the points whose cartesian coordinates are

(i) $(-2, -2)$ (ii) $(-3, 4)$

Sol. (i) Given, $x = -2, y = -2$

$\therefore$ $r = \sqrt{(x^2 + y^2)} = \sqrt{(4+4)} = 2\sqrt{2}$

and $\alpha = \tan^{-1}\left|\frac{y}{x}\right| = \tan^{-1}\left|\frac{-2}{-2}\right| = \tan^{-1}1 = \frac{\pi}{4}$

Since, point $(-2, -2)$ lies in III quadrant.

$\therefore$ $\theta = -\pi + \alpha = -\pi + \frac{\pi}{4} = -\frac{3\pi}{4}$

Hence, polar coordinates of the given points will be $\left(2\sqrt{2}, -\frac{3\pi}{4}\right)$.

Remark : If we find θ, from the equation,

$$\tan\theta = \frac{y}{x} = \frac{-2}{-2} = 1$$

then, $\theta = \frac{\pi}{4}$ and then

$$(x, y) = (r\cos\theta, r\sin\theta) = \left(2\sqrt{2}\times\frac{1}{\sqrt{2}}, 2\sqrt{2}\times\frac{1}{\sqrt{2}}\right)$$

$$= (2, 2) \neq (-2, -2)$$

(ii) Given, $x = -3, y = 4$

$\therefore$ $r = \sqrt{(x^2 + y^2)} = \sqrt{(9+16)} = 5$

and $\alpha = \tan^{-1}\left|\frac{y}{x}\right| = \tan^{-1}\left|\frac{4}{-3}\right| = \tan^{-1}\left(\frac{4}{3}\right)$

Since, point $(-3, 4)$ lies in II quadrant

$\therefore$ $\theta = \pi - \alpha = \pi - \tan^{-1}\left(\frac{4}{3}\right)$

Hence, polar coordinates of the given points, will be $\left(5, \pi - \tan^{-1}\left(\frac{4}{3}\right)\right)$.

Example 5. Transform the equation $r^2 = a^2\cos 2\theta$ into cartesian form.

Sol. $\because$ $r = \sqrt{(x^2 + y^2)}$ and $\theta = \tan^{-1}\left(\frac{y}{x}\right)$

or $r^2 = (x^2 + y^2)$ and $\tan\theta = \frac{y}{x}$

Given, $r^2 = a^2\cos 2\theta = a^2\left(\frac{1-\tan^2\theta}{1+\tan^2\theta}\right)$

or $(x^2 + y^2) = a^2\left(\frac{1 - \frac{y^2}{x^2}}{1 + \frac{y^2}{x^2}}\right)$

or $(x^2 + y^2)^2 = a^2(x^2 - y^2)$

This is the required equation in cartesian form.

Aliter :

$r^2 = a^2\cos 2\theta$

or $r^2 = a^2(\cos^2\theta - \sin^2\theta)$

$\because$ $x = r\cos\theta$ and $y = r\sin\theta$

and $r^2 = x^2 + y^2$

then $r^2 = a^2\left(\frac{x^2}{r^2} - \frac{y^2}{r^2}\right)$

or $r^4 = a^2(x^2 - y^2)$

or $(x^2 + y^2)^2 = a^2(x^2 - y^2)$.

Example 6. Transform the equation $x^2 + y^2 = ax$ into polar form.

Sol. $\because$ $x = r\cos\theta, y = r\sin\theta$

Given, $x^2 + y^2 = ax$

$\Rightarrow$ $r^2 = a(r\cos\theta)$

or $r = a\cos\theta$

This is the required equation in polar form.

Exercise for Session 1

1. The polar coordinates of the point whose cartesian coordinates are $(-1, -1)$ is

(a) $\left(\sqrt{2}, \frac{\pi}{4}\right)$ (b) $\left(\sqrt{2}, \frac{3\pi}{4}\right)$ (c) $\left(\sqrt{2}, -\frac{\pi}{4}\right)$ (d) $\left(\sqrt{2}, -\frac{3\pi}{4}\right)$

2. The cartesian coordinates of the point whose polar coordinates are $\left(13, \pi - \tan^{-1}\left(\frac{5}{12}\right)\right)$ is

(a) $(12, 5)$ (b) $(-12, 5)$ (c) $(-12, -5)$ (d) $(12, -5)$

3. The transform equation of $r^2 \cos^2 \theta = a^2 \cos 2\theta$ to cartesian form is $(x^2 + y^2) x^2 = a^2\lambda$, then value of λ is

(a) $y^2 - x^2$ (b) $x^2 - y^2$ (c) xy (d) x^2y^2

4. The coordinates of P' in the figure is

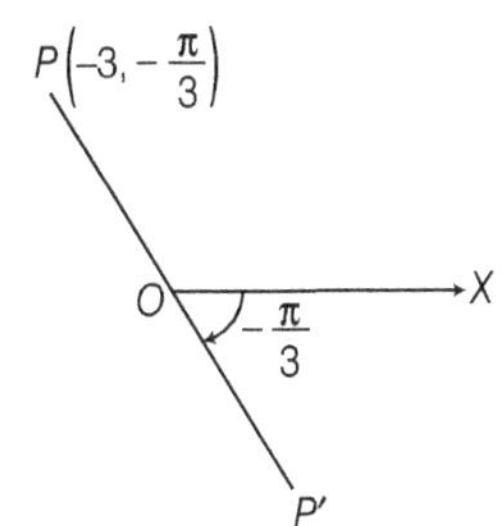

(a) $\left(3, \frac{\pi}{3}\right)$ (b) $\left(3, -\frac{\pi}{3}\right)$ (c) $\left(-3, -\frac{\pi}{3}\right)$ (d) $\left(-3, \frac{\pi}{3}\right)$

5. The cartesian coordinates of the point Q in the figure is

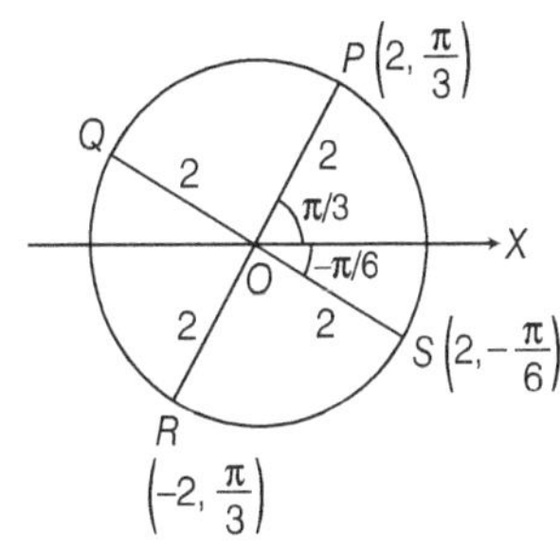

(a) $(\sqrt{3}, 1)$ (b) $(-\sqrt{3}, 1)$ (c) $(-\sqrt{3}, -1)$ (d) $(\sqrt{3}, -1)$

6. A point lies on X-axis at a distance 5 units from Y-axis. What are its coordinates ?

7. A point lies on *Y-axis at a distance 4 units from* X-axis. What are its coordinates ?

8. A point lies on negative direction of X-axis at a distance 6 units from Y-axis. What are its coordinates ?

9. Transform the equation $y = x \tan\alpha$ to polar form.

10. Transform the equation $r = 2a \cos\theta$ to cartesian form.

Session 2

Distance between Two Points, Choice of Axes, Distance between Two Points in Polar Coordinates

Distance Between Two Points

Theorem : The distance between two points $P(x_1, y_1)$ and $Q(x_2, y_2)$ is given by

$$|PQ| = \sqrt{(x_2 - x_1)^2 + (y_2 - y_1)^2}$$

Proof : Let $P(x_1, y_1)$ and $Q(x_2, y_2)$ be any two points in the plane. Let us assume that the points P and Q are both in 1st quadrant (for the sake of exactness).

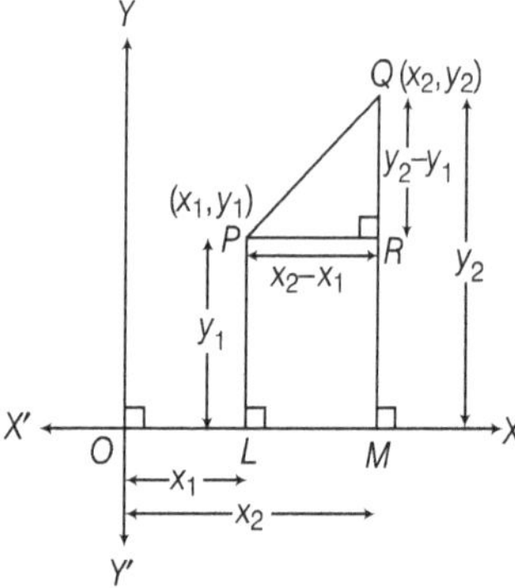

From P and Q draw PL and QM perpendiculars to X-axis. From P draw PR perpendicular to QM and join PQ. Then

$$OL = x_1, OM = x_2, PL = y_1, QM = y_2$$

$\therefore \quad PR = LM = OM - OL = x_2 - x_1$

and $\quad QR = QM - RM = QM - PL = y_2 - y_1$

Since, PRQ is a right angled triangle, therefore by pythagoras theorem.

$$(PQ)^2 = (PR)^2 + (QR)^2$$

$\therefore \quad |PQ| = \sqrt{(PR)^2 + (QR)^2}$ ($\because PQ$ is always positive)

$$= \sqrt{(x_2 - x_1)^2 + (y_2 - y_1)^2}$$

$\therefore$ The distance PQ between the points $P(x_1, y_1)$ and $Q(x_2, y_2)$ is given by $\sqrt{(x_2 - x_1)^2 + (y_2 - y_1)^2}$

or $\sqrt{(\text{difference in x coordinates})^2 + (\text{difference in y coordinates})^2}$

or $\sqrt{(\text{difference of abscissaes})^2 + (\text{difference of ordinates})^2}$

Notations : We shall denote the distance between two points P and Q of the coordinate plane, either by $|PQ|$ or by $\overline{PQ}$.

***Corollary* 1 :** The above formula is true for all positions of the points (i.e. either point or both points are not in the 1st quadrant) keeping in mind, the proper signs of their coordinates.

***Corollary* 2 :** The distance of the point $P(x, y)$ from the origin $O(0, 0)$ is given by

$$|OP| = \sqrt{(x - 0)^2 + (y - 0)^2} = \sqrt{(x^2 + y^2)}$$

***Corollary* 3 :** The above formula can also be used as

$$\sqrt{(x_1 - x_2)^2 + (y_1 - y_2)^2}$$

***Corollary* 4 :** (i) If PQ is parallel to X-axis, then $y_1 = y_2$ and so

$$|PQ| = \sqrt{(x_2 - x_1)^2} = |x_2 - x_1|$$

(ii) If PQ is parallel to Y-axis, then $x_1 = x_2$ and so

$$|PQ| = \sqrt{(y_2 - y_1)^2} = |y_2 - y_1|$$

***Corollary* 5 :** If distance between two points is given, then use $\pm$ sign.

Remarks

1. If three points $A(x_1, y_1)$, $B(x_2, y_2)$ and $C(x_3, y_3)$ are collinear, then $\quad |AB| \pm |BC| = |AC|$

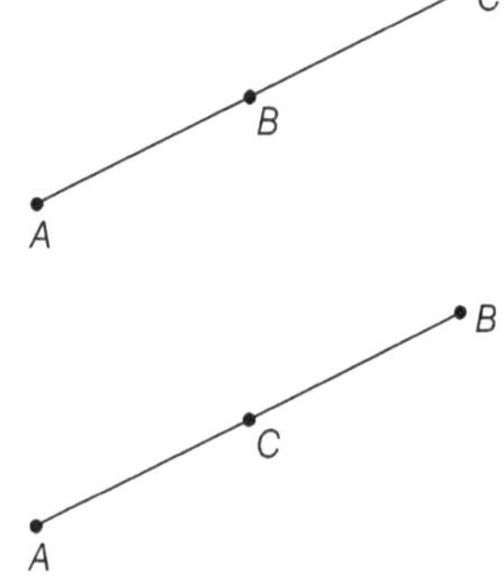

2. When three points are given and it is required to :

(i) an **Isosceles triangle**, show that two of its sides (or two angles) are equal.

(ii) an **Equilateral triangle**, show that its all sides are equal or each angle is of 60°.

(iii) a **Right angle triangle**, show that the sum of the squares of two sides is equal to the square of the third side.

(iv) an **Isosceles right angled triangle**, show that two of its sides are equal and the sum of the squares of two equal sides is equal to the square of the third side.

(v) a **Scalene triangle**, show that its all sides are unequal.

3. When four points are given and it is required to

(i) a **Square**, show that the four sides are equal and the diagonals are also equal.

(ii) a **Rhombus, (or equilateral trapezium)** show that the four sides are equal and the diagonals are not equal.

(iii) a **Rectangle**, show that the opposite sides are equal and the diagonals are also equal.

(iv) a **Parallelogram**, show that the opposite sides are equal and the diagonals are not equal.

(v) a **Trapezium**, show that the two sides are parallel and the other two sides are not parallel.

(vi) An Isosceles Trapezium, show that the two sides are parallel and the other two sides are not parallel but equal.

4. If A, B, C be the vertices of a triangle and we have to find the coordinates of the circumcentre then, let the circumcentre be $P(x, y)$ and use $PA^2 = PB^2$ and $PA^2 = PC^2$ this will give two equations in x and y then solve these two equations and (x, y).

Important Remarks for Objective Questions

(i) If (x_1, y_1) and (x_2, y_2) are the ends of the hypotenuse of a right angled isosceles triangle, then the third vertex is given by

$$\left(\frac{(x_1+x_2)\pm(y_1-y_2)}{2}, \frac{(y_1+y_2)\mp(x_1-x_2)}{2}\right)$$

(ii) If two vertices of an equilateral triangle are (x_1, y_1) and (x_2, y_2), then coordinates of the third vertex are

$$\left(\frac{x_1+x_2\mp\sqrt{3}(y_2-y_1)}{2}, \frac{y_1+y_2\pm\sqrt{3}(x_2-x_1)}{2}\right)$$

Example 7. Prove that the distance of the point $(a\cos\alpha, a\sin\alpha)$ from the origin is independent of α.

Sol. Let $P \equiv (a\cos\alpha, a\sin\alpha)$ and $O \equiv (0, 0)$

then
$$|OP| = \sqrt{(a\cos\alpha - 0)^2 + (a\sin\alpha - 0)^2}$$
$$= \sqrt{(a^2\cos^2\alpha + a^2\sin^2\alpha)}$$
$$= \sqrt{a^2(\cos^2\alpha + \sin^2\alpha)} = \sqrt{a^2}$$
$$= |a|, \text{ which is independent of } \alpha.$$

Example 8. Find the distance between the points $(a\cos\alpha, a\sin\alpha)$ and $(a\cos\beta, a\sin\beta)$, where $a > 0$.

Sol. Let $P \equiv (a\cos\alpha, a\sin\alpha)$ and $Q \equiv (a\cos\beta, a\sin\beta)$

then
$$|PQ| = \sqrt{(a\cos\alpha - a\cos\beta)^2 + (a\sin\alpha - a\sin\beta)^2}$$
$$= \sqrt{a^2\{(\cos\alpha - \cos\beta)^2 + (\sin\alpha - \sin\beta)^2\}}$$
$$= \sqrt{a^2\{\cos^2\alpha + \cos^2\beta - 2\cos\alpha\cos\beta + \sin^2\alpha + \sin^2\beta - 2\sin\alpha\sin\beta\}}$$
$$= \sqrt{a^2\{1 + 1 - 2(\cos\alpha\cos\beta + \sin\alpha\sin\beta)\}}$$
$$= \sqrt{a^2(2 - 2\cos(\alpha - \beta))}$$
$$= \sqrt{2a^2(1 - \cos(\alpha - \beta))}$$
$$= \sqrt{\left(2a^2 \cdot 2\sin^2\left(\frac{\alpha-\beta}{2}\right)\right)}$$
$$= \sqrt{4a^2\sin^2\left(\frac{\alpha-\beta}{2}\right)}$$
$$= \left|2a\sin\left(\frac{\alpha-\beta}{2}\right)\right|$$
$$= 2a\left|\sin\left(\frac{\alpha-\beta}{2}\right)\right| \qquad (\because a > 0)$$

Example 9. If the point (x, y) be equidistant from the points $(6, -1)$ and $(2, 3)$, prove that $x - y = 3$.

Sol. Let $P \equiv (x, y)$, $A \equiv (6, -1)$ and $B \equiv (2, 3)$

By the given condition, $PA = PB$

$\Rightarrow \quad \sqrt{(x-6)^2 + (y+1)^2} = \sqrt{(x-2)^2 + (y-3)^2}$

or $\quad (x-6)^2 + (y+1)^2 = (x-2)^2 + (y-3)^2$

or $\quad x^2 - 12x + 36 + y^2 + 2y + 1 = x^2 - 4x + 4 + y^2 - 6y + 9$

or $\quad 8x - 8y = 24$

or $\quad x - y = 3$

Example 10. Using distance formula, show that the points $(1, 5)$, $(2, 4)$ and $(3, 3)$ are collinear.

Sol. Let $A \equiv (1, 5)$, $B \equiv (2, 4)$ and $C \equiv (3, 3)$ be the given points, then

$$|AB| = \sqrt{(1-2)^2 + (5-4)^2} = \sqrt{2}$$

√2 C
B
√2
A

$$|BC| = \sqrt{(2-3)^2 + (4-3)^2} = \sqrt{2}$$

and $\quad |AC| = \sqrt{(1-3)^2 + (5-3)^2} = 2\sqrt{2}$

Clearly, $\quad |AB| + |BC| = \sqrt{2} + \sqrt{2} = 2\sqrt{2} = |AC|$.

Hence, A, B, C are collinear.

Example 11. An equilateral triangle has one vertex at the point (0, 0) and another at $(3, \sqrt{3})$. Find the coordinates of the third vertex.

Sol. Let $O \equiv (0, 0)$ and $A \equiv (3, \sqrt{3})$ be the given points and let $B \equiv (x, y)$ be the required point. Then

$$OA = OB = AB$$

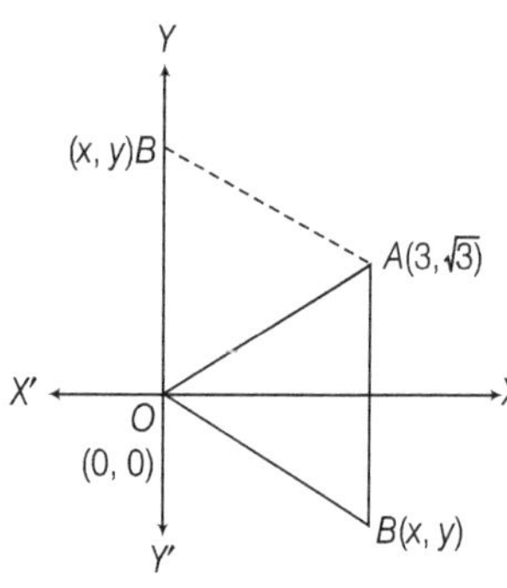

$$\Rightarrow \quad (OA)^2 = (OB)^2 = (AB)^2$$

$$\Rightarrow (3-0)^2 + (\sqrt{3}-0)^2 = (x-0)^2 + (y-0)^2$$

$$= (x-3)^2 + (y-\sqrt{3})^2$$

$$\Rightarrow \quad 12 = x^2 + y^2 = x^2 + y^2 - 6x - 2\sqrt{3}y + 12$$

Taking first two members then

$$x^2 + y^2 = 12 \qquad \ldots(i)$$

and taking last two members, then

$$6x + 2\sqrt{3}y = 12 \text{ or } y = \sqrt{3}(2-x) \qquad \ldots(ii)$$

From Eqs. (i) and (ii), we get

$$x^2 + 3(2-x)^2 = 12$$

or
$$4x^2 - 12x = 0$$

$$\Rightarrow \quad x = 0, 3$$

Putting $x = 0, 3$ in Eq. (ii), we get $y = 2\sqrt{3}, -\sqrt{3}$

Hence, the coordinates of the third vertex B are $(0, 2\sqrt{3})$ or $(3, -\sqrt{3})$.

Short Cut Method : According to important note :

$$\left(\frac{x_1 + x_2 \mp \sqrt{3}(y_2 - y_1)}{2}, \frac{y_1 + y_2 \pm \sqrt{3}(x_2 - x_1)}{2}\right)$$

i.e.
$$\left(\frac{0 + 3 \mp \sqrt{3}(\sqrt{3} - 0)}{2}, \frac{0 + \sqrt{3} \pm \sqrt{3}(3 - 0)}{2}\right)$$

or
$$\left(\frac{3 \mp 3}{2}, \frac{\sqrt{3} \pm 3\sqrt{3}}{2}\right)$$

$$\Rightarrow \quad (0, 2\sqrt{3}) \text{ or } (3, -\sqrt{3})$$

Example 12. Show that four points $(1, -2)$, $(3, 6)$, $(5, 10)$ and $(3, 2)$ are the vertices of a parallelogram.

Sol. Let $A \equiv (1, -2)$, $B \equiv (3, 6)$, $C \equiv (5, 10)$ and $D \equiv (3, 2)$ be the given points. Then

$$|AB| = \sqrt{(1-3)^2 + (-2-6)^2} = \sqrt{4 + 64} = 2\sqrt{17}$$

$$|BC| = \sqrt{(3-5)^2 + (6-10)^2} = \sqrt{4 + 16} = 2\sqrt{5}$$

$$|CD| = \sqrt{(5-3)^2 + (10-2)^2} = \sqrt{4 + 64} = 2\sqrt{17}$$

$$|AD| = \sqrt{(1-3)^2 + (-2-2)^2} = \sqrt{4 + 16} = 2\sqrt{5}$$

$$|AC| = \sqrt{(1-5)^2 + (-2-10)^2} = \sqrt{16 + 144} = 4\sqrt{10}$$

and
$$|BD| = \sqrt{(3-3)^2 + (6-2)^2} = 4$$

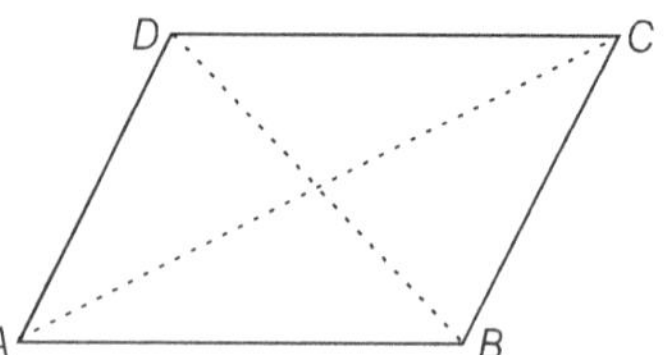

Clearly, $|AB| = |CD|$, $|BC| = |AD|$ and $|AC| \neq |BD|$

Hence, $ABCD$ is a parallelogram.

Example 13. Let the opposite angular points of a square be $(3, 4)$ and $(1, -1)$. Find the coordinates of the remaining angular points.

Sol. Let $A(3, 4)$ and $C(1, -1)$ be the given angular points of a square $ABCD$ and let $B(x, y)$ be the unknown vertex. Then

$$AB = BC$$

$$\Rightarrow \quad (AB)^2 = (BC)^2$$

$$\Rightarrow \quad (x-3)^2 + (y-4)^2 = (x-1)^2 + (y+1)^2$$

$$\Rightarrow \quad 4x + 10y - 23 = 0$$

$$\Rightarrow \quad x = \left(\frac{23 - 10y}{4}\right) \qquad \ldots(i)$$

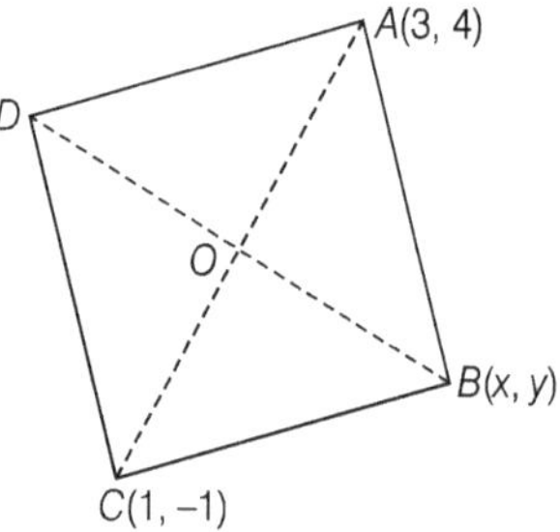

Also, in ΔABC,

$$(AB)^2 + (BC)^2 = (AC)^2$$

$$\Rightarrow \quad (x-3)^2 + (y-4)^2 + (x-1)^2 + (y+1)^2$$

$$= (3-1)^2 + (4+1)^2$$

$$\Rightarrow \quad x^2 + y^2 - 4x - 3y - 1 = 0 \qquad \ldots(ii)$$

Substituting the value of x from Eqs. (i) into (ii), we get

$$\left(\frac{23 - 10y}{4}\right)^2 + y^2 - 4\left(\frac{23 - 10y}{4}\right) - 3y - 1 = 0$$

$$\Rightarrow \quad 4y^2 - 12y + 5 = 0$$

or
$$(2y - 1)(2y - 5) = 0$$

$$\therefore \quad y = \frac{1}{2} \text{ or } \frac{5}{2}$$

Putting $y = \frac{1}{2}$ in Eq. (i), we get $x = \frac{9}{2}$,

and putting $y = \frac{5}{2}$ in Eq. (i), we get $x = -\frac{1}{2}$

Hence, the required vertices of the square are $\left(\frac{9}{2}, \frac{1}{2}\right)$ and $\left(-\frac{1}{2}, \frac{5}{2}\right)$.

Example 14. Find the circumcentre of the triangle whose vertices are $(-2, -3)$, $(-1, 0)$ and $(7, -6)$. Also find the radius of the circumcircle.

Sol. Let $A \equiv (-2, -3)$, $B \equiv (-1, 0)$ and $C \equiv (7, -6)$.

Let $P \equiv (x, y)$ be the circumcentre of ΔABC.

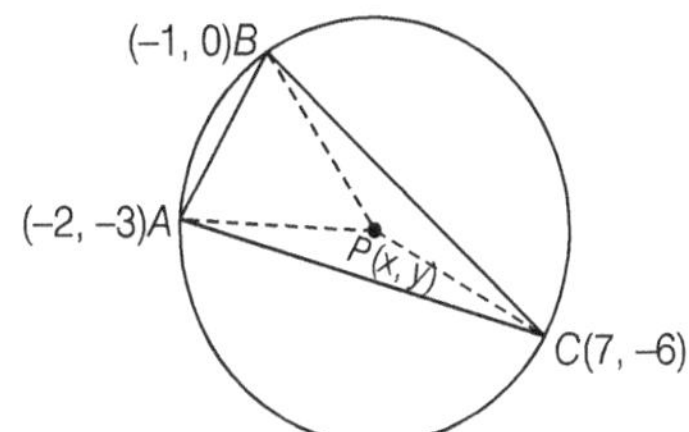

Since, P is the circumcentre

$\therefore \quad |PA| = |PB| = |PC| \Rightarrow (PA)^2 = (PB)^2 = (PC)^2$

$$(x+2)^2 + (y+3)^2 = (x+1)^2 + (y-0)^2$$
$$= (x-7)^2 + (y+6)^2$$

$$\Rightarrow \quad x^2 + y^2 + 4x + 6y + 13 = x^2 + y^2 + 2x + 1$$
$$= x^2 + y^2 - 14x + 12y + 85$$

Taking first two members, we get

$$x + 3y + 6 = 0 \quad \text{...(i)}$$

and taking 1st and last member then, we get

$$3x - y - 12 = 0 \quad \text{...(ii)}$$

Solving Eqs. (i) and (ii), we get

$$x = 3, y = -3$$

Hence, circumcentre is $(3, -3)$.

Radius of the circumcircle

$$= PB = \sqrt{(3+1)^2 + (-3-0)^2}$$
$$= \sqrt{16+9} = 5 \text{ units}$$

Example 15. If the line segment joining the points $A(a, b)$ and $B(c, d)$ subtends an angle θ at the origin O, prove that

$$\cos\theta = \frac{ac+bd}{\sqrt{(a^2+b^2)(c^2+d^2)}}$$

or $\quad OA.OB\cos\theta = ac + bd$

Sol. Let $OA = r_1$ and $OB = r_2$

Now, $\quad r_1 = |OA| = \sqrt{(a^2+b^2)} \quad \text{...(i)}$

and $\quad r_2 = |OB| = \sqrt{(c^2+d^2)} \quad \text{...(ii)}$

Also, $\quad |AB| = \sqrt{(a-c)^2 + (b-d)^2}$

$$= \sqrt{a^2 + b^2 + c^2 + d^2 - 2ac - 2bd}$$

$$= \sqrt{r_1^2 + r_2^2 - 2(ac+bd)} \quad \text{[from Eqs. (i) and (ii)]}$$

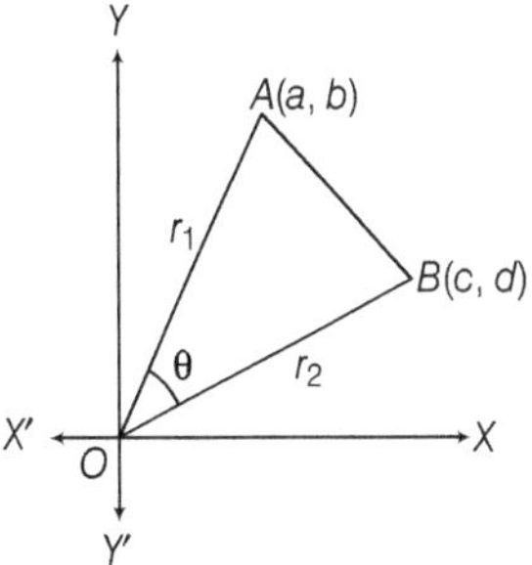

By using **Cosine formula** in ΔAOB

$$\cos\theta = \frac{(OA)^2 + (OB)^2 - (AB)^2}{2 \cdot OA \cdot OB}$$

$$= \frac{r_1^2 + r_2^2 - (r_1^2 + r_2^2 - 2(ac+bd))}{2r_1 r_2}$$

$$= \frac{2(ac+bd)}{2r_1 r_2} = \frac{(ac+bd)}{r_1 r_2} \quad \text{...(iii)}$$

$$= \frac{(ac+bd)}{\sqrt{(a^2+b^2)}\sqrt{(c^2+d^2)}} \quad \text{[from Eqs. (i) and (ii)]}$$

$$= \frac{(ac+bd)}{\sqrt{(a^2+b^2)(c^2+d^2)}}$$

Also from Eq. (iii),

$$r_1 r_2 \cos\theta = ac + bd \quad \text{or} \quad OA.OB\cos\theta = ac + bd$$

Choice of Axes

For simplification we carefully choose the axes or the origin. Some situations are given below :

(i) If two lines are perpendicular then point of intersection is taken as origin and these lines must be taken as the coordinate axes.

(ii) If two fixed points A and B are given then we take $|AB| = 2a$ and the mid-point of AB as origin 'O', line AOB as X-axis and the line perpendicular to AB through O is taken as Y-axis then the coordinates of the fixed points are $(\pm a, 0)$. Similarly if AOB as Y-axis and the line perpendicular to AB through O is taken as X-axis then the coordinates of the fixed points are $(0, \pm a)$.

(iii) If there is a symmetry of any kind then take the coordinates of the points in a general way i.e. (x_i, y_i), $i = 1, 2, 3, \ldots$ etc.

Example 16. Show that the triangle, the coordinates of whose vertices are given by integers, can never be an equilateral triangle.

Sol. Let $A \equiv (0, 0)$, $B \equiv (a, 0)$ and $C \equiv (b, c)$ be the vertices of equilateral triangle ABC where a, b, c are integers then,

$$|AB| = |BC| = |CA|$$

$$\Rightarrow \quad (AB)^2 = (BC)^2 = (CA)^2$$

$$\Rightarrow \quad a^2 = (a-b)^2 + c^2 = b^2 + c^2$$

From first two members, we get

$$b^2 + c^2 = 2ab \quad \text{...(i)}$$

and taking first and third members, then

$$b^2 + c^2 = a^2 \quad \text{...(ii)}$$

From Eqs. (i) and (ii) we get

$$a = 2b \quad (\because a \neq 0)$$

From Eq. (ii), $b^2 + c^2 = (2b)^2$

or $\quad c^2 = 3b^2$

or $\quad c = \pm b\sqrt{3}$

which is impossible, since b and c are integers.

Example 17. In any triangle ABC, show that

$$AB^2 + AC^2 = 2(AD^2 + BD^2)$$

where, D is the middle point of BC.

Sol. Let D as the origin and DC and DY as the X and Y-axes respectively. Let $BC = 2a$, then

$$B \equiv (-a, 0),\ C \equiv (a, 0) \text{ and let } A \equiv (b, c)$$

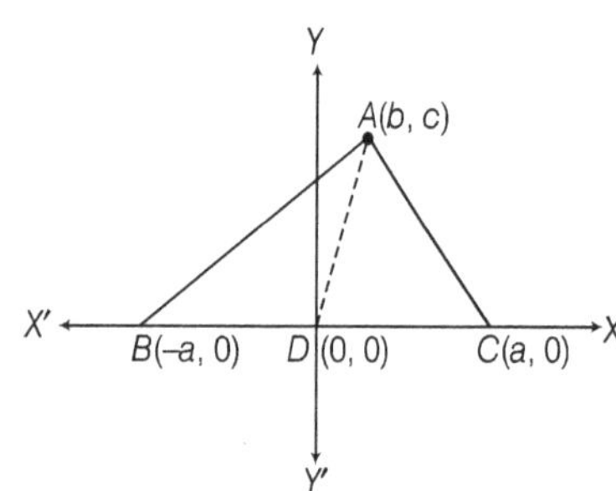

Now, $\quad \text{LHS} = AB^2 + AC^2$

$$= (b+a)^2 + (c-0)^2 + (b-a)^2 + (c-0)^2$$

$$= 2(a^2 + b^2 + c^2) \quad \text{...(i)}$$

and $\quad \text{RHS} = 2(AD^2 + BD^2)$

$$= 2\{(b-0)^2 + (c-0)^2 + a^2\}$$

$$= 2(a^2 + b^2 + c^2) \quad \text{...(ii)}$$

From Eqs. (i) and (ii), we get

$$AB^2 + AC^2 = 2(AD^2 + BD^2)$$

Example 18. Let $ABCD$ be a rectangle and P be any point in its plane. Show that $PA^2 + PC^2 = PB^2 + PD^2$

Sol. Let A as the origin and AB and AD as the X and Y-axes respectively. Let $AB = a$ and $AD = b$, then

$$B \equiv (a, 0),\ D \equiv (0, b) \text{ and } C \equiv (a, b)$$

Let $\quad P \equiv (\alpha, \beta)$

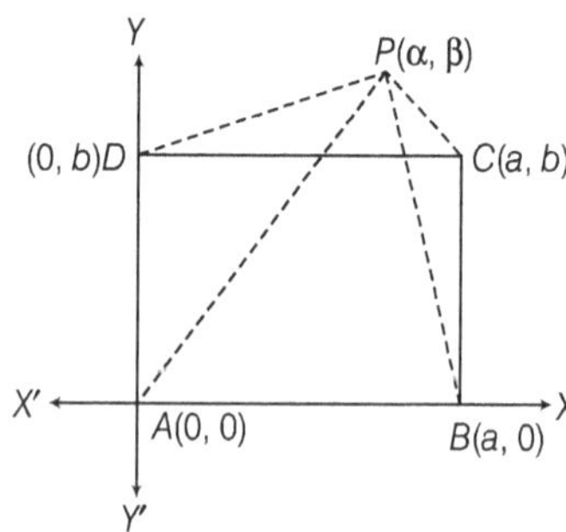

Now, $\text{LHS} = PA^2 + PC^2$

$$= (\alpha - 0)^2 + (\beta - 0)^2 + (\alpha - a)^2 + (\beta - b)^2$$

$$= 2\alpha^2 + 2\beta^2 - 2a\alpha - 2b\beta + a^2 + b^2 \quad \text{...(i)}$$

and $\quad \text{RHS} = PB^2 + PD^2$

$$= (\alpha - a)^2 + (\beta - 0)^2 + (\alpha - 0)^2 + (\beta - b)^2$$

$$= 2\alpha^2 + 2\beta^2 - 2a\alpha - 2b\beta + a^2 + b^2 \quad \text{...(ii)}$$

From Eqs. (i) and (ii), we get

$$PA^2 + PC^2 = PB^2 + PD^2$$

Distance between Two Points in Polar Coordinates

Let O be the pole and OX be the initial line. Let P and Q be two given points whose polar coordinates are (r_1, θ_1) and (r_2, θ_2) respectively.

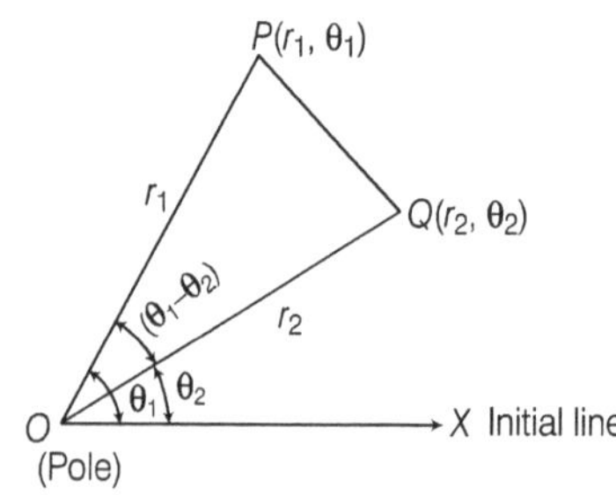

Then, $\quad OP = r_1,\ OQ = r_2$

and $\quad \angle POX = \theta_1,\ \angle QOX = \theta_2$

$\therefore \quad \angle POQ = \theta_1 - \theta_2$

By using **Cosine formula** in ΔPOQ,

$$\cos(\angle POQ) = \frac{(OP)^2 + (OQ)^2 - (PQ)^2}{2(OP)(OQ)}$$

or $$\cos(\theta_1 - \theta_2) = \frac{r_1^2 + r_2^2 - (PQ)^2}{2\,r_1 r_2}$$

$\therefore$ $$|PQ| = \sqrt{(r_1^2 + r_2^2 - 2\,r_1 r_2 \cos(\theta_1 - \theta_2))}$$

Remark

Always taking θ_1 and θ_2 in radians.

Example 19. Prove that the points $(0,0)$, $\left(3, \frac{\pi}{2}\right)$ and $\left(3, \frac{\pi}{6}\right)$ are the vertices of an equilateral triangle.

Sol. Let $A \equiv (0, 0)$, $B \equiv \left(3, \frac{\pi}{2}\right)$ and $C \equiv \left(3, \frac{\pi}{6}\right)$

Here, given coordinates are in polar form

$\therefore$ $$|AB| = \sqrt{\left(0^2 + 3^2 - 2\cdot 0\cdot 3 \cos\left(\frac{\pi}{2} - 0\right)\right)} = 3 \text{ units}$$

$$|BC| = \sqrt{\left(3^2 + 3^2 - 2\cdot 3\cdot 3 \cos\left(\frac{\pi}{2} - \frac{\pi}{6}\right)\right)}$$

$$= \sqrt{\left(18 - 18 \sin\frac{\pi}{6}\right)} = \sqrt{(18 - 9)} = 3 \text{ units}$$

and $$|CA| = \sqrt{\left(3^2 + 0^2 - 2\cdot 3\cdot 0 \cos\left(\frac{\pi}{6} - 0\right)\right)} = 3 \text{ units}$$

$\therefore$ $$|AB| = |BC| = |CA|$$

Hence, points A, B, C are the vertices of an equilateral triangle.

Aliter :

$\because$ $$\angle BAX = \frac{\pi}{2}$$

and $$\angle CAX = \frac{\pi}{6}$$

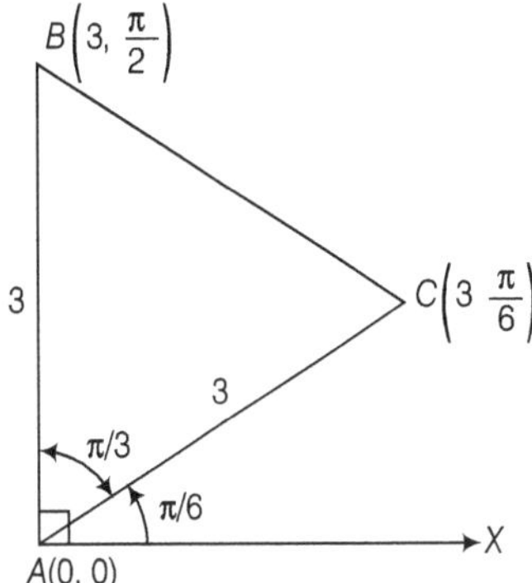

$\therefore$ $$\angle BAC = \frac{\pi}{2} - \frac{\pi}{6} = \frac{\pi}{3}$$

$\because$ In $\Delta\, ABC$

$$AB = AC$$

$\therefore$ $$\angle ACB = \angle ABC = \alpha \quad \text{(say)}$$

$\therefore$ $$\alpha + \alpha + \frac{\pi}{3} = \pi$$

or $$\alpha = \frac{\pi}{3}$$

Hence, $$|AB| = |BC| = |CA|.$$

Exercise for Session 2

1. If the distance between the points $(a, 2)$ and $(3, 4)$ be 8, then a equals to

(a) $2 + 3\sqrt{15}$ (b) $2 - 3\sqrt{15}$ (c) $2 \pm 3\sqrt{15}$ (d) $3 \pm 2\sqrt{15}$

2. The three points $(-2, 2)$, $(8, -2)$ and $(-4, -3)$ are the vertices of

(a) an isosceles triangle (b) an equilateral triangle (c) a right angled triangle (d) None of these

3. The distance between the points $\left(3, \frac{\pi}{4}\right)$ and $\left(7, \frac{5\pi}{4}\right)$ is

(a) 8 (b) 10 (c) 12 (d) 14

4. Let $A(6, -1)$, $B(1, 3)$ and $C(x, 8)$ be three points such that $AB = BC$, then the value of x are

(a) 3, 5 (b) −3, 5 (c) 3, −5 (d) −3, −5

5. The points $(a + 1, 1)$, $(2a + 1, 3)$ and $(2a + 2, 2a)$ are collinear, if

(a) $a = -1, 2$ (b) $a = \frac{1}{2}, 2$ (c) $a = 2, 1$ (d) $a = -\frac{1}{2}, 2$

6. If $A \equiv (3, 4)$ and B is a variable point on the lines $|x| = 6$. If $AB \le 4$ then the number of positions of B with integral coordinates is

(a) 5 (b) 6 (c) 10 (d) 12

7. The number of points on X-axis which are at a distance c units $(c < 3)$ from $(2, 3)$ is

(a) 1 (b) 2 (c) 0 (d) 3

8. The point on the axis of y which its equidistant from $(-1, 2)$ and $(3, 4)$, is

(a) (0, 3) (b) (0, 4) (c) (0, 5) (d) (0, −6)

9. Find the distance between the points $(at_1^2, 2at_1)$ and $(at_2^2, 2at_2)$, where t_1 and t_2 are the roots of the equation $x^2 - 2\sqrt{3}x + 2 = 0$ and $a > 0$.

10. If $P(at^2, 2at)$, $Q\left(\frac{a}{t^2}, -\frac{2a}{t}\right)$ and $S(a, 0)$ be any three points, show that $\frac{1}{SP} + \frac{1}{SQ}$ is independent of t.

11. Prove that the points $(3, 4)$, $(8, -6)$ and $(13, 9)$ are the vertices of a right angled triangle.

12. Show that the points $(0, -1)$, $(6, 7)$, $(-2, 3)$ and $(8, 3)$ are the vertices of a rectangle.

13. Find the circumcentre and circumradius of the triangle whose vertices are $(-2, 3)$, $(2, -1)$ and $(4, 0)$.

14. The vertices of a triangle are $A(1, 1)$, $B(4, 5)$ and $C(6, 13)$. Find $\cos A$.

15. Two opposite vertices of a square are $(2, 6)$ and $(0, -2)$. Find the coordinates of the other vertices.

16. If the point (x, y) is equidistant from the points $(a + b, b - a)$ and $(a - b, a + b)$, prove that $bx = ay$.

17. If a and b are real numbers between 0 and 1 such that the points $(a, 1)$, $(1, b)$ and $(0, 0)$ form an equilateral triangle, find a and b.

18. An equilateral triangle has one vertex at $(3, 4)$ and another at $(-2, 3)$. Find the coordinates of the third vertex.

19. If P be any point in the plane of square $ABCD$, prove that

$$PA^2 + PC^2 = PB^2 + PD^2$$

Session 3

Section Formula, Centroid of a Triangle, Incentre, Some Standard Results, Area of Triangle

Section Formula

Definition : If P be any point on the line AB between A and B then we say that P divides segment AB *internally* in the ratio $AP : PB$.

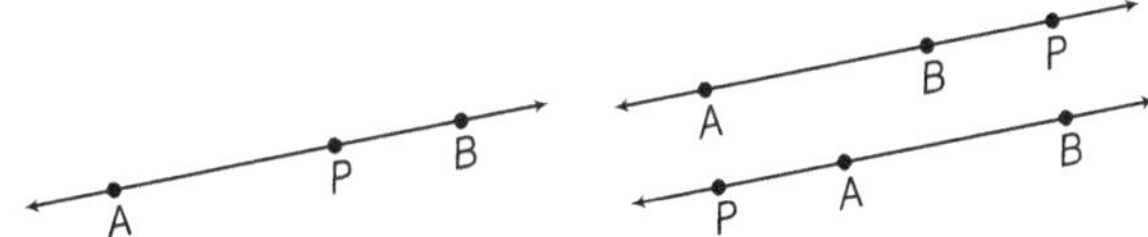

Also, if P be any point on the line AB but not between A and B (P may be to the right or the left of the points A, B) then P divides AB *externally* in the ratio $AP : PB$

> ***Note***
>
> $\frac{AP}{PB} = \begin{cases} \text{Positive, in internally division} \\ \text{Negative, in externally division} \end{cases}$

(i) Formula for Internal Division

Theorem : If the point $P(x, y)$ divides the line segment joining the points $A(x_1, y_1)$ and $B(x_2, y_2)$ internally in the ratio $m : n$, then prove that

$$x = \frac{mx_2 + nx_1}{m+n}$$

$$y = \frac{my_2 + ny_1}{m+n}$$

Proof : The given points are $A(x_1, y_1)$ and $B(x_2, y_2)$. Let us assume that the points A and B are both in 1st quadrant (for the sake of exactness). Since $P(x, y)$ divides AB internally in the ratio $m : n$ i.e. $AP : PB = m : n$. From A, B and P draw AL, BM and PN perpendiculars to X-axis. From A and P draw AH and PJ perpendiculars to PN and BM respectively, then

$OL = x_1, ON = x, OM = x_2, AL = y_1, PN = y$ and $BM = y_2$

$$\therefore \quad AH = LN = ON - OL = x - x_1$$

$$PJ = NM = OM - ON = x_2 - x$$

$$PH = PN - HN = PN - AL = y - y_1$$

and $\quad BJ = BM - JM = BM - PN = y_2 - y$

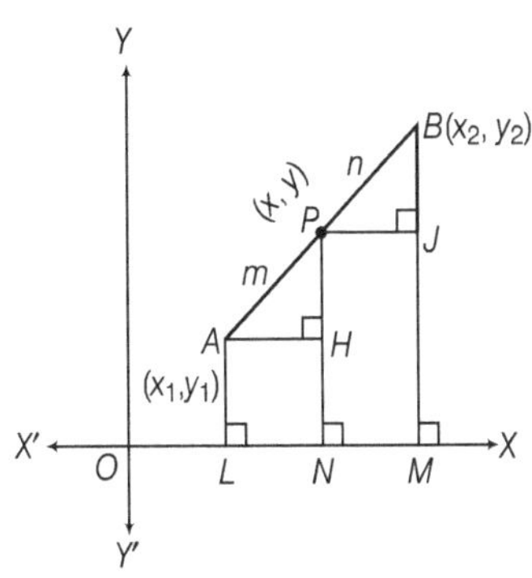

Clearly, the Δs AHP and PJB are similar and therefore, their sides are proportional

$$\therefore \quad \frac{AH}{PJ} = \frac{PH}{BJ} = \frac{AP}{PB}$$

or

$$\underset{\text{(i)}}{\frac{x - x_1}{x_2 - x}} = \underset{\text{(ii)}}{\frac{y - y_1}{y_2 - y}} = \underset{\text{(iii)}}{\frac{m}{n}}$$

From Eqs. (i) and (iii), we have

$$\frac{x - x_1}{x_2 - x} = \frac{m}{n}$$

$$\Rightarrow \quad nx - nx_1 = mx_2 - mx$$

$$\Rightarrow \quad (m+n)x = mx_2 + nx_1$$

$$\therefore \quad x = \frac{mx_2 + nx_1}{m+n}$$

and from Eqs. (ii) and (iii), we have

$$\frac{y - y_1}{y_2 - y} = \frac{m}{n}$$

$$\Rightarrow \quad ny - ny_1 = my_2 - my$$

$$\Rightarrow \quad (m+n)y = my_2 + ny_1$$

$$\therefore \quad y = \frac{my_2 + ny_1}{m+n}$$

Thus, the coordinates of P are

$$\left(\frac{mx_2 + nx_1}{m+n}, \frac{my_2 + ny_1}{m+n}\right)$$

***Corollary* 1 :** The above section formula is true for all positions of the points (i.e. either point or both points are not in the 1st quadrant), keeping in mind, the proper signs of their coordinates.

***Corollary* 2 :** If P is the mid-point of AB then $m = n$, the coordinates of the middle-point of AB are

$$\left(\frac{x_1 + x_2}{2}, \frac{y_1 + y_2}{2}\right)$$

Remarks

1. If $P(\alpha, \beta)$ be the mid-point of AB and if coordinates of A are (λ, μ) then the coordinates of B are $(2\alpha - \lambda, 2\beta - \mu)$, i.e. (Double the x-co-ordinate of mid point – x-coordinate of given point, Double the y-co-ordinate of mid point – y-coordinate of given point).
2. The following diagram will help to remember the section formula.

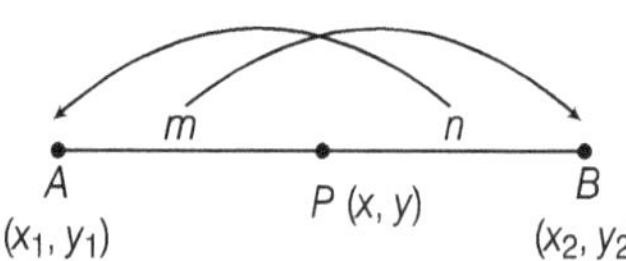

3. For finding ratio, use ratio $\lambda : 1$, then coordinates of P are $\left(\frac{x_1 + \lambda x_2}{1 + \lambda}, \frac{y_1 + \lambda y_2}{1 + \lambda}\right)$. If λ is positive then divides internally and if λ is negative, then divides externally.
4. The straight line $ax + by + c = 0$ divides the joint of points $A(x_1, y_1)$ and $B(x_2, y_2)$ in the ratio

$$\frac{AP}{PB} = \frac{\lambda}{1} = -\frac{(ax_1 + by_1 + c)}{(ax_2 + by_2 + c)}$$

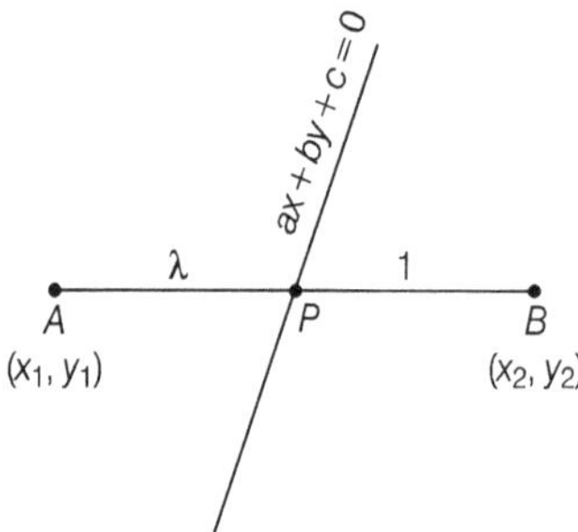

If ratio is positive, then divides internally and if ratio is negative then divides externally.

Proof : Coordinates of P are $\left(\frac{x_1 + \lambda x_2}{1 + \lambda}, \frac{y_1 + \lambda y_2}{1 + \lambda}\right)$

$\because P$ lies on the line $ax + by + c = 0$, then

$$a\left(\frac{x_1 + \lambda x_2}{1 + \lambda}\right) + b\left(\frac{y_1 + \lambda y_2}{1 + \lambda}\right) + c = 0$$

or $$(ax_1 + by_1 + c) + \lambda(ax_2 + by_2 + c) = 0$$

or $$\frac{\lambda}{1} = -\frac{(ax_1 + by_1 + c)}{(ax_2 + by_2 + c)}$$

5. The line joining the points (x_1, y_1) and (x_2, y_2) is divided by the X-axis in the ratio $-\frac{y_1}{y_2}$ and by Y-axis in the ratio $-\frac{x_1}{x_2}$.
6. In square, rhombus, rectangle and parallelogram diagonals bisect to each other.

Example 20. Find the coordinates of the point which divides the line segment joining the points $(5, -2)$ and $(9, 6)$ in the ratio $3 : 1$.

Sol. Let the required point be (x, y), then

$$x = \left(\frac{3 \times 9 + 1 \times 5}{3 + 1}\right) = 8$$

and $$y = \left(\frac{3 \times 6 + 1 \times (-2)}{3 + 1}\right) = 4$$

Thus, the coordinates of the required point are (8, 4).

Example 21. Find the length of median through A of a triangle whose vertices are $A(-1, 3), B(1, -1)$ and $C(5, 1)$.

Sol. Let D be the mid-point of BC, then coordinates of D are $\left(\frac{1+5}{2}, \frac{-1+1}{2}\right)$ i.e. $(3, 0)$

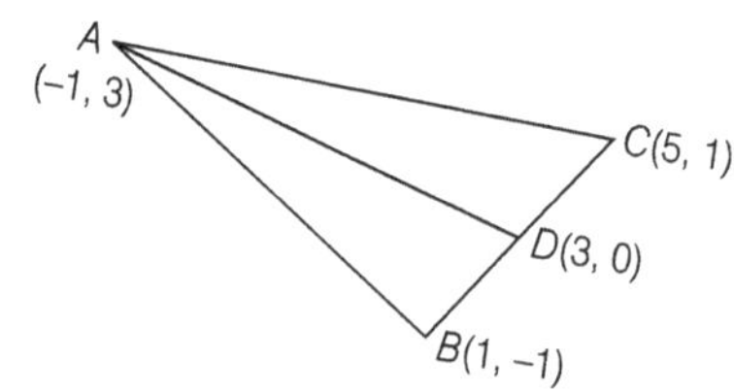

$\therefore$ $$\text{Median } AD = \sqrt{(3+1)^2 + (0-3)^2}$$
$$= \sqrt{16 + 9} = \sqrt{25}$$
$$= 5 \text{ units}$$

Example 22. Determine the ratio in which $y - x + 2 = 0$ divides the line joining $(3, -1)$ and $(8, 9)$.

Sol. Suppose the line $y - x + 2 = 0$ divides the line segment joining $A(3, -1)$ and $B(8, 9)$ in the ratio $\lambda : 1$ at point P, then the coordinates of the point P are $\left(\frac{8\lambda + 3}{\lambda + 1}, \frac{9\lambda - 1}{\lambda + 1}\right)$.

But P lies on $y - x + 2 = 0$ therefore

$$\left(\frac{9\lambda - 1}{\lambda + 1}\right) - \left(\frac{8\lambda + 3}{\lambda + 1}\right) + 2 = 0$$

$$\Rightarrow \quad 9\lambda - 1 - 8\lambda - 3 + 2\lambda + 2 = 0$$

$$\Rightarrow \quad 3\lambda - 2 = 0 \quad \text{or} \quad \lambda = \frac{2}{3}$$

So, the required ratio is $\frac{2}{3} : 1$, i.e. $2 : 3$ (internally) since here λ is positive.

Shortcut method

According to Remark 4 :

$$\lambda = -\left(\frac{-1 - 3 + 2}{9 - 8 + 2}\right) = \frac{2}{3}$$

or $$\lambda : 1 = 2 : 3$$

Example 23. The coordinates of three consecutive vertices of a parallelogram are (1, 3), (−1, 2) and (2, 5). Then find the coordinates of the fourth vertex.

Sol. Let the fourth vertex be $D(\alpha, \beta)$. Since $ABCD$ is a parallelogram, the diagonals bisect to each other.
i.e. mid-point of BD = mid-point of AC

$$\therefore \quad \left(\frac{\alpha-1}{2}, \frac{\beta+2}{2}\right) = \left(\frac{2+1}{2}, \frac{5+3}{2}\right)$$

$$\text{or} \quad \left(\frac{\alpha-1}{2}, \frac{\beta+2}{2}\right) = \left(\frac{3}{2}, 4\right)$$

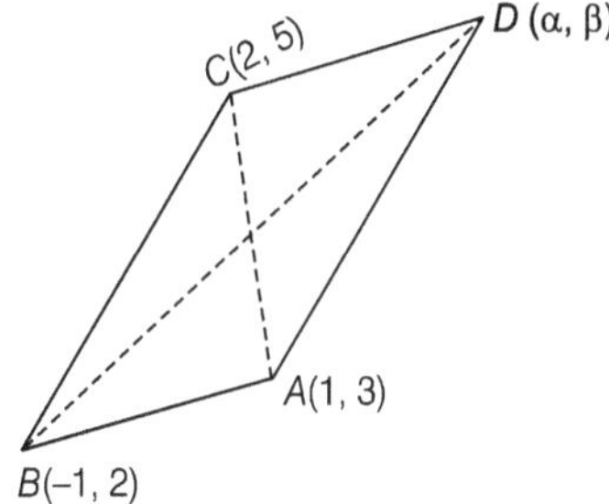

On equating abscissaes and ordinates, we get

$$\frac{\alpha-1}{2} = \frac{3}{2} \quad \text{or} \quad \alpha - 1 = 3 \quad \text{or} \quad \alpha = 4$$

$$\text{and} \quad \frac{\beta+2}{2} = 4 \quad \text{or} \quad \beta + 2 = 8 \quad \text{or} \quad \beta = 6$$

Hence, the coordinates of the fourth vertex $D(\alpha, \beta)$ is (4, 6).

Example 24. In what ratio does X-axis divide the line segment joining (2, − 3) and (5, 6)?

Sol. Let the given points be $A(2, -3)$ and $B(5, 6)$. Let AB be divided by the X-axis at $P(x, 0)$ in the ratio $\lambda : 1$ internally. Considering the ordinate of P, then

$$0 = \frac{\lambda \times 6 + 1 \times (-3)}{\lambda + 1}$$

$$\text{or} \quad \lambda = \frac{1}{2}$$

$\therefore$ The ratio is $\frac{1}{2} : 1$ i.e. 1 : 2 (Internally)

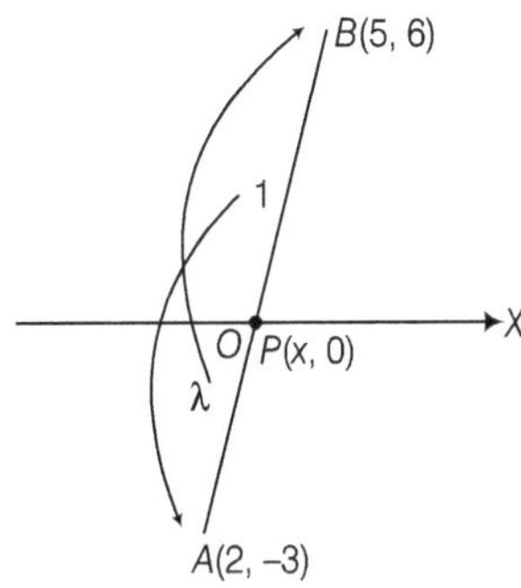

Shortcut Method

According to Remark 5 :

$$\frac{\lambda}{1} = -\frac{y_1}{y_2} = \frac{-(-3)}{6} = \frac{1}{2}$$

$\therefore$ The ratio is $\frac{1}{2} : 1$ i.e. 1 : 2 (internally)

Example 25. The mid-points of the sides of a triangle are (1, 2), (0, − 1) and (2, − 1). Find the coordinates of the vertices of a triangle with the help of two unknowns.

Sol. Let $D(1, 2)$, $E(0, -1)$ and $F(2, -1)$ be the mid-points of BC, CA and AB respectively.
Let the coordinates of A be (α, β) then coordinates of B and C are $(4-\alpha, -2-\beta)$ and $(-\alpha, -2-\beta)$ respectively
(see note 1)
$\because$ D is the mid-point of B and C

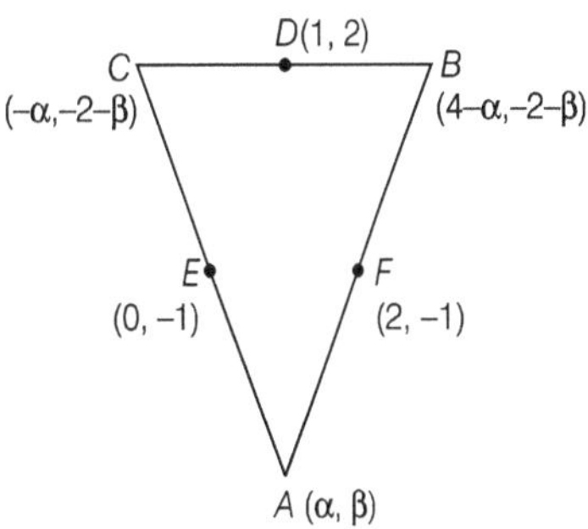

$$\text{then} \quad 1 = \frac{4-\alpha-\alpha}{2}$$

$$\Rightarrow \quad 1 = 2 - \alpha \quad \text{or} \quad \alpha = 1$$

$$\text{and} \quad 2 = \frac{-2-\beta-2-\beta}{2}$$

$$\Rightarrow \quad 2 = -2 - \beta \quad \text{or} \quad \beta = -4$$

Hence, coordinates of A, B and C are (1, − 4), (3, 2) and (−1, 2) respectively.

Example 26. Prove that in a right angled triangle the mid-point of the hypotenuse is equidistant from its vertices.

Sol. Let the given right angled triangle be ABC, with right angled at B. We take B as the origin and BA and BC as the X and Y-axes respectively.
Let $BA = a$ and $BC = b$
then $A \equiv (a, 0)$ and $C \equiv (0, b)$
Let M to be the mid-point of the hypotenuse AC, then coordinates of M are $\left(\frac{a}{2}, \frac{b}{2}\right)$

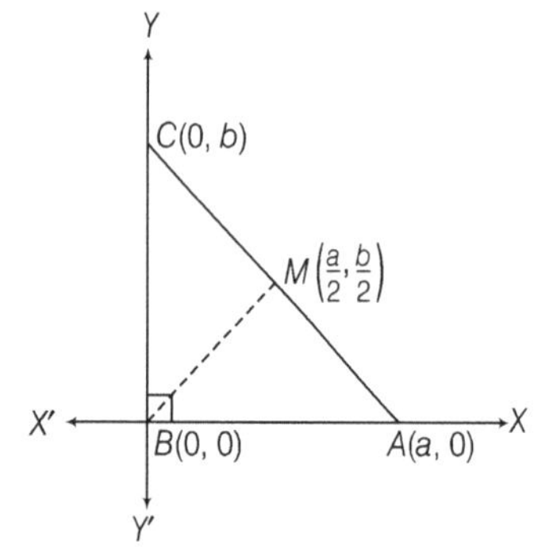

$$\therefore \quad |AM| = \sqrt{\left(a - \frac{a}{2}\right)^2 + \left(0 - \frac{b}{2}\right)^2} = \frac{\sqrt{(a^2 + b^2)}}{2} \quad \text{...(i)}$$

$$|BM| = \sqrt{\left(0 - \frac{a}{2}\right)^2 + \left(0 - \frac{b}{2}\right)^2} = \frac{\sqrt{(a^2 + b^2)}}{2} \quad \text{...(ii)}$$

$$\text{and} \quad |CM| = \sqrt{\left(0 - \frac{a}{2}\right)^2 + \left(b - \frac{b}{2}\right)^2} = \frac{\sqrt{(a^2 + b^2)}}{2} \quad \text{...(iii)}$$

From Eqs. (i), (ii) and (iii), we get

$$|AM| = |BM| = |CM|$$

Example 27 Show that the line joining the mid-points of any two sides of a triangle is half the third side.

Sol. We take O as the origin and OC and OY as the X and Y-axes respectively.

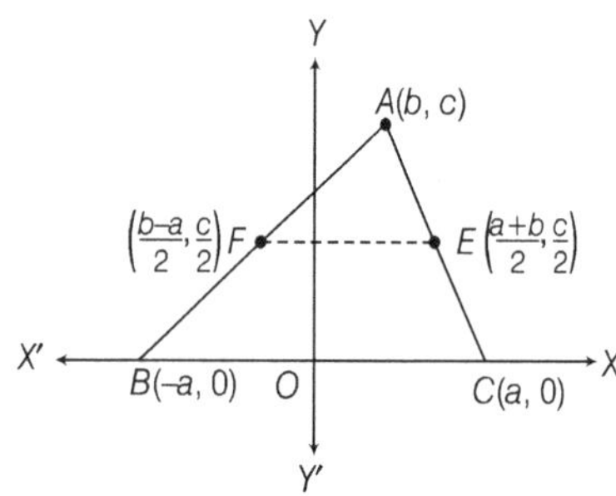

Let $BC = 2a$, then $B \equiv (-a, 0)$, $C \equiv (a, 0)$

Let $A \equiv (b, c)$, if E and F are the mid-points of sides AC and AB respectively.

Then, $\quad E \equiv \left(\dfrac{a+b}{2}, \dfrac{c}{2}\right)$ and $F \equiv \left(\dfrac{b-a}{2}, \dfrac{c}{2}\right)$

Now, $\quad FE = \sqrt{\left(\dfrac{a+b}{2} - \dfrac{b-a}{2}\right)^2 + \left(\dfrac{c}{2} - \dfrac{c}{2}\right)^2} = a$

$$= \frac{1}{2}(2a) = \frac{1}{2}(BG)$$

Hence, the line joining the mid-points of any two sides of a triangle is half the third side.

(ii) Formula for External Division

Theorem : If the point $P(x, y)$ divides the line joining the points $A(x_1, y_1)$ and $B(x_2, y_2)$ externally in the ratio $m : n$ then prove that

$$x = \frac{mx_2 - nx_1}{m - n}, y = \frac{my_2 - ny_1}{m - n}$$

Proof : The given points are $A(x_1, y_1)$ and $B(x_2, y_2)$. Let us assume that the points A and B are both in the 1st quadrant (for the sake of exactness). Let $P(x, y)$ be the point which divides AB externally in the ratio $m : n$, so that $\dfrac{AP}{BP} = \dfrac{m}{n}$.

From A, B and P draw AL, BM and PN perpendiculars on X-axis. Also, from A and B draw AR and BS perpendiculars on PN,

then $\quad AR = LN = ON - OL = x - x_1$

$BS = MN = ON - OM = x - x_2$

$PR = PN - RN = PN - AL = y - y_1$

and $\quad PS = PN - SN = PN - BM = y - y_2$

Clearly, the Δs APR and BPS are similar and therefore their sides are proportional.

$$\therefore \quad \frac{AP}{PB} = \frac{AR}{BS} = \frac{PR}{PS}$$

$$\text{or} \quad \underset{\text{(i)}}{\frac{m}{n}} = \underset{\text{(ii)}}{\frac{x - x_1}{x - x_2}} = \underset{\text{(iii)}}{\frac{y - y_1}{y - y_2}}$$

From Eqs. (i) and (ii), we have

$$\frac{m}{n} = \frac{x - x_1}{x - x_2}$$

$$\Rightarrow \quad mx - mx_2 = nx - nx_1$$

$$\Rightarrow \quad (m - n)x = mx_2 - nx_1$$

$$\text{or} \quad x = \frac{mx_2 - nx_1}{m - n}$$

Also, from Eqs. (i) and (iii), we have

$$\frac{m}{n}=\frac{y-y_1}{y-y_2}$$

$\Rightarrow$ $$my-my_2=ny-ny_1$$

$\Rightarrow$ $$(m-n)\,y=my_2-ny_1$$

or $$y=\frac{my_2-ny_1}{m-n}$$

Thus, the coordinates of P are $\left(\dfrac{mx_2-nx_1}{m-n},\dfrac{my_2-ny_1}{m-n}\right)$.

(Here, $m\neq n$)

***Corollary* 1 :** The above formula is true for all positions of the points, keeping in mind, the proper signs of their coordinates.

***Corollary* 2 :** The above coordinates can also be expressed as

$$\left(\frac{mx_2+(-n)\,x_1}{m+(-n)},\frac{my_2+(-n)\,y_1}{m+(-n)}\right)$$

and this can be thought of as the coordinates of the point dividing AB internally in the ratio $m:-n$

***Corollary* 3 :** $\because$ $$\frac{AP}{PB}=\frac{m}{n}$$

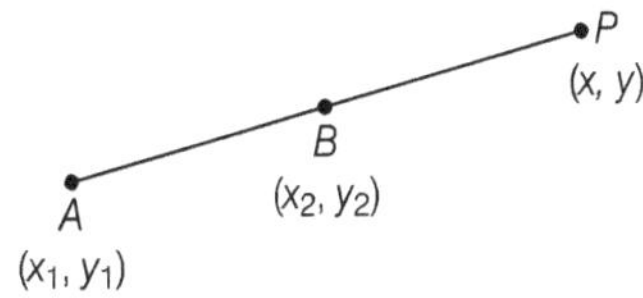

or $$\frac{AP}{PB}-1=\frac{m}{n}-1$$

or $$\frac{AP-PB}{PB}=\frac{m-n}{n}$$

or $$\frac{AB}{PB}=\frac{m-n}{n}$$

Now, we can say that B divides AP in the ratio $m-n:n$ internally.

i.e. $$x_2=\frac{(m-n)\,x+nx_1}{(m-n)+n}\Rightarrow x=\frac{mx_2-nx_1}{m-n}$$

and $$y_2=\frac{(m-n)\,y+ny_1}{(m-n)+n}\Rightarrow y=\frac{my_2-ny_1}{m-n}$$

***Corollary* 4 :** (for proving A, B and C are collinear)

If A, B, C three points are collinear then let C divides AB in the ratio $\lambda:1$ internally.

If $\lambda=+$ ve rational, then divide internally

and if $\lambda=-$ ve rational, then divide externally.

Remarks

1. The following diagram will help to remember the section formula

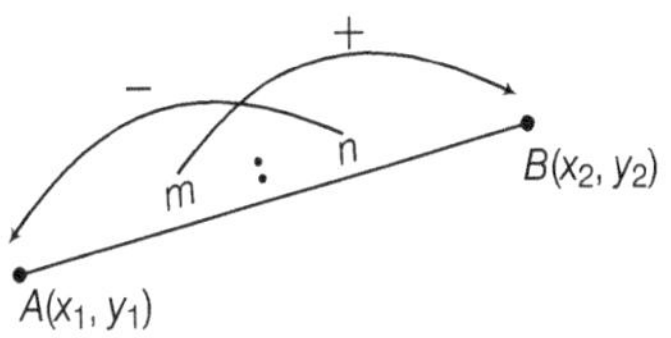

2. Let $\frac{m}{n}=\lambda$, then $\left(\dfrac{mx_2-nx_1}{m-n},\dfrac{my_2-ny_1}{m-n}\right)$

or $\left(\dfrac{\frac{m}{n}x_2-x_1}{\frac{m}{n}-1},\dfrac{\frac{m}{n}y_2-y_1}{\frac{m}{n}-1}\right)$ or $\left(\dfrac{\lambda x_2-x_1}{\lambda-1},\dfrac{\lambda y_2-y_1}{\lambda-1}\right)$

Example 28. Find the coordinates of a point which divides externally the line joining $(1,-3)$ and $(-3,9)$ in the ratio 1 : 3.

Sol. Let the coordinates of the required point be $P(x, y)$,

Then, $$x=\left(\frac{1\times(-3)-3\times1}{1-3}\right)$$

and $$y=\left(\frac{1\times9-3\times(-3)}{1-3}\right)$$

i.e. $x=3$ and $y=-9$

Hence, the required point is $(3,-9)$.

Example 29. The line segment joining $A(6,3)$ to $B(-1,-4)$ is doubled in length by having its length added to each end. Find the coordinates of the new ends.

Sol. Let P and Q be the required new ends

Let the coordinates of P be (x_1, y_1)

Given, $AB=2AP$

$\Rightarrow$ $$\frac{AB}{AP}=\frac{2}{1}$$

i.e. A divides BP internally in the ratio 2 : 1.

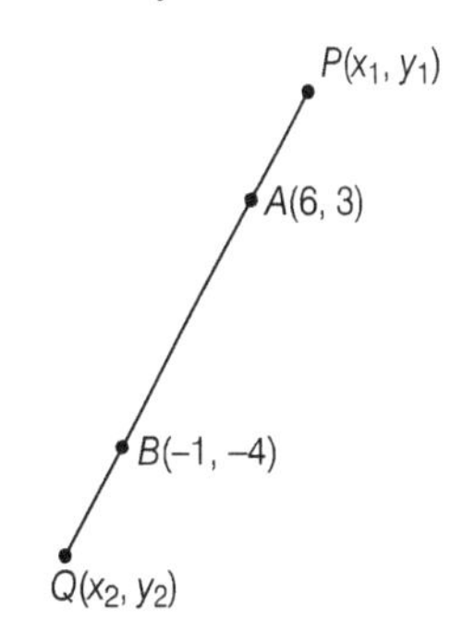

Then, $$6=\frac{2\times x_1+1\times(-1)}{2+1}$$

$\Rightarrow \quad 19 = 2x_1$ or $x_1 = \dfrac{19}{2}$

and $\quad 3 = \dfrac{2 \times y_1 + 1 \times (-4)}{2+1}$

$\Rightarrow \quad 13 = 2y_1$ or $y_1 = \dfrac{13}{2}$

$\therefore$ Coordinates of P are $\left(\dfrac{19}{2}, \dfrac{13}{2}\right)$.

Also, let coordinates of Q be (x_2, y_2)

Given, $\quad AB = 2BQ \Rightarrow \dfrac{AB}{BQ} = \dfrac{2}{1}$

i.e. B divides AQ internally in the ratio 2 : 1

Then $\quad -1 = \dfrac{2 \times x_2 + 1 \times 6}{2+1}$

$\Rightarrow \quad -9 = 2x_2$ or $x_2 = -\dfrac{9}{2}$

and $\quad -4 = \dfrac{2 \times y_2 + 1 \times 3}{2+1}$

$\Rightarrow \quad -15 = 2y_2$ or $y_2 = -\dfrac{15}{2}$

$\therefore$ Coordinates of Q are $\left(-\dfrac{9}{2}, -\dfrac{15}{2}\right)$

Aliter : $\because \quad AB = 2AP$

$\Rightarrow \quad \dfrac{AB}{AP} = \dfrac{2}{1} \Rightarrow \dfrac{AB}{AP} + 1 = \dfrac{2}{1} + 1$

$\Rightarrow \quad \dfrac{AB + AP}{AP} = \dfrac{3}{1} \Rightarrow \dfrac{BP}{AP} = \dfrac{3}{1}$

$\therefore$ P divides AB externally in the ratio 1 : 3

Then, $\quad x_1 = \dfrac{1 \times (-1) - 3 \times 6}{1 - 3} = \dfrac{19}{2}$

and $\quad y_1 = \dfrac{1 \times (-4) - 3 \times 3}{1-3} = \dfrac{13}{2}$

$\therefore$ Coordinates of P are $\left(\dfrac{19}{2}, \dfrac{13}{2}\right)$

Also, $\quad AB = 2BQ$

$\Rightarrow \quad \dfrac{AB}{BQ} = \dfrac{2}{1} \Rightarrow \dfrac{AB}{BQ} + 1 = \dfrac{2}{1} + 1$

$\Rightarrow \quad \dfrac{AB + BQ}{BQ} = \dfrac{3}{1} \Rightarrow \dfrac{AQ}{BQ} = \dfrac{3}{1}$

$\therefore$ Q divides AB externally in the ratio 3 : 1

then, $\quad x_2 = \dfrac{3 \times (-1) - 1 \times 6}{3 - 1} = -\dfrac{9}{2}$

and $\quad y_2 = \dfrac{3 \times (-4) - 1 \times 3}{3-1} = -\dfrac{15}{2}$

$\therefore$ Coordinates of Q are $\left(-\dfrac{9}{2}, -\dfrac{15}{2}\right)$.

Example 30. Using section formula show that the points $(1, -1), (2, 1)$ and $(4, 5)$ are collinear.

Sol. Let $A \equiv (1, -1)$, $B \equiv (2, 1)$ and $C \equiv (4, 5)$

Suppose C divides AB in the ratio $\lambda : 1$ internally, then

$$4 = \frac{\lambda \times 2 + 1 \times 1}{\lambda + 1}$$

$\Rightarrow \quad 4\lambda + 4 = 2\lambda + 1$

or $\quad \lambda = -\dfrac{3}{2}$

i.e. C divides AB in the ratio 3 : 2 (externally).

Hence, A, B, C are collinear.

C(4, 5)
B(2, 1)
A(1, –1)

Example 31. Find the ratio in which the point $(2, y)$ divides the line segment joining (4, 3) and (6, 3) and hence find the value of y.

Sol. Let $A \equiv (4, 3)$, $B \equiv (6, 3)$ and $P \equiv (2, y)$

Let P divides AB internally in the ratio $\lambda : 1$

then, $\quad 2 = \dfrac{6\lambda + 4}{\lambda + 1} \Rightarrow 2\lambda + 2 = 6\lambda + 4$

$\Rightarrow \quad -4\lambda = 2$ or $\lambda = -\dfrac{1}{2}$

A(2, 3) B(4, 3) C(6, 3)

$\therefore$ P divides AB externally in the ratio 1 : 2 ($\because \lambda$ is negative)

$$\text{Now, } y = \frac{1 \times 3 - 2 \times 3}{1 - 2} = 3$$

(iii) Harmonic Conjugates

If four points in a line, then the system is said to form a range. Let four points say P, Q, R, S.

If the range (PQ, RS) has a cross ratio equal to -1, then it is called harmonic.

i.e. $\quad \dfrac{PR}{RQ} \cdot \dfrac{SQ}{SP} = -1 \Rightarrow \dfrac{PR}{RQ} = -\dfrac{SP}{SQ} = \lambda \quad$ (say)

$\therefore \quad \dfrac{PR}{RQ} = \dfrac{\lambda}{1} \Rightarrow PR : RQ = \lambda : 1 \quad$ (internally)

and $\quad \dfrac{SP}{SQ} = -\dfrac{\lambda}{1} \Rightarrow PS : SQ = \lambda : 1 \quad$ (externally)

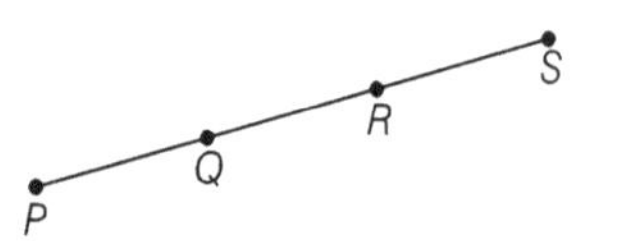

Hence, R and S are called the **harmonic conjugates** to each other with respect to the points P and Q.

Example 32 Find the harmonic conjugates of the point $R(5,1)$ with respect to the points $P(2,10)$ and $Q(6,-2)$.

Sol. Let $S(\alpha, \beta)$ (be the harmonic conjugates of the point $R(5, 1)$).
Suppose R divides PQ in the ratio $\lambda : 1$ internally, then S divides PQ in the ratio $\lambda : 1$ externally, then

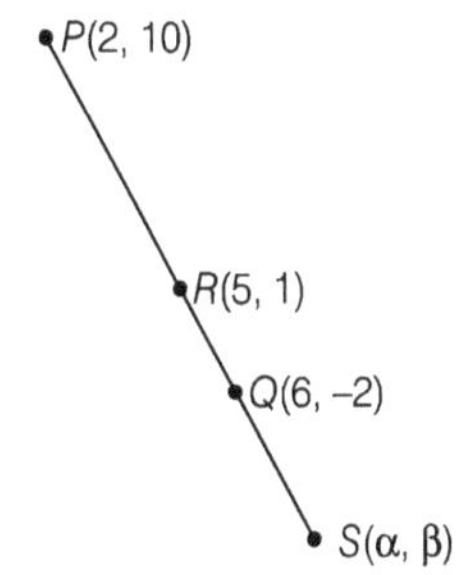

$$5 = \frac{6\lambda + 2}{\lambda + 1} \Rightarrow 5\lambda + 5 = 6\lambda + 2$$

$\therefore \quad \lambda = 3$

Also, $\quad 1 = \dfrac{-2\lambda + 10}{\lambda + 1}$

$$\lambda + 1 = -2\lambda + 10 \Rightarrow 3\lambda = 9$$

$\therefore \quad \lambda = 3$

Now, $\quad \alpha = \dfrac{3 \times 6 - 1 \times 2}{3 - 1} = 8$

and $\quad \beta = \dfrac{3 \times (-2) - 1 \times 10}{3 - 1}$

$$= -8$$

Hence, harmonic conjugates of $R(5, 1)$ is $S(8, -8)$.

Centroid of a Triangle

Definition : The point of intersection of the medians of a triangle is called the centroid of the triangle and it divides the median internally in the ratio 2 : 1.

Theorem : Prove that the coordinates of the centroid of the triangle whose vertices are $(x_1, y_1), (x_2, y_2)$ and (x_3, y_3) are

$$\left(\frac{x_1 + x_2 + x_3}{3}, \frac{y_1 + y_2 + y_3}{3}\right)$$

Also, deduce that the medians of a triangle are concurrent.

Proof : Let $A \equiv (x_1, y_1)$, $B \equiv (x_2, y_2)$ and $C \equiv (x_3, y_3)$ be the vertices of the triangle ABC. Let us assume that the points A, B and C are in the 1st quadrant (for the sake of exactness) whose medians are AD, BE and CF respectively so D, E and F are respectively the mid-points of BC, CA and AB then the coordinates of D, E, F are

$$D \equiv \left(\frac{x_2 + x_3}{2}, \frac{y_2 + y_3}{2}\right)$$

$$E \equiv \left(\frac{x_3 + x_1}{2}, \frac{y_3 + y_1}{2}\right)$$

and $\quad F \equiv \left(\dfrac{x_1 + x_2}{2}, \dfrac{y_1 + y_2}{2}\right)$

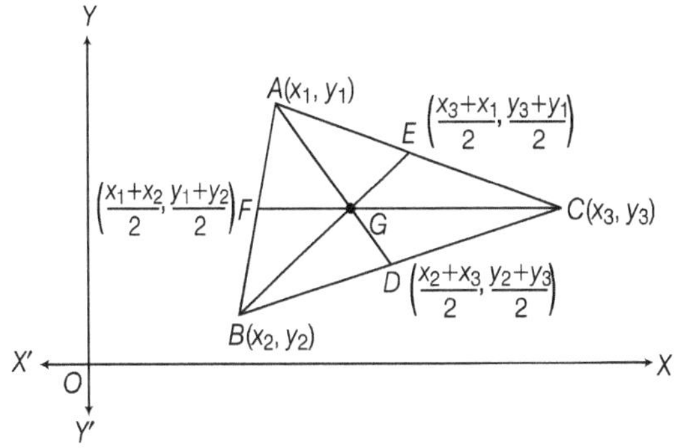

The coordinates of a point dividing AD in the ratio 2 : 1 are

$$\left(\frac{2 \cdot \left(\frac{x_2 + x_3}{2}\right) + 1 \cdot x_1}{2+1}, \frac{2 \cdot \left(\frac{y_2 + y_3}{2}\right) + 1 \cdot y_1}{2+1}\right)$$

or $\quad \left(\dfrac{x_1 + x_2 + x_3}{3}, \dfrac{y_1 + y_2 + y_3}{3}\right)$

and the coordinates of a point dividing BE in the ratio 2 : 1 are

$$\left(\frac{2 \cdot \left(\frac{x_3 + x_1}{2}\right) + 1 \cdot x_2}{2 + 1}, \frac{2 \cdot \left(\frac{y_3 + y_1}{2}\right) + 1 \cdot y_2}{2 + 1}\right)$$

or $\quad \left(\dfrac{x_1 + x_2 + x_3}{3}, \dfrac{y_1 + y_2 + y_3}{3}\right)$

Similarly the coordinates of a point dividing CF in the ratio 2 : 1 are

$$\left(\frac{x_1 + x_2 + x_3}{3}, \frac{y_1 + y_2 + y_3}{3}\right)$$

$\therefore$ The common point which divides AD, BE and CF in the ratio 2 : 1 is

$$\left(\frac{x_1 + x_2 + x_3}{3}, \frac{y_1 + y_2 + y_3}{3}\right)$$

Hence, medians of a triangle are concurrent and the coordinates of the centroid are

$$\left(\frac{x_1 + x_2 + x_3}{3}, \frac{y_1 + y_2 + y_3}{3}\right)$$

Important Theorem

Centroid of the triangle obtained by joining the middle points of the sides of a triangle is the same as the centroid of the original triangle.

Or

If $(a_1, b_1), (a_2, b_2)$ and (a_3, b_3) are the mid-points of the sides of a triangle, then its centroid is given by

$$\left(\frac{a_1 + a_2 + a_3}{3}, \frac{b_1 + b_2 + b_3}{3}\right)$$

Proof : Let D, E, F are the mid-points of BC, CA and AB respectively now let coordinates of A are (α, β) then coordinates of B and C are $(2a_3 - \alpha, 2b_3 - \beta)$ and $(2a_2 - \alpha, 2b_2 - \beta)$ are respectively.

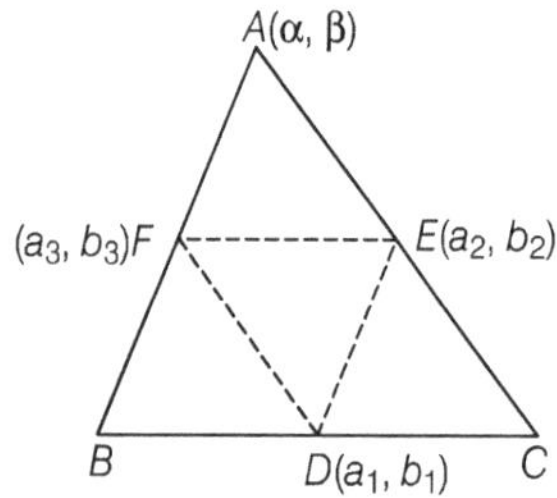

$\because$ $D(a_1, b_1)$ is the mid-point of B and C, then

$$2a_1 = 2a_3 - \alpha + 2a_2 - \alpha \Rightarrow \alpha = a_2 + a_3 - a_1$$

and $$2b_1 = 2b_3 - \beta + 2b_2 - \beta \Rightarrow \beta = b_2 + b_3 - b_1$$

Now, coordinates of B are $(2a_3 - \alpha, 2b_3 - \beta)$

or $$(a_3 + a_1 - a_2, b_3 + b_1 - b_2)$$

and coordinates of C are $(2a_2 - \alpha, 2b_2 - \beta)$

or $$(a_2 + a_1 - a_3, b_2 + b_1 - b_3)$$

Hence, coordinates of A, B and C are

$$A \equiv (a_2 + a_3 - a_1, b_2 + b_3 - b_1),$$
$$B \equiv (a_3 + a_1 - a_2, b_3 + b_1 - b_2)$$
and $$C \equiv (a_2 + a_1 - a_3, b_2 + b_1 - b_3)$$

$\therefore$ Coordinates of centroid of triangle ABC are

$$\left(\frac{a_1 + a_2 + a_3}{3}, \frac{b_1 + b_2 + b_3}{3}\right)$$

which is same as the centroid of triangle DEF.

***Corollary* 1 (Finger Rule) :** If mid-points of the sides of a triangle are $(x_1, y_1), (x_2, y_2)$ and (x_3, y_3), then coordinates of the original triangle are

$$(x_2 + x_3 - x_1, y_2 + y_3 - y_1),$$
$$(x_3 + x_1 - x_2, y_3 + y_1 - y_2)$$
and $$(x_1 + x_2 - x_3, y_1 + y_2 - y_3).$$

***Corollary* 2 :** If two vertices of a triangle are (x_1, y_1) and (x_2, y_2) and the coordinates of centroid are (α, β), then coordinates of the third vertex are

$$(3\alpha - x_1 - x_2, 3\beta - y_1 - y_2)$$

***Corollary* 3 :** According to important theorem $\Delta s\ ABC$ and DEF are similar

$$\therefore \quad \frac{\text{Area of } \Delta ABC}{\text{Area of } \Delta DEF} = \frac{(BC)^2}{(EF)^2}$$

$$= \frac{4\{(a_2 - a_3)^2 + (b_2 - b_3)^2\}}{\{(a_2 - a_3)^2 + (b_2 - b_3)^2\}} = 4$$

$\therefore$ Area of $\Delta\ ABC = 4 \times$ Area of ΔDEF

i.e. Area of a triangle is four times the area of the triangle formed by joining the mid-points of its sides.

Example 33. Two vertices of a triangle are $(-1, 4)$ and $(5, 2)$. If its centroid is $(0, -3)$, find the third vertex.

Sol. Let the third vertex be (x, y) then the coordinates of the centroid of triangle are

$$\left(\frac{-1 + 5 + x}{3}, \frac{4 + 2 + y}{3}\right) \text{ i.e. } \left(\frac{4 + x}{3}, \frac{6 + y}{3}\right)$$

Now, $$\left(\frac{4 + x}{3}, \frac{6 + y}{3}\right) = (0, -3)$$

$$\Rightarrow \quad \frac{4 + x}{3} = 0 \text{ and } \frac{6 + y}{3} = -3$$

$$\Rightarrow \quad 4 + x = 0 \text{ and } y + 6 = -9$$

or $$x = -4 \text{ and } y = -15$$

Hence, the third vertex is $(-4, -15)$.

Shortcut Method

According to corollary 2

$$(x, y) = (3 \times 0 - (-1) - 5, 3 \times (-3) - 4 - 2)$$
$$= (-4, -15)$$

Example 34. The vertices of a triangle are $(1, 2), (h, -3)$ and $(-4, k)$. Find the value of $\sqrt{\{(h + k)^2 + (h + 3k)^2\}}$. If the centroid of the triangle be at the point $(5, -1)$.

Sol. Here, $\frac{1 + h - 4}{3} = 5$ and $\frac{2 - 3 + k}{3} = -1$

then, we get $h = 18, k = -2$

$$\therefore \quad = \sqrt{(h + k)^2 + (h + 3k)^2}$$
$$= \sqrt{(18 - 2)^2 + (18 - 6)^2}$$
$$= \sqrt{(16^2 + 12^2)} = 20$$

Example 35. If $D(-2, 3)$, $E(4, -3)$ and $F(4, 5)$ are the mid-points of the sides BC, CA and AB of triangle ABC, then find $\sqrt{(|AG|^2 + |BG|^2 - |CG|^2)}$ where, G is the centroid of ΔABC.

Sol. Let the coordinates of A be (α, β)

then coordinates of B are $(8-\alpha, 10-\beta)$

and coordinates of C are $(8-\alpha, -6-\beta)$

$\because$ D is the mid-point of BC, then

$$\frac{8-\alpha+8-\alpha}{2} = -2$$

and $$\frac{10-\beta-6-\beta}{2} = 3$$

i.e. $$\alpha = 10 \text{ and } \beta = -1$$

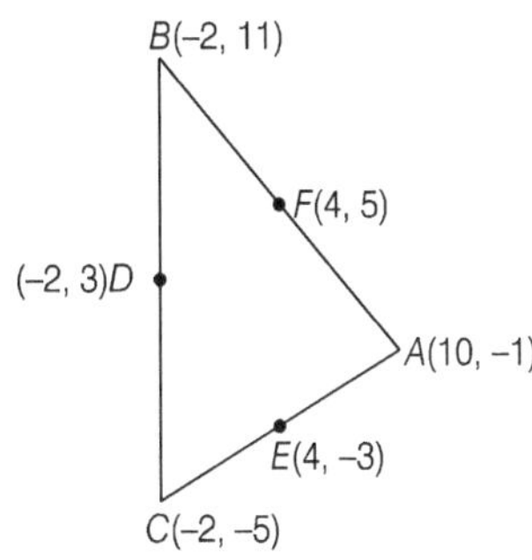

$\therefore$ Coordinates of A, B, C are $(10, -1)$, $(-2, 11)$ and $(-2, -5)$ respectively.

Now, coordinates of centroid

$$G \equiv \left(\frac{10-2-2}{3}, \frac{-1+11-5}{3}\right)$$

i.e. $$G \equiv \left(2, \frac{5}{3}\right)$$

$\therefore$ $$AG = \sqrt{(10-2)^2 + \left(-1-\frac{5}{3}\right)^2}$$

$$= \sqrt{\left(64 + \frac{64}{9}\right)} = \frac{8}{3}\sqrt{(10)}$$

$$BG = \sqrt{(-2-2)^2 + \left(11-\frac{5}{3}\right)^2}$$

$$= \sqrt{16 + \frac{(28)^2}{9}} = \frac{4}{3}\sqrt{(58)}$$

and $$CG = \sqrt{(-2-2)^2 + \left(-5-\frac{5}{3}\right)^2}$$

$$= \sqrt{\left(16 + \frac{400}{9}\right)} = \frac{4}{3}\sqrt{(34)}$$

Hence, $$\sqrt{(|AG|^2 + |BG|^2 - |CG|^2)}$$

$$= \sqrt{\left(\frac{64}{9} \times 10 + \frac{16}{9} \times 58 - \frac{16}{9} \times 34\right)}$$

$$= \sqrt{\frac{32}{9}(20 + 29 - 17)}$$

$$= \sqrt{\left(\frac{32}{9} \times 32\right)} = \frac{32}{3}$$

Example 36. If G be the centroid of the ΔABC and O be any other point in the plane of the triangle ABC, then show that
$OA^2 + OB^2 + OC^2 = GA^2 + GB^2 + GC^2 + 3GO^2$.

Sol. Let G be the origin and GO be X-axis.

$$O \equiv (a, 0),\ A \equiv (x_1, y_1),\ B \equiv (x_2, y_2)$$

and $C \equiv (x_3, y_3)$

Now, LHS $= OA^2 + OB^2 + OC^2$

$$= (x_1 - a)^2 + y_1^2 + (x_2 - a)^2 + y_2^2 + (x_3 - a)^2 + y_3^2$$

$$= (x_1^2 + x_2^2 + x_3^2) + (y_1^2 + y_2^2 + y_3^2) - 2a(x_1 + x_2 + x_3) + 3a^2$$

$$= \sum x_1^2 + \sum y_1^2 - 0 + 3a^2 \quad \left(\because \frac{x_1 + x_2 + x_3}{3} = 0 \text{ i.e., } x_1 + x_2 + x_3 = 0\right)$$

$$= \sum x_1^2 + \sum y_1^2 + 3a^2 \quad \text{...(i)}$$

and RHS $= GA^2 + GB^2 + GC^2 + 3GO^2$

$$= x_1^2 + y_1^2 + x_2^2 + y_2^2 + x_3^2 + y_3^2 + 3\{(a-0)^2\}$$

$$= \sum x_1^2 + \sum y_1^2 + 3a^2 \quad \text{... (ii)}$$

Hence, from Eqs. (i) and (ii), we get

$$OA^2 + OB^2 + OC^2 = GA^2 + GB^2 + GC^2 + 3GO^2.$$

Example 37. If G be the centroid of ΔABC, show that

$$AB^2 + BC^2 + CA^2 = 3(GA^2 + GB^2 + GC^2).$$

Sol. We take B as the origin and BC and BY as the X and Y-axes respectively.

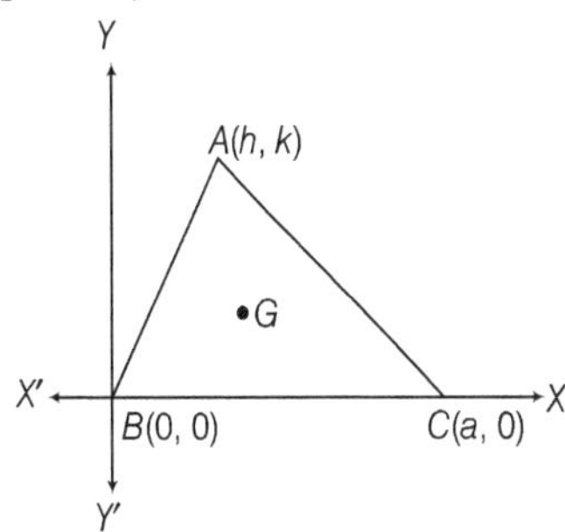

Let $BC = a$, then $B \equiv (0, 0)$ and $C \equiv (a, 0)$
and let $A \equiv (h, k)$
then, coordinates of G will be

$$\left(\frac{h+0+a}{3}, \frac{k+0+0}{3}\right), \text{ i.e. } \left(\frac{h+a}{3}, \frac{k}{3}\right)$$

Take $\Delta\, ABC$ as in 1st quadrant (for the sake of exactness).

Now, $\text{LHS} = (AB)^2 + (BC)^2 + (CA)^2$

$$= (h-0)^2 + (k-0)^2 + a^2 + (h-a)^2 + (k-0)^2$$

$$= 2h^2 + 2k^2 - 2ah + 2a^2 \quad \text{... (i)}$$

$$\text{RHS} = 3\,((GA)^2 + (GB)^2 + (GC)^2)$$

$$= 3\left\{\left(\frac{a+h}{3} - h\right)^2 + \left(\frac{k}{3} - k\right)^2 + \left(\frac{a+h}{3} - 0\right)^2 + \left(\frac{k}{3} - 0\right)^2 + \left(\frac{a+h}{3} - a\right)^2 + \left(\frac{k}{3} - 0\right)^2\right\}$$

$$= \frac{3}{9}\{(a-2h)^2 + (-2k)^2 + (a+h)^2 + k^2 + (h-2a)^2 + k^2\}$$

$$= \frac{1}{3}\{6a^2 + 6h^2 + 6k^2 - 6ah\}$$

$$= 2h^2 + 2k^2 - 2ah + 2a^2 \quad \text{... (ii)}$$

Hence, from Eqs. (i) and (ii), we get

$$AB^2 + BC^2 + CA^2 = 3(GA^2 + GB^2 + GC^2)$$

Example 38. The vertices of a triangle are $(1, a), (2, b)$ and $(c^2, -3)$

(i) Prove that its centroid can not lie on the Y-axis.

(ii) Find the condition that the centroid may lie on the X-axis.

Sol. Centroid of the triangle is

$$G \equiv \left(\frac{1+2+c^2}{3}, \frac{a+b-3}{3}\right) \text{ i.e. } \left(\frac{3+c^2}{3}, \frac{a+b-3}{3}\right)$$

(i) $\because$ G will lie on Y-axis, then

$$\frac{3+c^2}{3} = 0$$

$\Rightarrow$ $c^2 = -3$

or $c = \pm i\sqrt{3}$

$\because$ Both values of c are imaginary.
Hence, G can not lie on Y-axis.

(ii) $\because$ G will lie on X-axis, then $\dfrac{a+b-3}{3} = 0$

$\Rightarrow$ $a + b - 3 = 0$

or $a + b = 3$

Incentre

Definition : The point of intersection of internal angle bisectors of triangle is called the incentre of the triangle.

Theorem : Prove that the coordinates of the incentre of a triangle whose vertices are $A(x_1, y_1), B(x_2, y_2), C(x_3, y_3)$ are

$$\left(\frac{ax_1 + bx_2 + cx_3}{a+b+c}, \frac{ay_1 + by_2 + cy_3}{a+b+c}\right)$$

where, a, b, c are the lengths of sides BC, CA and AB respectively.

Also, prove that the internal bisectors of the angles of a triangle are concurrent.

Proof : Given $A \equiv (x_1, y_1), B(x_2, y_2), C \equiv (x_3, y_3)$ be the vertices of $\Delta\, ABC$ and $BC = a, CA = b$ and $AB = c$. Let AD be the bisector of A. We know that the bisector of an angle of a triangle divides the opposite side in the ratio of the sides containing the triangle.

$$\therefore \quad \frac{BD}{DC} = \frac{AB}{AC} = \frac{c}{b} \quad \text{... (i)}$$

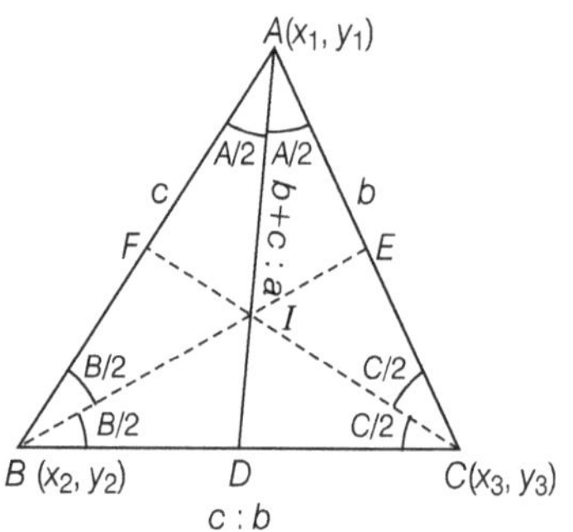

Hence, D divides BC in the ratio $c : b$

$\therefore$ Coordinates of D are $\left(\dfrac{cx_3 + bx_2}{c+b}, \dfrac{cy_3 + by_2}{c+b}\right)$

From Eq. (i), $\dfrac{DC}{BD} = \dfrac{b}{c}$ or $\dfrac{DC}{BD} + 1 = \dfrac{b}{c} + 1$

or $\dfrac{DC + BD}{BD} = \left(\dfrac{b+c}{c}\right)$ or $\dfrac{a}{BD} = \left(\dfrac{b+c}{c}\right)$

$$\therefore \quad BD = \frac{ac}{(b+c)}$$

Also, in $\Delta\, ABD$, BI is the bisector of B.

Then, $\dfrac{AI}{ID} = \dfrac{AB}{BD} = \dfrac{c}{\left(\dfrac{ac}{b+c}\right)} = \dfrac{b+c}{a}$

$\therefore$ I divides AD in the ratio $b+c:a$

$\therefore$ Coordinates of I are

$$\left(\frac{(b+c)\cdot\dfrac{cx_3+bx_2}{c+b}+a\cdot x_1}{b+c+a}, \frac{(b+c)\cdot\dfrac{cy_3+by_2}{c+b}+b\cdot y_1}{b+c+a} \right)$$

i.e. $$\left(\frac{ax_1+bx_2+cx_3}{a+b+c}, \frac{ay_1+by_2+cy_3}{a+b+c} \right)$$

Similarly we can show that the coordinates of the point which divides BE internally in the ratio $c+a:b$ and the coordinates of the point which divides CF internally in the ratio $a+b:c$ will be each

$$\left(\frac{ax_1+bx_2+cx_3}{a+b+c}, \frac{ay_1+by_2+cy_3}{a+b+c} \right)$$

and $$CE=\frac{ab}{(c+a)}, AE=\frac{bc}{(c+a)},$$

$$AF=\frac{bc}{a+b}, BF=\frac{ac}{a+b}$$

Thus, the three internal bisectors of the angles of a triangle meet in a point I.

$$I\equiv\left(\frac{ax_1+bx_2+cx_3}{a+b+c}, \frac{ay_1+by_2+cy_3}{a+b+c} \right)$$

***Corollary* 1 :** If ΔABC is equilateral, then $a=b=c$

$$\text{incentre}=\left(\frac{x_1+x_2+x_3}{3}, \frac{y_1+y_2+y_3}{3} \right)=\text{centroid}$$

i.e. incentre and centroid coincide in equilateral, triangle.

***Corollary* 2 :** $AE=AF=s-a$

$BD=BF=s-b$

$CD=CE=s-c$

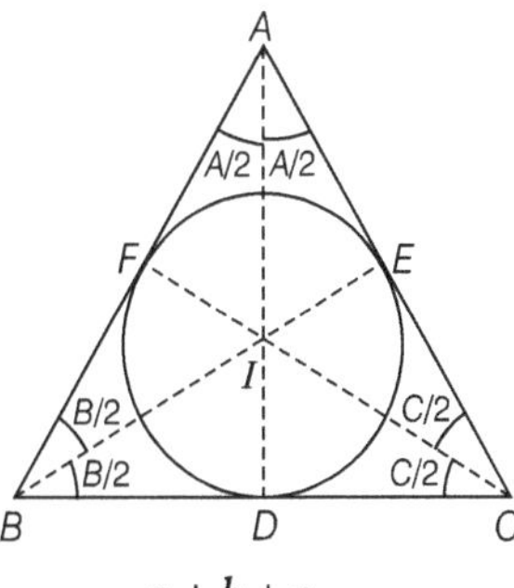

where, $$s=\frac{a+b+c}{2}$$

and $|BC|=a, |CA|=b, |AB|=c$

Proof : Let $AE=AF=\alpha$

($\because$ Lengths of tangents are equal from a point to a circle)

$BD=BF=\beta$

$CD=CE=\gamma$

Also, $a=BC=BD+DC=\beta+\gamma$ ....(i)

$b=CA=CE+AE=\gamma+\alpha$ ...(ii)

and $c=AB=AF+BF=\alpha+\beta$ ...(iii)

Adding all, we get

$$a+b+c=2(\alpha+\beta+\gamma)$$

or $$2s=2(\alpha+\beta+\gamma)$$

$\therefore$ $$s=\alpha+\beta+\gamma$$

From Eqs. (i), (ii) and (iii), we get

$$\alpha=s-a, \beta=s-b, \gamma=s-c$$

Example 39. Find the coordinates of incentre of the triangle whose vertices are $(4,-2)$, $(-2,4)$ and $(5,5)$.

Sol. Let $A(4,-2)$, $B(-2,4)$ and $C(5,5)$ be the vertices of the given triangle. Then

$$a=BC=\sqrt{(-2-5)^2+(4-5)^2}=\sqrt{50}=5\sqrt{2}$$

$$b=CA=\sqrt{(5-4)^2+(5+2)^2}=\sqrt{50}=5\sqrt{2}$$

and $$c=AB=\sqrt{(4+2)^2+(-2-4)^2}=\sqrt{72}=6\sqrt{2}$$

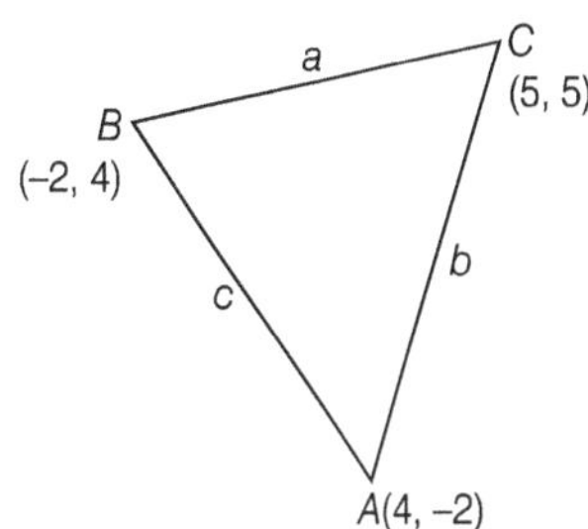

Let (x, y) be the coordinates of incentre of ΔABC. Then

$$x=\frac{ax_1+bx_2+cx_3}{a+b+c}$$

$$=\frac{5\sqrt{2}\times4+5\sqrt{2}\times(-2)+6\sqrt{2}\times5}{5\sqrt{2}+5\sqrt{2}+6\sqrt{2}}$$

$$=\frac{20\sqrt{2}-10\sqrt{2}+30\sqrt{2}}{16\sqrt{2}}$$

$$=\frac{40}{16}=\frac{5}{2}$$

and $$y=\frac{ay_1+by_2+cy_3}{a+b+c}$$

$$=\frac{5\sqrt{2}\times(-2)+5\sqrt{2}\times4+6\sqrt{2}\times5}{5\sqrt{2}+5\sqrt{2}+6\sqrt{2}}$$

$$=\frac{40}{16}=\frac{5}{2}$$

$\therefore$ The coordinates of the incentre are $\left(\frac{5}{2}, \frac{5}{2}\right)$

Example 40. If $\left(\frac{3}{2}, 0\right), \left(\frac{3}{2}, 6\right)$ and $(-1, 6)$ are mid-points of the sides of a triangle, then find

(i) Centroid of the triangle

(ii) Incentre of the triangle

Sol. Let $A \equiv (\alpha, \beta)$, then coordinates of $B \equiv (-2-\alpha, 12-\beta)$ and coordinates of $C \equiv (3-\alpha, 12-\beta)$. But mid-point of BC is $\left(\frac{3}{2}, 0\right)$

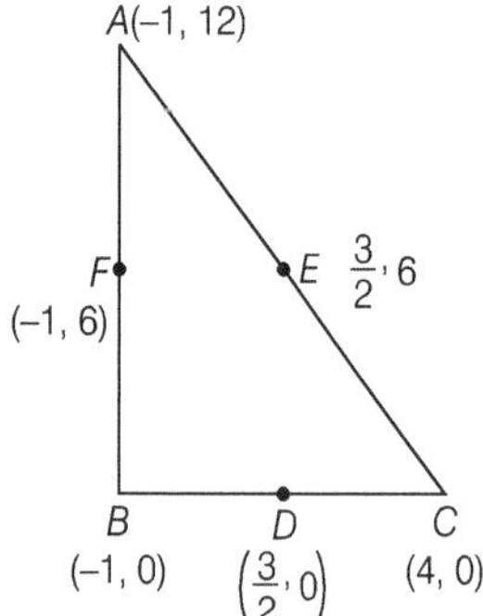

then $\quad 3 = -2 - \alpha + 3 - \alpha$

$\Rightarrow \quad \alpha = -1$

and $\quad 0 = 12 - \beta + 12 - \beta$

$\Rightarrow \quad \beta = 12$

$\therefore$ Coordinates of vertices are

$$A \equiv (-1, 12), B \equiv (-1, 0) \quad \text{and} \quad C \equiv (4, 0)$$

(i) Centroid : The centroid of ΔABC is

$$\left(\frac{x_1 + x_2 + x_3}{3}, \frac{y_1 + y_2 + y_3}{3}\right)$$

or $$\left(\frac{-1-1+4}{3}, \frac{12+0+0}{3}\right) \text{ i.e. } \left(\frac{2}{3}, 4\right)$$

(ii) Incentre : We have

$$a = BC = \sqrt{(-1-4)^2 + (0-0)^2} = 5$$

$$b = CA = \sqrt{(4+1)^2 + (0-12)^2} = 13$$

and $$c = AB = \sqrt{(-1+1)^2 + (12-0)^2} = 12$$

$\therefore$ The incentre of ΔABC is

$$\left(\frac{ax_1 + bx_2 + cx_3}{a+b+c}, \frac{ay_1 + by_2 + cy_3}{a+b+c}\right)$$

or $$\left(\frac{5 \times (-1) + 13 \times (-1) + 12 \times 4}{5 + 13 + 12}, \frac{5 \times 12 + 13 \times 0 + 12 \times 0}{5 + 13 + 12}\right)$$

i.e. $\quad (1, 2)$

Example 41. If a vertex of a triangle be (1, 1) and the middle points of two sides through it be $(-2, 3)$ and $(5, 2)$, then find the centroid and the incentre of the triangle.

Sol. Let coordinate of A be (1, 1) and mid-points of AB and AC are F and E.

$\therefore \quad F \equiv (-2, 3)$ and $E \equiv (5, 2)$

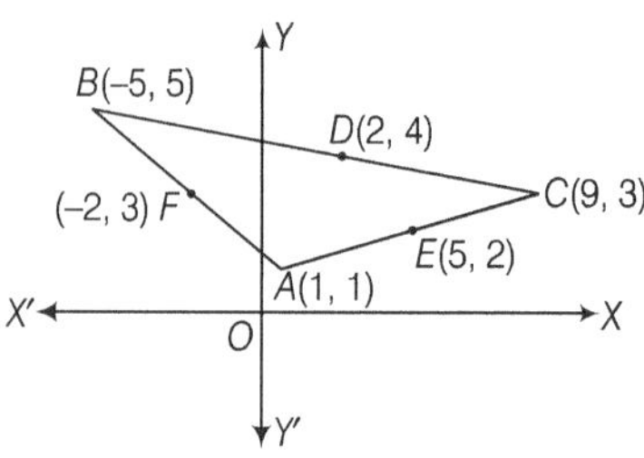

Hence, coordinates of B and C are $(2 \times (-2) - 1, (2 \times 3 - 1)$ and $(2 \times 2 - (-5), 2 \times 4 - 5)$ respectively.

i.e. $\quad B \equiv (-5, 5)$ and $C \equiv (9, 3)$

Then, centroid is $\left(\frac{1-5+9}{3}, \frac{1+5+3}{3}\right)$ i.e., $\left(\frac{5}{3}, 3\right)$

Also, $$a = |BC| = \sqrt{(-5-9)^2 + (5-3)^2} = \sqrt{200} = 10\sqrt{2}$$

$$b = |CA| = \sqrt{(9-1)^2 + (3-1)^2} = \sqrt{68} = 2\sqrt{17}$$

and $$c = |AB| = \sqrt{(1+5)^2 + (1-5)^2} = \sqrt{52} = 2\sqrt{13}$$

Then, incentre is

$$\left(\frac{10\sqrt{2} \times 1 + 2\sqrt{17} \times (-5) + 2\sqrt{13} \times 9}{10\sqrt{2} + 2\sqrt{17} + 2\sqrt{13}}, \frac{10\sqrt{2} \times 1 + 2\sqrt{17} \times 5 + 2\sqrt{13} \times 3}{10\sqrt{2} + 2\sqrt{17} + 2\sqrt{13}}\right)$$

i.e. $$\left(\frac{5\sqrt{2} - 5\sqrt{17} + 9\sqrt{13}}{5\sqrt{2} + \sqrt{17} + \sqrt{13}}, \frac{5\sqrt{2} + 5\sqrt{17} + 3\sqrt{13}}{5\sqrt{2} + \sqrt{17} + \sqrt{13}}\right)$$

Example 42. If G be the centroid and I be the incentre of the triangle with vertices $A(-36, 7), B(20, 7)$ and $C(0, -8)$ and $GI = \frac{25}{3}\sqrt{(205)}\,\lambda$, then find the value of λ.

Sol. Coordinates of centroid are

$$G \equiv \left(-\frac{16}{3}, 2\right)$$

and $$a = |BC| = \sqrt{(20-0)^2 + (7+8)^2}$$

$$= \sqrt{625} = 25$$

$$b = |CA| = \sqrt{(0+36)^2 + (-8-7)^2}$$

$$= \sqrt{1521} = 39$$

$$c = |AB| = \sqrt{(-36-20)^2 + (7-7)^2}$$

$$= \sqrt{(56)^2} = 56$$

Therefore, the coordinates of incentre are

$$I \equiv \left(\frac{25 \times (-36) + 39 \times 20 + 56 \times 0}{25 + 39 + 56}, \frac{25 \times 7 + 39 \times 7 + 56 \times (-8)}{25 + 39 + 56}\right)$$

i.e., $I \equiv (-1, 0)$

$\therefore \quad GI = \sqrt{\left(-\frac{16}{3}+1\right)^2 + (2-0)^2} = \frac{\sqrt{(205)}}{3}$

but given $GI = \frac{25}{3}\sqrt{(205)}\,\lambda$

$\therefore \quad \frac{1}{3}\sqrt{(205)} = \frac{25}{3}\sqrt{(205)}\,\lambda$

$\Rightarrow \quad \lambda = \frac{1}{25}$

Some Standard Results

1. Excentres of a Triangle

This is the point of intersection of the external bisectors of the angles of a triangle.

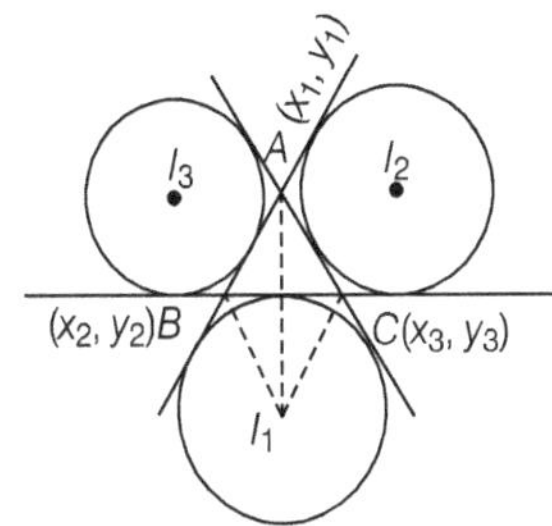

The circle opposite to the vertex A is called the escribed circle opposite A or the circle escribed to the side BC. If I_1 is the point of intersection of internal bisector of $\angle BAC$ and external bisector of $\angle ABC$ and $\angle ACB$, then

$$I_1 \equiv \left(\frac{ax_1 - bx_2 - cx_3}{a-b-c}, \frac{ay_1 - by_2 - cy_3}{a-b-c}\right)$$

or
$$I_1 \equiv \left(\frac{-ax_1 + bx_2 + cx_3}{-a+b+c}, \frac{-ay_1 + by_2 + cy_3}{-a+b+c}\right)$$

Similarly,
$$I_2 \equiv \left(\frac{ax_1 - bx_2 + cx_3}{a-b+c}, \frac{ay_1 - by_2 + cy_3}{a-b+c}\right)$$

and
$$I_3 \equiv \left(\frac{ax_1 + bx_2 - cx_3}{a+b-c}, \frac{ay_1 + by_2 - cy_3}{a+b-c}\right)$$

where, $|BC| = a, |CA| = b$ and $|AB| = c$

Example 43. If the coordinates of the mid-points of sides BC, CA and AB of triangle ABC are $(1, 1)$, $(2, -3)$ and $(3, 4)$, then find the excentre opposite to the vertex A.

Sol. Let $D(1, 1)$, $E(2, -3)$ and $F(3, 4)$ are the mid-points of the sides of the triangle BC, CA and AB respectively. Let $A \equiv (\alpha, \beta)$

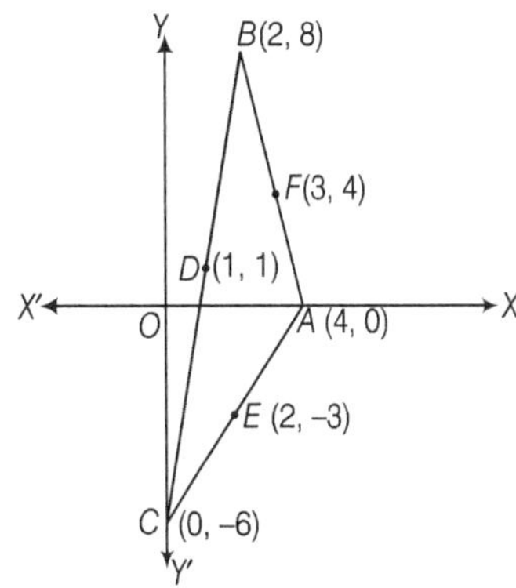

then $B \equiv (6-\alpha, 8-\beta)$

and $C \equiv (4-\alpha, -6-\beta)$

Also, D is the mid-point of B and C, then

$$1 = \frac{6-\alpha+4-\alpha}{2} \Rightarrow \alpha = 4$$

and
$$1 = \frac{8-\beta-6-\beta}{2} \Rightarrow \beta = 0$$

$\therefore \quad A \equiv (4, 0)$, $B \equiv (2, 8)$ and $C \equiv (0, -6)$, then

$$a = |BC| = \sqrt{(2-0)^2 + (8+6)^2} = \sqrt{200} = 10\sqrt{2}$$

$$b = |CA| = \sqrt{(0-4)^2 + (-6-0)^2} = \sqrt{52} = 2\sqrt{13}$$

and
$$c = |AB| = \sqrt{(4-2)^2 + (0-8)^2} = \sqrt{68} = 2\sqrt{17}$$

Hence, the coordinates of the excentre opposite to A are

$$\left(\frac{-ax_1 + bx_2 + cx_3}{-a+b+c}, \frac{ay_1 + by_2 + cy_3}{-a+b+c}\right)$$

i.e.,
$$\left(\frac{-10\sqrt{2}\times 4 + 2\sqrt{13}\times 2 + 2\sqrt{17}\times 0}{-10\sqrt{2} + 2\sqrt{13} + 2\sqrt{17}}, \frac{-10\sqrt{2}\times 0 + 2\sqrt{13}\times 8 + 2\sqrt{17}\times(-6)}{-10\sqrt{2} + 2\sqrt{13} + 2\sqrt{17}}\right)$$

or
$$\left(\frac{-20\sqrt{2} + 2\sqrt{13}}{-5\sqrt{2} + \sqrt{13} + \sqrt{17}}, \frac{8\sqrt{13} - 6\sqrt{17}}{-5\sqrt{2} + \sqrt{13} + \sqrt{17}}\right)$$

2. Circumcentre of a Triangle

The circumcentre of a triangle is the point of intersection of the perpendicular bisectors of the sides of a triangle (i.e., the lines through the mid-point of a side and perpendicular to it). Let $A(x_1, y_1)$, $B(x_2, y_2)$ and $C(x_3, y_3)$ be the vertices of ΔABC and if angles of ΔABC are given, then coordinates of circumcentre

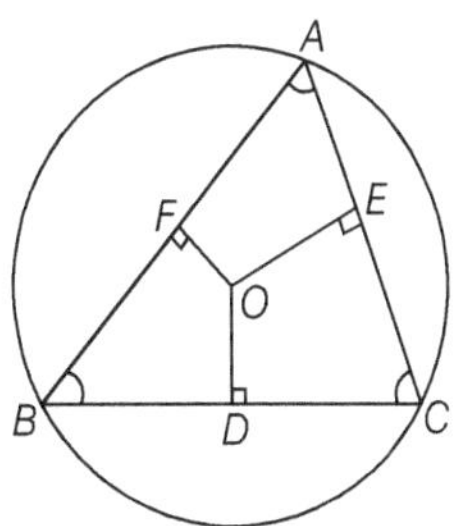

are $$\left(\frac{x_1 \sin 2A + x_2 \sin 2B + x_3 \sin 2C}{\sin 2A + \sin 2B + \sin 2C}, \frac{y_1 \sin 2A + y_2 \sin 2B + y_3 \sin 2C}{\sin 2A + \sin 2B + \sin 2C}\right)$$

Or

$$\left(\frac{ax_1 \cos A + bx_2 \cos B + cx_3 \cos C}{a\cos A + b\cos B + c\cos C}, \frac{ay_1 \cos A + by_2 \cos B + cy_3 \cos C}{a\cos A + b\cos B + c\cos C}\right)$$

where, $|BC| = a, |CA| - b$ and $|AB| = c$

Example 44. In a ΔABC with vertices $A(1, 2)$, $B(2, 3)$ and $C(3, 1)$ and $\angle A = \angle B = \cos^{-1}\left(\frac{1}{\sqrt{10}}\right)$, $\angle C = \cos^{-1}\left(\frac{4}{5}\right)$, then find the circumcentre of ΔABC.

Sol. Since, $\angle A = \angle B = \cos^{-1}\left(\frac{1}{\sqrt{10}}\right)$

$$\Rightarrow \quad \cos A = \cos B = \frac{1}{\sqrt{10}}$$

then, $\sin A = \sin B = \frac{3}{\sqrt{10}}$

$$\therefore \quad \sin 2A = \sin 2B = 2 \times \frac{3}{\sqrt{10}} \times \frac{1}{\sqrt{10}} = \frac{3}{5}$$

and $\quad \angle C = \cos^{-1}\left(\frac{4}{5}\right)$

$$\Rightarrow \quad \cos C = \frac{4}{5} \text{ then, } \sin C = \frac{3}{5}$$

$$\therefore \quad \sin 2C = 2 \times \frac{3}{5} \times \frac{4}{5} = \frac{24}{25}$$

Let the circumcenter be (x, y), then

$$x = \frac{x_1 \sin 2A + x_2 \sin 2B + x_3 \sin 2C}{\sin 2A + \sin 2B + \sin 2C}$$

$$= \frac{1 \times \frac{3}{5} + 2 \times \frac{3}{5} + 3 \times \frac{24}{25}}{\frac{3}{5} + \frac{3}{5} + \frac{24}{25}} = \frac{13}{6}$$

and $$y = \frac{y_1 \sin 2A + y_2 \sin 2B + y_3 \sin 2C}{\sin 2A + \sin 2B + \sin 2C}$$

$$= \frac{2 \times \frac{3}{5} + 3 \times \frac{3}{5} + 1 \times \frac{24}{25}}{\frac{3}{5} + \frac{3}{5} + \frac{24}{25}} = \frac{11}{6}$$

Hence, coordinates of circumcenter are $\left(\frac{13}{6}, \frac{11}{6}\right)$.

Two Important Tricks for Circumcentre

(a) If angles of triangle ABC are not given and the vertices $A(x_1, y_1)$, $B(x_2, y_2)$ and $C(x_3, y_3)$ are given, then the circumcentre of the ΔABC is given by

$$\left(\frac{(x_1 + x_2) + \lambda(y_1 - y_2)}{2}, \frac{(y_1 + y_2) - \lambda(x_1 - x_2)}{2}\right)$$

Here, we observe that

$$P = \begin{bmatrix} x_1 - x_3 & y_1 - y_3 \\ x_2 - x_3 & y_2 - y_3 \end{bmatrix}$$

$$\therefore \quad \lambda = \frac{\vec{\mathbf{R}}_1 \cdot \vec{\mathbf{R}}_2}{|P|}$$

(b) If the angle C is given instead of coordinates of the vertex C and the vertices $A(x_1, y_1)$, $B(x_2, y_2)$ of ΔABC are given, then the circumcentre of ΔABC is given by

$$\left(\frac{(x_1 + x_2) \pm \cot C(y_1 - y_2)}{2}, \frac{(y_1 + y_2) \pm \cot C(x_1 - x_2)}{2}\right)$$

Remark

Circumcentre of the right angled triangle ABC, right angled at A is $\frac{B + C}{2}$.

Example 45. Find the circumcentre of the triangle whose vertices are (2, 2), (4, 2) and (0, 4).

Sol. Let the given points are (x_1, y_1), (x_2, y_2) and (x_3, y_3) respectively.

for the matrix

$$P = \begin{bmatrix} x_1 - x_3 & y_1 - y_3 \\ x_2 - x_3 & y_2 - y_2 \end{bmatrix} = \begin{bmatrix} 2 & -2 \\ 4 & -2 \end{bmatrix}$$

$$\therefore \quad \lambda = \frac{\vec{\mathbf{R}}_1 \cdot \vec{\mathbf{R}}_2}{|P|}$$

$$= \frac{2 \times 4 + (-2) \times (-2)}{2 \times (-2) - 4 \times (-2)} = \frac{12}{4} = 3$$

$\therefore$ Circumcentre of the triangle

$$\equiv \left(\frac{(x_1 + x_2) + \lambda(y_1 - y_2)}{2}, \frac{(y_1 + y_2) - \lambda(x_1 - x_2)}{2}\right)$$

$$\equiv \left(\frac{2 + 4 + 3(2 - 2)}{2}, \frac{2 + 2 - 3(2 - 4)}{2}\right)$$

$$\equiv (3, 5)$$

Example 46. Find the circumcentre of triangle ABC if $A \equiv (7, 4)$, $B \equiv (3, -2)$ and $\angle C = \frac{\pi}{3}$.

Sol. Here, $x_1 = 7, y_1 = 4, x_2 = 3, y_2 = -2$ and $\angle C = \frac{\pi}{3}$

$\therefore$ The circumcentre of ΔABC

$$\equiv \left(\frac{(x_1 + x_2) \pm \cot C(y_1 - y_2)}{2}, \frac{(y_1 + y_2) \mp \cot C(x_1 - x_2)}{2}\right)$$

$$\equiv \left(\frac{(7+3) \pm \frac{1}{\sqrt{3}}(4+2)}{2}, \frac{(4-2) \mp \frac{1}{\sqrt{3}}(7-3)}{2}\right)$$

$$\equiv \left(5 + \sqrt{3}, 1 - \frac{2}{\sqrt{3}}\right) \text{ or } \left(5 - \sqrt{3}, 1 + \frac{2}{\sqrt{3}}\right)$$

3. Orthocentre of a Triangle

The orthocentre of a triangle is the point of intersection of altitudes
(i.e., the lines through the vertices and perpendicular to opposite sides).

Let $A(x_1, y_1)$, $B(x_2, y_2)$ and $C(x_3, y_3)$ be the vertices of ΔABC and if angles of ΔABC are given, then coordinates of orthocentre are

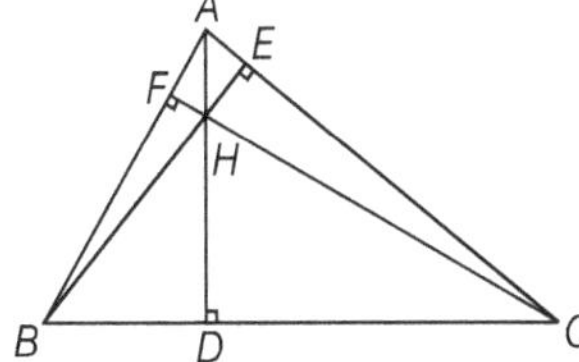

$$\left(\frac{x_1 \tan A + x_2 \tan B + x_3 \tan C}{\tan A + \tan B + \tan C}, \frac{y_1 \tan A + y_2 \tan B + y_3 \tan C}{\tan A + \tan B + \tan C}\right)$$

or
$$\left(\frac{ax_1 \sec A + bx_2 \sec B + cx_3 \sec C}{a \sec A + b \sec B + c \sec C}, \frac{ay_1 \sec A + by_2 \sec B + cy_3 \sec C}{a \sec A + b \sec B + c \sec C}\right)$$

where, $|BC| = a, |CA| = b$ and $|AB| = c$

Important trick for orthocentre :

orthocentre of the triangle whose vertices are (0, 0), (x_1, y_1) is given by

$$(\lambda(y_2 - y_1), -\lambda(x_2 - x_1))$$

where, $$\lambda = \frac{x_1x_2 + y_1y_2}{x_1y_2 - x_2y_1}$$

Remarks

1. The orthocentre of a triangle having vertices (α, β), (β, α) and (α, α) is (α, α).
2. The orthocentre of a triangle having vertices is $\left(-\frac{1}{\alpha\beta\gamma}, -\alpha\beta\gamma\right)$
3. The orthocentre of right angled triangle *ABC*, right angled at *A* is *A*.

Example 47. Find the orthocentre of ΔABC if $A \equiv (0, 0), B \equiv (3, 5)$ and $C \equiv (4, 7)$.

Sol. Here, $x_1 = 3, y_1 = 5, x_2 = 4, y_2 = 7$

$$\therefore \quad \lambda = \frac{3 \times 4 + 5 \times 7}{3 \times 7 - 4 \times 5} = 47$$

$\Rightarrow$ Orthocentre of $\Delta ABC \equiv (47(7-5), -47(4-3))$
$\equiv (94, -47)$

4. Nine Point Centre of a Triangle

If a circle passing through the feet of perpendiculars (i.e., D, E, F) mid-points of sides BC, CA, AB respectively (i.e., H, I, J) and the n x
mid-points of the line joining the orthocentre O to the angular points A, B, C (i.e., K, L, M) thus the nine points $D, E, F, H, I, J, K, L, M$ all lie on a circle.

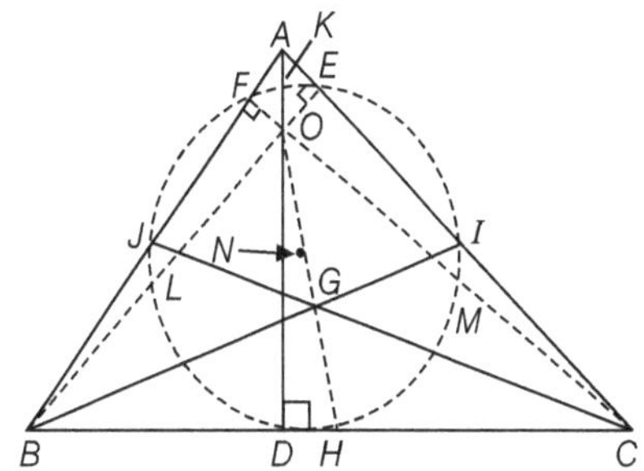

This circle is known as nine point circle and its centre is called the nine point centre. The nine-point centre of a triangle is collinear with the circumcentre and the orthocentre and bisects the segments joining them and radius of nine point circle of a triangle is half the radius of the circumcircle.

***Corollary* 1 :** The orthocentre, the nine point centre, the centroid and the circumcentre therefore all lie on a straight line.

Corollary* 2 :** If O is orthocentre, N is nine point centre, G is centroid and C is circumcentre, then to remember it see ***ONGC (i.e. Oil Natural Gas Corporation) in left of G are 2 and in right is 1, therefore G divides O and C in the ratio 2 : 1 (internally).

***Corollary* 3 :** N is the mid-point of O and C

***Corollary* 4 :** Radius of nine point circle $= \frac{1}{2} \times$ Radius of circumcircle

Remarks

1. The distance between the orthocentre and circumcentre in an equilateral triangle is zero.
2. If the circumcentre and centroid of a triangle are respectively (α, β) (γ, δ) then orthocentre will be $(3\gamma - 2\alpha, 3\delta - 2\beta)$.

Example 48. If a triangle has its orthocentre at (1,1) and circumcentre at $\left(\frac{3}{2}, \frac{3}{4}\right)$, then find the centroid and nine point centre.

Sol. Since, centroid divides the orthocentre and circumcentre in the ratio 2 : 1 (internally) and if centroid $G(x, y)$, then

$$O(1,1) \overset{2}{\text{———}} G(x,y) \overset{1}{\text{———}} C\left(\frac{3}{2}, \frac{3}{4}\right)$$

$$x = \frac{2 \times \frac{3}{2} + 1 \times 1}{2+1} = \frac{4}{3}$$

and $$y = \frac{2 \times \frac{3}{4} + 1 \times 1}{2+1} = \frac{5}{6}$$

$\therefore$ Centroid is $\left(\frac{4}{3}, \frac{5}{6}\right)$ and nine point centre is the mid-point of orthocentre and circumcentre.

$\therefore$ Nine point centre is $\left(\frac{1+\frac{3}{2}}{2}, \frac{1+\frac{3}{4}}{2}\right)$, i.e. $\left(\frac{5}{4}, \frac{7}{8}\right)$.

Example 49. The vertices of a triangle are $A(a, a\tan\alpha)$, $B(b, b\tan\beta)$ and $C(c, c\tan\gamma)$. If the circumcentre of ΔABC coincides with the origin and $H(\bar{x}, \bar{y})$ is the orthocentre, then show that

$$\frac{\bar{y}}{\bar{x}} = \left(\frac{\sin\alpha + \sin\beta + \sin\gamma}{\cos\alpha + \cos\beta + \cos\gamma}\right).$$

Sol. If R be the circumradius and O be the circumcentre

$\therefore$ $$OA = OB = OC = R$$

or $$\sqrt{(a^2 + a^2\tan^2\alpha)} = \sqrt{(b^2 + b^2\tan^2\beta)} = \sqrt{(c^2 + c^2\tan^2\gamma)} = R$$

or $$a\sec\alpha = b\sec\beta = c\sec\gamma = R$$

or $$a = R\cos\alpha,\ b = R\cos\beta,\ c = R\cos\gamma$$

then, $$a\tan\alpha = R\cos\alpha \cdot \frac{\sin\alpha}{\cos\alpha} = R\sin\alpha$$

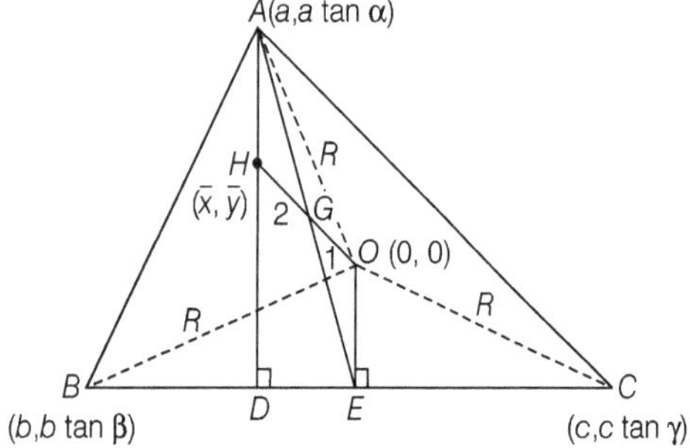

Similarly,

$$b\tan\beta = R\sin\beta \text{ and } c\tan\gamma = R\sin\gamma$$

$\therefore$ Coordinates of the vertices of a triangle are :

$$A(R\cos\alpha, R\sin\alpha), B(R\cos\beta, R\sin\beta)$$

and $$C(R\cos\gamma, R\sin\gamma)$$

$\therefore$ Centroid

$$(G) \equiv \left(\frac{R(\cos\alpha + \cos\beta + \cos\gamma)}{3}, \frac{R(\sin\alpha + \sin\beta + \sin\gamma)}{3}\right)$$

Since, G divides H and O in the ratio 2 : 1 (internally), then

$$\frac{R}{3}(\cos\alpha + \cos\beta + \cos\gamma) = \frac{2 \cdot 0 + 1 \cdot \bar{x}}{2+1}$$

or $$\frac{R}{3}(\cos\alpha + \cos\beta + \cos\gamma) = \frac{\bar{x}}{3} \quad \text{...(i)}$$

and $$\frac{R}{3}(\sin\alpha + \sin\beta + \sin\gamma) = \frac{2 \cdot 0 + 1 \cdot \bar{y}}{2+1}$$

or $$\frac{R}{3}(\sin\alpha + \sin\beta + \sin\gamma) = \frac{\bar{y}}{3} \quad \text{...(ii)}$$

Dividing Eqs. (ii) by (i), then we get

$$\frac{\bar{y}}{\bar{x}} = \left(\frac{\sin\alpha + \sin\beta + \sin\gamma}{\cos\alpha + \cos\beta + \cos\gamma}\right)$$

Area of a Triangle

Theorem : The area of a triangle, the coordinates of whose vertices are $(x_1, y_1), (x_2, y_2)$ and (x_3, y_3) is

$$\frac{1}{2}|x_1(y_2 - y_3) + x_2(y_3 - y_1) + x_3(y_1 - y_2)|$$

or $$\frac{1}{2}\left|\begin{vmatrix} x_1 & y_1 & 1 \\ x_2 & y_2 & 1 \\ x_3 & y_3 & 1 \end{vmatrix}\right|$$

Proof : Let ABC be a triangle with vertices $A(x_1, y_1)$, $B(x_2, y_2)$ and $C(x_3, y_3)$. Let us assume that the points A, B and C are in 1st quadrant (for the sake of exactness). Draw AL, BM and CN perpendicular on X-axis. Let Δ be the required area of the triangle ABC, then

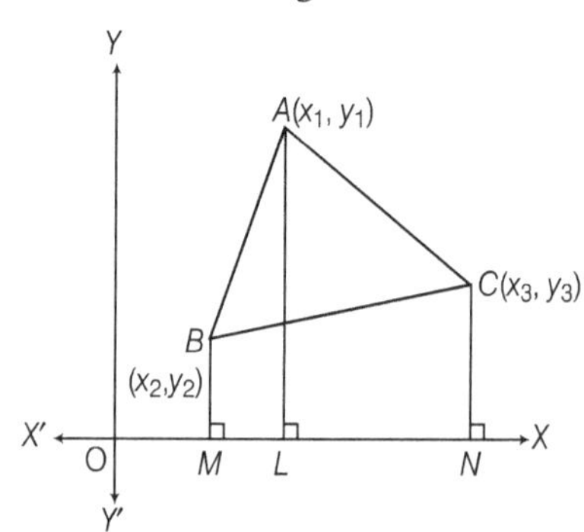

$\Delta =$ Area of triangle ABC

$=$ [Area of trapezium $ABML$ + Area of trapezium $ALNC$ − Area of trapezium $BMNC$]

[$\because$ Area of trapezium $= \frac{1}{2}$ (Sum of parallel sides) × (Distance between them)]

$$\therefore \Delta = \left[\frac{1}{2}(BM + AL)(ML) + \frac{1}{2}(AL + CN)(LN) - \frac{1}{2}(BM + CN)(MN)\right]$$

$$= \left[\frac{1}{2}(BM + AL)(OL - OM) + \frac{1}{2}(AL + CN)(ON - (OL) - \frac{1}{2}(BM + CN)(ON - OM)\right]$$

$$= \left[\frac{1}{2}(y_2 + y_1)(x_1 - x_2) + \frac{1}{2}(y_1 + y_3)(x_3 - x_1) - \frac{1}{2}(y_2 + y_3)(x_3 - x_2)\right]$$

$$= \frac{1}{2}[x_1(y_2 + y_1 - y_1 - y_3) + x_2(-y_2 - y_1 + y_2 + y_3) + x_3(y_1 + y_3 - y_2 - y_3)]$$

$$= \frac{1}{2}[x_1(y_2 - y_3) + x_2(y_3 - y_1) + x_3(y_1 - y_2)]$$

The area of triangle ABC will come out to be a positive quantity only when the vertices A, B, C are taken in anticlockwise direction and if points A, B, C are taken in clockwise direction then the area will be negative and if the points A, B, C are taken arbitrary then the area will be positive or negative, the numerical value being the same in all cases.

Thus in general (i.e., $\triangle ABC$ with + inside, $\triangle ABC$ with − inside)

$$\text{Area of } \Delta ABC = \frac{1}{2}|x_1(y_2 - y_3) + x_2(y_3 - y_1) + x_3(y_1 - y_2)|$$

This expression can be written in determinant form as follows

$$\frac{1}{2}\left|\begin{vmatrix} x_1 & y_1 & 1 \\ x_2 & y_2 & 1 \\ x_3 & y_3 & 1 \end{vmatrix}\right|$$

***Corollary* 1 :** Area of triangle can also be found by easy method

$$\Delta = \left|\frac{1}{2}\begin{vmatrix} x_1 & y_1 \\ x_2 & y_2 \end{vmatrix} + \frac{1}{2}\begin{vmatrix} x_2 & y_2 \\ x_3 & y_3 \end{vmatrix} + \frac{1}{2}\begin{vmatrix} x_3 & y_3 \\ x_1 & y_1 \end{vmatrix}\right|$$

and **Area of quadrilateral *ABCD* :** The area of a quadrilateral can be found out by dividing the quadrilateral into two triangles.

$\therefore$ Area of quadrilateral $ABCD$

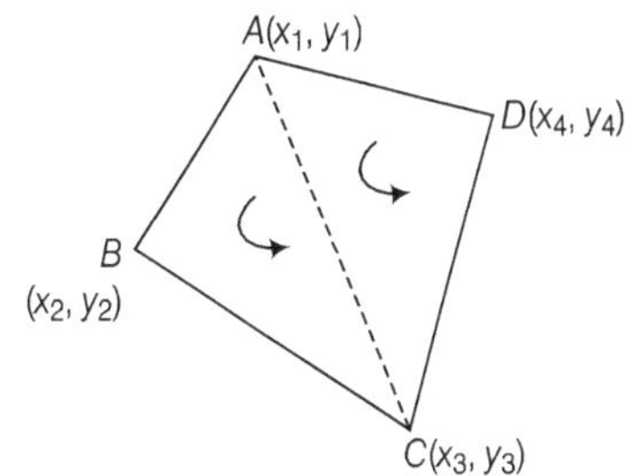

$= \text{Area of } \Delta ABC + \text{Area of } \Delta DAC$

$$= \frac{1}{2}\begin{vmatrix} x_1 & y_1 \\ x_2 & y_2 \end{vmatrix} + \frac{1}{2}\begin{vmatrix} x_2 & y_2 \\ x_3 & y_3 \end{vmatrix} + \frac{1}{2}\begin{vmatrix} x_3 & y_3 \\ x_1 & y_1 \end{vmatrix} + \frac{1}{2}\begin{vmatrix} x_4 & y_4 \\ x_1 & y_1 \end{vmatrix} + \frac{1}{2}\begin{vmatrix} x_1 & y_1 \\ x_3 & y_3 \end{vmatrix} + \frac{1}{2}\begin{vmatrix} x_3 & y_3 \\ x_4 & y_4 \end{vmatrix}$$

$$= \left|\frac{1}{2}\begin{vmatrix} x_1 & y_1 \\ x_2 & y_2 \end{vmatrix} + \frac{1}{2}\begin{vmatrix} x_2 & y_2 \\ x_3 & y_3 \end{vmatrix} + \frac{1}{2}\begin{vmatrix} x_3 & y_3 \\ x_4 & y_4 \end{vmatrix}\right| + \frac{1}{2}\begin{vmatrix} x_4 & y_4 \\ x_1 & y_1 \end{vmatrix}$$

$$\left(\because \begin{vmatrix} x_3 & y_3 \\ x_1 & y_1 \end{vmatrix} = -\begin{vmatrix} x_1 & y_1 \\ x_3 & y_3 \end{vmatrix}\right)$$

$\therefore$ **Area of polygon whose vertices are $(x_1, y_1), (x_2, y_2), (x_3, y_3), \ldots, (x_n, y_n)$ is**

$$\frac{1}{2}\left|\begin{vmatrix} x_1 & y_1 \\ x_2 & y_2 \end{vmatrix} + \begin{vmatrix} x_2 & y_2 \\ x_3 & y_3 \end{vmatrix} + \begin{vmatrix} x_3 & y_3 \\ x_4 & y_4 \end{vmatrix} + \ldots + \begin{vmatrix} x_n & y_n \\ x_1 & y_1 \end{vmatrix}\right|$$

Or

Stair Method Repeat first coordinates one time in last for down arrow use positive sign and for up arrow use negative sign.

$$\therefore \quad \text{Area of polygon} = \frac{1}{2}\left|\begin{vmatrix} x_1 & y_1 \\ x_2 & y_2 \\ x_3 & y_3 \\ -- & -- \\ -- & -- \\ x_n & y_n \\ x_1 & y_1 \end{vmatrix}\right|$$

$$= \frac{1}{2}|\{(x_1y_2 + x_2y_3 + \ldots + x_ny_1) - (y_1x_2 + y_2x_3 + \ldots + y_nx_1)\}|$$

***Corollary* 2 :** If the coordinates of the vertices of the triangle are given in polar form i.e.,

$A(r_1, \theta_1), B(r_2, \theta_2), C(r_3, \theta_3)$.

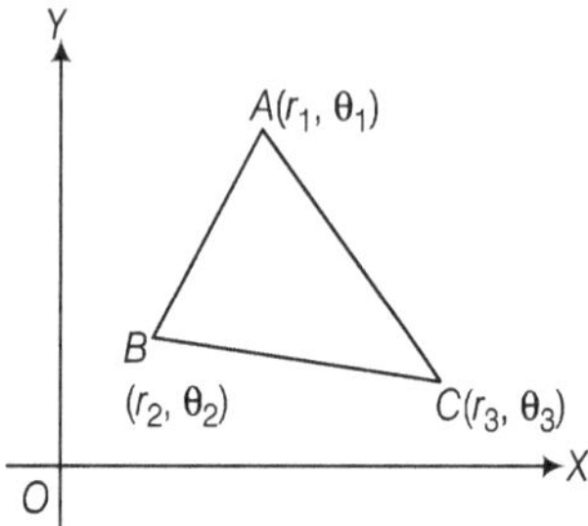

Then, area of triangle

$$= \frac{1}{2}| r_1 r_2 \sin(\theta_1 - \theta_2) + r_2 r_3 \sin(\theta_2 - \theta_3) + r_3 r_1 \sin(\theta_3 - \theta_1)|$$

$$= \frac{1}{2}| \sum r_1 r_2 \sin(\theta_1 - \theta_2)|$$

***Corollary* 3 :** If $a_1 x + b_1 y + c_1 = 0$, $a_2 x + b_2 y + c_2 = 0$ and $a_3 x + b_3 y + c_3 = 0$ are the sides of a triangle, then the area of the triangle is given by (without solving the vertices)

$$\Delta = \frac{1}{2|C_1 C_2 C_3|} \begin{vmatrix} a_1 & b_1 & c_1 \\ a_2 & b_2 & c_2 \\ a_3 & b_3 & c_3 \end{vmatrix}^2$$

where, C_1, C_2, C_3 are the cofactors of c_1, c_2, c_3 in the determinant

Here, $$C_1 = \begin{vmatrix} a_2 & b_2 \\ a_3 & b_3 \end{vmatrix} = (a_2 b_3 - a_3 b_2)$$

$$C_2 = \begin{vmatrix} a_3 & b_3 \\ a_1 & b_1 \end{vmatrix} = (a_3 b_1 - a_1 b_3)$$

and $$C_3 = \begin{vmatrix} a_1 & b_1 \\ a_2 & b_2 \end{vmatrix} = (a_1 b_2 - a_2 b_1)$$

and $$\begin{vmatrix} a_1 & b_1 & c_1 \\ a_2 & b_2 & c_2 \\ a_3 & b_3 & c_3 \end{vmatrix} = c_1 C_1 + c_2 C_2 + c_3 C_3$$

Or

$$\text{Area of triangle} = \frac{\Delta^2}{2|\Delta_1 \Delta_2 \Delta_3|}$$

where, $\Delta = \begin{vmatrix} a_1 & b_1 & c_1 \\ a_2 & b_2 & c_2 \\ a_3 & b_3 & c_3 \end{vmatrix}, \Delta_1 = \begin{vmatrix} a_1 & b_1 \\ a_2 & b_2 \end{vmatrix}, \Delta_2 = \begin{vmatrix} a_2 & b_2 \\ a_3 & b_3 \end{vmatrix}$

and $\Delta_3 = \begin{vmatrix} a_3 & b_3 \\ a_1 & b_1 \end{vmatrix}$

***Corollary* 4 :** Area of the triangle formed by the lines of the form $y = m_1 x + c_1, y = m_2 x + c_2$ and $y = m_3 x + c_3$ is

$$\Delta = \frac{1}{2}\left|\frac{(c_2 - c_3)^2}{(m_2 - m_3)} + \frac{(c_3 - c_1)^2}{(m_3 - m_1)} + \frac{(c_1 - c_2)^2}{(m_1 - m_2)}\right|$$

Remarks

1. If area of a triangle is given then, use ± sign.
2. The points $A(x_1, y_1)$, $B(x_2, y_2)$ and $C(x_3, y_3)$ are collinear, then area of $(\Delta ABC) = 0$.
3. Four given points will be collinear, then area of the quadrilateral is zero.
4. Area of the triangle formed by the points (x_1, y_1), (x_2, y_2) and (x_3, y_3) is $\Delta = \frac{1}{2}\left|\begin{vmatrix} x_1 - x_3 & x_2 - x_3 \\ y_1 - y_3 & y_2 - y_3 \end{vmatrix}\right|$
5. If one vertex (x_3, y_3) is at (0, 0) then, $\Delta = \frac{1}{2}| x_1 y_2 - x_2 y_1 |$

Example 50. The coordinates of A, B, C are $(6, 3), (-3, 5)$ and $(4, -2)$ respectively and P is any points (x, y). Show that the ratio of the areas of the triangles PBC and ABC is $\frac{|x + y - 2|}{7}$.

Sol. We have

$$\frac{\text{Area of } \Delta PBC}{\text{Area of } \Delta ABC} = \frac{\frac{1}{2}|\{x(5+2) - 3(-2-y) + 4(y-5)\}|}{\frac{1}{2}|\{6(5+2) - 3(-2-3) + 4(3-5)\}|}$$

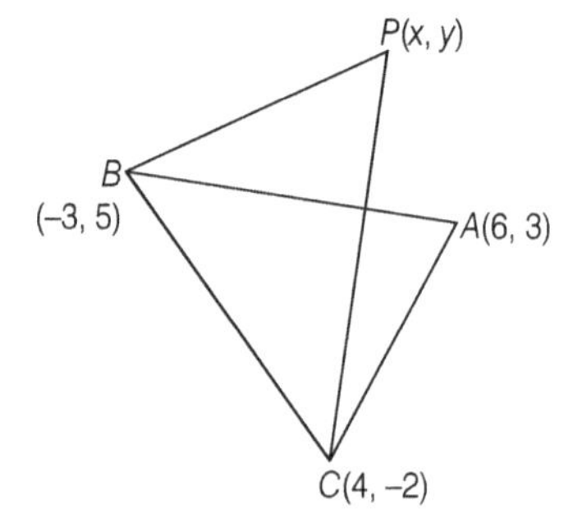

$$= \frac{|7x + 7y - 14|}{|49|} = \frac{7|x + y - 2|}{49} = \frac{|x + y - 2|}{7}$$

Example 51. Find the area of the pentagon whose vertices are $A(1, 1), B(7, 21), C(7 - 3), D(12, 2)$ and $E(0, -3)$.

Sol. The required area

$$= \frac{1}{2}\left|\begin{vmatrix} 1 & 1 \\ 7 & 21 \end{vmatrix} + \begin{vmatrix} 7 & 21 \\ 7 & -3 \end{vmatrix} + \begin{vmatrix} 7 & -3 \\ 12 & 2 \end{vmatrix} + \begin{vmatrix} 12 & 2 \\ 0 & -3 \end{vmatrix} + \begin{vmatrix} 0 & -3 \\ 1 & 1 \end{vmatrix}\right|$$

$$= \frac{1}{2}|(21 - 7) + (-21 - 147) + (14 + 36) + (-36 - 0) + (0 + 3)|$$

$$= \frac{1}{2}|-137| = \frac{137}{2} \text{ sq units}$$

Example 52. Show that the points $(a, 0), (0, b)$ and $(1, 1)$ are collinear, if $\frac{1}{a}+\frac{1}{b}=1$

Sol. Let $A \equiv (a, 0)$, $B \equiv (0, b)$ and $C \equiv (1, 1)$

Now, points A, B, C will be collinear, if area of $\Delta ABC = 0$

or $$\frac{1}{2}\left|\begin{vmatrix} a & 0 \\ 0 & b \end{vmatrix}+\begin{vmatrix} 0 & b \\ 1 & 1 \end{vmatrix}+\begin{vmatrix} 1 & 1 \\ a & 0 \end{vmatrix}\right|=0$$

$\Rightarrow$ $$|(ab-0)+(0-b)+(0-a)|=0$$

or $$ab-a-b=0$$

or $$a+b=ab \text{ or } \frac{1}{a}+\frac{1}{b}=1$$

Example 53. Prove that the coordinates of the vertices of an equilateral triangle can not all be rational.

Sol. Let $A(x_1, y_1)$, $B(x_2, y_2)$ and $C(x_3, y_3)$ be the vertices of a triangle ABC. If possible let $x_1, y_1, x_2, y_2, x_3, y_3$ be all rational.

Now, area of ΔABC $$=\frac{1}{2}|x_1(y_2-y_3)+x_2(y_3-y_1)+x_3(y_1-y_2)|$$

$$= \text{Rational} \quad \text{...(i)}$$

Since, ΔABC is equilateral

$\therefore$ Area of ΔABC $$=\frac{\sqrt{3}}{4}(\text{side})^2$$

$$=\frac{\sqrt{3}}{4}(AB)^2$$

$$=\frac{\sqrt{3}}{4}\{(x_1-x_2)^2+(y_1-y_2)^2\}$$

$$= \text{Irrational} \quad \text{...(ii)}$$

From Eqs. (i) and (ii),

Rational = Irrational

which is contradiction.

Hence, $x_1, y_1, x_2, y_2, x_3, y_3$ cannot all be rational.

Example 54. The coordinates of two points A and B are (3, 4) and (5, –2) respectively. Find the coordinates of any point P if $PA = PB$ and area of ΔAPB is 10.

Sol. Let coordinates of P be (h, k).

$\because$ $$PA = PB \Rightarrow (PA)^2=(PB)^2$$

$\Rightarrow$ $$(h-3)^2+(k-4)^2=(h-5)^2+(k+2)^2$$

$\Rightarrow$ $$(h-3)^2-(h-5)^2+(k-4)^2-(k+2)^2=0$$

$\Rightarrow$ $$(2h-8)(2)+(2k-2)(-6)=0$$

$\Rightarrow$ $$(h-4)-3(k-1)=0$$

$\Rightarrow$ $$h-3k-1=0 \quad \text{...(i)}$$

Now, Area of ΔPAB $$=\frac{1}{2}\left|\begin{vmatrix} h & k & 1 \\ 3 & 4 & 1 \\ 5 & -2 & 1 \end{vmatrix}\right|=10$$

or $$6h+2k-26=\pm 20$$

$\Rightarrow$ $$6h+2k-46=0 \text{ or } 6h+2k-6=0$$

$\Rightarrow$ $$3h+k-23=0 \text{ or } 3h+k-3=0$$

Solving $h-3k-1=0$ and $3h+k-23=0$,

we get $h=7, k=2$

Solving $h-3k-1=0$ and $3h+k-3=0$,

we get $h=1, k=0$

Hence, the coordinates of P are (7, 2) or (1, 0).

Example 55. Find the area of the triangle formed by the straight lines $7x-2y+10=0$, $7x+2y-10=0$ and $9x+y+2=0$ (without solving the vertices of the triangle).

Sol. The given lines are :

$$7x-2y+10=0$$
$$7x+2y-10=0$$
$$9x+y+2=0$$

$\therefore$ Area of triangle $$\Delta=\frac{1}{2|C_1C_2C_3|}\begin{vmatrix} 7 & -2 & 10 \\ 7 & 2 & -10 \\ 9 & 1 & 2 \end{vmatrix}^2 \quad \text{...(i)}$$

where, $$C_1=\begin{vmatrix} 7 & 2 \\ 9 & 1 \end{vmatrix}=7-18=-11,$$

$$C_2=\begin{vmatrix} 9 & 1 \\ 7 & -2 \end{vmatrix}=-18-7=-25$$

and $$C_3=\begin{vmatrix} 7 & -2 \\ 7 & 2 \end{vmatrix}=14+14=28,$$

and $$\begin{vmatrix} 7 & -2 & 10 \\ 7 & 2 & -10 \\ 9 & 1 & 2 \end{vmatrix}=10C_1-10C_2+2C_3$$

$$=10\times(-11)-10\times(-25)+2\times 28=196$$

$\therefore$ From Eq. (i), $$\Delta=\frac{1}{2|-11\times(-25)\times 28|}\times(196)^2$$

$$=\frac{196\times 196}{2\times 11\times 25\times 28}=\frac{686}{275} \text{ sq units}$$

Example 56. If Δ_1 is the area of the triangle with vertices $(0,0)$, $(a\tan\alpha, b\cot\alpha)$, $(a\sin\alpha, b\cos\alpha)$; Δ_2 is the area of the triangle with vertices (a,b), $(a\sec^2\alpha, b\,\text{cosec}^2\alpha)$, $(a+a\sin^2\alpha, b+b\cos^2\alpha)$ and Δ_3 is the area of the triangle with vertices $(0,0)$, $(a\tan\alpha, -b\cot\alpha)$, $(a\sin\alpha, b\cos\alpha)$. Show that there is no value of α for which Δ_1, Δ_2 and Δ_3 are in GP.

Sol. We have, $\Delta_1 = \frac{1}{2}|(a\tan\alpha)(b\cos\alpha) - (a\sin\alpha)(b\cot\alpha)|$ ($\because$ one vertex is (0,0))

$$= \frac{1}{2}|ab||\sin\alpha - \cos\alpha| \quad \text{... (i)}$$

and $\Delta_2 = \frac{1}{2}\left|\begin{vmatrix} a-(a+a\sin^2\alpha) & a\sec^2\alpha-(a+a\sin^2\alpha) \\ b-(b+b\cos^2\alpha) & b\operatorname{cosec}^2\alpha-(b+b\cos^2\alpha)\end{vmatrix}\right|$ (See remark 4)

$$= \frac{1}{2}\left|\begin{vmatrix} -a\sin^2\alpha & a(\tan^2\alpha-\sin^2\alpha) \\ -b\cos^2\alpha & b(\cot^2\alpha-\cos^2\alpha)\end{vmatrix}\right|$$

$$= \frac{1}{2}|ab|\times\left|\begin{vmatrix} -\sin^2\alpha & \sin^2\alpha(\sec^2\alpha-1) \\ -\cos^2\alpha & \cos^2\alpha(\operatorname{cosec}^2\alpha-1)\end{vmatrix}\right|$$

$$= \frac{1}{2}|ab|\times\left|\begin{vmatrix} -\sin^2\alpha & \sin^2\alpha\tan^2\alpha \\ -\cos^2\alpha & \cos^2\alpha\cot^2\alpha\end{vmatrix}\right|$$

$$= \frac{1}{2}|ab|\times|-\sin^2\alpha\cos^2\alpha\cot^2\alpha + \sin^2\alpha\cos^2\alpha\tan^2\alpha|$$

$$= \frac{1}{2}|ab|\times|-\cos^4\alpha + \sin^4\alpha|$$

$$= \frac{1}{2}|ab|\times|\sin^2\alpha + \cos^2\alpha|\times|\sin^2\alpha - \cos^2\alpha|$$

$$= \frac{1}{2}|ab|\times|1|\times|-\cos 2\alpha|$$

$$= \frac{1}{2}|ab|\times|\cos 2\alpha| \quad \text{... (ii)}$$

and $\Delta_3 = \frac{1}{2}|(a\tan\alpha)(b\cos\alpha) - (-b\cot\alpha)(a\sin\alpha)|$

$$= \frac{1}{2}|ab||\sin\alpha + \cos\alpha| \quad \text{... (iii)}$$

Since, $\Delta_1, \Delta_2, \Delta_3$ are in GP, then $\Delta_1\Delta_3 = \Delta_2^2$

$\Rightarrow \frac{1}{2}|ab||\sin\alpha - \cos\alpha| \times \frac{1}{2}|ab||\sin\alpha + \cos\alpha|$

$= \frac{1}{4}|ab|^2|\cos 2\alpha|^2$ [from Eqs. (i), (ii) and (iii)]

$\Rightarrow |\sin^2\alpha - \cos^2\alpha| = |\cos 2\alpha|^2$

$\Rightarrow |-\cos 2\alpha| = |\cos 2\alpha|^2$

$\Rightarrow |\cos 2\alpha| = |\cos 2\alpha|^2$

$\Rightarrow |\cos 2\alpha|(1 - |\cos 2\alpha|) = 0$

$\therefore 1 - |\cos 2\alpha| = 0$ ($\because |\cos 2\alpha| \neq 0$)

$\Rightarrow |\cos 2\alpha| = 1$

or $\cos 2\alpha = \pm 1$ or $\cos 2\alpha = 1$

and $\cos 2\alpha = -1$

or $2\alpha = 2n\pi, 2\alpha = (2p+1)\pi$

or $\alpha = n\pi, \alpha = p\pi + \frac{\pi}{2}; n, p \in I$

For these values of α the vertices of the given triangles are not defined. Hence Δ_1, Δ_2 and Δ_3 cannot be in GP for any value of α.

Exercise for Session 3

1. The coordinates of the middle points of the sides of a triangle are (4, 2), (3, 3) and (2, 2), then coordinates of centroid are

   (a) (3, 7/3) (b) (3, 3) (c) (4, 3) (d) (3, 4)

2. The incentre of the triangle whose vertices are (−36, 7), (20, 7) and (0, −8) is

   (a) (0, −1) (b) (−1, 0) (c) (1, 1) (d) $\left(\frac{1}{2}, 1\right)$

3. If the orthocentre and centroid of a triangle are (−3, 5) and (3, 3) then its circumcentre is

   (a) (6, 2) (b) (3, −1) (c) (−3, 5) (d) (−3, 1)

4. An equilateral triangle has each side equal to a. If the coordinates of its vertices are $(x_1, y_1), (x_2, y_2)$ and (x_3, y_3) then the square of the determinant $\begin{vmatrix} x_1 & y_1 & 1 \\ x_2 & y_2 & 1 \\ x_3 & y_3 & 1 \end{vmatrix}$ equals

   (a) $3a^4$ (b) $\frac{3a^4}{2}$ (c) $\frac{3}{4}a^4$ (d) $\frac{3}{8}a^4$

5. The vertices of a triangle are $A(0, 0), B(0, 2)$ and $C(2, 0)$. The distance between circumcentre and orthocentre is

   (a) $\sqrt{2}$ (b) $\frac{1}{\sqrt{2}}$ (c) 2 (d) $\frac{1}{2}$

6. $A(a, b)$, $B(x_1, y_1)$ and $C(x_2, y_2)$ are the vertices of a triangle. If a, x_1, x_2 are in GP with common ratio r and b, y_1, y_2 are in GP with common ratio s, then area of ΔABC is

(a) $ab\ (r-1)(s-1)(s-r)$
(b) $\frac{1}{2}ab\ (r+1)(s+1)(s-r)$
(c) $\frac{1}{2}ab\ (r-1)(s-1)(s-r)$
(d) $ab\ (r+1)(s+1)(r-s)$

7. The points $(x+1, 2)$, $(1, x+2)$, $\left(\frac{1}{x+1}, \frac{2}{x+1}\right)$ are collinear, then x is equal to

(a) -4
(b) -8
(c) 4
(d) 8

8. The vertices of a triangle are $(6, 0)$, $(0, 6)$ and $(6, 6)$. Then distance between its circumcentre and centroid, is

(a) $2\sqrt{2}$
(b) 2
(c) $\sqrt{2}$
(d) 1

9. The nine point centre of the triangle with vertices $(1, \sqrt{3})$, $(0, 0)$ and $(2, 0)$ is

(a) $\left(1, \frac{\sqrt{3}}{2}\right)$
(b) $\left(\frac{2}{3}, \frac{1}{\sqrt{3}}\right)$
(c) $\left(\frac{2}{3}, \frac{\sqrt{3}}{2}\right)$
(d) $\left(1 \frac{1}{\sqrt{3}}\right)$

10. The vertices of a triangle are $(0, 0)$, $(1, 0)$ and $(0, 1)$. Then excentre opposite to $(0, 0)$ is

(a) $\left(1-\frac{1}{\sqrt{2}}, 1+\frac{1}{\sqrt{2}}\right)$
(b) $\left(1+\frac{1}{\sqrt{2}}, 1+\frac{1}{\sqrt{2}}\right)$
(c) $\left(1+\frac{1}{\sqrt{2}}, 1-\frac{1}{\sqrt{2}}\right)$
(d) $\left(1-\frac{1}{\sqrt{2}}, 1-\frac{1}{\sqrt{2}}\right)$

11. If α, β, γ are the real roots of the equation $x^3 - 3px^2 + 3qx - 1 = 0$, then find the centroid of the triangle whose vertices are $\left(\alpha, \frac{1}{\alpha}\right)$, $\left(\beta, \frac{1}{\beta}\right)$ and $\left(\gamma, \frac{1}{\gamma}\right)$.

12. If centroid of a triangle be $(1, 4)$ and the coordinates of its any two vertices are $(4, -8)$ and $(-9, 7)$, find the area of the triangle.

13. Find the centroid and incentre of the triangle whose vertices are $(1, 2)$, $(2, 3)$ and $(3, 4)$.

14. Show that the area of the triangle with vertices $(\lambda, \lambda - 2)$, $(\lambda + 3, \lambda)$ and $(\lambda + 2, \lambda + 2)$ is independent of λ.

15. Prove that the points $(a, b+c)$, $(b, c+a)$ and $(c, a+b)$ are collinear.

16. Prove that the points (a, b), (c, d) and $(a-c, b-d)$ are collinear, if $ad = bc$.

17. If the points (x_1, y_1), (x_2, y_2) and (x_3, y_3) are collinear, show that $\sum \left(\frac{y_1 - y_2}{x_1 x_2}\right) = 0$, i.e.

$$\frac{y_1 - y_2}{x_1 x_2} + \frac{y_2 - y_3}{x_2 x_3} + \frac{y_3 - y_1}{x_3 x_1} = 0$$

18. The coordinates of points A, B, C and D are $(-3, 5)$, $(4, -2)$, $(x, 3x)$ and $(6, 3)$ respectively and $\frac{\Delta ABC}{\Delta BCD} = \frac{2}{3}$, find x.

19. Find the area of the hexagon whose vertices taken in order are $(5, 0)$, $(4, 2)$, $(1, 3)$, $(-2, 2)$, $(-3, -1)$ and $(0, -4)$.

Session 4

Locus and Its Equation, Change of Axes the Transformation of Axes, Removal of the Term *xy* from *F*(*x*, *y*) = $ax^2 + 2hxy + by^2$ without Changing the Origin, Position of a Point which lies Inside a Triangle

Locus and Its Equation

Locus : The locus of a moving point is the path traced out by that point under one or more given conditions.

For example 1. If a point P moves in a plane such that whose distance from a fixed point O (say) in the plane is always constant distance a. Thus the locus of the moving point P is clearly a circle with centre O and radius a.

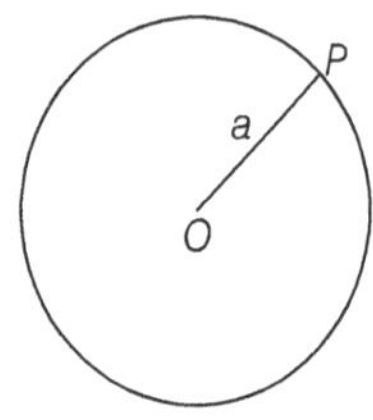

For example 2. If a point P moves in a plane such that whose distance from two fixed points A and B (say) are always equal i.e. $PA = PB$

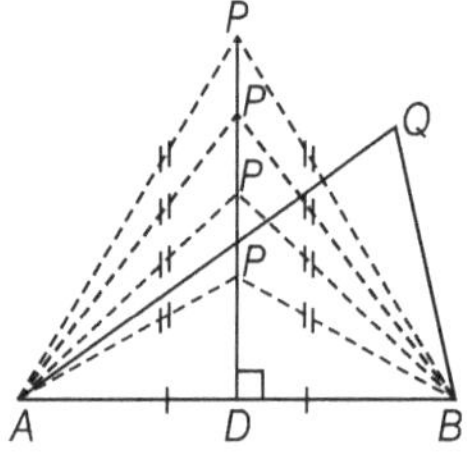

(The point P cannot be at Q because $AQ \neq BQ$)

Obviously all the positions of the moving point P lies on the right bisector of AB. Thus the locus of the moving point P is the right bisector of AB.

Equation of a Locus

A relation $f(x, y) = 0$ between x and y which is satisfied by each point on the locus and such that each point satisfying the equation is on the locus is called the ***equation of the locus***.

How to Find the Locus of a Point

Let (x_1, y_1) be the coordinates of the moving point say P. Now, apply the geometrical conditions on x_1, y_1. This gives a relation between x_1 and y_1. Now replace x_1 by x and y_1 by y in the eliminant and resulting equation would be the equation of the locus.

***Corollary* 1 :** If x and y are not there in the question, the coordinates of P may also be taken as (x, y).

***Corollary* 2 :** If coordinates and equation are not given in the question, suitable choice of origin and axes may be made.

***Corollary* 3 :** To find the locus of the point of intersection of two straight lines, eliminate the parameter or parameters from the given lines. If more than one parameter, then additional condition or conditions will also be given.

> ***Note***
>
> Simplify the equation by squaring both sides if square roots are there and taking LCM to remove the denominators.

Example 57. Find the locus of a point which moves such that its distance from the point (0, 0) is twice its distance from the Y-axis.

Sol. Let $P(x_1, y_1)$ be the moving point whose locus is required.

By hypothesis $|OP| = 2|PM|$ $\quad$ ($\because$ P lies in any quadrant)

$$\Rightarrow \sqrt{(x_1^2 + y_1^2)} = 2|x_1|$$

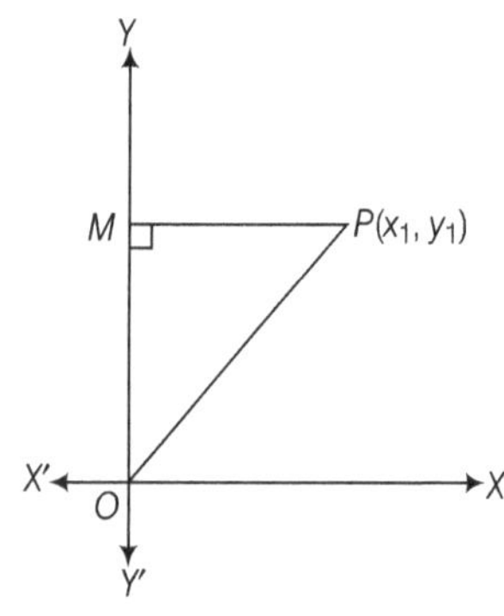

Squaring both sides, then

$$x_1^2 + y_1^2 = 4x_1^2$$

$$\Rightarrow \quad 3x_1^2 - y_1^2 = 0$$

Changing (x_1, y_1) to (x, y), then

$$3x^2 - y^2 = 0$$

which is the required locus of P.

Example 58. Find the locus of the moving point P such that $2PA = 3PB$, where A is $(0, 0)$ and B is $(4, -3)$.

Sol. Let $P(x_1, y_1)$ be the moving point whose locus is required.

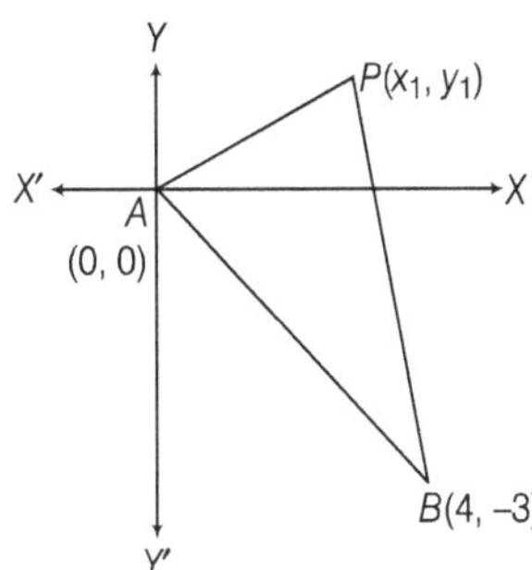

By hypothesis,

$$2PA = 3PB \text{ or } 4(PA)^2 = 9(PB)^2$$

$$\Rightarrow \quad 4\{x_1^2 + y_1^2\} = 9\{(x_1 - 4)^2 + (y_1 + 3)^2\}$$

$$\Rightarrow \quad 4(x_1^2 + y_1^2) = 9(x_1^2 + y_1^2 - 8x_1 + 6y_1 + 25)$$

$$\text{or} \quad 5x_1^2 + 5y_1^2 - 72x_1 + 54y_1 + 225 = 0$$

Changing (x_1, y_1) to (x, y), then

$$5x^2 + 5y^2 - 72x + 54y + 225 = 0$$

which is the required locus of P.

Example 59. A point moves so that the sum of the squares of its distances from two fixed points $A(a, 0)$ and $B(-a, 0)$ is constant and equal to $2c^2$, find the locus of the point.

Sol. Let $P(x_1, y_1)$ be the moving point whose locus is required.

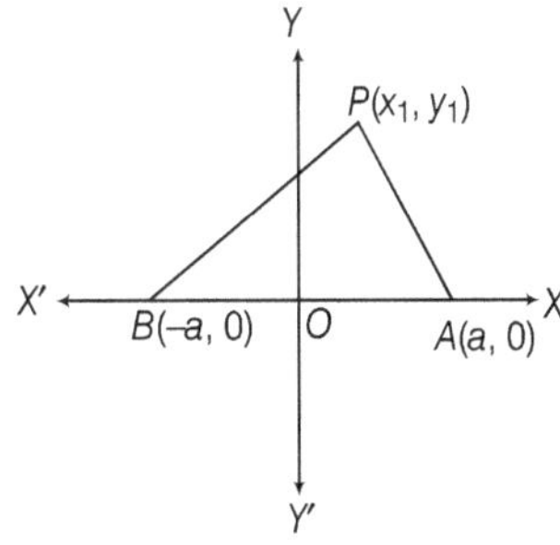

By hypothesis, $\quad (PA)^2 + (PB)^2 = 2c^2$

$$\Rightarrow \quad (x_1 - a)^2 + (y_1 - 0)^2 + (x_1 + a)^2 + (y_1 - 0)^2 = 2c^2$$

$$\Rightarrow \quad 2x_1^2 + 2y_1^2 + 2a^2 = 2c^2$$

$$\text{or} \quad x_1^2 + y_1^2 = c^2 - a^2$$

Changing (x_1, y_1) to (x, y), then

$$x^2 + y^2 = c^2 - a^2$$

which is the required locus of P.

Example 60. A point moves such that the sum of its distances from two fixed points $(ae, 0)$ and $(-ae, 0)$ is always $2a$. Prove that the equation of the locus is

$$\frac{x^2}{a^2} + \frac{y^2}{b^2} = 1, \quad \text{where } b^2 = a^2(1 - e^2)$$

Sol. Let $P(x_1, y_1)$ be the moving point whose locus is required and $A(ae, 0)$ and $B(-ae, 0)$ be the given fixed points.

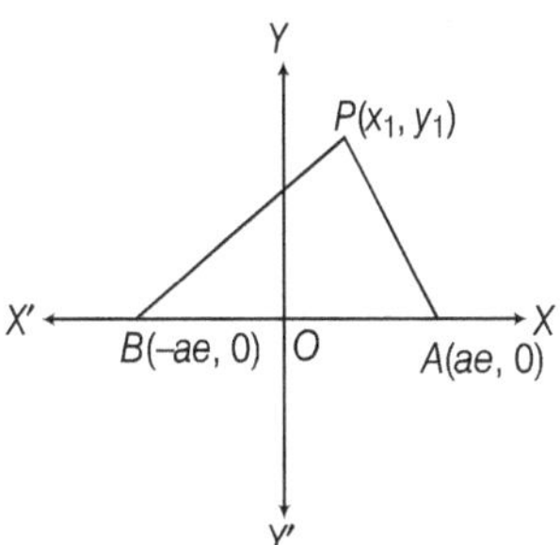

By hypothesis, $\quad |PA| + |PB| = 2a$

$$\text{or} \quad \sqrt{(x_1 - ae)^2 + (y_1 - 0)^2} + \sqrt{(x_1 + ae)^2 + (y_1 - 0)^2} = 2a$$

$$\text{or} \quad \sqrt{(x_1^2 + y_1^2 - 2aex_1 + a^2e^2)} + \sqrt{(x_1^2 + y_1^2 + 2aex_1 + a^2e^2)} = 2a \quad \text{...(i)}$$

Let $\quad l = x_1^2 + y_1^2 - 2aex_1 + a^2e^2$

and $\quad m = x_1^2 + y_1^2 + 2aex_1 + a^2e^2 \quad$ ($l - m$ method)

then, Eq. (i) can be written as

$$\sqrt{l} + \sqrt{m} = 2a \quad \text{...(ii)}$$

and $\quad l - m = -4aex_1$

$$\text{or} \quad (\sqrt{l} + \sqrt{m})(\sqrt{l} - \sqrt{m}) = -4aex_1$$

$$\text{or} \quad 2a(\sqrt{l} - \sqrt{m}) = -4aex_1 \quad \text{[from Eq. (ii)]}$$

$$\text{or} \quad \sqrt{l} - \sqrt{m} = -2ex_1 \quad \text{...(iii)}$$

Adding Eqs. (ii) and (iii), then

$$2\sqrt{l} = 2a - 2ex_1 \text{ or } \sqrt{l} = a - ex_1$$

Squaring both sides,

$$l = a^2 - 2aex_1 + e^2x_1^2$$

$$\Rightarrow \quad x_1^2 + y_1^2 - 2aex_1 + a^2e^2 = a^2 - 2aex_1 + e^2x_1^2$$

$$\Rightarrow \quad (1 - e^2)x_1^2 + y_1^2 = a^2(1 - e^2)$$

$$\text{or} \quad \frac{x_1^2}{a^2} + \frac{y_1^2}{a^2(1 - e^2)} = 1$$

$$\text{or} \quad \frac{x_1^2}{a^2} + \frac{y_1^2}{b^2} = 1 \quad [\because b^2 = a^2(1 - e^2)]$$

Changing (x_1, y_1) to (x, y), then

$$\frac{x^2}{a^2} + \frac{y^2}{b^2} = 1$$

which is the required locus of P.

Example 61. Find the equation of the locus of a point which moves so that the difference of its distances from the points $(3, 0)$ and $(-3, 0)$ is 4 units.

Sol. Let $P(x_1, y_1)$ be the moving point whose locus is required and $A(3, 0)$ and $B(-3, 0)$ be the given fixed points.

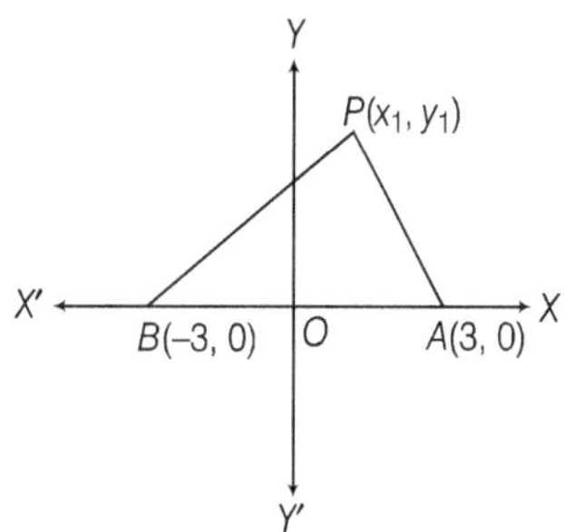

By hypothesis

$$|PB| - |PA| = 4 \text{ (assume } |PB| > |PA|)$$

$$\Rightarrow \sqrt{(x_1+3)^2+(y_1-0)^2} - \sqrt{(x_1-3)^2+(y_1-0)^2} = 4$$

$$\Rightarrow \sqrt{(x_1^2+y_1^2+6x_1+9)} = 4 + \sqrt{(x_1^2+y_1^2-6x_1+9)}$$

Squaring both sides then,

$$x_1^2+y_1^2+6x_1+9 = 16 + x_1^2+y_1^2-6x_1+9+8\sqrt{(x_1^2+y_1^2-6x_1+9)}$$

or $$(12x_1-16) = 8\sqrt{(x_1^2+y_1^2-6x_1+9)}$$

or $$(3x_1-4) = 2\sqrt{(x_1^2+y_1^2-6x_1+9)}$$

Again, squaring both sides, then

$$9x_1^2-24x_1+16 = 4x_1^2+4y_1^2-24x_1+36$$

or $$5x_1^2-4y_1^2 = 20$$

$$\Rightarrow \frac{x_1^2}{4} - \frac{y_1^2}{5} = 1$$

Changing (x_1, y_1) by (x, y), then

$$\frac{x^2}{4} - \frac{y^2}{5} = 1$$

which is the required locus of P.

Aliter ($l - m$ method) :

Since, $$|PB| - |PA| = 4$$

$$\Rightarrow \sqrt{(x_1+3)^2+(y_1-0)^2} - \sqrt{(x_1-3)^2+(y_1-0)^2} = 4$$

$$\Rightarrow \sqrt{(x_1^2+y_1^2+6x_1+9)} - \sqrt{(x_1^2+y_1^2-6x_1+9)} = 4 \quad \text{...(i)}$$

Let $$l = x_1^2+y_1^2+6x_1+9$$

and $$m = x_1^2+y_1^2-6x_1+9$$

then, Eq. (i) can be written as

$$\sqrt{l} - \sqrt{m} = 4 \quad \text{... (ii)}$$

and $$l - m = 12x_1$$

$$\Rightarrow (\sqrt{l}+\sqrt{m})(\sqrt{l}-\sqrt{m}) = 12x_1$$

$$\Rightarrow (\sqrt{l}+\sqrt{m})(4) = 12x_1 \quad \text{[from Eq. (ii)]}$$

$$\Rightarrow \sqrt{l}+\sqrt{m} = 3x_1 \quad \text{...(iii)}$$

Adding Eqs. (ii) and (iii),

$$2\sqrt{l} = (3x_1+4)$$

Squaring both sides,

$$4l = 9x_1^2+24x_1+16$$

$$\Rightarrow 4(x_1^2+y_1^2+6x_1+9) = 9x_1^2+24x_1+16$$

$$\Rightarrow 5x_1^2-4y_1^2 = 20 \quad \text{or} \quad \frac{x_1^2}{4} - \frac{y_1^2}{5} = 1$$

Changing (x_1, y_1) by (x, y), then

$$\frac{x^2}{4} - \frac{y^2}{5} = 1$$

which is the required locus of P.

Example 62. The ends of the hypotenuse of a right angled triangle are $(6, 0)$ and $(0, 6)$. Find the locus of the third vertex.

Sol. Let $C(x_1, y_1)$ be the moving point (third vertex) whose locus is required and $A(6, 0)$ and $B(0, 6)$ be the given vertices.

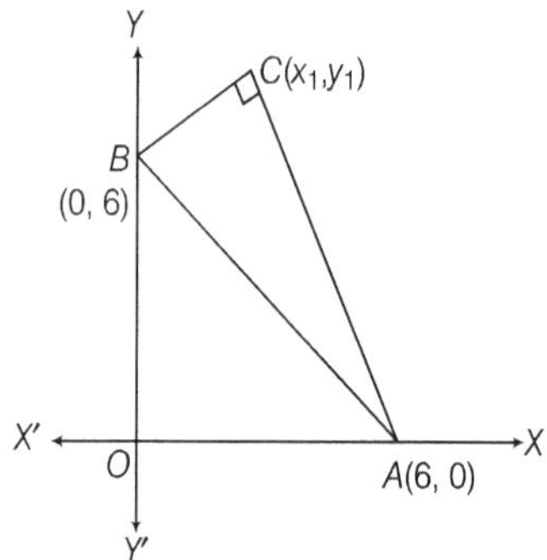

By hypothesis

$$(AC)^2 + (BC)^2 = (AB)^2 \quad (\because \angle ACB = 90^\circ)$$

$$\Rightarrow (x_1-6)^2+(y_1-0)^2+(x_1-0)^2+(y_1-6)^2 = 6^2+6^2$$

$$\Rightarrow 2x_1^2+2y_1^2-12x_1-12y_1 = 0$$

or $$x_1^2+y_1^2-6x_1-6y_1 = 0$$

Changing (x_1, y_1) by (x, y), then

$$x^2+y^2-6x-6y = 0$$

which is the required locus of third vertex C.

Aliter 1. Slope of $AC \times$ slope of $BC = -1$

$$\Rightarrow \left(\frac{y_1-0}{x_1-c}\right) \times \left(\frac{y_1-r}{x_1-0}\right) = -1$$

or $$x_1^2+y_1^2-6x_1-6y_1 = 0$$

Aliter 2. Mid-point of AB is $M \equiv (3, 3)$

$$\because \quad MA = MB = MC \Rightarrow (MA)^2 \equiv (MC)^2$$

$$(3-0)^2+(3-6)^2 = (x_1-3)^2(y_1-3)^2$$

or $$x_1^2+y_1^2-6x_1-6y_1 = 0$$

$\therefore$ Required locus is

$$x^2+y^2-6x-6y = 0$$

Example 63. Find the equation of the locus of a point which moves so that the sum of their distances from (3, 0) and (−3, 0) is less than 9.

Sol. Let $P(x_1, y_1)$ be the moving point whose locus is required and $A(3, 0)$ and $B(-3, 0)$ are the given points.

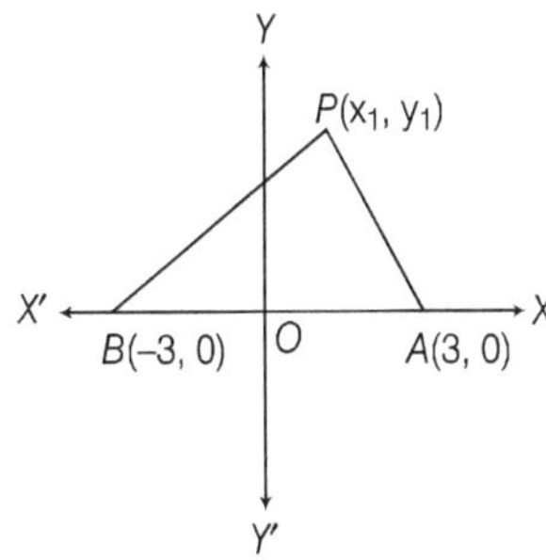

By hypothesis,

$$|PA| + |PB| < 9$$

$$\Rightarrow \quad \sqrt{\{(x_1 - 3)^2 + (y_1 - 0)^2\}} + \sqrt{\{(x_1 + 3)^2 + (y_1 - 0)^2\}} < 9$$

$$\Rightarrow \quad \sqrt{(x_1^2 + y_1^2 - 6x_1 + 9)} < 9 - \sqrt{(x_1^2 + y_1^2 + 6x_1 + 9)}$$

On squaring, we get

$$(x_1^2 + y_1^2 - 6x_1 + 9) < (81 + x_1^2 + y_1^2 + 6x_1 + 9) - 18\sqrt{(x_1^2 + y_1^2 + 6x_1 + 9)}$$

$$(\because a < b \Rightarrow a^2 < b^2 \text{ provided } a > 0)$$

$$\Rightarrow \quad -12x_1 - 81 < -18\sqrt{(x_1^2 + y_1^2 + 6x_1 + 9)}$$

$$\Rightarrow \quad (4x_1 + 27) > 6\sqrt{(x_1^2 + y_1^2 + 6x_1 + 9)}$$

$$(\because \text{If } a > b, \text{ then } -a < -b)$$

On squaring, we get

$$16x_1^2 + 729 + 216x > 36x_1^2 + 36y_1^2 + 216x_1 + 324$$

$$\Rightarrow \quad 20x_1^2 + 36y_1^2 < 405$$

Changing (x_1, y_1) by (x, y), then

$$20x^2 + 36y^2 < 405$$

which is the required locus of P.

Example 64. Find the locus of a point whose coordinate are given by $x = t + t^2$, $y = 2t + 1$, *where t is variable.*

Sol. Given, $\quad x = t + t^2 \quad$ ...(i)

and $\quad y = 2t + 1 \quad$ ...(ii)

From Eq. (ii), $\quad t = \left(\frac{y-1}{2}\right) \quad$ ...(iii)

On eliminating t from Eqs. (i) and (iii), we get required locus as

$$x = \left(\frac{y-1}{2}\right) + \left(\frac{y-1}{2}\right)^2$$

$$\Rightarrow \quad x = \left(\frac{y-1}{2}\right)\left(1 + \frac{y-1}{2}\right)$$

$$\Rightarrow \quad x = \left(\frac{y-1}{2}\right)\left(\frac{y+1}{2}\right)$$

or $\quad 4x = y^2 - 1$

or $\quad y^2 = 4x + 1$

Example 65. A stick of length *l* rests against the floor and a wall of a room. If the stick begins to slide on the floor, find the locus of its middle point.

Sol. Let the cross section of the floor and wall be taken as the coordinate axes and AB be one of the position of the stick. Let the mid-point of AB be $P(x_1, y_1)$, then coordinates of A and B are $(2x_1, 0)$ and $(0, 2y_1)$ respectively.

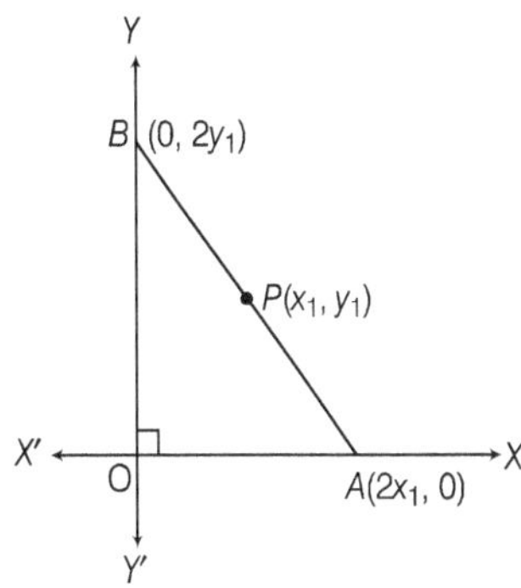

But given, $|AB| = l$

$$\Rightarrow \quad (AB)^2 = l^2$$

$$\Rightarrow \quad (2x_1 - 0)^2 + (0 - 2y_1)^2 = l^2$$

$$\Rightarrow \quad 4x_1^2 + 4y_1^2 = l^2$$

Changing (x_1, y_1) by (x, y), then

$$4(x^2 + y^2) = l^2$$

which is the required locus of P.

Aliter :

Since, $\quad |AB| = l$

Let $\quad \angle OAB = \alpha$

$\therefore \quad OA = l\cos\alpha$ and $OB = l\sin\alpha$

then, $\quad A \equiv (l\cos\alpha, 0)$

and $\quad B \equiv (0, l\sin\alpha)$

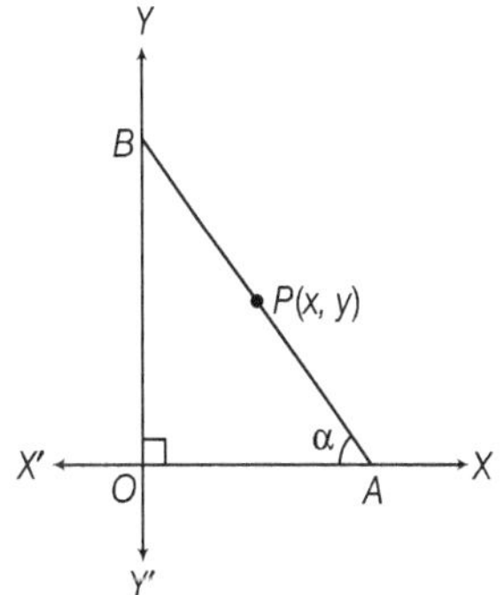

Let $P(x, y)$ be the mid-point of AB, then

$$2x = l\cos\alpha \quad \text{...(i)}$$

$$2y = l\sin\alpha \quad \text{...(ii)}$$

Squaring and adding Eqs. (i) and (ii), then

$$4(x^2 + y^2) = l^2$$

which is the required locus of P.

Example 66. Find the locus of the point of intersection of the lines $x\cos\alpha + y\sin\alpha = a$ and $x\sin\alpha - y\cos\alpha = b$, where α is variable.

Sol. Given equations are

$$x\cos\alpha + y\sin\alpha = a \quad \text{...(i)}$$

and $$x\sin\alpha - y\cos\alpha = b \quad \text{...(ii)}$$

Here, α is a variable, on eliminating α. Squaring and adding Eqs. (i) and (ii), we get required locus as

$$(x\cos\alpha + y\sin\alpha)^2 + (x\sin\alpha - y\cos\alpha)^2 = a^2 + b^2$$

or $$(x^2\cos^2\alpha + y^2\sin^2\alpha + 2xy\cos\alpha\sin\alpha) + (x^2\sin^2\alpha + y^2\cos^2\alpha - 2xy\sin\alpha\cos\alpha) = a^2 + b^2$$

$$\Rightarrow \quad x^2(\cos^2\alpha + \sin^2\alpha) + y^2(\sin^2\alpha + \cos^2\alpha) = a^2 + b^2$$

$$\Rightarrow \quad x^2 + y^2 = a^2 + b^2$$

Example 67. A variable line cuts X-axis at A, Y-axis at B, where $OA = a$, $OB = b$ (O as origin) such that $a^2 + b^2 = 1$.

Find the locus of

(i) centroid of ΔOAB

(ii) circumcentre of ΔOAB

Sol. (i) Coordinates of A and B are $(a, 0)$ and $(0, b)$ respectively. If centroid of ΔOAB be $G(x, y)$

then $$x = \frac{0 + a + 0}{3} \Rightarrow a = 3x$$

and $$y = \frac{0 + 0 + b}{3} \Rightarrow b = 3y$$

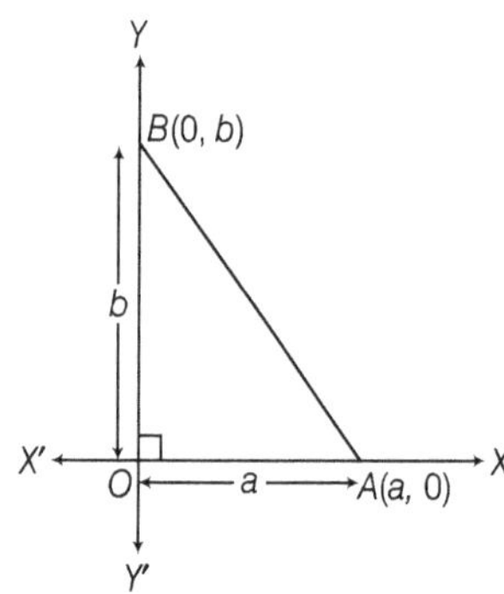

On substituting in $a^2 + b^2 = 1$, we get

$$(3x)^2 + (3y)^2 = 1$$

or $$x^2 + y^2 = \frac{1}{9}$$

which is the required locus of G.

(ii) If the circumcentre be $C(x, y)$. Since in semicircle angle $90°$, then AB is the diameter of the circumcircle OAB.

$\therefore$ Circumcentre is the mid-point of AB.

Then $$x = \frac{a + 0}{2} \Rightarrow a = 2x$$

and $$y = \frac{0 + b}{2} \Rightarrow b = 2y$$

On substituting in $a^2 + b^2 = 1$, we get

$$(2x)^2 + (2y)^2 = 1$$

or $$x^2 + y^2 = \frac{1}{4}$$

which is the required locus of C.

Example 68. Two points P and Q are given, R is a variable point on one side of the line PQ such that $\angle RPQ - \angle RQP$ is a positive constant 2α. Find the locus of the point R.

Sol. Let the X-axis along QP and the middle point of PQ is origin and let coordinates of moving point R be (x_1, y_1).

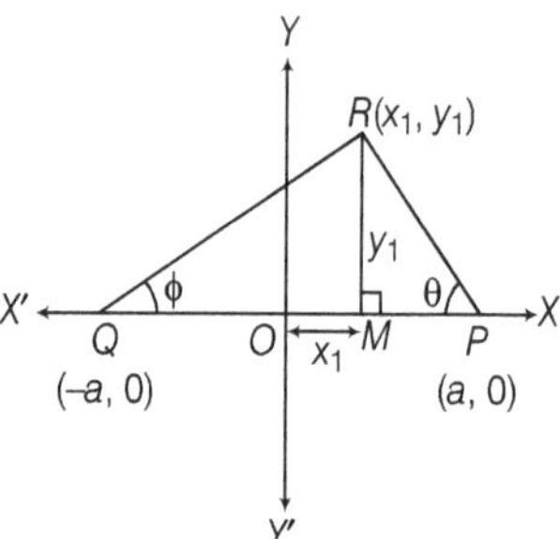

Let $$OP = OQ = a$$

then coordinates of P and Q are $(a, 0)$ and $(-a, 0)$ respectively.

Draw RM perpendicular on QP

$\therefore$ $$OM = x_1 \text{ and } MR = y_1$$

and let $$\angle RPM = \theta \text{ and } \angle RQM = \phi$$

Now, in ΔRMP,

$$\tan\theta = \frac{RM}{MP} = \frac{RM}{OP - OM} = \frac{y_1}{a - x_1} \quad \text{...(i)}$$

and in ΔRMQ,

$$\tan\phi = \frac{RM}{QM} = \frac{RM}{OQ + OM} = \frac{y_1}{a + x_1} \quad \text{...(ii)}$$

But given

$$\angle RPQ - \angle RQP = 2\alpha \quad \text{(constant)}$$

$$\Rightarrow \quad \theta - \phi = 2\alpha$$

$$\therefore \quad \tan(\theta - \phi) = \tan 2\alpha$$

$$\Rightarrow \quad \frac{\tan\theta - \tan\phi}{1 + \tan\theta\tan\phi} = \tan 2\alpha$$

$$\Rightarrow \quad \frac{\frac{y_1}{a-x_1}-\frac{y_1}{a+x_1}}{1+\left(\frac{y_1}{a-x_1}\right)\cdot\left(\frac{y_1}{a+x_1}\right)}=\tan 2\alpha$$

[from Eqs. (i) and (ii)]

$$\Rightarrow \quad \frac{2x_1y_1}{a^2-x_1^2+y_1^2}=\tan 2\alpha$$

or $\quad a^2-x_1^2+y_1^2=2x_1y_1\cot 2\alpha$

or $\quad x_1^2-y_1^2+2x_1y_1\cot 2\alpha=a^2$

Hence, locus of the point $R(x_1, y_1)$ is

$$x^2-y^2+2xy\cot 2\alpha=a^2$$

Change of Axes OR the Transformations of Axes

In coordinate geometry we have discussed the coordinates of a point or the equation of a curve are always considered on taking a fixed point O as the origin and two perpendicular straight lines through O as the coordinates axes. For convenient the coordinates of the point or the equation of the curve changes when either the origin is changed or the direction of axes or both are suitably. These processes in coordinate geometry are known as the *transformations or change of axes.* This process of transformation of coordinates will be of great advantage to solve most of the problems very easily.

(i) Change of origin OR Shifting of origin (Translation of Axes)

To change the origin of coordinates to another point (h, k) whereas the directions of axes remain unaltered.

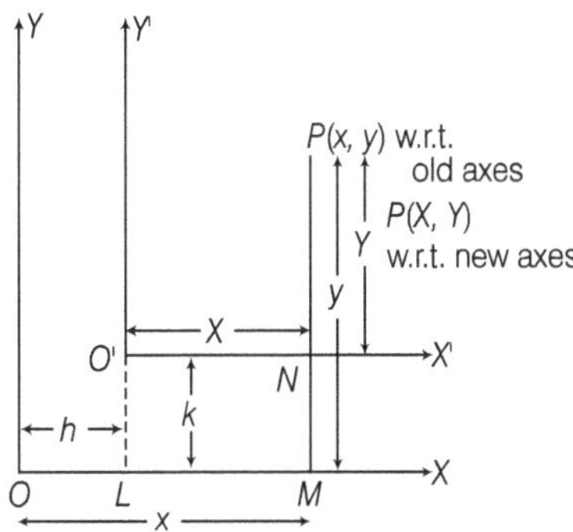

Let O be the origin of coordinates and OX, OY be the original coordinate axes. Let O' be the new origin and (h, k) its coordinates referred to the original axes. Draw two lines $O'X'$ and $O'Y'$ through O' and parallel to OX and OY respectively. Let $P(x, y)$ be any point referred to the original axes OX, OY. Again suppose that the coordinates of the same point P referred to the new axes $O'X', O'Y'$ are (X, Y).

From O' draw $O'L$ perpendicular to OX. from P draw PM perpendicular to OX to meet $O'X'$ in N. Then

$$OL=h, O'L=k, OM=x, PM=y, O'N=X$$

and $\quad PN=Y$

we have $\quad x=OM=OL+LM=OL+O'N=h+X$

i.e. $\quad \mathbf{x=X+h} \quad$ ...(i)

and $\quad y=PM=PN+NM=PN+O'L=Y+k$

i.e. $\quad \mathbf{y=Y+k} \quad$ ...(ii)

from Eqs. (i) and (ii),

$$\mathbf{X=x-h} \quad \text{and} \quad \mathbf{Y=y-k}$$

Thus, if origin is shifted to point (h, k) without rotation of axes, then new equation of curve can be obtained by putting $x+h$ in place of x and $y+k$ in place of y.

Remarks

1. In this case axes are shifted parallel to themselves, then it is also called **Transformation by parallel axes.**
2. **Inverse translation or shifting the origin back :** Some times it is required to shift the new origin back. Then putting $x-h$ in place of x and $y-k$ in place of y in any equation of curve referred to the new origin to get the corresponding equation referred to the old origin.
3. The above transformation is true whether the axes be rectangular or oblique.

Example 69. Find the equation of the curve $2x^2+y^2-3x+5y-8=0$ when the origin is transferred to the point $(-1, 2)$ without changing the direction of axes.

Sol. Here, we want to shift the origin to the point $(-1, 2)$ without changing the direction of axes. Then we replace x by $x-1$ and y by $y+2$ in the equation of given curve, then the transformed equation is

$$2(x-1)^2+(y+2)^2-3(x-1)+5(y+2)-8=0$$

$$\Rightarrow \quad 2x^2+y^2-7x+9y+11=0$$

Example 70. The equation of a curve referred to the new axes, axes retaining their direction and origin is $(4, 5)$ is $x^2+y^2=36$. Find the equation referred to the original axes.

Sol. Here we want to shift the $(4, 5)$ to the origin without changing the direction of axes. Then we replace x by $x-4$ and y by $y-5$ in the equation of given curve then the required equation is

$$(x-4)^2+(y-5)^2=36$$

$$\Rightarrow \quad x^2+y^2-8x-10y+5=0$$

Example 71. Shift the origin to a suitable point so that the equation $y^2 + 4y + 8x - 2 = 0$ will not contain term in y and the constant.

Sol. Let the origin be shifted to the point (h, k) without changing the direction of axes. Then we replace x by $x + h$ and y by $y + k$ in the equation of the given curve then the transformed equation is

$$(y + k)^2 + 4(y + k) + 8(x + h) - 2 = 0$$

$$\Rightarrow \quad y^2 + (2k + 4)y + 8x + (k^2 + 4k + 8h - 2) = 0$$

Since, this equation is required to be free from the term containing y and the constant, we have

$$2k + 4 = 0 \quad \text{and} \quad k^2 + 4k + 8h - 2 = 0$$

$$\therefore \quad k = -2 \quad \text{and} \quad h = \frac{3}{4}$$

Hence, the point to which the origin be shifted is $\left(\frac{3}{4}, -2\right)$.

Example 72. At what point the origin be shifted, if the coordinates of a point $(-1, 8)$ become $(-7, 3)$?

Sol. Let the origin be shifted to the point (h, k) without changing the direction of axes. Then we replace x by $x + h$ and y by $y + k$ and we get new co-ordinates. Here, given old coordinates and new coordinates are $(-1, 8)$ and $(-7, 3)$ respectively.

We have $\quad -1 + h = -7 \quad$ and $\quad 8 + k = 3$

$$\Rightarrow \quad h = -6 \quad \text{and} \quad k = -5$$

Hence, the origin must be shifted to $(-6, -5)$.

(ii) Rotation of Axes (Change of Directions of Axes)

To find the change in the coordinates of a point when the directions of axes are rotated through an angle θ the origin being fixed.

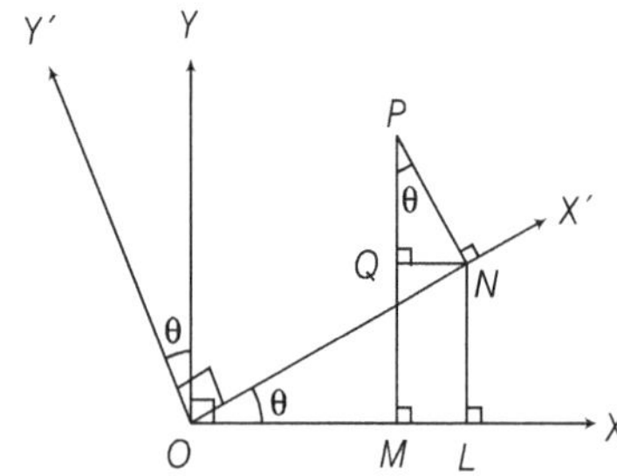

Let OX and OY be the original system of coordinate axes. Let OX' and OY' be the new axes obtained by rotating the original axes through an angle θ. Let P be a point in the plane whose coordinates are (x, y) and (X, Y) referred to old and new axes respectively. Draw PM and PN perpendiculars to OX and OX' and also NL and NQ perpendiculars to OX and PM. We have

$$OM = x, PM = y, ON = X, PN = Y$$

Now, $\quad x = OM = OL - ML$

$\left(\because \text{Angle between any two lines = Angle between their perpendiculars i.e. } \angle XOX' = \angle NPM = \theta\right)$

$$= OL - QN = ON\cos\theta - PN\sin\theta$$

$$= X\cos\theta - Y\sin\theta$$

i.e. $\quad \boldsymbol{x = X\cos\theta - Y\sin\theta} \quad$ ...(i)

and $\quad y = PM = PQ + QM = PQ + NL$

$$= PN\cos\theta + ON\sin\theta$$

$$= Y\cos\theta + X\sin\theta$$

i.e. $\quad \boldsymbol{y = X\sin\theta + Y\cos\theta} \quad$ ...(ii)

Now, multiplying Eqs. (i) by $\cos\theta$ and Eq. (ii) by $\sin\theta$ and adding we get

$$\boldsymbol{X = x\cos\theta + y\sin\theta} \quad \text{...(iii)}$$

Also, subtracting the product of Eq. (i) by $\sin\theta$ from the product of Eq. (ii) by $\cos\theta$, we get

$$\boldsymbol{Y = -x\sin\theta + y\cos\theta} \quad \text{...(iv)}$$

also $x^2 + y^2 = X^2 + Y^2 = OP^2$ are unchanged i.e. the distance of the point P from the origin O remains unaffected by the rotation of axes.

Rule : When the axes are rotated through θ, replace (x, y) by $(x\cos\theta - y\sin\theta, x\sin\theta + y\cos\theta)$.

Shifting the coordinate axes back : Some times it is required to shift the new coordinates axes back. Then replace (x, y) by

$$(x\cos\theta + y\sin\theta, -x\sin\theta + y\cos\theta).$$

Independent Proof (Aliter)

The relations $X = x\cos\theta + y\sin\theta$ and $Y = -x\sin\theta + y\cos\theta$ can be obtained independently.

Proof : Draw PM and PN perpendiculars to OX and OX' and also ML and MQ perpendiculars to PN and OX' respectively.

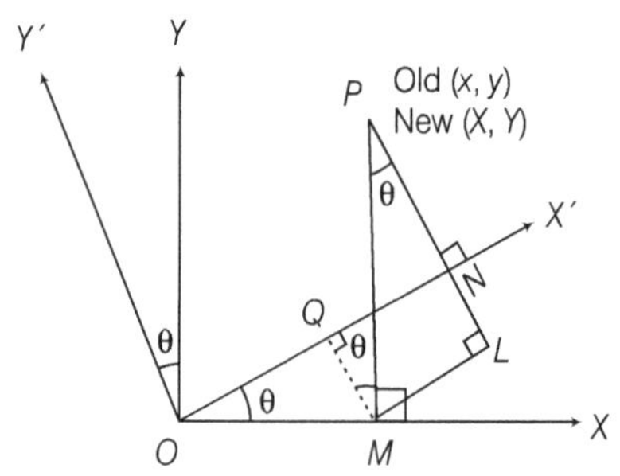

We have, $\quad OM = x, PM = y, ON = X$

and $\quad PN = Y$

Also, angle between any two lines

= Angle between their perpendiculars lines

i.e. $\angle XOX' = \angle MPN = \angle PMQ = \theta$

$\therefore$ $X = ON = OQ + QN$

$= OQ + ML$

$= OM\cos\theta + PM\sin\theta$

$(\because OQ = OM\cos\theta$ and $ML = PM\sin\theta)$

$= x\cos\theta + y\sin\theta$

i.e. $\mathbf{X = x\cos\theta + y\sin\theta}$

and $Y = PN = PL - NL = PL - QM$

$= PM\cos\theta - OM\sin\theta$

$(\because PL = PM\cos\theta$ and $QM = OM\sin\theta)$

$= y\cos\theta - x\sin\theta$

i.e. $\mathbf{Y = -x\sin\theta + y\cos\theta}$

Remark :

The results Eqs. (i), (ii), (iii) and (iv) can be conveniently remembered by the following methods.

(i) Light heavy method : Let x, y be light and X, Y be heavy then heavy X, Y down and x, y up then

	x	y
X	$\cos\theta$	$\sin\theta$
Y	$-\sin\theta$	$\cos\theta$

third row is obtained by differentiating second row with respect to θ.

For remembrance ***C*** ***S*** (Civil Services)

$\downarrow$ $\downarrow$

$\cos\theta$ $\sin\theta$ $\left(\text{i.e. } \begin{matrix} C \to \cos\theta \\ S \to \sin\theta \end{matrix}\right)$

$\downarrow$ $\downarrow$

$-\sin\theta$ $\cos\theta$ $\left(\begin{matrix} (\cos\theta)' = -\sin\theta \\ (\sin\theta)' = \cos\theta \end{matrix}\right)$

(a) Finding x and y in terms of X and Y

x = Sum of the products of the elements in the left most column with the corresponding elements of the first column

i.e. $x = X\cos\theta - Y\sin\theta$

and y = Sum of the products of the elements in the left most column with the corresponding elements of the second column.

i.e. $y = X\sin\theta + Y\cos\theta$

Hence, $\left.\begin{aligned} x &= X\cos\theta - Y\sin\theta \\ y &= X\sin\theta + Y\cos\theta \end{aligned}\right\}$

(b) Finding X and Y in terms of x and y

X = Sum of the products of the elements of top-row with the corresponding elements of first row.

i.e. $X = x\cos\theta + y\sin\theta$

and Y = Sum of the products of the elements of top-row with the corresponding elements of second row.

i.e. $Y = -x\sin\theta + y\cos\theta$

Hence, $\left.\begin{aligned} X &= x\cos\theta + y\sin\theta \\ Y &= -x\sin\theta + y\cos\theta \end{aligned}\right\}$

(ii) Matrix method :

$$\begin{bmatrix} X \\ Y \end{bmatrix} = \begin{bmatrix} \cos\theta & \sin\theta \\ -\sin\theta & \cos\theta \end{bmatrix} \begin{bmatrix} x \\ y \end{bmatrix} = A \begin{bmatrix} x \\ y \end{bmatrix} \text{(say)}$$

and $$\begin{bmatrix} x \\ y \end{bmatrix} = \begin{bmatrix} \cos\theta & -\sin\theta \\ \sin\theta & \cos\theta \end{bmatrix} \begin{bmatrix} X \\ Y \end{bmatrix} = A' \begin{bmatrix} X \\ Y \end{bmatrix}$$

where, A' is the transpose matrix of A.

(iii) Complex number method :

Let $z = x + iy$

and $Z = X + iY$, where $i = \sqrt{-1}$

then $z = Ze^{i\theta}$ ...(i)

i.e. $(x + iy) = (X + iY)(\cos\theta + i\sin\theta)$

On comparing real and imaginary parts, we get

$$\left.\begin{aligned} x &= X\cos\theta - Y\sin\theta \\ y &= X\sin\theta + Y\cos\theta \end{aligned}\right\}$$

Again from Eq. (i), $Z = ze^{-i\theta}$

i.e. $(X + iY) = (x + iy)(\cos\theta - i\sin\theta)$

On comparing real and imaginary parts, we get

$$\left.\begin{aligned} X &= x\cos\theta + y\sin\theta \\ Y &= -x\sin\theta + y\cos\theta \end{aligned}\right\}$$

Example 73. If the axes are turned through 45°, find the transformed form of the equation $3x^2 + 3y^2 + 2xy = 2$.

Sol. Here, $\theta = 45°$ so $\sin\theta = \cos\theta = \frac{1}{\sqrt{2}}$

Replacing (x, y) by $(x\cos\theta - y\sin\theta, x\sin\theta + y\cos\theta)$

i.e. $\left(\frac{x - y}{\sqrt{2}}, \frac{x + y}{\sqrt{2}}\right)$

Then, $3x^2 + 3y^2 + 2xy = 2$ becomes

$$3\left(\frac{x - y}{\sqrt{2}}\right)^2 + 3\left(\frac{x + y}{\sqrt{2}}\right)^2 + 2\left(\frac{x - y}{\sqrt{2}}\right)\left(\frac{x + y}{\sqrt{2}}\right) = 2$$

$\Rightarrow \quad 3(2x^2+2y^2)+2(x^2-y^2)=4$

$\Rightarrow \quad 8x^2+4y^2=4$

or $\quad 2x^2+y^2=1$

which is free from the term containing xy.

Example 74. Prove that if the axes be turned through $\frac{\pi}{4}$ the equation $x^2-y^2=a^2$ is transformed to the form $xy=\lambda$. Find the value of λ.

Sol. Here, $\theta=\frac{\pi}{4}$ so $\sin\theta=\cos\theta=\frac{1}{\sqrt{2}}$

Replacing (x, y) by $(x\cos\theta-y\sin\theta, x\sin\theta+y\cos\theta)$

i.e. $\quad \left(\frac{x-y}{\sqrt{2}}, \frac{x+y}{\sqrt{2}}\right)$

then, $x^2-y^2=a^2$ becomes

$$\left(\frac{x-y}{\sqrt{2}}\right)^2-\left(\frac{x+y}{\sqrt{2}}\right)^2=a^2$$

$$\Rightarrow \quad \left(\frac{x-y}{\sqrt{2}}+\frac{x+y}{\sqrt{2}}\right)\left(\frac{x-y}{\sqrt{2}}-\frac{x+y}{\sqrt{2}}\right)=a^2$$

$$\Rightarrow \quad \left(\frac{2x}{\sqrt{2}}\right)\left(\frac{-2y}{\sqrt{2}}\right)=a^2$$

$$\text{or} \quad xy=-\frac{a^2}{2}$$

Comparing it with $xy=\lambda$, then we get $\lambda=-\frac{a^2}{2}$.

Example 75. Through what angle should the axes be rotated so that the equation $9x^2-2\sqrt{3}\,xy+7y^2=10$ may be changed to $3x^2+5y^2=5$?

Sol. Let angle be θ then replacing (x, y) by $(x\cos\theta-y\sin\theta, x\sin\theta+y\cos\theta)$

then, $\quad 9x^2-2\sqrt{3}xy+7y^2=10$ becomes

$$9(x\cos\theta-y\sin\theta)^2-2\sqrt{3}(x\cos\theta-y\sin\theta)(x\sin\theta+y\cos\theta)+7(x\sin\theta+y\cos\theta)^2=10$$

$$\Rightarrow \quad x^2(9\cos^2\theta-2\sqrt{3}\sin\theta\cos\theta+7\sin^2\theta)+2xy(-9\sin\theta\cos\theta-\sqrt{3}\cos 2\theta+7\sin\theta\cos\theta)+y^2(9\cos^2\theta+2\sqrt{3}\sin\theta\cos\theta+7\cos^2\theta)=10$$

On comparing with $3x^2+5y^2=5$ (coefficient of xy)

we get $-9\sin\theta\cos\theta-\sqrt{3}\cos 2\theta+7\sin\theta\cos\theta=0$

or $\quad \sin 2\theta=-\sqrt{3}\cos 2\theta$

or $\quad \tan 2\theta=-\sqrt{3}=\tan(180^\circ-60^\circ)$

or $\quad 2\theta=120^\circ$

$\therefore \quad \theta=60^\circ$

Example 76. If (x, y) and (X, Y) be the coordinates of the same point referred to two sets of rectangular axes with the same origin and if $ux+vy$, when u and v are independent of X and Y become $VX+UY$, show that $u^2+v^2=U^2+V^2$

Sol. Let the axes rotate an angle θ and if (x, y) be the point with respect to old axes and (X, Y) be the co-ordinates with respect to new axes, then

$$x+iy=(X+iY)e^{i\theta}=(X+iY)(\cos\theta+i\sin\theta)$$

On comparing real and imaginary parts, we get

$$\begin{cases} x=X\cos\theta-Y\sin\theta \\ y=X\sin\theta+Y\cos\theta \end{cases}$$

Then, $ux+vy=u(X\cos\theta-Y\sin\theta)+v(X\sin\theta+Y\cos\theta)$

$=(u\cos\theta+v\sin\theta)X+(-u\sin\theta+v\cos\theta)Y$

but given new curve $VX+UY$

then, $VX+UY=(u\cos\theta+v\sin\theta)X+(-u\sin\theta+v\cos\theta)Y$

On comparing the coefficients of X and Y, we get

$$V=u\cos\theta+v\sin\theta \quad \text{...(i)}$$

and $$U=-u\sin\theta+v\cos\theta \quad \text{...(ii)}$$

Squaring and adding Eqs. (i) and (ii), we get

$$V^2+U^2=(u\cos\theta+v\sin\theta)^2+(-u\sin\theta+v\cos\theta)^2$$

$$=u^2+v^2$$

Hence, $\quad u^2+v^2=U^2+V^2$

Aliter 1 (By matrix method) :

$$\begin{bmatrix} x \\ y \end{bmatrix}=\begin{bmatrix} \cos\theta & -\sin\theta \\ \sin\theta & \cos\theta \end{bmatrix}\begin{bmatrix} X \\ Y \end{bmatrix}=\begin{bmatrix} X\cos\theta-Y\sin\theta \\ X\sin\theta+Y\cos\theta \end{bmatrix} \quad \text{...(i)}$$

$$\because \quad ux+vy=[u \quad v]\begin{bmatrix} x \\ y \end{bmatrix}=[u\ v]\begin{bmatrix} X\cos\theta+Y\sin\theta \\ X\sin\theta+Y\cos\theta \end{bmatrix} \quad \text{[from (i)]}$$

$$=uX\cos\theta-uY\sin\theta+vX\sin\theta+vY\cos\theta$$

$$=X(u\cos\theta+v\sin\theta)+Y(-u\sin\theta+v\cos\theta)$$

but given new curve $VX+UY$

Then, $VX+UY=X(u\cos\theta+v\sin\theta)+Y(-u\sin\theta+v\cos\theta)$

On comparing the coefficients of X and Y, we get

$$V=u\cos\theta+v\sin\theta \quad \text{...(ii)}$$

$$U=-u\sin\theta+v\cos\theta \quad \text{...(iii)}$$

Squaring and adding Eqs. (ii) and (iii), we get

$$u^2+v^2=U^2+V^2$$

Aliter 2 (Best approach) :

$$ux+vy=R_e((u-iv)(x+iy))$$

$$=R_e((u-iv)(X+iY)e^{i\theta}) \quad \text{...(i)}$$

and $$VX+UY=R_e((V-iU)(X+iY)) \quad \text{...(ii)}$$

From Eqs. (i) and (ii), we get

$$V-iU=(u-iv)e^{i\theta}$$

Taking modulus both sides, then

$$|V - iU| = |u - iv||e^{i\theta}|$$

$\Rightarrow$ $$\sqrt{(V^2 + U^2)} = \sqrt{u^2 + v^2} \cdot 1$$

or $$u^2 + v^2 = U^2 + V^2$$

(iii) Double Transformation (Origin Shifted and Axes Rotated)

If origin is shifted to the point. $O'(h, k)$ and at the same time the directions of axes are rotated through an angle θ in the anticlockwise sense such that new coordinates of $P(x, y)$ become (X, Y).

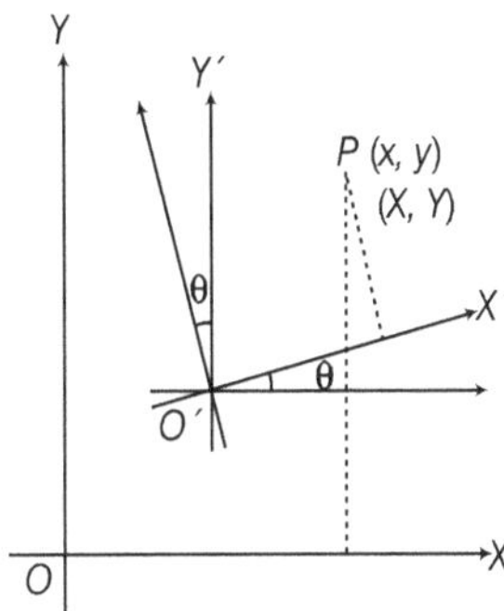

Then, we get $x = h + X\cos\theta - Y\sin\theta$ ...(i)

and $y = k + X\sin\theta + Y\cos\theta$ ...(ii)

In practice we have to replace x by $h + x\cos\theta - y\sin\theta$ and y by $k + x\sin\theta + y\cos\theta$.

Again, if we want to shift the coordinate axes back to their original positions, then we obtained X and Y by solving Eqs. (i) and (ii), then

$$X = (x - h)\cos\theta + (y - k)\sin\theta$$

and $$Y = -(x - h)\sin\theta + (y - k)\cos\theta$$

Example 77. What does the equation $2x^2 + 4xy - 5y^2 + 20x - 22y - 14 = 0$ becomes when referred to rectangular axes through the point $(-2, -3)$, the new axes being inclined at an angle of $45°$ *with the old ?*

Sol. Let $O'(-2, -3)$ be the new origin and axes are rotated about O' through an angle 45° in anticlockwise direction then replacing x and y by

$$-2 + x\cos 45° - y\sin 45°$$

and $$-3 + x\sin 45° + y\cos 45°$$

i.e. $-2 + \left(\frac{x - y}{\sqrt{2}}\right)$ and $-3 + \left(\frac{x + y}{\sqrt{2}}\right)$ respectively in the given curve, then the new equation of curve will be

$$2\left\{-2 + \left(\frac{x - y}{\sqrt{2}}\right)\right\}^2 + 4\left\{-2 + \left(\frac{x - y}{\sqrt{2}}\right)\right\}\left\{-3 + \left(\frac{x + y}{\sqrt{2}}\right)\right\}$$

$$-5\left\{-3 + \left(\frac{x + y}{\sqrt{2}}\right)\right\}^2 + 20\left\{-2 + \left(\frac{x - y}{\sqrt{2}}\right)\right\}$$

$$-22\left\{-3 + \left(\frac{x + y}{\sqrt{2}}\right)\right\} - 14 = 0$$

$\Rightarrow$ $$x^2 - 14xy - 7y^2 - 2 = 0$$

Removal of the Term xy from $f(x, y) = ax^2 + 2hxy + by^2$ without Changing the Origin

Clearly, $h \neq 0$

Rotating the axes through an angle θ, we have

$$x = X\cos\theta - Y\sin\theta$$

and $$y = X\sin\theta + Y\cos\theta$$

$\because$ $$f(x, y) = ax^2 + 2hxy + by^2$$

After rotation, new equation is

$$F(X, Y) = (a\cos^2\theta + 2h\cos\theta\sin\theta + b\sin^2\theta)X^2$$
$$+ 2\{(b - a)\cos\theta\sin\theta + h(\cos^2\theta - \sin^2\theta)\}XY$$
$$+ (a\sin^2\theta - 2h\cos\theta\sin\theta + b\cos^2\theta)Y^2$$

Now, coefficient of $XY = 0$

Then, we get $\cot 2\theta = \dfrac{a - b}{2h}$

Remark

Usually, we use the formula, $\tan 2\theta = \dfrac{2h}{a - b}$ for finding the angle of rotation, θ.

However, if $a = b$, we use $\cot 2\theta = \dfrac{a - b}{2h}$ as in this case $\tan 2\theta$ is not defined.

Example 78. Given the equation $4x^2 + 2\sqrt{3}xy + 2y^2 = 1$, through what angle should the axes be rotated so that the term in xy be wanting from the transformed equation.

Sol. Comparing the given equation with $ax^2 + 2hxy + by^2$, we get $a = 4$, $h = \sqrt{3}$ $b = 2$. If axes are to be rotated at θ, then

$$\tan 2\theta = \frac{2h}{a - b} = \frac{2\sqrt{3}}{2} = \sqrt{3} = \tan\frac{\pi}{3}$$

$$2\theta = \frac{\pi}{3}, \pi + \frac{\pi}{3} \Rightarrow 2\theta = \frac{\pi}{3}, \frac{4\pi}{3}$$

$\therefore$ $$\theta = \frac{\pi}{6}, \frac{2\pi}{3}$$

Position of a Point which Lies Inside a Triangle

If any point say (P) lies within the triangle ABC,

then $\Delta_1 + \Delta_2 + \Delta_3 = \Delta$

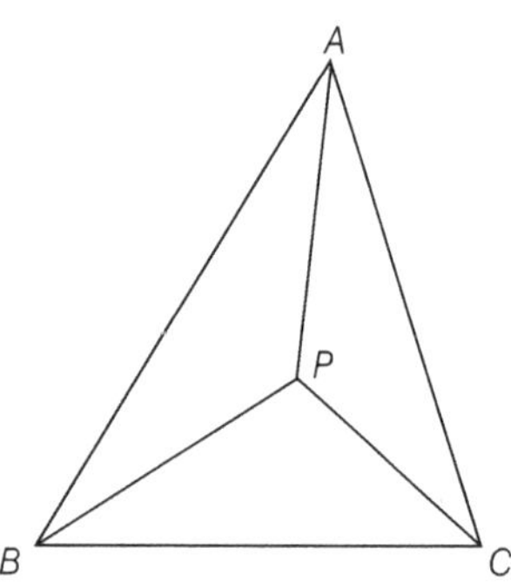

where, $\Delta =$ Area of triangle ABC,

$\Delta_1 =$ Area of ΔPBC,

$\Delta_2 =$ Area of ΔPCA,

$\Delta_3 =$ Area of ΔPAB

Also, $\Delta_1 \neq 0, \Delta_2 \neq 0, \Delta_3 \neq 0, \Delta \neq 0$

(Each individual area must be non-zero)

Example 79. Find λ if $(\lambda, \lambda + 1)$ is an interior point of ΔABC where, $A \equiv (0, 3); B \equiv (-2, 0)$ and $C \equiv (6, 1)$.

Sol. The point $P(\lambda, \lambda + 1)$ will be inside the triangle ABC, then

Area of ΔPBC + Area of ΔPCA + Area of ΔPAB = Area of ΔABC

$$\Rightarrow \frac{1}{2}\left|\begin{vmatrix} \lambda & \lambda+1 & 1 \\ -2 & 0 & 1 \\ 6 & 1 & 1 \end{vmatrix}\right| + \frac{1}{2}\left|\begin{vmatrix} \lambda & \lambda+1 & 1 \\ 6 & 1 & 1 \\ 0 & 3 & 1 \end{vmatrix}\right| + \frac{1}{2}\left|\begin{vmatrix} \lambda & \lambda+1 & 1 \\ 0 & 3 & 1 \\ -2 & 0 & 1 \end{vmatrix}\right|$$

$$= \frac{1}{2}\left|\begin{vmatrix} 0 & 3 & 1 \\ -2 & 0 & 1 \\ 6 & 1 & 1 \end{vmatrix}\right|$$

$$\Rightarrow \quad |7\lambda + 6| + |8\lambda - 12| + |\lambda + 4| = 22$$

For $\lambda < -4$:

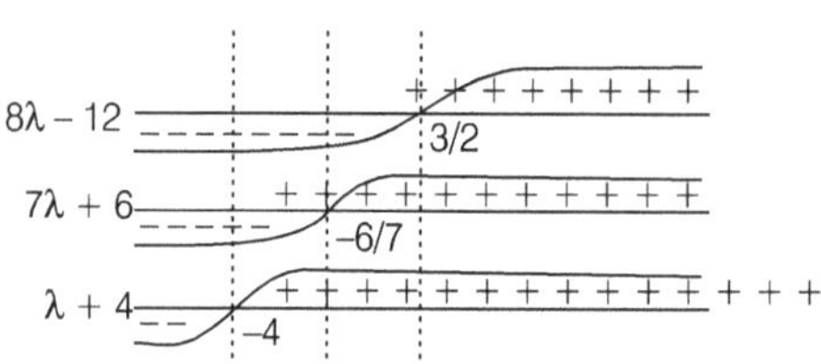

Then, $-(7\lambda + 6) - (8\lambda - 12) - (\lambda + 4) = 22$

$\Rightarrow \quad -16\lambda = 20 \quad \therefore \quad \lambda = -\frac{5}{4}$

which is impossible.

For $-4 \leq \lambda < -\frac{6}{7}$:

Then, $-(7\lambda + 6) - (8\lambda - 12) + (\lambda + 4) = 22$

$\Rightarrow \quad -14\lambda = 12 \quad \therefore \quad = -\frac{6}{7}$

which is impossible.

For $-\frac{6}{7} \leq \lambda < \frac{3}{2}$:

Then, $(7\lambda + 6) - (8\lambda - 12) + \lambda + 4 = 22 \Rightarrow 22 = 22$

$\because$ at $\lambda = -\frac{6}{7}$, area of $\Delta PBC = 0$

$\therefore \quad \lambda \neq \frac{-6}{7}$

$\therefore \quad \lambda \in \left(-\frac{6}{7}, \frac{3}{2}\right)$

For $\lambda \geq \frac{3}{2}$:

Then, $7\lambda + 6 + 8\lambda - 12 + \lambda + 4 = 22 \Rightarrow 16\lambda = 24$

$\therefore \quad \lambda = \frac{3}{2}$

$\because$ at $\lambda = \frac{3}{2}$, area of $\Delta PCA = 0$

$\therefore \quad \lambda \neq \frac{3}{2}$

Hence, value of $\lambda \in \left(-\frac{6}{7}, \frac{3}{2}\right)$.

Exercise for Session 4

1. The equation of the locus of points equidistant from $(-1, -1)$ and $(4, 2)$ is
(a) $3x - 5y - 7 = 0$ (b) $5x + 3y - 9 = 0$ (c) $4x + 3y + 2 = 0$ (d) $x - 3y + 5 = 0$

2. The equation of the locus of a point which moves so that its distance from the point $(ak, 0)$ is k times its distance from the point $\left(\frac{a}{k}, 0\right)$, $(k \neq 1)$ is
(a) $x^2 - y^2 = a^2$ (b) $2x^2 - y^2 = 2a^2$ (c) $xy = a^2$ (d) $x^2 + y^2 = a^2$

3. If the coordinates of a variable point P be $\left(t + \frac{1}{t}, t - \frac{1}{t}\right)$, where t is the variable quantity, then the locus of P is
(a) $xy = 8$ (b) $2x^2 - y^2 = 8$ (c) $x^2 - y^2 = 4$ (d) $2x^2 + 3y^2 = 5$

4. If the coordinates of a variable point P be $(\cos\theta + \sin\theta, \sin\theta - \cos\theta)$, where θ is the parameter, then the locus of P is
(a) $x^2 - y^2 = 4$ (b) $x^2 + y^2 = 2$ (c) $xy = 3$ (d) $x^2 + 2y^2 = 3$

5. If a point moves such that twice its distance from the axis of x exceeds its distance from the axis of y by 2, then its locus is
(a) $x - 2y = 2$ (b) $x + 2y = 2$ (c) $2y - x = 2$ (d) $2y - 3x = 5$

6. The equation $4xy - 3x^2 = a^2$ become when the axes are turned through an angle $\tan^{-1} 2$ is
(a) $x^2 + 4y^2 = a^2$ (b) $x^2 - 4y^2 = a^2$ (c) $4x^2 + y^2 = a^2$ (d) $4x^2 - y^2 = a^2$

7. Transform the equation $x^2 - 3xy + 11x - 12y + 36 = 0$ to parallel axes through the point $(-4, 1)$ becomes $ax^2 + bxy + 1 = 0$ then $b^2 - a =$
(a) $\frac{1}{4}$ (b) $\frac{1}{16}$ (c) $\frac{1}{64}$ (d) $\frac{1}{256}$

8. Find the equation of the locus of all points equidistant from the point $(2, 4)$ and the Y-axis.

9. Find the equation of the locus of the points twice as far from $(-a, 0)$ as from $(a, 0)$.

10. OA and OB are two perpendicular straight lines. A straight line AB is drawn in such a manner that $OA + OB = 8$. Find the locus of the mid point of AB.

11. The ends of a rod of length l move on two mutually perpendicular lines. Find the locus of the point on the rod which divides it in the ratio 1 : 2.

12. The coordinates of three points O, A, B are $(0, 0)$, $(0, 4)$ and $(6, 0)$ respectively. A point P moves so that the area of ΔPOA is always twice the area of ΔPOB. Find the equation to both parts of the locus of P.

13. What does the equation $(a - b)(x^2 + y^2) - 2abx = 0$ become, if the origin be moved to the point $\left(\frac{ab}{a - b}, 0\right)$?

14. The equation $x^2 + 2xy + 4 = 0$ is transformed to the parallel axes through the point $(6, \lambda)$. For what value of λ its new form passes through the new origin ?

15. Show that if the axes be turned through $7\frac{1^\circ}{2}$; the equation $\sqrt{3}x^2 + (\sqrt{3} - 1)xy - y^2 = 0$ become free of xy in its new form.

16. Find the angle through which the axes may be turned so that the equation $Ax + By + C = 0$ may reduce to the form $x =$ constant, and determine the value of this constant.

17. Transform $12x^2 + 7xy - 12y^2 - 17x - 31y - 7 = 0$ to rectangular axes through the point $(1, -1)$ inclined at an angle $\tan^{-1}\left(\frac{4}{3}\right)$ to the original axes.

Shortcuts and Important Results to Remember

1. If D, E, F are the mid-points of the sides BC, CA, AB of ΔABC, the $A = E + F - D$, $B = F + D - E$ and $C = D + E - F$

2. Orthocentre, nine point centre, centroid, circumcentre of a triangle are collinear. Centroid divides the line joining orthocentre and circumcentre in the ration 2 :1 (Internally) and nine point centre is the mid-point of orthocentre and circumcentre.

3. The circumcentre of a right angled triangle is the mid-point of the hypotenuse.

4. In an equilateral triangle orthocentre, nine point centre, centroid, circumcentre, incentre coincide.

5. The distance between the orthocentre and circumcentre in an equilateral triangle is zero.

6. The orthocentre of a triangle having vertices (α, β), (β, α) and (α, α) is (α, α).

7. Orthocentre of the triangle formed by the points $\left(\alpha, \frac{1}{\alpha}\right); \left(\beta, \frac{1}{\beta}\right); \left(\gamma, \frac{1}{\gamma}\right)$ is $\left(-\frac{1}{\alpha\beta\gamma}, -\alpha\beta\gamma\right)$

   i.e. all points and orthocentre lie on $xy = 1$.

8. **Points in a triangle :** Centroid (G), Incentre (I), Excentres (I_1, I_2, I_3), Orthocentre (O), Circumcentre (C) are given by $\left(\frac{m_1x_1 + m_2x_2 + m_3x_3}{m_1 + m_2 + m_3}, \frac{m_1y_1 + m_2y_2 + m_3y_3}{m_1 + m_2 + m_3}\right)$, where

	m_1	m_2	m_3
G	1	1	1
I	$\sin A$	$\sin B$	$\sin C$
I_1	$-\sin A$	$\sin B$	$\sin C$
I_2	$\sin A$	$-\sin B$	$\sin C$
I_3	$\sin A$	$\sin B$	$-\sin C$
O	$\tan A$	$\tan B$	$\tan C$
C	$\sin 2A$	$\sin 2B$	$\sin 2B$

   and vertices $A \equiv (x_1, y_1)$, $B \equiv (x_2, y_2)$, $C \equiv (x_3, y_3)$ and A, B, C are the angles of ΔABC.

9. If the circumcentre and centroid of a triangle are respectively (α, β), (γ, δ), then orthocentre will be $(3\gamma - 2\alpha, 3\delta - 2\beta)$.

10. If $ABCD$ is a parallelogram, then $D = A - B + C$.

11. If D, E, F are the mid-points of the sides BC, CA, AB of ΔABC, then the centroid of ΔABC = centroid of ΔDEF. If area of $\Delta ABC = \Delta$, then area of ΔAFE = area of ΔBDF = area of ΔCED = area of $\Delta DEF = \frac{\Delta}{4}$ and area of parallelogram $CEFD$ = area of parallelogram $BDEF$ = area of parallelogram $AEDF = \frac{\Delta}{2}$

12. Orthocentre of the right angle triangled ABC, right angled at A is A.

13. Circumcentre of the right angled triangle ABC, right angled at A is $\frac{B + C}{2}$.

14. X-axis divides the line segment joining (x_1, y_1), (x_2, y_2) in the ratio $-y_1 : y_2$ and Y-axis divides the same line segment in the ratio $-x_1 : x_2$.

15. Area of the triangle formed by (x_1, y_1), (x_2, y_2), (x_3, y_3) is $\frac{1}{2}\left|\begin{vmatrix} x_1 - x_3 & x_2 - x_3 \\ y_1 - y_3 & y_2 - y_3 \end{vmatrix}\right|$.

16. The area of the triangle formed by $y = m_1x + c_1$, $y = m_2x + c_2$, $y = m_3x + c_3$ is $\frac{1}{2}\Sigma\frac{(c_1 - c_2)^2}{|m_1 - m_2|}$.

17. Area of the quadrilateral formed by (x_1, y_1) (x_2, y_2) (x_3, y_3), (x_4, y_4) is

$$\frac{1}{2}\left|\begin{vmatrix} x_1 - x_3 & x_2 - x_4 \\ y_1 - y_3 & y_2 - y_4 \end{vmatrix}\right|$$

18. If (x_1, y_1), (x_2, y_2) are the ends of the hypotenuse of a right angled isosceles triangle, then the third vertex is given by

$$\left(\frac{x_1 + x_2 \pm (y_1 - y_2)}{2}, \frac{y_1 + y_2 \mp (x_1 - x_2)}{2}\right)$$

19. Given the two vertices (x_1, y_1) and (x_2, y_2) of an equilateral triangle, then its third vertex is given by

$$\left(\frac{x_1 + x_2 \pm \sqrt{3}(y_1 - y_2)}{2}, \frac{y_1 + y_2 \mp \sqrt{3}(x_1 - x_2)}{2}\right)$$

20. Circumcentre of the triangle formed by the points (x_1, y_1), (x_2, y_2) and (x_3, y_3) is same as that of triangle formed by the points $(0, 0)$, $(x_2 - x_1, y_2 - y_1)$, $(x_3 - x_1, y_3 - y_1)$.

JEE Type Solved Examples : Single Option Correct Type Questions

This section contains **5 multiple choice examples**. Each example has four choice (a), (b), (c) and (d) out of which **ONLY ONE** is correct.

Ex. 1. *Locus of centroid of the triangle whose vertices are $(a\cos t, a\sin t), (b\sin t, -b\cos t)$ and $(1, 0)$, where t is a parameter, is*

(a) $(3x-1)^2+(3y)^2=a^2-b^2$

(b) $(3x-1)^2+(3y)^2=a^2+b^2$

(c) $(3x+1)^2+(3y)^2=a^2+b^2$

(d) $(3x+1)^2+3y^2=a^2-b^2$

Sol. (b) Let $A\equiv(a\cos t, a\sin t)$, $B\equiv(b\sin t, -b\cos t)$ and $C\equiv(1,0)$

$\therefore$ Centroid $\equiv\left(\dfrac{a\cos t+b\sin t+1}{3}, \dfrac{a\sin t-b\cos t}{3}\right)$

Let $x=\dfrac{a\cos t+b\sin t+1}{3}\Rightarrow 3x-1=a\cos t+b\sin t$ ...(i)

and $y=\dfrac{a\sin t-b\cos t}{3}\Rightarrow 3y=a\sin t-b\cos t$ ...(ii)

On squaring and adding Eqs. (i) and (ii), we get

$$(3x-1)^2+(3y)^2=a^2+b^2$$

which is locus of centroid.

Ex. 2. *The incentre of triangle with vertices $(1,\sqrt{3}), (0,0)$ and $(2,0)$ is*

(a) $\left(1,\dfrac{\sqrt{3}}{2}\right)$ (b) $\left(\dfrac{2}{3},\dfrac{1}{\sqrt{3}}\right)$ (c) $\left(\dfrac{2}{3},\dfrac{\sqrt{3}}{2}\right)$ (d) $\left(1,\dfrac{1}{\sqrt{3}}\right)$

Sol. (d)

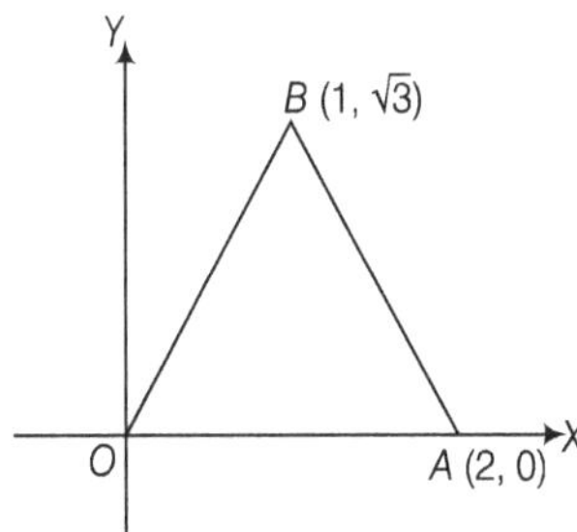

Let $O\equiv(0,0), A\equiv(2,0)$

and $B\equiv(1,\sqrt{3})$

$\because$ $OA=2=OB=AB$

$\Rightarrow \Delta OAB$ is an equilateral.

$\therefore$ Incentre = Centroid

$$\equiv\left(\frac{0+2+1}{3},\frac{0+0+\sqrt{3}}{3}\right)$$

$\therefore$ Incentre $\equiv\left(1,\dfrac{1}{\sqrt{3}}\right)$

Ex. 3. *Orthocentre of triangle with vertices $(0,0)$, $(3, 4)$ and $(4, 0)$ is*

(a) $\left(3,\dfrac{5}{4}\right)$ (b) $(3,12)$

(c) $\left(3,\dfrac{3}{4}\right)$ (d) $(3,9)$

Sol. (c) Denote the points are $(x_1,y_1),(x_2,y_2)$ and (x_3,y_3) from the matrix

$$P=\begin{bmatrix} x_1-x_3 & y_1-y_3\\ x_2-x_3 & y_2-y_3\end{bmatrix}=\begin{bmatrix}-4 & 0\\ -1 & 4\end{bmatrix}$$

$\therefore$ $$\lambda=\frac{\vec{\mathbf{R}}_1\cdot\vec{\mathbf{R}}_2}{|P|}=\frac{(-4)(-1)+0}{-16}=-\frac{1}{4}$$

$\therefore$ Circumcentre of the triangle

$$\equiv\left(\frac{x_1+x_2+\lambda(y_1-y_2)}{2},\frac{y_1+y_2-\lambda(x_1-x_2)}{2}\right)$$

$$\equiv\left(\frac{3-4\lambda}{2},\frac{4+3\lambda}{2}\right)\equiv\left(2,\frac{13}{8}\right)$$

i.e. $C\equiv\left(2,\dfrac{13}{8}\right)$

and centroid $G\equiv\left(\dfrac{7}{3},\dfrac{4}{3}\right)$

$\therefore$ Orthocentre

$$H\equiv\left(3\times\frac{7}{3}-2\times2, 3\times\frac{4}{3}-2\times\frac{13}{8}\right)\equiv\left(3,\frac{3}{4}\right)$$

Aliter : Let orthocentre

$$H\equiv(\alpha,\beta)$$

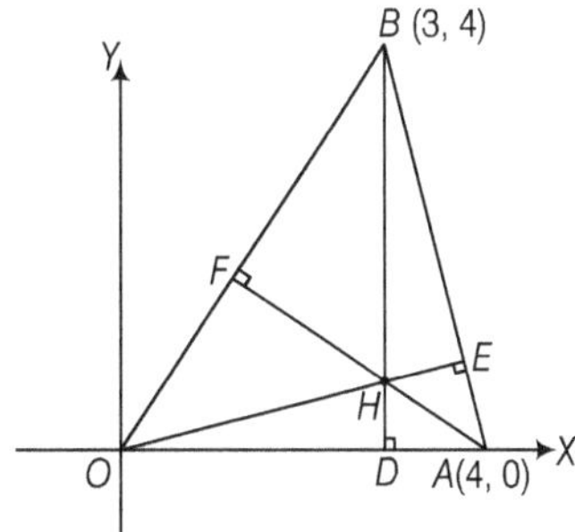

$\therefore$ Slope of $BH\times$ slope of $OA=-1$

$\Rightarrow$ $$\left(\frac{\beta-4}{\alpha-3}\right)\times\left(\frac{0}{4}\right)=-1$$

$\therefore \quad \alpha - 3 = 0$

$\Rightarrow \quad \alpha = 3 \quad \text{...(i)}$

and slope of $AH \times$ slope of $OB = -1$

$\Rightarrow \quad \left(\frac{\beta - 0}{\alpha - 4}\right) \times \left(\frac{4}{3}\right) = -1$

From Eq. (i), $\quad \beta = \frac{3}{4}$

Hence, orthocentre is $\left(3, \frac{3}{4}\right)$.

Ex. 4. *If x_1, x_2, x_3 as well as y_1, y_2, y_3 are in GP, with the same common ratio, then the points $(x_1, y_1), (x_2, y_2)$ and (x_3, y_3)*

(a) lie on a straight line
(b) lie on an ellipse
(c) lie on a circle
(d) are vertices of a triangle

Sol. (a) Let common ratio of GP is r, then $x_2 = x_1 r$, $x_3 = x_1 r^2$, $y_2 = y_1 r$ and $y_3 = y_1 r^2$.

Let $A \equiv (x_1, y_1)$, $B \equiv (x_2, y_2)$ and $C \equiv (x_3, y_3)$

$$\therefore \quad \text{Area of } \Delta ABC = \frac{1}{2}\left|\begin{vmatrix} x_1 & y_1 & 1 \\ x_2 & y_2 & 1 \\ x_3 & y_3 & 1 \end{vmatrix}\right|$$

$$= \frac{1}{2}\left|\begin{vmatrix} x_1 & y_1 & 1 \\ x_1 r & y_1 r & 1 \\ x_1 r^2 & y_1 r^2 & 1 \end{vmatrix}\right|$$

$$= \frac{1}{2}|x_1 y_1| \left|\begin{vmatrix} 1 & 1 & 1 \\ r & r & 1 \\ r^2 & r^2 & 1 \end{vmatrix}\right| = 0 \quad (\because C_1 \text{ and } C_2 \text{ are identical})$$

$\Rightarrow$ Points A, B, C are collinear.

Ex. 5. *Let A be the image of $(2, -1)$ with respect to Y-axis. Without transforming the origin, coordinate axis are turned at an angle 45° in the clockwise direction. Then, the coordiates of A in the new system are*

(a) $\left(-\frac{1}{\sqrt{2}}, -\frac{3}{\sqrt{2}}\right)$ (b) $\left(-\frac{3}{\sqrt{2}}, -\frac{1}{\sqrt{2}}\right)$
(c) $\left(\frac{1}{\sqrt{2}}, \frac{3}{\sqrt{2}}\right)$ (d) $\left(\frac{3}{\sqrt{2}}, \frac{1}{\sqrt{2}}\right)$

Sol. (a) Since, the image of (h, k) w.r.t. Y-axis is $(-h, k)$.

$\therefore$ Coordinate of A are $(-2, -1)$.

If (X, Y) are the coordinates of A w.r.t. the new coordinate axes obtained by turning the axes through an angle 45° in the clockwise direction, then

$$X = -2\cos(-45°) - \sin(-45°)$$
$$= -\frac{2}{\sqrt{2}} + \frac{1}{\sqrt{2}} = -\frac{1}{\sqrt{2}}$$

and
$$Y = 2\sin(-45°) - \cos(-45°)$$
$$= -\frac{2}{\sqrt{2}} - \frac{1}{\sqrt{2}} = -\frac{3}{\sqrt{2}}$$

$\therefore$ Required coordinates are $\left(-\frac{1}{\sqrt{2}}, -\frac{3}{\sqrt{2}}\right)$.

JEE Type Solved Examples :
More than One Correct Option Type Questions

- This section contains **3 multiple choice examples**. Each example has four choices (a), (b), (c) and (d). Out of which **MORE THAN ONE** may be correct.

Ex. 6. *Let $S_1, S_2, \ldots$, be squares such that for each $n \geq 1$, the length of a side of S_n equals the length of a diagonal of S_{n+1}. If the length of a side S_1 is 10 cm, then for which of the following value of n is the area of S_n less than 1 sq cm?*

(a) 7 (b) 8 (c) 9 (d) 10

Sol. (b,c,d)

If a be the side of the square, then diagonal $d = a\sqrt{2}$ by hypothesis

$$a_n = \sqrt{2}\, a_{n+1}$$

$$\Rightarrow \quad a_{n+1} = \frac{a_n}{\sqrt{2}} = \frac{a_{n-1}}{(\sqrt{2})^2} = \frac{a_{n-2}}{(\sqrt{2})^3} = \ldots = \frac{a_1}{(\sqrt{2})^n}$$

$$\Rightarrow \quad a_n = \frac{a_1}{(\sqrt{2})^{n-1}} = \frac{10}{(2)^{(n-1)/2}}$$

$\because$ Area of $S_n < 1 \Rightarrow a_n^2 < 1$

$$\Rightarrow \quad \frac{100}{2^{n-1}} < 1$$

$$\Rightarrow \quad 2^{n-1} > 100 > 2^6$$

$$\Rightarrow \quad n - 1 > 6$$

$$\Rightarrow \quad n > 7$$

$\therefore \quad n = 8, 9, 10, \ldots$

Ex 7. *If each of the vertices of a triangle has integral coordinates, then the triangles may be*

(a) right angled (b) equilateral
(c) isosceles (d) scalene

Sol. (a,c,d) Let $A \equiv (x_1, y_1)$, $B \equiv (x_2, y_2)$ and $C \equiv (x_3, y_3)$ be the vertices of triangle ABC. Given $x_1, y_1, x_2, y_2, x_3, y_3$ be all integers.

Now, area of $\Delta ABC = \frac{1}{2}|x_1(y_2 - y_3) + x_2(y_3 - y_1) + x_3(y_1 - y_2)|$

$= \text{Rational} \quad \text{...(i)}$

If ΔABC is equilateral then,

$$\text{Area of } \Delta ABC = \frac{\sqrt{3}}{4}(\text{side})^2$$

$$= \frac{\sqrt{3}}{4}\{(x_1 - x_2)^2 + (y_1 - y_2)^2\}$$

$$= \text{Irrational} \quad \text{...(ii)}$$

It is clear from Eqs. (i) and (ii), ΔABC can not be equilateral.

Ex. 8. *ABC is an isosceles triangle. If the coordinates of the base are $B(1, 3)$ and $C(-2, 7)$. The coordinates of vertex A can be*

(a) $(1, 6)$ (b) $\left(-\frac{1}{2}, 5\right)$ (c) $\left(\frac{5}{6}, 6\right)$ (d) $\left(-7, \frac{1}{8}\right)$

Sol. (b,c,d) Let vertex of the ΔABC be $A(x, y)$

$\therefore \quad AB = AC$

$\Rightarrow \quad (AB)^2 = (AC)^2$

$\Rightarrow \quad (x-1)^2 + (y-3)^2 = (x+2)^2 + (y-7)^2$

$\Rightarrow \quad 6x - 8y + 43 = 0 \quad \text{...(i)}$

Here, use observe that the coordinates $\left(-\frac{1}{2}, 5\right), \left(\frac{5}{6}, 6\right)$ and $\left(-7, \frac{1}{8}\right)$ satisfy the Eq. (i).

JEE Type Solved Examples : Paragraph Based Questions

- This section contains **one solved paragraph** based 3 **multiple choice questions**. Each of these questions has four choices (a), (b), (c) and (d) out of which **ONLY ONE** is correct.

Paragraph

(Q. Nos. 9 to 11)

If $A\left(\alpha, \frac{1}{\alpha}\right), B\left(\beta, \frac{1}{\beta}\right), C\left(\gamma, \frac{1}{\gamma}\right)$ be the vertices of a ΔABC, where α, β are the roots of $x^2 - 6ax + 2 = 0$; β, γ are the roots of $x^2 - 6bx + 3 = 0$ and γ, α are the roots of $x^2 - 6cx + 6 = 0$; a, b, c being positive.

9. The value of $a + b + c$ is

(a) 1 (b) 2
(c) 3 (d) 5

10. The coordinates of centroid of ΔABC is

(a) $\left(1, \frac{11}{9}\right)$ (b) $\left(\frac{1}{3}, \frac{11}{18}\right)$
(c) $\left(2, \frac{11}{18}\right)$ (d) $\left(\frac{2}{3}, \frac{11}{19}\right)$

11. The coordinates of orthocentre of ΔABC is

(a) $\left(-\frac{1}{2}, -2\right)$ (b) $\left(-\frac{1}{3}, -3\right)$
(c) $\left(-\frac{1}{5}, -5\right)$ (d) $\left(-\frac{1}{6}, -6\right)$

Sol. $\because \alpha, \beta$ are the roots of $x^2 - 6ax + 2 = 0$

$\therefore \quad \alpha + \beta = 6a \quad \text{...(i)}$

and $\quad \alpha\beta = 2 \quad \text{...(ii)}$

Again, β, γ are the roots of $x^2 - 6bx + 3 = 0$

$\therefore \quad \beta + \gamma = 6b \quad \text{...(iii)}$

and $\quad \beta\gamma = 3 \quad \text{...(iv)}$

Again, γ, α are the roots of $x^2 - 6cx + 6 = 0$

$\therefore \quad \gamma + \alpha = 6c \quad \text{...(v)}$

and $\quad \gamma\alpha = 6 \quad \text{...(vi)}$

from Eqs. (ii), (iv) and (vi), we get

$$\alpha\beta \cdot \beta\gamma \cdot \gamma\alpha = 2 \cdot 3 \cdot 6$$

$\Rightarrow \quad \alpha\beta\gamma = 6$

$\therefore \quad \alpha = 2, \beta = 1, \gamma = 3$

9. (b) Adding Eqs. (i), (iii) and (v), we get

$$2(\alpha + \beta + \gamma) = 6(a + b + c)$$

or $\quad a + b + c = \frac{1}{3}(2 + 1 + 3) = 2$

10. (c) Centroid of $\Delta ABC \equiv \left(\frac{\Sigma\alpha}{3}, \frac{\Sigma\alpha\beta}{3\alpha\beta\gamma}\right)$

$$\equiv \left(\frac{2+1+3}{3}, \frac{2\cdot1 + 1\cdot3 + 3\cdot2}{3\cdot2\cdot1\cdot3}\right)$$

$$\equiv \left(2, \frac{11}{18}\right)$$

11. (d) Orthocentre of $\Delta ABC \equiv \left(-\frac{1}{\alpha\beta\gamma}, -\alpha\beta\gamma\right)$

$$\equiv \left(-\frac{1}{6}, -6\right)$$

JEE Type Solved Examples : Single Integer Answer Type Questions

- This section contains **one solved example**. The answer to this example is **a single digit integer** ranging from 0 to 9 (both inclusive).

Ex.12. *If the points* $(-2,0), \left(-1,\frac{1}{\sqrt{3}}\right)$ *and* $(\cos\theta, \sin\theta)$ *are collinear, then the number of values of* $\theta \in [0, 2\pi]$ *is*

Sol. (1) Since, the given points are collinear, then

$$\begin{vmatrix} -2 & 0 & 1 \\ -1 & \frac{1}{\sqrt{3}} & 1 \\ \cos\theta & \sin\theta & 1 \end{vmatrix} = 0$$

$$\Rightarrow \quad -2\left(\frac{1}{\sqrt{3}} - \sin\theta\right) - 0 + 1\left(-\sin\theta - \frac{\cos\theta}{\sqrt{3}}\right) = 0$$

$$\Rightarrow \quad \sqrt{3}\sin\theta - \cos\theta = 2$$

$$\Rightarrow \quad \frac{\sqrt{3}}{2}\sin\theta - \frac{1}{2}\cos\theta = 1$$

$$\text{or} \quad \sin\left(\theta - \frac{\pi}{6}\right) = 1$$

$$\text{or} \quad \theta - \frac{\pi}{6} = 2n\pi + \frac{\pi}{2}$$

$$\text{for } n = 0, \quad \theta = \frac{\pi}{6} + \frac{\pi}{2} = \frac{2\pi}{3} \in [0, 2\pi]$$

Number of values θ is 1.

JEE Type Solved Examples : Matching Type Questions

- This section contains **one solved example**. Which has four statements (A, B, C and D) given in **Column I** and four statements (p, q, r and s) in **Column II**. Any given statements in **Column I** can have correct matching with one or more statement(s) given in **Column II**.

Ex. 13. *Match the following*

	Column I		Column II
A.	The points $(\lambda+1, 1), (2\lambda+1, 3)$ and $(2\lambda+2, 2\lambda)$ are collinear then number of values of λ is	(p)	a prime number
B.	Area of ΔABC is 20 sq units, where A, B and C are $(4, 6), (10, 14)$ and (x, y) respectively. AC is perpendicular to BC, then number of positions of C is	(q)	an odd number
C.	In a ΔABC coordinates of orthocentre, centroid and vertex A are respectively $(2,2), (2,1)$ and $(0,2)$. The x-coordinate of vertex B is	(r)	a composite number
D.	A man starts from $P(-3,4)$ and reaches the point Q $(0,1)$ touching the X-axis at $R(\lambda, 0)$ such that $PR + RQ$ is minimum, then $10\lvert\lambda\rvert$ is	(s)	a perfect number

Sol. (A) → (p); (B) → (r); (C) → (p, q); (D) → (r, s)

(A) ∵ Points are collinear

$$\therefore \quad \begin{vmatrix} \lambda+1 & 1 & 1 \\ 2\lambda+1 & 3 & 1 \\ 2\lambda+2 & 2\lambda & 1 \end{vmatrix} = 0$$

$$\Rightarrow \quad (\lambda+1)(3-2\lambda) - 1(2\lambda+1-2\lambda-2) + 1(4\lambda^2+2\lambda-6\lambda-6) = 0$$

$$\text{or} \quad 2\lambda^2 - 3\lambda - 2 = 0$$

$$\text{or} \quad (2\lambda+1)(\lambda-2) = 0$$

$$\therefore \quad \lambda = 2, -\frac{1}{2}$$

Number of values of λ is 2.

(B) ∵ Area of triangles ABC is 20 sq units.

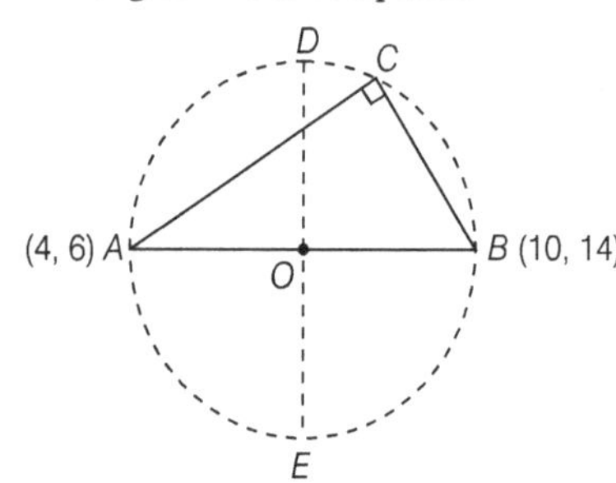

∵ C can not be at D and E

∴ Four positions are possible two above AB and two below AB.

(C)

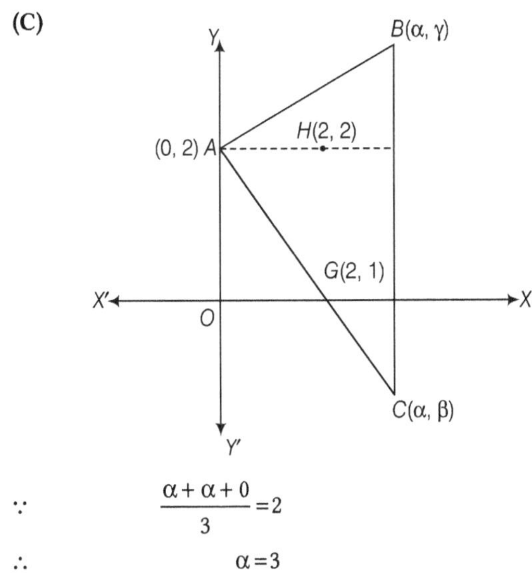

$\because \quad \dfrac{\alpha+\alpha+0}{3}=2$

$\therefore \quad \alpha=3$

$\Rightarrow$ x-coordinates of vertex $B=3$

(D) For $PR + RQ$ to be minimum, it should be the path of light

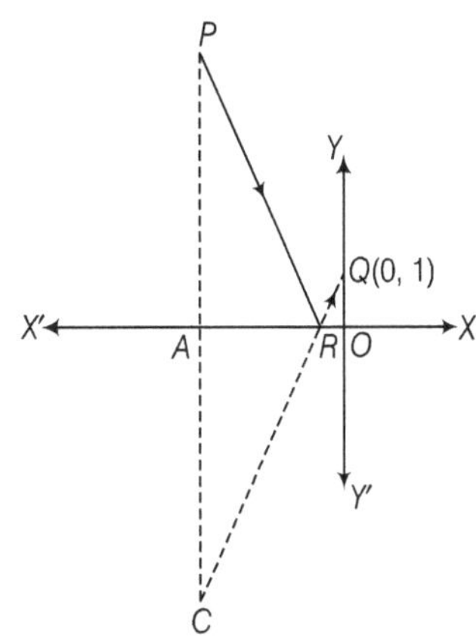

$\because \quad \angle PRA = \angle QRO$

From similar triangles PAR and QOR

$$\frac{AR}{RO}=\frac{PA}{QO} \quad \text{or} \quad \frac{\lambda+3}{0-\lambda}=\frac{4}{1}$$

or $\quad \lambda=-\dfrac{3}{5} \quad \therefore \quad 10|\lambda|=6.$

JEE Type Solved Examples :
Statement I and II Type Questions

- **Directions** (Ex. Nos. 14 and 15) are Assertion-Reason type examples. Each of these examples contains two statements.

Statement I (Assertion) and **Statement II** (Reason)

Each of these examples also has four alternative choices, (a), (b), (c) and (d) only one out of which is the correct answer. You have to select the correct choice as given below :

(a) Statement I is true, Statement II is true; Statement II is a correct explanation for Statement I

(b) Statement I is true, Statement II is true; Statement II is not a correct explanation for Statement I

(c) Statement I is true, Statement II is false

(d) Statement I is false, Statement II is true

Ex. 14. Statement I *The area of the triangle formed by the points* $A(100,102), B(102,105), C(104,107)$ *is same as the area formed by* $A'(0,0), B'(2,3), C'(4,5)$.

Statement II *The area of the triangle is constant with respect to translation :*

Sol. (a) Area of triangle is unaltered by shifting origin to any point. If origin is shifted to (100, 102), then A, B, C becomes $A'(0,0)$, $B'(2,3)$, $C'(4,5)$ respectively. Hence, both statements are true and Statement II is correct explanation for Statement I.

Ex. 15. Statement I *If centroid and circumcentre of a triangle are known its orthocentre can be found*

Statement II *Centroid, orthocentre and circumcentre of a triangle are collinear.*

Sol. (b) $\because$ Centroid divides orthocentre and circumcentre in the ratio 2 : 1 (internally).

$\therefore$ We can find easily orthocentre.

$\Rightarrow$ Statement I is true, and centroid, orthocentre and circumcentre are collinear Statement II is true but Statement II is not correct explanation for Statement I.

Subjective Type Examples

- In this section, there are **7 subjective solved examples**.

Ex. 16. *The four points $A(\alpha, 0), B(\beta, 0), C(\gamma, 0)$ and $D(\delta, 0)$ are such that α, β are the roots of equation $ax^2 + 2hx + b = 0$ and γ, δ are those of equation $a'x^2 + 2h'x + b' = 0$. Show that the sum of the ratios in which C and D divide AB is zero, if $ab' + a'b = 2hh'$.*

Sol. Since, α, β are the roots of $ax^2 + 2hx + b = 0$

$$\therefore \quad \alpha + \beta = -\frac{2h}{a} \text{ and } \alpha\beta = \frac{b}{a} \quad \text{...(i)}$$

and γ, δ are the roots of $a'x^2 + 2h'x + b' = 0$

$$\text{then,} \quad \gamma + \delta = -\frac{2h'}{a'} \text{ and } \gamma\delta = \frac{b'}{a'} \quad \text{...(ii)}$$

Let C divides AB in the ratio $\lambda : 1$

then $A(\alpha, 0)$ —λ— $C(\gamma, 0)$ —1— $B(\beta, 0)$

$$\gamma = \frac{\lambda \cdot \beta + 1 \cdot \alpha}{\lambda + 1}$$

$$\therefore \quad \lambda = \frac{\gamma - \alpha}{\beta - \gamma}$$

and let D divides AB in the ratio $\mu : 1$

then $A(\alpha, 0)$ —μ— $D(\delta, 0)$ —1— $B(\beta, 0)$

$$\delta = \frac{\mu \cdot \beta + 1 \cdot \alpha}{\mu + 1}$$

$$\therefore \quad \mu = \frac{\delta - \alpha}{\beta - \delta}$$

but given $\lambda + \mu = 0$

$$\Rightarrow \quad \frac{\gamma - \alpha}{\beta - \gamma} + \frac{\delta - \alpha}{\beta - \delta} = 0$$

$$\Rightarrow \quad (\alpha + \beta)(\gamma + \delta) - 2\alpha\beta - 2\gamma\delta = 0$$

$$\Rightarrow \quad \left(-\frac{2h}{a}\right)\left(-\frac{2h'}{a'}\right) - \frac{2b}{a} - \frac{2b'}{a'} = 0$$

[from Eqs. (i) and (ii)]

$$\text{or} \quad ab' + a'b = 2hh'$$

Ex. 17. *If m_1 and m_2 are the roots of the equation $x^2 + (\sqrt{3} + 2)x + (\sqrt{3} - 1) = 0$. Show that the area of the triangle formed by the lines $y = m_1x, y = m_2x$ and $y = c$ is $\left(\frac{\sqrt{33} + \sqrt{11}}{4}\right)c^2$.*

Sol. Since, m_1 and m_2 are the roots of the equation

$$x^2 + (\sqrt{3} + 2)x + (\sqrt{3} - 1) = 0$$

$$\text{then} \quad m_1 + m_2 = -(\sqrt{3} + 2), m_1m_2 = (\sqrt{3} - 1)$$

$$\therefore \quad m_1 - m_2 = \sqrt{(m_1 + m_2)^2 - 4m_1m_2}$$

$$= \sqrt{(3 + 4 + 4\sqrt{3} - 4\sqrt{3} + 4)} = \sqrt{11}$$

and coordinates of the vertices of the given triangle are $(0, 0)$, $(c/m_1, c)$ and $(c/m_2, c)$.

Hence, the required area of triangle $= \frac{1}{2}\left|\frac{c}{m_1} \times c - \frac{c}{m_2} \times c\right|$

$$= \frac{1}{2}c^2\left|\left(\frac{1}{m_1} - \frac{1}{m_2}\right)\right| = \frac{1}{2}c^2\frac{|m_2 - m_1|}{|m_1m_2|}$$

$$= \frac{1}{2}c^2\frac{\sqrt{11}}{(\sqrt{3} - 1)}$$

$$= \frac{1}{2}c^2 \cdot \frac{\sqrt{11}(\sqrt{3} + 1)}{(\sqrt{3} - 1)(\sqrt{3} + 1)}$$

$$= \left(\frac{\sqrt{33} + \sqrt{11}}{4}\right)c^2$$

Ex. 18. *If x coordinates of two points B and C are the roots of equation $x^2 + 4x + 3 = 0$ and their y coordinates are the roots of equation $x^2 - x - 6 = 0$. If x coordinate of B is less than x coordinate of C and y coordinate of B is greater than the y coordinate of C and coordinates of a third point A be $(3, -5)$, find the length of the bisector of the interior angle at A.*

Sol. $\because \quad x^2 + 4x + 3 = 0 \Rightarrow x = -1, -3$

and $\quad x^2 - x - 6 = 0 \Rightarrow x = -2, 3$

Also, given that x and y coordinates of B are respectively less than and greater than the corresponding coordinates of C.

$$\therefore \quad B \equiv (-3, 3) \text{ and } C \equiv (-1, -2)$$

$$\text{Now,} \quad AB = \sqrt{(3 + 3)^2 + (-5 - 3)^2} = 10$$

$$\text{and} \quad AC = \sqrt{(3 + 1)^2 + (-5 + 2)^2} = 5$$

$$\therefore \quad \frac{AB}{AC} = \frac{2}{1}$$

Let AD be the bisector of $\angle BAC$, then

$$\frac{BD}{DC} = \frac{AB}{AC} = \frac{2}{1}$$

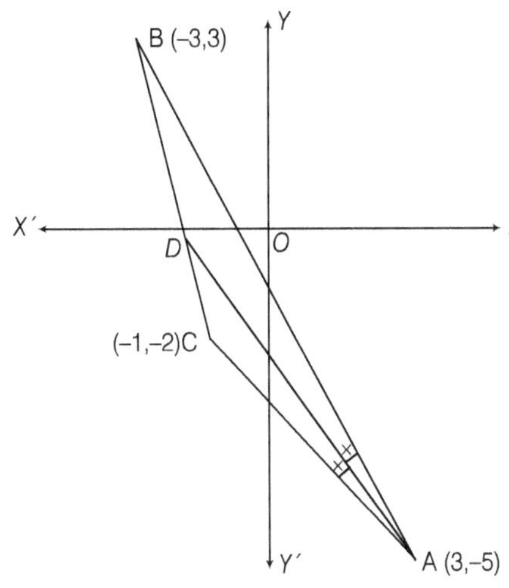

Thus, D divides BC internally in the ratio 2 : 1

$$\therefore \quad D \equiv \left(\frac{2(-1)+1(-3)}{2+1}, \frac{2(-2)+1(3)}{2+1} \right)$$

Thus, $$D \equiv \left(-\frac{5}{3}, -\frac{1}{3} \right)$$

Now, $$AD = \sqrt{\left(3+\frac{5}{3}\right)^2 + \left(-5+\frac{1}{3}\right)^2}$$

$$= \sqrt{\frac{196}{9}+\frac{196}{9}} = \frac{14\sqrt{2}}{3} \text{ units}$$

Ex. 19. *The distance between two parallel lines is unity. A point P lies between the lines at a distance a from one of them. Find the length of a side of an equilateral triangle PQR, vertex Q of which lies on one of the parallel lines and vertex R lies on the other line.*

Sol. Let $PQ = QR = RP = r$

and $\angle PQL = \theta$

then, $\angle XQR = \theta + 60°$

Given, $PL = a$ and $RN = 1$ unit

In ΔPQL, $\sin\theta = \dfrac{PL}{QP} = \dfrac{a}{r}$

$$\therefore \quad a = r\sin\theta \qquad \text{...(i)}$$

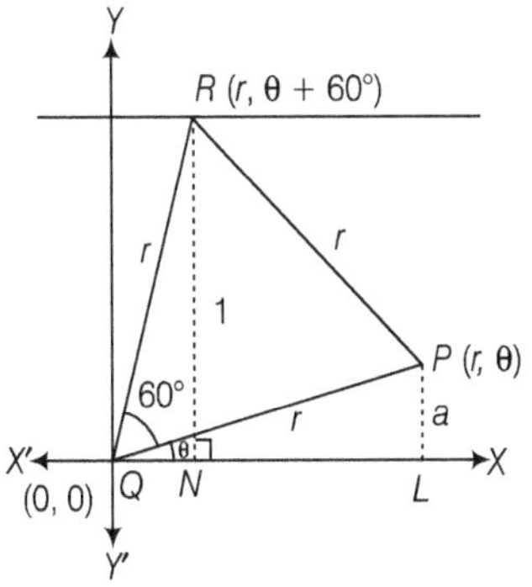

and in ΔQRN, $\sin(\theta + 60°) = \dfrac{RN}{QR} = \dfrac{1}{r}$

$$\therefore \quad r\sin(\theta+60°) = 1$$

$$r\{\sin\theta\cos 60° + \cos\theta \sin 60°\} = 1$$

$$\Rightarrow \quad r\left\{\frac{1}{2}\sin\theta + \frac{\sqrt{3}}{2}\cos\theta\right\} = 1$$

$$\Rightarrow \quad r\left\{\frac{1}{2}\times\frac{a}{r} + \frac{\sqrt{3}}{2}\times\sqrt{1-\frac{a^2}{r^2}}\right\} = 1 \qquad \text{[from Eq. (i)]}$$

$$\Rightarrow \quad \frac{a}{2} + \frac{\sqrt{3}}{2}\sqrt{(r^2-a^2)} = 1$$

$$\Rightarrow \quad \frac{\sqrt{3}}{2}\sqrt{(r^2-a^2)} = 1 - \frac{a}{2}$$

$$\text{or} \quad \frac{3}{4}(r^2-a^2) = 1 + \frac{a^2}{4} - a$$

$$\Rightarrow \quad 3r^2 - 3a^2 = 4 + a^2 - 4a$$

$$\Rightarrow \quad 3r^2 = 4a^2 - 4a + 4$$

$$= 4(a^2 - a + 1)$$

$$\therefore \quad r = \frac{2}{\sqrt{3}}\sqrt{(a^2-a+1)}$$

Hence, length of side of an equilateral triangle

$$= \frac{2}{\sqrt{3}}\sqrt{(a^2-a+1)} \text{ units.}$$

Ex. 20. *In a ΔABC, $A \equiv (\alpha, \beta)$, $B \equiv (1, 2)$, $C \equiv (2, 3)$ and point A lies on the line $y = 2x + 3$ where $\alpha, \beta \in I$. If the area of ΔABC be such that $[\Delta] = 2$, where [.] denotes the greatest integer function, find all possible coordinates of A.*

Sol. $\because (\alpha, \beta)$ lies on $y = 2x + 3$

then $\beta = 2\alpha + 3$

Thus, the coordinates of A are $(\alpha, 2\alpha+3)$ ...(i)

$$\Delta = \frac{1}{2}\left|\left\{ \begin{vmatrix} \alpha & 2\alpha+3 \\ 1 & 2 \end{vmatrix} + \begin{vmatrix} 1 & 2 \\ 2 & 3 \end{vmatrix} + \begin{vmatrix} 2 & 3 \\ \alpha & 2\alpha+3 \end{vmatrix} \right\}\right|$$

$$= \frac{1}{2}|2\alpha - (2\alpha+3) + 3 - 4 + 4\alpha + 6 - 3\alpha|$$

$$= \frac{1}{2}|\alpha + 2|$$

but $[\Delta] = 2$

$$\Rightarrow \quad \left[\frac{1}{2}|\alpha+2|\right] = 2$$

$$\Rightarrow \quad 2 \le \frac{|\alpha+2|}{2} < 3$$

$$\Rightarrow \quad 4 \le |\alpha+2| < 6$$

$$\Rightarrow \quad 4 \le \alpha + 2 < 6$$

$$\text{and} \quad -6 < \alpha + 2 \le -4$$

$$\Rightarrow \quad 2 \le \alpha < 4 \text{ and } -8 < \alpha \le -6$$

$$\because \quad \alpha \in I$$

$$\therefore \quad \alpha = 2, 3, -7, -6$$

Hence, possible coordinates of A are $(2, 7), (3, 9), (-7, -11)$ and $(-6, -9)$.

Ex. 21. *Let S be the square of unit area. Consider any quadrilateral which has one vertex on each side of S. If a,b,c and d denote the lengths of the sides of the quadrilateral, prove that* $2 \le a^2 + b^2 + c^2 + d^2 \le 4$.

Sol. Given S be the area of square with vertices

$O(0, 0), A(1, 0), B(1, 1), C(0, 1)$.

Let $PQRM$ be the quadrilateral with vertices

$P(p, 0), Q(1, q), R(r, 1)$ and $M(0, m)$

and sides $MP = a, PQ = b, QR = c, RM = d$

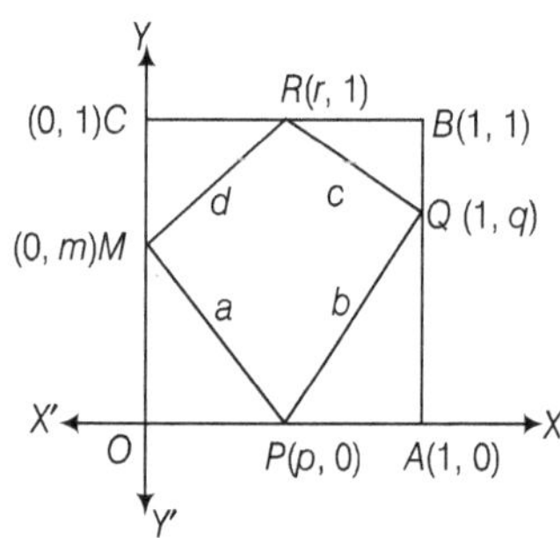

Then,
$$a^2 = p^2 + m^2$$
$$b^2 = (1-p)^2 + q^2$$
$$c^2 = (1-q)^2 + (1-r)^2$$
$$d^2 = r^2 + (1-m)^2$$

$$\therefore a^2 + b^2 + c^2 + d^2 = p^2 + (1-p)^2 + q^2 + (1-q)^2 + r^2 + (1-r)^2 + m^2 + (1-m)^2$$
$$= 2[p^2 + q^2 + r^2 + m^2 - p - q - r - m + 2]$$
$$= 2\left[\left(p-\frac{1}{2}\right)^2 + \left(q-\frac{1}{2}\right)^2 + \left(r-\frac{1}{2}\right)^2 + \left(m-\frac{1}{2}\right)^2 + 1\right] \ge 2$$

$$\Rightarrow \quad a^2 + b^2 + c^2 + d^2 \ge 2 \quad \text{...(i)}$$

also, since $0 \le x \le 1$

$\therefore \quad x^2 \le 1$

$\therefore \quad a^2 \le 1, b^2 \le 1, c^2 \le 1, d^2 \le 1$

$$\Rightarrow \quad a^2 + b^2 + c^2 + d^2 \le 4 \quad \text{...(ii)}$$

From Eqs. (i) and (ii), we get

$$2 \le a^2 + b^2 + c^2 + d^2 \le 4$$

Ex. 22. *The circumcentre of a triangle with vertices* $(a, a\tan\alpha), B(b, b\tan\beta)$ *and* $C(c, c\tan\gamma)$ *lies at the origin, where* $0 < \alpha, \beta, \gamma < \pi/2$ *and* $\alpha + \beta + \gamma = \pi$. *Show that its orthocentre lies on the line*

$$4\cos\left(\frac{\alpha}{2}\right)\cos\left(\frac{\beta}{2}\right)\cos\left(\frac{\gamma}{2}\right)x - 4\sin\left(\frac{\alpha}{2}\right)\sin\left(\frac{\beta}{2}\right)\sin\left(\frac{\gamma}{2}\right)y = y$$

Sol. Since, the circumcentre of the triangle is at the origin O, we have $OA = OB = OC = R$, where R is the circumradius of the circumcircle.

$$\therefore \quad (OA)^2 = R^2 \Rightarrow a^2 + a^2\tan^2\alpha = R^2 \Rightarrow a = R\cos\alpha$$

Therefore, the coordinates of A are $(R\cos\alpha, R\sin\alpha)$.

Similarly, the coordinates of B are $(R\cos\beta, R\sin\beta)$ and those of C are $(R\cos\gamma, R\sin\gamma)$.

Thus the coordinates of centroid G of ΔABC are

$$\left(\frac{R}{3}(\cos\alpha + \cos\beta + \cos\gamma), \frac{R}{3}(\sin\alpha + \sin\beta + \sin\gamma)\right)$$

Now, if $P(h, k)$ is the orthocentre of ΔABC, then

$$\frac{R}{3}(\cos\alpha + \cos\beta + \cos\gamma) = \frac{1\cdot h + 2\cdot 0}{1+2} \quad (\because PG : GO = 2:1)$$

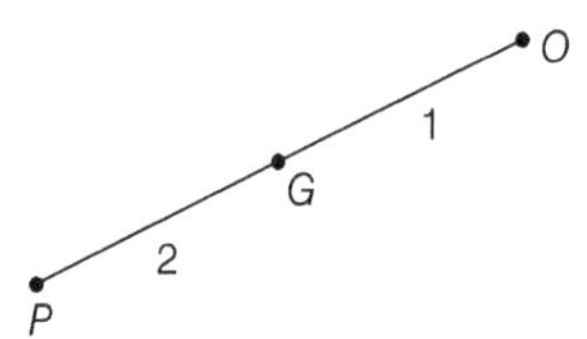

$$\Rightarrow \quad R(\cos\alpha + \cos\beta + \cos\gamma) = h \quad \text{...(i)}$$

and
$$\frac{R}{3}(\sin\alpha + \sin\beta + \sin\gamma) = \frac{1\cdot k + 2\cdot 0}{1+2}$$

$$\Rightarrow \quad R(\sin\alpha + \sin\beta + \sin\gamma) = k \quad \text{...(ii)}$$

Dividing (ii) by (i), then

$$\Rightarrow \quad \frac{\sin\alpha + \sin\beta + \sin\gamma}{\cos\alpha + \cos\beta + \cos\gamma} = \frac{k}{h}$$

$$\Rightarrow \quad \frac{4\cos(\alpha/2)\cos(\beta/2)\cos(\gamma/2)}{1 + 4\sin(\alpha/2)\sin(\beta/2)\sin(\gamma/2)} = \frac{k}{h}$$

(Because, $\alpha + \beta + y = \pi$ by identity)

Hence, the orthocentre $P(h, k)$ lies on the line

$$4\cos\left(\frac{\alpha}{2}\right)\cos\left(\frac{\beta}{2}\right)\cos\left(\frac{\gamma}{2}\right)x - 4\sin\left(\frac{\alpha}{2}\right)\sin\left(\frac{\beta}{2}\right)\sin\left(\frac{\gamma}{2}\right)y = y$$

Coordinate System and Coordinates Exercise 1 : Single Option Correct Type Questions

- This section contains **15 multiple choice questions.** Each question has four choices (a), (b), (c), (d) out of which **ONLY ONE** is correct.

1. Vertices of a variable triangle are (3, 4), $(5\cos\theta, 5\sin\theta)$ and $(5\sin\theta, -5\cos\theta)$, where $\theta \in R$. Locus of its orthocentre is

(a) $x^2 + y^2 + 6x + 8y - 25 = 0$

(b) $x^2 + y^2 - 6x + 8y - 25 = 0$

(c) $x^2 + y^2 + 6x - 8y - 25 = 0$

(d) $x^2 + y^2 - 6x - 8y - 25 = 0$

2. If a rod AB of length 2 units slides on coordinate axes in the first quadrant. An equilateral triangle ABC is completed with C on the side away from O. Then, locus of C is

(a) $x^2 + y^2 - xy + 1 = 0$

(b) $x^2 + y^2 - xy\sqrt{3} + 1 = 0$

(c) $x^2 + y^2 + xy\sqrt{3} - 1 = 0$

(d) $x^2 + y^2 - xy\sqrt{3} - 1 = 0$

3. The sides of a triangle are $3x + 4y$, $4x + 3y$ and $5x + 5y$ units, where $x > 0$, $y > 0$. The triangle is

(a) right angled (b) acute angled

(c) obtuse angled (d) isosceles

4. Let P and Q be the points on the line joining $A(-2, 5)$ and $B(3, 1)$ such that $AP = PQ = QB$. Then, the mid-point of PQ is

(a) $\left(\frac{1}{2}, 3\right)$ (b) $\left(-\frac{1}{4}, 4\right)$

(c) $(2, 3)$ (d) $(-1, 4)$

5. A triangle ABC right angled at A has points A and B as $(2, 3)$ and $(0, -1)$ respectively. If $BC = 5$ units, then the point C is

(a) $(4, 2)$ (b) $(-4, 2)$

(c) $(-4, 4)$ (d) $(4, -4)$

6. The locus of a point P which divides the line joining $(1, 0)$ and $(2\cos\theta, 2\sin\theta)$ internally in the ratio $2:3$ for all θ is

(a) a straight line (b) a circle

(c) a pair of straight lines (d) a parabola

7. The points with the coordinates $(2a, 3a)$, $(3b, 2b)$ and (c, c) are collinear

(a) for no value of a, b, c (b) for all values of a, b, c

(c) if $a, \frac{c}{5}, b$ are in HP (d) if $a, \frac{2c}{5}, b$ are in HP

8. The vertices of a triangle are (0, 3), (−3, 0) and (3, 0). The coordinates of its orthocentre are

(a) $(0, -2)$ (b) $(0, 2)$

(c) $(0, 3)$ (d) $(0, -3)$

9. ABC is an equilateral triangle such that the vertices B and C lie on two parallel lines at a distance 6. If A lies between the parallel lines at a distance 4 from one of them, then the length of a side of the equilateral triangle is

(a) 8 (b) $\sqrt{\frac{88}{3}}$

(c) $\frac{4\sqrt{7}}{\sqrt{3}}$ (d) None of these

10. A, B, C are respectively the points $(1, 2), (4, 2), (4, 5)$. If T_1, T_2 are the points of trisection of the line segment AC and S_1, S_2 are the points of trisection of the line segment BC, the area of the quadrilateral $T_1S_1S_2T_2$ is

(a) 1 (b) $\frac{3}{2}$ (c) 2 (d) $\frac{5}{2}$

11. (i) The points $(-1, 0), (4, -2)$ and $(\cos 2\theta, \sin 2\theta)$ are collinear

(ii) The points $(-1, 0), (4, -2)$ and $\left(\frac{1-\tan^2\theta}{1+\tan^2\theta}, \frac{2\tan\theta}{1+\tan^2\theta}\right)$ are collinear

(a) both statements are equivalent

(b) statemetn (i) has more solution than statement (ii) for θ

(c) statement (ii) has more solution than statement (i) for θ

(d) None of the above

12. If $\alpha_1, \alpha_2, \alpha_3, \beta_1, \beta_2, \beta_3$ are the values of n for which $\sum_{r=0}^{n-1} x^{2r}$ is divisible by $\sum_{r=0}^{n-1} x^r$, then the triangle having vertices $(\alpha_1, \beta_1), (\alpha_2, \beta_2)$ and (α_3, β_3) cannot be

(a) an isosceles triangle

(b) a right angled isosceles triangle

(c) a right angled triangle

(d) an equilateral triangle

13. A triangle ABC with vertices $A(-1, 0)$, $B\left(-2, \frac{3}{4}\right)$ and $C\left(-3, -\frac{7}{6}\right)$ has its orthocentre at H. Then, the orthocentre of triangle BCH will be

(a) $(-3, -2)$ (b) $(1, 3)$

(c) $(-1, 2)$ (d) None of these

14. If $\sum_{i=1}^{4}(x_i^2 + y_i^2) \le 2x_1x_3 + 2x_2x_4 + 2y_2y_3 + 2y_1y_4$, the points $(x_1, y_1), (x_2, y_2), (x_3, y_3), (x_4, y_4)$ are
(a) the vertices of a rectangle
(b) collinear
(c) the vertices of a trapezium
(d) None of the above

15. Without change of axes the origin is shifted to (h, k), then from the equation $x^2 + y^2 - 4x + 6y - 7 = 0$, then term containing linear powers are missing, then point (h, k) is
(a) (3, 2) (b) (−3, 2)
(c) (2, −3) (d) (−2, −3)

Coordinate System and Coordinates Exercise 2 : More than One Correct Option Type Questions

- This section contains **7 multiple choicc questions**. Each questions has four choices (a), (b), (c), (d) out of which **MORE THAN ONE** may be correct.

16. If $(-6, -4), (3, 5), (-2, 1)$ are the vertices of a parallelogram, then remaining vertex can be
(a) $(0, -1)$ (b) $(-1, 0)$
(c) $(-11, -8)$ (d) $(7, 10)$

17. If the point $P(x, y)$ be equidistant from the points $A(a + b, a - b)$ and $B(a - b, a + b)$ then
(a) $ax = by$
(b) $bx = ay$
(c) $x^2 - y^2 = 2(ax + by)$
(d) P can be (a, b)

18. If the coordinates of the vertices of a triangle are rational numbers, then which of the following points of the triangle will always have rational coordinates
(a) centroid (b) incentre
(c) circumcentre (d) orthocentre

19. The points $A(-4, -1), B(-2, -4), C(4, 0)$ and $D(2, 3)$ are the vertices of a
(a) parallelogram (b) rectangle
(c) rhombus (d) square

20. The medians AD and BE of the triangle with vertices $A(0, b), B(0, 0)$ and $C(a, 0)$ are mutually perpendicular if
(a) $b = a\sqrt{2}$ (b) $a = b\sqrt{2}$
(c) $b = -a\sqrt{2}$ (d) $a = -b\sqrt{2}$

21. The points $A(x, y), B(y, z)$ and $C(z, x)$ represents the vertices of a right angled triangle, if
(a) $x = y$ (b) $y = z$
(c) $z = x$ (d) $x = y = z$

22. Let the base of a triangle lie along the line $x = a$ and be of length $2a$. The area of this triangles is a^2, if the vertex lies on the line
(a) $x = -a$ (b) $x = 0$
(c) $x = \frac{a}{2}$ (d) $x = 2a$

Coordinate System and Coordinates Exercise 3 : Paragraph Based Questions

- This section contains **2 solved paragraphs** based upon each of the paragraph, **3 multiple choice questions** have to be answered. Each of these question has four choices (a), (b), (c) and (d) out of which **ONLY ONE** is correct.

Paragraph I

(Q. Nos. 23 to 25)

ABC is a triangle right angled at A, $AB = 2AC$. $A \equiv (1, 2)$, $B \equiv (-3, 1)$. ACD is an equilateral triangle. The vertices of two triangles are in anticlockwise sense. $BCEF$ is a square with vertices in clockwise sense.

23. If area of ΔACF is S, then the value of $8S$ is
(a) 42 (b) 51
(c) 62 (d) 102

24. Length of DE is
(a) $\sqrt{17}\sqrt{(4 - \sqrt{3})}$
(b) $\frac{\sqrt{17}}{2}\sqrt{(8 + \sqrt{3})}$
(c) $\frac{\sqrt{17}}{2}\sqrt{(4 + \sqrt{3})}$
(d) $\sqrt{15}\sqrt{(4 + \sqrt{3})}$

25. The y-coordinate of the centroid of the square $BCEF$ is
(a) $-\frac{1}{4}$ (b) $-\frac{3}{4}$
(c) $-\frac{5}{4}$ (d) $-\frac{7}{4}$

Paragraph II

(Q. Nos. 26 to 28)

Let $O(0,0)$, $A(2,0)$ *and* $B\left(1, \frac{1}{\sqrt{3}}\right)$ *be the vertices of a triangle.*

Let R be the region consisting of all those points P inside ΔOAB *satisfying.*

$d(P, OA) \leq \min \{d(P, OB), d(P, AB)\}$, *where, d denotes the distance from the point P to the corresponding line. Let M be the peak of region R.*

26. Length of perpendicular from M to OA is equal to

(a) $\sqrt{3}$ (b) $\frac{1}{\sqrt{3}}$ (c) 3 (d) $2-\sqrt{3}$

27. The perimeter of region R is equal to

(a) $4-\sqrt{3}$ (b) $4+\sqrt{3}$

(c) $4+3\sqrt{3}$ (d) $2+4\sqrt{(2-\sqrt{3})}$

28. The area of region R is equal to

(a) $2-\sqrt{3}$ (b) $2+\sqrt{3}$ (c) $2\sqrt{3}$ (d) $4+\sqrt{3}$

Coordinate System and Coordinates Exercise 4 :
Single Integer Answer Type Questions

- This section contains **5 questions**. The answer to each example is **a single digit integer** ranging from 0 to 9 (both inclusive).

29. If the area of the triangle formed by the points $(2a, b), (a+b, 2b+a)$ and $(2b, 2a)$ be Δ_1 and the area of the triangle whose vertices are $(a+b, a-b), (3b-a, b+3a)$ and $(3a-b, 3b-a)$ be Δ_2, then the value of Δ_2 / Δ_1 is

30. The diameter of the nine point circle of the triangle with vertices $(3, 4)$, $(5\cos\theta, 5\sin\theta)$ and $(5\sin\theta, -5\cos\theta)$, where $\theta \in R$, is

31. The ends of the base of an isosceles triangle are $(2\sqrt{2}, 0)$ and $(0, \sqrt{2})$. One side is of length $2\sqrt{2}$. If Δ be the area of triangle, then the value of $[\Delta]$ is (where $[\cdot]$ denotes the greatest integer function)

32. If (x, y) is the incentre of the triangle formed by the points $(3, 4), (4, 3)$ and $(1, 2)$, then the value of x^2 is

33. Let P and Q be points on the line joining $A(-2, 5)$ and $B(3, 1)$ such that $AP = PQ = QB$. If mid-point of PQ is (a, b), then the value of $\frac{b}{a}$ is

Coordinate System and Coordinates Exercise 5 :
Matching Type Questions

- The section contains **2 questions**. Each question has four statements (A, B, C and D) given in **Column I** and four statements (p, q, r and s) in **Column II**. Any given statement in **Column I** can have correct matching with one or more statement(s) given in **Column II**.

34. Consider the triangle with vertices $A(0, 0)$, $B(5, 12)$ and $C(16, 12)$.

	Column I		Column II
A.	If (λ, μ) are the coordinates of centroid of triangle ABC, then $(\lambda + \mu)$ is divisible by	(p)	3
B.	If (λ, μ) are the coordinates of circumcentre of triangle ABC, then 2λ is divisible by	(q)	5
C.	If (λ, μ) are the coordinates of incentre of triangle ABC, then μ is divisible by	(r)	7
D.	If (λ, μ) are the coordinates of excentre opposite to vertex B, then $\lambda + \mu$ is divisible by	(s)	9

35. The vertices of a triangle are $A(-10, 8)$, $B(14, 8)$ and $C(-10, 26)$. Let G, I, H, O be the centroid, incentre, orthocentre, circumcentre respectively of ΔABC.

	Column I		Column II
A.	The inradius r is	(p)	a prime number
B.	The circumradius R is	(q)	an even number
C.	The area of ΔIGH is	(r)	a composite number
D.	The area of ΔOGI is	(s)	a perfect number

Coordinate System and Coordinates Exercise 6 : Statement I and II Type Questions

- **Directions** (Q. Nos. 36 to 39) are Assertion-Reason type questions. Each of these questions contains two statements :

Statement I (Assertion) and

Statement II (Reason)

Each of these question also has four alternative choices (a), (b), (c) and (d), only one out of which is the correct answer.

You have to select the correct choice as given below

(a) Statement I is true, statement II is true; statement II is a correct explanation for statement I

(b) Statement I is true, statement II is true; statement II is not a correct explanation for statement I

(c) Statement I is true, statement II is false

(d) Statement I is false, statement II is true

36. The vertices of a triangle an $A(1,2)$, $B(-1,3)$ and $C(3,4)$. Let D, E, F divide BC, CA, AB respectively in the same ratio.

Statement I The centroid of triangle DEF is (1, 3).

Statement II The triangle ABC and DEF have the same centroid.

37. Statement I Let the vertices of a ΔABC be $A(-5,-2)$, $B(7,6)$ and $C(5,-4)$. Then, the coordinates of the circumcentre are (1, 2).

Statement II In a right angled triangle, the mid point of the hypotenuse is the circumcentre of the triangle.

38. A line segment AB is divided internally and externally in the same ratio at P and Q respectively and M is the mid-point of AB.

A M P B Q

Statement I MP, MB, MQ are in G.P

Statement II AP, AB and AQ are in H.P.

39. Statement I Transformation of the equation $x^2-3xy+11x-12y+36=0$ to parallel axes through the point $(-4,1)$ becomes $ax^2+bxy+1=0$, then $b^2-a=\frac{1}{64}$.

Statement II If the axes turned through an angle θ, then the equation $f(x,y)=0$ is transformed by replacing (x,y) by $((x\cos\theta-y\sin\theta),(x\sin\theta+y\cos\theta))$.

Coordinate System and Coordinates Exercise 7 : Subjective Type Questions

- In this section, there are **7 subjective questions.**

40. If $A(x_1,y_1)$, $B(x_2,y_2)$ and $C(x_3,y_3)$ are the vertices of a ΔABC and (x,y) be a point on the internal bisector of angle A, then prove that

$$b\begin{vmatrix} x & y & 1 \\ x_1 & y_1 & 1 \\ x_2 & y_2 & 1 \end{vmatrix}+c\begin{vmatrix} x & y & 1 \\ x_1 & y_1 & 1 \\ x_3 & y_3 & 1 \end{vmatrix}=0$$

where, $AC=b$ and $AB=c$.

41. If a, b, c be the pth, qth and rth terms respectively of a HP, show that the points (bc,p), (ca,q) and (ab,r) are collinear.

42. A line L intersects three sides BC, CA and AB of a triangle in P, Q, R respectively, show that

$$\frac{BP}{PC}\cdot\frac{CQ}{QA}\cdot\frac{AR}{RB}=-1$$

43. If the points, $\left(\frac{a^3}{a-1},\frac{a^2-3}{a-1}\right)$, $\left(\frac{b^3}{b-1},\frac{b^2-3}{b-1}\right)$ and $\left(\frac{c^3}{c-1},\frac{c^2-3}{c-1}\right)$ are collinear for three distinct values a, b, c and $a\neq1$, $b\neq1$ and $c\neq1$, then show that

$$abc-(bc+ca+ab)+3(a+b+c)=0$$

44. Show that the area of the triangle whose sides are $a_rx+b_ry+c_r=0$, $r=1,2,3$ is $\frac{\Delta^2}{2|C_1C_2C_3|}$, where C_1, C_2 and C_3 are the cofactors of c_1, c_2 and c_3 respectively in the determinant

$$\Delta=\begin{vmatrix} a_1 & b_1 & c_1 \\ a_2 & b_2 & c_2 \\ a_3 & b_3 & c_3 \end{vmatrix}$$

45. If $A_1, A_2, A_3, ..., A_n$ are n points in a plane whose coordinates are $(x_1, y_1), (x_2, y_2), (x_3, y_3), ..., (x_n, y_n)$ respectively. A_1A_2 is bisected in the point G_1; G_1A_3 is divided at G_2 in the ratio $1:2$; G_2A_4 is divided at G_3 in the ratio 1 : 3; G_3A_5 at G_4 in the 1 : 4 and so on until all the points are exhausted. Show that the coordinates of the final point so obtained are

$$\frac{x_1 + x_2 + ... + x_n}{n} \text{ and } \frac{y_1 + y_2 + ... + y_n}{n}$$

46. If by change of axes without change of origin, the expression $ax^2 + 2hxy + by^2$ becomes $a_1x_1^2 + 2h_1x_1y_1 + b_1y_1^2$, prove that

(i) $a + b = a_1 + b_1$

(ii) $ab - h^2 = a_1b_1 - h_1^2$

(iii) $(a-b)^2 + 4h^2 = (a_1 - b_1)^2 + 4h_1^2$

Coordinate System and Coordinates Exercise 8 :

Questions Asked in Previous 13 Year's Exams

- This section contains questions asked in **IIT-JEE, AIEEE, JEE Main & JEE Advanced** from year **2005** to **2017**.

47. If a vertex of a triangle is (1, 1) and the mid-points of two side through this vertex are (– 1, 2) and (3, 2), then the centroid of the triangle is **[AIEEE 2005, 3M]**

(a) $\left(\frac{1}{3}, \frac{7}{3}\right)$ (b) $\left(1, \frac{7}{3}\right)$

(c) $\left(-\frac{1}{3}, \frac{7}{3}\right)$ (d) $\left(-1, \frac{7}{3}\right)$

48. Let $O(0, 0)$, $P(3, 4)$, $Q(6, 0)$ be the vertices of the triangle OPQ. The point R inside the triangle OPQ is such that the triangles OPR, PQR, OQR are of equal area. The coordinates of R are **[IIT-JEE 2007, 3M]**

(a) $\left(\frac{4}{3}, 3\right)$ (b) $\left(3, \frac{2}{3}\right)$

(c) $\left(3, \frac{4}{3}\right)$ (d) $\left(\frac{4}{3}, \frac{2}{3}\right)$

49. Let $A(h, k)$, $B(1, 1)$ and $C(2, 1)$ be the vertices of a right angled triangle with AC as its hypotenuse. If the area of the triangle is 1, then the set of values which 'k' can take is given by **[AIEEE 2007, 3M]**

(a) {1, 3} (b) {0, 2}

(c) (– 1, 3} (d) {–3, – 2}

50. Three distinct points A, B and C are given in the 2-dimensional coordinates plane such that the ratio of the distance of any one of them from the point (1, 0) to the distance from the point (–1, 0) is equal to $\frac{1}{3}$. Then, the circumcentre of the triangle ABC is at the point **[AIEEE 2009, 4M]**

(a) $\left(\frac{5}{4}, 0\right)$ (b) $\left(\frac{5}{2}, 0\right)$

(c) $\left(\frac{5}{3}, 0\right)$ (d) (0, 0)

51. The x-coordinate of the incentre of the triangle that has the coordinates of mid-points of its sides are (0, 1), (1, 1) and (1, 0) is **[JEE Main 2013, 4M]**

(a) $2 + \sqrt{2}$ (b) $2 - \sqrt{2}$

(c) $1 + \sqrt{2}$ (d) $1 - \sqrt{2}$

52. The number of points, having both coordinates are integers, that lie in the interior of the triangle with vertices (0, 0), (0, 41) and (41, 0) is **[JEE Main 2015, 4M]**

(a) 820 (b) 780

(c) 901 (d) 861

53. Let k be an integer such that the triangle with vertices $(k, -3k)$, $(5, k)$ and $(-k, 2)$ has area 28 sq units. Then, the orthocentre of this triangle is at the point **[JEE Main 2017, 4M]**

(a) $\left(2, \frac{1}{2}\right)$ (b) $\left(2, -\frac{1}{2}\right)$

(c) $\left(1, \frac{3}{4}\right)$ (d) $\left(1, -\frac{3}{4}\right)$

Answers

Exercise for Session 1

1. (d) 2. (b) 3. (b) 4. (b) 5. (b) 6. $(\pm 5, 0)$ 7. $(0, \pm 4)$ 8. $(-6, 0)$ 9. $\theta = \alpha$ 10. $x^2 + y^2 = 2ax$

Exercise for Session 2

1. (d) 2. (c) 3. (b) 4. (b) 5. (d) 6. (a) 7. (c) 8. (c) 9. $8a$ 13. $\left(\frac{3}{2}, \frac{5}{2}\right)$ and $\frac{5\sqrt{2}}{2}$ 14. $\frac{63}{65}$ 15. (5, 1) and (−3, 3) 17. $a = b = 2 - \sqrt{3}$ 18. $\left(\frac{1+\sqrt{3}}{2}, \frac{7-5\sqrt{3}}{2}\right)$ or $\left(\frac{1-\sqrt{3}}{2}, \frac{7+5\sqrt{3}}{2}\right)$

Exercise for Session 3

1. (a) 2. (b) 3. (a) 4. (c) 5. (a) 6. (c) 7. (a) 8. (c) 9. (d) 10. (b) 11. (p,q) 12. $\frac{333}{2}$ sq units 13. Centroid = incentre ≡ (2, 3) 18. $-\frac{3}{67}, \frac{45}{17}$ 19. 34 sq units

Exercise for Session 4

1. (b) 2. (d) 3. (c) 4. (b) 5. (c) 6. (b) 7. (c) 8. $y^2 - 8y - 4x + 20 = 0$ 9. $3x^2 + 3y^2 - 10ax + 3a^2 = 0$ 10. $x + y = 4$ 11. $9x^2 + 36y^2 = 4l^2$ 12. $x^2 - 9y^2 = 0$ 13. $(a-b)^2 (x^2 + y^2) = a^2b^4$ 14. $-3\frac{1}{3}$ 16. $\tan^{-1}\left(\frac{B}{A}\right), -\frac{C}{\sqrt{(A^2 + B^2)}}$ 17. $xy = 0$

Chapter Exercises

1. (d) 2. (d) 3. (c) 4. (a) 5. (a) 6. (b) 7. (d) 8. (c) 9. (c) 10. (b) 11. (b) 12. (d) 13. (d) 14. (a) 15. (c) 16. (b,c,d) 17. (b,d) 18. (a,c,d) 19. (a,b) 20. (b,d) 21. (a,b,c) 22. (b,d) 23. (b) 24. (b) 25. (d) 26. (d) 27. (d) 28. (a) 29. (4) 30. (5) 31. (3) 32. (9) 33. (6)
34. $(A) \to (p,q)$; $(B) \to (p,r)$; $(C) \to (p,s)$; $(D) \to (p)$
35. $(A) \to (q,r,s)$; $(B) \to (r)$; $(C) \to (q,r,s)$; $(D) \to (p)$
36. (a) 37. (a) 38. (a) 39. (b) 47. (b) 48. (c) 49. (c) 50. (a) 51. (b) 52. (b) 53. (a)

Solutions

1. Since, the distance of all points from $O(0, 0) = 5$

$\therefore$ $O(0, 0)$ be the circumcentre.

Centroid of triangle (G)

$$\equiv \left(\frac{3 + 5\cos\theta + 5\sin\theta)}{3}, \frac{4 + 5\sin\theta - 5\cos\theta}{3}\right)$$

Let $H(\alpha, \beta)$ be the orthocentre of the triangle, then

$$\alpha = 3 + 5\cos\theta + 5\sin\theta$$

$$\Rightarrow \quad (\alpha - 3) = 5\cos\theta + 5\sin\theta \quad \text{...(i)}$$

and $\beta = 4 + 5\sin\theta - 5\cos\theta$

$$\Rightarrow \quad (\beta - 4) = 5\sin\theta - 5\cos\theta \quad \text{...(ii)}$$

On squaring and adding Eqs. (i) and (ii), we get

$$(\alpha - 3)^2 + (\beta - 4)^2 = 25 + 25$$

$$\Rightarrow \quad \alpha^2 + \beta^2 - 6\alpha - 8\beta - 25 = 0$$

Hence, the locus of $H(\alpha, \beta)$ is

$$x^2 + y^2 - 6x - 8y - 25 = 0$$

2.

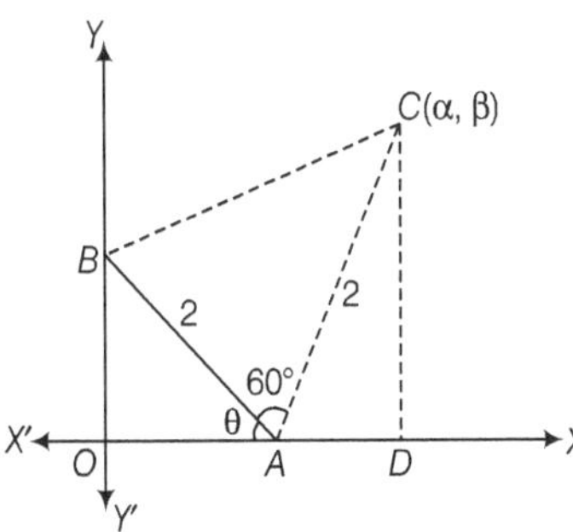

Let $AB = AC = 2$

and $\angle BAO = \theta$

Let $C \equiv (\alpha, \beta)$

$$\therefore \quad \alpha = 2\cos\theta + 2\cos(180^\circ - (60^\circ + \theta))$$

$$= 2\cos\theta - 2\cos(60^\circ + \theta)$$

$$= 2\cos\theta - 2\left\{\cos\theta \times \frac{1}{2} - \sin\theta \times \frac{\sqrt{3}}{2}\right\}$$

$$= \cos\theta + \sqrt{3}\sin\theta \quad \text{...(i)}$$

and $\beta = 2\sin(180^\circ - (60^\circ + \theta))$

$$= 2\sin(60^\circ + \theta)$$

$$= 2\left(\sin\theta \times \frac{1}{2} + \cos\theta \times \frac{\sqrt{3}}{2}\right)$$

$$= \sin\theta + \sqrt{3}\cos\theta \quad \text{...(ii)}$$

Eliminating θ from Eqs. (i) and (ii), we get

$$\alpha^2 + \beta^2 - \alpha\beta\sqrt{3} - 1 = 0$$

Hence, the locus of $H(\alpha, \beta)$ is

$$x^2 + y^2 - xy\sqrt{3} - 1 = 0$$

3. Let $a = 3x + 4y$, $b = 4x + 3y$, $c = 5x + 5y$

$$\therefore \quad \cos C = \frac{a^2 + b^2 - c^2}{2ab}$$

$$= \frac{(3x + 4y)^2 + (4x + 3y)^2 - (5x + 5y)^2}{2(3x + 4y)(4x + 3y)}$$

$$= -\frac{xy}{(3x + 4y)(4x + 3y)} < 0$$

$$\Rightarrow \quad C > 90^\circ$$

Hence, triangle is obtuse angled.

4. A———P———Q———B

$$\because \quad AP = PQ = QB$$

$\therefore$ mid-point of PQ = mid-point of $AB = \left(\frac{1}{2}, 3\right)$

5. $z_A = 2 + 3i$; $z_B = -i$ and $AB = \sqrt{(4 + 16)} = \sqrt{20} = 2\sqrt{5}$

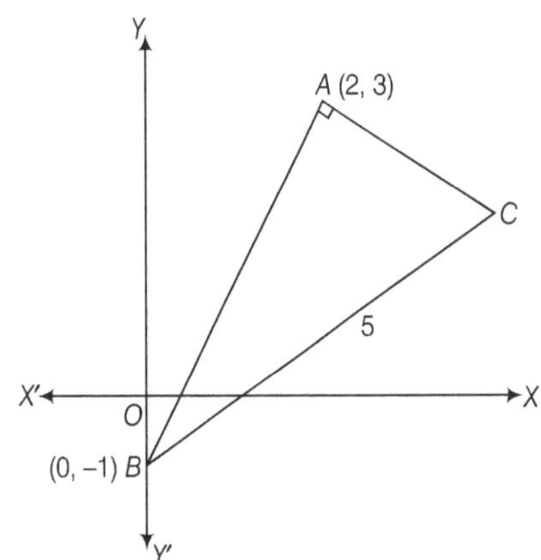

$$\therefore \quad (AC) = \sqrt{(BC)^2 - (AC)^2} = \sqrt{5}$$

$$\therefore \quad \frac{z_C - z_A}{z_B - z_A} = \frac{AC}{AB} e^{i\pi/2} = \frac{i}{2}$$

$$\Rightarrow \quad z_C - (2 + 3i) = \frac{i}{2}(-i - 2 - 3i)$$

or $z_C = 2 + 3i - i + 2 = 4 + 2i$

$$\therefore \quad C \equiv (4, 2)$$

6. Let $P \equiv (h, k)$ and $A \equiv (1, 0)$, $B \equiv (2\cos\theta, 2\sin\theta)$

$\because$ $PA : PB = 2 : 3$

$$\therefore \quad h = \frac{4\cos\theta + 3}{5} \Rightarrow 5h - 3 = 4\cos\theta \quad \text{...(i)}$$

and $k = \dfrac{4\sin\theta + 0}{5} \Rightarrow 5k = 4\sin\theta \quad \text{...(ii)}$

OA squaring and adding Eqs. (i) and (ii), we get

$$(5h - 3)^2 + (5k)^2 = 16$$

$\therefore$ Locus of C is $(5x - 3)^2 + (5y)^2 = 16$

or $25(x^2 + y^2) - 30x - 7 = 0$

which is a circle.

7. $\frac{1}{2}\begin{vmatrix} 2a & 3a & 1 \\ 3b & 2b & 1 \\ c & c & 1 \end{vmatrix} = 0$

$\Rightarrow \quad 2a(2b-c) - 3a(3b-c) + 1(3bc - 2bc) = 0$

or $\quad -5ab + ac + bc = 0$

or $\quad c = \dfrac{5ab}{a+b}$

or $\quad \dfrac{2c}{5} = \dfrac{2ab}{a+b}$

Hence, $a, \dfrac{2c}{5}, b$ are in HP.

8.

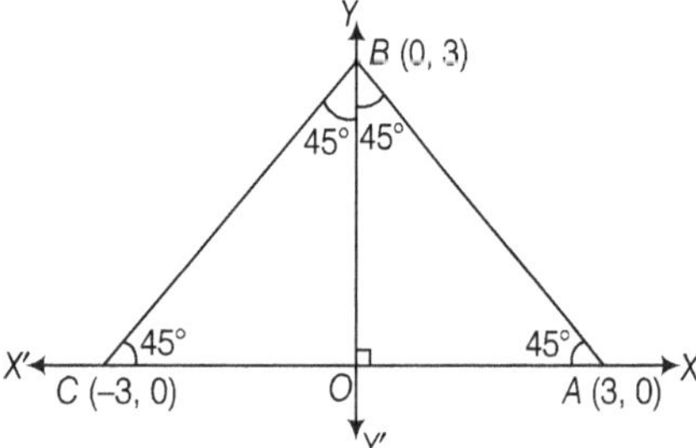

It is clear from the figure orthocentre $\equiv (0, 3)$

9. Let, $A(0, 0)$

Coordinate of B are $(2\cot\theta, 2)$ and coordinate of C are $\{4\cot(60° - \theta), -4\}$

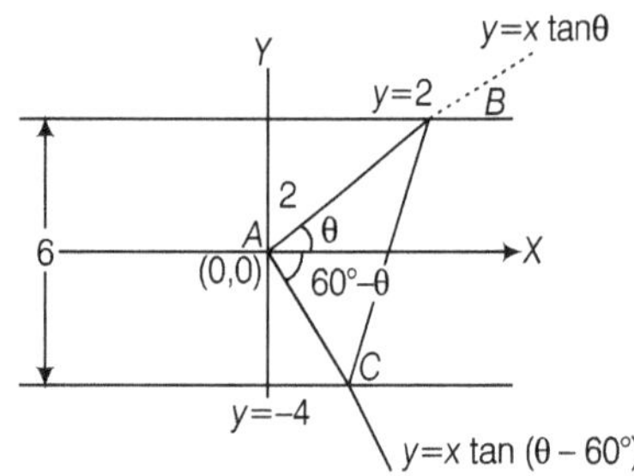

$\therefore \quad AB = AC$

$\Rightarrow \quad (AB)^2 = (AC)^2$

$4\cot^2\theta + 4 = 16\cot^2(60° - \theta) + 16$

$4\text{cosec}^2\theta = 16\text{cosec}^2(60° - \theta)$

$\Rightarrow \quad \sin(60° - \theta) = 2\sin\theta$

$\Rightarrow \quad \left(\dfrac{\sqrt{3}}{2}\cos\theta - \dfrac{1}{2}\sin\theta\right) = 2\sin\theta$

$\therefore \quad \tan\theta = \dfrac{\sqrt{3}}{5}$

$\therefore$ The required length

$= AB = \sqrt{(4\cot^2\theta + 4)}$

$= 2\sqrt{\dfrac{28}{3}} = \dfrac{4\sqrt{7}}{\sqrt{3}}$

10. A ——•T_1——•T_2—— C

$\because \quad A \equiv (1, 2), B \equiv (4, 2), C \equiv (4, 5) \qquad (\because AT_1 = T_1T_2 = T_2C)$

T_1 divides AC in the ratio 1 : 2 internally, then

$T_1 \equiv \left(\dfrac{1\times4 + 2\times1}{1+2}, \dfrac{1\times5 + 2\times2}{1+2}\right)$

or $\quad T_1 \equiv (2, 3)$

and T_2 is the mid-point of T_1 and C, then

$T_2 \equiv \left(\dfrac{2+4}{2}, \dfrac{3+5}{2}\right)$

or $\quad T_2 \equiv (3, 4)$

S_1 divides BC in the ratio 1 : 2 (internally), then

B ——S_1——S_2—— C

$(\because BS_1 = S_1S_2 = S_2C)$

$S_1 \equiv \left(\dfrac{1\times4 + 2\times4}{1+2}, \dfrac{1\times5 + 2\times2}{1+2}\right)$

or $\quad S_1 \equiv (4, 3)$

and S_2 is the mid-point of S_1 and C, then

$S_2 \equiv \left(\dfrac{4+4}{2}, \dfrac{3+5}{2}\right)$

or $\quad S_2 = (4, 4)$

Area of quadrilateral $T_1S_1S_2T_2$

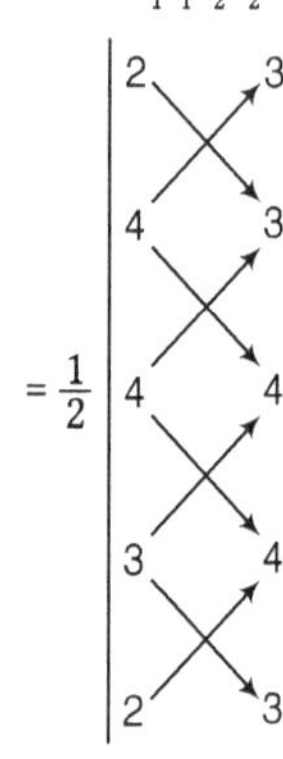

$= \dfrac{1}{2}|(6 + 16 + 16 + 9) - (12 + 12 + 12 + 8)|$

$= \dfrac{3}{2}$ sq units.

11. **Statement (i)** :

$\because$ Points $(-1, 0), (4, -2)$ and $(\cos 2\theta, \sin 2\theta)$ are collinear.

$\therefore \quad \begin{vmatrix} -1 - \cos 2\theta & 0 - \sin 2\theta \\ 4 - \cos 2\theta & -2 - \sin 2\theta \end{vmatrix} = 0$

$\Rightarrow \quad 2 + \sin 2\theta + 2\cos 2\theta + \sin 2\theta\cos 2\theta$

$+ 4\sin 2\theta - \sin 2\theta\cos 2\theta = 0$

$\Rightarrow \quad 5\sin 2\theta + 2(1 + \cos 2\theta) = 0$

or $\quad 10\sin\theta\cos\theta + 4\cos^2\theta = 0$

or $\quad 2\cos\theta(5\sin\theta + 2\cos\theta) = 0$

or $\quad \cos\theta = 0$ and $\tan\theta = -\dfrac{2}{5}$

or $\quad \theta = m\pi + \dfrac{\pi}{2}$

and $\quad \theta = n\pi + \tan^{-1}\left(\dfrac{-2}{5}\right); m, n \in I$

Statement (ii) :

$\because$ Points $(-1, 0), (4, -2)$ and $\left(\frac{1-\tan^2\theta}{1+\tan^2\theta}, \frac{2\tan\theta}{1+\tan^2\theta}\right)$ are collinear.

$$\therefore \quad \begin{vmatrix} -1-\frac{1-\tan^2\theta}{1+\tan^2\theta} & 0-\frac{2\tan\theta}{1+\tan^2\theta} \\ 4-\frac{1-\tan^2\theta}{1+\tan^2\theta} & -2-\frac{2\tan^2\theta}{1+\tan^2\theta} \end{vmatrix} = 0$$

$\Rightarrow \; 10\tan^3\theta + 4\tan^2\theta + 10\tan\theta + 4 = 0$

or $\quad (2\tan^2\theta + 2)(5\tan\theta + 2) = 0$

or $\quad \tan^2\theta \neq -1$

$\therefore \quad \tan\theta = -\frac{2}{5}$

$\Rightarrow \; \theta = p\pi + \tan^{-1}\left(\frac{-2}{5}\right), p \in I$

12. $\because \quad \dfrac{\sum_{r=0}^{n-1} x^{2r}}{\sum_{r=0}^{n-1} x^r} = \text{integer}$

$$\Rightarrow \quad \frac{\frac{1\cdot(1-x^{2n})}{(1-x^2)}}{\frac{1\cdot(1-x^n)}{(1-x)}} = \text{integer}$$

$$\Rightarrow \quad \frac{1+x^n}{1+x} = \text{integer}$$

n must be 1, 3, 5, 7, 9, 11, ...

$\therefore$ vertices are (1, 7), (3, 9), (5, 11)

Here, $(AB)^2 = 8, (BC)^2 = 8, (CA)^2 = 32$

$\therefore$ triangle cannot be an equilateral.

13. The orthocentre of ΔBCH is the vertex $A(-1, 0)$.

14. Given, $x_1^2 + y_1^2 + x_2^2 + y_2^2 + x_3^2 + y_3^2 + x_4^2 + y_4^2 \leq 2x_1x_3 + 2x_2x_4 + 2y_2y_3 + 2y_1y_4$

$\Rightarrow (x_1 - x_3)^2 + (x_2 - x_4)^2 + (y_2 - y_3)^2 + (y_1 - y_4)^2 \leq 0$

or $(x_1 - x_3)^2 + (x_2 - x_4)^2 + (y_2 - y_3)^2 + (y_1 - y_4)^2 = 0$

or $\quad x_1 = x_3, x_2 = x_4, y_2 = y_3, y_1 = y_4$

or $\quad \dfrac{x_1 + x_2}{2} = \dfrac{x_3 + x_4}{2}$

and $\quad \dfrac{y_1 + y_2}{2} = \dfrac{y_3 + y_4}{2}$

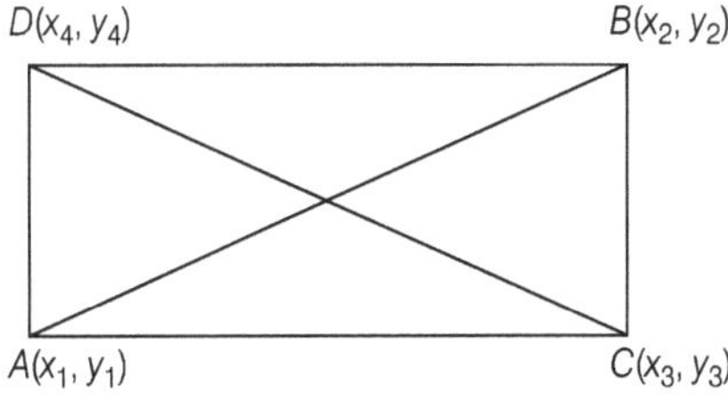

Hence, AB and CD bisect each other

Therefore, $ACBD$ is a parallelogram. Also,

$(AB)^2 = (x_1 - x_2)^2 + (y_1 - y_2)^2 = (x_3 - x_4)^2 + (y_3 - y_4)^2 = (CD)^2$

Thus, $ACBD$ is a parallelogram and $AB = CD$.

Hence, it is a rectangle.

15. $(x + h)^2 + (y + k)^2 - 4(x + h) + 6(y + k) - 7 = 0$

$\Rightarrow \; x^2 + y^2 + 2x(h-2) + 2y(k+3) + (h^2 + k^2 - 4h + 6k - 7) = 0$

According to question

$h - 2 = 0, k + 3 = 0$

$\therefore \quad h = 2, k = -3$

hence, $\quad (h, k) \equiv (2, -3)$.

16. If the remaining vertex is (h, k), then

Case I

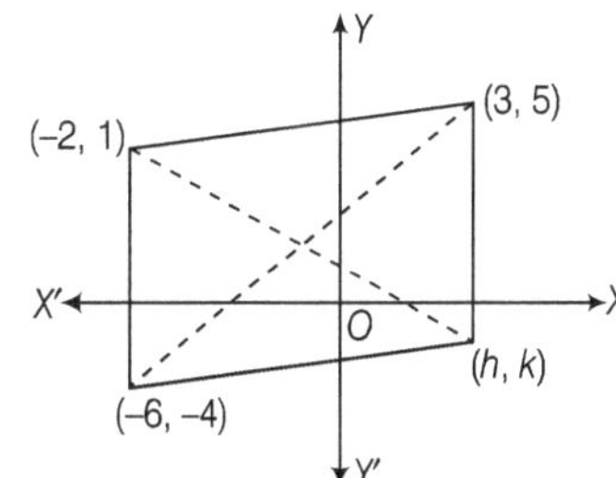

$h - 2 = 3 - 6, k + 1 = 5 - 4 \quad$ or $\quad h = -1, k = 0$

$\therefore$ Fourth vertex is $(-1, 0)$.

Case II

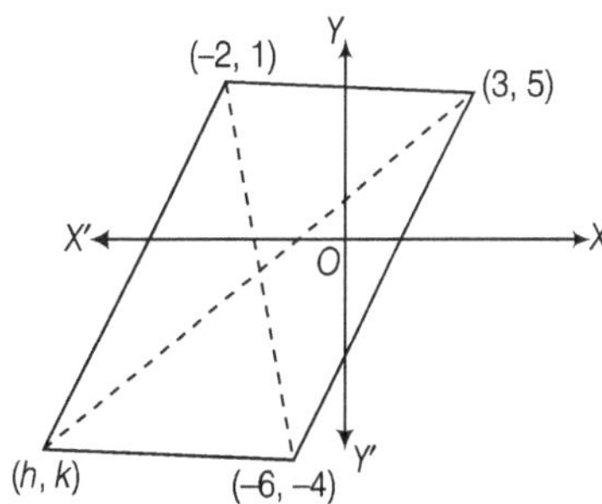

$h + 3 = -2 - 6, k + 5 = 1 - 4 \quad$ or $\quad h = -11, k = -8$

$\therefore$ Fourth vertex is $(-11, -8)$.

Case III

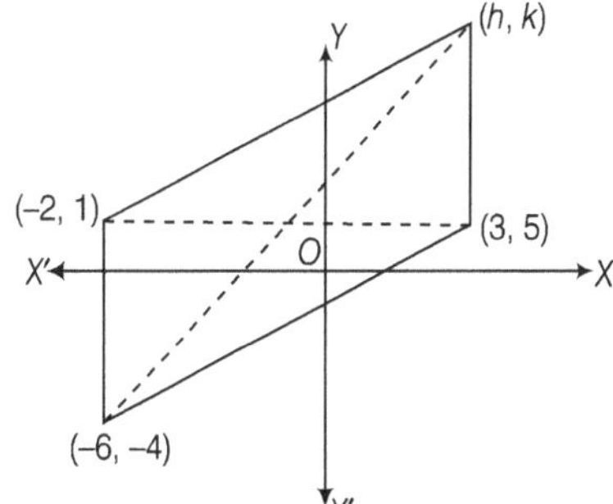

$h - 6 = -2 + 3, k - 4 = 1 + 5$

or $\quad h = 7, k = 10$

$\therefore$ Fourth vertex is $(7, 10)$.

17. $(PA)^2 = (PB)^2$

$\Rightarrow \; (x - a - b)^2 + (y - a + b)^2 = (x - a + b)^2 + (y - a - b)^2$

$\Rightarrow \; (x - a + b)^2 - (x - a - b)^2 = (y - a + b)^2 - (y - a - b)^2$

$\Rightarrow \quad (2x - 2a)(2b) = (2y - 2a)(2b)$

or $\quad x = y$

and P is the mid-point of AB i.e., (a, a)

If P be (a, b), then $bx = ay \qquad (\because a = b)$

18. Let vertices of triangle ABC are

$$A \equiv (x_1, y_1), B \equiv (x_2, y_2) \text{ and } C \equiv (x_3, y_3)$$

where, $x_1, x_2, x_3, y_1, y_2, y_3 \in Q$

$\therefore \quad a = BC = \sqrt{(x_2 - x_3)^2 + (y_2 - y_3)^2}$

$= \text{rational or irrational}$

similarly, $b = CA, c = AB$

Then, incentre

$$\equiv \left(\frac{ax_1 + bx_2 + cx_3}{a+b+c}, \frac{ay_1 + by_2 + cy_3}{a+b+c} \right)$$

$\therefore$ Incentre has rational or irrational coordinates but centroid, circumcentre and orthocentre have always rational coordinates.

19. Since, $A = (-4 -1), B \equiv (-2, -4), C \equiv (4, 0), D \equiv (2, 3)$

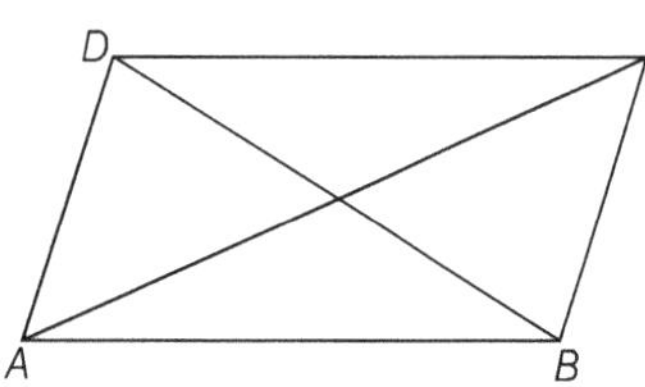

$\therefore \quad (AB)^2 = (-4 + 2)^2 + (-1 + 4)^2 = 13$

$(BC)^2 = (-2 - 4)^2 + (-4 - 0)^2 = 52$

$(CD)^2 = (4 - 2)^2 + (0 - 3)^2 = 13$

and $(DA)^2 = (2 + 4)^2 + (3 + 1)^2 = 52$

Clearly, $AB = CD$ and $BC = AD$

$\therefore ABCD$ is a parallelogram.

Again, $(AC)^2 = (-4 - 4)^2 + (-1 - 0)^2 = 65$

and $(BD)^2 = (-2 - 2)^2 + (-4 - 3)^2 = 65$

$\therefore \quad AC = BD$

Hence, $ABCD$ is a rectangle.

20.

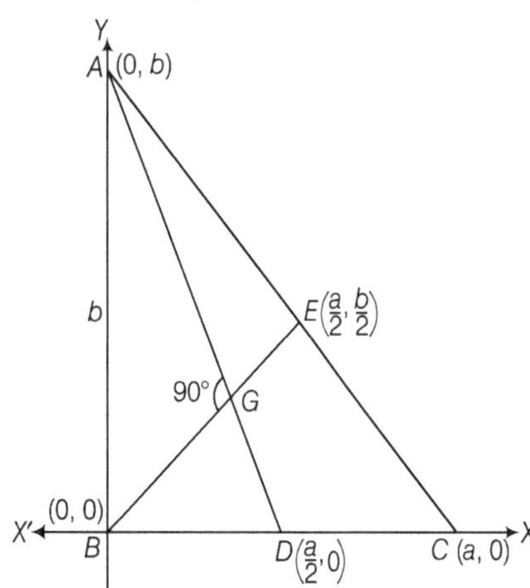

$\because \quad BG = \frac{2}{3} BE = \frac{2}{3} \times \frac{\sqrt{(a^2 + b^2)}}{2}$

$\Rightarrow \quad (BG)^2 = \frac{1}{9}(a^2 + b^2) \quad \text{...(i)}$

and $\quad AG = \frac{2}{3} AD = \frac{2}{3} \times \sqrt{\left(\frac{a^2}{4} + b^2\right)}$

$\Rightarrow \quad (AG)^2 = \frac{1}{9}(a^2 + 4b^2) \quad \text{...(ii)}$

Now, in right angled triangle ABG,

$(BA)^2 = (AG)^2 + (BG)^2$

$\Rightarrow \quad b^2 = \frac{1}{9}(a^2 + 4b^2) + \frac{1}{9}(a^2 + b^2)$ [from Eqs. (i) and (ii)]

$\Rightarrow \quad a^2 = 2b^2$

$\therefore \quad a = \pm b\sqrt{2}$

21. $\because \quad (AB)^2 = (x - y)^2 + (y - z)^2$

$(BC)^2 = (y - z)^2 + (z - x)^2$

and $(CA)^2 = (z - x)^2 + (x - y)^2$

Case I If $x = y$, then

$(AB)^2 + (CA)^2 = (BC)^2$

Case II If $y = z$, then

$(AB)^2 + (BC)^2 = (CA)^2$

Case III If $z = x$, then

$(BC)^2 + (CA)^2 = (AB)^2$

22.

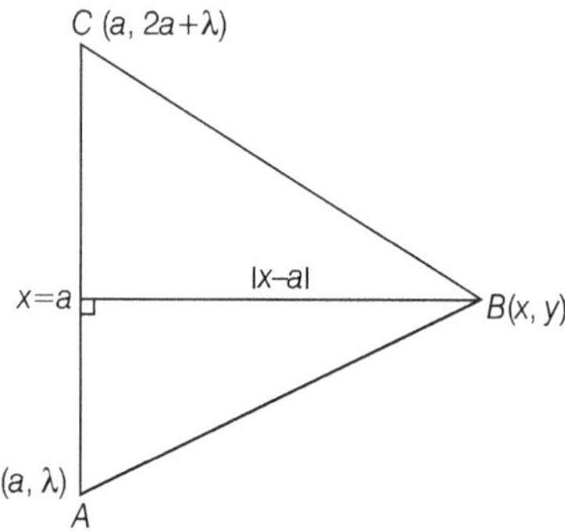

Let $\quad A \equiv (a, \lambda)$

then, $\quad B \equiv (a, 2a + \lambda)$

and $\quad C \equiv (x, y)$

Area of $\quad \Delta ABC = a^2 \quad$ (given)

$\Rightarrow \quad \frac{1}{2} \times 2a \times |x - a| = a^2$

$\Rightarrow \quad |x - a| = a$

$\Rightarrow \quad x - a = \pm a$

$\Rightarrow \quad x = 0, x = 2a$

Sol. (Q. Nos. 23 to 25)

$AB = \sqrt{(1 + 3)^2 + (2 - 1)^2} = \sqrt{17}$

$AC = \frac{1}{2} AB = \frac{1}{2}\sqrt{17}$

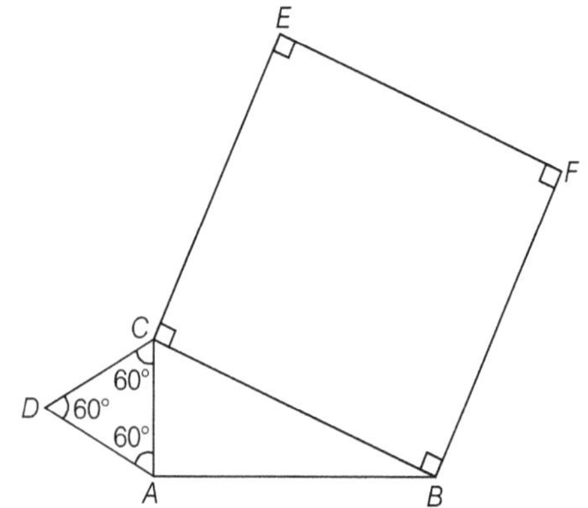

For coordinates of C:

$$\frac{z_c - z_A}{z_B - z_A} = \frac{AC}{AB} e^{i\pi/2} = \frac{i}{2}$$

$$\Rightarrow z_c - (1 + 2i) = \frac{i}{2}(-3 + i - 1 - 2i)$$

$$= \frac{i}{2}(-4 - i) = -2i + \frac{1}{2}$$

or $$z_c = \frac{3}{2}$$

$\therefore$ $$C \equiv \left(\frac{3}{2}, 0\right)$$

For coordinates of D:

$$\frac{z_D - z_A}{z_C - z_A} = e^{i\pi/3}$$

$$\Rightarrow z_D - (1 + 2i) = \left(\frac{1}{2} + \frac{i\sqrt{3}}{2}\right)\left(\frac{1}{2} - 2i\right)$$

$$= \frac{1}{4} + \sqrt{3} - i + \frac{i\sqrt{3}}{4}$$

or $$z_D = \left(\frac{5}{4} + \sqrt{3}\right) + i\left(1 + \frac{\sqrt{3}}{4}\right)$$

$\therefore$ $$D \equiv \left(\frac{5}{4} + \sqrt{3}, 1 + \frac{\sqrt{3}}{4}\right)$$

For coordinates of F:

$$\frac{z_F - z_B}{z_C - z_B} = e^{-i\pi/2} = -i$$

$$\Rightarrow z_F - (-3 + i) = -i\left(\frac{9}{2} - i\right)$$

$$\Rightarrow \quad z_F = -4 - \frac{7}{2}i$$

$\therefore$ $$F \equiv \left(-4, -\frac{7}{2}\right), \text{ then}$$

$$E \equiv \left(\frac{1}{2}, -\frac{9}{2}\right)$$

23. $$S = \frac{1}{2}\left|\begin{vmatrix} 1 & 2 & 1 \\ \frac{3}{2} & 0 & 1 \\ -4 & -\frac{7}{2} & 1 \end{vmatrix}\right| = \frac{51}{8}$$

$\therefore$ $$8S = 51$$

24. $$DE = \sqrt{\left(\frac{5}{4} + \sqrt{3} - \frac{1}{2}\right)^2 + \left(1 + \frac{\sqrt{3}}{4} + \frac{9}{2}\right)^2}$$

$$= \sqrt{\left(\frac{3}{4} + \sqrt{3}\right)^2 + \left(\frac{11}{2} + \frac{\sqrt{3}}{4}\right)^2} = \frac{\sqrt{17}}{2}\sqrt{(8 + \sqrt{3})}$$

25. y-coordinate of the centroid of the square

$$BCEF = \frac{0 - \frac{7}{2}}{2} = -\frac{7}{4}$$

■ ***Sol.*** (Q. Nos. 26 to 28)

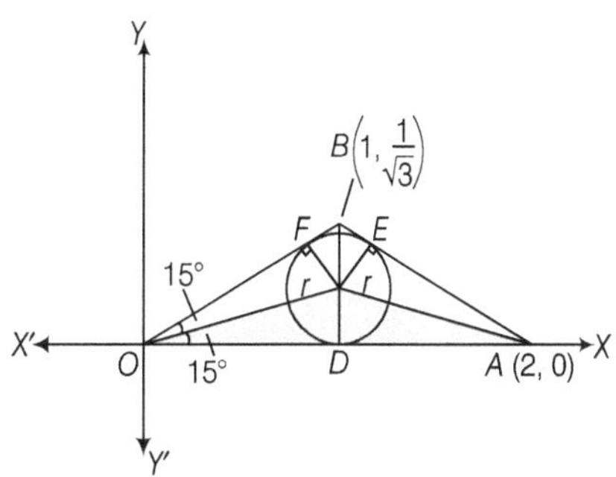

Given, $O \equiv (0, 0)$ $A \equiv (2, 0)$

and $B \equiv \left(1, \frac{1}{\sqrt{3}}\right)$

Let $P \equiv (x, y)$

If I be the incentre of ΔOAB.

If in radius $= r$, then

$ID = IE = IF = r$, if P at I,

then $d(P, OA) = d(P, OB) = d(P, AB) = r$,

But $d(P, OA) \le \min.\{d(P, OB), d(P, AB)\}$

which is possible only P lies in the ΔOIA

$\therefore$ M be the peak of region R.

$\therefore$ $M = I$

26. Length of perpendicular from M to $OA = ID = r = OD \tan 15°$

$$= 1 \times (2 - \sqrt{3})$$

$$= 2 - \sqrt{3}$$

27. Perimeter of region

$$R = IO + OA + AI$$

$$= r \operatorname{cosec} 15° + 2 + r \operatorname{cosec} 15°$$

$$= 2r \operatorname{cosec} 15° + 2$$

$$= 2(2 - \sqrt{3}) \cdot \frac{2\sqrt{2}}{(\sqrt{3} - 1)} + 2$$

$$= (\sqrt{3} - 1)^2 \cdot \frac{2\sqrt{2}}{(\sqrt{3} - 1)} + 2$$

$$= 2\sqrt{2}(\sqrt{3} - 1) + 2$$

$$\Rightarrow \quad = 2 + 4\sqrt{(2 - \sqrt{3})}$$

28. Area of region $R = \frac{1}{2} \times OA \times r$

$$= \frac{1}{2} \times 2 \times (2 - \sqrt{3}) = (2 - \sqrt{3})$$

29. We know that the area of the triangle formed by joining the mid-points of any triangle is one fourth of that triangle, then

$$\Delta_2 = 4\Delta_1$$

$\therefore$ $$\frac{\Delta_2}{\Delta_1} = 4$$

30. Since, the distance of all points from $O(0, 0) = 5$

$\therefore$ Circumradius $(R) = 5$

Hence, diameter of nine point circle $= R = 5$

31. Let $B \equiv (2\sqrt{2}, 0)$, $C \equiv (0, \sqrt{2})$

$\therefore \quad BC = \sqrt{(8+2)} = \sqrt{10}$

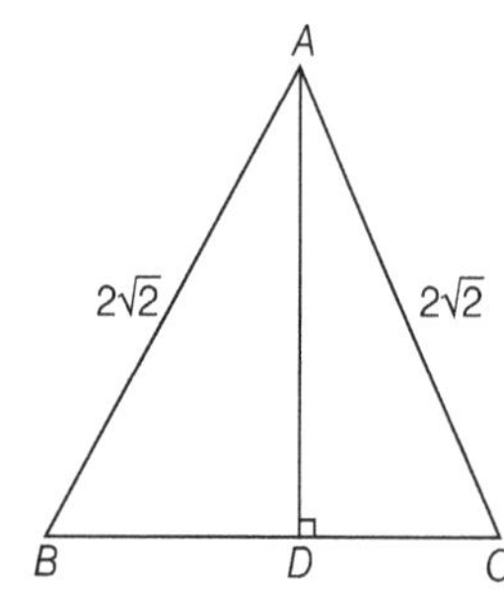

and $\quad AD = \sqrt{(AB)^2 - (BD)^2}$

$$= \sqrt{\left(8 - \frac{10}{4}\right)} = \sqrt{\frac{11}{2}}$$

$\therefore \quad \Delta = \frac{1}{2} \cdot BC \cdot AD$

$$= \frac{1}{2} \cdot \sqrt{10} \cdot \frac{\sqrt{11}}{\sqrt{2}} = \frac{\sqrt{55}}{2}$$

$\Rightarrow \quad [\Delta] = 3$

32. Let $A \equiv (3, 4)$, $B \equiv (4, 3)$ and $C \equiv (1, 2)$

$\therefore \quad a = |BC| = \sqrt{(9+1)} = \sqrt{10}$

$b = |CA| = \sqrt{(4+4)} = 2\sqrt{2}$

$c = |AB| = \sqrt{(1+1)} = \sqrt{2}$

$\Rightarrow \quad x = \dfrac{\sqrt{10} \times 3 + 2\sqrt{2} \times 4 + \sqrt{2} \times 1}{\sqrt{10} + 2\sqrt{2} + \sqrt{2}}$

$$= \frac{3(\sqrt{10} + 3\sqrt{2})}{(\sqrt{10} + 3\sqrt{2})} = 3$$

$\therefore \quad x^2 = 9$

33. A———P R Q———B

$\because \quad AP = PQ = QB$

Let R is the mid-point of PQ such that $PR = RQ$.

Now, $\quad AR = AP + PR = QB + RQ = RB$

$\Rightarrow \quad AR = RB$

$\therefore$ R bisects the line segment AB, then

$$R \equiv \left(\frac{-2+3}{2}, \frac{5+1}{2}\right)$$

$$\equiv \left(\frac{1}{2}, 3\right) = (a, b) \qquad \text{(given)}$$

$\therefore \quad a = \frac{1}{2},\ b = 3 \Rightarrow \frac{b}{a} = 6$

34. **(A)** Centroid of ΔABC is

$$\left(\frac{0+5+16}{3}, \frac{0+12+12}{3}\right) \equiv (7, 8)$$

Here, $\quad \lambda = 7, \mu = 8$

$\therefore \quad \lambda + \mu = 15$

(B)

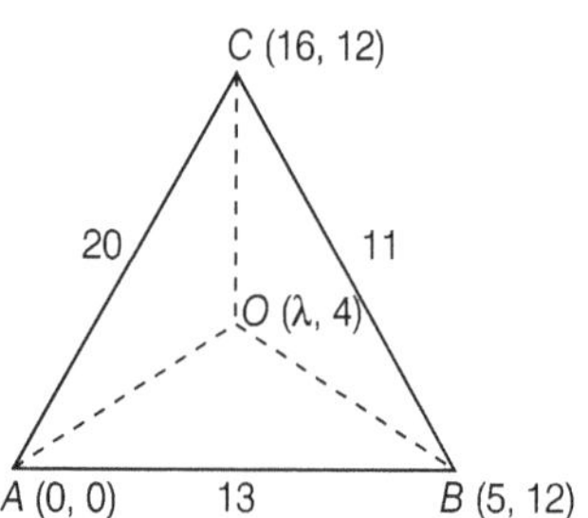

$$(OA)^2 = (OB)^2 = (OC)^2$$

$\Rightarrow \lambda^2 + \mu^2 = (\lambda - 5)^2 + (\mu - 12)^2 = (\lambda - 16)^2 + (\mu - 12)^2$

$\Rightarrow (\lambda - 5)^2 + (\mu - 12)^2 = (\lambda - 16)^2 + (\mu - 12)^2$

or $\quad (\lambda - 5) = -(\lambda - 16)$

$\therefore \quad \lambda = \frac{21}{2} \Rightarrow 2\lambda = 21$

(C) Incentre of ΔABC is

$$\left(\frac{11 \times 0 + 13 \times 16 + 20 \times 5}{11 + 13 + 20}, \frac{11 \times 0 + 13 \times 12 + 20 \times 12}{11 + 13 + 20}\right)$$

$$\equiv (7, 9)$$

Here, $\quad \mu = 9$

(D) Excentre opposite to vertex B is

$$\left(\frac{11 \times 0 + 13 \times 16 - 20 \times 5}{11 + 13 - 20}, \frac{11 \times 0 + 13 \times 12 - 20 \times 12}{11 + 13 - 20}\right)$$

$$\equiv (27, -21)$$

Here, $\quad \lambda = 27, \mu = -21$

$\therefore \quad \lambda + \mu = 6$

35.

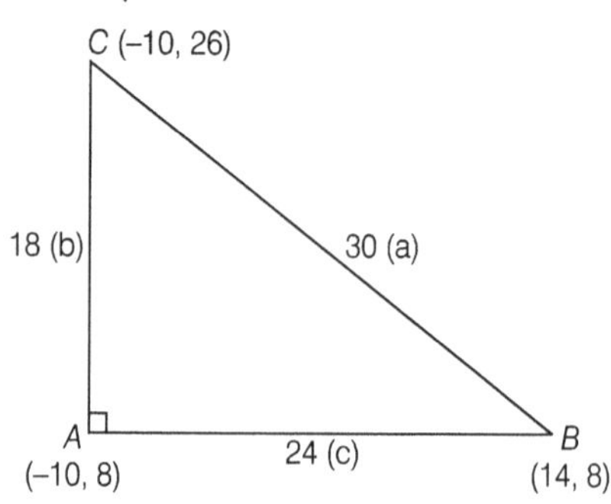

$$\Delta = \frac{1}{2}\left|\begin{vmatrix} -10 & 8 & 1 \\ 14 & 8 & 1 \\ -10 & 26 & 1 \end{vmatrix}\right| = 216$$

$$s = \frac{a+b+c}{2} = \frac{30+18+24}{2} = 36$$

$$G \equiv \left(\frac{-10+14-10}{3}, \frac{8+8+26}{3}\right)$$

$$\equiv (-2, 14)$$

$$I \equiv \left(\frac{30 \times -10 + 24 \times -10 + 18 \times 14}{30 + 24 + 18}, \frac{30 \times 8 + 24 \times 26 + 18 \times 8}{30 + 24 + 18}\right)$$

$$\equiv (-4, 14)$$

$H = A \equiv (-10, 8)$

$O =$ mid-point of $BC \equiv (2, 17)$

(A) $r = \frac{\Delta}{s} = \frac{216}{36} = 6$

(B) $R = \frac{BC}{2} = \frac{30}{2} = 15$

(C) Area of $\Delta IGH = \frac{1}{2}\left|\begin{vmatrix} -4 & 14 & 1 \\ -2 & 14 & 1 \\ -10 & 8 & 1 \end{vmatrix}\right| = 6$

(D) Area of $\Delta OGI = \frac{1}{2}\left|\begin{vmatrix} 2 & 17 & 1 \\ -2 & 14 & 1 \\ -4 & 14 & 1 \end{vmatrix}\right| = 3$

36. The centroid of triangle ABC is $G(1, 3)$. If D divided BC in the ratio $\lambda : 1$, then

$$D \equiv \left(\frac{3\lambda - 1}{\lambda + 1}, \frac{4\lambda + 3}{\lambda + 1}\right), E \equiv \left(\frac{\lambda + 3}{\lambda + 1}, \frac{3\lambda + 4}{\lambda + 1}\right)$$

and $$F \equiv \left(\frac{-\lambda + 1}{\lambda + 1}, \frac{3\lambda + 2}{\lambda + 1}\right)$$

$\therefore$ The centroid of triangle DEF is $(1, 3)$.

Both statements are true and statement II is correct explanation of statement I.

37. $\because$ $$|AB| = \sqrt{(-5-7)^2 + (-2-6)^2} = 4\sqrt{13}$$

$$|BC| = \sqrt{(7-5)^2 + (6+4)^2} = 2\sqrt{26}$$

and $$|CA| = \sqrt{(5+5)^2 + (-4+2)^2} = 2\sqrt{26}$$

$\because$ $(BC)^2 + (CA)^2 = (AB)^2$ and $|BC| = |CA|$

$\Rightarrow \Delta ABC$ is right angled isosceles triangle and right angle at C.

$\therefore$ Circumcentre is mid-point of $A, B \equiv (1, 2)$. Both statements are true and statement II is correct explanation of statement I.

38. Let $A \equiv (0, 0)$, $M \equiv (h, k)$, $B \equiv (2h, 2k)$ and let same ratio $\lambda : 1$

$$P \equiv \left(\frac{2h\lambda}{\lambda + 1}, \frac{2k\lambda}{\lambda + 1}\right), Q = \left(\frac{2h\lambda}{\lambda - 1}, \frac{2k\lambda}{\lambda - 1}\right)$$

$$AP = \frac{2\lambda}{(\lambda + 1)}\sqrt{(h^2 + k^2)}, \; AB = 2\sqrt{(h^2 + k^2)},$$

$$AQ = \frac{2\lambda}{(\lambda - 1)}\sqrt{(h^2 + k^2)}$$

$\because$ $$\frac{AP - AB}{AB - AQ} = \frac{\lambda - 1}{\lambda + 1} = \frac{AP}{AQ}$$

$\therefore$ AP, AB and AQ are in HP.

$\Rightarrow$ $AM + MP$, $AM + MB$ and $AM + MQ$ are in HP

$\therefore$ MP, MB and MQ are in GP.

Both statements are true and statement II is correct explanation of statement I.

39. Replacing x by $(x - 4)$ and y by $y + 1$ is

$x^2 - 3xy + 11x - 12y + 36 = 0$, then

$(x-4)^2 - 3(x-4)(y+1) + 11(x-4) - 12(y+1) + 36 = 0$

$\Rightarrow$ $$x^2 - 3xy + 8 = 0$$

or $$\frac{x^2}{8} - \frac{3xy}{8} + 1 = 0$$

comparing with $ax^2 + bxy + 1 = 0$.

$\therefore$ $$a = \frac{1}{8}, b = -\frac{3}{8}$$

$\therefore$ $$b^2 - a$$

$$= \frac{9}{64} - \frac{1}{8} = \frac{1}{64}$$

$\Rightarrow$ Statement I is true.

Hence, both statements are true and statement II is not correct explanation of statement I.

40. Let AD be the internal bisector of angle A.

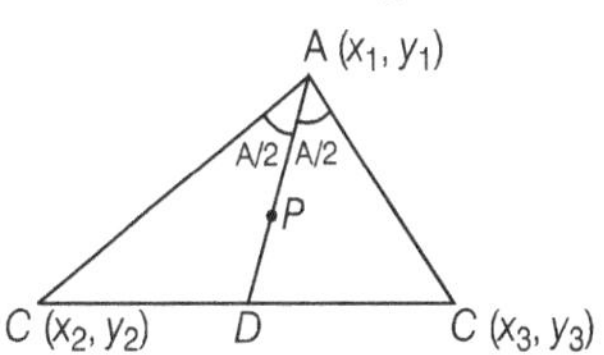

Then, $$\frac{BD}{DC} = \frac{AB}{AC} = \frac{c}{b}$$

$\therefore$ $$D \equiv \left(\frac{cx_3 + bx_2}{c + b}, \frac{cy_3 + by_2}{c + b}\right)$$

Let $P \equiv (x, y)$. According to question, $P(x, y)$ lies on AD, therefore P, A, D are collinear

$\therefore$ $$\begin{vmatrix} x & y & 1 \\ x_1 & y_1 & 1 \\ \frac{cx_3 + bx_2}{c + b} & \frac{cy_3 + by_2}{c + b} & 1 \end{vmatrix} = 0$$

or $$\frac{1}{(c+b)}\begin{vmatrix} x & y & 1 \\ x_1 & y_1 & 1 \\ cx_3 + bx_2 & cy_3 + by_2 & c + b \end{vmatrix} = 0$$

or $$\begin{vmatrix} x & y & 1 \\ x_1 & y_1 & 1 \\ cx_3 & cy_3 & c \end{vmatrix} + \begin{vmatrix} x & y & 1 \\ x_1 & y_1 & 1 \\ bx_2 & by_2 & b \end{vmatrix} = 0$$

(using the addition property of determinants)

or $$c\begin{vmatrix} x & y & 1 \\ x_1 & y_1 & 1 \\ x_3 & y_3 & 1 \end{vmatrix} + b\begin{vmatrix} x & y & 1 \\ x_1 & y_1 & 1 \\ x_2 & y_2 & 1 \end{vmatrix} = 0$$

Hence, $$b\begin{vmatrix} x & y & 1 \\ x_1 & y_1 & 1 \\ x_2 & y_2 & 1 \end{vmatrix} + c\begin{vmatrix} x & y & 1 \\ x_1 & y_1 & 1 \\ x_3 & y_3 & 1 \end{vmatrix} = 0$$

41. Let first term and common difference of corresponding AP are A and D.

Since, pth term of HP $= a$

$\therefore$ pth term of AP $= \frac{1}{a}$

$\Rightarrow$ $$A + (p-1)D = \frac{1}{a} \quad \text{...(i)}$$

Similarly, $$A + (q-1)D = \frac{1}{b} \quad \text{...(ii)}$$

and $$A + (r-1)D = \frac{1}{c} \quad \text{...(iii)}$$

Subtracting Eq. (ii) from Eq. (i),

$$(p-q)D = \frac{1}{a} - \frac{1}{b} \quad \text{...(iv)}$$

and subtracting Eq. (iii) from Eq. (ii),

$$(q-r)D = \frac{1}{b} - \frac{1}{c} \quad \text{...(v)}$$

Dividing Eq. (iv) by Eq. (v),

$$\frac{p-q}{q-r} = \frac{\frac{1}{a} - \frac{1}{b}}{\frac{1}{b} - \frac{1}{c}} = \frac{(b-a)}{ba} \times \frac{bc}{(c-b)}$$

$$\Rightarrow \quad \frac{p-q}{q-r} = \frac{bc-ac}{ac-ab} \quad \text{...(vi)}$$

Let $A(bc, p)$, $B(ca, q)$, $C(ab, r)$

$$\text{Slope of } AB = \frac{q-p}{ca-bc}$$

and $$\text{Slope of } BC = \frac{r-q}{ab-ca}$$

$$= \frac{q-p}{ca-bc} \quad \text{[from Eq. (vi)]}$$

Since, Slope of AB = slope of BC

Hence, A, B, C are collinear.

42. Suppose the equation of the line L is $ax + by + c = 0$. Let the coordinates of A, B, C be respectively (x_1, y_1); (x_2, y_2); (x_3, y_3). Suppose P divides BC in the ratio $\lambda : 1$, then coordinates of P are $\left(\frac{\lambda x_3 + x_2}{\lambda + 1}, \frac{\lambda y_3 + y_2}{\lambda + 1}\right)$ since P lies on L.

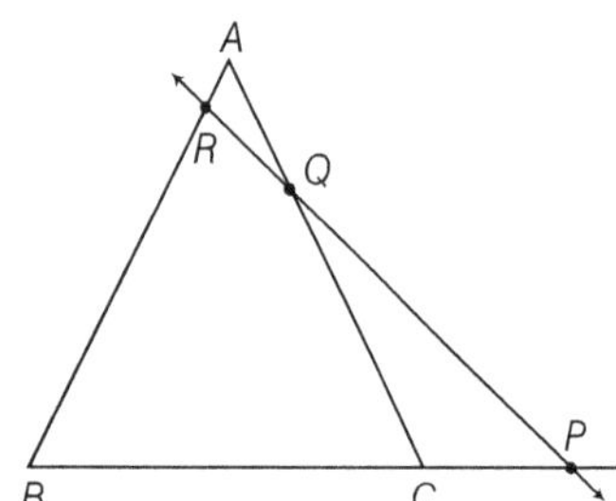

$$\Rightarrow \quad a\left(\frac{\lambda x_3 + x_2}{\lambda + 1}\right) + b\left(\frac{\lambda y_3 + y_2}{\lambda + 1}\right) + c = 0$$

$$\Rightarrow \quad a(\lambda x_3 + x_2) + b(\lambda y_3 + y_2) + c(\lambda + 1) = 0$$

$$\Rightarrow \quad \lambda(ax_3 + by_3 + c) + (ax_2 + by_2 + c) = 0$$

$$\therefore \quad \frac{\lambda}{1} = \frac{BP}{CP} = -\frac{(ax_2 + by_2 + c)}{(ax_3 + by_3 + c)}$$

Similarly, $$\frac{CQ}{QA} = -\frac{(ax_3 + by_3 + c)}{(ax_1 + by_1 + c)}$$

and $$\frac{AR}{RB} = -\frac{(ax_1 + by_1 + c)}{(ax_2 + by_2 + c)}$$

Hence, $$\frac{BP}{PC} \cdot \frac{CQ}{QA} \cdot \frac{AR}{RB} = -1$$

Aliter :

Let middle point O of BC as the origin, BC as the X-axis and yy' as Y-axis.

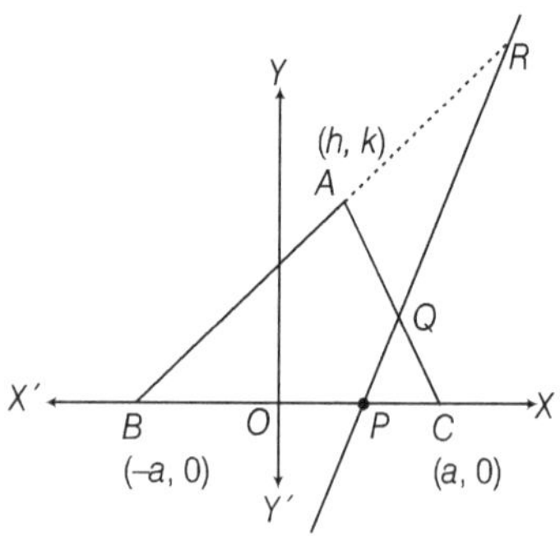

Let $BC = 2a$

$\therefore$ $OB = OC = a$

Then, $B \equiv (-a, 0)$

and $C \equiv (a, 0)$

Let $A \equiv (h, k)$

Let P, Q, R divides BC, CA and AB in the ratio $\lambda : 1$, $\mu : 1$ and $\nu : 1$

i.e. $$\frac{BP}{PC} = \lambda, \frac{CQ}{QA} = \mu, \frac{AR}{RB} = \nu$$

Case I : Two sides divided internally and one side divided externally.

Hence, λ, μ are positive and ν is negative

Now, $$P \equiv \left(\frac{\lambda a - a}{\lambda + 1}, 0\right); Q \equiv \left(\frac{\mu h + a}{\mu + 1}, \frac{\mu k}{\mu + 1}\right)$$

and $$R \equiv \left(\frac{-a\nu + h}{\nu + 1}, \frac{k}{\nu + 1}\right)$$

Since, points P, Q, R are collinear.

$$\therefore \quad \frac{1}{2}\begin{vmatrix} \frac{\lambda a - a}{\lambda + 1} & 0 & 1 \\ \frac{\mu h + a}{\mu + 1} & \frac{\mu k}{\mu + 1} & 1 \\ \frac{-a\nu + h}{\nu + 1} & \frac{k}{\nu + 1} & 1 \end{vmatrix} = 0$$

or $$\begin{vmatrix} \lambda a - a & 0 & \lambda + 1 \\ \mu h + a & \mu k & \mu + 1 \\ -a\nu + h & k & \nu + 1 \end{vmatrix} = 0$$

or $$k\begin{vmatrix} \lambda a - a & 0 & \lambda + 1 \\ \mu h + a & \mu & \mu + 1 \\ -a\nu + h & 1 & \nu + 1 \end{vmatrix} = 0$$

Applying $R_2 \to R_2 - \mu R_3$, then

$$k\begin{vmatrix} \lambda a - a & 0 & \lambda + 1 \\ a + a\mu\nu & 0 & 1 - \mu\nu \\ -a\nu + h & 1 & \nu + 1 \end{vmatrix} = 0$$

or $$-k\begin{vmatrix} \lambda a - a & \lambda + 1 \\ a + a\mu\nu & 1 - \mu\nu \end{vmatrix} = 0$$

or $\quad -ka\begin{vmatrix}\lambda-1 & \lambda+1\\ 1+\mu\nu & 1-\mu\nu\end{vmatrix}=0$

or $\quad -ka\{(\lambda-1)(1-\mu\nu)-(\lambda+1)(1+\mu\nu)\}=0$

or $\quad -ka\{-2\lambda\mu\nu-2\}$

$\Rightarrow \quad 2ka(\lambda\mu\nu+1)=0$

or $\quad \lambda\mu\nu=-1 \qquad (\because ka\neq 0)$

or $\quad \dfrac{BP}{PC}\cdot\dfrac{CQ}{QA}\cdot\dfrac{AR}{RB}=-1$

Case II : All the three sides will be divided externally

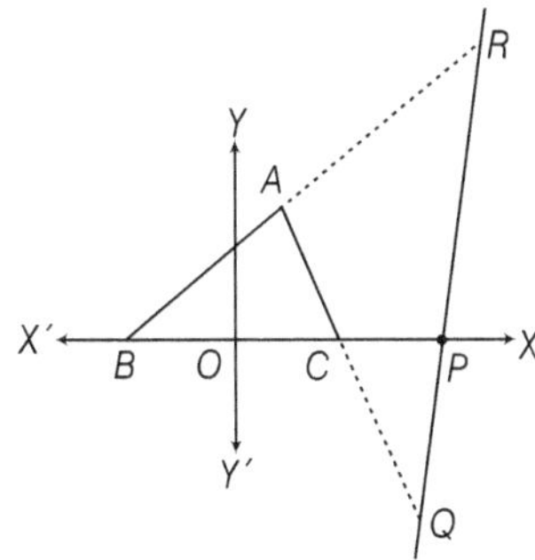

Here, λ, μ and ν are negative.

Now, in case I formula for internal division will be used then we can show that

$$\lambda\mu\nu=-1$$

i.e. $\quad \dfrac{BP}{PC}\cdot\dfrac{CQ}{QA}\cdot\dfrac{AR}{RB}=-1$

43. Since, given points are collinear, then

$$\frac{1}{2}\begin{vmatrix}\frac{a^3}{a-1} & \frac{a^2-3}{a-1} & 1\\ \frac{b^3}{b-1} & \frac{b^2-3}{b-1} & 1\\ \frac{c^3}{c-1} & \frac{c^2-3}{c-1} & 1\end{vmatrix}=0$$

$$\Rightarrow \quad \frac{1}{(a-1)(b-1)(c-1)}\begin{vmatrix}a^3 & a^2-3 & a-1\\ b^3 & b^2-3 & b-1\\ c^3 & c^2-3 & c-1\end{vmatrix}=0$$

or $$\begin{vmatrix}a^3 & a^2-3 & a-1\\ b^3 & b^2-3 & b-1\\ c^3 & c^2-3 & c-1\end{vmatrix}=0$$

$$\Rightarrow \quad \begin{vmatrix}a^3 & a^2 & a\\ b^3 & b^2 & b\\ c^3 & c^2 & c\end{vmatrix}+\begin{vmatrix}a^3 & a^2 & -1\\ b^3 & b^2 & -1\\ c^3 & c^2 & -1\end{vmatrix}+\begin{vmatrix}a^3 & -3 & a\\ b^3 & -3 & b\\ c^3 & -3 & c\end{vmatrix}$$

$$+\begin{vmatrix}a^3 & -3 & -1\\ b^3 & -3 & -1\\ c^3 & -3 & -1\end{vmatrix}=0$$

or $$-abc\begin{vmatrix}1 & a & a^2\\ 1 & b & b^2\\ 1 & c & c^2\end{vmatrix}+\begin{vmatrix}1 & a^2 & a^3\\ 1 & b^2 & b^3\\ 1 & c^2 & c^3\end{vmatrix}-3\begin{vmatrix}1 & a & a^3\\ 1 & b & b^3\\ 1 & c & c^3\end{vmatrix}+0=0$$

or $\quad -abc(a-b)(b-c)(c-a)$
$\qquad +(ab+bc+ca)(a-b)(b-c)(c-a)$
$\qquad -3(a+b+c)(a-b)(b-c)(c-a)=0$

$\Rightarrow \quad -(a-b)(b-c)(c-a)$
$\qquad \{abc-(ab+bc+ca)+3(a+b+c)\}=0$

$\therefore \quad abc-(ab+bc+ca)+3(a+b+c)=0$

$$\left\{\begin{array}{l}\because a,b,c \text{ are distinct}\\ \therefore a\neq b,\ b\neq c,\ c\neq a\\ \therefore (a-b)(b-c)(c-a)\neq 0\end{array}\right\}$$

a, b, c are distinct.

Aliter : Suppose the given points lie on the line $lx+my+n=0$

then, $\quad l\left(\dfrac{t^3}{t-1}\right)+m\left(\dfrac{t^2-3}{t-1}\right)+n=0$

where, $t=a, b, c$

$\Rightarrow \quad lt^3+mt^2+nt-(3m+n)=0 \qquad$ ...(i)

i.e. a, b, c are the roots of Eq. (i)

then, $\quad a+b+c=-\dfrac{m}{l}$

$\quad ab+bc+ca=\dfrac{n}{l}$

$\quad abc=\dfrac{(3m+n)}{l}$

Now, $\quad abc-(bc+ca+ab)+3(a+b+c)$
$\quad =\dfrac{(3m+n)}{l}-\dfrac{n}{l}-\dfrac{3m}{l}=0$

Hence, $\quad abc-(bc+ca+ab)+3(a+b+c)=0$

44. $\because \Delta^c=\Delta^2$

where, Δ^c be the determinant of cofactors of Δ.

Let, $\quad \Delta^c=\begin{vmatrix}A_1 & B_1 & C_1\\ A_2 & B_2 & C_2\\ A_3 & B_3 & C_3\end{vmatrix}$

then, $\quad A_1=b_2c_3-b_3c_2,\ B_1=a_3c_2-a_2c_3,\ C_1=a_2b_3-a_3b_2$
$\quad A_2=b_3c_1-b_1c_3,\ B_2=c_3a_1-c_1a_3,\ C_2=a_3b_1-a_1b_3$
$\quad A_3=b_1c_2-b_2c_1,\ B_3=a_2c_1-a_1c_2,\ C_3=a_1b_2-a_2b_1$

Given lines are

$a_1x+b_1y+c_1=0 \qquad$ ...(i)

$a_2x+b_2y+c_2=0 \qquad$ ...(ii)

$a_3x+b_3y+c_3=0 \qquad$ ...(iii)

Let P be the point of intersection of Eqs. (ii) and (iii), then

$$\frac{x}{b_2c_3-b_3c_2}=\frac{y}{c_2a_3-c_3a_2}=\frac{1}{a_2b_3-a_3b_2}$$

i.e. $\quad \dfrac{x}{A_1}=\dfrac{y}{B_1}=\dfrac{1}{C_1}$

$\therefore \quad P\equiv\left(\dfrac{A_1}{C_1},\dfrac{B_1}{C_1}\right)$

Similarly, if Q and R be the points of intersections of Eqs. (iii) and (i) and Eqs. (i) and (ii) respectively, then

$$Q\equiv\left(\frac{A_2}{C_2},\frac{B_2}{C_2}\right),\ R\equiv\left(\frac{A_3}{C_3},\frac{B_3}{C_3}\right)$$

$$\therefore \text{ Area of } \Delta PQR = \frac{1}{2}\left|\begin{vmatrix} \frac{A_1}{C_1} & \frac{B_1}{C_1} & 1 \\ \frac{A_2}{C_2} & \frac{B_2}{C_2} & 1 \\ \frac{A_3}{C_3} & \frac{B_3}{C_3} & 1 \end{vmatrix}\right| = \frac{1}{2|C_1C_2C_3|}\begin{vmatrix} A_1 & B_1 & C_1 \\ A_2 & B_2 & C_2 \\ A_3 & B_3 & C_3 \end{vmatrix}$$

$$= \frac{1}{2|C_1C_2C_3|}\begin{vmatrix} a_1 & b_1 & c_1 \\ a_2 & b_2 & c_2 \\ a_3 & b_3 & c_3 \end{vmatrix}^2 = \frac{\Delta^2}{2|C_1C_2C_3|}$$

45. Since, G_1 is the middle point of A_1A_2 where

$$A_1 \equiv (x_1, y_1) \text{ and } A_2 \equiv (x_2, y_2)$$

$$\therefore \quad G_1 \equiv \left(\frac{x_1 + x_2}{2}, \frac{y_1 + y_2}{2}\right)$$

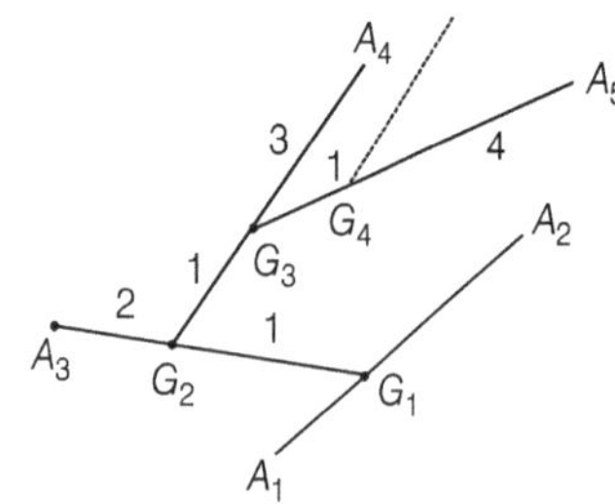

Since, G_2 divided G_1A_3 internally in the ratio 1:2

$$\therefore \quad G_2 \equiv \left(\frac{2\cdot\left(\frac{x_1 + x_2}{2}\right) + 1.\ x_3}{2+1}, \frac{2\cdot\left(\frac{y_1 + y_2}{2}\right) + 1.y_3}{2+1}\right)$$

i.e. $$G_2 \equiv \left(\frac{x_1 + x_2 + x_3}{3}, \frac{y_1 + y_2 + y_3}{3}\right)$$

Again G_3 divides G_2A_4 internally in the ratio 1:3

$$\therefore \quad G_3 \equiv \left(\frac{3\cdot\left(\frac{x_1 + x_2 + x_3}{3}\right) + 1.x_4}{3+1}, \frac{3\cdot\left(\frac{y_1 + y_2 + y_3}{3}\right) + 1.y_4}{3+1}\right)$$

i.e. $$G_3 \equiv \left(\frac{x_1 + x_2 + x_3 + x_4}{4}, \frac{y_1 + y_2 + y_3 + y_4}{4}\right)$$

Proceeding in this way, we can show that

$$G_{n-1} \equiv \left(\frac{x_1 + x_2 + \ldots + x_n}{n}, \frac{y_1 + y_2 + \ldots + y_n}{n}\right)$$

or we can say that the coordinates of the final point are

$$\frac{x_1 + x_2 + \ldots + x_n}{n} \text{ and } \frac{y_1 + y_2 + \ldots + y_n}{n}$$

46. Let the axes be rotated through an angle α, since (x, y) be the coordinates with respect to old axes and (x_1, y_1) be the coordinates with respect to new axes, then

$$x = x_1 \cos\alpha - y_1 \sin\alpha$$

and $$y = x_1 \sin\alpha + y_1 \cos\alpha$$

Now, the expression $ax^2 + 2hxy + by^2$ becomes

$$a(x_1\cos\alpha - y_1\sin\alpha)^2 + 2h(x_1\cos\alpha - y_1\sin\alpha)(x_1\sin\alpha + y_1\cos\alpha) + b(x_1\sin\alpha + y_1\cos\alpha)^2$$

$$= x_1^2(a\cos^2\alpha + h\sin 2\alpha + b\sin^2\alpha) + x_1y_1(2h\cos 2\alpha - a\sin 2\alpha + b\sin 2\alpha) + y_1^2(a\sin^2\alpha - h\sin 2\alpha + b\cos^2\alpha) \quad \ldots(i)$$

But, from question the expression $ax^2 + 2hxy + by^2$ transforms into

$$a_1x_1^2 + 2h_1x_1y_1 + b_1y_1^2 \quad \ldots(ii)$$

Therefore, the expressions (i) and (ii) are the same. Hence, equating the coefficients, we get

$$a_1 = a\cos^2\alpha + h\sin 2\alpha + b\sin^2\alpha \quad \ldots(iii)$$

$$2h_1 = 2h\cos 2\alpha - a\sin 2\alpha + b\sin 2\alpha \quad \ldots(iv)$$

$$b_1 = a\sin^2\alpha - h\sin 2\alpha + b\cos^2\alpha \quad \ldots(v)$$

On adding Eqs. (iii) and (v), we get

$$a_1 + b_1 = a(\cos^2\alpha + \sin^2\alpha) + b(\sin^2\alpha + \cos^2\alpha)$$

or $$a_1 + b_1 = a + b \quad \ldots(vi)$$

Again, $$a_1 - b_1 = a(\cos^2\alpha - \sin^2\alpha) + 2h\sin 2\alpha + b(\sin^2\alpha - \cos^2\alpha)$$

$$\Rightarrow \quad (a_1 - b_1) = (a - b)\cos 2\alpha + 2h\sin 2\alpha$$

$$(a_1 - b_1)^2 = (a - b)^2\cos^2 2\alpha + 4h^2\sin^2 2\alpha + 4h(a - b)\sin 2\alpha\cos 2\alpha \quad \ldots(vii)$$

Again, from Eq. (iv)

$$2h_1 = 2h\cos 2\alpha - (a - b)\sin 2\alpha$$

$$\therefore \quad 4h_1^2 = 4h^2\cos^2 2\alpha + (a - b)^2\sin^2 2\alpha - 4h(a - b)\sin 2\alpha\cos 2\alpha \quad \ldots(viii)$$

On adding Eqs. (vii) and (viii), we get

$$(a_1 - b_1)^2 + 4h_1^2 = (a - b)^2 + 4h^2$$

Again, $$4a_1b_1 - 4h_1^2 = (a_1 + b_1)^2 - (a_1 - b_1)^2 - 4h^2 = (a + b)^2 - (a - b)^2 - 4h^2 \quad \text{[from Eq. (vi)]}$$

Hence, $$a_1b_1 - h_1^2 = ab - h^2$$

47. Vertex of triangle is (1, 1) and mid-point of sides through this vertex are (−1,2) and (3, 2)

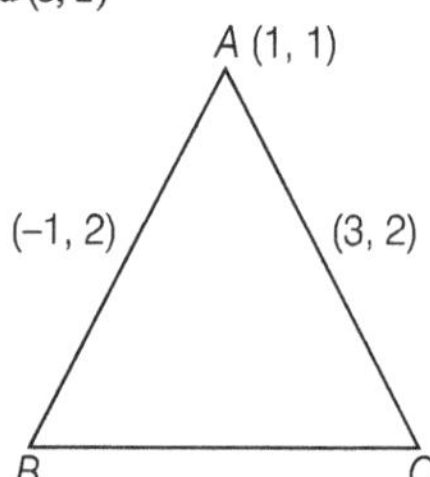

$\Rightarrow$ Vertex B and C come out to be (−3, 3) and (5, 3)

$$\therefore \text{ Centroid is } \frac{1 - 3 + 5}{3}, \frac{1 + 3 + 5}{3} \Rightarrow \left(1, \frac{7}{3}\right)$$

48.

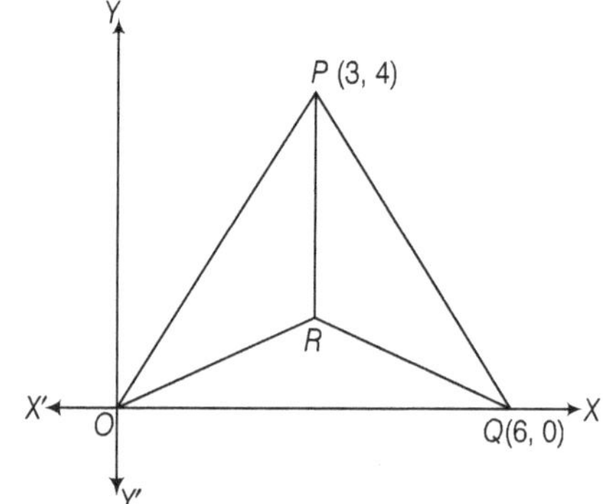

$\because$ Area of (ΔOPR) = Area of (ΔPQR) = Area of (ΔOQR)

$\therefore$ By geometry R should be the centroid of ΔOPQ

$$\therefore \quad R \equiv \left(\frac{0+3+6}{3}, \frac{0+4+0}{3}\right) \equiv \left(3, \frac{4}{3}\right)$$

49. Given, the vertices of a right angled triangle are $A(1, k)$, $B(1, 1)$ and $C(2, 1)$ and area of $\Delta ABC = 1$ sq unit

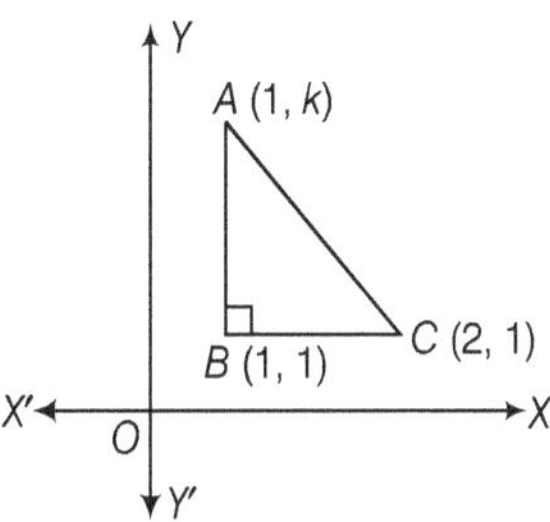

We know that, area of right angled triangle

$$= \frac{1}{2} \times BC \times AB = \frac{1}{2}(1)\,|(k-1)|$$

$$= \frac{1}{2}|k-1| \Rightarrow \pm(k-1) = 2$$

$$\Rightarrow \quad k = -1, 3$$

$$\therefore \quad K = \{-1, 3\}$$

50. Let $P \equiv (1, 0)$ and $Q \equiv (-1, 0)$

Given that, $\dfrac{AP}{AQ} = \dfrac{BP}{BQ} = \dfrac{CP}{CQ} = \dfrac{1}{3}$

$$\Rightarrow \quad 3AP = AQ \text{ or } 9(AP)^2 = (AQ)^2$$

Let $\quad A \equiv (x, y)$, then

$$a((x-1)^2 + (y-0)^2) = (x+1)^2 + (y-0)^2$$

$$\Rightarrow \quad 8x^2 + 8y^2 - 20x + 8 = 0$$

$$\Rightarrow \quad x^2 + y^2 - \frac{5}{2}x + 1 = 0 \quad \text{...(i)}$$

Circumcentre of ΔABC = Centre of circle Eq. (i)

$$= \left(\frac{5}{4}, 0\right)$$

51. From the figure, we have

$$a = 2, b = 2\sqrt{2}, c = 2$$

$$x_1 = 0, x_2 = 0, x_3 = 2 \quad (\because BC = a, CA = b, AB = c)$$

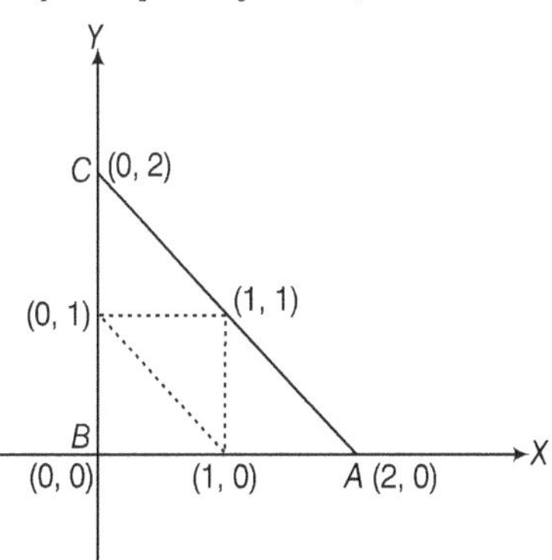

Now, x-coordinate of incentre is given as

$$\frac{ax_1 + bx_2 + cx_3}{a+b+c}$$

$\Rightarrow$ x-coordinate of incentre

$$= \frac{2 \times 0 + 20\sqrt{2} \times 0 + 2 \times 2}{2 + 2 + 2\sqrt{2}}$$

$$= \frac{2}{2+\sqrt{2}} = 2 - \sqrt{2}$$

52.

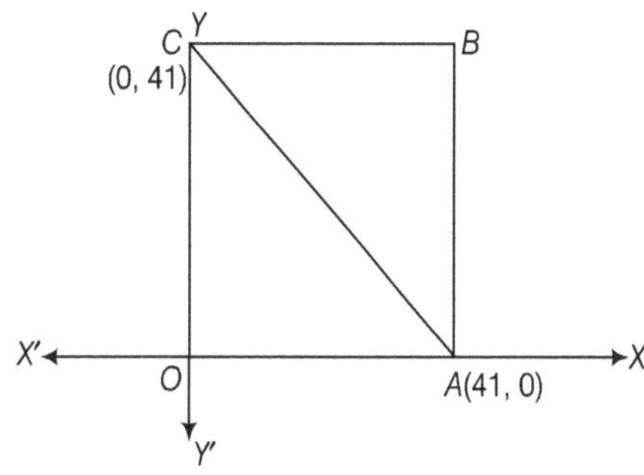

Total number of integral points inside the square

$$OABC = 40 \times 40 = 1600.$$

Number of integral points on AC = Number of integral points on OB = 40 (namely (1, 1), (2, 2), (3, 3), ..., (40, 40))

Hence, number of integral points inside the

$$\Delta OAC = \frac{1600 - 40}{2} = 780$$

Aliter : $x > 0, y > 0\ x + y < 41$ or $0 < x + y < 41$

$\therefore$ Number of integral points inside the $\Delta OAC = {}^{40}C_2 = 780$.

53. $$\frac{1}{2}\left|\begin{vmatrix} k & -3k & 1 \\ 5 & k & 1 \\ -k & 2 & 1 \end{vmatrix}\right| = 28$$

$$\Rightarrow \quad 5k^2 + 13k + 10 = \pm 56$$

$$\Rightarrow \quad 5k^2 + 13k - 46 = 0$$

$$\text{or} \quad 5k^2 + 13k + 66 = 0$$

$$\therefore \quad 5k^2 + 13k - 46 = 0$$

$$\text{and} \quad 5k^2 + 13k + 66 \neq 0 \quad (\because D < 0)$$

$$\Rightarrow \quad k = 2, -\frac{23}{5}$$

$$\therefore \quad k = 2, k \neq -\frac{23}{5} \quad (\because k \in I)$$

$\therefore$ Vertices an $A \equiv (2, -6)$, $B \equiv (5, 2)$, $C \equiv (-2, 2)$.

Denote the points are (x_1, y_1), (x_2, y_2) and (x_3, y_3) from the matrix $P = \begin{bmatrix} x_1 - x_3 & y_1 - y_3 \\ x_2 - x_3 & y_2 - y_3 \end{bmatrix} = \begin{bmatrix} 4 & -8 \\ 7 & 0 \end{bmatrix}$

$$\therefore \quad \lambda = \frac{\vec{\mathbf{R}}_1 \cdot \vec{\mathbf{R}}_2}{|P|} = \frac{28}{56} = \frac{1}{2}$$

$\therefore$ Circumcentre of triangle is $\left(\dfrac{7 + \frac{1}{2} \times -8}{2}, \dfrac{-4 - \frac{1}{2} \times -3}{2}\right)$

or $\left(\dfrac{3}{2}, -\dfrac{5}{4}\right)$ and centroid is $\left(\dfrac{5}{3}, -\dfrac{2}{3}\right)$

then, orthocentre

$$= \left(\frac{5}{3} \times 3 - 2 \times \frac{3}{2}, -\frac{2}{3} \times 3 + 2 \times \frac{5}{4}\right) \text{ or } \left(2, \frac{1}{2}\right),$$

CHAPTER

02

The Straight Lines

Learning Part

Session 1

- Definition
- Slope or Gradient of a Line
- Lines Parallel to Coordinate Axes
- Different Forms of the Equation of a Straight Line
- The Distance Form or Symmetric Form or Parametric Form of a Line
- Angle of Inclination of a Line
- Angle Between Two Lines
- Intercepts of a Line on Axes
- Reduction of General Equation to Standard Form

Session 2

- Position of Two Points Relative to a Given Line
- Equations of Lines Parallel and Perpendicular to a Given Line
- Distance Between Two Parallel Lines
- Position of a Point which Lies Inside a Triangle
- Distance of a Point From a Line
- Area of Parallelogram

Session 3

- Points of Intersection of Two Lines
- Family of Lines
- Concurrent Lines
- How to Find Circumcentre and Orthocentre by Slopes

Session 4

- Equations of Straight Lines Passing Through a Given Point and Making a Given Angle with a Given Line
- Equation of the Bisectors
- Equation of that Bisector of the Angle Between Two Lines Which Contains a Given Point
- A Line Equally Inclined with Two Lines
- Bisector of the Angle Containing The Origin
- How to Distinguish the Acute (Internal) and Obtuse (External) Angle Bisectors

Session 5

- The Foot of Perpendicular Drawn from the Point (x_1, y_1) to the Line $ax+by+c=0$
- Image or Reflection of a Point (x_1, y_1) in Different Cases
- Image or Reflection of a Point (x_1, y_1) about a Line Mirror
- Use of Image or Reflection

Session 6

- Reflection of Light
- Refraction of Light
- Condition of Collineirty If Three Given Points are in Cyclic Order

Practice Part

- JEE Type Examples
- Chapter Exercises

Arihant on Your Mobile !

Exercises with the symbol can be practised on your mobile. See inside cover page to activate for free.

Session 1

Definition, Angle of Inclination of a Line, Slope or Gradient of a Line, Angle Between Two Lines, Lines Parallel to Coordinate Axes, Intercepts of a Line on Axes, Different Forms of the Equation of A Straight Line, Reduction of General Equation to Standard Form, The Distance Form or Symmetric Form or Parametric Form of a Line

Definition

A straight line defined as the curve which is such that the line segment joining any two points on it lies wholly on it.

Theorem : Show that the general equation of the first degree in x, y represents a straight line.

Proof : The general equation of the first degree is

$$ax + by + c = 0 \quad \text{...(i)}$$

Let $P(x_1, y_1)$ and $Q(x_2, y_2)$ be the coordinates of any two points on the curve given by Eq. (i), then

$$ax_1 + by_1 + c = 0 \quad \text{...(ii)}$$

$$ax_2 + by_2 + c = 0 \quad \text{...(iii)}$$

Multiplying Eq. (iii) by λ and adding to Eq. (ii), we have

$$a(x_1 + \lambda x_2) + b(y_1 + \lambda y_2) + c(1 + \lambda) = 0$$

or $$a\left(\frac{x_1 + \lambda x_2}{1 + \lambda}\right) + b\left(\frac{y_1 + \lambda y_2}{1 + \lambda}\right) + c = 0 \quad (\lambda \neq -1)$$

This relation shows that the point

$$\left(\frac{x_1 + \lambda x_2}{1 + \lambda}, \frac{y_1 + \lambda y_2}{1 + \lambda}\right) \text{ lies on Eq. (i).}$$

But from previous chapter we know that this point divides the join of $P(x_1, y_1)$ and $Q(x_2, y_2)$ is the ratio $\lambda : 1$.

Since, λ can have any value, so each point on the line PQ lies on Eq. (i) i.e. the line wholly lies on Eq. (i). Hence, by the definition of the straight line as given above we conclude that Eq. (i) represents a straight line.

Hence, the general equation of first degree in x, y *viz* $ax + by + c = 0$ represents a straight line.

Remarks

1. The number of **arbitrary constants** in the equation of a straight line is two (we observe three constants a, b and c in the equation $ax + by + c = 0$ of a straight line. The given equation of line can be rewritten as $\left(\frac{a}{c}\right)x + \left(\frac{b}{c}\right)y + 1 = 0$ or

   $px + qy + 1 = 0$ where $p = \frac{a}{c}$ and $q = \frac{b}{c}$.

   Thus, we have only two arbitrary constants p and q in the equation of a straight line.

   Hence, to completely determine the equation of a straight line, we require two conditions to determine the two unknowns in general.
2. A straight line is briefly written as a 'line.'
3. The equation of a straight line is the relation between x and y, which is satisfied by the coordinates of each and every point on the line.

Angle of Inclination of a Line

The angle of inclination of a line is the measure of the angle between the X-axis and the line measured in the anticlockwise direction.

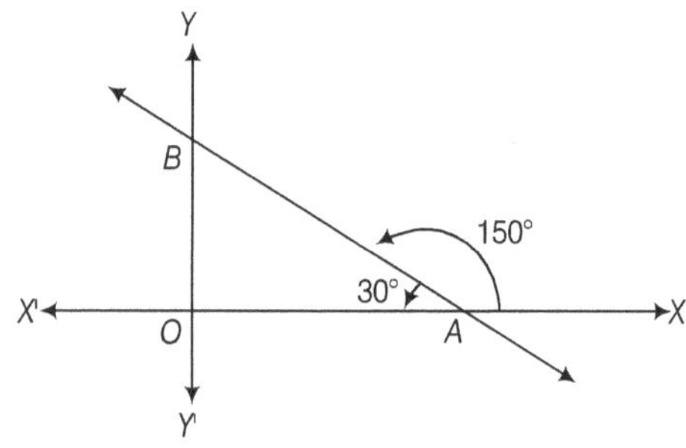

Here, angle of inclination of line $AB = 150°$.

Remarks

1. When two lines are parallel, they have the same inclination.
2. The inclination of a line which is parallel to X-axis or coinciding with X-axis is 0°.
3. The angle of inclination of the line lies between 0° and 180° i.e. $0 < \theta \le \pi$ and $\theta \ne \frac{\pi}{2}$.

Slope or Gradient of a Line

If inclination of a line is $(\theta \ne 90°)$, then $\tan\theta$ is called the slope or gradient of the line. It is usually denoted by m.

θ is positive or negative according as it is measured in anticlockwise or clockwise direction.

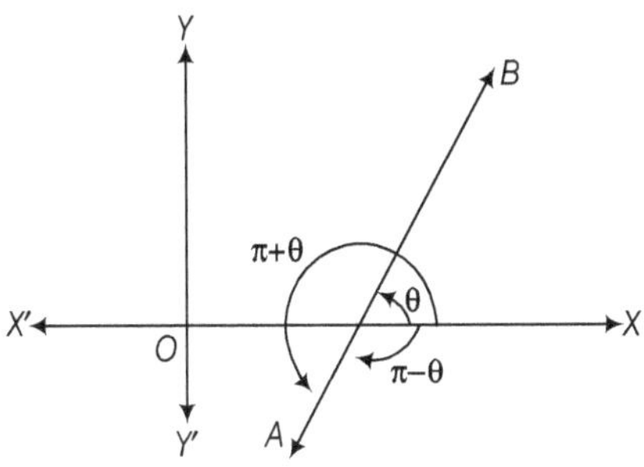

i.e. Slope of $AB = m$ of $AB = m(AB)$

$$\begin{aligned} &= \tan\theta \text{ or } \tan[-(\pi-\theta)] \\ &= \tan(\pi+\theta) \\ &= \text{slope of } BA = m \text{ of } BA \\ &= m(BA) \end{aligned}$$

$\therefore \quad m(AB) = m(BA)$

Hence, we do not take into consideration the direction of a line segment while talking of its slope.

Remarks

1. Slope of a line is not the angle but is the tangent of the inclination of the line.
2. If a line is parallel to X-axis, then its slope $= \tan 0° = 0$.
3. Slope of a line parallel to Y-axis or perpendicular to X-axis is not defined. Whenever we say that the slope of a line is not defined.
4. If a line is equally inclined to the axes, then it will make an angle of 45° or 135° with the positive direction of X-axis. Slope in this case will be tan 45° or tan135°. i.e. ± 1

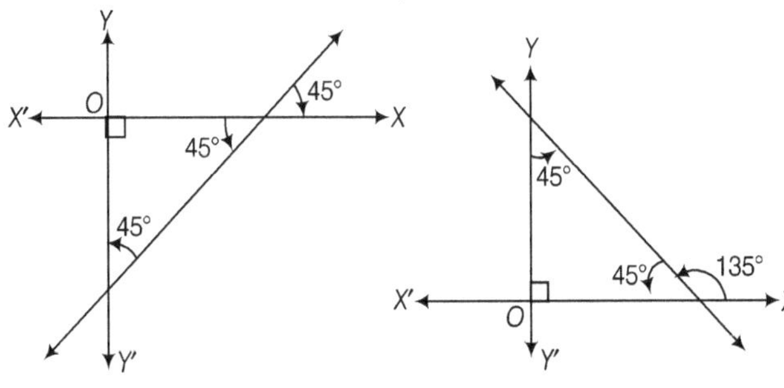

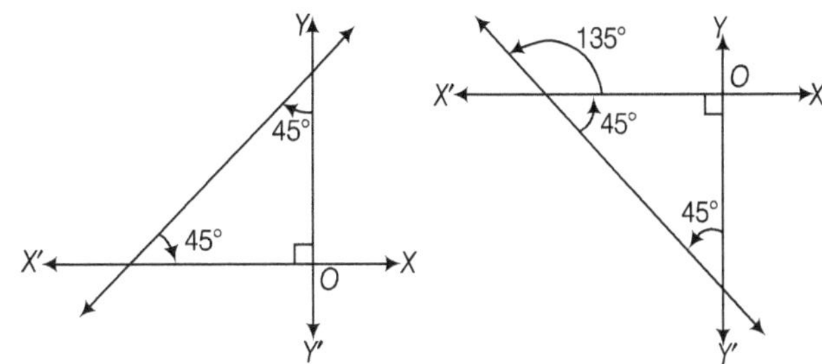

Theorem : If $P(x_1, y_1)$ and $Q(x_2, y_2)$ are two points on a line l, then the slope m of the line l is given by

$$m = \frac{y_2 - y_1}{x_2 - x_1}, x_1 \ne x_2$$

If $x_1 = x_2$, then m is not defined. In that case the line is perpendicular to X-axis.

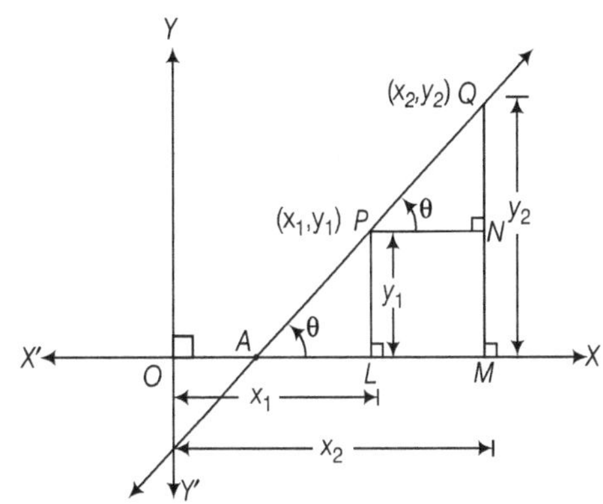

Proof : Given $P(x_1, y_1)$ and $Q(x_2, y_2)$ are two points on a line l, let line l makes an angle θ with positive direction of X-axis. Draw PL, QM perpendiculars on X-axis and

$$PN \perp QM$$

Then, $\quad PN = LM = OM - OL = x_2 - x_1$

and $\quad QN = QM - NM = QM - PL$

$$= y_2 - y_1$$

Also, $\quad \angle QAM = \angle QPN = \theta$

Now, in ΔQPN

$$\tan\theta = \frac{QN}{PN} = \frac{y_2 - y_1}{x_2 - x_1} = \frac{\text{Difference of ordinates}}{\text{Difference of abscissaes}}$$

or $\quad m = \dfrac{y_2 - y_1}{x_2 - x_1}$

If $x_1 = x_2$, then $\tan\theta = \infty$ or $\theta = \frac{\pi}{2}$ i.e. m is not defined or the line is perpendicular to X-axis.

Remarks

1. When the two lines are parallel, then their slopes are equal i.e. $m_1 = m_2$.
2. If three points A, B, C are collinear, then slope of $AB =$ slope of $BC =$ slope of AC.

Example 1. Find the inclination of the line whose slope is $-\frac{1}{\sqrt{3}}$.

Sol. Let α be the inclination of a line then its slope $= \tan\alpha$

$$\therefore \quad \tan\alpha = -\frac{1}{\sqrt{3}} = -\tan 30^\circ$$

$$= \tan(180^\circ - 30^\circ) = \tan 150^\circ$$

$$\Rightarrow \quad \alpha = 150^\circ$$

Example 2. Find the slope of the line through the points $(4, -6), (-2, -5)$.

Sol. Slope of the line $m = \frac{-5-(-6)}{-2-(4)} = -\frac{1}{6}$

Example 3. Determine λ, so that 2 is the slope of the line through $(2, 5)$ and $(\lambda, 3)$.

Sol. Slope of the line joining $(2, 5)$ and $(\lambda, 3)$

$$= \frac{3-5}{\lambda-2} = \frac{-2}{\lambda-2} = 2 \quad \text{(given)}$$

$$\Rightarrow \quad -2 = 2\lambda - 4$$

$$\Rightarrow \quad 2\lambda = 2$$

$$\therefore \quad \lambda = 1$$

Example 4. Show that the line joining the points $(2, -3)$ and $(-5, 1)$ is parallel to the line joining $(7, -1)$ and $(0, 3)$.

Sol. Slope of the line joining the points $(2, -3)$ and $(-5, 1)$ is

$$m_1 = \frac{1-(-3)}{-5-2} = -\frac{4}{7}$$

and slope of the line joining the points $(7, -1)$ and $(0, 3)$ is

$$m_2 = \frac{3-(-1)}{0-7} = \frac{-4}{7}$$

Here, $m_1 = m_2$

Hence, lines are parallel.

Example 5. Find whether the points $(-a, -b), [-(s+1)a, -(s+1)b]$ and $[(t-1)a, (t-1)b]$ are collinear?

Sol. Let $A \equiv (-a, -b)$, $B \equiv [-(s+1)a, -(s+1)b]$ and $C \equiv ((t-1)a, (t-1)b)$

Then, slope of $AB = \frac{-(s+1)b + b}{-(s+1)a + a} = \frac{b}{a}$

and slope of $BC = \frac{(t-1)b + (s+1)b}{(t-1)a + (s+1)a} = \frac{b}{a}$

Hence, given points are collinear.

Example 6. For what value of k the points $(k, 2-2k), (-k+1, 2k)$ and $(-4-k, 6-2k)$ are collinear?

Sol. Let $A \equiv (k, 2-2k)$, $B \equiv (-k+1, 2k)$ and $C \equiv (-4-k, 6-2k)$ are collinear, then

Slope of AB = Slope of AC

$$\Rightarrow \quad \frac{2k-(2-2k)}{-k+1-k} = \frac{6-2k-(2-2k)}{-4-k-k}$$

$$\Rightarrow \quad \frac{4k-2}{-2k+1} = \frac{4}{-4-2k} \quad \left(k \neq \frac{1}{2} (\because \text{Denominator} \neq 0)\right)$$

$$\Rightarrow \quad (4k-2)(-4-2k) = 4(-2k+1)$$

$$\Rightarrow \quad (2k-1)(-2-k) - (-2k+1) = 0$$

$$\Rightarrow \quad (2k-1)(-2-k+1) = 0$$

$$\therefore \quad k \neq \frac{1}{2}, \quad \therefore \quad k = -1$$

Angle Between Two Lines

Theorem : The acute angle θ between the lines having slopes m_1 and m_2 is given by

$$\theta = \tan^{-1}\left|\frac{m_1 - m_2}{1 + m_1 m_2}\right|$$

Proof : Let l_1 and l_2 be two non-perpendicular lines, neither of which is parallel to the Y-axis.

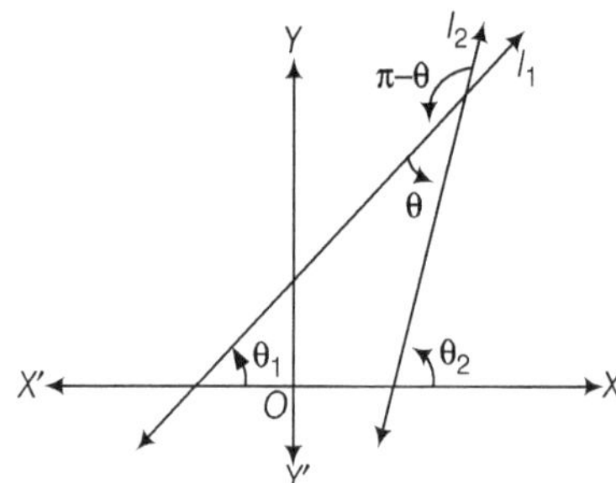

Let m_1 and m_2 be the slopes of two given lines l_1 and l_2 respectively. Let θ_1 and θ_2 be the inclinations of these lines.

$$\therefore \quad m_1 = \tan\theta_1 \text{ and } m_2 = \tan\theta_2$$

Let θ and $\pi - \theta$ be the angles between the lines $\left(\theta \neq \frac{\pi}{2}\right)$.

Then, $\theta_2 = \theta + \theta_1$ or $\theta = \theta_2 - \theta_1$

$$\Rightarrow \quad \tan\theta = \tan(\theta_2 - \theta_1)$$

$$\Rightarrow \quad \tan\theta = \left(\frac{\tan\theta_2 - \tan\theta_1}{1 + \tan\theta_2 \tan\theta_1}\right) = \left(\frac{m_2 - m_1}{1 + m_1 m_2}\right) \quad \text{...(i)}$$

Also, $\tan(\pi - \theta) = -\tan\theta = -\left(\frac{m_2 - m_1}{1 + m_2 m_1}\right)$ ...(ii)

From Eqs. (i) and (ii) the angle between two lines of slopes m_1 and m_2 is given by

$$\tan\theta = \pm\left(\frac{m_1 - m_2}{1 + m_1 m_2}\right)$$

$$\Rightarrow \qquad \theta = \tan^{-1}\left[\pm\left(\frac{m_1 - m_2}{1 + m_1 m_2}\right)\right]$$

Hence, the acute angle between the lines l_1 and l_2 is given by

$$\theta = \tan^{-1}\left|\frac{m_1 - m_2}{1 + m_1 m_2}\right|.$$

***Corollary* 1 :** If two lines, whose slopes are m_1 and m_2 are parallel,

iff $\qquad \theta = 0° \text{ (or } \pi) \Leftrightarrow \tan\theta = 0$

$\qquad \Leftrightarrow m_1 = m_2$

Thus, when two lines are parallel, their slopes are equal.

***Corollary* 2 :** If two lines, whose slopes are m_1 and m_2 are perpendicular,

iff $\qquad \theta = \frac{\pi}{2}\left(\text{or } -\frac{\pi}{2}\right) \Leftrightarrow \cot\theta = 0$

$\qquad \Leftrightarrow m_1 m_2 = -1$

Thus, when two lines are perpendicular, the product of their slopes is -1. The slope of each is the negative reciprocal of the slope of other i.e. if m is the slope of a line, then the slope of a line perpendicular to it is $-\frac{1}{m}$.

Example 7. Find the angle between the lines joining the points $(0, 0), (2, 3)$ and $(2, -2), (3, 5)$.

Sol. Let the given points be $A \equiv (0, 0)$, $B \equiv (2, 3)$, $C \equiv (2, -2)$ and $D \equiv (3, 5)$. Let m_1 and m_2 be the slopes of the lines AB and CD respectively.

$$\therefore \qquad m_1 = \frac{3-0}{2-0} = \frac{3}{2} \text{ and } m_2 = \frac{5-(-2)}{3-2} = 7$$

Let θ be the acute angle between the lines

$$\therefore \qquad \tan\theta = \left|\frac{m_1 - m_2}{1 + m_1 m_2}\right| = \left|\frac{\frac{3}{2} - 7}{1 + \left(\frac{3}{2}\right)\cdot 7}\right|$$

$$= \left|\frac{-11}{23}\right| = \frac{11}{23}$$

$$\therefore \qquad \theta = \tan^{-1}\left(\frac{11}{23}\right)$$

Example 8. The angle between two lines is $\frac{\pi}{4}$ and the slope of one of them is $\frac{1}{2}$. Find the slope of the other line.

Sol. If θ be the acute angle between the lines with slopes m_1 and m_2, then

$$\tan\theta = \left|\frac{m_1 - m_2}{1 + m_1 m_2}\right|$$

Let $\qquad \theta = \frac{\pi}{4}$ and $m_1 = \frac{1}{2}$

then $\qquad \tan\frac{\pi}{4} = \left|\frac{\frac{1}{2} - m_2}{1 + \frac{1}{2}\cdot m_2}\right|$

$$\Rightarrow \qquad 1 = \left|\frac{1 - 2m_2}{2 + m_2}\right|$$

$$\Rightarrow \qquad \frac{1 - 2m_2}{2 + m_2} = \pm 1$$

Taking positive sign then,

$$1 - 2m_2 = 2 + m_2$$

$$\therefore \qquad m_2 = -\frac{1}{3}$$

and taking negative sign then,

$$1 - 2m_2 = -2 - m_2$$

$$\therefore \qquad m_2 = 3$$

Hence, the slope of the other line is either $-\frac{1}{3}$ or 3.

Example 9. Without using pythagoras theorem, show that the points $A(-1, 3), B(0, 5)$ and $C(3, 1)$ are the vertices of a right angled triangle.

Sol. In ΔABC, we have

$$\text{Slope of side } AB = \frac{5-3}{0-(-1)} = 2 = m_1 \qquad \text{(say)}$$

$$\text{Slope of side } BC = \frac{1-5}{3-0} = -\frac{4}{3} = m_2 \qquad \text{(say)}$$

and $\qquad \text{Slope of side } CA = \frac{3-1}{-1-3} = -\frac{1}{2} = m_3 \qquad \text{(say)}$

Clearly, $\qquad m_1 m_3 = 2 \times \left(-\frac{1}{2}\right) = -1$

$\therefore$ AB and CA are perpendicular to each other i.e.

$$\angle BAC = 90°$$

Hence, the given points are the vertices of a right angled triangle.

Example 10. A line passes through the points $A(2, -3)$ and $B(6, 3)$. Find the slopes of the lines which are

(i) parallel to AB (ii) perpendicular to AB

Sol. Let m be the slope of AB. Then $m = \frac{3-(-3)}{6-2} = \frac{6}{4} = \frac{3}{2}$

(i) Let m_1 be the slope of a line parallel to AB, then

$$m_1 = m = \frac{3}{2}$$

(ii) The slope of a line perpendicular to AB is

$$-\frac{1}{m} = -\frac{1}{\frac{3}{2}} = -\frac{2}{3}$$

Example 11. Show that the triangle which has one of the angles as 60°, can not have all vertices with integral coordinates.

Sol. Let ABC be a triangle whose vertices are $A(x_1, y_1), B(x_2, y_2)$ and $C(x_3, y_3)$. Assume $x_1, x_2, x_3, y_1, y_2, y_3$ all are integers.

Let $\angle BAC = 60°$

$$\text{Slope of } AC = \frac{y_3 - y_1}{x_3 - x_1} = m_1 \quad \text{(say)}$$

and $$\text{Slope of } AB = \frac{y_2 - y_1}{x_2 - x_1} = m_2 \quad \text{(say)}$$

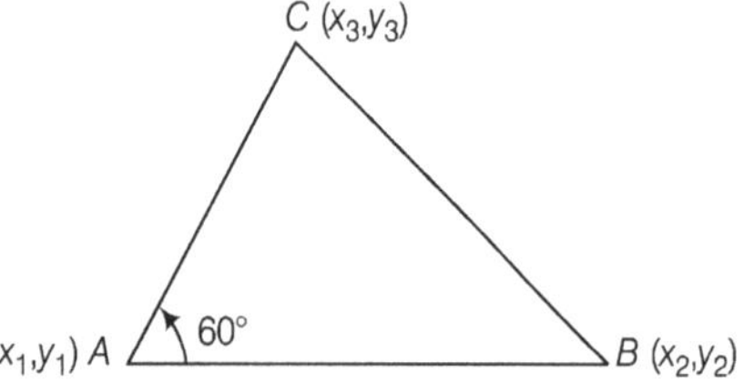

Here, m_1 and m_2 are rational numbers ($\because x_1, x_2, x_3, y_1, y_2, y_3$ are integers)

$$\therefore \quad \tan(\angle BAC) = \frac{m_1 - m_2}{1 + m_1 m_2}$$

$$= \text{Rational} \quad (\because m_1 \text{ and } m_2 \text{ are rational})$$

But $\tan(\angle BAC) = \tan 60° = \sqrt{3} = $ Irrational

$\because$ Rational number $\neq$ Irrational number

Which is contradiction so our assumption that the vertices are integers is wrong. Hence, the triangle having one angle of 60° can not have all vertices with integral coordinates.

Lines Parallel to Coordinate Axes

(i) **Equation of a line parallel to Y-axis :** Let l be a straight line parallel to Y-axis and at a distance a from it, a being the directed distance of the line from the Y-axis . Therefore, the line lies on the right of Y-axis if $a > 0$ and if $a < 0$, then the line would lies on the left of Y-axis.

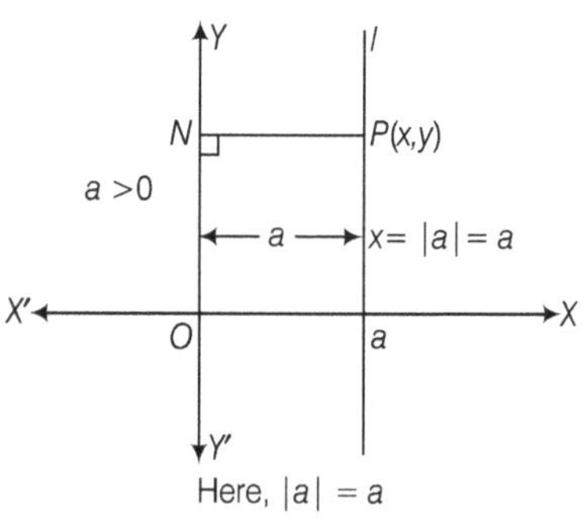

Here, $|a| = a$

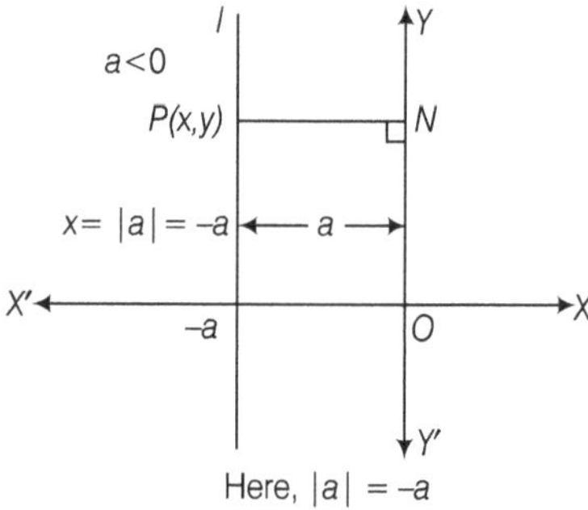

Here, $|a| = -a$

Let $P(x, y)$ be any point on the line l, then

$x = a$ is the required equation. (Here, $|a| = a$)

Remarks

1. In particular equation of Y-axis is $x = 0$ ($\because a = 0$)
2. A line is parallel to Y-axis, at a distance from it and is on the negative side of Y-axis, then its equation is $x = -a$.

(ii) **Equation of a line parallel to X-axis :** Let l be a straight line parallel to X-axis and at a distance b from it, b being the directed distance of the line from the X-axis. Therefore, the line lies above the X-axis, if $b > 0$ and if $b < 0$, then the line would lie below the X-axis.

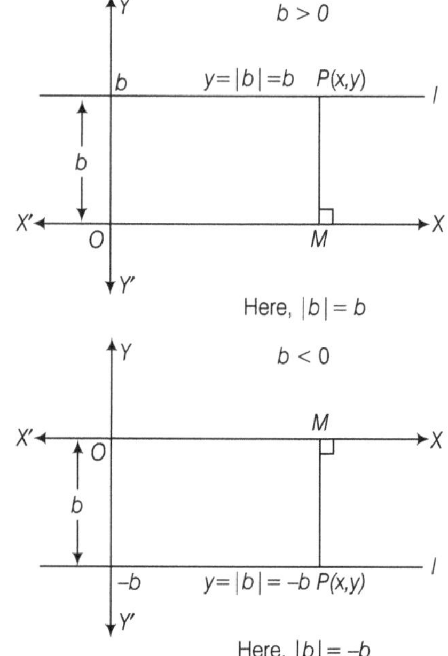

Let $P(x, y)$ be any point on the line l, then $y = b$ is the required equation (Here, $|b| = b$).

Remarks

1. In particular equation of X-axis is $y = 0$ $(\because b = 0)$
2. A line parallel to X-axis at a distance b from it and is on the negative side of X-axis, then its equation is $y = -b$.

Example 12. Find the equation of the straight line parallel to Y-axis and at a distance (i) 3 units to the right (ii) 2 units to the left.

Sol. (i) Equation of straight line parallel to Y-axis at a distance a units to the right is $x = a$.

$\therefore$ Required equation is $x = 3$

(ii) Equation of straight line parallel to Y-axis at a distance a units to the left is $x = -a$.

$\therefore$ Required equation is $x = -2$.

Example 13. Find the equation of the straight line parallel to X-axis and at a distance

(i) 5 units above the X-axis

(ii) 9 units below the X-axis.

Sol. (i) Equation of a straight line parallel to X-axis at a distance b units above the X-axis is $y = b$.

$\therefore$ Required equation is $y = 5$

(ii) Equation of a straight line parallel to X-axis at a distance b units below the X-axis is $y = -b$.

$\therefore$ Required equation is $y = -9$

Example 14. Find the equation of the straight line which passes through the point $(2, -3)$ and is

(i) parallel to the X-axis

(ii) perpendicular to the X-axis

Sol. (i) Let equation of any line parallel to X-axis is

$$y = b \qquad \text{....(i)}$$

Since, it passes through the point $(2, -3)$.

Putting $y = -3$ in Eq. (i), then

$$b = -3$$

Hence, required equation of the line is $y = -3$.

Eq. (i) Let equation of any line perpendicular to X-axis = Equation of any line parallel to Y-axis is

$$x = a \qquad \text{...(ii)}$$

Since, it passes through the point $(2, -3)$ putting $x = 2$ in Eq. (ii)

Then, $2 = a \Rightarrow a = 2$

Hence, required equation of the line $x = 2$.

Example 15. Find the equation of a line which is equidistant from the lines $x = -\frac{7}{2}$ and $x = \frac{15}{2}$.

Sol. Since, the given (both) lines are parallel to Y-axis and the required line is equidistant from these lines, so it is also parallel to Y-axis. Let equation of any line parallel to Y-axis is

$$x = a$$

Here, $a = \dfrac{\left(-\frac{7}{2} + \frac{15}{2}\right)}{2} = \frac{8}{4} = 2$ units

Hence, its equation is $x = 2$.

Intercepts of a Line on Axes

If a line cuts X-axis at $A(a, 0)$ and the Y-axis at $B(0, b)$ then OA and OB are known as the intercepts of the line on X-axis and Y-axis respectively. $|a|$ is called the length of intercept of the line on X-axis. Intercept of a line on X-axis may be positive or negative and $|b|$ is called the length of intercept of the line on Y-axis. Intercept of a line on Y-axis may be positive or negative.

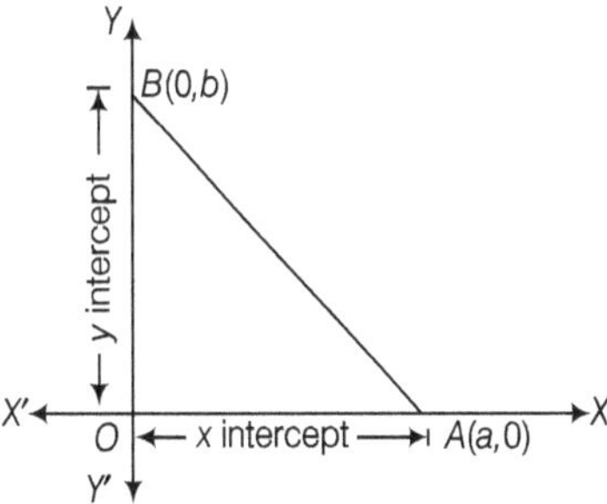

Remark

If a line parallel to Y-axis, then its intercept on Y-axis is not defined and if a line parallel to X-axis, then its intercept on X-axis is not defined.

Intercepts in II quadrant

Intercept on X-axis = $-a$, length of intercept on X-axis = $|a|$
Intercept on Y-axis = b, length of intercept on Y-axis = $|b|$

Intercepts in I quadrant

Intercept on X-axis = a, length of intercept on X-axis = $|a|$
Intercept on Y-axis = b, length of intercept on Y-axis = $|b|$

Intercepts in III quadrant

Intercept on X-axis = $-a$, length of intercept on X-axis = $|a|$
Intercept on Y-axis = $-b$, length of intercept on Y-axis = $|b|$

Intercepts in IV quadrant

Intercept on X-axis = a, length of intercept on X-axis = $|a|$
Intercept on Y-axis = $-b$, length of intercept on Y-axis = $|b|$

Different Forms of the Equation of a Straight Line

(i) Slope-Intercept Form

Theorem : The equation of the straight line whose slope is m and which cuts an intercept c on the Y-axis is

$$y = mx + c$$

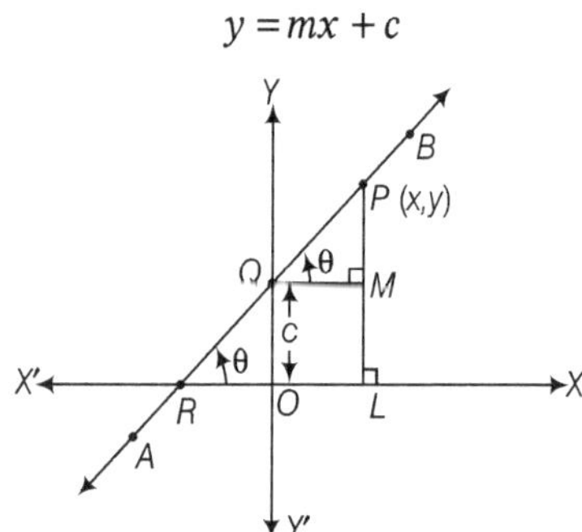

Proof : Let AB be a line whose slope is m and which cuts an intercept c on Y-axis. Let $P(x, y)$ be any point on the line. Draw $PL \perp$ to X-axis and $QM \perp$ to PL.

Then, from figure,

$$\angle PRL = \angle PQM = \theta, OQ = c$$

$\therefore$ $$PM = PL - ML = PL - OQ = y - c$$

and $$QM = OL = x$$

Now in ΔPQM, $\tan\theta = \dfrac{PM}{QM}$

$\Rightarrow$ $$m = \frac{y-c}{x} \Rightarrow y = mx + c$$

which is the required equation of the line.

Remarks

1. If the line passes through the origin, then $c = 0$ ($\because 0 = m.0 + c \Rightarrow c = 0$) and hence equation of the line will become $y = mx$.
2. Equation of any line may be taken as $y = mx + c$.
3. If the line is parallel to X-axis, then $\theta = 0°$ i.e. $m = \tan 0° = 0$. Hence, equation of the line parallel to X-axis is $y = c$.

Example 16. If the straight line $y = mx + c$ passes through the points $(2, 4)$ and $(-3, 6)$, find the values of m and c.

Sol. Since, $(2, 4)$ lies on $y = mx + c$

$\therefore$ $$4 = 2m + c \quad ...(i)$$

Again, $(-3, 6)$ lies on $y = mx + c$

$\therefore$ $$6 = -3m + c \quad ...(ii)$$

On solving Eqs. (i) and (ii), we get $m = -\dfrac{2}{5}, c = \dfrac{24}{5}$

Example 17. What are the inclination to the X-axis and intercept on Y-axis of the line

$$3y = \sqrt{3}x + 6\,?$$

Sol. The given equation can be written as

$$y = \frac{x}{\sqrt{3}} + 2 \quad ...(i)$$

Now, comparing Eq. (i) with $y = mx + c$, then we get

$$m = \frac{1}{\sqrt{3}}$$

Let θ be the inclination to the X-axis, then

$$\tan\theta = \tan 30°$$

$\therefore$ $$\theta = 30° \quad \text{and} \quad c = 2.$$

Example 18. Find the equation of the straight line cutting off an intercept of 3 units on negative direction of Y-axis and inclined at an angle $\tan^{-1}\left(\dfrac{3}{5}\right)$ to the axis of x.

Sol. Here, $c = -3$ and $\theta = \tan^{-1}\left(\dfrac{3}{5}\right)$

or $$\tan\theta = \frac{3}{5} = m$$

Hence, the equation of the line

$$y = mx + c$$

i.e. $$y = \frac{3}{5}x - 3$$

or $$3x - 5y - 15 = 0$$

Example 19. Find the equation to the straight line cutting off an intercept of 5 units on negative direction of Y-axis and being equally inclined to the axes.

Sol. Here, $c = -5$

$$m = \tan 45° \quad \text{or} \quad \tan 135°$$

i.e. $$m = \pm 1$$

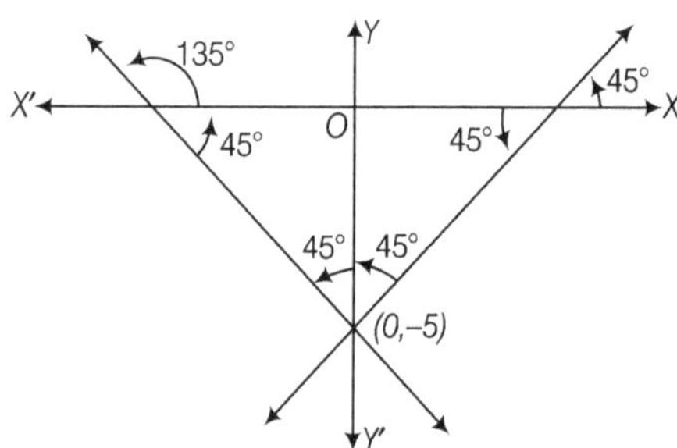

Hence, required equation is

$$y = (\pm 1)\,x - 5$$

or $$y = \pm\,x - 5$$

Example 20. Find the equations of the bisectors of the angle between the coordinate axes.

Sol. Let L_1 and L_2 be the straight lines bisecting the co-ordinate axes.

Both L_1 and L_2 pass through origin

$\therefore$ Equation of line through origin is $y = mx$

for L_1, $m = \tan 45° = 1$

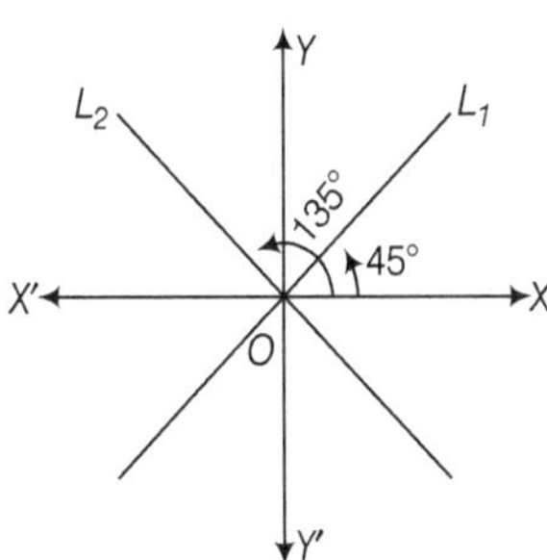

$\therefore$ Equation of line L_1 is $y = x$

i.e. $\quad x - y = 0$

For L_2, $m = \tan 135° = -1$

$\therefore$ Equation of line L_2 is $y = -x$

i.e. $\quad x + y = 0$

Hence, equations of the bisectors of the angle between the coordinate axes are $x \pm y = 0$.

(ii) The Point-Slope Form of a Line

Theorem : The equation of the straight line which passes through the point (x_1, y_1) and has the slope 'm' is

$$y - y_1 = m(x - x_1)$$

Proof : Let AB be a straight line whose slope is m and which pass through the point $Q(x_1, y_1)$. Let the line AB cuts X-axis at R and $\angle BRX = \theta$, then

$$\tan\theta = m$$

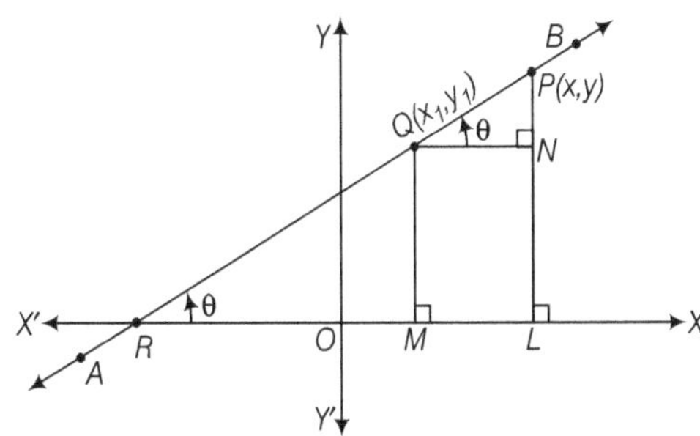

Let $P(x, y)$ be any point on the line AB. Draws PL and QM perpendiculars from P and Q on X-axis respectively. Also draw QN perpendicular from Q on PL, then from figure

$$\angle PRL = \angle PQN = \theta, OL = x, OM = x_1, PL = y, QM = y_1$$

Then, $QN = ML = OL - OM = x - x_1$

and $\quad PN = PL - NL = PL - QM = y - y_1$

Now, in triangle PQN,

$$\tan\theta = \frac{PN}{QN} = \frac{y - y_1}{x - x_1}$$

$$\therefore \quad m = \frac{y - y_1}{x - x_1}$$

or $\quad y - y_1 = m(x - x_1)$

which is the required equation of the line.

Aliter : Let the equation of the required line be

$$y = mx + c \quad \text{...(i)}$$

where, m is the slope of the line.

Since line Eq. (i) passes through the point (x_1, y_1), therefore

$$y_1 = mx_1 + c \quad \text{...(ii)}$$

Subtracting (ii) form (i), we get

$$\mathbf{y - y_1 = m(x - x_1)}$$

which is the required equation of the line.

***Corollary* :** If the line passes through the origin, then putting $x_1 = 0$ and $y_1 = 0$ in $y - y_1 = m(x - x_1)$.

It becomes $y = mx$, which is the equation of the line passing through the origin and having slope m.

Remark

The equation $y - y_1 = m(x - x_1)$ is called **point-slope** form or **one point** form of the equation.

Example 21. Find the equation of a line which makes an angle of 135° with the positive direction of X-axis and passes through the point $(3, 5)$.

Sol. The slope of the line $= m = \tan 135° = -1$

Here $x_1 = 3, y_1 = 5$.

$\therefore$ The required equation of the line is

$$y - 5 = -1(x - 3)$$

or $\quad x + y - 8 = 0$

Example 22. Find the equation of the straight line bisecting the segment joining the points $(5, 3)$ and $(4, 4)$ and making an angle of 45° with the positive direction of X-axis.

Sol. Here, m = slope of the line $= \tan 45° = 1$.

Let A be the mid-point of $(5, 3)$ and $(4, 4)$. Then, the coordinates of A are

$$\left(\frac{5+4}{2}, \frac{3+4}{2}\right) \text{ i.e. } \left(\frac{9}{2}, \frac{7}{2}\right).$$

Hence, the required equation of the line is

$$y - \frac{7}{2} = 1\left(x - \frac{9}{2}\right)$$

or $\quad x - y - 1 = 0$

Example 23. Find the equation of the right bisector of the line joining (1, 1) and (3, 5).

Sol. Let m be the slope of the line joining (1, 1) and (3, 5).

Then, $$m = \frac{5-1}{3-1} = \frac{4}{2} = 2$$

$\therefore$ Slope (M) of right bisector of the join of (1, 1)

and $$(3, 5) = -\frac{1}{m}$$

$\therefore$ $$M = -\frac{1}{2}$$

Mid-point of the join of (1, 1) and (3, 5) is $\left(\frac{1+3}{2}, \frac{1+5}{2}\right)$

i.e. (2, 3).

Hence, equation of the right bisector passing through (2, 3) and having slope $M = -\frac{1}{2}$ is

$$y - 3 = -\frac{1}{2}(x-2)$$

or $$x + 2y - 8 = 0$$

(iii) The Two-Point Form of a Line

Theorem : The equation of a line passing through two given points (x_1, y_1) and (x_2, y_2) is given by

$$y - y_1 = \left(\frac{y_2 - y_1}{x_2 - x_1}\right)(x - x_1)$$

Proof :

Let AB be a line which passes through two points $Q(x_1, y_1)$ and $R(x_2, y_2)$. Let $P(x, y)$ be any point on the line AB.

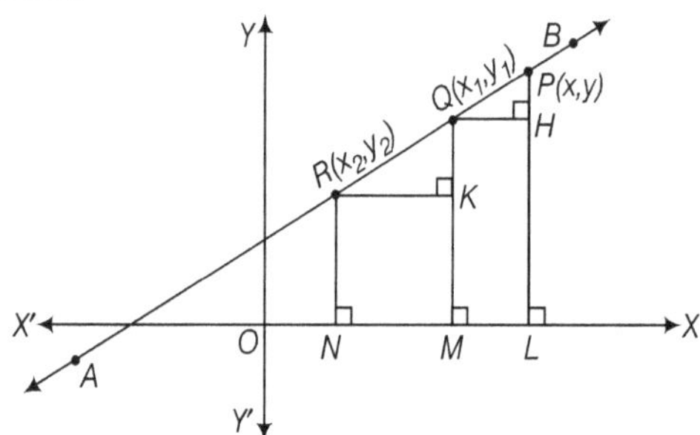

Draws PL, QM and RN are perpendiculars from P, Q and R on X-axis respectively. Also draws QH and RK are perpendiculars on PL and QM respectively. Then from figure

$$ON = x_2, OM = x_1, OL = x, RN = y_2,$$
$$QM = y_1 \text{ and } PL = y$$

then, $$RK = NM = OM - ON = x_1 - x_2$$
$$QH = ML = OL - OM = x - x_1$$
$$QK = QM - KM = QM - RN = y_1 - y_2$$
and $$PH = PL - HL = PL - QM = y - y_1$$

Now, triangles PHQ and QKR are similar, then

$$\frac{PH}{QK} = \frac{QH}{RK}$$

$\Rightarrow$ $$\frac{y - y_1}{y_1 - y_2} = \frac{x - x_1}{x_1 - x_2}$$

or $$y - y_1 = \left(\frac{y_2 - y_1}{x_2 - x_1}\right)(x - x_1)$$

which is the required equation of the line.

Aliter I : Let the equation of the required line be

$$y = mx + c \quad \text{...(i)}$$

where m is the slope of the line.

Since, line Eq. (i) passes through the points (x_1, y_1) and (x_2, y_2) therefore

$$y_1 = mx_1 + c \quad \text{...(ii)}$$

and $$y_2 = mx_2 + c \quad \text{...(iii)}$$

Now, subtracting Eqs. (ii) from (i), we get

$$y - y_1 = m(x - x_1) \quad \text{...(iv)}$$

and subtracting Eqs. (ii) from (iii), we get

$$y_2 - y_1 = m(x_2 - x_1) \quad \text{...(v)}$$

Dividing Eqs. (iv) by (v) then, we get

$$\frac{y - y_1}{y_2 - y_1} = \frac{x - x_1}{x_2 - x_1}$$

or $$y - y_1 = \left(\frac{y_2 - y_1}{x_2 - x_1}\right)(x - x_1)$$

which is the required equation of the line.

Aliter II : Since points, $P(x, y)$, $Q(x_1, y_1)$ and $R(x_2, y_2)$ are collinear then area of $\Delta PQR = 0$

i.e. $$\frac{1}{2}\left|\begin{vmatrix} x & y & 1 \\ x_1 & y_1 & 1 \\ x_2 & y_2 & 1 \end{vmatrix}\right| = 0 \text{ or } \begin{vmatrix} x & y & 1 \\ x_1 & y_1 & 1 \\ x_2 & y_2 & 1 \end{vmatrix} = 0$$

which is the required equation of the line.

Example 24. Find the equation to the straight line joining the points $\left(at_1, \frac{a}{t_1}\right)$ and $\left(at_2, \frac{a}{t_2}\right)$.

Sol. The equation of the line joining the points $\left(at_1, \frac{a}{t_1}\right)$ and $\left(at_2, \frac{a}{t_2}\right)$ is

$$y - \frac{a}{t_1} = \left(\frac{\frac{a}{t_2} - \frac{a}{t_1}}{at_2 - at_1}\right)(x - at_1)$$

$$\Rightarrow \quad y - \frac{a}{t_1} = -\frac{a(t_1 - t_2)}{at_1t_2(t_1 - t_2)}(x - at_1)$$

or $$y - \frac{a}{t_1} = -\frac{1}{t_1t_2}(x - at_1)$$

or $$t_1t_2y - at_2 = -x + at_1$$

or $$x + t_1t_2y = a(t_1 + t_2)$$

which is the required equation of the line.

Example 25. Let ABC be a triangle with $A(-1, -5)$, $B(0, 0)$ and $C(2, 2)$ and let D be the middle point of BC. Find the equation of the perpendicular drawn from B to AD.

Sol. $\because D$ is the middle point of BC.

$\therefore$ Coordinates of D are $\left(\frac{0+2}{2}, \frac{0+2}{2}\right)$

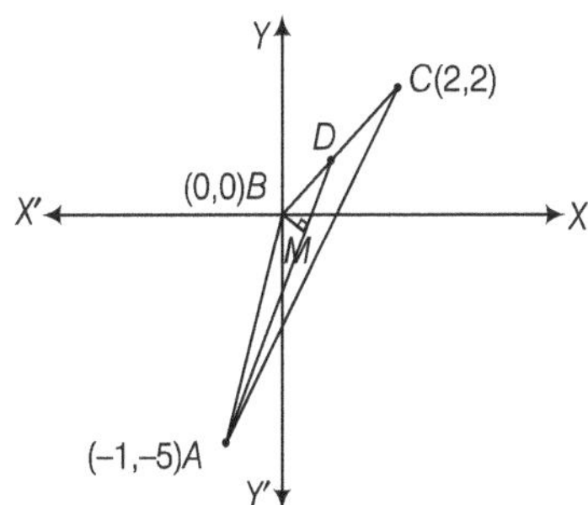

i.e. $D(1, 1)$

Slope of median $AD = \frac{1+5}{1+1} = 3$

$\therefore$ Slope of BM which is perpendicular to $AD = -\frac{1}{3}$.

Hence, equation of the line BM is

$$y - 0 = -\frac{1}{3}(x - 0) \Rightarrow x + 3y = 0$$

which is the required equation of the line.

Example 26. The vertices of a triangle are $A(10, 4), B(-4, 9)$ and $C(-2, -1)$. Find the equation of the altitude through A.

Sol. $\because$ Slope of $BC = \frac{-1-9}{-2+4} = \frac{-10}{2} = -5$

$\therefore$ Slope of altitude $AD = -\frac{1}{-5} = \frac{1}{5}$

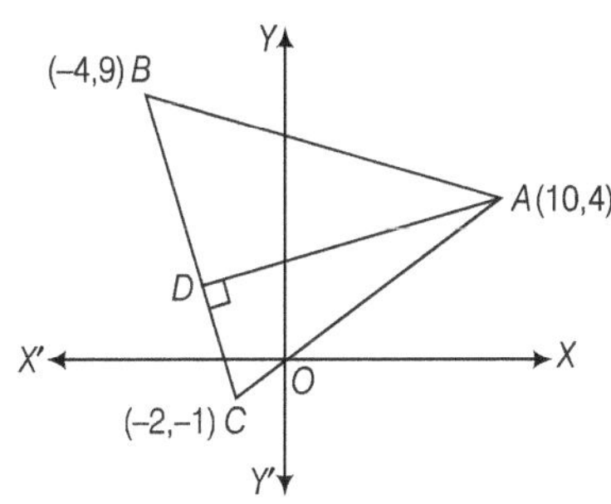

Hence, equation of altitude AD which passes through $(0, 4)$ and having slope $\frac{1}{5}$ is

$$y - 4 = \frac{1}{5}(x - 10)$$

or $$x - 5y + 10 = 0$$

Example 27. Find the equations of the medians of a triangle, the coordinates of whose vertices are $(-1, 6), (-3, -9)$ and $(5, -8)$.

Sol. Let $A(-1, 6)$, $B(-3, -9)$ and $C(5, -8)$ be the vertices of ΔABC. Let D, E and F be the mid-points of the sides BC, CA and AB respectively.

Coordinates of $D \equiv \left(\frac{-3+5}{2}, \frac{-9-8}{2}\right)$

i.e. $\left(1, -\frac{17}{2}\right)$

Coordinates of $E \equiv \left(\frac{5-1}{2}, \frac{-8+6}{2}\right)$

i.e. $(2, -1)$

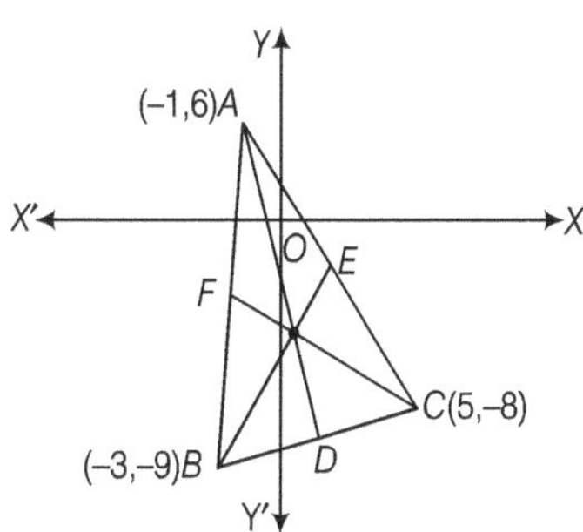

and coordinates of $F \equiv \left(\frac{-1-3}{2}, \frac{6-9}{2}\right)$

i.e. $(-2, -3/2)$

$\therefore$ Equation of the median AD = Equation of line through $(-1, 6)$ and $\left(1, -\frac{17}{2}\right)$ is

$$y - 6 = \frac{-\frac{17}{2} - 6}{1+1}(x + 1)$$

$$\Rightarrow \quad y - 6 = -\frac{29}{4}(x + 1) \quad \text{or} \quad 29x + 4y + 5 = 0$$

Equation of median BE is

$$y + 9 = \frac{-1+9}{2+3}(x + 3) \quad \text{or} \quad 8x - 5y - 21 = 0$$

and equation of median CF is

$$y + 8 = \frac{-\frac{3}{2} + 8}{-2-5}(x - 5)$$

or $$13x + 14y + 47 = 0$$

Example 28. Find the ratio in which the line segment joining the points $(2, 3)$ and $(4, 5)$ is divided by the line joining $(6, 8)$ and $(-3, -2)$.

Sol. The equation of line passing through $(6, 8)$ and $(-3, -2)$ is

$$y - 8 = \frac{-2-8}{-3-6}(x - 6)$$

$$\Rightarrow \quad 9y - 72 = 10x - 60$$

$$\text{or} \quad 10x - 9y + 12 = 0 \quad \text{...(i)}$$

Let the required ratio be $\lambda : 1$.

Now, the coordinates of the point P which divide the line segment joining the points $(2, 3)$ and $(4, 5)$ in the ratio $\lambda : 1$ is

$$P\left(\frac{2+4\lambda}{1+\lambda}, \frac{3+5\lambda}{1+\lambda}\right)$$

Clearly P lies on Eq. (i), then

$$10\left(\frac{2+4\lambda}{1+\lambda}\right) - 9\left(\frac{3+5\lambda}{1+\lambda}\right) + 12 = 0$$

$$\text{or} \quad 20 + 40\lambda - 27 - 45\lambda + 12 + 12\lambda = 0$$

$$\text{or} \quad 7\lambda + 5 = 0 \quad \text{or} \quad \lambda = -\frac{5}{7}$$

$\therefore$ The required ratio $= \lambda : 1 = -\frac{5}{7} : 1 = -5 : 7$

Hence, the required ratio is $5 : 7$ (externally).

(iv) The Intercept Form of a Line :

Theorem : The equation of the straight line which cuts off intercepts of lengths of a and b on X-axis and Y-axis respectively, is

$$\frac{x}{a} + \frac{y}{b} = 1$$

Proof : Let QR be a line which cuts off intercepts $OA = a$ and $OB = b$ on the X-axis and Y-axis respectively, where $a \neq 0$. The line is non vertical, because b is finite. Let $P(x, y)$ be a general point on the line.

Draws PL and PM perpendiculars on X-axis and Y-axis respectively. Then $PL = y$ and $OL = x$ also join OP. Clearly,

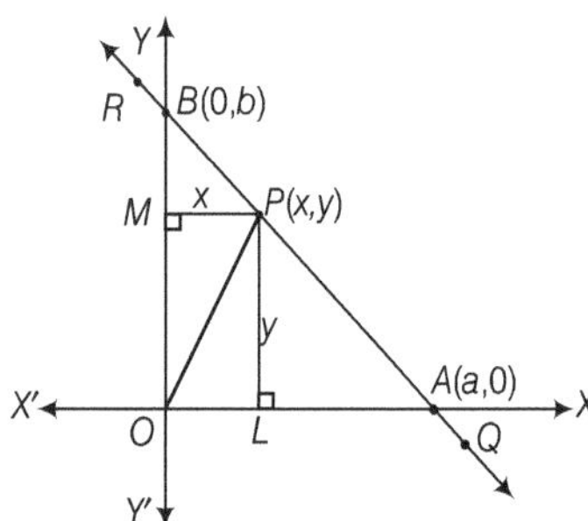

Area of ΔOAB = Area of ΔOAP + Area of ΔOPB

$$\Rightarrow \quad \frac{1}{2} \cdot OA \cdot OB = \frac{1}{2} \cdot OA \cdot PL + \frac{1}{2} \cdot OB \cdot PM$$

$$\Rightarrow \quad \frac{1}{2} \cdot OA \cdot OB = \frac{1}{2} \cdot OA \cdot PL + \frac{1}{2} \cdot OB \cdot OL$$

$$\text{or} \quad \frac{1}{2} ab = \frac{1}{2} ay + \frac{1}{2} bx$$

$$\Rightarrow \quad ab = ay + bx$$

$$\text{or} \quad \frac{x}{a} + \frac{y}{b} = 1$$

which is the required equation of the line.

Aliter I : Equation of the line through $A(a, 0)$ and $B(0, b)$ is

$$y - 0 = \frac{b-0}{0-a}(x - a)$$

$$\text{or} \quad -ay = bx - ab$$

$$\text{or} \quad bx + ay = ab$$

$$\text{or} \quad \frac{x}{a} + \frac{y}{b} = 1$$

which is the required equation of the line.

Aliter II : Points $A(a, 0)$, $P(x, y)$ and $B(0, b)$ are collinear, we have

slope of AB = slope of AP

$$\Rightarrow \quad \frac{b-0}{0-a} = \frac{y-0}{x-a} \Rightarrow bx - ab = -ay$$

$$\Rightarrow \quad bx + ay = ab \Rightarrow \frac{x}{a} + \frac{y}{b} = 1$$

or

$$\begin{vmatrix} a & 0 & 1 \\ x & y & 1 \\ 0 & b & 1 \end{vmatrix} = 0$$

$$\Rightarrow \quad a(y - b) - 0 + 1 \cdot (bx) = 0$$

$$\text{or} \quad bx + ay = ab$$

$$\text{or} \quad \frac{x}{a} + \frac{y}{b} = 1$$

which is the required equation of the line.

Example 29. Find the equation of the line through $(2, 3)$ so that the segment of the line intercepted between the axes is bisected at this point.

Sol. Let the required line segment be AB.

Let O be the origin and $OA = a$ and $OB = b$.

Then the coordinates of A and B are $(a, 0)$ and $(0, b)$ respectively.

$\therefore \quad \dfrac{a+0}{2} = 2 \Rightarrow a = 4$

and $\quad \dfrac{0+b}{2} = 3 \Rightarrow b = 6$

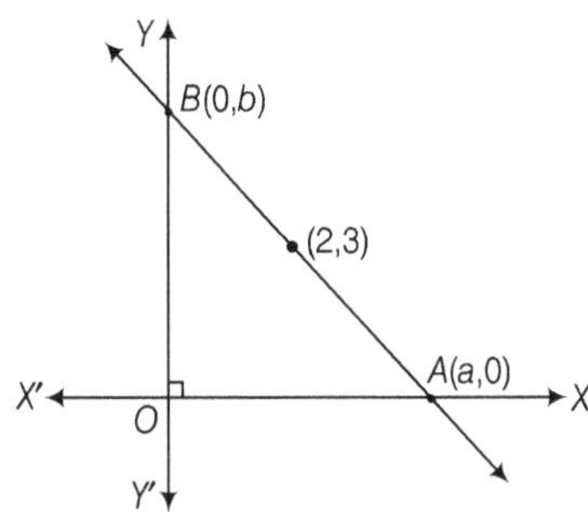

Hence, the equation of the required line is

$$\frac{x}{4} + \frac{y}{6} = 1$$

i.e. $\quad 3x + 2y = 12$

Example 30. Find the equation to the straight line which passes through the points (3, 4) and have intercepts on the axes :

(a) equal in magnitude but opposite in sign

(b) such that their sum is 14

Sol. (a) Let intercepts on the axes be a and $-a$ respectively.

$\therefore$ The equation of the line in intercept form is

$$\frac{x}{a} + \frac{y}{-a} = 1 \quad \text{or} \quad x - y = a \qquad \text{...(i)}$$

Since, Eq. (i) passes through (3, 4), then

$$3 - 4 = a$$

$\therefore \quad a = -1$

From Eq. (i), $\quad x - y + 1 = 0$

which is the required equation of the line.

(b) Let the equation of the line be $\dfrac{x}{a} + \dfrac{y}{b} = 1$

This passes through (3, 4).

Therefore $\quad \dfrac{3}{a} + \dfrac{4}{b} = 1 \qquad \text{...(ii)}$

It is given that $a + b = 14$

$\therefore \quad b = 14 - a$

Putting $b = 14 - a$ in Eq. (ii), we get

$$\frac{3}{a} + \frac{4}{14-a} = 1$$

$\Rightarrow \quad 42 - 3a + 4a = 14a - a^2$

$\Rightarrow \quad a^2 - 13a + 42 = 0$

$\Rightarrow \quad (a-7)(a-6) = 0$

$\therefore \quad a = 6, 7$

Then, $\quad b = 8, 7 \qquad (\because b = 14 - a)$

Hence, the required equations are

$$\frac{x}{6} + \frac{y}{8} = 1 \quad \text{and} \quad \frac{x}{7} + \frac{y}{7} = 1$$

i.e. $\quad 4x + 3y = 24$ and $x + y = 7$

Example 31. Find the equation of the straight line through the point $P(a, b)$ parallel to the line $\dfrac{x}{a} + \dfrac{y}{b} = 1$. Also find the intercepts made by it on the axes.

Sol. Let the line $\dfrac{x}{a} + \dfrac{y}{b} = 1$

meets the axes in A and B respectively. So that

$$OA = a, OB = b$$

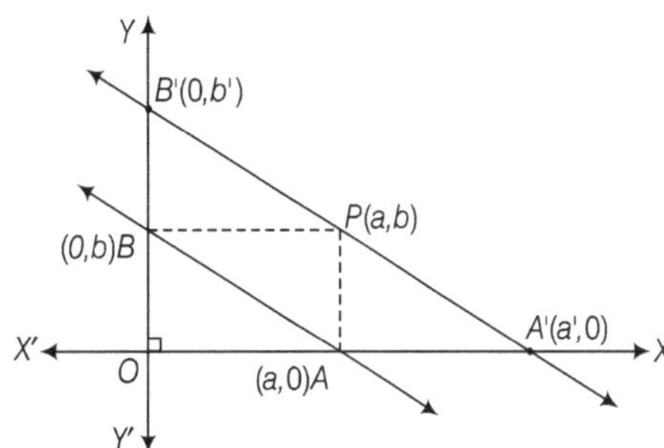

Let the required parallel line meet in A' and B' respectively, so that

$OA' = a' \qquad$ (say)

and $\quad OB' = b' \qquad$ (say)

$\therefore$ Equation of required line is

$$\frac{x}{a'} + \frac{y}{b'} = 1 \qquad \text{...(i)}$$

Since, Δ's OAB and $OA'B'$ are similar, then

$$\frac{OA'}{OA} = \frac{OB'}{OB}$$

i.e. $\quad \dfrac{a'}{a} = \dfrac{b'}{b} = \lambda \qquad$ (say)

$\Rightarrow \quad a' = a\lambda, b' = b\lambda$

Substituting these values in Eq. (i), then

$$\frac{x}{a\lambda} + \frac{y}{b\lambda} = 1 \qquad \text{...(ii)}$$

It passes through (a, b), then

$$\frac{a}{a\lambda} + \frac{b}{b\lambda} = 1$$

$\Rightarrow \quad \dfrac{2}{\lambda} = 1$ or $\lambda = 2$

From Eq. (ii) required equation is

$$\frac{x}{2a} + \frac{y}{2b} = 1$$

Evidently intercepts on the axes are $2a$ and $2b$.

(v) The Normal Form or Perpendicular Form of a Line

Theorem : The equation of the straight line upon which the length of perpendicular from the origin is p and this normal makes an angle α with the positive direction of X-axis is

$$x\cos\alpha + y\sin\alpha = p.$$

Proof : Let AB be a line such that the length of perpendicular from O to the line be p

i.e. $\quad ON = p$

and $\quad \angle NOX = \alpha$

Let $P(x, y)$ be any point on the line. Draw PL perpendicular from P on X-axis.

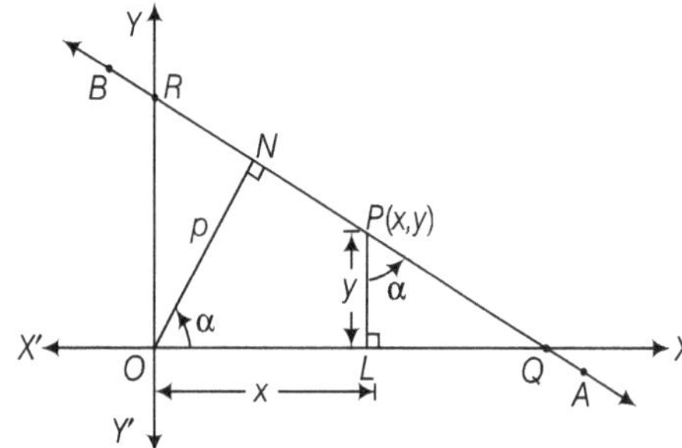

Let line AB cuts X and Y-axes at Q and R respectively.

Now, $\quad \angle NQO = 90° - \alpha$

$\therefore \quad \angle LPQ = 90° - (90° - \alpha) = \alpha$

In ΔPLQ, $\quad \tan\alpha = \dfrac{LQ}{PL} = \dfrac{LQ}{y}$

$\therefore \quad LQ = y\tan\alpha \quad$ ...(i)

Also, in ΔONQ, $\quad \cos\alpha = \dfrac{ON}{OQ}$

$\Rightarrow \quad \cos\alpha = \dfrac{p}{OL + LQ}$

$\Rightarrow \quad OL\cos\alpha + LQ\cos\alpha = p$

$\Rightarrow \quad x\cos\alpha + y\tan\alpha\cos\alpha = p$

$(\because OL = x \text{ and } LQ = y\tan\alpha)$

$\therefore \quad \boldsymbol{x\cos\alpha + y\sin\alpha = p}$

which is the required equation of the line AB.

Aliter I : $\because \angle NOQ = \alpha$

then $\quad \angle NOR = 90° - \alpha$

Now, in ΔONQ, $\quad \sec\alpha = \dfrac{OQ}{ON} = \dfrac{OQ}{p}$

or $\quad OQ = p\sec\alpha$

Also in ΔONR, $\sec(90° - \alpha) = \dfrac{OR}{ON}$

$\Rightarrow \quad \operatorname{cosec}\alpha = \dfrac{OR}{p}$

or $\quad OR = p\operatorname{cosec}\alpha$

Thus, AB makes intercepts $p\sec\alpha$ and $p\operatorname{cosec}\alpha$ on X-axis and Y-axis respectively.

$\therefore$ Equation of AB is $\dfrac{x}{p\sec\alpha} + \dfrac{y}{p\operatorname{cosec}\alpha} = 1$

or $\quad \boldsymbol{x\cos\alpha + y\sin\alpha = p}$

which is the required equation of the line AB.

Aliter II : The points $Q(p\sec\alpha, 0)$, $P(x, y)$ and $R(0, p\operatorname{cosec}\alpha)$ are collinear, then

$$\begin{vmatrix} p\sec\alpha & 0 & 1 \\ x & y & 1 \\ 0 & p\operatorname{cosec}\alpha & 1 \end{vmatrix} = 0$$

or $\quad p\sec\alpha(y - p\operatorname{cosec}\alpha) - 0 + 1(px\operatorname{cosec}\alpha) = 0$

or $\quad p(y\sin\alpha - p) + px\cos\alpha = 0$

or $\quad \boldsymbol{x\cos\alpha + y\sin\alpha = p}$

which is the required equation of the line AB.

Remarks

1. Here, p is always taken as positive and α is measured from positive direction of X-axis in anticlockwise direction between 0 and 2π (i.e. $0 \le \alpha < 2\pi$).
2. (Coefficient of $x)^2$ + (Coefficient of $y)^2 = \cos^2\alpha + \sin^2\alpha = 1$
3. $\cos\alpha$ and $\cos(90° - \alpha)$ are the direction cosines of ON.
4.

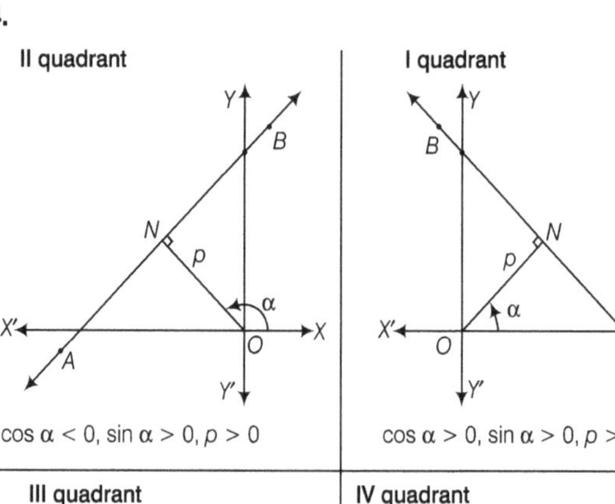

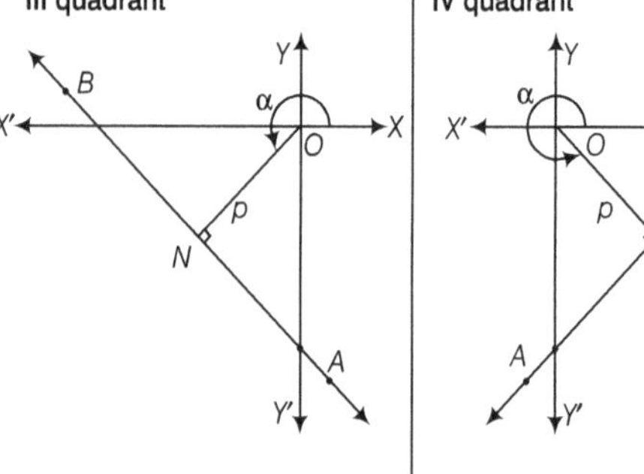

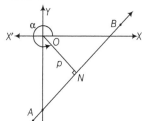

***Corollary* 1 :** If $\alpha = 0°$, then equation $x \cos\alpha + y \sin\alpha = p$ becomes $x \cos 0° + y \sin 0° = p$

i.e. $x = p$ (Equation of line parallel to Y-axis)

***Corollary* 2 :** If $\alpha = \frac{\pi}{2}$, then equation $x \cos\alpha + y \sin\alpha = p$

becomes $x \cos\left(\frac{\pi}{2}\right) + y \sin\left(\frac{\pi}{2}\right) = p$

i.e. $y = p$ (Equation of line parallel to X-axis).

***Corollary* 3 :** If $\alpha = 0°$, $p = 0$ then equation $x \cos\alpha + y \sin\alpha = p$ becomes $x \cos 0° + y \sin 0° = 0$

i.e. $x = 0$ (Equation of Y-axis)

***Corollary* 4 :** If $\alpha = \frac{\pi}{2}$, $p = 0$ then equation

$x \cos\alpha + y \sin\alpha = p$ becomes $x \cos\left(\frac{\pi}{2}\right) + y \sin\left(\frac{\pi}{2}\right) = 0$

i.e. $\quad y = 0 \quad$ (Eq. (i) of X-axis).

Example 32. The length of perpendicular from the origin to a line is 9 and the line makes an angle of 120° with the positive direction of Y-axis. Find the equation of the line.

Sol. Here, $\alpha = 60°$ and $p = 9$.

$\therefore$ Equation of the required line is

$$x \cos 60° + y \sin 60° = 9$$

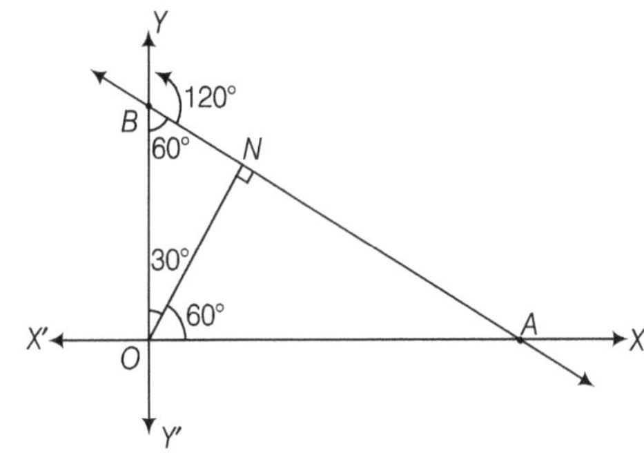

$$\Rightarrow \quad x\left(\frac{1}{2}\right) + y\left(\frac{\sqrt{3}}{2}\right) = 9$$

or $\quad x + y\sqrt{3} = 18$

Example 33. Find the equation of the straight line on which the perpendicular from origin makes an angle of 30° with X-axis and which forms a triangle of area $\left(\frac{50}{\sqrt{3}}\right)$ sq units with the coordinates axes.

Sol. Let $\angle NOA = 30°$

Let $ON = p > 0, OA = a, OB = b$

In ΔONA, $\quad \cos 30° = \frac{ON}{OA} = \frac{p}{a}$

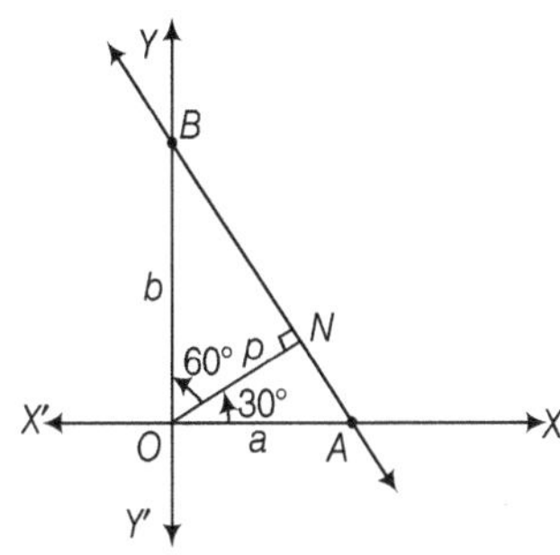

$$\Rightarrow \quad \frac{\sqrt{3}}{2} = \frac{p}{a} \text{ or } a = \frac{2p}{\sqrt{3}}$$

and in ΔONB, $\cos 60° = \frac{ON}{OB} = \frac{p}{b}$

$$\Rightarrow \quad \frac{1}{2} = \frac{p}{b} \text{ or } b = 2p$$

$$\because \quad \text{Area of } \Delta OAB = \frac{1}{2}ab = \frac{1}{2}\left(\frac{2p}{\sqrt{3}}\right)$$

$$(2p) = \frac{2p^2}{\sqrt{3}}$$

$$\therefore \quad \frac{2p^2}{\sqrt{3}} = \frac{50}{\sqrt{3}} \quad \text{(given)}$$

$$\Rightarrow \quad p^2 = 25$$

$$\text{or} \quad p = 5 \quad (\because p > 0)$$

$\therefore$ Using $x \cos\alpha + y \sin\alpha = p$, the equation of the line AB is

$$x \cos 30° + y \sin 30° = 5$$

or $\quad x\sqrt{3} + y = 10$

Reduction of General Equation to Standard Form

Let $Ax + By + C = 0$ be the general equation of a straight line where A and B are not both zero.

(i) Reduction of 'Slope-Intercept' Form

Given equation is $Ax + By + C = 0$

$$\Rightarrow \quad By = -Ax - C$$

$$\Rightarrow \quad y = \left(-\frac{A}{B}\right)x + \left(-\frac{C}{B}\right) \quad \text{(Assuming } B \neq 0\text{)}$$

Comparing it with $y = mx + c$

we get $\quad \text{slope } (m) = -\frac{A}{B} = -\frac{\text{coefficient of } x}{\text{coefficient of } y}$

and $\quad y \text{ intercept } (c) = -\frac{C}{B} = -\frac{\text{constant term}}{\text{coefficient of } y}$

***Corollary* 1 :** Find angle between the lines $A_1x + B_1y + C_1 = 0$ and $A_2x + B_2y + C_2 = 0$.

Slope of the line

$$A_1x + B_1y + C_1 = 0 \text{ is } -\frac{A_1}{B_1} = m_1 \quad \text{(say)}$$

and slope of the line

$$A_2x + B_2y + C_2 = 0 \text{ is } -\frac{A_2}{B_2} = m_2 \quad \text{(say)}$$

If θ is the angle between the two lines, then

$$\tan\theta = \left|\frac{m_1 - m_2}{1 + m_1m_2}\right| = \left|\frac{\left(-\frac{A_1}{B_1}\right) - \left(-\frac{A_2}{B_2}\right)}{1 + \left(-\frac{A_1}{B_1}\right)\left(-\frac{A_2}{B_2}\right)}\right|$$

$$= \left|\frac{A_1B_2 - A_2B_1}{A_1A_2 + B_1B_2}\right|$$

$$\therefore \quad \theta = \tan^{-1}\left|\frac{A_1B_2 - A_2B_1}{A_1A_2 + B_1B_2}\right|$$

***Corollary* 2 :** Find the condition of (i) parallelism (ii) perpendicularity of the lines

$$A_1x + B_1y + C_1 = 0$$

$$\text{and} \quad A_2x + B_2y + C_2 = 0$$

(i) If the two lines are parallel, $\theta = 0°$

$$\therefore \quad \tan\theta = \tan 0° = 0$$

$$\Rightarrow \quad \left|\frac{A_1B_2 - A_2B_1}{A_1A_2 + B_1B_2}\right| = 0$$

$$\Rightarrow \quad A_1B_2 - A_2B_1 = 0$$

$$\text{or} \quad \frac{A_1}{A_2} = \frac{B_1}{B_2} \quad \textbf{(Remember)}$$

which is required condition of parallelism.

(ii) If the two lines are perpendicular, $\theta = 90°$

$$\therefore \quad \tan\theta = \tan 90° = \infty$$

$$\Rightarrow \quad \left|\frac{A_1B_2 - A_2B_1}{A_1A_2 + B_1B_2}\right| = \infty$$

$$\Rightarrow \quad A_1A_2 + B_1B_2 = 0 \quad \textbf{(Remember)}$$

which is required condition of perpendicularity.

Remark

If two lines are coincident, then

$$\frac{A_1}{A_2} = \frac{B_1}{B_2} = \frac{C_1}{C_2} \quad \textbf{(Remember)}$$

(ii) Reduction to 'Intercept' Form

Given equation is $Ax + By + C = 0$

$$\Rightarrow \quad Ax + By = -C$$

$$\Rightarrow \quad \frac{A}{-C}x + \frac{B}{-C}y = 1 \quad \text{(Assuming } C \neq 0)$$

$$\Rightarrow \quad \frac{x}{(-C/A)} + \frac{y}{(-C/B)} = 1 \quad \text{(Assuming } A \neq 0, B \neq 0)$$

Comparing with $\frac{x}{a} + \frac{y}{b} = 1$

we get, x-intercept $(a) = -\frac{C}{A} = -\frac{\text{constant term}}{\text{coefficient of } x}$

and y-intercept $(b) = -\frac{C}{B} = -\frac{\text{constant term}}{\text{coefficient of } y}$

(iii) Reduction to 'Normal' Form

Given equation is $Ax + By + C = 0$. Let its **normal form** be $x\cos\alpha + y\sin\alpha = p$.

Clearly, equations $Ax + By + C = 0$ and $x\cos\alpha + y\sin\alpha = p$ represent the same line.

$$\text{Therefore,} \quad \frac{A}{\cos\alpha} = \frac{B}{\sin\alpha} = \frac{C}{-p}$$

$$\Rightarrow \quad \cos\alpha = -\frac{Ap}{C}$$

$$\text{and} \quad \sin\alpha = -\frac{Bp}{C} \quad \text{...(i)}$$

$$\cos^2\alpha + \sin^2\alpha = 1$$

$$\left(-\frac{Ap}{C}\right)^2 + \left(-\frac{Bp}{C}\right)^2 = 1$$

$$\text{or} \quad p^2 = \frac{C^2}{A^2 + B^2}$$

$$\Rightarrow \quad p = \frac{|C|}{\sqrt{(A^2 + B^2)}}$$

From Eq. (i), $\cos\alpha = -\frac{|C|}{C} \cdot \frac{A}{\sqrt{(A^2 + B^2)}}$,

$$\sin\alpha = -\frac{|C|}{C} \cdot \frac{B}{\sqrt{(A^2 + B^2)}}.$$

Putting the values of $\cos\alpha, \sin\alpha$ and p in $x\cos\alpha + y\sin\alpha = p$, we get

$$x\left(\frac{-|C|}{C}\cdot\frac{A}{\sqrt{(A^2+B^2)}}\right)x+y\left(\frac{-|C|}{C}\cdot\frac{B}{\sqrt{(A^2+B^2)}}\right)$$

$$=\frac{|C|}{\sqrt{(A^2+B^2)}}$$

$$\Rightarrow \left(-\frac{A}{\sqrt{(A^2+B^2)}}\right)x+\left(-\frac{B}{\sqrt{(A^2+B^2)}}\right)y=\frac{C}{\sqrt{(A^2+B^2)}}$$

This is the normal form of the line $Ax+By+C=0$.

Rule : First shift the constant term on the RHS and make it positive, if it is not so by multiplying the whole equation by '-1' and then divide both sides by

$$\sqrt{(\text{coefficient of } x)^2+(\text{coefficient of } y)^2}$$

Example 34. Reduce $x+\sqrt{3}y+4=0$ to the :

(i) Slope-intercept form and find its slope and y-intercept

(ii) Intercept form and find its intercepts on the axes

(iii) Normal form and find the values of p and α

Sol. (i) Given equation is $x+\sqrt{3}\,y+4=0$

$$\Rightarrow \quad \sqrt{3}y=-x-4$$

$$\Rightarrow \quad y=\left(-\frac{1}{\sqrt{3}}\right)x+\left(-\frac{4}{\sqrt{3}}\right)$$

which is in the slope-intercept form $y=mx+c$

Where slope $(m)=-\dfrac{1}{\sqrt{3}}$ and y-intercept $(c)=-\dfrac{4}{\sqrt{3}}$

(ii) Given equation is

$$x+\sqrt{3}y+4=0$$

$$\Rightarrow \quad x+\sqrt{3}y=-4$$

$$\Rightarrow \quad \frac{x}{-4}+\frac{\sqrt{3}y}{-4}=1$$

$$\Rightarrow \quad \frac{x}{-4}+\frac{y}{-4/\sqrt{3}}=1$$

which is in the intercept form $\dfrac{x}{a}+\dfrac{y}{b}=1$

where x-intercept $(a)=-4$ and y-intercept $(b)=-\dfrac{4}{\sqrt{3}}$

(iii) Given equation is $x+\sqrt{3}y+4=0$

$$\Rightarrow \quad x+\sqrt{3}y=-4$$

$$\Rightarrow \quad -x-\sqrt{3}y=4 \qquad \text{(RHS made positive)}$$

Dividing both sides by $\sqrt{(-1)^2+(-\sqrt{3})^2}=2$, we get

$$\left(-\frac{1}{2}\right)x+\left(-\frac{\sqrt{3}}{2}\right)y=2$$

Which is the normal form $x\cos\alpha+y\sin\alpha=p$.

where, $\cos\alpha=-\dfrac{1}{2}=-\cos 60°=\cos(180°-60°)$

or $\cos(180°+60°)$

$\therefore$ $\alpha=120°$ or $240°$

and $\sin\alpha=-\dfrac{\sqrt{3}}{2}=-\sin 60°=\sin(180°+60°)$

or $\sin(360°-60°)$

$\therefore$ $\alpha=240°$ or $300°$

Hence, $\alpha=240°,\ p=2$

$\therefore$ Required normal form is

$$x\cos 240°+y\sin 240°=2$$

Example 35. Find the measure of the angle of intersection of the lines whose equations are $3x+4y+7=0$ and $4x-3y+5=0$.

Sol. Given lines are $3x+4y+7=0$, $4x-3y+5=0$. Comparing the given lines with $A_1x+B_1y+C_1=0$, $A_2x+B_2y+C_2=0$ respectively, we get

$$A_1=3, B_1=4 \quad \text{and} \quad A_2=4, B_2=-3$$

$$\because \quad A_1A_2+B_1B_2=3\times 4+4(-3)=0$$

Hence, the given lines are perpendicular.

Example 36. Find the angle between the lines

$$(a^2-ab)\,y=(ab+b^2)\,x+b^3$$

and $\quad (ab+a^2)\,y=(ab-b^2)\,x+a^3$

where $a>b>0$.

Sol. The given equations of lines can be written as

$$(ab+b^2)\,x-(a^2-ab)\,y+b^3=0 \qquad \text{...(i)}$$

and $\quad (ab-b^2)\,x-(ab+a^2)\,y+a^3=0 \qquad$ ...(ii)

Comparing the given lines (i) and (ii) with the lines

$$A_1x+B_1y+C_1=0 \quad \text{and} \quad A_2x+B_2y+C_2=0$$

respectively, we get

$$A_1=ab+b^2,\ B_1=-(a^2-ab)$$

and $\quad A_2=ab-b^2,\ B_2=-(ab+a^2)$

Let θ be the acute angle between the lines, then

$$\tan\theta=\left|\frac{A_1B_2-A_2B_1}{A_1A_2+B_1B_2}\right|$$

$$\tan\theta=\left|\frac{(ab+b^2)\times(-(ab+a^2))-(ab-b^2)\times(-(a^2-ab))}{(ab+b^2)(ab-b^2)+(a^2-ab)(ab+a^2)}\right|$$

$$=\left|\frac{-\{a^2b^2+a^3b+ab^3+a^2b^2-a^3b+a^2b^2+a^2b^2-b^3a\}}{(a^2b^2-b^4+a^4-a^2b^2)}\right|$$

$$=\left|\frac{-4a^2b^2}{a^4-b^4}\right|=\frac{4a^2b^2}{a^4-b^4}$$

$$\therefore\ \theta=\tan^{-1}\left(\frac{4a^2b^2}{a^4-b^4}\right)$$

Example 37. Two equal sides of an isosceles triangle are given by the equations $7x - y + 3 = 0$ and $x + y - 3 = 0$ and its third side passes through the point $(1, -10)$. Determine the equation of the third side.

Sol. Given equations

$$7x - y + 3 = 0 \quad \text{...(i)}$$

and $$x + y - 3 = 0 \quad \text{...(ii)}$$

represents two equal sides AB and AC of an isosceles triangle ABC. Since its third side passes through $D(1, -10)$ then its equation is

$$y + 10 = m(x - 1) \quad \text{...(iii)}$$

$\because$ $AB = AC$

Let $\angle ABC = \angle ACB = \theta$

then $\angle ACE = \pi - \theta$

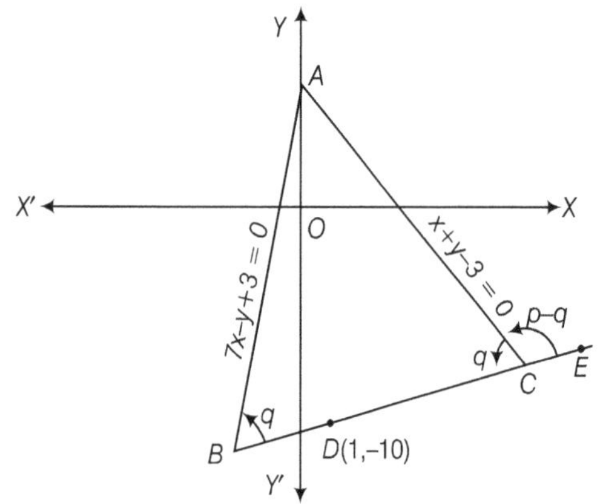

From Eqs. (i) and (ii), slopes of AB and AC are

$$m_1 = 7 \quad \text{and} \quad m_2 = -1$$

respectively.

$\therefore$ $$\tan\theta = \frac{7 - m}{1 + 7m}$$

and $$\tan(\pi - \theta) = \frac{-1 - m}{1 + (-1)m} = -\left(\frac{1 + m}{1 - m}\right)$$

$\Rightarrow$ $$-\tan\theta = -\left(\frac{1 + m}{1 - m}\right) \Rightarrow \tan\theta = \left(\frac{1 + m}{1 - m}\right)$$

$\therefore$ $$\frac{7 - m}{1 + 7m} = \frac{1 + m}{1 - m}$$

$\Rightarrow$ $(7 - m)(1 - m) = (1 + 7m)(1 + m)$

$\Rightarrow$ $6m^2 + 16m - 6 = 0$

or $3m^2 + 8m - 3 = 0$ or $(3m - 1)(m + 3) = 0$

$\Rightarrow$ $$m = \frac{1}{3}, -3$$

Hence from Eq. (iii), the third side BC has two equations

$$y + 10 = \frac{1}{3}(x - 1) \text{ and } y + 10 = -3(x - 1)$$

or $x - 3y - 31 = 0$ and $3x + y + 7 = 0$

The Distance form or Symmetric form or Parametric form of a line

Theorem : The equation of the straight line passing through (x_1, y_1) and making an angle θ with the positive direction of X-axis is

$$\frac{x - x_1}{\cos\theta} = \frac{y - y_1}{\sin\theta} = r$$

where, r is the directed distance between the points (x, y) and (x_1, y_1).

Proof : Let AB be a line which passes through the point $Q(x_1, y_1)$ and meet X-axis at R and makes an angle θ with the positive direction of X-axis.

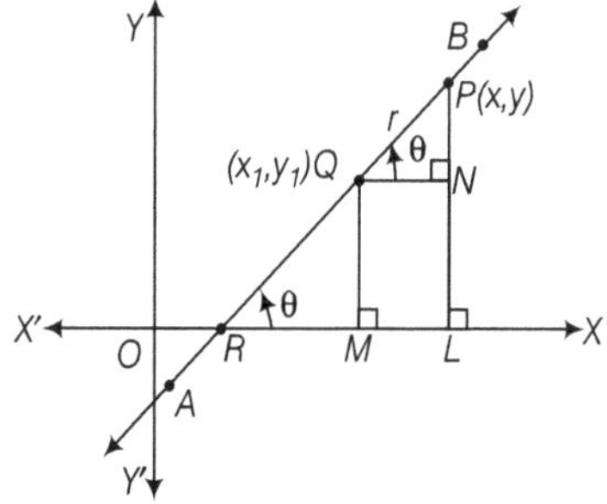

Let $P(x, y)$ be any point on the line at a distance r from Q. Draws PL and QM are perpendiculars from P and Q on X-axis respectively and draw QN perpendicular on PL. Then,

$$QN = ML = OL - OM = x - x_1$$

and $$PN = PL - NL = PL - QM = y - y_1$$

from ΔPQN,

$$\cos\theta = \frac{QN}{PQ} = \frac{x - x_1}{r} \quad \text{or} \quad \frac{x - x_1}{\cos\theta} = r \quad \text{...(i)}$$

and $$\sin\theta = \frac{PN}{PQ} = \frac{y - y_1}{r} \quad \text{or} \quad \frac{y - y_1}{\sin\theta} = r \quad \text{...(ii)}$$

From Eqs. (i) and (ii), we get

$$\frac{x - x_1}{\cos\theta} = \frac{y - y_1}{\sin\theta} = r$$

***Corollary* 1 :** $\because \dfrac{x - x_1}{\cos\theta} = \dfrac{y - y_1}{\sin\theta} = r$, then

$$\left.\begin{aligned} x &= x_1 + r\cos\theta \\ y &= y_1 + r\sin\theta \end{aligned}\right\}$$

parametric equations of straight line AB.

***Corollary* 2 :** If P point above Q then r is positive then coordinates of P are $(x_1 + r\cos\theta, y_1 + r\sin\theta)$ and if P below Q then r is negative then coordinates of P are $(x_1 - r\cos\theta, y_1 - r\sin\theta)$.

Example 38. The slope of a straight line through $A(3,2)$ is $\frac{3}{4}$. Find the coordinates of the points on the line that are 5 units away from A.

Sol. Let straight line makes an angle θ with positive direction of X-axis,

then $\tan\theta = \frac{3}{4}$

$\therefore \quad \sin\theta = \frac{3}{5}$ and $\cos\theta = \frac{4}{5}$

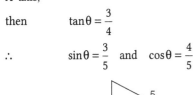

$\therefore$ Equation of the straight line through $A(3, 2)$ in parametric form is

$$\frac{x-3}{\cos\theta} = \frac{y-2}{\sin\theta} = \pm 5$$

$\therefore \quad x = 3 \pm 5\cos\theta = 3 \pm 5 \times \frac{4}{5} = 3 \pm 4 = 7$ or -1

and $\quad y = 2 \pm 5\sin\theta = 2 \pm 5 \times \frac{3}{5} = 2 \pm 3 = 5$ or -1

Hence, the coordinates of the points are $(7, 5)$ and $(-1, -1)$.

Example 39. Find the direction in which a straight line must be drawn through the point $(1, 2)$ so that its point of intersection with the line $x + y = 4$ may be at a distance $\frac{1}{3}\sqrt{6}$ from this point.

Sol. Let the straight line makes an angle θ with the positive direction of X-axis.

$\therefore$ Equation of the line through $(1, 2)$ in parametric form is

$$\frac{x-1}{\cos\theta} = \frac{y-2}{\sin\theta} = \frac{1}{3}\sqrt{6}$$

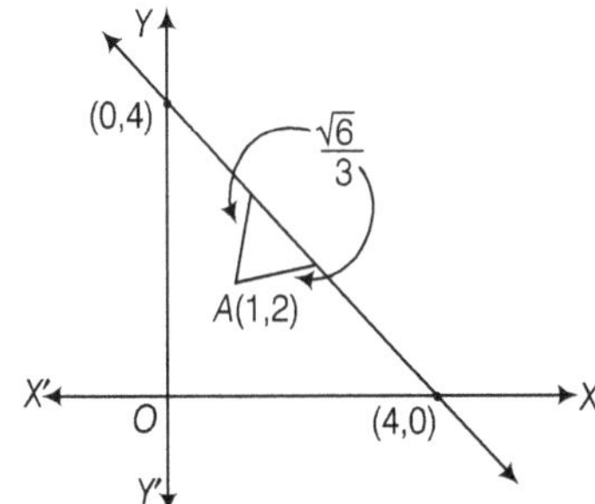

or $\quad x = 1 + \frac{\sqrt{6}}{3}\cos\theta$ and $y = 2 + \frac{\sqrt{6}}{3}\sin\theta$

Since, the point $\left(1 + \frac{\sqrt{6}}{3}\cos\theta, 2 + \frac{\sqrt{6}}{3}\sin\theta\right)$ lies on the line

$$x + y = 4$$

$$\therefore \quad 1 + \frac{\sqrt{6}}{3}\cos\theta + 2 + \frac{\sqrt{6}}{3}\sin\theta = 4$$

$$\Rightarrow \quad \frac{\sqrt{6}}{3}(\cos\theta + \sin\theta) = 1$$

$$\Rightarrow \quad \cos\theta + \sin\theta = \frac{3}{\sqrt{6}} = \frac{\sqrt{3}}{\sqrt{2}}$$

$$\Rightarrow \quad \frac{1}{\sqrt{2}}\cos\theta + \frac{1}{\sqrt{2}}\sin\theta = \frac{\sqrt{3}}{2}$$

$$\Rightarrow \quad \cos\left(\theta - \frac{\pi}{4}\right) = \cos\left(\frac{\pi}{6}\right)$$

$$\theta - \frac{\pi}{4} = 2n\pi \pm \frac{\pi}{6}; n \in I$$

for $n = 0$, $\quad \theta = \pm\frac{\pi}{6} + \frac{\pi}{4} \qquad (\because 0 \le \theta < \pi)$

$$= 15°, 75°$$

Example 40. A line through $(2, 3)$ makes an angle $\frac{3\pi}{4}$ with the negative direction of X-axis. Find the length of the line segment cut off between $(2, 3)$ and the line $x + y - 7 = 0$.

Sol. $\because$ Line makes an angle $\frac{3\pi}{4}$ with the negative direction of X-axis.

$\therefore$ Line makes an angle $\frac{\pi}{4}$ with the positive direction of X-axis.

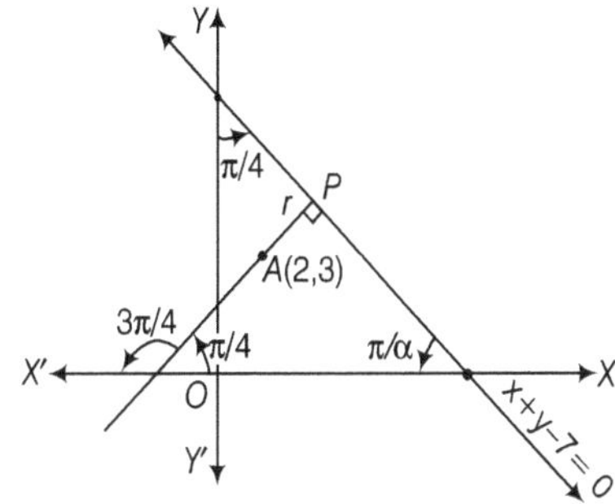

$\therefore$ The equation of the line through $(1, 2)$ in parametric form is

$$\frac{x-2}{\cos\left(\frac{\pi}{4}\right)} = \frac{y-3}{\sin\left(\frac{\pi}{4}\right)} = r$$

i.e. $$\frac{x-2}{\frac{1}{\sqrt{2}}} = \frac{y-3}{\frac{1}{\sqrt{2}}} = r \qquad \text{...(i)}$$

$\therefore \quad x = 2 + \frac{r}{\sqrt{2}}$ and $y = 3 + \frac{r}{\sqrt{2}}$

Let the line (i) meet the line $x + y - 7 = 0$ in P

$\therefore$ Coordinates of $P\left(2 + \frac{r}{\sqrt{2}}, 3 + \frac{r}{\sqrt{2}}\right)$ lies on $x + y - 7 = 0$

then $\quad 2 + \frac{r}{\sqrt{2}} + 3 + \frac{r}{\sqrt{2}} - 7 = 0$

or $\quad \frac{2r}{\sqrt{2}} = 2$ or $r = \sqrt{2}$

$\therefore \quad AP = \sqrt{2}$

Example 41. Find the distance of the point $(2, 3)$ from the line $2x - 3y + 9 = 0$ measured along the line $2x - 2y + 5 = 0$.

Sol. Since, slope of the line $2x - 2y + 5 = 0$ is 1, its makes an angle $\frac{\pi}{4}$ with positive direction of X-axis.

The equation of the line through $(2, 3)$ and making an angle $\frac{\pi}{4}$ in parametric form

$$\frac{x-2}{\cos\left(\frac{\pi}{4}\right)} = \frac{y-3}{\sin\left(\frac{\pi}{4}\right)} = r \text{ or } \frac{x-2}{\frac{1}{\sqrt{2}}} = \frac{y-3}{\frac{1}{\sqrt{2}}} = r$$

Coordinates of any point on this line are $\left(2 + \frac{r}{\sqrt{2}}, 3 + \frac{r}{\sqrt{2}}\right)$.

This point lies on the line $2x - 3y + 9 = 0$

$$\Rightarrow \quad 2\left(2 + \frac{r}{\sqrt{2}}\right) - 3\left(3 + \frac{r}{\sqrt{2}}\right) + 9 = 0$$

$$\Rightarrow \quad -\frac{r}{\sqrt{2}} + 4 = 0$$

$$\therefore \quad r = 4\sqrt{2}$$

Example 42. If the line $y - \sqrt{3}x + 3 = 0$ cuts the parabola $y^2 = x + 2$ at A and B, then find the value of $PA.\ PB$ {where $P \equiv (\sqrt{3}, 0)$}.

Sol. Slope of line $y - \sqrt{3}x + 3 = 0$ is $\sqrt{3}$

If line makes an angle θ with X-axis, then $\tan\theta = \sqrt{3}$

$$\therefore \quad \theta = 60^\circ$$

$$\frac{x - \sqrt{3}}{\cos 60^\circ} = \frac{y - 0}{\sin 60^\circ} = r$$

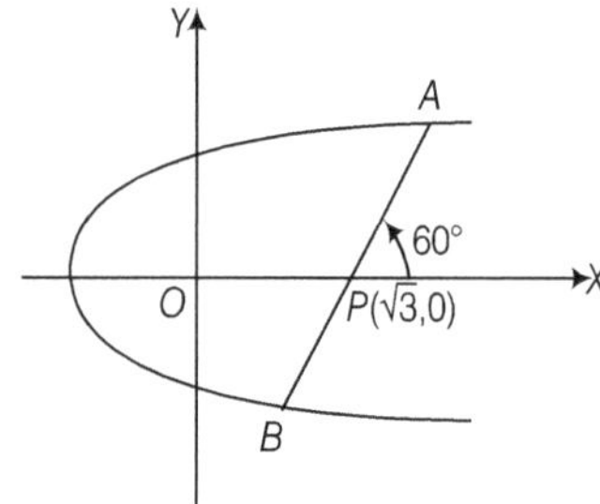

$\Rightarrow \left(\sqrt{3} + \frac{r}{2}, \frac{r\sqrt{3}}{2}\right)$ be a point on the parabola $y^2 = x + 2$

then, $\frac{3}{4}r^2 = \sqrt{3} + \frac{r}{2} + 2 \Rightarrow 3r^2 - 2r - 4(2 + \sqrt{3}) = 0$

$$\therefore \quad PA \cdot PB = r_1 r_2 = \left|\frac{-4(2+\sqrt{3})}{3}\right| = \frac{4(2+\sqrt{3})}{3}$$

Special Corollaries

(i) **Angle made by AB with positive X-axis (where A and B are given points)** :be two points and let AB makes an angle θ with the positive direction of X-axis and let d be the distance between A and B. Then Let $A(x_1, y_1)$ and $B(x_2, y_2)$

$$\cos\theta = \frac{x_2 - x_1}{d}, \sin\theta = \frac{y_2 - y_1}{d}$$

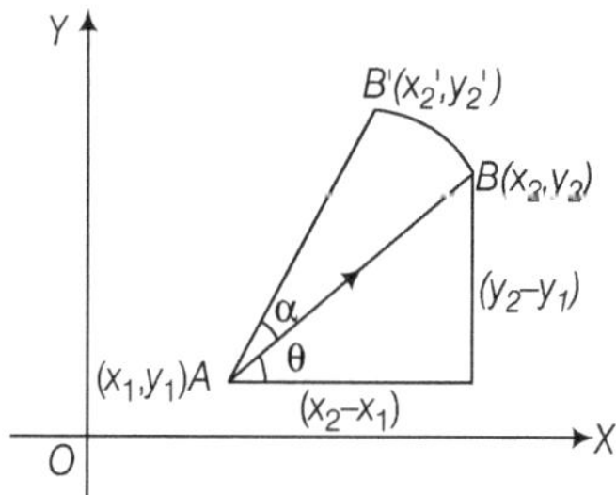

where, $d = \sqrt{(x_2 - x_1)^2 + (y_2 - y_1)^2} = AB$

and $x_2 = x_1 + d\cos\theta, y_2 = y_1 + d\sin\theta$

If AB rotates an angle α about A, then new coordinates of B are

$$x_2' = x_1 + d\cos(\theta + \alpha),$$
$$y_2' = y_1 + d\sin(\theta + \alpha)$$

and here, $AB = AB' = d$.

(ii) **Complex number as a rotating arrow in Argand plane** :

Let $z = r(\cos\theta + i\sin\theta) = re^{i\theta}$, where $i = \sqrt{-1}$ ... (i)

be a complex number representing a point P in the Argand plane.

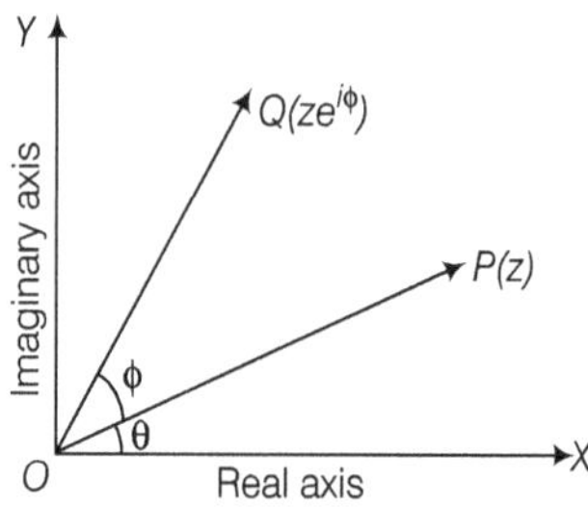

Then, $OP = |z| = r$ and $\angle POX = \theta$

Now, consider complex number $z_1 = ze^{i\phi}$

or $z_1 = re^{i\theta} \cdot e^{i\phi} = r \cdot e^{i(\theta + \phi)}$ [from Eq. (i)]

Clearly the complex number z_1 represents a point Q in the Argand plane, when

$$OQ = r \quad \text{and} \quad \angle QOX = \theta + \phi$$

Clearly multiplication of z with $e^{i\phi}$ rotates the vector $\vec{OP}$ through angle ϕ in anti-clockwise sense. Similarly multiplication of z with $e^{-i\phi}$ will rotate the vector $\vec{OP}$ in clockwise sense.

Remark

If z_1, z_2 and z_3 are the affixes of the three points A, B and C such that $AC = AB$ and $\angle CAB = \theta$. Therefore

$$\vec{AB} = z_2 - z_1, \vec{AC} = z_3 - z_1$$

Then $\vec{AC}$ will be obtained by rotating $\vec{AB}$ through an angle θ in anticlockwise sense and therefore

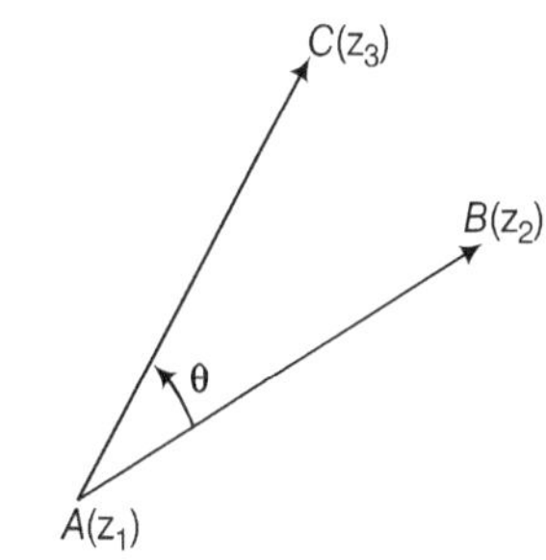

$$\vec{AC} = \vec{AB}e^{i\theta}$$

or $\quad (z_3 - z_1) = (z_2 - z_1)\,e^{i\theta}$ or $\left(\dfrac{z_3 - z_1}{z_2 - z_1}\right) = e^{i\theta}$

Example 43. The line joining the points $A(2, 0)$ and $B(3, 1)$ is rotated about A in the anticlockwise direction through an angle of 15°. Find the equation of the line in the new position. If B goes to C in the new position, what will be the coordinates of C?

Sol. By special corollary (i)

Here $\quad AB = \sqrt{(2-3)^2 + (0-1)^2} = \sqrt{2}$

and $\quad$ slope of $AB = \dfrac{1-0}{3-2} = 1 = \tan 45^\circ$

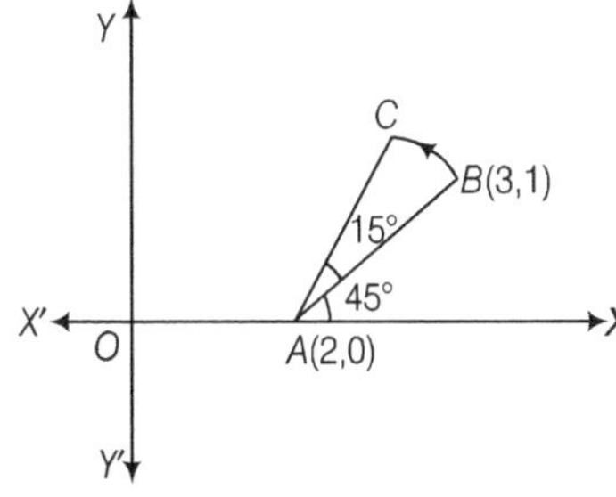

$\therefore \quad \angle BAX = 45^\circ$

Now line AB is rotated through an angle of 15°

$\Rightarrow \quad \angle CAX = 45^\circ + 15^\circ = 60^\circ$

and $\quad AB = AC = \sqrt{2}$

Equation of line AC in parametric form is

$$\left.\begin{aligned} x &= 2 + r\cos 60^\circ \\ y &= 0 + r\sin 60^\circ \end{aligned}\right\} \quad \text{...(i)}$$

Since, $AC = r = \sqrt{2}$

Put $\quad r = \sqrt{2}$ in Eq. (i), then

$$x = 2 + \sqrt{2}\cdot\frac{1}{2} = \frac{4+\sqrt{2}}{2}$$

and $\quad y = \sqrt{2}\,.\,\dfrac{\sqrt{3}}{2} = \dfrac{\sqrt{6}}{2}$

Equation of the line AC is

$$\frac{x-2}{y} = \cot 60^\circ = \frac{1}{\sqrt{3}}$$

or $\quad x\sqrt{3} - y - 2\sqrt{3} = 0$

and coordinates of C are $\left(\dfrac{4+\sqrt{2}}{2}, \dfrac{\sqrt{6}}{2}\right)$.

Aliter (By special corollary (ii))

$\because \quad A \equiv (2, 0), B \equiv (3, 1)$, let $C \equiv (x, y)$

$\therefore \quad z_A = 2, z_B = 3 + i,\ z_C = x + iy$, where $i = \sqrt{-1}$

$$\frac{z_C - z_A}{z_B - z_A} = e^{i\frac{5\pi}{12}} \qquad \left(\because 15^\circ = \frac{5\pi}{12}\right)$$

$\Rightarrow \quad z_C - 2 = (1+i)(\cos 15^\circ + i\sin 15^\circ)$

or $\quad z_C = 2 + (1+i)\left(\dfrac{\sqrt{3}+1}{2\sqrt{2}} + i\left(\dfrac{\sqrt{3}-1}{2\sqrt{2}}\right)\right)$

$$= \left(2 + \frac{\sqrt{3}+1}{2\sqrt{2}} - \frac{\sqrt{3}-1}{2\sqrt{2}}\right) + i\left(\frac{\sqrt{3}+1}{2\sqrt{2}} + \frac{\sqrt{3}-1}{2\sqrt{2}}\right)$$

$$= \left(2 + \frac{1}{\sqrt{2}}\right) + i\left(\frac{\sqrt{3}}{\sqrt{2}}\right) = \frac{4+\sqrt{2}}{2} + i\left(\frac{\sqrt{6}}{2}\right)$$

$\therefore \quad C \equiv \left(\dfrac{4+\sqrt{2}}{2}, \dfrac{\sqrt{6}}{2}\right)$

and equation of AC

$$y - 0 = \tan 60^\circ (x - 2) \Rightarrow x\sqrt{3} - y - 2\sqrt{3} = 0$$

Example 44. The centre of a square is at the origin and one vertex is $A(2, 1)$. Find the coordinates of other vertices of the square.

Sol. [By special corollary (ii)]

$\because \quad A \equiv (2, 1)$

$\therefore \quad z_A = 2 + i$, where $i = \sqrt{-1}$

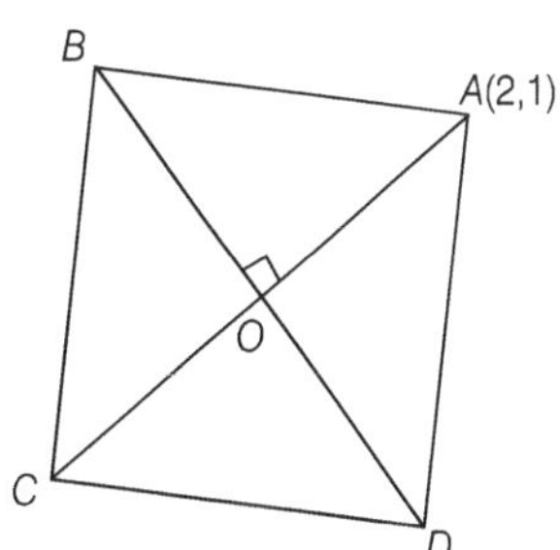

Now, in triangle AOB,

$$OA = OB, \angle AOB = 90° = \frac{\pi}{2}$$

$\therefore \quad z_B = z_A e^{i\frac{\pi}{2}} = iz_A = 2i - 1$

$\therefore \quad B \equiv (-1, 2)$

$\because O$ is the mid-point of AC and BD

$\therefore \quad C \equiv (-2, -1)$ and $D \equiv (1, -2)$.

Example 45. The extremities of the diagonal of a square are $(1, 1)$, $(-2, -1)$. Obtain the other two vertices and the equation of the other diagonal.

Sol. **(By special corollary (ii))**

$\because \quad A \equiv (1, 1)$

$\therefore \quad z_A = 1 + i$, where $i = \sqrt{-1}$

and $\quad C \equiv (-2, -1)$

$\therefore \quad z_C = -2 - i$

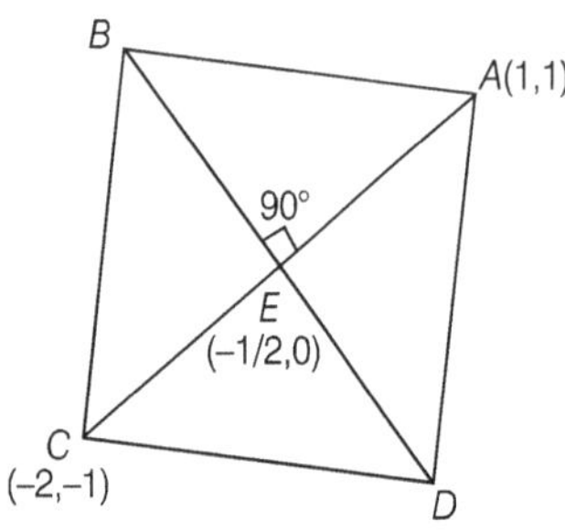

then centre of square $E \equiv \left(-\frac{1}{2}, 0\right)$

$\therefore \quad z_E = -\frac{1}{2}$

Now, in ΔAEB, $(EA = EB)$

$$\frac{z_B - z_E}{z_A - z_E} = e^{i\frac{\pi}{2}} = i$$

$\Rightarrow \quad z_B + \frac{1}{2} = i\left(1 + i + \frac{1}{2}\right)$

$\therefore \quad z_B = -\frac{3}{2} + \frac{3}{2}i$

$$B \equiv \left(-\frac{3}{2}, \frac{3}{2}\right)$$

then $\quad D \equiv \left(-1 + \frac{3}{2}, -\frac{3}{2}\right)$

or $\quad D \equiv \left(\frac{1}{2}, -\frac{3}{2}\right)$

Hence, equation of other diagonal BD is

$$y - 0 = \frac{\frac{3}{2} - 0}{-\frac{3}{2} + \frac{1}{2}}\left(x + \frac{1}{2}\right)$$

$\Rightarrow \quad 6x + 4y + 3 = 0$

Exercise for Session 1

1. The distance of the point (3, 5) from the line $2x + 3y - 14 = 0$ measured parallel to the line $x - 2y = 1$ is

(a) $\frac{7}{\sqrt{5}}$ (b) $\frac{7}{\sqrt{13}}$ (c) $\sqrt{5}$ (d) $\sqrt{13}$

2. The lines $x \cos\alpha + y \sin\alpha = p_1$ and $x \cos\beta + y \sin\beta = p_2$ will be perpendicular, if

(a) $\alpha = \beta$ (b) $|\alpha - \beta| = \pi/2$

(c) $\alpha = \pi/2$ (d) $\alpha \pm \beta = \pi/2$

3. If each of the points $(x_1, 4)$, $(-2, y_1)$ lies on the line joining the points $(2, -1)$, $(5, -3)$, then the point $P(x_1, y_1)$ lies on the line

(a) $6(x + y) - 25 = 0$ (d) $2x + 6y + 1 = 0$

(c) $2x + 3y - 6 = 0$ (d) $6(x + y) + 25 = 0$

4. The equation of the straight line passing through the point (4, 3) and making intercepts on the coordinate axes whose sum is –1 is

(a) $\frac{x}{2} + \frac{y}{3} = -1$ and $\frac{x}{-2} + \frac{y}{1} = -1$ (b) $\frac{x}{2} - \frac{y}{3} = -1$ and $\frac{x}{-2} + \frac{y}{1} = -1$

(c) $\frac{x}{2} + \frac{y}{3} = 1$ and $\frac{x}{-2} + \frac{y}{1} = 1$ (d) $\frac{x}{2} - \frac{y}{3} = 1$ and $\frac{x}{-2} + \frac{y}{1} = 1$

5. If the straight lines $ax + by + c = 0$ and $x \cos\alpha + y \sin\alpha = c$ enclose an angle $\pi/4$ between them and meet the straight line $x \sin\alpha - y \cos\alpha = 0$ in the same point, then

(a) $a^2 + b^2 = c^2$ (b) $a^2 + b^2 = 2$ (c) $a^2 + b^2 = 2c^2$ (d) $a^2 + b^2 = 4$

6. The angle between the lines $2x - y + 3 = 0$ and $x + 2y + 3 = 0$ is

(a) 30° (b) 45° (c) 60° (d) 90°

7. The inclination of the straight line passing through the point (–3, 6) and the mid-point of the line joining the points (4, –5) and (–2, 9) is

(a) $\pi/4$ (b) $\pi/2$ (c) $3\pi/4$ (d) π

8. A square of side a lies above the X-axis and has one vertex at the origin. The side passing through the origin makes an angle $\pi/6$ with the positive direction of X-axis. The equation of its diagonal not passing through the origin is

(a) $y(\sqrt{3} - 1) - x(1 - \sqrt{3}) = 2a$ (b) $y(\sqrt{3} + 1) + x(1 - \sqrt{3}) = 2a$
(c) $y(\sqrt{3} + 1) + x(1 + \sqrt{3}) = 2a$ (d) $y(\sqrt{3} + 1) + x(\sqrt{3} - 1) = 2a$

9. $A(1, 3)$ and $C(7, 5)$ are two opposite vertices of a square. The equation of side through A is

(a) $x + 2y - 7 = 0$ (b) $x - 2y + 5 = 0$
(c) $2x + y - 5 = 0$ (d) $2x - y + 1 = 0$

10. The equation of a straight line passing through the point $(-5, 4)$ and which cuts off an intercept of $\sqrt{2}$ units between the lines $x + y + 1 = 0$ and $x + y - 1 = 0$ is

(a) $x - 2y + 13 = 0$ (b) $2x - y + 14 = 0$
(c) $x - y + 9 = 0$ (d) $x - y + 10 = 0$

11. Equation to the straight line cutting off an intercept 2 from negative direction of the axis of y and inclined at 30° to the positive direction of axis of x is

(a) $y + x - \sqrt{3} = 0$ (b) $y - x + 2 = 0$
(c) $y - x\sqrt{3} - 2 = 0$ (d) $y\sqrt{3} - x + 2\sqrt{3} = 0$

12. What is the value of y so that the line through $(3, y)$ and (2, 7) is parallel to the line through (–1, 4) and (0, 6) ?

13. A straight line is drawn through the point $P(2, 2)$ and is inclined at an angle of 30° with the X-axis. Find the coordinates of two points on it at a distance 4 from P on either side of P.

14. If the straight line through the point $P(3, 4)$ makes an angle $\frac{\pi}{6}$ with X-axis and meets the line $12x + 5y + 10 = 0$ at Q, find the length of PQ.

15. Find the distance of the point (2, 3) from the line $2x - 3y + 9 = 0$ measured along the line $x - y + 1 = 0$.

16. A line is such that its segment between the straight line $5x - y - 4 = 0$ and $3x + 4y - 4 = 0$ is bisected at the point $(1, 5)$. Obtain the equation.

17. The side AB and AC of a ΔABC are respectively $2x + 3y = 29$ and $x + 2y = 16$. If the mid-point of BC is (5, 6), then find the equation of BC.

18. A straight line through $A(-15, -10)$ meets the lines $x - y - 1 = 0$, $x + 2y = 5$ and $x + 3y = 7$ respectively at A, B and C. If $\frac{12}{AB} + \frac{40}{AC} = \frac{52}{AD}$, prove that the line passes through the origin.

Session 2

Position of Two Points Relative to a Given Line, Position of a Point Which Lies Inside a Triangle, Equations of Lines Parallel and Perpendicular to a Given Line, Distance of a Point From a Line, Distance Between Two Parallel Lines, Area of Parallelogram,

Position of Two Points Relative to a Given Line

Theorem : The points $P(x_1, y_1)$ and $Q(x_2, y_2)$ lie on the same or opposite sides of the line $ax + by + c = 0$ according as

$$\frac{ax_1 + by_1 + c}{ax_2 + by_2 + c} > 0 \text{ or } < 0.$$

Proof : Let the line PQ be divided by the line $ax + by + c = 0$ in the ratio $\lambda : 1$ (internally) at the point R.

$\therefore$ The coordinates of R are $\left(\frac{x_1 + \lambda x_2}{1+\lambda}, \frac{y_1 + \lambda y_2}{1+\lambda}\right)$.

The point of R lies on the line $ax + by + c = 0$

then $\quad a\left(\frac{x_1 + \lambda x_2}{1+\lambda}\right) + b\left(\frac{y_1 + \lambda y_2}{1+\lambda}\right) + c = 0$

$\Rightarrow \quad \lambda(ax_2 + by_2 + c) + (ax_1 + by_1 + c) = 0$

$\Rightarrow \quad \lambda = -\left(\frac{ax_1 + by_1 + c}{ax_2 + by_2 + c}\right) \qquad (\because ax_2 + by_2 + c \neq 0)$

Case I : Let P and Q are on same side of the line $ax + by + c = 0$.

$\therefore$ R divides PQ externally.

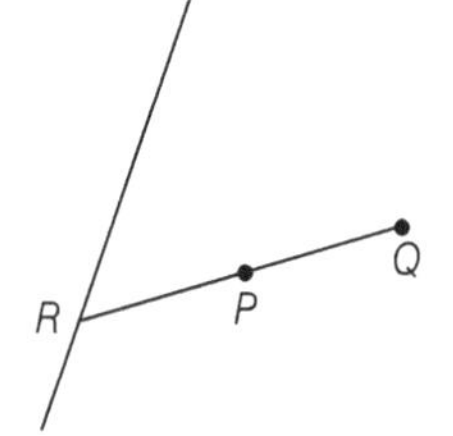

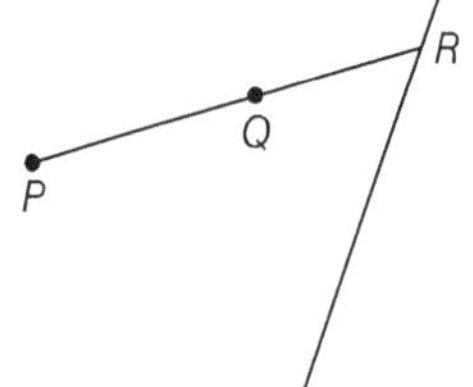

$\therefore$ λ is negative

$$\Rightarrow \quad -\left(\frac{ax_1 + by_1 + c}{ax_2 + by_2 + c}\right) < 0$$

$$\Rightarrow \quad \left(\frac{ax_1 + by_1 + c}{ax_2 + by_2 + c}\right) > 0$$

$$\text{or} \quad \frac{f(x_1, y_1)}{f(x_2, y_2)} > 0$$

where, $f(x, y) \equiv ax + by + c$.

Case II : Let P and Q are on opposite sides of the line $ax + by + c = 0$

$\therefore$ R divides PQ internally.

$\therefore$ λ is positive

$$\Rightarrow \quad -\left(\frac{ax_1 + by_1 + c}{ax_2 + by_2 + c}\right) > 0$$

$$\Rightarrow \quad \left(\frac{ax_1 + by_1 + c}{ax_2 + by_2 + c}\right) < 0$$

$$\text{or} \quad \frac{f(x_1, y_1)}{f(x_2, y_2)} < 0$$

where, $f(x, y) = ax + by + c$

Remarks

1. The side of the line where origin lies is known as origin side.
2. A point (α, β) will lie on origin side of the line $ax + by + c = 0$, if $a\alpha + b\beta + c$ and c have same sign.
3. A point (α, β) will lie on non-origin side of the line $ax + by + c = 0$, if $a\alpha + b\beta + c$ and c have opposite sign.

Example 46. Are the points (2,1) and (–3, 5) on the same or opposite side of the line $3x-2y+1=0$?

Sol. Let $f(x, y) \equiv 3x - 2y + 1$

$$\therefore \quad \frac{f(2,1)}{f(-3,5)} = \frac{3(2)-2(1)+1}{3(-3)-2(5)+1} = -\frac{5}{18} < 0$$

Therefore, the two points are on the opposite sides of the given line.

Example 47. Is the point (2, –7) lies on origin side of the line $2x+y+2=0$?

Sol. Let $f(x, y) \equiv 2x + y + 2$

$$\therefore \quad f(2,-7) = 2(2) - 7 + 2 = -1$$

$$f(2,-7) < 0 \quad \text{and} \quad \text{constant } 2 > 0$$

Hence, the point (2, – 7) lies on non-origin side.

Example 48. A straight canal is at a distance of $4\frac{1}{2}$ km from a city and the nearest path from the city to the canal is in the north-east direction. Find whether a village which is at 3 km north and 4 km east from the city lies on the canal or not. If not, then on which side of the canal is the village situated ?

Sol. Let $O(0, 0)$ be the given city and AB be the straight canal.

Given, $OL = \frac{9}{2}$ km

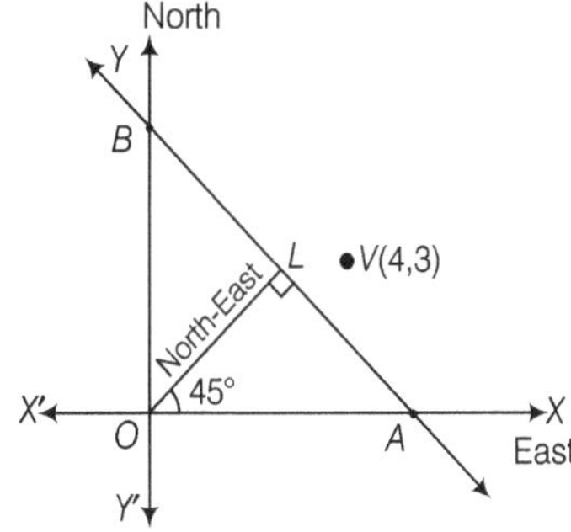

$\therefore$ Equation of AB

i.e. Equation of canal is

$$x\cos 45° + y\sin 45° = \frac{9}{2}$$

or $$x + y = \frac{9}{\sqrt{2}} \qquad \text{...(i)}$$

Let V be the given village, then $V \equiv (4, 3)$

Putting $x = 4$ and $y = 3$ in Eq. (i),

then $4 + 3 = \frac{9}{\sqrt{2}}$, i.e. $7 = \frac{9}{\sqrt{2}}$ which is impossible.

Hence, the given village V does not lie on the canal.

Also if $f(x, y) \equiv x + y - \frac{9}{\sqrt{2}}$

$$\therefore \quad \frac{f(4,3)}{f(0,0)} = \left(\frac{4+3-\frac{9}{\sqrt{2}}}{0+0-\frac{9}{\sqrt{2}}}\right) = -\left(\frac{7\sqrt{2}-9}{9}\right) < 0$$

Hence, the village is on that side of the canal on which origin or the city lies.

Position of a Point Which Lies Inside a Triangle

Let $P(x_1, y_1)$ be the point and equations of the sides of a triangle are

$$BC: a_1x + b_1y + c_1 = 0$$

$$CA: a_2x + b_2y + c_2 = 0$$

and $$AB: a_3x + b_3y + c_3 = 0$$

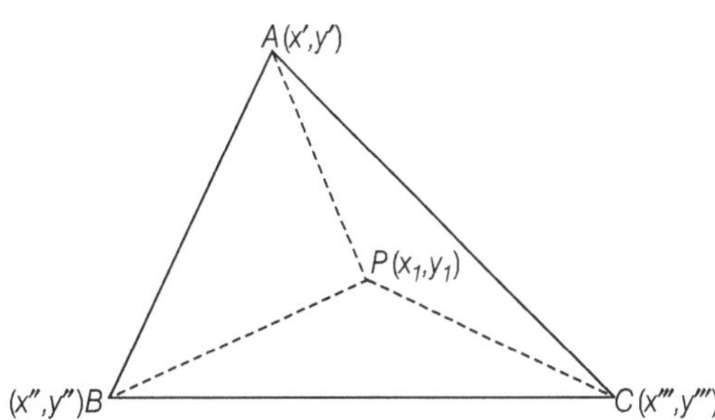

First find the coordinates of A, B and C say,

$$A \equiv (x', y');\ B \equiv (x'', y'') \text{ and } C \equiv (x''', y''')$$

and if coordinates of A, B, C are given, then find equations of BC, CA and AB.

If $P(x_1, y_1)$ lies inside the triangle, then P and A must be on the same side of BC, P and B must be on the same side of AC, P and C must be on the same side of AB , then

$$\frac{a_1x_1 + b_1y_1 + c_1}{a_1x' + b_1y' + c_1} > 0 \qquad \text{...(i)}$$

$$\frac{a_2x_1 + b_2y_1 + c_2}{a_2x'' + b_2y'' + c_2} > 0 \qquad \text{...(ii)}$$

and $$\frac{a_3x_1 + b_3y_1 + c_3}{a_3x''' + b_3y''' + c_3} > 0 \qquad \text{...(iii)}$$

The required values of $P(x_1, y_1)$ must be intersection of these inequalities Eqs. (i), (ii) and (iii).

Aliter (Best Method) : First draw the exact diagram of the problem. If the point $P(x_1, y_1)$ move on the line $y = ax + b$ for all x_1, then

$$P \equiv (x_1, ax_1 + b)$$

and the portion DE of the line $y = ax + b$ (Excluding D and E) lies within the triangle. Now line $y = ax + b$ cuts any two sides out of three sides, then find coordinates of D and E.

$$D \equiv (\alpha, \beta)$$

and $\quad E \equiv (\gamma, \delta)$ (say)

then $\quad \alpha < x_1 < \gamma$

and $\quad \beta < ax_1 + b < \delta$

Example 49. For what values of the parameter t does the point $P(t, t+1)$ lies inside the triangle ABC where $A \equiv (0, 3), B \equiv (-2, 0)$ and $C \equiv (6, 1)$.

Sol. Equations of sides

$$BC : x - 8y + 2 = 0$$

$$CA : x + 3y - 9 = 0$$

and $\quad AB : 3x - 2y + 6 = 0$

Since, $P(t, t+1)$ lies inside the triangle ABC, then P and A must be on the same side of BC

$\therefore \quad \dfrac{\text{value of } (x - 8y + 2) \text{ at } P(t, t+1)}{\text{value of } (x - 8y + 2) \text{ at } A(0, 3)} > 0$

i.e. $\quad \dfrac{t - 8(t+1) + 2}{0 - 24 + 2} > 0$

or $\quad \dfrac{-7t - 6}{-22} > 0$

or $\quad 7t + 6 > 0$

$\therefore \quad t > -\dfrac{6}{7} \quad$ ...(i)

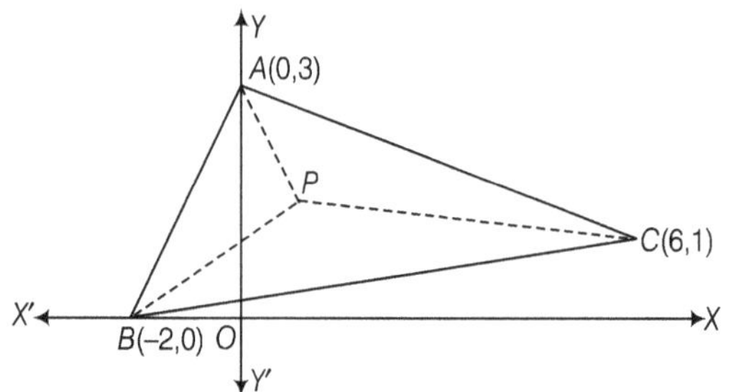

and P, B must be on the same side of CA

$\therefore \quad \dfrac{\text{value of } (x + 3y - 9) \text{ at } P(t, t+1)}{\text{value of } (x + 3y - 9) \text{ at } B(-2, 0)} > 0$

i.e. $\quad \dfrac{t + 3(t+1) - 9}{-2 + 0 - 9} > 0$

or $\quad \dfrac{4t - 6}{-11} > 0$

or $\quad 4t - 6 < 0$

$\therefore \quad t < \dfrac{3}{2} \quad$ ...(ii)

and P, C must be on the same side of AB

$\therefore \quad \dfrac{\text{value of } (3x - 2y + 6) \text{ at } P(t, t+1)}{\text{value of } (3x - 2y + 6) \text{ at } C(6, 1)} > 0$

i.e. $\quad \dfrac{3t - 2(t+1) + 6}{18 - 2 + 6} > 0$

or $\quad \dfrac{t + 4}{22} > 0$

or $\quad t + 4 > 0$

$\therefore \quad t > -4 \quad$ ...(iii)

From Eqs. (i), (ii) and (iii), we get

$$-\frac{6}{7} < t < \frac{3}{2}$$

i.e. $\quad t \in \left(-\dfrac{6}{7}, \dfrac{3}{2}\right)$

Aliter : First draw the exact diagram of ΔABC, the point $P(t, t+1)$ move on the line

$$y = x + 1$$

for all t.

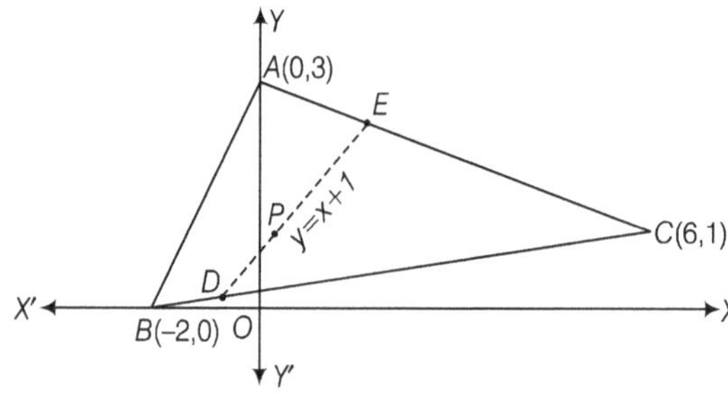

Now, D and E are the intersection of

$$y = x + 1, x - 8y + 2 = 0$$

and $\quad y = x + 1, \quad x + 3y - 9 = 0$

respectively.

$\therefore \quad D \equiv \left(-\dfrac{6}{7}, \dfrac{1}{7}\right)$

and $\quad E \equiv \left(\dfrac{3}{2}, \dfrac{5}{2}\right)$

Thus, the points on the line $y = x + 1$ whose x-coordinates lies between $-\dfrac{6}{7}$ and $\dfrac{3}{2}$ lie within the triangle ABC.

Hence, $\quad -\dfrac{6}{7} < t < \dfrac{3}{2}$

i.e. $\quad t \in \left(-\dfrac{6}{7}, \dfrac{3}{2}\right)$

Example 50. Find λ if $(\lambda, 2)$ is an interior point of ΔABC formed by $x+y=4$, $3x-7y=8$ and $4x-y=31$.

Sol. Let $P \equiv (\lambda, 2)$

First draw the exact diagram of ΔABC, the point $P(\lambda, 2)$ move on the line $y=2$ for all λ.

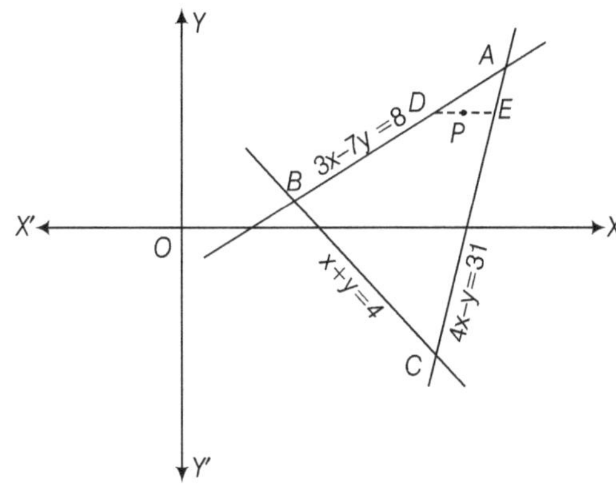

Now, D and E are the intersection of

$$3x-7y=8, y=2$$

and $4x-y=31$, $y=2$ respectively.

$$\therefore \quad D \equiv \left(\frac{22}{3}, 2\right) \text{ and } E \equiv \left(\frac{33}{4}, 2\right)$$

Thus, the points on the line $y=2$ whose x-coordinates lies between $\frac{22}{3}$ and $\frac{33}{4}$ lie within the ΔABC.

Hence, $\frac{22}{3} < \lambda < \frac{33}{4}$

i.e. $\lambda \in \left(\frac{22}{3}, \frac{33}{4}\right)$

Example 51. Determine all values of α for which the point (α, α^2) lies inside the triangle formed by the lines $2x+3y-1=0$, $x+2y-3=0$ and $5x-6y-1=0$.

Sol. The coordinates of the vertices are

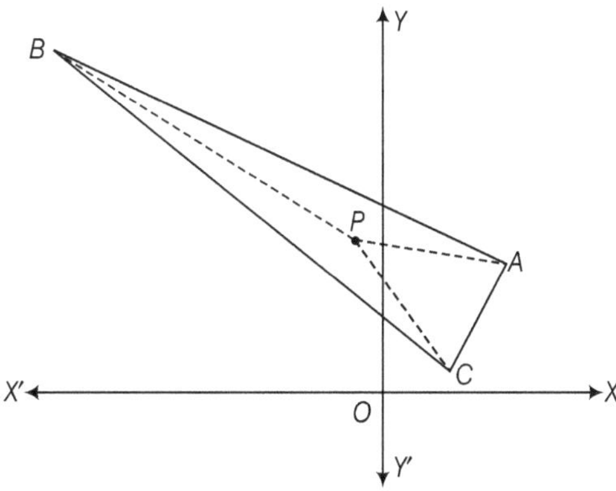

$$A\left(\frac{5}{4}, \frac{7}{8}\right), B(-7, 5) \text{ and } C\left(\frac{1}{3}, \frac{1}{9}\right)$$

$\because P(\alpha, \alpha^2)$ lies inside the ΔABC, then

(i) A and P must lie on the same side of BC

(ii) B and P must lie on the same side of CA

(iii) C and P must lie on the same side of AB, then

$$\frac{\frac{5}{2}+\frac{21}{8}-1}{2\alpha+3\alpha^2-1} > 0$$

$$\Rightarrow \quad \frac{33}{2\alpha+3\alpha^2-1} > 0$$

or $\quad 3\alpha^2+2\alpha-1>0$

$$\Rightarrow \quad (\alpha+1)\left(\alpha-\frac{1}{3}\right)>0$$

$$\Rightarrow \quad \alpha \in (-\infty, -1) \cup \left(\frac{1}{3}, \infty\right) \quad \text{...(i)}$$

and $\quad \frac{-35-30-1}{5\alpha-6\alpha^2-1} > 0$

$$\Rightarrow \quad 5\alpha-6\alpha^2-1<0$$

$$\Rightarrow \quad \left(\alpha-\frac{1}{3}\right)\left(\alpha-\frac{1}{2}\right)>0$$

$$\therefore \quad \alpha \in (-\infty, 1/3) \cup (1/2, \infty) \quad \text{..(ii)}$$

and $\quad \frac{\frac{1}{3}+\frac{2}{9}-3}{\alpha+2\alpha^2-3} > 0$

$$\Rightarrow \quad \alpha+2\alpha^2-3<0$$

$$\Rightarrow \quad (2\alpha+3)(\alpha-1)<0$$

$$\therefore \quad \alpha \in (-3/2, 1) \quad \text{...(iii)}$$

From Eq. (i), Eq. (ii) and Eq. (iii), we get

$$\alpha \in (-3/2, -1) \cup (1/2, 1).$$

Aliter : Let $P(\alpha, \alpha^2)$ first draw the exact diagram of ΔABC.

The point $P(\alpha, \alpha^2)$ move on the curve $y=x^2$ for all α.

Now, intersection of $y=x^2$

and $\quad 2x+3y-1=0$

or $\quad 2x+3x^2-1=0$

$$\therefore \quad x=-1, x=\frac{1}{3}$$

Let intersection points

$$D \equiv (-1, 1) \text{ and } E \equiv \left(\frac{1}{3}, \frac{1}{9}\right)$$

intersection of $y=x^2$

and $\quad x+2y-3=0$

or $\quad x+2x^2-3=0$

$$\therefore \quad x=1, x=-3/2$$

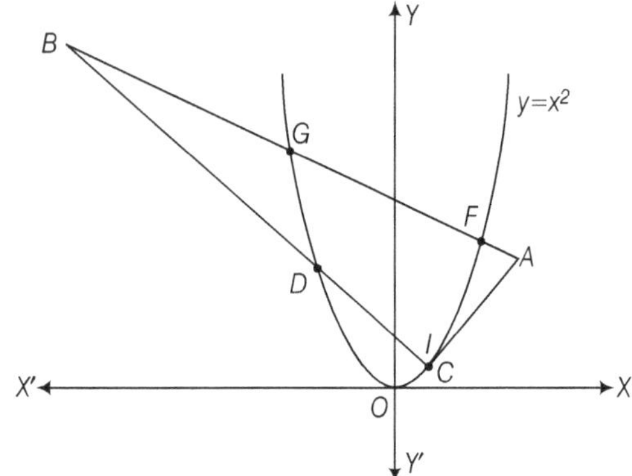

Let intersection points

$$F \equiv (1, 1) \text{ and } G \equiv \left(-\frac{3}{2}, \frac{9}{4}\right)$$

and intersection of $y = x^2$ and $5x - 6y - 1 = 0$

or $\quad 5x - 6x^2 - 1 = 0$

$\therefore \quad x = \frac{1}{3}, x = \frac{1}{2}$

Let intersection points

$$H \equiv \left(\frac{1}{3}, \frac{1}{9}\right) \text{ and } I \equiv \left(\frac{1}{2}, \frac{1}{4}\right).$$

Thus the points on the curve $y = x^2$ whose x-coordinate lies between $-3/2$ & -1 and $\frac{1}{2}$ & 1 lies within the triangle ABC.

Hence, $\quad -\frac{3}{2} < \alpha < -1$ or $\frac{1}{2} < \alpha < 1$

i.e. $\quad \alpha \in \left(-\frac{3}{2}, -1\right) \cup \left(\frac{1}{2}, 1\right)$

Equations of Lines Parallel and Perpendicular to a Given Line

Theorem 1: The equation of line parallel to $ax + by + c = 0$ is $ax + by + \lambda = 0$, where λ is some constant.

Proof : Let the equation of any line parallel to

$$ax + by + c = 0 \qquad \text{...(i)}$$

be $\quad a_1 x + b_1 y + c_1 = 0 \qquad$ ...(ii)

then $\quad \frac{a_1}{a} = \frac{b_1}{b} = k \qquad$ (say)

$\therefore \quad a_1 = ak, b_1 = bk$

Then from Eq. (ii),

$$akx + bky + c = 0$$

Dividing it by k, then

$$ax + by + \frac{c}{k} = 0$$

or $\quad ax + by + \lambda = 0 \qquad \left(\text{writing } \lambda \text{ for } \frac{c}{k}\right)$

Hence, any line parallel to $ax + by + c = 0$ is

$$ax + by + \lambda = 0$$

where λ is some constant.

Aliter : The given line is

$$ax + by + c = 0 \qquad \text{...(i)}$$

Its slope $= -\frac{a}{b}$

Thus, any line parallel to Eq. (i) is given by

$$y = \left(-\frac{a}{b}\right) x + \lambda_1$$

$\Rightarrow \quad ax + by - b\lambda_1 = 0$

$\Rightarrow \quad ax + by + \lambda = 0 \qquad$ (writing λ for $-b\lambda_1$)

where, λ is some constant.

***Corollary*:** The equation of the line parallel to $ax + by + c = 0$ and passing through (x_1, y_1) is

$$a(x - x_1) + b(y - y_1) = 0$$

Working Rule :

(i) Keep the terms containing x and y unaltered.

(ii) Change the constant.

(iii) The constant λ is determined from an additional condition given in the problem.

Theorem 2 : The equation of the line perpendicular to the line $ax + by + c = 0$ is

$bx - ay + \lambda = 0$, where λ is some constant.

Proof : Let the equation of any line perpendicular to

$$ax + by + c = 0 \qquad \text{... (i)}$$

be $\quad a_1 x + b_1 y + c_1 = 0 \qquad$ ...(ii)

then $\quad aa_1 + bb_1 = 0$

or $\quad aa_1 = -bb_1$

$\Rightarrow \quad \frac{a_1}{b} = \frac{b_1}{-a} = k \qquad$ (say)

$\therefore \quad a_1 = bk, b_1 = -ak$

Then, from Eq. (ii), $bkx - aky + c_1 = 0$ dividing it by k, then

$$bx - ay + \frac{c_1}{k} = 0$$

or $\quad bx - ay + \lambda = 0 \quad \left(\text{writing } \lambda \text{ for } \frac{c_1}{k}\right)$

Hence, any line perpendicular to $ax + by + c = 0$ is

$$bx - ay + \lambda = 0$$

where, λ is some constant.

Aliter : The given line is

$$ax + by + c = 0 \quad \text{...(i)}$$

$$\text{Its slope} = -\frac{a}{b}$$

Slope of perpendicular line of Eq. (i) is $\frac{b}{a}$.

Thus any line perpendicular to Eq. (i) is given by

$$y = \left(\frac{b}{a}\right)x + \lambda_1$$

$\Rightarrow \quad bx - ay + a\lambda_1 = 0$

or $\quad bx - ay + \lambda = 0 \quad (\text{writing } \lambda \text{ for } a\lambda_1)$

where, λ is some constant.

***Corollary* 1 :** The equation of the line through (x_1, y_1) and perpendicular to $ax + by + c = 0$ is

$$b(x - x_1) - a(y - y_1) = 0$$

***Corollary* 2 :** Also equation of the line perpendicular to $ax + by + c = 0$ is written as

$$\frac{x}{a} - \frac{y}{b} + k = 0, \text{ where } k \text{ is some constant.}$$

Working Rule :

(i) Interchange the coefficients of x and y and changing sign of one of these coefficients.

(ii) Changing the constant term.

(iii) The value of λ can be determined from an additional condition given in the problem.

Example 52. Find the general equation of the line which is parallel to $3x - 4y + 5 = 0$. Also find such line through the point $(-1, 2)$.

Sol. Equation of any parallel to $3x - 4y + 5 = 0$ is

$$3x - 4y + \lambda = 0 \quad \text{...(i)}$$

which is general equation of the line.

Also Eq. (i) passes through $(-1, 2)$, then

$$3(-1) - 4(2) + \lambda = 0$$

$\therefore \quad \lambda = 11$

Then from Eq. (i) required line is

$$3x - 4y + 11 = 0$$

Example 53. Find the general equation of the line which is perpendicular to $x + y + 4 = 0$. Also find such line through the point $(1, 2)$.

Sol. Equation of any line perpendicular to $x + y + 4 = 0$ is

$$x - y + \lambda = 0 \quad \text{...(i)}$$

which is general equation of the line.

Also Eq. (i) passes through $(1, 2)$, then

$$1 - 2 + \lambda = 0$$

$\therefore \quad \lambda = 1$

Then from Eq. (i), required line is

$$x - y + 1 = 0$$

Example 54. Show that the equation of the line passing through the point $(a\cos^3\theta, a\sin^3\theta)$ and perpendicular to the line

$x \sec\theta + y \operatorname{cosec}\theta = a$ is

$x \cos\theta - y \sin\theta = a\cos 2\theta$

Sol. The given equation $x \sec\theta + y \operatorname{cosec}\theta = a$ can be written as

$$x \sin\theta + y \cos\theta = a \sin\theta \cos\theta \quad \text{...(i)}$$

$\therefore$ equation of perpendicular line of Eq. (i) is

$$x \cos\theta - y \sin\theta = \lambda \quad \text{...(ii)}$$

Also it is pass through $(a\cos^3\theta, a\sin^3\theta)$

$\therefore \quad a\cos^3\theta \cdot \cos\theta - a\sin^3\theta \cdot \sin\theta = \lambda$

$\Rightarrow \quad \lambda = a(\cos^4\theta - \sin^4\theta)$

$= a(\cos^2\theta + \sin^2\theta)(\cos^2\theta - \sin^2\theta)$

$= a \cdot 1 \cdot \cos 2\theta = a\cos 2\theta$

From Eq. (ii), the required equation of the line is

$$x \cos\theta - y \sin\theta = a\cos 2\theta$$

Aliter : (From corollary (2) of Theorem (2)

Equation of any line perpendicular to the line

$$x \sec\theta + y \operatorname{cosec}\theta = a, \text{ is}$$

$$\frac{x}{\sec\theta} - \frac{y}{\operatorname{cosec}\theta} = k$$

or $\quad x\cos\theta - y\sin\theta = k \quad \text{...(iii)}$

Also, it pass through $(a\cos^3\theta, a\sin^3\theta)$

$\therefore \quad a\cos^3\theta \cdot \cos\theta - a\sin^3\theta \cdot \sin\theta = k$

or $\quad k = a(\cos^4\theta - \sin^4\theta)$

$= a(\cos^2\theta + \sin^2\theta)(\cos^2\theta - \sin^2\theta)$

$= a \cdot 1 \cdot \cos 2\theta$

$= a\cos 2\theta$

From Eq. (iii), the required equation of the line is

$$x\cos\theta - y\sin\theta = a\cos 2\theta$$

Distance of a Point From a Line

Theorem : The length of perpendicular from a point (x_1, y_1) to the line $ax + by + c = 0$ is

$$\frac{|ax_1 + by_1 + c|}{\sqrt{(a^2 + b^2)}}$$

Proof : Given line is $ax + by + c = 0$

$$\Rightarrow \quad \frac{x}{\left(-\frac{c}{a}\right)} + \frac{y}{\left(-\frac{c}{b}\right)} = 1$$

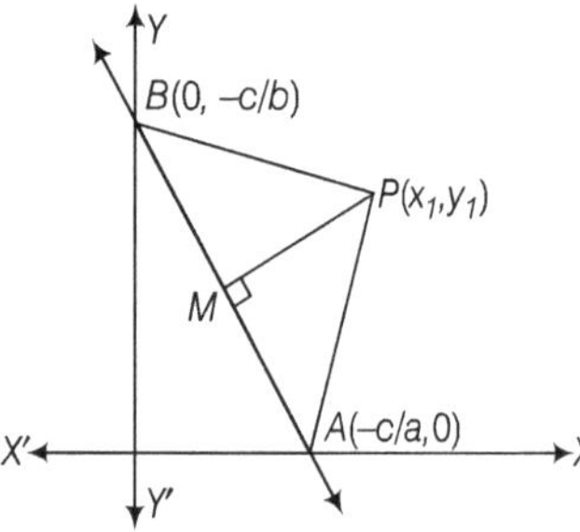

Let the given line intersects the X-axis and Y-axis at A and B respectively, then coordinates of A and B are $\left(-\frac{c}{a}, 0\right)$ and $\left(0, -\frac{c}{b}\right)$ respectively.

Draw PM perpendicular to AB.

Now, Area of $\Delta\, PAB$

$$= \frac{1}{2}\left| x_1\left(0 + \frac{c}{b}\right) - \frac{c}{a}\left(-\frac{c}{b} - y_1\right) + 0\,(y_1 - 0)\right|$$

$$= \frac{1}{2}\left|\frac{c}{ab}\right| |ax_1 + by_1 + c| \quad \text{...(i)}$$

Let $PM = p$

Also, area of $\Delta\, PAB$

$$= \frac{1}{2} \cdot AB \cdot PM = \frac{1}{2}\sqrt{\left\{\left(-\frac{c}{a} - 0\right)^2 + \left(0 + \frac{c}{b}\right)^2\right\}} \cdot p$$

$$= \frac{1}{2}\left|\frac{c}{ab}\right| \sqrt{(a^2 + b^2)} \cdot p \quad \text{... (ii)}$$

From Eqs. (i) and (ii), we have

$$\frac{1}{2}\left|\frac{c}{ab}\right| \sqrt{(a^2 + b^2)} \cdot p = \frac{1}{2}\left|\frac{c}{ab}\right| |ax_1 + by_1 + c|$$

or $$p = \frac{|ax_1 + by_1 + c|}{\sqrt{(a^2 + b^2)}}$$

Aliter I : Let PM makes an angle θ with positive direction of X-axis.

Then, equation of PM in distance form will be

$$\frac{x - x_1}{\cos\theta} = \frac{y - y_1}{\sin\theta} = p \quad (\because PM = p)$$

Therefore coordinates of M will be

$$(x_1 + p\cos\theta, y_1 + p\sin\theta)$$

Since, M lies on $ax + by + c = 0$, then

$$a(x_1 + p\cos\theta) + b(y_1 + p\sin\theta) + c = 0$$

or $$p(a\cos\theta + b\sin\theta) = -(ax_1 + by_1 + c) \quad \text{...(iii)}$$

Since, slope of $AB = -\frac{a}{b}$

$\therefore$ Slope of $PM = \frac{b}{a}$

$\therefore$ $\tan\theta = \frac{b}{a}$ ($\because$ PM makes an angle θ with positive direction of X-axis)

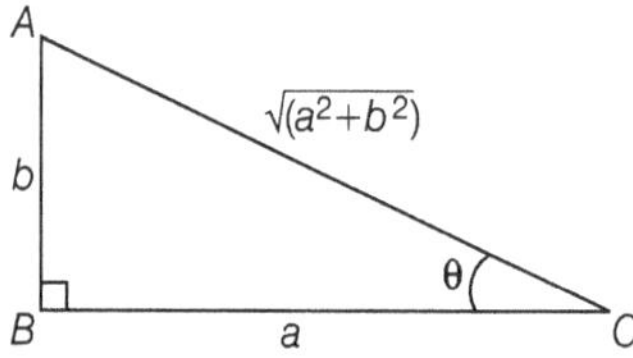

then $$\sin\theta = \frac{b}{\sqrt{(a^2 + b^2)}}$$

and $$\cos\theta = \frac{a}{\sqrt{(a^2 + b^2)}}$$

Now, from Eq. (iii),

$$p\left(\frac{a^2}{\sqrt{(a^2 + b^2)}} + \frac{b^2}{\sqrt{(a^2 + b^2)}}\right) = -(ax_1 + by_1 + c)$$

or $$p = -\frac{(ax_1 + by_1 + c)}{\sqrt{(a^2 + b^2)}}$$

Since, p is positive

$$\therefore \quad p = \frac{|ax_1 + by_1 + c|}{\sqrt{(a^2 + b^2)}}$$

Aliter II : Let $Q(x, y)$ be any point on the line

$$ax + by + c = 0$$

Hence, the length of perpendicular from P on AB will be least value of PQ.

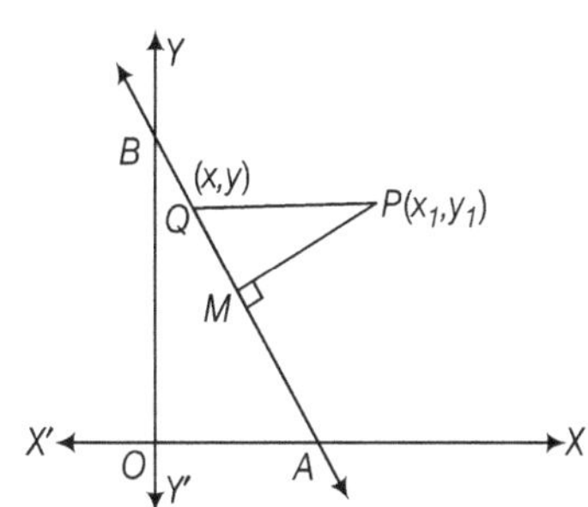

Let $z = (PQ)^2$

$$= (x - x_1)^2 + (y - y_1)^2 \quad \text{...(iv)}$$

$$= (x - x_1)^2 + \left(-\frac{c}{b} - \frac{ax}{b} - y_1\right)^2$$

$$\left(\because ax + by + c = 0 \;\; \therefore y = -\frac{c}{b} - \frac{ax}{b}\right)$$

$\therefore$ $$\frac{dz}{dx} = 2(x - x_1) + 2\left(-\frac{c}{b} - \frac{ax}{b} - y_1\right)\left(-\frac{a}{b}\right)$$

and $$\frac{d^2z}{dx^2} = 2 + 2\left(-\frac{a}{b}\right)\left(-\frac{a}{b}\right) = 2\left(1 + \frac{a^2}{b^2}\right) = \text{positive}$$

$\because$ z is minimum

$\therefore$ PQ is also minimum.

For maximum or minimum, $\frac{dz}{dx} = 0$

$$2(x - x_1) + 2\left(-\frac{c}{b} - \frac{ax}{b} - y_1\right)\left(-\frac{a}{b}\right) = 0$$

or $$2(x - x_1) + 2(y - y_1)\left(-\frac{a}{b}\right) = 0 \quad \left(\because y = -\frac{c}{b} - \frac{ax}{b}\right)$$

or $$\frac{(x - x_1)}{a} = \frac{(y - y_1)}{b} = \frac{a(x - x_1) + b(y - y_1)}{a \cdot a + b \cdot b}$$

$$= \frac{(ax + by + c) - (ax_1 + by_1 + c)}{(a^2 + b^2)}$$

(by law of proportion)

$$= \frac{0 - (ax_1 + by_1 + c)}{(a^2 + b^2)} \quad (\because ax + by + c = 0)$$

$\Rightarrow$ $$(x - x_1) = -\frac{a(ax_1 + by_1 + c)}{(a^2 + b^2)}$$

and $$(y - y_1) = -\frac{b(ax_1 + by_1 + c)}{(a^2 + b^2)}$$

$\therefore$ From Eq. (iv),

$$PQ = \sqrt{(ax_1 + by_1 + c)^2 \frac{(a^2 + b^2)}{(a^2 + b^2)^2}} = \frac{|ax_1 + by_1 + c|}{\sqrt{(a^2 + b^2)}}$$

$\because$ Least value of PQ is PM

$\therefore$ $$p = PM = \frac{|ax_1 + by_1 + c|}{\sqrt{(a^2 + b^2)}}$$

Aliter III : Let $M \equiv (h, k)$

Since, $M(h, k)$ lies on AB,

$$ah + bk + c = 0 \quad \text{..(v)}$$

Now, AB and PM are perpendicular to each other, then

$$(\text{slope of } PM) \times (\text{slope of } AB) = -1$$

$\Rightarrow$ $$\frac{y_1 - k}{x_1 - h} \times \left(-\frac{a}{b}\right) = -1$$

$\Rightarrow$ $$\frac{x_1 - h}{a} = \frac{y_1 - k}{b} = \frac{a(x_1 - h) + b(y_1 - k)}{a.a + b.b}$$

(by law of proportion)

$$= \frac{(ax_1 + by_1 + c) - (ah + bk + c)}{a^2 + b^2}$$

$$= \frac{ax_1 + by_1 + c}{a^2 + b^2} \quad \text{[from Eq. (v)]}$$

$\therefore$ $$(PM)^2 = (x - x_1)^2 + (y - y_1)^2$$

$$= \left(\frac{ax_1 + by_1 + c}{a^2 + b^2}\right)^2 (a^2 + b^2)$$

$\therefore$ Length of perpendicular

$$PM = \pm \frac{(ax_1 + by_1 + c)}{\sqrt{(a^2 + b^2)}}$$

Hence, $$PM = p = \frac{|ax_1 + by_1 + c)}{\sqrt{(a^2 + b^2)}}$$

Aliter IV : Equation of AB in normal form is

$$\frac{a}{\sqrt{(a^2 + b^2)}} x + \frac{b}{\sqrt{(a^2 + b^2)}} y = \frac{-c}{\sqrt{(a^2 + b^2)}}$$

$\Rightarrow$ $$OL = -\frac{c}{\sqrt{(a^2 + b^2)}}$$

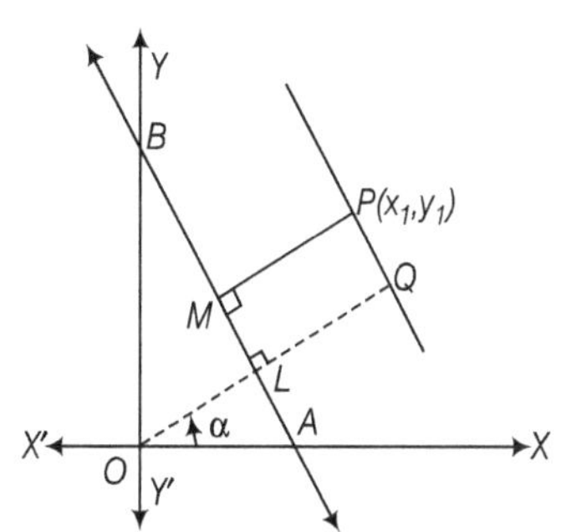

Equation of line parallel to AB and passes through (x_1, y_1) is

$$a(x - x_1) + b(y - y_1) = 0$$

or $$ax + by = ax_1 + by_1$$

Normal form is

$$\frac{a}{\sqrt{(a^2 + b^2)}} x + \frac{b}{\sqrt{(a^2 + b^2)}} y = \frac{ax_1 + by_1}{\sqrt{(a^2 + b^2)}}$$

$$\Rightarrow \quad OQ = \frac{ax_1 + by_1}{\sqrt{(a^2 + b^2)}}$$

$$\therefore \quad PM = QL = OQ - OL = \frac{ax_1 + by_1 + c}{\sqrt{(a^2 + b^2)}}$$

Hence, required perpendicular distance

$$p = \frac{|ax_1 + by_1 + c|}{\sqrt{(a^2 + b^2)}}$$

Aliter V : The equation of line through $P(x_1, y_1)$ and perpendicular to $ax + by + c = 0$ is

$$b(x - x_1) - a(y - y_1) = 0 \qquad \text{...(vi)}$$

If this perpendicular meet the line $ax + by + c = 0$ in $M(x_2, y_2)$ then (x_2, y_2) lie on both the lines $ax + by + c = 0$ and Eq. (vi), then

$$b(x_2 - x_1) - a(y_2 - y_1) = 0, ax_2 + by_2 + c = 0$$

$$ax_2 + by_2 + c = a(x_2 - x_1) + b(y_2 - y_1) + ax_1 + by_1 + c = 0$$

or $$b(x_2 - x_1) - a(y_2 - y_1) = 0 \qquad \text{...(vii)}$$

and $$a(x_2 - x_1) + b(y_2 - y_1) = -(ax_1 + by_1 + c) \qquad \text{...(viii)}$$

On squaring and adding Eqs. (vii) and (viii), we get

$$(a^2 + b^2)((x_2 - x_1)^2 + (y_2 - y_1)^2) = (ax_1 + by_1 + c)^2$$

or $$PM = \sqrt{(x_2 - x_1)^2 + (y_2 - y_1)^2}$$

$$= \frac{|ax_1 + by_1 + c|}{\sqrt{(a^2 + b^2)}}$$

Hence, length of perpendicular

$$PM = p = \frac{|ax_1 + by_1 + c|}{\sqrt{(a^2 + b^2)}}$$

***Corollary* 1 :** The length of perpendicular from the origin to the line $ax + by + c = 0$ is

$$\frac{|a \cdot 0 + b \cdot 0 + c|}{\sqrt{(a^2 + b^2)}} \text{ i.e. } \frac{|c|}{\sqrt{(a^2 + b^2)}}$$

***Corollary* 2 :** The length of perpendicular from (x_1, y_1) to the line $x \cos\alpha + y \sin\alpha = p$ is

$$\frac{|x_1 \cos\alpha + y_1 \sin\alpha - p|}{\sqrt{(\cos^2\alpha + \sin^2\alpha)}} = |x_1 \cos\alpha + y_1 \sin\alpha - p|$$

Working Rule :

(i) Put the point (x_1, y_1) for (x, y) on the LHS while the RHS is zero.

(ii) Divide LHS after Eq. (i) by $\sqrt{(a^2 + b^2)}$, where a and b are the coefficients of x and y respectively.

Example 55. Find the sum of the abscissas of all the points on the line $x + y = 4$ that lie at a unit distance from the line $4x + 3y - 10 = 0$.

Sol. Any point on the line $x + y = 4$ can be taken as $(x_1, 4 - x_1)$. As it is at a unit distance from the line $4x + 3y - 10 = 0$, we get

$$\frac{|4x_1 + 3(4 - x_1) - 10|}{\sqrt{(4^2 + 3^2)}} = 1$$

$$\Rightarrow \quad |x_1 + 2| = 5 \Rightarrow x_1 + 2 = \pm 5$$

$$\Rightarrow \quad x_1 = 3 \text{ or } -7$$

$\therefore$ Required sum $= 3 - 7 = -4$.

Example 56. If p and p' are the length of the perpendiculars from the origin to the straight lines whose equations are $x \sec\theta + y \operatorname{cosec}\theta = a$ and $x \cos\theta - y \sin\theta = a \cos 2\theta$, then find the value of $4p^2 + p'^2$.

Sol. We have, $p = \dfrac{|-a|}{\sqrt{(\sec^2\theta + \operatorname{cosec}^2\theta)}}$

$$\therefore \quad p^2 = \frac{a^2}{\sec^2\theta + \operatorname{cosec}^2\theta} = \frac{a^2 \sin^2\theta \cos^2\theta}{1}$$

$$\Rightarrow \quad 4p^2 = a^2 \sin^2 2\theta \qquad \text{...(i)}$$

and $$p' = \frac{|-a \cos 2\theta|}{\sqrt{(\cos^2\theta + \sin^2\theta)}} = |-a \cos 2\theta|$$

$$\therefore \quad (p')^2 = a^2 \cos^2 2\theta \qquad \text{...(ii)}$$

$\therefore$ Adding Eqs. (i) and (ii), we get

$$4p^2 + p'^2 = a^2$$

Example 57. If p is the length of the perpendicular from the origin to the line $\dfrac{x}{a} + \dfrac{y}{b} = 1$, then prove that $\dfrac{1}{a^2} + \dfrac{1}{b^2} = \dfrac{1}{p^2}$.

Sol. p = length of perpendicular from origin to

$$\frac{x}{a} + \frac{y}{b} = 1$$

$$= \frac{|0 + 0 - 1|}{\sqrt{\left(\frac{1}{a}\right)^2 + \left(\frac{1}{b}\right)^2}} = \frac{1}{\sqrt{\left(\frac{1}{a^2} + \frac{1}{b^2}\right)}}$$

or $$\frac{1}{p^2} = \frac{1}{a^2} + \frac{1}{b^2} \text{ or } \frac{1}{a^2} + \frac{1}{b^2} = \frac{1}{p^2}$$

Example 58. Prove that no line can be drawn through the point (4, – 5) so that its distance from (–2, 3) will be equal to 12.

Sol. Suppose, if possible.

Equation of line through (4, – 5) with slope of m is

$$y + 5 = m(x - 4)$$

$$\Rightarrow \quad mx - y - 4m - 5 = 0$$

Then, $\dfrac{|m(-2) - 3 - 4m - 5|}{\sqrt{m^2 + 1}} = 12$

$$\Rightarrow \quad |-6m - 8| = 12\sqrt{(m^2 + 1)}$$

On squaring, $(6m + 8)^2 = 144(m^2 + 1)$

$$\Rightarrow \quad 4(3m + 4)^2 = 144(m^2 + 1)$$

$$\Rightarrow \quad (3m + 4)^2 = 36(m^2 + 1)$$

$$\Rightarrow \quad 27m^2 - 24m + 20 = 0 \quad \text{...(i)}$$

Since, the discriminant of Eq. (i) is $(-24)^2 - 4 \cdot 27 \cdot 20 = -1584$ which is negative, there is no real value of m. Hence no such line is possible.

Distance between Two Parallel Lines

Let the two parallel lines be

$$ax + by + c = 0 \quad \text{and} \quad ax + by + c_1 = 0$$

The distance between the parallel lines is the perpendicular distance of any point on one line from the other line.

Let (x_1, y_1) be any point on $ax + by + c = 0$

$$\therefore \quad ax_1 + by_1 + c = 0 \quad \text{...(i)}$$

Now, perpendicular distance of the point (x_1, y_1) from the line $ax + by + c_1 = 0$ is

$$\frac{|ax_1 + by_1 + c_1|}{\sqrt{(a^2 + b^2)}} = \frac{|c_1 - c|}{\sqrt{(a^2 + b^2)}} \quad \text{[from Eq. (i)]}$$

This is required distance between the given parallel lines.

Aliter I : The distance between the lines is

$$d = \frac{\lambda}{\sqrt{(a^2 + b^2)}}$$

(i) $\lambda = |c_1 - c|$, if both the lines are on the same side of the origin.

(ii) $\lambda = |c_1| + |c|$, if the lines are on the opposite side of the origin.

Aliter II : Find the coordinates of any point on one of the given lines, preferably putting $x = 0$ or $y = 0$. Then the perpendicular distance of this point from the other line is the required distance between the lines.

Example 59. Find the distance between the lines $5x - 12y + 2 = 0$ and $5x - 12y - 3 = 0$.

Sol. The distance between the lines

$$5x - 12y + 2 = 0 \quad \text{and} \quad 5x - 12y - 3 = 0 \text{ is}$$

$$\frac{|2 - (-3)|}{\sqrt{(5)^2 + (-12)^2}} = \frac{5}{13}$$

Aliter I : The constant term in both equations are 2 and –3 which are of opposite sign. Hence origin lies between them.

$\therefore$ Distance between lines is $\dfrac{|2| + |-3|}{\sqrt{(5)^2 + (-12)^2}} = \dfrac{5}{13}$

Aliter II : Putting $y = 0$ in $5x - 12y - 3 = 0$ then $x = \dfrac{3}{5}$

$\therefore \quad \left(\dfrac{3}{5}, 0\right)$ lie on $5x - 12y - 3 = 0$

Hence, distance between the lines

$5x - 12y + 2 = 0$ and $(5x - 12y - 3 = 0)$

= Distance from $\left(\dfrac{3}{5}, 0\right)$ to the line $5x - 12y + 2 = 0$

$$= \frac{\left|5 \times \frac{3}{5} - 0 + 2\right|}{\sqrt{5^2 + (-12)^2}} = \frac{5}{13}$$

Example 60. Find the equations of the line parallel to $5x - 12y + 26 = 0$ and at a distance of 4 units from it.

Sol. Equation of any line parallel to $5x - 12y + 26 = 0$ is

$$5x - 12y + \lambda = 0 \quad \text{...(i)}$$

Since, the distance between the parallel lines is 4 units, then

$$\frac{|\lambda - 26|}{\sqrt{(5)^2 + (-12)^2}} = 4$$

or $\quad |\lambda - 26| = 52$ or $\lambda - 26 = \pm 52$

or $\quad \lambda = 26 \pm 52 \quad \therefore \lambda = -26$ or 78

Substituting the values of λ in Eq. (i), we get

$$5x - 12y - 26 = 0$$

and $\quad 5x - 12y + 78 = 0$

Area of Parallelogram

Theorem : Area of parallelogram *ABCD* whose sides *AB, BC, CD* and *DA* are represented by $a_1x + b_1y + c_1 = 0$, $a_2x + b_2y + c_2 = 0$, $a_1x + b_1y + d_1 = 0$ and $a_2x + b_2y + d_2 = 0$ is

$$\frac{p_1 p_2}{\sin\theta} \quad \text{or} \quad \frac{|c_1 - d_1||c_2 - d_2|}{\left|\begin{vmatrix} a_1 & b_1 \\ a_2 & b_2 \end{vmatrix}\right|}$$

where, p_1 and p_2 are the distances between parallel sides and θ is the angle between two adjacent sides.

Proof : Since, p_1 and p_1 are the distances between the pairs of parallel sides of the parallelogram and θ is the angle between two adjacent sides, then

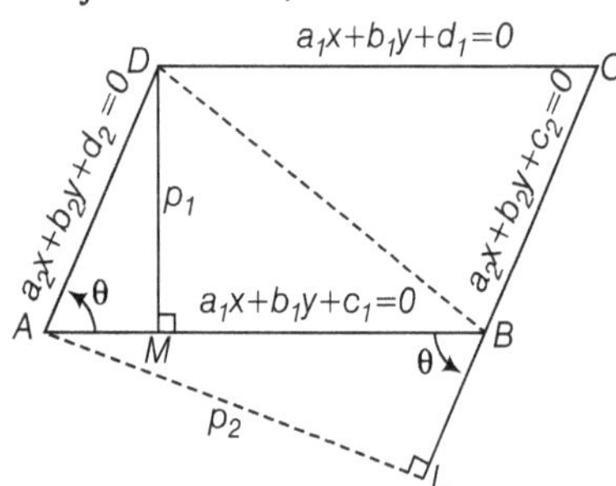

Area of parallelogram $ABCD$

$$= 2 \times \text{Area of } \Delta ABD$$

$$= 2 \times \frac{1}{2} \times AB \times p_1$$

$$= AB \times p_1$$

$$= \frac{p_2}{\sin\theta} \times p_1 \quad \left(\because \text{in } \Delta ABL, \sin\theta = \frac{p_2}{AB} \right)$$

$$= \frac{p_1 p_2}{\sin\theta} \quad \text{...(i)}$$

Now, p_1 = Distance between parallel sides AB and DC

$$= \frac{|c_1 - d_1|}{\sqrt{(a_1^2 + b_1^2)}}$$

and p_2 = Distance between parallel sides AD and BC

$$= \frac{|c_2 - d_2|}{\sqrt{(a_2^2 + b_2^2)}}$$

Also, $\tan\theta = \left| \dfrac{m_1 - m_2}{1 + m_1 m_2} \right| = \left| \dfrac{-\dfrac{a_1}{b_1} - \left(-\dfrac{a_2}{b_2}\right)}{1 + \left(-\dfrac{a_1}{b_1}\right)\left(-\dfrac{a_2}{b_2}\right)} \right|$

$$\left(\because m_1 = \text{slope of } AB = -\frac{a_1}{b_1} \text{ and } m_2 = \text{slope of } AD = -\frac{a_2}{b_2} \right)$$

$$= \left| \frac{a_1 b_2 - a_2 b_1}{a_1 a_2 + b_1 b_2} \right|$$

$\therefore$ $$\sin\theta = \frac{|a_1 b_2 - a_2 b_1|}{\sqrt{(a_1^2 + b_1^2)(a_2^2 + b_2^2)}}$$

Now, substitute the values of p_1, p_2 and $\sin\theta$ in Eq. (i)

$\therefore$ Area of parallelogram $ABCD = \dfrac{|c_1 - d_1||c_2 - d_2|}{|a_1 b_2 - a_2 b_1|}$

$$= \frac{|c_1 - d_1||c_2 - d_2|}{\left| \begin{vmatrix} a_1 & b_1 \\ a_2 & b_2 \end{vmatrix} \right|}$$

Corollaries :

1. If $p_1 = p_2$, then $ABCD$ becomes a rhombus

$\therefore$ Area of rhombus $ABCD = \dfrac{p_1^2}{\sin\theta}$

$$= \frac{(c_1 - d_1)^2}{|a_1 b_2 - a_2 b_1| \sqrt{\left(\dfrac{a_1^2 + b_1^2}{a_2^2 + b_2^2} \right)}}$$

2. If d_1 and d_2 are the lengths of two perpendicular diagonals of a rhombus, then

Area of rhombus $= \dfrac{1}{2} d_1 d_2$

3. Area of the parallelogram whose sides are $y = mx + a$, $y = mx + b$, $y = nx + c$ and $y = nx + d$ is $\dfrac{|a - b||c - d|}{|m - n|}$.

Example 61. Show that the area of the parallelogram formed by the lines $x + 3y - a = 0$, $3x - 2y + 3a = 0$, $x + 3y + 4a = 0$ and $3x - 2y + 7a = 0$ is $\dfrac{20}{11} a^2$ sq units.

Sol. Required area of the parallelogram

$$= \frac{|-a - 4a||3a - 7a|}{\left| \begin{vmatrix} 1 & 3 \\ 3 & -2 \end{vmatrix} \right|} = \frac{20}{11} a^2 \text{ sq units}$$

Example 62. Show that the area of the parallelogram formed by the lines

$$x\cos\alpha + y\sin\alpha = p,\ x\cos\alpha + y\sin\alpha = q,$$
$$x\cos\beta + y\sin\beta = r,\ x\cos\beta + y\sin\beta = s \text{ is}$$
$$|(p - q)(r - s)\operatorname{cosec}(\alpha - \beta)|.$$

Sol. The equation of sides of the parallelogram are

$$x\cos\alpha + y\sin\alpha - p = 0,$$
$$x\cos\alpha + y\sin\alpha - q = 0,$$
$$x\cos\beta + y\sin\beta - r = 0,$$
and $$x\cos\beta + y\sin\beta - s = 0$$

$\therefore$ Required area of the parallelogram

$$= \frac{|-p-(-q)||-r-(-s)|}{\left|\begin{vmatrix}\cos\alpha & \sin\alpha\\ \cos\beta & \sin\beta\end{vmatrix}\right|} = \frac{|p-q||r-s|}{|\sin(\beta-\alpha)|}$$

$$= |(p-q)(r-s)\operatorname{cosec}(\alpha-\beta)|$$

Example 63. Prove that the diagonals of the parallelogram formed by the lines

$$\frac{x}{a}+\frac{y}{b}=1, \frac{x}{b}+\frac{y}{a}=1, \frac{x}{a}+\frac{y}{b}=2 \text{ and } \frac{x}{b}+\frac{y}{a}=2$$

are at right angles. Also find its area $(a \neq b)$.

Sol. The distance between the parallel sides

$$\frac{x}{a}+\frac{y}{b}=1 \text{ and } \frac{x}{a}+\frac{y}{b}=2$$

is $$\frac{|2-1|}{\sqrt{\left(\frac{1}{a^2}+\frac{1}{b^2}\right)}} = \frac{1}{\sqrt{\left(\frac{1}{a^2}+\frac{1}{b^2}\right)}} = p_1 \quad \text{(say)}$$

and the distance between the parallel sides

$$\frac{x}{b}+\frac{y}{a}=1 \text{ and } \frac{x}{b}+\frac{y}{a}=2$$

is $$\frac{|2-1|}{\sqrt{\left(\frac{1}{b^2}+\frac{1}{a^2}\right)}} = \frac{1}{\sqrt{\left(\frac{1}{a^2}+\frac{1}{b^2}\right)}} = p_2 \quad \text{(say)}$$

Here, $p_1 = p_2$.

$\therefore$ Parallelogram is a rhombus.

But we know that diagonals of rhombus are perpendicular to each other.

$\therefore$ Area of the rhombus $$= \frac{|(-1+2)(-1+2)|}{\left|\begin{vmatrix}\frac{1}{a} & \frac{1}{b}\\ \frac{1}{b} & \frac{1}{a}\end{vmatrix}\right|}$$

$$= \frac{a^2b^2}{|b^2-a^2|} (a \neq b)$$

Example 64. Show that the four lines $ax \pm by \pm c = 0$ enclose a rhombus whose area is $\frac{2c^2}{|ab|}$.

Sol. The given lines are

$$ax + by + c = 0 \quad \text{...(i)}$$
$$ax + by - c = 0 \quad \text{...(ii)}$$
$$ax - by + c = 0 \quad \text{...(iii)}$$
and $$ax - by - c = 0 \quad \text{...(iv)}$$

Distance between the parallel lines Eqs. (i) and (ii) is $\frac{2c}{\sqrt{(a^2+b^2)}} = p_1$ (say) and distance between the parallel lines Eqs. (iii) and (iv) is

$$\frac{2c}{\sqrt{(a^2+b^2)}} = p_2 \quad \text{(say)}$$

Here, $p_1 = p_2$

$\therefore$ it is a rhombus.

$\therefore$ Area of rhombus $$= \frac{|(c+c)(c+c)|}{\left|\begin{vmatrix}a & b\\ a & -b\end{vmatrix}\right|} = \frac{4c^2}{|-2ab|} = \frac{2c^2}{|ab|}$$

Exercise for Session 2

1. The number of lines that are parallel to $2x + 6y - 7 = 0$ and have an intercept 10 between the coordinate axes is
   (a) 1 (b) 2 (c) 4 (d) infinitely many

2. The distance between the lines $4x + 3y = 11$ and $8x + 6y = 15$ is
   (a) $\frac{7}{2}$ (b) $\frac{7}{5}$ (c) $\frac{7}{10}$ (d) $\frac{9}{10}$

3. If the algebraic sum of the perpendicular distances from the points (2, 0), (0, 2) and (1, 1) to a variable straight line is zero, then the line passes through the point
   (a) (1, 1) (b) (–1, 1) (c) (–1, –1) (d) (1, –1)

4. If the quadrilateral formed by the lines $ax + by + c = 0$, $a'x + b'y + c' = 0$, $ax + by + c' = 0$ and $a'x + b'y + c' = 0$ have perpendicular diagonals, then
   (a) $b^2 + c^2 = b'^2 + c'^2$ (b) $c^2 + a^2 = c'^2 + a'^2$ (c) $a^2 + b^2 = a'^2 + b'^2$ (d) None of these

5. The area of the parallelogram formed by the lines $3x - 4y + 1 = 0$, $3x - 4y + 3 = 0$, $4x - 3y - 1 = 0$ and $4x - 3y - 2 = 0$, is
   (a) $\frac{1}{7}$ sq units (b) $\frac{2}{7}$ sq units (c) $\frac{3}{7}$ sq units (d) $\frac{4}{7}$ sq units

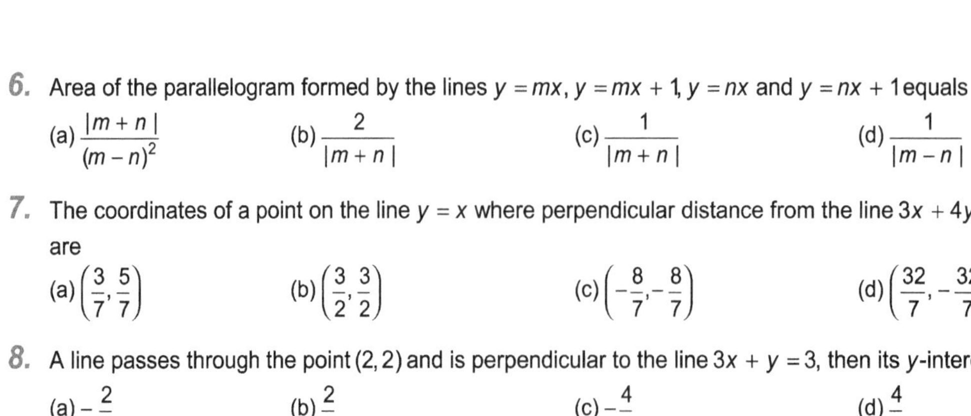

6. Area of the parallelogram formed by the lines $y = mx$, $y = mx + 1$, $y = nx$ and $y = nx + 1$ equals

(a) $\frac{|m+n|}{(m-n)^2}$ (b) $\frac{2}{|m+n|}$ (c) $\frac{1}{|m+n|}$ (d) $\frac{1}{|m-n|}$

7. The coordinates of a point on the line $y = x$ where perpendicular distance from the line $3x + 4y = 12$ is 4 units, are

(a) $\left(\frac{3}{7}, \frac{5}{7}\right)$ (b) $\left(\frac{3}{2}, \frac{3}{2}\right)$ (c) $\left(-\frac{8}{7}, -\frac{8}{7}\right)$ (d) $\left(\frac{32}{7}, -\frac{32}{7}\right)$

8. A line passes through the point $(2, 2)$ and is perpendicular to the line $3x + y = 3$, then its y-intercept is

(a) $-\frac{2}{3}$ (b) $\frac{2}{3}$ (c) $-\frac{4}{3}$ (d) $\frac{4}{3}$

9. If the points (1, 2) and (3, 4) were to be on the opposite side of the line $3x - 5y + a = 0$, then

(a) $7 < a < 11$ (b) $a = 7$ (c) $a = 11$ (d) $a < 7$ or $a > 11$

10. The lines $y = mx$, $y + 2x = 0$, $y = 2x + k$ and $y + mx = k$ form a rhombus if m equals

(a) -1 (b) $\frac{1}{2}$ (c) 1 (d) 2

11. The points on the axis of x, whose perpendicular distance from the straight line $\frac{x}{a} + \frac{y}{b} = 1$ is a

(a) $\frac{b}{a}(a \pm \sqrt{(a^2 + b^2)}, 0)$ (b) $\frac{a}{b}(b \pm \sqrt{(a^2 + b^2)}, 0)$

(c) $\frac{b}{a}(a + b, 0)$ (d) $\frac{a}{b}(a \pm \sqrt{(a^2 + b^2)}, 0)$

12. The three sides of a triangle are given by $(x^2 - y^2)(2x + 3y - 6) = 0$. If the point $(-2, a)$ lies inside and $(b, 1)$ lies outside the triangle, then

(a) $a \in \left(2, \frac{10}{3}\right)$; $b \in (-1, 1)$ (b) $a \in \left(-2, \frac{10}{3}\right)$; $b \in \left(-1, \frac{9}{2}\right)$

(c) $a \in \left(1, \frac{10}{3}\right)$; $b \in (-3, 5)$ (d) None of these

13. Are the points (3, 4) and (2, –6) on the same or opposite sides of the line $3x - 4y = 8$?

14. If the points (4, 7) and $(\cos\theta, \sin\theta)$, where $0 < \theta < \pi$, lie on the same side of the line $x + y - 1 = 0$, then prove that θ lies in the first quadrant.

15. Find the equations of lines parallel to $3x - 4y - 5 = 0$ at a unit distance from it.

16. Show that the area of the parallelogram formed by the lines $2x - 3y + a = 0$, $3x - 2y - a = 0$, $2x - 3y + 3a = 0$ and $3x - 2y - 2a = 0$ is $\frac{2a^2}{5}$ sq units.

17. A line 'L' is drawn from $P(4, 3)$ to meet the lines $L_1: 3x + 4y + 5 = 0$ and $L_2: 3x + 4y + 15 = 0$ at point A and B respectively. From 'A' a line, perpendicular to L is drawn meeting the line L_2 at A_1. Similarly from point 'B' a line, perpendicular to L is drawn meeting the line L_1 at B_1. Thus a parallelogram AA_1BB_1 is formed. Find the equation (s) of 'L' so that the area of the parallelogram AA_1BB_1 is least.

18. The vertices of a ΔOBC are $O(0, 0)$, $B(-3, -1)$, $C(-1, -3)$. Find the equation of the line parallel to BC and intersecting the sides OB and OC and whose perpendicular distance from the origin is $\frac{1}{2}$.

Session 3

Point of Intersection of Two Lines, Concurrent Lines Family of Lines, How to Find Circumcentre and Orthocentre by Slopes

Points of Intersection of Two Lines

Let $a_1x + b_1y + c_1 = 0$ and $a_2x + b_2y + c_2 = 0$ be two non-parallel lines. If (x_1, y_1) be the coordinates of their point of intersection,

then $a_1x_1 + b_1y_1 + c_1 = 0$ and $a_2x_1 + b_2y_1 + c_2 = 0$

Solving these two by cross multiplication, then

$$\frac{x_1}{b_1c_2 - b_2c_1} = \frac{y_1}{c_1a_2 - c_2a_1} = \frac{1}{a_1b_2 - a_2b_1}$$

we get $$(x_1, y_1) \equiv \left(\frac{b_1c_2 - b_2c_1}{a_1b_2 - a_2b_1}, \frac{c_1a_2 - c_2a_1}{a_1b_2 - a_2b_1}\right)$$

$$\equiv \left(\frac{\begin{vmatrix} b_1 & b_2 \\ c_1 & c_2 \end{vmatrix}}{\begin{vmatrix} a_1 & a_2 \\ b_1 & b_2 \end{vmatrix}}, \frac{\begin{vmatrix} c_1 & c_2 \\ a_1 & a_2 \end{vmatrix}}{\begin{vmatrix} a_1 & a_2 \\ b_1 & b_2 \end{vmatrix}}\right)$$

Remarks

1. Here lines are not parallel, they have unequal slopes, then, $a_1b_2 - a_2b_1 \neq 0$
2. In solving numerical questions, we should not be remember the coordinates (x_1, y_1) given above, but we solve the equations directly.

Concurrent Lines

The three given lines are concurrent, if they meet in a point. Hence to prove that three given lines are concurrent, we proceed as follows :

I Method : Find the point of intersection of any two lines by solving them simultaneously. If this point satisfies the third equation also, then the given lines are concurrent.

II Method : The three lines $a_ix + b_iy + c_i = 0, i = 1, 2, 3$ are concurrent if

$$\begin{vmatrix} a_1 & b_1 & c_1 \\ a_2 & b_2 & c_2 \\ a_3 & b_3 & c_3 \end{vmatrix} = 0$$

III Method : The condition for the lines $P = 0, Q = 0$ and $R = 0$ to be concurrent is that three constants l, m, n (not all zeros at the same time) can be obtained such that

$$lP + mQ + nR = 0$$

Remarks

1. The reader is advised to follow method I in numerical problems.
2. For finding unknown quantity applying method II.

Example 65. Show that the lines

$2x + 3y - 8 = 0$, $x - 5y + 9 = 0$ and $3x + 4y - 11 = 0$

are concurrent.

Sol. **I Method :** Solving the first two equations, we see that their point of intersection is (1, 2) which also satisfies the third equation

$$3 \times 1 + 4 \times 2 - 11 = 0$$

Hence the given lines are concurrent.

II Method : We have $\begin{vmatrix} a_1 & b_1 & c_1 \\ a_2 & b_2 & c_2 \\ a_3 & b_3 & c_3 \end{vmatrix} = \begin{vmatrix} 2 & 3 & 8 \\ 1 & -5 & 9 \\ 3 & 4 & -11 \end{vmatrix}$

Applying $C_3 \to C_3 + C_1 + 2C_2$

$$= \begin{vmatrix} 2 & 3 & 0 \\ 1 & -5 & 0 \\ 3 & 4 & 0 \end{vmatrix} = 0$$

Hence the given lines are concurrent.

III Method : Suppose

$$l(2x + 3y - 8) + m(x - 5y + 9) + n(3x + 4y - 11) = 0$$

$$\Rightarrow x(2l + m + 3n) + y(3l - 5m + 4n) + (-8l + 9m - 11n) = 0$$

$$= 0 \cdot x + 0 \cdot y + 0$$

On comparing,

$$2l + m + 3n = 0, 3l - 5m + 4n = 0, -8l + 9m - 11n = 0$$

After solving, we get $l = 19, m = 1, n = -13$

Hence, $19(2x + 3y - 8) + (x - 5y + 9) - 13(3x + 4y - 11) = 0$

Hence the given lines are concurrent.

Example 66. If the lines $ax+y+1=0$, $x+by+1=0$ and $x+y+c=0$ (a, b and c being distinct and different from 1) are concurrent, then find the value of $\frac{1}{1-a}+\frac{1}{1-b}+\frac{1}{1-c}$.

Sol. The given lines are concurrent, then

$$\begin{vmatrix} a & 1 & 1 \\ 1 & b & 1 \\ 1 & 1 & c \end{vmatrix}=0 \Rightarrow \begin{vmatrix} a & 1-a & 1-a \\ 1 & b-1 & 0 \\ 1 & 0 & c-1 \end{vmatrix}=0$$

(applying $C_2 \to C_2 - C_1$ and $C_3 \to C_3 - C_1$)

Expanding along first row

$$\Rightarrow \quad a(b-1)(c-1)-(1-a)(c-1)-(1-a)(b-1)=0$$

$$\Rightarrow \quad a(1-b)(1-c)+(1-a)(1-c)+(1-a)(1-b)=0$$

Dividing by $(1-a)(1-b)(1-c)$, then

$$\frac{a}{1-a}+\frac{1}{1-b}+\frac{1}{1-c}=0$$

$$\Rightarrow \quad -1+\frac{1}{1-a}+\frac{1}{1-b}+\frac{1}{1-c}=0$$

Hence, $$\frac{1}{1-a}+\frac{1}{1-b}+\frac{1}{1-c}=1$$

Example 67. Show that the three straight lines $2x-3y+5=0$, $3x+4y-7=0$ and $9x-5y+8=0$ meet in a point.

Sol. If we multiply these three equations by 3, 1 and −1, we have

$$3(2x-3y+5)+(3x+4y-7)-(9x-5y+8)=0$$

which is an identity.

Hence, three lines meet in a point.

Family of Lines

Theorem : Any line through the point of intersection of the lines $a_1x+b_1y+c_1=0$ and $a_2x+b_2y+c_2=0$ can be represented by the equation

$$(a_1x+b_1y+c_1)+\lambda(a_2x+b_2y+c_2)=0$$

where λ is a parameter which depends on the other property of line.

Proof : The equations of the lines are

$$a_1x+b_1y+c_1=0 \quad \text{...(i)}$$

and $$a_2x+b_2y+c_2=0 \quad \text{...(ii)}$$

Multiplying μ and ν in Eqs. (i) and (ii) and adding, we get

$$\mu(a_1x+b_1y+c_1)+\nu(a_2x+b_2y+c_2)=0$$

where μ, ν are any constants not both zero.

Dividing both sides by μ, then

$$(a_1x+b_1y+c_1)+\frac{\nu}{\mu}(a_2x+b_2y+c_2)=0$$

$$\Rightarrow (a_1x+b_1y+c_1)+\lambda(a_2x+b_2y+c_2)=0 \left(\text{where, } \lambda=\frac{\nu}{\mu}\right)$$

It is a first degree equation in x and y. So it represents family of lines through the point of intersection of Eqs. (i) and (ii).

Thus, the family of straight lines through the intersection of lines

$$L_1 \equiv a_1x+b_1y+c_1=0$$

and $L_2 \equiv a_2x+b_2y+c_2=0$ is

$$(a_1x+b_1y+c_1)+\lambda(a_2x+b_2y+c_2)=0$$

i.e. $$L_1+\lambda L_2=0$$

Corollaries :

1. The equation $L_1+\lambda L_2=0$ or $\mu L_1+\nu L_2=0$ represent a line passing through the intersection of the lines $L_1=0$ and $L_2=0$ which is a fixed point, where λ, μ, ν are constants.
2. For finding fixed point, the number of constants in family of lines are one or two. If number of constants more than two, then convert in two or one constant form.

Example 68. Find the equation of the straight line passing through the point (2, 1) and through the point of intersection of the lines $x+2y=3$ and $2x-3y=4$.

Sol. Equation of any straight line passing through the intersection of the lines $x+2y=3$ and $2x-3y=4$ is

$$\lambda(x+2y-3)+(2x-3y-4)=0 \quad \text{...(i)}$$

Since, it passes through the point (2, 1)

$$\therefore \quad \lambda(2+2-3)+(4-3-4)=0$$

$$\Rightarrow \quad \lambda-3=0$$

$$\therefore \quad \lambda=3$$

Now, substituting this value of λ in (i), we get

$$3(x+2y-3)+(2x-3y-4)=0$$

i.e. $$5x+3y-13=0$$

which is the equation of required line.

Example 69. The family of lines $x(a+2b)+y(a+3b)=a+b$ passes through the point for all values of a and b. Find the point.

Sol. The given equation can be written as

$$a(x+y-1)+b(2x+3y-1)=0$$

which is equation of a line passing through the point of intersection of the lines $x+y-1=0$ and $2x+3y-1=0$. The point of intersection of these lines is $(2, -1)$. Hence the given family of lines passes through the point $(2, -1)$ for all values of a and b.

Example 70. If $3a+2b+6c=0$ the family of straight lines $ax+by+c=0$ passes through a fixed point. Find the coordinates of fixed point.

Sol. Given, $3a + 2b + 6c = 0$

or $$\frac{a}{2}+\frac{b}{3}+c=0 \qquad \text{...(i)}$$

and family of straight lines is

$$ax + by + c = 0 \qquad \text{...(ii)}$$

Subtracting Eqs. (i) from (ii), then

$$a\left(x-\frac{1}{2}\right)+b\left(y-\frac{1}{3}\right)=0$$

which is equation of a line passing through the point of intersection of the lines

$$x-\frac{1}{2}=0 \quad \text{and} \quad y-\frac{1}{3}=0$$

$\therefore$ The coordinates of fixed point are $\left(\frac{1}{2},\frac{1}{3}\right)$.

Example 71. If $4a^2+9b^2-c^2+12ab=0$, then the family of straight lines $ax+by+c=0$ is either concurrent at ... or at ....

Sol. Given, $4a^2+9b^2-c^2+12ab=0$

or $$(2a+3b)^2-c^2=0$$

or $$c=\pm(2a+3b) \qquad \text{...(i)}$$

and family of straight lines is

$$ax+by+c=0 \qquad \text{...(ii)}$$

Substituting the value of c from Eqs. (i) in (ii), then

$$ax+by\pm(2a+3b)=0$$

$$\Rightarrow \quad a(x\pm 2)+b(y\pm 3)=0$$

Taking '+' sign : $a(x+2)+b(y+3)=0$

which is equation of a line passing through the point of intersection of the lines $x+2=0$ and $y+3=0$

$\therefore$ coordinates of fixed point are $(-2,-3)$.

Taking '–' sign : $a(x-2)+b(y-3)=0$

which is equation of a line passing through the point of intersection of the lines

$$x-2=0 \quad \text{and} \quad y-3=0$$

$\therefore$ coordinates of fixed point are $(2, 3)$

Hence, the family of straight lines $ax+by+c=0$ is either concurrent at $(-2,-3)$ or *at* $(2,3)$.

Example 72. Find the equation of the line passing through the point of intersection of the lines $x+5y+7=0, 3x+2y-5=0$

and (a) parallel to the line $7x+2y-5=0$

(b) perpendicular to the line $7x+2y-5=0$

Sol. Any line passing through the point of intersection of the given lines is

$$(x+5y+7)+\lambda(3x+2y-5)=0$$

$$\Rightarrow \quad x(1+3\lambda)+y(5+2\lambda)+(7-5\lambda)=0 \qquad \text{...(i)}$$

Its slope $= -\dfrac{(1+3\lambda)}{(5+2\lambda)}$

(a) Line Eq. (i) is to be parallel to $7x+2y-5=0$

then $$-\frac{(1+3\lambda)}{(5+2\lambda)}=-\frac{7}{2}$$

$$\Rightarrow \quad 2+6\lambda=35+14\lambda$$

$$\Rightarrow \quad 8\lambda=-33$$

$$\Rightarrow \quad \lambda=-\frac{33}{8}$$

Substituting this value of λ in Eq. (i), we get the required equation as $7x+2y-17=0$

(b) Line, (i) is to be perpendicular to $7x+2y-5=0$

$$\therefore \quad -\frac{(1+3\lambda)}{(5+2\lambda)}\times-\left(\frac{7}{2}\right)=-1$$

or $$7+21\lambda=-10-4\lambda$$

$$\therefore \quad \lambda=-\frac{17}{25}$$

Substituting this value of λ is Eq. (i), we get the required equation as

$$2x-7y-20=0.$$

Aliter :

The point of intersection of the given lines

$x+5y-7=0$ and $3x+2y-5=0$ is $(3,-2)$.

$\therefore$ Equation of line through $(3,-2)$ is

$$y+2=m(x-3) \qquad \text{...(ii)}$$

(a) Line (ii) is parallel to $7x+2y-5=0$

$$\therefore \quad m=-\frac{7}{2}$$

Hence, the equation of the required line is

$$y+2=-\frac{7}{2}(x-3)$$

or $$7x+2y-17=0$$

(b) Line (ii) is perpendicular to $7x+2y-5=0$

then $$m\times\left(-\frac{7}{2}\right)=-1$$

or $$m=\frac{2}{7}$$

Hence, the equation of the required line is

$$y+2=\frac{2}{7}(x-3)$$

or $$2x-7y-20=0$$

Example 73. Find the equation of straight line which passes through the intersection of the straight lines

$$3x-4y+1=0 \quad and \quad 5x+y-1=0$$

and cuts off equal intercepts from the axes.

Solution : Equation of any line passing through the intersection of the given lines is

$$(3x-4y+1)+\lambda(5x+y-1)=0$$

$$\Rightarrow \quad x(3+5\lambda)+y(-4+\lambda)+(1-\lambda)=0 \quad ...(i)$$

$$\Rightarrow \quad \frac{x}{\left(\frac{\lambda-1}{3+5\lambda}\right)}+\frac{y}{\left(\frac{\lambda-1}{\lambda-4}\right)}=1$$

but given x-intercept = y-intercept

i.e. $$\left(\frac{\lambda-1}{3+5\lambda}\right)=\left(\frac{\lambda-1}{\lambda-4}\right)$$

$$\Rightarrow \quad \frac{1}{3+5\lambda}=\frac{1}{\lambda-4}$$

($\lambda \neq 1 \because$ if $\lambda=1$ then line (i) pass through origin)

$$\therefore \quad \lambda-4=3+5\lambda$$

or $$4\lambda=-7$$

$$\therefore \quad \lambda=-\frac{7}{4}$$

Substituting the value of λ in Eq. (i), we get required equation is $23x+23y=11$.

Example 74. If t_1 and t_2 are roots of the equation $t^2+\lambda t+1=0$, where λ is an arbitrary constant. Then prove that the line joining the points $(at_1^2, 2at_1)$ and $(at_2^2, 2at_2)$ always passes through a fixed point. Also find that point.

Sol. $\because t_1$ and t_2 are the roots of the equation $t^2+\lambda t+1=0$

$$\therefore \quad t_1+t_2=-\lambda \quad \text{and} \quad t_1t_2=1 \quad ...(i)$$

Equation of the line joining the points $(at_1^2, 2at_1)$ and $(at_2^2, 2at_2)$ is

$$y-2at_1=\frac{2at_2-2at_1}{at_2^2-at_1^2}(x-at_1^2)$$

$$\Rightarrow \quad y-2at_1=\frac{2}{(t_2+t_1)}(x-at_1^2)$$

$$\Rightarrow \quad y(t_1+t_2)-2at_1t_2-2at_1^2=2x-2at_1^2$$

$$\Rightarrow \quad y(t_1+t_2)-2at_1t_2=2x$$

$$\Rightarrow \quad y(-\lambda)-2a=2x \quad \text{[from Eq. (i)]}$$

or $$(x+a)+\lambda\left(\frac{y}{2}\right)=0$$

which is equation of a line passing through the point of intersection of the lines $x+a=0$ and $\frac{y}{2}=0$.

$\therefore$ coordinates of fixed point are $(-a, 0)$.

Example 75. A variable straight line through the point of intersection of the lines $\frac{x}{a}+\frac{y}{b}=1$ and $\frac{x}{b}+\frac{y}{a}=1$ meets the coordinate axes in A and B. Show that the locus of the mid-point of AB is the curve $2xy(a+b)=ab(x+y)$.

Sol. Any line through the point of intersection of given lines is

$$\left(\frac{x}{a}+\frac{y}{b}-1\right)+\lambda\left(\frac{x}{b}+\frac{y}{a}-1\right)=0$$

$$x\left(\frac{1}{a}+\frac{\lambda}{b}\right)+y\left(\frac{1}{b}+\frac{\lambda}{a}\right)=(1+\lambda)$$

$$\Rightarrow \quad x\left(\frac{b+a\lambda}{ab}\right)+y\left(\frac{a+b\lambda}{ab}\right)=(1+\lambda)$$

$$\Rightarrow \quad \frac{x}{\left\{\frac{ab(1+\lambda)}{b+a\lambda}\right\}}+\frac{y}{\left\{\frac{ab(1+\lambda)}{a+b\lambda}\right\}}=1$$

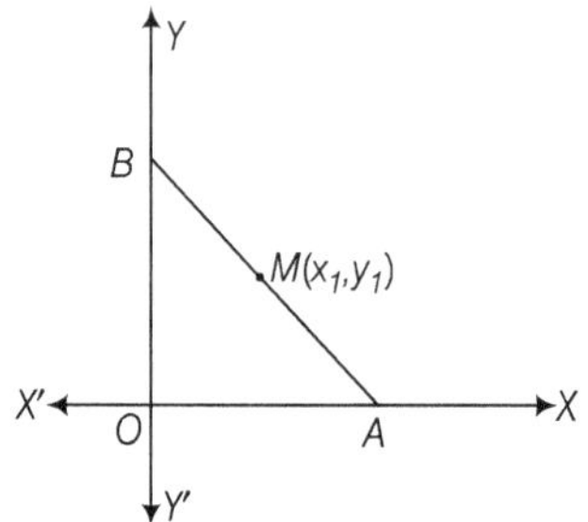

This meets the X-axis at

$$A \equiv \left(\frac{ab(1+\lambda)}{b+a\lambda}, 0\right)$$

and meets the Y-axis at

$$B \equiv \left(0, \frac{ab(1+\lambda)}{a+b\lambda}\right)$$

Let the mid-point of AB is $M(x_1, y_1)$, then

$$x_1=\frac{ab(1+\lambda)}{2(b+a\lambda)} \quad \text{and} \quad y_1=\frac{ab(1+\lambda)}{2(a+b\lambda)}$$

$$\therefore \quad \frac{1}{x_1}+\frac{1}{y_1}=\frac{2(b+a\lambda)}{ab(1+\lambda)}+\frac{2(a+b\lambda)}{ab(1+\lambda)}$$

$$=\frac{2}{ab(1+\lambda)}(b+a\lambda+a+b\lambda)$$

$$=\frac{2}{ab(1+\lambda)}(a+b)(1+\lambda)$$

$$\Rightarrow \quad \frac{(x_1+y_1)}{x_1y_1}=\frac{2(a+b)}{ab}$$

$$\Rightarrow \quad 2x_1y_1(a+b)=ab(x_1+y_1)$$

Hence, the locus of mid point of AB is

$$2xy(a+b)=ab(x+y).$$

How to Find Circumcentre and Orthocentre by Slopes

(i) Circumcentre

The circumcentre of a triangle is the point of intersection of the perpendicular bisectors of the sides of a triangle. It is the centre of the circle which passes through the vertices of the triangle and so its distance from the vertices of the triangle is the same and this distance is known as the **circumradius** of the triangle.

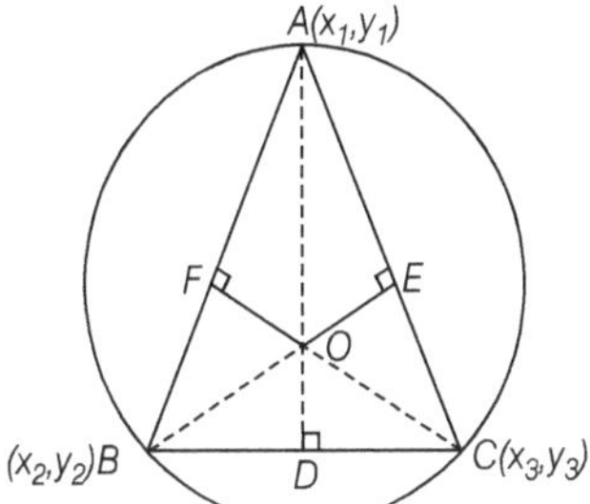

Let $O(x, y)$ be the circumcentre.

If D, E and F are the mid points of BC, CA and AB respectively and $OD \perp BC$, $OE \perp CA$ and $OF \perp AB$

$\therefore$ slope of $OD \times$ slope of $BC = -1$

and slope of $OE \times$ slope of $CA = -1$

and slope of $OF \times$ slope of $AB = -1$

Solving any two, we get (x, y).

Example 76. Find the coordinates of the circumcentre of the triangle whose vertices are $A(5, -1)$, $B(-1, 5)$ and $C(6, 6)$. Find its radius also.

Sol. Let circumcentre be $O'(\alpha, \beta)$ and mid points of sides BC, CA and AB are $D\left(\frac{5}{2}, \frac{11}{2}\right)$, $E\left(\frac{11}{2}, \frac{5}{2}\right)$ and $F(2, 2)$ respectively. Since $O'D \perp BC$.

$\therefore$ Slope of $O'D \times$ slope of $BC = -1$

$$\Rightarrow \quad \frac{\beta - \frac{11}{2}}{\alpha - \frac{5}{2}} \times \frac{6-5}{6+1} = -1$$

$$\Rightarrow \quad \frac{2\beta - 11}{7(2\alpha - 5)} = -1$$

$$\Rightarrow \quad 2\beta - 11 = -14\alpha + 35$$

$$\Rightarrow \quad 14\alpha + 2\beta = 46$$

$$\therefore \quad 7\alpha + \beta = 23 \quad \text{...(i)}$$

and $O'E \perp CA$

$\therefore$ Slope of $O'E \times$ Slope of $CA = -1$

$$\Rightarrow \quad \frac{\beta - \frac{5}{2}}{\alpha - \frac{11}{2}} \times \frac{-1-6}{5-6} = -1$$

$$\Rightarrow \quad \frac{2\beta - 5}{2\alpha - 11} \times \frac{7}{1} = -1$$

$$\Rightarrow \quad 14\beta - 35 = -2\alpha + 11$$

$$\therefore \quad 2\alpha + 14\beta = 46$$

$$\therefore \quad \alpha + 7\beta = 23 \quad \text{... (ii)}$$

Solving Eqs. (i) and (ii), we get

$$\alpha = \beta = \frac{23}{8}$$

$$\therefore \text{ Circumcentre} = \left(\frac{23}{8}, \frac{23}{8}\right)$$

$$\therefore \text{ Circumradius} = O'A = O'B = O'C$$

$$= O'C = \sqrt{(\alpha - 6)^2 + (\beta - 6)^2}$$

$$= \sqrt{\left(\frac{23}{8} - 6\right)^2 + \left(\frac{23}{8} - 6\right)^2}$$

$$= \sqrt{\left(\frac{25}{8}\right)^2 + \left(\frac{25}{8}\right)^2} = \frac{25\sqrt{2}}{8} \text{ units.}$$

(ii) Orthocentre

The orthocentre of a triangle is the point of intersection of altitudes.

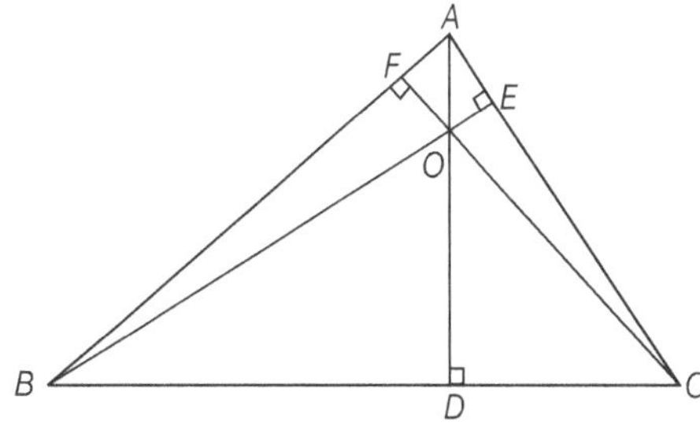

Here O is the orthocentre since $AD \perp BC$, $BE \perp CA$ and $CF \perp AB$, then $OA \perp BC$, $OB \perp CA$, and $OC \perp AB$

Solving any two we can get coordinates of O.

Remarks

1. If any two lines out of three lines i.e. AB, BC and CA are perpendicular, then orthocentre is the point of intersection of two perpendicular lines.
2. Firstly find the slope of lines BC, CA and AB.

Example 77. Find the orthocentre of the triangle formed by the lines $xy = 0$ and $x + y = 1$.

Sol. Three sides of the triangle are $x = 0, y = 0$ and $x + y = 1$. The coordinates of the vertices are $O(0, 0)$, $A(1, 0)$ and $B(0, 1)$. The triangle OAB is a right angled triangle having right angle at O. Therefore $O(0, 0)$ is the orthocentre. Since we know that the point of intersection of two perpendicular lines is the orthocentre of the triangle OAB.

Example 78. Find the orthocentre of the triangle ABC whose angular points are $A(1, 2), B(2, 3)$ and $C(4, 3)$..

Sol. Now, Slope of $BC = \dfrac{3-3}{4-2} = 0$

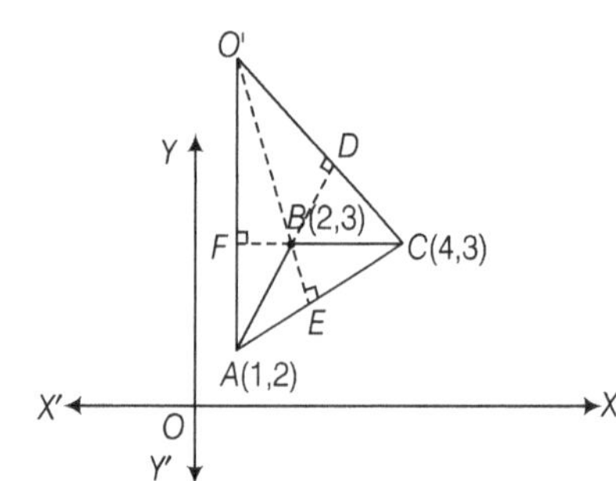

Slope of $CA = \dfrac{2-3}{1-4} = \dfrac{1}{3}$

and Slope of $AB = \dfrac{3-2}{2-1} = 1$

Let orthocentre be $O'(\alpha, \beta)$ then

Slope of $O'A \times$ slope of $BC = -1$

$$\frac{2-\beta}{1-\alpha} \times 0 = -1$$

$$\Rightarrow \quad \frac{0}{1-\alpha} = -1$$

$$\Rightarrow \quad 1 - \alpha = 0$$

$$\therefore \quad \alpha = 1$$

and Slope of $OB \times$ slope of $CA = -1$

$$\Rightarrow \quad \frac{3-\beta}{2-\alpha} \times \frac{1}{3} = -1$$

$$\Rightarrow \quad 3 - \beta = 3\alpha - 6$$

$$\Rightarrow \quad 3\alpha + \beta = 9$$

$$\therefore \quad \beta = 6 \qquad (\because \alpha = 1)$$

Hence, orthocentre of the given triangle is $(1, 6)$.

Example 79. The equations of two sides of a triangle are $3x - 2y + 6 = 0$ and $4x + 5y = 20$ and the orthocentre is $(1, 1)$. Find the equation of the third side.

Sol. Let $3x - 2y + 6 = 0$ and $4x + 5y = 20$ are the equations of the sides AB and AC. The point of intersection of AB and AC is $\left(\dfrac{10}{23}, \dfrac{84}{23}\right)$. Let slope of BC is m. Since $O'A \perp BC$

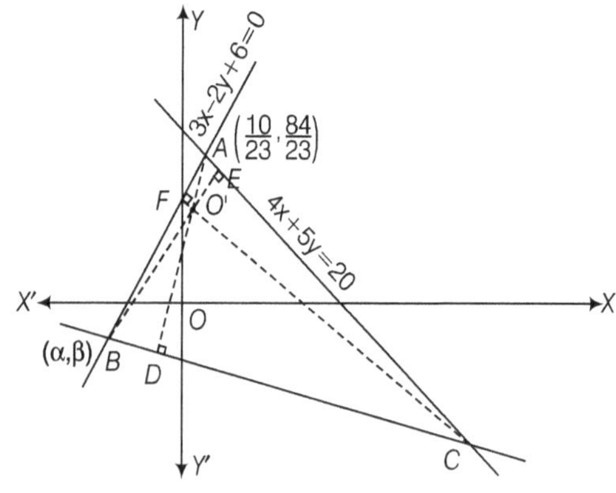

$\therefore$ Slope of $O'A \times$ Slope of $BC = -1$

$$\Rightarrow \quad \frac{\frac{84}{23} - 1}{\frac{10}{23} - 1} \times m = -1$$

$$\Rightarrow \quad \frac{61}{-13} m = -1$$

$$\therefore \quad m = \frac{13}{61}$$

Let the vertex B is (α, β).

(α, β) lies on $3x - 2y + 6 = 0$

$$\therefore \quad 3\alpha - 2\beta + 6 = 0 \qquad \text{...(i)}$$

and $O'B \perp AC$

$\therefore$ Slope of $O'B \times$ slope of $AC = -1$

$$\frac{\beta - 1}{\alpha - 1} \times \left(-\frac{4}{5}\right) = -1$$

$$\Rightarrow \quad 4\beta - 4 = 5\alpha - 5$$

$$\Rightarrow \quad 5\alpha - 4\beta - 1 = 0 \qquad \text{...(ii)}$$

Solving Eqs. (i) and (ii), we get

$$\alpha = -13 \quad \text{and} \quad \beta = -\frac{33}{2}$$

Since, third side passes through $\left(-13, -\dfrac{33}{2}\right)$ with slope $\dfrac{13}{61}$, therefore its equation is

$$y + \frac{33}{2} = \frac{13}{61}(x + 13)$$

$$\Rightarrow \quad 122y + 33 \times 61 = 26x + 2 \times 169$$

$$\Rightarrow \quad 26x - 122y - 1675 = 0$$

Aliter : The equation of line through A. i.e. point of intersection of AB and AC is

$$(3x - 2y + 6) + \lambda(4x + 5y - 20) = 0 \qquad \text{...(i)}$$

it passes through $(1, 1)$, then

$$(3 - 2 + 6) + \lambda(4 + 5 - 20) = 0$$

$$\Rightarrow \quad 7 - 11\lambda = 0$$

$$\therefore \quad \lambda = \frac{7}{11}$$

From Eq. (i), $(3x-2y+6)+\frac{7}{11}(4x+5y-20)=0$

$\Rightarrow \quad 61x+13y-74=0$

$\therefore \quad$ Slope of $AD=-\frac{61}{13}$

$\Rightarrow \quad$ Slope of $BC=\frac{13}{61}$

If coordinates of $B(\alpha,\beta)$, B lies on AB

$\therefore \quad 3\alpha-2\beta+6=0 \quad$ ...(ii)

and $\quad O'B\perp CA$

then $\quad \frac{\beta-1}{\alpha-1}\times\left(-\frac{4}{5}\right)=-1$

$\Rightarrow \quad 5\alpha-4\beta-1=0 \quad$ ...(iii)

Solving Eqs. (ii) and (iii), we get

$$\alpha=-13 \quad\text{and}\quad \beta=-\frac{33}{2}$$

$\therefore$ Equation of third side i.e. BC is

$$y+\frac{33}{2}=\frac{13}{61}(x+13)$$

$\therefore \quad 26x-122y-1675=0$

Example 80. If the orthocentre of the triangle formed by the lines $2x+3y-1=0$, $x+2y-1=0$, $ax+by-1=0$ is at origin, then find (a,b).

Sol. The equation of a line through A i.e. the point of intersection of AB and AC, is

$$(2x+3y-1)+\lambda(ax+by-1)=0 \quad \text{...(i)}$$

It passes through $O(0,0)$, then

$$-1-\lambda=0$$

$\therefore \quad \lambda=-1$

From Eq. (i),

$$2x+3y-1-ax-by+1=0$$

$\Rightarrow \quad (2-a)x+(3-b)y=0$

Since, $AD\perp BC$

$\therefore \quad -\frac{(2-a)}{(3-b)}\times\left(-\frac{1}{2}\right)=-1$

$\Rightarrow \quad 2-a=-6+2b$

$\Rightarrow \quad a+2b=8 \quad$ ...(ii)

Similarly, $BE\perp AC$, we get

$$a+b=0 \quad \text{...(iii)}$$

Solving Eqs. (ii) and (iii), we get

$$b=8 \quad\text{and}\quad a=-8$$

$\therefore \quad (a,b)$ is $(-8,8)$.

Example 81. If the equations of the sides of a triangle are $a_rx+b_ry=1; r=1,2,3$ and the orthocentre is the origin, then prove that

$$a_1a_2+b_1b_2=a_2a_3+b_2b_3=a_3a_1+b_3b_1.$$

Sol. The equation of the line through A, i.e. the point of intersection of AB and AC is

$$(a_2x+b_2y-1)+\lambda(a_3x+b_3y-1)=0 \quad \text{...(i)}$$

It passes through (0, 0), then

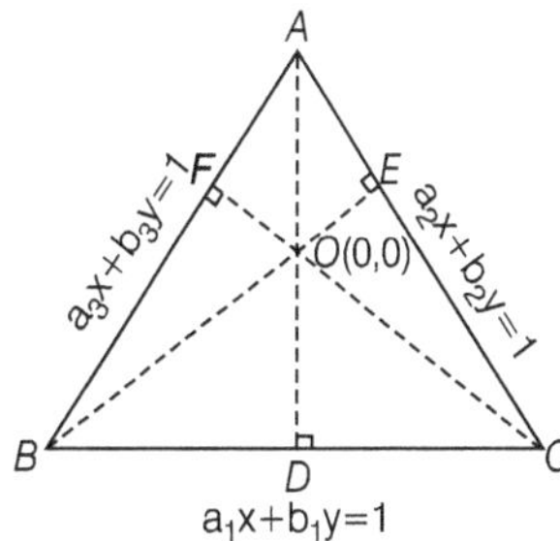

$$-1-\lambda=0$$

$\therefore \quad \lambda=-1$

From Eq. (i), $a_2x+b_2y-1-a_3x-b_3y+1=0$

$\therefore \quad (a_2-a_3)x+(b_2-b_3)y=0$

Since, $AD\perp BC$

$\therefore$ Slope of $AD\times$ slope of $BC=-1$

$$-\frac{(a_2-a_3)}{(b_2-b_3)}\times\left(-\frac{a_1}{b_1}\right)=-1$$

$\Rightarrow \quad a_1a_2-a_3a_1=-b_1b_2+b_1b_3$

$\Rightarrow \quad a_1a_2+b_1b_2=a_3a_1+b_3b_1 \quad$ ...(ii)

Similarly, $BE\perp CA$, then we get

$$a_1a_2+b_1b_2=a_2a_3+b_2b_3 \quad \text{...(iii)}$$

From Eqs. (ii) and (iii), we get

$$a_1a_2+b_1b_2=a_2a_3+b_2b_3=a_3a_1+b_3b_1$$

Exercise for Session 3

1. The locus of the point of intersection of lines $x \cos \alpha + y \sin \alpha = a$ and $x \sin \alpha - y \cos \alpha = b$ (α is a parameter) is

(a) $2(x^2 + y^2) = a^2 + b^2$
(b) $x^2 - y^2 = a^2 - b^2$
(c) $x^2 + y^2 = a^2 + b^2$
(d) $x^2 - y^2 = a^2 + b^2$

2. If a, b, c are in AP then $ax + by + c = 0$ represents

(a) a straight line
(b) a family of concurrent lines
(c) a family of parallel lines
(d) None of these

3. If the lines $x + 2ay + a = 0$, $x + 3by + b = 0$ and $x + 4cy + c = 0$ are concurrent, then a, b, c are in

(a) AP
(b) GP
(c) HP
(d) AGP

4. The set of lines $ax + by + c = 0$, where $3a + 2b + 4c = 0$ is concurrent at the point

(a) $\left(\frac{3}{4}, \frac{1}{2}\right)$
(b) $\left(\frac{1}{2}, \frac{3}{4}\right)$
(c) $\left(-\frac{3}{4}, -\frac{1}{2}\right)$
(d) $\left(-\frac{1}{2}, -\frac{3}{4}\right)$

5. If the lines $ax + y + 1 = 0$, $x + by + 1 = 0$ and $x + y + c = 0$, (a, b and c being distinct and different from 1) are concurrent, then the value of $\frac{a}{a-1} + \frac{b}{b-1} + \frac{c}{c-1}$ is

(a) -2
(b) -1
(c) 1
(d) 2

6. If $u \equiv a_1x + b_1y + c_1 = 0$ and $v \equiv a_2x + b_2y + c_2 = 0$ and $\frac{a_1}{a_2} = \frac{b_1}{b_2} = \frac{c_1}{c_2}$, then $u + kv = 0$ represents

(a) $u = 0$
(b) a family of concurrent lines
(c) a family of parallel lines
(d) None of these

7. The straight lines $x + 2y - 9 = 0$, $3x + 5y - 5 = 0$ and $ax + by - 1 = 0$ are concurrent, if the straight line $35x - 22y + 1 = 0$ passes through the point

(a) (a, b)
(b) (b, a)
(c) $(a, -b)$
(d) $(-a, b)$

8. If the straight lines $x + y - 2 = 0$, $2x - y + 1 = 0$ and $ax + by - c = 0$ are concurrent, then the family of lines $2ax + 3by + c = 0$ (a, b, c are non-zero) is concurrent at

(a) (2, 3)
(b) $\left(\frac{1}{2}, \frac{1}{3}\right)$
(c) $\left(-\frac{1}{6}, -\frac{5}{9}\right)$
(d) $\left(\frac{2}{3}, -\frac{7}{5}\right)$

9. The straight line through the point of intersection of $ax + by + c = 0$ and $a'x + b'y + c' = 0$ are parallel to Y-axis has the equation

(a) $x(ab' - a'b) + (cb' - c'b) = 0$
(b) $x(ab' + a'b) + (cb' + c'b) = 0$
(c) $y(ab' - a'b) + (c'a - ca') = 0$
(d) $y(ab' + a'b) + (c'a + ca') = 0$

10. If the equations of three sides of a triangle are $x + y = 1$, $3x + 5y = 2$ and $x - y = 0$, then the orthocentre of the triangle lies on the line/lines

(a) $5x - 3y = 1$
(b) $5y - 3x = 1$
(c) $2x - 3y = 1$
(d) $5x - 3y = 2$

11. Find the equation of the line through the intersection of $2x-3y+4=0$ and $3x+4y-5=0$ and perpendicular to $6x-7y+c=0$

(a) $199y+120x=125$
(b) $199y-120x=125$
(c) $119x+102y=125$
(d) $119x-102y=125$

12. The locus of the point of intersection of the lines $\frac{x}{a}-\frac{y}{b}=m, \frac{x}{a}+\frac{y}{b}=\frac{1}{m}$ is

(a) a circle
(b) an ellipse
(c) a hyperbola
(d) a parabola

13. Find the condition on a and b, such that the portion of the line $ax+by-1=0$, intercepted between the lines $ax+y+1=0$ and $x+by=0$ subtends a right angled at the origin.

14. If the lines $(a-b-c)x+2ay+2a=0, 2bx+(b-c-a)y+2b=0$ and $(2c+1)x+2cy+c-a-b=0$ are concurrent, then prove that either $a+b+c=0$ or $(a+b+c)^2+2a=0$.

15. Prove that the lines $ax+by+c=0, bx+cy+a=0$ and $cx+ay+b=0$ are concurrent if $a+b+c=0$ or $a+b\omega+c\omega^2=0$ or $a+b\omega^2+c\omega=0$, where ω is a complex cube root of unity.

16. Find the equation of the straight line which passes through the intersection of the lines $x-y-1=0$ and $2x-3y+1=0$ and is parallel to (i) X-axis (ii) Y-axis (iii) $3x+4y=14$.

17. Let a, b, c be parameters. Then, the equation $ax+by+c=0$ will represent a family of straight lines passing through a fixed-point, if there exists a linear relation between a, b and c.

18. Prove that the family of lines represented by $x(1+\lambda)+y(2-\lambda)+5=0, \lambda$ being arbitrary, pass through a fixed point. Also find the fixed point.

19. Prove that $\left(-a, -\frac{a}{2}\right)$ is the orthocentre of the triangle formed by the lines $y=m_i x+\frac{a}{m_i}, i=1,2,3; m_1, m_2, m_3$ being the roots of the equation $x^3-3x^2+2=0$.

Session 4

Equations of Straight Lines Passing Through a Given Point and Making a Given Angle with a Given Line, A Line Equally Inclined With Two Lines, Equation of the Bisectors, Bisector of the Angle Containing the Origin, Equation of that Bisector of the Angle Between Two Lines which Contains a Given Point, How to Distinguish the Acute (Internal) and Obtuse (External) Angle Bisectors

Equations of Straight Lines Passing Through a Given Point and Making a Given Angle with a Given Line

Theorem : Prove that the equations of the straight lines which pass through a given point (x_1, y_1) and make a given angle α with the given straight line $y = mx + c$ are

$$y - y_1 = \tan(\theta \pm \alpha)(x - x_1)$$

where, $m = \tan\theta$.

Proof : Let AB be the given line which makes an angle θ with X-axis.

$\therefore \quad m = \tan\theta$

Let CD and EF are two required lines which make angle α with the given line. Let these lines meet the given line AB at Q and R respectively

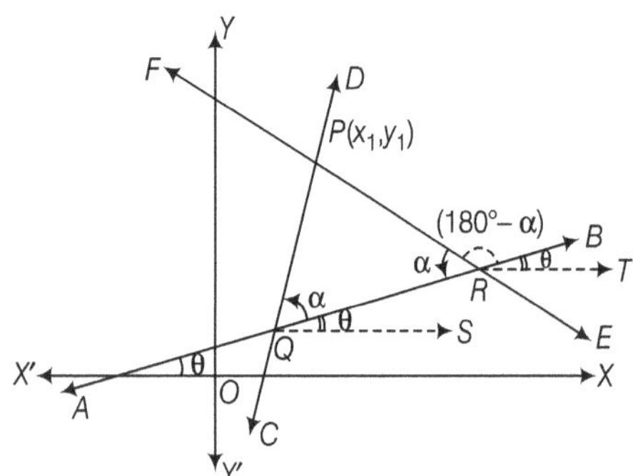

$\therefore \quad \angle DQS = \angle PQR + \angle RQS = (\alpha + \theta)$

$\therefore$ Equation of line CD is

$$y - y_1 = \tan(\theta + \alpha)(x - x_1) \quad \text{...(i)}$$

and $\angle FRT = \angle FRB + \angle BRT$

$$= 180^\circ - \alpha + \theta$$

$$= 180^\circ + (\theta - \alpha)$$

$\therefore$ Equation of line EF is

$$y - y_1 = \tan(180^\circ + \theta - \alpha)(x - x_1)$$

or $y - y_1 = \tan(\theta - \alpha)(x - x_1) \quad \text{...(ii)}$

From Eqs. (i) and (ii), we get

$$y - y_1 = \tan(\theta \pm \alpha)(x - x_1)$$

These are the equations of the two required lines.

Example 82. Find the equations of the straight lines passing through the point (2, 3) and inclined at $\pi/4$ radians to the line $2x + 3y = 5$.

Sol. Let the line $2x + 3y = 5$ make an angle θ with positive X-axis.

Then $\tan\theta = -\dfrac{2}{3}$

Now $\tan\theta \cdot \tan\dfrac{\pi}{4} = -\dfrac{2}{3} \times 1$

$$= -\frac{2}{3} \neq \pm 1$$

Slopes of required lines are

$$\tan\left(\theta + \frac{\pi}{4}\right) \text{ and } \tan\left(\theta - \frac{\pi}{4}\right)$$

$$\therefore \quad \tan\left(\theta+\frac{\pi}{4}\right)=\frac{\tan\theta+\tan\left(\frac{\pi}{4}\right)}{1-\tan\theta\tan\left(\frac{\pi}{4}\right)}=\frac{\left(-\frac{2}{3}\right)+1}{1-\left(-\frac{2}{3}\right)(1)}=\frac{1}{5}$$

$$\text{and} \quad \tan\left(\theta-\frac{\pi}{4}\right)=\frac{\tan\theta-\tan\left(\frac{\pi}{4}\right)}{1+\tan\theta\tan\left(\frac{\pi}{4}\right)}$$

$$=\frac{\left(-\frac{2}{3}\right)-1}{1+\left(-\frac{2}{3}\right)(1)}=-5$$

$\therefore$ Equations of required lines are

$$y-3=\frac{1}{5}(x-2) \text{ and } y-3=-5(x-2)$$

i.e. $x-5y+13=0$ and $5x+y-13=0$

Example 83. A vertex of an equilateral triangle is $(2, 3)$ and the opposite side is $x+y=2$. Find the equations of the other sides.

Sol. Let $A(2, 3)$ be one vertex and $x+y=2$ be the opposite side of an equilateral triangle. Clearly remaining two sides pass through the point $A(2, 3)$ and make an angle 60° with $x+y=2$

$\because$ Slope of $x+y=2$ is -1

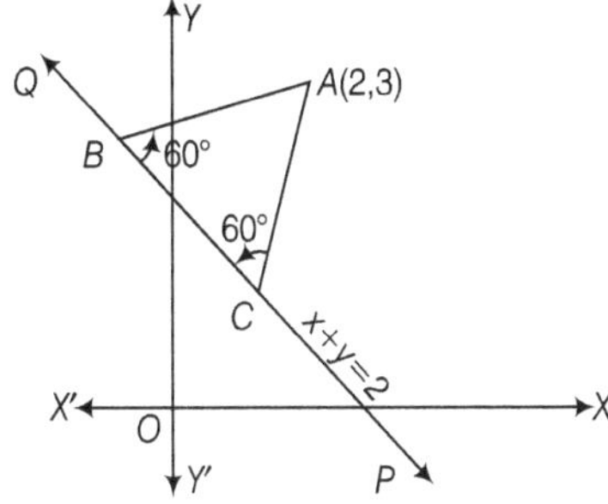

Let $\tan\theta=-1$

$\therefore \quad \theta=135°$

$\therefore$ Equations of the other two sides are

$$y-3=\tan(135°\pm 60°)(x-2)$$

i.e. sides are

$$y-3=\tan(195°)(x-2) \quad \text{(taking '+' sign)}$$

$$\Rightarrow \quad y-3=\tan(180°+15°)(x-2)$$

$$\Rightarrow \quad y-3=\tan 15°(x-2)$$

$$\Rightarrow \quad y-3=(2-\sqrt{3})(x-2)$$

$$\Rightarrow \quad (2-\sqrt{3})x-y=1-2\sqrt{3}$$

$$\text{and} \quad y-3=\tan(75°)(x-2) \quad \text{(taking '–' sign)}$$

$$\Rightarrow \quad y-3=\cot 15°(x-2)$$

$$\Rightarrow \quad y-3=(2+\sqrt{3})(x-2)$$

$$\Rightarrow \quad (2+\sqrt{3})x-y=1+2\sqrt{3}$$

Hence, equations of other sides are

$$(2-\sqrt{3})x-y=1-2\sqrt{3}$$

$$\text{and} \quad (2+\sqrt{3})x-y=1+2\sqrt{3}$$

Example 84. The straight lines $3x+4y=5$ and $4x-3y=15$ intersect at a point A. On these lines, the points B and C are chosen so that $AB=AC$. Find the possible equations of the line BC passing through the point $(1, 2)$.

Sol. Clearly $\angle BAC=90°$

$\because \quad AB=AC$

$\therefore \quad \angle ABC=\angle BCA=45°$

$\alpha=45°$

$\because$ Slope of $3x+4y=5$ is $-\frac{3}{4}$

Let $\tan\theta=-\frac{3}{4}$

So, possible equations of BC are given by

$$y-2=\tan(\theta\pm\alpha)(x-1)$$

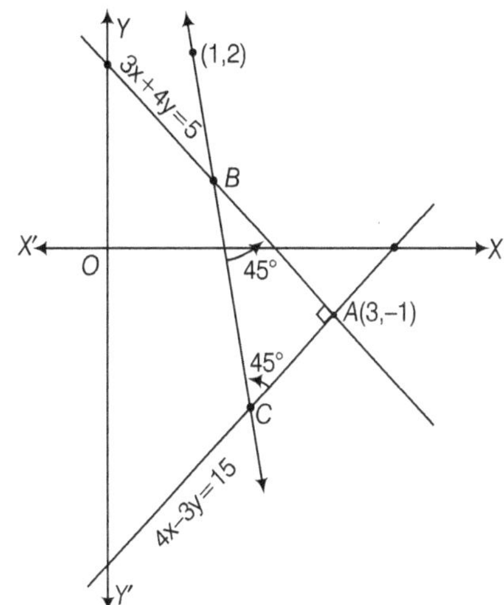

$$\Rightarrow \quad y-2=\left(\frac{\tan\theta\pm\tan\alpha}{1\mp\tan\theta\tan\alpha}\right)(x-1)$$

$$\Rightarrow \quad y-2=\left(\frac{-\frac{3}{4}\pm 1}{1\mp\left(-\frac{3}{4}\right)(1)}\right)(x-1)$$

$$\Rightarrow \quad y-2=\left(\frac{-3\pm 4}{4\mp(-3)}\right)(x-1)$$

$$\Rightarrow \quad y-2=\frac{1}{4-(-3)}(x-1) \quad \text{(taking upper sign)}$$

$$\text{or} \quad x-7y+13=0$$

and $\quad y-2=\frac{(-3-4)}{(4+(-3))}(x-1)$ (taking below sign)

or $\quad 7x+y-9=0$

Hence, possible equation of the line BC are $x-7y+13=0$ and $7x+y-9=0$

A Line Equally Inclined with Two Lines

Theorem : If two lines with slopes m_1 and m_2 be equally inclined to a line with slope m, then

$$\left(\frac{m_1-m}{1+mm_1}\right)=-\left(\frac{m_2-m}{1+mm_2}\right)$$

Proof : Let be two lines of slopes m_1 and m_2 intersecting at a point P.

Let $\angle CPA=\angle BPC=\theta$

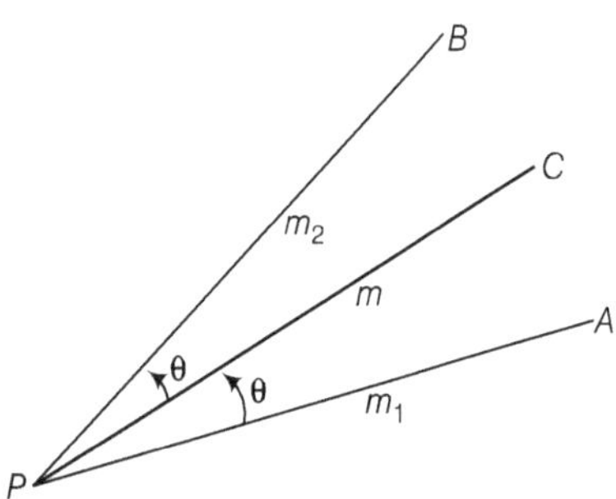

$\therefore \quad \tan(\angle CPA)=\left(\frac{m-m_1}{1+mm_1}\right)$

or $\quad \tan\theta=\left(\frac{m-m_1}{1+mm_1}\right) \quad (\because m>m_1) \quad$ ...(i)

and $\quad \tan(\angle BPC)=\left(\frac{m_2-m}{1+m_2m}\right)$

or $\quad \tan\theta=\left(\frac{m_2-m}{1+m_2m}\right) \quad (\because m_2>m) \quad$ ... (ii)

From Eqs. (i) and (ii), we get

$$\left(\frac{m-m_1}{1+mm_1}\right)=\left(\frac{m_2-m}{1+m_2m}\right) \text{ or } \left(\frac{m_1-m}{1+mm_1}\right)=-\left(\frac{m_2-m}{1+mm_2}\right)$$

Remarks

1. The above equation gives two values of m which are the slopes of the lines parallel to the bisectors of the angles between the two given lines.
2. Sign of m in both brackets is same.

Example 85. Find the equations to the straight lines passing through the point $(2, 3)$ and equally inclined to the lines $3x-4y-7=0$ and $12x-5y+6=0$.

Sol. Let m be the slope of the required line. Then its equation is

$$y-3=m(x-2) \quad \text{...(i)}$$

It is given that line (i) is equally inclined to the lines

$3x-4y-7=0$ and $12x-5y+6=0$ then

$$\Rightarrow \left(\frac{\frac{3}{4}-m}{1+\frac{3}{4}m}\right)=-\left(\frac{\frac{12}{5}-m}{1+\frac{12}{5}m}\right)$$

$$\left(\begin{array}{l}\text{slope of } 3x-4y-7=0 \text{ is } \frac{3}{4}\\ \text{and slope of } 12x-5y+6=0 \text{ is } \frac{12}{5}\end{array}\right)$$

$\Rightarrow \quad \left(\frac{3-4m}{4+3m}\right)=-\left(\frac{12-5m}{5+12m}\right)$

$\Rightarrow \quad (3-4m)(5+12m)+(4+3m)(12-5m)=0$

$\Rightarrow \quad 63m^2-32m-63=0$

$\Rightarrow \quad (7m-9)(9m+7)=0$

$\therefore \quad m=\frac{9}{7},-\frac{7}{9}$

Putting these values of m in Eq. (i) we obtain the equations of required lines as $9x-7y+3=0$ and $x+9y-41=0$.

Example 86. Two equal sides of an isosceles triangle are given by the equations $7x-y+3=0$ and $x+y-3=0$ and its third side passes through the point $(1,-10)$. Determine the equation of the third side.

Sol. Let m be the slope of BC. Since $AB=AC$.

Therefore BC makes equal angles with AB and AC.

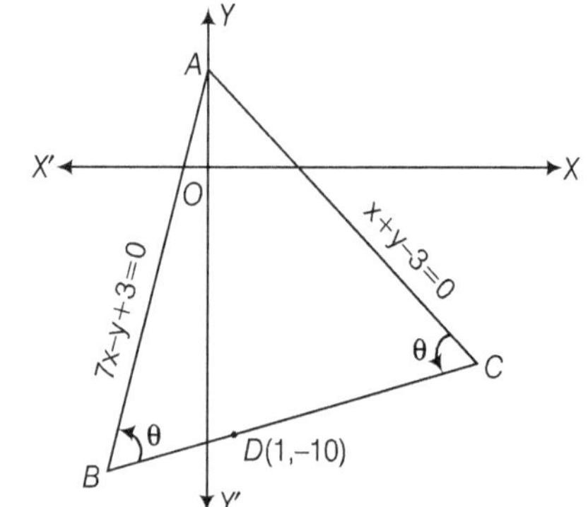

Then $\left(\frac{7-m}{1+7m}\right)=-\left(\frac{-1-m}{1+(-1)m}\right)$

$\Rightarrow \quad (7-m)(1-m)-(1+7m)(1+m)=0$

$\Rightarrow \quad 6m^2+16m-6=0$

$\Rightarrow \quad 3m^2+8m-3=0$

$\Rightarrow \quad (3m-1)(m+3)=0$

$\Rightarrow \quad m=\frac{1}{3},-3$

Equation of third side BC is $y+10=m(x-1)$

i.e. $\quad y+10=\frac{1}{3}(x-1) \quad$ and $\quad y+10=-3(x-1)$

or $\quad x-3y-31=0 \quad$ and $\quad 3x+y+7=0$

Equation of the Bisectors

Theorem : Prove that the equation of the bisectors of the angles between the lines

$$a_1x+b_1y+c_1=0 \quad \text{and} \quad a_2x+b_2y+c_2=0$$

are given by $\quad \dfrac{(a_1x+b_1y+c_1)}{\sqrt{(a_1^2+b_1^2)}}=\pm\dfrac{(a_2x+b_2y+c_2)}{\sqrt{(a_2^2+b_2^2)}}$

Proof : Let the given lines be AA' and BB' whose equations are

$$a_1x+b_1y+c_1=0 \qquad \text{...(i)}$$

and $\quad a_2x+b_2y+c_2=0 \qquad$ ...(ii)

Since bisectors of the angles between the two lines are the locus of a point which moves in a plane such that whose distance from two lines are equal.

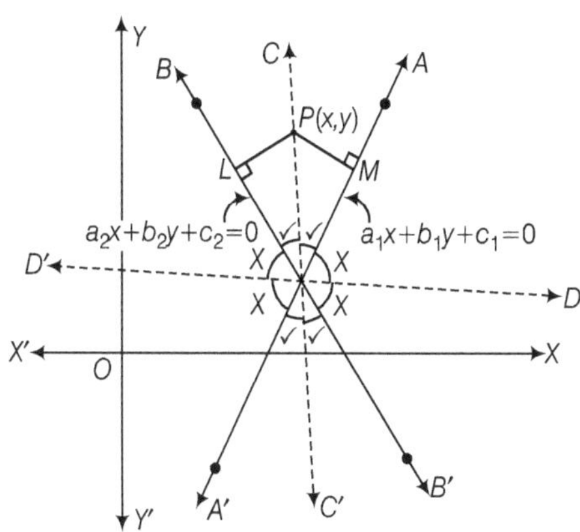

Let CC' and DD' be the two bisectors of the angle between the lines AA' and BB'. Let $P(x,y)$ be any point on CC', then

Length of the perpendicular from P on AA'

= length of the perpendicular from P on BB'

$\therefore \quad \dfrac{|a_1x+b_1y+c_1|}{\sqrt{(a_1^2+b_1^2)}}=\dfrac{|a_2x+b_2y+c_2|}{\sqrt{(a_2^2+b_2^2)}}$

or $\quad \dfrac{(a_1x+b_1y+c_1)}{\sqrt{(a_1^2+b_1^2)}}=\pm\dfrac{(a_2x+b_2y+c_2)}{\sqrt{(a_2^2+b_2^2)}}$

These are the required equations of the bisectors.

Note

The two bisectors are perpendicular to each other.

Example 87. Find the equations of the bisectors of the angles between the straight lines $3x-4y+7=0$ and $12x+5y-2=0$.

Sol. The equations of the bisectors of the angles between $3x-4y+7=0$ and $12x+5y-2=0$ are

$$\frac{(3x-4y+7)}{\sqrt{(3)^2+(-4)^2}}=\pm\frac{(12x+5y-2)}{\sqrt{(12)^2+(5)^2}}$$

or $\quad \dfrac{(3x-4y+7)}{5}=\pm\dfrac{(12x+5y-2)}{13}$

or $\quad (39x-52y+91)=\pm(60x+25y-10)$

Taking the positive sign, we get

$$21x+77y-101=0$$

as one bisector.

Taking the negative sign, we get $99x-77y+81=0$ as the second bisector.

Bisector of the Angle Containing the Origin

Let equations of lines be

$$a_1x+b_1y+c_1=0 \qquad \text{...(i)}$$

$$a_2x+b_2y+c_2=0 \qquad \text{...(ii)}$$

where c_1 and c_2 are positive.

Let $P(x,y)$ be taken on the bisector of the angle which contains the origin.

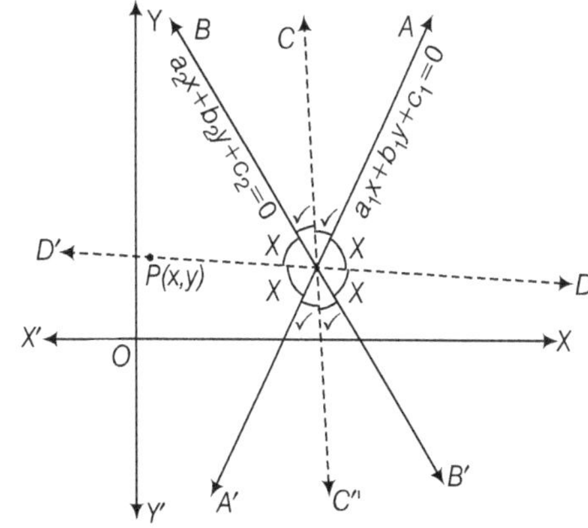

(i) Let $P(x,y)$ lies on DD' ,then either $O(0,0)$ and $P(x,y)$ will lie on the same side of the two lines Eqs. (i) and (ii), then

$$\frac{a_1x+b_1y+c_1}{0+0+c_1}>0$$

and $\quad \dfrac{a_2x+b_2y+c_2}{0+0+c_2}>0$

or $\quad a_1x+b_1y+c_1>0$

and $\quad a_2x+b_2y+c_2>0 \qquad (\because c_1,c_2>0)$

If the origin $O(0,0)$ and $P(x,y)$ lie on the opposite side of the two lines Eqs. (i) and (ii), then

$$\frac{a_1x+b_1y+c_1}{0+0+c_1}<0 \quad \text{and} \quad \frac{a_2x+b_2y+c_2}{0+0+c_2}<0$$

or $\quad a_1x+b_1y+c_1<0 \quad \text{and} \quad a_2x+b_2y+c_2<0$

$$(\because c_1, c_2>0)$$

Then equation of bisectors will be

$$\frac{|a_1x+b_1y+c_1|}{\sqrt{(a_1^2+b_1^2)}}=\frac{|a_2x+b_2y+c_2|}{\sqrt{(a_2^2+b_2^2)}}$$

Case I : If $a_1x+b_1y+c_1>0$ and $a_2x+b_2y+c_2>0$

then $$\frac{(a_1x+b_1y+c_1)}{\sqrt{(a_1^2+b_1^2)}}=\frac{(a_2x+b_2y+c_2)}{\sqrt{(a_2^2+b_2^2)}}$$

Case II : If $a_1x+b_1y+c_1<0$ and $a_2x+b_2y+c_2<0$

then $$-\frac{(a_1x+b_1y+c_1)}{\sqrt{(a_1^2+b_1^2)}}=-\frac{(a_2x+b_2y+c_2)}{\sqrt{(a_2^2+b_2^2)}}$$

i.e. $$\frac{(a_1x+b_1y+c_1)}{\sqrt{(a_1^2+b_1^2)}}=\frac{(a_2x+b_2y+c_2)}{\sqrt{(a_2^2+b_2^2)}}$$

Thus is both cases equation of the bisector containing the origin, when c_1 and c_2 are positive is

$$\frac{(a_1x+b_1y+c_1)}{\sqrt{(a_1^2+b_1^2)}}=\frac{(a_2x+b_2y+c_2)}{\sqrt{(a_2^2+b_2^2)}}$$

and equation of the bisector of the angle between the lines

$$a_1x+b_1y+c_1=0 \quad \text{and} \quad a_2x+b_2y+c_2=0$$

which does not contain the origin when c_1 and c_2 are positive is

$$\frac{(a_1x+b_1y+c_1)}{\sqrt{(a_1^2+b_1^2)}}=-\frac{(a_2x+b_2y+c_2)}{\sqrt{(a_2^2+b_2^2)}}$$

Working Rule :

(i) First re-write the equations of the two lines so that their constant terms are positive.

(ii) The bisector of the angle containing the origin and does not containing the origin, then taking +ve and – ve sign in

$$\frac{(a_1x+b_1y+c_1)}{\sqrt{(a_1^2+b_1^2)}}=\pm\frac{(a_2x+b_2y+c_2)}{\sqrt{(a_2^2+b_2^2)}} \text{ respectively.}$$

Example 88. Find the equations of angular bisector bisecting the angle containing the origin and not containing the origin of the lines $4x+3y-6=0$ and $5x+12y+9=0$.

Sol. Firstly make the constant terms (c_1, c_2) positive, then

$$-4x-3y+6=0 \text{ and } 5x+12y+9=0$$

$\therefore$ The equation of the bisector bisecting the angle containing origin is

$$\frac{(-4x-3y+6)}{\sqrt{(-4^2)+(-3)^2}}=\frac{(5x+12y+9)}{\sqrt{(5)^2+(12)^2}}$$

$$\Rightarrow \quad \left(\frac{-4x-3y+6}{5}\right)=\left(\frac{5x+12y+9}{13}\right)$$

$$\Rightarrow \quad -52x-39y+78=25x+60y+45$$

$$\Rightarrow \quad 77x+99y-33=0 \text{ or } 7x+9y-3=0$$

and the equation of the bisector bisecting the angle not containing origin is

$$\frac{(-4x-3y+6)}{\sqrt{(-4)^2+(-3)^2)}}=-\frac{(5x+12y+9)}{\sqrt{(5^2)+(12)^2}}$$

$$\Rightarrow \quad \left(\frac{-4x-3y+6}{5}\right)=-\left(\frac{5x+12y+9}{13}\right)$$

$$\Rightarrow \quad -52x-39y+78=-25x-60y-45$$

$$\Rightarrow \quad 27x-21y-123=0 \text{ or } 9x-7y-41=0$$

Equation of that Bisector of the Angle between Two Lines which Contains a Given Point

Let the equations of the two lines be

$$a_1x+b_1y+c_1=0 \qquad \text{...(i)}$$

and $$a_2x+b_2y+c_2=0 \qquad \text{...(ii)}$$

The equation of the bisector of the angle between the two lines containing the points (h,k) will be

$$\frac{(a_1x+b_1y+c_1)}{\sqrt{(a_1^2+b_1^2)}}=\frac{(a_2x+b_2y+c_2)}{\sqrt{(a_2^2+b_2^2)}}$$

or $$\frac{(a_1x+b_1y+c_1)}{\sqrt{(a_1^2+b_1^2)}}=-\frac{(a_2x+b_2y+c_2)}{\sqrt{(a_2^2+b_2^2)}}$$

according as $a_1h+b_1k+c_1$ and $a_2h+b_2k+c_2$ are of the same sign or opposite sign.

Example 89. Find the bisector of the angle between the lines $2x+y-6=0$ and $2x-4y+7=0$ which contains the point (1, 2).

Sol. Value of $2x+y-6$ at (1, 2) is – 2 (negative)

and value of $2x-4y+7$ at (1, 2) is 1 (positive)

i.e. opposite sign.

$\therefore$ Equation of bisector containing the point (1, 2) is

$$\frac{(2x+y-6)}{\sqrt{(2^2+1^2)}}=-\frac{(2x-4y+7)}{\sqrt{(2)^2+(-4)^2}}$$

$$\Rightarrow \quad 2(2x+y-6)+(2x-4y+7)=0$$

or $$6x-2y-5=0$$

How to Distinguish the Acute (Internal) and Obtuse (External) Angle Bisectors?

Let the equations of the two lines be

$$a_1x + b_1y + c_1 = 0 \quad ...(i)$$

and $$a_2x + b_2y + c_2 = 0 \quad ...(ii)$$

where, $c_1 > 0, c_2 > 0$.

$\because$ Equations of bisectors are

$$\frac{(a_1x + b_1y + c_1)}{\sqrt{(a_1^2 + b_1^2)}} = \pm \frac{(a_2x + b_2y + c_2)}{\sqrt{(a_2^2 + b_2^2)}} \quad ...(iii)$$

when Eq. (iii) be simplified, let the bisectors be

$$p_1x + q_1y + r_1 = 0 \quad ...(iv)$$

and $$p_2x + q_2y + r_2 = 0 \quad ...(v)$$

Since the two bisectors are at right angles, the angle α between the acute (internal) bisector and any one of the given lines must lie between 0 and 45° i.e. $0 < \alpha < 45°$.

$\therefore \quad 0 < \tan\alpha < 1$

If m_1 and m_2 are the slopes of Eqs. (i) and (iii) respectively.

Then, $\quad m_1 = -\frac{a_1}{b_1}$ and $m_2 = -\frac{p_1}{q_1}$

$$\therefore \quad \tan\alpha = \left|\frac{m_1 - m_2}{1 + m_1 m_2}\right|$$

$$= \left|\frac{\left(-\frac{a_1}{b_1}\right) - \left(-\frac{p_1}{q_1}\right)}{1 + \left(-\frac{a_1}{b_1}\right)\left(-\frac{p_1}{q_1}\right)}\right| = \left|\frac{a_1q_1 - b_1p_1}{b_1q_1 + a_1p_1}\right|$$

Hence, if $0 < \tan\alpha < 1$, $p_1x + q_1y + r_1 = 0$ is the acute (internal) bisector and if $\tan\alpha > 1$, $p_2x + q_2y + r_2 = 0$ is the obtuse (external) bisector.

Shortcut Method for finding Acute (Internal) and Obtuse (External) Angle Bisectors

Let the equations of the two lines be

$$a_1x + b_1y + c_1 = 0$$

$$a_2x + b_2y + c_2 = 0$$

Taking $\quad c_1 > 0, c_2 > 0$ and $a_1b_2 \neq a_2b_1$

Then equations of the bisectors are

$$\frac{(a_1x + b_1y + c_1)}{\sqrt{(a_1^2 + b_1^2)}} = \pm \frac{(a_2x + b_2y + c_2)}{\sqrt{(a_2^2 + b_2^2)}}$$

Conditions	Acute angle bisector	Obtuse angle bisector
$a_1a_2 + b_1b_2 > 0$	–	+
$a_1a_2 + b_1b_2 < 0$	+	–

Remarks

1. Bisectors are perpendiculars to each other.
2. '+' sign gives the bisector of the angle containing origin.
3. If $a_1a_2 + b_1b_2 > 0$ then the origin lies in obtuse angle and if $a_1a_2 + b_1b_2 < 0$, then the origin lies in acute angle.

Explanation : Equations of given lines in normal form will be respectively

$$-\frac{a_1x}{\sqrt{(a_1^2 + b_1^2)}} - \frac{b_1y}{\sqrt{(a_1^2 + b_1^2)}} = \frac{c_1}{\sqrt{(a_1^2 + b_1^2)}} \quad (\because c_1 > 0)$$

and $$-\frac{a_2x}{\sqrt{(a_2^2 + b_2^2)}} - \frac{b_2y}{\sqrt{(a_2^2 + b_2^2)}} = \frac{c_2}{\sqrt{(a_2^2 + b_2^2)}} \quad (\because c_2 > 0)$$

If $\quad \cos\alpha = -\frac{a_1}{\sqrt{(a_1^2 + b_1^2)}}$ then $\sin\alpha = -\frac{b_1}{\sqrt{(a_1^2 + b_1^2)}}$

and $\quad \cos\beta = -\frac{a_2}{\sqrt{(a_2^2 + b_2^2)}}$ then $\sin\beta = -\frac{b_2}{\sqrt{(a_2^2 + b_2^2)}}$

Now, $\cos(\alpha - \beta) = \cos\alpha\cos\beta + \sin\alpha\sin\beta$

$$= \frac{(a_1a_2 + b_1b_2)}{\sqrt{(a_1^2 + b_1^2)}\sqrt{(a_2^2 + b_2^2)}}$$

$$\cos(\alpha - \beta) > 0 \quad \text{or} \quad < 0$$

according as $(\alpha - \beta)$ is acute or obtuse.

i.e. $\quad a_1a_2 + b_1b_2 > 0 \quad$ or $\quad < 0$

Hence, bisector of the angle between the lines will be the bisector of the acute or obtuse angle according as origin lies in the acute or obtuse angle according as $a_1a_2 + b_1b_2 < 0$ or > 0.

Example 90. Find the equation of the bisector of the obtuse angle between the lines $3x - 4y + 7 = 0$ and $12x + 5y - 2 = 0$.

Sol. Firstly make the constant terms (c_1, c_2) positive

$$3x - 4y + 7 = 0 \quad \text{and} \quad -12x - 5y + 2 = 0$$

$\because \quad a_1a_2 + b_1b_2 = (3)(-12) + (-4)(-5) = -36 + 20 = -16$

$\therefore \quad a_1a_2 + b_1b_2 < 0$

Hence "–" sign gives the obtuse bisector.

$\therefore$ Obtuse bisector is

$$\frac{(3x - 4y + 7)}{\sqrt{(3)^2 + (-4)^2}} = -\frac{(-12x - 5y + 2)}{\sqrt{(-12)^2 + (-5)^2}}$$

$\Rightarrow \quad 13(3x - 4y + 7) = -5(-12x - 5y + 2)$

$\Rightarrow \quad 21x + 77y - 101 = 0$ is the obtuse angle bisector.

Example 91. Find the bisector of acute angle between the lines $x+y-3=0$ and $7x-y+5=0$.

Sol. Firstly, make the constant terms (c_1, c_2) positive then

$-x-y+3=0$ and $7x-y+5=0$

$\because \quad a_1a_2+b_1b_2=(-1)(7)+(-1)(-1)=-7+1=-6$

i.e. $\quad a_1a_2+b_1b_2<0$

Hence "+" sign gives the acute bisector.

$\therefore$ Acute bisector is $\dfrac{-x-y+3}{\sqrt{(-1)^2+(-1)^2}}=+\dfrac{7x-y+5}{\sqrt{(7)^2+(-1)^2}}$

$$\Rightarrow \quad \frac{-x-y+3}{\sqrt{2}}=\frac{7x-y+5}{5\sqrt{2}}$$

$$\Rightarrow \quad -5x-5y+15=7x-y+5$$

$$\therefore \quad 12x+4y-10=0 \quad \text{or} \quad 6x+2y-5=0$$

is the acute angle bisector.

Example 92. Find the coordinates of incentre of the triangle. The equation of whose sides are

$AB: x+y-1=0, BC: 7x-y-15=0$

and $CA: x-y-1=0$.

Sol. Firstly, make the constant terms $(c_1, c_2$, and $c_3)$ positive

i.e. $\quad AB: -x-y+1=0 \quad$ ...(i)

$BC: -7x+y+15=0 \quad$ ...(ii)

$CA: -x+y+1=0 \quad$ ...(iii)

$\because$ The incentre of triangle is the point of intersection of internal or acute angle bisectors.

Internal bisector of AB and BC :

$$-x-y+1=0$$

$$-7x+y+15=0$$

$\because \quad a_1a_2+b_1b_2=(-1)(-7)+(-1)(1)=6>0$

$\therefore$ Acute or internal bisector is

$$\frac{(-x-y+1)}{\sqrt{(-1)^2+(-1)^2}}=-\frac{(-7x+y+15)}{\sqrt{(-7)^2+(1)^2}}$$

$$\Rightarrow \quad \frac{(-x-y+1)}{\sqrt{2}}=-\frac{(-7x+y+15)}{5\sqrt{2}}$$

$$\Rightarrow \quad -5x-5y+5=7x-y-15$$

or $\quad 12x+4y-20=0$

or $\quad 3x+y-5=0 \quad$ ...(iv)

Internal bisector of BC and CA :

$$-7x+y+15=0$$

$$-x+y+1=0$$

$\because \quad a_1a_2+b_1b_2=(-7)(-1)+(1)(1)=8>0$

$\because$ Acute or internal bisector is

$$\frac{(-7x+y+15)}{\sqrt{(-7)^2+(1)^2}}=-\frac{(-x+y+1)}{\sqrt{(-1)^2+(1)^2}}$$

$$\Rightarrow \quad \frac{-7x+y+15}{5\sqrt{2}}=\frac{(x-y-1)}{\sqrt{2}}$$

$$\Rightarrow \quad -7x+y+15=5x-5y-5$$

or $\quad 12x-6y-20=0$

or $\quad 6x-3y-10=0 \quad$ ...(v)

Finally, solve Eqs. (iv) and (v), we get

$$x=\frac{5}{3} \text{ and } y=0$$

Hence coordinates of incentre are $\left(\dfrac{5}{3}, 0\right)$.

Exercise for Session 4

1. The straight lines $2x+11y-5=0$, $24x+7y-20=0$ and $4x-3y-2=0$
   (a) form a triangle
   (b) are only concurrent
   (c) are concurrent with one line bisecting the angle between the other two
   (d) None of the above

2. The line $x+3y-2=0$ bisects the angle between a pair of straight lines of which one has the equation $x-7y+5=0$. The equation of other line is
   (a) $3x+3y-1=0$ (b) $x-3y+2=0$ (c) $5x+5y+3=0$ (d) $5x+5y-3=0$

3. P is a point on either of the two lines $y-\sqrt{3}\,|x|=2$ at a distance of 5 units from their point of intersection. The coordinates of the foot of the perpendicular from P on the bisector of the angle between them are
   (a) $\left(0, \dfrac{4+5\sqrt{3}}{2}\right)$ or $\left(0, \dfrac{4-5\sqrt{3}}{2}\right)$ depending on which the point P is taken
   (b) $\left(0, \dfrac{4+5\sqrt{3}}{2}\right)$ (c) $\left(0, \dfrac{4-5\sqrt{3}}{2}\right)$ (d) $\left(\dfrac{5}{2}, \dfrac{5\sqrt{3}}{2}\right)$

4. In a triangle ABC, the bisectors of angles B and C lie along the lines $x = y$ and $y = 0$. If A is (1, 2), then the equation of line BC is

(a) $2x + y = 1$ (b) $3x - y = 5$ (c) $x - 2y = 3$ (d) $x + 3y = 1$

5. In ΔABC, the coordinates of the vertex A are (4, –1) and lines $x - y - 1 = 0$ and $2x - y = 3$ are the internal bisecters of angles B and C. Then, the radius of the incircle of triangle ABC is

(a) $\frac{5}{\sqrt{5}}$ (b) $\frac{3}{\sqrt{5}}$ (c) $\frac{6}{\sqrt{5}}$ (d) $\frac{7}{\sqrt{5}}$

6. The equation of the straight line which bisects the intercepts made by the axes on the lines $x + y = 2$ and $2x + 3y = 6$ is

(a) $2x = 3$ (b) $y = 1$ (c) $2y = 3$ (d) $x = 1$

7. The equation of the bisector of the acute angle between the lines $2x - y + 4 = 0$ and $x - 2y = 1$ is

(a) $x + y + 5 = 0$ (b) $x - y + 1 = 0$ (c) $x - y = 5$ (d) $x - y + 5 = 0$

8. The equation of the bisector of that angle between the lines $x + y = 3$ and $2x - y = 2$ which contains the point (1, 1) is

(a) $(\sqrt{5} - 2\sqrt{2})x + (\sqrt{5} + \sqrt{2})y = 3\sqrt{5} - 2\sqrt{2}$ (b) $(\sqrt{5} + 2\sqrt{2})x + (\sqrt{5} - \sqrt{2})y = 3\sqrt{5} + 2\sqrt{2}$

(c) $3x = 10$ (d) $3x - 5y + 2 = 0$

9. Find the equations of the two straight lines through (7, 9) and making an angle of 60° with the line $x - \sqrt{3}y - 2\sqrt{3} = 0$.

10. Equation of the base of an equilateral triangle is $3x + 4y = 9$ and its vertex is at the point (1, 2). Find the equations of the other sides and the length of each side of the triangle.

11. Find the coordinates of those points on the line $3x + 2y = 5$ which are equidistant from the lines $4x + 3y - 7 = 0$ and $2y - 5 = 0$.

12. Two sides of rhombus $ABCD$ are parallel to the lines $y = x + 2$ and $y = 7x + 3$. If the diagonal of the rhombus intersect at the point (1, 2) and the vertex A lies on Y-axis, find the possible coordinates of A.

13. The bisector of two lines L_1 and L_2 are given by $3x^2 - 8xy - 3y^2 + 10x + 20y - 25 = 0$. If the line L_1 passes through origin, find the equation of line L_2.

14. Find the equation of the bisector of the angle between the lines $x + 2y - 11 = 0$ and $3x - 6y - 5 = 0$ which contains the point (1, –3).

15. Find the equation of the bisector of the angle between the lines $2x - 3y - 5 = 0$ and $6x - 4y + 7 = 0$ which is the supplement of the angle containing the point (2, –1).

Session 5

The Foot of Perpendicular Drawn from the Point (x_1, y_1) to the Line $ax + by + c = 0$, Image or Reflection of a Point (x_1, y_1) about a Line Mirror, Image or Reflection of a Point In Different Cases, Use of Image or Reflection

The Foot of Perpendicular Drawn from the Point (x_1, y_1) to the Line $ax+by+c=0$

Let $P \equiv (x_1, y_1)$ and let M be the foot of perpendicular drawn from P on $ax + by + c = 0$.

In order to find the coordinates of M, find the equation of the line PM which is perpendicular to RS and passes through $P(x_1, y_1)$, i.e. $bx - ay = bx_1 - ay_1$

or $b(x - x_1) - a(y - y_1) = 0$ and solving it with $ax + by + c = 0$, then we get coordinates of M.

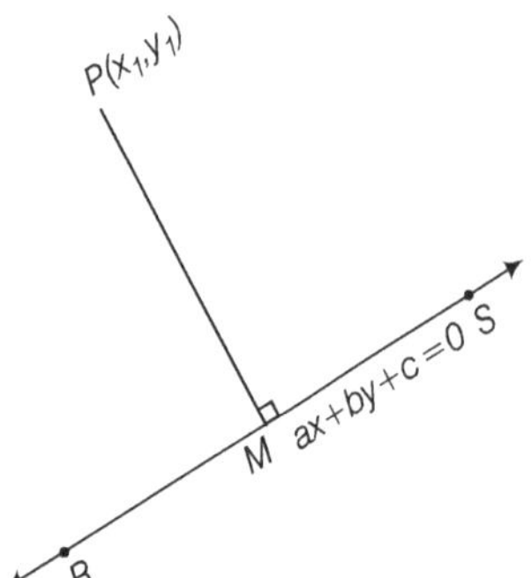

Aliter I : Let the coordinates of M are (x_2, y_2) then $M(x_2, y_2)$ lies on $ax + by + c = 0$

$$\Rightarrow \quad ax_2 + by_2 + c = 0 \quad \text{...(i)}$$

and $\because PM \perp RS$

then (Slope of PM) (Slope of RS) $= -1$

$$\Rightarrow \quad \left(\frac{y_2 - y_1}{x_2 - x_1}\right) \times \left(-\frac{a}{b}\right) = -1$$

$$\text{or} \quad bx_2 - ay_2 = bx_1 - ay_1 \quad \text{...(ii)}$$

Solving Eqs. (i) and (ii), we get (x_2, y_2).

Aliter II : Let the coordinates of M are (x_2, y_2)

$$\because \quad PM \perp RS$$

and M lies on $\quad ax + by + c = 0$

$$\text{i.e.} \quad ax_2 + by_2 + c = 0 \quad \text{...(iii)}$$

$$\text{and} \quad \left(\frac{y_2 - y_1}{x_2 - x_1}\right) \times \left(-\frac{a}{b}\right) = -1 \quad (\because PM \perp RS)$$

$$\text{or} \quad \frac{x_2 - x_1}{a} = \frac{y_2 - y_1}{b}$$

$$\text{or} \quad \frac{x_2 - x_1}{a} = \frac{y_2 - y_1}{b} = \frac{a(x_2 - x_1) + b(y_2 - y_1)}{(a^2 + b^2)}$$

(By ratio proportion method)

$$= \frac{(ax_2 + by_2) - (ax_1 + by_1)}{a^2 + b^2}$$

$$= \frac{-c - (ax_1 + by_1)}{a^2 + b^2} \quad \text{[from Eq. (iii)]}$$

$$\text{or} \quad \frac{x_2 - x_1}{a} = \frac{y_2 - y_1}{b} = -\frac{(ax_1 + by_1 + c)}{(a^2 + b^2)}$$

Example 93. Find the coordinates of the foot of the perpendicular drawn from the point (2, 3) to the line $y = 3x + 4$.

Sol. Given line is

$$3x - y + 4 = 0 \quad \text{...(i)}$$

Let Eq. $\quad P \equiv (2, 3)$.

Let, M be the foot of perpendicular drawn from P on RS.

Then equation of PM passes through $P(2, 3)$ and perpendicular to RS is

$$x + 3y - (2 + 3 \times 3) = 0$$

$$\text{i.e.} \quad x + 3y - 11 = 0 \quad \text{...(ii)}$$

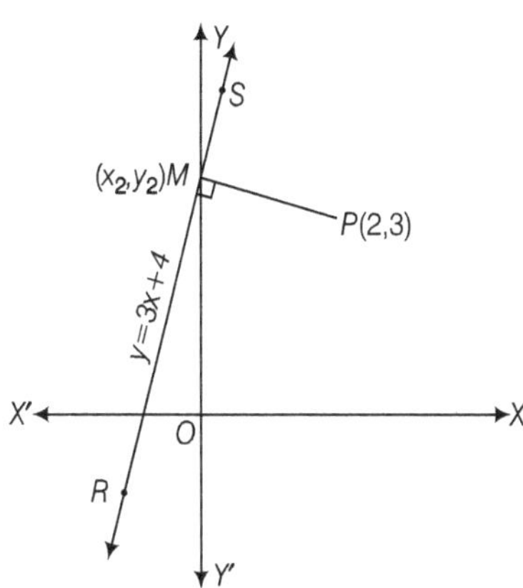

Solving Eqs. (i) and (ii), we get

$$x = -\frac{1}{10}, y = \frac{37}{10}$$

$$\therefore \quad M \equiv \left(-\frac{1}{10}, \frac{37}{10}\right)$$

Aliter I : Let the coordinates of M be (x_2, y_2) then $M(x_2, y_2)$ lies on $3x - y + 4 = 0$

$$\Rightarrow \quad 3x_2 - y_2 + 4 = 0 \quad \text{...(iii)}$$

and $\because$ $PM \perp RS$

$\therefore$ (Slope of PM) $\times$ (Slope of RS) $= -1$

$$\Rightarrow \quad \left(\frac{y_2 - 3}{x_2 - 2}\right) \times (3) = -1$$

or

$$x_2 + 3y_2 - 11 = 0 \quad \text{...(iv)}$$

Solving Eqs. (iii) and (iv), we get

$$x_2 = -\frac{1}{10}, y_2 = \frac{37}{10}$$

$$\therefore \quad M \equiv \left(-\frac{1}{10}, \frac{37}{10}\right)$$

Aliter II : By Ratio Proportion Method :

$$\frac{x_2 - 2}{3} = \frac{y_2 - 3}{-1} = \frac{-(3 \times 2 - 3 + 4)}{3^2 + (-1)^2}$$

$$\Rightarrow \quad \frac{x_2 - 2}{3} = \frac{y_2 - 3}{-1} = -\frac{7}{10}$$

$$x_2 = -\frac{1}{10} \text{ and } y_2 = \frac{37}{10}$$

$$\therefore \quad M \equiv \left(-\frac{1}{10}, \frac{37}{10}\right)$$

Image or Reflection of a Point (x_1, y_1) About a Line Mirror

Let $Q \equiv (x_2, y_2)$ be the image of $P \equiv (x_1, y_1)$ then find coordinates of the foot of perpendicular M drawn from the point $P(x_1, y_1)$ on RS and use fact that M is the mid- point P and Q.

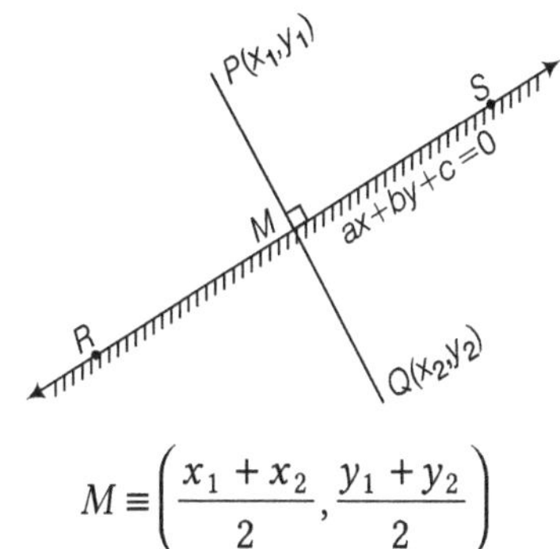

i.e.

$$M \equiv \left(\frac{x_1 + x_2}{2}, \frac{y_1 + y_2}{2}\right)$$

Aliter I : Ratio Proportion Method :

$$\because \quad PQ \perp RS$$

$$\therefore \quad (\text{Slope of } PQ) \times (\text{Slope of } RS) = -1$$

or

$$\left(\frac{y_2 - y_1}{x_2 - x_1}\right) \times \left(-\frac{a}{b}\right) = -1$$

or

$$\frac{(x_2 - x_1)}{a} = \frac{(y_2 - y_1)}{b}$$

or

$$\frac{x_2 - x_1}{a} = \frac{y_2 - y_1}{b} = \frac{a(x_2 - x_1) + b(y_2 - y_1)}{a^2 + b^2}$$

$$= \frac{a(2x - x_1 - x_1) + b(2y - y_1 - y_1)}{a^2 + b^2}$$

$$\left(\begin{array}{l}\because M(x, y) \text{ is mid-point of } P \text{ and } Q \\ \therefore x_2 = 2x - x_1 \text{ and } y_2 = 2y - y_1\end{array}\right)$$

$$= \frac{-2ax_1 - 2by_1 + 2(ax + by)}{a^2 + b^2}$$

$$= \frac{-2ax_1 - 2by_1 + 2(-c)}{a^2 + b^2} \quad (\because ax + by = -c)$$

$$= \frac{-2(ax_1 + by_1 + c)}{(a^2 + b^2)}$$

i.e.

$$\frac{x_2 - x_1}{a} = \frac{y_2 - y_1}{b} = -\frac{2(ax_1 + by_1 + c)}{(a^2 + b^2)}$$

Aliter II : By Distance form or Symmetric form or parametric form :

$$\because \quad \text{Slope of } RS = -\frac{a}{b}$$

$$\therefore \quad \text{Slope of } PQ = \frac{b}{a}$$

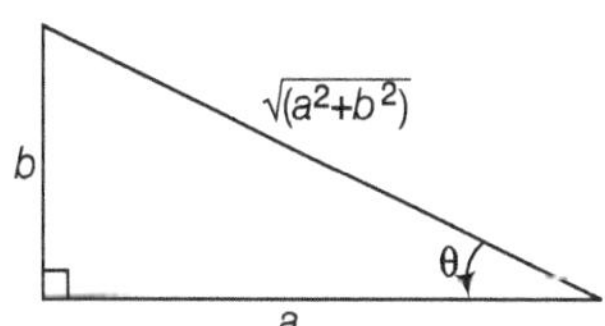

Let $\tan\theta = \frac{b}{a}$

$\therefore \quad \sin\theta = \frac{b}{\sqrt{(a^2+b^2)}}$

and $\cos\theta = \frac{a}{\sqrt{(a^2+b^2)}}$

Put the equation of the mirror line such that the coefficient of y becomes negative.

Suppose if $b > 0$

then $ax + by + c = 0$

becomes $-ax - by - c = 0$

and $p = PM =$ Directed distance from $P(x_1, y_1)$ on $-ax - by - c = 0$ (i.e. p +ve or −ve)

$$= \left(\frac{-ax_1 - by_1 - c}{\sqrt{(a^2+b^2)}}\right)$$

$$\therefore \quad PQ = 2PM = 2p = 2\left(\frac{-ax_1 - by_1 - c}{\sqrt{(a^2+b^2)}}\right) = r$$

$\Rightarrow$ Required image has the coordinates $(x_1 + r\cos\theta, y_1 + r\sin\theta)$.

Example 94. Find the image of the point $(4, -13)$ with respect to the line mirror $5x + y + 6 = 0$.

Sol. Let, $P \equiv (4, -13)$ and Let, $Q \equiv (x_2, y_2)$ be mirror image P with respect to line mirror $5x + y + 6 = 0$.

Let, $M(\alpha, \beta)$ be the foot of perpendicular from $P(4, -13)$ on the line mirror $5x + y + 6 = 0$, then

$$\frac{\alpha - 4}{5} = \frac{\beta + 13}{1} = \frac{-(5 \times 4 - 13 + 6)}{5^2 + 1^2}$$

or $$\frac{\alpha - 4}{5} = \frac{\beta + 13}{1} = -\frac{1}{2}$$

$$\therefore \quad M \equiv \left(\frac{3}{2}, -\frac{27}{2}\right)$$

$\because M$ is the mid-point of P and Q, then

$$Q \equiv (x_2, y_2) \equiv \left(2 \times \frac{3}{2} - 4, 2 \times \left(-\frac{27}{2}\right) + 13\right)$$

i.e. $Q \equiv (-1, -14)$

Aliter I :

By Ratio Proportion Method : Let, $Q(x_2, y_2)$ the image of $P(4, -13)$ with respect to line mirror $5x + y + 6 = 0$, then

$$\frac{x_2 - 4}{5} = \frac{y_2 + 13}{1} = -\frac{2(5 \times 4 - 13 + 6)}{5^2 + 1^2} = -1$$

or $x_2 - 4 = -5$ and $y_2 + 13 = -1$

$\therefore \quad x_2 = -1$ and $y_2 = -14$

Hence $Q \equiv (-1, -14)$.

Aliter II :

By distance form or Symmetric form or Parametric form : Let, $P \equiv (4, -13)$ and Q be the image of P with respect to line mirror (RS) $5x + y + 6 = 0$

$\because$ Slope of $RS = -5$

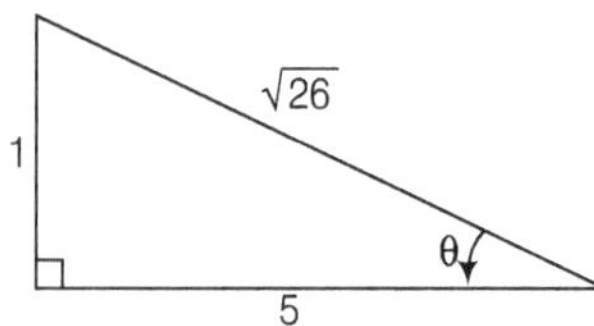

$\therefore$ Slope of $PQ = \frac{1}{5} = \tan\theta$

$\therefore \quad \sin\theta = \frac{1}{\sqrt{26}}$ and $\cos\theta = \frac{5}{\sqrt{26}}$

Now, put the equation of the mirror line such that the coefficient of y becomes negative.

Then, $5x + y + 6 = 0$ becomes $-5x - y - 6 = 0$ and

$p = \perp$ Directed distance from $P(4, -13)$ on $(-5x - y - 6 = 0)$

$$= \frac{-5 \times 4 + 13 - 6}{\sqrt{(-5)^2 + (-1)^2}} = -\frac{13}{\sqrt{26}}$$

$$\therefore \quad PQ = r = 2p = -\frac{26}{\sqrt{26}} = -\sqrt{26}$$

Hence, required image has the coordinates

$$Q \equiv (4 - \sqrt{26}\cos\theta, -13 - \sqrt{26}\sin\theta)$$

i.e. $$\left(4 - \sqrt{26} \times \frac{5}{\sqrt{26}}, -13 - \sqrt{26} \times \frac{1}{\sqrt{26}}\right)$$

i.e. $(4 - 5, -13 - 1)$

Hence, $Q \equiv (-1, -14)$

Image or Reflection of a Point in Different Cases

(i) The image or reflection of a point with respect to *X*-axis

Let $P(\alpha, \beta)$ be any point and $Q(x, y)$ be its image about X-axis, then (M is the mid-point of P and Q)

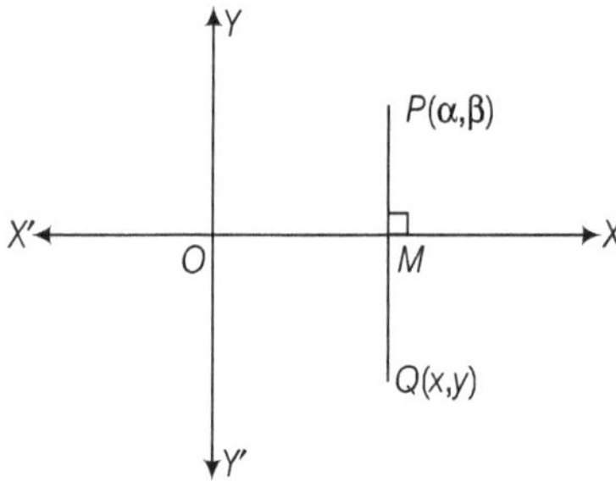

$$x = \alpha \text{ and } y = -\beta$$

$\therefore \quad Q \equiv (\alpha, -\beta)$

i.e. sign change of ordinate.

Remark

The image of the line $ax + by + c = 0$ about X-axis is $ax - by + c = 0$

(ii) The image or reflection of a point with respect to *Y*-axis

Let $P(\alpha, \beta)$ be any point and $Q(x, y)$ be its image about Y-axis, then (M is the mid-point of PQ)

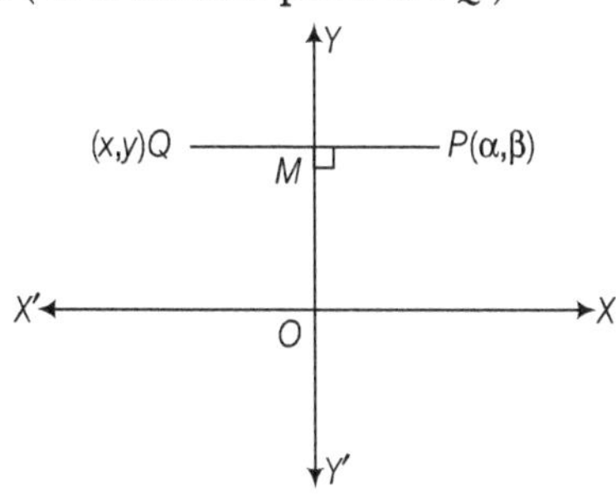

$$x = -\alpha \text{ and } y = \beta$$

$\therefore \quad Q \equiv (-\alpha, \beta)$

i.e. sign change of abscissae.

Remark

The image of the line $ax + by + c = 0$ about Y-axis is $-ax + by + c = 0$

(iii) The image or reflection of a point with respect to origin

Let $P(\alpha, \beta)$ be any point and $Q(x, y)$ be its image about the origin (O is the mid point of PQ), then

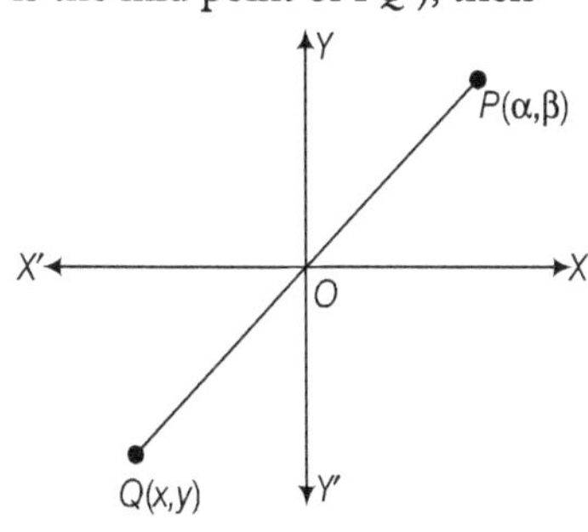

$$x = -\alpha \text{ and } y = -\beta$$

$\therefore \quad Q \equiv (-\alpha, -\beta)$

i.e. sign change of abscissae and ordinate.

Remark

The image of the line $ax + by + c = 0$ about origin is $-ax - by + c = 0$.

(iv) The image or reflection of a point with respect to the line $x = a$

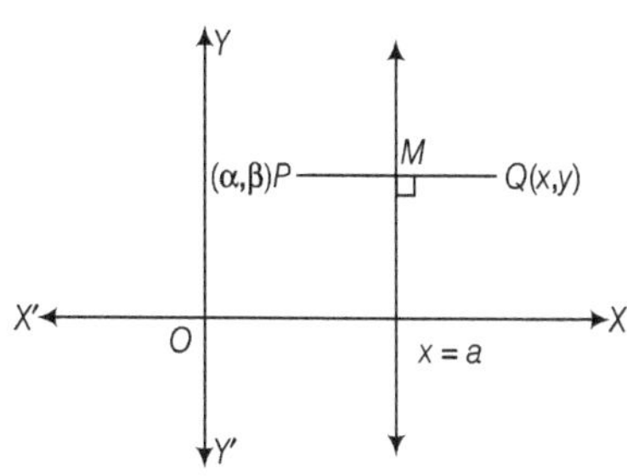

Let $P(\alpha, \beta)$ be any point and $Q(x, y)$ be its image about the line $x = a$, then $y = \beta$

$\therefore$ Coordinates of M are (a, β)

$\because$ M is the mid-point of PQ

$\therefore \; Q \equiv (2a - \alpha, \beta)$

Remark

The image of the line $ax + by + c = 0$ about the line $x = \lambda$ is

$$a(2\lambda - x) + by + c = 0$$

(v) The image or reflection of a point with respect to the line $y = b$

Let $P(\alpha, \beta)$ be any point and $Q(x, y)$ be its image about the line y =b, then $x = \alpha$

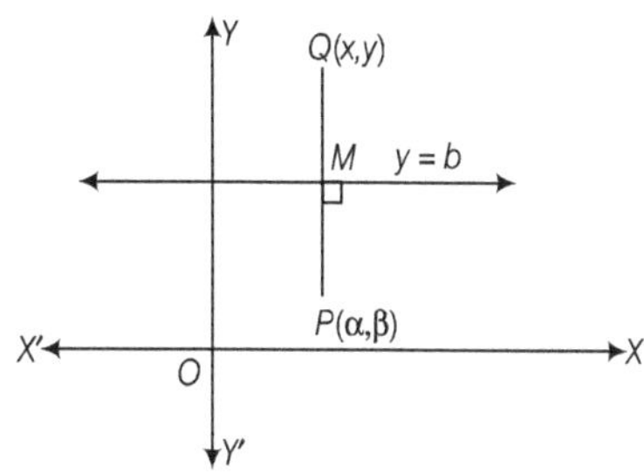

$\therefore$ Co-ordinates of M are (α, b)

$\because$ M is the mid-point of PQ $\therefore \; Q \equiv (\alpha, 2b - \beta)$

Remark

The image of the line $ax + by + c = 0$ about the line $y = \mu$ is

$$ax + b(2\mu - y) + c = 0.$$

(vi) The image or reflection of a point with respect to the line $y = x$

Let $P(\alpha, \beta)$ be any point and $Q(x_1, y_1)$ be its image about the line $y = x$ (RS), then $PQ \perp RS$

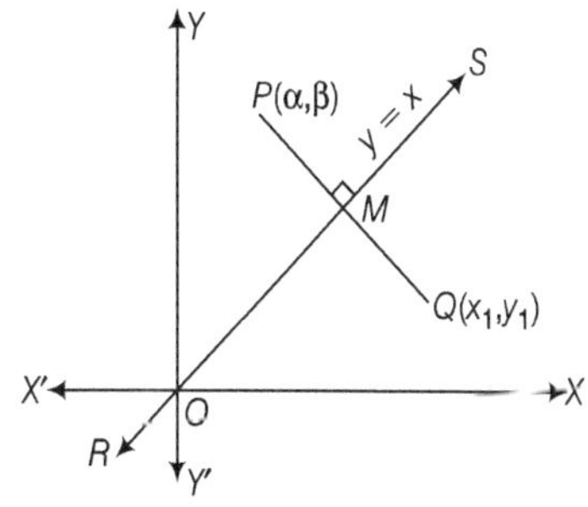

$\therefore$ (Slope of PQ) $\times$ (Slope of RS) $= -1$

or $$\frac{y_1 - \beta}{x_1 - \alpha} \times 1 = -1$$

or $$x_1 - \alpha = \beta - y_1 \quad \text{...(i)}$$

and mid--point of PQ lie on $y = x$

i.e. $$\left(\frac{y_1 + \beta}{2}\right) = \left(\frac{x_1 + \alpha}{2}\right)$$

or $$x_1 + \alpha = \beta + y_1 \quad \text{...(ii)}$$

Solving Eqs. (i) and (ii), we get $x_1 = \beta$ and $y_1 = \alpha$

$\therefore$ $Q \equiv (\beta, \alpha)$ i.e. interchange of x and y.

Remark

The image of the line $ax + by + c = 0$ about the line $y = x$ is $ay + bx + c = 0$.

(vii) The image or reflection of a point with respect to the line $y = x \tan\theta$

Let $P(\alpha, \beta)$ be any point and $Q(x_1, y_1)$ be its image about the line $y = x \tan\theta$ (RS), then $PQ \perp RS$

$\therefore$ (Slope of PQ) $\times$ (Slope of RS) $= -1$

or $$\frac{y_1 - \beta}{x_1 - \alpha} \times \tan\theta = -1$$

$\Rightarrow$ $$y_1 - \beta = (\alpha - x_1)\cot\theta \quad \text{...(i)}$$

and mid-point of PQ lie on $y = x \tan\theta$

i.e. $$\left(\frac{y_1 + \beta}{2}\right) = \left(\frac{x_1 + \alpha}{2}\right)\tan\theta$$

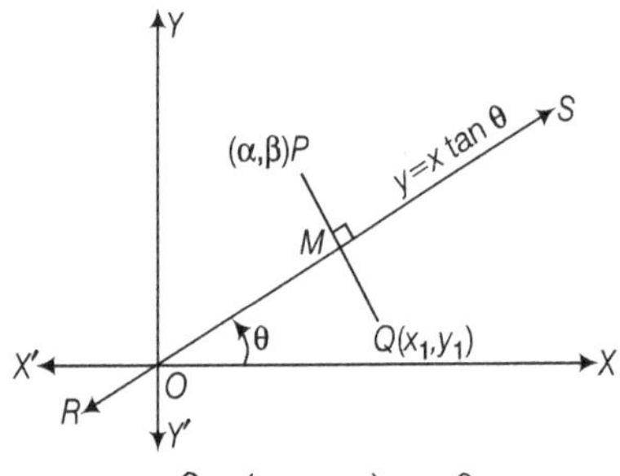

or $$y_1 + \beta = (x_1 + \alpha)\tan\theta \quad \text{...(ii)}$$

Solving Eqs. (i) and (ii), we get

$$x_1 = \alpha\cos 2\theta + \beta\sin 2\theta$$

and $$y_1 = \alpha\sin 2\theta - \beta\cos 2\theta$$

$\therefore$ $$Q \equiv (\alpha\cos 2\theta + \beta\sin 2\theta, \alpha\sin 2\theta - \beta\cos 2\theta)$$

Example 95. The point $P(\alpha, \beta)$ undergoes a reflection in the X-axis followed by a reflection in the Y-axis. Show that their combined effect is the same as the single reflection of $P(\alpha, \beta)$ in the origin when $\alpha, \beta > 0$.

Sol. Let $P_1(x_1, y_1)$ be the image of (α, β) after reflection in the X-axis. Then

$$x_1 = \alpha \quad \text{and} \quad y_1 = -\beta \quad \text{...(i)}$$

Now, let $P_2(x_2, y_2)$ be the image of $P_1(x_1, y_1)$ in the Y-axis. Then

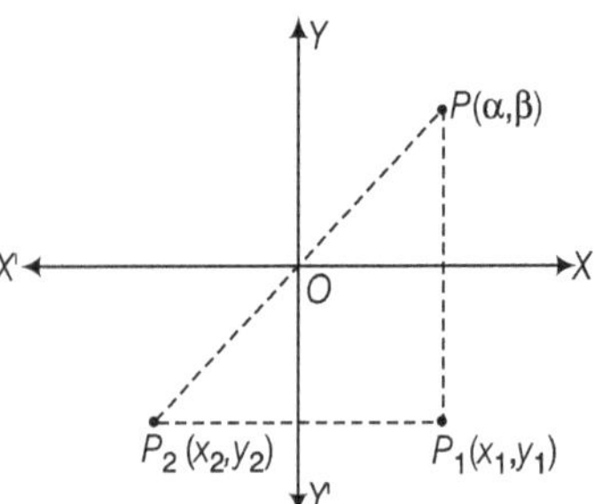

$$x_2 = -x_1, y_2 = y_1$$

$\Rightarrow$ $$x_2 = -\alpha, y_2 = -\beta \quad \text{[from Eq. (i)] ...(ii)}$$

further let $P_3(x_3, y_3)$ be the image of $P(\alpha, \beta)$ in the origin O. Then

$$x_3 = -\alpha, y_3 = -\beta \quad \text{...(iii)}$$

From Eqs. (ii) and (iii) ,we get

$$x_3 = x_2 \text{ and } y_3 = y_2.$$

Hence the image of P_2 of P after successive reflection in their X-axis and Y-axis is the same as the single reflection of P in the origin.

Example 96. Find the image of the point $(-2, -7)$ under the transformations $(x, y) \to (x - 2y, -3x + y)$.

Sol. Let (x_1, y_1) be the image of the point (x, y) under the given transformation. Then

$$x_1 = x - 2y = (-2) - 2(-7) = 12$$

$\therefore$ $x_1 = 12$ and $y_1 = -3x + y = -3(-2) - 7 = -1$

$\therefore$ $y_1 = -1$

Hence, the image is $(12, -1)$.

Example 97. The image of the point $A(1, 2)$ by the line mirror $y = x$ is the point B and the image of B by the line mirror $y = 0$ is the point (α, β). Find α and β.

Sol. Let (x_1, y_1) be the image of the point $(1, 2)$ about the line $y = x$.

Then $$x_1 = 2, y_1 = 1 \quad \text{...(i)}$$

Also given image of $B(x_1, y_1)$ by the line mirror $y = 0$ is (α, β). Then $\alpha = x_1 = 2$

and $$\beta = -y_1 = -1 \quad \text{[from Eq. (i)]}$$

Hence, $$\alpha = 2 \quad \text{and} \quad \beta = -1$$

Example 98. The point (4, 1) undergoes the following three transformations successively :

(i) Reflection about the line $y = x$.

(ii) Translation through a distance 2 units along the positive direction of X-axis.

(iii) Rotation through an angle $\pi/4$ about the origin in the anticlockwise direction.

Then, find the coordinates of the final position.

Sol. Let $Q(x_1, y_1)$ be the reflection of P about the line $y = x$. Then

$$\left.\begin{aligned} x_1 &= 1 \\ y_1 &= 4 \end{aligned}\right\}$$

$\therefore$ Coordinates of Q is (1, 4).

Given that Q move 2 units along the positive direction of X-axis.

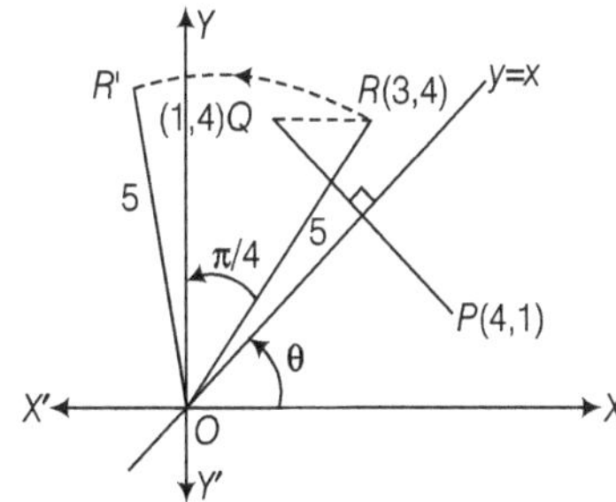

$\therefore$ Coordinates of R is $(x_1 + 2, y_1)$

or $\quad R(3, 4)$

If OR makes an angle θ, then

$$\tan\theta = \frac{4}{3}$$

$$\therefore \quad \sin\theta = \frac{4}{5} \quad \text{and} \quad \cos\theta = \frac{3}{5}$$

After rotation of $\frac{\pi}{4}$ let new position of R is R' and

$$OR = OR' = \sqrt{3^2 + 4^2} = 5$$

$\therefore \quad OR'$ makes an angle $(\pi/4 + \theta)$ with X-axis.

Coordinates of $R'\left(OR' \cos\left(\frac{\pi}{4} + \theta\right), OR' \sin\left(\frac{\pi}{4} + \theta\right)\right)$

i.e. $\quad R'\left(OR'\left(\frac{1}{\sqrt{2}}\cos\theta - \frac{1}{\sqrt{2}}\sin\theta\right),\right.$

$$\left. OR' \sin\left(\frac{1}{\sqrt{2}}\cos\theta + \frac{1}{\sqrt{2}}\sin\theta\right)\right)$$

$$\Rightarrow \quad R'\left(5\left(\frac{3}{5\sqrt{2}} - \frac{4}{5\sqrt{2}}\right), 5\left(\frac{3}{5\sqrt{2}} + \frac{4}{5\sqrt{2}}\right)\right)$$

$$\Rightarrow \quad R'\left(-\frac{1}{\sqrt{2}}, \frac{7}{\sqrt{2}}\right)$$

Aliter (Use of complex number) :

Let Q be the reflection of $P(4, 1)$ about the line $y = x$, then $Q \equiv (1, 4)$

$\because Q$ move 2 units along the +ve direction of X-axis, if new point is ,R then $R \equiv (3, 4)$.

If $\quad R(3, 4) = R(z_1)$

when $\quad z_1 = (3 + 4i)$

then $\quad R'(x, y) = R'(z_2)$

$$\therefore \quad z_2 = z_1 e^{i\pi/4} \qquad \left(\because \angle ROR' = \frac{\pi}{4}\right)$$

$$= (3 + 4i)\left(\cos\frac{\pi}{4} + i\sin\frac{\pi}{4}\right)$$

$$= (3 + 4i)\left(\frac{1}{\sqrt{2}} + \frac{i}{\sqrt{2}}\right) = \left(-\frac{1}{\sqrt{2}} + \frac{7i}{\sqrt{2}}\right)$$

Hence, new coordinates are $\left(-\frac{1}{\sqrt{2}}, \frac{7}{\sqrt{2}}\right)$.

Use of Image or Reflection

To make problems simpler and easier use Image or reflection.

Types of problems : (i) If vertex of a $\Delta\, ABC$ and equations of perpendicular bisectors of AB and AC are given, then B and C are the images or reflections of A about the perpendicular bisectors of AB and AC (where M and N are the mid-points of AB and AC).

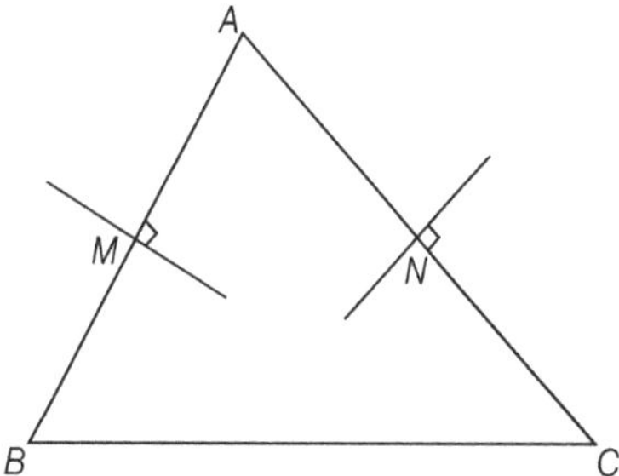

Example 99. The base of a triangle passes through a fixed point (f, g) and its sides are respectively bisected at right angles by the lines $y + x = 0$ and $y - 9x = 0$. Determine the locus of its vertex.

Sol. Let $A \equiv (\alpha, \beta)$ the image of $A(\alpha, \beta)$ about $y + x = 0$ is B, then $B \equiv (-\beta, -\alpha)$ and if image of $A(\alpha, \beta)$ about $y - 9x = 0$ is $C(x_2, y_2)$, then

$$\frac{x_2 - \alpha}{-9} = \frac{y_2 - \beta}{1} = \frac{-2(\beta - 9\alpha)}{1 + 81}$$

$$\therefore \quad x_2 = \frac{9\beta - 40\alpha}{41} \text{ and } y_2 = \frac{40\beta + 9\alpha}{41}$$

$$\therefore \quad C \equiv \left(\frac{9\beta - 40\alpha}{41}, \frac{40\beta + 9\alpha}{41}\right)$$

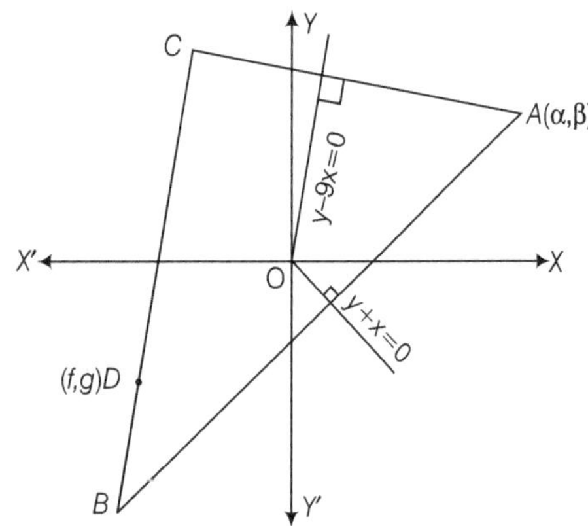

Hence, B, D, C are collinear, then

$$\frac{1}{2}\begin{vmatrix} -\beta & -\alpha & 1 \\ f & g & 1 \\ \frac{9\beta-40\alpha}{41} & \frac{40\beta+9\alpha}{41} & 1 \end{vmatrix} = 0$$

$$\Rightarrow \quad 4(\alpha^2+\beta^2)+(4g+5f)\alpha+(4f-5g)\beta=0$$

Hence, locus of vertex is

$$4(x^2+y^2)+(4g+5f)x+(4f-5g)y=0$$

(ii) The images or reflections of vertex A of a ΔABC about the angular bisectors of angles B and C lie on the side BC. (By congruence) A_1 and A_2 are the images of A about the angle bisectors BE and CF respectively, where M and N are the mid-points of AA_1 and AA_2.

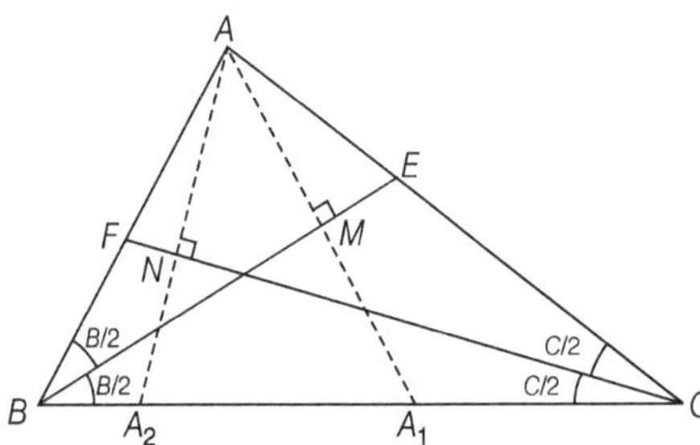

Example 100. Find the equations of the sides of the triangle having $(3, -1)$ as a vertex, $x-4y+10=0$ and $6x+10y-59=0$ being the equations of an angle bisector and a median respectively drawn from different vertices.

Sol. Let BE be the angle bisector and CF be the median. Given equations of BE and CF are $x-4y+10=0$ and $6x+10y-59=0$ respectively.

Since, image of A with respect to BE lie on BC. If image of A is $L(h, k)$.

then $$\frac{h-3}{1}=\frac{k+1}{-4}=\frac{-2(3+4+10)}{1^2+(-4)^2}=-2$$

i.e. $h=1, k=7$

$\therefore$ $L \equiv (1, 7)$

$\because$ F be the mid-point of AB.

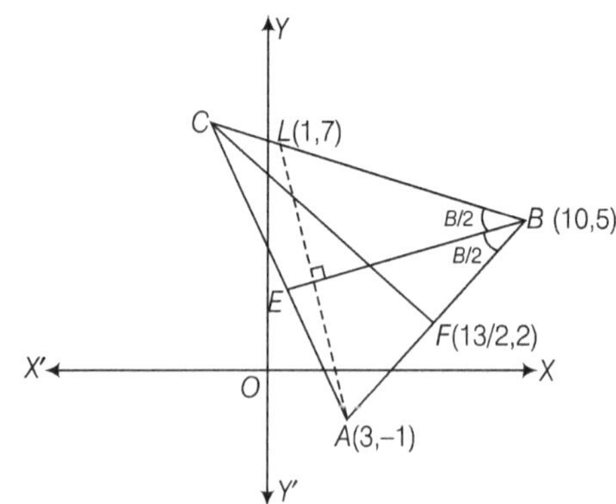

Let $F \equiv (\alpha, \beta)$

then $B \equiv (2\alpha-3, 2\beta+1)$

$\because$ B lie on BE, then

$$(2\alpha-3)-4(2\beta+1)+10=0$$

i.e. $2\alpha-8\beta+3=0$ ...(i)

and F lie on CF, then

$6\alpha+10\beta-59=0$ ...(ii)

Solving Eqs. (i) and (ii), we get

$$\alpha=\frac{13}{2}, \beta=2$$

then $F \equiv \left(\frac{13}{2}, 2\right)$

and $B=(10, 5)$

Equation of AB is

$$y+1=\frac{2+1}{\frac{13}{2}-3}(x-3)$$

$$\Rightarrow \quad y+1=\frac{6}{7}(x-3)$$

or $6x-7y-25=0$

Equation of BC is

$$y-5=\frac{7-5}{1-10}(x-10)$$

$$\Rightarrow \quad y-5=-\frac{2}{9}(x-10)$$

or $2x+9y-65=0$

$\because$ CA is the family of lines of CB and CF

then $(2x+9y-65)+\lambda(6x+10y-59)=0$ ...(iii)

it pass through $A(3, -1)$

then $(6-9-65)+\lambda(18-10-59)=0$

$\therefore$ $\lambda=-\frac{4}{3}$

From Eq. (iii), we get equation of AC is

$$18x+13y-41=0$$

(iii) Optimization (Minimization or Maximization)

(a) **Minimization :** Let A and B are two given points on the same side of $ax + by + c = 0$. Suppose we want to determine a point P on $ax + by + c = 0$ such that $PA + PB$ is minimum. Then find the image of A or B about the line $ax + by + c = 0$ (say A' or B') then join B' with A or A' with B wherever it intersects $ax + by + c = 0$ is the required point.

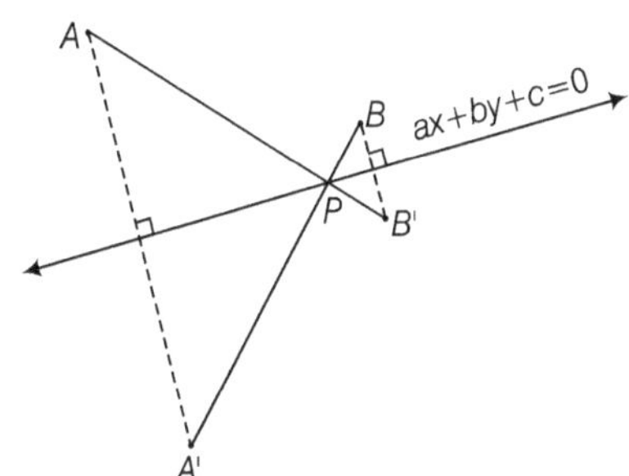

$\therefore \quad PA + PB = PA + PB'$

or $\quad PA + PB = PA' + PB$

Remark

By triangle in equality

Sum of two sides of a triangle > Third side

i.e. $|PA + PB| = |PA + PB'| = |AB'|$ (minimum value).

Example 101. Find a point R on the X-axis such that $PR + RQ$ is the minimum, when $P \equiv (1, 1)$ and $Q \equiv (3, 2)$.

Sol. Since P and Q lie on the same side of X-axis.

The image of Q (3, 2) about X-axis is Q' (3, – 2) then the equation of line PQ' is

$$y - 1 = \frac{-2-1}{3-1}(x-1)$$

$$\Rightarrow \quad 3x + 2y - 5 = 0$$

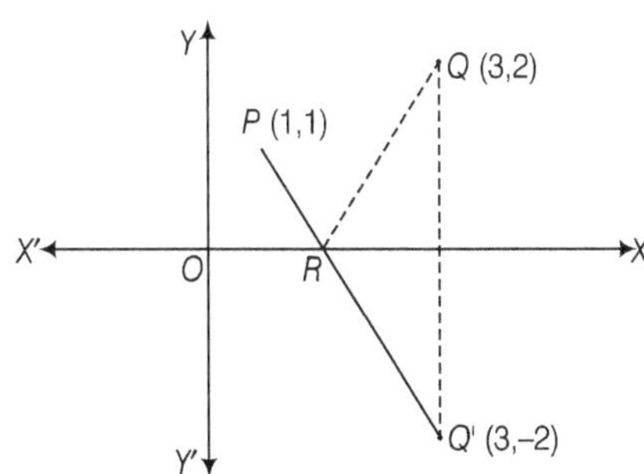

This line meets X-axis at $R\left(\frac{5}{3}, 0\right)$ which is the required point.

(b) **Maximization :** Let A and B are two given points on the same side of $ax + by + c = 0$. Suppose we want to determine a point P on $ax + by + c = 0$ such that $|PA - PB|$ is maximum, then find the equation of line AB wherever it intersects $ax + by + c = 0$ is the required point.

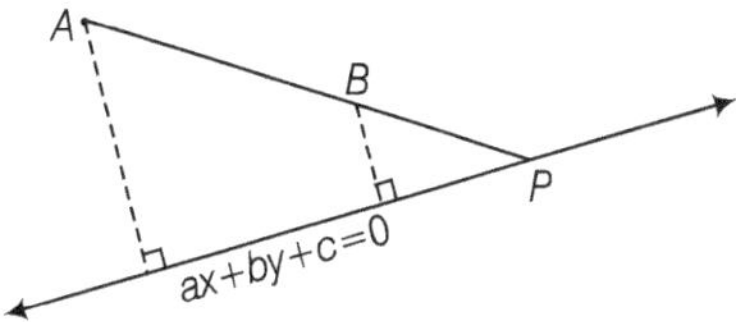

Remark

By triangle inequality

Difference of two sides of a triangle < Third side

i.e. $\quad |PA - PB| = |AB|$ (maximum value)

Example 102. Find a point P on the line $3x + 2y + 10 = 0$ such that $|PA - PB|$ is maximum where A is (4, 2) and B is (2, 4).

Sol. Let, $\quad L(x, y) = 3x + 2y + 10$

$\therefore \quad L(4, 2) = 12 + 4 + 10 = 26$

and $\quad L(2, 4) = 6 + 8 + 10 = 24$

$\therefore$ A and B lie on the same side of the line

$$3x + 2y + 10 = 0 \quad \text{...(i)}$$

Equation of line AB is

$$y - 2 = \frac{4-2}{2-4}(x-4)$$

or $\quad x + y - 6 = 0 \quad$ ...(ii)

This line Eq. (ii) meets Eq. (i) at $P \equiv (-22, 28)$ which is the required point.

Aliter

Let $\quad$ P be (x_1, y_1) and $\angle APB = \theta$

then $\quad \cos\theta = \dfrac{(PA)^2 + (PB)^2 - (AB)^2}{2PA \cdot PB}$

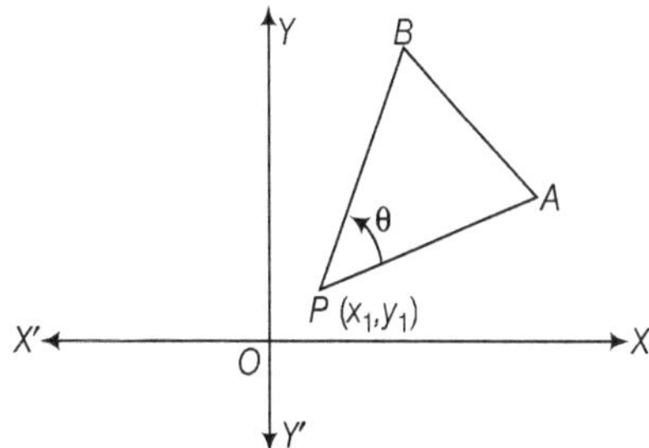

since $\qquad \cos\theta \le 1$

$$\Rightarrow \quad \frac{(PA)^2 + (PB)^2 - (AB)^2}{2PA \cdot PB} \le 1$$

$$\Rightarrow \quad (PA - PB)^2 \le (AB)^2$$

$$\Rightarrow \quad |PA - PB| \le |AB|$$

$$\Rightarrow \quad |PA - PB| \le 2\sqrt{2}$$

Maximum value of $|PA - PB|$ is $2\sqrt{2}$ when, $\theta = 0$.

i.e. P lies on the line AB as well as on the given line.

$\therefore$ Equation of AB is

$$y - 2 = \frac{4-2}{2-4}(x - 4)$$

$$\Rightarrow \quad y - 2 = -x + 4$$

$$\Rightarrow \quad x + y = 6 \qquad \text{...(i)}$$

and given line

$$3x + 2y + 10 = 0 \qquad \text{...(ii)}$$

Solving Eqs. (i) and (ii), we get $P(-22, 28)$.

P
B
A

Exercise for Session 5

1. The coordinates of the foot of the perpendicular from (2, 3) to the line $3x + 4y - 6 = 0$ are

(a) $\left(-\frac{14}{25}, -\frac{27}{25}\right)$ (b) $\left(\frac{14}{25}, -\frac{17}{25}\right)$

(c) $\left(-\frac{14}{25}, \frac{17}{25}\right)$ (d) $\left(\frac{14}{25}, \frac{27}{25}\right)$

2. If the foot of the perpendicular from the origin to a straight line is at the point $(3, -4)$. Then the equation of the line is

(a) $3x - 4y = 25$ (b) $3x - 4y + 25 = 0$

(c) $4x + 3y - 25 = 0$ (d) $4x - 3y + 25 = 0$

3. The coordinates of the foot of the perpendicular from (a, 0) on the line $y = mx + \frac{a}{m}$ are

(a) $\left(0, -\frac{1}{a}\right)$ (b) $\left(0, \frac{a}{m}\right)$ (c) $\left(0, -\frac{a}{m}\right)$ (d) $\left(0, \frac{1}{a}\right)$

4. If the equation of the locus of a point equidistant from the points (a_1, b_1) and (a_2, b_2) is $(a_1 - a_2)x + (b_1 - b_2)y + c = 0$, then the value of c is

(a) $a_1^2 - a_2^2 + b_1^2 - b_2^2$ (b) $\sqrt{(a_1^2 + b_1^2 - a_2^2 - b_2^2}$

(c) $\frac{1}{2}(a_1^2 + a_2^2 + b_1^2 + b_2^2)$ (d) $\frac{1}{2}(a_2^2 + b_2^2 - a_1^2 - b_1^2)$

5. The image of the point (3, 8) in the line $x + 3y = 7$ is

(a) (1, 4) (b) (4, 1) (c) (–1 – 4) (d) (–4, – 1)

6. The image of the point (4, –3) with respect to the line $y = x$ is

(a) (–4, – 3) (b) (3, 4) (c) (–4, 3) (d) (–3, 4)

7. The coordinates of the image of the origin O with respect to the straight line $x + y + 1 = 0$ are

(a) $\left(-\frac{1}{2}, -\frac{1}{2}\right)$ (b) (–2, – 2)

(c) (1, 1) (d) (–1, – 1)

8. If (–2, 6) is the image of the point (4, 2) with respect to the line $L = 0$, then $L \equiv$

(a) $6x - 4y - 7 = 0$ (b) $2x - 3y - 5 = 0$

(c) $3x - 2y + 5 = 0$ (d) $3x - 2y + 10 = 0$

9. The image of $P(a, b)$ on the line $y = -x$ is Q and the image of Q on the line $y = x$ is R. Then the mid-point of PR is

(a) $(a + b, a + b)$ (b) $\left(\frac{a+b}{2}, \frac{b+2}{2}\right)$

(c) $(a - b, b - a)$ (d) $(0, 0)$

10. The nearest point on the line $3x - 4y = 25$ from the origin is

(a) $(3, 4)$ (b) $(3, -4)$ (c) $(3, 5)$ (d) $(-3, 5)$

11. Consider the points $A(0, 1)$ and $B(2, 0)$, P be a point on the line $4x + 3y + 9 = 0$. The coordinates of P such that $|PA - PB|$ is maximum are

(a) $\left(-\frac{12}{5}, \frac{17}{5}\right)$ (b) $\left(-\frac{84}{5}, \frac{13}{5}\right)$ (c) $\left(-\frac{6}{5}, \frac{17}{5}\right)$ (d) $(0, -3)$

12. Consider the points $A(3, 4)$ and $B(7, 13)$. If P is a point on the line $y = x$ such that $PA + PB$ is minimum, then the coordinates of P are

(a) $\left(\frac{12}{7}, \frac{12}{7}\right)$ (b) $\left(\frac{13}{7}, \frac{13}{7}\right)$ (c) $\left(\frac{31}{7}, \frac{31}{7}\right)$ (d) $(0, 0)$

13. The image of a point $P(2, 3)$ in the line mirror $y = x$ is the point Q and the image of Q in the line mirror $y = 0$ is the point $R(x, y)$. Find the coordinates of R.

14. The equations of perpendicular bisector of the sides AB and AC of a ΔABC are $x - y + 5 = 0$ and $x + 2y = 0$ respectively. If the point A is $(1, -2)$, find the equation of line BC.

15. In a ΔABC, the equation of the perpendicular bisector of AC is $3x - 2y + 8 = 0$. If the coordinates of the point A and B are $(1, -1)$ and $(3, 1)$ respectively, find the equation of the line BC and the centre of the circumcircle of ΔABC.

16. Is there a real value of λ for which the image of the point $(\lambda, \lambda - 1)$ by the line mirror $3x + y = 6\lambda$ is the point $(\lambda^2 + 1, \lambda)$? If so find λ.

Session 6

Reflection of Light, Refraction of Light, Conditions of Collinearity if Three Given Points be in Cyclic Order

Reflection of Light

When a ray of light falls on a smooth polished surface (Mirror) separating two media, a part of it is reflected back into the first medium.

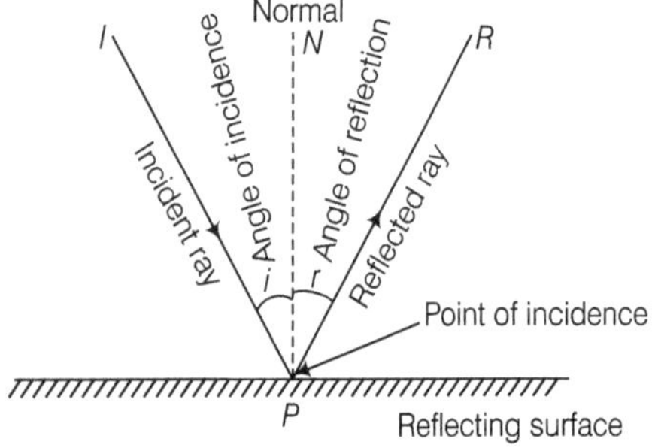

IP is the incident ray and *PR* is the reflected ray. A perpendicular drawn to the surface, at the point of incidence *P* is called the normal. Hence *PN* is the normal. The angle between the incident ray and the normal ($\angle IPN$) is called the **angle of incidence** which is represented by $\angle i$

i.e. $\angle IPN = \angle i =$ Angle of incidence and the angle between the reflected ray and the normal ($\angle IPR$) is called the **angle of reflection** which is represented by $\angle r$.

i.e. $\angle IPR = \angle r =$ Angle of reflection.

Laws of Reflection :

(i) The incident ray, normal and the reflected ray to a surface at the point of incidence all lie in the same plane.

(ii) The angle of incidence = angle of reflection

i.e. $\angle i = \angle r$

Example 103. A ray of light is sent along the line $x - 2y - 3 = 0$. Upon reaching the line $3x - 2y - 5 = 0$, the ray is reflected from it. Find the equation of the line containing the reflected ray.

Sol. To get coordinates of point *P*, we solve the given equation of lines together as

$$x - 2y - 3 = 0$$

$$3x - 2y - 5 = 0$$

$\therefore \quad x = 1, y = -1$

$\therefore$ Coordinates of *P* are $(1, -1)$.

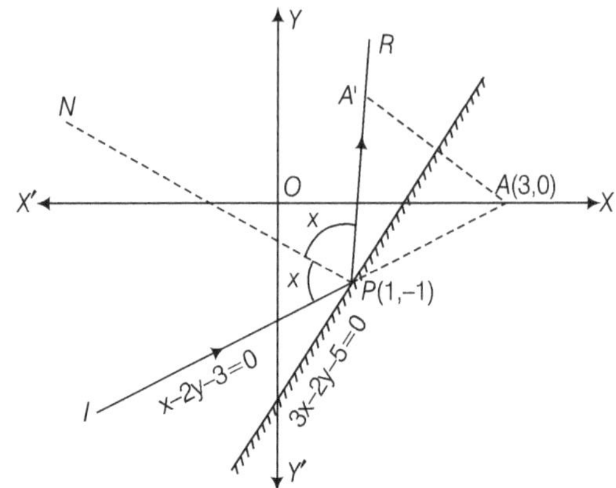

Let slope of reflected ray be *m*.

Since, slope of line mirror is 3/2.

$\therefore \quad$ Slope of $PN = -2/3$ and

slope of $IP = 1/2$, line *PN* is equally inclined to *IP* and *PR*, then

$$\left(\frac{m - \left(-\frac{2}{3}\right)}{1 + m\left(-\frac{2}{3}\right)}\right) = -\left(\frac{\frac{1}{2} - \left(-\frac{2}{3}\right)}{1 + \frac{1}{2}\left(-\frac{2}{3}\right)}\right)$$

$\Rightarrow \quad \dfrac{3m + 2}{3 - 2m} = -\dfrac{7}{4}$

$\Rightarrow \quad 12m + 8 = -21 + 14m$

$\therefore \quad 2m = 29$

$\Rightarrow \quad m = \dfrac{29}{2}$

$\therefore$ Equation of reflected ray $y + 1 = \dfrac{29}{2}(x - 1)$

$\Rightarrow \quad 2y + 2 = 29x - 29$

$\Rightarrow \quad 29x - 2y - 31 = 0.$

Aliter (Image method) : Take A (3, 0) be any point on IP and if $A'(\alpha, \beta)$ be the image of A about the mirror line $3x - 2y - 5 = 0$, then

$$\frac{\alpha - 3}{3} = \frac{\beta - 0}{-2} = \frac{-2(9 - 0 - 5)}{9 + 4}$$

$\therefore \quad \alpha = \frac{15}{13}$ and $\beta = \frac{16}{13}$

$\therefore \quad A' \equiv \left(\frac{15}{13}, \frac{16}{13}\right)$

$\therefore$ Equation of $A'P$ is the equation of the reflected ray then its equation is,

$$y + 1 = \frac{\left(\frac{16}{13} + 1\right)}{\left(\frac{15}{13} - 1\right)}(x - 1)$$

$$\Rightarrow \quad y + 1 = \frac{29}{2}(x - 1) \text{ or } 29x - 2y - 31 = 0$$

Example 104. A light beam, emanating from the point (3, 10) reflects from the straight line $2x + y - 6 = 0$ and, then passes through the point (7, 2). Find the equations of the incident and reflected beams.

Sol. Let images of A and B about the line $2x + y - 6 = 0$ are $A'(\alpha, \beta)$ and $B'(\gamma, \delta)$ respectively.

Then, $\quad \frac{\alpha - 3}{2} = \frac{\beta - 10}{1} = \frac{-2(6 + 10 - 6)}{2^2 + 1^2}$

$$= -4$$

$\therefore \quad \alpha = -5, \beta = 6$

i.e. $\quad A' \equiv (-5, 6)$

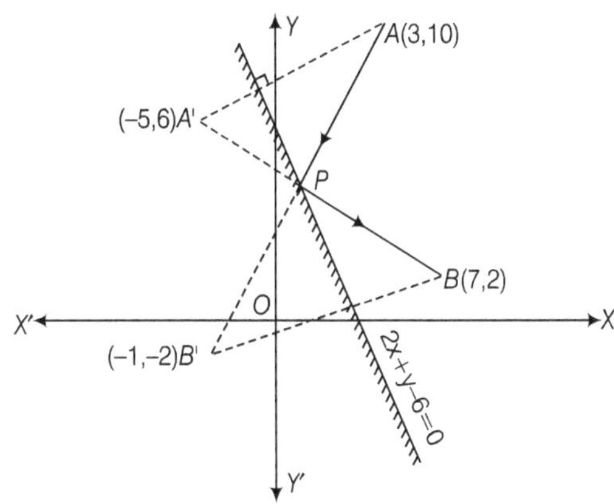

and $\quad \frac{\gamma - 7}{2} = \frac{\delta - 2}{1} = \frac{-2(14 + 2 - 6)}{2^2 + 1^2} = -4$

$\therefore \quad \gamma = -1, \delta = -2$

i.e. $\quad B' \equiv (-1, -2)$.

$\therefore$ Equation of incident ray AB' is

$$y + 2 = \frac{10 + 2}{3 + 1}(x + 1) \text{ or } 3x - y + 1 = 0$$

and equation of reflected ray $A'B$ is

$$y - 6 = \frac{2 - 6}{7 + 5}(x + 5)$$

$$\Rightarrow \quad y - 6 = -\frac{1}{3}(x + 5)$$

or $\quad x + 3y - 13 = 0$

Refraction of Light

When a ray of light falls on the boundary separating the two transparent media, there is a change in direction of ray. This phenomenon is called refraction.

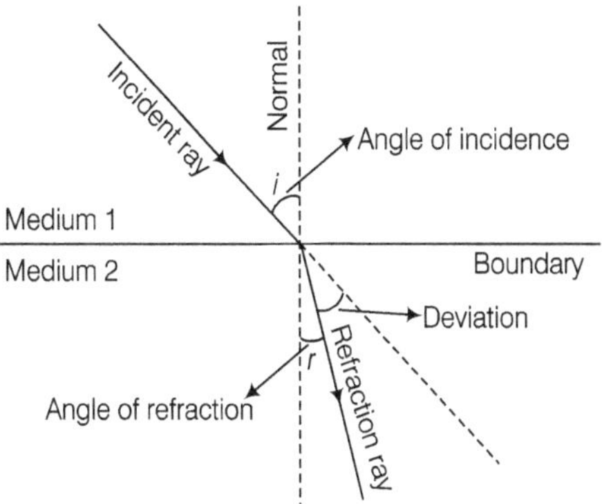

Laws of Refraction

(i) The incident ray, normal and the refracted ray to the surface separating the two transparent media all lie in the same plane.

(ii) The ratio of sine of angle of incidence to the sine of the angle of refraction is constant for the two given media. The constant is called the refractive index of medium 2 with respect to medium 1.

i.e. $\quad {}_1\mu_2 = \frac{\sin i}{\sin r}$

Example 105. A ray of light is sent along the line $x - 6y = 8$. After refracting across the line $x + y = 1$ it enters the opposite side after turning by 15° away from the line $x + y = 1$. Find the equation of the line along which the refracted ray travels.

Sol. The point of intersection of $x - 6y = 8$ and $x + y = 1$ is $A \equiv (2, -1)$. Let the required ray have the slope $= m$, then

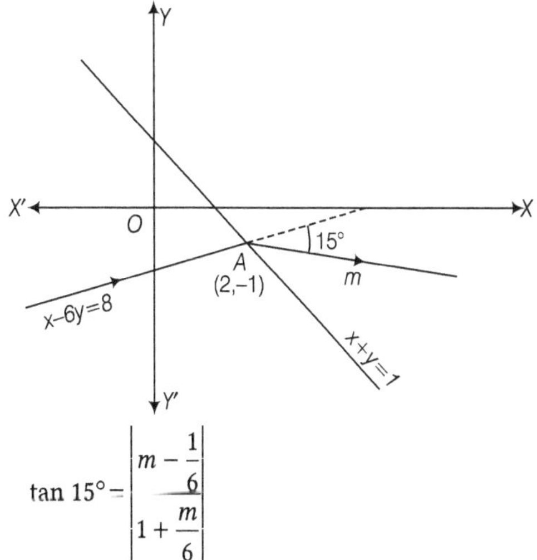

$$\tan 15° = \left|\frac{m - \frac{1}{6}}{1 + \frac{m}{6}}\right|$$

$\Rightarrow \quad 2-\sqrt{3}=\pm\left(\frac{6m-1}{m+6}\right)$

then, $\quad \frac{6m-1}{m+6}=2-\sqrt{3}$ or $\sqrt{3}-2$

$\Rightarrow \quad m=\frac{70-37\sqrt{3}}{13}$

or $\quad m=\frac{37\sqrt{3}-70}{61}$

Let the angle between $x+y=1$ and the line through $A(2,-1)$ with the slope $\frac{70-37\sqrt{3}}{13}$ be α, then

$$\tan\alpha=\left|\frac{\frac{70-37\sqrt{3}}{13}-(-1)}{1-\left(\frac{70-37\sqrt{3}}{13}\right)}\right|=\left|\frac{83-37\sqrt{3}}{37\sqrt{3}-57}\right|$$

$$=\frac{83-37\sqrt{3}}{37\sqrt{3}-57}$$

and if angle between $x+y=1$ and the line through $A(2,-1)$ with the slope $\frac{37\sqrt{3}-70}{61}$ be β, then

$$\tan\beta=\left|\frac{\frac{37\sqrt{3}-70}{61}-(-1)}{1-\left(\frac{37\sqrt{3}-70}{61}\right)}\right|=\left|\frac{37\sqrt{3}-9}{131-37\sqrt{3}}\right|$$

$$=\frac{37\sqrt{3}-9}{131-37\sqrt{3}}$$

Here $\tan\alpha>\tan\beta, \therefore \alpha>\beta$

therefore the slope of the refracted ray $=\frac{70-37\sqrt{3}}{13}$

$\therefore$ The equation of the refracted ray is

$$y+1=\frac{(70-37\sqrt{3})}{13}(x-2)$$

$\Rightarrow \quad 13y+13=(70-37\sqrt{3})x-140+74\sqrt{3}$

or $\quad (70-37\sqrt{3})x-13y-153+74\sqrt{3}=0$

Conditions of Collinearity if Three given points are in Cyclic Order

Let the three given points

$$A\equiv(f(a),g(a)), B\equiv(f(b),g(b))$$

and $C\equiv(f(c),g(c))$ lie on the line

$lx+my+n=0$, where l, m and n are constants.

Then $\quad lf(t)+m\,g(t)+n=0 \quad$ ...(i)

where, $\quad t=a,b,c$

i.e. a, b, c are the roots of the Eq. (i).

In this case Eq. (i) must be cubic in t.

$$At^3+Bt^2+Ct+D=0 \quad \text{(say)}$$

then $\quad a+b+c=-\frac{B}{A}, ab+bc+ca=\frac{C}{A}$

and $\quad abc=-\frac{D}{A}$

which are the required conditions.

Example 106. If the points $\left(\frac{a^3}{a-1},\frac{a^2-3}{a-1}\right),\left(\frac{b^3}{b-1},\frac{b^2-3}{b-1}\right)$ and $\left(\frac{c^3}{c-1},\frac{c^2-3}{c-1}\right)$ are collinear for three distinct values a,b,c and different from 1, then show that $abc-(bc+ca+ab)+3(a+b+c)=0$.

Sol. Let the three given points lie on the line

$lx+my+n=0$, where l, m and n are constants.

Then, $l\left(\frac{t^3}{t-1}\right)+m\left(\frac{t^2-3}{t-1}\right)+n=0$

$\Rightarrow \quad lt^3+mt^2+nt-(3m+n)=0$

for $t=a,b,c$

i.e. a, b, c are the roots of

$$lt^3+mt^2+nt-3m-n=0$$

then $\quad a+b+c=-\frac{m}{l}, ab+bc+ca=\frac{n}{l}$

and $\quad abc=\left(\frac{3m+n}{l}\right)$

Now, $abc-(bc+ca+ab)+3(a+b+c)$

$$=\left(\frac{3m+n}{l}\right)-\frac{n}{l}-\frac{3m}{l}=0$$

Hence, $abc-(bc+ca+ab)+3(a+b+c)=0$

Example 107. If t_1, t_2 and t_3 are distinct, the points $(t_1, 2at_1+at_1^3), (t_2, 2at_2+at_2^3)$ and $(t_3, 2at_3+at_3^3)$ are collinear, then prove that $t_1+t_2+t_3=0$.

Sol. Let the three given points lie on the line $lx+my+n=0$, where l, m and n are constants. Then,

$$l(t)+m(2at+at^3)+n=0$$

$\Rightarrow \quad (am)t^3+(2am+l)t+n=0 \quad$ ...(i)

for $t=t_1, t_2, t_3$

i.e., t_1, t_2, t_3 are the roots of Eq. (i), then

$$t_1+t_2+t_3=0$$

Exercise for Session 6

1. A ray of light passing through the point (1, 2) is reflected on the X-axis at a point P and passes through the point (5, 3). The abscissae of the point P is

(a) 3 (b) $\frac{13}{3}$ (c) $\frac{13}{5}$ (d) $\frac{13}{4}$

2. The equation of the line segment AB is $y = x$. If A and B lie on the same side of the line mirror $2x - y = 1$, then the image of AB has the equation

(a) $x + y = 2$ (b) $8x + y = 9$ (c) $7x - y = 6$ (d) None of these

3. A ray of light travelling along the line $x + y = 1$ is incident on the X-axis and after refraction it enters the other side of the X-axis by turning $\pi/6$ away from the X-axis. The equation of the line along which the refracted ray travels is

(a) $x + (2 - \sqrt{3})\, y = 1$ (b) $x\,(2 + \sqrt{3}) + y = 2 + \sqrt{3}$

(c) $(2 - \sqrt{3})x + y = 1$ (d) $x + (2 + \sqrt{3})y = (2 + \sqrt{3})$

4. All the points lying inside the triangle formed by the points (0, 4), (2, 5) and (6, 2) satisfy

(a) $3x + 2y + 8 \geq 0$ (b) $2x + y - 10 \geq 0$

(c) $2x - 3y - 11 \geq 0$ (d) $-2x + y - 3 \geq 0$

5. Let O be the origin and let $A(1, 0)$, $B(0, 1)$ be two points. If $P(x, y)$ is a point such that $xy > 0$ and $x + y < 1$ then

(a) P lies either inside in ΔOAB or in third quadrant (b) P cannot be inside in ΔOAB

(c) P lies inside the ΔOAB (d) None of these

6. A ray of light coming along the line $3x + 4y - 5 = 0$ gets reflected from the line $ax + by - 1 = 0$ and goes along the line $5x - 12y - 10 = 0$ then

(a) $a = \frac{64}{115}, b = \frac{112}{15}$ (b) $a = -\frac{64}{115}, b = \frac{8}{115}$

(c) $a = \frac{64}{115}, b = \frac{8}{115}$ (d) $a = -\frac{64}{115}, b = \frac{-8}{115}$

7. Two sides of a triangle have the joint equation $x^2 - 2xy - 3y^2 + 8y - 4 = 0$. The third side, which is variable, always passes through the point $(-5, -1)$. Find the range of values of the slope of the third side, so that the origin is an interior point of the triangle.

8. Determine the range of values of $\theta \in [0, 2\pi]$ for which $(\cos\theta, \sin\theta)$ lies inside the triangle formed by the lines $x + y - 2 = 0$, $x - y - 1 = 0$ and $6x + 2y - \sqrt{10} = 0$.

9. Let $P(\sin\theta, \cos\theta)$, where $0 \leq \theta \leq 2\pi$ be a point and let OAB be a triangle with vertices (0, 0), $\left(\frac{\sqrt{3}}{2}, 0\right)$ and $\left(0, \frac{\sqrt{3}}{2}\right)$.

Find θ if P lies inside the $\Delta\, OAB$.

10. Find all values of θ for which the point $(\sin^2\theta, \sin\theta)$ lies inside the square formed by the line $xy = 0$ and $4xy - 2x - 2y + 1 = 0$.

11. Determine whether the point $(-3, 2)$ lies inside or outside the triangle whose sides are given by the equations $x + y - 4 = 0$, $3x - 7y + 8 = 0$, $4x - y - 31 = 0$.

12. A ray of light is sent along the line $x - 2y + 5 = 0$, upon reaching the line $3x - 2y + 7 = 0$, the ray is reflected from it. Find the equation of the line containing the reflected ray.

Shortcuts and Important Results to Remember

1. Area of parallelogram formed by the lines $a_1x + b_1y + c_1 = 0$, $a_2x + b_2y + d_1 = 0$, $a_1x + b_1y + c_2 = 0$ and $a_2x + b_2y + d_2 = 0$ is

$$\frac{|c_1 - c_2||d_1 - d_2|}{\left|\begin{vmatrix} a_1 & b_1 \\ a_2 & b_2 \end{vmatrix}\right|}$$

2. Area of parallelogram formed by the lines $y = m_1x + c_1$, $y = m_2x + d_1$, $y = m_1x + c_2$ and $y = m_2x + d_2$ is

$$\frac{|c_1 - c_2||d_1 - d_2|}{|m_1 - m_2|}$$

3. If $A \equiv (x_1, y_1)$, $B \equiv (x_2, y_2)$ and $C \equiv (x_3, y_3)$ are the vertices of a ΔABC, then angle A is acute or obtuse according as

$$(x_1 - x_2)(x_1 - x_3) + (y_1 - y_2)(y_1 - y_3) > 0 \quad \text{or} \quad < 0$$

Similarly, for $\angle B$

$$(x_2 - x_3)(x_2 - x_1) + (y_2 - y_3)(y_2 - y_1) > 0 \quad \text{or} \quad < 0$$

and for $\angle C$

$$(x_3 - x_1)(x_3 - x_2) + (y_3 - y_1)(y_3 - y_2) > 0 \quad \text{or} \quad < 0$$

4. If the origin lies in the acute angle or obtuse angle between the lines

$$a_1x + b_1y + c_1 = 0$$

and $$a_2x + b_2y + c_2 = 0$$

according as $(a_1a_2 + b_1b_2)c_1c_2 < 0$ or > 0.

5. If $A \equiv (x_1, y_1)$, $B \equiv (x_2, y_2)$ and $C \equiv (x_3, y_3)$ are the vertices of a ΔABC then the equations of the right bisectors (perpendicular bisectors) of the sides BC, CA and AB are

$$y(y_2 - y_3) + x(x_2 - x_3) = \left(\frac{x_2^2 - x_3^2}{2}\right) + \left(\frac{y_2^2 - y_3^2}{2}\right);$$

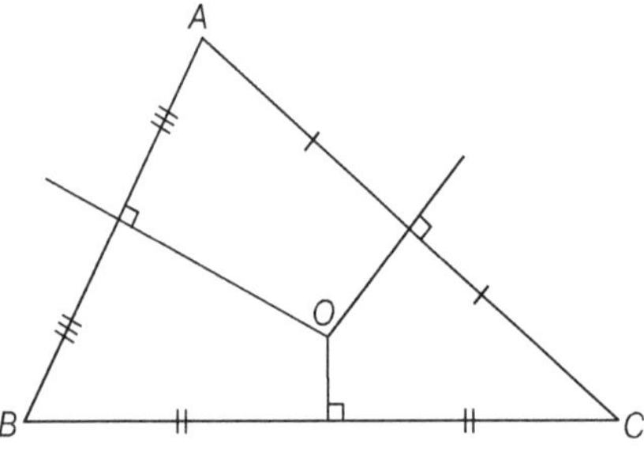

$$y(y_3 - y_1) + x(x_3 - x_1) = \left(\frac{x_3^2 - x_1^2}{2}\right) + \left(\frac{y_3^2 - y_1^2}{2}\right)$$

and $$y(y_1 - y_2) + x(x_1 - x_2) = \left(\frac{x_1^2 - x_2^2}{2}\right) + \left(\frac{y_1^2 - y_2^2}{2}\right)$$

respectively. Where O is the circumcentre of ΔABC.

6. If $A \equiv (x_1, y_1)$, $B \equiv (x_2, y_2)$ and $C \equiv (x_3, y_3)$ are the vertices of a ΔABC then the equations of medians AD, BE and CF are

$$y(x_2 + x_3 - 2x_1) - x(y_2 + y_3 - 2y_1) = y_1(x_2 + x_3) - x_1(y_2 + y_3);$$

$$y(x_3 + x_1 - 2x_2) - x(y_3 + y_1 - 2y_2) = y_2(x_3 + x_1) - x_2(y_3 + y_1)$$

and $y(x_1 + x_2 - 2x_3) - x(y_1 + y_2 - 2y_3) = y_3(x_1 + x_2) - x_3(y_1 + y_2)$ respectively.

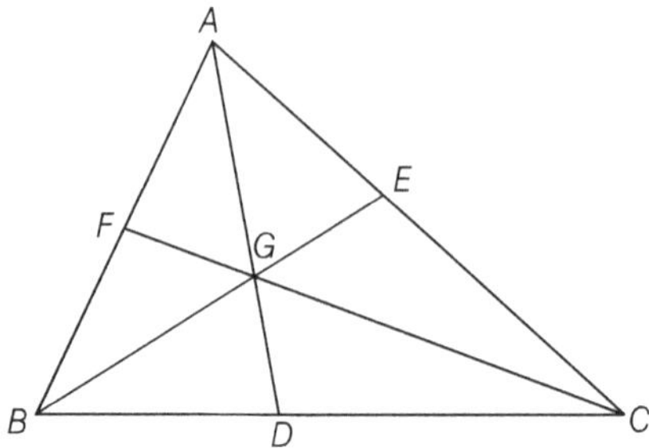

Where, G is the centroid of ΔABC.

7. If $A \equiv (x_1, y_1)$, $B \equiv (x_2, y_2)$ and $C \equiv (x_3, y_3)$ are the vertices of a ΔABC then the equations of the altitudes AL, BM and CN are

$$y(y_2 - y_3) + x(x_2 - x_3) = y_1(y_2 - y_3) + x_1(x_2 - x_3);$$

$$y(y_3 - y_1) + x(x_3 - x_1) = y_2(y_3 - y_1) + x_2(x_3 - x_1)$$

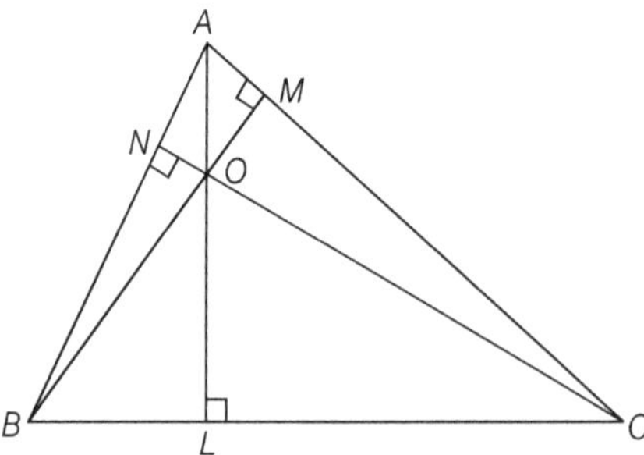

and $y(y_1 - y_2) + x(x_1 - x_2) = y_3(x_1 - x_2) + x_3(x_1 - x_2)$ respectively. Where O is the orthocentre of ΔABC.

8. If sides of a triangle ABC are represented by

$BC: a_1x + b_1y + c_1 = 0$,

$CA: a_2x + b_2y + c_2 = 0$

and $AB: a_3x + b_3y + c_3 = 0$

then $|BC| : |CA| : |AB|$

$$= \sqrt{(a_1^2 + b_1^2)}\left|\begin{vmatrix} a_2 & b_2 \\ a_3 & b_3 \end{vmatrix}\right| : \sqrt{(a_2^2 + b_2^2)}\left|\begin{vmatrix} a_3 & b_3 \\ a_1 & b_1 \end{vmatrix}\right| : \sqrt{(a_3^2 + b_3^2)}\left|\begin{vmatrix} a_1 & b_1 \\ a_2 & b_2 \end{vmatrix}\right|$$

JEE Type Solved Examples :
Single Option Correct Type Questions

- This section contains **10 multiple choice examples**. Each example has four choices (a), (b), (c) and (d) out of which **ONLY ONE** is correct.

Ex. 1 *A rectangle ABCD has its side AB parallel to $y = x$ and vertices A, B and D lie on $y = 1$, $x = 2$ and $x = -2$ respectively, then locus of vertex C is*

(a) $x = 5$ (b) $x - y = 5$

(c) $y = 5$ (d) $x + y = 5$

Sol. (c) Since AB is parallel to $y = x$.

$\therefore$ Equation of AB is $y = x + a$ (say)

$\because$ A lies on $y = 1$

$\therefore$ $A \equiv (1 - a, 1)$

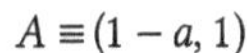

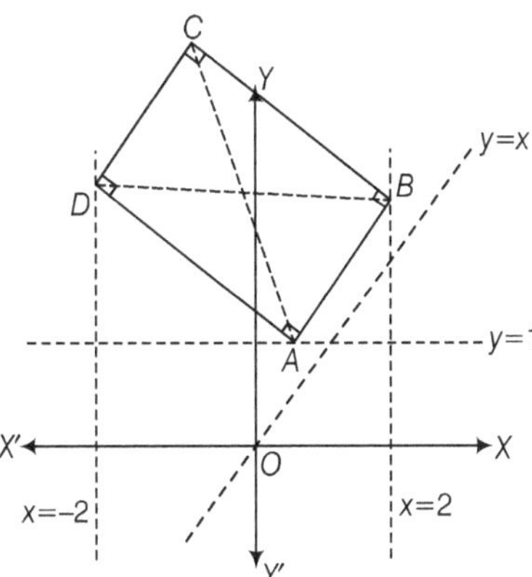

Again, B lies on $x = 2$

$\therefore$ $B = (2, 2 + a)$

$\Rightarrow$ Equation of AD is

$$y - 1 = -[x - (1 - a)] \text{ or } y = 2 - x - a$$

$\because$ D lies on $x = -2$

$\therefore$ $D \equiv (-2, 4 - a)$

Let $C \equiv (h, k)$

$\because$ Diagonals of rectangle bisects to each other

$\therefore$ $h + 1 - a = 2 - 2 \Rightarrow a = 1 + h$

and $k + 1 = 2 + a + 4 - a$

$\Rightarrow$ $k = 5$

$\therefore$ Locus of C is $y = 5$

Ex. 2 *The line $(\lambda + 1)^2 x + \lambda y - 2\lambda^2 - 2 = 0$ passes through a point regardless of the value λ. Which of the following is the line with slope 2 passing through the point?*

(a) $y = 2x - 8$ (b) $y = 2x - 5$

(c) $y = 2x - 4$ (d) $y = 2x + 8$

Sol. (a)

$\because$ $(\lambda + 1)^2 x + \lambda y - 2\lambda^2 - 2 = 0$

or $(\lambda^2 + 2\lambda + 1)x + \lambda y - 2\lambda^2 - 2 = 0$

or $(\lambda^2 + 1)(x - 2) + \lambda(2x + y) = 0$

$\therefore$ For fixed point

$$x - 2 = 0 \text{ and } 2x + y = 0$$

$\therefore$ Fixed point is $(2, -4)$

$\therefore$ Equation of required line is $y + 4 = 2(x - 2)$

or $y = 2x - 8$

Ex. 3 *A man starts from the point $P(-3, 4)$ and reaches point $Q(0, 1)$ touching X-axis at R such that $PR + RQ$ is minimum, then the point R is*

(a) $\left(\frac{3}{5}, 0\right)$ (b) $\left(-\frac{3}{5}, 0\right)$ (c) $\left(-\frac{2}{5}, 0\right)$ (d) $(-2, 0)$

Sol. (b) Let $R = (\alpha, 0)$

For $PR + PQ$ to be minimum it should be the path of light and thus we have

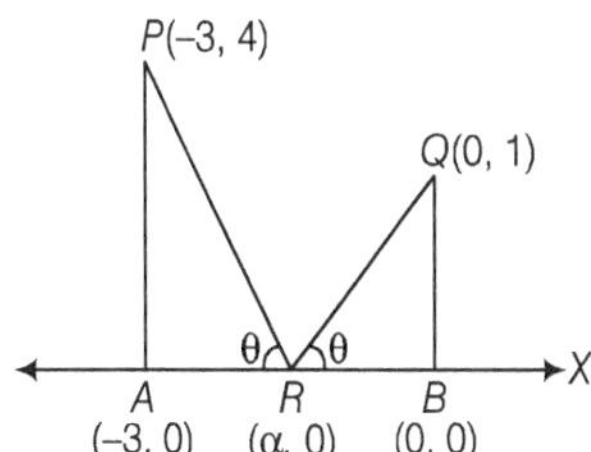

$$\Delta APR \sim \Delta BQR$$

$\Rightarrow$ $\frac{AR}{RB} = \frac{PA}{QB} \Rightarrow \frac{\alpha + 3}{0 - \alpha} = \frac{4}{1} \Rightarrow \alpha = -\frac{3}{5}$

Hence, $R \equiv \left(-\frac{3}{5}, 0\right)$

Ex. 4 *If the point $P(a, a^2)$ lies inside the triangle formed by the lines $x = 0$, $y = 0$ and $x + y = 2$, then exhaustive range of 'a' is*

(a) $(0, 1)$ (b) $(1, \sqrt{2})$

(c) $(\sqrt{2} - 1, 1)$ (d) $(\sqrt{2} - 1, 2)$

Sol. (a) Since the point $P(a, a^2)$ lies on $y = x^2$

Solving, $y = x^2$

and $x + y = 2$, we get

$$x^2 + x - 2 = 0$$

$\Rightarrow$ $(x + 2)(x - 1) = 0$

$\Rightarrow$ $x = -2, 1$

It is clear from figure,

$$A \equiv (1, 1)$$

also $a > 0$ for I quadrant.

$\therefore$ $a \in (0, 1)$

Ex. 5 *If $5a + 4b + 20c = t$, then the value of t for which the line $ax + by + c - 1 = 0$ always passes through a fixed point is*

(a) 0 (b) 20
(c) 30 (d) None of these

Sol. (b) Equation of line $\frac{ax}{c-1} + \frac{by}{c-1} + 1 = 0$ has two independent parameters. It can pass through a fixed point if it contains only one independent parameter. Now there must be one relation between $\frac{a}{c-1}$ and $\frac{b}{c-1}$ independent of a, b and c so that $\frac{a}{c-1}$ can be cxpressed in terms of $\frac{b}{c-1}$ and straight line contains only one independent parameter. Now that given relation can be expressed as $\frac{5a}{c-1} + \frac{4b}{c-1} = \frac{t-20c}{c-1}$.

RHS is independent of c if $t = 20$.

Ex. 6 *If the straight lines, $ax + amy + 1 = 0$, $bx + (m+1)by + 1 = 0$ and $cx + (m+2)cy + 1 = 0$, $m \neq 0$ are concurrent, then a, b, c are in*

(a) AP only for $m = 1$ (b) AP for all m
(c) GP for all m (d) HP for all m

Sol. (d) The three lines are concurrent if

$$\begin{vmatrix} a & am & 1 \\ b & m+1 & 1 \\ c & (m+2)c & 1 \end{vmatrix} = 0$$

Applying $C_2 \to C_2 - mC_1$, then

$$\begin{vmatrix} a & 0 & 1 \\ b & b & 1 \\ c & 2c & 1 \end{vmatrix} = 0$$

or $a(b - 2c) - 0 + 1(2bc - bc) = 0$

or $b = \frac{2ac}{a+c}$, which is independent of m.

$\therefore$ a, b, c are in HP for all m.

Ex. 7 *If a ray travelling the line $x = 1$ gets reflected the line $x + y = 1$, then the equation of the line along which the reflected ray travels is*

(a) $y = 0$ (b) $x - y = 1$
(c) $x = 0$ (d) None of these

Sol. (a) Reflected ray is X-axis.

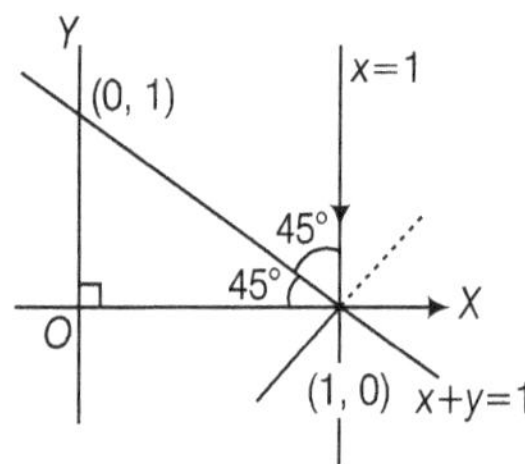

$\therefore$ Equation $y = 0$

Ex. 8 *Through the point $P(\alpha, \beta)$, when $\alpha\beta > 0$, the straight line $\frac{x}{a} + \frac{y}{b} = 1$ is drawn so as to form with coordinate axes a triangle of area Δ. If $ab > 0$, then the least value of Δ is*

(a) $\alpha\beta$ (b) $2\alpha\beta$
(c) $4\alpha\beta$ (d) $8\alpha\beta$

Sol. (b) Given line is

$$\frac{x}{a} + \frac{y}{b} = 1 \quad \text{...(i)}$$

$\therefore$ $A \equiv (a, 0), B \equiv (0, b)$

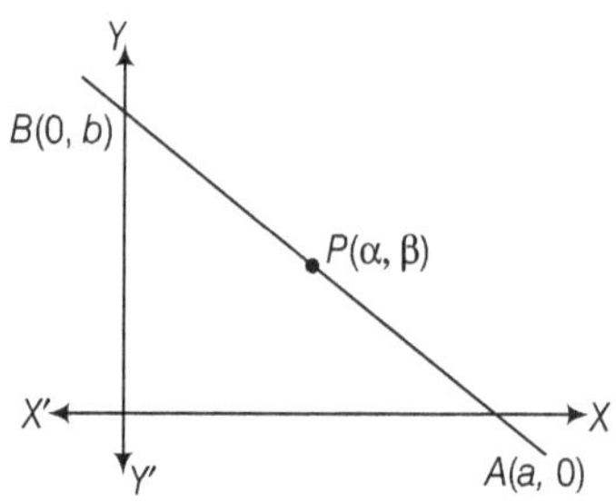

$\because$ Area of $(\Delta AOB) = \Delta$

$\therefore$ $\frac{1}{2}|ab| = \Delta \Rightarrow ab = 2\Delta$ $(\because ab > 0)$

Since, the line (i) passes through the point $P(\alpha, \beta)$.

$\therefore$ $\frac{\alpha}{a} + \frac{\beta}{b} = 1 \Rightarrow \frac{\alpha}{a} + \frac{a\beta}{2\Delta} = 1$ $\left(\because b = \frac{2\Delta}{a}\right)$

$\Rightarrow$ $\alpha^2\beta - 2a\Delta + 2\Delta\alpha = 0$

$\because a$ is real

$\therefore$ $D \geq 0$

$\Rightarrow$ $4\Delta^2 - 4\beta(2\Delta\alpha) \geq 0$ or $\Delta \geq 2\alpha\beta$

$\therefore$ Least value of Δ is $2\alpha\beta$.

Ex. 9 *The coordinates of the point P on the line $2x + 3y + 1 = 0$, such that $|PA - PB|$ is maximum, where A is $(2, 0)$ and B is $(0, 2)$ is*

(a) $(5, -3)$ (b) $(7, -5)$
(c) $(9, -7)$ (d) $(11, -9)$

Sol. (b) $|PA - PB| \leq |AB|$

Maximum value of $|PA - PB|$ is $|AB|$, which is possible only when P, A, B are collinear

if $P(x, y)$, then equation AB is

$$\frac{x}{2} + \frac{y}{2} = 1$$

$\Rightarrow$ $x + y = 2$ ...(i)

Now solving Eq. (i)

and $2x + 3y + 1 = 0$ ...(ii)

Then, we get,

$$x = 7, y = -5$$

$\therefore$ $P \equiv (7, -5)$

Ex. 10 *Equation of the straight line which belongs to the system of straight lines $a(2x+y-3)+b(3x+2y-5)=0$ and is farthest from the point (4, −3) is*

(a) $4x+11y-15=0$ (b) $3x-4y+1=0$

(c) $7x+y-8=0$ (d) None of these

Sol. (b) The system of straight lines $a(2x+y-3)+b(3x+2y-5)=0)$ passes through the point of intersection of the lines $2x+y-3=0$ and $3x+2y-5=0$ i.e. (1, 1)

The line of this family which is farthest from (4, −3) is the line through (1, 1) and perpendicular to the line joining (1, 1) and (4, −3)

∴ The required line is

$$y-1=\frac{3}{4}(x-1)$$

or $$3x-4y+1=0$$

JEE Type Solved Examples : More than One Correct Option Type Questions

- This section contains **5 multiple choice examples**. Each example has four choices (a), (b), (c) and (d) out of which **MORE THAN ONE** may be correct.

Ex. 11 *The vertices of a square inscribed in the triangle with vertices A(0, 0), B(2, 1) and C(3, 0), given that two of its vertices are on the side AC, are*

(a) $\left(\frac{3}{2},0\right)$ (b) $\left(\frac{3}{2},\frac{3}{4}\right)$ (c) $\left(\frac{9}{4},\frac{3}{4}\right)$ (d) $\left(\frac{9}{4},0\right)$

Sol. (a, b, c, d)

Let $PQRS$ be a square inscribed in ΔABC and

$$PQ=QR=RS=SP=\lambda \quad \text{(say)}$$

Let $P\equiv(a,0)$,

∴ $Q\equiv(a+\lambda,\lambda)$, $R\equiv(a+\lambda,\lambda)$ and $S\equiv(a,\lambda)$

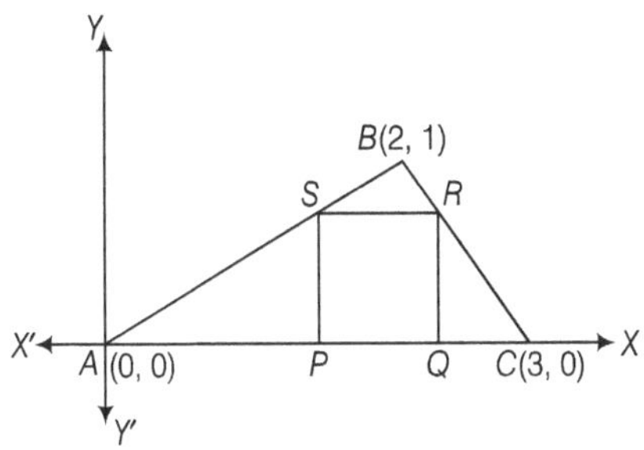

Now equation of AB is

$$x-2y=0 \quad \text{...(i)}$$

and equation of BC is

$$x+y-3=0 \quad \text{...(ii)}$$

∵ S lies on AB, then

$$a-2\lambda=0 \quad \text{...(iii)}$$

and R lies on BC, then

$$a+\lambda+\lambda-3=0 \text{ or } a+2\lambda-3=0 \quad \text{...(iv)}$$

From Eqs. (iii) and (iv), we get $a=\frac{3}{2}, \lambda=\frac{3}{4}$

Hence, $P\equiv\left(\frac{3}{2},0\right)$, $Q\equiv\left(\frac{9}{4},0\right)$,

$R\equiv\left(\frac{9}{4},\frac{3}{2}\right)$, $S\equiv\left(\frac{3}{2},\frac{3}{4}\right)$

Ex. 12 *Line $\frac{x}{a}+\frac{y}{b}=1$ cuts the coordinate axes at $A(a,0)$ and $B(0,b)$ and the line $\frac{x}{a'}+\frac{y}{b'}=-1$ at $A'(-a',0)$ and $B'(0,-b')$. If the points A, B, A', B' are concyclic, then the orthocentre of the triangle ABA' is*

(a) (0, 0) (b) $(0,b')$

(c) $\left(0,\frac{-aa'}{b}\right)$ (d) $\left(0,\frac{bb'}{a}\right)$

Sol. (b, c)

∵ A, B, A', B' are concyclic then,

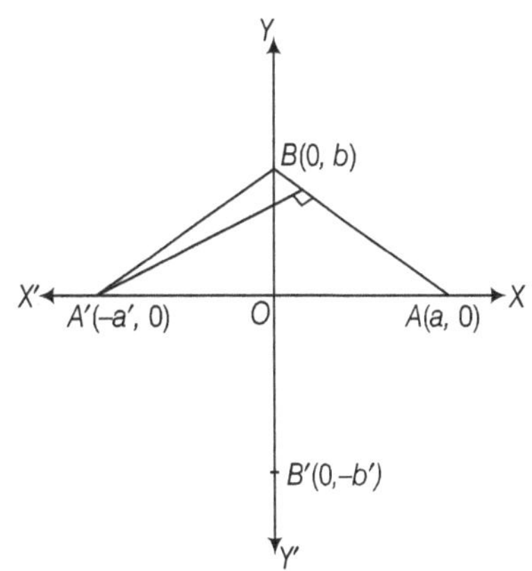

$$OA\cdot OA'=OB\cdot OB'$$

or $$(a)\cdot(-a')=(b)\cdot(-b')$$

or $$aa'=bb' \quad \text{...(i)}$$

The equation of altitude through A' is

$$y-0=\frac{a}{b}(x+a')$$

It intersects the altitude

$$x=0 \text{ at } y=\frac{aa'}{b}$$

∴ Orthocentre is $\left(0,\frac{aa'}{b}\right)$ or $(0,b')$ [from Eq. (i)]

Ex. 13 *Two straight lines $u=0$ and $v=0$ passes through the origin and angle between them is $\tan^{-1}\left(\frac{7}{9}\right)$. If the ratio of the slope of $v=0$ and $u=0$ is $\frac{9}{2}$, then their equations are*

(a) $y = 3x$ and $3y = 2x$
(b) $2y = 3x$ and $3y = x$
(c) $y + 3x = 0$ and $3y + 2x = 0$
(d) $2y + 3x = 0$ and $3y + x = 0$

Sol. (a, b, c, d)

Let the slope of $u = 0$ be m, then the slope of $v = 0$ is $\frac{9m}{2}$.

Therefore, $$\left|\frac{m - \frac{9m}{2}}{1 + m \times \frac{9m}{2}}\right| = \frac{7}{9}$$

or $$\left|\frac{-7m}{2 + 9m^2}\right| = \frac{7}{9}$$

$\Rightarrow$ $$9m^2 + 9m + 2 = 0 \text{ or } 9m^2 - 9m + 2 = 0$$

$\Rightarrow$ $$m = -\frac{2}{3}, -\frac{1}{3} \text{ or } m = \frac{2}{3}, \frac{1}{3}$$

Therefore, the equation of lines are
(i) $2x + 3y = 0$ and $3x + y = 0$
(ii) $x + 3y = 0$ and $3x + 2y = 0$
(iii) $2x = 3y$ and $3x = y$
(iv) $x = 3y$ and $3x = 2y$

Ex. 14 *Two sides of a rhombus OABC (lying entirely in the first or third quadrant) of are equal to 2 sq units are $y = \frac{x}{\sqrt{3}}$, $y = \sqrt{3}x$. Then the possible coordinates of B is/are (O being the origin)*

(a) $(1+\sqrt{3}, 1+\sqrt{3})$ (b) $(-1-\sqrt{3}, -1-\sqrt{3})$
(c) $(3+\sqrt{3}, 3+\sqrt{3})$ (d) $(\sqrt{3}-1, \sqrt{3}-1)$

Sol. (a, b)

Here, $\angle COA = 30°$

Let $OA = AB = BC = CO = x$

$\because$ Area of rhombus $OABC$

$$= 2 \times \frac{1}{2} \times x \times x \sin 30°$$

$$= \frac{x^2}{2} = 2 \qquad \text{[given]}$$

$\therefore$ $x = 2$

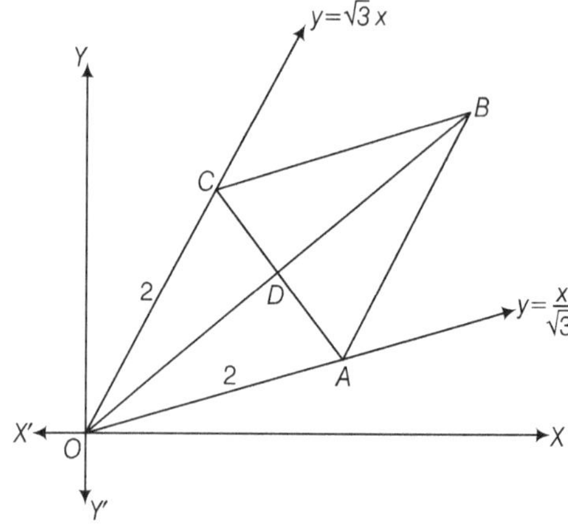

Coordinates of A and C are $(\sqrt{3}, 1)$ and $(1, \sqrt{3})$ in I quadrant and in III quadrant are $(-\sqrt{3}, -1)$ and $(-1, -\sqrt{3})$

Hence, coordinates of B are $(\sqrt{3}+1, \sqrt{3}+1)$ and $(-\sqrt{3}-1, -\sqrt{3}-1)$

Ex. 15 *A and B are two fixed points whose coordinates are (3, 2) and (5, 4) respectively. The coordinates of a point P, if ABP is an equilateral triangle are*

(a) $(4-\sqrt{3}, 3+\sqrt{3})$ (b) $(4+\sqrt{3}, 3-\sqrt{3})$
(c) $(3-\sqrt{3}, 4+\sqrt{3})$ (d) $(3+\sqrt{3}, 4-\sqrt{3})$

Sol. (a, b)

$\because$ $$AB = AP = BP = 2\sqrt{2}$$

$\therefore$ Coordinates of P are $(3 + 2\sqrt{2}\cos 105°, 2 + 2\sqrt{2}\sin 105°)$

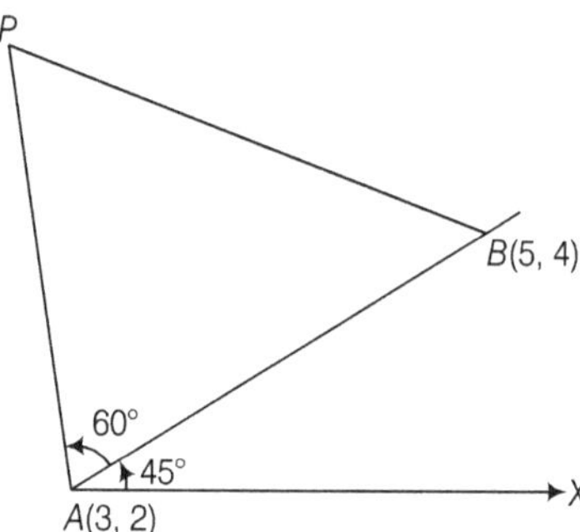

or $$(3 - (\sqrt{3}-1), 2 + \sqrt{3} + 1)$$

or $$(4-\sqrt{3}, 3+\sqrt{3})$$

If P below AB, then coordinates of P are

$$(3 + 2\sqrt{2}\cos 15°, 2 - 2\sqrt{2}\sin 15°)$$

or $$[(3 + \sqrt{3} + 1, 2 - (\sqrt{3}-1)]$$

or $$(4+\sqrt{3}, 3-\sqrt{3})$$

JEE Type Solved Examples : Paragraph Based Questions

- This section contains **2 solved paragraphs** based upon each of the paragraph **3 multiple choice questions** have to be answered. Each of these question has four choices (a), (b), (c) and (d) out of which **ONLY ONE** is correct.

Paragraph I

(Q. Nos. 16 to18)

Let $d(P, OA) \le \min \cdot \{d(P, AB), d(P, BC), d(P, OC)\}$, where d denotes the distance from the point to the corresponding the line and R be the region consisting of all those points P inside the rectangle OABC such that $O \equiv (0,0)$, $A \equiv (3,0)$, $B \equiv (3,2)$ and $C \equiv (0,2)$. Let M be the peak of region R.

16. Length of the perpendicular from M to OA is

(a) 4 (b) 3 (c) 2 (d) 1

17. If λ be the perimeter of region R, then λ is

(a) $4 - \sqrt{2}$ (b) $4 + \sqrt{2}$ (c) $4 + 2\sqrt{2}$ (d) 10

18. If Δ be the area of region R, then Δ is

(a) 2 (b) 4 (c) 6 (d) 8

Sol. Let $P \equiv (x, y)$

$\because \quad d(P, OA) \le \min \cdot \{d(P, AB), d(P, BC), d(P, OC)\}$

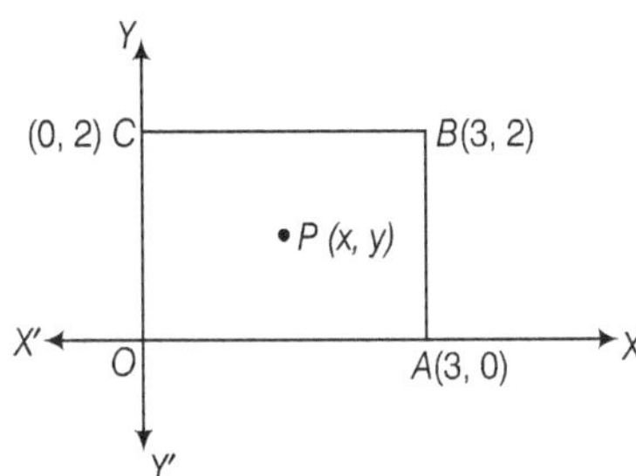

$\Rightarrow \quad |y| \le \min \{|3 - x|, |2 - y|, |x|\}$

As the rectangle $OABC$ lies in I quadrant,

$\therefore \quad y \le \min \cdot [3 - x, 2 - y.x]$

We draw the graph of

$y = 3 - x, y = 2 - y, y = x$

or $\quad x + y = 3, y = 1, y = x$

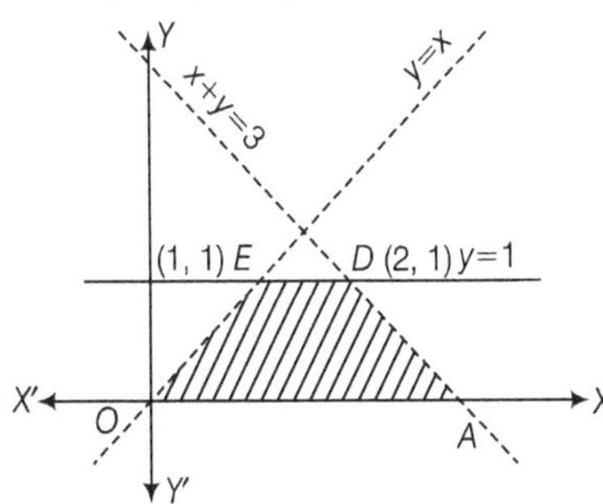

$\therefore \quad E \equiv (1, 1)$ and $D \equiv (2, 1)$

16. (d) $\because$ M lie on $y = 1$

$\therefore$ Length of $\perp$ from M to OA is 1.

17. (c) λ = Perimeter of region R

$$= OA + AD + DE + EO$$
$$= 3 + \sqrt{2} + 1 + \sqrt{2}$$
$$= 4 + 2\sqrt{2}$$

18. (a) Δ = Area of region R

$$= \frac{1}{2}(OA + ED) \times 1$$
$$= \frac{1}{2}(3 + 1) = 2$$

Paragraph II

(Q. Nos. 19 to 21)

A variable straight line 'L' is drawn through O(0, 0) to meet this lines $L_1 : y - x - 10 = 0$ and $L_2 : y - x - 20 = 0$ at the points A and B respectively.

19. A point P is taken on 'L' such that $\dfrac{2}{OP} = \dfrac{1}{OA} + \dfrac{1}{OB}$, then the locus of P is

(a) $3x + 3y - 40 = 0$ (b) $3x + 3y + 40 = 0$

(c) $3x - 3y - 40 = 0$ (d) $3x - 3y + 40 = 0$

20. A point P is taken on 'L' such that $(OP)^2 = OA \cdot OB$, then the locus of P is

(a) $(y - x)^2 = 25$ (b) $(y - x)^2 = 50$

(c) $(y - x)^2 = 100$ (d) $(y - x)^2 = 200$

21. A point P is taken on 'L' such that $\dfrac{1}{(OP)^2} = \dfrac{1}{(OA)^2} + \dfrac{1}{(OB)^2}$, then locus of P is

(a) $(y - x)^2 = 32$ (b) $(y - x)^2 = 64$

(c) $(y - x)^2 = 80$ (d) $(y - x)^2 = 100$

Sol. Let the equation of line 'L' through origin is

$$\frac{x - 0}{\cos\theta} = \frac{y - 0}{\sin\theta} = r$$

$\therefore \quad P \equiv (r\cos\theta, r\sin\theta)$

Let $\quad OA = r_1$ and $OB = r_2$

$\therefore \quad A \equiv (r_1 \cos\theta, r_1 \sin\theta)$

and $\quad B \equiv (r_2 \cos\theta, r_2 \sin\theta)$

A lies on $\quad L_1 : y - x - 10 = 0$

$\therefore \quad r_1 \sin\theta - r_1 \cos\theta - 10 = 0$

$\Rightarrow \quad r_1 = \dfrac{10}{\sin\theta - \cos\theta} \quad$ ...(i)

$\Rightarrow$ B lies on $L_1 : y - x - 20 = 0$

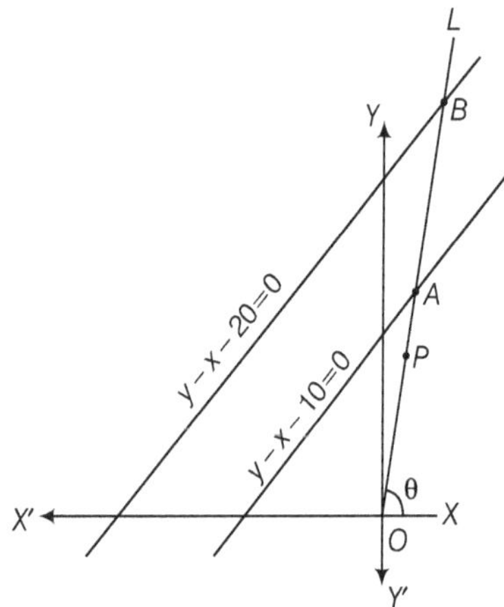

$\therefore \quad r_2 \sin\theta - r_2 \cos\theta - 20 = 0$

$\Rightarrow \quad r_2 = \dfrac{20}{\sin\theta - \cos\theta}$ ...(ii)

19. (d) $\because \quad \dfrac{2}{OP} = \dfrac{1}{OA} + \dfrac{1}{OB} \Rightarrow \dfrac{2}{r} = \dfrac{1}{r_1} + \dfrac{1}{r_2}$

$\Rightarrow \quad \dfrac{2}{r} = \dfrac{\sin\theta - \cos\theta}{10} + \dfrac{\sin\theta - \cos\theta}{20}$ [from Eqs. (i) and (ii)]

or $\quad 2 = \dfrac{r\sin\theta - r\cos\theta}{10} + \dfrac{r\sin\theta - r\cos\theta}{20}$

or $\quad 2 = \dfrac{y-x}{10} + \dfrac{y-x}{20}$ $[\because P \equiv (r\cos, r\sin\theta)]$

$\therefore$ Locus of P is $3x - 3y + 40 = 0$

20. (d) $\because (OP)^2 = OA \cdot OB$

$\Rightarrow \quad r^2 = r_1 \cdot r_2$

$\Rightarrow \quad r^2 = \dfrac{10}{(\sin\theta - \cos\theta)} \cdot \dfrac{20}{(\sin\theta - \cos\theta)}$ [from Eqs. (i) and (ii)]

or $\quad (r\sin\theta - r\cos\theta)^2 = 200$

$\therefore$ Locus of P is $(y - x)^2 = 200$

21. (c) $\because \quad \dfrac{1}{(OP)^2} = \dfrac{1}{(OA)^2} + \dfrac{1}{(OB)^2}$

$\Rightarrow \quad \dfrac{1}{r^2} = \dfrac{1}{r_1^2} + \dfrac{1}{r_2^2}$

$\Rightarrow \quad \dfrac{1}{r^2} = \dfrac{(\sin\theta - \cos\theta)^2}{100} + \dfrac{(\sin\theta - \cos\theta)^2}{400}$

or $\quad 400 = 4(r\sin\theta - r\cos\theta)^2 + (r\sin\theta - r\cos\theta)^2$

$\therefore$ Locus of P is $(y - x)^2 = 80$

JEE Type Solved Examples :
Single Integer Answer Type Questions

- This section contains **2 examples**. The answer to each example is **a single digit integer,** ranging from 0 to 9 (both inclusive).

● **Ex. 22** *$P(x, y)$ is called a natural point if $x, y \in N$. The total number of points lying inside the quadrilateral formed by the lines $2x + y = 2$, $x = 0$, $y = 0$ and $x + y = 5$ is*

Sol. (6) First, we construct the graph of the given quadrilateral.

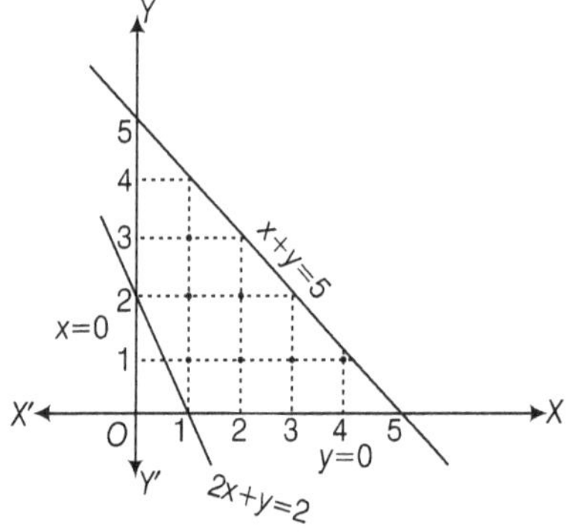

It is clear from the graph that there are six points lying inside the quadrilateral.

● **Ex. 23** *The distance of the point (x, y) from the origin is defined as $d = \max \cdot \{|x|, |y|\}$. Then the distance of the common point for the family of lines $x(1 + \lambda) + \lambda y + 2 + \lambda = 0$ (λ being parameter) from the origin is*

Sol. (2) Given family of lines is

$$x(1 + \lambda) + \lambda y + 2 + \lambda = 0$$

$\Rightarrow \quad (x + 2) + \lambda(x + y + 1) = 0$

for common point or fixed point

$$x + 2 = 0$$

and $\quad x + y + 1 = 0$

or $\quad x = -2, y = 1$

$\therefore$ Common point is $(-2, 1)$

or $\quad d = \max\{|-2|, |1|\}$

$\quad = \max\{2, 1\} = 2$

JEE Type Solved Examples : Matching Type Questions

- This section contains **2 examples**. Examples 24 and 25 has four statements (A, B, C and D) given in **Column I** and four statements (p, q, r and s) in **Column II**. Any given statement in **Column I** can have correct matching with one or more statement(s) given in **Column II**.

Ex. 24 *Consider the following linear equations x and y*

$$ax + by + c = 0$$
$$bx + cy + a = 0$$
$$cx + ay + b = 0$$

	Column I		Column II
(A)	$a + b + c \neq 0$ and $a^2 + b^2 + c^2 = ab + bc + ca$	(p)	Lines are sides of a triangle
(B)	$a + b + c = 0$ and $a^2 + b^2 + c^2 \neq ab + bc + ca$	(q)	Lines are different and concurrent
(C)	$a + b + c \neq 0$ and $a^2 + b^2 + c^2 \neq ab + bc + ca$	(r)	Number of pair (x, y) satisfying the equations are infinite
(D)	$a + b + c = 0$ and $a^2 + b^2 + c^2 = ab + bc + ca$	(s)	Lines are identical

Sol. (A) → (r, s); (B) → (q); (C) → (p); (D) → (r)

(A) if $a + b + c \neq 0$ and $a^2 + b^2 + c^2 = ab + bc + ca$

or $\frac{1}{2}\{(a-b)^2 + (b-c)^2 + (c-a)^2\} = 0$

or $a - b = 0, b - c = 0, c - a = 0$

or $a = b = c \Rightarrow$ All the lines an identical

and number of pair (x, y) are infinite.

(B) If $a + b + c = 0$ and $a^2 + b^2 + c^2 \neq ab + bc + ca$

$\Rightarrow a + b + c = 0$, but a, b, c are not simultaneously equal.

Hence, lines are different and concurrent.

(C) If $a + b + c \neq 0$ and $a^2 + b^2 + c^2 \neq ab + bc + ca$

$$\Rightarrow \Delta = \begin{vmatrix} a & b & c \\ b & c & a \\ c & a & b \end{vmatrix} \neq 0 \text{ and } a, b, c \text{ are not all simultaneously equal.}$$

$\therefore$ Lines are sides of a triangle.

(D) If $a + b + c = 0$ and $a^2 + b^2 + c^2 = ab + bc + ca$

$\Rightarrow \Delta = 0$ and $a = b = c$

$\therefore$ Equations are satisfied for any (x, y).

Ex. 25 *The equation of the sides of a triangle are $x + 2y + 1 = 0$, $2x + y + 2 = 0$ and $px + qy + 1 = 0$ and area of triangle is Δ.*

	Column I		Column II
(A)	$p = 2, q = 3$, then 8Δ is divisible by	(p)	3
(B)	$p = 3, q = 2$, then 8Δ is divisible by	(q)	4
(C)	$p = 3, q = 4$, then 10Δ is divisible by	(r)	6
(D)	$p = 4, q = 3$, then 20Δ is divisible by	(s)	9

Sol. (A) → (p); (B) → (p, q, r); (C) → (p, r); (D) → (p, s)

$$\because \quad \Delta = \frac{D^2}{2|C_1 C_2 C_3|}, \text{ where}$$

$$D = \begin{vmatrix} 1 & 2 & 1 \\ 2 & 1 & 2 \\ p & q & 1 \end{vmatrix} = 3(p-1)$$

and C_1, C_2, C_3 are co-factors of third column, then

$$C_1 = 2q - p, C_2 = 2p - q, C_3 = -3$$

$$\therefore \quad \Delta = \frac{3(p-1)^2}{2|2q-p||2p-q|}$$

(A) for $p = 2, q = 3$

$\Rightarrow \quad \Delta = \frac{3}{8}$

$\therefore \quad 8\Delta = 3$

(B) for $p = 3, q = 2$

$\Rightarrow \quad \Delta = \frac{3}{2}$

$\therefore \quad 8\Delta = 12$

(C) for $p = 3, q = 4$

$\Rightarrow \quad \Delta = \frac{6}{10}$

$\therefore \quad 10\Delta = 6$

(D) for $p = 4, q = 3$

$\Rightarrow \quad \Delta = \frac{27}{20}$

$\therefore \quad 20\Delta = 27$

JEE Type Solved Examples : Statement I and II Type Questions

- **Directions** (Ex. Nos. 26 and 27) are Assertion-Reason type examples. Each of these examples contains two statements.

  Statement I (Assertion) and **Statement II** (Reason)

  Each of these examples also has four alternative choices. Only one of which is the correct answer. You have to select the correct choice as given below.

  (a) Statement I is true, statement II is true; statement II is a correct explanation for statement I.

  (b) Statement I is true, statement II is true; statement II is not a correct explanation for statement I.

  (c) Statement I is true, statement II is false.

  (d) Statement I is false, statement II is true.

Ex. 26 *Consider the lines,* $L_1 : \frac{x}{3} + \frac{y}{4} = 1$; $L_2 : \frac{x}{4} + \frac{y}{3} = 1$; $L_3 : \frac{x}{3} + \frac{y}{4} = 2$ *and* $L_4 : \frac{x}{4} + \frac{y}{3} = 2$

Statement I : The quadrilateral formed by these four lines is a rhombus.

Statement II : If diagonals of a quadrilateral formed by any four lines are unequal and intersect at right angle, then it is a rhombus.

Sol. (c) $\because$ L_1, L_3 are parallel.

$\therefore$ Distance between L_1 and $L_3 = \frac{1}{\sqrt{\left(\frac{1}{9} + \frac{1}{16}\right)}} = \frac{12}{5}$ and

L_2, L_4 are parallel.

$\therefore$ Distance between L_2 and $L_4 = \frac{1}{\sqrt{\left(\frac{1}{16} + \frac{1}{9}\right)}} = \frac{12}{5}$

$\therefore$ Distance between L_1 and L_3 = Distance between L_2 and L_4.

$\therefore$ Quadrilateral formed by L_1, L_2, L_3, L_4 is a rhombus.

Hence, statement I is true and statement II is false.

Ex. 27

Statement I : Incentre of the triangle formed by the lines whose sides are $3x + 4y = 0$; $5x - 12y = 0$ and $y - 15 = 0$ is the point P whose coordinates are $(1, 8)$.

Statement II : Point P equidistant from the three lines forming the triangle.

Sol. (b) Let $L_1 \equiv 3x + 4y = 0$,

$L_2 \equiv 5x - 12y = 0$ and $L_3 \equiv y - 15 = 0$

Length of $\perp$ from P to $L_1 = \frac{3 + 32}{5} = 7$

Length of $\perp$ from P to $L_2 = \frac{|5 - 96|}{13} = 7$

and Length of $\perp$ from P to $L_3 = \frac{|8 - 15|}{1} = 7$

$\therefore$ Statement II is true

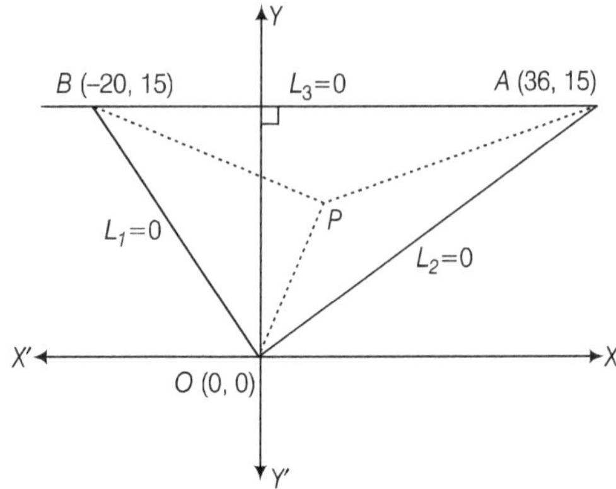

Also, Area of $\Delta OPA = \frac{1}{2} \times OA \times 7$

$= \frac{1}{2} \times 39 \times 7 = \Delta_1$

Area of $\Delta OPB = \frac{1}{2} \times OB \times 7$

$= \frac{1}{2} \times 25 \times 7 = \Delta_2$

and Area of $\Delta APB = \frac{1}{2} \times AB \times 7$

$= \frac{1}{2} \times 56 \times 7 = \Delta_3$

$\therefore$ $\Delta_1 + \Delta_2 + \Delta_3 = \frac{7}{2}(39 + 25 + 56)$

$= \frac{7 \times 120}{2} = \frac{1}{2} \times 56 \times 15 =$ Area of ΔAOB

$\Rightarrow P$ inside the triangle.

Hence, both statements are true and statement II is not correct explanation of statement I.

Subjective Type Examples

- In this section, there are **15 subjective solved examples**.

Ex. 28. *If x-coordinates of two points B and C are the roots of equation $x^2+4x+3=0$ and their y-coordinates are the roots of equation $x^2-x-6=0$. If x-coordinate of B is less than x-coordinate of C and y-coordinate of B is greater than the y-coordinate of C and coordinates of a third point A be $(3,-5)$. Find the length of the bisector of the interior angle at A.*

Sol. $\because$ $x^2+4x+3=0 \Rightarrow x=-1,-3$

and $x^2-x-6=0 \Rightarrow x=-2,3$

Also given that x and y-coordinates of B are respectively less than and greater than the corresponding coordinates of C.

$\therefore$ $B \equiv (-3,3)$ and $C \equiv (-1,-2)$

Now $AB=\sqrt{(3+3)^2+(-5-3)^2}=10$

and $AC=\sqrt{(3+1)^2+(-5+2)^2}=5$

$\therefore$ $\dfrac{AB}{AC}=\dfrac{2}{1}$

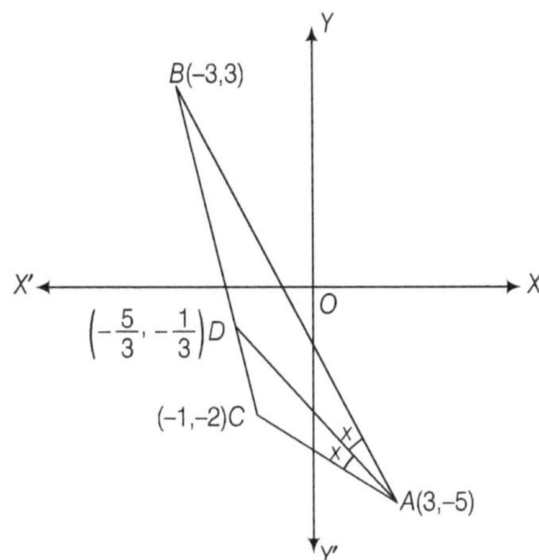

Let AD be the bisector of $\angle BAC$, then

$$\frac{BD}{DC}=\frac{AB}{AC}=\frac{2}{1}$$

Thus D divides BC internally in the ratio 2 : 1

$\therefore$ $D \equiv \left(\dfrac{2(-1)+1(-3)}{2+1}, \dfrac{2(-2)+1(3)}{2+1}\right)$

Thus, $D \equiv \left(-\dfrac{5}{3}, -\dfrac{1}{3}\right)$

Now, $AD=\sqrt{\left(3+\dfrac{5}{3}\right)^2+\left(-5+\dfrac{1}{3}\right)^2}$

$$=\sqrt{\frac{196}{9}+\frac{196}{9}}=\frac{14\sqrt{2}}{3} \text{ units.}$$

Ex. 29. *Let the sides of a parallelogram be $u=p, u=q, v=r$ and $v=s$ where, $u=lx+my+n$ and $v=l'x+m'y+n'$. Show that the equation of the diagonal through the point of intersection of $u=p$ and $v=r$ and $u=q$ and $v=s$, is given by* $\begin{vmatrix} u & v & 1 \\ p & r & 1 \\ q & s & 1 \end{vmatrix}=0$

Sol. Equation of the line through point of intersection D of lines $u-p=0$ and $v-r=0$ is

$$(u-p)+\lambda(v-r)=0 \quad \text{...(i)}$$

it is also passing through $u=q$ and $v=s$, then Eq. (i) becomes

$$(q-p)+\lambda(s-r)=0$$

$\therefore$ $\lambda=-\dfrac{(q-p)}{(s-r)}$ ...(ii)

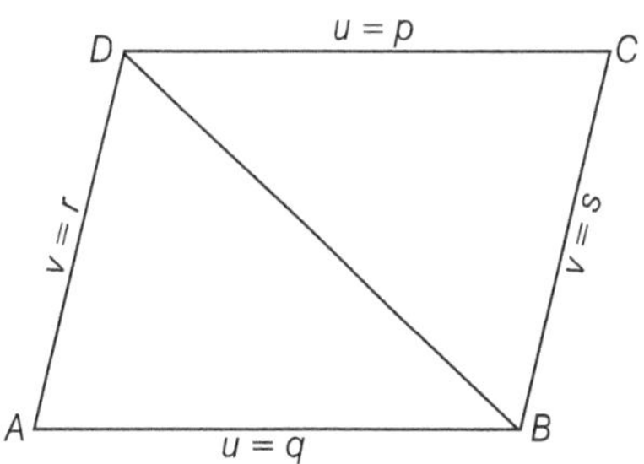

From Eqs. (i) and (ii), we get

$$(u-p)-\frac{(q-p)}{(s-r)}(v-r)=0$$

$\Rightarrow$ $u(s-r)-p(s-r)-v(q-p)+r(q-p)=0$

$\Rightarrow$ $u(r-s)-v(p-q)+ps-qr=0$

$\Rightarrow$ $\begin{vmatrix} u & v & 1 \\ p & r & 1 \\ q & s & 1 \end{vmatrix}=0$

Ex. 30. *The vertices B and C of a triangle ABC lie on the lines $3y=4x$ and $y=0$ respectively and the side BC passes through the point $\left(\dfrac{2}{3},\dfrac{2}{3}\right)$. If ABOC is a rhombus, O being the origin, find the equation of the line BC and the coordinates of A.*

Sol. Let the side of the rhombus be a

$\therefore$ $OB=BA=AC=CO=a$

Co-ordinates of A is $\left(a+x_1, \dfrac{4x_1}{3}\right)$

$\therefore$ $(OB)^2=(BA)^2=(AC)^2=(CO)^2=a^2 \Rightarrow (OB)^2=a^2$

$$\Rightarrow \quad x_1^2 + \frac{16x_1^2}{9} = a^2 \Rightarrow \frac{25x_1^2}{9} = a^2 \Rightarrow a = \frac{5x_1}{3}$$

$$\therefore \quad C \equiv \left(\frac{5x_1}{3}, 0\right), \ A \equiv \left(\frac{8x_1}{3}, \frac{4x_1}{3}\right),$$

$$B \equiv \left(x_1, \frac{4x_1}{3}\right), \ O \equiv (0, 0)$$

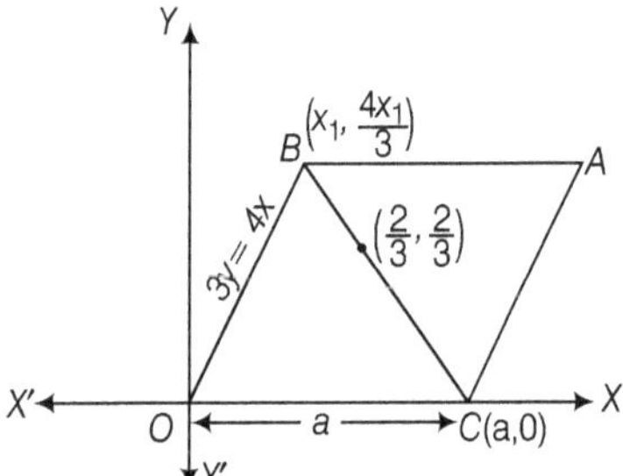

$\therefore$ Equation of BC

$$y - 0 = \frac{\frac{4x_1}{3} - 0}{x_1 - \frac{5x_1}{3}}\left(x - \frac{5x_1}{3}\right)$$

$$\Rightarrow \quad y = -2x + \frac{10x_1}{3} \qquad \text{...(1)}$$

it is passing through $\left(\frac{2}{3}, \frac{2}{3}\right)$, then

$$\frac{2}{3} = -\frac{4}{3} + \frac{10x_1}{3}$$

$$\Rightarrow \quad 2 = \frac{10x_1}{3}$$

$$\therefore \quad x_1 = \frac{3}{5}$$

Hence, coordinates are

$$C \equiv (1, 0), \ A \equiv \left(\frac{8}{5}, \frac{4}{5}\right)$$

$$B \equiv \left(\frac{3}{5}, \frac{4}{5}\right), \ O \equiv (0, 0)$$

From Eq. (i), equation of BC is

$$y = -2x + 2$$

$$\Rightarrow \quad 2x + y = 2$$

Ex. 31 *The ends AB of a straight line segment of constant length c slide upon the fixed rectangular axes OX and OY respectively. If the rectangle OAPB be completed, then show that the locus of the foot of perpendicular drawn from P to AB is* $x^{2/3} + y^{2/3} = c^{2/3}$.

Sol. Let $A \equiv (a, 0)$, $B \equiv (0, b)$ then $P \equiv (a, b)$

Since $\quad AB = c$

$$\sqrt{a^2 + b^2} = c$$

or $\quad a^2 + b^2 = c^2 \qquad$ ...(i)

and $\quad$ let $Q \equiv (x_1, y_1)$

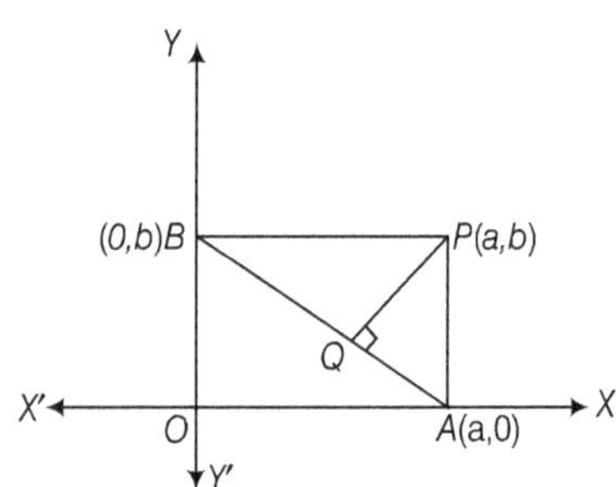

$\because \ PQ \perp AB$

$\therefore$ Slope of $PQ \times$ Slope of $AB = -1$

$$\Rightarrow \quad \left(\frac{b - y_1}{a - x_1}\right) \times \left(\frac{b - 0}{0 - a}\right) = -1$$

$$\Rightarrow \quad ax_1 - by_1 = a^2 - b^2 \qquad \text{...(ii)}$$

$\because$ Equation of AB is $\frac{x}{a} + \frac{y}{b} = 1$

But Q lies on AB then $\frac{x_1}{a} + \frac{y_1}{b} = 1$

$$\Rightarrow \quad bx_1 + ay_1 = ab \qquad \text{...(iii)}$$

From Eqs. (ii) and (iii), we get

$$x_1 = \frac{a^3}{a^2 + b^2}, \ y_1 = \frac{b^3}{a^2 + b^2}$$

Now, $\quad x_1^{2/3} + y_1^{2/3} = \frac{(a^2 + b^2)}{(a^2 + b^2)^{2/3}}$

$$= (a^2 + b^2)^{1/3} = c^{2/3} \qquad \text{[from Eq. (i)]}$$

Hence, required locus is $x^{2/3} + y^{2/3} = c^{2/3}$.

Aliter :

Since, $\quad AB = c$

Let $\quad \angle BAO = \theta$

$\therefore \quad OA = c\cos\theta$ and $OB = c\sin\theta$

$\because \quad OB = PA = c\sin\theta$

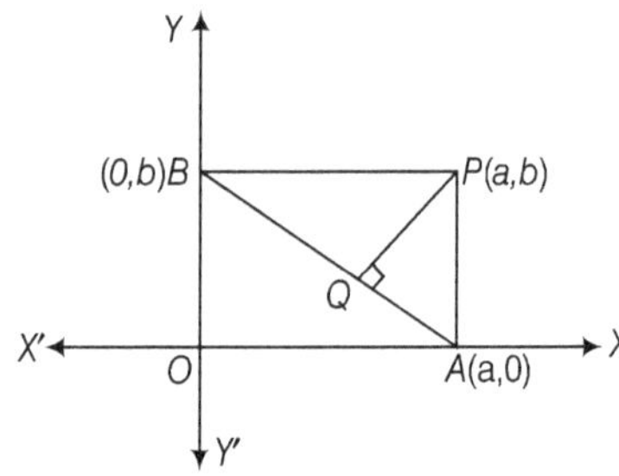

In ΔPQA, $\quad \sin\theta = \frac{QA}{PA} = \frac{QA}{c\sin\theta}$

$$\therefore \quad QA = c\sin^2\theta$$

Now, in ΔQAM, $\quad \sin\theta = \frac{QM}{QA} = \frac{QM}{c\sin^2\theta}$

$$\therefore \quad QM = c\sin^3\theta$$

and $\quad \cos\theta = \frac{MA}{QA} = \frac{MA}{c\sin^2\theta}$

$$\Rightarrow \quad MA = c\sin^2\theta\cos\theta$$

If coordinates of Q be (x_1, y_1)

then $\quad x_1 = OM = OA - MA = c\cos\theta - c\sin^2\theta\cos\theta$

$$x_1 = c\cos^3\theta \quad \text{...(i)}$$

and $\quad y_1 = MQ = c\sin^3\theta \quad$ ...(ii)

From Eqs. (i) and (ii),

$$x_1^{2/3} + y_1^{2/3} = c^{2/3}\cos^2\theta + c^{2/3}\sin^2\theta = c^{2/3}$$

$$\Rightarrow \quad x_1^{2/3} + y_1^{2/3} = c^{2/3}$$

Hence, locus of Q is $x^{2/3} + y^{2/3} = c^{2/3}$

Ex. 32 *A square lies above the X-axis and has one vertex at the origin. The side passing through the origin makes an angle α $(0 < \alpha < \pi/4)$ with the positive direction of the X-axis. Prove that the equation of its diagonals are*

$$y(\cos\alpha - \sin\alpha) = x(\sin\alpha + \cos\alpha)$$

and $\quad y(\sin\alpha + \cos\alpha) + x(\cos\alpha - \sin\alpha) = a$

where, is the length of each side of the square.

Sol. Here, $OA = AB = BC = CO = a$

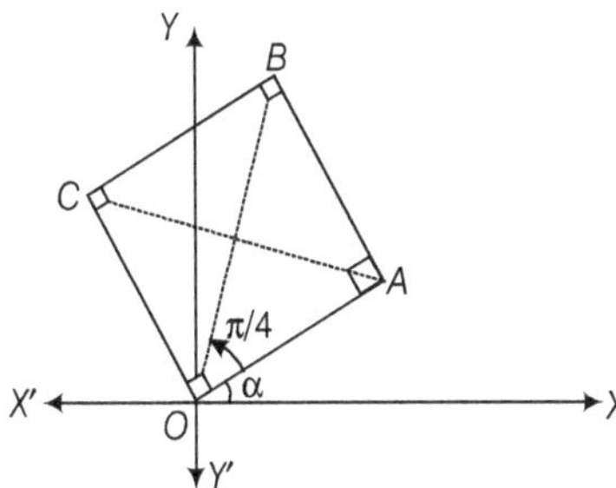

Equation of OB is $y - 0 = \tan\left(\frac{\pi}{4} + \alpha\right)(x - 0)$

$$\Rightarrow \quad y\cos\left(\frac{\pi}{4} + \alpha\right) = x\sin\left(\frac{\pi}{4} + \alpha\right)$$

$$\Rightarrow \quad y(\cos\alpha - \sin\alpha) = x(\cos\alpha + \sin\alpha)$$

Hence, equation of diagonal OB is

$$x(\cos\alpha + \sin\alpha) + y(\sin\alpha - \cos\alpha) = 0$$

Coordinates of A are $(a\cos\alpha, a\sin\alpha)$

Diagonal AC is perpendicular to the diagonal OB,

$$\text{Slope of } AC = -\frac{1}{\text{slope of } OB}$$

$$= -\frac{1}{\tan\left(\frac{\pi}{4} + \alpha\right)} = -\cot\left(\frac{\pi}{4} + \alpha\right)$$

Hence, equation of diagonal AC is

$$y - a\sin\alpha = -\cot\left(\frac{\pi}{4} + \alpha\right)(x - a\cos\alpha)$$

$$\Rightarrow \quad y - a\sin\alpha = -\left(\frac{\cos\alpha - \sin\alpha}{\cos\alpha + \sin\alpha}\right)(x - a\cos\alpha)$$

$$\Rightarrow \quad y(\cos\alpha + \sin\alpha) - a\sin\alpha\cos\alpha - a\sin^2\alpha$$

$$= -x(\cos\alpha - \sin\alpha) + a\cos^2\alpha - a\sin\alpha\cos\alpha$$

$$\Rightarrow \quad x(\cos\alpha - \sin\alpha) + y(\cos\alpha + \sin\alpha) = a$$

Ex. 33 *In a ΔABC, $A \equiv (\alpha, \beta)$, $B \equiv (1, 2)$, $C \equiv (2, 3)$ and point A lies on the line $y = 2x + 3$, where $\alpha, \beta \in I$. If the area of ΔABC be such that $[\Delta] = 2$, where $[.]$ denotes the greatest integer function, find all possible coordinates of A.*

Sol. $\because$ (α, β) lies on $y = 2x + 3$

then $\quad \beta = 2\alpha + 3$

Thus ,the coordinates of A are $(\alpha, 2\alpha + 3)$

$$\Delta = \frac{1}{2}\left|\begin{vmatrix}\alpha & 2\alpha+3\\ 1 & 2\end{vmatrix} + \begin{vmatrix}1 & 2\\ 2 & 3\end{vmatrix} + \begin{vmatrix}2 & 3\\ \alpha & 2\alpha+3\end{vmatrix}\right|$$

$$= |2\alpha - 2\alpha - 3 + 3 - 4 + 4\alpha + 6 - 3\alpha|$$

$$\Delta = \frac{1}{2}|\alpha + 2|$$

But $\quad [\Delta] = \left[\frac{1}{2}|\alpha + 2|\right] = 2 \quad$ (given)

$$\therefore \quad 2 \le \frac{|\alpha + 2|}{2} < 3$$

$$\Rightarrow \quad 4 \le |\alpha + 2| < 6$$

$$\Rightarrow \quad 4 \le \alpha + 2 < 6 \text{ or } -6 < \alpha + 2 \le -4$$

$$\Rightarrow \quad 2 \le \alpha < 4 \text{ or } -8 < \alpha \le -6$$

$$\therefore \quad \alpha = 2, 3, -7, -6$$

then $\quad \beta = 7, 9, -11, -9$

Hence, coordinates of A are $(2, 7), (3, 9), (-7, -11)$ and $(-6, -9)$.

Ex. 34 *Find the values of non-negative real numbers $\lambda_1, \lambda_2, \lambda_3, \mu_1, \mu_2, \mu_3$ such that the algebraic sum of the perpendiculars drawn from points $(\lambda_1, 4), (\lambda_2, 5), (\lambda_3, -3), (2, \mu_1), (3, \mu_2)$ and $(7, \mu_3)$ on a variable line passing through $(2,1)$ is zero.*

Sol. Let the equation of the variable line be $ax + by + c = 0$. It is given that

$$\Rightarrow \frac{(a\lambda_1 + 4b + c)}{\sqrt{(a^2 + b^2)}} + \frac{(a\lambda_2 + 5b + c)}{\sqrt{(a^2 + b^2)}} + \frac{(a\lambda_3 - 3b + c)}{\sqrt{(a^2 + b^2)}} + \frac{(2a + b\mu_1 + c)}{\sqrt{(a^2 + b^2)}} + \frac{(3a + b\mu_2 + c)}{\sqrt{(a^2 + b^2)}} + \frac{(7a + b\mu_3 + c)}{\sqrt{(a^2 + b^2)}} = 0$$

$$\Rightarrow a(\lambda_1 + \lambda_2 + \lambda_3 + 12) + b(\mu_1 + \mu_2 + \mu_3 + 6) + 6c = 0$$

$$\Rightarrow a\left(\frac{\lambda_1 + \lambda_2 + \lambda_3 + 12}{6}\right) + b\left(\frac{\mu_1 + \mu_2 + \mu_3 + 6}{6}\right) + c = 0 \quad \text{...(i)}$$

But the line passes through $(2,1)$, therefore

$$2a + b + c = 0 \quad \text{...(ii)}$$

From Eqs. (i) and (ii), we get

$$\frac{\lambda_1 + \lambda_2 + \lambda_3 + 12}{6} = 2 \text{ and } \frac{\mu_1 + \mu_2 + \mu_3 + 6}{6} = 1$$

$$\Rightarrow \lambda_1 + \lambda_2 + \lambda_3 = 0 \text{ and } \mu_1 + \mu_2 + \mu_3 = 0$$

$$\Rightarrow \lambda_1 = \lambda_2 = \lambda_3 \text{ and } \mu_1 = \mu_2 = \mu_3 \quad [\because \lambda_i, \mu_i \ge 0 \text{ for all i}]$$

$$\lambda_1 = \lambda_2 = \lambda_3 = \alpha \quad \text{(say)}$$

and $\quad \mu_1 = \mu_2 = \mu_3 = \beta \quad$ (say)

where $\alpha \ge 0$ and $\beta \ge 0$.

Ex. 35 *The three sides of a triangle are $L_r \equiv x\cos\theta_r + y\sin\theta_r - p_r = 0$, where r= 1,2,3. Show that the orthocentre is given by $L_1\cos(\theta_2-\theta_3) = L_2\cos(\theta_3-\theta_1) = L_3\cos(\theta_1-\theta_2)$.*

Sol. The given lines are

$$L_1 \equiv x\cos\theta_1 + y\sin\theta_1 - p_1 = 0$$
$$L_2 \equiv x\cos\theta_2 + y\sin\theta_2 - p_2 = 0$$
$$L_3 \equiv x\cos\theta_3 + y\sin\theta_3 - p_3 = 0$$

Now, equation of AD is $L_2 + \lambda L_3 = 0$ ...(i)

$\Rightarrow (x\cos\theta_2 + y\sin\theta_2 - p_2) + \lambda(x\cos\theta_3 + y\sin\theta_3 - p_3) = 0$

$\Rightarrow x(\cos\theta_2 + \lambda\cos\theta_3) + y(\sin\theta_2 + \lambda\sin\theta_3) - (p_2 + \lambda p_3) = 0$

$\therefore$ Slope of $AD = -\dfrac{(\cos\theta_2 + \lambda\cos\theta_3)}{(\sin\theta_2 + \lambda\sin\theta_3)}$

and Slope of $BC = -\dfrac{\cos\theta_1}{\sin\theta_1}$

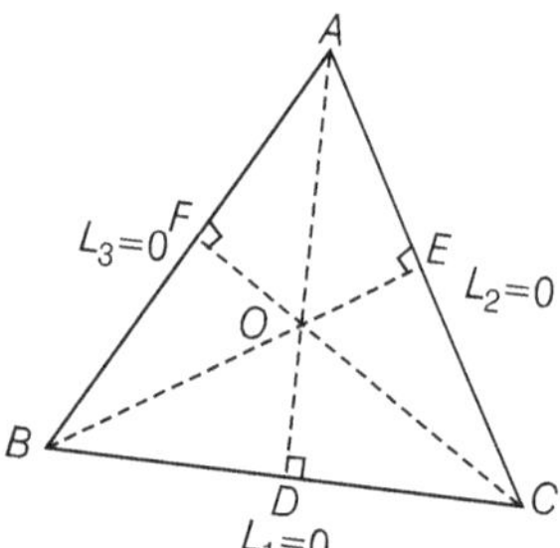

Since, $AD \perp BC$

$\therefore$ Slope of $BC \times$ slope of $AD = -1$

$\Rightarrow -\dfrac{\cos\theta_1}{\sin\theta_1} \times \left[-\dfrac{(\cos\theta_2 + \lambda\cos\theta_3)}{(\sin\theta_2 + \lambda\sin\theta_3)}\right] = -1$

$\Rightarrow \cos\theta_1\cos\theta_2 + \lambda\cos\theta_3\cos\theta_1 = -\sin\theta_1\sin\theta_2 - \lambda\sin\theta_3\sin\theta_1$

$\Rightarrow \cos(\theta_1-\theta_2) + \lambda\cos(\theta_3-\theta_1) = 0$

$\therefore \lambda = -\dfrac{\cos(\theta_1-\theta_2)}{\cos(\theta_3-\theta_1)}$

Now from Eq. (i),

$$L_2 - \frac{\cos(\theta_1-\theta_2)}{\cos(\theta_3-\theta_1)}L_3 = 0$$

$\therefore L_2\cos(\theta_3-\theta_1) = L_3\cos(\theta_1-\theta_2)$ ...(ii)

Similarly, we can obtain equation of altitude BE as

$L_3\cos(\theta_1-\theta_2) = L_1\cos(\theta_2-\theta_3)$ ...(iii)

From Eqs. (ii) and (iii), we get

$$L_1\cos(\theta_2-\theta_3) = L_2\cos(\theta_3-\theta_1) = L_3\cos(\theta_1-\theta_2)$$

Ex. 36 *Let (h, k) be a fixed point, where $h>0, k>0$. A straight line passing through this point cuts the positive direction of the co-ordinate axes at the points P and Q. Find the minimum area of the triangle OPQ ,O being the origin.*

Sol. Equation of any line passing through the fixed point (h, k) and having slope m can be taken as

$y - k = m(x-h)$ ...(i)

$\Rightarrow \dfrac{y}{m} - \dfrac{k}{m} = x - h$ or $x - \dfrac{y}{m} = h - \dfrac{k}{m}$

$\Rightarrow \dfrac{x}{\left(h-\dfrac{k}{m}\right)} - \dfrac{y}{m\left(h-\dfrac{k}{m}\right)} = 1$

$\Rightarrow \dfrac{x}{\left(h-\dfrac{k}{m}\right)} + \dfrac{y}{(k-mh)} = 1$

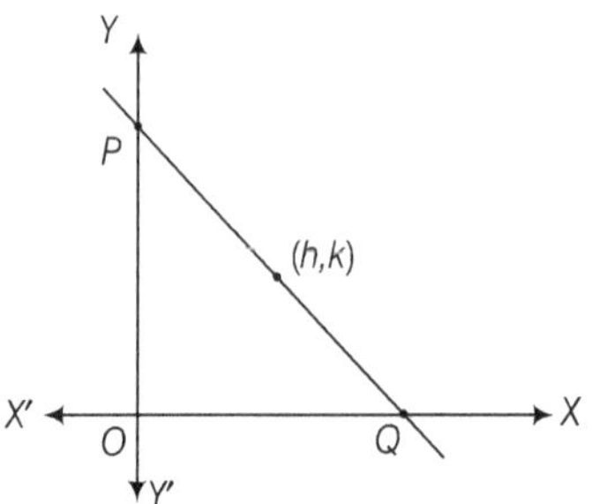

$\therefore OQ = h - \dfrac{k}{m}$ and $OP = k - mh$

Area of triangle $OPQ = \dfrac{1}{2}.OQ.OP = \dfrac{1}{2}.\left(h-\dfrac{k}{m}\right)(k-mh)$

$\Rightarrow = \dfrac{1}{2}\left(2hk - mh^2 - \dfrac{k^2}{m}\right)$

$\Rightarrow A(m) = hk - \dfrac{mh^2}{2} - \dfrac{k^2}{2m}$ ...(ii)

To minimise, $\dfrac{dA}{dm} = 0$

$\Rightarrow 0 - \dfrac{h^2}{2} + \dfrac{k^2}{2m^2} = 0 \Rightarrow m = \pm\dfrac{k}{h}$

$\therefore \dfrac{d^2A}{dm^2}\Bigg| = -\dfrac{2k^2}{2m^3}$

$\dfrac{d^2A}{dm^2}\Bigg|_{m=-k/h} = \dfrac{h^3}{k} > 0$ $(\because h>0, k>0)$

Hence for $m = -\dfrac{k}{h}$, $A(m)$ is minimum . Put $m = -\dfrac{k}{h}$ in Eq. (ii), we get minimum area.

$\Rightarrow$ Minimum area of $\Delta OPQ = hk + \dfrac{hk}{2} + \dfrac{hk}{2} = 2hk$

Ex. 37 *The distance between two parallel lines is unity. A point P lies between the lines at a distance a from one of them. Find the length of a side of an eqilateral triangle PQR, vertex Q of which lies on one of the parallel lines and vertex R lies on the other line.*

Sol. Let $PQ = QR = RP = r$

and $\angle PQL = \theta$

then $\angle XQR = \theta + 60°$

Given $PL = a$ and $RN = 1$ unit

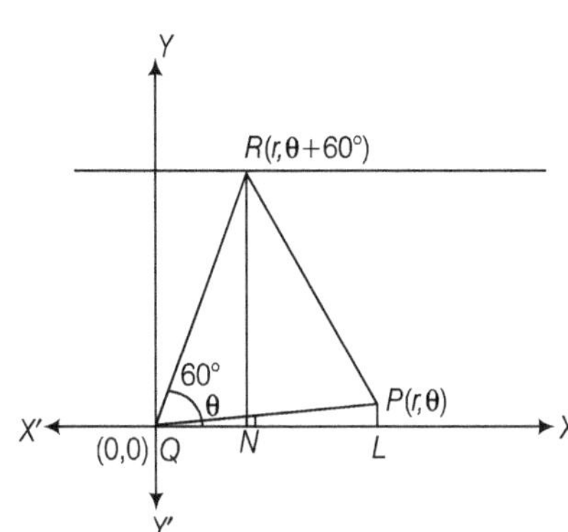

In ΔPQL

$$\sin\theta = \frac{PL}{QP} = \frac{a}{r}$$

$$\therefore \quad a = r\sin\theta \quad \text{...(i)}$$

and in ΔQRN,

$$r\sin(\theta + 60°) = \frac{RN}{QR} = \frac{1}{r}$$

$$\sin(\theta + 60°) = 1$$

$$(\sin\theta\cos 60° + \cos\theta\sin 60°) = 1$$

$$\Rightarrow \quad r\left(\frac{1}{2}\sin\theta + \frac{\sqrt{3}}{2}\cos\theta\right) = 1$$

$$\Rightarrow \quad r\left(\frac{1}{2}\times\frac{a}{r} + \frac{\sqrt{3}}{2}\times\sqrt{1-\frac{a^2}{r^2}}\right) = 1 \quad \text{[from Eq. (i)]}$$

$$\Rightarrow \quad \frac{a}{2} + \frac{\sqrt{3}}{2}\sqrt{(r^2 - a^2)} = 1$$

$$\Rightarrow \quad \frac{\sqrt{3}}{2}\sqrt{(r^2 - a^2)} = 1 - \frac{a}{2}$$

$$\text{or} \quad \frac{3}{4}(r^2 - a^2) = 1 + \frac{a^2}{4} - a$$

$$\Rightarrow \quad 3r^2 - 3a^2 = 4 + a^2 - 4a$$

$$\Rightarrow \quad 3r^2 = 4(a^2 - a + 1)$$

$$\therefore \quad r = \frac{2}{\sqrt{3}}\sqrt{(a^2 - a + 1)}$$

Ex. 38 *A ray of light travelling along the line OA (O being origin) is reflected by the line mirror $x - y + 1 = 0$, is the point of incidence being A (1, 2) the reflected ray, travelling along AB is again reflected by the line mirror $x - y = 2$, the point of incidence being B. If this reflected ray moves along BC, find the equation of the line BC.*

Sol. Since, slope of $OA = \frac{2-0}{1-0} = 2 = m_1$ (say)

and slope of normal to $x - y + 1 = 0$ is

$$-1 = m_2 \quad \text{(say)}$$

Now, let slope of AB is m

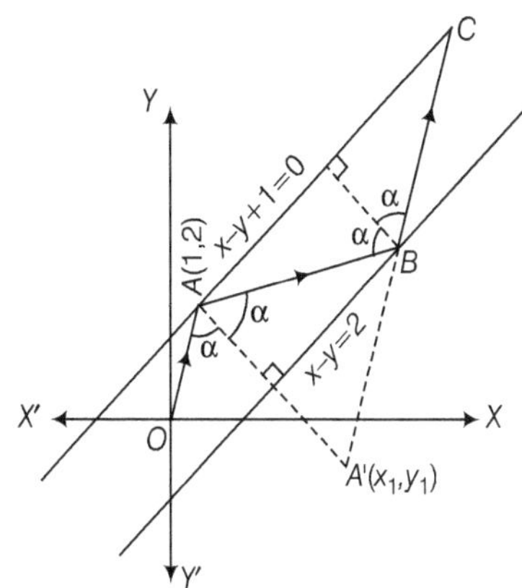

$\because$ OA and AB are equally inclined to normal of $x - y + 1 = 0$ then,

$$\left(\frac{m_1 - m_2}{1 + m_1 m_2}\right) = -\left(\frac{m - m_2}{1 + m m_2}\right)$$

$$\Rightarrow \quad \left(\frac{2-(-1)}{1+2(-1)}\right) = -\left(\frac{m-(-1)}{1+m(-1)}\right)$$

$$\Rightarrow \quad 3(1 - m) = m + 1$$

$$\text{or} \quad m = \frac{1}{2}$$

$\therefore$ Equation of AB is

$$y - 2 = \frac{1}{2}(x - 1)$$

$$\text{or} \quad x - 2y + 3 = 0$$

Now, solving $x - 2y + 3 = 0$

and $x - y = 2$

then, we get $x = 7, y = 5$

i.e. $B \equiv (7, 5)$

$\because$ BC is parallel to OA

$\therefore$ Equation of BC is

$$y - 5 = m_1(x - 7)$$

$$\Rightarrow \quad y - 5 = 2(x - 7)$$

$$\text{i.e.} \quad 2x - y - 9 = 0$$

Aliter :

If image of A (1, 2) with respect to line mirror $x - y = 2$ be $A'(x_1, y_1)$, then

$$\frac{x_1 - 1}{1} = \frac{y_1 - 2}{-1} = \frac{-2(1-2-2)}{1+1}$$

$$\text{or} \quad x_1 = 4, y_1 = -1$$

$$\text{i.e.} \quad A' \equiv (4, -1)$$

$\because$ BC is parallel to OA

then equation of BC = equation of $A'C$ is

$$y - y_1 = 2(x - x_1)$$

$$\Rightarrow \quad y + 1 = 2(x - 4)$$

$$\text{or} \quad 2x - y - 9 = 0$$

Ex. 39 *Consider two lines $L_1 \equiv x - y = 0$ and $L_2 \equiv x + y = 0$ and a moving point $P(x, y)$. Let $d(P, L_i), i = 1, 2$ represents the distance of the point 'P' from L_i. If point 'P' moves in certain region 'R' in such a way $\sum_{i=1}^{2} d(P, L_i) \in [2, 4]$.*

Find the area of region 'R'.

Sol. $\because$ Given $\sum_{i=1}^{2} d(P, L_i) \in [2, 4]$

$$\Rightarrow \quad 2 \le \sum_{i=1}^{2} d(P, L_i) \le 4$$

$$\Rightarrow \quad 2 \le d(P, L_1) + d(P, L_2) \le 4$$

$$\Rightarrow \quad 2 \le \frac{|x-y|}{\sqrt{2}} + \frac{|x+y|}{\sqrt{2}} \le 4$$

$$\Rightarrow \quad 2\sqrt{2} \le |x-y| + |x+y| \le 4\sqrt{2}$$

Case I : If $x - y > 0, x + y > 0$

then $\quad 2\sqrt{2} \le (x-y) + (x+y) \le 4\sqrt{2}$

$\Rightarrow \quad 2\sqrt{2} \le 2x \le 4\sqrt{2}$ or $\sqrt{2} \le x \le 2\sqrt{2}$

Case II : If $x - y > 0, x + y < 0$

then $\quad 2\sqrt{2} \le (x-y) - (x+y) \le 4\sqrt{2}$

$\Rightarrow \quad 2\sqrt{2} \le -2y \le 4\sqrt{2}$

or $\quad -\sqrt{2} \ge y \ge -2\sqrt{2}$ or $-2\sqrt{2} \le y \le -\sqrt{2}$

Case III : If $x - y < 0, x + y > 0$

then $\quad 2\sqrt{2} \le -(x-y) + (x+y) \le 4\sqrt{2}$

$\Rightarrow \quad 2\sqrt{2} \le 2y \le 4\sqrt{2}$ or $\sqrt{2} \le y \le 2\sqrt{2}$

Case IV : If $x - y < 0, x + y < 0$

then $\quad 2\sqrt{2} \le -(x-y) - (x+y) \le 4\sqrt{2}$

$\Rightarrow \quad 2\sqrt{2} \le -2x \le 4\sqrt{2}$

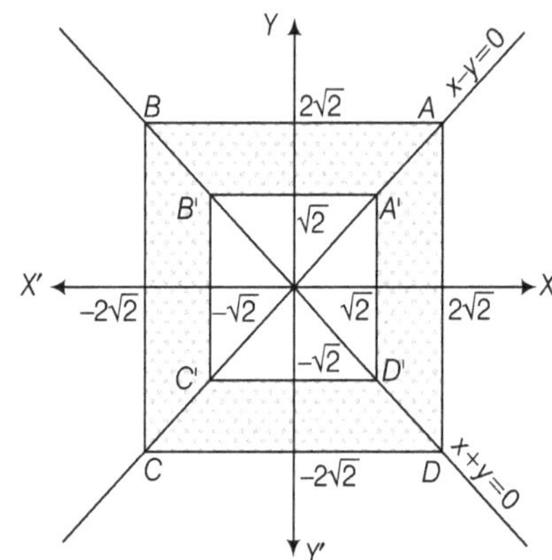

or $\quad -\sqrt{2} \ge x \ge -2\sqrt{2}$

or $\quad -2\sqrt{2} \le x \le -\sqrt{2}$

Combining all cases, we get

$$x \in [-2\sqrt{2}, -\sqrt{2}] \cup [\sqrt{2}, 2\sqrt{2}]$$

and $\quad y \in [-2\sqrt{2}, -\sqrt{2}] \cup [\sqrt{2}, 2\sqrt{2}]$

Hence, area of the required region

$$= (4\sqrt{2})^2 - (2\sqrt{2})^2$$

$$= 32 - 8 = 24 \text{ sq units.}$$

Ex. 40 *A rectangle PQRS has its side PQ parallel to the line $y = mx$ and vertices P, Q and S on the lines $y = a, x = b$ and $x = -b$ respectively. Find the locus of the vertex R.*

Sol. $\because$ PQ is parallel to $y = mx$

$\therefore$ Equation of PQ is $y = mx + \lambda$ ...(i)

$\because$ Diagonals bisect to each other

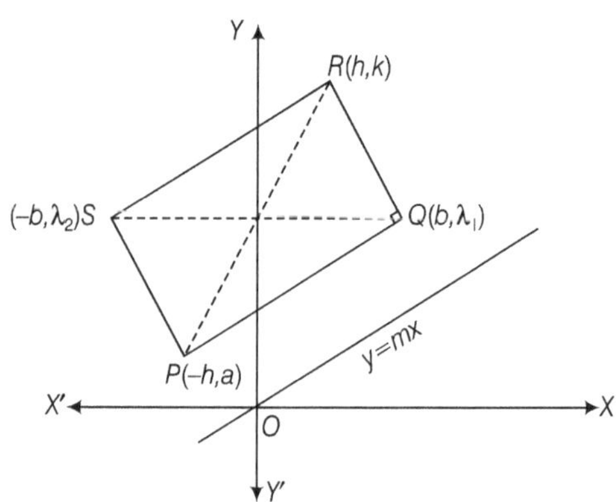

$\therefore$ x-coordinate of P is $-h$.

Suppose y-coordinate of Q and S are λ_1 and λ_2 respectively.

$\because$ Eq. (i) pass through $P(-h, a)$

then $\quad a = -mh + \lambda$

$\therefore \quad \lambda = a + mh$

$\Rightarrow \quad y = mx + a + mh$

Q also lie on it, then

$$\lambda_1 = mb + a + mh$$

$\therefore \quad Q \equiv (b, mb + a + mh)$

Also, slope of $PQ \times$ slope of $QR = -1$

$$m \times \frac{(k - (mb + a + mh))}{(h - b)} = -1$$

$$\Rightarrow \quad mk - m^2b - am - m^2h = -h + b$$

$$\Rightarrow \quad (m^2 - 1)h - mk + b(m^2 + 1) + am = 0$$

$\therefore$ Locus of R is

$$(m^2 - 1)x - my + b(m^2 + 1) + am = 0$$

Ex. 41. *For points $P \equiv (x_1, y_1)$ and $Q \equiv (x_2, y_2)$ of the coordinate plane, a new distance $d(P, Q)$ is defined by $d(P, Q) = |x_1 - x_2| + |y_1 - y_2|$. Let $O \equiv (0, 0)$ and $A \equiv (3, 2)$. Prove that the set of the points in the first quadrant which are equidistant (with respect to the new distance) from O and A consists of the union of a line segment of finite length and an infinite ray. Sketch this set in a labelled diagram.*

Sol. Let $P(x, y)$ be any point in the first quadrant, we have $x > 0, y > 0$

$$d(P, Q) = |x - 0| + |y - 0| = |x| + |y| = x + y$$

and $\quad d(P, A) = |x - 3| + |y - 2|$

Given, $\quad d(P, Q) = d(P, A)$

$$x + y = |x - 3| + |y - 2| \qquad \text{...(i)}$$

Case I : $0 \le x < 3, 0 \le y < 2$

then Eq. (i) becomes

$$x + y = 3 - x + 2 - y$$

or $$x + y = 5/2$$

Case II : $0 \le x < 3, y \ge 2$

then Eq. (i) becomes

$$x + y = 3 - x + y - 2$$

or $$x = \frac{1}{2}$$

Case III : $x \ge 3, 0 \le y < 2$

then Eq. (i) becomes

$$x + y = x - 3 + 2 - y$$

$\Rightarrow$ $$y = -\frac{1}{2} \quad \text{(Impossible)}$$

Case IV : $x \ge 3, y \ge 2$

$$x + y = x - 3 + y - 2$$

$\Rightarrow$ $$0 = -5 \quad \text{(Impossible)}$$

Combining all cases, then

$$x + y = 5/2; 0 \le x < 3, 0 \le y < 2$$

and $$x = \frac{1}{2}; 0 \le x < 3, y \ge 2$$

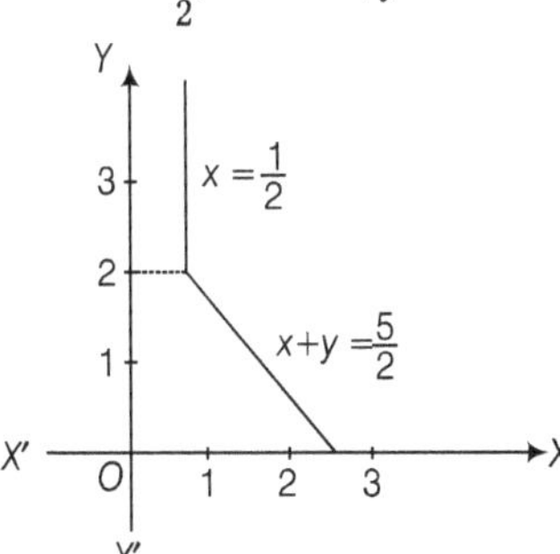

The labelled diagram is given in adjoining figure.

● ***Ex. 42.*** *A line through the variable point $A(k+1, 2k)$ meets the lines $7x + y - 16 = 0, 5x - y - 8 = 0, x - 5y + 8 = 0$ at B, C, D respectively, prove that AC, AB, AD are in HP.*

Sol. Given lines are

$$7x + y - 16 = 0 \quad \text{...(i)}$$

$$5x - y - 8 = 0 \quad \text{...(ii)}$$

$$x - 5y + 8 = 0 \quad \text{...(iii)}$$

Let the equation of line passing through $A(k+1, 2k)$ making an angle θ with the + ve direction of X-axis, be

$$\frac{x - (k+1)}{\cos\theta} = \frac{y - 2k}{\sin\theta} = r_1, r_2, r_3 \quad (\text{if } AB = r_1, AC = r_2, AD = r_3)$$

$\therefore$ $$B \equiv [(k+1) + r_1 \cos\theta, 2k + r_1 \sin\theta]$$

$$C \equiv [(k+1) + r_2 \cos\theta, 2k + r_2 \sin\theta]$$

$$D \equiv [(k+1) + r_3 \cos\theta, 2k + r_3 \sin\theta]$$

Points B, C, D satisfying Eqs. (i), (ii) and (iii) respectively

then $$r_1 = \frac{9(1-k)}{7\cos\theta + \sin\theta}$$

$$r_2 = \frac{3(1-k)}{5\cos\theta - \sin\theta}$$

and $$r_3 = \frac{9(1-k)}{5\sin\theta - \cos\theta}$$

$\therefore$ $$\frac{1}{r_2} + \frac{1}{r_3} = \frac{(5\cos\theta - \sin\theta)}{3(1-k)} + \frac{(5\sin\theta - \cos\theta)}{9(1-k)}$$

$$= \frac{15\cos\theta - 3\sin\theta + 5\sin\theta - \cos\theta}{9(1-k)}$$

$$= \frac{14\cos\theta + 2\sin\theta}{9(1-k)} = \frac{2}{r_1}$$

Hence r_2, r_1, r_3 are in HP

i.e. AC, AB, AD are in HP.

The Straight Lines Exercise 1 : Single Option Correct Type Questions

- This section contains **30 multiple choice questions**. Each question has four choices (a), (b), (c), (d) out of which **ONLY ONE** is correct.

1. The straight line $y = x - 2$ rotates about a point where it cuts X-axis and becomes perpendicular on the straight line $ax + by + c = 0$, then its equation is

(a) $ax + by + 2a = 0$ (b) $ay - bx + 2b = 0$
(c) $ax + by + 2b = 0$ (d) None of these

2. If $\frac{2}{1!9!} + \frac{2}{3!7!} + \frac{1}{5!5!} = \frac{2^m}{n!}$, then orthocentre of the triangle having sides $x - y + 1 = 0$, $x + y + 3 = 0$ and $2x + 5y - 2 = 0$ is

(a) $(2m - 2n, m - n)$ (b) $(2m - 2n, n - m)$
(c) $(2m - n, m + n)$ (d) $(2m - n, m - n)$

3. If $f(x + y) = f(x)f(y) \forall x, y \in R$ and $f(1) = 2$, then area enclosed by $3|x| + 2|y| \le 8$ is

(a) $f(4)$ sq units (b) $\frac{1}{2}f(6)$ sq units
(c) $\frac{1}{3}f(6)$ sq units (d) $\frac{1}{3}f(5)$ sq units

4. The graph of the function $y = \cos x \cos(x + 2) - \cos^2(x + 1)$ is

(a) a straight line passing through $(0, -\sin^2 1)$ with slope 2
(b) a straight line passing through (0, 0)
(c) a parabola with vertex $(1, -\sin^2 1)$
(d) a straight line passing through the point $\left(\frac{\pi}{2}, -\sin^2 1\right)$ are parallel to the X-axis.

5. A line passing through the point (2, 2) and the axes enclose an area λ. The intercepts on the axes made by the line are given by the two roots of

(a) $x^2 - 2|\lambda|x + |\lambda| = 0$ (b) $x^2 + |\lambda|x + 2|\lambda| = 0$
(c) $x^2 - |\lambda|x + 2|\lambda| = 0$ (d) None of these

6. The set of value of 'b' for which the origin and the point (1, 1) lie on the same side of the straight line $a^2x + aby + 1 = 0 \forall a \in R, b > 0$ are

(a) $b \in (2, 4)$ (b) $b \in (0, 2)$
(c) $b \in [0, 2]$ (d) None of these

7. Line L has intercepts a and b on the co-ordinates axes, when the axes are rotated through a given angle; keeping the origin fixed, the same line has intercepts p and q, then

(a) $a^2 + b^2 = p^2 + q^2$ (b) $\frac{1}{a^2} + \frac{1}{b^2} = \frac{1}{p^2} + \frac{1}{q^2}$
(c) $a^2 + p^2 = b^2 + q^2$ (d) $\frac{1}{a^2} + \frac{1}{p^2} = \frac{1}{b^2} + \frac{1}{q^2}$

8. If the distance of any point (x, y) from the origin is defined as $d(x, y) = \max\{|x|, |y|\}$, $d(x, y) = a$ non-zero constant, then the locus is

(a) a circle (b) a straight line
(c) a square (d) a triangle

9. If p_1, p_2, p_3 be the perpendiculars from the points $(m^2, 2m)$, $(mm', m + m')$ and $(m'^2, 2m')$ respectively on the line $x\cos\alpha + y\sin\alpha + \frac{\sin^2\alpha}{\cos\alpha} = 0$, then p_1, p_2, p_3 are in

(a) AP (b) GP
(c) HP (d) None of these

10. $ABCD$ is a square whose vertices A, B, C and D are (0, 0), (2, 0), (2, 2) and (0, 2) respectively. This square is rotated in the xy plane with an angle of 30° in anti-clockwise direction about an axis passing through the vertex A the equation of the diagonal BD of this rotated square is .... If E is the centre of the square, the equation of the circumcircle of the triangle ABE is

(a) $\sqrt{3}x + (1 - \sqrt{3})y = \sqrt{3}$, $x^2 + y^2 = 4$
(b) $(1 + \sqrt{3})x - (1 - \sqrt{2})y = 2$, $x^2 + y^2 = 9$
(c) $(2 - \sqrt{3})x + y = 2(\sqrt{3} - 1)$, $x^2 + y^2 - x\sqrt{3} - y = 0$
(d) None of the above

11. The point (4, 1) undergoes the following three successive transformations

(i) reflection about the line $y = x - 1$.
(ii) translation through a distance 1 unit along the positive direction of X-axis.
(iii) rotation through an angle $\frac{\pi}{4}$ about the origin in the anti-clockwise direction

Then, the coordinates of the final point are

(a) (4, 3) (b) $\left(\frac{7}{2}, \frac{7}{2}\right)$
(c) $(0, 3\sqrt{2})$ (d) (3, 4)

12. If the square $ABCD$, where $A(0, 0)$, $B(2, 0)$, $C(2, 2)$ and $D(0, 2)$ undergoes the following three transformations successively

(i) $f_1(x, y) \to (y, x)$
(ii) $f_2(x, y) \to (x + 3y, y)$
(iii) $f_3(x, y) \to \left(\frac{x - y}{2}, \frac{x + y}{2}\right)$

then the final figure is a

(a) square (b) parallelogram
(c) rhombus (d) None of these

13. The line $x+y=a$ meets the axes of x and y at A and B respectively. A triangle AMN is inscribed in the triangle OAB, O being the origin, with right angle at N, M and N lie respectively on OB and AB. If the area of the triangle AMN is $\frac{3}{8}$ of the area of the triangle OAB, then $\frac{AN}{BN}$ is equal to

(a) 1 (b) 2 (c) 3 (d) 4

14. If $P(1,0)$, $Q(-1,0)$ and $R(2,0)$ are three given points, then the locus of point S satisfying the relation $(SQ)^2+(SR)^2=2(SP)^2$ is

(a) a straight line parallel to X-axis
(b) a circle through the origin
(c) a circle with centre at the origin
(d) a straight line parallel to Y-axis

15. If $A\left(\frac{\sin\alpha}{3}-1, \frac{\cos\alpha}{2}-1\right)$ and $B(1,1)$, $\alpha\in[-\pi,\pi]$ are two points on the same side of the line $3x-2y+1=0$, then α belongs to the interval

(a) $\left(-\pi,-\frac{3\pi}{4}\right]\cup\left(\frac{\pi}{4},\pi\right)$ (b) $[-\pi,\pi]$
(c) ϕ (d) None of these

16. The line $x+y=1$ meets X-axis at A and Y-axis at B, P is the mid-point of AB. P_1 is the foot of the perpendicular from P to OA; M_1 is that of P_1 from OP; P_2 is that of M_1 from OA; M_2 is that of P_2 from OP; P_3 is that of M_2 from OA and so on. If P_n denotes the nth foot of the perpendicular on OA form M_{n-1}, then OP_n is equal to

(a) $\frac{1}{2n}$ (b) $\frac{1}{2^n}$
(c) 2^n-1 (d) 2^n+3

17. The line $x=c$ cuts the triangle with corners (0, 0); (1, 1) and (9, 1) into two regions. For the area of the two regions to be the same, then c must be equal to

(a) $\frac{5}{2}$ (b) 3
(c) $\frac{7}{2}$ (d) 3 or 15

18. If the straight lines $x+2y=9$, $3x-5y=5$ and $ax+by=1$ are concurrent, then the straight line $5x+2y=1$, passes through the point

(a) $(a,-b)$ (b) $(-a,b)$
(c) (a,b) (d) $(-a,-b)$

19. The ends of the base of the isosceles triangle are at (2, 0) and (0, 1) and the equation of one side is $x=2$, then the orthocentre of the triangle is

(a) $\left(\frac{3}{4},\frac{3}{2}\right)$ (b) $\left(\frac{5}{4},1\right)$
(c) $\left(\frac{3}{4},1\right)$ (d) $\left(\frac{4}{3},\frac{7}{12}\right)$

20. Suppose that a ray of light leaves the point (3, 4), reflects off the Y-axis towards the X-axis, reflects off the X-axis, and finally arrives at the point (8, 2). The value of x is

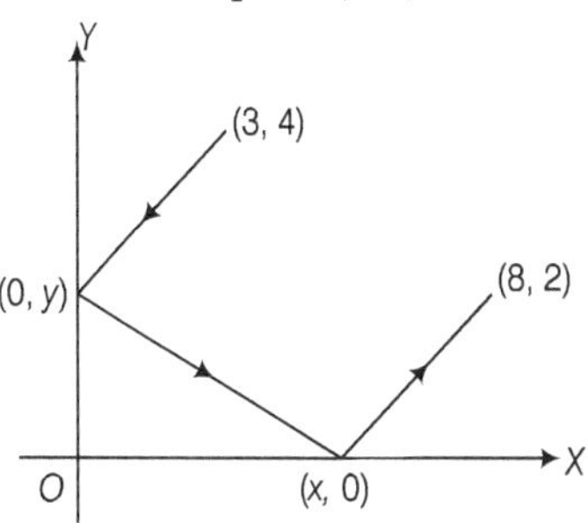

(a) $4\frac{1}{2}$ (b) $4\frac{1}{3}$ (c) $4\frac{2}{3}$ (d) $5\frac{1}{3}$

21. m, n are two integers with $0<n<m$. A is the point (m,n) on the cartesian plane. B is the reflection of A in the line $y=x$. C is the reflection of B in the Y-axis, D is the reflection of C in the X-axis and E is the reflection of D in the Y-axis. The area of the pentagon $ABCDE$ is

(a) $2m(m+n)$ (b) $m(m+3n)$
(c) $m(2m+3n)$ (d) $2m(m+3n)$

22. A straight line L with negative slope passes through the point (8, 2) and cuts the positive coordinates axes at points P and Q. As L varies, the absolute minimum value of $OP+OQ$ is (O is origin)

(a) 10 (b) 18 (c) 16 (d) 12

23. Drawn from origin are two mutually perpendicular lines forming an isosceles triangle together with the straight line $2x+y=a$, then the area of this triangle is

(a) $\frac{a^2}{2}$ sq units (b) $\frac{a^2}{3}$ sq units
(c) $\frac{a^2}{5}$ sq units (d) None of these

24. The number of integral values of m for which the x-coordinate of the point of intersection of the lines $3x+4y=9$ and $y=mx+1$ is also an integer is

(a) 2 (b) 0 (c) 4 (d) 1

25. A ray of light coming from the point (1, 2) is reflected at a point A on the X-axis and then passes through the point (5, 3). The coordinates of the point A are

(a) $\left(\frac{13}{5},0\right)$ (b) $\left(\frac{5}{13},0\right)$
(c) $(-7,0)$ (d) None of these

26. Consider the family of lines $5x+3y-2+\lambda(3x-y-4)=0$ and $x-y+1+\mu(2x-y-2)=0$. Equation of straight line that belong to both families is $ax+by-7=0$, then $a+b$ is

(a) 1 (b) 3 (c) 5 (d) 7

27. In ΔABC equation of the right bisectors of the sides AB and AC are $x+y=0$ and $x-y=0$ respectively. If $A\equiv(5,7)$, then equation of side BC is

(a) $7y=5x$ (b) $5x=y$
(c) $5y=7x$ (d) $5y=x$

28. Two particles start from the point $(2,-1)$, one moving 2 units along the line $x+y=1$ and the other 5 units along the line $x-2y=4$. If the particles move towards increasing y, then their new positions are

(a) $(2-\sqrt{2},\sqrt{2}-1);(2\sqrt{2}+2,\sqrt{5}-1)$
(b) $(2\sqrt{2}+2,\sqrt{5}-1);(2\sqrt{2},\sqrt{2}+1)$
(c) $(2+\sqrt{2},\sqrt{2}+1);(2\sqrt{2}+2,\sqrt{5}+1)$
(d) $(2-\sqrt{2},\sqrt{5}-1);(\sqrt{2}-1,2\sqrt{2}+2)$

29. Let P be $(5,3)$ and a point R on $y=x$ and Q on the X-axis be such that $PQ+QR+RP$ is minimum, then the coordinates of Q are

(a) $\left(\frac{17}{8},0\right)$ (b) $\left(\frac{17}{4},0\right)$
(c) $\left(\frac{17}{2},0\right)$ (d) $(17,0)$

30. In the adjacent figure combined equation of the incident and refracted ray is

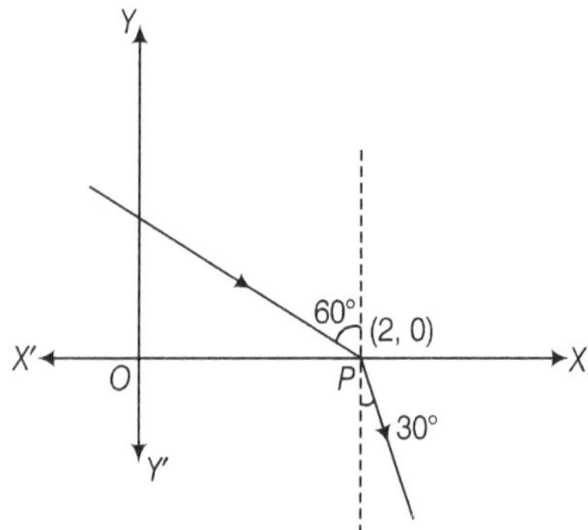

(a) $(x-2)^2+y^2+\frac{4}{\sqrt{3}}(x-2)y=0$
(b) $(x-2)^2+y^2-\frac{4}{\sqrt{3}}(x-2)y=0$
(c) $(x-2)^2+y^2+\frac{y}{\sqrt{3}}(x-2)=0$
(d) $(x-2)^2+y^2-\frac{y}{\sqrt{3}}(x-2)=0$

The Straight Lines Exercise 2 :
More than One Correct Option Type Questions

- The section contains **15 multiple choice questions**. Each question has four choices (a), (b), (c), and (d) out of which **MORE THAN ONE** may be correct.

31. The point of intersection of the lines $\frac{x}{a}+\frac{y}{b}=1$ and $\frac{x}{b}+\frac{y}{a}=1$ lies on

(a) $x-y=0$
(b) $(x+y)(a+b)=2ab$
(c) $(lx+my)(a+b)=(l+m)ab$
(d) $(lx-my)(a+b)=(l-m)ab$

32. The equations $(b-c)x+(c-a)y+a-b=0$ and $(b^3-c^3)x+(c^3-a^3)y+a^3-b^3=0$ will represent the same line, if

(a) $b=c$ (b) $c=a$
(c) $a=b$ (d) $a+b+c=0$

33. The area of a triangle is 5. Two of its vertices are (2, 1) and (3, –2). The third vertex lies on $y=x+3$. The coordinates of the third vertex cannot be

(a) $\left(\frac{-3}{2},\frac{3}{2}\right)$ (b) $\left(\frac{3}{4},\frac{-3}{2}\right)$
(c) $\left(\frac{7}{2},\frac{13}{2}\right)$ (d) $\left(\frac{-1}{4},\frac{11}{4}\right)$

34. If the lines $x-2y-6=0$, $3x+y-4=0$ and $\lambda x+4y+\lambda^2=0$ are concurrent, then

(a) $\lambda=2$ (b) $\lambda=-3$ (c) $\lambda=4$ (d) $\lambda=-4$

35. Equation of a straight line passing through the point of intersection of $x-y+1=0$ and $3x+y-5=0$ are perpendicular to one of them is

(a) $x+y+3=0$ (b) $x+y-3=0$
(c) $x-3y-5=0$ (d) $x-3y+5=0$

36. If one vertex of an equilateral triangle of side a lies at the origin and the other lies on the line $x-\sqrt{3}y=0$, the coordinates of the third vertex are

(a) $(0,a)$ (b) $\left(\frac{\sqrt{3}a}{2},\frac{-a}{2}\right)$ (c) $(0,-a)$ (d) $\left(\frac{-\sqrt{3}a}{2},\frac{a}{2}\right)$

37. If the line $ax+by+c=0$, $bx+cy+a=0$ and $cx+ay+b=0$ are concurrent $(a+b+c\neq 0)$ then

(a) $a^3+b^3+c^3-3abc=0$ (b) $a=b$
(c) $a=b=c$ (d) $a^2+b^2+c^2-bc-ca-ab=0$

38. $A(1,3)$ and $C(7,5)$ are two opposite vertices of a square. The equation of a side through A is

(a) $x+2y-7=0$ (b) $x-2y+5=0$
(c) $2x+y-5=0$ (d) $2x-y+1=0$

39. If $6a^2 - 3b^2 - c^2 + 7ab - ac + 4bc = 0$, then the family of lines $ax + by + c = 0$ is concurrent at

(a) $(-2, -3)$ (b) $(3, -1)$
(c) $(2, 3)$ (d) $(-3, 1)$

40. Consider the straight lines $x + 2y + 4 = 0$ and $4x + 2y - 1 = 0$. The line $6x + 6y + 7 = 0$ is

(a) bisector of the angle including origin
(b) bisector of acute angle
(c) bisector of obtuse angle
(d) None of the above

41. Two roads are represented by the equations $y - x = 6$ and $x + y = 8$. An inspection bungalow has to be so constructed that it is at a distance of 100 from each of the roads. Possible location of the bungalow is given by

(a) $(100\sqrt{2} + 1, 7)$ (b) $(1 - 100\sqrt{2}, 7)$
(c) $(1, 7 + 100\sqrt{2})$ (d) $(1, 7 - 100\sqrt{2})$

42. If (a, b) be an end of a diagonal of a square and the other diagonal has the equation $x - y = a$, then another vertex of the square can be

(a) $(a - b, a)$ (b) $(a, 0)$
(c) $(0, -a)$ (d) $(a + b, b)$

43. Consider the equation $y - y_1 = m(x - x_1)$. If m and x_1 are fixed and different lines are drawn for different values of y_1, then

(a) the lines will pass through a fixed point
(b) there will be a set of parallel lines
(c) all the lines intersect the line $x = x_1$
(d) all the lines will be parallel to the line $y = x_1$

44. Let $L_1 \equiv ax + by + a\sqrt[3]{b} = 0$ and $L_2 \equiv bx - ay + b\sqrt[3]{a} = 0$ be two straight lines. The equations of the bisectors of the angle formed by the foci whose equations are $\lambda_1 L_1 - \lambda_2 L_2 = 0$ and $\lambda_1 L_1 + \lambda_2 L_2 = 0$, λ_1 and λ_2 being non-zero real numbers, are given by

(a) $L_1 = 0$ (b) $L_2 = 0$
(c) $\lambda_1 L_1 + \lambda_2 L_2 = 0$ (d) $\lambda_2 L_1 - \lambda_1 L_2 = 0$

45. The equation of the bisectors of the angles between the two intersecting lines $\frac{x-3}{\cos\theta} = \frac{y+5}{\sin\theta}$ and $\frac{x-3}{\cos\phi} = \frac{y+5}{\sin\phi}$ are $\frac{x-3}{\cos\alpha} = \frac{y+5}{\sin\alpha}$ and $\frac{x-3}{\beta} = \frac{y+5}{\gamma}$, then

(a) $\alpha = \frac{\theta + \phi}{2}$ (b) $\beta = -\sin\alpha$
(c) $\gamma = \cos\alpha$ (d) $\beta = \sin\alpha$

The Straight Lines Exercise 3 : Paragraph Based Questions

- The section contains **5 Paragraphs** based upon each of the paragraphs **3 multiple choice questions** have to be answered. Each of these questions has four choices (a), (b), (c), and (d) out of which **ONLY ONE** is correct.

Paragraph I

(Q. Nos. 46 to 48)

For points $P \equiv (x_1, y_1)$ and $Q = (x_2, y_2)$ of the coordinate plane, a new distance $d(P, Q)$ is defined by
$d(P, Q) = |x_1 - x_2| + |y_1 - y_2|$
Let $O \equiv (0, 0)$, $A \equiv (1, 2)$, $B \equiv (2, 3)$ and $C \equiv (4, 3)$ are four fixed points on x-y plane.

46. Let $R(x, y)$, such that R is equidistant from the point O and A with respect to new distance and if $0 \le x < 1$ and $0 \le y < 2$, then R lie on a line segment whose equation is

(a) $x + y = 3$ (b) $x + 2y = 3$
(c) $2x + y = 3$ (d) $2x + 2y = 3$

47. Let $S(x, y)$, such that S is equidistant from points O and B with respect to new distance and if $x \ge 2$ and $0 \le y < 3$, then locus of S is

(a) a line segment of finite length
(b) a line of infinite length
(c) a ray of finite length
(d) a ray of infinite length

48. Let $T(x, y)$, such that T is equidistant from point O and C with respect to new distance and if T lie in first quadrant, then T consists of the union of a line segment of finite length and an infinite ray whose labelled diagram is

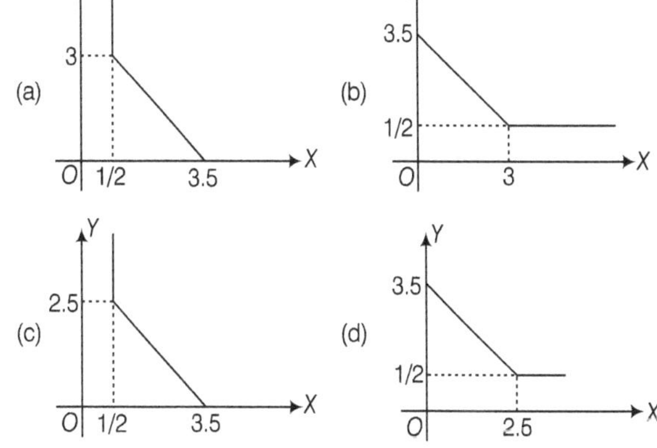

Paragraph II

(Q. Nos. 49 to 51)

In a triangle ABC, if the equation of sides AB, BC and CA are $2x - y + 4 = 0$, $x - 2y - 1 = 0$ and $x + 3y - 3 = 0$ respectively.

49. Tangent of internal angle A is equal to

(a) -7 (b) -3
(c) $\frac{1}{2}$ (d) 7

50. The equation of external bisector of angle B is

(a) $x - y - 1 = 0$ (b) $x - y + 1 = 0$
(c) $x + y - 5 = 0$ (d) $x + y + 5 = 0$

51. The image of point B w.r.t the side CA is

(a) $\left(-\frac{3}{5}, \frac{26}{5}\right)$ (b) $\left(-\frac{3}{5}, -\frac{26}{5}\right)$
(c) $\left(\frac{3}{5}, -\frac{26}{5}\right)$ (d) $\left(\frac{3}{5}, \frac{26}{5}\right)$

Paragraph III

(Q. Nos. 52 to 54)

$A(1, 3)$ and $C\left(-\frac{2}{5}, \frac{-2}{5}\right)$ are the vertices of a triangle ABC and the equation of the angle bisector of $\angle ABC$ is $x + y = 2$.

52. Equation of BC is

(a) $7x + 3y - 4 = 0$ (b) $7x + 3y + 4 = 0$
(c) $7x - 3y + 4 = 0$ (d) $7x - 3y - 4 = 0$

53. Coordinates of vertex B are

(a) $\left(\frac{3}{10}, \frac{17}{10}\right)$ (b) $\left(\frac{17}{10}, \frac{3}{10}\right)$
(c) $\left(-\frac{5}{2}, \frac{9}{2}\right)$ (d) $\left(\frac{9}{2}, -\frac{5}{2}\right)$

54. Equation of AB is

(a) $3x + 7y = 24$
(b) $3x + 7y + 24 = 0$
(c) $13x + 7y + 8 = 0$
(d) $13x - 7y + 8 = 0$

Paragraph IV

(Q. Nos. 55 to 57)

Let $S' = 0$ be the image or reflection of the curve $S = 0$ about line mirror $L = 0$. Suppose P be any point on the curve $S = 0$ and Q be the image or reflection about the line mirror $L = 0$, then Q will lie on $S' = 0$.

How to find the image or reflection of a curve?

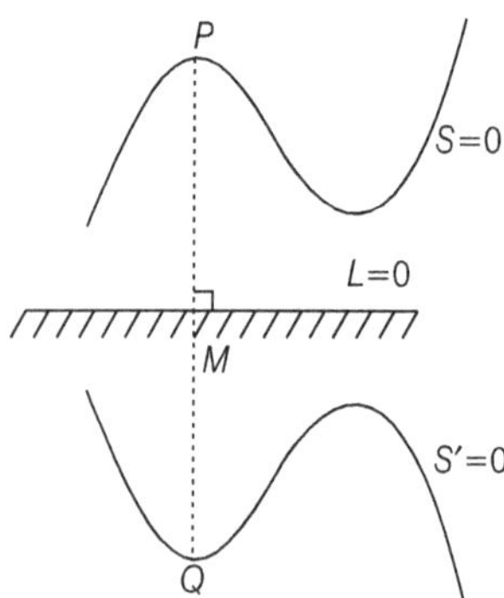

Let the given curve be $S : f(x, y) = 0$ and line mirror $L : ax + by + c = 0$. We take a point P on the given curve in parametric form. Suppose Q be the image or reflection of point P about line mirror $L = 0$, which again contains the same parameter. Let $Q \equiv (\phi(t), \psi(t))$, where t is parameter. Now let $x = \phi(t)$ and $y = \psi(t)$

Eliminating t, we get the equation of the reflected curve S'.

55. The image of the line $3x - y = 2$ in the line $y = x - 1$ is

(a) $x + 3y = 2$ (b) $3x + y = 2$
(c) $x - 3y = 2$ (d) $x + y = 2$

56. The image of the circle $x^2 + y^2 = 4$ in the line $x + y = 2$ is

(a) $x^2 + y^2 - 2x - 2y = 0$ (b) $x^2 + y^2 - 4x - 4y + 6 = 0$
(c) $x^2 + y^2 - 2x - 2y + 2 = 0$ (d) $x^2 + y^2 - 4x - 4y + 4 = 0$

57. The image of the parabola $x^2 = 4y$ in the line $x + y = a$ is

(a) $(x - a)^2 = 4(a - y)$ (b) $(y - a)^2 = 4(a - x)$
(c) $(x - a)^2 = 4(a + y)$ (d) $(y - a)^2 = 4(a + x)$

Paragraph V

(Q. Nos. 58 to 60)

In a ΔABC, the equation of the side BC is $2x - y = 3$ and its circumcentre and orhtocentre are (2, 4) and (1, 2) respectively.

58. Circumradius of ΔABC is

(a) $\sqrt{\frac{61}{5}}$ (b) $\sqrt{\frac{51}{5}}$ (c) $\sqrt{\frac{41}{5}}$ (d) $\sqrt{\frac{43}{5}}$

59. $\sin B \cdot \sin C =$

(a) $\frac{9}{2\sqrt{61}}$ (b) $\frac{9}{4\sqrt{61}}$ (c) $\frac{9}{\sqrt{61}}$ (d) $\frac{9}{5\sqrt{61}}$

60. The distance of orthocentre from vertex A is

(a) $\frac{1}{\sqrt{5}}$ (b) $\frac{6}{\sqrt{5}}$ (c) $\frac{3}{\sqrt{5}}$ (d) $\frac{2}{\sqrt{5}}$

The Straight Lines Exercise 4 :
Single Integer Answer Type Questions

- The section contains **10 questions**. The answer to eaeh question is a **single digit integer**, ranging from 0 to 9 (both inclusive).

61. The number of possible straight lines passing through (2, 3) and forming a triangle with the coordinate axes, whose area is 12 sq units, is

62. The portion of the line $ax + 3y - 1 = 0$, intercepted between the lines $ax + y + 1 = 0$ and $x + 3y = 0$ subtend a right angle at origin, then the value of $|a|$ is

63. Let ABC be a triangle and $A \equiv (1, 2)$, $y = x$ be the perpendicular bisector of AB and $x - 2y + 1 = 0$ be the angle bisector of $\angle C$. If the equation of BC is given by $ax + by - 5 = 0$, then the value of $a - 2b$ is

64. A lattice point in a plane is a point for which both coordinates are integers. If n be the number of lattice points inside the triangle whose sides are $x = 0$, $y = 0$ and $9x + 223y = 2007$, then tens place digit in n is

65. The number of triangles that the four lines $y = x + 3$, $y = 2x + 3$, $y = 3x + 2$ and $y + x = 3$ form is

66. In a plane there are two families of lines : $y = x + n$, $y = -x + n$, where $n \in \{0, 1, 2, 3, 4\}$. The number of squares of the diagonal of length 2 formed by these lines is

67. Given $A(0, 0)$ and $B(x, y)$ with $x \in (0, 1)$ and $y > 0$. Let the slope of line AB be m_1. Point C lies on line $x = 1$ such that the slope of BC is equal to m_2, where $0 < m_2 < m_1$. If the area of triangle ABC can be expressed as $(m_1 - m_2) f(x)$ and the largest possible value of $f(x)$ is λ, then the value of $\frac{1}{\lambda}$ is

68. If $(\lambda, \lambda + 1)$ is an interior point of ΔABC, where $A \equiv (0, 3)$, $B \equiv (-2, 0)$ and $C \equiv (6, 1)$, then the number of integral values of λ is

69. For all real values of a and b, lines $(2a + b)x + (a + 3b)y + (b - 3a) = 0$ and $\lambda x + 2y + 6 = 0$ and $\lambda x + 2y + 6 = 0$ are concurrent, then the value of $|\lambda|$ is

70. If from point (4, 4) perpendiculars to the straight lines $3x + 4y + 5 = 0$ and $y = mx + 7$ meet at Q and R and area of triangle PQR is maximum, then the value of $3m$ is

The Straight Lines Exercise 5 :
Matching Type Questions

- The section contains **5 questions**. Questions 1, 2 and 3 have four statement (A, B, C and D) given in **Column I** and four statements (p, q, r and s) in **Column II** and questions 74 and 75 have three statements (A, B and C) given in **Column I** and five statements (p, q, r, s and t) in **Column II**. Any given statement in **Column I** can have correct matching with one or more statement (s) given in **Column II**.

71. Let L_1, L_2, L_3 be three straight lines a plane and n be the number of circles touching all the lines.

	Column I		Column II
(A)	The lines are concurrent, then $n + 1$ is a	(p)	natural number
(B)	The lines are parallel, then $2n + 3$ is a	(q)	prime number
(C)	Two lines are parallel, then $n + 2$ is a	(r)	composite number
(D)	The lines are neither concurrent nor parallel, then $n + 2$ is a	(s)	perfect number

72. Match the Columns

	Column I		Column II
(A)	Lines $x - 2y - 6 = 0$, $3x + y - 4 = 0$ and $\lambda x + 4y + \lambda^2 = 0$ are concurrent, then the value of $|\lambda|$ is	(p)	2
(B)	The variable straight lines $3x(a + 1) + 4y(a - 1) - 3(a - 1) = 0$ for different value of 'a' passes through a fixed point (p, q) if $\lambda = p - q$, then the value of $4|\lambda|$	(q)	3
(C)	If the line $x + y - 1 - \left|\frac{\lambda}{2}\right| = 0$ passing through the intersection of $x - y + 1 = 0$ and $3x + y - 5 = 0$, is perpendicular to one of them, then the value of $|\lambda + 1|$ is	(r)	4
(D)	If the line $y - x - 1 + \lambda = 0$ is equidistant from the points $(1, -2)$ and $(3, 4)$, then the value of $|\lambda|$ is	(s)	5

73. Consider the triangle formed by the lines $y + 3x + 2 = 0$, $3y - 2x - 5 = 0$ and $4y + x - 14 = 0$

	Column I		Column II
(A)	If $(0, \lambda)$ lies inside the triangle, then integral values are less than $\|3\lambda\|$	(p)	4
(B)	If $(1, \lambda)$ lies inside the triangle, then integral values are less than $\|3\lambda\|$	(q)	5
(C)	If $(\lambda, 2)$ lies inside the triangle, then integral values of $\|6\lambda\|$ are	(r)	6
(D)	If $(\lambda, 7/2)$ lies inside the triangle, then integral value of $\|6\lambda\|$ are	(s)	7

74. Match the following

	Column I		Column II
(A)	The area bounded by the curve max. $\{\|x\|, \|y\|\} = 1$ is	(p)	0
(B)	If the point (a, a) lies between the lines $\|x + y\| = 6$, then $[\|a\|]$ is (where $[.]$ denotes the greatest integer function)	(q)	1
(C)	Number of integral values of b for which the origin and the point (1, 1) lie on the same side of the st. line $a^2x + aby + 1 = 0$ for all $a \in R \sim \{0\}$ is	(r)	2
		(s)	3
		(t)	4

75. Match the following

	Column I		Column II
(A)	If the distance of any point (x, y) from origin is defined as $d(x, y) = 2\|x\| + 3\|y\|$. If perimeter and area of figure bounded by $d(x, y) = 6$ are λ unit and μ sq units respectively, then	(p)	(λ, μ) lies on $x = 3y$
(B)	If the vertices of a triangle are (6, 0), (0, 6) and (6, 6). If distance between circumcentre and orthocentre and distance between circumcentre and centroid are λ unit and μ unit respectively, then	(q)	(λ, μ) lies on $x^2 - y^2 = 64$
(C)	The ends of the hypotenuse of a right angled triangle are (6, 0) and (0, 6). If the third vertex is (λ, μ), then	(r)	(λ, μ) lies on $x^2 + y^2 - 6x - 6y = 0$
		(s)	(λ, μ) lies on $x^2 - 16y = 16$
		(t)	(λ, μ) lies on $x^2 - y^2 = 16$

The Straight Lines Exercise 6 : Statement I and II Type Questions

- **Directions** (Q. Nos 76 to 83) are Assertion-Reason type questions. Each of these question contains two statements.

Statement I (Assertion) and

Statement II (Reason)

Each of these questions has four alternative choices, only one of which is the correct answer.

You have to select the correct choice.

(a) Statement I is true, statement II is true; statement II is a correct explanation for statement I
(b) Statement I is true, statement II is true; statement II is not a correct explanation for statement I
(c) Statement I is true, statement II is false
(d) Statement I is false, statement II is true

76. Statement I The lines $x(a + 2b) + y(a + 3b) = a + b$ are concurrent at the point $(2, -1)$

Statement II The lines $x + y - 1 = 0$ and $2x + 3y - 1 = 0$ intersect at the point $(2, -1)$

77. Statement I The points (3, 2) and (1, 4) lie on opposite side of the line $3x - 2y - 1 = 0$

Statement II The algebraic perpendicular distance from the given point to the line have opposite sign.

78. Statement I If sum of algebraic distances from points $A(1, 2)$, $B(2, 3)$, $C(6, 1)$ is zero on the line $ax + by + c = 0$, then $2a + 3b + c = 0$

Statement II The centroid of the triangle is (3, 2)

79. Statement I Let $A \equiv (0, 1)$ and $B \equiv (2, 0)$ and P be a point on the line $4x + 3y + 9 = 0$, then the co-ordinates of P such that $|PA - PB|$ is maximum is $\left(-\frac{12}{5}, \frac{17}{5}\right)$.

Statement II $|PA - PB| \le |AB|$

80. Statement I The incentre of a triangle formed by the line $x\cos\left(\frac{\pi}{9}\right) + y\sin\left(\frac{\pi}{9}\right) = \pi$, $x\cos\left(\frac{8\pi}{9}\right) + y\sin\left(\frac{8\pi}{9}\right) = \pi$ and $x\cos\left(\frac{13\pi}{9}\right) + y\sin\left(\frac{13\pi}{9}\right) = \pi$ is (0, 0).

Statement II Any point equidistant from the given three non-concurrent straight lines in the plane is the incentre of the triangle.

81. **Statement I** Reflection of the point (5, 1) in the line $x + y = 0$ is $(-1, -5)$.

Statement II Reflection of a point $P(\alpha, \beta)$ in the line $ax + by + c = 0$ is $Q(\alpha', \beta')$, if $\left(\frac{\alpha+\alpha'}{2}, \frac{\beta+\beta'}{2}\right)$ lies on the line.

82. **Statement I** The internal angle bisector of angle C of a triangle ABC with sides AB, AC and BC as $y = 0$, $3x + 2y = 0$, and $2x + 3y + 6 = 0$, respectively, is $5x + 5y + 6 = 0$.

Statement II The image of point A with respect to $5x + 5y + 6 = 0$ lies on the side BC of the triangle.

83. **Statement I** If the point $(2a - 5, a^2)$ is on the same side of the line $x + y - 3 = 0$ as that of the origin, then $a \in (2, 4)$.

Statement II The point (x_1, y_1) and (x_2, y_2) lie on the same or opposite sides of the line $ax + by + c = 0$, as $ax_1 + by_1 + c$ and $ax_2 + by_2 + c$ have the same or opposite signs.

The Straight Lines Exercise 7 :
Subjective Type Questions

- In this section, there are **15 subjective questions**.

84. If $A(x_1, y_1)$, $B(x_2, y_2)$ and $C(x_3, y_3)$ are the vertices of a triangle, then show that the equation of the line joining A and the circumcentre is given by

$$(\sin 2B)\begin{vmatrix} x & y & 1 \\ x_1 & y_1 & 1 \\ x_2 & y_2 & 1 \end{vmatrix} + (\sin 2C)\begin{vmatrix} x & y & 1 \\ x_1 & y_1 & 1 \\ x_3 & y_3 & 1 \end{vmatrix} = 0$$

85. Find the coordinates of the point at unit distance from the lines

$3x - 4y + 1 = 0, 8x + 6y + 1 = 0$.

86. A variable line makes intercepts on the coordinate axes, the sum of whose squares is constant and equal to k^2. Show that the locus of the foot of the perpendicular from the origin to this line is $(x^2 + y^2)^2 (x^{-2} + y^{-2}) = k^2$.

87. A variable line intersects n lines $y = mx, (m = 1, 2, 3, \dots, n)$ in the points $A_1, A_2, A_3, \dots, A_n$ respectively.

If $\sum_{p=1}^{n} \frac{1}{OA_p} = c$ (constant). Show that line passes through a fixed point. Find the coordinates of this fixed point (O being origin).

88. Given n straight lines and a fixed point O. A straight line is drawn through O meeting these lines in the points $R_1, R_2, R_3, \dots, R_n$ and a point R is taken on it such that

$$\frac{n}{OR} = \sum_{r=1}^{n} \frac{1}{OR_r}$$

Prove that the locus of R is a straight line.

89. Prove that all lines represented by the equation

$$(2\cos\theta + 3\sin\theta)\, x + (3\cos\theta - 5\sin\theta)\, y = 5\cos\theta - 2\sin\theta$$

pass through a fixed point for all θ. What are the coordinates of this fixed point and its reflection in the line $x + y = \sqrt{2}$? Prove that all lines through reflection point can be represented by equation

$$(2\cos\theta + 3\sin\theta)\, x + (3\cos\theta - 5\sin\theta)\, y = (\sqrt{2} - 1)(5\cos\theta - 2\sin\theta)$$

90. P is any point on the line $x - a = 0$. If A is the point $(a, 0)$ and PQ, the bisector of the angle OPA, meets the X-axis in Q. Prove that the locus of the foot of the perpendicular from Q on OP is

$(x - a)^2 (x^2 + y^2) = a^2 y^2$.

91. Having given the bases and the sum of the areas of a number of triangles is constant, which have a common vertex. Show that the locus of this vertex is a straight line.

92. $A(3, 0)$ and $B(6, 0)$ are two fixed points and $U(\alpha, \beta)$ is a variable point on the plane. AU and BU meet the y-axis at C and D respectively and AD meets OU at V. Prove that CV passes through (2, 0) for any position of U in the plane.

93. A variable line is drawn through O to cut two fixed straight lines L_1 and L_2 in R and S. A point P is chosen on the variable line such that $\frac{m+n}{OP} = \frac{m}{OR} + \frac{n}{OS}$. Show that the locus of P is a straight line passing through the point of intersection of L_1 and L_2.

94. A line through $A(-5, -4)$ meets the lines $x + 3y + 2 = 0$, $2x + y + 4 = 0$ and $x - y - 5 = 0$ at the points B, C and D respectively, if

$$\left(\frac{15}{AB}\right)^2 + \left(\frac{10}{AC}\right)^2 = \left(\frac{6}{AD}\right)^2$$

find the equation of the line.

95. Two fixed straight lines X-axis and $y = mx$ are cut by a variable line in the points $A(a, 0)$ and $B(b, mb)$ respectively. P and Q are the feet of the perpendiculars drawn from A and B upon the lines $y = mx$ and X-axis. Show that, if AB passes through a fixed point (h, k), then PQ will also pass through a fixed point. Find the fixed point.

96. Find the equation of straight lines passing through point $(2, 3)$ and having an intercept of length 2 units between the straight lines $2x + y = 3$, $2x + y = 5$.

97. Let $O(0, 0)$, $A(2, 0)$ and $B\left(1, \frac{1}{\sqrt{3}}\right)$ be the vertices of a triangle. Let R be the region consisting of all those points P inside ΔOAB which satisfy

$d(P, OA) \le \min\{d(P, OB), d(P, AB)\}$

where d denotes the distance from the point to the corresponding line. Sketch the region R and find its area.

98. Two triangles ABC and PQR are such that the perpendiculars from A to QR, B to RP and C to PQ are concurrent. Show that the perpendicular from P to BC, Q to CA and R to AB are also concurrent.

The Straight Lines Exercise 8 :
Questions Asked in Previous 13 Year's Exams

- This section contains questions asked in **IIT-JEE, AIEEE, JEE Main & JEE Advanced** from year **2005** to **2017**.

99. The line parallel to the X-axis and passing through the intersection of the lines $ax + 2by + 3b = 0$ and $bx - 2ay - 3a = 0$, where $(a, b) \ne (0, 0)$ is **[AIEEE 2005, 3M]**

(a) below the X-axis at a distance of $\frac{3}{2}$ from it

(b) below the X-axis at a distance of $\frac{2}{3}$ from it

(c) above the X-axis at a distance of $\frac{3}{2}$ from it

(d) above the X-axis at a distance of $\frac{2}{3}$ from it

100. A straight line through the point $A(3, 4)$ is such that its intercept between the axes is bisected at A. Its equation is **[AIEEE 2006, 4.5M]**

(a) $x + y = 7$ (b) $3x - 4y + 7 = 0$
(c) $4x + 3y = 24$ (d) $3x + 4y = 25$

101. If (a, a^2) falls inside the angle made by the lines $y = \frac{x}{2}$, $x > 0$ and $y = 3x$, $x > 0$, then a belong to **[AIEEE 2006, 6M]**

(a) $\left(0, \frac{1}{2}\right)$ (b) $(3, \infty)$
(c) $\left(\frac{1}{2}, 3\right)$ (d) $\left(-3, -\frac{1}{2}\right)$

102. Lines $L_1 : y - x = 0$ and $L_2 : 2x + y = 0$ intersect the line $L_3 : y + 2 = 0$ at P and Q respectively. The bisector of the acute angle between L_1 and L_2 intersects L_3 at R. **[IIT-JEE 2007, 3M]**

Statement I The ratio $PR : RQ$ equals $2\sqrt{2} : \sqrt{5}$ because

Statement II In any triangle, bisector of an angle divides the triangle into two similar triangles.

(a) Statement I is true, statement II is true; statement II is not a correct explanation for statement I

(b) Statement I is true, statement II is true; statement II is not a correct explanation for statement I

(c) Statement I is true, statement II is false

(d) Statement I is false, statement II is true

103. Let $P = (-1, 0)$, $Q = (0, 0)$ and $R = (3, 3\sqrt{3})$ be three point. The equation of the bisector of the angle PQR is **[AIEEE 2007, 3M]**

(a) $\frac{\sqrt{3}}{2}x + y = 0$ (b) $x + \sqrt{3}y = 0$
(c) $\sqrt{3}x + y = 0$ (d) $x + \frac{\sqrt{3}}{2}y = 0$

104. Consider the lines given by

$$L_1 : x + 3y - 5 = 0$$
$$L_2 : 3x - ky - 1 = 0$$
$$L_3 : 5x + 2y - 12 = 0$$

Match the statements/Expressions in **Column I** with the statements/Expressions in **Column II**

	Column I		Column II
(A)	L_1, L_2, L_3 are concurrent, if	(p)	$k = -9$
(B)	one of L_1, L_2, L_3 is parallel to at least one of the other two, if	(q)	$k = -\frac{6}{5}$
(C)	L_1, L_2, L_3 form a triangle, if	(r)	$k = \frac{5}{6}$
(D)	L_1, L_2, L_3 do not form a triangle, if	(s)	$k = 5$

[IIT-JEE 2008, 6M]

105. The perpendicular bisector of the line segment joining $P(1, 4)$ and $Q(k, 3)$ has y-intercept -4. Then a possible value of k is **[AIEEE 2008, 3M]**

(a) 1 (b) 2 (c) -2 (d) -4

106. The lines $p(p^2+1)x-y+q=0$ and $(p^2+1)^2x+(p^2+1)y+2q=0$ are perpendicular to a common line for **[AIEEE 2009, 4M]**

(a) exactly one values of p
(b) exactly two values of p
(c) more than two values of p
(d) no value of p

107. The line L given by $\frac{x}{5}+\frac{y}{b}=1$ passes through the point (13, 32). The line K is parallel to L and has the equation $\frac{x}{c}+\frac{y}{3}=1$. Then the distance between L and K is **[AIEEE 2010, 4M]**

(a) $\sqrt{17}$ (b) $\frac{17}{\sqrt{15}}$
(c) $\frac{23}{\sqrt{17}}$ (d) $\frac{23}{\sqrt{15}}$

108. A straight line L through the point $(3,-2)$ is inclined at an angle $60°$ to the line $\sqrt{3}x+y=1$. If L also intersects the X-axis, then the equation of L is **[IIT-JEE 2011, 3M]**

(a) $y+\sqrt{3}x+2-3\sqrt{3}=0$ (b) $y-\sqrt{3}x+2+3\sqrt{3}=0$
(c) $\sqrt{3}y-x+3+2\sqrt{3}=0$ (d) $\sqrt{3}y+x-3+2\sqrt{3}=0$

109. The lines $L_1: y-x=0$ and $L_2: 2x+y=0$ intersect the line $L_3: y+2=0$ at P and Q respectively. The bisector of the acute angle between L_1 and L_2 intersects L_3 at R. **[AIEEE 2011, 4M]**

Statement I : The ratio $PR:RQ$ equals $2\sqrt{2}:\sqrt{5}$

Statement II : In any triangle, bisector of an angle divides the triangle into two similar triangles.

(a) Statement I is true, statement II is true; statement II is not a correct explanation for statement I.
(b) Statement I is true, statement II is false.
(c) Statement I is false, statement II is true.
(d) Statement I is true, statement II is true; statement II is a correct explanation for statement I

110. If the line $2x+y=k$ passes through the point which divides the line segment joining the points (1, 1) and (2, 4) in the ratio 3 : 2, then k equals **[AIEEE 2012, 4M]**

(a) $\frac{29}{5}$ (b) 5
(c) 6 (d) $\frac{11}{5}$

111. A ray of light along $x+\sqrt{3}y=\sqrt{3}$ gets reflected upon reaching X-axis, the equation of the reflected ray is **[JEE Main 2013, 4M]**

(a) $y=x+\sqrt{3}$ (b) $\sqrt{3}y=x-\sqrt{3}$
(c) $y=\sqrt{3}x-\sqrt{3}$ (d) $\sqrt{3}y=x-1$

112. For $a>b>c>0$, the distance between (1, 1) and the point of intersection of the lines $ax+by+c=0$ and $bx+ay+c=0$ is less than $2\sqrt{2}$. Then **[JEE Advanced 2013, 3M]**

(a) $a+b-c>0$ (b) $a-b+c<0$
(c) $a-b+c>0$ (d) $a+b-c<0$

113. Let PS be the median of the triangle with vertices $P(2,2)$, $Q(6,-1)$ and $R(7,3)$. The equation of the line passing through $(1,-1)$ and parallel to PS is **[JEE Main 2014, 4M]**

(a) $4x+7y+3=0$ (b) $2x-9y-11=0$
(c) $4x-7y-11=0$ (d) $2x+9y+7=0$

114. Let a, b, c and d be non-zero numbers. If the point of intersection of the lines $4ax+2ay+c=0$ and $5bx+2by+d=0$ lies in the fourth quadrant and is equidistant from the two axes, then **[JEE Main 2014, 4M]**

(a) $3bc-2ad=0$ (b) $3bc+2ad=0$
(c) $2bc-3ad=0$ (d) $2bc+3ad=0$

115. For a point P in the plane, let $d_1(P)$ and $d_2(P)$ be the distance of the point P from the lines $x-y=0$ and $x+y=0$ respectively. The area of the region R consisting of all points P lying in the first quadrant of the plane and satisfying $2\le d_1(P)+d_2(P)\le 4$, is **[JEE Advanced 2014, 3M]**

116. The number of points, having both co-ordinates as integers, that lie in the interior of the triangle with vertices (0, 0), (0, 41) and (41, 0) is **[JEE Advanced 2015, 4M]**

(a) 820 (b) 780 (c) 901 (d) 861

117. Two sides of a rhombus are along the lines, $x-y+1=0$ and $7x-y-5=0$. If its diagonals intersect at $(-1,-2)$, then which one of the following is a vertex of this rhombus? **[JEE Main 2016, 4M]**

(a) $\left(\frac{1}{3},-\frac{8}{3}\right)$ (b) $\left(-\frac{10}{3},-\frac{7}{3}\right)$
(c) $(-3,-9)$ (d) $(-3,-8)$

Answers

Exercise for Session 1

1. (c) **2.** (b) **3.** (b) **4.** (d) **5.** (b) **6.** (d) **7.** (c) **8.** (d) **9.** (a,d) **10.** (c) **11.** (d) **12.** $y = 9$ **13.** $(2 + 2\sqrt{3}, 4)$ and $(2 - 2\sqrt{3}, 0)$

14. $PQ = \dfrac{132}{12\sqrt{3} + 5}$ **15.** $4\sqrt{2}$ units

16. $83x - 35y + 92 = 0$ **17.** $x + y - 11 = 0$

Exercise for Session 2

1. (b) **2.** (c) **3.** (a) **4.** (c) **5.** (b) **6.** (d) **7.** (c,d) **8.** (d) **9.** (d) **10.** (d) **11.** (b) **12.** (d)

13. The two points are on the opposite side of the given line.

15. $3x - 4y = 0$ and $3x - 4y - 10 = 0$

17. $7x + y - 31 = 0$ **18.** $2x + 2y + \sqrt{2} = 0$

Exercise for Session 3

1. (c) **2.** (b) **3.** (c) **4.** (a) **5.** (d) **6.** (a) **7.** (a) **8.** (c) **9.** (a) **10.** (a,b) **11.** (c) **12.** (c)

13. $2a + b^2 + b = 0$ **16.** (i) $y = 3$ (ii) $x = 4$, (iii) $3x + 4y = 24$

18. $\left(\dfrac{-5}{3}, \dfrac{-5}{3}\right)$

Exercise for Session 4

1. (c) **2.** (d) **3.** (b) **4.** (b) **5.** (c) **6.** (b) **7.** (c) **8.** (a) **9.** $x = 7$ and $x + \sqrt{3}y = 7 + 9\sqrt{3}$

10. $x(4\sqrt{3} + 3) + y(4 - 3\sqrt{3}) = 11 - 2\sqrt{3}$ and

$y(4 + 3\sqrt{3}) - x(4\sqrt{3} - 3) = 11 + 2\sqrt{3}, \dfrac{4\sqrt{3}}{15}$

11. $\left(-\dfrac{1}{14}, \dfrac{73}{28}\right)$ and $\left(\dfrac{1}{16}, \dfrac{77}{32}\right)$

12. $\left(0, \dfrac{5}{2}\right)$ and $(0, 0)$ **13.** $x + 2y - 6 = 0$

14. $3x = 19$ **15.** $10x - 10y - 3 = 0$

Exercise for Session 5

1. (d) **2.** (a) **3.** (b) **4.** (d) **5.** (c) **6.** (d) **7.** (d) **8.** (c) **9.** (d) **10.** (b) **11.** (b) **12.** (c) **13.** $(3, -2)$ **14.** $14x + 23y - 40 = 0$

15. $4x - y + 6 = 0, \left(-\dfrac{4}{5}, \dfrac{14}{5}\right)$ **16.** (2)

Exercise for Session 6

1. (c) **2.** (c) **3.** (a,b) **4.** (a) **5.** (a) **6.** (c) **7.** $m \in \left(-1, \dfrac{1}{5}\right)$

8. $\theta \in \left(0, \dfrac{5\pi}{6} - \tan^{-1} 3\right)$ **9.** $\theta \in \left(0, \dfrac{\pi}{12}\right) \cup \left(\dfrac{5\pi}{12}, \dfrac{\pi}{2}\right)$

10. $\theta \in \left\{\bigcup_{n=z}\left(2n\pi, 2n\pi + \dfrac{\pi}{6}\right)\right\} \cup \left\{\bigcup_{m=z}\left(2m\pi + \dfrac{5\pi}{6}, 2m\pi\right)\right\}$

11. Outside **12.** $29x - 2y + 33 = 0$

Chapter Exercises

1. (b) **2.** (a) **3.** (c) **4.** (d) **5.** (c) **6.** (b) **7.** (b) **8.** (b) **9.** (b) **10.** (c) **11.** (c) **12.** (b) **13.** (c) **14.** (d) **15.** (a) **16.** (b) **17.** (b) **18.** (c) **19.** (b) **20.** (b) **21.** (b) **22.** (b) **23.** (c) **24.** (a) **25.** (a) **26.** (b) **27.** (a) **28.** (a) **29.** (b) **30.** (a) **31.** (a,b,c,d) **32.** (a,b,c,d) **33.** (a,c) **34.** (a,d) **35.** (b,d) **36.** (a,b,c,d) **37.** (a,c,d) **38.** (a,d) **39.** (a,b) **40.** (a,b) **41.** (a,b,c,d) **42.** (b,d) **43.** (a,b,c) **44.** (a,b) **45.** (a,b,c) **46.** (d) **47.** (d) **48.** (a) **49.** (a) **50.** (d) **51.** (a) **52.** (b) **53.** (c) **54.** (a) **55.** (c) **56.** (d) **57.** (b) **58.** (a) **59.** (a) **60.** (b) **61.** (3) **62.** (6) **63.** (5) **64.** (8) **65.** (3) **66.** (9) **67.** (8) **68.** (2) **69.** (2) **70.** (4) **71.** (A) → (p); (B) → (p,q); (C) → (p,r) (D) → (p,r,s)

72. (A) → (p,r); (B) → (q); (C) → (q,s) (D) → (p)

73. (A) → (p,q); (B) → (p, q,r,s); (C) → (p,q,r,s); (D) → (p,q,r,s)

74. (A) → (t); (B) → (p,q,r); (C) → (s)

75. (A) → (q,s); (B) → (p,t); (C) → (r) **76.** (a) **77.** (a) **78.** (d) **79.** (d) **80.** (c) **81.** (b) **82.** (b) **83.** (d)

85. $\left(\dfrac{6}{5}, \dfrac{-1}{10}\right), \left(-\dfrac{2}{5}, \dfrac{-13}{10}\right), \left(0, \dfrac{3}{2}\right), \left(\dfrac{-8}{5}, \dfrac{3}{10}\right)$

87. $\left(\dfrac{\pm\sum_{p=1}^{n}\dfrac{1}{\sqrt{(1+p^2)}}}{c}, \dfrac{\pm\sum_{p=1}^{n}\dfrac{p}{\sqrt{(1+p^2)}}}{c}\right)$ **94.** $2x + 3y + 22 = 0$

95. $\left(\dfrac{h + mk}{1 + m^2}, \dfrac{mh - k}{1 + m^2}\right)$ **96.** $3x + 4y - 18 = 0$ and $x - 2 = 0$

97. $(2 - \sqrt{3})$ sq units. **99.** (a) **100.** (c) **101.** (c) **102.** (c) **103.** (c) **103.** (c) **104.** (A) → (s); (B) → (p,q); (C) → (r); (D) → (p,q,s)

105. (a) **106.** (a) **107.** (c) **108.** (b) **109.** (b) **110.** (c) **111.** (b) **112.** (a) **113.** (d) **114.** (a) **115.** (6) **116.** (b) **117.** (a)

Solutions

1. Equation of line passing through (2, 0) and perpendicular to $ax + by + c = 0$

Then, required equation is

$$y - 0 = \frac{b}{a}(x - 2)$$

$$ay = bx - 2b$$

$$\Rightarrow \quad ay - bx + 2b = 0$$

2. $\because \frac{2}{1!9!} + \frac{2}{3!7!} + \frac{1}{5!5!} = \frac{2^m}{n!}$

$$\frac{1}{10!}\left\{\frac{2 \times 10!}{1!9!} + \frac{2 \times 10!}{3!7!} + \frac{10!}{5!5!}\right\} = \frac{2^m}{n!}$$

$$\Rightarrow \quad \frac{1}{10!}\{2\,{}^{10}C_1 + 2\,{}^{10}C_3 + {}^{10}C_5\} = \frac{2^m}{n!}$$

$$\frac{1}{10!}\{{}^{10}C_1 + {}^{10}C_3 + {}^{10}C_5 + {}^{10}C_7 + {}^{10}C_9\} = \frac{2^m}{n!}$$

$$\Rightarrow \quad \frac{1}{10!}(2)^{10-1} = \frac{2^m}{n!}$$

$$\therefore \quad m = 9 \text{ and } n = 10$$

Hence, $x - y + 1 = 0$ and $x + y + 3 = 0$ are perpendicular to each other, then orthocentre is the point of intersection which is $(-2, -1)$

$\therefore \quad -2 = 2m - 2n$ and $-1 = m - n$

$\therefore$ Point is $(2m - 2n, m - n)$.

3. $\therefore$ Required area

$$= 4 \times \frac{1}{2}\left(\frac{8}{3} \times 4\right) = \frac{64}{3} = \frac{2^6}{3} \quad \text{...(i)}$$

$$\because \quad f(x + y) = f(x)f(y)$$

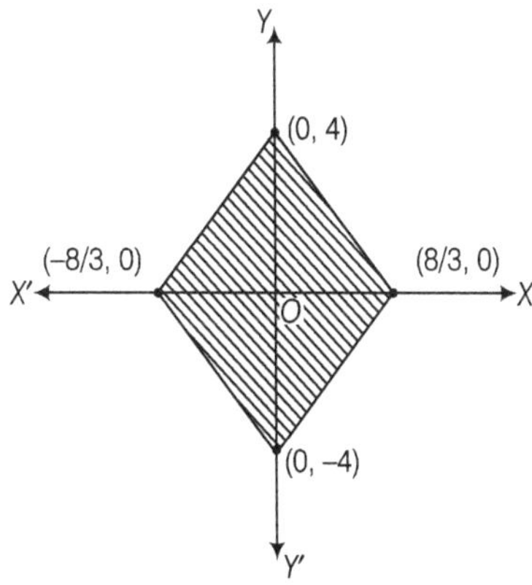

$$\therefore \quad f(2) = f(1)f(1) = 2^2$$

$$f(3) = f(1 + 2) = f(1)f(2) = 2^3$$

....

....

$$\therefore \quad f(n) = 2^n$$

$$\therefore \quad \text{Area} = \frac{2^6}{3} = \frac{f(6)}{3} \text{ sq units}$$

4. We have, $\quad y = \cos x \cos(x + 2) - \cos^2(x + 1)$

$$y = \frac{1}{2}\{2\cos x \cos(x + 2) - 2\cos^2(x + 1)\}$$

$$= \frac{1}{2}\{\cos(2x + 2) + \cos 2 - 1 - \cos(2x + 2)\}$$

$$= \frac{1}{2}(\cos 2 - 1)$$

$$= \frac{1}{2}(1 - 2\sin^2 1 - 1)$$

$$= -\sin^2 1$$

which is a straight line passing through $(\lambda, -\sin^2 1)$; $\forall \lambda \in R$ and parallel to the X-axis.

5. Let line $\frac{x}{a} + \frac{y}{b} = 1 \quad$ ...(i)

Its passes through (2, 2), then

$$\frac{2}{a} + \frac{2}{b} = 1$$

$$\Rightarrow \quad 2(a + b) = ab \quad \text{...(ii)}$$

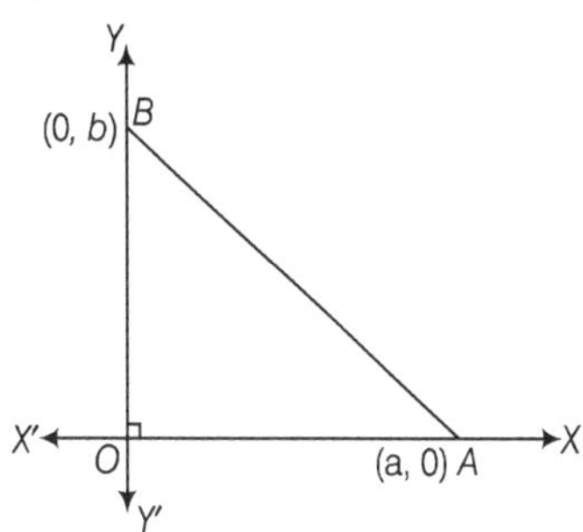

$\because$ Area of $\Delta AOB = \frac{1}{2}ab = |\lambda| \quad$ (given)

$$\therefore \quad ab = 2|\lambda|$$

from Eq. (ii), $\quad a + b = |\lambda|$

Hence, required equation is

$$x^2 - (a + b)x + ab = 0$$

$$\text{or} \quad x^2 - |\lambda|x + 2|\lambda| = 0$$

6. $\frac{\text{Value of } (a^2x + aby + 1) \text{ at } (1, 1)}{\text{Value of } (a^2x + aby + 1) \text{ at } (0, 0)} > 0$

$$\text{or} \quad \frac{a^2 + ab + 1}{1} > 0; \forall a \in R$$

$$\text{or} \quad a^2 + ab + 1 > 0; \forall a \in R$$

$$\therefore \quad D < 0$$

$$\Rightarrow \quad b^2 - 4 < 0$$

$$\Rightarrow \quad -2 < b < 2 \text{ but } b > 0$$

$$\therefore \quad 0 < b < 2$$

$$\text{i.e.} \quad b \in (0, 2)$$

7. Equation of L is $\frac{x}{a}+\frac{y}{b}=1$ and let the axis be rotated through an angle θ and let (X, Y) be the new coordinates of any point $P(x, y)$ in the plane, then
$x = X\cos\theta - Y\sin\theta$, $y = X\sin\theta + Y\cos\theta$, the equation of the line with reference to original coordinates is

$$\frac{x}{a}+\frac{y}{b}=1$$

i.e.
$$\frac{X\cos\theta - Y\sin\theta}{a}+\frac{X\sin\theta + Y\cos\theta}{b}=1 \quad \text{...(i)}$$

and with reference to new coordinates is

$$\frac{X}{p}+\frac{Y}{q}=1 \quad \text{...(ii)}$$

Comparing Eqs. (i) and (ii), we get

$$\frac{\cos\theta}{a}+\frac{\sin\theta}{b}=\frac{1}{p} \quad \text{...(iii)}$$

and
$$-\frac{\sin\theta}{a}+\frac{\cos\theta}{b}=\frac{1}{q} \quad \text{...(iv)}$$

Squaring and adding Eqs. (iii) and (iv), we get

$$\frac{1}{a^2}+\frac{1}{b^2}=\frac{1}{p^2}+\frac{1}{q^2}$$

8. $d(x, y) = \max\{|x|, |y|\}$ ...(i)

but $d(x, y) = a$ ...(ii)

From Eqs. (i) and (ii), we get

$a = \max\{|x|, |y|\}$

if $|x| > |y|$, then $a = |x|$

$\therefore$ $x = \pm a$

and if $|y| > |x|$, then $a = |y|$

$\therefore$ $y = \pm a$

Therefore locus represents a straight line.

9. $P_1 = |m^2\cos\alpha + 2m\sin\alpha + \frac{\sin^2\alpha}{\cos\alpha}|$

$$= \frac{(m\cos\alpha + \sin\alpha)^2}{|\cos\alpha|}$$

$$p_2 = \left|mm'\cos\alpha + (m+m')\sin\alpha + \frac{\sin^2\alpha}{\cos\alpha}\right|$$

$$= \frac{|(m\cos\alpha + \sin\alpha)|\,|m'\cos\alpha + \sin\alpha|}{|\cos\alpha|}$$

and
$$p_3 = |m'^2\cos\alpha + 2m'\sin\alpha + \frac{\sin^2\alpha}{\cos\alpha}|$$

$$= \frac{(m'\cos\alpha + \sin\alpha)^2}{|\cos\alpha|}$$

$\because$ $p_2^2 = p_1 p_3$

Hence, p_1, p_2, p_3 are in GP.

10. Side of the square = 2 unit

Coordinates of B, C and D are $(\sqrt{3}, 1)$, $(\sqrt{3}-1, \sqrt{3}+1)$ and $(-1, \sqrt{3})$ respectively.

Slope of $BD = \frac{\sqrt{3}-1}{-1-\sqrt{3}} = \frac{(\sqrt{3}-1)(\sqrt{3}-1)}{-2} = \sqrt{3}-2$

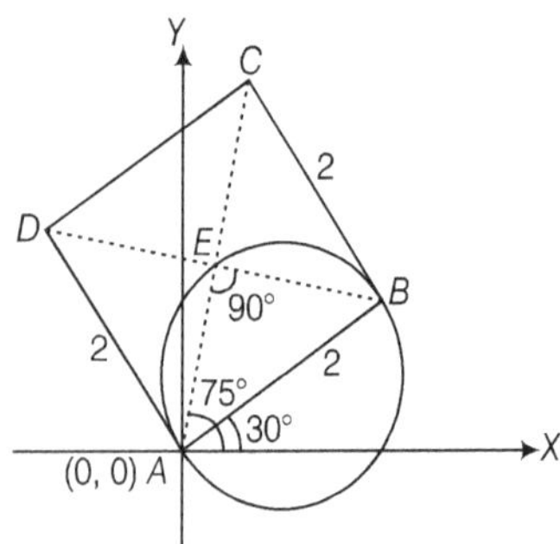

$\therefore$ Equation of BD is

$$y - 1 = (\sqrt{3}-2)(x-\sqrt{3})$$

$\Rightarrow$ $(2-\sqrt{3})x + y = 2(\sqrt{3}-1)$

and equation of the circumcircle of the triangle ABE (Apply diametric form as AB is diameter)

$$(x-0)(x-\sqrt{3}) + (y-0)(y-1) = 0$$

$\Rightarrow$ $x^2 + y^2 - x\sqrt{3} - y = 0$

11. If (α, β) be the image of $(4, 1)$ w.r.t $y = x - 1$, then $(\alpha, \beta) = (2, 3)$, say point Q

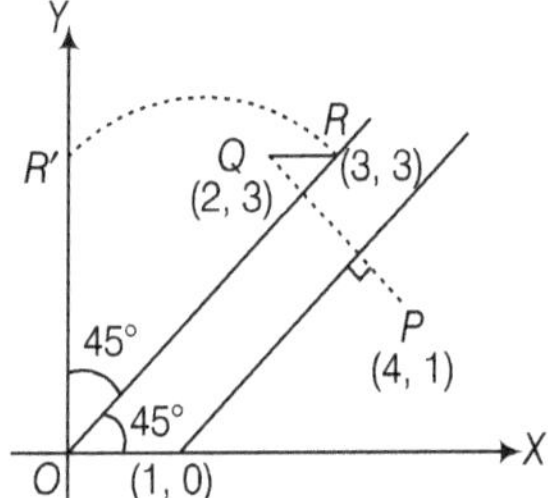

After translation through a distance 1 unit along the positive direction of X-axis at the point whose coordinate are $R \equiv (3, 3)$.
After rotation through are angle $\frac{\pi}{4}$ about the origin in the anticlockwise direction, then R goes to R' such that

$$OR = OR' = 3\sqrt{2}$$

$\therefore$ The coordinates of the final point are $(0, 3\sqrt{2})$.

12. $\because$ $A \equiv (0, 0); B \equiv (2, 0); C \equiv (2, 2); D \equiv (0, 2)$

(i) $f_1(x, y) \to (y, x)$, then

$A \equiv (0, 0); B \equiv (0, 2); C \equiv (2, 2), D \equiv (2, 0)$

(ii) $f_2(x, y) \to (x + 3y, y)$, then

$A \equiv (0, 0); B \equiv (6, 2); C \equiv (8, 2), D \equiv (2, 0)$

(iii) $f_3(x, y) \to \left(\frac{x-y}{2}, \frac{x+y}{2}\right)$, then

$A \equiv (0, 0); B \equiv (2, 4); C \equiv (3, 5), D \equiv (1, 1)$

Now, $AB = DC = 2\sqrt{5}$, $AD = BC = \sqrt{2}$

and $AC = \sqrt{34}$, $BD = \sqrt{10}$

i.e. $AC \neq BD$

$\therefore$ Final figure is a parallelogram.

13. Let $\frac{AN}{BN} = \lambda$

Then, coordinate of N are $\left(\frac{a}{1+\lambda}, \frac{a\lambda}{1+\lambda}\right)$

$\because$ Slope of $AB = -1$

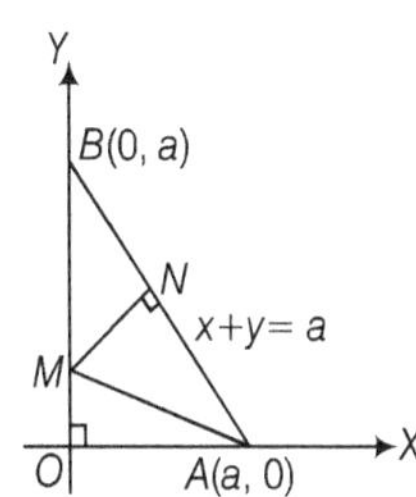

$\therefore$ Slope of $MN = 1$

$\therefore$ Equation on MN is

$$y - \frac{a\lambda}{1+\lambda} = x - \frac{a}{1+\lambda} \Rightarrow x - y = a\left(\frac{1-\lambda}{\lambda+1}\right)$$

So, the coordinates of M are $\left(0, a\left(\frac{\lambda-1}{\lambda+1}\right)\right)$

Therefore, area of $\Delta AMN = \frac{3}{8}$ area of ΔOAB

$$\Rightarrow \quad \frac{1}{2} \cdot AN \cdot MN = \frac{3}{8} \cdot \frac{1}{2} a \cdot a$$

$$\Rightarrow \quad \frac{1}{2} \cdot \left| \frac{a\lambda\sqrt{2}}{1+\lambda} \cdot \frac{a\sqrt{2}}{1+\lambda} \right| = \frac{3}{8} \cdot \frac{1}{2} a \cdot a$$

$$\Rightarrow \quad \frac{a^2\lambda}{(1+\lambda)^2} = \frac{3}{8} \cdot \frac{1}{2} a^2$$

$$\therefore \quad \lambda = 3 \text{ or } \lambda = \frac{1}{3}$$

For $\lambda = \frac{1}{3}$, then M lies outside the segment OB and hence the required value of $\lambda = 3$.

14. Let $S = (x, y)$, given $(SQ)^2 + (SR)^2 = 2(SP)^2$

$$\Rightarrow \quad (x+1)^2 + y^2 + (x-2)^2 + y^2 = 2[(x-1^2) + y^2]$$

$$\Rightarrow \quad 2x^2 + 2y^2 - 2x + 5 = 2(x^2 + y^2 - 2x + 1)$$

$$\Rightarrow \quad 2x + 3 = 0 \Rightarrow x = -\frac{3}{2}$$

A straight line parallel to Y-axis.

15. $\frac{\text{Value of}(3x - 2y + 1) \text{ at } A}{\text{Value of } (3x - 2y + 1) \text{ at } B} > 0$

$$\Rightarrow \quad \frac{(\sin\alpha - 3) - (\cos\alpha - 2) + 1}{(3 - 2 + 1)} > 0$$

$$\Rightarrow \quad \sin\alpha - \cos\alpha > 0 \Rightarrow \sin\alpha > \cos\alpha$$

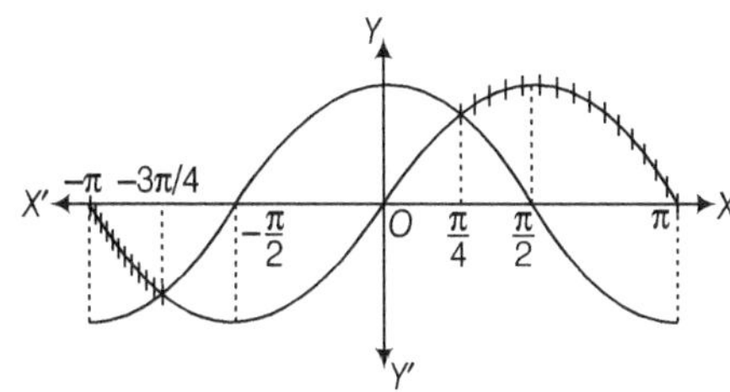

It is clear from the figure

$$\alpha \in \left(-\pi, \frac{-3\pi}{4}\right) \cup \left(\frac{\pi}{4}, \pi\right).$$

16. $\because$ Equation of AB is $x + y = 1$, then coordinates of A and B are $(1, 0)$ and $(0, 1)$ respectively.

$\therefore$ Coordinates of P are $\left(\frac{1}{2}, \frac{1}{2}\right)$

$\because$ PP_1 is perpendicular to OA

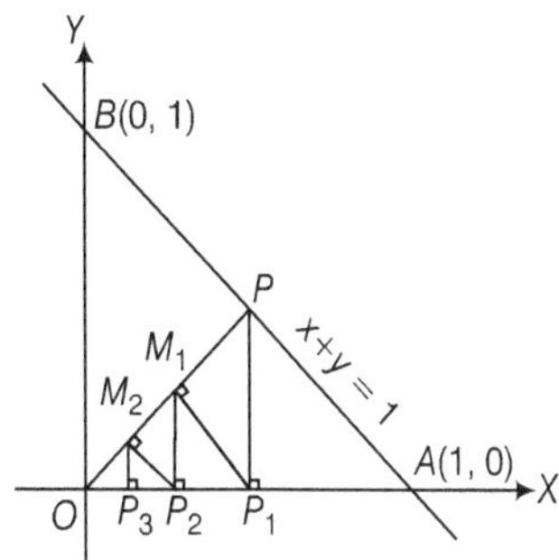

Equation of OP is $y = x$

Then, $\quad OP_1 = PP_1 = \frac{1}{2}$

We have, $\quad (OM_{n-1})^2 = (OP_n)^2 + (P_nM_{n-1})^2$

$$= 2(OP_n)^2 \quad \{\because y = x\}$$

$$= 2\alpha_n^2 \text{ (say)}$$

Also, $\quad (OP_{n-1})^2 = (OM_{n-1})^2 + (P_{n-1}M_{n-1})^2$

$$\alpha_{n-1}^2 = 2\alpha_n^2 + \frac{1}{2}\alpha_{n-1}^2$$

$$\Rightarrow \quad \frac{1}{2}\alpha_{n-1}^2 = 2\alpha_n^2$$

$$\Rightarrow \quad \alpha_n = \frac{1}{2}\alpha_{n-1}$$

$$\therefore \quad OP_n = \alpha_n = \frac{1}{2}\alpha_{n-1}$$

$$= \frac{1}{2^2}\alpha_{n-2} = \frac{1}{2^3}\alpha_{n-3}$$

....

....

....

$$= \frac{1}{2^{n-1}}\alpha_1$$

$$= \frac{1}{2^{n-1}}\left(\frac{1}{2}\right) = \frac{1}{2^n}.$$

17. Let $O \equiv (0, 0)$, $A \equiv (1, 1)$ and $B \equiv (9, 1)$

Area of $\Delta OAB = \frac{1}{2} \times 8 \times 1 = 4$

It is clear that $1 < c < 9$

and $\quad M \equiv (c, 1)$ and $N \equiv \left(c, \frac{c}{9}\right)$

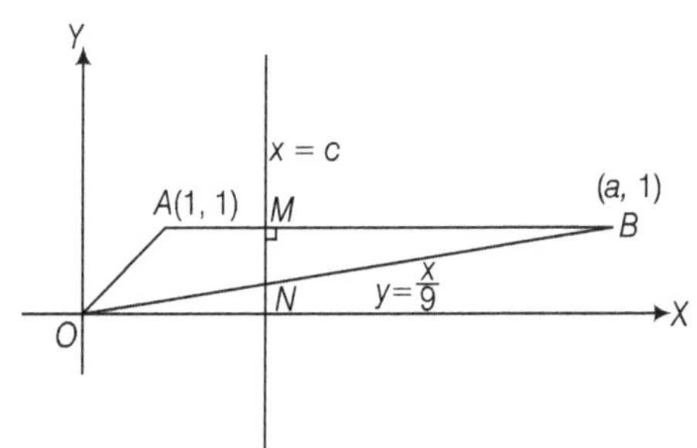

$\therefore$ Area of $\Delta BMN = 2$ (given)

$$\rightarrow \quad \frac{1}{2}\times(9-c)\times\left(1-\frac{c}{9}\right)=2$$

or $(9-c)^2 = 36$

or $9 - c = \pm 6 \Rightarrow c = 3$ or 15

but $1 < c < 9$

$\therefore$ $c = 3$

18. The three lines are concurrent if

$$\begin{vmatrix} 1 & 2 & -9 \\ 3 & -5 & -5 \\ a & b & -1 \end{vmatrix} = 0$$

or $5a + 2b = 1$

which is three of the line $5x + 2y = 1$ passes through (a, b).

19. $\because BC = AC$

$$\Rightarrow \quad 2^2 + (\lambda - 1)^2 = \lambda^2$$

$$\Rightarrow \quad 4 = \lambda^2 - (\lambda - 1)^2$$

$$= (2\lambda - 1)(1)$$

$$\therefore \quad \lambda = \frac{5}{2}$$

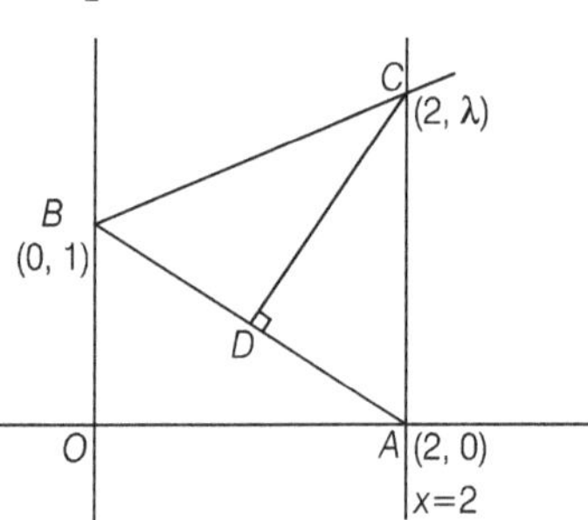

$\because$ Equation. of AB is $\frac{x}{2}+\frac{y}{1}=1$, $D\equiv\left(1,\frac{1}{2}\right)$ (mid-point of AB)

$\therefore$ Equation of CD is $2x - y = \mu$

$\because CD$ pass through D, thus

$$2-\frac{1}{2}=\mu \text{ or } \mu=\frac{3}{2}$$

$\therefore$ Equation of CD is $\quad 2x - y = \frac{3}{2}$ ...(i)

and Eq. (i) of line $\perp$ to AC and pass through B is $y = 1$ ...(ii)

from Eqs. (i) and (ii), we get

Orthocentre $\equiv\left(\frac{5}{4}, 1\right)$

20. Let $A \equiv (3, 4)$, $B \equiv (0, y)$, $C \equiv (x, 0)$, $D \equiv (8, 2)$

$\therefore$ Slope of AB = – Slope of BC

$$\Rightarrow \quad \frac{y-4}{0-3} = -\left(\frac{0-y}{x-0}\right)$$

or $4x - xy = 3y$ ...(i)

and slope of BC = – slope of CD

$$\Rightarrow \quad \left(\frac{0-y}{x-0}\right) = -\left(\frac{2-0}{8-x}\right)$$

or $2x + xy = 8y$ ...(ii)

adding Eqs. (i) and (ii), we get

$6x = 11y$ ...(iii)

from Eqs. (ii) and (iii), we get

$$x = \frac{13}{3} = 4\frac{1}{3}$$

21.

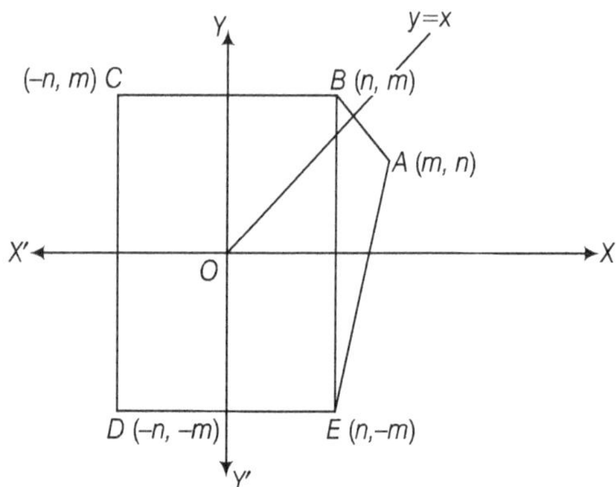

Area of rectangle $BCDE = (2n)(2m)$

$= 4mn$

and area of $\Delta ABE = \frac{1}{2}\times 2m \times (m-n)$

$= m(m-n)$

$\therefore$ Area of pentagon $= 4mn + m(m-n)$

$= m(m+3n)$

22. The equation of the line L, be $y - 2 = m(x - 8)$, $m < 0$

coordinates of P and Q are $P\left(8-\frac{2}{m}, 0\right)$ and $Q(0, 2-8m)$.

So, $\quad OP + OQ = 8 - \frac{2}{m} + 2 - 8m$

$$= 10 + \frac{2}{(-m)} + 8(-m) \geq$$

$$10 + 2\sqrt{\frac{2}{(-m)}\times 8(-m)} \geq 18$$

So, absolute minimum value of $OP + OQ = 18$

23. Let the two perpendiculars through the origin intersect $2x + y = a$ at A and B so that the triangle OAB is isosceles.

OM = length of perpendicular from O to

AB, $OM = \frac{a}{\sqrt{5}}$.

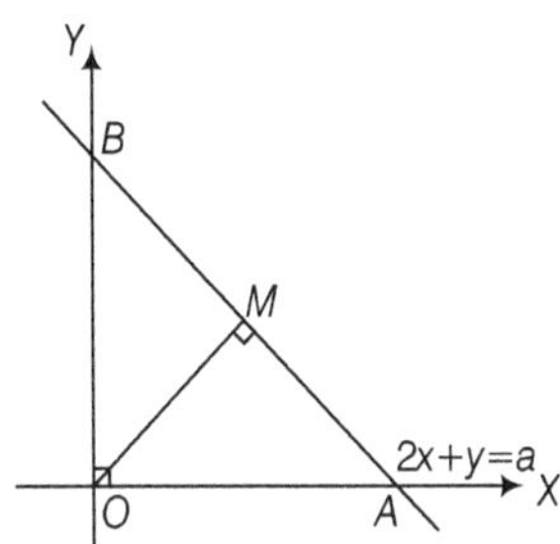

Also, $AM = MB = OM$

$\Rightarrow \quad AB = \dfrac{2a}{\sqrt{5}}$

Area of $\Delta OAB = \dfrac{1}{2} \cdot AB \cdot OM$

$$= \frac{1}{2} \cdot \frac{2a}{\sqrt{5}} \cdot \frac{a}{\sqrt{5}} = \frac{a^2}{5} \text{ sq units}$$

24. Solving given equations, we get

$$x = \frac{5}{3 + 4m}$$

x is an integer, if $3 + 4m = 1, -1, 5, -5$

or $\quad m = \dfrac{-2}{4}, \dfrac{-4}{4}, \dfrac{2}{4}, \dfrac{-8}{4}$

or $\quad m = -\dfrac{1}{2}, -1, \dfrac{1}{2}, -2$

Hence, m has two integral values.

25. Let the coordinates of A be $(a, 0)$. Then the slope of the reflected ray is

$$\frac{3 - 0}{5 - a} = \tan\theta \quad \text{(say) ...(i)}$$

Then the slope of the incident ray

$$= \frac{2 - 0}{1 - a} = \tan(\pi - \theta)$$

From Eqs. (i) and (ii), we get

$$\tan\theta + \tan(\pi - \theta) = 0$$

$\Rightarrow \quad \dfrac{3}{5 - a} + \dfrac{2}{1 - a} = 0$

$\Rightarrow \quad 3 - 3a + 10 - 2a = 0$

$$a = \frac{13}{5}$$

Thus, the coordinate of A is $\left(\dfrac{13}{5}, 0\right)$

26. Lines $5x + 3y - 2 + \lambda(3x - y - 4) = 0$ are concurrent at $(1, -1)$ and lines

$x - y + 1 + \mu(2x - y - 2) = 0$ are concurrent at $(3, 4)$.

Thus equation of line common to both family is

$$y + 1 = \frac{4 + 1}{3 - 1}(x - 1)$$

or $\quad 5x - 2y - 7 = 0$

$\therefore \quad a = 5, b = -2 \Rightarrow a + b = 3$

27. $\because B$ is the reflection of $A(5, 7)$ w.r.t the line $x + y = 0$

$\therefore \quad B \equiv (-7, -5)$

and C is the reflection of $A(5, 7)$ w.r.t the line $x - y = 0$

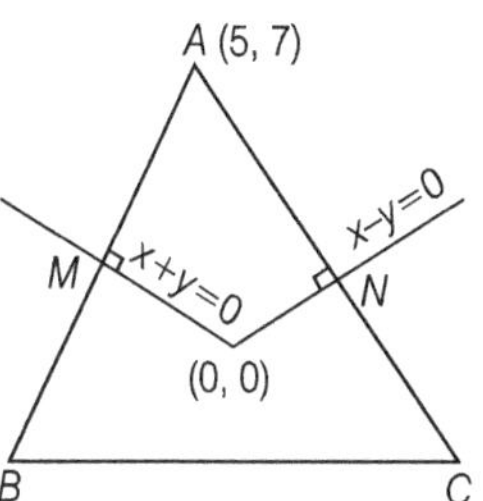

$\therefore \quad C \equiv (7, 5)$

$\therefore \quad$ Equation of BC is $y + 5 = \dfrac{5 + 5}{7 + 7}(x + 7)$ or $7y = 5x$

28. Let $P \equiv (2, -1)$

$P(2, -1)$ goes 2 units along $x + y = 1$ upto A and 5 units along $x - 2y = 4$ upto B.

Now, $\quad$ slope of $x + y = -1$ is $-1 = \tan\theta \quad$ (say)

$\therefore \quad \theta = 135°$

and $\quad$ slope $x - 2y = 4$ is $\dfrac{1}{2} = \tan\phi \quad$ (say)

$\therefore \quad \sin\phi = \dfrac{1}{\sqrt{5}}, \cos\phi = \dfrac{2}{\sqrt{5}}$

The coordinates of A

i.e. $\quad (2 + 2\cos 135°, -1 + 2\sin 135°)$

or $\quad (2 - \sqrt{2}, \sqrt{2} - 1)$

The coordinates of B

i.e. $(2 + 5\cos\phi, -1 + 5\sin\phi)$ or $(2 + 2\sqrt{5}, \sqrt{5} - 1)$

29. $\because \quad P \equiv (5, 3)$

Let P' and P'' be the images of P w.r.t $y = x$ and $y = 0$ (X-axis) respectively, then $P' \equiv (3, 5)$ and $P'' \equiv (5, -3)$

$\because \quad PQ + QR + RP$ is minimum

$\therefore \quad P', R, Q, P''$ are collinear.

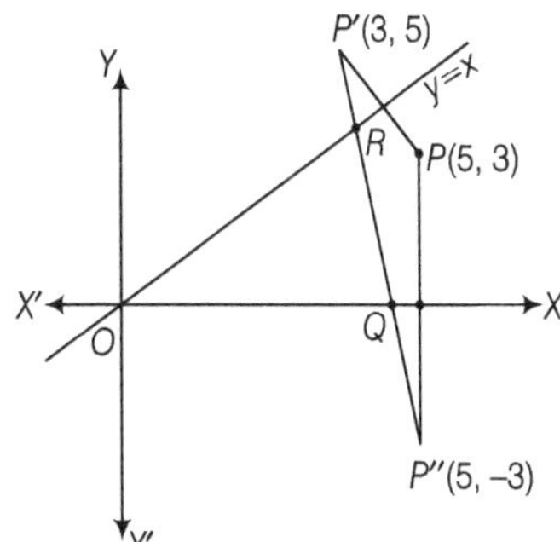

$\therefore \quad$ Equation of $P'P''$ is

$$y + 3 = \left(\frac{5 + 3}{3 - 5}\right)(x - 5)$$

or $\quad 4x + y = 17$

$\therefore \quad Q \equiv \left(\dfrac{17}{4}, 0\right) \quad (\because Q \text{ on } Y\text{-axis})$

30. Equation of incident ray is

$$y - 0 = \tan(90° + 60°)(x - 2)$$

or $$y = -\frac{1}{\sqrt{3}}(x - 2)$$

or $$(x - 2) + y\sqrt{3} = 0$$

and equation of refracted ray is

$$y - 0 = -\tan 60°(x - 2)$$

or $$y = -\sqrt{3}(x - 2)$$

or $$(x - 2) + \frac{y}{\sqrt{3}} = 0$$

$\therefore$ Combined equation is

$$[(x - 2) + y\sqrt{3}]\left((x - 2) + \frac{y}{\sqrt{3}}\right) = 0$$

i.e. $$(x - 2)^2 + y^2 + \frac{4}{\sqrt{3}}(x - 2)y = 0$$

31. Point of intersection of $\frac{x}{a} + \frac{y}{b} = 1$ and $\frac{x}{b} + \frac{y}{a} = 1$ is $P\left(\frac{ab}{a + b}, \frac{ab}{a + b}\right)$, this point P satisfies alternates (a), (b), (c) and (d).

32. The two lines will be identical if their exists some real number k such that

$b^3 - c^3 = k(b - c)$, $c^3 - a^3 = k(c - a)$ and $a^3 - b^3 = k(a - b)$

$\Rightarrow$ $b - c = 0$ or $b^2 + c^2 + bc = k$

$c - a = 0$ or $c^2 + a^2 + ca = k$

and $a - b = 0$ or $a^2 + b^2 + ab = k$

$\Rightarrow$ $a = b$ or $b = c$ or $c = a$

or $b^2 + c^2 + bc = c^2 + a^2 + ca$

$\Rightarrow$ $b = c$ or $c = a$

or $a = b$ or $a + b + c = 0$

33. As the third vertex lies on the line $y = x + 3$, its coordinates are of the form $(x, x + 3)$. The area of the triangle with vertices $(2, 1)$, $(3, -2)$ and $(x, x + 3)$ is given by

$$\frac{1}{2}\left|\begin{vmatrix} x & x+3 & 1 \\ 2 & 1 & 1 \\ 3 & -2 & 1 \end{vmatrix}\right| = |2x - 2| = 5 \quad \text{(given)}$$

$\therefore$ $$2x - 2 = \pm 5 \Rightarrow x = \frac{-3}{2}, \frac{7}{2}$$

Thus, the coordinates of the third vertex are $\left(\frac{7}{2}, \frac{13}{2}\right)$ or $\left(\frac{-3}{2}, \frac{3}{2}\right)$.

34. $$\begin{vmatrix} 1 & -2 & -6 \\ 3 & 1 & -4 \\ \lambda & 4 & \lambda^2 \end{vmatrix} = 0$$

$\Rightarrow$ $$\lambda^2 + 2\lambda - 8 = 0$$

$\therefore$ $$(\lambda + 4)(\lambda - 2) = 0$$

$\Rightarrow$ $$\lambda = -4, 2$$

35. Equation of any line through the point of intersection of the given lines is $(3x + y - 5) + \lambda(x - y + 1) = 0$.

Since this line is perpendicular to one of the given lines

$$\frac{3 + \lambda}{\lambda - 1} = -1 \text{ or } \frac{1}{3}$$

$\Rightarrow \lambda = -1$ or -5, therefore the required straight line is

$$x + y - 3 = 0$$

or $$x - 3y + 5 = 0$$

36. If B lies on Y-axis, then coordinates of B are $(0, a)$ or $(0, -a)$

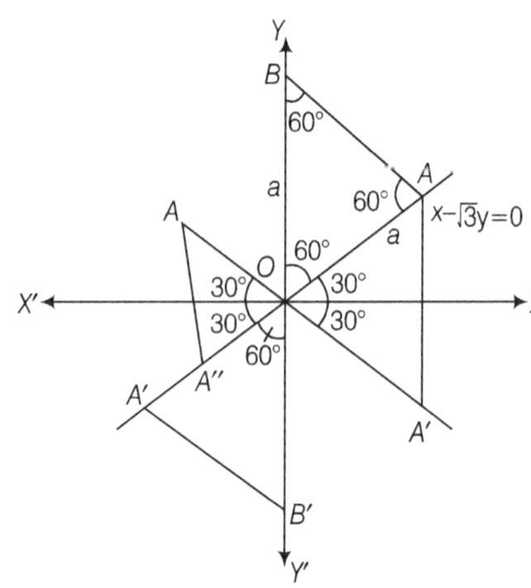

If third vertex in IV quadrant or in II quadrant, then its coordinates are $(a\cos 30°, -a\sin 30°)$ and $(-a\cos 30°, a\sin 30°)$

i.e. $$\left(\frac{a\sqrt{3}}{2}, -\frac{a}{2}\right) \text{ and } \left(-\frac{a\sqrt{3}}{2}, \frac{a}{2}\right),$$

37. Since, $ax + by + c = 0$, $bx + cy + a = 0$ and $cx + ay + b = 0$ are concurrent

$\therefore$ $$\begin{vmatrix} a & b & c \\ b & c & a \\ c & a & b \end{vmatrix} = 0$$

$\Rightarrow$ $$3abc - a^3 - b^3 - c^3 = 0$$

$\Rightarrow$ $$-(a + b + c)(a^2 + b^2 + c^2 - ab - bc - ca) = 0$$

$$a + b + c \neq 0$$

$\therefore$ $$a^2 + b^2 + c^2 - ab - bc - ca = 0$$

$$\frac{1}{2}\{(a - b)^2 + (b - c)^2 + (c - a)^2\} = 0$$

As a, b, c are real numbers

$\therefore$ $$b - c = 0, c - a = 0, a - b = 0$$

$\Rightarrow$ $$a = b = c$$

38. $\because$ $E \equiv (4, 4)$

$\therefore z_C = 7 + 5i$, $z_E = 4 + 4i$

Now, (in ΔBEC)

$$\frac{z_B - z_E}{z_C - z_E} = e^{i\frac{\pi}{2}} = i$$

$\Rightarrow$ $$z_B - 4 - 4i = i(7 + 5i - 4 - 4i)$$

or $$z_B = 3 + 7i$$

$\therefore \quad B \equiv (3, 7)$, then $D \equiv (5, 1)$

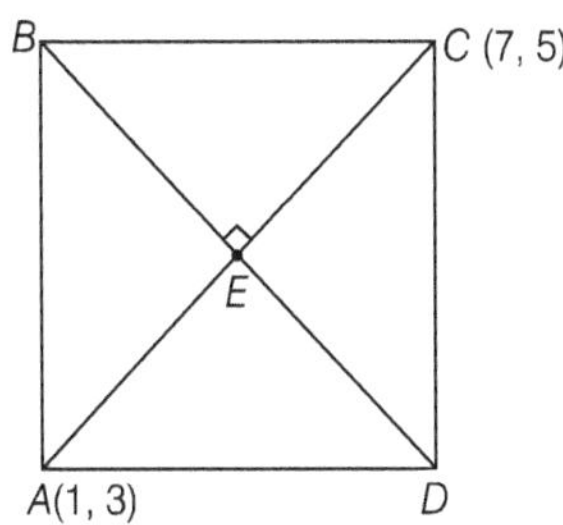

Equation of AB is

$$y - 3 = \frac{7-3}{3-1}(x-1) \text{ or } 2x - y + 1 = 0$$

and equation of AD is

$$y - 3 = \frac{1-3}{5-1}(x-1) \text{ or } x + 2y - 7 = 0$$

39. Given,

$$6a^2 - 3b^2 - c^2 + 7ab - ac + 4bc = 0$$

$$\Rightarrow 6a^2 + (7b - c)a - (3b^2 - 4bc + c^2) = 0$$

$$\Rightarrow a = \frac{-(7b-c) \pm \sqrt{(7b-c)^2 + 24(3b^2 - 4bc + c^2)}}{12}$$

$$\Rightarrow \quad 12a + 7b - c = \pm(11b - 5c)$$

$$\Rightarrow \quad 12a - 4b + 4c = 0$$

or $\quad 12a + 18b - 6c = 0$

$$\Rightarrow \quad 3a - b + c = 0$$

or $\quad -2a - 3b + c = 0$

Hence $(3, -1)$ or $(-2, -3)$ lies on the line $ax + by + c = 0$,

40. $x + 2y + 4 = 0$ and $4x + 2y - 1 = 0$

$$\Rightarrow \quad x + 2y + 4 = 0$$

and $\quad -4x - 2y + 1 = 0$

Here, $\quad (1)(-4) + (2)(-2) = -8 < 0$

$\therefore$Bisector of the angle including the acute angle bisectors and origin is

$$\frac{x + 2y + 4}{\sqrt{5}} = \frac{(-4x - 2y + 1)}{2\sqrt{5}}$$

$$\Rightarrow \quad 6x + 6y + 7 = 0$$

41. Let position of bunglow is $P(x_1, y_1)$, then $PM = 100$ and $PN = 100$

$$\therefore \quad \frac{x_1 + y_1 - 8}{\sqrt{2}} = \pm 100$$

and $\quad \dfrac{x_1 - y_1 + 6}{\sqrt{2}} = \pm 100$

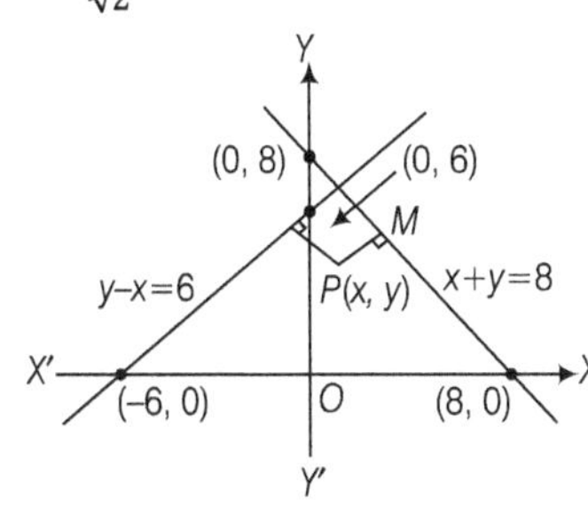

After solving, we get

$$x_1 = 1 \pm 100\sqrt{2}, 1$$

and $\quad y_1 = 7, 7 \pm 100\sqrt{2}$

Hence, $\quad (1 + 100\sqrt{2}, 7), (1 - 100\sqrt{2}, 7),$
$(1, 7 + 100\sqrt{2}), (1, 7 - 100\sqrt{2})$

42. Equation of the other diagonal is $x + y = \lambda$ which pass through (a, b), then

$$a + b = \lambda$$

$\therefore$ Equation of other diagonal is

$$x + y = a + b$$

i.e. then centre of the square is the point of intersection of $x - y = a$ and $x + y = a + b$ is $\left(a + \frac{b}{2}, \frac{b}{2}\right)$, then vertex

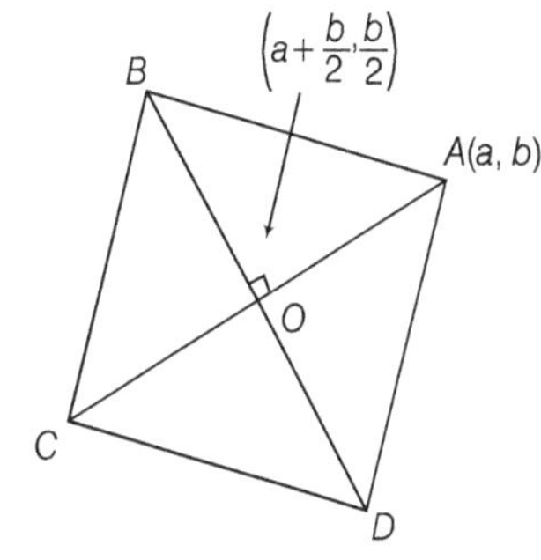

$$C \equiv (2a + b - a, b - b)$$

$\therefore \quad C \equiv (a + b, 0)$

If $\quad B \equiv z$

Then, $$\frac{z - \left(a + \frac{b}{2} + \frac{ib}{2}\right)}{(a + ib) - \left(a + \frac{b}{2} + \frac{ib}{2}\right)} = \frac{BO}{AO} e^{i\frac{\pi}{2}} = i \quad (\because BO = AO)$$

$$\Rightarrow \quad z - \left(a + \frac{b}{2} + \frac{ib}{2}\right) = i\left(-\frac{b}{2} + \frac{ib}{2}\right) = -\frac{ib}{2} - \frac{b}{2}$$

$\therefore \quad z = a$

$\therefore \quad B \equiv (a, 0)$

then, $\quad D \equiv (a + b, b)$

Hence, other vertices are $(a + b, 0), (a, 0)$ and $(a + b, b)$.

43. $(y - y_1) - m(x - x_1) = 0$ is family of lines

$\therefore \quad y - y_1 = 0, x - x_1 = 0$

Then, $\quad y = y_1$ and $x = x_1$

44. Given lines $L_1 = 0$ and $L_2 = 0$ are perpendicular and given bisectors are $\lambda_1 L_1 - \lambda_2 L_2 = 0$ and $\lambda_1 L_1 + \lambda_2 L_2 = 0$

$\therefore$bisectors are perpendicular to each other.

Hence, bisectors of $\lambda_1 L_1 - \lambda_2 L_2 = 0$ and $\lambda_1 L_1 + \lambda_2 L_2 = 0$ are $L_1 = 0$ and $L_2 = 0$.

45. $\therefore$ One bisector makes an angle $\left(\frac{\theta + \phi}{2}\right)$ with X-axis, then other bisector makes an angle $90° + \left(\frac{\theta + \phi}{2}\right)$ with X-axis.

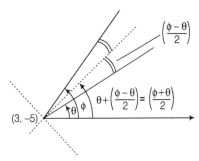

$\therefore$ Equations of bisectors are

$$\frac{x-3}{\cos\left(\frac{\theta+\phi}{2}\right)}=\frac{y+5}{\sin\left(\frac{\theta+\phi}{2}\right)} \quad \text{...(i)}$$

and
$$\frac{x-3}{\cos\left(\frac{\pi}{2}+\frac{\theta+\phi}{2}\right)}=\frac{y+5}{\sin\left(\frac{\pi}{2}+\frac{\theta+\phi}{2}\right)}$$

$$\Rightarrow \quad \frac{x-3}{-\sin\left(\frac{\theta+\phi}{2}\right)}=\frac{y+5}{\cos\left(\frac{\theta+\phi}{2}\right)} \quad \text{...(ii)}$$

But given bisector are $\frac{x-3}{\cos\alpha}=\frac{y+5}{\sin\alpha}$

$$\therefore \quad \alpha=\frac{\theta+\phi}{2} \text{ and } \frac{x-3}{\beta}=\frac{y+5}{\gamma} \quad \text{[from Eq. (i)]...(iii)}$$

$$\therefore \quad \beta=-\sin\left(\frac{\theta+\phi}{2}\right)=-\sin\alpha \quad \text{[from Eq. (ii)]}$$

and
$$\gamma=\cos\left(\frac{\theta+\phi}{2}\right)=\cos\alpha$$

46. $\because OR = AR$

$\Rightarrow \quad |x-0|+|y-0|=|x-1|+|y-2|$

$\Rightarrow \quad |x|+|y|=|x-1|+|y-2|$

$\because \quad 0 \le x < 1$ and $0 \le y < 2$

$\therefore \quad x+y=-(x-1)-(y-2)$

$\Rightarrow \quad 2x+2y=3$

47. $OS = BS$

$\Rightarrow |x-0|+|y-0|=|x-2|+|y-3|$

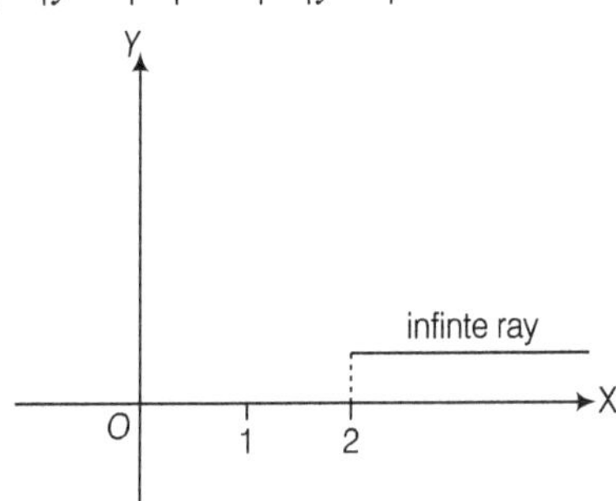

$\Rightarrow |x|+|y|=|x-2|+|y-3|$

$\because \quad x \ge 2$ and $0 \le y < 3$

$\therefore \quad x+y=x-2+3-y$

$\Rightarrow \quad 2y=1$

$\therefore \quad y=\frac{1}{2}$

48. $\because OT = CT$

$\Rightarrow \quad |x-0|+|y-0|=|x-4|+|y-3|$

$\because \quad x \ge 0, y \ge 0$

$\Rightarrow \quad x+y=|x-4|+|y-3|$

Case I : If $0 \le x \le 4$ and $0 \le y \le 3$

$x+y=4-x+3-y$

$\Rightarrow \quad x+y=\frac{7}{2}$

Case II : If $0 \le x \le 4$ and $y \ge 3$

$x+y=4-x+y-3$

$\Rightarrow \quad x=\frac{1}{2}$

Case III : If $x \ge 4$ and $0 \le y \le 3$

$x+y=x-4+3-y$

$y=-1/2$ (impossible)

Case IV : If $x \ge 4$ and $y \ge 3$

$x+y=x-4+y-3$

$\Rightarrow \quad 0=-7$ (impossible)

Combining all cases, we get

$x+y=\frac{7}{2}, \forall\ 0 \le x \le 4$ and $0 \le y \le 3$

and $\quad x=\frac{1}{2}, \forall\ 0 \le x \le 4$ and $y \ge 3$

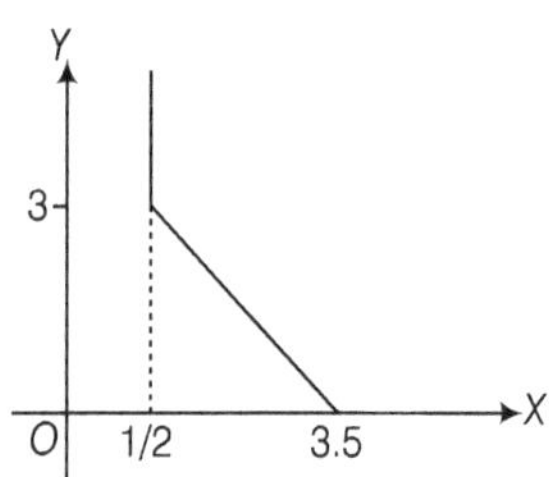

Sol. (Q. Nos. 49 to 51)

$AB : 2x-y+4=0,$

$BC : x-2y-1=0$

and $\quad CA : x+3y-3=0$

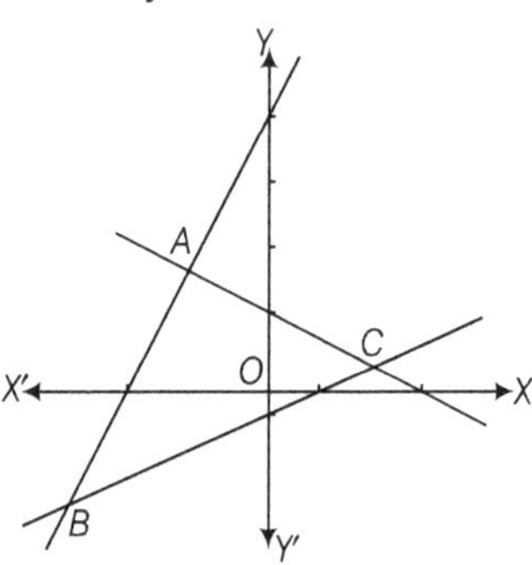

$\therefore \quad m_{AB}=m_1=2$

$m_{BC}=m_2=\frac{1}{2}$

and $\quad m_{CA}=m_3=-\frac{1}{3}$

$\because \quad m_1 > m_2 > m_3$

49. $\because \angle A$ is obtuse

$$\therefore \quad \tan A = \frac{m_3 - m_1}{1 + m_3 m_1}$$

$$= \frac{-\frac{1}{3} - 2}{1 - \frac{2}{3}} = -7$$

50. For external bisector of B

$$AB : 2x - y + 4 = 0$$

$$BC : -x + 2y + 1 = 0$$

$\because \quad (2)(-1) + (-1)(2) = -4 < 0$

$\therefore$ External bisector of B is

$$\left(\frac{2x - y + 4}{\sqrt{5}}\right) = -\frac{(-x + 2y + 1)}{\sqrt{5}}$$

or $\quad x + y + 5 = 0$

51. Let (α, β) be the image of $B(-3, -2)$ w.r.t. the line $x + 3y - 3 = 0$, then

$$\frac{\alpha + 3}{1} = \frac{\beta + 2}{3} = \frac{-2(-3 - 6 - 3)}{1 + 9}$$

or $\quad \dfrac{\alpha + 3}{1} = \dfrac{\beta + 2}{3} = \dfrac{12}{5}$

or $\quad \alpha = -\dfrac{3}{5}$ and $\beta = \dfrac{26}{5}$

$\therefore$ Required image is $\left(-\dfrac{3}{5}, \dfrac{26}{5}\right)$,

Sol. (Q. Nos. 52 to 54)

Let $\quad B \equiv (\lambda, 2 - \lambda) \quad (\because B$ lies on $x + y = 2)$

Slope of line $AB = m_1 = \dfrac{1 + \lambda}{1 - \lambda}$

and Slope of line $BC = m_2 = \dfrac{5\lambda - 12}{-5\lambda - 2}$

$$= \frac{12 - 5\lambda}{2 + 5\lambda}$$

Let slope of bisector $(x + y = 2) = m_3 = -1$

Now, $\quad \dfrac{m_3 - m_1}{1 + m_3 m_1} = \dfrac{m_2 - m_3}{1 + m_2 m_3}$

$$\Rightarrow \quad \frac{-1 - \frac{1 + \lambda}{1 - \lambda}}{1 - \frac{1 + \lambda}{1 - \lambda}} = \frac{\frac{12 - 5\lambda}{2 + 5\lambda} + 1}{1 - \frac{12 - 5\lambda}{2 + 5\lambda}}$$

or $\quad \dfrac{-2}{-2\lambda} = \dfrac{14}{-10 + 10\lambda}$

or $\quad 14\lambda = -10 + 10\lambda$

$\therefore \quad \lambda = \dfrac{-5}{2} \quad$ ...(i)

52. Equation of BC is

$$y - (2 - \lambda) = \frac{-\frac{2}{5} - (2 - \lambda)}{-\frac{2}{5} - \lambda}(x - \lambda)$$

or $\quad y - 2 - \dfrac{5}{2} = \dfrac{-\frac{2}{5} - \frac{9}{2}}{-\frac{2}{5} + \frac{5}{2}}\left(x + \dfrac{5}{2}\right)$

or $\quad 7x + 3y + 4 = 0$

53. Coordinates of vertex B are $(\lambda, 2 - \lambda)$

i.e. $\quad \left(-\dfrac{5}{2}, \dfrac{9}{2}\right) \quad$ [from Eq. (i)]

54. $A \equiv (1, 3)$ and $B \equiv \left(-\dfrac{5}{2}, \dfrac{9}{2}\right)$

$\therefore$ Equation of AB is

$$y - 3 = \frac{\frac{9}{2} - 3}{-\frac{5}{2} - 1}(x - 1)$$

or $\quad 3x + 7y = 24$

55. Any point on the line $3x - y = 2$ is $(t, 3t - 2)$, t being parameter. If (x, y) be image of the point $(t, 3t - 2)$ in the line $y = x - 1$ or $x - y - 1 = 0$, then

$$\frac{x - t}{1} = \frac{y - (3t - 2)}{-1}$$

$$= -\frac{2(t - 3t + 2 - 1)}{1 + 1}$$

$\Rightarrow \quad \dfrac{x - t}{1} = \dfrac{y - 3t + 2}{-1} = 2t - 1$

or $\quad x - t = 2t - 1$

$\Rightarrow \quad x + 1 = 3t \quad$ ...(i)

and $\quad y - 3t + 2 = -2t + 1$

$\Rightarrow \quad y + 1 = t \quad$ ...(ii)

From Eqs. (i) and (ii), we get

$$x + 1 = 3(y + 1)$$

$\Rightarrow \quad x - 3y = 2$

56. Any point on the circle $x^2 + y^2 = 4$ is $(2\cos\theta, 2\sin\theta)$, θ being parameter.

If (x, y) be image of the point $(2\cos\theta, 2\sin\theta)$, in the line $x + y = 2$, then

$$\frac{x - 2\cos\theta}{1} = \frac{y - 2\sin\theta}{1}$$

$$= \frac{-2(2\cos\theta + 2\sin\theta - 2)}{1 + 1}$$

or $\quad x - 2\cos\theta = y - 2\sin\theta$

$= -2\cos\theta - 2\sin\theta + 2 \quad$ ...(i)

or $\quad x - 2\cos\theta = -2\cos\theta - 2\sin\theta + 2$

$\Rightarrow \quad x - 2 = -2\sin\theta$

and $\quad y - 2\sin\theta = -2\cos\theta - 2\sin\theta + 2$

$\Rightarrow \quad y - 2 = -2\cos\theta \quad$ ...(ii)

From Eqs. (i) and (ii),

$$(x - 2)^2 + (y - 2)^2 = 4$$

$\Rightarrow \quad x^2 + y^2 - 4x - 4y + 4 = 0$

57. Any point on the parabola $x^2 = 4y$ is $(2t, t^2)$, t being parameter. If (x, y) be image of the point $(2t, t^2)$ in the $x + y = a$, then

$$\frac{x-2t}{1} = \frac{y-t^2}{1} = \frac{-2(2t+t^2-a)}{1+1} = -2t - t^2 + a$$

or $\quad x - 2t = -2t - t^2 + a$

$\Rightarrow \quad x - a = -t^2 \qquad \text{...(i)}$

and $\quad y - t^2 = -2t - t^2 + a$

$\Rightarrow \quad y - a = -2t \qquad \text{...(ii)}$

From Eqs. (i) and (ii) we get

$$(y-a)^2 = 4t^2 = -4(x-a)$$

or $\quad (y-a)^2 = 4(a-x)$

Sol. (Q. Nos. 58 to 60)

Given orthocentre $O \equiv (1, 2)$

and circumcentre

$$O' = (2, 4)$$

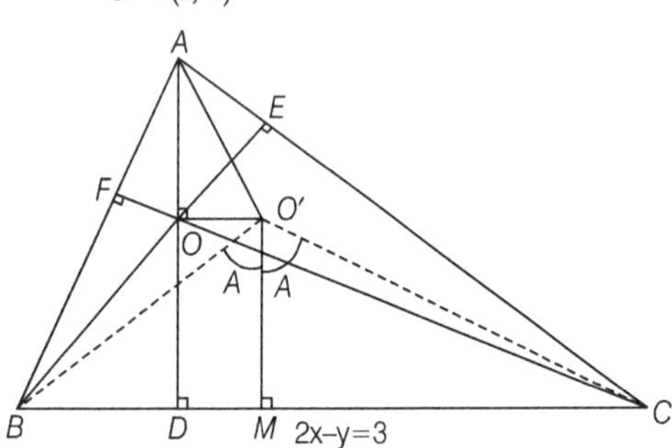

$\because$ Slope of OO' = Slope of $(2x - y = 3)$

and $\quad OD = O'M = \frac{3}{\sqrt{5}}$

Let R be the circumradius

$\therefore \quad O'M = R\cos A$

$\Rightarrow \quad R\cos A = \frac{3}{\sqrt{5}} \qquad \text{...(i)}$

58. $R = AO' = \sqrt{(AO)^2 + (OO')^2}$

$$= \sqrt{(2R\cos A)^2 + 5}$$

$$= \sqrt{\left(\frac{6}{\sqrt{5}}\right)^2 + 5} \qquad \text{[from Eq. (i)]}$$

$$= \sqrt{\frac{61}{5}}$$

59. $\because OD = 2R\cos B\cos C$

$\therefore \quad 2R\cos B\cos C = \frac{3}{\sqrt{5}}$

$$= R\cos A \qquad \text{[from Eq. (i)] ...(ii)}$$

$\Rightarrow \quad \cos A = 2\cos B\cos C$

$\Rightarrow \quad -\cos(B+C) = 2\cos B\cos C \qquad (\because A + B + C = \pi)$

$\Rightarrow \quad -(\cos B\cos C - \sin B\sin C) = 2\cos B\cos C$

or $\quad \sin B\sin C = 3\cos B\cos C$

$$= 3 \times \frac{3}{2R\sqrt{5}}$$

$$= \frac{9}{2\sqrt{61}} \qquad \left(\because R = \sqrt{\frac{61}{5}}\right)$$

60. $\because AO = 2R\cos A$

$$= 2 \times \frac{3}{\sqrt{5}} \qquad \text{[from Eq. (i)]}$$

$$= \frac{6}{\sqrt{5}}$$

61. The equation of straight line through (2, 3) with slope m is

$$y - 3 = m(x-2)$$

or $\quad mx - y = 2m - 3$

or $\quad \dfrac{x}{\left(\dfrac{2m-3}{m}\right)} + \dfrac{y}{(3-2m)} = 1$

Here, $\quad OA = \dfrac{2m-3}{m}$ or $OB = 3 - 2m$

$\because$ The area of $\Delta OAB = 12$

$\Rightarrow \quad \left|\frac{1}{2} \times OA \times OB\right| = 12$

or $\quad \frac{1}{2}\left(\frac{2m-3}{m}\right)(3-2m) = \pm 12$

or $\quad (2m-3)^2 = \pm 24m$

Taking positive sign, we get $4m^2 - 36m + 9 = 0$

Here $D > 0$, This is a quadratic in m which given two value of m, and taking negative sign, we get $(2m+3)^2 = 0$.

This gives one line of m as $\frac{-3}{2}$.

Hence, three straight lines are possible.

62. $\because$ Point of intersection of $ax + 3y - 1 = 0$ and $ax + y + 1 = 0$ is $A\left(-\frac{2}{a}, 1\right)$ and point of intersection of $ax + 3y - 1 = 0$ and $x + 3y = 0$ is $B\left(\frac{1}{a-1}, -\frac{1}{3(a-1)}\right)$

$\Rightarrow \quad$ Slope of OA is $m_{OA} = -\frac{a}{2}$

and $\quad$ Slope of OB is $m_{OB} = -\frac{1}{3}$

$\because \quad m_{OA} \times m_{OB} = -1$

$\therefore \quad -\frac{a}{2} \times -\frac{1}{3} = -1$

or $\quad a = -6$

$\therefore \quad |a| = 6$

63. Here, B is the image of A w.r.t line $y = x$

$\therefore$ $B \equiv (2, 1)$ and C is the image of A w.r.t line $x - 2y + 1 = 0$ if $C \equiv (\alpha, \beta)$, then

$$\frac{\alpha - 1}{1} = \frac{\beta - 2}{-2} = \frac{-2(1 - 4 + 1)}{1 + 4}$$

or $$\alpha = \frac{9}{5} \text{ and } \beta = \frac{2}{5}$$

$\therefore$ $$C \equiv \left(\frac{9}{5}, \frac{2}{5}\right)$$

$\Rightarrow$ Equation of BC is

$$y - 1 = \frac{\left(\frac{2}{5} - 1\right)}{\left(\frac{9}{5} - 2\right)}(x - 2)$$

or $$3x - y - 5 = 0 \quad (\because \text{Eq. of } BC \text{ is } ax + by - 5 = 0)$$

Here, $a = 3, b = -1$

$\therefore$ $a - 2b = 5$

64. On the line $y = 1$, the number of lattice points is $\left[\frac{2007 - 223}{9}\right] = 198$

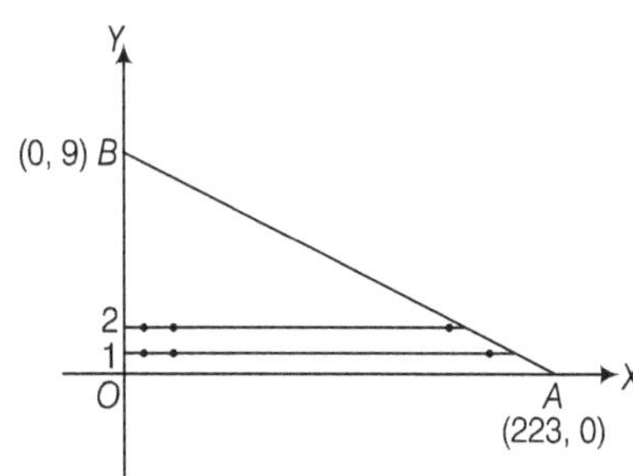

Hence, the total number of points

$$= \sum_{y=1}^{8}\left[\frac{2007 - 223y}{9}\right]$$

$$= 198 + 173 + 148 + 123 + 99 + 74 + 49 + 24 = 888$$

Hence, tens place digit is 8.

65. A rough sketch of the lines is given.

There are three triangle namely ABC, BCD and ABD

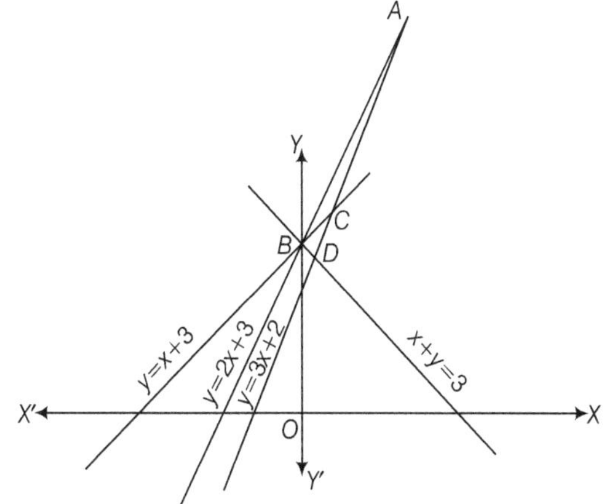

66. Let a be the length of side of square

$\therefore$ $$a^2 + a^2 = 2^2 \Rightarrow a = \sqrt{2}$$

i.e. distance between parallel lines is $\sqrt{2}$

Now, let two lines of family $y = x + n$ are $y = x + n$, and $y = x + n_2$, where

$$n_1, n_2 \in \{0, 1, 2, 3, 4\}$$

$\therefore$ $$\frac{|n_1 - n_2|}{\sqrt{2}} = \sqrt{2}$$

or $$|n_1 - n_2| = 2$$

$\Rightarrow$ $\{n_1, n_2\}$ are $\{0, 2\}$, $\{1, 3\}$ and $\{2, 4\}$

Hence, both the family have three such pairs. So, the number of squares possible is $3 \times 3 = 9$.

67. Let the coordinate of C be $(1, c)$, then

$$m_2 = \frac{c - y}{1 - x}$$

or $$m_2 = \frac{c - m_1 x}{1 - x} \quad (\because \text{slope of } AB = m_1)$$

$\Rightarrow$ $$m_2(1 - x) = c - m_1 x$$

or $$c = (m_1 - m_2)x + m_2$$

Now, the area of ΔABC is $\frac{1}{2}|cx - y|$

$$= \frac{1}{2}|((m_1 - m_2)x + m_2)x - m_1 x| \quad (\because y = m_1 x)$$

$$= \frac{1}{2}(m_1 - m_2)(x - x^2) \quad [\because m_1 > m_2 \text{ and } x \in (0, 1)]$$

Hence, $$f(x) = \frac{1}{2}(x - x^2)$$

$\therefore$ $$\frac{df(x)}{dx} = \frac{1}{2}(1 - 2x)$$

and $$\frac{d^2 f(x)}{dx^2} = -1 < 0$$

For maximum of

$$f(x), \frac{df(x)}{dx} = 0 \Rightarrow x = \frac{1}{2}$$

$\therefore$ $$f(x)|_{\max} = \frac{1}{2}\left(\frac{1}{2} - \frac{1}{4}\right)$$

$$= \frac{1}{8} = \lambda \quad \text{(given)}$$

$\Rightarrow$ $$\frac{1}{\lambda} = 8$$

68. Equation of AB is $3x - 2y + 6 = 0$

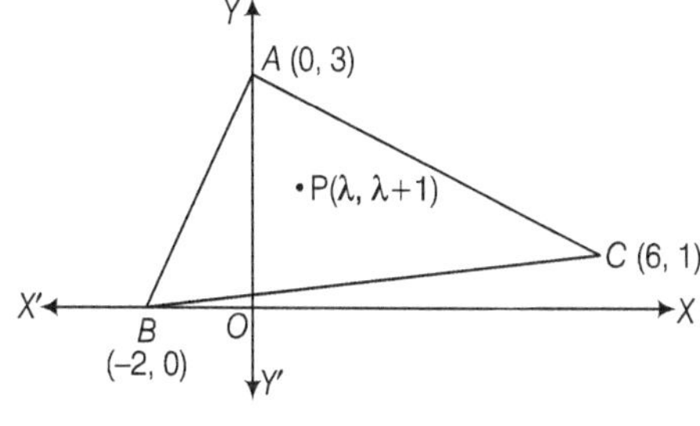

Equation of BC is $x - 8y + 2 = 0$,
Equation of CA is $x + 3y - 9 = 0$
Let $P \equiv (\lambda, \lambda + 1)$
$\because B$ and P lie on one side of AC, then

$$\frac{\lambda + 3(\lambda + 1) - 9}{-2 + 0 - 9} > 0$$

or $4\lambda - 6 < 0$

or $\lambda < \frac{3}{2}$ ...(i)

and C and P lie on one side of AB, then

$$\frac{3\lambda - 2(\lambda + 1) + 6}{18 - 2 + 6} > 0$$

or $\lambda + 4 > 0$

or $\lambda > -4$ ...(ii)

Finally, A and P lie on one side of BC, then

$$\frac{\lambda - 8(\lambda + 1) + 2}{0 - 24 + 2} > 0$$

or $-7\lambda - 6 < 0$

or $\lambda > -\frac{6}{7}$ ...(iii)

From Eqs. (i), (ii) and (iii), we get

$$-\frac{6}{7} < \lambda < \frac{3}{2}$$

Integral values of λ are 0 and 1.
Hence, number of integral values of λ is 2.

69. Lines

$$(2a + b)x + (a + 3b)y + b - 3a = 0$$

or $a(2x + y - 3) + b(x + 3y + 1) = 0$

are concurrent at the point of intersection of lines $2x + y - 3 = 0$ and $x + 3y + 1 = 0$ which is $(2, -1)$.
Now, line $\lambda x + 2y + 6 = 0$ must pass through $(2, -1)$, therefore,

$$2\lambda - 2 + 6 \text{ or } \lambda = -2$$

$\therefore$ $|\lambda| = 2$

70. Since, PQ is of fixed length.

Area of $\Delta PQR = \frac{1}{2}|PQ||RP|\sin\theta$

This will be maximum, if $\sin\theta = 1$ and RP is maximum.

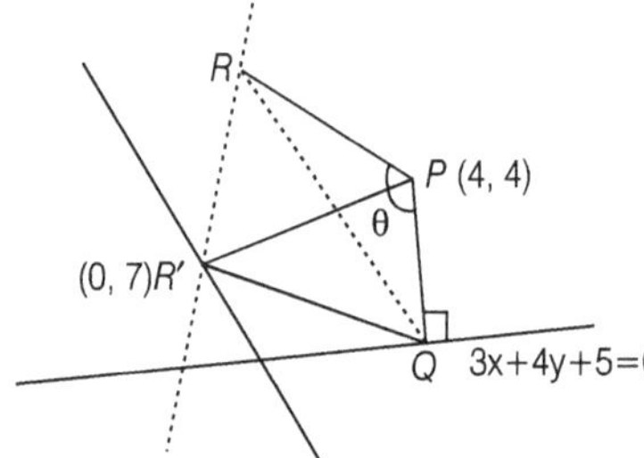

Since, line $y = mx + 7$ rotates about $(0, 7)$, if PR' is perpendicular to the line than PR' is maximum value of PR.

$\therefore$ $m = -\left(\frac{4 - 0}{4 - 7}\right) = \frac{4}{3}$

Hence, $3m = 4$

71. **(A)**

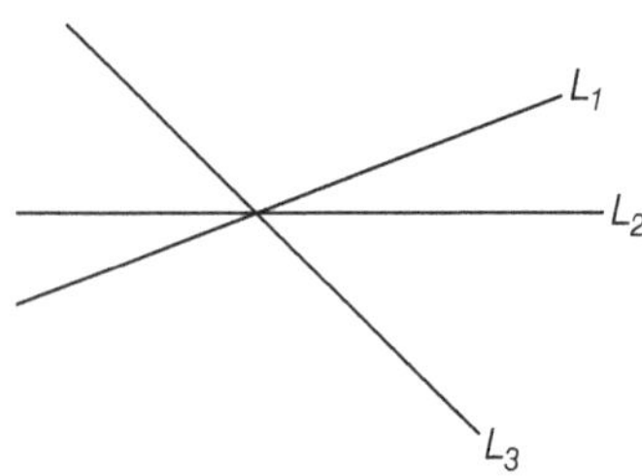

In this case no circle

$\therefore$ $n = 0 \Rightarrow n + 1 = 1$

(B)

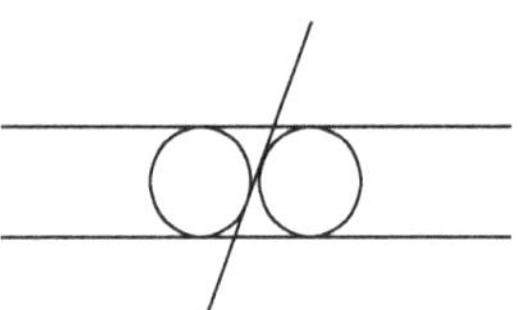

In this case no circle

$\therefore$ $n = 0 \Rightarrow 2n + 3 = 3$

(C)

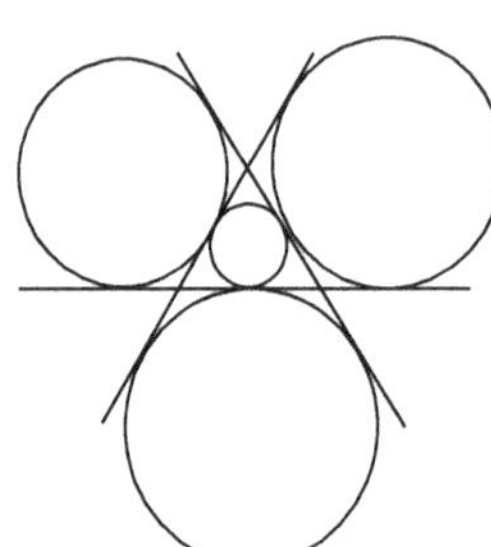

In this case two circle which are touching all three lines

$\therefore$ $n = 2 \Rightarrow n + 2 = 4$

(D)

In this case four circle which are touching all three lines

$\therefore$ $n = 4 \Rightarrow n + 2 = 6$

72. **(A)** The given lines an concurrent. So,

$$\begin{vmatrix} 1 & -2 & -6 \\ 3 & 1 & -4 \\ \lambda & 4 & \lambda^2 \end{vmatrix} = 0$$

or $\lambda^2 + 2\lambda - 8 = 0$

or $\lambda = 2, -4$

$\therefore$ $|\lambda| = 2, 4$

(B) Given family is

$$3x(a + 1) + 4y(a - 1) - 3(a - 1) = 0$$

or $a(3x + 4y - 3) + (3x - 4y + 3) = 0$

for fixed point=

$$3x + 4y - 3 = 0$$

and $3x - 4y + 3 = 0$

$\therefore$ $x = 0, y = \frac{3}{4}$

Fixed point is $\left(0, \frac{3}{4}\right)$,

Here $\quad p = 0, q = \frac{3}{4}$

$\therefore \quad 4|\lambda| = 4|p - q| = 3$

(C) The point of intersection of $x - y + 1 = 0$ and $3x + y - 5 = 0$ is $(1, 2)$. It lies on the line

$$x + y - 1 - \left|\frac{\lambda}{2}\right| = 0$$

$\Rightarrow \quad 1 + 2 - 1 - \left|\frac{\lambda}{2}\right| = 0$

or $\quad |\lambda| = 4$ or $\lambda = -4, 4$

$\therefore \quad \lambda + 1 = -3, 5$ or $|\lambda + 1| = 3, 5$

(D) The mid-point of $(1, -2)$ and $(3, 4)$ will satisfy

$$y - x - 1 + \lambda = 0$$

or $\quad 1 - 2 - 1 + \lambda = 0$

$\therefore \quad \lambda = 2$ or $|\lambda| = 2$

73.

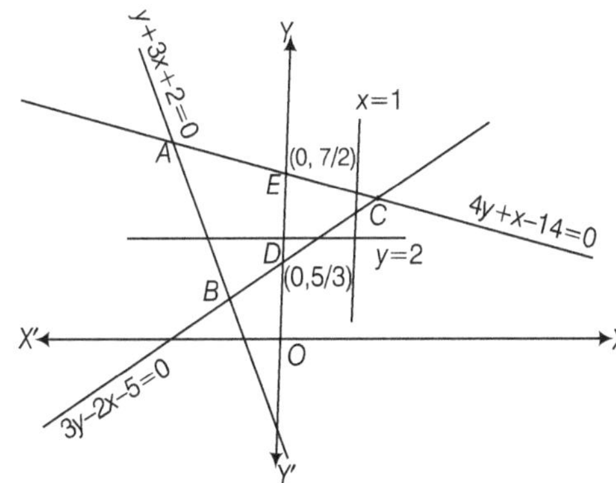

(A) The points on the line $x = 0$, whose y-coordinate lies between $\frac{5}{3}$ and $\frac{7}{2}$ inside the triangle ABC.

$\therefore \quad \frac{5}{3} < \lambda < \frac{7}{2}$ or $5 < 3\lambda < 10.5$

$\therefore \quad |3\lambda| = 6, 7, 8, 9, 10$

(B) $\because C \equiv (2, 3)$

The points on the line $x = 1$, whose y-coordinate lies between

$\frac{8}{3} \quad$ (put $x = 1$ in $3y - 2x - 5 = 0$)

and $\frac{13}{4} \quad$ (put $x = 1$ in $4y + x - 14 = 0$)

$\therefore \quad \frac{8}{3} < \lambda < \frac{13}{4}$ or $8 < 3\lambda < 9.75$

$\therefore \quad |3\lambda| = 9$

(C) $\because B \equiv (-1, 1)$

The point on the line $y = 2$, whose x-coordinate lies between

$\frac{-4}{3} \quad$ (put $y = 2$ in $y + 3x + 2 = 0$)

and $\frac{1}{2} \quad$ (put $y = 2$ in $3y - 2x - 5 = 0$)

$\therefore \quad \frac{-4}{3} < \lambda < \frac{1}{2}$ or $-8 < 6\lambda < 3$

Integral values of 6λ are

$$-7, -6, -5, -4, -3, -2, -1, 0, 1, 2$$

$\therefore \quad |6\lambda| = 7, 6, 5, 4, 3, 2, 1, 0$

(D) $\because A \equiv (-2, 4)$

The points on the line $y = \frac{7}{2}$, whose x-coordinates lies between

$0 \quad$ (put $y = \frac{7}{2}$ in $4y + x - 14 = 0$)

and $\frac{-11}{6} \quad$ (put $y = \frac{7}{2}$ in $y + 3x + 2 = 0$)

$\therefore \quad \frac{-11}{6} < \lambda < 0$

or $\quad -11 < 6\lambda < 0$

Integral value of 6λ are

$$-10, -9, -8, -7, -6, -3, -2, -1$$

$\therefore \quad |6\lambda| = 10, 9, 8, 7, 6, 5, 4, 3, 2, 1$

74. **(A)** $\because \max.\{|x|, |y|\} = 1$

If $|x| = 1$ and if $|y| = 1$

then $x = \pm 1$ and $y = \pm 1$

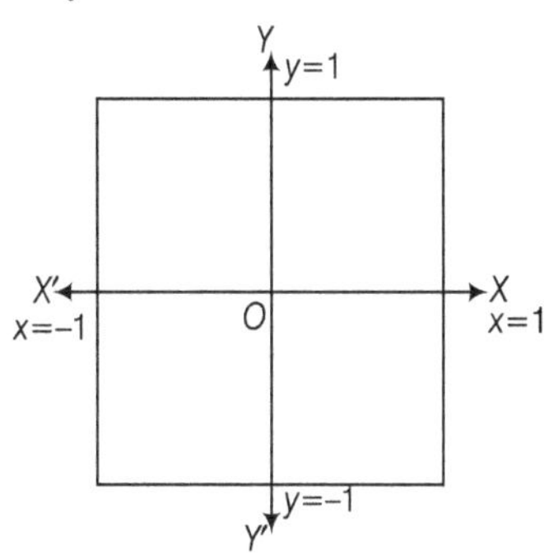

$\therefore$ Required area $= 2 \times 2 = 4$ sq units

(B) The line $y = x$ cuts the lines $|x + y| = 6$

i.e. $\quad x + y = \pm 6$

at $\quad x = \pm 3, y = \pm 3$

or $(-3, -3)$ and $(3, 3)$

then $\quad -3 < a < 3$

$\therefore \quad 0 \le |a| < 3$

$\therefore \quad [|a|] = 0, 1, 2$

(C) Since $(0, 0)$ and $(1, 1)$ lie on the same side.

So, $\quad a^2 + ab + 1 > 0$

$\because$ Coefficient of a^2 is > 0

$\therefore \quad D < 0$

$\quad b^2 - 4 < 0$ or $-2 < b < 2$

$\Rightarrow \quad b = -1, 0, 1$

$\therefore$ Number of values of b is 3.

75. **(A)** $\because$ $d(x, y) = 2|x| + 3|y| = 6$ (given)

$\therefore$ $$\frac{|x|}{3} + \frac{|y|}{2} = 1$$

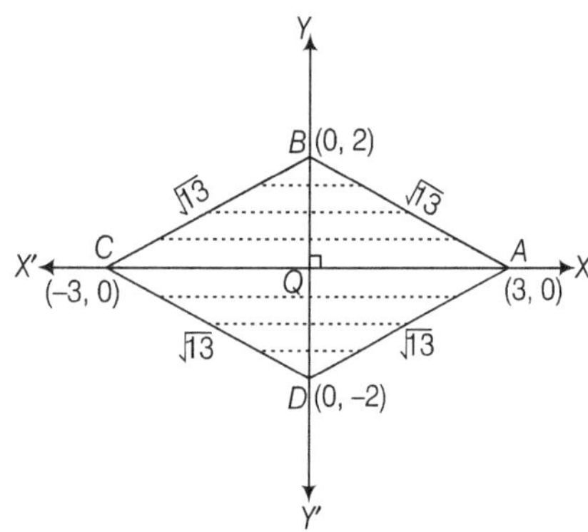

$\therefore$ Perimeter, $\lambda = 4\sqrt{13}$

and area, $\mu = 4 \times \frac{1}{2} \times 3 \times 2 = 12$

then $\frac{\lambda^2}{16} - \mu = 1$

and $\lambda^2 - \mu^2 = 64$

Hence, locus of (λ, μ) are

$$x^2 - 16y = 16$$

and $$x^2 - y^2 = 64$$

(B) It is clear that orthocentre is (6, 6)

$O' \equiv (6, 6)$,

Circumcentre is $C' \equiv (3, 3)$ and centroid is $G' \equiv (4, 4)$

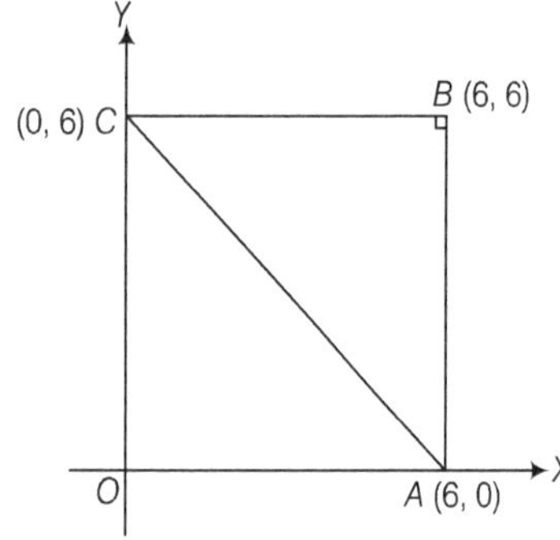

$\therefore$ $\lambda = O'C' = \sqrt{(0-3)^2 + (6-3)^2}$

$= \sqrt{9+9} = 3\sqrt{2}$

and $\mu = C'G' = \sqrt{(4-3)^2 + (4-3)^2}$

$= \sqrt{1+1} = \sqrt{2}$

$\therefore$ $\lambda^2 - \mu^2 = 16$ and $\lambda = 3\mu$

Hence, locus of (λ, μ) are

$x^2 - y^2 = 16$ and $x = 3y$

(C) $\therefore$ Slope of $AC \times$ slope of $BC = -1$

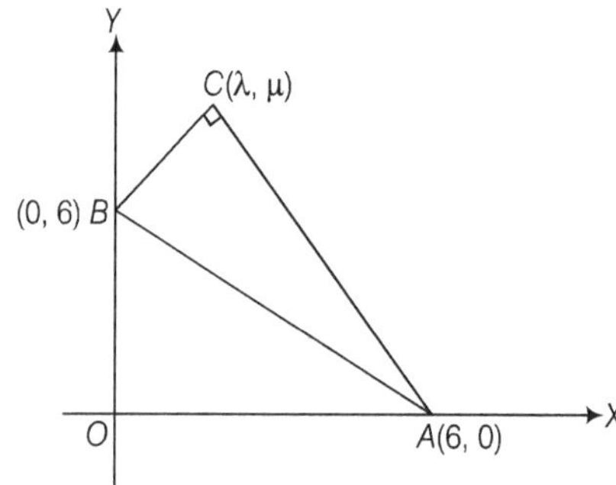

$\Rightarrow$ $$\left(\frac{\mu - 0}{\lambda - 6}\right) \times \left(\frac{\mu - 6}{\lambda - 0}\right) = -1$$

$\Rightarrow$ $\mu^2 - 6\mu = -\lambda^2 + 6\lambda$

or $\lambda^2 + \mu^2 - 6\lambda - 6\mu = 0$

Hence, locus of (λ, μ) is

$$x^2 + y^2 - 6x - 6y = 0$$

76. $\because$ $x(a + 2b) + y(a + 3b) = a + b$

$\Rightarrow$ $a(x + y - 1) + b(2x + 3y - 1) = 0$

then $x + y - 1 = 0$ and $2x + 3y - 1 = 0$

$\therefore$ point of intersection is $(2, -1)$

Hence, both statement are true and statement II is correct explanation for statement I.

77. $\because$ Algebraic perpendicular from (3, 2) to the line

$3x - 2y + 1 = 0$ is $\frac{9 - 4 + 1}{\sqrt{(9 + 4)}}$ i.e. $\frac{6}{\sqrt{13}} = p_1$ (say)

and algebraic perpendicular distance from (1, 4) to the line $3x - 2y + 1 = 0$ is

$\frac{3 - 8 + 1}{\sqrt{9 + 4}}$ i.e. $\frac{-4}{\sqrt{13}} = p_2$ (say)

$\therefore$ $$p_1 p_2 = \frac{6}{\sqrt{13}} \times \frac{-4}{\sqrt{13}} = \frac{-24}{13} < 0$$

Hence, both statements are true and statement II is a correct explanation for statement I.

78. Sum of algebraic distances from points $A(1, 2)$, $B(2, 3)$, $C(6, 1)$ to the line $ax + by + c = 0$ is zero (given), then

$$\frac{a + 2b + c}{\sqrt{(a^2 + b^2)}} + \frac{(2a + 3b + c)}{\sqrt{(a^2 + b^2)}} + \frac{(6a + b + c)}{\sqrt{(a^2 + b^2)}} = 0$$

$\Rightarrow$ $9a + 6b + 3c = 0$

or $3a + 2b + c = 0$

$\therefore$ Statement I is false.

Also, centroid of ΔABC is $\left(\frac{1 + 2 + 6}{3}, \frac{2 + 3 + 1}{3}\right)$

i.e. (3, 2)

$\therefore$ Statement II is true.

79. Equation of AB is

$$y - 1 = \frac{0-1}{2-0}(x - 0) \Rightarrow x + 2y - 2 = 0$$

$\because \quad |PA - PB| \le |AB|$

$\Rightarrow |PA - PB|$ to be maximum, then A, B and P must be collinear.

Solving $\quad x + 2y - 2 = 0$

and $\quad 4x + 3y + 9 = 0,$

we get, $\quad P \equiv \left(\frac{24}{5}, \frac{17}{5}\right)$

Hence, Statement I is false and Statement II is obviously true.

80. Statement II is false as the point satisfying such a property can be the excentre of the triangle.

Let $\quad L_1 \equiv x\cos\left(\frac{\pi}{9}\right) + y\sin\left(\frac{\pi}{9}\right) - \pi = 0,$

$L_2 \equiv x\cos\left(\frac{8\pi}{9}\right) + y\sin\left(\frac{8\pi}{9}\right) - \pi = 0$ and

$L_3 \equiv x\cos\left(\frac{13\pi}{9}\right) + y\sin\left(\frac{8\pi}{9}\right) - \pi = 0$

and $\quad P \equiv (0, 0)$

Length $\perp$ from P to L_1 = Length of $\perp$ from P to L_2 = Length of $\perp$ from P to $L_3 = \pi$ and P lies inside the triangle.

$\therefore P(0, 0)$ is incentre of triangle.

Hence, statement I is true and statement II is false.

81. $\because$ Mid-point of $(5, 1)$ and $(-1, -5)$ i.e. $(2, -2)$ lies on $x + y = 0$ and (slope of $x + y = 0$) $\times$ (slope of line joining $(5, 1)$ and $(-1, -5)) = (-1) \times \frac{-6}{-6}$

$\therefore$ Statement I is true.

Statement II is also true.

Hence, both statements are true but statement II is not correct explanation of statement I.

82. Equation of AC and BC are $3x + 2y = 0$ and $2x + 3y + 6 = 0$

$\because (3)(2) + (2)(3) = 12 > 0$

$\therefore$ Internal angle bisector of C is

$$\left(\frac{3x + 2y}{\sqrt{13}}\right) = -\left(\frac{2x + 3y + 6}{\sqrt{13}}\right)$$

or $\quad 5x + 5y + 6 = 0$

$\Rightarrow$ Statement I is true.

Also, the image of A about the angle bisectors of angle B and C lie on the side BC. (by congruence).

$\therefore$ Statement II is true.

Both statements are true and statement II is not correct explanation of statement I.

83. $\because$ Points (x_1, y_1) and (x_2, y_2) lie on the same or opposite sides of the line

$$ax + by + c = 0, \text{ as}$$

$$\frac{ax_1 + by_1 + c}{ax_2 + by_2 + c} > 0 \text{ or } < 0$$

$\therefore \quad$ Statement II is true.

Also, $(2a - 5, a^2)$ and $(0, 0)$ on the same side of $x + y - 3 = 0$, then

$$\frac{2a - 5 + a^2 - 3}{0 + 0 - 3} > 0$$

$\Rightarrow \quad a^2 + 2a - 8 < 0$

or $\quad (a + 4)(a - 2) < 0$

$\therefore \quad a \in (-4, 2)$

$\Rightarrow$ Statement I is false

Hence, statement I is false and statement II is true.

84. In ΔOBD, $\quad \frac{BD}{\sin(\pi - 2C)} = \frac{R}{\sin\theta}$ ...(i)

In ΔODC, $\quad \frac{DC}{\sin(\pi - 2B)} = \frac{R}{\sin(\pi - \theta)}$ ...(ii)

From Eqs. (i) and (ii), $\quad \frac{BD}{DC} = \frac{\sin 2C}{\sin 2B}$

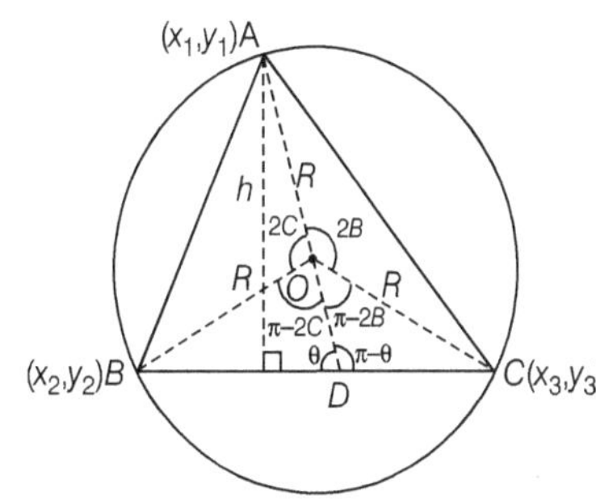

$\therefore$ Coordinates of D are

$$\left(\frac{x_2 \sin 2B + x_3 \sin 2C}{\sin 2B + \sin 2C}, \frac{y_2 \sin 2B + y_3 \sin 2C}{\sin 2B + \sin 2C}\right)$$

Let (x, y) be any point on AD, then equation of AD is

$$\begin{vmatrix} x & y & 1 \\ x_1 & y_1 & 1 \\ \frac{x_2 \sin 2B + x_3 \sin 2C}{\sin 2B + \sin 2C} & \frac{y_2 \sin 2B + y_3 \sin 2C}{\sin 2B + \sin 2C} & 1 \end{vmatrix} = 0$$

or $$\begin{vmatrix} x & y & 1 \\ x_1 & y_1 & 1 \\ x_2 \sin 2B + x_3 \sin 2C & y_2 \sin 2B + y_3 \sin 2C & \sin 2B + \sin 2C \end{vmatrix} = 0$$

or $$\begin{vmatrix} x & y & 1 \\ x_1 & y_1 & 1 \\ x_2 \sin 2B & y_2 \sin 2B & \sin 2B \end{vmatrix} + \begin{vmatrix} x & y & 1 \\ x_1 & y_1 & 1 \\ x_3 \sin 2C & y_3 \sin 2C & \sin 2C \end{vmatrix} = 0$$

or $$(\sin 2B)\begin{vmatrix} x & y & 1 \\ x_1 & y_1 & 1 \\ x_2 & y_2 & 1 \end{vmatrix} + (\sin 2C)\begin{vmatrix} x & y & 1 \\ x_1 & y_1 & 1 \\ x_3 & y_3 & 1 \end{vmatrix} = 0$$

85. Let (x_1, y_1) be the coordinates of a point at unit distance from each of the given lines.

$$\Rightarrow \quad \frac{|3x_1 - 4y_1 + 1|}{\sqrt{3^2 + 4^2}} = 1 \text{ and } \frac{|8x_1 + 6y_1 + 1|}{\sqrt{8^2 + 6^2}} = 1$$

$$\Rightarrow \quad 3x_1 - 4y_1 + 1 = \pm 5 \text{ and } 8x_1 + 6y_1 + 1 = \pm 10$$

$$\Rightarrow \quad 3x_1 - 4y_1 - 4 = 0 \quad \text{...(i)}$$

$$\text{or} \quad 3x_1 - 4y_1 + 6 = 0 \quad \text{...(ii)}$$

$$8x_1 + 6y_1 - 9 = 0 \quad \text{...(iii)}$$

$$\text{or} \quad 8x_1 + 6y_1 + 11 = 0 \quad \text{...(iv)}$$

$(1) \cap (3)$

$$\Rightarrow \quad x_1 / 60 = y_1 / -5 = 1/50,$$

$$\therefore \quad (x_1, y_1) = \left(\frac{6}{5}, -\frac{1}{10}\right)$$

$(1) \cap (4)$

$$\Rightarrow \quad x_1 / -20 = y_1 / -65 = 1/50,$$

$$\therefore \quad (x_1, y_1) = \left(-\frac{2}{5}, -\frac{13}{10}\right)$$

$(2) \cap (3)$

$$\Rightarrow \quad x_1 / 0 = y_1 / 75 = 1/50, \therefore (x_1, y_1) = (0, 3/2)$$

$(2) \cap (4)$

$$\Rightarrow \quad x_1 / -80 = y_1 / 15 = 1/50, \therefore (x_1, y_1) = \left(-\frac{8}{5}, \frac{3}{10}\right)$$

Hence, the required four points have the coordinates

$$\left(\frac{6}{5}, -\frac{1}{10}\right), \left(-\frac{2}{5}, -\frac{13}{10}\right), \left(0, \frac{3}{2}\right), \left(-\frac{8}{5}, \frac{3}{10}\right).$$

86. Let $\angle OAB = \alpha$

$$\therefore \quad OA = AB \cos\alpha \text{ and } OB = AB \sin\alpha$$

$$\because \quad (OA)^2 + (OB)^2 = k^2$$

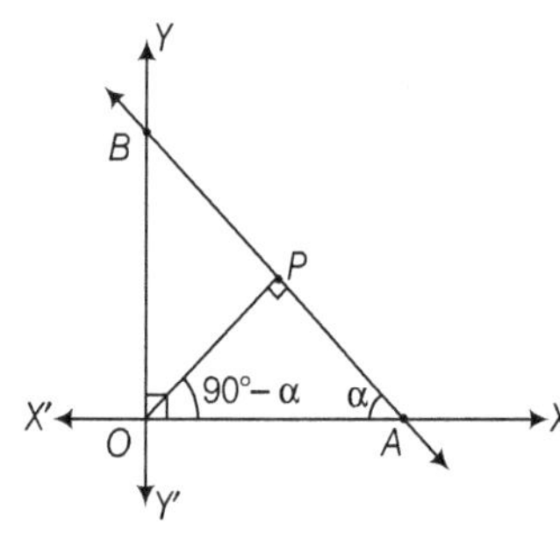

$$\text{i.e.} \quad (AB)^2 (\cos^2\alpha + \sin^2\alpha) = k^2$$

$$\text{or} \quad AB = k$$

$$\text{then} \quad OA = k \cos\alpha \text{ and } OB = k \sin\alpha$$

$$\therefore \text{ Equation of } AB \text{ is } \frac{x}{k\cos\alpha} + \frac{y}{k\sin\alpha} = 1$$

$$\text{or} \quad \frac{x}{\cos\alpha} + \frac{y}{\sin\alpha} = k \quad \text{...(i)}$$

Let P be the foot of perpendicular from O on AB.

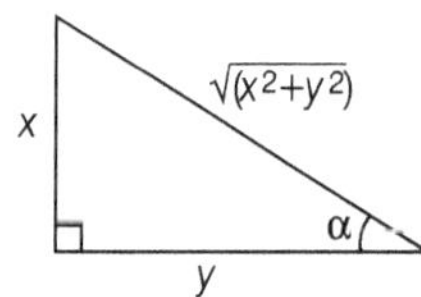

$$\therefore \text{ Equation of } OP \text{ is } y = x\tan(90° - \alpha)$$

$$\text{or} \quad \cot\alpha = \frac{y}{x}$$

$$\therefore \quad \sin\alpha = \frac{x}{\sqrt{(x^2 + y^2)}}$$

$$\text{and} \quad \cos\alpha = \frac{y}{\sqrt{(x^2 + y^2)}} \quad \text{...(ii)}$$

Substituting the values of $\sin\alpha$ and $\cos\alpha$ from Eq. (i) in (i) then we get the required locus of P

$$\therefore \quad \frac{x}{y/\sqrt{(x^2+y^2)}} + \frac{y}{x/\sqrt{(x^2+y^2)}} = k$$

$$\Rightarrow \quad (x^2 + y^2)\sqrt{(x^2 + y^2)} = kxy$$

Squaring both sides, we get

$$(x^2 + y^2)^2 (x^2 + y^2) = k^2 x^2 y^2$$

$$\text{or} \quad (x^2 + y^2)^2 \left(\frac{x^2}{x^2y^2} + \frac{y^2}{x^2y^2}\right) = k^2$$

$$\text{or} \quad (x^2 + y^2)^2 (x^{-2} + y^{-2}) = k^2$$

87. Let the equation of variable line be $ax + by = 1$. Then the coordinates of A_p will be

$$A_p \equiv \left(\frac{1}{a + bp}, \frac{p}{a + bp}\right)$$

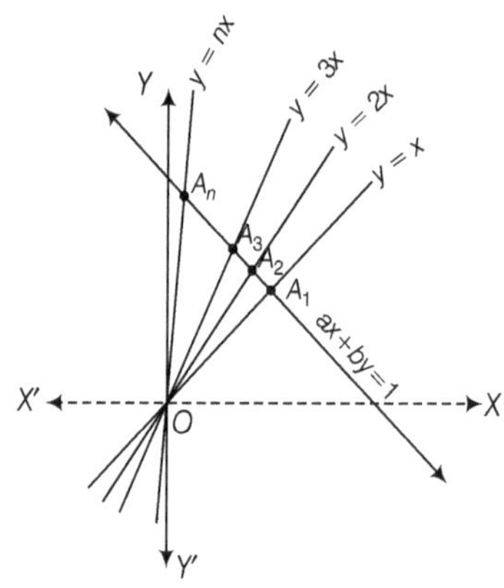

$$\therefore \quad OA_p = \frac{\sqrt{(1 + p^2)}}{|a + bp|} \quad \text{...(i)}$$

$$\text{Given,} \quad \sum_{p=1}^{n} \frac{1}{OA_p} = c$$

$$\Rightarrow \quad \sum_{p=1}^{n} \frac{|a + bp|}{\sqrt{(1 + p^2)}} = c \quad \text{[from Eq. (1)]}$$

$$\Rightarrow a\left(\pm \sum_{p=1}^{n} \frac{1}{\sqrt{(1+p^2)}}\right) + b\left(\pm \sum_{p=1}^{n} \frac{p}{\sqrt{(1+p^2)}}\right) = c$$

$$\text{or } a\left(\pm \frac{\sum_{p=1}^{n} \frac{1}{\sqrt{(1+p^2)}}}{c}\right) + b\left(\pm \frac{\sum_{p=1}^{n} \frac{p}{\sqrt{(1+p^2)}}}{c}\right) = 1$$

So, line always passes through a fixed point whose coordinates are

$$\left(\frac{\pm \sum_{p=1}^{n} \frac{1}{\sqrt{(1+p^2)}}}{c}, \frac{\pm \sum_{p=1}^{n} \frac{p}{\sqrt{(1+p^2)}}}{c} \right)$$

88. Let the equation of given n lines be

$$y = m_r x + c_r,$$

where $\quad r = 1, 2, 3, \dots, n \qquad \dots(i)$

Let equation of line through origin O is

$$y = mx \qquad \dots(ii)$$

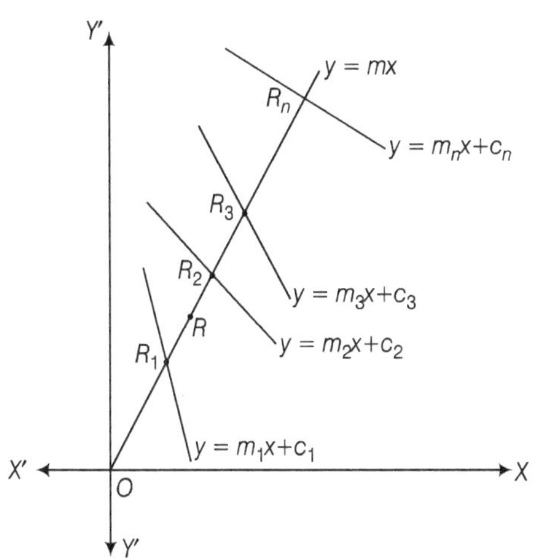

Solving Eqs. (i) and (ii), we get

$$R_r \equiv \left(\frac{c_r}{m - m_r}, \frac{mc_r}{m - m_r} \right)$$

$$\therefore \quad OR_r = \sqrt{\left(\frac{c_r}{m - m_r} \right)^2 + \left(\frac{m\, c_r}{m - m_r} \right)^2}$$

$$= \left| \frac{c_r}{m - m_r} \right| \sqrt{(1+m^2)} \qquad \dots(iii)$$

Let $\quad R \equiv (x_1, y_1)$

$$\therefore \quad y_1 = mx_1 \Rightarrow m = \frac{y_1}{x_1} \qquad \dots(iv)$$

Given, $\dfrac{n}{OR} = \sum_{r=1}^{n} \dfrac{1}{OR_r}$

$$\Rightarrow \frac{n}{\sqrt{(x_1^2 + y_1^2)}} = \sum_{r=1}^{n} \left| \frac{m - m_r}{c_r} \right| \frac{1}{\sqrt{(1+m^2)}} \qquad \text{[from Eq. (iii)]}$$

$$= \frac{1}{\sqrt{(1+m^2)}} \left\{ m \left(\sum_{r=1}^{n} \left(\pm \frac{1}{c_r} \right) \right) + \sum_{r=1}^{n} \left(\mp \frac{m_r}{c_r} \right) \right\}$$

$$= \frac{1}{\sqrt{(1+m^2)}} (ma + b)$$

$$\left\{ \text{where } a = \sum_{r=1}^{n} \left(\pm \frac{1}{c_r} \right) \text{ and } b = \sum_{r=1}^{n} \left(\mp \frac{m_r}{c_r} \right) \right.$$

then $$\frac{n}{\sqrt{(x_1^2 + y_1^2)}} = \frac{\frac{y_1}{x_1} a + b}{\sqrt{1 + \left(\frac{y_1}{x_1} \right)^2}} \qquad \text{[from Eq. (iv)]}$$

$$\Rightarrow \quad n = ay_1 + bx_1$$

Hence, locus of point R is $bx + ay = n$.

89. First equation can be expressed as

$$(2x + 3y - 5) \cos\theta + (3x - 5y + 2) \sin\theta = 0$$

$$\Rightarrow \quad (2x + 3y - 5) + (3x - 5y + 2) \tan\theta = 0$$

It is clear that these lines will pass through the point of intersection of the lines

$$\left. \begin{aligned} 2x + 3y - 5 = 0 \\ 3x - 5y + 2 = 0 \end{aligned} \right\} \qquad \dots(i)$$

for all values of θ.

Solving the system of Eq. (i), we get (1, 1).

Hence, the fixed point is P (1, 1). Let $Q(\alpha, \beta)$ be the reflection of P (1, 1) in the line $x + y = \sqrt{2}$.

Then $$\frac{\alpha - 1}{1} = \frac{\beta - 1}{1} = \frac{-2(1 + 1 - \sqrt{2})}{1^2 + 1^2} = \sqrt{2} - 2$$

$$\therefore \quad \alpha = \sqrt{2} - 1, \beta = \sqrt{2} - 1$$

i.e. $\quad Q \equiv (\sqrt{2} - 1, \sqrt{2} - 1)$

If the required family of lines is

$$(2\cos\theta + 3\sin\theta)\, x + (3\cos\theta - 5\sin\theta)\, y = \lambda$$

in order that each member of the family pass through Q, we have

$$\lambda = (\sqrt{2} - 1)(2\cos\theta + 3\sin\theta + 3\cos\theta - 5\sin\theta)$$

$$\lambda = (\sqrt{2} - 1)(5\cos\theta - 2\sin\theta)$$

Hence, equation of required family is

$$(2\cos\theta + 3\sin\theta)\, x + (3\cos\theta - 5\sin\theta)\, y = (\sqrt{2} - 1)(5\cos\theta - 2\sin\theta).$$

90. Let $R\,(h, k)$ be the foot of perpendicular from Q on OP.

Let equation of OP be

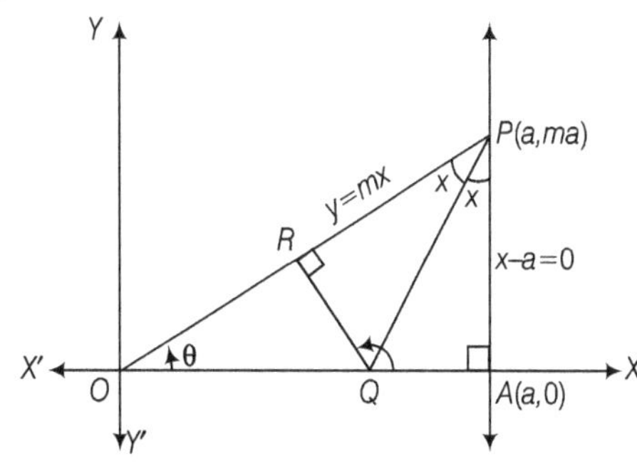

$$y = mx$$

then $\quad k = mh$

or $$m = \frac{k}{h} \qquad \dots(i)$$

and coordinates of $P \equiv (a, ma)$

$\because$ PQ is the bisector of OPA

$\therefore$ $\angle APQ = \angle RPQ$

and $\angle PAQ = \angle QRP = 90°$

$\therefore$ $PA = PR$

then $|ma| = \sqrt{(h-a)^2 + (k-ma)^2}$

From Eq. (i), $\left|\frac{ak}{h}\right| = \sqrt{(h-a)^2 + \left(k - \frac{ak}{h}\right)^2}$

$\Rightarrow$ $a|k| = |(h-a)|\sqrt{(h^2+k^2)}$

Hence, required locus is

$$(x-a)^2(x^2+y^2) = a^2y^2$$

91. Let the coordinates of the vertex be (h, k) and equations of the bases be

$$x\cos\alpha_r + y\sin\alpha_r - p_r = 0 \quad \text{where } r = 1, 2, 3, \ldots, n$$

and their lengths be respectively $l_1, l_2, l_3, \ldots, l_n$.

$\because$ Length of perpendicular from (h, k) on $x\cos\alpha_r + y\sin\alpha_r - p_r = 0$ is

$$\frac{|h\cos\alpha_r + k\sin\alpha_r - p_r|}{\sqrt{(\cos^2\alpha + \sin^2\alpha)}},$$

i.e. $|h\cos\alpha_r + k\sin\alpha_r - p_r|$

Given, sum of areas of all triangles = constant

then

$$\sum_{r=1}^{n}\frac{1}{2}l_r\cdot|h\cos\alpha_r + k\sin\alpha_r - p_r| = C'$$

$$\Rightarrow \sum_{r=1}^{n}\frac{1}{2}.l_r.(\pm(h\cos\alpha_r + k\sin\alpha_r - p_r)) = C'$$

$$\Rightarrow h\left(\sum_{r=1}^{n}\pm\frac{1}{2}l_r\cos\alpha_r\right) + k\left(\sum_{r=1}^{n}\pm\frac{1}{2}l_r.\sin\alpha_r\right)$$

$$= \sum_{r=1}^{n}\pm\frac{1}{2}l_r.p_r + C'$$

$\Rightarrow Ah + Bk = -C$

$\therefore$ Required locus is

$$Ax + By + C = 0$$

where A, B, C are constants.

92. The equation of BU is

$$y - \beta = \frac{0-\beta}{6-\alpha}(x-\alpha)$$

So that the coordinates of D are $\left(0, \frac{6\beta}{6-\alpha}\right)$

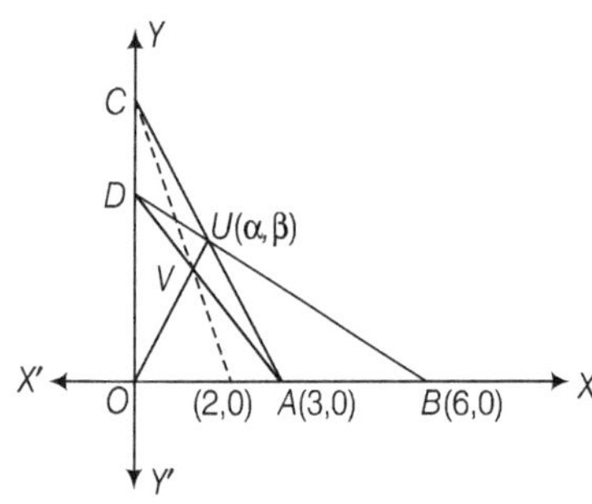

Similarly, the coordinates of C are $\left(0, \frac{3\beta}{3-\alpha}\right)$

Now, the equation of AD is

$$\frac{x}{3} + \frac{(6-\alpha)}{6\beta}y = 1 \quad \text{...(i)}$$

and the equation of OU is

$$\beta x = \alpha y \quad \text{...(ii)}$$

Solving Eqs. (i) and (ii), we get

$$x = \frac{6\alpha}{6+\alpha}, y = \frac{6\beta}{6+\alpha}$$

Hence, coordinates of V are $\left(\frac{6\alpha}{6+\alpha}, \frac{6\beta}{6+\alpha}\right)$

Then, the equation of CV is

$$y - \frac{3\beta}{3-\alpha} = \frac{\frac{6\beta}{6+\alpha} - \frac{3\beta}{3-\alpha}}{\frac{6\alpha}{6+\alpha} - 0}(x-0)$$

$$\Rightarrow y - \frac{3\beta}{3-\alpha} = \frac{-9\alpha\beta}{6\alpha(3-\alpha)}x$$

$$\Rightarrow y = \frac{3\beta}{(3-\alpha)}\left(1 - \frac{x}{2}\right)$$

which pass through the point (2, 0) for all values of (α, β).

93. Let the equation of the variable line through 'O' be

$$\frac{x}{\cos\theta} = \frac{y}{\sin\theta}$$

and let $OR = r_1$, $OS = r_2$ and $OP = r_3$

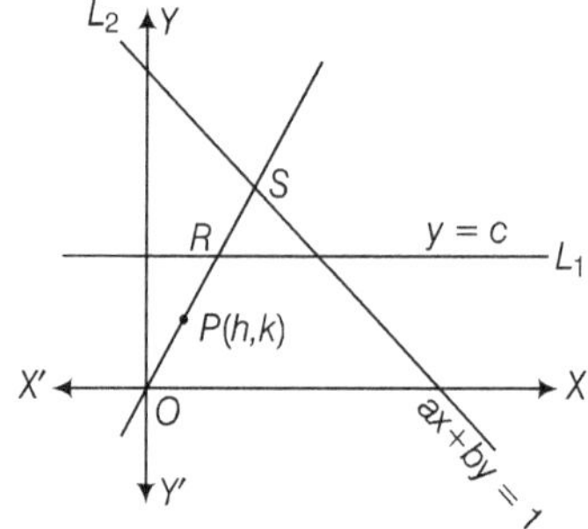

Then coordinates of R, S and P are :

$R(r_1\cos\theta, r_1\sin\theta)$, $S(r_2\cos\theta, r_2\sin\theta)$, $P(r_3\cos\theta, r_3\sin\theta)$

R lies on L_1 and S lies on L_2.

Let $L_1 \equiv y - c = 0$

and $L_2 \equiv ax + by - 1 = 0$

$\therefore$ $r_1\sin\theta = c$ and $ar_2\cos\theta + br_2\sin\theta = 1$

$\therefore$ $r_1 = \frac{c}{\sin\theta}$ and $r_2 = \frac{1}{a\cos\theta + b\sin\theta}$

From the given condition

$$\frac{m+n}{r_3} = \frac{m}{r_1} + \frac{n}{r_2}$$

$$\Rightarrow \frac{m+n}{r_3} = \frac{m\sin\theta}{c} + n(a\cos\theta + b\sin\theta) \quad \text{...(i)}$$

Let the coordinates of P be (h, k), then

$$h = r_3 \cos\theta, k = r_3 \sin\theta$$

From Eq. (i), $$m + n = \frac{mr_3 \sin\theta}{c} + n(ar_3 \cos\theta + br_3 \sin\theta)$$

$$\Rightarrow \quad m + n = \frac{mk}{c} + n(ah + bk)$$

Locus of P is $n(ax + by) + \frac{my}{c} = (m + n)$

$$\Rightarrow \quad n(ax + by - 1) + \frac{m}{c}(y - c) = 0$$

$$\Rightarrow \quad (ax + by - 1) + \frac{m}{nc}(y - c) = 0$$

$$\Rightarrow \quad L_2 + \lambda L_1 = 0 \quad \left(\text{where, } \lambda = \frac{m}{nc}\right)$$

Hence, locus of P is a point of intersection of L_1 and L_2.

94. The given lines are

$$x + 3y + 2 = 0 \quad \text{...(i)}$$

$$2x + y + 4 = 0 \quad \text{...(ii)}$$

$$x - y - 5 = 0 \quad \text{...(iii)}$$

Equation of the line passing through $A(-5, -4)$ and making an angle θ with the positive direction of X-axis is

$$\frac{x + 5}{\cos\theta} = \frac{y + 4}{\sin\theta} = r(AB, AC, AD) \quad \text{...(iv)}$$

$\therefore$ Points $(-5 + AB\cos\theta, -4 + AB\sin\theta)$, $(-5 + AC\cos\theta, -4 + AC\sin\theta)$ and $(-5 + AD\cos\theta, -4 + AD\sin\theta)$ lie on Eqs. (i), (ii) and (iii) respectively.

$$(-5 + AB\cos\theta) + 3(-4 + AB\sin\theta) + 2 = 0$$

$$\Rightarrow \quad AB(\cos\theta + 3\sin\theta) = 15$$

$$\Rightarrow \quad \frac{15}{AB} = \cos\theta + 3\sin\theta$$

Similarly, $$\frac{10}{AC} = 2\cos\theta + \sin\theta$$

and $$\frac{6}{AD} = \cos\theta - \sin\theta$$

From given condition

$$\left(\frac{15}{AB}\right)^2 + \left(\frac{10}{AC}\right)^2 = \left(\frac{6}{AD}\right)^2$$

we get $(\cos\theta + 3\sin\theta)^2 + (2\cos\theta + \sin\theta)^2 = (\cos\theta - \sin\theta)^2$

$$\Rightarrow \quad 4\cos^2\theta + 9\sin^2\theta + 12\sin\theta\cos\theta = 0$$

$$\Rightarrow \quad (2\cos\theta + 3\sin\theta)^2 = 0$$

$$\therefore \quad \tan\theta = -\frac{2}{3}$$

Hence the equation of the line from Eq. (iv) is

$$y + 4 = -\frac{2}{3}(x + 5) \Rightarrow 2x + 3y + 22 = 0$$

95. $\because A, R$ and B are collinear

then, $$\frac{k - 0}{h - a} = \frac{mb - 0}{b - a}$$

$$\therefore \quad \frac{a}{b}k - am + mh - k = 0 \quad \text{...(i)}$$

Let $P \equiv (\alpha, \beta)$

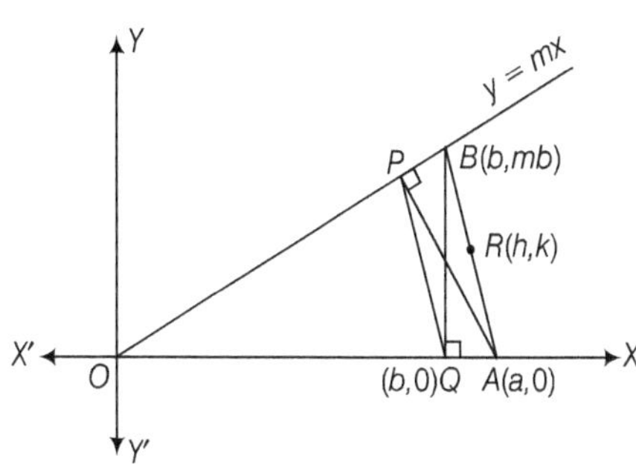

$\because$ P be the foot of perpendicular from A on $y = mx$, then

$$\frac{\alpha - a}{-m} = \frac{\beta - 0}{1} = \frac{-(0 - ma)}{(1 + m^2)}$$

$$\therefore \quad \alpha = \frac{a}{1 + m^2}, \beta = \frac{am}{1 + m^2}$$

i.e. $$P \equiv \left(\frac{a}{1 + m^2}, \frac{am}{1 + m^2}\right)$$

$\therefore$ Equation of PQ is

$$y - 0 = \frac{\frac{am}{1 + m^2} - 0}{\frac{a}{1 + m^2} - b}(x - b)$$

$$\Rightarrow \quad \frac{a}{b}(y - mx) + am - (1 + m^2)y = 0 \quad \text{...(ii)}$$

Adding Eqs. (i) and (ii), then

$$\frac{a}{b}(y - mx + k) + (mh - k - (1 + m^2)y) = 0$$

$$\Rightarrow \quad (mh - k - (1 + m^2)y) + \lambda(y - mx + k) = 0$$

$$\left(\text{where, } \lambda = \frac{a}{b}\right)$$

Hence PQ pass through a fixed point.

For fixed point

$$mh - k - (1 + m^2)y = 0, y - mx + k = 0$$

$$y = \frac{mh - k}{(1 + m^2)}, x = \frac{h + mk}{(1 + m^2)}$$

Hence, fixed point is $\left(\frac{h + mk}{1 + m^2}, \frac{mh - k}{1 + m^2}\right)$.

96. Given lines are parallel and distance between them < 2

Given lines are

$$2x + y = 3 \quad \text{...(i)}$$

and $$2x + y = 5 \quad \text{...(ii)}$$

Equation of any line through Eqs. (ii) and (iii) is

$$y - 3 = m(x - 2)$$

or $$y = mx - 2m + 3 \quad \text{...(iii)}$$

Let line (iii) cut lines (i) and (ii) at A and B respectively.

Solving Eqs. (i) and (iii), we get

$$A \equiv \left(\frac{2m}{m + 2}, \frac{6 - m}{m + 2}\right)$$

and solving Eqs. (ii) and (iii), we get

$$B \equiv \left(\frac{2m+2}{m+2}, \frac{m+6}{m+2} \right)$$

According to question $AB = 2$

$$\Rightarrow \qquad (AB)^2 = 4$$

$$\Rightarrow \qquad \left(\frac{2}{m+2} \right)^2 + \left(\frac{2m}{m+2} \right)^2 = 4$$

$$\Rightarrow \qquad 1 + m^2 = m^2 + 4m + 4 \qquad \text{...(iv)}$$

Case I : When m is finite (line is not perpendicular to X-axis) then from Eq. (iv).

$$1 = 4m + 4$$

$$\therefore \qquad m = -\frac{3}{4}$$

Case II : When m is infinite (line is perpendicular to X-axis) then from Eq. (iv),

$$\frac{1}{m^2} + 1 = 1 + \frac{4}{m} + \frac{4}{m^2}$$

$$0 + 1 = 1 + 0 + 0$$

$$1 = 1 \text{ which is true}$$

Hence $m \to \infty$ acceptable.

Hence, equation of the required lines are

$$y - 3 = -\frac{3}{4}(x - 2)$$

and $$\frac{y-3}{\infty} = x - 2 \Rightarrow x - 2 = 0$$

i.e. $\quad 3x + 4y = 18 \quad$ and $\quad x - 2 = 0$

Aliter I :

$\because \; 2x + y = 3$ cuts Y-axis at $(0, 3)$ and line $2x + y = 5$ cuts Y-axis at $(0, 5)$

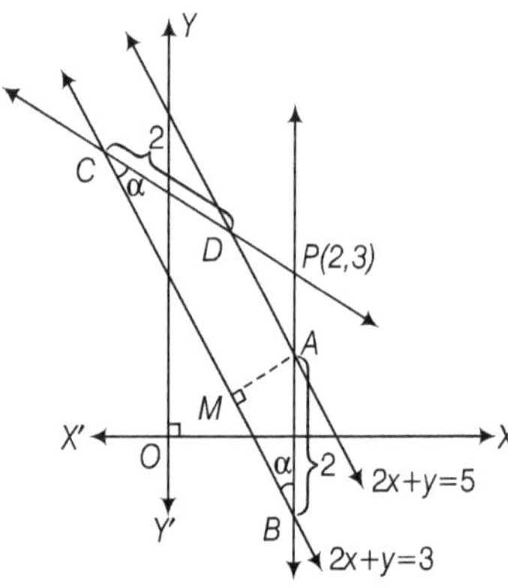

Therefore intercept on Y-axis is 2.

Also, $\quad AM =$ distance between parallel lines

$$= \frac{|-5+3|}{\sqrt{2^2 + 1^2}} = \frac{2}{\sqrt{5}}$$

$$\therefore \qquad MB = \sqrt{(AB)^2 - (AM)^2} = \sqrt{4 - \frac{4}{5}} = \frac{4}{\sqrt{5}}$$

then $$\tan\alpha = \frac{AM}{MB} = \frac{1}{2}$$

Also $\quad \tan\theta = -2 \qquad$ (slope of $2x + y = 5$)

Now, equation of required lines are

$$y - 3 = \tan(\theta \pm \alpha)(x - 2)$$

$$\Rightarrow \qquad y - 3 = \left(\frac{\tan\theta \pm \tan\alpha}{1 \mp \tan\theta \tan\alpha} \right)(x - 2)$$

$$\Rightarrow \qquad y - 3 = \frac{(-2) \pm \frac{1}{2}}{1 \mp (-2)\left(\frac{1}{2}\right)}(x - 2)$$

$$\Rightarrow \qquad y - 3 = \frac{\left(-2 \pm \frac{1}{2}\right)}{1 \mp (-1)}(x - 2)$$

$$\Rightarrow (1 \mp (-1))(y - 3) = \left(-2 \pm \frac{1}{2}\right)(x - 2)$$

$$\Rightarrow \qquad x - 2 = 0 \quad \text{and} \quad 2y - 6 = -\frac{3}{2}(x - 2)$$

i.e. $$x - 2 = 0 \quad \text{and} \quad 3x + 4y - 18 = 0$$

Aliter II : Any line through $(2, 3)$ is

$$\frac{x-2}{\cos\theta} = \frac{y-3}{\sin\theta} = r$$

Suppose this line cuts $2x + y = 5$ and $2x + y = 3$ at D and C respectively but given $DC = 2$

then $\quad D \equiv (2 + r\cos\theta, 3 + r\sin\theta)$

and $\quad C \equiv (2 + (r + 2)\cos\theta, 3 + (r + 2)\sin\theta)$

$\because \; D$ and C lies on

$$2x + y = 5 \quad \text{and} \quad 2x + y = 3$$

then $$2(2 + r\cos\theta) + (3 + r\sin\theta) = 5 \qquad \text{... (v)}$$

and $$2(2 + (r + 2)\cos\theta) + (3 + (r + 2)\sin\theta) = 3 \qquad \text{... (vi)}$$

Subtracting Eq. (v) from Eq. (vi), then

$$4\cos\theta + 2\sin\theta = -2$$

or $$2\cos\theta + \sin\theta = -1$$

$$\Rightarrow \qquad 2\left(\frac{1 - \tan^2\left(\frac{\theta}{2}\right)}{1 + \tan^2\left(\frac{\theta}{2}\right)} \right) + \left(\frac{2\tan\left(\frac{\theta}{2}\right)}{1 + \tan^2\left(\frac{\theta}{2}\right)} \right) = -1$$

$$\Rightarrow \qquad 2 - 2\tan^2\left(\frac{\theta}{2}\right) + 2\tan\left(\frac{\theta}{2}\right) = -1 - \tan^2\left(\frac{\theta}{2}\right)$$

$$\Rightarrow \qquad \tan^2\left(\frac{\theta}{2}\right) - 2\tan\left(\frac{\theta}{2}\right) - 3 = 0$$

$$\therefore \qquad \tan\left(\frac{\theta}{2}\right) = -1 \text{ or } 3$$

$$\therefore \qquad \tan\theta = \infty \quad \text{or} \quad -\frac{3}{4}$$

$\therefore$ Required lines are

$$y - 3 = \infty(x - 2)$$

and $$y - 3 = -\frac{3}{4}(x - 2)$$

i.e. $\quad x - 2 = 0$

and $\quad 3x + 4y - 18 = 0$

97. If I be the incentre of ΔOAB.

If inradius $= r$

then $\quad ID = IE = IF = r$

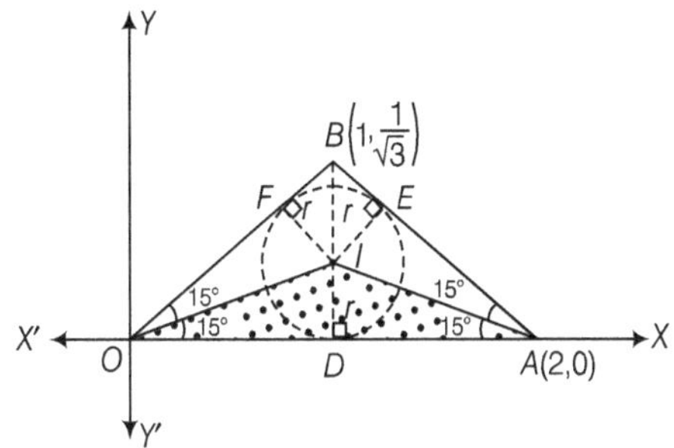

If P at I,then

$$d(P, OA) = d(P, OB) = d(P, AB) = r$$

But $\quad d(P, OA) \le \min\{d(P, OB), d(P, AB)\}$

which is possible only when P lies in the ΔOIA.

$$\therefore \quad \tan 15° = \frac{ID}{OD} = \frac{r}{1}$$

$$\Rightarrow \quad r = (2 - \sqrt{3})$$

$\therefore$ Required area $= \frac{1}{2} \cdot 2 \cdot r = r = (2 - \sqrt{3})$ sq units.

98. Let $A \equiv (x_1, y_1)$, $B \equiv (x_2, y_2)$ and $C \equiv (x_3, y_3)$ are the vertices of a triangle ABC and $P \equiv (a_1, b_1)$, $Q \equiv (a_2, b_2)$ and $R \equiv (a_3, b_3)$ are the vertices of triangle PQR.

Equation of perpendicular from A to QR is

$$y - y_1 = -\frac{(a_2 - a_3)}{(b_2 - b_3)}(x - x_1)$$

or $\quad (a_2 - a_3)x + (b_2 - b_3)y - x_1(a_2 - a_3) - y_1(b_2 - b_3) = 0 \quad$ ...(i)

Similarly, equations of perpendiculars from B to RP and C to PQ are respectively,

$$(a_3 - a_1)x + (b_3 - b_1)y - x_2(a_3 - a_1) - y_2(b_3 - b_1) = 0 \quad \text{...(ii)}$$

and $(a_1 - a_2)x + (b_1 - b_2)y - x_3(a_1 - a_2) - y_3(b_1 - b_2) = 0$ ...(iii)

Given that lines (i), (ii) and (iii) are concurrent, then adding, we get

$$(x_2 - x_3)a_1 + (x_3 - x_1)a_2 + (x_1 - x_2)a_3 + (y_2 - y_3)b_1 + (y_3 - y_1)b_2 + (y_1 - y_2)b_3 = 0 \quad \text{...(iv)}$$

Now, equation of perpendicular from P to BC is

$$y - b_1 = -\frac{(x_2 - x_3)}{(y_2 - y_3)}(x - a_1)$$

or $\quad (x_2 - x_3)x + (y_2 - y_3)y - a_1(x_2 - x_3) - b_1(y_2 - y_3) = 0 \quad$ ...(v)

Similarly, equations of perpendiculars from Q to CA and R to AB are respectively,

$$(x_3 - x_1)x + (y_3 - y_1)y - a_2(x_3 - x_1) - b_2(y_3 - y_1) = 0 \quad \text{...(vi)}$$

and $\quad (x_1 - x_2)x + (y_1 - y_2)y - a_3(x_1 - x_2) - b_3(y_1 - y_2) = 0 \quad$ ...(vii)

Adding Eqs. (v), (vi) and (vii), we get

LHS = 0 (identically) [from Eq. (iv)]

Hence perpendiculars from P to BC, Q to CA and R to AB are concurrent.

99. The line passing through the intersection of lines $ax + 2by + 3b = 0$ and $bx - 2ay - 3a = 0$ is

$$ax + 2by + 3b + \lambda(bx - 2ay - 3a) = 0$$

$$\Rightarrow (a + b\lambda)x + (2b - 2a\lambda)y + 3b - 3\lambda a = 0$$

As this line is parallel to X-axis.

$$\therefore \quad a + b\lambda = 0 \Rightarrow \lambda = -\frac{a}{b}$$

$$\Rightarrow \quad ax + 2by + 3a - \frac{a}{b}(bx - 2ay - 3a) = 0$$

$$\Rightarrow \quad ax + 2by + 3b - ax + \frac{2a^2}{b}y + \frac{3a^2}{b} = 0$$

$$y\left(2b + \frac{2a^2}{b}\right) + 3b + \frac{3a^2}{b} = 0$$

$$y\left(\frac{2b^2 + 2a^2}{b}\right) = -\left(\frac{3b^2 + 3a^2}{b}\right)$$

$$y = \frac{-3(a^2 + b^2)}{2(b^2 + a^2)} = \frac{-3}{2}$$

So, it is $\frac{3}{2}$ units below X-axis.

100.

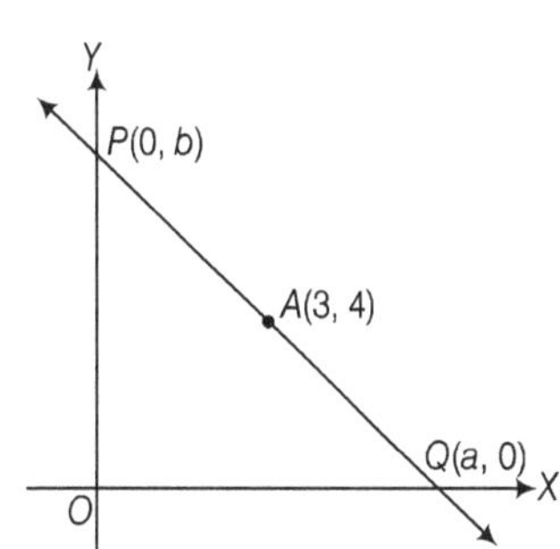

$\because A$ is the mid-point of PQ, therefore

$$\frac{a + 0}{2} = 3, \frac{0 + b}{2} = 4$$

$$\Rightarrow \quad a = 6, b = 8$$

$\therefore$ Equation of line is $\frac{x}{6} + \frac{y}{8} = 1$

or $\quad 4x + 3y = 24$

101. Clearly for point P,

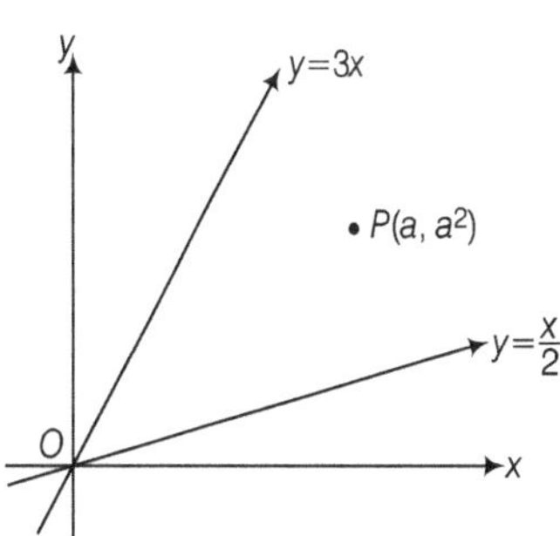

$$a^2 - 3a < 0 \text{ and } a^2 - \frac{a}{2} > 0$$

$$\Rightarrow \quad \frac{1}{2} < a < 3$$

102. Point of intersection of L_1 and L_2 is $A(0, 0)$.

Also $P(-2, -2)$, $Q(1, -2)$

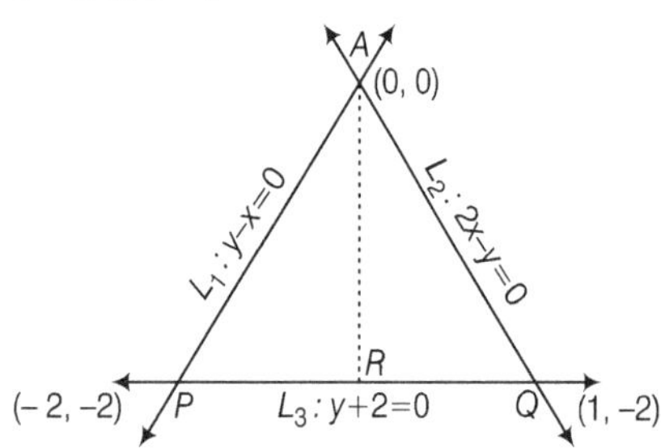

$\because AR$ is the bisector of $\angle PAQ$, therefore R divides PQ in the same ratio as $AP : AQ$.

Thus $PR : RQ = AP : AQ = 2\sqrt{2} : \sqrt{5}$

$\therefore$ Statement I is true.

Statement II is clearly false.

103. Given : The coordinates of points P, Q, R are $(-1, 0), (0, 0), (3, 3\sqrt{3})$ respectively.

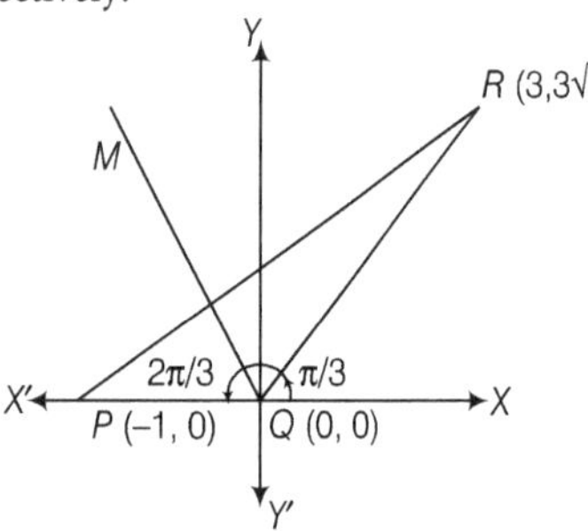

Slope of equation $QR = \dfrac{y_2 - y_1}{x_2 - x_1} = \dfrac{3\sqrt{3}}{3}$

$\Rightarrow \quad \tan\theta = \sqrt{3} \Rightarrow \theta = \dfrac{\pi}{3}$

$\Rightarrow \quad \angle RQX = \dfrac{\pi}{3}$

$\therefore \quad \angle RQP = \pi - \dfrac{\pi}{3} = \dfrac{2\pi}{3}$

Let QM bisects the $\angle PQR$,

$\therefore$ Slope of the line $QM = \tan\dfrac{2\pi}{3} = -\sqrt{3}$

$\therefore$ Equation of line QM is $(y - 0) = -\sqrt{3}(x - 0)$

$\Rightarrow \quad y = -\sqrt{3}x \Rightarrow \sqrt{3}x + y = 0$

104. **(A)** $\because L_1, L_2, L_3$ are concurrent, then

$$\begin{vmatrix} 1 & 3 & -5 \\ 3 & -k & -1 \\ 5 & 2 & -12 \end{vmatrix} = 0 \Rightarrow k = 5$$

(B) slope of (L_1) = slope of (L_2)

$\Rightarrow \quad -\dfrac{1}{3} = \dfrac{3}{k} \quad \therefore k = -9$

and slope of (L_3) = slope of (L_2)

$\rightarrow \quad \dfrac{5}{2} = \dfrac{3}{k} \quad \therefore k = -\dfrac{6}{5}$

(C) Lines are not concurrent or not parallel, then

$$k \neq 5, k \neq -9, k \neq -\frac{6}{5}$$

$\therefore \quad k = \dfrac{5}{6}$

(D) The given lines do not form a triangle if they are concurrent or any two of them are parallel.

$\therefore \quad k = 5, k = -9, k = -\dfrac{6}{5}$

105. Slope of $PQ = \dfrac{3-4}{k-1} = \dfrac{-1}{k-1}$

$\therefore$ Slope of perpendicular bisector of $PQ = (k-1)$

Also mid-point of $PQ \left(\dfrac{k+1}{2}, \dfrac{7}{2}\right)$

$\therefore$ Equation of perpendicular bisector is

$$y - \frac{7}{2} = (k-1)\left(x - \frac{k+1}{2}\right)$$

$\Rightarrow \quad 2y - 7 = 2(k-1)x - (k^2 - 1)$

$\Rightarrow \quad 2(k-1)x - 2y + (8 - k^2) = 0$

$\therefore \quad Y\text{-intercept} = -\dfrac{8-k^2}{-2} = -4$

$\Rightarrow \quad 8 - k^2 = -8 \text{ or } k^2 = 16 \Rightarrow k = \pm 4$

106. If the line $p(p^2 + 1)x - y + q = 0$

and $\quad (p^2 + 1)^2 x + (p^2 + 1)y + 2q = 0$

are perpendicular to a common line, then these lines must be parallel to each other,

$\therefore \quad m_1 = m_2 \Rightarrow -\dfrac{p(p^2+1)}{-1} = -\dfrac{(p^2+1)^2}{p^2+1}$

$\Rightarrow \quad (p^2 + 1)(p + 1) = 0$

$\Rightarrow \quad p = -1$

$\therefore p$ can have exactly one value.

107. Slope of line $L = -\dfrac{b}{5}$

Slope of line $K = -\dfrac{3}{c}$

Line L is parallel to line K.

$\Rightarrow \quad \dfrac{b}{5} = \dfrac{3}{c} \Rightarrow bc = 15$

$(13, 32)$ is a point on L.

$\therefore \quad \dfrac{13}{5} + \dfrac{32}{b} = 1 \Rightarrow \dfrac{32}{b} = -\dfrac{8}{5}$

$\Rightarrow \quad b = -20 \Rightarrow c = -\dfrac{3}{4}$

Equation of $K : y - 4x = 3$

$\Rightarrow \quad 4x - y + 3 = 0$

Distance between L and $K = \dfrac{|52 - 32 + 3|}{\sqrt{17}}$

$= \dfrac{23}{\sqrt{17}}$

108. Let the slope of line L be m.

Then $$\left|\frac{m+\sqrt{3}}{1-\sqrt{3}m}\right| = \sqrt{3}$$

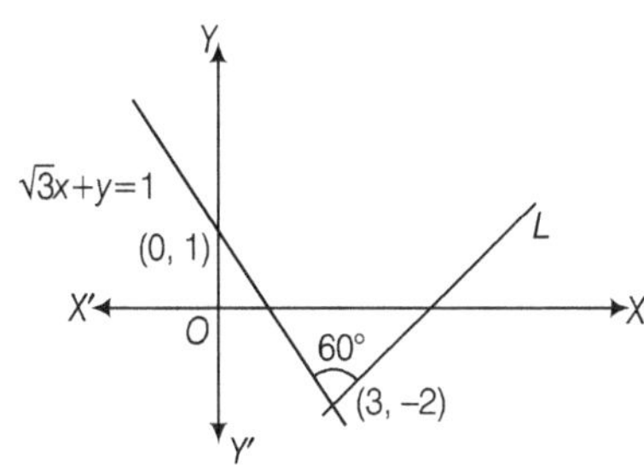

$\Rightarrow \quad m+\sqrt{3} = \pm(\sqrt{3}-3m)$

$\Rightarrow \quad 4m = 0$ or $2m = 2\sqrt{3}$

$\Rightarrow \quad m = 0$ or $m = \sqrt{3}$

$\because L$ intersects X-axis,

$\therefore \quad m = \sqrt{3}$

$\therefore$Equation of L is $y+2=\sqrt{3}(x-3)$

or $\quad \sqrt{3}x - y - (2+3\sqrt{3}) = 0$

109.

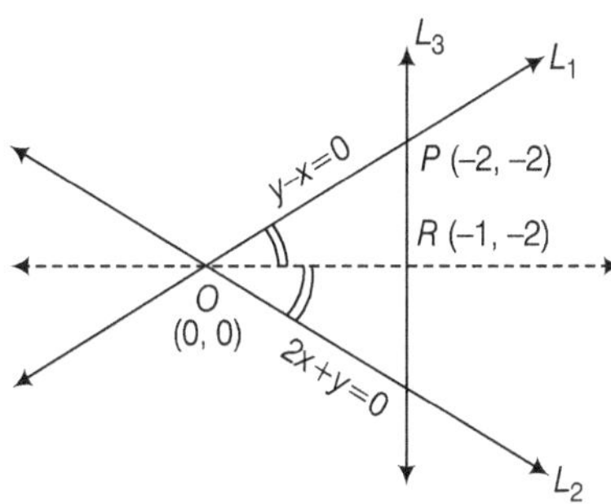

$$L_1 : y - x = 0,\quad L_2 : 2x + y = 0,\quad L_3 : y + 2 = 0$$

On solving the equation of lines L_1 and L_2, we get their point of intersection (0, 0) i.e. origin O.

On solving the equation of lines L_1 and L_3,

we get $\quad P = (-2, -2)$

Similarly, we get $\quad Q = (-1, -2)$

We know that bisector of an angle of a triangle, divide the opposite side the triangle in the ratio of the sides including the angle [Angle Bisector Theorem of a Triangle]

$$\therefore \quad \frac{PR}{RQ} = \frac{OP}{OQ} = \frac{\sqrt{(-2)^2+(-2)^2}}{\sqrt{(-1)^2+(-2)^2}} = \frac{2\sqrt{2}}{\sqrt{5}}$$

110. Let the joining points be $A(1, 1)$ and $B(2, 4)$.

Let point C divides line AB in the ratio 3 : 2. So, by section formula we have

$$C = \left(\frac{3\times2+2\times1}{3+2}, \frac{3\times4+2\times1}{3+2}\right) = \left(\frac{8}{5}, \frac{14}{5}\right)$$

Since Line $2x+y=k$ passes through $C\left(\frac{8}{5}, \frac{14}{5}\right)$

$\therefore C$ satisfies the equation $2x+y=k$.

$$\Rightarrow \quad \frac{2+8}{5} + \frac{14}{5} = k \Rightarrow k = 6$$

111. Suppose $B(0, 1)$ be any point on given line and coordinate of A is $(\sqrt{3}, 0)$. So, equation of

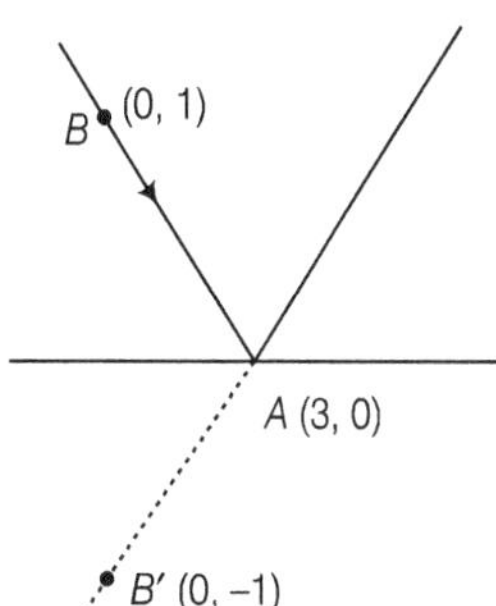

Reflected ray is $\dfrac{-1-0}{0-\sqrt{3}} = \dfrac{y-0}{x-\sqrt{3}}$

$\Rightarrow \quad \sqrt{3}y = x - \sqrt{3}$

112. The intersection point of two lines is $\left(\dfrac{-c}{a+b}, \dfrac{-c}{a+b}\right)$

Distance between (1, 1) and $\left(\dfrac{-c}{a+b}, \dfrac{-c}{a+b}\right) < 2\sqrt{2}$

$$\Rightarrow \quad 2\left(1+\frac{c}{a+b}\right)^2 < 8$$

$$\Rightarrow \quad 1+\frac{c}{a+b} < 2$$

$$\Rightarrow \quad a+b-c > 0$$

113. Let P, Q, R, be the vertices of ΔPQR

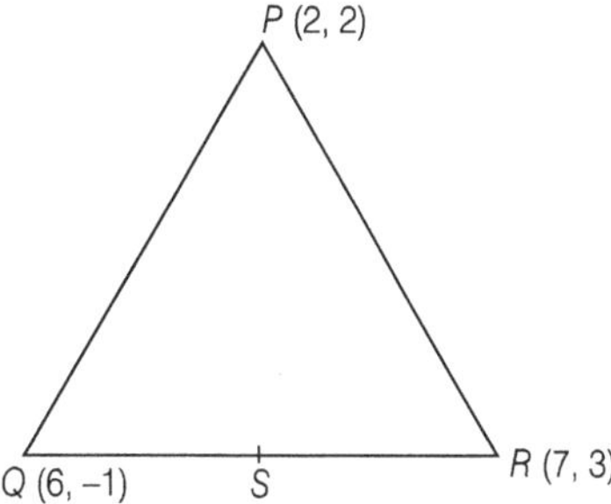

Since, PS is the median, S is mid-point of QR

So, $$S = \left(\frac{7+6}{2}, \frac{3-1}{2}\right) = \left(\frac{13}{2}, 1\right)$$

Now, slope of $PS = \dfrac{2-1}{2-\dfrac{13}{2}} = -\dfrac{2}{9}$

Since, required line is parallel to PS therefore slope of required line = slope of PS Now, eqn of line passing through $(1, -1)$ and having slope $-\dfrac{2}{9}$ is

$$y-(-1) = -\frac{2}{9}(x-1)$$

$$9y+9 = -2x+2$$

$$\Rightarrow \quad 2x+9y+7=0$$

114. Given lines are

$$4ax + 2ay + c = 0$$
$$5bx + 2by + d = 0$$

The point of intersection will be

$$\frac{x}{2ad - 2bc} = \frac{-y}{4ad - 5bc} = \frac{1}{8ab - 10ab}$$

$$\Rightarrow \quad x = \frac{2(ad - bc)}{-2ab} = \frac{bc - ad}{ab}$$

$$\Rightarrow \quad y = \frac{5bc - 4ad}{-2ab} = \frac{4ad - 5bc}{2ab}$$

$\because$ Point of intersection is in fourth quadrant so x is positive and y is negative.

Also distance from axes is same

So $\quad x = -y \quad$ ($\because$ distance from X-axis is $-y$ as y is negative)

$$\frac{bc - ad}{ab} = \frac{5bc - 4ad}{2ab} \Rightarrow 3bc - 2ad = 0$$

115. Let the point P be (x, y)

Then $\quad d_1(P) = \left|\frac{x - y}{\sqrt{2}}\right|$ and $d_2(P) = \left|\frac{x + y}{\sqrt{2}}\right|$

For P lying in first quadrant $x > 0, y > 0$.

Also $\quad 2 \le d_1(P) + d_2(P) \le 4$

$$\Rightarrow \quad 2 \le \left|\frac{x - y}{\sqrt{2}}\right| + \left|\frac{x + y}{\sqrt{2}}\right| \le 4$$

If $x > y$, then

$$2 \le \frac{x - y + x + y}{\sqrt{2}} \le 4 \text{ or } \sqrt{2} \le x \le 2\sqrt{2}$$

If $x < y$, then

$$2 \le \frac{y - x + x + y}{2} \le 4 \text{ or } \sqrt{2} \le y \le 2\sqrt{2}$$

The required region is the shaded region in the figure given below.

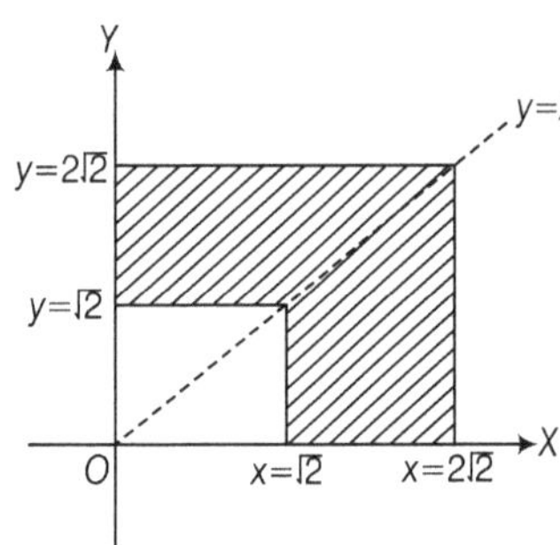

$\therefore$ Required area $= (2\sqrt{2})^2 - (\sqrt{2})^2 = 8 - 2 = 6$ sq units

116. Total number of integral points inside the square $OABC$

$$= 40 \times 40 = 1600$$

Number of integral points on AC

$$= \text{Number of integral points on } OB$$
$$= 40 \text{ [namely (1, 1), (2, 2) ... (40, 40)]}$$

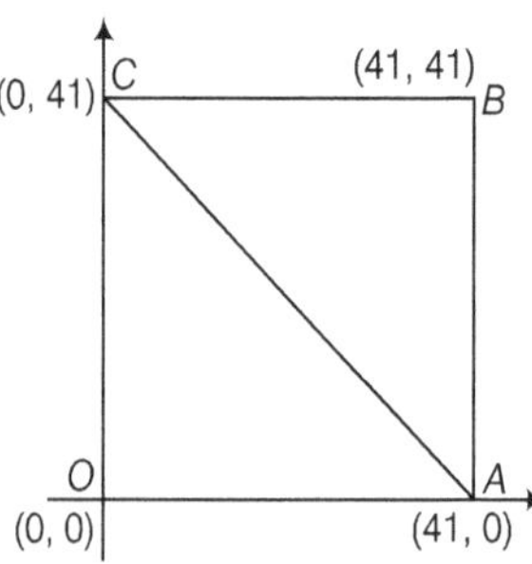

$\therefore$ Number of integral points inside the ΔOAC

$$= \frac{1600 - 40}{2} = 780$$

117.

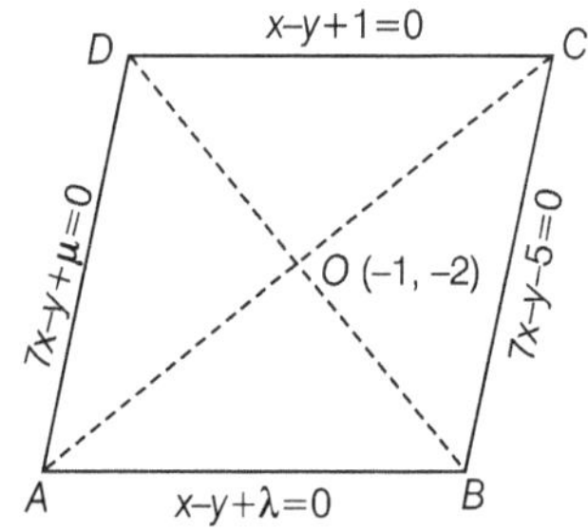

Let other two sides of rhombus are

$$x - y + \lambda = 0$$

and $\quad 7x - y + \mu = 0$

then O is equidistant from AB and DC and from AD and BC

$\therefore \quad |-1 + 2 + 1| = |-1 + 2 + \lambda| \Rightarrow \lambda = -3$

and $\quad |-7 + 2 - 5| = |-7 + 2 + \mu| \Rightarrow \mu = 15$

$\therefore$ Other two sides are

$$x - y - 3 = 0$$

and $\quad 7x - y + 15 = 0$

On solving the equation of sides pairwise, we get the vertices as $\left(\frac{1}{3}, \frac{-8}{3}\right)$, $(1, 2)$, $\left(\frac{-7}{3}, \frac{-4}{3}\right)$, $(-3, -6)$

CHAPTER

03

Pair of Straight Lines

Learning Part

Session 1

- Introduction
- Homogeneous Equation in Two Variables

Session 2

- Angle between the Pair of Lines $ax^2 + 2hxy + by^2$

Session 3

- Bisectors of the Angle between the Lines Given by a Homogeneous Equation

Session 4

- General Equation of Second Degree
- Important Theorems

Session 5

- To Find the Point of Intersection of Lines Represented by $ax^2 + 2hxy + by^2 + 2gx + 2fy + c = 0$ with the Help of Partial Differentiation
- Removal of First Degree Term
- Equation of the Lines Joining the Origin to the Points of Intersection of a Given Line and a Given Curve

Practice Part

- JEE Type Examples
- Chapter Exercises

Session 1

Introduction, Homogeneous Equation in Two Variables

Introduction

Let the equation of two lines be

$$ax + by + c = 0 \quad \text{...(i)}$$

and $$a_1x + b_1y + c_1 = 0 \quad \text{...(ii)}$$

Hence, $(ax + by + c)(a_1x + b_1y + c_1) = 0$ is called the joint equation of lines Eqs. (i) and (ii) and conversely, if joint equation of two lines be

$$(ax + by + c)(a_1x + b_1y + c_1) = 0,$$

then their separate equations will be

$$ax + by + c = 0 \quad \text{and} \quad a_1x + b_1y + c_1 = 0$$

Remark

In order to find the joint equation of two lines, make RHS of two lines equal to zero and then multiply the two equations.

Example 1 Find the joint equation of lines $y = x$ and $y = -x$.

Sol. The given lines can be rewritten as

$$x - y = 0 \quad \text{and} \quad x + y = 0$$

$\therefore$ Joint equation of lines is $(x - y)(x + y) = 0$

or $$x^2 - y^2 = 0$$

Wrong process : Since, the lines are

$$y = x \quad \text{and} \quad y = -x$$

Then joint equation is $\quad y^2 = -x^2$

$$\Rightarrow \quad x^2 + y^2 = 0$$

This process is wrong, since RHS of two equations are not equal to zero.

Remark

In order to find the separate equations of two lines when their joint equation is given, first of all make RHS equal to zero and then resolve LHS into two linear factors or use Shri Dharacharya method. The two factors equated to zero will give the separate equations of lines.

Example 2 Find the separate equation of lines represented by the equation $x^2 - 6xy + 8y^2 = 0$.

Sol. Separate equation of lines represented by the equation

$$x^2 - 6xy + 8y^2 = 0$$

i.e. $$(x - 4y)(x - 2y) = 0$$

$$\Rightarrow \quad x - 4y = 0 \quad \text{and} \quad x - 2y = 0$$

Aliter :

We have, $\quad x^2 - 6xy + 8y^2 = 0$

By Shri Dharacharya method, $x = \dfrac{6y \pm \sqrt{(-6y)^2 - 4 \cdot 8y^2}}{2}$

$$\Rightarrow \quad x = 3y \pm y\sqrt{(9 - 8)}$$

$$x = 3y \pm y$$

$$\therefore \quad x = 4y \quad \text{and} \quad x = 2y$$

Hence, the lines are

$$x - 4y = 0 \quad \text{and} \quad x - 2y = 0.$$

Homogeneous Equation in Two Variables

An equation of the form

$$a_0y^n + a_1y^{n-1}x + a_2y^{n-2}x^2 + \ldots + a_nx^n = 0 \quad \text{...(i)}$$

in which the sum of the powers of x and y in every term is the same (here n), is called a **homogeneous** equation (of degree n).

We will prove that Eq. (i) represents n straight lines passing through the origin.

$$a_0y^n + a_1y^{n-1}x + a_2y^{n-2}x^2 + \ldots + a_nx^n = 0$$

Dividing each term by x^n, we get

$$a_0\left(\frac{y}{x}\right)^n + a_1\left(\frac{y}{x}\right)^{n-1} + a_2\left(\frac{y}{x}\right)^{n-2} + \ldots + a_n = 0$$

Above is an equation of nth degree in $\dfrac{y}{x}$. Let the roots of this equation be $m_1, m_2, m_3, \ldots, m_n$.

Then, the above equation will be identical with

$$a_0\left(\frac{y}{x} - m_1\right)\left(\frac{y}{x} - m_2\right)\left(\frac{y}{x} - m_3\right)\ldots\left(\frac{y}{x} - m_n\right) = 0$$

$$\Rightarrow a_0(y - m_1x)(y - m_2x)(y - m_3x)\ldots(y - m_nx) = 0$$

Hence, Eq. (i) represents n straight lines

$$y-m_1 x=0, y-m_2 x=0,$$
$$y-m_3 x=0, \ldots, y-m_n x=0$$

all of which clearly pass through the origin.

***Corollary*:** Since, $ax^2+2hxy+by^2=0$ is a homogeneous equation of second degree, it represents two straight lines through origin. The given equation is

$$ax^2+2hxy+by^2=0 \quad \text{...(i)}$$

Dividing by x^2, we get

$$a+2h\left(\frac{y}{x}\right)+b\left(\frac{y}{x}\right)^2=0$$

$$\Rightarrow \quad b\left(\frac{y}{x}\right)^2+2h\left(\frac{y}{x}\right)+a=0 \quad \text{...(ii)}$$

Putting $\frac{y}{x}=m$

then, $bm^2+2hm+a=0$ ...(iii)

If m_1 and m_2 be two roots, then

$$m_1+m_2=-\frac{2h}{b}=-\frac{\text{coefficient of } xy}{\text{coefficient of } y^2}$$

and $m_1m_2=\frac{a}{b}=\frac{\text{coefficient of } x^2}{\text{coefficient of } y^2}$

$$\therefore \quad |m_1-m_2|=\sqrt{\{(m_1+m_2)^2-4m_1m_2\}}$$
$$=\frac{2}{|b|}\sqrt{(h^2-ab)}$$

Thus, $y=m_1x$ and $y=m_2x$ are two straight lines which are given by Eq. (i). Also, from Eq. (iii),

$$m=\frac{-2h\pm2\sqrt{(h^2-ab)}}{2b}$$
$$=\frac{-h\pm\sqrt{(h^2-ab)}}{b}=\frac{y}{x} \quad \left[\because m=\frac{y}{x}\right]$$

$$\therefore \quad by=\{-h+\sqrt{(h^2-ab)}\}x$$

and $by=\{-h-\sqrt{(h^2-ab)}\}x$

are two lines represented by Eq. (i).

(i) The lines are real and distinct, if $h^2-ab>0$.
(ii) The lines are coincident, if $h^2-ab=0$.
(iii) The lines are imaginary, if $h^2-ab<0$.

Remarks

1. In further discussions, we will consider only real cases.
2. **Two very useful identities** When lines represented by
$$ax^2+2hxy+by^2=0$$
pass through the origin, let their equations be
$$y=m_1x \text{ and } y=m_2x$$
then, $(y-m_1x)$ and $(y-m_2x)$
must be factors of $ax^2+2hxy+by^2=0$
then $ax^2+2hxy+by^2=b(y-m_1x)(y-m_2x)$
[Making coefficient of y^2 equal on both sides]
Now, comparing both sides, we get
$$2h=-b(m_1+m_2) \text{ and } a=bm_1m_2$$
$$\therefore \quad m_1+m_2=-\frac{2h}{b} \text{ and } m_1m_2=\frac{a}{b}$$

Example 3 Find the condition that the slope of one of the lines represented by $ax^2+2hxy+by^2=0$ should be n times the slope of the other.

Sol. Let the lines represented by
$ax^2+2hxy+by^2=0$ are $y=m_1x$ and $y=m_2x$.

Therefore, $m_1+m_2=-\frac{2h}{b}$ ...(i)

and $m_1m_2=\frac{a}{b}$ ...(ii)

Given, $m_2=nm_1$

From Eq. (i), $m_1+nm_1=-\frac{2h}{b}$

$$\therefore \quad m_1=-\frac{2h}{b(1+n)} \quad \text{...(iii)}$$

and from Eq. (ii), $m_1(nm_1)=\frac{a}{b}$

$$\therefore \quad nm_1^2=\frac{a}{b}$$

$$\Rightarrow \quad n\left\{\frac{-2h}{b(1+n)}\right\}^2=\frac{a}{b} \quad \text{[from Eq. (iii)]}$$

$$\Rightarrow \quad \frac{4nh^2}{b^2(1+n)^2}=\frac{a}{b}$$

$$\Rightarrow \quad 4nh^2=ab(1+n)^2 \quad \text{...(iv)}$$

This is the required condition.

***Corollary*:** If slope of one line is double of the other, then put $n=2$ in Eq. (iv), we have

$$8h^2=9ab.$$

Example 4 If the slope of one of the lines represented by $ax^2+2hxy+by^2=0$ be the nth power of the other, prove that, $(ab^n)^{\frac{1}{n+1}}+(a^nb)^{\frac{1}{n+1}}+2h=0$.

Sol. Let m and m^n be the slopes of the lines represented by
$$ax^2+2hxy+by^2=0$$

then $m+m^n=-\frac{2h}{b}$ ...(i)

and $\quad m\cdot m^n=\frac{a}{b}\Rightarrow m^{n+1}=\frac{a}{b}$

$\Rightarrow \quad m=\left(\frac{a}{b}\right)^{\frac{1}{(n+1)}}$ ...(ii)

Substituting the value of m from Eq. (ii) in Eq. (i), then

$$\left(\frac{a}{b}\right)^{\frac{1}{(n+1)}}+\left(\frac{a}{b}\right)^{\left(\frac{n}{n+1}\right)}=-\frac{2h}{b}$$

$$\Rightarrow \quad a^{\frac{1}{n+1}}\cdot b^{\frac{n}{n+1}}+a^{\frac{n}{n+1}}\cdot b^{\frac{1}{n+1}}+2h=0$$

***Corollary*:** If slope of one line is square of the other, then put $n=2$, then

$$(ab^2)^{\frac{1}{3}}+(a^2b)^{\frac{1}{3}}=-2h$$

On cubing both sides, we get

$$ab^2+a^2b+3(ab^2)^{\frac{1}{3}}(a^2b)^{\frac{1}{3}}\left((ab^2)^{\frac{1}{3}}+(a^2b)^{\frac{1}{3}}\right)=-8h^3$$

$$\Rightarrow \quad ab(a+b)+3ab(-2h)=-8h^3$$

$$\therefore \quad \frac{(a+b)}{h}+\frac{8h^2}{ab}=6.$$

Example 5 Find the product of the perpendiculars drawn from the point (x_1, y_1) on the lines $ax^2+2hxy+by^2=0$.

Sol. Let the lines represented by $ax^2+2hxy+by^2=0$ be $y=m_1x$ and $y=m_2x$.

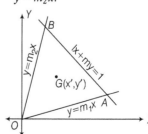

Therefore, $m_1+m_2=-\frac{2h}{b}$ and $m_1m_2=\frac{a}{b}$

The lengths of the perpendiculars from (x_1, y_1) on these lines are

$$\frac{|y_1-m_1x_1|}{\sqrt{1+m_1^2}} \text{ and } \frac{|y_1-m_2x_1|}{\sqrt{1+m_2^2}}$$

$$\text{Their product}=\frac{|y_1-m_1x_1|}{\sqrt{1+m_1^2}}\times\frac{|y_1-m_2x_1|}{\sqrt{1+m_2^2}}$$

$$=\frac{|(y_1-m_1x_1)(y_1-m_2x_1)|}{\sqrt{(1+m_1^2)(1+m_2^2)}}$$

$$=\frac{|y_1^2-(m_1+m_2)x_1y_1+m_1m_2x_1^2|}{\sqrt{1+m_1^2+m_2^2+m_1^2m_2^2}}$$

$$=\frac{|y_1^2-(m_1+m_2)x_1y_1+m_1m_2x_1^2|}{\sqrt{1+(m_1+m_2)^2-2m_1m_2+(m_1m_2)^2}}$$

$$=\frac{\left|y_1^2+\frac{2h}{b}x_1y_1+\frac{a}{b}x_1^2\right|}{\sqrt{\left(1+\frac{4h^2}{b^2}-\frac{2a}{b}+\frac{a^2}{b^2}\right)}}$$

$$=\frac{|ax_1^2+2hx_1y_1+by_1^2|}{\sqrt{\{(a-b)^2+4h^2\}}}$$

Example 6 Find the condition that one of the lines given by $ax^2+2hxy+by^2=0$ may be perpendicular to one of the lines given by $a'x^2+2h'xy+b'y^2=0$.

Sol. Since, both pair are passing through origin, let $y=mx$ be one of the lines represented by

$$ax^2+2hxy+by^2=0$$

then, $ax^2+2hx(mx)+b(mx)^2=0$

$\Rightarrow \quad bm^2+2hm+a=0$ ...(i)

then, $y=-\frac{1}{m}x$ be one of the line represented by

$$a'x^2+2h'xy+b'y^2=0$$

$\left[\because y=-\frac{1}{m}x \text{ is perpendicular to } y=mx \text{ and passing through origin}\right]$

then $a'x^2+2h'x\left(-\frac{1}{m}x\right)+b'\left(-\frac{1}{m}x\right)^2=0$

$\Rightarrow \quad a'm^2-2h'm+b'=0$ ...(ii)

On solving Eqs. (i) and (ii), by cross-multiplication rule i.e.

$$\begin{matrix} m^2 & m & 1 & m^2 & m \\ b & 2h & a & b & 2h \\ a' & -2h' & b' & a' & -2h' \end{matrix}$$

$$\Rightarrow \quad \frac{m^2}{2hb'+2h'a}=\frac{m}{aa'-bb'}=\frac{1}{-2h'b-2a'h}$$

$$\therefore \quad m^2=-\frac{(hb'+h'a)}{(h'b+a'h)},\ m=\frac{(bb'-aa')}{2(a'h+h'b)}$$

On eliminating m, we obtain

$$4(ha'+h'b)(h'a+hb')+(bb'-aa')^2=0.$$

Example 7 Show that the centroid (x', y') of the triangle with sides $ax^2+2hxy+by^2=0$ and $lx+my=1$, is given by

$$\frac{x'}{bl-hm}=\frac{y'}{am-hl}=\frac{2}{3(am^2-2hlm+bl^2)}.$$

Sol. Let the lines represented by

$$ax^2+2hxy+by^2=0$$

be $\quad y=m_1x$

and $\quad y=m_2x$.

Therefore, $m_1 + m_2 = -\dfrac{2h}{b}$

and $m_1 m_2 = \dfrac{a}{b}$

Coordinates of A and B are

$$\left(\frac{1}{l+mm_1}, \frac{m_1}{l+mm_1}\right) \text{ and } \left(\frac{1}{l+mm_2}, \frac{m_2}{l+mm_2}\right)$$

Since, centroid $= (x', y')$,

then, $x' = \left(\dfrac{\dfrac{1}{l+mm_1}+\dfrac{1}{l+mm_2}+0}{3}\right)$

$$= \left(\frac{2l + m(m_1+m_2)}{3\{l^2 + ml(m_1+m_2) + m^2 m_1 m_2)\}}\right)$$

$$= \left(\frac{2l - \dfrac{2hm}{b}}{3\left(l^2 - \dfrac{2hml}{b} + \dfrac{m^2 a}{b}\right)}\right)$$

$$= \frac{2}{3}\cdot\frac{(bl - hm)}{(am^2 - 2hlm + bl^2)} \quad \text{...(i)}$$

and $y' = \left(\dfrac{\dfrac{m_1}{l+mm_1}+\dfrac{m_2}{l+mm_2}+0}{3}\right)$

$$= \left(\frac{l(m_1+m_2) + 2mm_1m_2}{3\{l^2 + lm(m_1+m_2) + m^2 m_1 m_2)\}}\right)$$

$$= \left(\frac{-\dfrac{2hl}{b} + \dfrac{2ma}{b}}{3\left(l^2 - \dfrac{2hlm}{b} + \dfrac{m^2 a}{b}\right)}\right)$$

$$= \frac{2}{3}\cdot\frac{(am - hl)}{(am^2 - 2hlm + bl^2)} \quad \text{...(ii)}$$

From Eqs. (i) and (ii), we get

$$\frac{x'}{bl - hm} = \frac{y'}{am - hl} = \frac{2}{3(am^2 - 2hlm + bl^2)}$$

Example 8 Show that the area of the triangle formed by the lines $ax^2 + 2hxy + by^2 = 0$ and $lx + my + n = 0$ is $\dfrac{n^2\sqrt{(h^2 - ab)}}{|(am^2 - 2hlm + bl^2)|}$.

Sol. Let equation of lines represented by

$ax^2 + 2hxy + by^2 = 0$ be $y = m_1 x$ and $y = m_2 x$

therefore, $m_1 + m_2 = -\dfrac{2h}{b}$ and $m_1 m_2 = \dfrac{a}{b}$.

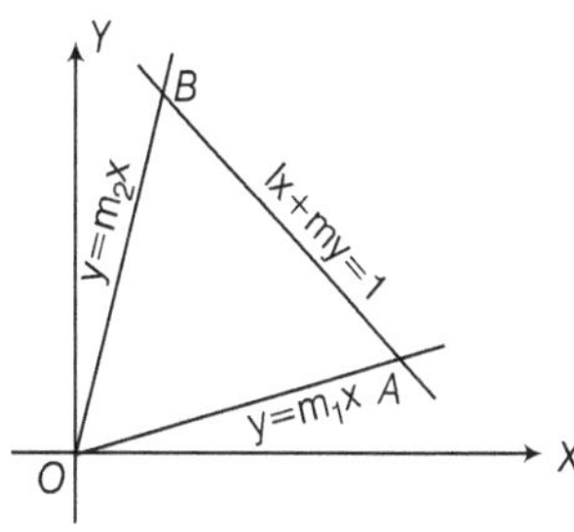

Coordinates of A and B are

$$\left(\frac{-n}{l+mm_1}, \frac{-nm_1}{l+mm_1}\right) \text{ and } \left(\frac{-n}{l+mm_2}, \frac{-nm_2}{l+mm_2}\right),$$

respectively.

Then, required area

$$= \frac{1}{2}\left|\left(\frac{-n}{l+mm_1}\right)\left(\frac{-nm_2}{l+mm_2}\right) - \left(\frac{-n}{l+mm_2}\right)\left(\frac{-nm_1}{l+mm_1}\right)\right|$$

[$\because$ if coordinates are $(0, 0), (x_1, y_1)$ and, (x_2, y_2), then area $= \frac{1}{2}|x_1y_2 - x_2y_1|$]

$$= \frac{1}{2}\left|\frac{n^2(m_2 - m_1)}{l^2 + lm(m_1+m_2) + m^2 m_1 m_2}\right|$$

$$= \frac{1}{2}\left|\frac{n^2\sqrt{(m_1+m_2)^2 - 4m_1m_2}}{l^2 + lm(m_1+m_2) + m^2 m_1 m_2}\right|$$

$$= \frac{1}{2}\left|\frac{n^2\sqrt{\left(\dfrac{4h^2}{b^2} - \dfrac{4a}{b}\right)}}{l^2 - \dfrac{2hlm}{b} + \dfrac{m^2 a}{b}}\right|$$

$$= \frac{n^2\sqrt{(h^2 - ab)}}{|(am^2 - 2hlm + bl^2)|}$$

Example 9 Show that the two straight lines $x^2(\tan^2\theta + \cos^2\theta) - 2xy\tan\theta + y^2\sin^2\theta = 0$ move with the axis of x angles such that the difference of their tangents is 2.

Sol. Given equation is

$$x^2(\tan^2\theta + \cos^2\theta) - 2xy\tan\theta + y^2\sin^2\theta = 0 \quad \text{...(i)}$$

and homogeneous equation of second degree

$$ax^2 + 2hxy + by^2 = 0 \quad \text{...(ii)}$$

On comparing Eqs. (i) and (ii), we get

$a = \tan^2\theta + \cos^2\theta$

$h = -\tan\theta$

and $b = \sin^2\theta$

Let separate lines of Eq. (ii) are

$y = m_1 x$

and $y = m_2 x$

where, $m_1 = \tan\theta_1$ and $m_2 = \tan\theta_2$

therefore, $m_1 + m_2 = -\frac{2h}{b} = \frac{2\tan\theta}{\sin^2\theta}$

and $m_1 \cdot m_2 = \frac{a}{b} = \frac{\tan^2\theta + \cos^2\theta}{\sin^2\theta}$

$\therefore \quad m_1 \sim m_2 = \sqrt{(m_1 + m_2)^2 - 4m_1m_2}$

$\Rightarrow \tan\theta_1 \sim \tan\theta_2 = \sqrt{\frac{4\tan^2\theta}{\sin^4\theta} - \frac{4(\tan^2\theta + \cos^2\theta)}{\sin^2\theta}}$

$= \frac{2}{\sin^2\theta}\sqrt{\tan^2\theta - \sin^2\theta(\tan^2\theta + \cos^2\theta)}$

$= \frac{2\sin\theta}{\sin^2\theta}\sqrt{(\sec^2\theta - \tan^2\theta - \cos^2\theta)}$

$= \frac{2\sin\theta}{\sin^2\theta}\sqrt{(1 - \cos^2\theta)}$

$= \frac{2}{\sin\theta}\sin\theta = 2$

Exercise for Session 1

1. The lines given by the equation $(2y^2 + 3xy - 2x^2)(x + y - 1) = 0$ form a triangle which is

(a) equilateral
(b) isosceles
(c) right angled
(d) obtuse angled

2. Area of the triangle formed by the lines $y^2 - 9xy + 18x^2 = 0$ and $y = 9$ is

(a) 27/4
(b) 0
(c) 9/4
(d) 27

3. The equation $3x^2 + 2hxy + 3y^2 = 0$ represents a pair of straight lines passing through the origin. The two lines are

(a) real and distinct, if $h^2 > 3$
(b) real and distinct, if $h^2 > 9$
(c) real and coincident, if $h^2 = 3$
(d) real and coincident, if $h^2 > 3$

4. If one of the lines of the pair $ax^2 + 2hxy + by^2 = 0$ bisects the angle between positive directions of the axes, then a, b, h satisfy the relation

(a) $a + b = 2|h|$
(b) $a + b = -2h$
(c) $a - b = 2|h|$
(d) $(a - b)^2 = 4h^2$

5. If the slope of one of the lines given by $a^2x^2 + 2hxy + b^2y^2 = 0$ be three times of the other, then h is equal to

(a) $2\sqrt{3}ab$
(b) $-2\sqrt{3}ab$
(c) $\frac{2}{\sqrt{3}}ab$
(d) $-\frac{2}{\sqrt{3}}ab$

6. Find the separate equations of two straight lines whose joint equation is $ab(x^2 - y^2) + (a^2 - b^2)xy = 0$.

7. Find the coordinates of the centroid of the triangle whose sides are $12x^2 - 20xy + 7y^2 = 0$ and $2x - 3y + 4 = 0$.

8. If the lines $ax^2 + 2hxy + by^2 = 0$ be two sides of a parallelogram and the line $lx + my = 1$ be one of its diagonal, show that the equation of the other diagonal is $y(bl - hm) = x(am - hl)$.

9. Find the condition that one of the lines given by $ax^2 + 2hxy + by^2 = 0$ may coincide with one of the lines given by $a'x^2 + 2h'xy + b'y^2 = 0$.

Session 2

Angle between the Pair of Lines $ax^2 + 2hxy + by^2$

Angle between the Pair of Lines $ax^2 + 2hxy + by^2$

Theorem The angle θ between the pair of lines represented by $ax^2 + 2hxy + by^2 = 0$

is given by $\theta = \tan^{-1}\left\{\frac{2\sqrt{(h^2 - ab)}}{|a+b|}\right\}$.

Proof Let $y = m_1 x$ and $y = m_2 x$ be the lines represented by

$$ax^2 + 2hxy + by^2 = 0.$$

Then, $m_1 + m_2 = -\frac{2h}{b}, m_1 m_2 = \frac{a}{b}$

Since, θ be the angle between the lines

$$y = m_1 x \quad \text{and} \quad y = m_2 x.$$

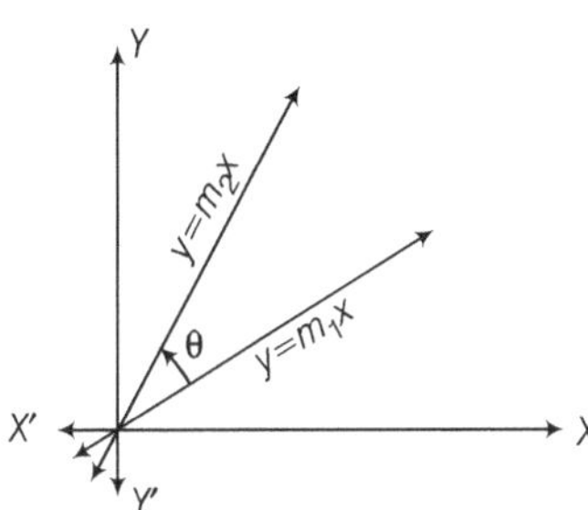

Then, $\tan\theta = \left|\frac{m_1 - m_2}{1 + m_1 m_2}\right| = \frac{\sqrt{(m_1 + m_2)^2 - 4m_1 m_2}}{|1 + m_1 m_2|}$

$$= \frac{\sqrt{\left(\frac{-2h}{b}\right)^2 - 4\left(\frac{a}{b}\right)}}{\left|1 + \frac{a}{b}\right|} = \frac{2\sqrt{(h^2 - ab)}}{|a+b|}$$

$$\therefore \quad \theta = \tan^{-1}\left\{\frac{2\sqrt{(h^2 - ab)}}{|a+b|}\right\}$$

Remark

$$\theta = \sin^{-1}\left\{\frac{2\sqrt{h^2 - ab}}{\sqrt{(a-b)^2 + 4h^2}}\right\}$$

Corollary 1 *Condition for the lines to be perpendicular.*

The lines are perpendicular if the angle between them is $\frac{\pi}{2}$.

i.e. $\theta = \frac{\pi}{2}$

$\Rightarrow \quad \cot\theta = \cot\frac{\pi}{2}$

$\Rightarrow \quad \cot\theta = 0$

$\Rightarrow \quad \frac{|a+b|}{2\sqrt{(h^2 - ab)}} = 0 \quad \Rightarrow \quad a + b = 0$

i.e. Coefficient of x^2 + Coefficient of $y^2 = 0$

Hence, the lines represented by $ax^2 + 2hxy + by^2 = 0$ are perpendicular, iff $a + b = 0$ i.e. coefficient of x^2 + coefficient of $y^2 = 0$.

Remark

Pair of any two perpendicular lines through the origin.

$\because$ Lines represented by $ax^2 + 2hxy + by^2 = 0$

be perpendicular, then $a + b = 0$ or $b = -a$

Hence, the equation becomes $ax^2 + 2hxy - ay^2 = 0$

$\Rightarrow \quad x^2 + \left(\frac{2h}{a}\right)xy - y^2 = 0$

$\Rightarrow \quad x^2 + pxy - y^2 = 0$, (Remember)

where, p is any constant.

Corollary 2 *Pair of lines perpendicular to the lines represented by*

$$ax^2 + 2hxy + by^2 = 0$$

and through origin.

Let lines represented by

$ax^2 + 2hxy + by^2 = 0$ be $y = m_1 x$ and $y = m_2 x$

then $\quad m_1 + m_2 = -\frac{2h}{b}$

and $\quad m_1 m_2 = \frac{a}{b}$

lines perpendiculars to $y = m_1 x$

and $y = m_2 x$

and passing through origin are

$$y = -\frac{1}{m_1} x$$

and $$y = -\frac{1}{m_2} x$$

then, pair is $$\left(y + \frac{x}{m_1}\right)\left(y + \frac{x}{m_2}\right) = 0$$

$$\Rightarrow \quad x^2 + xy(m_1 + m_2) + m_1 m_2 y^2 = 0$$

$$\Rightarrow \quad x^2 - \frac{2hxy}{b} + \frac{a}{b} y^2 = 0$$

$$\therefore \quad bx^2 - 2hxy + ay^2 = 0$$

Aid to memory For perpendicular pairs interchange the coefficients of x^2 and y^2 and change the sign of xy.

***Corollary* 3** *Condition for the lines to be coincident.*

The lines are coincident, if the angle between them is $0°$ (or π)

i.e. $$\theta = 0 \text{ (or } \pi)$$

$$\therefore \quad \tan\theta = 0°$$

$$\Rightarrow \quad \frac{2\sqrt{(h^2 - ab)}}{|a + b|} = 0$$

$$\Rightarrow \quad h^2 - ab = 0$$

$$\Rightarrow \quad h^2 = ab$$

Hence, the lines represented by $ax^2 + 2hxy + by^2 = 0$ are coincident, iff $h^2 = ab$, then $ax^2 + 2hxy + by^2$ is a perfect square.

Remark

The parallel lines will be coincident only as both pass through a point.

Example 10 Find the angle between the lines $(x^2 + y^2)\sin^2\alpha = (x\cos\beta - y\sin\beta)^2$.

Sol. Given equation is

$$(x^2 + y^2)\sin^2\alpha = (x\cos\beta - y\sin\beta)^2$$

$$\Rightarrow \quad x^2(\sin^2\alpha - \cos^2\beta) + 2xy\sin\beta\cos\beta + y^2(\sin^2\alpha - \sin^2\beta) = 0 \quad \text{...(i)}$$

The homogeneous equation of second degree is

$$ax^2 + 2hxy + by^2 = 0 \quad \text{...(ii)}$$

On comparing Eqs. (i) and (ii), we get

$$a = \sin^2\alpha - \cos^2\beta,\ h = \sin\beta\cos\beta,$$
$$b = \sin^2\alpha - \sin^2\beta$$

Let the angle between the lines representing by Eq. (i) is θ.

$$\therefore \quad \tan\theta = 2\frac{\sqrt{h^2 - ab}}{|a + b|}$$

$$= 2\frac{\sqrt{\sin^2\beta\cos^2\beta - (\sin^2\alpha - \cos^2\beta)(\sin^2\alpha - \sin^2\beta)}}{|\sin^2\alpha - \cos^2\beta + \sin^2\alpha - \sin^2\beta|}$$

$$= 2\frac{\sqrt{\{\sin^2\beta\cos^2\beta - \sin^4\alpha + \sin^2\alpha\sin^2\beta + \sin^2\alpha\cos^2\beta - \sin^2\beta\cos^2\beta\}}}{|(2\sin^2\alpha - 1)|}$$

$$= 2\frac{\sqrt{\sin^2\alpha(1 - \sin^2\alpha)}}{|-\cos 2\alpha|}$$

$$= \frac{2\sin\alpha\cos\alpha}{|-\cos 2\alpha|} = \tan 2\alpha$$

$$\therefore \quad \theta = 2\alpha$$

Example 11 Show that the angle between the lines given by $(a + 2hm + bm^2)x^2 + 2\{(b - a)m - (m^2 - 1)h\}xy + (am^2 - 2hm + b)y^2 = 0$ is the same whatever be the value of m.

Sol. Given equation is

$$(a + 2hm + bm^2)x^2 + 2\{(b - a)m - (m^2 - 1)h\}xy + (am^2 - 2hm + b)y^2 = 0 \quad \text{...(i)}$$

The homogeneous equation of second degree

$$Ax^2 + 2Hxy + By^2 = 0 \quad \text{...(ii)}$$

On comparing Eqs. (i) and (ii), we get

$$A = a + 2hm + bm^2,\ H = (b - a)m - (m^2 - 1)h,$$
$$B = am^2 - 2hm + b$$

Let the angle between the lines representing by Eq. (i) is θ.

$$\therefore \quad \tan\theta = \frac{2\sqrt{(H^2 - AB)}}{|A + B|}$$

$$= \frac{2\sqrt{\{(b - a)m - (m^2 - 1)h\}^2 - (a + 2hm + bm^2)(am^2 - 2hm + b)}}{|a + 2hm + bm^2 + am^2 - 2hm + b|}$$

$$= \frac{2\sqrt{(m^2 + 1)^2(h^2 - ab)}}{|a + b|(m^2 + 1)} = \frac{2\sqrt{(h^2 - ab)}}{|a + b|}$$

$$\Rightarrow \quad \theta = \tan^{-1}\left\{\frac{2\sqrt{(h^2 - ab)}}{|a + b|}\right\}$$

which is independent of m. Hence, the angle between the lines representing by Eq. (i) is same for all values of m.

Example 12 Show that the straight lines $x^2+4xy+y^2=0$ and the line $x-y=4$ form an equilateral triangle.

Sol. Equation $\quad x^2+4xy+y^2=0 \quad$ ...(i)

is a homogeneous equation of second degree in x and y. Therefore, it represents two lines OP and OQ through the origin.

Equation, $\quad x-y=4 \quad$ ...(ii)

represent the line PQ.

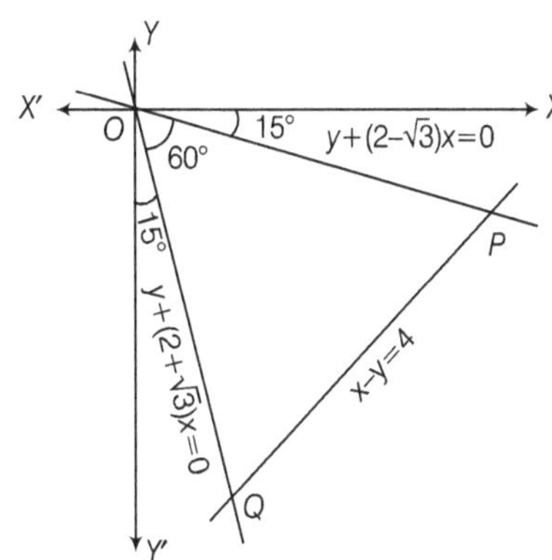

Let $\angle POQ=\theta$.

then, $\quad \tan\theta=\dfrac{2\sqrt{[(2)^2-1\cdot1]}}{|1+1|}=\sqrt{3}$

$\therefore \quad \theta=60^\circ$

From Eq. (i), $\quad x^2+4xy+y^2=0$

$\Rightarrow \quad \left(\dfrac{y}{x}\right)^2+4\left(\dfrac{y}{x}\right)+1=0$

$\Rightarrow \quad \dfrac{y}{x}=\dfrac{-4\pm\sqrt{(4^2-4)}}{2}=-2\pm\sqrt{3}$

$\Rightarrow \quad y=(-2\pm\sqrt{3})\,x$

i.e. $\quad OP: y+(2-\sqrt{3})\,x=0$

and $\quad OQ: y+(2+\sqrt{3})\,x=0$

$\because$ Slope of $PQ=1$ and Slope of $OP=-(2-\sqrt{3})$.

If $\quad \angle OPQ=\alpha$

then $\quad \tan\alpha=\left|\dfrac{1-(-2+\sqrt{3})}{1-2+\sqrt{3}}\right|=\left|\dfrac{3-\sqrt{3}}{-1+\sqrt{3}}\right|=\sqrt{3}$

$\therefore \quad \alpha=60^\circ$

Hence, $\angle OQP=180^\circ-(60^\circ+60^\circ)=60^\circ$

Hence, ΔOPQ is an equilateral triangle.

Example 13 Show that the condition that two of the three lines represented by $ax^3+bx^2y+cxy^2+dy^3=0$ may be at right angles is $a^2+ac+bd+d^2=0$.

Sol. The given equation being homogeneous of third degree represents three straight lines through the origin. Since, two of these lines are to be at right angles.

Let pair of these lines be $(x^2+pxy-y^2)$, p is constant and the other factor is $(ax-dy)$.

Hence, $ax^3+bx^2y+cxy^2+dy^3=(x^2+pxy-y^2)(ax-dy)$

Comparing the coefficients of similar terms, we get

$$b=ap-d \quad \text{...(i)}$$

$$c=-pd-a \quad \text{...(ii)}$$

Multiplying Eq. (i) by d and Eq. (ii) by a and adding, we get

$$bd+ac=-d^2-a^2$$

$\Rightarrow \quad a^2+ac+bd+d^2=0$

Aliter :

Let $y=m_1x$, $y=m_2x$ and $y=m_3x$ be the lines represented by the equation

$$ax^3+bx^2y+cxy^2+dy^3=0.$$

Then

$$ax^3+bx^2y+cxy^2+dy^3=d\,(y-m_1x)(y-m_2x)(y-m_3x) \quad \text{...(i)}$$

On equating the coefficients of x^3, x^2y and xy^2 on both sides, we get

$$m_1+m_2+m_3=-\frac{c}{d}$$

$$m_1m_2+m_2m_3+m_3m_1=\frac{b}{d}$$

and $\quad m_1m_2m_3=-\dfrac{a}{d} \quad$ ...(ii)

Let the perpendicular lines be $y=m_1x$ and $y=m_2x$, then

$$m_1m_2=-1$$

From Eq. (ii), $\quad m_3=\dfrac{a}{d} \quad$ ...(iii)

On putting $y=m_3x$ in Eq. (i), we get

$$ax^3+bm_3x^3+cm_3^2x^3+dm_3^3x^3=0$$

$\Rightarrow \quad dm_3^3+cm_3^2+bm_3+a=0$

$\Rightarrow \quad d\left(\dfrac{a}{d}\right)^3+c\left(\dfrac{a}{d}\right)^2+b\left(\dfrac{a}{d}\right)+a=0 \quad$ [from Eq. (iii)]

Hence, $\quad a^2+ac+bd+d^2=0$

Exercise for Session 2

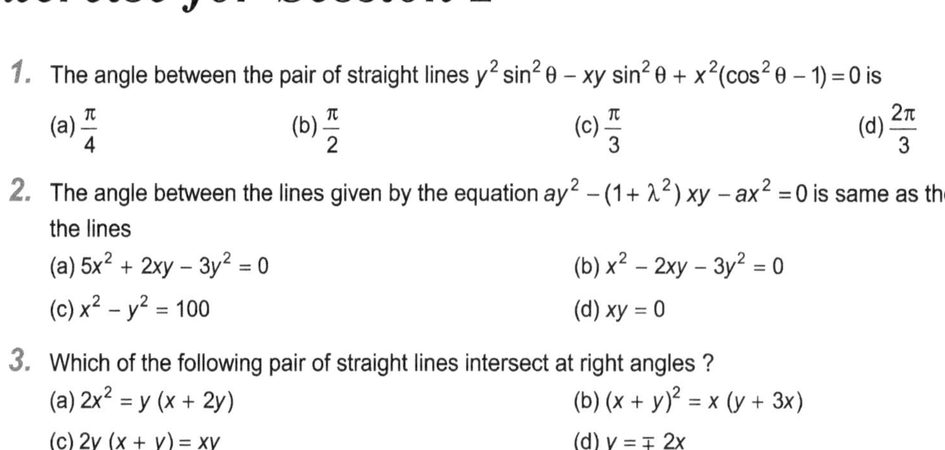

1. The angle between the pair of straight lines $y^2 \sin^2 \theta - xy \sin^2 \theta + x^2(\cos^2 \theta - 1) = 0$ is

   (a) $\frac{\pi}{4}$ (b) $\frac{\pi}{2}$ (c) $\frac{\pi}{3}$ (d) $\frac{2\pi}{3}$

2. The angle between the lines given by the equation $ay^2 - (1 + \lambda^2) xy - ax^2 = 0$ is same as the angle between the lines

   (a) $5x^2 + 2xy - 3y^2 = 0$ (b) $x^2 - 2xy - 3y^2 = 0$
   (c) $x^2 - y^2 = 100$ (d) $xy = 0$

3. Which of the following pair of straight lines intersect at right angles ?

   (a) $2x^2 = y(x + 2y)$ (b) $(x + y)^2 = x(y + 3x)$
   (c) $2y(x + y) = xy$ (d) $y = \mp 2x$

4. If $h^2 = ab$, then the lines represented by $ax^2 + 2hxy + by^2 = 0$ are

   (a) parallel (b) perpendicular
   (c) coincident (d) None of these

5. Equation $ax^3 - 9x^2y - xy^2 + 4y^3 = 0$ represents three straight lines. If the two of the lines are perpendicular, then a is equal to

   (a) –5 (b) 5
   (c) –4 (d) 4

6. Find the angle between the lines whose joint equation is $2x^2 - 3xy + y^2 = 0$.

7. Show that the lines $(1 - \cos \theta \tan \alpha) y^2 - (2 \cos \theta + \sin^2 \theta \tan \alpha) xy + \cos \theta (\cos \theta + \tan \alpha) x^2 = 0$ include an angle α between them.

8. Find the angle between the lines represented by the equation $x^2 - 2pxy + y^2 = 0$.

9. Show that the lines $x^2 - 4xy + y^2 = 0$ and $x + y = 1$ form an equilateral triangle and find its area.

10. Prove that the triangle formed by the lines $ax^2 + 2hxy + by^2 = 0$ and $lx + my = 1$ is isosceles, if $h(l^2 - m^2) = (a - b)m$.

Session 3

Bisectors of the Angle between the Lines Given by a Homogeneous Equation

Bisectors of the Angle between the Lines Given by a Homogeneous Equation

Theorem The joint equation of the bisectors of the angles between the lines represented by the equation

$$ax^2 + 2hxy + by^2 = 0 \quad \text{is} \quad \frac{x^2 - y^2}{a - b} = \frac{xy}{h}.$$

Proof Let the lines represented by $ax^2 + 2hxy + by^2 = 0$ be $y - m_1 x = 0$ and $y - m_2 x = 0$, then

$$m_1 + m_2 = -\frac{2h}{b} \quad \text{and} \quad m_1 m_2 = \frac{a}{b}$$

Since, the bisectors of the angles between the lines are the locus of a point which is equidistant from the two given lines.

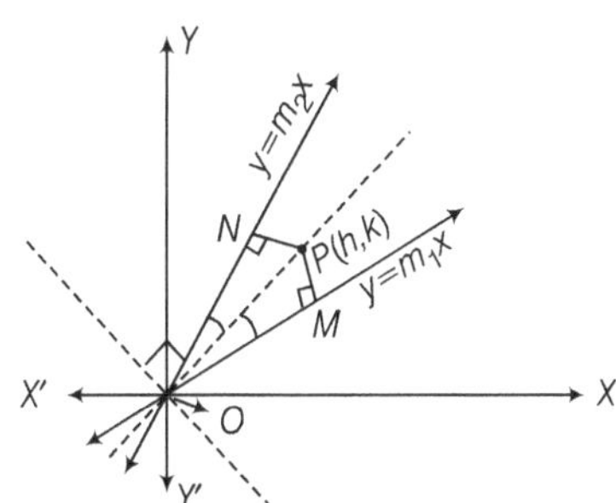

Let $P(h, k)$ be a point on a bisector of the angle between the given lines. Then, $PM = PN$

$$\Rightarrow \quad \frac{|k - m_1 h|}{\sqrt{(1 + m_1^2)}} = \frac{|k - m_2 h|}{\sqrt{(1 + m_2^2)}}$$

$$\Rightarrow \quad \frac{(k - m_1 h)}{\sqrt{(1 + m_1^2)}} = \pm \frac{(k - m_2 h)}{\sqrt{(1 + m_2^2)}}$$

Hence, the locus of a $P(h, k)$ is

$$\frac{(y - m_1 x)}{\sqrt{(1 + m_1^2)}} = \pm \frac{(y - m_2 x)}{\sqrt{(1 + m_2^2)}}$$

$\therefore$ The pair of bisectors is

$$\left(\frac{(y - m_1 x)}{\sqrt{(1 + m_1^2)}} + \frac{(y - m_2 x)}{\sqrt{(1 + m_2^2)}}\right)\left(\frac{(y - m_1 x)}{\sqrt{(1 + m_1^2)}} - \frac{(y - m_2 x)}{\sqrt{(1 + m_2^2)}}\right) = 0$$

$$\Rightarrow \quad \frac{(y - m_1 x)^2}{(1 + m_1^2)} - \frac{(y - m_2 x)^2}{(1 + m_2^2)} = 0$$

$$\Rightarrow \quad (1 + m_2^2)(y^2 + m_1^2 x^2 - 2m_1 xy) - (1 + m_1^2)(y^2 + m_2^2 x^2 - 2m_2 xy) = 0$$

$$\Rightarrow \quad (m_2^2 - m_1^2) y^2 - (m_2^2 - m_1^2) x^2 + 2xy(m_2 - m_1) - 2m_1 m_2 (m_2 - m_1) xy = 0$$

$$\Rightarrow \quad (m_2 + m_1)(y^2 - x^2) + 2xy - 2m_1 m_2 xy = 0 \qquad [\because m_1 - m_2 \neq 0]$$

$$\Rightarrow \quad (x^2 - y^2)\left(-\frac{2h}{b}\right) = 2xy\left(1 - \frac{a}{b}\right) \qquad \left[\because m_1 + m_2 = -\frac{2h}{b},\ m_1 m_2 = \frac{a}{b}\right]$$

$$\therefore \quad \frac{x^2 - y^2}{a - b} = \frac{xy}{h} \qquad [b \neq 0]$$

Aliter :

Let the equation $ax^2 + 2hxy + by^2 = 0$ represent two lines L_1OM_1 and L_2OM_2 making angles θ_1 and θ_2 with the positive direction of X-axis.

If slopes of L_1OM_1 and L_2OM_2 are m_1 and m_2, then

$$m_1 = \tan\theta_1 \quad \text{and} \quad m_2 = \tan\theta_2$$

and $$m_1 + m_2 = -\frac{2h}{b},\ m_1 m_2 = \frac{a}{b} \qquad \text{...(i)}$$

Let NON_1 and KOK_1 are the required bisectors,

Since $$\angle NOL_1 = \angle NOL_2 = \frac{\theta_2 - \theta_1}{2}$$

$$\angle NOX = \theta_1 + \frac{\theta_2 - \theta_1}{2} = \frac{\theta_1 + \theta_2}{2}$$

Since, $$\angle NOK = \frac{\pi}{2}$$

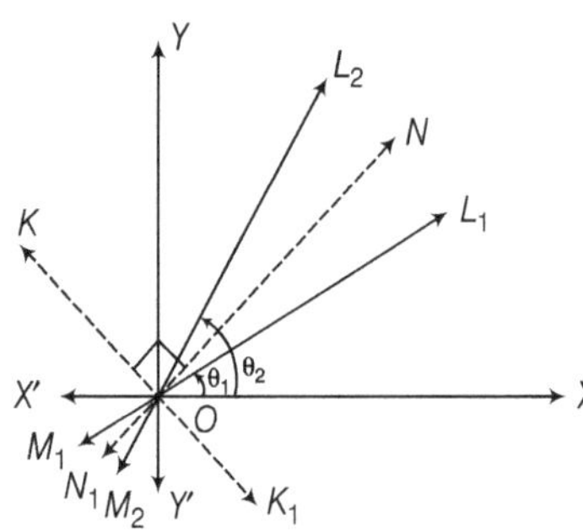

$$\therefore \quad \angle KOX = \frac{\pi}{2} + \angle NOX = \frac{\pi}{2} + \left(\frac{\theta_1 + \theta_2}{2}\right)$$

Equation of bisectors are $y = x \tan\left(\frac{\theta_1 + \theta_2}{2}\right)$

$$\Rightarrow \quad y - x \tan\left(\frac{\theta_1 + \theta_2}{2}\right) = 0 \quad \text{...(ii)}$$

and
$$y = x \tan\left(\frac{\pi}{2} + \frac{\theta_1 + \theta_2}{2}\right)$$

$$\Rightarrow \quad y = -x \cot\left(\frac{\theta_1 + \theta_2}{2}\right)$$

$$\Rightarrow \quad y + x \cot\left(\frac{\theta_1 + \theta_2}{2}\right) = 0 \quad \text{...(iii)}$$

$\therefore$ Pair of bisectors

$$\left[y - x \tan\left(\frac{\theta_1 + \theta_2}{2}\right)\right]\left[y + x \cot\left(\frac{\theta_1 + \theta_2}{2}\right)\right] = 0$$

$$\Rightarrow \quad y^2 - x^2 + xy\left(\cot\left(\frac{\theta_1 + \theta_2}{2}\right) - \tan\left(\frac{\theta_1 + \theta_2}{2}\right)\right) = 0$$

$$\Rightarrow \quad x^2 - y^2 = xy\left(\frac{1 - \tan^2\left(\frac{\theta_1 + \theta_2}{2}\right)}{\tan\left(\frac{\theta_1 + \theta_2}{2}\right)}\right)$$

$$\Rightarrow \quad x^2 - y^2 = xy\left(\frac{2}{\tan(\theta_1 + \theta_2)}\right)$$

$$\Rightarrow \quad x^2 - y^2 = 2xy\left(\frac{1 - \tan\theta_1 \tan\theta_2}{\tan\theta_1 + \tan\theta_2}\right)$$

$$\Rightarrow \quad x^2 - y^2 = 2xy\left(\frac{1 - m_1 m_2}{m_1 + m_2}\right)$$

$$\Rightarrow \quad x^2 - y^2 = 2xy\left(\frac{1 - a/b}{-2h/b}\right)$$

$$\therefore \quad \frac{(x^2 - y^2)}{(a - b)} = \frac{xy}{h}$$

Remark

The joint equation of the bisectors is $\frac{x^2 - y^2}{a - b} = \frac{xy}{h}$

or $\quad hx^2 - (a - b)\, xy - hy^2 = 0$

i.e. coefficient of x^2 + coefficient of $y^2 = 0$.

Hence, the bisectors of the angle between the lines are always perpendicular to each other.

Corollaries

1. If $a = b$, the bisectors are $x^2 - y^2 = 0$

   i.e. $\quad x - y = 0, x + y = 0$

2. If $h = 0$, the bisectors are $xy = 0$

   i.e. $\quad x = 0, y = 0$

Example 14 Find the equation of the bisectors of the angle between the lines represented by $3x^2 - 5xy + 4y^2 = 0$.

Sol. Given equation is

$$3x^2 - 5xy + 4y^2 = 0 \quad \text{...(i)}$$

Comparing it with the equation

$$ax^2 + 2hxy + by^2 = 0 \quad \text{...(ii)}$$

then $\quad a = 3, h = -\frac{5}{2}, b = 4$

Hence, the equation of bisectors of the angle between the pair of the lines (i) is

$$\frac{x^2 - y^2}{3 - 4} = \frac{xy}{-5/2}$$

$$\Rightarrow \quad \frac{x^2 - y^2}{-1} = \frac{2xy}{-5}$$

$$\therefore \quad 5x^2 - 2xy - 5y^2 = 0$$

Example 15 Show that the line $y = mx$ bisects the angle between the lines

$$ax^2 - 2hxy + by^2 = 0,$$

if $\quad h(1 - m^2) + m(a - b) = 0.$

Sol. Equation of pair of bisectors of angles between lines $ax^2 - 2hxy + by^2 = 0$ is

$$\frac{x^2 - y^2}{a - b} = \frac{xy}{-h}$$

$$\Rightarrow \quad -h(x^2 - y^2) = (a - b)\, xy \quad \text{...(i)}$$

But $y = mx$ is one of these lines, then it will satisfy it. Substituting $y = mx$ in Eq. (i),

$$-h(x^2 - m^2x^2) = (a - b)x \cdot mx$$

Dividing by x^2, $h(1 - m^2) + m(a - b) = 0$

Example 16 If pairs of straight lines $x^2 - 2pxy - y^2 = 0$ and $x^2 - 2qxy - y^2 = 0$ be such that each pair bisects the angle between the other pair, then prove that $pq = -1$.

Sol. According to the question, the equation of the bisectors of the angle between the lines

$$x^2 - 2pxy - y^2 = 0 \quad \text{...(i)}$$

is $$x^2 - 2qxy - y^2 = 0 \quad \text{...(ii)}$$

$\therefore$ The equation of bisectors of the angle between the lines (i) is

$$\frac{x^2 - y^2}{1-(-1)} = \frac{xy}{-p}$$

$$\Rightarrow \quad -px^2 - 2xy + py^2 = 0 \quad \text{...(iii)}$$

Since, Eqs. (ii) and (iii) are identical, comparing Eqs. (ii) and (iii), we get

$$\frac{1}{-p} = \frac{-2q}{-2} = \frac{-1}{p} \Rightarrow pq = -1$$

Remark

By taking the bisectors of the angles between the pair of lines (ii), we will get the same result.

Example 17 Prove that the angle between one of the lines given by $ax^2 + 2hxy + by^2 = 0$ and one of the lines $ax^2 + 2hxy + by^2 + \lambda(x^2 + y^2) = 0$ is equal to angle between other two lines of the system.

Sol. The equation of the bisectors of the angle between the lines

$$ax^2 + 2hxy + by^2 = 0 \quad \text{...(i)}$$

is $$\frac{x^2 - y^2}{a-b} = \frac{xy}{h}$$

and the equation of bisectors of the angle between the lines

$$ax^2 + 2hxy + by^2 + \lambda(x^2 + y^2) = 0 \quad \text{...(ii)}$$

$$\Rightarrow \quad (a+\lambda)x^2 + 2hxy + (b+\lambda)y^2 = 0$$

is $$\frac{x^2 - y^2}{(a+\lambda)-(b+\lambda)} = \frac{xy}{h} \Rightarrow \frac{x^2 - y^2}{a-b} = \frac{xy}{h}$$

$\therefore$ Bisectors of angles between lines given by Eqs. (i) and (ii) are the same. Hence the result.

Example 18 Show that the pair of lines given by $a^2x^2 + 2h(a+b)xy + b^2y^2 = 0$ is equally inclined to the pair given by $ax^2 + 2hxy + by^2 = 0$.

Sol. Given pair of lines are

$$a^2x^2 + 2h(a+b)xy + b^2y^2 = 0 \quad \text{...(i)}$$

and $$ax^2 + 2hxy + by^2 = 0 \quad \text{...(ii)}$$

Equation of bisectors of first pair is

$$\frac{x^2 - y^2}{a^2 - b^2} = \frac{xy}{h(a+b)} \Rightarrow \frac{x^2 - y^2}{a-b} = \frac{xy}{h}$$

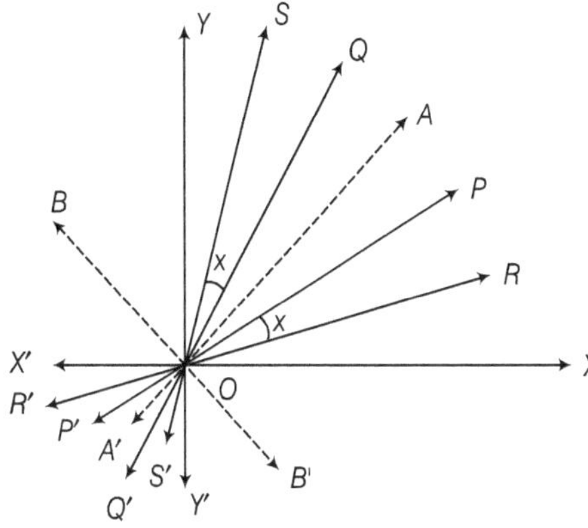

which are also the bisectors of the second pair.

Let $P'OP, Q'OQ, R'OR, S'OS$ be the lines of the Eqs. (i) and (ii) pairs respectively and $A'OA$ and $B'OB$ be their bisectors. We have,

$$\angle ROA = \angle SOA$$

and $$\angle POA = \angle QOA$$

$$\Rightarrow \quad \angle ROA - \angle POA = \angle SOA - \angle QOA$$

$$\Rightarrow \quad \angle ROP = \angle SOQ$$

Hence the result.

Example 19 If the lines represented by $x^2 - 2pxy - y^2 = 0$ are rotated about the origin through an angle θ, one in clockwise direction and the other in anti-clockwise direction, then find the equation of the bisectors of the angle between the lines in the new position.

Sol. Since, lines represented by $x^2 - 2pxy - y^2 = 0$ are perpendicular to each other. The bisectors of the angles between the lines in new position are same as the bisectors of the angles between their old positions. i.e. OC, OD ; OA, OB be the old and new pairs respectively and OE and OF be their bisectors, we have

$$\angle COE = \angle DOE$$

and $$\angle COA = \angle DOB = \theta \quad \text{[given]}$$

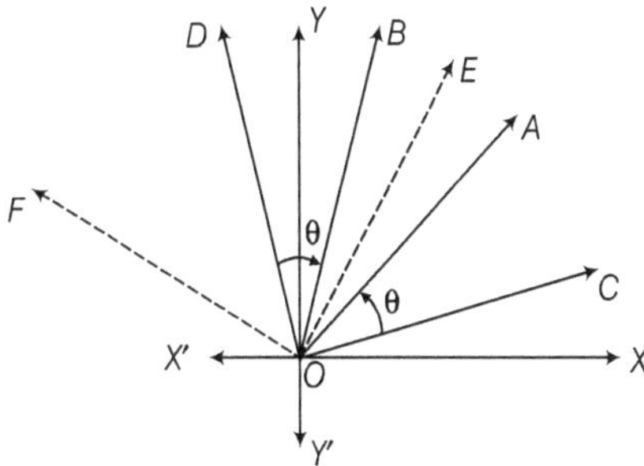

$$\Rightarrow \quad \angle COE - \angle COA = \angle DOE - \angle DOB$$

$$\Rightarrow \quad \angle AOE = \angle BOE$$

Therefore, the required equation is $\dfrac{x^2 - y^2}{1-(-1)} = \dfrac{xy}{-p}$

i.e. $\quad px^2 + 2xy - py^2 = 0.$

Exercise for Session 3

1. If coordinate axes are the angle bisectors of the pair of lines $ax^2 + 2hxy + by^2 = 0$, then

(a) $a = b$ (b) $h = 0$

(c) $a^2 + b = 0$ (d) $a + b^2 = 0$

2. If the line $y = mx$ is one of the bisector of the lines $x^2 + 4xy - y^2 = 0$, then the value of m is

(a) $\frac{\sqrt{5} - 1}{2}$ (b) $\frac{\sqrt{5} + 1}{2}$

(c) $-\left(\frac{\sqrt{5} + 1}{2}\right)$ (d) $-\left(\frac{\sqrt{5} - 1}{2}\right)$

3. If one of the lines of $my^2 + (1 - m^2)xy - mx^2 = 0$ is a bisector of the angle between the lines $xy = 0$, then $\cos^{-1}(m)$ is

(a) 0 (b) $\pi/2$

(c) π (d) $3\pi/2$

4. The bisectors of the angles between the lines $(ax + by)^2 = c(bx - ay)^2, c > 0$ are respectively parallel and perpendicular to the line

(a) $bx - ay + \mu = 0$ (b) $ax + by + \lambda = 0$

(c) $ax - by + \nu = 0$ (d) $bx + ay + \tau = 0$

5. If the pairs of straight lines $ax^2 + 2hxy - ay^2 = 0$ and $bx^2 + 2gxy - by^2 = 0$ be such that each bisects the angles between the other, then prove that $hg + ab = 0$.

6. Prove that the lines $2x^2 + 6xy + y^2 = 0$ are equally inclined to the lines $4x^2 + 18xy + y^2 = 0$.

7. Show that the lines bisecting the angle between the bisectors of the angles between the lines $ax^2 + 2hxy + by^2 = 0$ are given by $(a - b)(x^2 - y^2) + 4hxy = 0$.

8. Prove that the bisectors of the angle between the lines $ax^2 + acxy + cy^2 = 0$ and $\left(3 + \frac{1}{c}\right)x^2 + xy + \left(3 + \frac{1}{a}\right)y^2 = 0$ are always the same.

9. The lines represented by $x^2 + 2\lambda xy + 2y^2 = 0$ and the lines represented by $(1 + \lambda)x^2 - 8xy + y^2 = 0$ are equally inclined, find the values of λ.

Session 4

General Equation of Second Degree, Important Theorems

General Equation of Second Degree

The equation $ax^2 + 2hxy + by^2 + 2gx + 2fy + c = 0$

is the general equation of second degree and represents a conics (pair of straight lines, circle, parabola, ellipse, hyperbola). It contains six constants a, b, c, f, g, h.

i.e. $a =$ coefficient of x^2, $b =$ coefficient of y^2,

$c =$ constant term, $g =$ half the coefficient of x,

$f =$ half the coefficient of y,

$h =$ half the coefficient of xy.

Theorem The necessary and sufficient condition for

$$ax^2 + 2hxy + by^2 + 2gx + 2fy + c = 0$$

to represent a pair of straight lines is that

$$abc + 2fgh - af^2 - bg^2 - ch^2 = 0 \text{ or } \begin{vmatrix} a & h & g \\ h & b & f \\ g & f & c \end{vmatrix} = 0.$$

Proof Necessary condition : Let the equation be

$$ax^2 + 2hxy + by^2 + 2gx + 2fy + c = 0 \quad \text{...(i)}$$

represent a pair of lines. Assuming that these lines are not parallel, we suppose further that their point of intersection is (x_1, y_1). Shifting the origin at (x_1, y_1) without rotating the coordinate axes, we have the Eq. (i) transforms to

$$a(X + x_1)^2 + 2h(X + x_1)(Y + y_1) + b(Y + y_1)^2$$
$$+ 2g(X + x_1) + 2f(Y + y_1) + c = 0 \quad \text{...(ii)}$$

Now this Eq. (ii) represents a pair of lines through the new origin and consequently, it is homogeneous in X and Y.

Hence, the coefficients of X and Y and the constant term in Eq. (ii) must vanish separately.

i.e. coefficient of $X =$ coefficient of $Y =$ constant term $= 0$

$$\Rightarrow \quad ax_1 + hy_1 + g = 0 \quad \text{...(iii)}$$
$$hx_1 + by_1 + f = 0 \quad \text{...(iv)}$$

and $ax_1^2 + 2hx_1y_1 + by_1^2 + 2gx_1 + 2fy_1 + c = 0$ ...(v)

Now, $ax_1^2 + 2hx_1y_1 + by_1^2 + 2gx_1 + 2fy_1 + c = 0$

$$\Rightarrow x_1(ax_1 + hy_1 + g) + y_1(hx_1 + by_1 + f) + (gx_1 + fy_1 + c) = 0$$

$$\Rightarrow x_1 \cdot 0 + y_1 \cdot 0 + gx_1 + fy_1 + c = 0$$

[from Eqs. (iii) and (iv)]

$$\Rightarrow \quad gx_1 + fy_1 + c = 0 \quad \text{...(vi)}$$

On eliminating x_1, y_1 from Eqs. (iii), (iv) and (vi), we get the determinant

$$\begin{vmatrix} a & h & g \\ h & b & f \\ g & f & c \end{vmatrix} = 0$$

$\therefore$ $abc + 2fgh - af^2 - bg^2 - ch^2 = 0$,

as the required condition.

Remarks

1. **Without using determinant** On solving Eqs. (iii) and (iv), we get
$$(x_1, y_1) = \left(\frac{hf - bg}{ab - h^2}, \frac{gh - af}{ab - h^2}\right)$$
and then substituting the values of x_1 and y_1 in Eqs. (vi), we obtain
$$g\left(\frac{hf - bg}{ab - h^2}\right) + f\left(\frac{gh - af}{ab - h^2}\right) + c = 0$$
$$\Rightarrow \quad abc + 2fgh - af^2 - bg^2 - ch^2 = 0$$
2. By making $ax^2 + 2hxy + by^2 + 2gx + 2fy + c = 0$
homogeneous with the help of a new variable z, i.e.
$ax^2 + 2hxy + by^2 + 2gxz + 2fyz + cz^2 = 0$
Let $f(x, y, z) \equiv ax^2 + 2hxy + by^2 + 2gxz + 2fyz + cz^2 = 0$
$$\therefore \quad \frac{\partial f}{\partial x} = 2ax + 2hy + 2gz = 0$$
$$\frac{\partial f}{\partial y} = 2hx + 2by + 2fz = 0$$
$$\frac{\partial f}{\partial z} = 2gx + 2fy + 2cz = 0$$
and finally putting $z = 1$, we obtain equations
$$ax + hy + g = 0, hx + by + f = 0, gx + fy + c = 0$$
which are same as Eqs. (iii), (iv) and (vi), respectively.
3. If $ab - h^2 = 0$, the lines given by Eq. (i) are parallel. In this case, the method followed in the above proof fails and we follow the following method.

Aliter I : (Proof)

Let the lines represented by

$$ax^2 + 2hxy + by^2 + 2gx + 2fy + c = 0 \quad \text{...(i)}$$

be $lx + my + n = 0$ and $l'x + m'y + n' = 0$

then $ax^2 + 2hxy + by^2 + 2gx + 2fy + c$

$$\equiv (lx + my + n)(l'x + m'y + n') \quad \text{...(ii)}$$

Comparing the coefficients of similar terms in both sides of Eq. (ii), we get

$$\left\{\begin{matrix} ll' = a, mm' = b, nn' = c \\ lm' + l'm = 2h, ln' + l'n = 2g, \\ mn' + m'n = 2f \end{matrix}\right\} \quad \text{...(iii)}$$

We now eliminate l, m, n, l', m' and n' from these equations, we have

$$\begin{vmatrix} l & l' & 0 \\ m & m' & 0 \\ n & n' & 0 \end{vmatrix} \times \begin{vmatrix} l' & l & 0 \\ m' & m & 0 \\ n' & n & 0 \end{vmatrix} = 0$$

[$\because$ each determinant $= 0$]

$$\Rightarrow \begin{vmatrix} 2ll' & lm' + l'm & ln' + l'n \\ ml' + m'l & 2mm' & mn' + m'n \\ nl' + n'l & nm' + n'm & 2nn' \end{vmatrix} = 0$$

$$\Rightarrow \begin{vmatrix} 2a & 2h & 2g \\ 2h & 2b & 2f \\ 2g & 2f & 2c \end{vmatrix} = 0$$

$$\Rightarrow \Delta = \begin{vmatrix} a & h & g \\ h & b & f \\ g & f & c \end{vmatrix} = 0$$

$\therefore \quad \Delta = abc + 2fgh - af^2 - bg^2 - ch^2 = 0,$

which is the required necessary condition.

Remark

Without using determinant

Now, $(lm' + l'm)(ln' + l'n)(mn' + m'n) = 2h \cdot 2g \cdot 2f$

$\Rightarrow \quad 2ll'mm'nn' + ll'(m^2n'^2 + m'^2n^2)$

$\qquad + mm'(n^2l'^2 + n'^2l^2) + nn'(l^2m'^2 + l'^2m^2) = 8fgh$

$\Rightarrow \quad 2ll'mm'nn' + ll'\{(mn' + m'n)^2 - 2mm'nn'\}$

$\qquad + mm'\{(nl' + n'l)^2 - 2nn'll'\} + nn'\{(lm' + l'm)^2 - 2ll'mm'\}$

$\qquad = 8fgh \qquad$ [from Eq. (iii)]

$\Rightarrow 2abc + a(4f^2 - 4bc) + b(4g^2 - 4ca) + c(4h^2 - 4ab) = 8fgh$

$\therefore \qquad abc + 2fgh - af^2 - bg^2 - ch^2 = 0,$

which is the required necessary condition.

Aliter II : (Proof)

Given equation is

$$ax^2 + 2hxy + by^2 + 2gx + 2fy + c = 0 \quad \text{...(i)}$$

Case I If $a \neq 0$, then writing Eq. (i) as a quadratic equation in x, we get

$$ax^2 + 2x(hy + g) + by^2 + 2fy + c = 0$$

Solving, we have

$$x = \frac{-2(hy + g) \pm \sqrt{4(hy + g)^2 - 4a(by^2 + 2fy + c)}}{2a}$$

$$\therefore x = \frac{-(hy + g) \pm \sqrt{\{(h^2 - ab)y^2 + 2(gh - af)y + (g^2 - ac)\}}}{a}$$

Eq. (i), will represent two straight lines, if LHS of Eq. (i), can be resolved into two linear factors, therefore the expression under the square root should be a perfect square.

[$\because Ax^2 + Bx + C = 0$ is a perfect square $\Leftrightarrow B^2 - 4AC = 0$]

Hence, $4(gh - af)^2 - 4(h^2 - ab)(g^2 - ac) = 0$

or $\quad abc + 2fgh - af^2 - bg^2 - ch^2 = 0 \quad \text{...(ii)}$

Ths is called discriminant of the Eq. (i).

Case II If $a = 0, b \neq 0$, then writing Eq. (i) as a quadratic equation in y

i.e. $\quad by^2 + 2y(hx + f) + 2gx + c = 0$

and proceeding above we get the condition

$$2fgh - bg^2 - ch^2 = 0$$

which is condition obtained by putting $a = 0$ in Eq. (ii).

Case III If $a = 0, b = 0$ but $h \neq 0$, then Eq. (i) becomes

$$2hxy + 2gx + 2fy + c = 0$$

Multiplying by $\frac{h}{2}$ $\qquad [\because h \neq 0]$

$$\Rightarrow \quad h^2xy + hgx + hfy + \frac{ch}{2} = 0$$

$$\Rightarrow \quad (hx + f)(hy + g) = fg - \frac{ch}{2}$$

Above equation represents two straight lines, if

$$fg - \frac{ch}{2} = 0 \Rightarrow 2fgh - ch^2 = 0$$

which is condition obtained by putting $a = 0, b = 0$ in Eq. (ii).

Hence in each case, the condition that

$$ax^2 + 2hxy + by^2 + 2gx + 2fy + c = 0$$

represents two straight lines is

$$abc + 2fgh - af^2 - bg^2 - ch^2 = 0$$

which is the required necessary condition.

Sufficient condition (Conversely)

Here, we have to show that the equation $ax^2 + 2hxy + by^2 + 2gx + 2fy + c = 0$ represents a pair of straight lines.

$$\begin{vmatrix} a & h & g \\ h & b & f \\ g & f & c \end{vmatrix} = 0$$

i.e. lines $ax + hy + g = 0$, $hx + by + f = 0$, $gx + fy + c = 0$ are concurrent.

Let the point of concurrency be (x_1, y_1).

Then, $\quad ax_1 + hy_1 + g = 0 \quad$ ...(iii)

$hx_1 + by_1 + f = 0 \quad$ ...(iv)

and $\quad gx_1 + fy_1 + c = 0 \quad$ ...(v)

Now, shifting the origin at (x_1, y_1) without rotating the coordinate axes the equation

$ax^2 + 2hxy + by^2 + 2gx + 2fy + c = 0$ reduces to

$$a(X + x_1)^2 + 2h(X + x_1)(Y + y_1) + b(Y + y_1)^2 + 2g(X + x_1) + 2f(Y + y_1) + c = 0$$

$$\Rightarrow aX^2 + 2hXY + bY^2 + 2X(ax_1 + hy_1 + g) + 2Y(hx_1 + by_1 + f) + x_1(ax_1 + hy_1 + g) + y_1(hx_1 + by_1 + f) + (gx_1 + fy_1 + c) = 0$$

$$\Rightarrow aX^2 + 2hXY + bY^2 + 0 + 0 + 0 + 0 + 0 = 0$$

[from Eqs. (iii), (iv) and (v)]

i.e. $\quad aX^2 + 2hXY + bY^2 = 0$

It is homogeneous equation of second degree. So, it represents a pair of straight lines through the new origin.

Hence, the equation $ax^2 + 2hxy + by^2 + 2gx + 2fy + c = 0$ represents a pair of straight lines, if

$$abc + 2fgh - af^2 - bg^2 - ch^2 = 0.$$

Some useful identities If $y = m_1x + c_1$, $y = m_2x + c_2$ be lines represented by Eq. (i). Then,

$$ax^2 + 2hxy + by^2 + 2gx + 2fy + c = b(y - m_1x - c_1)(y - m_2x - c_2)$$
$$= b(y^2 - (m_1 + m_2)xy + m_1m_2x^2 + (m_1c_2 + m_2c_1)x - (c_1 + c_2)y + c_1c_2)$$

On equating coefficients, we get

$$m_1 + m_2 = -\frac{2h}{b}, m_1m_2 = \frac{a}{b}, m_1c_2 + m_2c_1 = \frac{2g}{b},$$

$$c_1 + c_2 = -\frac{2f}{b}, c_1c_1 = \frac{c}{b}$$

These five relations are very useful to solve many problems.

Important Theorems

Theorem 1 The angle between the lines represented by

$$ax^2 + 2hxy + by^2 + 2gx + 2fy + c = 0$$

is given by

$$\theta = \tan^{-1}\left\{\frac{2\sqrt{(h^2 - ab)}}{|a + b|}\right\}.$$

Proof Let $\quad y = m_1x + c_1$

and $\quad y = m_2x + c_2$

be the lines represented by

$$ax^2 + 2hxy + by^2 + 2gx + 2fy + c = 0$$

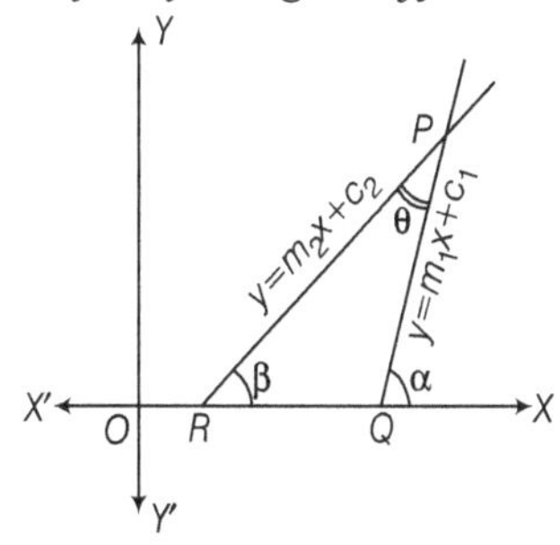

where, $m_1 = \tan\alpha, m_2 = \tan\beta$

Then, $ax^2 + 2hxy + by^2 + 2gx + 2fy + c$

$$\equiv (y - m_1x - c_1)(y - m_2x - c_2)$$

Comparing coefficients of like powers, we obtain

$$m_1 + m_2 = -\frac{2h}{b}, m_1m_2 = \frac{a}{b}$$

Now, if θ be the acute angle between the lines $y = m_1x + c_1$ and $y = m_2x + c_2$, then

$$\tan\theta = \left|\frac{m_1 - m_2}{1 + m_1m_2}\right| = \frac{\sqrt{(m_1 + m_2)^2 - 4m_1m_2}}{|1 + m_1m_2|}$$

$$= \frac{\sqrt{\left(-\frac{2h}{b}\right)^2 - 4\left(\frac{a}{b}\right)}}{\left|1 + \frac{a}{b}\right|} = \frac{2\sqrt{(h^2 - ab)}}{|a + b|}$$

$$\therefore \quad \theta = \tan^{-1}\left\{\frac{2\sqrt{(h^2 - ab)}}{|a + b|}\right\}$$

***Corollary* 1.** The angle between the lines represented by

$$ax^2 + 2hxy + by^2 + 2gx + 2fy + c = 0$$

is the same as the angle between the lines represented by

$$ax^2 + 2hxy + by^2 = 0$$

***Corollary* 2.** The lines represented by

$$ax^2 + 2hxy + by^2 + 2gx + 2fy + c = 0$$

are perpendicular iff $a + b = 0$ and parallel iff $h^2 = ab$.

Theorem 2 The lines represented by

$$ax^2 + 2hxy + by^2 + 2gx + 2fy + c = 0$$

will be coincident, if $h^2 - ab = 0, g^2 - ac = 0$

and $\quad f^2 - bc = 0.$

Proof Let the lines represented by

$$ax^2 + 2hxy + by^2 + 2gx + 2fy + c = 0$$

be $\quad lx + my + n = 0 \quad$ and $\quad l'x + m'y + n' = 0$

then $\quad ax^2 + 2hxy + by^2 + 2gx + 2fy + c$

$$\equiv (lx + my + n)(l'x + m'y + n')$$

Comparing the coefficients of similar terms in both sides, we get

$$\left.\begin{array}{l} ll' = a, mm' = b, nn' = c \\ lm' + l'm = 2h, ln' + l'n = 2g \\ mn' + m'n = 2f \end{array}\right\}$$

$\because$ Lines $lx + my + n = 0$ and $l'x + m'y + n' = 0$ are coincident, then $\dfrac{l}{l'} = \dfrac{m}{m'} = \dfrac{n}{n'}$.

Taking the ratios in pairs, then

$$lm' - l'm = 0, mn' - m'n = 0, ln' - l'n = 0$$

$$\Rightarrow \quad \sqrt{(lm' + l'm)^2 - 4ll'mm'} = 0,$$

$$\sqrt{(mn' + m'n)^2 - 4mm'nn'} = 0$$

and $\quad \sqrt{(ln' + l'n)^2 - 4ll'nn'} = 0$

i.e. $\quad \sqrt{(4h^2 - 4ab)} = 0, \sqrt{(4f^2 - 4bc)} = 0$

and $\quad \sqrt{(4g^2 - 4ac)} = 0$

i.e. $\quad h^2 - ab = 0, f^2 - bc = 0, g^2 - ac = 0$

Theorem 3 The point of intersection of the lines represented by

$ax^2 + 2hxy + by^2 + 2gx + 2fy + c = 0$ is

$$\left(\sqrt{\left(\frac{f^2 - bc}{h^2 - ab}\right)}, \sqrt{\left(\frac{g^2 - ca}{h^2 - ab}\right)}\right) \text{ or } \left(\frac{bg - hf}{h^2 - ab}, \frac{af - gh}{h^2 - ab}\right).$$

Proof Let the lines represented by

$$ax^2 + 2hxy + by^2 + 2gx + 2fy + c = 0$$

be $\quad lx + my + n = 0 \quad$ and $\quad l'x + m'y + n' = 0$

then $\quad ax^2 + 2hxy + by^2 + 2gx + 2fy + c$

$$\equiv (lx + my + n)(l'x + m'y + n')$$

Comparing the coefficients of similar terms in both sides

then $\quad ll' = a, mm' = b, nn' = c$

$$lm' + l'm = 2h, ln' + l'n = 2g, mn' + m'n = 2f$$

$$\Rightarrow \quad (lm' - l'm) = \sqrt{(lm' + l'm)^2 - 4ll'mm'} = 2\sqrt{(h^2 - ab)}$$

$$\Rightarrow \quad (nl' - n'l) = \sqrt{(ln' + l'n)^2 - 4ll'nn'} = 2\sqrt{(g^2 - ac)}$$

and $\quad (mn' - m'n) = \sqrt{(mn' + m'n)^2 - 4mm'nn'}$

$$= 2\sqrt{(f^2 - bc)}$$

Now, solving $lx + my + n = 0$ and $l'x + m'y + n' = 0$

then $\quad \dfrac{x}{(mn' - m'n)} = \dfrac{y}{(nl' - n'l)} = \dfrac{1}{(lm' - l'm)}$

$$\Rightarrow \quad \frac{x}{2\sqrt{(f^2 - bc)}} = \frac{y}{2\sqrt{(g^2 - ac)}} = \frac{1}{2\sqrt{(h^2 - ab)}}$$

$$\therefore \quad (x, y) = \left(\sqrt{\left(\frac{f^2 - bc}{h^2 - ab}\right)}, \sqrt{\left(\frac{g^2 - ac}{h^2 - ab}\right)}\right)$$

Also, $x = \sqrt{\left(\dfrac{f^2 - bc}{h^2 - ab}\right)} = \dfrac{\sqrt{(f^2 - bc)(h^2 - ab)}}{(h^2 - ab)}$

$$= \frac{\sqrt{f^2h^2 - abf^2 - bch^2 + b(abc)}}{(h^2 - ab)}$$

$$= \frac{\sqrt{f^2h^2 - abf^2 - bch^2 + b(af^2 + bg^2 + ch^2 - 2fgh)}}{(h^2 - ab)}$$

$$[\because abc + 2fgh - af^2 - bg^2 - ch^2 = 0]$$

$$= \frac{\sqrt{(f^2h^2 + b^2g^2 - 2bfgh)}}{(h^2 - ab)} = \frac{\sqrt{(bg - hf)^2}}{(h^2 - ab)}$$

$$= \left(\frac{bg - hf}{h^2 - ab}\right)$$

Similarly, $\quad y = \left(\dfrac{af - gh}{h^2 - ab}\right)$

Hence, $\quad (x, y) = \left(\dfrac{bg - hf}{h^2 - ab}, \dfrac{af - gh}{h^2 - ab}\right).$

Remembering Method (For second point)

Since, $\quad \Delta = \begin{vmatrix} a & h & g \\ h & b & f \\ g & f & c \end{vmatrix}$

taking first two rows (repeat first column)

$$\begin{matrix} a & & h & & g & & a \\ & \times & & \times & & \times & \\ h & & b & & f & & h \end{matrix}$$

$\Rightarrow \quad ab-h^2, hf-bg, gh-af$

$\Rightarrow \quad h^2-ab, bg-hf, af-gh$

$\Rightarrow \quad 1, \dfrac{bg-hf}{h^2-ab}, \dfrac{af-gh}{h^2-ab}$

Hence, point of intersection is $\left(\dfrac{bg-hf}{h^2-ab}, \dfrac{af-gh}{h^2-ab}\right)$.

OR

Cofactors of third column are C_{13}, C_{23}, C_{33}

$\because \quad C_{13} = \begin{vmatrix} h & b \\ g & f \end{vmatrix} = hf-bg$

$C_{23} = -\begin{vmatrix} a & h \\ g & f \end{vmatrix} = hg-af$

and $\quad C_{33} = \begin{vmatrix} a & h \\ h & b \end{vmatrix} = ab-h^2$

Point of intersection is $\left(\dfrac{C_{13}}{C_{33}}, \dfrac{C_{23}}{C_{33}}\right)$ i.e.

$$\left(\frac{hf-bg}{ab-h^2}, \frac{hg-af}{ab-h^2}\right) \text{ or } \left(\frac{bg-hf}{h^2-ab}, \frac{af-hg}{h^2-ab}\right).$$

Remembering Mehod (For first point)

Cofactors of leading diagonal are

C_{11}, C_{22}, C_{33}

$\because \quad C_{11} = \begin{vmatrix} b & f \\ f & c \end{vmatrix} = bc-f^2,$

$C_{22} = \begin{vmatrix} a & g \\ g & c \end{vmatrix} = ac-g^2$

and $\quad C_{33} = \begin{vmatrix} a & h \\ h & b \end{vmatrix} = ab-h^2$

$\therefore$ Point of intersection are $\left(\sqrt{\dfrac{C_{11}}{C_{33}}}, \sqrt{\dfrac{C_{22}}{C_{33}}}\right)$

i.e. $\quad \left(\sqrt{\left(\dfrac{bc-f^2}{ab-h^2}\right)}, \sqrt{\left(\dfrac{ac-g^2}{ab-h^2}\right)}\right)$

or $\quad \left(\sqrt{\left(\dfrac{f^2-bc}{h^2-ab}\right)}, \sqrt{\left(\dfrac{g^2-ac}{h^2-ab}\right)}\right)$

Theorem 4 The pair of bisectors of the lines represented by

$$ax^2+2hxy+by^2+2gx+2fy+c=0,$$

is $\quad \dfrac{(x-\alpha)^2-(x-\beta)^2}{(a-b)} = \dfrac{(x-\alpha)(y-\beta)}{h}$

where (α, β) be the point of intersection of the pair of straight lines represented by Eq. (i).

Proof Since (α, β) be the point of intersection of the lines represented by

$$ax^2+2hxy+by^2+2gx+2fy+c=0 \quad \text{...(i)}$$

Shifting the origin at (α, β) without rotating the coordinate axes, the Eq. (i) reduces to

$$a(X+\alpha)^2+2h(X+\alpha)(Y+\beta)$$
$$+b(Y+\beta)^2+2g(X+\alpha)+2f(Y+\beta)+c=0$$

$[\because x = X+\alpha \text{ and } y = Y+\beta]$

$\Rightarrow \quad (aX^2+2hXY+bY^2)+2X(a\alpha+h\beta+g)$
$$+2Y(h\alpha+b\beta+f)$$
$$+a\alpha^2+2h\alpha\beta+b\beta^2+2g\alpha+2f\beta+c=0 \quad \text{...(ii)}$$

This equation represents a pair of straight lines passing through the new origin. So, it must be homogeneous equation of second degree in X and Y.

$\therefore \quad a\alpha+h\beta+g=0 \quad$ ...(iii)

$h\alpha+b\beta+f=0 \quad$ ....(iv)

and $a\alpha^2+2h\alpha\beta+b\beta^2+2g\alpha+2f\beta+c=0 \quad$ ...(v)

Now, from Eq. (ii), $\quad aX^2+2hXY+bY^2=0 \quad$ ...(vi)

The equation of the bisectors of the angles between the lines given by Eq. (vi) is

$$\frac{X^2-Y^2}{a-b} = \frac{XY}{h} \quad \text{...(vii)}$$

[with reference to new origin]

Replacing X by $x-\alpha$ and Y by $y-\beta$ in Eq. (vii), then

$$\frac{(x-\alpha)^2-(y-\beta)^2}{(a-b)} = \frac{(x-\alpha)(y-\beta)}{h}$$

[with reference to old origin]

which is the required equation of the bisectors of the angles between the lines given by Eq. (i).

Remark

If $ax^2+2hxy+by^2+2gx+2fy+c=0$

represents two straight lines, then the equation of lines through the origin and parallel to them is $ax^2+2hxy+by^2=0$.

Example 20 For what value of λ does the equation $12x^2 - 10xy + 2y^2 + 11x - 5y + \lambda = 0$ represent a pair of straight lines? Find their equations and the angle between them.

Sol. Comparing the given equation with the equation

$$ax^2 + 2hxy + by^2 + 2gx + 2fy + c = 0,$$

we get $a = 12, h = -5, b = 2, g = \frac{11}{2}, f = -\frac{5}{2}$ and $c = \lambda$

If the given equation represents a pair of straight lines, then

$$abc + 2fgh - af^2 - bg^2 - ch^2 = 0$$

$$\Rightarrow \quad 12 \times 2 \times \lambda + 2 \times \left(-\frac{5}{2}\right) \times \frac{11}{2} \times (-5) - 12 \times \frac{25}{4}$$

$$- 2 \times \frac{121}{4} - \lambda \times 25 = 0$$

$\therefore \quad \lambda = 2$, also $h^2 - ab = 25 - 24 = 1 > 0$

$\therefore$ The given equation will represent a pair of straight lines, if $\lambda = 2$.

To find the two lines

First method

Substituting $\lambda = 2$ in the given equation, we get

$$12x^2 - 10xy + 2y^2 + 11x - 5y + 2 = 0 \quad ...(i)$$

Since, $\quad 12x^2 - 10xy + 2y^2 = 2(3x - y)(2x - y)$

factors of Eq. (i) can be taken as

$$2(3x - y + l)(2x - y + m)$$

$$= 12x^2 - 10xy + 2y^2 + 2(2l + 3m)x + 2(-l - m)y + 2lm$$

On comparing, $2l + 3m = \frac{11}{2}, l + m = \frac{5}{2}, lm = 1$

Solving, we get $l = 2, m = \frac{1}{2}$.

Thus, the factors of Eq. (i) are

$$2(3x - y + 2)\left(2x - y + \frac{1}{2}\right) = 0$$

or $\quad (3x - y + 2)(4x - 2y + 1) = 0.$

$\therefore$ The two straight lines represented by the given equation are

$$3x - y + 2 = 0 \text{ and } 4x - 2y + 1 = 0.$$

Second Method

Writing Eq. (i) as quadratic equation in x, we get

$$12x^2 + (-10y + 11)x + 2y^2 - 5y + 2 = 0$$

$\therefore$

$$x = \frac{-(-10y + 11) \pm \sqrt{(-10y + 11)^2 - 48(2y^2 - 5y + 2)}}{24}$$

i.e. $\quad 24x = (10y - 11) \pm \sqrt{(4y^2 + 20y + 25)}$

$$= (10y - 11) \pm (2y + 5)$$

$\therefore \quad 24x = 12y - 6$, i.e. $4x - 2y + 1 = 0$

and $\quad 24x = 8y - 16$, i.e. $3x - y + 2 = 0$

are the required lines.

To find the angle between the lines

If θ be the angle between the lines, then

$$\tan\theta = \frac{2\sqrt{h^2 - ab}}{|a + b|}$$

$$= \frac{2\sqrt{25 - 24}}{|12 + 2|} = \frac{1}{7}$$

$$\therefore \quad \theta = \tan^{-1}\left(\frac{1}{7}\right).$$

Example 21 Prove that the equation $8x^2 + 8xy + 2y^2 + 26x + 13y + 15 = 0$ represents a pair of parallel straight lines. Also, find the perpendicular distance between them.

Sol. Given equation is

$$8x^2 + 8xy + 2y^2 + 26x + 13y + 15 = 0 \quad ...(i)$$

Writing Eq. (i) as quadratic equation in x, we get

$$8x^2 + 2x(4y + 13) + 2y^2 + 13y + 15 = 0$$

$$\therefore \quad x = \frac{-2(4y + 13) \pm \sqrt{4(4y + 13)^2 - 32(2y^2 + 13y + 15)}}{16}$$

$$\Rightarrow \quad x = \frac{-(4y + 13) \pm \sqrt{(4y + 13)^2 - 8(2y^2 + 13y + 15)}}{8}$$

$$\Rightarrow \quad x = \frac{-(4y + 13) \pm 7}{8}$$

$\Rightarrow \quad 8x = -4y - 13 + 7$, i.e. $4x + 2y + 3 = 0$

and $\quad 8x = -4y - 13 - 7$, i.e. $2x + y + 5 = 0$

i.e. the given Eq. (i) represents two straight lines

$$2x + y + 5 = 0$$

and $\quad 4x + 2y + 3 = 0$

i.e. $\quad 2x + y + \frac{3}{2} = 0$

both lines are parallel.

$\therefore$ Distance between them $= \dfrac{\left|5 - \frac{3}{2}\right|}{\sqrt{2^2 + 1^2}} = \dfrac{7}{2\sqrt{5}}$

Aliter : Here, $\Delta = 8 \times 2 \times 15 + 2 \times \frac{13}{2} \times 13 \times 4$

$$- 8 \times \left(\frac{13}{2}\right)^2 - 2 \times (13)^2 - 15 \times (4)^2 = 0$$

and $\quad h^2 = (4)^2 = 16 = 8 \times 2 = ab$

$\therefore$ Given equation

$$8x^2 + 8xy + 2y^2 + 26x + 13y + 15 = 0 \quad ...(i)$$

represents two parallel straight lines.

Since, $\quad 8x^2 + 8xy + 2y^2 = 2(2x + y)^2$

factors of Eq. (i) can be taken as

$$2(2x + y + l)(2x + y + m)$$

$$= 8x^2 + 8xy + 2y^2 + 2(2m + 2l)x + 2(m + l)y + 2lm$$

On comparing, we get $l + m = \frac{13}{2}$ and $lm = \frac{15}{2}$

$\therefore$ Distance between them

$$= \frac{|l - m|}{\sqrt{(2^2 + 1^2)}} = \frac{\sqrt{(l + m)^2 - 4lm}}{\sqrt{5}}$$

$$= \frac{\sqrt{\frac{169}{4} - \frac{60}{2}}}{\sqrt{5}} = \frac{7}{2\sqrt{5}}$$

Remark

For comparing coefficients write equation in form

$$\begin{matrix} 2x + y + l \\ 2x + y + m \end{matrix}$$

coefficient of x is $2m + 2l$, cofficient of y is $l + m$ and coefficients of constant term is lm.

i.e. $l + m = \frac{13}{2}, lm = \frac{15}{2}$

Example 22 Find the combined equation of the straight lines passing through the point (1, 1) and parallel to the lines represented by the equation $x^2 - 5xy + 4y^2 + x + 2y - 2 = 0$.

Sol. Given equation of lines is

$$x^2 - 5xy + 4y^2 + x + 2y - 2 = 0. \quad \text{...(i)}$$

Since, $x^2 - 5xy + 4y^2 = (x - 4y)(x - y)$

Factors of Eq. (i) taken as $(x - 4y + l)(x - y + m)$.

Now, equation of line through (1, 1) and parallel to

$$x - 4y + l = 0 \text{ is } x - 4y + \lambda = 0$$

i.e. $1 - 4 + \lambda = 0$

$\therefore$ $\lambda = 3$

then line is $x - 4y + 3 = 0$ ...(ii)

and equation of line through (1, 1) and parallel to

$$x - y + m = 0 \text{ is } x - y + \mu = 0$$

i.e. $1 - 1 + \mu = 0$

$\therefore$ $\mu = 0$

then line is $x - y = 0$ ...(iii)

Hence, equation of lines Eqs. (ii) and (iii) is

$$(x - 4y + 3)(x - y) = 0$$

i.e. $x^2 - 5xy + 4y^2 + 3x - 3y = 0$

Example 23 If $ax^2 + 2hxy + by^2 + 2gx + 2fy + c = 0$ represents a pair of lines, prove that the area of the triangle formed by their bisectors and axis of x is $\frac{\sqrt{(a-b)^2 + 4h^2}}{|2h|} \cdot \left|\frac{ca - g^2}{ab - h^2}\right|$.

Sol. Given $ax^2 + 2hxy + by^2 + 2gx + 2fy + c = 0$ ...(i)

The point of intersection of the lines given by Eq. (i) are

$$\alpha = \sqrt{\left(\frac{f^2 - bc}{h^2 - ab}\right)}, \beta = \sqrt{\left(\frac{g^2 - ca}{h^2 - ab}\right)}$$

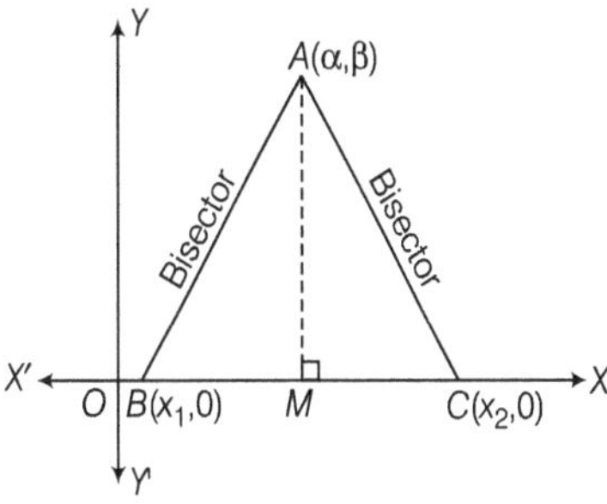

Hence, equation of the bisectors of the lines given by Eq. (i) is

$$\frac{(x - \alpha)^2 - (y - \beta)^2}{a - b} = \frac{(x - \alpha)(y - \beta)}{h}$$

For X-axis, $y = 0$.

$$\therefore \quad \frac{(x - \alpha)^2 - \beta^2}{a - b} = \frac{-\beta(x - \alpha)}{h}$$

or $h(x - \alpha)^2 + \beta(x - \alpha)(a - b) - h\beta^2 = 0$ ...(ii)

Eq. (ii) is a quadratic in $(x - \alpha)$ and let two values of x be x_1 and x_2, so that its roots are

$$x_1 - \alpha \text{ and } x_2 - \alpha$$

$\therefore$ $(x_1 - \alpha) + (x_2 - \alpha) = \text{Sum of roots} = \frac{-\beta(a - b)}{h}$

$(x_1 - \alpha)(x_2 - \alpha) = \text{Products of roots} = -\beta^2$

$\therefore$ $|x_2 - x_1| = |(x_2 - \alpha) - (x_1 - \alpha)|$

$$= \sqrt{[(x_2 - \alpha) + (x_1 - \alpha)]^2 - 4(x_2 - \alpha)(x_1 - \alpha)}$$

$\therefore$ $|x_2 - x_1| = \sqrt{\left\{\frac{\beta^2(a - b)^2}{h^2} + 4\beta^2\right\}}$

$$= \left|\frac{\beta}{h}\right| \sqrt{(a - b)^2 + 4h^2}$$

$\therefore$ Area of $\Delta ABC = \frac{1}{2}|BC||AM|$

$$= \frac{1}{2}|x_2 - x_1||\beta|$$

$$= \frac{1}{2}\left|\frac{\beta}{h}\right|\sqrt{(a - b)^2 + 4h^2} \times |\beta|$$

$$= \frac{\sqrt{(a - b)^2 + 4h^2}}{|2h|} \cdot \beta^2$$

$$= \frac{\sqrt{(a - b)^2 + 4h^2}}{|2h|} \cdot \frac{ca - g^2}{ab - h^2}$$

Exercise for Session 4

1. If $\lambda x^2 + 10xy + 3y^2 - 15x - 21y + 18 = 0$ represents a pair of straight lines. Then, the value of λ is

(a) -3 (b) 3 (c) 4 (d) -4

2. The point of intersection of the straight lines given by the equation $3y^2 - 8xy - 3x^2 - 29x + 3y - 18 = 0$ is

(a) $\left(1, \frac{1}{2}\right)$ (b) $\left(1, -\frac{1}{2}\right)$ (c) $\left(-\frac{3}{2}, \frac{5}{2}\right)$ (d) $\left(-\frac{3}{2}, -\frac{5}{2}\right)$

3. If the equation $12x^2 + 7xy - py^2 - 18x + qy + 6 = 0$ represents two perpendicular lines, then the value of p and q are

(a) 12, 1 (b) 12, -1 (c) 12, $\frac{23}{2}$ (d) 12, $-\frac{23}{2}$

4. If the angle between the two lines represented by $2x^2 + 5xy + 3y^2 + 7y + 4 = 0$ is $\tan^{-1}(m)$, then m is equal to

(a) $-\frac{1}{5}$ (b) $\frac{1}{5}$ (c) $-\frac{3}{5}$ (d) $\frac{3}{5}$

5. The equation of second degree $x^2 + 2\sqrt{2}xy + 2y^2 + 4x + 4\sqrt{2}\,y + 1 = 0$ represents a pair of straight lines, the distance between them is

(a) 2 (b) $2\sqrt{3}$ (c) 4 (d) $4\sqrt{3}$

6. Find the area of the parallelogram formed by the lines $2x^2 + 5xy + 3y^2 = 0$ and $2x^2 + 5xy + 3y^2 + 3x + 4y + 1 = 0$.

7. Find the locus of the incentre of the triangle formed by

$$xy - 4x - 4y + 16 = 0 \quad \text{and} \quad x + y = a \quad (a > 4, a \neq 4\sqrt{2} \text{ and } a \text{ is the parameter}).$$

8. If the equation $2hxy + 2gx + 2fy + c = 0$ represents two straight lines, then show that they form a rectangle of area $\frac{|fg|}{h^2}$ with the coordinate axes.

9. Find the area of the triangle formed by the lines represented by $ax^2 + 2hxy + by^2 + 2gx + 2fy + c = 0$ and axis of x.

10. Find the equations of the straight lines passing through the point (1, 1) and parallel to the lines represented by the equation $x^2 - 5xy + 4y^2 + x + 2y - 2 = 0$.

Session 5

To Find the Point of Intersection of Lines Represented by $ax^2 + 2hxy + by^2 + 2gx + 2fy + c = 0$ with the Help of Partial Differentiation, Removal of First Degree Terms, Equation of the Lines Joining the Origin to the Points of Intersection of a Given Line and a Given Curve

To Find the Point of Intersection of Lines Represented by $ax^2 + 2hxy + by^2 + 2gx + 2fy + c = 0$

Let $\phi(x, y) \equiv ax^2 + 2hxy + by^2 + 2gx + 2fy + c = 0$

$\therefore \quad \dfrac{\partial\phi}{\partial x} = 2ax + 2hy + 2g \quad$ [treating y as constant]

and $\quad \dfrac{\partial\phi}{\partial y} = 2hx + 2by + 2f \quad$ [treating x as constant]

For point of intersection $\dfrac{\partial\phi}{\partial x} = 0$ and $\dfrac{\partial\phi}{\partial y} = 0$,

we obtain $\quad ax + hy + g = 0$ and $hx + by + f = 0$

Solving them $\quad \dfrac{x}{fh - bg} = \dfrac{y}{gh - af} = \dfrac{1}{ab - h^2}$

$$(x, y) = \left(\frac{bg - fh}{h^2 - ab}, \frac{af - gh}{h^2 - ab}\right)$$

Working rule In practice, therefore, the general equation of second degree $\phi = 0$, represents a pair of straight lines, we solve its partial derivatives $\dfrac{\partial\phi}{\partial x} = 0, \dfrac{\partial\phi}{\partial y} = 0$ for their intersecting point $(x, y) = (\alpha, \beta)$.

Remembering Method (without use of partial derivatives)

Since, $\quad \Delta = \begin{vmatrix} a & h & g \\ h & b & f \\ g & f & c \end{vmatrix}$

from first two rows

$a \quad h \quad g \quad \Rightarrow \quad ax + hy + g = 0$

and $\quad h \quad b \quad f \quad \Rightarrow \quad hx + by + f = 0$ and then solve.

Example 24 Find the point of intersection of lines represented by $2x^2 - 7xy - 4y^2 - x + 22y - 10 = 0$.

Sol. Let $\quad \phi \equiv 2x^2 - 7xy - 4y^2 - x + 22y - 10 = 0$

$\therefore \quad \dfrac{\partial\phi}{\partial x} \equiv 4x - 7y - 1 = 0$

and $\quad \dfrac{\partial\phi}{\partial y} \equiv -7x - 8y + 22 = 0$

then, the point of intersection is $(x, y) = (2, 1)$.

Removal of First Degree Terms

Let point of intersection of lines represented by

$$ax^2 + 2hxy + by^2 + 2gx + 2fy + c = 0 \quad \text{...(i)}$$

is (α, β).

Here, $(\alpha, \beta) = \left(\dfrac{bg - fh}{h^2 - ab}, \dfrac{af - gh}{h^2 - ab}\right)$

For removal of first degree terms, shift the origin to (α, β).

i.e. Replacing x by $(X + \alpha)$ and y be $(Y + \beta)$ in Eq. (i).

Aliter : Direct equation after removal of first degree terms is

$aX^2 + 2hXY + bY^2 + (g\alpha + f\beta + c) = 0$

where, $\quad \alpha = \dfrac{bg - fh}{h^2 - ab}$

and $\quad \beta = \dfrac{af - gh}{h^2 - ab}$.

Example 25 Find the new equation of curve $12x^2+7xy-12y^2-17x-31y-7=0$ after removing the first degree terms.

Sol. Let $\phi \equiv 12x^2+7xy-12y^2-17x-31y-7=0$ ...(i)

$$\therefore \quad \frac{\partial\phi}{\partial x}=24x+7y-17=0$$

and $$\frac{\partial\phi}{\partial y}\equiv 7x-24y-31=0$$

Their point of intersection is $(x, y) \equiv (1, -1)$

Here, $\alpha = 1, \beta = -1$

Shift the origin to $(1, -1)$ then replacing $x = X+1$ and $y = Y-1$ in Eq. (i) the required equation is

$$12(X+1)^2+7(X+1)(Y-1)-12(Y-1)^2-17(X+1)-31(Y-1)-7=0$$

i.e. $12X^2+7XY-12Y^2=0$

Aliter :

Here, $\alpha = 1$ and $\beta = -1$

and $g=-\frac{17}{2}, f=-\frac{31}{2}, c=-7$

$$\therefore \quad g\alpha+f\beta+c=-\frac{17}{2}\times 1-\frac{31}{2}\times -1-7=0$$

$\therefore$ Removed equation is

$$aX^2+2hXY+by^2+(g\alpha+f\beta+c)=0$$

$$12X^2+7XY-12Y^2+0=0$$

$$12X^2+7XY-12Y^2=0.$$

Example 26 Transform the equation $x^2+4xy+y^2-2x+2y+4=0$ into the form $\frac{Y'^2}{b^2}-\frac{X'^2}{a^2}=1$.

Sol. To remove the first degree terms, we shift the origin to the point (α, β).

Then, $$\alpha=\frac{bg-fh}{h^2-ab}=\frac{1\times(-1)-1\times 2}{4-1\times 1}=-1$$

and $$\beta=\frac{af-gh}{h^2-ab}=\frac{1\times 1-(-1)\times(2)}{4-1\times 1}=1$$

then, the transformed equation is

$$X^2+4XY+Y^2+(g\alpha+f\beta+c)=0$$

$$\Rightarrow X^2+4XY+Y^2+(-1\times(-1)+1\times 1+4)=0$$

$$\therefore \quad X^2+4XY+Y^2+6=0 \quad ...(i)$$

Now, to remove the XY term from Eq. (i), we rotate the axes through an angle θ given by

$$\cot 2\theta=\frac{a-b}{2h}=0 \quad [\because \text{ here } a=b]$$

$$\Rightarrow \cot 2\theta = 0$$

$$\Rightarrow 2\theta=\frac{\pi}{2} \text{ or } \frac{3\pi}{2}$$

$$\Rightarrow \theta=\frac{\pi}{4} \text{ or } \frac{3\pi}{4}$$

Taking $\theta=\frac{\pi}{4}$ $\left[\text{we can also take } \theta=\frac{3\pi}{4}\right]$

$$\Rightarrow \cos\theta=\frac{1}{\sqrt{2}}, \sin\theta=\frac{1}{\sqrt{2}}$$

Now, if (X', Y') be the coordinates of the point when the axes are rotated through $\theta=\frac{\pi}{4}$, we have

$$X=\frac{X'-Y'}{\sqrt{2}}, Y=\frac{X'+Y'}{\sqrt{2}}$$

then Eq. (i) becomes

$$\frac{Y'^2}{6}-\frac{X'^2}{2}=1 \Rightarrow \frac{Y'^2}{b^2}-\frac{X'^2}{a^2}=1$$

where, $a^2=2$ and $b^2=6$.

Equation of the Lines Joining the Origin to the Points of Intersection of a Given Line and a Given Curve

Theorem The combined equation of the straight lines joining the origin to the points of intersection of a second degree curve

$$ax^2+2hxy+by^2+2gx+2fy+c=0$$

and a straight line $lx+my+n=0$ is :

$$ax^2+2hxy+by^2+2gx\left(\frac{lx+my}{-n}\right)+2fy\left(\frac{lx+my}{-n}\right)+c\left(\frac{lx+my}{-n}\right)^2=0$$

Proof The equation of the curve (PAQ) is

$$ax^2+2hxy+by^2+2gx+2fy+c=0 \quad ...(i)$$

and the equation of the line PQ be

$$lx+my+n=0 \quad ...(ii)$$

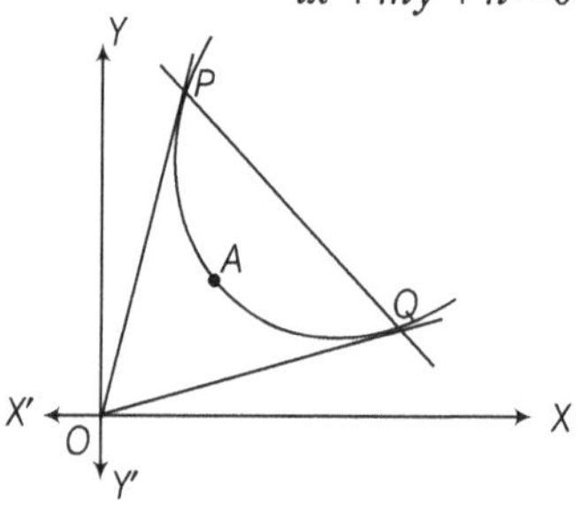

From the equation of the line Eq. (ii), find the value of '1' in terms of x and y,

i.e. $$\frac{lx+my}{-n}=1 \quad ...(iii)$$

Now, the Eq. (i) can be written as

or $ax^2+2hxy+by^2+(2gx+2fy)(1)+c(1)^2=0$

or $ax^2+2hxy+by^2+(2gx+2fy)\left(\frac{lx+my}{-n}\right)$

$$+c\left(\frac{lx+my}{-n}\right)^2=0 \quad ...(iv)$$

[replacing 1 by $\frac{lx+my}{-n}$ from Eq. (iii)]

Hence, the Eq. (iv) is homogeneous equation of second degree. Above Eq. (iv) on simplification will be of the form $Ax^2+2Hxy+By^2=0$ and will represent the required straight lines. If θ be the angle between them, then

$$\theta=\tan^{-1}\left(\frac{2\sqrt{(H^2-AB)}}{|A+B|}\right)$$

Hence, the equation of pairs of straight lines passing through the origin and the points of intersection of a curve and a line is obtained by making the curve homogeneous with the help of the line.

Example 27 Prove that the angle between the lines joining the origin to the points of intersection of the straight line $y=3x+2$ with the curve $x^2+2xy+3y^2+4x+8y-11=0$ is $\tan^{-1}\left(\frac{2\sqrt{2}}{3}\right)$.

Sol. Equation of curve is $x^2+2xy+3y^2+4x+8y-11=0$ ...(i)

and line $\quad y=3x+2 \Rightarrow \frac{y-3x}{2}=1$ ...(ii)

Making Eq. (i) homogeneous with the help of Eq. (ii), then

$$x^2+2xy+3y^2+4x\left(\frac{y-3x}{2}\right)+8y\left(\frac{y-3x}{2}\right)-11\left(\frac{y-3x}{2}\right)^2=0$$

$$\Rightarrow \quad x^2+2xy+3y^2+2xy-6x^2+4y^2-12xy-\frac{11}{4}(y-3x)^2=0$$

$$\Rightarrow \quad -5x^2-8xy+7y^2-\frac{11}{4}(y^2-6xy+9x^2)=0$$

$$\Rightarrow \quad -20x^2-32xy+28y^2-11y^2+66xy-99x^2=0$$

$$\Rightarrow \quad 119x^2-34xy-17y^2=0$$

$$\Rightarrow \quad 7x^2-2xy-y^2=0 \quad ...(iii)$$

This is the equation of lines joining the origin to the points of intersection of Eqs. (i) and (ii).

Comparing Eq. (iii) with $ax^2+2hxy+by^2=0$

$$a=7, h=-1, b=-1$$

If θ is the acute angle between pair of lines of Eq. (iii), then

$$\tan\theta=\frac{2\sqrt{h^2-ab}}{|a+b|}=\frac{2\sqrt{(1+7)}}{|7-1|}=\frac{2\sqrt{8}}{6}=\frac{4\sqrt{2}}{6}=\frac{2\sqrt{2}}{3}$$

$$\therefore \quad \theta=\tan^{-1}\left(\frac{2\sqrt{2}}{3}\right)$$

Example 28 Find the condition that the pair of straight lines joining the origin to the intersections of the line $y=mx+c$ and the circle $x^2+y^2=a^2$ may be at right angles.

Sol. The equations of the line and the circle are

$$y=mx+c \quad ...(i)$$

and $\quad x^2+y^2=a^2$ ...(ii)

The pair of straight lines joining the origin to the intersections of Eqs. (i) and (ii), is obtained by making homogeneous Eq. (ii) with the help of Eq. (i).

$$\because \quad y=mx+c \Rightarrow \frac{y-mx}{c}=1$$

$$\therefore \quad x^2+y^2=a^2(1)^2 \Rightarrow x^2+y^2=a^2\left(\frac{y-mx}{c}\right)^2$$

$$\Rightarrow x^2(c^2-a^2m^2)+2ma^2xy+y^2(c^2-a^2)=0 \quad ...(iii)$$

The lines given by Eq. (iii), are at right angles, then coefficient of x^2 + coefficient of $y^2=0$

$$\Rightarrow \quad c^2-a^2m^2+c^2-a^2=0$$

$$\therefore \quad 2c^2=a^2(1+m^2)$$

which is the required condition.

Example 29 Prove that the pair of lines joining the origin to the intersection of the curve $\frac{x^2}{a^2}+\frac{y^2}{b^2}=1$ by the line $lx+my+n=0$ are coincident, if a $a^2l^2+b^2m^2=n^2$.

Sol. The given curve is $\frac{x^2}{a^2}+\frac{y^2}{b^2}=1$ ...(i)

and line $\quad lx+my+n=0$

$$\Rightarrow \quad lx+my=-n$$

$$\Rightarrow \quad \frac{lx+my}{-n}=1 \quad ...(ii)$$

Making Eq. (i) homogeneous with the help of Eq. (ii), then

$$\frac{x^2}{a^2}+\frac{y^2}{b^2}=\left(\frac{lx+my}{-n}\right)^2$$

$$\Rightarrow \quad \frac{n^2x^2}{a^2}+\frac{n^2y^2}{b^2}=l^2x^2+m^2y^2+2lmxy$$

$$\Rightarrow \quad \left(\frac{n^2}{a^2}-l^2\right)x^2-2lmxy+\left(\frac{n^2}{b^2}-m^2\right)y^2=0 \quad ...(iii)$$

This is of the form $Ax^2 + 2Hxy + By^2 = 0$,

then $A = \frac{n^2}{a^2} - l^2, H = -lm$

and $B = \frac{n^2}{b^2} - m^2$

The lines given by Eq. (iii) will be coincident, if

$$H^2 - AB = 0 \Rightarrow H^2 = AB$$

$$\Rightarrow \quad l^2m^2 = \left(\frac{n^2}{a^2} - l^2\right)\left(\frac{n^2}{b^2} - m^2\right)$$

$$\Rightarrow \quad l^2m^2 = \frac{n^4}{a^2b^2} - \frac{n^2m^2}{a^2} - \frac{l^2n^2}{b^2} + l^2m^2$$

$$\Rightarrow \quad \frac{n^4}{a^2b^2} = \frac{n^2m^2}{a^2} + \frac{n^2l^2}{b^2}$$

$$\Rightarrow \quad n^2 = b^2m^2 + a^2l^2$$

$$\Rightarrow \quad a^2l^2 + b^2m^2 = n^2$$

Example 30 Show that the straight lines joining the origin to the points of intersection of curves

$$ax^2 + 2hxy + by^2 + 2gx = 0$$

and $a'x^2 + 2h'xy + b'y^2 + 2g'x = 0$

are at right angles, if $g'(a+b) = g(a'+b')$.

Sol. The two curves meet in two points and the required lines joining the origin to these points will be obtained by making one equation homogeneous with the help of the other.

$$ax^2 + 2hxy + by^2 + 2gx = 0 \quad \text{...(i)}$$

$$a'x^2 + 2h'xy + b'y^2 + 2g'x = 0 \quad \text{...(ii)}$$

Multiplying Eq. (i) by g' and Eq. (ii) by g and subtracting, we get $(ag' - a'g)x^2 + (2hg' - 2h'g)xy + (bg' - b'g)y^2 = 0$

If the lines are at right angles, then coefficient of x^2 + coefficient of $y^2 = 0$

$$\Rightarrow \quad ag' - a'g + bg' - b'g = 0$$

$$\therefore \quad (a+b)g' = (a'+b')g.$$

Exercise for Session 5

1. If the straight lines joining origin to the points of intersection of the line $x + y = 1$ with the curve $x^2 + y^2 + x - 2y - m = 0$ are perpendicular to each other, then the value of m should be
   (a) $-\frac{1}{2}$ (b) 0 (c) $\frac{1}{2}$ (d) 1
2. The pair of straight lines joining the origin to the common points of $x^2 + y^2 = 4$ and $y = 3x + c$ are perpendicular, if c^2 is equal to
   (a) –1 (b) 6 (c) 13 (d) 20
3. Mixed term xy is to be removed from the general equation of second degree $ax^2 + 2hxy + by^2 + 2gx + 2fy + c = 0$, one should rotate the axes through an angle θ, then $\tan 2\theta$ is equal to
   (a) $\frac{(a-b)}{2h}$ (b) $\frac{2h}{(a+b)}$ (c) $\frac{(a+b)}{2h}$ (d) $\frac{2h}{(a-b)}$
4. The lines joining the origin to the points of intersection of $2x^2 + 3xy - 4x + 1 = 0$ and $3x + y = 1$ are given by
   (a) $x^2 - y^2 - 5xy = 0$ (b) $x^2 - y^2 + 5xy = 0$ (c) $x^2 + y^2 - 5xy = 0$ (d) $x^2 + y^2 + 5xy = 0$
5. The equation of the line joining the origin to the point of intersection of the lines $2x^2 + xy - y^2 + 5x - y + 2 = 0$ is
   (a) $x + y = 0$ (b) $x - y = 0$ (c) $x - 2y = 0$ (d) $2x + y = 0$
6. Find the equation of the lines joining the origin to the points of intersection of $3x - 2y = 1$ with $3x^2 + 5xy - 3y^2 + 2x + 3y = 0$ and show that they are at right angles.
7. If the straight line joining the origin and the points of intersection of $y = mx + 1$ and $x^2 + y^2 = 1$ be perpendicular to each other, then find the value of m.
8. Prove that the straight lines joining the origin to the points of intersection of the straight line $kx + hy = 2hk$ with the curve $(x-h)^2 + (y-k)^2 = c^2$ are at right angles, if $h^2 + k^2 = c^2$.
9. Show that for all values of λ, the lines joining the origin to the points common to $x^2 + 2hxy - y^2 + gx + fy = 0$ and $fx - gy = \lambda$ are at right angles.
10. Find the equations of the straight lines joining the origin to the points of intersection of $x^2 + y^2 - 4x - 2y = 0$ and $x^2 + y^2 - 2x - 4y = 4$.

Shortcuts and Important Results to Remember

1 If slope of one of the lines represented by $ax^2 + 2hxy + by^2 = 0$ should be n times the slope of the other, then $4nh^2 = ab(1+n)^2$.

2 If the slope of one of the lines represented by $ax^2 + 2hxy + by^2 = 0$ be the nth power of the other, then $(ab^n)^{1/n+1} + (a^n b)^{1/n+1} + 2h = 0$

3 If two of the three lines represented by $ax^3 + bx^2y + cxy^2 + dy^3 = 0$ may be at right angles, then $a^2 + ac + bd + d^2 = 0$

4 If pairs of straight lines $x^2 + 2m_1xy - y^2 = 0$ and $x^2 + 2m_2xy - y^2 = 0$ be such that each pair bisects the angle between the other pair, then $m_1m_2 = -1$

5 If the equation $ax^2 + 2hxy + by^2 + 2gx + 2fy + c = 0$ represents a pair of parallel lines, then

(i) $h^2 = ab$, $bg^2 = af^2$.

(ii) the distance between them $= 2\sqrt{\dfrac{(g^2 - ac)}{a(a+b)}}$.

6 If $ax^2 + 2hxy + by^2 + 2gx + 2fy + c = 0$ and $ax^2 + 2hxy + by^2 - 2gx - 2fy + c = 0$ each represent a pair of lines, then the area of the parallelogram enclosed by them is $\dfrac{2|c|}{\sqrt{(h^2 - ab)}}$.

JEE Type Solved Examples :
Single Option Correct Type Questions

- This section contains **6 multiple choice examples**. Each example has four choices (a), (b), (c) and (d) out of which **ONLY ONE** is correct.

Ex. 1 *If the pairs of lines $x^2 + 2xy + \lambda y^2 = 0$ and $\lambda x^2 + 2xy + y^2 = 0$ have exactly one line in common, then the joint equation of the other two lines is given by*

(a) $3x^2 + 8xy - 3y^2 = 0$ (b) $3x^2 + 10xy + 3y^2 = 0$

(c) $x^2 + 2xy - 3y^2 = 0$ (d) $3x^2 + 2xy - y^2 = 0$

Sol. (b) Let $y = mx$, be a line common to the given pairs of lines, then

$$\lambda m^2 + 2m + 1 = 0 \text{ and } m^2 + 2m + \lambda = 0$$

$$\Rightarrow \quad \frac{m^2}{2(\lambda - 1)} = \frac{m}{(1 - \lambda^2)} = \frac{1}{2(\lambda - 1)}$$

$$\Rightarrow \quad m^2 = 1 \text{ and } m = -\frac{1}{2}(\lambda + 1)$$

$$\Rightarrow \quad (\lambda + 1)^2 = 4 \Rightarrow \lambda + 1 = 2, -2$$

$$\therefore \quad \lambda = 1 \text{ or } -3$$

But for $\lambda = 1$, the two pairs have both the lines common.

So, $\lambda = -3$ and the slope m of the line common to both the pairs is 1. Now,

$$x^2 + 2xy + \lambda y^2 = x^2 + 2xy - 3y^2 = (x - y)(x + 3y)$$

and $\lambda x^2 + 2xy + y^2 = -3x^2 + 2xy + y^2 = -(x - y)(3x + y)$

Hence, the joint equation of other two lines is

$$(x + 3y)(3x + y) = 0 \text{ or } 3x^2 + 10xy + 3y^2 = 0.$$

Ex. 2 *The combined equation of the lines l_1 and l_2 is $2x^2 + 6xy + y^2 = 0$ and that of the lines m_1 and m_2 is $4x^2 + 18xy + y^2 = 0$. If the angle between l_1 and m_2 is α, then the angle between l_2 and m_1 will be*

(a) $\frac{\pi}{2} - \alpha$ (b) $\frac{\pi}{4} + \alpha$ (c) α (d) 2α

Sol. (c) The combined equation of the bisectors of the angles between the lines of the first pair is

$$\frac{x^2 - y^2}{2 - 1} = \frac{xy}{3} \Rightarrow x^2 - y^2 = \frac{1}{3}xy$$

and the combined equation of the bisectors of the angles between the lines of the second pair is

$$\frac{x^2 - y^2}{4 - 1} = \frac{xy}{9} \Rightarrow x^2 - y^2 = \frac{1}{3}xy$$

It is clear that the two pairs are equally inclined to each other.

Hence, the angle between l_2 and m_1 is α.

Ex. 3 *The pair of lines $\sqrt{3}x^2 - 4xy + \sqrt{3}y^2 = 0$ are rotated about the origin by $\frac{\pi}{6}$ in the anti-clockwise sense. The equation of the pair in the new position is*

(a) $x^2 - \sqrt{3}xy = 0$ (b) $y^2 - \sqrt{3}xy = 0$

(c) $\sqrt{3}x^2 - xy = 0$ (d) $\sqrt{3}y^2 - xy = 0$

Sol. (c) The given equation of pair of straight lines can be written as

$$(\sqrt{3}x - y)(x - \sqrt{3}y) = 0$$

$$\Rightarrow \quad y = \sqrt{3}x \text{ and } y = \frac{1}{\sqrt{3}}x$$

$$\Rightarrow \quad y = x \tan 60^\circ \text{ and } y = x \tan 30^\circ$$

After rotation, the separate equations are

$$y = x \tan 90^\circ \text{ and } y = x \tan 60^\circ$$

$$\Rightarrow \quad x = 0 \text{ and } y = x\sqrt{3}$$

Hence, the combined equation in the new position is

$$x(\sqrt{3}x - y) = 0$$

or

$$\sqrt{3}x^2 - xy = 0.$$

Ex. 4 *If the pair of lines $ax^2 - 2xy + by^2 = 0$ and $bx^2 - 2xy + ay^2 = 0$ be such that each pair bisects the angle between the other pair, then $|a - b|$ equals to*

(a) 1 (b) 2

(c) 3 (d) 4

Sol. (b) According to the example, the equation of the bisectors of the angle between the lines

$$ax^2 - 2xy + by^2 = 0 \quad ...(i)$$

is

$$bx^2 - 2xy + ay^2 = 0 \quad ...(ii)$$

$\therefore$ The equation of bisectors of the angle between the lines Eq. (i) is

$$\frac{x^2 - y^2}{a - b} = \frac{xy}{-1}$$

$$\Rightarrow \quad x^2 + (a - b)xy - y^2 = 0 \quad ...(iii)$$

Since, Eqs. (ii) and (iii) are identical, comparing Eqs. (ii) and (iii), we get

$$\frac{b}{1} = \frac{-2}{a - b} = \frac{a}{-1}$$

$$\Rightarrow \quad (a - b)b = -2$$

and

$$(a - b)a = 2$$

$$\therefore \quad (a - b)^2 = 4$$

or

$$|a - b| = 2$$

Ex. 5 *The equation of line which is parallel to the line common to the pair of lines given by $3x^2 + xy - 4y^2 = 0$ and $6x^2 + 11xy + 4y^2 = 0$ and at a distance of 2 units from it is*

(a) $3x - 4y = -10$ (b) $x - y = 2$
(c) $3x + 4y = 10$ (d) $2x + y = -2$

Sol. (c) We have, $3x^2 + xy - 4y^2 = 0$

or $(x - y)(3x + 4y) = 0$ ...(i)

and $6x^2 + 11xy + 4y^2 = 0$

or $(2x + y)(3x + 4y) = 0$ ...(ii)

Equation of line common to Eqs. (i) and (ii) is

$$3x + 4y = 0 \quad \text{...(iii)}$$

Equation of any line parallel to Eq. (iii) is

$$3x + 4y = \lambda$$

Since, its distance from Eq. (iii) is 2, we have

$$\frac{|\lambda - 0|}{\sqrt{(3^2 + 4^2)}} = 2 \text{ or } \lambda = \pm 10$$

Hence, required lines are $3x + 4y = \pm 10$.

Ex. 6 *The lines joining the origin to the points of intersection of $x^2 + y^2 + 2gx + c = 0$ and $x^2 + y^2 + 2fy - c = 0$ are at right angles, if*

(a) $g^2 + f^2 = c$ (b) $g^2 - f^2 = c$
(c) $g^2 - f^2 = 2c$ (d) $g^2 + f^2 = c^2$

Sol. (c) Given,

$$x^2 + y^2 + 2gx + c = 0 \quad \text{...(i)}$$

and $$x^2 + y^2 + 2fy - c = 0 \quad \text{...(ii)}$$

On subtracting Eq. (ii) from Eq. (i), we get

$$2gx - 2fy + 2c = 0$$

or $$\frac{fy - gx}{c} = 1 \quad \text{...(iii)}$$

On adding Eqs. (i) and (ii), we get

$$2(x^2 + y^2 + gx + fy) = 0$$

or $$x^2 + y^2 + gx + fy = 0 \quad \text{...(iv)}$$

Homogenising Eq. (iv) with the help of Eq. (iii), then

$$x^2 + y^2 + (gx + fy)\left(\frac{fy - gx}{c}\right) = 0$$

$\therefore$ The lines will be at right angles, when

$$\left(1 - \frac{g^2}{c}\right) + \left(1 + \frac{f^2}{c}\right) = 0$$

$\Rightarrow$ $$g^2 - f^2 = 2c$$

JEE Type Solved Examples :
More than One Correct Option Type Questions

- This section contains **3 multiple choice examples**. Each example has four choices (a), (b), (c) and (d) out of which **MORE THAN ONE** may be correct.

Ex. 7 *The lines joining the origin to the point of intersection of $3x^2 + mxy - 4x + 1 = 0$ and $2x + y - 1 = 0$ are at right angles. Which of the following is/are possible value of m?*

(a) -4 (b) 3 (c) 4 (d) 7

Sol. (a,b,c,d) Given line is $2x + y = 1$ ...(i)

and curve is $3x^2 + mxy - 4x + 1 = 0$ ...(ii)

Homogenising Eq. (ii) with the help of Eq. (i), then

$$3x^2 + mxy - 4x(2x + y) + (2x + y)^2 = 0$$

or $$-x^2 + mxy + y^2 = 0$$

the lines are at right angles as $a + b = 0$, when $h^2 > ab$

i.e. $$\frac{m^2}{4} + 1 > 0$$

which is true for all $m \in R$.

Ex. 8 *The lines $(lx + my)^2 - 3(mx - ly)^2 = 0$ and $lx + my + n = 0$ form*

(a) an isosceles triangle (b) a right angled triangle
(c) an equilateral triangle (d) None of these

Sol. (a,c) $(lx + my)^2 - 3(mx - ly)^2 = 0$

$\Rightarrow (l^2 - 3m^2)x^2 + 8mlxy + (m^2 - 3l^2)y^2 = 0$

$\Rightarrow \{(l + m\sqrt{3})x + (m - l\sqrt{3})y\}\{(l - \sqrt{3}m)x + (m + \sqrt{3}l)y\} = 0$

Let slope of $(l + m\sqrt{3})x + (m - l\sqrt{3})y = 0$ be m_1 and slope of $(l - m\sqrt{3})x + (m + l\sqrt{3})y = 0$ be m_2 and slope of $lx + my + n = 0$ is m_3.

Now, $$\tan\theta_1 = \left|\frac{m_3 - m_1}{1 + m_3 m_1}\right| = \left|\frac{-\frac{l}{m} + \frac{l + m\sqrt{3}}{m - l\sqrt{3}}}{1 + \frac{l}{m}\cdot\left(\frac{l + m\sqrt{3}}{m - l\sqrt{3}}\right)}\right|$$

$$= \left|\frac{\sqrt{3}(l^2 + m^2)}{(l^2 + m^2)}\right| = \sqrt{3}$$

$\Rightarrow$ $$\theta_1 = 60^\circ$$

Similarly, $\tan\theta_2 = \left|\dfrac{m_2 - m_1}{1 + m_2 m_1}\right| = \sqrt{3}$

$\Rightarrow \qquad \theta_2 = 60^\circ$

Hence, an equilateral triangle is formed which is also an isosceles one.

Ex. 9 *If the equation $ax^2 - 6xy + y^2 + bx + cy + d = 0$ represents a pair of lines whose slopes are m and m^2, then the value(s) of a is/are*

(a) -27 (b) -8
(c) 8 (d) 27

Sol. (a,c) $\because$ m and m^2 are the roots of the equation

$$\left(\frac{y}{x}\right)^2 - 6\left(\frac{y}{x}\right) + a = 0$$

$\therefore \qquad m + m^2 = 6$ and $m \cdot m^2 = a$ ...(i)

Now, $\qquad (m + m^2)^3 = (6)^3$

$\Rightarrow m^3 + m^6 + 3m \cdot m^2 (m + m^2) = 216$

$\Rightarrow \qquad a + a^2 + 3a(6) = 216$ [from Eq. (i)]

$\Rightarrow \qquad a^2 + 19a - 216 = 0$

$\Rightarrow \qquad (a + 27)(a - 8) = 0$

$\therefore \qquad a = -27, 8$

JEE Type Solved Examples : Paragraph Based Questions

- This section contains **one solved paragraph** based upon each paragraph **2 multiple choice questions** have to be answered. Each of these questions has four choices (a), (b), (c) and (d) out of which **ONLY ONE** is correct.

Paragraph

(Q. Nos. 10 to11)

Consider the equation of a pair of straight lines as $\lambda xy - 8x + 9y - 12 = 0$

10. The value of λ is

(a) 0 (b) 2
(c) 4 (d) 6

11. The point of intersection of lines is (α, β), then the equation whose roots are α, β, is

(a) $4x^2 + x - 8 = 0$ (b) $6x^2 + x - 12 = 0$
(c) $4x^2 - x - 8 = 0$ (d) $6x^2 - x - 12 = 0$

Sol. Given equation is,

$$\lambda xy - 8x + 9y - 12 = 0$$

Here, $\qquad a = 0, b = 0, c = -12,$

$$f = \frac{9}{2}, g = -4 \text{ and } h = \frac{\lambda}{2}$$

10. (d) For $\Delta = 0$,

$$0 + 2 \times \frac{9}{2} \times -4 \times \frac{\lambda}{2} - 0 - 0 + 12 \times \frac{\lambda^2}{4} = 0$$

$\Rightarrow \qquad 3\lambda^2 - 18\lambda = 0$

$\therefore \qquad \lambda = 0, 6$

Hence, $\qquad \lambda = 6$ [$\because$ for $\lambda = 0$, it will give an equation of first degree]

11. (b) Let $f(x,y) = 6xy - 8x + 9y - 12$ [$\because \lambda = 6$]

$\therefore \qquad \dfrac{\partial f}{\partial x} = 6y - 8$ and $\dfrac{\partial f}{\partial y} = 6x + 9$

For point of intersection $\dfrac{\partial f}{\partial x} = 0$ and $\dfrac{\partial f}{\partial y} = 0$, we get

$$x = -\frac{3}{2}, y = \frac{4}{3}$$

$\therefore \qquad \alpha = -\dfrac{3}{2}$ and $\beta = \dfrac{4}{3}$

Hence, required equation is

$$x^2 - \left(-\frac{3}{2} + \frac{4}{3}\right)x - 2 = 0$$

$\Rightarrow \qquad 6x^2 + x - 12 = 0$

JEE Type Solved Examples : Single Integer Answer Type Questions

- This section contains **2 examples**. The answer to each example is **a single digit integer**, ranging from 0 to 9 (both inclusive).

Ex. 12 *If the sum of the slopes of the lines given by $x^2 - 2cxy - 7y^2 = 0$ is four times their product, then the value of c is*

Sol. (2) Given, $m_1 + m_2 = 4m_1m_2$

$$\Rightarrow \quad -\frac{2h}{b} = 4 \cdot \frac{a}{b} \Rightarrow h = -2a$$

$$\therefore \quad -c = -2 \times 1 \Rightarrow c = 2$$

Ex. 13 *If one of the lines given by $6x^2 - xy + 4cy^2 = 0$ is $3x + 4y = 0$, then the value of $|c|$ is*

Sol. (3) $\because 3x + 4y = 0$ is one of the lines given by $6x^2 - xy + 4cy^2 = 0$, then

$$6x^2 - x\left(-\frac{3x}{4}\right) + 4c\left(-\frac{3x}{4}\right)^2 = 0 \qquad \left[\because y = -\frac{3x}{4}\right]$$

$$\Rightarrow \quad 6 + \frac{3}{4} + \frac{9c}{4} = 0 \; ; \quad \therefore c = -3$$

Hence, $\quad |c| = 3$

JEE Type Solved Examples : Matching Type Questions

- This section contains **one solved example**. This example has four statements (A, B, C and D) is **Column I** and four statements (p, q, r and s) in **Column II**. Any given statements in **Column I** can have correct matching with one or more statement(s) given in **Column II**.

Ex. 14 *Match the following*

	Column I		Column II
(A)	If the slope of one of the lines represented by $ax^2 + 2hxy + by^2 = 0$ is the square of the other, then $\frac{a+b}{h} + \frac{8h^2}{ab}$ is a	(p)	Odd prime number
(B)	The product of perpendiculars drawn from the point (1, 2) to the pair of lines $x^2 + 4xy + y^2 = 0$ is λ units, then $[\lambda]$ is a (where $[\cdot]$ denotes the greatest integer function).	(q)	Composite number
(C)	Distance between two lines represented by the line pair $x^2 - 4xy + 4y^2 + x - 2y - 6 = 0$ is λ unit, then $[\lambda]$ is a (where $[\cdot]$ denotes the greatest integer function).	(r)	Even prime number
(D)	If the pairs $a_1x^2 + 2h_1xy + b_1y^2 = 0$ and $a_2x^2 + 2h_2xy + b_2y^2 = 0$ have one line common, then $\frac{(a_1b_2 - a_2b_1)^2}{(b_1h_2 - b_2h_1)(a_2h_1 - a_1h_2)}$ is a	(s)	Perfect number

Sol. (A) → (q, s); (B) → (p); (C) → (r); (D) → (q)

(A) Let m and m^2 be the slopes of the lines represented by $ax^2 + 2hxy + by^2 = 0$, then

$$m + m^2 = -\frac{2h}{b} \qquad \text{...(i)}$$

and $$m \cdot m^2 = \frac{a}{b} \qquad \text{...(ii)}$$

From Eq. (i), $(m + m^2)^3 = \left(-\frac{2h}{b}\right)^3$

$$\Rightarrow m^3 + m^6 + 3m \cdot m^2(m + m^2) = -\frac{8h^3}{b^3}$$

$$\Rightarrow \frac{a}{b} + \frac{a^2}{b^2} + \frac{3a}{b}\left(-\frac{2h}{b}\right) = -\frac{8h^3}{b^3} \quad \text{[from Eqs. (i) and (ii)]}$$

$$\Rightarrow \quad ab + a^2 - 6ah = -\frac{8h^3}{b}$$

$$\therefore \quad \frac{a+b}{h} + \frac{8h^2}{ab} = 6$$

(B) Let $y = m_1x$ and $y = m_2x$ lines represented by $x^2 + 4xy + y^2 = 0$, then $m_1 + m_2 = -4$, $m_1m_2 = 1$. Then, product of perpendiculars drawn from the point (1, 2)

$$= \frac{|(2 - m_1)(2 - m_2)|}{\sqrt{(1 + m_1^2)}\sqrt{(1 + m_2^2)}}$$

$$= \frac{|4 - 2(m_1 + m_2) + m_1m_2|}{\sqrt{1 + (m_1 + m_2)^2 - 2m_1m_2 + (m_1m_2)^2}}$$

$$= \frac{|4 + 8 + 1|}{\sqrt{(1 + 16 - 2 + 1)}} = \frac{13}{4} \text{ units}$$

$$\because \quad \lambda = \frac{13}{4}$$

$$\therefore \quad [\lambda] = 3$$

(C) Given, line pair is $x^2 - 4xy + 4y^2 + x - 2y - 6 = 0$

$\Rightarrow \quad (x - 2y)^2 + (x - 2y) - 6 = 0$

$\Rightarrow \quad (x - 2y + 3)(x - 2y - 2) = 0$

$\therefore$ Lines are $x - 2y + 3 = 0$ and $x - 2y - 2 = 0$

Hence, distance between lines $= \dfrac{|3-(-2)|}{\sqrt{1+4}} = \sqrt{5}$ unit

$\therefore \quad \lambda = \sqrt{5}$

Hence, $\quad [\lambda] = [\sqrt{5}] = 2$

(D) Let $y = mx$ be the common line, then
$b_1m^2 + 2h_1m + a_1 = 0$ and $b_2m^2 + 2h_2m + a_2 = 0$.

$$\Rightarrow \begin{vmatrix} b_1 & 2h_1 \\ b_2 & 2h_2 \end{vmatrix} \times \begin{vmatrix} 2h_1 & a_1 \\ 2h_2 & a_2 \end{vmatrix} = \begin{vmatrix} a_1 & b_1 \\ a_2 & b_2 \end{vmatrix}^2$$

$$\Rightarrow 4(b_1h_2 - b_2h_1)(a_2h_1 - a_1h_2) = (a_1b_2 - a_2b_1)^2$$

$$\therefore \frac{(a_1b_2 - a_2b_1)^2}{(b_1h_2 - b_2h_1)(a_2h_1 - a_1h_2)} = 4$$

JEE Type Solved Examples : Statement I and II Type Questions

- **Directions** (Ex. Nos. 15-16) Each of these examples contains two statements.

Statement I (Assertion) and

Statement II (Reason)

Each of these examples also has four alternative choices, only one of which is the correct answer. You have to select the correct choice, as given below :

(a) Statement I is true, Statement II is true and Statement II is a correct explanation for Statement I

(b) Statement I is true, Statement II is true and Statement II is not a correct explanation for Statement I

(c) Statement I is true, Statement II is false

(d) Statement I is false, Statement II is true

Ex. 15 **Statement I** *The combined equation of* l_1, l_2 *is* $3x^2 + 6xy + 2y^2 = 0$ *and that of* m_1, m_2 *is* $5x^2 + 18xy + 2y^2 = 0$. *If angle between* l_1, m_2 *is* θ, *then angle between* l_2, m_1 *is* θ.

Statement II *If the pairs of lines* $l_1l_2 = 0, m_1m_2 = 0$ *are equally inclinded that angle between* l_1 *and* m_2 = *angle between* l_2 *and* m_1.

Sol. (a) The pair of bisectors of $3x^2 + 6xy + 2y^2 = 0$ is $\dfrac{x^2 - y^2}{3-2} = \dfrac{xy}{3}$, i.e. $3x^2 - xy - 3y^2 = 0$ and pair of bisectors of $5x^2 + 18xy + 2y^2 = 0$ is $\dfrac{x^2 - y^2}{5-2} = \dfrac{xy}{9}$

i.e. $3x^2 - xy - 3y^2 = 0$ are coincides.

$\therefore$ Angle between l_1, m_2 is same as angle between l_2, m_1.

$\therefore$ Both statements are true and Statement II is a correct explanation for Statement I.

Ex. 16 **Statement I** *The equation* $2x^2 - 3xy - 2y^2 + 5x - 5y + 3 = 0$ *represents a pair of perpendicular straight lines.*

Statement II *A pair of lines given by* $ax^2 + 2hxy + by^2 + 2gx + 2fy + c = 0$ *are perpendicular if* $a + b = 0$.

Sol. (d) Here, $\Delta \neq 0$, $h^2 > ab$ and $a + b = 0$

$\therefore \quad 2x^2 - 3xy - 2y^2 + 5x - 5y + 3 = 0$

represents a rectangular hyperbola.

$\therefore$ Statement I is false and Statement II is true.

Subjective Type Examples

- In this section, there are **10 subjective solved examples**.

Ex. 17 *If the lines represented by* $2x^2 - 5xy + 2y^2 = 0$ *be the two sides of a parallelogram and the line* $5x + 2y = 1$ *be one of its diagonal. Find the equation of the other diagonal, and area of the parallelogram.*

Sol. Given pair of lines, $2x^2 - 5xy + 2y^2 = 0$

i.e. $\quad (x - 2y)(2x - y) = 0$

$\therefore \quad x - 2y = 0$ and $2x - y = 0$

and the diagonal $5x + 2y = 1$ does not pass through origin, hence it is AC.

On solving, $x - 2y = 0$ and $5x + 2y = 1$, we get

$$A = \left(\frac{1}{6}, \frac{1}{12}\right)$$

and solving $2x - y = 0$ and $5x + 2y = 1$, we get

$$C \equiv \left(\frac{1}{9}, \frac{2}{9}\right).$$

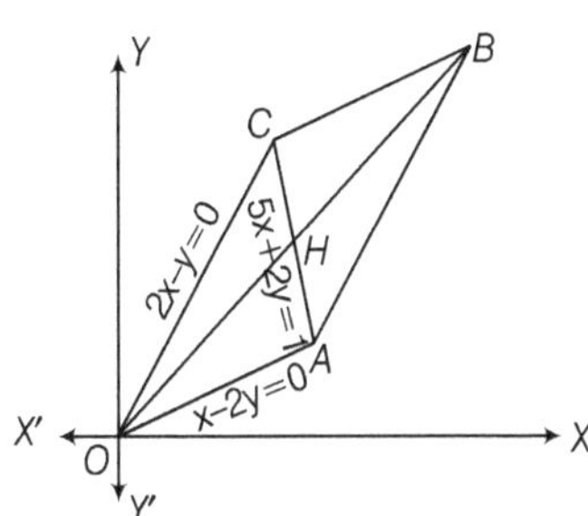

Since, diagonals of parallelogram bisect each other, if bisect at H.

Then, $$H \equiv \left\{\frac{1}{2}\left(\frac{1}{6}+\frac{1}{9}\right), \frac{1}{2}\left(\frac{1}{12}+\frac{2}{9}\right)\right\}$$

i.e. $$H = \left(\frac{5}{36}, \frac{11}{72}\right)$$

Hence, the equation of other diagonal which passes through O and H is

$$y - 0 = \frac{\frac{11}{72} - 0}{\frac{5}{36} - 0}(x - 0)$$

$$\Rightarrow \quad y = \frac{11}{10}x$$

$$\Rightarrow \quad 11x - 10y = 0$$

Now, area of parallelogram $= 2 \times$ Area of ΔOAC

$$= 2 \times \frac{1}{2}\left|\frac{1}{6} \times \frac{2}{9} - \frac{1}{9} \times \frac{1}{12}\right| = \frac{1}{36} \text{ sq units}$$

Ex. 18 *Prove that the equation $(a+2h+b)x^2 - 2(a-b)xy + (a-2h+b)y^2 = 0$ represents a pair of lines each inclined at an angle of 45° to one or other of the lines given by, $ax^2 + 2hxy + by^2 = 0$.*

Sol. Given equation is

$$ax^2 + 2hxy + by^2 = 0 \quad \text{...(i)}$$

Let the lines represented by Eq. (i) are

$$y - m_1 x = 0 \quad \text{...(ii)}$$

and $$y - m_2 x = 0 \quad \text{...(iii)}$$

therefore, $m_1 + m_2 = -\frac{2h}{b}$, $m_1 m_2 = \frac{a}{b}$

If $m_1 = \tan\theta_1$ and $m_2 = \tan\theta_2$, the equation of lines through the origin making 45° with the lines Eqs. (ii) and (iii) will be

$$y - x\tan(\theta_1 - 45°) = 0$$

and $$y - x\tan(\theta_2 - 45°) = 0$$

Their combined equation is

$$\{y - x\tan(\theta_1 - 45°)\}\{y - x\tan(\theta_2 - 45°)\} = 0$$

$$\Rightarrow \left(y - \frac{m_1 - 1}{1 + m_1}x\right)\left(y - \frac{m_2 - 1}{1 + m_2}x\right) = 0$$

$$\Rightarrow \{(1+m_1)y - (m_1 - 1)x\}\{(1+m_2)y - (m_2 - 1)x\} = 0$$

$$\Rightarrow (1+m_1)(1+m_2)y^2 - xy\{(1+m_1)(m_2-1) + (m_1-1)(1+m_2)\} + (m_1-1)(m_2-1)x^2 = 0$$

$$\Rightarrow (1 + m_1 + m_2 + m_1 m_2)y^2 - 2xy(m_1 m_2 - 1) + \{m_1 m_2 - (m_1 + m_2) + 1\}x^2 = 0$$

$$\Rightarrow \left(1 - \frac{2h}{b} + \frac{a}{b}\right)y^2 - 2xy\left(\frac{a}{b} - 1\right) + \left(\frac{a}{b} + \frac{2h}{b} + 1\right)x^2 = 0$$

$$\therefore \quad (a + 2h + b)x^2 - 2(a - b)xy + (a - 2h + b)y^2 = 0$$

Ex. 19 *If $u \equiv ax^2 + 2hxy + by^2 + 2gx + 2fy + c = 0$ represents a pair of straight lines, prove that the equation of the third pair of straight lines passing through the points where these meet the axes is $cu + 4(fg - ch)xy = 0$.*

Sol. $u \equiv ax^2 + 2hxy + by^2 + 2gx + 2fy + c = 0$

$\because$ u represents a pair of straight line, then $\Delta = 0$

$$\therefore \quad abc + 2fgh - af^2 - bg^2 - ch^2 = 0 \quad \text{...(i)}$$

Combined equation of axes is $xy = 0$

Now, the curve through the intersection of $u = 0$ and $xy = 0$ is

$$u + \lambda xy = 0 \quad \text{...(ii)}$$

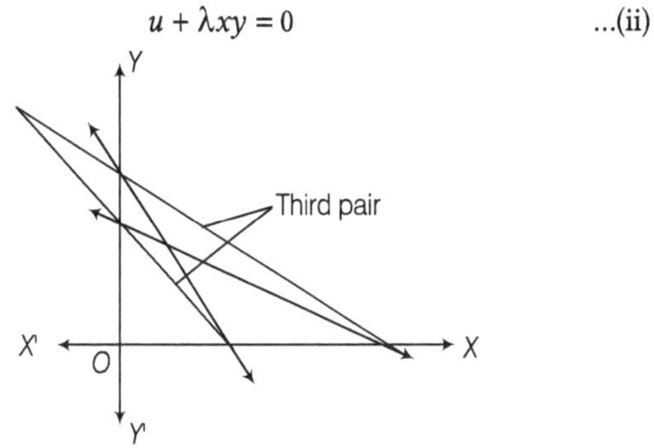

i.e. $$ax^2 + 2hxy + by^2 + 2gx + 2fy + c + \lambda xy = 0$$

$$\Rightarrow \quad ax^2 + xy(2h + \lambda) + by^2 + 2gx + 2fy + c = 0$$

If it represents a pair of lines, then

$$abc + 2fg\left(h + \frac{\lambda}{2}\right) - af^2 - bg^2 - c\left(h + \frac{\lambda}{2}\right)^2 = 0$$

$$\Rightarrow (abc + 2fgh - af^2 - bg^2 - ch^2) + \lambda(fg - ch) - \frac{c\lambda^2}{4} = 0$$

$$\Rightarrow \quad 0 + \lambda(fg - ch) - \frac{c\lambda^2}{4} = 0 \quad \text{[from Eq. (i)]}$$

$$\therefore \quad \lambda = \frac{4(fg - ch)}{c} \quad \text{...(iii)}$$

Hence, the equation of third pair from Eqs. (ii) and (iii) is

$$u + \frac{4(fg - ch)}{c}xy = 0$$

$$\therefore \quad cu + 4(fg - ch)xy = 0$$

Ex. 20 *If the equation $ax^2 + 2hxy + by^2 + 2gx + 2fy + c = 0$ represents a pair of parallel lines, prove that*
(i) $h = \sqrt{ab}$ and $g\sqrt{b} = f\sqrt{a}$ or ($h = -\sqrt{ab}$ and $g\sqrt{b} = -f\sqrt{a}$).
(ii) the distance between them is $2\sqrt{\left(\frac{g^2 - ac}{a(a+b)}\right)}$.

Sol. Given equation is,

$$ax^2 + 2hxy + by^2 + 2gx + 2fy + c = 0 \quad \text{...(i)}$$

Let the equation of the parallel lines represented by Eq. (i) be

$$lx + my + n = 0 \quad \text{and } lx + my + n_1 = 0.$$

Then, $(lx + my + n)(lx + my + n_1)$

$$\equiv ax^2 + 2hxy + by^2 + 2gx + 2fy + c$$

Equating the coefficients, we get

$$l^2 = a \quad \text{...(ii)}$$

$$m^2 = b \quad \text{...(iii)}$$

$$nn_1 = c \quad \text{...(iv)}$$

$$2lm = 2h \quad \text{...(v)}$$

$$(n + n_1)l = 2g \quad \text{...(vi)}$$

$$m(n + n_1) = 2f \quad \text{...(vii)}$$

Eq. (i) From Eq. (v)

$\Rightarrow \quad h = lm = \pm\sqrt{ab}$

Now, $\quad h = \sqrt{ab} \quad$ or $\quad h = -\sqrt{ab}$

$\because \quad abc + 2fgh - af^2 - bg^2 - ch^2 = 0$

$\Rightarrow abc + 2fg\sqrt{ab} - af^2 - bg^2 - c \cdot ab = 0$

[substituting the value of $h = \sqrt{ab}$]

$\Rightarrow \quad -(f\sqrt{a} - g\sqrt{b})^2 = 0 \Rightarrow \quad f\sqrt{a} = g\sqrt{b}$

Thus, the given equation represents a pair of lines.

Also, if $h = -\sqrt{ab}$, then $g\sqrt{b} = -f\sqrt{a}$

(ii) The distance between parallel lines

$$= \frac{|n - n_1|}{\sqrt{(l^2 + m^2)}} = \frac{\sqrt{(n + n_1)^2 - 4nn_1}}{\sqrt{l^2 + m^2}}$$

$$= \frac{\sqrt{\left(\frac{4g^2}{l^2} - 4c\right)}}{\sqrt{(a+b)}} \quad \text{[from Eqs. (vi), (ii) and (iii)]}$$

$$= 2\sqrt{\left(\frac{g^2 - ac}{a(a+b)}\right)} \quad [\because l^2 = a]$$

Remark

In some books, the conditions for parallel lines are stated as $h^2 = ab$ and $bg^2 = af^2$ we show that by an example that these conditions are not sufficient because

$$h^2 = ab \Rightarrow \quad h = \pm\sqrt{ab}$$

and $\quad bg^2 = af^2 \Rightarrow g\sqrt{b} = \pm f\sqrt{a}$

$\Rightarrow \quad h = \sqrt{ab}, g\sqrt{b} = f\sqrt{a} \quad$ or $\quad (h = -\sqrt{ab}, g\sqrt{b} = -f\sqrt{a})$

Consider, for example, $4x^2 + 4xy + y^2 + 4x - 2y + 5 = 0$

Here, $a = 4, h = 2, b = 1, g = 2, f = -1, c = 5$ and

$$h = \sqrt{ab}, g\sqrt{b} = -f\sqrt{a}$$

But $abc + 2fgh - af^2 - bg^2 - ch^2$

$$= 4 \times 1 \times 5 + 2 \times (-1) \times 2 \times 2 - 4 \times (-1)^2 - 1 \times (2)^2 - 5 \times (2)^2$$

$$= 20 - 8 - 4 - 4 - 20 = -16 \neq 0$$

Hence, the Eq. (i) does not represent a pair of lines at all.

Ex. 21 *A parallelogram is formed by the lines $ax^2 + 2hxy + by^2 = 0$ and the lines through (p, q) parallel to them. Show that the equation of the diagonal of the parallelogram which does not pass through origin is $(2x - p)(ap + hq) + (2y - q)(hp + bq) = 0$.*
Show also that the area of the parallelogram is

$$|(ap^2 + 2hpq + bq^2)| / 2\sqrt{(h^2 - ab)}.$$

Sol. The combined equation of AB and AD is

$$S_1 \equiv ax^2 + 2hxy + by^2 = 0$$

Now, equation of lines through (p, q) and parallel to $S_1 \equiv 0$ is $S_2 \equiv a(x - p)^2 + 2h(x - p)(y - q) + b(y - q)^2 = 0$

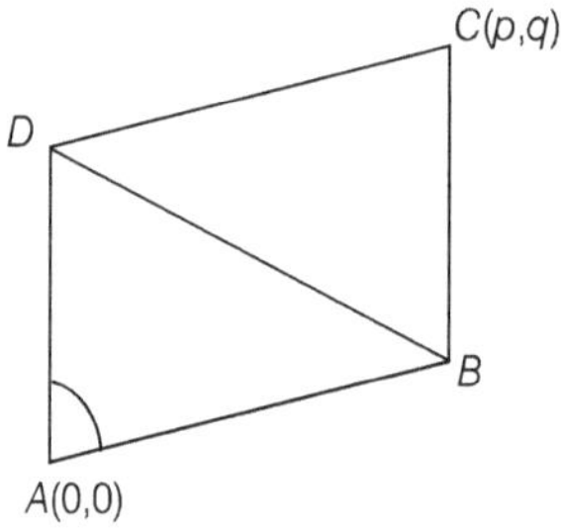

Hence, the equation of diagonal BD is $S_1 - S_2 = 0$

$$a(-2xp + p^2) + 2h(-py - qx + pq) + b(-2qy + q^2) = 0$$

$$-ap(2x - p) - hq(2x - p) - hp(2y - q) - bq(2y - q) = 0$$

[$\because 2hpq$ is written as $hpq + hpq$]

Hence, diagonal of BD is

$$(2x - p)(ap + hq) + (2y - q)(bq + hp) = 0$$

Area of parallelogram $= \frac{p_1 p_2}{\sin\theta}$

$\Rightarrow p_1 p_2 =$ product of perpendiculars from (p, q) on AB and AD whose combined equation is

$ax^2 + 2hxy + by^2 = 0$

$$\therefore \quad p_1 p_2 = \frac{|ap^2 + 2hpq + bq^2|}{\sqrt{\{(a - b)^2 + 4h^2\}}}$$

$$\therefore \quad \tan\theta = \frac{2\sqrt{(h^2 - ab)}}{|(a+b)|}$$

$$\therefore \quad \sin\theta = \frac{2\sqrt{(h^2 - ab)}}{\sqrt{(a-b)^2 + 4h^2}}$$

$$\therefore \text{ Required area} = \frac{|ap^2 + 2hpq + bq^2|}{2\sqrt{(h^2 - ab)}}$$

Ex. 22 *A point moves so that the distance between the feet of perpendiculars drawn from it to the lines $ax^2 + 2hxy + by^2 = 0$ is a constant $2k$. Show that the equation of its locus is $(x^2 + y^2)(h^2 - ab) = k^2 \{(a-b)^2 + 4h^2\}$.*

Sol. $\because \angle ONP = \angle OMP = \frac{\pi}{2}$

$\therefore$ O, M, P, N are concyclic with diameter OP.

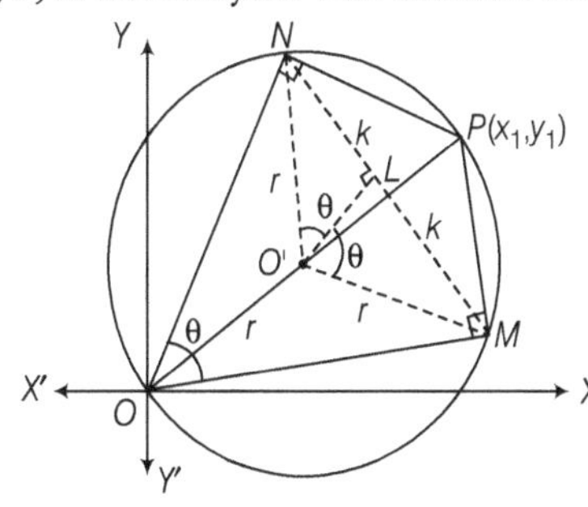

Let $\quad P \equiv (x_1, y_1)$

$\therefore$ Coordinates of centre are $O' = \left(\frac{x_1}{2}, \frac{y_1}{2}\right)$

$\therefore$ Radius $r = O'N = OM = OO'$

$$= \sqrt{\left(\frac{x_1}{2}\right)^2 + \left(\frac{y_1}{2}\right)^2} = \frac{\sqrt{(x_1^2 + y_1^2)}}{2}$$

Let $\quad \angle MON = \theta$

$\therefore \quad \angle MO'N = 2\theta \Rightarrow \angle NO'L = \angle MO'L = \theta$

and given $MN = 2k$, then $NL = LM = k$

Now, in $\Delta NO'L$,

$$\sin\theta = \frac{NL}{O'N} = \frac{k}{r} = \frac{k}{\frac{\sqrt{(x_1^2 + y_1^2)}}{2}} = \frac{2k}{\sqrt{(x_1^2 + y_1^2)}} \quad \text{...(i)}$$

But angle between the lines represented by

$ax^2 + 2hxy + by^2 = 0$ is $\tan\theta = \frac{2\sqrt{(h^2 - ab)}}{|a+b|}$.

$$\therefore \quad \sin\theta = \frac{2\sqrt{(h^2 - ab)}}{\sqrt{(a-b)^2 + 4h^2}} \quad \text{...(ii)}$$

From Eqs. (i) and (ii), we get

$$\frac{2\sqrt{(h^2 - ab)}}{\sqrt{(a-b)^2 + 4h^2}} = \frac{2k}{\sqrt{(x_1^2 + y_1^2)}}$$

On squaring both sides, we get

$$(x_1^2 + y_1^2)(h^2 - ab) = k^2 \{(a-b)^2 + 4h^2\}$$

Hence, locus of $P(x_1, y_1)$ is

$$(x^2 + y^2)(h^2 - ab) = k^2 \{(a-b)^2 + 4h^2\}.$$

Ex. 23 *Show that if two of the lines $ax^3 + bx^2y + cxy^2 + dy^3 = 0 \, (a \neq 0)$ make complementary angles with X-axis in anti-clockwise sense, then $\quad a(a-c) + d(b-d) = 0$.*

Sol. The given equation can be written as

$$dm^3 + cm^2 + bm + a = 0, \text{ where } m = \frac{y}{x}$$

Let its roots be m_1, m_2, m_3.

$$\therefore \quad m_1 m_2 m_3 = -\frac{a}{d} \quad \text{...(i)}$$

If $m_1 = \tan\alpha$, then $m_2 = \tan(90° - \alpha)$

[$\because$ two lines makes complementary angles with X-axis]

$\therefore \quad m_2 = \cot\alpha$ then $m_1 m_2 = 1$

From Eq. (i), $\quad m_3 = -\frac{a}{d}$

Since, m_3 is root of the above cubic, we have

$$d\left(-\frac{a^3}{d^3}\right) + c\left(\frac{a^2}{d^2}\right) + b\left(-\frac{a}{d}\right) + a = 0$$

$$\Rightarrow \quad \left(-\frac{a^3}{d^2}\right) + \left(\frac{ca^2}{d^2}\right) - \left(\frac{ab}{d}\right) + a = 0$$

$$\Rightarrow \quad -a^3 + ca^2 - abd + ad^2 = 0$$

On dividing each by a, we get

$$-a^2 + ca - bd + d^2 = 0$$

$$\therefore \quad a(a-c) + d(b-d) = 0.$$

Ex. 24 *Show that the equation $a(x^4 + y^4) - 4bxy(x^2 - y^2) + 6cx^2y^2 = 0$ represents two pairs of lines at right angles and that if $2b^2 = a^2 + 3ac$, the two pairs will coincide.*

Sol. Given equation is

$$a(x^4 + y^4) - 4bxy(x^2 - y^2) + 6c\,x^2y^2 = 0 \quad \text{...(i)}$$

Eq. (i) is a homogeneous equation of fourth degree and since it represents two pairs at right angles. i.e. sum of the coefficients of x^2 and y^2 should be zero.

Let $a(x^4 + y^4) - 4bxy(x^2 - y^2) + 6cx^2y^2$

$$= (ax^2 + pxy - ay^2)(x^2 + qxy - y^2),$$

where, p and q are constants.

On comparing similar powers, we get

$$p + aq = -4b \quad \text{...(ii)}$$

$$-2a + pq = 6c \quad \text{...(iii)}$$

Again, given two pairs coincide, then

$$\frac{p}{a} = q$$

or $\qquad p = aq \qquad$ ...(iv)

From Eqs. (ii) and (iv),

$$q = -\frac{2b}{a}$$

and $\qquad p = -2b$

Substituting the values of p and q in Eq. (iii), we get

$$-2a + \frac{4b^2}{a} = 6c$$

$\Rightarrow \qquad -a^2 + 2b^2 = 3ac$

$\therefore \qquad 2b^2 = a^2 + 3ac$

• **Ex. 25** *Show that the locus of a point such that the product of the perpendiculars let fall from it on three lines represented by $ay^3 + by^2x + cyx^2 + dx^3 = 0$ is constant $= k^3$, is*

$$ay^3 + by^2x + cyx^2 + dx^3 = k^3\sqrt{(a-c)^2 + (b-d)^2}.$$

Sol. Let the three represented lines are

$$y = m_1x,\ y = m_2x \text{ and } y = m_3x$$

$$ay^3 + by^2x + cyx^2 + dx^3 = a(y - m_1x)(y - m_2x)(y - m_3x)$$

On comparing similar powers on both sides

$\Rightarrow \qquad m_1 + m_2 + m_3 = -\frac{b}{a} \qquad$ ...(i)

$m_1m_2 + m_2m_3 + m_3m_1 = \frac{c}{a} \qquad$ ...(ii)

$m_1m_2m_3 = -\frac{d}{a} \qquad$ ...(iii)

Let the point $P(x_1, y_1)$, from given condition

$$\frac{(y_1 - m_1x_1)}{\sqrt{(1+m_1^2)}} \cdot \frac{(y_1 - m_2x_1)}{\sqrt{(1+m_2^2)}} \cdot \frac{(y_1 - m_3x_1)}{\sqrt{(1+m_3^2)}} = k^3$$

$$\Rightarrow \quad \frac{1}{a}(ay_1^3 + by_1^2x_1 + cy_1x_1^2 + dx_1^3)$$

$$= k^3\sqrt{(1+m_1^2)(1+m_2^2)(1+m_3^2)}$$

$$[\because ay^3 + by^2x + cyx^2 + dx^3 = a(y - m_1x)(y - m_2x)(y - m_3x)]$$

$$\Rightarrow (ay_1^3 + by_1^2x_1 + cy_1x_1^2 + dx_1^3)$$

$$= ak^3\sqrt{(1 + \Sigma m_1^2 + \Sigma m_1^2m_2^2 + m_1^2m_2^2m_3^2)}$$

$$= ak^3\sqrt{\{1 + (\Sigma m_1)^2 - 2\Sigma m_1m_2 + (\Sigma m_1m_2)^2 - 2m_1m_2m_3\Sigma m_1 + (m_1m_2m_3)^2\}}$$

$$= ak^3\sqrt{1 + \frac{b^2}{a^2} - \frac{2c}{a} + \frac{c^2}{a^2} + \frac{2d}{a}\cdot\left(-\frac{b}{a}\right) + \left(-\frac{d}{a}\right)^2}$$

$$= k^3\sqrt{(a^2 + b^2 - 2ac + c^2 - 2bd + d^2)}$$

$$= k^3\sqrt{\{(a-c)^2 + (b-d)^2\}}$$

Hence, locus of P is

$$(ay^3 + by^2x + cyx^2 + dx^3) = k^3\sqrt{\{(a-c)^2 + (b-d)^2\}}$$

• **Ex. 26** *If one of the lines given by the equation $ax^2 + 2hxy + by^2 = 0$ coincides with one of the lines given by $a'x^2 + 2h'xy + b'y^2 = 0$ and the other lines represented by them be perpendicular, then.*

$$\frac{ha'b'}{b'-a'} = \frac{h'ab}{b-a} = \frac{1}{2}\sqrt{(-aa'bb')}$$

Sol. Let the two lines represented by

$$ax^2 + 2hxy + by^2 = 0 \qquad \text{...(i)}$$

be $\qquad y = m_1x$

and $\qquad y = m_2x$

$\therefore \qquad m_1 + m_2 = -\frac{2h}{b} \qquad$ ...(ii)

and $\qquad m_1m_2 = \frac{a}{b} \qquad$ ...(iii)

and the lines represented by

$$a'x^2 + 2h'xy + b'y^2 = 0 \qquad \text{...(iv)}$$

be $\qquad y = -\frac{1}{m_1}x \quad$ and $\quad y = m_2x$

$\therefore \qquad -\frac{1}{m_1} + m_2 = -\frac{2h'}{b'} \qquad$ ...(v)

and $\qquad -\left(\frac{1}{m_1}\right)m_2 = \frac{a'}{b'} \qquad$ ...(vi)

From Eqs. (iii) and (vi), we get

$$-m_2^2 = \frac{aa'}{bb'} \Rightarrow m_2 = \frac{\sqrt{(-aba'b')}}{bb'}$$

From Eqs. (iii), we get $\quad m_1 = -\frac{\sqrt{(-aba'b')}}{a'b}$

Substituting these values of m_1 and m_2 in Eqs. (ii) and (v), we get

$$-\frac{\sqrt{-aba'b'}}{a'b} + \frac{\sqrt{-aba'b'}}{bb'} = -\frac{2h}{b}$$

$\Rightarrow \qquad \frac{ha'b'}{b'-a'} = \frac{1}{2}\sqrt{-aa'bb'} \qquad$ ...(vii)

and $\qquad \frac{a'b}{\sqrt{-aba'b'}} + \frac{\sqrt{-aba'b'}}{bb'} = -\frac{2h'}{b'}$

$\qquad \frac{h'ab}{b-a} = \frac{1}{2}\sqrt{-aba'b'} \qquad$ ...(viii)

From Eqs. (vii) and (viii), we get

$$\frac{ha'b'}{b'-a'} = \frac{h'ab}{b-a} = \frac{1}{2}\sqrt{-aba'b'}$$

Pair of Straight Lines Exercise 1 :
Single Option Correct Type Questions

- This section contains **12 multiple choice questions**. Each question has four choices (a), (b), (c), (d) out of which **ONLY ONE** is correct.

1. If the sum of the slopes of the lines given by $4x^2 + 2\lambda xy - 7y^2 = 0$ is equal to the product of the slopes, then λ is equal to

(a) -4 (b) -2 (c) 2 (d) 4

2. The equation $3ax^2 + 9xy + (a^2 - 2)y^2 = 0$ represents two perpendicular straight lines for

(a) only one value of a (b) for all values of a
(c) for only two values of a (d) for no value of a

3. The image of the pair of lines represented by $ax^2 + 2hxy + by^2 = 0$ by the line mirror $y = 0$ is

(a) $ax^2 - 2hxy - by^2 = 0$ (b) $bx^2 - 2hxy + ay^2 = 0$
(c) $bx^2 + 2hxy + ay^2 = 0$ (d) $ax^2 - 2hxy + by^2 = 0$

4. Number of points lying on the line $7x + 4y + 2 = 0$ which is equidistant from the lines $15x^2 + 56xy + 48y^2 = 0$ is

(a) 0 (b) 1
(c) 2 (d) 4

5. Orthocentre of the triangle formed by the lines $xy - 3x - 5y + 15 = 0$ and $3x + 5y = 15$ is

(a) $(-5, -3)$ (b) $(5, 3)$
(c) $(-3, -5)$ (d) $(3, 5)$

6. Two of the straight lines given by $3x^3 + 3x^2y - 3xy^2 + dy^3 = 0$ are at right angles, if d equal to

(a) -4 (b) -3
(c) -2 (d) -1

7. Two lines are given by $(x - 2y)^2 + \lambda(x - 2y) = 0$. The value of $|\lambda|$ so that the distance between them is 3, is

(a) $\sqrt{5}$ (b) $2\sqrt{5}$
(c) $3\sqrt{5}$ (d) $4\sqrt{5}$

8. The four straight lines given by the equations $12x^2 + 7xy - 12y^2 = 0$ and $12x^2 + 7xy - 12y^2 - x + 7y - 1 = 0$ lie along the sides of a

(a) square (b) rhombus
(c) rectangle (d) parallelogram

9. Distance between the parallel lines $4x^2 + 20xy + 25y^2 + 2x + 5y - 12 = 0$ is

(a) $\frac{3}{\sqrt{29}}$ (b) $\frac{5}{\sqrt{29}}$
(c) $\frac{7}{\sqrt{29}}$ (d) $\frac{9}{\sqrt{29}}$

10. The point of intersection of the two lines given by $2x^2 - 5xy + 2y^2 + 3x + 3y + 1 = 0$ is

(a) $(-2, 2)$ (b) $(-3, 3)$
(c) $(3, 3)$ (d) $(2, 2)$

11. If $\alpha, \beta > 0$ and $\alpha < \beta$ and $\alpha x^2 + 4\gamma xy + \beta y^2 + 4p(x + y + 1) = 0$ represents a pair of straight lines, then

(a) $\alpha \le p \le \beta$ (b) $p \le \alpha$
(c) $p \ge \alpha$ (d) $p \le \alpha$ or $p \ge \beta$

12. If the equation of the pair of straight lines passing through the point (1, 1), one making an angle θ with the positive direction of the X-axis and the other making the same angle with the positive direction of the Y-axis, is $x^2 - (a+2)xy + y^2 + a(x + y - 1) = 0$, $a \ne -2$, then the value of $\sin 2\theta$ is

(a) $a - 2$ (b) $a + 2$
(c) $\frac{2}{(a+2)}$ (d) $\frac{2}{a}$

Pair of Straight Lines Exercise 2 :
More than One Option Correct Type Questions

- This section contains **6 multiple choice questions**. Each questions has four choices (a), (b), (c), (d) out of which **MORE THAN ONE** may be correct.

13. The equation of image of pair of lines $y = |x - 1|$ in Y-axis is

(a) $y = |x + 1|$ (b) $y = |x - 1| + 3$
(c) $x^2 - y^2 + 2x + 1 = 0$ (d) $x^2 - y^2 + 2x - 1 = 0$

14. The equation $ax^2 + by^2 + cx + cy = 0$ represent a pair of straight lines, if

(a) $a + b = 0$
(b) $c = 0$
(c) $a + c = 0$
(d) $c(a + b) = 0$

15. If $x^2 + \alpha y^2 + 2\beta y = a^2$ represents a pair of perpendicular straight lines, then
(a) $\alpha = 1, \beta = a$
(b) $\alpha = 1, \beta = -a$
(c) $\alpha = -1, \beta = -a$
(d) $\alpha = -1, \beta = a$

16. If the pair of lines $ax^2 + 2hxy + by^2 + 2gx + 2fy + c = 0$ intersect on Y-axis, then
(a) $f^2 = bc$
(b) $abc = 2fgh$
(c) $bg^2 \neq ch^2$
(d) $2fgh = bg^2 + ch^2$

17. Two pair of straight lines have the equations $y^2 + xy - 12x^2 = 0$ and $ax^2 + 2hxy + by^2 = 0$. One line will be common among them, if
(a) $a = -3(2h + 3b)$ (b) $a = 8(h - 2b)$
(c) $a = 2(b + h)$ (d) $a = -3(b + h)$

18. The combined equation of three sides of a triangle is $(x^2 - y^2)(2x + 3y - 6) = 0$. If $(-2, a)$ is an interior and $(b, 1)$ is an exterior point of the triangle, then
(a) $2 < a < \frac{10}{3}$ (b) $-2 < a < \frac{10}{3}$
(c) $-1 < b < \frac{9}{2}$ (d) $-1 < b < 1$

Pair of Straight Lines Exercise 3 : Paragraph Based Questions

- This section contains **3 paragraphs** based upon each of the paragraph, **3 multiple choice questions** have to be answered. Each of these question has four choices (a), (b), (c) and (d) out of which **ONLY ONE** is correct.

Paragraph I
(Q. Nos. 19 to 21)

Consider the equation of a pair of straight lines as
$x^2 - 3xy + \lambda y^2 + 3x - 5y + 2 = 0$

19. The value of λ is
(a) 1 (b) 2
(c) 3 (d) 4

20. The point of intersection of lines is (α, β), then the value of $\alpha^2 + \beta^2$ is
(a) 2 (b) 5
(c) 10 (d) 17

21. The angle between the lines is θ, then the value of $\cos 2\theta$ is
(a) $\frac{1}{3}$ (b) $\frac{2}{3}$
(c) $\frac{3}{5}$ (d) $\frac{4}{5}$

Paragraph II
(Q. Nos. 22 to 24)

Let $f_1(x, y) \equiv ax^2 + 2hxy + by^2 = 0$ *and let* $f_{i+1}(x, y) = 0$ *denote the equation of the bisectors of* $f_i(x, y) = 0$ *for all* $i = 1, 2, 3, \ldots$

22. $f_3(x, y) = 0$ is
(a) $hx^2 - (a - b)xy - hy^2 = 0$
(b) $(a - b)x^2 + 4hxy - (a - b)y^2 = 0$
(c) $ax^2 + 2hxy + by^2 = 0$
(d) None of the above

23. If $f_{i+1}(x, y) = 0$ represents the equation of a pair of perpendicular lines, then $f_3(x, y) = 0$ is same as
(a) $f_1(x, y) = 0$
(b) $f_2(x, y) = 0$
(c) $hx^2 - (a - b)xy - hy^2 = 0$
(d) None of the above

24. The value of $\sum_{n=2}^{5} \frac{f_{n+2}(x, y)}{f_n(x, y)}$ is
(a) 14 (b) 4
(c) 54 (d) 6

Paragraph III
(Q. Nos. 25 to 27)

Consider a pair of perpendicular straight lines
$2x^2 + 3xy + by^2 - 11x + 13y + c = 0$

25. The value of c is
(a) -2 (b) 2
(c) -3 (d) 3

26. The value of $|b + 2c|$ is
(a) 4 (b) 6
(c) 8 (d) 10

27. If point of intersection of lines is C and points of intersection of the lines with the X-axis are A and B, if distance between the orthocentre and the circumcentre of ΔABC is λ, then $[\lambda]$ is (where $[.]$ denotes the greatest integer function
(a) 2 (b) 3
(c) 4 (d) 5

Pair of Straight Lines Exercise 4 : Single Integer Answer Type Questions

- This section contains **5 questions**. The answer to each question is **a single digit integer**, ranging from 0 to 9 (both inclusive).

28. Equation $\lambda x^3 - 10x^2y - xy^2 + 4y^3 = 0$ represented three straight lines, out of these three, two lines makes equal angle with $y = x$ and $\lambda > 0$, then the value of λ is

29. Area enclosed by curves $y^2 - 5xy + 6x^2 + 3x - y = 0$ and $y^2 - 5xy + 6x^2 + 2x - y = 0$ is λ sq units, then the value of λ is

30. The lines represented by $x^2 + 2\lambda xy + 2y^2 = 0$ and $(\lambda + 1)x^2 - 8xy + y^2 = 0$ are equally inclined, then the value of $|\lambda|$ is

31. If the lines joining the origin to the intersection of the line $y = nx + 2$ and the curve $x^2 + y^2 = 1$ are at right angles, then the value of n^2 is

32. If area of the triangle formed by the line $x + y = 3$ and the angle bisectors of the pair of straight lines $x^2 - y^2 + 2y = 1$ is λ sq units, then the value of λ is

Pair of Straight Lines Exercise 5 : Matching Type Questions

- This section contains **one question.** This question has four statements (A,B,C and D) given in **Column I** and four statements (p, q, r and s) in **Column II**. Any given statements in **Column I** can have correct matching with one or more statement(s) given in **Column II**.

33. Match the following

	Column I		Column II
(A)	The pair of lines joining the origin to the points of intersection of the curve $9x^2 + 16y^2 = 144$ by the line $2x + 2y + \lambda = 0$ are coincident, then $|\lambda|$ is divisible by	(p)	2
(B)	If the straight lines joining the origin to the points of intersection of the straight line $4x + 3y = 24$ and the curve $(x - 3)^2 + (y - 4)^2 = \lambda^2$, are at right angles, then $|\lambda|$ is divisible by	(q)	3
(C)	The two line pairs $y^2 - 4y + 3 = 0$ and $x^2 + 4xy + 4y^2 - 5x - 10y + 4 = 0$ enclose a 4 sided convex polygon, if area of polygon is λ sq units, then λ is divisible by	(r)	5
(D)	If the pairs of lines $3x^2 - 2pxy - 3y^2 = 0$ and $5x^2 - 2qxy - 5y^2 = 0$ are such that each pair bisects the angle between the other pair. If $\lambda = |pq|$, then λ is divisible by	(s)	6

Pair of Straight Lines Exercise 6 : Statement I and II Types Questions

- **Directions** (Q. Nos. 34-37) are Assertion-Reason type questions. Each of these questions contains two statements:
Statement I (Assertion) and **Statement II** (Reason)
Each of these questions also has four alternative choices, only one of which is the correct answer. You have to select the correct choice as given below :
(a) Statement I is true, Statement II is true; Statement II is a correct explanation for Statement I
(b) Statement I is true, Statement II is true; Statement II is not a correct explanation for Statement I
(c) Statement I is true, Statement II is false
(d) Statement I is false, Statement II is true

34. **Statement I** The four straight lines given by $6x^2+5xy-6y^2=0$ and $6x^2+5xy-6y^2-x+5y-1=0$ are the sides of a square.

Statement II The lines represented by general equation of second degree $ax^2+2hxy+by^2+2gx+2fy+c=0$ are perpendicular if $a+b=0$.

35. **Statement I** Two of the straight lines represented by $dx^3+cx^2y+bxy^2+ay^3=0$ will be at right angles if $d^2+bd+bc+a^2=0$.

Statement II Product of the slopes of two perpendicular lines is -1.

36. **Statement I** If $\alpha\beta=-1$, then the pair of straight lines $x^2-2\alpha xy-y^2=0$ and $y^2+2\beta xy-x^2=0$ are the angle bisector of each other.

Statement II Pair of angle bisector lines of the pair of lines $ax^2+2hxy+by^2=0$ is $h(x^2-y^2)=(a-b)xy$.

37. **Statement I** If $a+b=-2h$, then one line of the pair of lines $ax^2+2hxy+by^2=0$ bisects the angle between coordinate axes in positive quadrant.

Statement II If $ax+y(2h+a)=0$ is a factor of $ax^2+2hxy+by^2=0$, then $b+2h+a=0$.

Pair of Straight Lines Exercise 7 : Subjective Type Questions

- In this section, there are **7 subjective questions**.

38. Prove that the straight lines represented by $(y-mx)^2=a^2(1+m^2)$ and $(y-nx)^2=a^2(1+n^2)$ form a rhombus.

39. Prove that the equation $m(x^3-3xy^2)+y^3-3x^2y=0$ represents three straight lines equally inclined to each other.

40. Show that the straight lines $(A^2-3B^2)x^2+8ABxy+(B^2-3A^2)y^2=0$ form with the line $Ax+By+C=0$ an equilateral triangle whose area is $\dfrac{C^2}{\sqrt{3}(A^2+B^2)}$

41. Find the equations of the diagonals of the parallelogram formed by the lines $L^2-aL=0$ and $L'^2-aL'=0$, where $L=x\cos\theta+y\sin\theta-p$ *and* $L'=x\cos\theta'+y\sin\theta'-p'$.

42. If $ax^2+2hxy+by^2+2gx+2fy+c=0$ and $ax^2+2hxy+by^2-2gx-2fy+c=0$ each represents a pair of lines, then prove that the area of the parallelogram enclosed by them is $\dfrac{2|c|}{\sqrt{(h^2-ab)}}$.

43. Prove that lines $ax^2+2hxy+by^2+2gx+2fy+c=0$ are equidistant from the origin, if $f^4-g^4=c(bf^2-ag^2)$. Also, find the product of their distances from the origin.

44. Prove that if two of the lines represented by $ax^4+bx^3y+cx^2y^2+dxy^3+ay^4=0$ bisects the angle between the other two, then $c+6a=0$ and $b+d=0$.

Pair of Straight Lines Exercise 8 : Question Asked in Previous 13 Years Exams

- This section contains questions asked in **IIT-JEE, AIEEE, JEE Main & JEE Advanced** from year **2005** to **2017**.

45. If the pair of lines $ax^2 + 2(a+b)xy + by^2 = 0$ lie long diameters of a circle and divide the circle into four sectors such that the area of one of the sector is thrice the area of the another sector, then **[AIEEE 2005, 3M]**

(a) $3a^2 + 2ab + 3b^2 = 0$ (b) $3a^2 + 10ab + 3b^2 = 0$
(c) $3a^2 - 2ab + 3b^2 = 0$ (d) $3a^2 - 10ab + 3b^2 = 0$

46. If one of the lines of $my^2 + (1-m^2)xy - mx^2 = 0$ is a bisector of the angle between the lines $xy = 0$, then m is **[AIEEE 2007, 3M]**

(a) $-\frac{1}{2}$ (b) -2
(c) 1 (d) 2

Answers

Exercise for Session 1

1. (c) 2. (a) 3. (b) 4. (b) 5. (c, d)
6. $bx + ay = 0,\ ax - by = 0$ 7. $\left(\frac{8}{3}, \frac{8}{3}\right)$
9. $(ab' - a'b)^2 = 4(ah' - a'h)(h'b - hb')$

Exercise for Session 2

1. (b) 2. (c, d) 3. (a) 4. (c) 5. (b, c)
6. $\tan^{-1}\left(\frac{1}{3}\right)$ 8. $\sec^{-1}(\pm p)$ 9. $\frac{1}{6}\sqrt{3}$ sq units

Exercise for Session 3

1. (b) 2. (a, c) 3. (a, c) 4. (b) 9. ± 2

Exercise for Session 4

1. (b) 2. (d) 3. (a, d) 4. (b) 5. (a)
6. 1 sq unit 7. $x - y = 0$ 9. $\frac{|g^2 - ac|}{|a|\sqrt{h^2 - ab}}$
10. $x^2 - 5xy + 4y^2 + 3x - 3y = 0$

Exercise for Session 5

1. (c) 2. (d) 3. (d) 4. (a) 5. (b)
6. $9x^2 + 10xy - 9y^2 = 0$ 7. ± 1 10. $x^2 - xy - 2y^2 = 0$

Chapter Exercises

1. (b) 2. (c) 3. (d) 4. (c) 5. (b) 6. (b)
7. (c) 8. (a) 9. (c) 10. (c) 11. (d) 12. (c)
13. (a, c) 14. (a, b, d) 15. (c, d) 16. (a, d) 17. (a, b) 18. (a, d)
19. (b) 20. (c) 21. (d) 22. (b) 23. (a) 24. (b)
25. (a) 26. (b) 27. (c) 28. (7) 29. (1) 30. (2)
31. (7) 32. (2)
33. (A) → (p, r); (B) → (r); (C) → (p, q, s); (D) → (q, r)
34. (b) 35. (b) 36. (a) 37. (b)
41. $\begin{cases} x(\cos\theta - \cos\theta') + y(\sin\theta - \sin\theta') - p + p' = 0 \\ \text{and } x(\cos\theta + \cos\theta') + y(\sin\theta + \sin\theta') - p - p' - a = 0 \end{cases}$
43. $\frac{|c|}{\sqrt{(a-b)^2 + 4h^2}}$
45. (a) 46. (c)

Solutions

1. $\because m_1 + m_2 = m_1 m_2 \Rightarrow \dfrac{-2\lambda}{-7} = \dfrac{4}{-7}$

$\therefore \qquad \lambda = -2$

2. For perpendicular lines

$$3a + (a^2 - 2) = 0$$

$$\Rightarrow \qquad a = \frac{-3 \pm \sqrt{(9+8)}}{6} = \frac{-3 \pm \sqrt{17}}{6}$$

3. For mirror image with respect to $y = 0$ replace y by $-y$, then image of the pair of lines $ax^2 + 2hxy + by^2 = 0$ is

$$ax^2 + 2hx(-y) + b(-y)^2 = 0$$

or $$ax^2 - 2hxy + by^2 = 0$$

4. $\because \quad 15x^2 + 56xy + 48y^2 = 0 \qquad \text{...(i)}$

$\Rightarrow (3x + 4y)(5x + 12y) = 0$

Equation of lines represented by Eq. (i) are

$3x + 4y = 0$ and $5x + 12y = 0$

Let any point on $7x + 4y + 2 = 0$ is $\left(\lambda, \dfrac{-7\lambda - 2}{4}\right)$.

According to questions,

$$\left|\frac{3\lambda + 4\left(\frac{-7\lambda - 2}{4}\right)}{5}\right| = \left|\frac{5\lambda + 12\left(\frac{-7\lambda - 2}{4}\right)}{13}\right|$$

$$\Rightarrow \qquad \frac{1}{5}|-4\lambda - 2| = \frac{1}{13}|-16\lambda - 6|$$

$$\Rightarrow \qquad \frac{|2\lambda + 1|}{5} = \frac{|8\lambda + 3|}{13}$$

$$\Rightarrow \qquad 13(2\lambda + 1) = \pm 5(8\lambda + 3)$$

$$\therefore \qquad \lambda = -\frac{1}{7}, -\frac{14}{33}$$

5. Given lines are $xy - 3x - 5y + 15 = 0$

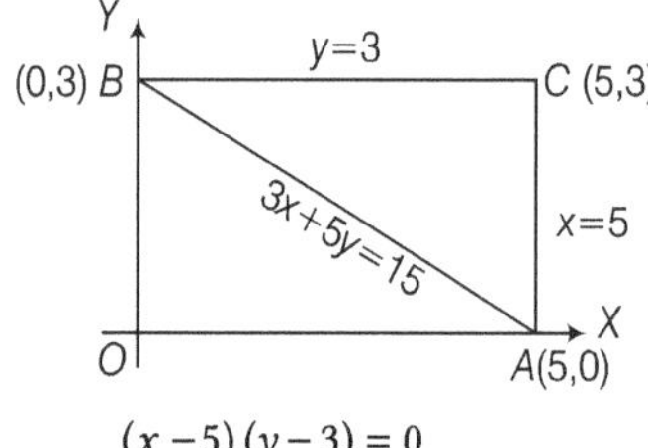

$$\Rightarrow \qquad (x-5)(y-3) = 0$$

$$\therefore \qquad x = 5 \text{ and } y = 3$$

Hence, orthocentre is (5, 3).

6. $3x^3 + 3x^2y - 3xy^2 + dy^3 = (x^2 + pxy - y^2)(3x - dy)$

On comparing coefficients of x^2y and xy^2, we get

$$3p - d = 3$$

and $$-3 - pd = -3$$

$$\therefore \qquad p = 0,\ d = -3$$

7. $\because \qquad (x - 2y)^2 + \lambda(x - 2y) = 0$

$\Rightarrow \qquad (x - 2y)(x - 2y + \lambda) = 0$

$\therefore$ Lines are $x - 2y = 0$ and $x - 2y + \lambda = 0$

Distance between lines = 3 (given)

$$\Rightarrow \qquad \frac{|\lambda - 0|}{\sqrt{(1+4)}} = 3$$

$$\therefore \qquad |\lambda| = 3\sqrt{5}$$

8. $\therefore \quad 12x^2 + 7xy - 12y^2 = 0 \qquad \text{...(i)}$

$\Rightarrow \quad (3x + 4y)(4x - 3y) = 0$

$\therefore$ Lines represented by Eq. (i) are

$$3x + 4y = 0 \text{ and } 4x - 3y = 0$$

and $\quad 12x^2 + 7xy - 12y^2 - x + 7y - 1 = 0 \qquad \text{...(ii)}$

$\Rightarrow \qquad (3x + 4y - 1)(4x - 3y + 1) = 0$

$\therefore$ Lines represented by Eq. (ii) are

$$3x + 4y - 1 = 0 \text{ and } 4x - 3y + 1 = 0$$

Distance between parallel lines $3x + 4y = 0$ and

$3x + 4y - 1 = 0$ is $\dfrac{1}{5}$.

And distance between parallel lines $4x - 3y = 0$ and

$4x - 3y + 1 = 0$ is $\dfrac{1}{5}$.

Hence, all sides along a square.

9. Given,

$$4x^2 + 20xy + 25y^2 + 2x + 5y - 12 = 0 \qquad \text{...(i)}$$

$$\Rightarrow \qquad (2x + 5y)^2 + (2x + 5y) - 12 = 0$$

$$\Rightarrow \qquad (2x + 5y + 4)(2x + 5y - 3) = 0$$

$\therefore$ Lines represented by Eq. (i) are

$$2x + 5y + 4 = 0 \text{ and } 2x + 5y - 3 = 0$$

Hence, distance between parallel lines $= \dfrac{|4 - (-3)|}{\sqrt{4 + 25}} = \dfrac{7}{\sqrt{29}}$.

10. Let $f(x, y) \equiv 2x^2 - 5xy + 2y^2 + 3x + 3y + 1 = 0$

$$\therefore \qquad \frac{\partial f}{\partial x} = 4x - 5y + 3 \text{ and } \frac{\partial f}{\partial y} = -5x + 4y + 3$$

For point of intersection $\dfrac{\partial f}{\partial x} = 0$ and $\dfrac{\partial f}{\partial y} = 0$

$\Rightarrow \ 4x - 5y + 3 = 0$ and $-5x + 4y + 3 = 0$, we get

$x = 3, y = 3$

$\therefore$ Point of intersection is (3, 3).

11. $\alpha x^2 + 4\gamma\, xy + \beta y^2 + 4p(x + y + 1) = 0$

represents a pair of straight lines.

$\therefore \Delta = 0$

$\Rightarrow 4\alpha\beta p + 16p^2\gamma - 4p^2\alpha - 4p^2\beta - 16\gamma^2 p = 0$

$\Rightarrow \quad (16p)\gamma^2 - 16p^2\gamma + 4p(p\alpha + p\beta - \alpha\beta) = 0$

$$\therefore \qquad B^2 - 4AC \ge 0$$

$$\Rightarrow \quad (16p^2)^2 - 4 \cdot (16p) \cdot 4p\,(p\alpha + p\beta - \alpha\beta) \ge 0$$

$$\Rightarrow \qquad p^2(p^2 - p\alpha - p\beta + \alpha\beta) \ge 0$$

$$\Rightarrow \qquad (p - \alpha)(p - \beta) \ge 0$$

$$\therefore \qquad p \le \alpha \text{ or } p \ge \beta \qquad [\because \alpha < \beta]$$

12. Equation of first line is $y - 1 = \tan\theta(x - 1)$

Equation of second line is $y - 1 = \cot\theta(x - 1)$

So, their joint equation is

$$[(y-1) - \tan\theta(x-1)][(y-1) - \cot\theta(x-1)] = 0$$

$$\Rightarrow (y-1)^2 - (x-1)(y-1)(\tan\theta + \cot\theta) + (x-1)^2 = 0$$

$$x^2 - (\tan\theta + \cot\theta)xy + y^2 + (\tan\theta + \cot\theta - 2)(x + y - 1) = 0$$

On comparing with the given equation, we get

$$\tan\theta + \cot\theta = a + 2$$

or $$\frac{1}{\sin\theta\cos\theta} = a + 2$$

or $$\sin 2\theta = \frac{2}{(a+2)}$$

13. For image w.r.t., Y-axis replace x by $-x$, then required image of lines is

$$y = |-x-1| \text{ or } y = |x+1|$$

and on squaring both sides, then

$$y^2 = x^2 + 2x + 1$$

$$\Rightarrow \quad x^2 - y^2 + 2x + 1 = 0$$

14. Given equation is

$$ax^2 + by^2 + cx + cy = 0 \quad \text{...(i)}$$

Eq. (i) represents a pair of straight lines.

$\therefore \quad \Delta = 0$

$$\Rightarrow \quad 0 + 2\cdot 0 - a \times \frac{c^2}{4} - b \times \frac{c^2}{4} = 0$$

or $$c^2(a + b) = 0$$

$\therefore \quad c = 0$ or $a + b = 0$

15. Given, equation is

$$x^2 + \alpha y^2 + 2\beta y - a^2 = 0 \quad \text{...(i)}$$

Equation (i) represents a pair of perpendicular straight lines

$\therefore$ $\Delta = 0$ and coefficient of x^2 + coefficient of $y^2 = 0$

$\Rightarrow \quad -a^2\alpha - \beta^2 = 0$ and $1 + \alpha = 0$

$\therefore \quad \alpha = -1$ and $\beta = \pm a$

16. Given pair of lines is

$$ax^2 + 2hxy + by^2 + 2gx + 2fy + c = 0 \quad \text{...(i)}$$

$\because$ Point of intersection of lines represented by (i) is

$$\left(\frac{hf - bg}{ab - h^2}, \frac{gh - af}{ab - h^2}\right) \text{ or } \left(\sqrt{\left(\frac{f^2 - bc}{h^2 - ab}\right)}, \sqrt{\left(\frac{g^2 - ac}{h^2 - ab}\right)}\right)$$

For Y-axis put $x = 0$

$\therefore \quad hf = bg, f^2 = bc$ and $h^2 \neq ab$

Also, $\Delta = 0$

$\therefore \quad abc + 2fgh - af^2 - bg^2 - ch^2 = 0$

For $$f^2 = bc, 2fgh = bg^2 + ch^2$$

17. Let $y = mx$ be the common line, then $m^2 + m - 12 = 0$ and $bm^2 + 2hm + a = 0$, then from first equation $m = -4, 3$

Substitute $m = -4$ in second equation, then $a = 8(h - 2b)$ and substitute $m = 3$ in second equation, then $a = -3(2h + 3b)$.

18. The separate equations of the sides are $x + y = 0$, $x - y = 0$ and $\frac{x}{3} + \frac{y}{2} = 1$.

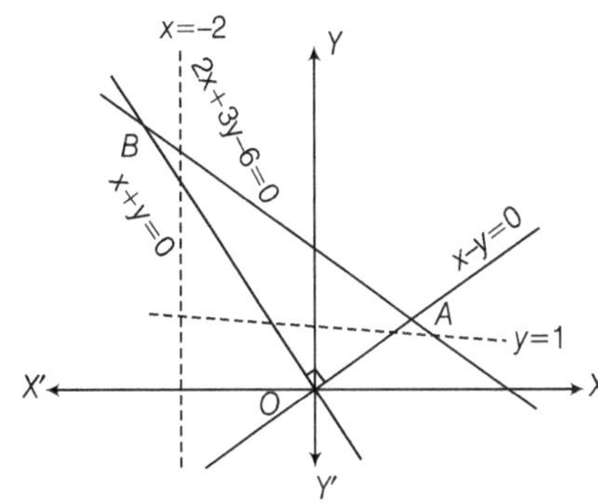

Intersection of $x = -2$ with $y = -x$ and $2x + 3y - 6 = 0$ gives the range of values of a.

$$\therefore \quad 2 < a < \frac{10}{3}$$

and intersection of $y = 1$ with $y = x$ and $2x + 3y - 6 = 0$ given the range of values of b

$$-1 < b < 1 \quad [\because (b, 1) \text{ is exterior point}]$$

Sol. (Q. Nos. 19 to 21)

Given equation is $x^2 - 3xy + \lambda y^2 + 3x - 5y + 2 = 0$

Here, $a = 1, b = \lambda, c = 2,$

$$f = -\frac{5}{2}, g = \frac{3}{2} \text{ and } h = -\frac{3}{2}.$$

19. $\Delta = 0$

$$1 \times \lambda \times 2 + 2 \times -\frac{5}{2} \times \frac{3}{2} \times -\frac{3}{2} - 1 \times \frac{25}{4} - \lambda \times \frac{9}{4} - 2 \times \frac{9}{4} = 0$$

$$\Rightarrow \quad 2\lambda + \frac{45}{4} - \frac{25}{4} - \frac{9\lambda}{4} - \frac{9}{2} = 0$$

$$\Rightarrow \quad -\frac{\lambda}{4} + \frac{1}{2} = 0$$

$$\therefore \quad \lambda = 2$$

20. Let $f(x, y) = x^2 - 3xy + 2y^2 + 3x - 5y + 2$ $\quad [\because \lambda = 2]$

$$\therefore \quad \frac{\partial f}{\partial x} = 2x - 3y + 3, \frac{\partial f}{\partial y} = -3x + 4y - 5$$

For point of intersection $\frac{\partial f}{\partial x} = 0$ and $\frac{\partial f}{\partial y} = 0$, we get

$$x = -3, y = -1$$

$\therefore \quad \alpha = -3$ and $\beta = -1$

$\therefore$ The value of $\alpha^2 + \beta^2$ is 10.

21. $$\tan\theta = \frac{2\sqrt{(h^2 - ab)}}{(a + b)} = \frac{2\sqrt{\left(\frac{9}{4} - 2\right)}}{1 + 2} = \frac{1}{3}$$

$$\therefore \quad \cos 2\theta = \frac{1 - \tan^2\theta}{1 + \tan^2\theta} = \frac{1 - \frac{1}{9}}{1 + \frac{1}{9}} = \frac{4}{5}$$

Solutions (Q. Nos. 22 to 24)

22. $\because \quad f_1(x, y) \equiv ax^2 + 2hxy + by^2 = 0$ ...(i)

bisectors of $f_1(x, y)$ is $f_2(x, y)$

$\therefore$ Equation of bisectors of (i) is $\dfrac{x^2 - y^2}{a - b} = \dfrac{xy}{h}$

$$\Rightarrow \quad hx^2 - (a - b)xy - hy^2 = 0$$

$$\therefore \quad f_2(x, y) \equiv hx^2 - (a - b)xy - hy^2 = 0 \quad \text{...(ii)}$$

Now, equation of bisectors of (ii) is

$$\frac{x^2 - y^2}{h - (-h)} = \frac{xy}{-\frac{(a-b)}{2}}$$

$$\Rightarrow \quad \frac{x^2 - y^2}{2h} = -\frac{2xy}{(a - b)}$$

$$\Rightarrow \quad (a - b)x^2 + 4hxy - (a - b)y^2 = 0$$

$$\therefore \quad f_3(x, y) \equiv (a - b)x^2 + 4hxy - (a - b)y^2 = 0$$

23. $f_2(x, y) \equiv bx^2 - 2hxy + ay^2 = 0$

and $f_3(x, y) \equiv ax^2 + 2hxy + by^2 = 0$

is same as $f_1(x, y) = 0$

24. For all $n \geq 2$

$$f_{n+2}(x, y) = f_n(x, y)$$

$$\therefore \quad \frac{f_{n+2}(x, y)}{f_n(x, y)} = 1$$

Now, $\displaystyle\sum_{n=2}^{5} \frac{f_{n+2}(x, y)}{f_n(x, y)} = \sum_{n=2}^{5} 1 = 1 + 1 + 1 + 1 = 4$

Sol. (Q. Nos. 25 to 27)

For perpendicular straight lines, then coefficient of x^2 + coefficient of $y^2 = 0$

$$\Rightarrow \quad 2 + b = 0$$

$$\therefore \quad b = -2$$

25. $2x^2 + 3xy - 2y^2 - 11x + 13y + c = 0$

represents a pair of straight lines, then we have

$$2 \times -2 \times c + 2 \times \frac{13}{2} \times -\frac{11}{2} \times \frac{3}{2} - 2 \times \frac{169}{4} + 2 \times \frac{121}{4} - c \times \frac{9}{4} = 0$$

$$\Rightarrow \quad -4c - \frac{429}{4} - \frac{169}{2} + \frac{121}{2} - \frac{9c}{4} = 0$$

$$\Rightarrow \quad c = -2$$

26. $|b + 2c| = |-2 - 4| = 6$

27. Now, pair of lines is $2x^2 + 3xy - 2y^2 - 11x + 13y - 2 = 0$

Let $f(x, y) \equiv 2x^2 + 3xy - 2y^2 - 11x + 13y - 2 = 0$

$$\therefore \quad \frac{\partial f}{\partial x} = 4x + 3y - 11 \text{ and } \frac{\partial f}{\partial y} = 3x - 4y + 13$$

For point of intersection, $\dfrac{\partial f}{dx} = 0$ and $\dfrac{\partial f}{\partial y} = 0$

$$\Rightarrow \quad 4x + 3y - 11 = 0 \text{ and } 3x - 4y + 13 = 0$$

$$\therefore \quad C \equiv \left(\frac{1}{5}, \frac{19}{5}\right)$$

Also, intersection on X-axis put $y = 0$.

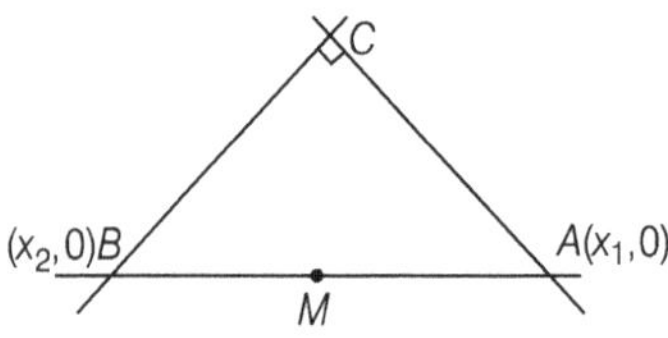

$$\therefore \quad 2x^2 - 11x + 2 = 0 \Rightarrow x_1 + x_2 = \frac{11}{2}$$

$\therefore$ Circumcentre of $\Delta ABC \Rightarrow M\left(\dfrac{x_1 + x_2}{2}, 0\right)$

$$\therefore \quad M \equiv \left(\frac{11}{4}, 0\right)$$

and orthocentre is $\quad C \equiv \left(\dfrac{1}{5}, \dfrac{19}{5}\right)$

$\therefore$ Required distance $= \sqrt{\left(\dfrac{11}{4} - \dfrac{1}{5}\right)^2 + \left(0 - \dfrac{19}{5}\right)^2}$

$$\therefore \quad \lambda = \sqrt{\frac{8377}{400}} = \sqrt{20.94} = 4.57$$

$$[\lambda] = [4.57] = 4$$

28. Given, $4y^3 - xy^2 - 10x^2y + \lambda x^3 = 0$

$$\Rightarrow \quad 4\left(\frac{y}{x}\right)^3 - \left(\frac{y}{x}\right)^2 - 10\left(\frac{y}{x}\right) + \lambda = 0$$

Let $y = mx$, then

$$4m^3 - m^2 - 10m + \lambda = 0$$

and let m_1, m_2, m_3 be the slopes of three lines, then

$$m_1 + m_2 + m_3 = \frac{1}{4} \quad \text{...(i)}$$

$$m_1m_2 + m_2m_3 + m_3m_1 = -\frac{10}{4} \quad \text{...(ii)}$$

$$m_1m_2m_3 = -\frac{\lambda}{4} \quad \text{...(iii)}$$

Since, two lines are equally inclined with $y = x$, so let $m_2m_3 = 1$

From Eq. (iii), $\quad m_1 = -\dfrac{\lambda}{4}$

From Eq. (i), $\quad m_2 + m_3 = \dfrac{\lambda + 1}{4}$ ...(iv)

and from Eq. (ii), $\quad 1 + \left(-\dfrac{\lambda}{4}\right)\left(\dfrac{\lambda + 1}{4}\right) = -\dfrac{10}{4}$

$$\Rightarrow \quad 16 - \lambda^2 - \lambda = -40$$

$$\Rightarrow \quad \lambda^2 + \lambda - 56 = 0$$

$$\Rightarrow \quad (\lambda + 8)(\lambda - 7) = 0$$

$$\lambda = -8, 7$$

Hence, $\quad \lambda = 7 \quad [\because \lambda > 0]$

29. $\because y^2 - 5xy + 6x^2 + 3x - y = 0$

$$\Rightarrow \quad (3x - y)(2x - y + 1) = 0$$

and $\; y^2 - 5xy + 6x^2 + 2x - y = 0$

$$\Rightarrow \quad (3x - y + 1)(2x - y) = 0$$

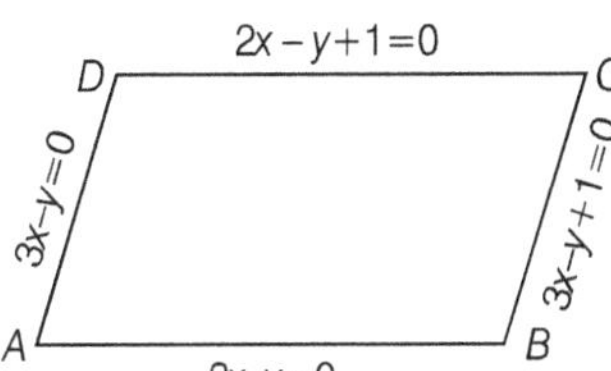

$\therefore$ Required Area $= \dfrac{(1-0)(1-0)}{\begin{vmatrix} 3 & -1 \\ 2 & -1 \end{vmatrix}} = 1$ sq unit

$\therefore \quad \lambda = 1$

30. Given pairs are

$$x^2 + 2\lambda xy + 2y^2 = 0 \quad \text{...(i)}$$

and $\quad (\lambda + 1)x^2 - 8xy + y^2 = 0 \quad$ ...(ii)

$\because$ Equations of angle bisectors of (i) and (ii) are equal

$\Rightarrow \dfrac{x^2 - y^2}{1-2} = \dfrac{xy}{\lambda}$ and $\dfrac{x^2 - y^2}{(\lambda+1)-1} = \dfrac{xy}{-4}$ must be same

$\Rightarrow \quad \dfrac{\lambda}{-1} = -\dfrac{4}{\lambda} \Rightarrow \lambda^2 = 4 \Rightarrow \lambda = \pm 2$

$\therefore \quad |\lambda| = 2$

31. Given, $\quad \dfrac{y - nx}{2} = 1 \quad$ ...(i)

and $\quad x^2 + y^2 = 1 \quad$ ...(ii)

Homogenising Eq. (ii) with Eq. (i), we get

$$x^2 + y^2 = \left(\frac{y - nx}{2}\right)^2$$

$\Rightarrow \quad \left(\dfrac{n^2}{4} - 1\right)x^2 - nxy + \left(\dfrac{1}{4} - 1\right)y^2 = 0$

or $\quad (n^2 - 4)x^2 - 4\,nxy - 3y^2 = 0$

The lines will be at right angles, when

$$(n^2 - 4) + (-3) = 0 \Rightarrow n^2 = 7$$

32. $\because \quad x^2 - y^2 + 2y = 1$

$\Rightarrow \quad x^2 = (y^2 - 2y + 1) = (y-1)^2$

$\Rightarrow \quad x = \pm (y - 1)$

i.e. $\quad x - y + 1 = 0$ and $x + y - 1 = 0$

$\therefore$ Bisectors are $y = 1$ and $x = 0$

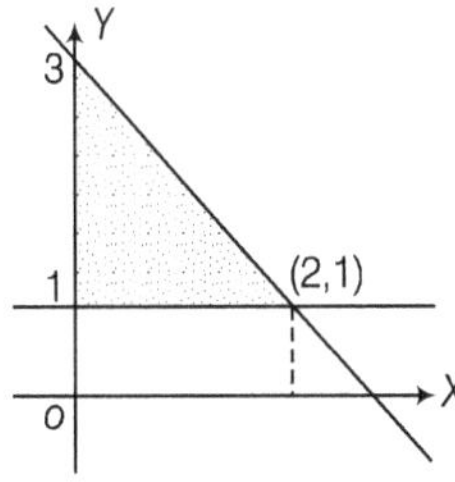

So, area between $x = 0$, $y = 1$ and $x + y = 3$ is given by

$$\frac{1}{2} \times 2 \times 2 = 2 \text{ sq units}$$

$\therefore \quad \lambda = 2$

33. (A) $\to$ (p, r); (B) $\to$ (r); (C) $\to$ (p, q, s); (D) $\to$ (q, r)

(A) Given $\quad \dfrac{2x + 2y}{-\lambda} = 1 \quad$ ...(i)

and $\quad 9x^2 + 16y^2 = 144 \quad$ ...(ii)

Homogenising Eq. (ii) with Eq. (i), we get

$$9x^2 + 16y^2 = 144\left(\frac{2x + 2y}{-\lambda}\right)^2$$

$\Rightarrow (9\lambda^2 - 576)x^2 - 1152xy + (16\lambda^2 - 576)y^2 = 0$

The lines are coincident, then

$$(-576)^2 = (9\lambda^2 - 576)(16\lambda^2 - 576)$$

$\Rightarrow \quad 144\lambda^4 - 576\lambda^2(25) = 0$

or $\quad \lambda^2 = 100$

$\therefore \quad |\lambda| = 10$

(B) Given, $\quad \dfrac{4x + 3y}{24} = 1 \quad$ ...(i)

and $\quad (x - 3)^2 + (y - 4)^2 = \lambda^2$

or $\quad x^2 + y^2 - (6x + 8y) + 25 - \lambda^2 = 0 \quad$ ...(ii)

Homogenising Eq. (ii) with Eq. (i), we get

$$x^2 + y^2 - (6x + 8y)\frac{(4x + 3y)}{24} + (25 - \lambda^2)\left(\frac{4x + 3y}{24}\right)^2 = 0$$

$\Rightarrow \quad 16(25 - \lambda^2)x^2 + 9(25 - \lambda^2)y^2 + (-600 - 24\lambda^2)xy = 0$

The lines will be at right angles, when

$$16(25 - \lambda^2) + 9(25 - \lambda^2) = 0$$

$\Rightarrow \quad 625 - 25\lambda^2 = 0$

$\Rightarrow \quad \lambda^2 = 25$

$\therefore \quad |\lambda| = 5$

(C) The lines pairs are $(y - 1)(y - 3) = 0$ i.e. $y = 1$ and $y = 3$ the other line pair is $x^2 + 4xy + 4y^2 - 5x - 10y + 4 = 0$

i.e. $\quad (x + 2y - 4)(x + 2y - 1) = 0$

or $\quad x + 2y - 4 = 0$ and $x + 2y - 1 = 0$

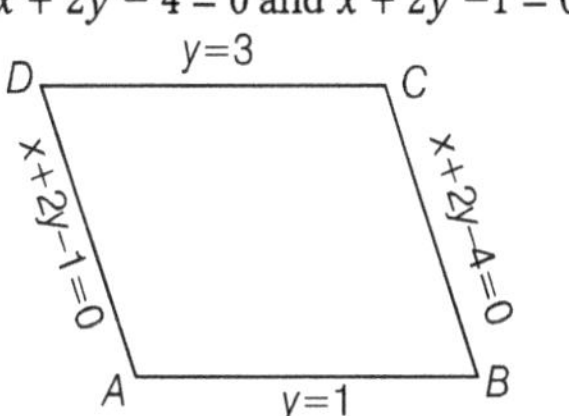

Required area $= \dfrac{(3-1)(4-1)}{\begin{vmatrix} 1 & 2 \\ 0 & 1 \end{vmatrix}} = 6$ sq units

$\therefore \quad \lambda = 6$

(D) Equation of the bisectors of $3x^2 - 2pxy - 3y^2 = 0$ is

$$\frac{x^2 - y^2}{3 - (-3)} = \frac{xy}{-p} \Rightarrow px^2 + 6xy - py^2 = 0$$

Which is same as $5x^2 - 2qxy - 5y^2 = 0$

i.e. $\quad \dfrac{p}{5} = \dfrac{6}{-2q} = \dfrac{-p}{-5} \Rightarrow pq = -15$

$\therefore \quad \lambda = |pq| = |-15| = 15$

34. $\because$ Lines represented by $6x^2 + 5xy - 6y^2 = 0$ are $l_1 : 2x + 3y = 0$, $l_2 : 3x - 2y = 0$
and lines represented by

$$6x^2 + 5xy - 6y^2 - x + 5y - 1 = 0$$

are $l_3 : 2x + 3y - 1 = 0$

$l_4 : 3x - 2y + 1 = 0$

$\because \quad l_1 \perp l_2, l_2 \perp l_3, l_3 \perp l_4$ and $l_4 \perp l_1$.

Also, l_1, l_2 intersect at (0, 0) and (0, 0) is equidistant from l_3 and l_4. These lines form sides of square.

$\therefore$ Statement I is true.

Statement II is true but Statement II is not a correct explanation for Statement I.

35. $dx^3 + cx^2y + bxy^2 + ay^3 = (x^2 + pxy - y^2)(dx - ay)$

On comparing, we get

$$c = -a + pd \Rightarrow p = \frac{c + a}{d} \quad \text{...(i)}$$

and $$b = -ap - d \Rightarrow p = \frac{-b - d}{a} \quad \text{...(ii)}$$

From Eq. (i) and Eq. (ii),

$$\frac{c + a}{d} = \frac{-b - d}{a}$$

$$\Rightarrow \quad d^2 + bd + ac + a^2 = 0$$

$\therefore$ Statement I is true.

Hence, both statements are true but Statement II is not correct explanation for Statement I.

36. Pair of bisectors between the lines $x^2 - 2\alpha xy - y^2 = 0$ is

$$\frac{x^2 - y^2}{1 - (-1)} = \frac{xy}{-\alpha}$$

$$\Rightarrow \quad \alpha x^2 + 2xy - \alpha y^2 = 0 \quad \text{...(i)}$$

Comparing it with $y^2 + 2\beta xy - x^2 = 0$, then

$$-\frac{\alpha}{1} = \frac{1}{\beta} = \frac{\lambda}{-1}$$

$$\Rightarrow \quad \alpha\beta = -1$$

Hence, both statements are true and Statement II is correct explanation for Statement I.

37. Put $2h = -(a + b)$ in $ax^2 + 2hxy + by^2 = 0$

$$\Rightarrow \quad ax^2 - (a + b)xy + by^2 = 0$$

$$\Rightarrow \quad (x - y)(ax - by) = 0$$

$\Rightarrow$ One of the line bisects the angle between coordinate axes in positive quadrant.

Also, put $b = -2h - a$ in $ax - by$, we have

$$ax - by = ax - (-2h - a)y$$
$$= ax + (2h + a)y$$

Hence, $ax + (2h + a)y$ is a factor of

$$ax^2 + 2hyx + by^2 = 0$$

$\therefore$ Both statements are true but Statement II is not correct explanation for Statement I.

38. From $(y - mx)^2 = a^2(1 + m^2)$

$$\Rightarrow \quad y - mx = \pm a\sqrt{(1 + m^2)}$$

$\therefore$ Lines $$y - mx = a\sqrt{1 + m^2} \quad \text{...(i)}$$

and $$y - mx = -a\sqrt{1 + m^2} \quad \text{...(ii)}$$

and from $$(y - nx)^2 = a^2(1 + n^2)$$

$$\Rightarrow \quad y - nx = \pm a\sqrt{(1 + n^2)}$$

$\therefore$ Lines $$y - nx = a\sqrt{1 + n^2} \quad \text{...(iii)}$$

and $$y - nx = -a\sqrt{1 + n^2} \quad \text{...(iv)}$$

Since, lines (i) and (ii) are parallel, the distance between lines (i) and (ii) is

$$\frac{|a\sqrt{1 + m^2} + a\sqrt{1 + m^2}|}{\sqrt{1 + m^2}} = |2a|$$

Similarly, (iii) and (iv) are parallel lines and the distance between them = $|2a|$. Therefore, distance between parallel lines are same.

Hence, lines (i), (ii), (iii) and (iv) form a rhombus.

39. Dividing by x^3, the given equation can be written as

$$m\left(1 - 3\left(\frac{y}{x}\right)^2\right) + \left(\frac{y}{x}\right)^3 - 3\left(\frac{y}{x}\right) = 0$$

writing $\frac{y}{x} = \tan\theta$, we have

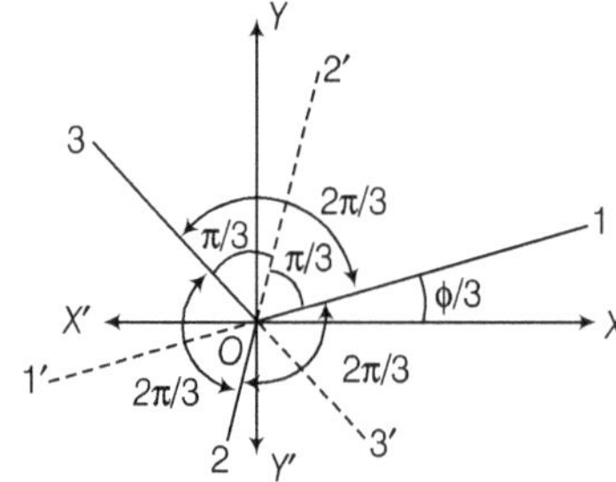

$$m(1 - 3\tan^2\theta) + \tan^3\theta - 3\tan\theta = 0$$

$$\therefore \quad m = \frac{3\tan\theta - \tan^3\theta}{1 - 3\tan^2\theta} = \tan 3\theta$$

Let $m = \tan\phi$,

then $\tan 3\theta = \tan\phi$

$$\therefore \quad 3\theta = \phi, \ \phi + \pi, \ \phi + 2\pi$$

$$\Rightarrow \quad \theta = \frac{\phi}{3}, \ \frac{\phi}{3} + \frac{\pi}{3}, \ \frac{\phi}{3} + \frac{2\pi}{3}$$

Thus, the given equation represents three lines through the origin and they are inclined at angles $\frac{\phi}{3}, \frac{\phi}{3} + \frac{\pi}{3}, \frac{\phi}{3} + \frac{2\pi}{3}$ with the X-axis. Clearly, they are equally inclined to each other.

40. Given pair of lines is

$$(A^2 - 3B^2)x^2 + 8ABxy + (B^2 - 3A^2)y^2 = 0 \quad \text{...(i)}$$

Given line is $\quad Ax + By + C = 0 \quad$ ...(ii)

Comparing Eq. (i) with $ax^2 + 2hxy + by^2 = 0$

$$a = A^2 - 3B^2,\ h = 4AB,\ b = B^2 - 3A^2$$

If θ be the acute angle between the lines represented by Eq. (i), then

$$\tan\theta = \frac{2\sqrt{(h^2 - ab)}}{|a+b|} = \frac{2\sqrt{16A^2B^2 - (A^2 - 3B^2)(B^2 - 3A^2)}}{|(A^2 - 3B^2 + B^2 - 3A^2)|}$$

$$= \frac{2\sqrt{(3A^4 + 3B^4 + 6A^2B^2)}}{|-2(A^2 + B^2)|} = \frac{\sqrt{3}(A^2 + B^2)}{(A^2 + B^2)} = \sqrt{3}$$

$\therefore \quad \theta = 60^\circ$

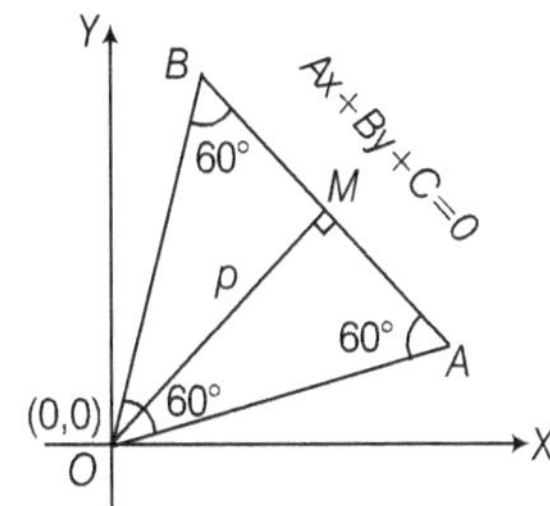

Eq. (i) can be written as

$$(B^2 - 3A^2)\left(\frac{y}{x}\right)^2 + 8AB\left(\frac{y}{x}\right) + (A^2 - 3B^2) = 0$$

Solving for y/x, we have

$$\frac{y}{x} = \frac{-8AB \pm \sqrt{64A^2B^2 - 4(B^2 - 3A^2)(A^2 - 3B^2)}}{2(B^2 - 3A^2)}$$

$$= \frac{-4AB \pm \sqrt{16A^2B^2 - (A^2B^2 - 3B^4 - 3A^4 + 9A^2B^2)}}{(B^2 - 3A^2)}$$

$$\Rightarrow \quad \frac{y}{x} = \frac{-4AB \pm \sqrt{3}(A^2 + B^2)}{(B^2 - 3A^2)}$$

$$\Rightarrow \quad y = \left\{\frac{-4AB \pm \sqrt{3}(A^2 + B^2)}{B^2 - 3A^2}\right\}x$$

Taking the positive sign, slope of one of the lines

$$= \frac{\sqrt{3}(A^2 + B^2) - 4AB}{B^2 - 3A^2}$$

and slope of the line $Ax + By + C = 0$ is $-A/B$.

Acute angle between these lines

$$= \tan^{-1}\left|\frac{\dfrac{\sqrt{3}(A^2 + B^2) - 4AB}{B^2 - 3A^2} + \dfrac{A}{B}}{1 - \left(\dfrac{A}{B}\right)\left[\dfrac{\sqrt{3}(A^2 + B^2) - 4AB}{B^2 - 3A^2}\right]}\right|$$

$$= \tan^{-1}\left|\frac{-3A^2 + \sqrt{3}A^2B - 3AB^2 + \sqrt{3}B^3}{-\sqrt{3}A^3 + A^2B - \sqrt{3}AB^2 + B^3}\right|$$

$$= \tan^{-1}(\sqrt{3}) = 60^\circ$$

then remaining third angle is $180^\circ - (60^\circ + 60^\circ) = 60^\circ$.

$\therefore$ The ΔAOB is equilateral.

In ΔOAB,

$$\text{Length of } \perp \text{ from } O \text{ on } AB = p = OM = \frac{|0 + 0 + C|}{\sqrt{(A^2 + B^2)}}$$

$$p = \frac{|C|}{\sqrt{(A^2 + B^2)}}$$

and in ΔOAM,

$$\sin 60^\circ = \frac{p}{OA} \Rightarrow OA = \frac{2p}{\sqrt{3}}$$

$$\therefore \quad OA = \frac{2|C|}{\sqrt{3}\sqrt{(A^2 + B^2)}}$$

$\therefore$ Area of the equilateral triangle $= \frac{\sqrt{3}}{4}(\text{side})^2 = \frac{\sqrt{3}}{4}(OA)^2$

$$= \frac{\sqrt{3}}{4} \times \frac{4|C|^2}{3 \times (A^2 + B^2)} = \frac{C^2}{\sqrt{3}(A^2 + B^2)}$$

41. Lines of parallelogram are

$$L = 0,\ L = a$$
$$L' = 0,\ L' = a$$

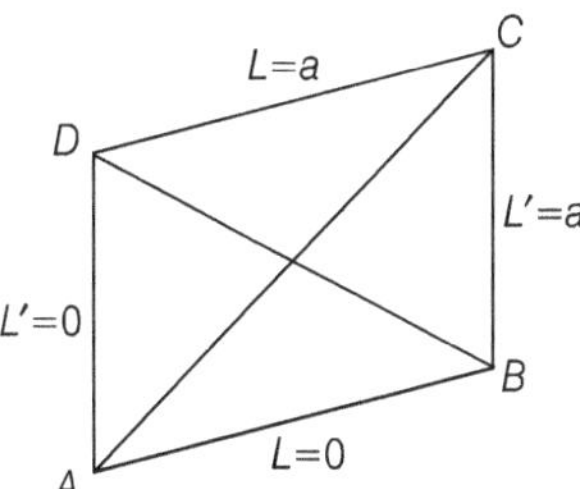

where, $\quad L = x\cos\theta + y\sin\theta - p$

$$L' = x\cos\theta' + y\sin\theta' - p'$$

Equation of the line AC, through the point of intersection of $L = 0$ and $L' = 0$ is

$$L + \lambda L' = 0$$

It also passes through

$$L = a \text{ and } L' = a, \quad \text{...(i)}$$

then, $\quad a + \lambda a = 0$

$\therefore \quad \lambda = -1$

Hence, diagonal of AC is $L - L' = 0$

i.e. $\quad x(\cos\theta - \cos\theta') + y(\sin\theta - \sin\theta') - p + p' = 0$

Equation of the line BD through point of intersection of $L = 0$ and $L' = a$ is

$$L + \lambda(L' - a) = 0$$

it also passes through $L = a$ and $L' = 0$.

$\therefore \quad a + \lambda(0 - a) = 0$

$\therefore \quad \lambda = 1$

Equation of diagonal BD is $L + L' - a = 0$

$\Rightarrow x(\cos\theta + \cos\theta') + y(\sin\theta + \sin\theta') - p - p' - a = 0$

42. Let the first equation represents lines

$$(lx + my + n)(l_1x + m_1y + n_1) = 0$$

then the second equation represents lines

$$(lx + my - n)(l_1x + m_1y - n_1) = 0$$

On comparing coefficients, $ll_1 = a, mm_1 = b, nn_1 = c$

$$mn_1 + m_1n = 2f, nl_1 + n_1l = 2g, \ lm_1 + l_1 m = 2h.$$

Let the angle between two non-parallel lines be θ, then

$$\tan\theta = \frac{2\sqrt{(h^2 - ab)}}{|a + b|}$$

$$\therefore \quad \sin\theta = \frac{2\sqrt{(h^2 - ab)}}{\sqrt{(a - b)^2 + 4h^2}}$$

$\therefore$ Area of parallelogram $= \dfrac{p_1p_2}{\sin\theta}$,

where, p_1 and p_2 are distance between two parallel sides.

$$\therefore \quad p_1 = \frac{|n - (-n)|}{\sqrt{l^2 + m^2}} \text{ and } p_2 = \frac{|n_1 - (-n_1)|}{\sqrt{l_1^2 + m_1^2}}$$

$$\therefore \quad p_1p_2 = \frac{|4nn_1|}{\sqrt{(l^2l_1^2 + l^2m_1^2 + m^2l_1^2 + m^2m_1^2)}}$$

$$= \frac{4|nn_1|}{\sqrt{\{l^2l_1^2 + m^2m_1^2 + (lm_1 + l_1m)^2 - 4ll_1mm_1\}}}$$

$$= \frac{4|c|}{\sqrt{a^2 + b^2 + 4h^2 - 2ab}} = \frac{4|c|}{\sqrt{(a - b)^2 + 4h^2}}$$

$$\therefore \quad \text{Area} = \frac{p_1p_2}{\sin\theta}$$

$$= \frac{4|c|}{(\sqrt{(a - b)^2 + 4h^2})\left(\dfrac{2\sqrt{h^2 - ab}}{\sqrt{(a - b)^2 + 4h^2}}\right)}$$

$$= \frac{2|c|}{\sqrt{(h^2 - ab)}}$$

43. Given, equation

$$ax^2 + 2hxy + by^2 + 2gx + 2fy + c = 0$$

represents two lines

$$lx + my + n = 0 \quad \text{and} \quad l_1x + m_1y + n_1 = 0$$

then, $ax^2 + 2hxy + by^2 + 2gx + 2fy + c$

$$= (lx + my + n)(l_1x + m_1y + n_1)$$

Comparing the coefficients of similar terms, we get

$$\left.\begin{aligned} &ll_1 = a, mm_1 = b, nn_1 = c \\ &lm_1 + ml_1 = 2h, n_1l + nl_1 = 2g, nm_1 + n_1m = 2f \end{aligned}\right\} \quad \text{...(i)}$$

Since, the lines $lx + my + n = 0$ and $l_1x + m_1y + n_1 = 0$ are equidistant from the origin, then

$$\frac{|n|}{\sqrt{l^2 + m^2}} = \frac{|n_1|}{\sqrt{l_1^2 + m_1^2}}$$

$$\Rightarrow \quad n^2l_1^2 + n^2m_1^2 = n_1^2l^2 + n_1^2m^2$$

$$\Rightarrow \quad n^2l_1^2 - n_1^2l^2 = n_1^2m^2 - n^2m_1^2$$

$$\Rightarrow (nl_1 - n_1l)(nl_1 + n_1l) = (n_1m - nm_1)(n_1m + nm_1)$$

On squaring both sides, we get

$$(nl_1 - n_1l)^2 (nl_1 + n_1l)^2 = (n_1m - nm_1)^2(n_1m + nm_1)^2$$

$$\Rightarrow \ [(nl_1 + n_1l)^2 - 4ll_1nn_1][nl_1 + n_1l]^2$$

$$= [(n_1m + nm_1)^2 - 4mm_1nn_1][n_1m + nm_1]^2$$

$$\Rightarrow \quad (4g^2 - 4ac)(4g^2) = (4f^2 - 4bc)(4f^2)$$

[using the six relations]

$$\Rightarrow \quad (g^2 - ac)g^2 = (f^2 - bc)f^2 \qquad \text{[from Eq. (i)]}$$

$$\Rightarrow \quad f^4 - g^4 = c(bf^2 - ag^2)$$

Also, product of distances from origin to the lines represented by

$$ax^2 + 2hxy + by^2 + 2gx + 2fy + c = 0$$

is $\dfrac{|n|}{\sqrt{(l^2 + m^2)}} \cdot \dfrac{|n_1|}{\sqrt{(l_1^2 + m_1^2)}}$

$$= \frac{|nn_1|}{\sqrt{(l^2l_1^2 + l^2m_1^2 + m^2l_1^2 + m^2m_1^2)}}$$

$$= \frac{|nn_1|}{\sqrt{(l^2l_1^2 + l^2m_1^2 + m^2l_1^2 + m^2m_1^2)}}$$

$$= \frac{|nn_1|}{\sqrt{(l^2l_1^2 + m^2m_1^2 + (lm_1 + ml_1)^2 - 2ll_1mm_1)}}$$

$$= \frac{|c|}{\sqrt{(a^2 + b^2 + 4h^2 - 2ab)}} \qquad \text{[from Eq. (i)]}$$

$$= \frac{|c|}{\sqrt{(a - b)^2 + 4h^2}}$$

44. We know that bisectors are mutually perpendicular to each other, then

$$ax^4 + bx^3y + cx^2y^2 + dxy^3 + ay^4 = 0$$

represents two pairs of mutually perpendicular lines.

Let $ax^4 + bx^3y + cx^2y^2 + dxy^3 + ay^4$

$$= (ax^2 + pxy - ay^2)(x^2 + qxy - y^2)$$

where, p and q are constants.

Comparing the coefficients of similar terms, we get

$$b = aq + p \qquad \text{...(i)}$$

$$c = pq - 2a \qquad \text{...(ii)}$$

$$d = -p - aq \qquad \text{...(iii)}$$

On adding Eqs. (i) and (iii), we have

$$b + d = 0$$

From Eq. (ii), $\quad pq = c + 2a \quad$ ...(iv)

But given that bisectors of one pair are given by the other, i.e.

$$\frac{x^2 - y^2}{a - (-a)} = \frac{xy}{(p/2)}$$

$$\Rightarrow \quad \frac{x^2 - y^2}{4xy} = \frac{a}{p} \quad \text{...(v)}$$

is the same as the other pair.

$$x^2 + qxy - y^2 = 0$$

or $$\frac{x^2 - y^2}{4xy} = -\frac{q}{4} \quad \text{...(vi)}$$

From Eqs. (v) and (vi), $\quad \frac{a}{p} = -\frac{q}{4}$

$$\therefore \quad pq = -4a$$

Again from Eq. (iv), $\quad -4a = c + 2a$

$$\therefore \quad c + 6a = 0$$

45. Let A be the area of small sector, then area of major sector is $3A$.

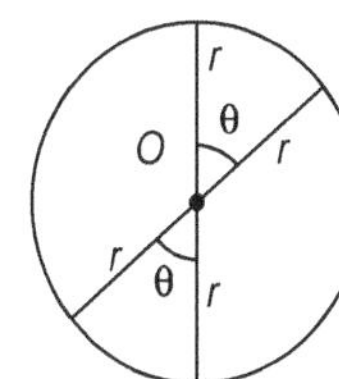

$$\therefore \quad A + 3A + A + 3A = \pi r^2$$

$$\Rightarrow \quad A = \frac{\pi}{8} r^2$$

$$\Rightarrow \quad \frac{1}{2} r^2 \theta = \frac{\pi}{8} r^2 \quad \left[\because \text{area of sector} = \frac{1}{2} r^2 \theta\right]$$

$$\therefore \quad \theta = \frac{\pi}{4}$$

$\therefore$ Angle between lines represented by

$$ax^2 + 2(a + b)xy + by^2 = 0 \text{ is } \frac{\pi}{4}.$$

$$\Rightarrow \quad \tan \frac{\pi}{4} = \frac{2\sqrt{(a + b)^2 - ab}}{|a + b|}$$

$$\Rightarrow \quad 1 = \frac{2\sqrt{(a + b)^2 - ab}}{|a + b|}$$

$$\Rightarrow \quad (a + b)^2 = 4(a + b)^2 - 4ab$$

$$\therefore \quad 3a^2 + 2ab + 3b^2 = 0$$

46. The equation of the bisectors of the lines $xy = 0$ are $y = \pm x$.

Putting $y = \pm x$ in

$$my^2 + (1 - m^2)xy - mx^2 = 0, \text{ we get}$$

$$\pm (1 - m^2)x^2 = 0$$

$$\Rightarrow \quad m^2 = 1$$

$\therefore$

CHAPTER

04

Circle

Learning Part

Session 1
- Definition
- Equation of Circle in Different Forms
- Locus of the Mid-point of the Chords of the Circle that Subtends an Angle of 2θ at its Centre

Session 2
- Diametric Form of a Circle
- Equation of Circle Passing Through Three Non-Collinear Points

Session 3
- Intercepts Made on the Axes by a Circle
- Different Forms of the Equations of a Circle
- Position of a Point with Respect to Circle
- Maximum and Minimum Distance of a Point from the Circle

Session 4
- Intersection of a Line and a Circle
- Product of the Algebraical Distances *PA* and *PB* is Constant when from *P*, *A* Secant be Drawn to Cut the Circle in the Points *A* and *B*
- The Length of Intercept Cut-off from a Line by a Circle
- Tangent to a Circle at a Given Point
- Normal to a Circle at a Given Point

Session 5
- Tangents from a Point to the Circle
- Length of the Tangent from a Point to a Circle
- Power of a Point with Respect to a Circle
- Chord of Contact
- Chord Bisected at a Given Point
- Pair of Tangents
- Director Circle

Session 6
- Diameter of a Circle
- Two Circles Touching Each Other
- Common Tangents to Two Circles
- Common Chord of Two Circles
- Family of Circles

Session 7
- Angle of Intersection of Two Circles
- Radical Axis
- Radical Centre
- Co-axial System of Circles
- Limiting Point
- Image of the Circle by the Line Mirror

Practice Part
- JEE Type Examples
- Chapter Exercises

Arihant on Your Mobile !

Exercises with the symbol can be practised on your mobile. See inside cover page to activate for free.

Session 1

Definition, Equation of Circle in Different Forms, Locus of the Mid-point of the Chords of the Circle that Subtends an Angle of 2θ at its Centre

Definition

A circle is the locus of a point which moves in a plane, so that its distance from a *fixed point* in the plane is always *constant.*

The fixed point is called the *centre* of the circle and the constant distance is called its *radius.*

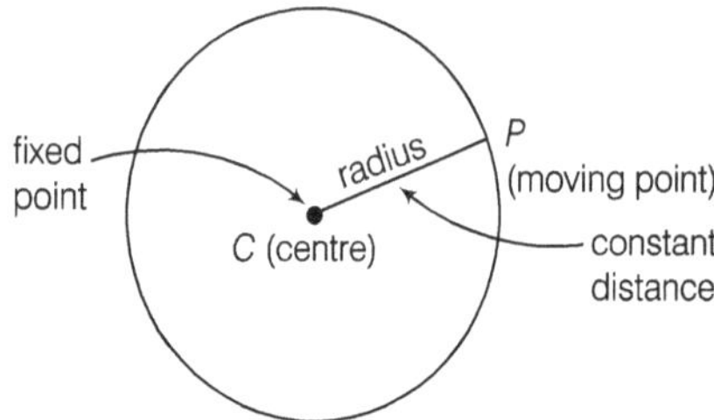

i.e. CP = constant distance = Radius

Equation of a Circle : The curve traced by the moving point is called its *circumference.* i.e. the equation of any circle is satisfied by co-ordinates of all points on its circumference.

OR

The equation of the circle is meant the equation of the circumference.

OR

It is the set of all points lying on the circumference of the circle.

Chord and Diameter : The line joining any two points on the circumference is called a chord. If any chord passing through its centre is called its diameter.

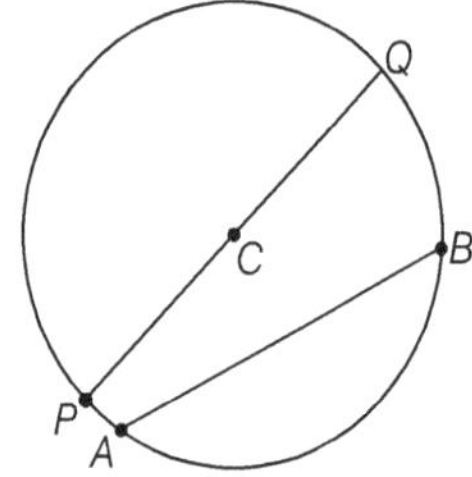

AB = Chord, PQ = Diameter

where, C is centre of the circle.

Equation of Circle in Different Forms

1. Centre-radius form

Let a be the *radius* and $C(h, k)$ be the *centre* of any circle.

If $P(x, y)$ be any point on the circumference.

Then, $CP = a \Rightarrow (CP)^2 = a^2$

$\Rightarrow$ $(x-h)^2 + (y-k)^2 = a^2$

This equation is known as the central form of the equation of a circle.

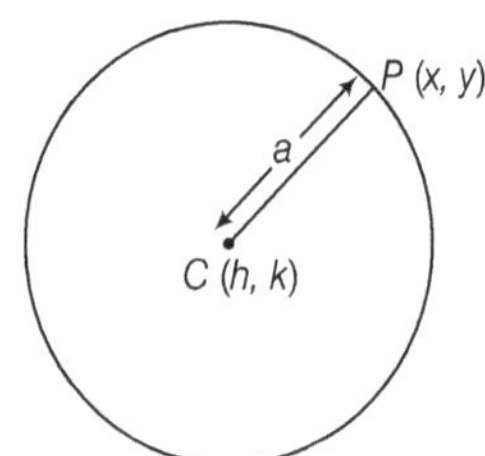

Remark

When, $C(h, k) = C(0, 0)$, then equation of circle becomes $x^2 + y^2 = a^2$ which is known as **standard form** of the circle.

2. Parametric form

If the radius of a circle whose centre is at $C(0, 0)$ makes an angle θ with the positive direction of X-axis, then θ is called the parameter.

Let $CP = a$

$\therefore$ $CM = x, PM = y \Rightarrow x = a\cos\theta, y = a\sin\theta$

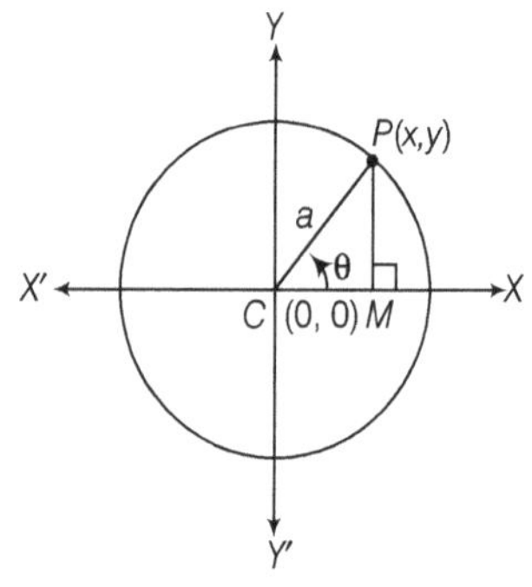

Hence, $(a\cos\theta, a\sin\theta)$ or 'θ' are the parametric coordinates of the circle $x^2+y^2=a^2$ and $x=a\cos\theta$ and $y=a\sin\theta$ are called parametric equations of the circle $x^2+y^2=a^2$ with parameters a and θ. $(0\le\theta<2\pi)$.

Remarks

1. The parametric coordinates of any point on the circle $(x-h)^2+(y-k)^2=a^2$ are given by $(h+a\cos\theta, k+a\sin\theta)$ $(0\le\theta<2\pi)$ and parametric equations of the circle $(x-h)^2+(y-k)^2=a^2$ are $x=h+a\cos\theta$, $y=k+a\sin\theta$.
2. Equation of the chord of the circle $x^2+y^2=a^2$ joining $(a\cos\alpha, a\sin\alpha)$ and $(a\cos\beta, a\sin\beta)$ is
$$x\cos\left(\frac{\alpha+\beta}{2}\right)+y\sin\left(\frac{\alpha+\beta}{2}\right)=a\cos\left(\frac{\alpha-\beta}{2}\right).$$

General form The equation of the circle with centre (h,k) and radius a is $(x-h)^2+(y-k)^2=a^2$

or $$x^2+y^2-2hx-2ky+h^2+k^2-a^2=0 \quad \text{...(i)}$$

which is of the form

$$x^2+y^2+2gx+2fy+c=0 \quad \text{...(ii)}$$

This is known as the **general equation** of a circle comparing Eqs. (i) and (ii), we get

$$h=-g, k=-f \quad \text{and} \quad a=\sqrt{(g^2+f^2-c)}$$

$\therefore$ Coordinates of the centre are $(-g,-f)$ and

$$\text{Radius}=\sqrt{(g^2+f^2-c)}\ (g^2+f^2\ge c)$$

Remarks

1. **Rule for finding the centre and radius of a circle**
   (i) Make the coefficients of x^2 and y^2 equal to 1 and right hand side equal to zero.
   (ii) Then, coordinates of centre will be (α,β), where, $\alpha=-\frac{1}{2}$(coefficient of x) and $\beta=-\frac{1}{2}$(coefficient of y)
   (iii) Radius $=\sqrt{\alpha^2+\beta^2-\text{(constant term)}}$
2. **Conditions for a circle** A general equation of second degree
$$ax^2+2hxy+by^2+2gx+2fy+c=0$$
   in x, y represent a circle, if
   (i) coefficient of x^2 = coefficient of y^2
   i.e. $a=b$
   (ii) coefficient of xy is zero
   i.e. $h=0$
3. **Nature of the circle** Radius of the circle $x^2+y^2+2gx+2fy+c=0$ is $\sqrt{(g^2+f^2-c)}$
   Now, the following cases are possible :
   (i) If $g^2+f^2-c>0$, then the radius of circle will be real. Hence in this case, real circle is possible.
   (ii) If $g^2+f^2-c=0$, then the radius of circle will be real. Hence in this case, circle is called a point circle.
   (iii) If $g^2+f^2-c<0$, then the radius of circle will be imaginary number. Hence in this case, circle is called a virtual circle or imaginary circle.
4. **Concentric circle** Two circles having the same centre $C(h,k)$ but different radii r_1 and r_2 respectively are called concentric circles. Thus, the circles $(x-h)^2+(y-k)^2=r_1^2$ and $(x-h)^2+(y-k)^2=r_2^2, r_1\ne r_2$ are concentric circles. Therefore, the equations of concentric circles differ only in constant terms.

Example 1. Find the centre and radius of the circle
$$2x^2+2y^2=3x-5y+7$$

Sol. The given equation of circle is
$$2x^2+2y^2=3x-5y+7$$
or $$x^2+y^2-\frac{3}{2}x+\frac{5}{2}y-\frac{7}{2}=0$$
If centre is (α,β), then
$$\alpha=-\frac{1}{2}\left(-\frac{3}{2}\right)=\frac{3}{4}$$
and $$\beta=-\frac{1}{2}\left(\frac{5}{2}\right)=-\frac{5}{4}$$
$\therefore$ Centre of circle is (α,β) i.e. $\left(\frac{3}{4},-\frac{5}{4}\right)$

and radius of the circle
$$=\sqrt{\alpha^2+\beta^2-\text{(constant term)}}$$
$$=\sqrt{\frac{9}{16}+\frac{25}{16}+\frac{7}{2}}=\sqrt{\frac{9+25+56}{16}}=\frac{3\sqrt{10}}{4}$$

Example 2. Prove that the radii of the circles $x^2+y^2=1, x^2+y^2-2x-6y=6$ and $x^2+y^2-4x-12y=9$ are in AP.

Sol. Given circles are $$x^2+y^2=1 \quad \text{...(i)}$$
$$x^2+y^2-2x-6y-6=0 \quad \text{...(ii)}$$
and $$x^2+y^2-4x-12y-9=0 \quad \text{...(iii)}$$
Let r_1, r_2 and r_3 be the radii of the circles Eqs. (i), (ii) and (iii), respectively.

Then, $$r_1=1$$
$$r_2=\sqrt{(-1)^2+(-3)^2+6}=4$$
and $$r_3=\sqrt{(-2)^2+(-6)^2+9}=7$$
Clearly, $r_2-r_1=4-1=3=r_3-r_2$

Hence, r_1, r_2, r_3 are in AP.

Example 3. Find the equation of the circle whose centre is the point of intersection of the lines $2x-3y+4=0$ and $3x+4y-5=0$ and passes through the origin.

Sol. The point of intersection of the lines $2x - 3y + 4 = 0$ and $3x + 4y - 5 = 0$ is $\left(-\frac{1}{17}, \frac{22}{17}\right)$.

Therefore, the centre of the circle is at $\left(-\frac{1}{17}, \frac{22}{17}\right)$.

Since, the origin lies on the circle, its distance from the centre of the circle is radius of the circle, therefore,

$$r = \sqrt{\left(-\frac{1}{17} - 0\right)^2 + \left(\frac{22}{17} - 0\right)^2} = \sqrt{\frac{485}{289}}$$

$\therefore$ The equation of the circle becomes

$$\left(x + \frac{1}{17}\right)^2 + \left(y - \frac{22}{17}\right)^2 = \frac{485}{289}$$

or $\quad 17(x^2 + y^2) + 2x - 44y = 0$

Aliter : $\because$ Point of intersection of the lines $2x - 3y + 4 = 0$ and $3x + 4y - 5 = 0$ is $\left(-\frac{1}{17}, \frac{22}{17}\right)$.

Therefore, the centre of the circle is at $\left(-\frac{1}{17}, \frac{22}{17}\right)$

Let required circle is

$$x^2 + y^2 + 2gx + 2fy + c = 0 \quad \text{...(i)}$$

Here, $-g = -\frac{1}{17}, -f = \frac{22}{17}, c = 0$

[$\because$ Circle passes through origin]

From Eq. (i), $\quad x^2 + y^2 + \frac{2x}{17} - \frac{44}{17}y = 0$

or $\quad 17(x^2 + y^2) + 2x - 44y = 0$

Example 4. Find the equation of the circle concentric with the circle $x^2 + y^2 - 8x + 6y - 5 = 0$ and passing through the point $(-2, -7)$.

Sol. The given equation of circle is

$$x^2 + y^2 - 8x + 6y - 5 = 0$$

Therefore, the centre of the circle is at $(4, -3)$. Since, the required circle is concentric with this circle, therefore, the centre of the required circle is also at $(4, -3)$. Since, the point $(-2, -7)$ lies on the circle, the distance of the centre from this point is the radius of the circle. Therefore, we get

$$r = \sqrt{(4+2)^2 + (-3+7)^2} = \sqrt{52}$$

Hence, the equation of the circle becomes

$$(x - 4)^2 + (y + 3)^2 = 52$$

or $\quad x^2 + y^2 - 8x + 6y - 27 = 0$

Aliter : Equation of concentric circle is

$$x^2 + y^2 - 8x + 6y + \lambda = 0 \quad \text{...(i)}$$

which pass through $(-2, -7)$, then

$$4 + 49 + 16 - 42 + \lambda = 0$$

$\therefore \quad \lambda = -27$

From Eq. (i), required circle is

$$x^2 + y^2 - 8x + 6y - 27 = 0$$

Example 5. A circle has radius 3 units and its centre lies on the line $y = x - 1$. Find the equation of the circle if it passes through (7, 3).

Sol. Let the centre of the circle be (h, k). Since, the centre lies on $y = x - 1$, we get

$$k = h - 1 \quad \text{...(i)}$$

Since, the circle passes through the point (7, 3), therefore the distance of the centre from this point is the radius r of the circle. We have,

$$r = \sqrt{(h-7)^2 + (k-3)^2}$$

or $\quad 3 = \sqrt{(h-7)^2 + (h-1-3)^2} \quad$ [from Eq. (i)]

$\Rightarrow \quad 9 = (h-7)^2 + (h-4)^2$

$\Rightarrow \quad h^2 - 11h + 28 = 0$

or $\quad (h-7)(h-4) = 0$

or $\quad h = 7$ and $h = 4$

For $h = 7$, we get $k = 6$ from Eq. (i)

and for $h = 4$, we get $k = 3$, from Eq. (i).

Hence, there are two circles which satisfy the given conditions. They are

$$(x-7)^2 + (y-6)^2 = 9$$

or $\quad x^2 + y^2 - 14x - 12y + 76 = 0$

and $\quad (x-4)^2 + (y-3)^2 = 9$

or $\quad x^2 + y^2 - 8x - 6y + 16 = 0$

Example 6. Find the area of an equilateral triangle inscribed in the circle

$$x^2 + y^2 + 2gx + 2fy + c = 0.$$

Sol. Given circle is

$$x^2 + y^2 + 2gx + 2fy + c = 0 \quad \text{...(i)}$$

Let O be the centre and ABC be an equilateral triangle inscribed in the circle Eq. (i).

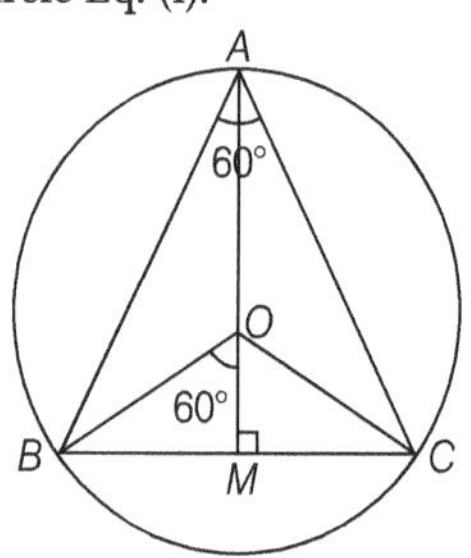

$$O \equiv (-g, -f)$$

and $\quad OA = OB = OC = \sqrt{g^2 + f^2 - c} \quad$ ...(ii)

In ΔBOM, $\sin 60^\circ = \dfrac{BM}{OB}$

$$\Rightarrow \quad BM = OB \sin 60^\circ = (OB)\frac{\sqrt{3}}{2}$$

$$\therefore \quad BC = 2BM = \sqrt{3}\,(OB) \qquad \text{...(iii)}$$

$$\therefore \quad \text{Area of } \Delta ABC = \frac{\sqrt{3}}{4}(BC)^2$$

$$= \frac{\sqrt{3}}{4} 3\,(OB)^2 \qquad \text{[from Eq. (iii)]}$$

$$= \frac{3\sqrt{3}}{4}(g^2 + f^2 - c) \text{ sq units.}$$

Example 7. Find the parametric form of the equation of the circle

$$x^2 + y^2 + px + py = 0.$$

Sol. Equation of the circle can be re-written in the form

$$\left(x + \frac{p}{2}\right)^2 + \left(y + \frac{p}{2}\right)^2 = \frac{p^2}{2}$$

Therefore, the parametric form of the equation of the given circle is

$$x = -\frac{p}{2} + \frac{p}{\sqrt{2}}\cos\theta = \frac{p}{2}(-1 + \sqrt{2}\cos\theta)$$

and

$$y = -\frac{p}{2} + \frac{p}{\sqrt{2}}\sin\theta = \frac{p}{2}(-1 + \sqrt{2}\sin\theta)$$

where, $0 \le \theta < 2\pi$.

Example 8. If the parametric of form of a circle is given by

(a) $x = -4 + 5\cos\theta$ and $y = -3 + 5\sin\theta$

(b) $x = a\cos\alpha + b\sin\alpha$ and $y = a\sin\alpha - b\cos\alpha$

find its cartesian form.

Sol. (a) The given equations are

$$x = -4 + 5\cos\theta$$

and $y = -3 + 5\sin\theta$

or $(x + 4) = 5\cos\theta$ ...(i)

and $(y + 3) = 5\sin\theta$ ...(ii)

Squaring and adding Eqs. (i) and (ii), then

$$(x + 4)^2 + (y + 3)^2 = 5^2$$

or $(x + 4)^2 + (y + 3)^2 = 25$

(b) The given equations are

$$x = a\cos\alpha + b\sin\alpha \qquad \text{...(iii)}$$

$$y = a\sin\alpha - b\cos\alpha \qquad \text{...(iv)}$$

Squaring and adding Eqs. (iii) and (iv), then

$$x^2 + y^2 = (a\cos\alpha + b\sin\alpha)^2 + (a\sin\alpha - b\cos\alpha)^2$$

$$\Rightarrow \quad x^2 + y^2 = a^2 + b^2$$

Locus of the Mid-point of the Chords of the Circle that Subtends an Angle of 2θ at its Centre

Let mid-point $M(x_1, y_1)$ and centre, radius of circle are (h,k), r respectively, then

$$\cos\theta = \frac{CM}{r} = \frac{\sqrt{(x_1 - h)^2 + (y_1 - k)^2}}{r}$$

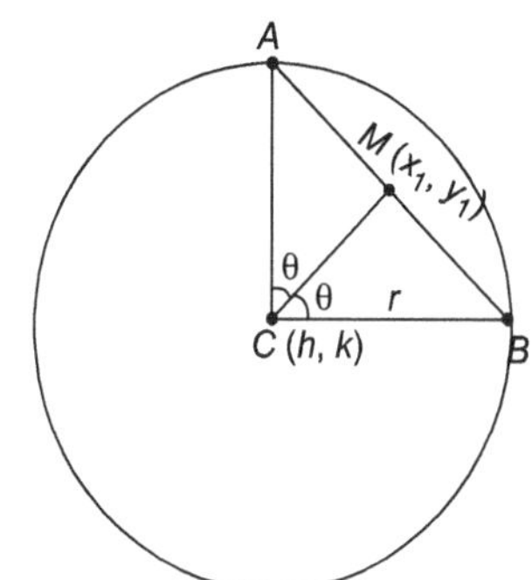

$\therefore$ Required locus is $\dfrac{(x - h)^2 + (y - k)^2 - r^2}{r^2} = -\sin^2\theta$

Remembering Method :

First make coefficient of x^2 = coefficient of $y^2 = 1$ and RHS of circle is zero, then $\dfrac{\text{LHS of circle}}{(\text{radius})^2} = -\sin^2\theta$

Example 9. Find the locus of mid-points of the chords of the circle $4x^2 + 4y^2 - 12x + 4y + 1 = 0$ that subtend an angle of $\dfrac{2\pi}{3}$ at its centre.

Sol. Here, $2\theta = \dfrac{2\pi}{3} \Rightarrow \theta = \dfrac{\pi}{3}$

Equation of circle can be written as

$$x^2 + y^2 - 3x + y + \frac{1}{4} = 0$$

$\therefore$ Required locus is

$$\frac{x^2 + y^2 - 3x + y + \frac{1}{4}}{\left(\sqrt{\frac{9}{4} + \frac{1}{4} - \frac{1}{4}}\right)^2} = -\sin^2\left(\frac{\pi}{3}\right) = -\frac{3}{4}$$

$$\Rightarrow \quad x^2 + y^2 - 3x + y + \frac{1}{4} = -\frac{27}{16}$$

or $16(x^2 + y^2) - 48x + 16y + 31 = 0$

Exercise for Session 1

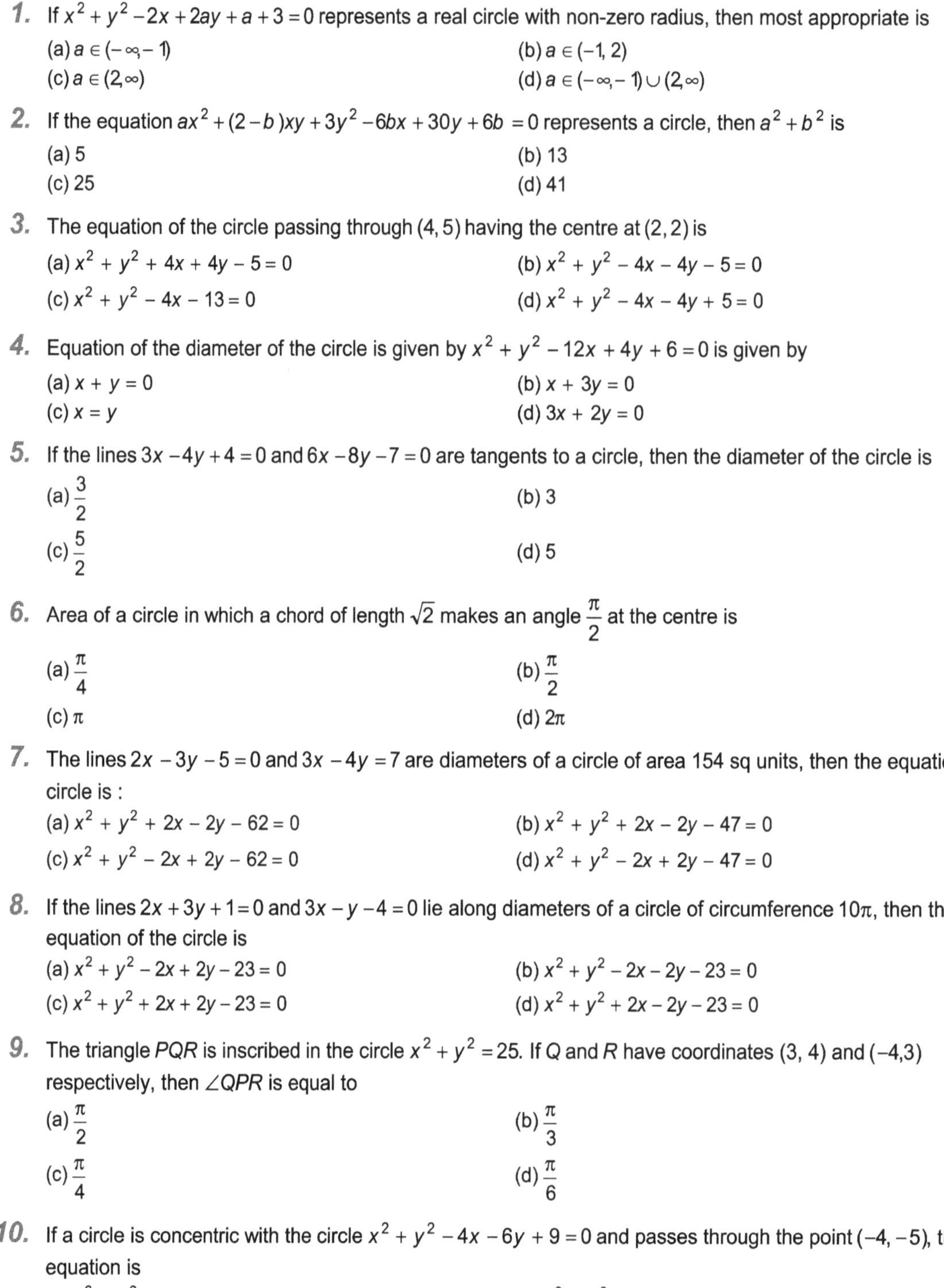

1. If $x^2 + y^2 - 2x + 2ay + a + 3 = 0$ represents a real circle with non-zero radius, then most appropriate is
(a) $a \in (-\infty, -1)$
(b) $a \in (-1, 2)$
(c) $a \in (2, \infty)$
(d) $a \in (-\infty, -1) \cup (2, \infty)$

2. If the equation $ax^2 + (2-b)xy + 3y^2 - 6bx + 30y + 6b = 0$ represents a circle, then $a^2 + b^2$ is
(a) 5
(b) 13
(c) 25
(d) 41

3. The equation of the circle passing through (4, 5) having the centre at (2, 2) is
(a) $x^2 + y^2 + 4x + 4y - 5 = 0$
(b) $x^2 + y^2 - 4x - 4y - 5 = 0$
(c) $x^2 + y^2 - 4x - 13 = 0$
(d) $x^2 + y^2 - 4x - 4y + 5 = 0$

4. Equation of the diameter of the circle is given by $x^2 + y^2 - 12x + 4y + 6 = 0$ is given by
(a) $x + y = 0$
(b) $x + 3y = 0$
(c) $x = y$
(d) $3x + 2y = 0$

5. If the lines $3x - 4y + 4 = 0$ and $6x - 8y - 7 = 0$ are tangents to a circle, then the diameter of the circle is
(a) $\frac{3}{2}$
(b) 3
(c) $\frac{5}{2}$
(d) 5

6. Area of a circle in which a chord of length $\sqrt{2}$ makes an angle $\frac{\pi}{2}$ at the centre is
(a) $\frac{\pi}{4}$
(b) $\frac{\pi}{2}$
(c) π
(d) 2π

7. The lines $2x - 3y - 5 = 0$ and $3x - 4y = 7$ are diameters of a circle of area 154 sq units, then the equation of the circle is :
(a) $x^2 + y^2 + 2x - 2y - 62 = 0$
(b) $x^2 + y^2 + 2x - 2y - 47 = 0$
(c) $x^2 + y^2 - 2x + 2y - 62 = 0$
(d) $x^2 + y^2 - 2x + 2y - 47 = 0$

8. If the lines $2x + 3y + 1 = 0$ and $3x - y - 4 = 0$ lie along diameters of a circle of circumference 10π, then the equation of the circle is
(a) $x^2 + y^2 - 2x + 2y - 23 = 0$
(b) $x^2 + y^2 - 2x - 2y - 23 = 0$
(c) $x^2 + y^2 + 2x + 2y - 23 = 0$
(d) $x^2 + y^2 + 2x - 2y - 23 = 0$

9. The triangle PQR is inscribed in the circle $x^2 + y^2 = 25$. If Q and R have coordinates (3, 4) and (–4,3) respectively, then $\angle QPR$ is equal to
(a) $\frac{\pi}{2}$
(b) $\frac{\pi}{3}$
(c) $\frac{\pi}{4}$
(d) $\frac{\pi}{6}$

10. If a circle is concentric with the circle $x^2 + y^2 - 4x - 6y + 9 = 0$ and passes through the point (–4, –5), then its equation is
(a) $x^2 + y^2 + 4x + 6y - 87 = 0$
(b) $x^2 + y^2 - 4x + 6y + 87 = 0$
(c) $x^2 + y^2 - 4x - 6y - 87 = 0$
(d) $x^2 + y^2 + 4x + 6y + 87 = 0$

11. Let AB be a chord of the circle $x^2 + y^2 = r^2$ subtending a right angle at the centre. Then, the locus of the centroid of the ΔPAB as P moves on the circle is

(a) a parabola
(b) a circle
(c) an ellipse
(d) a pair of straight lines

12. Let PQ and RS be tangents extremities of the diameter PR of a circle of radius r. If PS and RQ intersect at a point X on the circumference of the circle, then $2r$ equals

(a) $\sqrt{PQ \cdot RS}$
(b) $\dfrac{PQ + RS}{2}$
(c) $\dfrac{2PQ.RS}{PQ + RS}$
(d) $\sqrt{\dfrac{(PQ)^2 + (RS)^2}{2}}$

13. Find the centre and radius of the circle $5x^2 + 5y^2 + 4x - 8y = 16$.

14. Prove that the centres of the circles $x^2 + y^2 = 1, x^2 + y^2 + 6x - 2y - 1 = 0$ and $x^2 + y^2 - 12x + 4y = 1$ are collinear.

15. Find the equation of the circle whose centre is $(1, 2)$ and which passes through the point of intersection of $3x + y = 14$ and $2x + 5y = 18$.

16. Find the equation of the circle passing through the centre of the circle $x^2 + y^2 - 4x - 6y = 8$ and being concentric with the circle $x^2 + y^2 - 2x - 8y = 5$.

17. Prove that the locus of the centre of the circle $\frac{1}{2}(x^2 + y^2) + x\cos\theta + y\sin\theta - 4 = 0$ is $x^2 + y^2 = 1$.

18. Find the equation of the following curves in cartesian form. If the curve is a circle, then find its centre and radius

$x = -1 + 2\cos\alpha,\ y = 3 + 2\sin\alpha \qquad (0 \le \alpha < 2\pi)$

Session 2

Diametric Form of a Circle, Equation of Circle Passing Through Three Non-Collinear Points

Diametric Form of a Circle

Theorem : The equation of the circle on the line segment joining (x_1, y_1) and (x_2, y_2) as diameter is

$$(x - x_1)(x - x_2) + (y - y_1)(y - y_2) = 0.$$

Proof : Let $A(x_1, y_1)$ and $B(x_2, y_2)$ be the end points of a diameter and let $P(x, y)$ be any point on the circle

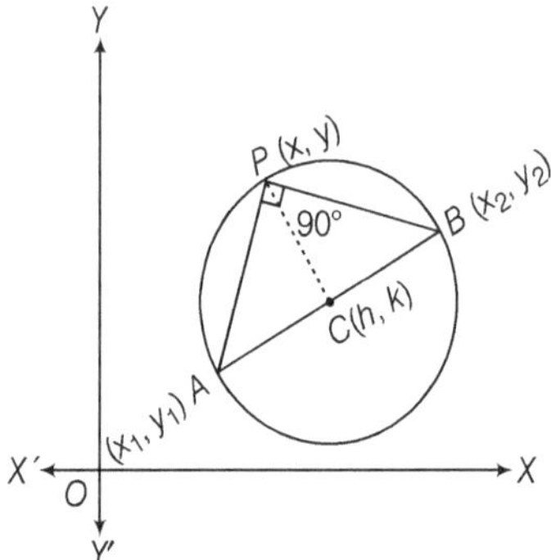

Now, Slope of $AP = \dfrac{y - y_1}{x - x_1}$

and Slope of $BP = \dfrac{y - y_2}{x - x_2}$

Since, $\angle APB = 90°$

$\therefore$ Slope of $AP \times$ Slope of $BP = -1$

$$\Rightarrow \quad \frac{(y - y_1)}{(x - x_1)} \times \frac{(y - y_2)}{(x - x_2)} = -1$$

$$\Rightarrow \quad (x - x_1)(x - x_2) + (y - y_1)(y - y_2) = 0$$

Remark

The diameteric form of a circle can also be written as

$$x^2 + y^2 - x(x_1 + x_2) - y(y_1 + y_2) + x_1x_2 + y_1y_2 = 0$$

or $x^2 + y^2 - x$ (sum of abscissae) $-y$ (sum of ordinates) + product of abscissae + product of ordinates $= 0$

Example 10. Find the equation of the circle the end points of whose diameter are the centres of the circles $x^2 + y^2 + 6x - 14y = 1$ and $x^2 + y^2 - 4x + 10y = 2$.

Sol. The centres of the given circles

$$x^2 + y^2 + 6x - 14y - 1 = 0$$

and $x^2 + y^2 - 4x + 10y - 2 = 0$ are $(-3, 7)$ and $(2, -5)$, respectively.

According to the question, the points $(-3, 7)$ and $(2, -5)$ are the extremities of the diameter of required circle.

Hence, equation of circle is

$$(x + 3)(x - 2) + (y - 7)(y + 5) = 0$$

$$\Rightarrow \quad x^2 + y^2 + x - 2y - 41 = 0$$

Example 11. The sides of a square are $x = 2, x = 3, y = 1$ and $y = 2$. Find the equation of the circle drawn on the diagonals of the square as its diameter.

Sol. Let *ABCD* be a square and equation of its sides *AB*, *BC*, *CD* and *DA* are $y = 1$, $x = 3$, $y = 2$, and $x = 2$, respectively.

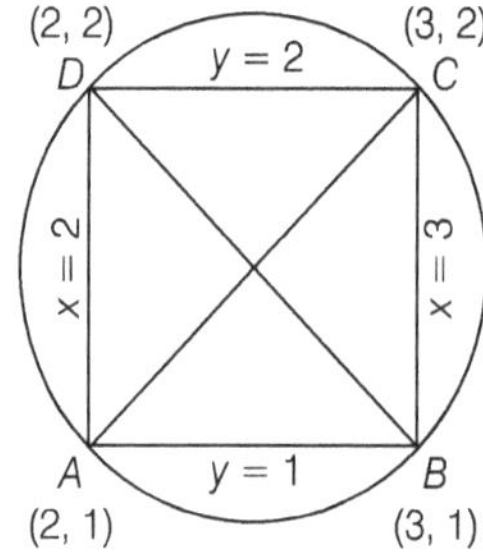

Then, $A \equiv (2, 1)$, $B \equiv (3, 1)$, $C \equiv (3, 2)$ and $D \equiv (2, 2)$

Since, diagonals of squares are the diameters of the circle, then equation of circle is

$$(x - 2)(x - 3) + (y - 1)(y - 2) = 0$$

$$\Rightarrow \quad x^2 + y^2 - 5x - 3y + 8 = 0 \text{ (If } AC \text{ as diameter).}$$

Example 12. The abscissae of two points *A* and *B* are the roots of the equation $x^2 + 2ax - b^2 = 0$ and their ordinates are the roots of the equation $x^2 + 2px - q^2 = 0$. Find the equation and the radius of the circle with *AB* as diameter.

Sol. Given equations are

$$x^2 + 2ax - b^2 = 0 \quad \text{...(i)}$$

and $\qquad x^2 + 2px - q^2 = 0 \qquad$ ...(ii)

Let the roots of the Eq. (i) be α and β and those of Eq. (ii) be γ and δ. Then,

$$\left.\begin{aligned}\alpha + \beta &= -2a\\ \alpha\beta &= -b^2\end{aligned}\right\} \text{ and } \left.\begin{aligned}\gamma + \delta &= -2p\\ \gamma\delta &= -q^2\end{aligned}\right\}$$

Let $A \equiv (\alpha, \gamma)$ and $B \equiv (\beta, \delta)$.

Now, equation of circle whose diameter is AB will be

$$(x - \alpha)(x - \beta) + (y - \gamma)(y - \delta) = 0$$

$$\Rightarrow \quad x^2 + y^2 - (\alpha + \beta)x - (\gamma + \delta)y + \alpha\beta + \gamma\delta = 0$$

$$\Rightarrow \quad x^2 + y^2 + 2ax + 2py - b^2 - q^2 = 0$$

and $\qquad \text{radius} = \sqrt{(a^2 + p^2 + b^2 + q^2)}$

Equation of Circle Passing Through Three Non-Collinear Points

Let the equation of circle be

$$x^2 + y^2 + 2gx + 2fy + c = 0 \qquad \text{...(i)}$$

If three points $(x_1, y_1), (x_2, y_2), (x_3, y_3)$ lie on the circle Eq. (i), their coordinates must satisfy its equation. Hence, solving equations

$$x_1^2 + y_1^2 + 2gx_1 + 2fy_1 + c = 0, \qquad \text{...(ii)}$$

$$x_2^2 + y_2^2 + 2gx_2 + 2fy_2 + c = 0, \qquad \text{...(iii)}$$

and $\qquad x_3^2 + y_3^2 + 2gx_3 + 2fy_3 + c = 0, \qquad$ ...(iv)

g, f, c are obtained from Eqs. (ii), (iii) and (iv). Then, to find the circle Eq. (i).

Aliter : Eliminate g, f, c from Eqs. (i), (ii), (iii) and (iv) with the help of determinant

$$\begin{vmatrix} x^2 + y^2 & x & y & 1 \\ x_1^2 + y_1^2 & x_1 & y_1 & 1 \\ x_2^2 + y_2^2 & x_2 & y_2 & 1 \\ x_3^2 + y_3^2 & x_3 & y_3 & 1 \end{vmatrix} = 0$$

which is the required equation of circle

Applying $R_1 \to R_1 - R_4, R_2 \to R_2 - R_4$ and $R_3 \to R_3 - R_4$ then, we get

$$\begin{vmatrix} x^2 + y^2 - x_3^2 - y_3^2 & x - x_3 & y - y_3 & 0 \\ x_1^2 + y_1^2 - x_3^2 - y_3^2 & x_1 - x_3 & y_1 - y_3 & 0 \\ x_2^2 + y_2^2 - x_3^2 - y_3^2 & x_2 - x_3 & y_2 - y_3 & 0 \\ x_3^2 + y_3^2 & x_3 & y_3 & 1 \end{vmatrix} = 0$$

i.e.

$$\begin{vmatrix} x^2 + y^2 - x_3^2 - y_3^2 & x - x_3 & y - y_3 \\ x_1^2 + y_1^2 - x_3^2 - y_3^2 & x_1 - x_3 & y_1 - y_3 \\ x_2^2 + y_2^2 - x_3^2 - y_3^2 & x_2 - x_3 & y_2 - y_3 \end{vmatrix} = 0$$

Remarks

1. **Cyclic quadrilateral** If all four vertices of a quadrilateral lie on a circle, then the quadrilateral is called a cyclic quadrilateral. The four vertices are said to be concyclic.
2. **Concyclic points** If A, B, C, D are concyclic, then

$$OA \cdot OD = OB \cdot OC$$

where, O' be the centre of the circle.

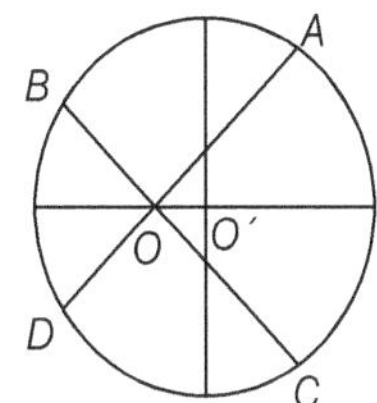

Example 13. Find the equation of the circle which passes through the points $(4, 1), (6, 5)$ and has its centre on the line $4x + y = 16$.

Sol. Let the equation of circle be

$$x^2 + y^2 + 2gx + 2fy + c = 0 \qquad \text{...(i)}$$

Since, the centre of Eq. (i) i.e. $(-g, -f)$ lies on $4x + y = 16$

then, $\qquad -4g - f = 16$

or $\qquad 4g + f + 16 = 0 \qquad$ ...(ii)

Since, the points $(4, 1)$ and $(6, 5)$ lie on circle $x^2 + y^2 + 2gx + 2fy + c = 0$, we get the equations

$$16 + 1 + 8g + 2f + c = 0$$

or $\qquad 17 + 8g + 2f + c = 0 \qquad$ ...(iii)

and $\qquad 36 + 25 + 12g + 10f + c = 0$

or $\qquad 61 + 12g + 10f + c = 0 \qquad$ ...(iv)

Subtracting Eq. (iii) from Eq. (iv), then

$$44 + 4g + 8f = 0 \qquad \text{...(v)}$$

Solving Eqs. (ii) and (v), we get

$$f = -4 \text{ and } g = -3$$

Now, from Eq. (iii), $17 - 24 - 8 + c = 0$

$\Rightarrow \qquad c = 15$

Hence, the equation of circle becomes

$$x^2 + y^2 - 6x - 8y + 15 = 0$$

Example 14. Find the equation of the circle passing through the three non-collinear points $(1, 1), (2, -1)$ and $(3, 2)$.

Sol. Let the equation of circle be

$$x^2 + y^2 + 2gx + 2fy + c = 0 \qquad \text{...(i)}$$

Since, the three given points lie on circle Eq. (i), we get

$$1 + 1 + 2g + 2f + c = 0$$

or $\quad 2g + 2f + c + 2 = 0 \quad$ ...(ii)

$\Rightarrow \quad 4 + 1 + 4g - 2f + c = 0$

or $\quad 4g - 2f + c + 5 = 0 \quad$ ...(iii)

$\Rightarrow \quad 9 + 4 + 6g + 4f + c = 0$

or $\quad 6g + 4f + c + 13 = 0 \quad$ ...(iv)

Subtracting Eq. (ii) from Eq. (iii) and subtracting Eq. (iii) from Eq. (iv), then

$$2g - 4f + 3 = 0 \quad \text{...(v)}$$

and $\quad 2g + 6f + 8 = 0 \quad$ ...(vi)

Solving Eq. (v) and Eq. (vi), we get

$$f = -\frac{1}{2} \text{ and } g = -\frac{5}{2}$$

Now, from Eq. (ii), $-5 - 1 + c + 2 = 0$

$\therefore \quad c = 4$

Hence, from Eq. (i), equation of circle is

$$x^2 + y^2 - 5x - y + 4 = 0$$

Aliter I Equation of circle passing through three points $(1, 1), (2, -1)$ and $(3, 2)$ is

$$\begin{vmatrix} x^2 + y^2 & x & y & 1 \\ 1^2 + 1^2 & 1 & 1 & 1 \\ 2^2 + (-1)^2 & 2 & -1 & 1 \\ 3^2 + 2^2 & 3 & 2 & 1 \end{vmatrix} = 0$$

$$\Rightarrow \quad \begin{vmatrix} x^2 + y^2 & x & y & 1 \\ 2 & 1 & 1 & 1 \\ 5 & 2 & -1 & 1 \\ 13 & 3 & 2 & 1 \end{vmatrix} = 0$$

Applying $R_1 \to R_1 - R_2, R_3 \to R_3 - R_2$ and $R_4 \to R_4 - R_2$, then

$$\Rightarrow \quad \begin{vmatrix} x^2 + y^2 - 2 & x - 1 & y - 1 & 0 \\ 2 & 1 & 1 & 1 \\ 3 & 1 & -2 & 0 \\ 11 & 2 & 1 & 0 \end{vmatrix} = 0$$

Expand with respect to fourth column, then

$$\begin{vmatrix} x^2 + y^2 - 2 & x - 1 & y - 1 \\ 3 & 1 & -2 \\ 11 & 2 & 1 \end{vmatrix} = 0$$

Expand with respect to first now, then

$$(x^2 + y^2 - 2)(5) - (x - 1)(25) + (y - 1)(-5) = 0$$

or $\quad x^2 + y^2 - 5x - y + 4 = 0$

Aliter II The centre of the circumcircle is the point of intersection of the right bisectors of the sides of the triangle and the radius is the distance of the circumcentre from any of the vertices of the triangle.

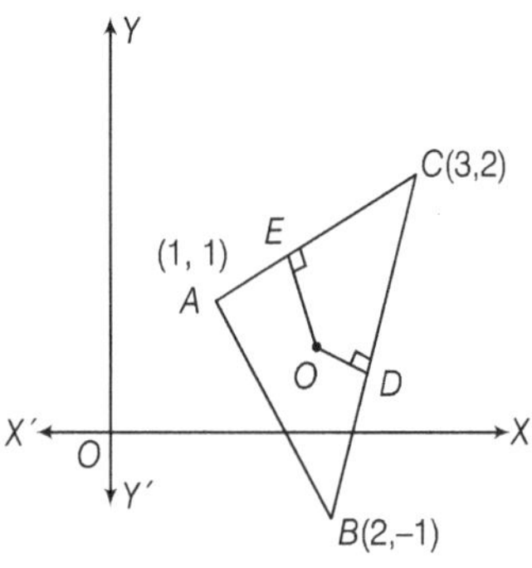

Let D and E are the mid-points of BC and CA, then

$$D \equiv \left(\frac{5}{2}, \frac{1}{2}\right) \text{ and } E \equiv \left(2, \frac{3}{2}\right)$$

Slope of $BC = \dfrac{2 - (-1)}{3 - 2} = 3$

$\therefore \quad$ Slope of $OD = -\dfrac{1}{3}$

$\therefore$ Equation of OD, $y - \dfrac{1}{2} = -\dfrac{1}{3}\left(x - \dfrac{5}{2}\right)$

$\Rightarrow \quad 6y - 3 = -2x + 5$

$\therefore \quad 2x + 6y - 8 = 0 \quad$ ...(i)

or $\quad x + 3y - 4 = 0$

and $\quad$ Slope of $CA = \dfrac{1 - 2}{1 - 3} = \dfrac{1}{2}$

$\therefore \quad$ Slope of $OE = -2$

$\therefore$ Equation of OE,

$$y - \frac{3}{2} = -2(x - 2)$$

$\Rightarrow \quad 2y - 3 = -4x + 8$

$\Rightarrow \quad 4x + 2y - 11 = 0 \quad$ ...(ii)

Solving Eq. (i) and Eq. (ii), we get $x = \dfrac{5}{2}$ and $y = \dfrac{1}{2}$

$\therefore$ Circumcentre is $\left(\dfrac{5}{2}, \dfrac{1}{2}\right)$ and radius

$$OC = \sqrt{\left(3 - \frac{5}{2}\right)^2 + \left(2 - \frac{1}{2}\right)^2} = \sqrt{\frac{5}{2}}$$

$\therefore$ Equation of circle is

$$(x - 5/2)^2 + (y - 1/2)^2 = 5/2$$

$\Rightarrow \quad x^2 + y^2 - 5x - y + 4 = 0$

Example 15. Show that the four points $(1, 0), (2, -7), (8, 1)$ and $(9, -6)$ are concyclic.

Sol. Since, the given four points are concyclic, we are to show that they lie on a circle. Let the general equation of circle is

$$x^2 + y^2 + 2gx + 2fy + c = 0 \quad \text{...(i)}$$

has three parameters, it is sufficient to obtain the equation of the circle passing through any three of these points. For concyclic, the fourth point should lie on this circle.

Let three points $A(1, 0)$, $B(2, -7)$ and $D(8, 1)$ lie on Eq. (i), then

$$1 + 0 + 2g + 0 + c = 0 \text{ or } 1 + 2g + c = 0 \quad \text{...(ii)}$$

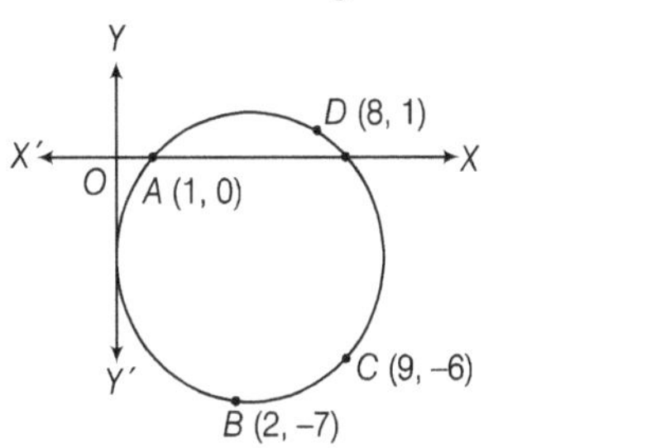

$$(2)^2 + (-7)^2 + 2g(2) + 2f(-7) + c = 0$$

or $$53 + 4g - 14f + c = 0 \quad \text{...(iii)}$$

and $$(8)^2 + (1)^2 + 2g(8) + 2f(1) + c = 0$$

$\Rightarrow$ $$65 + 16g + 2f + c = 0 \quad \text{...(iv)}$$

Now, subtracting Eq. (ii) from Eq. (iii), we get

$$52 + 2g - 14f = 0$$

or $$26 + g - 7f = 0 \quad \text{...(v)}$$

and subtracting Eq. (iii) from Eq. (iv), we get

$$12 + 12g + 16f = 0$$

$\Rightarrow$ $$3 + 3g + 4f = 0 \quad \text{...(vi)}$$

Solving Eq. (v) and Eq. (vi), we get

$$g = -5 \text{ and } f = 3$$

From Eq. (ii), $1 - 10 + c = 0$

$\therefore$ $c = 9$

Therefore, equation of circle passing through these points is

$$x^2 + y^2 - 10x + 6y + 9 = 0$$

Substituting the fourth point in the equation of this circle, we get

$$(9)^2 + (-6)^2 - 10(9) + 6(-6) + 9 = 0$$

Hence, the point $C(9, -6)$ lies on the circle, that is, the four points are concyclic.

Exercise for Session 2

1. If the line $x + 2\lambda y + 7 = 0$ is a diameter of the circle $x^2 + y^2 - 6x + 2y = 0$, then the value of λ is

(a) 1
(b) 3
(c) 5
(d) 7

2. If one end of a diameter of the circle $2x^2 + 2y^2 - 4x - 8y + 2 = 0$ is $(-1, 2)$, then the other end of the diameter is

(a) (2, 1)
(b) (3, 2)
(c) (4, 3)
(d) (5, 4)

3. If a circle passes through the points (0,0), (a, 0) and (0, b), then centre of the circle is

(a) (a, b)
(b) $\left(\frac{a}{2}, \frac{b}{2}\right)$
(c) $\left(\frac{a}{2}, \frac{b}{4}\right)$
(d) $\left(\frac{a}{4}, \frac{b}{2}\right)$

4. A circle passes through the points (–1, 3) and (5, 11) and its radius is 5. Then, its centre is

(a) (–5, 0)
(b) (–5, 7)
(c) (2, 7)
(d) (5, 0)

5. The radius of the circle, having centre at (2, 1) whose one of the chord is a diameter of the circle $x^2 + y^2 - 2x - 6y + 6 = 0$ is

(a) 3
(b) 2
(c) 1
(d) $\sqrt{3}$

6. The centre of the circle inscribed in the square formed by the lines $x^2 - 8x + 12 = 0$ and $y^2 - 14y + 45 = 0$ is

(a) (4, 7)
(b) (7, 4)
(c) (9, 4)
(d) (4, 9)

7. $ABCD$ is a square whose side is a. The equation of the circle circumscribing the square, taking AB and AD as the axes of reference is
(a) $x^2 + y^2 + ax + ay = 0$
(b) $x^2 + y^2 - ax + ay = 0$
(c) $x^2 + y^2 - ax - ay = 0$
(d) $x^2 + y^2 + ax - ay = 0$

8. The locus of the centre of the circle for which one end of the diameter is (3, 3) while the other end lies on the line $x + y = 4$ is
(a) $x + y = 3$
(b) $x + y = 5$
(c) $x + y = 7$
(d) $x + y = 9$

9. The equation of the circle which passes through (1, 0) and (0, 1) and has its radius as small as possible is
(a) $x^2 + y^2 + x + y = 0$
(b) $x^2 + y^2 - x + y = 0$
(c) $x^2 + y^2 + x - y = 0$
(d) $x^2 + y^2 - x - y = 0$

10. If the points $(2, 0), (0, 1), (4, 5)$ and $(0, c)$ are concyclic, then the value of c is
(a) 1
(b) −1
(c) $\frac{14}{3}$
(d) $-\frac{14}{3}$

11. The point on a circle nearest to the point $P(2,1)$ is at a distance of 4 units and farthest point is (6, 5), then the centre of the circle is
(a) $(3+\sqrt{2}, 2+\sqrt{2})$
(b) $(2+\sqrt{2}, 3+\sqrt{2})$
(c) $(4+\sqrt{2}, 3+\sqrt{2})$
(d) $(3+\sqrt{2}, 4+\sqrt{2})$

12. The intercept on the line $y = x$ by the circle $x^2 + y^2 - 2x = 0$ is AB. Equation of the circle on AB as a diameter is
(a) $x^2 + y^2 - x - y = 0$
(b) $x^2 + y^2 - x + y = 0$
(c) $x^2 + y^2 + x + y = 0$
(d) $x^2 + y^2 + x - y = 0$

13. Find the equation of the circle, the end points of whose diameter are $(2, -3)$ and $(-2, 4)$. Find the centre and radius.

14. If (4, 1) be an extremity of a diameter of the circle $x^2 + y^2 - 2x + 6y - 15 = 0$, find the coordinates of the other extremity of the diameter.

15. Find the equation of the circle drawn on the diagonal of the rectangle as its diameter whose sides are $x = 4$, $x = -2$, $y = 5$ and $y = -2$.

16. Find the equation of the circle which passes through the points $(1, 1), (2, 2)$ and whose radius is 1.

17. Find the equation of the circle which passes through the points $(3, 4), (3, -6)$ and $(1, 2)$.

Session 3

Intercepts Made on the Axes by a Circle, Different Forms of the Equations of a Circle, Position of a Point with Respect to Circle, Maximum and Minimum Distance of a Point from the Circle

Intercepts Made on the Axes by a Circle

Let the circle $x^2 + y^2 + 2gx + 2fy + c = 0$ ...(i)

Length of intercepts on X-axis and Y-axis are

$$|AB| = |x_2 - x_1| \text{ and } |CD| = |y_2 - y_1| \text{ respectively.}$$

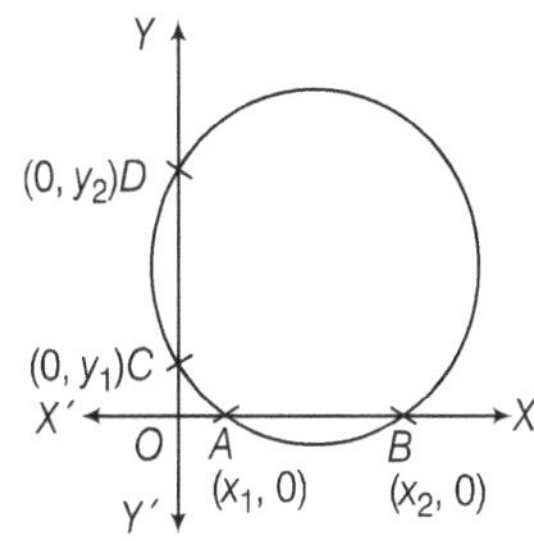

The circle intersects the X-axis, when $y = 0$

then $$x^2 + 2gx + c = 0$$

Since, the circle intersects the X-axis at $A(x_1, 0)$ and $B(x_2, 0)$

then, $$x_1 + x_2 = -2g, x_1x_2 = c$$

$$\therefore \quad |AB| = |x_2 - x_1| = \sqrt{(x_2 + x_1)^2 - 4x_1x_2}$$

$$= 2\sqrt{(g^2 - c)}$$

and the circle intersects the Y-axis, when $x = 0$, then

$$y^2 + 2fy + c = 0$$

Since, the circle intersects the Y-axis at $C(0, y_1)$ and $D(0, y_2)$

then, $$y_1 + y_2 = -2f, y_1y_2 = c$$

$$\therefore \quad |CD| = |y_2 - y_1| = \sqrt{(y_2 + y_1)^2 - 4y_2y_1}$$

$$= 2\sqrt{(f^2 - c)}$$

Remarks

1. Intercepts are always positive.
2. If circle touches X-axis, then $|AB| = 0$

   $\therefore \quad c = g^2$

   and if circle touches Y-axis, then $|CD| = 0$

   $\therefore \quad c = f^2$
3. If circle touches both axes, then $|AB| = 0 = |CD|$

   $\therefore \quad c = g^2 = f^2$

Example 16. Find the equation of the circle whose diameter is the line joining the points $(-4, 3)$ and $(12, -1)$. Find also the intercept made by it on Y-axis.

Sol. Equation of circle having $(-4, 3)$ and $(12, -1)$ as the ends of a diameter is

$$(x + 4)(x - 12) + (y - 3)(y + 1) = 0$$

$$\Rightarrow \quad x^2 + y^2 - 8x - 2y - 51 = 0 \quad \text{...(i)}$$

Comparing Eq. (i) with standard equation of circle

$$x^2 + y^2 + 2gx + 2fy + c = 0$$

then, $$g = -4, f = -1, c = -51$$

$\therefore$ Intercept on Y-axis $= 2\sqrt{(f^2 - c)} = 2\sqrt{(1 + 51)} = 4\sqrt{13}$.

Different Forms of the Equations of a Circle

(i) When the circle passes through the origin $(0, 0)$ and has intercepts 2α and 2β on the X-axis and Y-axis, respectively

Here, $$OA = 2\alpha, OB = 2\beta$$

then, $$OM = \alpha \quad \text{and} \quad ON = \beta$$

Centre of the circle is $C(\alpha, \beta)$ and radius

$$OC = \sqrt{(\alpha^2 + \beta^2)}$$

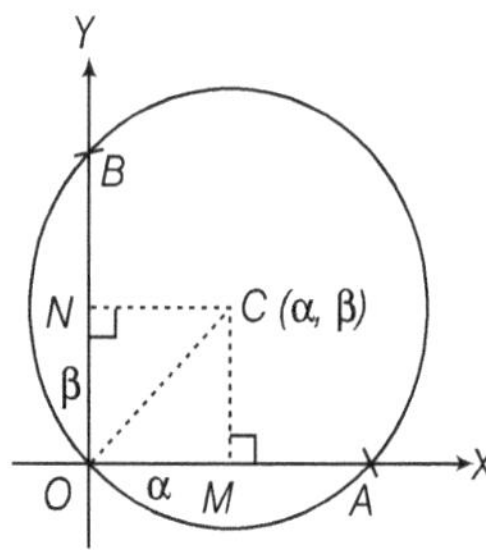

then, equation of circle is

$$(x-\alpha)^2+(y-\beta)^2=\alpha^2+\beta^2$$

or $$x^2+y^2-2\alpha x-2\beta y=0$$

Remark

If a circle is passing through origin, then constant term is absent

i.e. $x^2+y^2+2gx+2fy=0$

(ii) When the circle touches *X*-axis

Let (α, β) be the centre of the circle, then radius $=|\beta|$

$\therefore$ Equation of circle is

$$(x-\alpha)^2+(y-\beta)^2=\beta^2$$

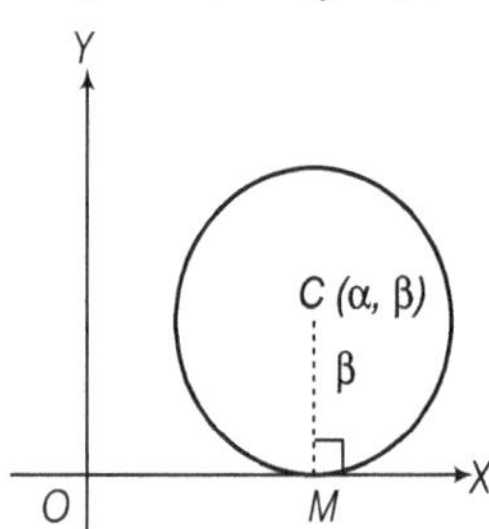

$\Rightarrow$ $$x^2+y^2-2\alpha x-2\beta y+\alpha^2=0$$

Remark

If the circle $x^2+y^2+2gx+2fy+c=0$ touches the *X*-axis, then

$$|-f|=\sqrt{g^2+f^2-c} \quad \text{or} \quad c=g^2$$

(iii) When the circle touches *Y*-axis

Let (α, β) be the centre of the circle, then

radius $=|\alpha|$

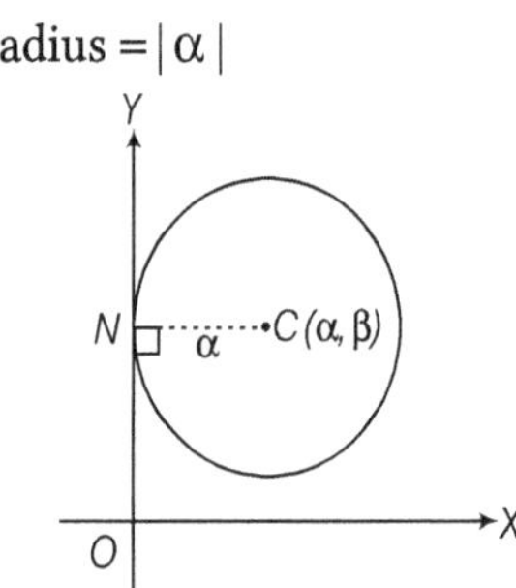

$\therefore$ Equation of circle is

$$(x-\alpha)^2+(y-\beta)^2=\alpha^2$$

$$\Rightarrow \quad x^2+y^2-2\alpha x-2\beta y+\beta^2=0$$

Remark

If the circle $x^2+y^2+2gx+2fy+c=0$ touches the *Y*-axis, then

$$|-g|=\sqrt{g^2+f^2-c}$$

or $$c=f^2$$

(iv) When the circle touches both axes

Here, $|OM|=|ON|$

Since, length of tangents are equal from any point on circle.

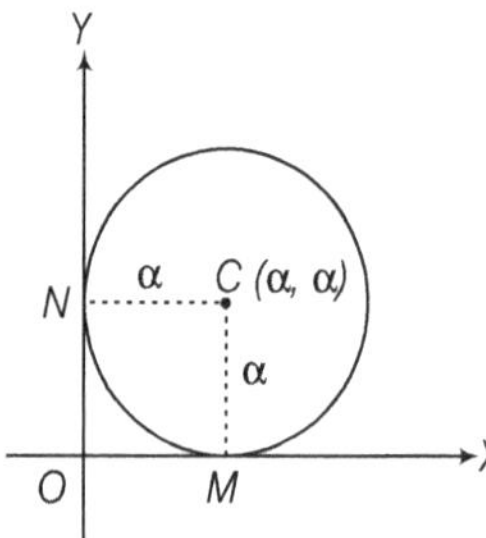

$\therefore$ Let centre is (α, α) also radius $=\alpha$

$\therefore$ Equation of circle is $(x-\alpha)^2+(y-\alpha)^2=\alpha^2$

$$\Rightarrow \quad x^2+y^2-2\alpha x-2\alpha y+\alpha^2=0$$

Remarks

1. If the circle $x^2+y^2+2gx+2fy+c=0$ touches both the axes, then $|-g|=|-f|=\sqrt{g^2+f^2-c}$

   $\therefore$ $c=g^2=f^2$

   $\therefore$ $g=f=\pm\sqrt{c}$

   $\therefore$ Equation of circle is

   $$x^2+y^2\pm 2\sqrt{c}\,x\pm 2\sqrt{c}\,y+c=0$$

   $\Rightarrow$ $$(x\pm\sqrt{c})^2+(y\pm\sqrt{c})^2=c^2$$

2. If $\alpha>0$, then centres for I, II, III and IV quadrants are $(\alpha, \alpha), (-\alpha, \alpha), (-\alpha, -\alpha)$ and $(\alpha, -\alpha)$, respectively.

   Then, equation of circles in these quadrants are

   $$(x-\alpha)^2+(y-\alpha)^2=\alpha^2, (x+\alpha)^2+(y-\alpha)^2=\alpha^2,$$

   $(x+\alpha)^2+(y+\alpha)^2=\alpha^2$ and $(x-\alpha)^2+(y+\alpha)^2=\alpha^2$, respectively.

(v) When the circle touches *X*-axis and cut-off intercepts on *Y*-axis of length $2l$

Let centre be (α, β)

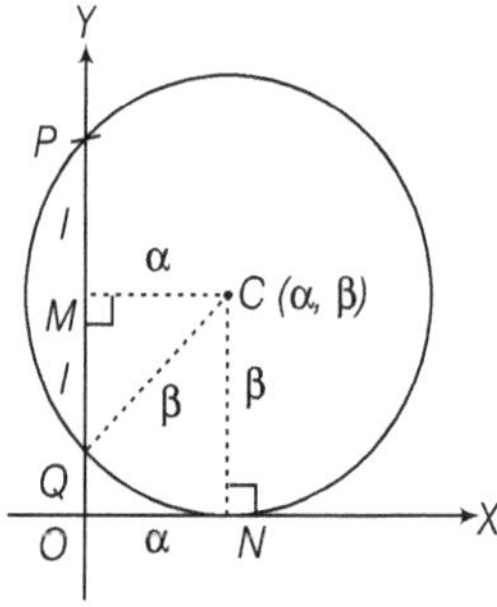

$\therefore$ radius $= \beta$

$$CQ = CN = \beta$$

In $\Delta CMQ, \beta^2 = \alpha^2 + l^2, \alpha = \sqrt{(\beta^2 - l^2)}$ (for I quadrant)

$\therefore$ Equation of circle is

$$[x - \sqrt{(\beta^2 - l^2)}]^2 + (y - \beta)^2 = \beta^2$$

Remark

$\because$ Length of intercepts on Y-axis of the circle

$x^2 + y^2 + 2gx + 2fy + c = 0$ is $2l = 2\sqrt{(f^2 - c)}$

i.e. $l^2 = f^2 - c$

and also circle touches X-axis

then, $c = g^2$

$\therefore$ $l^2 = f^2 - g^2$ or $l^2 = (-f)^2 - (-g)^2$

$\therefore$ Locus of centre is $y^2 - x^2 = l^2$ (rectangular hyperbola)

(vi) When the circle touches Y-axis and cut-off intercept on X-axis of length $2k$

Let centre be (α, β)

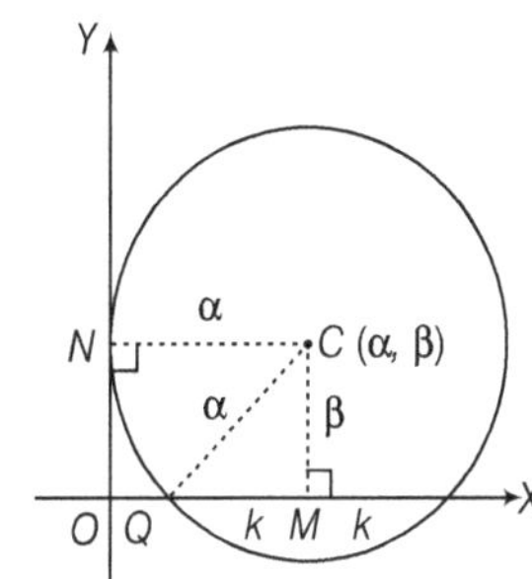

$\therefore$ radius $= \alpha$

$$CN = CQ = \alpha$$

In ΔCMQ, $\alpha^2 = \beta^2 + k^2$

$$\beta = \sqrt{(\alpha^2 - k^2)} \quad \text{(for I quadrant)}$$

$\therefore$ Equation of circle is

$$(x - \alpha)^2 + (y - \sqrt{\alpha^2 - k^2})^2 = \alpha^2$$

Remarks

$\because$ Length of intercept on X-axis of the circle

$x^2 + y^2 + 2gx + 2fy + c = 0$ is $2k = 2\sqrt{(g^2 - c)}$

i.e. $k^2 = g^2 - c$

and also circle touches Y-axis

then, $c = f^2$

$\therefore$ $k^2 = g^2 - f^2 = (-g)^2 - (-f)^2$

$\therefore$ Locus of centre is $x^2 - y^2 = k^2$ (rectangular hyperbola)

(vii) When the circle cut-off intercepts on X-axis and Y-axis of lengths $2l$ and $2k$ and not passing through origin

Let centre be (α, β)

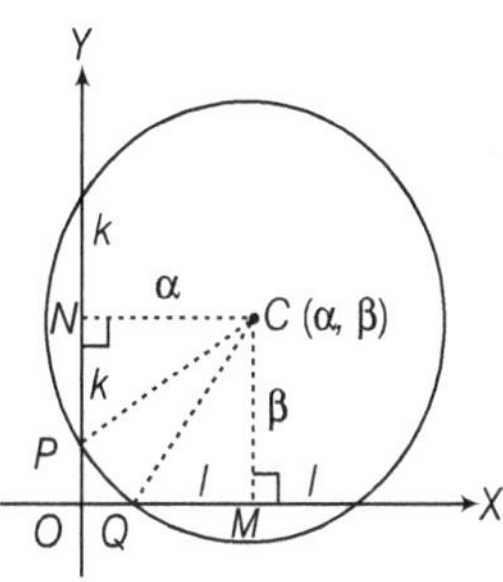

$\therefore$ radius $= CP = CQ = \lambda$ (say)

$$(CP)^2 = (CQ)^2 = \lambda^2$$

$$\alpha^2 + k^2 = \beta^2 + l^2 = \lambda^2$$

$\therefore$ $\alpha = \sqrt{\lambda^2 - k^2}$ and $\beta = \sqrt{\lambda^2 - l^2}$

$\therefore$ Equation of circle is (for I quadrant)

$$(x - \sqrt{\lambda^2 - k^2})^2 + (y - \sqrt{\lambda^2 - l^2})^2 = \lambda^2$$

(viii) When the circle passes through the origin and centre lies on X-axis

Let centre of circle be $C(a, 0)$

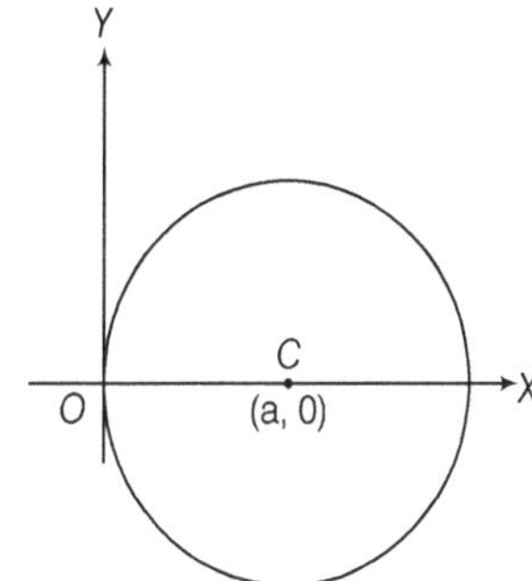

$\therefore$ radius $= a$

$\therefore$ Equation of circle is

$$(x - a)^2 + (y - 0)^2 = a^2 \text{ or } x^2 + y^2 - 2ax = 0$$

(ix) When the circle passes through origin and centre lies on Y-axis

Let centre of circle be $C(0, a)$

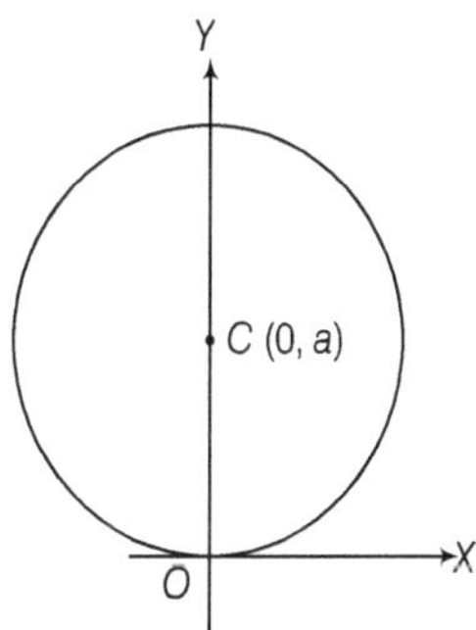

$\therefore$ radius $= a$

$\therefore$ Equation of circle is

$$(x-0)^2 + (y-a)^2 = a^2$$

or $$x^2 + y^2 - 2ay = 0$$

Example 17. Find the equation of the circle which touches the axis of y at a distance of 4 units from the origin and cuts the intercept of 6 units from the axis of x.

Sol. $\because$ $CM = NO = 4$

In ΔPCM, $(PC)^2 = (3)^2 + (4)^2$

$\therefore$ $PC = 5$

radius of circle $= 5$

$\therefore$ $NC = 5$

Centre of circle is (5, 4).

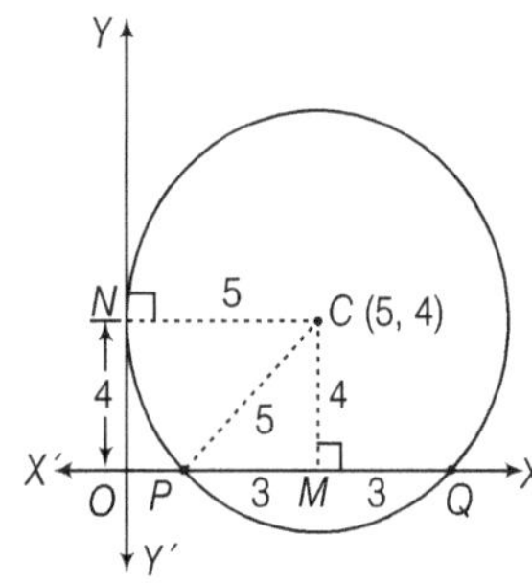

$\therefore$ Equation of circle, if centre in I quadrant

$$(x-5)^2 + (y-4)^2 = 25$$

If centre in II, III and IV quadrant, then equations are

$$(x+5)^2 + (y-4)^2 = 25,$$

$$(x+5)^2 + (y+4)^2 = 25$$

and $$(x-5)^2 + (y+4)^2 = 25$$

Hence, there are 4 circles which satisfy the given conditions. They are

$$(x \pm 5)^2 + (y \pm 4)^2 = 25$$

or $$x^2 + y^2 \pm 10x \pm 8y + 16 = 0$$

Aliter : Let the equation of the circle be

$$x^2 + y^2 + 2gx + 2fy + c = 0 \quad \text{...(i)}$$

Since, the circle touches the Y-axis

$\therefore$ $c = f^2$

or $f = \pm\sqrt{c}$

Also given the circle makes an intercept of 6 units along X-axis. Therefore,

$$2\sqrt{g^2 - c} = 6$$

or $g^2 - c = 9$

or $g = \pm\sqrt{(c+9)}$

From Eq. (i), the equation of circle can be written as

$$x^2 + y^2 \pm 2\sqrt{(c+9)}\, x \pm 2\sqrt{c}y + c = 0$$

The circle touches the Y-axis

$\therefore$ $x = 0$

$\therefore$ $y^2 \pm 2\sqrt{c}y + c = 0$

or $(y \pm \sqrt{c})^2 = 0$

$\therefore$ $y \pm \sqrt{c} = 0$

$y = \mp\sqrt{c}$

Since, the circle touches the Y-axis at a distance of 4 units from the origin, we have

$$y = \mp\sqrt{c} = 4$$

or $c = 16$

therefore, $f = \pm\sqrt{c} = \pm 4$

and $g = \pm\sqrt{c+9} = \pm\sqrt{16+9} = \pm 5$

Hence, there are 4 circles which satisfy the given conditions. They are

$$x^2 + y^2 \pm 10x \pm 8y + 16 = 0$$

Example 18. Find the equation of the circle which passes through the origin and makes intercepts of length a and b on the X and Y axes, respectively.

Sol. Let the equation of the circle be

$$x^2 + y^2 + 2gx + 2fy + c = 0 \quad \text{...(i)}$$

Since, the circle passes through the origin, we get $c = 0$ and given the intercepts on X and Y axes are a and b

then, $2\sqrt{(g^2 - c)} = a$

or $2\sqrt{(g^2 - 0)} = a$

$\therefore$ $g = \pm a/2$

and $2\sqrt{(f^2 - c)} = b$

or $2\sqrt{(f^2 - 0)} = b$

$\therefore$ $f = \pm b/2$

Hence, the equation of circle from Eq. (i) becomes

$$x^2 + y^2 \pm ax \pm by = 0$$

Example 19. Find the equation of the circle which touches the axes and whose centre lies on the line $x - 2y = 3$.

Sol. Since, the circle touches both the axes, let the radius of the circle by a, then

Case I If centre (a, a) but given centre lies on

$$x - 2y = 3$$

$\therefore$ $a - 2a = 3$

$\therefore$ $a = -3$

$\therefore$ Centre $= (-3, -3)$

and $\quad$ radius $= |-3| = 3$

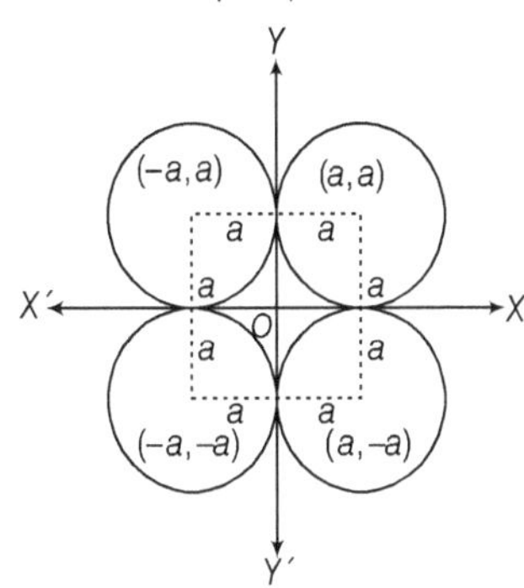

$\therefore$ Equation of circle is

$$(x+3)^2+(y+3)^2=3^2$$

and $\quad x^2+y^2+6x+6y+9=0$

Case II If centre $(-a, a)$ but centre lies on $x-2y=3$

$\therefore \quad -a-2a=3$

$\therefore \quad a=-1$

then, centre $=(1,-1)$ and radius $=|-1|=1$

$\therefore$ Equation of circle is $\quad (x-1)^2+(y+1)^2=1$

or $\quad x^2+y^2-2x+2y+1=0$

Case III If the centre $=(-a,-a)$

but centre lies on $x-2y=3$

$\therefore \quad -a+2a=3$

$\therefore \quad a=3$

then centre $(-3,-3)$ and radius $=|3|=3$

$\therefore$ Equation of circle is

$$(x+3)^2+(y+3)^2=3^2$$

or $\quad x^2+y^2+6x+6y+9=0$

Case IV If centre $=(a,-a)$ but centre lies on $x-2y=3$

or $\quad a+2a=3$

$\therefore \quad a=1$

then centre $=(1,-1)$ and radius $=1$

$\therefore$ Equation of circle is

$$(x-1)^2+(y+1)^2=1$$

or $\quad x^2+y^2-2x+2y+1=0$

Aliter I : Since, the circle touches both the axes, therefore its centre will be $(a, \pm a)$ and radius will be $|a|$, where a is positive or negative number.

Case I If centre $=(a, a)$

Since, centre lies on $x-2y=3$

$\therefore \quad a-2a=3$

$\quad a=-3$

$\therefore$ Centre of circle is $(-3,-3)$ and radius $=|-3|=3$.

Hence, equation of circle will be

$$(x+3)^2+(y+3)^2=3^2$$

or $\quad x^2+y^2+6x+6y+9=0$

Case II If centre $=(a,-a)$

Since, centre lies on $x-2y=3$

$\therefore \quad a+2a=3$

$\therefore \quad a=1$

$\therefore$ Centre of circle is $(1,-1)$ and radius $=|1|=1$

Hence, equation of circle will be

$$(x-1)^2+(y+1)^2=1$$

or $\quad x^2+y^2-2x+2y+1=0$

Aliter II : Let the equation of circle is

$$x^2+y^2+2gx+2fy+c=0 \quad \text{...(i)}$$

centre $=(-g,-f)$

Since, centre $(-g,-f)$ lies on $x-2y=3$

or $\quad -g+2f=3 \quad$ ...(ii)

Since, circle touches both axes

$\therefore \quad g^2=f^2=c$ or $g=\pm f$

if $g=f$, then from Eq. (ii), $-f+2f=3$

$\therefore \quad f=3$ and $g=3$

but $\quad c=f^2=g^2=9$

$\therefore$ Equation of circle from Eq. (i) is

$$x^2+y^2+6x+6y+9=0$$

and if $g=-f$, then from Eq. (ii)

$$f+2f=3$$

$\therefore \quad f=1$ and $g=-1$

but $\quad c=g^2=f^2=1$

$\therefore$ Equation of circle from Eq. (i) is

$$x^2+y^2-2x+2y+1=0$$

Aliter III : Since, centre of circle lies on $x-2y=3$, also since circle touches the axes, therefore, its centre will lie on the line $y=x$ or $y=-x$

Case I When the centre lies on the line $y=x$

but $\quad x-2y=3$

or $\quad x-2x=3$

$\therefore \quad x=-3=y$

Hence, the centre $=(-3,-3)$ and radius $=|-3|=3$

Therefore, the equation of circle in this case will be

$$(x+3)^2+(y+3)^2=3^2$$

or $\quad x^2+y^2+6x+6y+9=0$

Case II When the centre lies on the line $y=-x$

but $\quad x-2y=3$

or $\quad x+2x=3$

$\therefore \quad x=1$ then $y=-1$

$\therefore$ Centre of circle $(1,-1)$ and radius is $|1|=1$

Hence, equation of circle will be

$$(x-1)^2+(y+1)^2=1$$

or $\quad x^2+y^2-2x+2y+1=0$

Example 20. A circle of radius 2 lies in the first quadrant and touches both the axes of coordinates. Find the equation of the circle with centre at (6, 5) and touching the above circle externally.

Sol. Given, $AC = 2$ units

and $A \equiv (2, 2), B \equiv (6, 5)$

then $AB = \sqrt{(2-6)^2 + (2-5)^2}$

$= \sqrt{16+9} = 5$

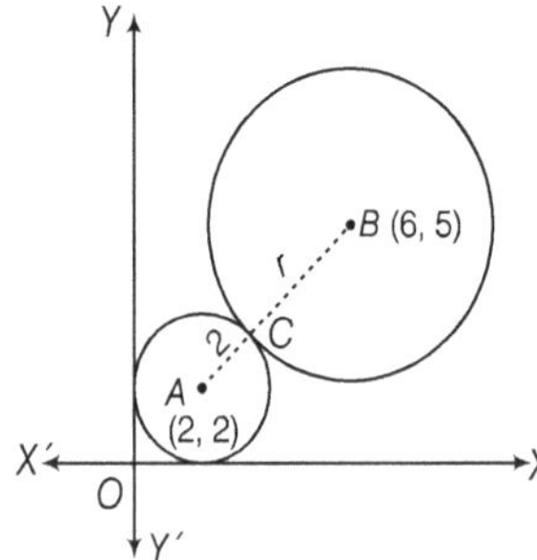

Since $AC + CB = AB$

$\therefore$ $2 + CB = 5$

$\therefore$ $CB = 3$

Hence, equation of required circle with centre at (6, 5) and radius 3 is

$$(x-6)^2 + (y-5)^2 = 3^2$$

or $$x^2 + y^2 - 12x - 10y + 52 = 0$$

Example 21. A circle of radius 5 units touches the coordinate axes in first quadrant. If the circle makes one complete roll on X-axis along the positive direction of X-axis, find its equation in the new position.

Sol. Let C be the centre of the circle in its initial position and D be its centre in the new position.

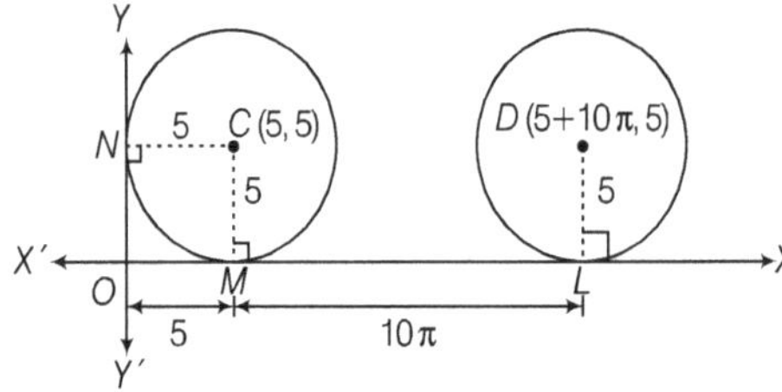

Since, the circle touches the coordinates axes in first quadrant and the radius of circle be 5 units.

$\therefore$ Centre of circle is (5, 5)

Moving length of circle = circumference of the circle

$= 2\pi r = 2\pi(5) = 10\pi$

Now, centre of circle in new position is $(5 + 10\pi, 5)$ and radius is 5 units, therefore, its equation will be

$$(x - 5 - 10\pi)^2 + (y-5)^2 = 5^2$$

or $$x^2 + y^2 - 10(1 + 2\pi)x - 10y + 100\pi^2 + 100\pi + 25 = 0$$

Position of a Point with Respect to Circle

Theorem : A point (x_1, y_1) lies outside, on or inside a circle

$$S \equiv x^2 + y^2 + 2gx + 2fy + c = 0$$

according as $S_1 >, =, \text{or} < 0$

where, $S_1 = x_1^2 + y_1^2 + 2gx_1 + 2fy_1 + c.$

Proof : Let $P(x_1, y_1)$ be the given point and let C be the centre of the circle

Then, $C \equiv (-g, -f)$

$\therefore$ $CP = \sqrt{(x_1+g)^2 + (y_1+f)^2}$

If r be the radius of the circle, then

$$r = \sqrt{(g^2 + f^2 - c)}$$

The point P lies outside, on or inside the circle according as

$CP >, =, \text{ or } < r$

$\Rightarrow$ $(CP)^2 >, =, \text{ or } < r^2$

$\Rightarrow$ $(x_1+g)^2 + (y_1+f)^2 >, =, \text{ or } < g^2 + f^2 - c$

$\Rightarrow$ $x_1^2 + y_1^2 + 2gx_1 + 2fy_1 + c >, =, \text{ or } < 0$

$\Rightarrow$ $S_1 >, =, \text{ or } < 0$

where, $S_1 = x_1^2 + y_1^2 + 2gx_1 + 2fy_1 + c.$

Example 22. Discuss the position of the points (1, 2) and (6, 0) with respect to the circle

$$x^2 + y^2 - 4x + 2y - 11 = 0.$$

Sol. Let $S \equiv x^2 + y^2 - 4x + 2y - 11 = 0$ for the point (1, 2)

$S_1 = 1^2 + 2^2 - 4 \cdot 1 + 2 \cdot 2 - 11 = -6$

$\therefore$ $S_1 < 0$

and for the point (6, 0)

$S_2 = 6^2 + 0 - 4 \cdot 6 + 2 \cdot 0 - 11$

$= 36 - 24 - 11$

$= 36 - 35 = 1$

$\therefore$ $S_2 > 0$

Hence, the point (1, 2) lies inside the circle and the point (6, 0) lies outside the circle.

Example 23. The circle $x^2 + y^2 - 6x - 10y + \lambda = 0$ does not touch or intersect the coordinate axes and the point (1, 4) is inside the circle. Find the range of values of λ.

Sol. Let $S \equiv x^2 + y^2 - 6x - 10y + \lambda = 0$

$\because$ Point (1, 4) is inside the circle, then $S_1 < 0$

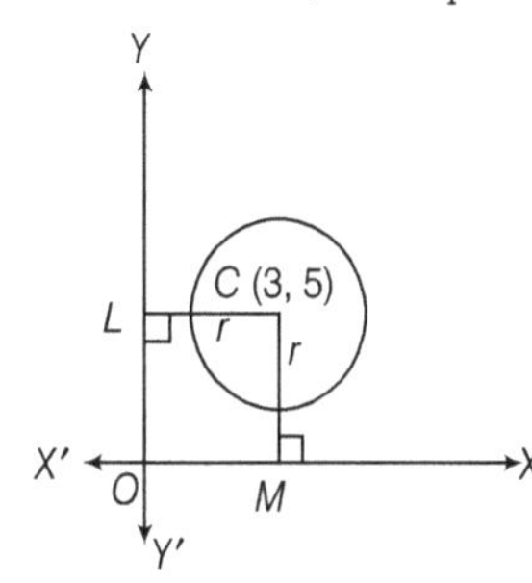

$$1 + 16 - 6 - 40 + \lambda < 0$$

$\Rightarrow \quad \lambda < 29 \quad$ ...(i)

Centre and radius of the circle are (3, 5) and $\sqrt{(34 - \lambda)}$, respectively.

$\because$ Circle does not touch or intersect the coordinate axes.

$\therefore \quad 5 > r$ and $3 > r$

or $\quad 5 > \sqrt{(34 - \lambda)}$ and $3 > \sqrt{(34 - \lambda)}$

$\Rightarrow \quad 25 > 34 - \lambda$ and $9 > 34 - \lambda$

$\Rightarrow \quad \lambda > 9$ and $\lambda > 25$

$\therefore \quad \lambda > 25 \quad$ ...(ii)

Also, $\quad 34 - \lambda > 0$

$\therefore \quad \lambda < 34 \quad$ ...(iii)

From Eqs. (i), (ii) and (iii), we get $25 < \lambda < 29$

Maximum and Minimum Distance of a Point from the Circle

Let any point $P(x_1, y_1)$ and circle

$$S \equiv x^2 + y^2 + 2gx + 2fy + c = 0 \quad \text{...(i)}$$

The centre and radius of the circle are

$$C(-g, -f) \quad \text{and} \quad \sqrt{(g^2 + f^2 - c)} \text{ respectively}$$

Case I If *P* inside the circle

In this case $S_1 < 0$

$\because \quad r = \sqrt{(g^2 + f^2 - c)} = CA = CB$

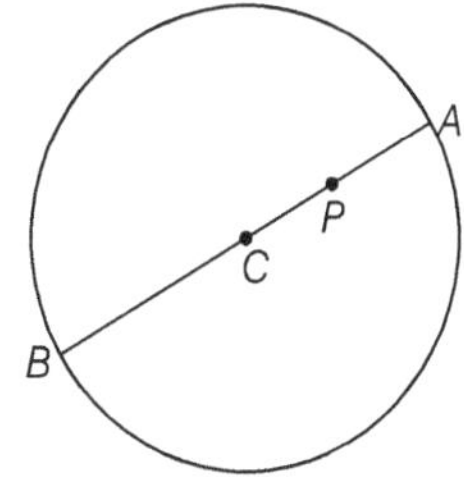

The **minimum distance** of P from circle $= PA = CA - CP$

$$= r - CP$$

and the **maximum distance** of P from circle $= PB$

$$= CB + CP = r + CP$$

Case II If *P* outside the circle

In this case $S_1 > 0$ the **minimum distance** of P from circle

$$= PA = CP - CA = CP - r$$

and the **maximum distance** of P from the circle

$$= PB = CP + CB = r + CP$$

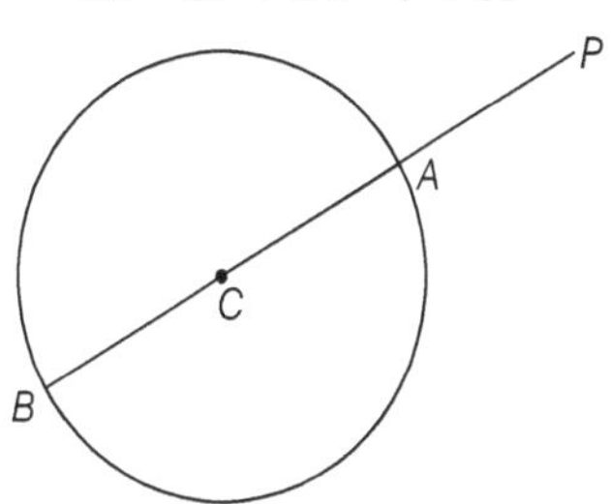

Case III If *P* on the circle

In this case $S_1 = 0$

the **minimum distance** of P from the circle $= 0$

and the **maximum distance** of P from the circle

$$= PA = 2r$$

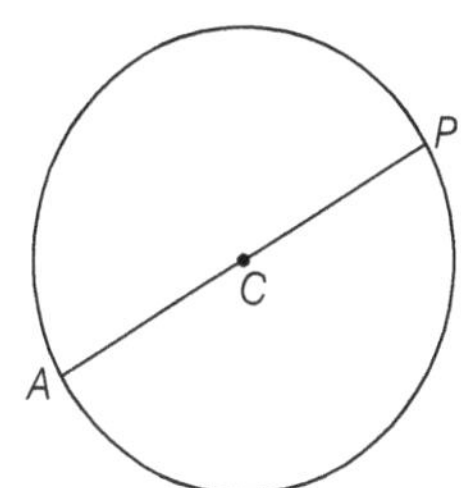

Remark

If point P inside or outside or on the circle and centre of circle at C and radius r, then minimum distance of P from the circle $= |CP - r|$ and maximum distance of P from the circle $= CP + r$

Example 24. Find the shortest and largest distance from the point $(2, -7)$ to the circle

$$x^2 + y^2 - 14x - 10y - 151 = 0$$

Sol. Let $\quad S \equiv x^2 + y^2 - 14x - 10y - 151 = 0$

$\therefore \quad S_1 = (2)^2 + (-7)^2 - 14(2) - 10(-7) - 151 = -56 < 0$

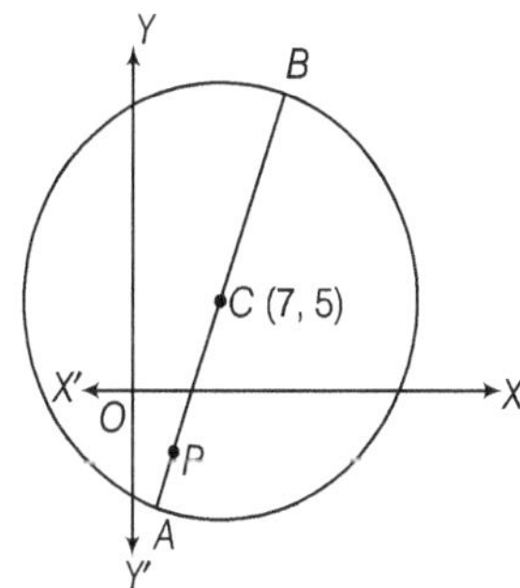

$\therefore P(2,-7)$ inside the circle

radius of the circle, $r = \sqrt{(-7)^2 + (-5)^2 + 151} = 15$

$\because$ Centre of circle $C \equiv (7,5)$

$$\therefore \qquad CP = \sqrt{(7-2)^2 + (5+7)^2} = 13$$

$\therefore$ **Shortest distance** $= PA = r - CP = 15 - 13 = 2$

and **Largest distance** $= PB = r + CP = 15 + 13 = 28$

Example 25. Find the points on the circle $x^2 + y^2 - 2x + 4y - 20 = 0$ which are farthest and nearest to the point $(-5,6)$.

Sol. The given circle is $S \equiv x^2 + y^2 - 2x + 4y - 20 = 0$

Let $\qquad P \equiv (-5,6)$

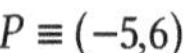

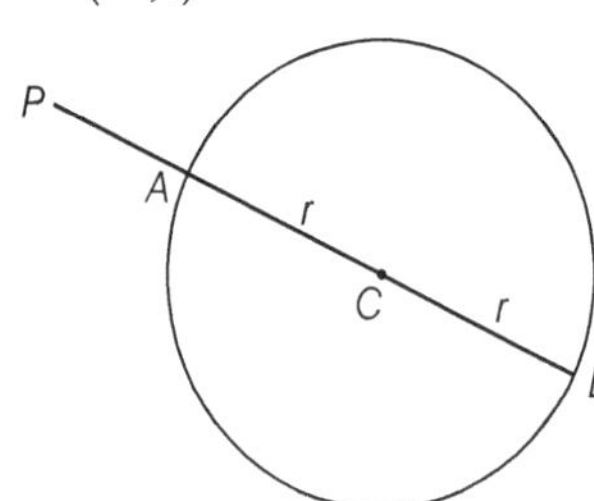

For the point P

$$S_1 = 25 + 36 + 10 + 24 - 20 = 75 > 0$$

$\therefore$ Point $P(-5,6)$ lies outside the circle.

The centre and radius of the circle are $(1,-2)$ and 5, respectively.

$$\because \qquad CP = \sqrt{(1+5)^2 + (-2-6)^2} = 10$$

Now, point A divides CP in the ratio

$$\frac{AP}{AC} = \frac{CP - r}{r} = \frac{10-5}{5} = 1$$

$\therefore A$ is mid-point of CP.

$$\therefore \qquad A \equiv \left(\frac{1-5}{2}, \frac{-2+6}{2}\right)$$

or $\qquad A \equiv (-2,2)$

and C is the mid-point of AB.

$$\therefore \qquad B \equiv (2 \times 1 - (-2), 2 \times -2 - 2)$$

or $\qquad B \equiv (4,-6)$

Hence, point $A(-2,2)$ is nearest to P and $B(4,-6)$ is farthest from P.

Exercise for Session 3

1. The length of intercept, the circle $x^2 + y^2 + 10x - 6y + 9 = 0$ makes on the X-axis is

(a) 2 (b) 4 (c) 6 (d) 8

2. The circle $x^2 + y^2 + 4x - 7y + 12 = 0$ cuts an intercept on Y-axis is of length

(a) 1 (b) 3 (c) 5 (d) 7

3. The locus of the centre of a circle which passes through the origin and cuts-off a length $2b$ from the line $x = c$ is

(a) $y^2 + 2cx = b^2 + c^2$ (b) $x^2 + cx = b^2 + c^2$ (c) $y^2 + 2cy = b^2 + c^2$ (d) $x^2 + cy = b^2 + c^2$

4. If a straight line through $C(-\sqrt{8}, \sqrt{8})$ making an angle of 135° with the X-axis cuts the circle $x = 5\cos\theta$, $y = 5\sin\theta$ at points A and B, then the length of AB is

(a) 3 (b) 5 (c) 8 (d) 10

5. If a circle of constant radius $3k$ passes through the origin and meets the axes at A and B, the locus of the centroid of ΔOAB is

(a) $x^2 + y^2 = k^2$ (b) $x^2 + y^2 = 2k^2$ (c) $x^2 + y^2 = 3k^2$ (d) $x^2 + y^2 = 4k^2$

6. The centre of the circle touching Y-axis at $(0,3)$ and making an intercept of 2 units on positive X-axis is

(a) $(10, \sqrt{3})$ (b) $(\sqrt{3}, 10)$ (c) $(\sqrt{10}, 3)$ (d) $(3, \sqrt{10})$

7. A circle passes through the points $A(1,0)$ and $B(5,0)$ and touches the Y-axis at $C(0,\lambda)$. If $\angle ACB$ is maximum, then

(a) $|\lambda| = \sqrt{5}$ (b) $|\lambda| = 2\sqrt{5}$ (c) $|\lambda| = 3\sqrt{5}$ (d) $|\lambda| = 4\sqrt{5}$

8. The equation of a circle whose centre is $(3, -1)$ and which intercept chord of 6 units length on straight line $2x - 5y + 18 = 0$ is

(a) $x^2 + y^2 - 6x + 2y - 28 = 0$
(b) $x^2 + y^2 + 6x - 2y - 28 = 0$
(c) $x^2 + y^2 + 4x - 2y + 24 = 0$
(d) $x^2 + y^2 + 2x - 2y - 12 = 0$

9. The locus of the centre of a circle which touches externally the circle $x^2 + y^2 - 6x - 6y + 14 = 0$ and also touches the Y-axis, is given by the equation

(a) $x^2 - 6x - 10y + 14 = 0$
(b) $x^2 - 10x - 6y + 14 = 0$
(c) $y^2 - 6x - 10y + 14 = 0$
(d) $y^2 - 10x - 6y + 14 = 0$

10. The locus of the centre of a circle of radius 2 which rolls on the outside of circle $x^2 + y^2 + 3x - 6y - 9 = 0$ is

(a) $x^2 + y^2 + 3x - 6y + 5 = 0$
(b) $x^2 + y^2 + 3x - 6y - 31 = 0$
(c) $x^2 + y^2 + 3x - 6y + 11 = 0$
(d) $x^2 + y^2 + 3x - 6y - 36 = 0$

11. The point $([\lambda + 1], [\lambda])$ is lying inside the circle $x^2 + y^2 - 2x - 15 = 0$. Then, the set of all values of λ is (where [.] represents the greatest integer function)

(a) $[-2, 3]$ (b) $(-2, 3)$ (c) $[-2, 0) \cup (0, 3)$ (d) $[0, 3)$

12. The greatest distance of the point $(10, 7)$ from the circle $x^2 + y^2 - 4x - 2y - 20 = 0$ is

(a) 5 (b) 10 (c) 15 (d) 20

13. Find equations to the circles touching Y-axis at $(0, 3)$ and making intercept of 8 units on the X-axis.

14. Show that the circle $x^2 + y^2 - 2ax - 2ay + a^2 = 0$ touches both the coordinate axes.

15. If the point $(\lambda, -\lambda)$ lies inside the circle $x^2 + y^2 - 4x + 2y - 8 = 0$, then find range of λ.

16. Find the equation of the circle which passes through the origin and cuts-off chords of lengths 4 and 6 on the positive side of the X-axis and Y-axis, respectively.

Session 4

Intersection of a Line and a Circle, Product of the Algebraical Distances *PA* and *PB* is Constant when from *P*, *A* Secant be Drawn to Cut the Circle in the Points *A* and *B*, The Length of Intercept Cut-off from a Line by a Circle, Tangent to a Circle at a Given Point, Normal to a Circle at a Given Point

Intersection of a Line and a Circle

Let the equation of the circle be

$$x^2 + y^2 = a^2 \quad \text{...(i)}$$

and the equation of the line be

$$y = mx + c \quad \text{...(ii)}$$

From Eq. (i) and Eq. (ii)

$$x^2 + (mx + c)^2 = a^2$$

or $$(1 + m^2)x^2 + 2mcx + c^2 - a^2 = 0 \quad \text{...(iii)}$$

Case I When points of intersection are real and distinct, then Eq. (iii) has two distinct roots.

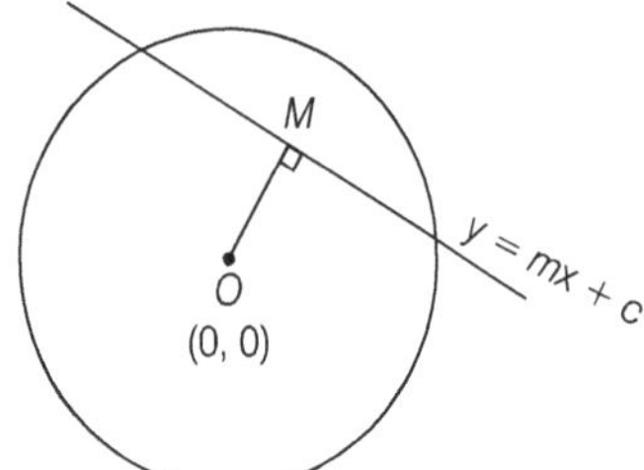

$\therefore$ $$B^2 - 4AC > 0$$

or $$4m^2c^2 - 4(1 + m^2)(c^2 - a^2) > 0$$

or $$a^2 > \frac{c^2}{1 + m^2}$$

or $$a > \frac{|c|}{\sqrt{(1 + m^2)}} = \text{length of perpendicular}$$

from $(0, 0)$ to $y = mx + c$

$\Rightarrow$ $a >$ length of perpendicular from $(0, 0)$ to $y = mx + c$

Thus, a line intersects a given circle at two distinct points if radius of circle is greater than the length of perpendicular from centre of the circle to the line.

Case II When the points of intersection are coincident, then Eq. (iii) has two equal roots

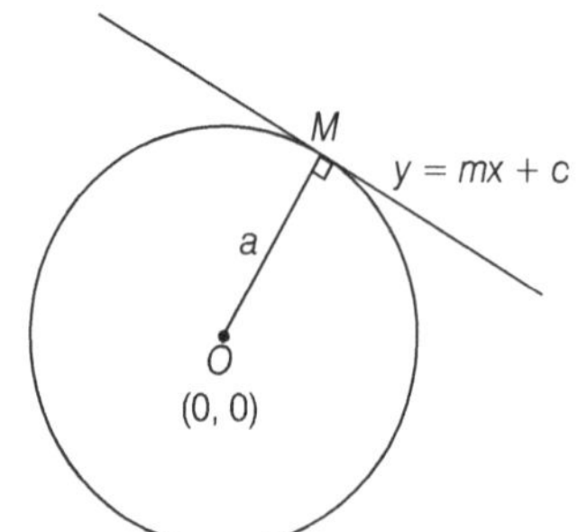

$\therefore$ $$B^2 - 4AC = 0$$

$\Rightarrow$ $$4m^2c^2 - 4(1 + m^2)(c^2 - a^2) = 0$$

$\therefore$ $$a^2 = \frac{c^2}{(1 + m^2)}$$

or $$a = \frac{|c|}{\sqrt{(1 + m^2)}}$$

a = length of the perpendicular from the point $(0, 0)$ to $y = mx + c$

Thus, a line touches the circle if radius of circle is equal to the length of perpendicular from centre of the circle to the line.

Case III When the points of intersection are imaginary. In this case (iii) has imaginary roots

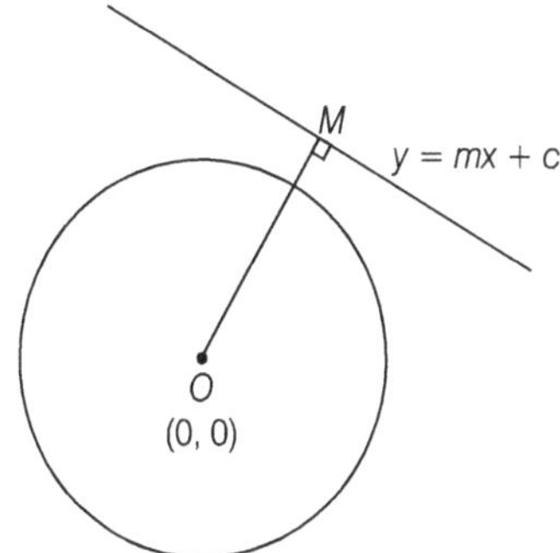

$$\therefore \quad B^2 - 4AC < 0$$

$$4m^2c^2 - 4(1+m^2)(c^2 - a^2) = 0$$

$$\therefore \quad a^2 < \frac{c^2}{1+m^2}$$

or $a < \frac{|c|}{\sqrt{1+m^2}}$ = length of perpendicular from $(0, 0)$ to $y = mx + c$

or $a <$ length of perpendicular from $(0, 0)$ to $y = mx + c$

Thus, a line does not intersect a circle if the radius of circle is less than the length of perpendicular from centre of the circle to the line.

| Example 26. Find the points of intersection of the line $2x + 3y = 18$ and the circle $x^2 + y^2 = 25$.

Sol. We have, $2x + 3y = 18$ ....(i)

and $x^2 + y^2 = 25$ ...(ii)

From Eq. (i), $y = \frac{18 - 2x}{3}$

Substituting in Eq. (ii), then $x^2 + \left(\frac{18 - 2x}{3}\right)^2 = 25$

$$\Rightarrow \quad 9x^2 + 4(9 - x)^2 = 225$$

$$\Rightarrow \quad 9x^2 + 4(81 - 18x + x^2) = 225$$

$$\Rightarrow \quad 13x^2 - 72x + 324 - 225 = 0$$

$$\Rightarrow \quad 13x^2 - 72x + 99 = 0$$

$$\Rightarrow \quad (x - 3)(13x - 33) = 0$$

$$\Rightarrow \quad x = 3 \quad \text{or} \quad x = \frac{33}{13}$$

From Eq. (i), $y = 4$ or $y = \frac{56}{13}$

Hence, the points of intersection of the given line and the given circle are $(3, 4)$ and $\left(\frac{33}{13}, \frac{56}{13}\right)$.

Product of the Algebraical Distances *PA* and *PB* is Constant when from *P*, A Secant be Drawn to Cut the Circle in the Points *A* and *B*

If a straight line through $P(\alpha, \beta)$ makes an angle θ with the positive direction of X-axis, then its equation is

$$\frac{x - \alpha}{\cos\theta} = \frac{y - \beta}{\sin\theta} = r$$

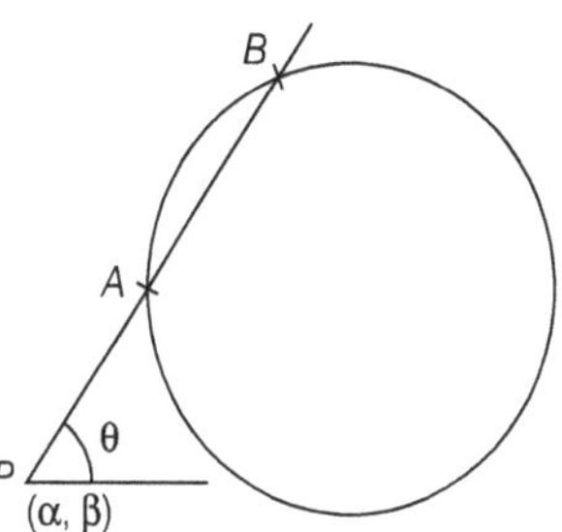

where, r is the algebraical distance of the point (x, y) from the point $P(\alpha, \beta)$.

$$\therefore \quad (x, y) = (\alpha + r\cos\theta, \beta + r\sin\theta)$$

If this point lies on the circle $x^2 + y^2 + 2gx + 2fy + c = 0$

or $\quad (\alpha + r\cos\theta)^2 + (\beta + r\sin\theta)^2 + 2g(\alpha + r\cos\theta) + 2f(\beta + r\sin\theta) + c = 0$

$$\Rightarrow \quad r^2 + 2r(\alpha\cos\theta + \beta\sin\theta + g\cos\theta + f\sin\theta) + (\alpha^2 + \beta^2 + 2g\alpha + 2f\beta + c) = 0$$

This is quadratic equation in r, then PA and PB are the roots of this equation.

$$\therefore \quad PA \cdot PB = \alpha^2 + \beta^2 + 2g\alpha + 2f\beta + c = \text{constant}$$

Since, RHS is independent of θ.

Remark

Secants are drawn from a given point A to cut a given circle at the pairs of points $P_1, Q_1; P_2, Q_2; \dots; P_n, Q_n$, then

$$AP_1 \cdot AQ_1 = AP_2 \cdot AQ_2 = \dots = AP_n \cdot AQ_n$$

The Length of Intercept Cut-off from a Line by a Circle

Theorem : The length of the intercept cut-off from the line $y = mx + c$ by the circle $x^2 + y^2 = a^2$ is

$$2\sqrt{\left\{\frac{a^2(1+m^2) - c^2}{(1+m^2)}\right\}}$$

Proof : Draw OM perpendicular to PQ

Now, OM = length of perpendicular from $O(0,0)$ to

$$(y = mx + c) = \frac{|c|}{\sqrt{(1+m^2)}}$$

and OP = radius of the circle = a

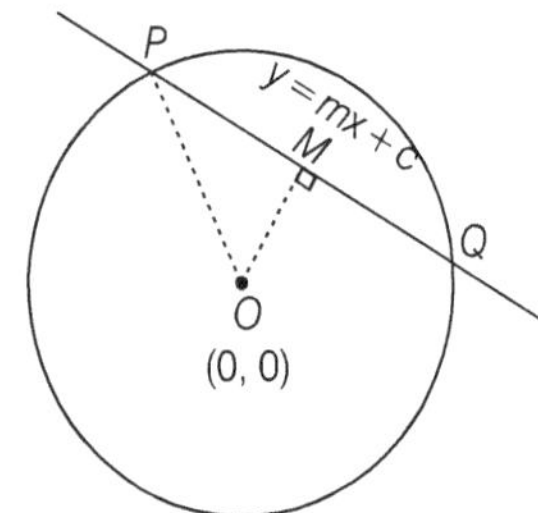

In ΔOPM, $PM = \sqrt{(OP)^2 - (OM)^2}$

$$= \sqrt{a^2 - \frac{c^2}{(1+m^2)}} = \sqrt{\left\{\frac{a^2(1+m^2) - c^2}{1+m^2}\right\}}$$

$\therefore$ $$PQ = 2PM = 2\sqrt{\left\{\frac{a^2(1+m^2) - c^2}{1+m^2}\right\}}$$

Remarks

1. If the line $y = mx + c$ touches the circle $x^2 + y^2 = a^2$, then intercepted length is zero

   i.e. $PQ = 0 \Rightarrow 2\sqrt{\left\{\frac{a^2(1+m^2) - c^2}{1+m^2}\right\}} = 0$

   $\therefore$ $c^2 = a^2(1+m^2)$

   which is the required condition for tangency.
2. If a line touches the circle, then length of perpendicular from the centre upon the line is equal to the radius of the circle.

Example 27. Find the length of the intercept on the straight line $4x - 3y - 10 = 0$ by the circle $x^2 + y^2 - 2x + 4y - 20 = 0$.

Sol. Centre and radius of the circle $x^2 + y^2 - 2x + 4y - 20 = 0$ are $(1, -2)$ and $\sqrt{1 + 4 + 20} = 5$ respectively.

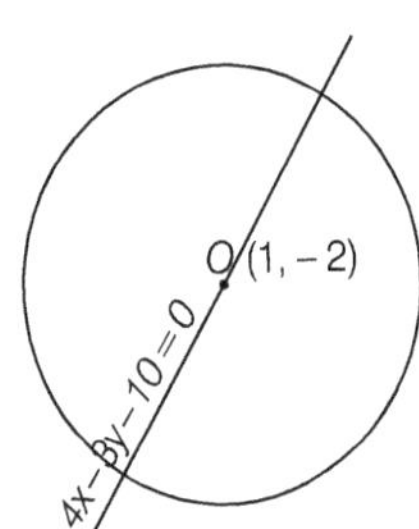

Let OM be the perpendicular from O on the line

$$4x - 3y - 10 = 0$$

then $$OM = \frac{|4 \times 1 - 3 \times (-2) - 10|}{\sqrt{4^2 + (-3)^2}} = 0$$

Hence, line $4x - 3y - 10 = 0$ passes through the centre of the circle.

Hence, intercepted length = diameter of the circle

$$= 2 \times 5 = 10$$

Example 28. Find the coordinates of the middle point of the chord which the circle $x^2 + y^2 + 4x - 2y - 3 = 0$ cuts-off the line $x - y + 2 = 0$.

Sol. Centre and radius of the circle $x^2 + y^2 + 4x - 2y - 3 = 0$ are $(-2, 1)$ and $\sqrt{4 + 1 + 3} = 2\sqrt{2}$ respectively.

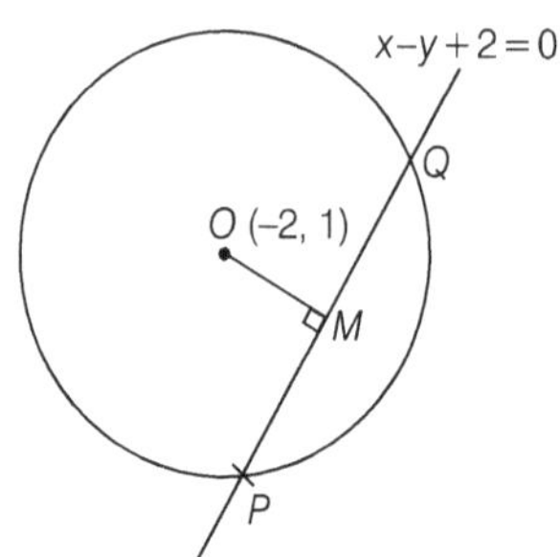

Draw perpendicular from O upon $x - y + 2 = 0$ is OM.

Equation of OM which is perpendicular to $x - y + 2 = 0$ is $x + y = \lambda$, it passes through $(-2, 1)$

Then, $-2 + 1 = \lambda$

$\therefore$ $\lambda = -1$

then equation of OM is $x + y + 1 = 0$

Since, M is the mid-point of PQ which is point of intersection of $x - y + 2 = 0$ and $x + y + 1 = 0$, coordinates of M is $\left(-\frac{3}{2}, \frac{1}{2}\right)$.

Aliter : Let $M \equiv (\alpha, \beta)$, then

$$\frac{\alpha + 2}{1} = \frac{\beta - 1}{-1} = -\frac{(-2 - 1 + 2)}{1 + 1}$$

(Here, M is foot of perpendicular)

$\Rightarrow$ $$\frac{\alpha + 2}{1} = \frac{\beta - 1}{-1} = \frac{1}{2}$$

or $$\alpha = -\frac{3}{2} \text{ and } \beta = \frac{1}{2}$$

$\therefore$ $$M \equiv \left(-\frac{3}{2}, \frac{1}{2}\right)$$

Example 29. For what value of λ will the line $y = 2x + \lambda$ be a tangent to the circle $x^2 + y^2 = 5$?

Sol. Comparing the given line with $y = mx + c$, we get

$m = 2$, $c = \lambda$ and given circle with $x^2 + y^2 = a^2$

then $a^2 = 5$

$\because$ Condition for tangency is

$$c^2 = a^2(1+m^2)$$

$$\Rightarrow \quad \lambda^2 = 5(1+4)$$

$$\lambda^2 = 25$$

$$\therefore \quad \lambda = \pm 5$$

Aliter : Since, line $y = 2x + \lambda$

or $\quad 2x - y + \lambda = 0$

is the tangent to the circle $x^2 + y^2 = 5$ then length of perpendicular from centre upon the line is equal to the radius of the circle

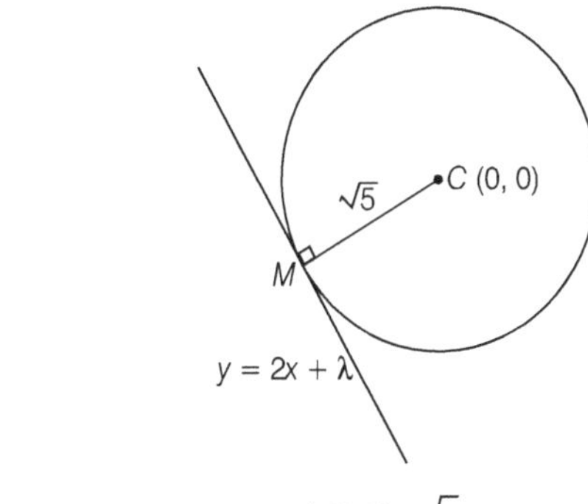

$$\therefore \quad |CM| = \sqrt{5}$$

$$\text{or} \quad \frac{|0-0+\lambda|}{\sqrt{4+1}} = \sqrt{5}$$

$$\Rightarrow \quad \frac{|\lambda|}{\sqrt{5}} = \sqrt{5}$$

$$\Rightarrow \quad |\lambda| = 5$$

$$\text{or} \quad \lambda = \pm 5$$

Tangent to a Circle at a Given Point

Let PQ be a chord and AB be a secant passing through P. Let P be the fixed point and move along the circle towards P, then the secant PQ turns about P. In the limit, when Q coincides with P, then the secant AB becomes a tangent to the circle at the point P.

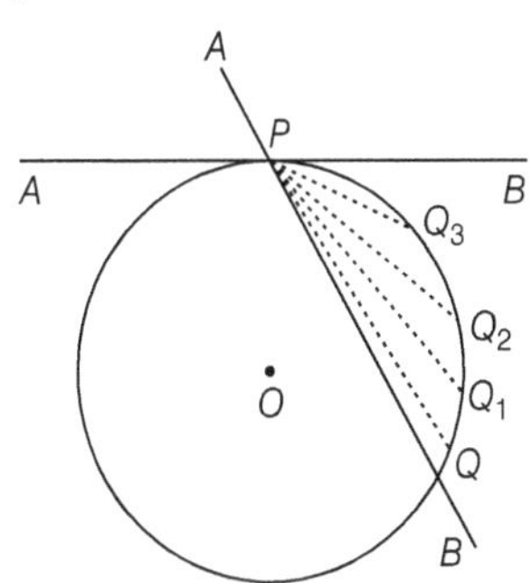

Different forms of the equations of tangents

1. Point form :

Theorem : The equation of tangent at the point $P(x_1, y_1)$ to a circle

$$x^2 + y^2 + 2gx + 2fy + c = 0 \text{ is}$$

$$xx_1 + yy_1 + g(x + x_1) + f(y + y_1) + c = 0$$

Proof : Since, $P(x_1, y_1)$ be a point on the circle

$$x^2 + y^2 + 2gx + 2fy + c = 0 \quad \text{...(i)}$$

Let $Q(x_2, y_2)$ be any other point on the circle Eq. (i). Since, points $P(x_1, y_1)$ and $Q(x_2, y_2)$ lie on the circle, therefore

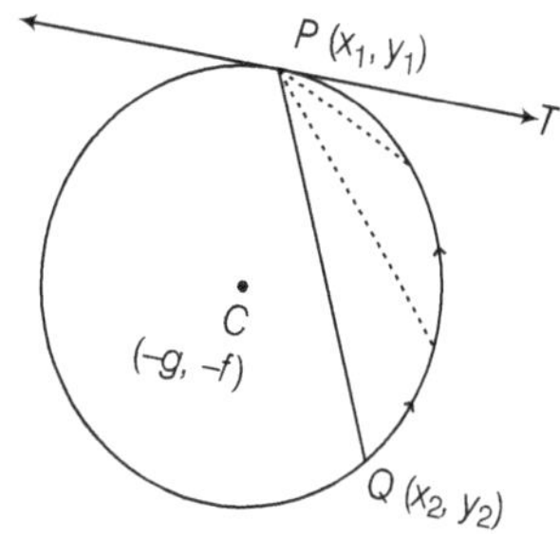

$$x_1^2 + y_1^2 + 2gx_1 + 2fy_1 + c = 0 \quad \text{...(ii)}$$

$$\text{and} \quad x_2^2 + y_2^2 + 2gx_2 + 2fy_2 + c = 0 \quad \text{...(iii)}$$

On subtracting Eq. (ii) from Eq. (iii), we have

$$(x_2^2 - x_1^2) + (y_2^2 - y_1^2) + 2g$$

$$(x_2 - x_1) + 2f(y_2 - y_1) = 0$$

$$\Rightarrow \quad (x_2 - x_1)(x_2 + x_1 + 2g) + (y_2 - y_1)$$

$$(y_2 + y_1 + 2f) = 0$$

$$\Rightarrow \quad \left(\frac{y_2 - y_1}{x_2 - x_1}\right) = -\left(\frac{x_1 + x_2 + 2g}{y_1 + y_2 + 2f}\right) \quad \text{...(iv)}$$

Now, the equation of the chord PQ is

$$y - y_1 = \left(\frac{y_2 - y_1}{x_2 - x_1}\right)(x - x_1) \quad \text{...(v)}$$

Putting the value of $\left(\frac{y_2 - y_1}{x_2 - x_1}\right)$ from Eq. (iv) in Eq. (v), then equation PQ becomes

$$y - y_1 = -\left(\frac{x_1 + x_2 + 2g}{y_1 + y_2 + 2f}\right)(x - x_1) \quad \text{...(vi)}$$

Now, when $Q \to P$ (along the circle), line PQ becomes tangent at P, we have $x_2 \to x_1, y_2 \to y_1$. So, the equation of tangent at $P(x_1, y_1)$ is :

$$y-y_1=-\left(\frac{x_1+x_1+2g}{y_1+y_1+2f}\right)(x-x_1)$$

$$\Rightarrow \quad y-y_1=-\left(\frac{x_1+g}{y_1+f}\right)(x-x_1)$$

$$\Rightarrow \quad (y-y_1)(y_1+f)+(x-x_1)(x_1+g)=0$$

$$\Rightarrow \quad xx_1+yy_1+gx+fy=x_1^2+y_1^2+gx_1+fy_1$$

On adding gx_1+fy_1+c to both sides, we get

$$xx_1+yy_1+g(x+x_1)+f(y+y_1)+c$$
$$=x_1^2+y_1^2+2gx_1+2fy_1+c=0 \quad \text{[from Eq. (ii)]}$$

$$\Rightarrow \quad xx_1+yy_1+g(x+x_1)+f(y+y_1)+c=0$$

This is the required equation of the tangent PT to the circle at the point (x_1, y_1).

Aliter : Since, circle is $x^2+y^2+2gx+2fy+c=0$

$P(x_1, y_1)$ lie on the circle

$$\therefore \quad x_1^2+y_1^2+2gx_1+2fy_1+c=0 \quad \text{...(i)}$$

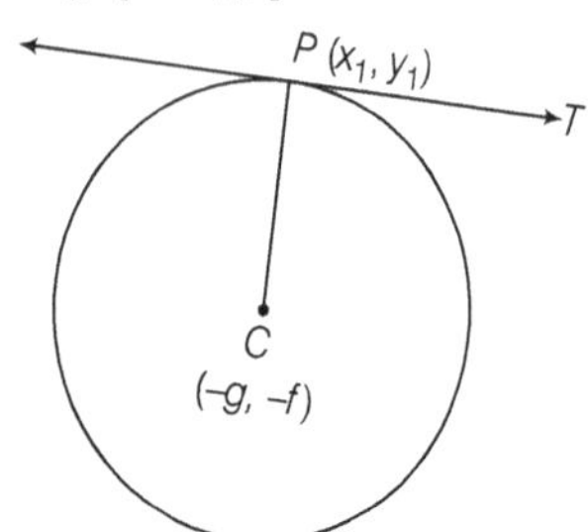

Its centre is $C(-g, -f)$

$$\therefore \quad \text{Slope of } CP=\frac{y_1-(-f)}{x_1-(-g)}=\frac{y_1+f}{x_1+g}$$

Since, tangent PT is perpendicular to CP.

$$\therefore \quad \text{Slope of tangent}=-\left(\frac{x_1+g}{y_1+f}\right)$$

$\therefore$ Equation of tangent at $P(x_1, y_1)$ is

$$y-y_1=-\left(\frac{x_1+g}{y_1+f}\right)(x-x_1)$$

$$\Rightarrow \quad (y-y_1)(y_1+f)+(x_1+g)(x-x_1)=0$$

$$\Rightarrow \quad xx_1+yy_1+gx+fy=x_1^2+y_1^2+gx_1+fy_1$$

On adding gx_1+fy_1+c to both sides, we get

$$xx_1+yy_1+g(x+x_1)+f(y+y_1)+c$$
$$=x_1^2+y_1^2+2gx_1+2fy_1+c=0 \quad \text{[from Eq. (i)]}$$

or $\quad xx_1+yy_1+g(x+x_1)+f(y+y_1)+c=0$

This is the required equation of the tangent PT to the circle at the point $P(x_1, y_1)$.

Remarks

1. For equation of tangent of circle at (x_1, y_1), substitute xx_1 for x^2, yy_1 for y^2, $\frac{x+x_1}{2}$ for x, $\frac{y+y_1}{2}$ for y and $\frac{xy_1+x_1y}{2}$ for xy and keep the constant as such.
2. This method of tangent at (x_1, y_1) is applied only for any conics of second degree. i.e. equation of tangent of $ax^2+2hxy+by^2+2gx+2fy+c=0$ at (x_1, y_1) is $axx_1+h(xy_1+x_1y)+byy_1+g(x+x_1)+f(y+y_1)+c=0$

Wrong process : Mostly students use wrong process **Suppose** any curve

$$ax^3+by^3=c$$

or $\quad a(x)(x^2)+b(y)(y^2)=c$

Equation of tangent at (x_1, y_1)

$$\Rightarrow \quad a\left(\frac{x+x_1}{2}\right)xx_1+b\left(\frac{y+y_1}{2}\right)yy_1=c^2$$

which is a second degree conic not the equation of tangent.

Reason : This method is applicable only for second degree conic, its a third degree conic. (find its tangent only by calculus)

Example 30. Prove that the tangents to the circle $x^2+y^2=25$ at $(3,4)$ and $(4,-3)$ are perpendicular to each other.

Sol. The equations of tangents to $x^2+y^2=25$ at (3, 4) and (4, – 3) are

$$3x+4y=25 \quad \text{...(i)}$$

and $\quad 4x-3y=25 \quad$ ...(ii)

respectively.

Now, $\quad$ slope of Eq. (i) $=-\frac{3}{4}=m_1$ $\quad$ (say)

and $\quad$ slope of Eq. (ii) $=\frac{4}{3}=m_2$ $\quad$ (say)

Clearly, $\quad m_1m_2=-1$

Hence, Eq. (i) and Eq. (ii) are perpendicular to each other.

Example 31. Find the equation of tangent to the circle $x^2+y^2-2ax=0$ at the point $[a(1+\cos\alpha), a\sin\alpha]$.

Sol. The equation of tangent of $x^2+y^2-2ax=0$ at $[a(1+\cos\alpha), a\sin\alpha]$ is

$$x\cdot a(1+\cos\alpha)+y\cdot a\sin\alpha-a[x+a(1+\cos\alpha)]=0$$

$$\Rightarrow \quad ax\cos\alpha+ay\sin\alpha-a^2(1+\cos\alpha)=0$$

or $\quad x\cos\alpha+y\sin\alpha=a(1+\cos\alpha)$

Example 32. Show that the circles $x^2+y^2-4x+6y+8=0$ and $x^2+y^2-10x-6y+14=0$ touch at $(3,-1)$.

Sol. Equation of tangent at $(3,-1)$ of the circle

$x^2+y^2-4x+6y+8=0$ is

$$3x+(-1)y-2(x+3)+3(y-1)+8=0$$

or $$x+2y-1=0 \quad \text{...(i)}$$

and equation of tangent at $(3,-1)$ of the circle

$x^2+y^2-10x-6y+14=0$ is

$$3\cdot x+(-1)\cdot y-5(x+3)-3(y-1)+14=0$$

or $$-2x-4y+2=0$$

or $$x+2y-1=0 \quad \text{...(ii)}$$

which is the same as Eq (i).

Hence, the given circles touch at $(3,-1)$.

2. Parametric form :

Theorem : The equation of tangent to the circle $x^2+y^2=a^2$ at the point $(a\cos\theta, a\sin\theta)$ is

$x\cos\theta+y\sin\theta=a$

Proof : The equation of tangent of $x^2+y^2=a^2$ at (x_1,y_1) is $xx_1+yy_1=a^2$ (using point form of the tangent)

Putting $\quad x_1=a\cos\theta,\ y_1=a\sin\theta$

then, we get $\quad x\cos\theta+y\sin\theta=a$

***Corollary* 1 :** Equation of chord joining $(a\cos\theta, a\sin\theta)$ and $(a\cos\phi, a\sin\phi)$ is

$$x\cos\left(\frac{\theta+\phi}{2}\right)+y\sin\left(\frac{\theta+\phi}{2}\right)=a\cos\left(\frac{\theta-\phi}{2}\right)$$

***Corollary* 2 :** Point of intersection of tangents at $(a\cos\theta, a\sin\theta)$ and $(a\cos\phi, a\sin\phi)$ is

$$\left(\frac{a\cos\left(\frac{\theta+\phi}{2}\right)}{\cos\left(\frac{\theta-\phi}{2}\right)}, \frac{a\sin\left(\frac{\theta+\phi}{2}\right)}{\cos\left(\frac{\theta-\phi}{2}\right)}\right)$$

Remembering method :

$\because$ $$x\cos\left(\frac{\theta+\phi}{2}\right)+y\sin\left(\frac{\theta+\phi}{2}\right)=a\cos\left(\frac{\theta-\phi}{2}\right)$$

or $$x\left\{\frac{a\cos\left(\frac{\theta+\phi}{2}\right)}{\cos\left(\frac{\theta-\phi}{2}\right)}\right\}+y\left\{\frac{a\sin\left(\frac{\theta+\phi}{2}\right)}{\cos\left(\frac{\theta-\phi}{2}\right)}\right\}=a^2$$

We get $$\left(\frac{a\cos\left(\frac{\theta+\phi}{2}\right)}{\cos\left(\frac{\theta-\phi}{2}\right)}, \frac{a\sin\left(\frac{\theta+\phi}{2}\right)}{\cos\left(\frac{\theta-\phi}{2}\right)}\right)$$

***Corollary* 3 :** The angle between a pair of tangents from a point P to the circle $x^2+y^2=a^2$ is α. Then, the locus of the point P is

$$x^2+y^2=\frac{a^2}{\sin^2\left(\frac{\alpha}{2}\right)}$$

Proof

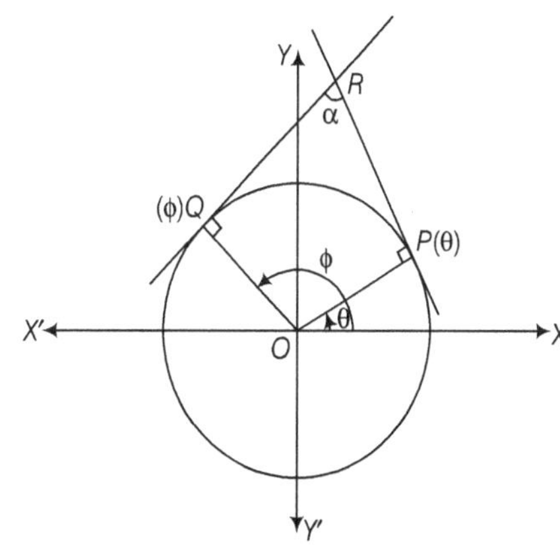

$\because$ $$\phi-\theta+\alpha=180^\circ$$

$\therefore$ $$\frac{\theta-\phi}{2}=-\left(90^\circ-\frac{\alpha}{2}\right)$$

or $$\cos\left(\frac{\theta-\phi}{2}\right)=\sin\left(\frac{\alpha}{2}\right)$$

Now, point of intersection is

$$\left(\frac{a\cos\left(\frac{\theta+\phi}{2}\right)}{\sin\left(\frac{\alpha}{2}\right)}, \frac{a\sin\left(\frac{\theta+\phi}{2}\right)}{\sin\left(\frac{\alpha}{2}\right)}\right)$$

Let $$x=\frac{a\cos\left(\frac{\theta+\phi}{2}\right)}{\sin\left(\frac{\alpha}{2}\right)} \text{ and } y=\frac{a\sin\left(\frac{\theta+\phi}{2}\right)}{\sin\left(\frac{\alpha}{2}\right)}$$

$\therefore$ $$x^2+y^2=\frac{a^2}{\sin^2\left(\frac{\alpha}{2}\right)}$$

Remarks

1. The angle between a pair of tangents from a point P to the circle $x^2+y^2+2gx+2fy+c=0$ is 2θ, then the locus of P is $x^2+y^2+2gx+2fy+c=(g^2+f^2-c)\cot^2\theta$
2. If angle between a pair of tangents from a point P to the circle $x^2+y^2=a^2$ is $\frac{\pi}{2}$, then the locus of P is
$$x^2+y^2=2a^2 \qquad \left(\text{Here, } \alpha=\frac{\pi}{2}\right)$$
which is **director circle** of $x^2+y^2=a^2$.
($\because$ locus of point of intersection of perpendicular tangents is **director circle**)
3. The equation of the tangent to the circle $(x-a)^2+(y-b)^2=r^2$ at the point $(a+r\cos\theta, b+r\sin\theta)$ is
$$(x-a)\cos\theta+(y-b)\sin\theta=r.$$

Example 33. The angle between a pair of tangents from a point P to the circle $x^2+y^2=25$ is $\frac{\pi}{3}$. Find the equation of the locus of the point P.

Sol. Here, $\alpha=\frac{\pi}{3}$

$\therefore$ Required locus is $x^2+y^2=\dfrac{25}{\sin^2\left(\frac{\pi}{6}\right)}=100$

Example 34. The angle between a pair of tangents from a point P to the circle $x^2+y^2-6x-8y+9=0$ is $\frac{\pi}{3}$. Find the equation of the locus of the point P.

Sol. Here, $2\theta=\frac{\pi}{3}$ or $\theta=\frac{\pi}{6}$

$\therefore$ Required locus is
$$x^2+y^2-6x-8y+9=(9+16-9)\cot^2\frac{\pi}{6}$$
or $$x^2+y^2-6x-8y+9=16\times3$$
or $$x^2+y^2-6x-8y-39=0$$

3. Slope form :

Theorem : The equation of a tangent of slope m to the circle $x^2+y^2=a^2$ is $y=mx\pm a\sqrt{(1+m^2)}$ and the coordinates of the point of contact are
$$\left(\pm\frac{am}{\sqrt{(1+m^2)}}, \mp\frac{a}{\sqrt{(1+m^2)}}\right)$$

Proof : Let $y=mx+c$ is the tangent of the circle $x^2+y^2=a^2$.

$\therefore$ Length of perpendicular from centre of circle $(0,0)$ on $(y=mx+c)$ = radius of circle

$$\therefore \quad \frac{|c|}{\sqrt{(1+m^2)}}=a \Rightarrow c=\pm a\sqrt{(1+m^2)}$$

On substituting this value of c in $y=mx+c$, we get
$$\boldsymbol{y=mx\pm a\sqrt{(1+m^2)}} \qquad \text{...(i)}$$
which are the required equations of tangents.

Also, let (x_1, y_1) be the point of contact, then equation of tangent at (x_1, y_1) to the circle $x^2+y^2=a^2$ is
$$xx_1+yy_1=a^2 \qquad \text{...(ii)}$$
On comparing Eq. (i) and Eq. (ii), we get
$$\frac{x_1}{m}=\frac{y_1}{-1}=\frac{a^2}{\pm a\sqrt{(1+m^2)}}$$
$$\Rightarrow \quad \frac{x_1}{m}=-\frac{y_1}{1}=\pm\frac{a}{\sqrt{(1+m^2)}}$$
$$\Rightarrow \quad x_1=\pm\frac{am}{\sqrt{1+m^2}} \quad \text{and} \quad y_1=\mp\frac{a}{\sqrt{(1+m^2)}}$$
Hence, $(x_1, y_1)=\left(\pm\dfrac{am}{\sqrt{(1+m^2)}}, \mp\dfrac{a}{\sqrt{(1+m^2)}}\right)$

Corollary **:** It also follows that $y=mx+c$ is a tangent to $x^2+y^2=a^2$, if $c^2=a^2(1+m^2)$ which is condition of tangency.

Remarks

1. The reason why there are two equations $y=mx\pm a\sqrt{1+m^2}$, there are two tangents, both are parallel and at the ends of diameter.
2. The line $ax+by+c=0$ is tangent to the circle $x^2+y^2=r^2$ if and only if $c^2=r^2(a^2+b^2)$.
3. If the line $y=mx+c$ is the tangent to the circle $x^2+y^2=r^2$, then point of contact is given by $\left(-\frac{mr^2}{c}, \frac{r^2}{c}\right)$
4. If the line $ax+by+c=0$ is the tangent to the circle $x^2+y^2=r^2$, then point of contact is given by $\left(-\frac{ar^2}{c}, -\frac{br^2}{c}\right)$.
5. The condition that the line $lx+my+n=0$ touches the circle $x^2+y^2+2gx+2fy+c=0$ is $(lg+mf-n)^2=(l^2+m^2)(g^2+f^2-c)$.
6. Equation of tangent of the circle $x^2+y^2+2gx+2fy+c=0$ in terms of slope is
$y+f=m(x+g)\pm\sqrt{(g^2+f^2-c)(1+m^2)}$
7. The equation of tangents of slope m to the circle $(x-a)^2+(y-b)^2=r^2$ are given by
$(y-b)=m(x-a)\pm r\sqrt{(1+m^2)}$
and the coordinates of the points of contact are
$\left(a\pm\frac{mr}{\sqrt{(1+m^2)}}, b\mp\frac{r}{\sqrt{(1+m^2)}}\right)$

Example 35. Find the equations of the tangents to the circle $x^2 + y^2 = 9$, which

(i) are parallel to the line $3x+4y-5=0$

(ii) are perpendicular to the line $2x+3y+7=0$

(iii) make an angle of 60° with the X-axis

Sol. (i) Slope of $3x + 4y - 5 = 0$ is $-\dfrac{3}{4}$

$$\text{Let } m = -\frac{3}{4}$$

and equation of circle is $x^2 + y^2 = 9$

$\therefore$ Equations of tangents

$$y = -\frac{3}{4}x \pm 3\sqrt{\left(1+\left(-\frac{3}{4}\right)^2\right)}$$

$$\Rightarrow \quad 4y = -3x \pm 15 \quad \text{or} \quad 3x + 4y \pm 15 = 0$$

(ii) Slope of $2x + 3y + 7 = 0$ is $-\dfrac{2}{3}$

$\therefore$ Slope of perpendicular to $2x + 3y + 7 = 0$ is $\dfrac{3}{2} = m$ (say)

and given circle is $x^2 + y^2 = 9$

$\therefore$ Equations of tangents perpendicular to $2x + 3y + 7 = 0$ is

$$y = \frac{3}{2}x \pm 3\sqrt{1+\left(\frac{3}{2}\right)^2}$$

$$\Rightarrow \quad 2y = 3x \pm 3\sqrt{13}$$

$$\text{or} \quad 3x - 2y \pm 3\sqrt{13} = 0$$

(iii) Since, tangent make an angle 60° with the X-axis

$$\therefore \quad m = \tan 60° = \sqrt{3}$$

and given circle $x^2 + y^2 = 9$

$\therefore$ Equation of tangents $y = \sqrt{3}x \pm 3\sqrt{1+(\sqrt{3})^2}$

$$\text{or} \quad \sqrt{3}\,x - y \pm 6 = 0$$

Aliter :

(i) Let tangent parallel to $3x + 4y - 5 = 0$ is

$$3x + 4y + \lambda = 0 \quad \text{...(i)}$$

and circle $x^2 + y^2 = 9$

then perpendicular distance from (0, 0) on Eq. (i) = radius

$$\frac{|\lambda|}{\sqrt{(3^2+4^2)}} = 3$$

$$\text{or} \quad |\lambda| = 15$$

$$\therefore \quad \lambda = \pm 15$$

From Eq. (i), equations of tangents are

$$3x + 4y \pm 15 = 0$$

(ii) Let tangent perpendicular to $2x + 3y + 7 = 0$ is

$$3x - 2y + \lambda = 0 \quad \text{...(ii)}$$

and circle $x^2 + y^2 = 9$

then, perpendicular distance from (0, 0) on Eq. (ii) = radius

$$\frac{|\lambda|}{\sqrt{3^2+(-2)^2}} = 3$$

$$\text{or} \quad |\lambda| = 3\sqrt{13}$$

$$\text{or} \quad \lambda = \pm 3\sqrt{13}$$

From Eq. (ii), equations of tangents are

$$3x - 2y \pm 3\sqrt{13} = 0$$

(iii) Let equation of tangent which makes an angle of 60° with the X-axis is

$$y = \sqrt{3}x + c \quad \text{...(iii)}$$

$$\text{or} \quad \sqrt{3}x - y + c = 0$$

and circle $x^2 + y^2 = 9$

then, perpendicular distance from (0, 0) to Eq. (iii) = radius

$$\frac{|c|}{\sqrt{(\sqrt{3})^2+(-1)^2}} = 3$$

$$\text{or} \quad |c| = 6$$

$$\text{or} \quad c = \pm 6$$

From Eq. (iii), equations of tangents are

$$\sqrt{3}x - y \pm 6 = 0$$

Example 36. Prove that the line $lx + my + n = 0$ touches the circle $(x-a)^2 + (y-b)^2 = r^2$ if $(al+bm+n)^2 = r^2(l^2+m^2)$.

Sol. If the line $lx + my + n = 0$ touches the circle $(x-a)^2 + (y-b)^2 = r^2$, then length of the perpendicular from the centre = radius

$$\frac{|la + mb + n|}{\sqrt{(l^2+m^2)}} = r$$

$$\Rightarrow \quad (la + mb + n)^2 = r^2(l^2 + m^2)$$

Aliter :

Here, line is $lx + my + n = 0$ and circle is $(x-a)^2 + (y-b)^2 = r^2$. Here, centre of circle (a, b) shift at (0, 0), then replacing x by $x + a$ and y by $y + b$ in the equation of straight line $lx + my + n = 0$ and circle $(x-a)^2 + (y-b)^2 = r^2$, the new form of straight line and circle are

$$l(x+a) + m(y+b) + n = 0$$

$$\text{or} \quad lx + my + (al + mb + n) = 0 \quad \text{...(i)}$$

$$\text{and} \quad x^2 + y^2 = r^2 \quad \text{...(ii)}$$

respectively.

On comparing Eq. (i) with $y = Mx + C$

$$\text{then} \quad M = -\frac{l}{m}$$

$$\text{and} \quad C = -\frac{(al + bm + n)}{m}$$

Since, Eq. (i) is the tangent of Eq. (ii), then

$$C^2 = r^2 (1 + M^2)$$

or $$\frac{(al + bm + n)^2}{m^2} = r^2 \left(1 + \frac{l^2}{m^2}\right)$$

or $$(al + bm + n)^2 = r^2 (l^2 + m^2)$$

Example 37. Show that the line $3x - 4y = 1$ touches the circle $x^2 + y^2 - 2x + 4y + 1 = 0$. Find the coordinates of the point of contact.

Sol. The centre and radius of the circle

$$x^2 + y^2 - 2x + 4y + 1 = 0 \text{ are } (1, -2)$$

and $\sqrt{(-1) + (2)^2 - 1} = 2$ respectively.

Since, length of perpendicular from centre $(1, -2)$ on $3x - 4y = 1$ is

$$\frac{|3 \times 1 - 4 \times (-2) - 1|}{\sqrt{(3)^2 + (-4)^2}} = \frac{10}{5}$$

$$= 2 = \text{radius of the circle}$$

Hence, $3x - 4y = 1$ touches the circle

$$x^2 + y^2 - 2x + 4y + 1 = 0$$

Second part : Let point of contact is (x_1, y_1), then tangent at (x_1, y_1) on $x^2 + y^2 - 2x + 4y + 1 = 0$ is

$$xx_1 + yy_1 - (x + x_1) + 2(y + y_1) + 1 = 0$$

$$\Rightarrow \quad x(x_1 - 1) + y(y_1 + 2) - x_1 + 2y_1 + 1 = 0 \quad \text{...(i)}$$

and given line $\quad 3x - 4y - 1 = 0 \quad$ ...(ii)

Since, Eq. (i) and Eq. (ii) are identical, then comparing Eq. (i) and Eq. (ii), we get

$$\frac{x_1 - 1}{3} = \frac{y_1 + 2}{-4} = \frac{-x_1 + 2y_1 + 1}{-1}$$

or $$x_1 = -\frac{1}{5} \text{ and } y_1 = -\frac{2}{5}$$

$\therefore$ Point of contact is $\left(-\frac{1}{5}, -\frac{2}{5}\right)$.

Aliter for second part : Since, perpendicular line to tangent always passes through the centre of the circle, perpendicular line to

$$3x - 4y = 1 \quad \text{...(i)}$$

is $$4x + 3y = \lambda \quad \text{...(ii)}$$

which passes through $(1, -2)$, then

$$4 - 6 = \lambda$$

$$\therefore \quad \lambda = -2$$

From Eq. (ii), $\quad 4x + 3y = -2 \quad$ ...(iii)

Solving Eq. (i) and Eq. (iii), we get the point of contact i.e. $x = -\frac{1}{5}$ and $y = -\frac{2}{5}$

Hence, point of contact is $\left(-\frac{1}{5}, -\frac{2}{5}\right)$.

Example 38. If $lx + my = 1$ touches the circle $x^2 + y^2 = a^2$, prove that the point (l, m) lies on the circle $x^2 + y^2 = a^{-2}$.

Sol. Since, $lx + my = 1$ touches the circle $x^2 + y^2 = a^2$.

Then, length of perpendicular from $(0, 0)$ on $lx + my = 1$ is equal to radius

then, $\frac{|-1|}{\sqrt{l^2 + m^2}} = a$ or $l^2 + m^2 = a^{-2}$

Hence, locus of (l, m) is $x^2 + y^2 = a^{-2}$

Aliter : Let the point of contact of line $lx + my = 1$ and circle $x^2 + y^2 = a^2$ is (x_1, y_1), then tangent of circle at (x_1, y_1) is $xx_1 + yy_1 = a^2$

Since, $\quad xx_1 + yy_1 = a^2 \quad$ and $\quad lx + my = 1$

are identical, then $\frac{x_1}{l} = \frac{y_1}{m} = \frac{a^2}{1}$

$$\therefore \quad x_1 = la^2, y_1 = ma^2$$

but (x_1, y_1) lie on $x^2 + y^2 = a^2$

then, $$l^2a^4 + m^2a^4 = a^2$$

$$\therefore \quad l^2 + m^2 = a^{-2}$$

$\therefore$ Locus of (l, m) is $x^2 + y^2 = a^{-2}$

Example 39. Show that the line $(x - 2)\cos\theta + (y - 2)\sin\theta = 1$ touches a circle for all values of θ. Find the circle.

Sol. Given line is $(x - 2)\cos\theta + (y - 2)\sin\theta$

$$1 = \cos^2\theta + \sin^2\theta$$

On comparing

$$x - 2 = \cos\theta \quad \text{...(i)}$$

and $$y - 2 = \sin\theta \quad \text{...(ii)}$$

Squaring and adding Eq. (i) and Eq. (ii), then

$$(x - 2)^2 + (y - 2)^2 = \cos^2\theta + \sin^2\theta$$

$$\Rightarrow \quad (x - 2)^2 + (y - 2)^2 = 1$$

or $$x^2 + y^2 - 4x - 4y + 7 = 0$$

Aliter : Since, tangent at $(\cos\theta, \sin\theta)$ of

$$x^2 + y^2 = 1 \quad \text{...(i)}$$

is $$x\cos\theta + y\sin\theta = 1 \quad \text{...(ii)}$$

replacing x by $x - 2$ and y by $y - 2$ in Eqs. (i) and (ii), then

$$(x - 2)^2 + (y - 2)^2 = 1 \quad \text{...(iii)}$$

$$(x - 2)\cos\theta + (y - 2)\sin\theta = 1 \quad \text{...(iv)}$$

Hence, Eq. (iv) touches the circle Eq. (iii).

$\therefore$ Equation of circle is

$$(x - 2)^2 + (y - 2)^2 = 1$$

or $$x^2 + y^2 - 4x - 4y + 7 = 0$$

Normal to a Circle at a Given Point

The normal of a circle at any point is a straight line which is perpendicular to the tangent at the point and always passes through the centre of the circle.

Different form of the Equation of Normals

1. Point form :

Theorem : The equation of normal at the point $P(x_1, y_1)$ to the circle $x^2+y^2+2gx+2fy+c=0$ is

$$\frac{x-x_1}{x_1+g}=\frac{y-y_1}{y_1+f}$$

Proof :

Equation of the given circle is

$$x^2+y^2+2gx+2fy+c=0 \quad \text{...(i)}$$

Its centre C is $(-g, -f)$

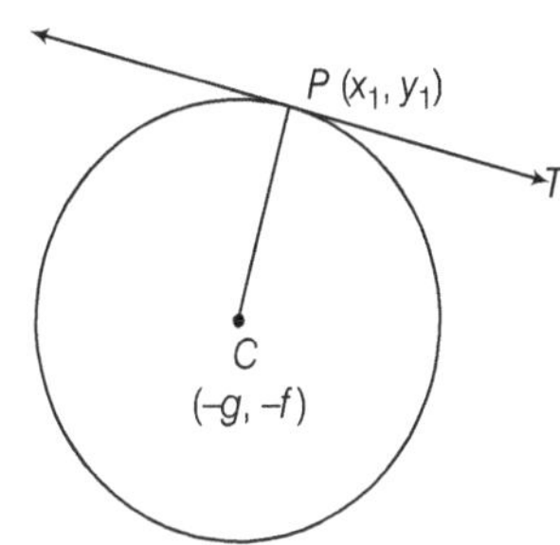

Let $P(x_1, y_1)$ be the given point.

$\because$ Normal of the circle at $P(x_1, y_1)$ passes through centre $C(-g, -f)$ of the circle.

Then, equation of normal CP passes through the points $C(-g, -f)$ and $P(x_1, y_1)$ is

$$y-y_1=\frac{(y_1+f)}{(x_1+g)}(x-x_1)$$

or
$$\frac{x-x_1}{x_1+g}=\frac{y-y_1}{y_1+f}$$

This is the required equation of normal at $P(x_1, y_1)$ of the given circle.

Remark

Easy method to find normal at (x_1, y_1) of second degree conics

$$ax^2+2hxy+by^2+2gx+2fy+c=0 \quad \text{...(i)}$$

then, according to determinant $\begin{vmatrix} a & h & g \\ h & b & f \\ g & f & c \end{vmatrix}$ write first two rows as ax_1+hy_1+g and hx_1+by_1+f

Then, normal at (x_1, y_1) of conic (i)

$$\frac{x-x_1}{ax_1+hy_1+g}=\frac{y-y_1}{hx_1+by_1+f}$$

***Corollary* 1 :** Equation of normal of $x^2+y^2=a^2$ at (x_1, y_1) is

$$\frac{x-x_1}{1\cdot x_1+0+0}=\frac{y-y_1}{0+1\cdot y_1+0}$$

(Here, $g, f=0$ and $a=b=1$)

$$\Rightarrow \quad \frac{x-x_1}{x_1}=\frac{y-y_1}{y_1}$$

or
$$\frac{x}{x_1}=\frac{y}{y_1}$$

***Corollary* 2 :** Equation of normal of $x^2+y^2+2gx+2fy+c=0$ at (x_1, y_1) is

$$\frac{x-x_1}{x_1+g}=\frac{y-y_1}{y_1+f} \quad \text{(Here, } a=b=1 \text{ and } h=0)$$

Remarks

1. Normal always passes through the centre of the circle. Just write the equation of the line joining (x_1, y_1) and the centre of the circle.
2. The equations of the normals show that they pass through the centre i.e. the normals are the radii which we know from *Euclidean geometry*.

Example 40. Find the equation of the normal to the circle $x^2+y^2=2x$, which is parallel to the line $x+2y=3$.

Sol. Given circle is $x^2+y^2-2x=0$

Centre of given circle is (1, 0)

Since, normal is parallel to $x+2y=3$

let the equation of normal is $x+2y=\lambda$

Since, normal passes through the centre of the circle i.e. (1, 0)

then $1+0=\lambda$

$\therefore \quad \lambda=1$

then, equation of normal is $x+2y=1$

or $x+2y-1=0$

Aliter Equation of normal at (x_1, y_1) of $x^2+y^2-2x=0$ is

$$\frac{x-x_1}{x_1-1}=\frac{y-y_1}{y_1-0}$$

or
$$\text{Slope}=\frac{y_1}{x_1-1}=m_1 \quad \text{(say)}$$

Since normal is parallel to $x + 2y = 3$

$\therefore \quad \text{Slope} = -\frac{1}{2} = m_2 \quad \text{(say)}$

but given $m_1 = m_2$

$$\frac{y_1}{x_1 - 1} = -\frac{1}{2} \text{ or } x_1 + 2y_1 - 1 = 0$$

$\therefore$ Locus of (x_1, y_1) is $x + 2y - 1 = 0$

Example 41. Find the equation of the normal to the circle $x^2 + y^2 - 5x + 2y - 48 = 0$ at the point $(5, 6)$.

Sol. Equation of the normal at $(5, 6)$ is

$$\frac{x-5}{5-\frac{5}{2}} = \frac{y-6}{6+1} \Rightarrow \frac{x-5}{\frac{5}{2}} = \frac{y-6}{7} \Rightarrow \frac{2x-10}{5} = \frac{y-6}{7}$$

$\Rightarrow \quad 14x - 70 = 5y - 30$

$\therefore \quad 14x - 5y - 40 = 0$

Aliter I : Since, centre of the circle $x^2 + y^2 - 5x + 2y - 48 = 0$ is $\left(\frac{5}{2}, -1\right)$, normal at (5,6) is the equation of a line, which passes through $\left(\frac{5}{2}, -1\right)$ and $(5, 6)$ is

$$y + 1 = \frac{6+1}{5-\frac{5}{2}}\left(x - \frac{5}{2}\right) \Rightarrow y + 1 = \frac{14}{5}\left(x - \frac{5}{2}\right)$$

$\Rightarrow \quad y + 1 = \frac{7}{5}(2x - 5)$

$\Rightarrow \quad 5y + 5 = 14x - 35 \quad \text{or} \quad 14x - 5y - 40 = 0$

Aliter II : Equation of tangent at $(5, 6)$ is

$$5 \cdot x + 6 \cdot y - \frac{5}{2}(x + 5) + (y + 6) - 48 = 0$$

$\Rightarrow \quad 10x + 12y - 5x - 25 + 2y + 12 - 96 = 0$

$\Rightarrow \quad 5x + 14y - 109 = 0$

Slope of tangent $= -\frac{5}{14}$

$\therefore \quad$ Slope of normal $= \frac{14}{5}$

$\therefore$ Equation of normal at $(5, 6)$ with slope $\frac{14}{5}$ is

$$y - 6 = \frac{14}{5}(x - 5)$$

$\Rightarrow \quad 5y - 30 = 14x - 70$

or $\quad 14x - 5y - 40 = 0$

2. Parametric form

Since, parametric coordinates of circle $x^2 + y^2 = a^2$ is $(a\cos\theta, a\sin\theta)$.

$\therefore$ Equation of normal at $(a\cos\theta, a\sin\theta)$ is

$$\frac{x}{a\cos\theta} = \frac{y}{a\sin\theta}$$

or $\quad \frac{x}{\cos\theta} = \frac{y}{\sin\theta}$ or $y = x\tan\theta$

or $\quad y = mx$, where $m = \tan\theta$

which is slope form of normal.

Exercise for Session 4

1. The length of the chord cut-off by $y = 2x + 1$ from the circle $x^2 + y^2 = 2$ is
   (a) $\frac{5}{6}$ (b) $\frac{6}{5}$ (c) $\frac{6}{\sqrt{5}}$ (d) $\frac{\sqrt{5}}{6}$

2. Circle $x^2 + y^2 - 4x - 8y - 5 = 0$ will intersect the line $3x - 4y = \lambda$ in two distinct points, if
   (a) $-10 < \lambda < 5$ (b) $9 < \lambda < 20$ (c) $-35 < \lambda < 15$ (d) $-16 < \lambda < 30$

3. If the line $3x - 4y + \lambda = 0$, $(\lambda > 0)$ touches the circle $x^2 + y^2 - 4x - 8y - 5 = 0$ at (a, b), then $\lambda + a + b$ is equal to
   (a) -22 (b) -20 (c) 20 (d) 22

4. Tangent which is parallel to the line $x - 3y - 2 = 0$ of the circle $x^2 + y^2 - 4x + 2y - 5 = 0$, has point/points of contact
   (a) $(1, -2)$ (b) $(-1, 2)$ (c) $(3, 4)$ (d) $(3, -4)$

5. If a circle, whose centre is $(-1, 1)$ touches the straight line $x + 2y = 12$, then the co-ordinates of the point of contact are
   (a) $\left(-\frac{7}{2}, -4\right)$ (b) $\left(-\frac{18}{5}, -\frac{21}{5}\right)$ (c) $(2, -7)$ (d) $(-2, -5)$

6. The area of the triangle formed by the tangent at the point (a, b) to the circle $x^2 + y^2 = r^2$ and the coordinate axes is

(a) $\frac{r^4}{2ab}$ (b) $\frac{r^4}{2|ab|}$ (c) $\frac{r^4}{ab}$ (d) $\frac{r^4}{|ab|}$

7. The equation of the tangent to the circle $x^2 + y^2 + 4x - 4y + 4 = 0$ which make equal intercepts on the positive coordinate axes is

(a) $x + y = 2$ (b) $x + y = 2\sqrt{2}$ (c) $x + y = 4$ (d) $x + y = 8$

8. If $a > 2b > 0$, then the positive value of m for which $y = mx - b\sqrt{(1+m^2)}$ is a common tangent to $x^2 + y^2 = b^2$ and $(x-a)^2 + y^2 = b^2$ is

(a) $\frac{2b}{\sqrt{(a^2 - 4b^2)}}$ (b) $\frac{\sqrt{(a^2 - 4b^2)}}{2b}$ (c) $\frac{2b}{a - 2b}$ (d) $\frac{b}{a - 2b}$

9. The angle between a pair of tangents from a point P to the circle $x^2 + y^2 = 16$ is $\frac{\pi}{3}$ and locus of P is $x^2 + y^2 = r^2$, then value of r is

(a) 5 (b) 6 (c) 7 (d) 8

10. The normal at the point $(3, 4)$ on a circle cuts the circle at the point $(-1, -2)$. Then, the equation of the circle is

(a) $x^2 + y^2 + 2x - 2y - 13 = 0$ (b) $x^2 + y^2 - 2x - 2y - 11 = 0$

(c) $x^2 + y^2 - 2x + 2y + 12 = 0$ (d) $x^2 + y^2 - 2x - 2y + 14 = 0$

11. The line $ax + by + c = 0$ is a normal to the circle $x^2 + y^2 = r^2$. The portion of the line $ax + by + c = 0$ intercepted by this circle is of length

(a) $\sqrt{r}$ (b) r (c) r^2 (d) $2r$

12. If the line $ax + by + c = 0$ touches the circle $x^2 + y^2 - 2x = \frac{3}{5}$ and is normal to the circle $x^2 + y^2 + 2x - 4y + 1 = 0$, then (a, b) are

(a) (1,3) (b) (3,1) (c) (1, 2) (d) (2, 1)

13. Show that for all values of θ, $x \sin\theta - y \cos\theta = a$ touches the circle $x^2 + y^2 = a^2$.

14. Find the equation of the tangents to the circle $x^2 + y^2 - 2x - 4y - 4 = 0$

which are (i) parallel (ii) perpendicular to the line $3x - 4y - 1 = 0$.

15. Find the equation of the family of circle which touch the pair of straight lines $x^2 - y^2 + 2y - 1 = 0$.

16. Find the value of λ so that the line $3x - 4y = \lambda$ may touch the circle $x^2 + y^2 - 4x - 8y - 5 = 0$.

17. Show that the area of the triangle formed by the positive X-axis, the normal and tangent to the circle $x^2 + y^2 = 4$ at $(1, \sqrt{3})$ is $2\sqrt{3}$.

Session 5

Tangents from a Point to the Circle, Length of the Tangent from a Point to a Circle, Power of a Point with Respect to a Circle, Chord of Contact, Chord Bisected at a Given Point, Pair of Tangents, Director Circle

Tangent from a Point to the Circle

Theorem : From a given point two tangents can be drawn to a circle which are real, coincident or imaginary according as the given point lies outside,on or inside the circle .

Proof : If circle is $\quad x^2 + y^2 = a^2 \quad$ ...(i)

any tangent to the circle Eq. (i) is

$$y = mx + a\sqrt{(1+m^2)} \quad \text{...(ii)}$$

If outside point is (x_1, y_1)

then, $\quad y_1 = mx_1 + a\sqrt{1+m^2}$

or $\quad (y_1 - mx_1)^2 = a^2(1+m^2)$

or $\quad y_1^2 + m^2x_1^2 - 2mx_1y_1 = a^2 + a^2m^2$

$\Rightarrow \quad m^2(x_1^2 - a^2) - 2mx_1y_1 + y_1^2 - a^2 = 0 \quad$ ...(iii)

which is quadratic in m which gives two values of m.

(real coincident or imaginary) corresponding to any value of x_1 and y_1.

The tangents are real, coincident or imaginary according as the values of m obtained from Eq. (iii) are real, coincident or imaginary.

or Discriminant $>, =,$ or <0

$\Rightarrow \quad 4x_1^2y_1^2 - 4(x_1^2 - a^2)(y_1^2 - a^2) >, =,$ or <0

$\Rightarrow \quad (x_1^2 + y_1^2 - a^2) >, =$ or <0

i.e. $P(x_1, y_1)$ lies outside, on or inside the circle $x^2 + y^2 = a^2$.

If P outside the circle, then substituting these values of m in Eq. (ii), we get the equation of tangents.

Aliter :

First write equation of line through (x_1, y_1) say

$$y - y_1 = m(x - x_1) \quad \text{...(i)}$$

which is tangent of the circle $x^2 + y^2 = a^2$, then

length of perpendicular from centre $(0, 0)$ to Eq. (i) = radius of the circle

then, $\quad \dfrac{|mx_1 - y_1|}{\sqrt{(1+m^2)}} = a$

or $\quad (mx_1 - y_1)^2 = a^2(1+m^2)$

or $\quad m^2x_1^2 - 2mx_1y_1 + y_1^2 = a^2 + a^2m^2$

$\Rightarrow \quad m^2(x_1^2 - a^2) - 2mx_1y_1 + y_1^2 - a^2 = 0$

which is quadratic in m which gives two values of m.

Example 42. Find the equations of the tangents to the circle $x^2 + y^2 = 16$ drawn from the point $(1, 4)$.

Sol. Given circle is

$$x^2 + y^2 = 16 \quad \text{...(i)}$$

Any tangent of Eq. (i) in terms of slope is

$$y = mx + 4\sqrt{(1+m^2)} \quad \text{...(ii)}$$

which passes through (1, 4)

then, $\quad 4 = m + 4\sqrt{(1+m^2)}$

$\Rightarrow \quad (4 - m)^2 = 16(1+m^2)$

$\Rightarrow \quad 15m^2 + 8m = 0$

$\therefore \quad m = 0, -\dfrac{8}{15}$

From Eq. (ii), equations of tangents drawn from (1, 4) are

$$y = 4$$

and $$y = -\frac{8}{15}x + 4\sqrt{\left(1 + \frac{64}{225}\right)}$$

or $8x + 15y = 68$ respectively.

Aliter : Equation of line through (1, 4) is $y - 4 = m(x - 1)$

$$\Rightarrow \quad mx - y + 4 - m = 0 \quad \text{...(i)}$$

Then, perpendicular length from centre (0, 0) to $mx - y + 4 - m = 0$ is equal to radius

then, $$\frac{|4 - m|}{\sqrt{m^2 + 1}} = 4$$

or $$(4 - m)^2 = 16(m^2 + 1)$$

$$\Rightarrow \quad 15m^2 + 8m = 0$$

$$\therefore \quad m = 0, -\frac{8}{15}$$

From Eq. (i), equation of tangents from (1, 4) are $y = 4$ and $8x + 15y = 68$, respectively.

Example 43. The angle between a pair of tangents from a point P to the circle $x^2 + y^2 + 4x - 6y + 9\sin^2\alpha + 13\cos^2\alpha = 0$ is 2α. Find the equation of the locus of the point P.

Sol. Let coordinates of P be (x_1, y_1) and given circle is

$$x^2 + y^2 + 4x - 6y + 9\sin^2\alpha + 13\cos^2\alpha = 0$$

or $$(x + 2)^2 + (y - 3)^2 - 4 - 9 + 9\sin^2\alpha + 13\cos^2\alpha = 0$$

$$\Rightarrow \quad (x + 2)^2 + (y - 3)^2 + 9\sin^2\alpha - 13(1 - \cos^2\alpha) = 0$$

$$\Rightarrow \quad (x + 2)^2 + (y - 3)^2 = 4\sin^2\alpha$$

$\therefore$ Centre and radius are $(-2, 3)$ and $2\sin\alpha$, respectively.

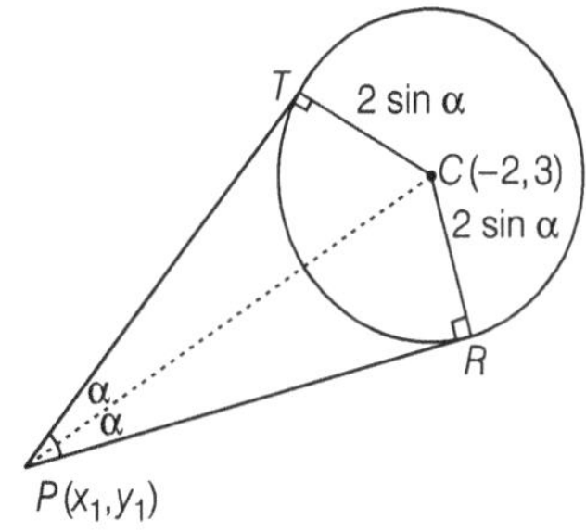

Distance between $P(x_1, y_1)$ and centre of circle $C(-2, 3)$ is

$$CP = \sqrt{(x_1 + 2)^2 + (y_1 - 3)^2}$$

In ΔPCT, $$\sin\alpha = \frac{CT}{CP} = \frac{2\sin\alpha}{\sqrt{(x_1 + 2)^2 + (y_1 - 3)^2}}$$

or $$\sqrt{(x_1 + 2)^2 + (y_1 - 3)^2} = 2$$

or $$(x_1 + 2)^2 + (y_1 - 3)^2 = 4$$

The required locus of $P(x_1, y_1)$ is

$$(x + 2)^2 + (y - 3)^2 = 4$$

Length of the Tangent from a Point to a Circle

Theorem : The length of tangent from the point $P(x_1, y_1)$ to the circle $x^2 + y^2 + 2gx + 2fy + c = 0$ is

$$\sqrt{(x_1^2 + y_1^2 + 2gx_1 + 2fy_1 + c)} = \sqrt{S_1}$$

Proof : Let PT and PT' be two tangents from the given point $P(x_1, y_1)$ to the circle $x^2 + y^2 + 2gx + 2fy + c = 0$. Then, the centre and radius are $C(-g, -f)$ and $\sqrt{(g^2 + f^2 - c)}$ $(= CT = CT')$ respectively.

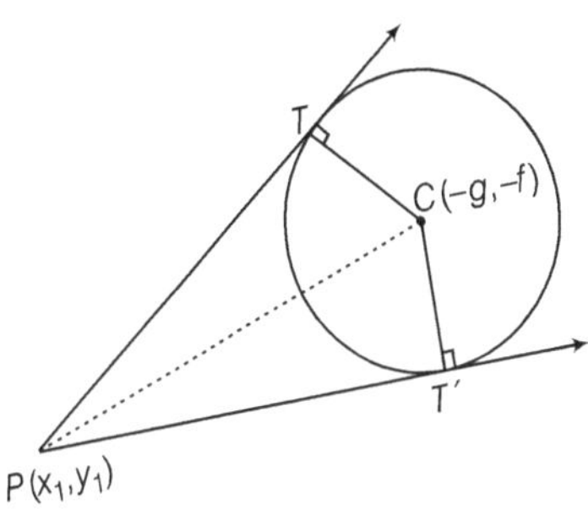

In ΔPCT,

$$PT = \sqrt{(PC)^2 - (CT)^2}$$

$$= \sqrt{(x_1 + g)^2 + (y_1 + f)^2 - g^2 - f^2 + c}$$

$$= \sqrt{(x_1^2 + y_1^2 + 2gx_1 + 2fy_1 + c)} = \sqrt{S_1} = PT'$$

where, $S_1 = x_1^2 + y_1^2 + 2gx_1 + 2fy_1 + c$

Remarks

1. To find length of tangent
   let $S = x^2 + y^2 + 2gx + 2fy + c$
   then, $S_1 = x_1^2 + y_1^2 + 2gx_1 + 2fy_1 + c$
   where, $P(x_1, y_1)$
   $\therefore$ length of tangent $= \sqrt{S_1}$
2. For S_1 first write the equation of circle in general form i.e. coefficient of x^2 = coefficient of $y^2 = 1$ and making RHS of circle is zero, then let LHS by S.

Example 44. Find the length of tangents drawn from the point $(3, -4)$ to the circle $2x^2 + 2y^2 - 7x - 9y - 13 = 0$.

Sol. The equation of the given circle is

$$2x^2 + 2y^2 - 7x - 9y - 13 = 0$$

Re-writing the given equation of the circle

i.e. $$x^2 + y^2 - \frac{7}{2}x - \frac{9}{2}y - \frac{13}{2} = 0$$

Let $S = x^2 + y^2 - \frac{7}{2}x - \frac{9}{2}y - \frac{13}{2}$

$\therefore$ $S_1 = (3)^2 + (-4)^2 - \frac{7}{2} \times 3 - \frac{9}{2} \times (-4) - \frac{13}{2}$

$= 25 - \frac{21}{2} + 18 - \frac{13}{2} = 43 - 17 = 26$

$\therefore$ Length of tangent $= \sqrt{S_1} = \sqrt{26}$

Example 45. If the length of tangent from (f, g) to the circle $x^2 + y^2 = 6$ be twice the length of the tangent from (f, g) to circle $x^2 + y^2 + 3x + 3y = 0$, then find the value of $f^2 + g^2 + 4f + 4g$.

Sol. According to the question

$$\sqrt{(g^2 + f^2 - 6)} = 2\sqrt{(f^2 + g^2 + 3f + 3g)}$$

On squaring $g^2 + f^2 - 6 = 4f^2 + 4g^2 + 12f + 12g$

or $3f^2 + 3g^2 + 12f + 12g + 6 = 0$

or $f^2 + g^2 + 4f + 4g + 2 = 0$

or $f^2 + g^2 + 4f + 4g = -2$

Example 46. Show that the area of the triangle formed by tangents from the point (4, 3) to the circle $x^2 + y^2 = 9$ and the line segment joining their points of contact is $7\frac{17}{25}$ square units in length.

Sol. Since, $PQ = PR = \sqrt{4^2 + 3^2 - 9} = 4$ units

$\therefore$ $\angle CPQ = \angle CPR = \alpha$ (let)

$\therefore$ $PC = \sqrt{(4-0)^2 + (3-0)^2} = 5$ units

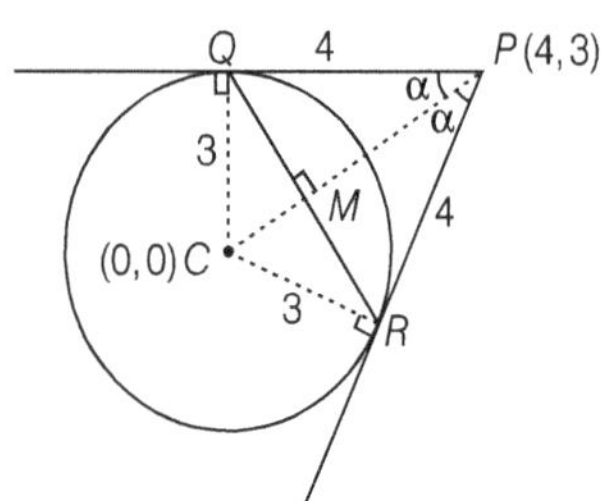

$\therefore$ In ΔPQC, $\tan\alpha = \frac{3}{4}$,

$\therefore$ $\sin\alpha = \frac{3}{5}$

and $\cos\alpha = \frac{4}{5}$

In ΔPMQ, $\cos\alpha = \frac{PM}{4} = \frac{4}{5}$

$\therefore$ $PM = \frac{16}{5}$

and $\sin\alpha = \frac{QM}{4} = \frac{3}{5}$

$\therefore$ $QM = \frac{12}{5}$

$\therefore$ Area of $\Delta PQR = \frac{1}{2} \cdot QR \cdot PM$

$= \frac{1}{2}(2QM) \cdot PM = (QM)(PM)$

$= \left(\frac{12}{5}\right)\left(\frac{16}{5}\right) = \frac{192}{25}$

$= 7\frac{17}{25}$ sq units

Example 47. Show that the length of the tangent from any point on the circle $x^2 + y^2 + 2gx + 2fy + c = 0$ to the circle $x^2 + y^2 + 2gx + 2fy + c_1 = 0$ is $\sqrt{(c_1 - c)}$.

Sol. Let (x_1, y_1) be any point on

$$x^2 + y^2 + 2gx + 2fy + c = 0$$

then $x_1^2 + y_1^2 + 2gx_1 + 2fy_1 + c = 0$ ...(i)

$\therefore$ Length of tangent from (x_1, y_1) to the circle

$x^2 + y^2 + 2gx + 2fy + c_1 = 0$ is

$\sqrt{x_1^2 + y_1^2 + 2gx_1 + 2fy_1 + c_1}$

$= \sqrt{(-c + c_1)} = \sqrt{(c_1 - c)}$ [From Eq. (i)]

Power of a Point With Respect to a Circle

Theorem : The power of a point $P(x_1, y_1)$ with respect to the circle

$$x^2 + y^2 + 2gx + 2fy + c = 0 \text{ is } S_1$$

where, $S_1 = x_1^2 + y_1^2 + 2gx_1 + 2fy_1 + c$

Proof : Let $P(x_1, y_1)$ be a point outside the circle and PAB and PCD drawn two secants. The power of $P(x_1, y_1)$ with respect to

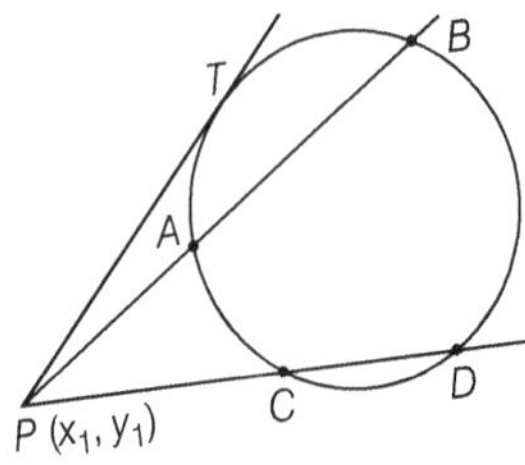

$$S \equiv x^2 + y^2 + 2gx + 2fy + c = 0$$

is equal to $PA \cdot PB$ which is

$$x_1^2 + y_1^2 + 2gx_1 + 2fy_1 + c = S_1$$

$\therefore$ Power remains constant for the circle

i.e. independent of A and B.

$\therefore\ PA\cdot PB = PC\cdot PD = (PT)^2 = S_1 = (\sqrt{S_1})^2$

$\therefore\ PA\cdot PB = (\sqrt{S_1})^2$ = square of the length of tangent.

Remark

If P outside, inside or on the circle, then $PA\cdot PB$ is + ve, − ve or zero, respectively.

Example 48. Find the power of point (2, 4) with respect to the circle $x^2 + y^2 - 6x + 4y - 8 = 0$

Sol. The power of the point (2, 4) with respect to the circle

$$x^2 + y^2 - 6x + 4y - 8 = 0 \text{ is } (\sqrt{S_1})^2 \text{ or } S_1$$

where, $S = x^2 + y^2 - 6x + 4y - 8$

$\therefore\quad S_1 = (2)^2 + (4)^2 - 6\times 2 + 4\times 4 - 8$

$= 4 + 16 - 12 + 16 - 8 = 16$

[$\because$ (2, 4) is outside from the circle $x^2 + y^2 - 6x + 4y - 8 = 0$]

Example 49. Show that the locus of the point, the powers of which with respect to two given circles are equal, is a straight line.

Sol. Let the given circles be

$$x^2 + y^2 + 2gx + 2fy + c = 0 \quad \text{...(i)}$$

and $$x^2 + y^2 + 2g_1x + 2f_1y + c_1 = 0 \quad \text{...(ii)}$$

Let $P(x_1, y_1)$ be a point, the powers of which with respect to the circles Eqs. (i) and (ii) are equal. Then,

$\therefore\quad [\sqrt{(x_1^2 + y_1^2 + 2gx_1 + 2fy_1 + c)}]^2$

$= [\sqrt{(x_1^2 + y_1^2 + 2g_1x_1 + 2f_1y_1 + c_1)}]^2$

or $\quad x_1^2 + y_1^2 + 2gx_1 + 2fy_1 + c$

$= x_1^2 + y_1^2 + 2g_1x_1 + 2f_1y_1 + c_1$

$\Rightarrow\quad 2(g - g_1)x_1 + 2(f - f_1)y_1 + c - c_1 = 0$

then, locus of $P(x_1, y_1)$ is

$$2(g - g_1)x + 2(f - f_1)y + c - c_1 = 0$$

which is a straight line.

Chord of Contact

From any external point, two tangents can be drawn to a given circle. The chord joining the points of contact of the two tangents is called the chord of contact of tangents.

Theorem : The equation of the chord of contact of tangents drawn from a point (x_1, y_1) to the circle $x^2 + y^2 = a^2$ is $xx_1 + yy_1 = a^2$.

Sol. Let $T(x', y')$ and $T'(x'', y'')$ be the points of contact of tangents drawn from $P(x_1, y_1)$ to $x^2 + y^2 = a^2$.

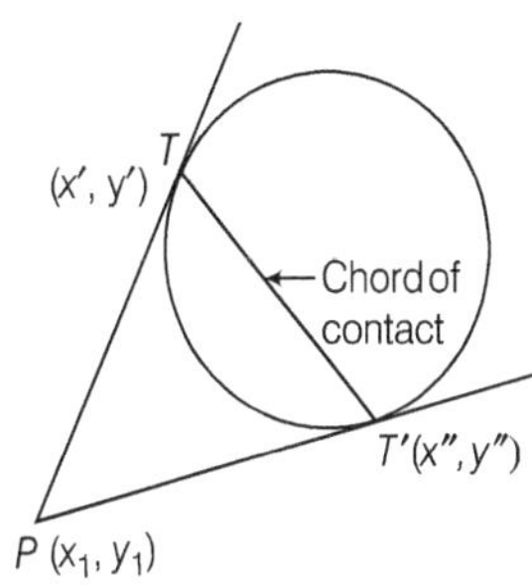

Then, equations of tangents PT and PT' are

$$xx' + yy' = a^2 \text{ and } xx'' + yy'' = a^2 \text{ respectively.}$$

Since, both tangents pass through $P(x_1, y_1)$, then

$$x_1x' + y_1y' = a^2$$

and $$x_1x'' + y_1y'' = a^2$$

$\because$ Points $T(x', y')$ and $T'(x'', y'')$ lie on

$$xx_1 + yy_1 = a^2$$

$\therefore$ Equation of **chord of contact** TT' is $xx_1 + yy_1 = a^2$

Remark

Equation of chord of contact like as equation of tangent at that point but point different.

Now, for chord of contact at (x_1, y_1), replacing x^2 by xx_1, y^2 by yy_1, x by $\dfrac{x + x_1}{2}$, y by $\dfrac{y + y_1}{2}$ and xy by $\dfrac{xy_1 + x_1y}{2}$.

***Corollary* 1 :** If R is the radius of the circle and L is the length of the tangent from $P(x_1, y_1)$ on $S = 0$.

Here, $L = \sqrt{S_1}$, then

(a) Length of chord of contact $TT' = \dfrac{2LR}{\sqrt{(R^2 + L^2)}}$

(b) Area of triangle formed by the pair of tangents and its chord of contact $= \dfrac{RL^3}{R^2 + L^2}$

(c) Angle between the pair of tangents from $P(x_1, y_1)$ $= \tan^{-1}\left(\dfrac{2RL}{L^2 - R^2}\right)$

***Corollary* 2 :** Equation of the circle circumscribing the triangle PTT' is

$$(x - x_1)(x + g) + (y - y_1)(y + f) = 0,$$

where, $O(-g, -f)$ is the centre of the circle

$$x^2 + y^2 + 2gx + 2fx + c = 0$$

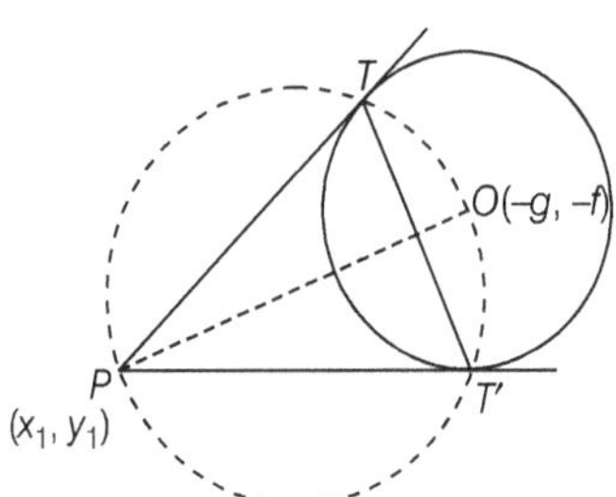

i.e. Required circle always passes through the centre of the given circle (Here, OP is the diameter of the required circle).

Example 50. If the pair of tangents are drawn from the point (4,5) to the circle $x^2+y^2-4x-2y-11=0$, then,

(i) Find the length of chord of contact.
(ii) Find the area of the triangle formed by a pair of tangents and their chord of contact.
(iii) Find the angle between the pair of tangents.

Sol. Here, $P \equiv (4,5)$,

$$R = \sqrt{((2)^2+(1)^2+11)} = 4$$

and $L = \sqrt{S_1} = \sqrt{((4)^2+(5)^2-4\times4-2\times5-11)} = 2$

(i) Length of chord of contact

$$= \frac{2LR}{\sqrt{(R^2+L^2)}} = \frac{2\times2\times4}{\sqrt{(4)^2+(2)^2}} = \frac{8}{\sqrt{5}} \text{ unit}$$

(ii) Area of triangle $= \dfrac{RL^3}{R^2+L^2} = \dfrac{4\times8}{16+4} = \dfrac{8}{5}$ sq units

(iii) Angle between the pair of tangents

$$= \pi + \tan^{-1}\left(\frac{2\times4\times2}{2^2-4^2}\right)$$

$$= \pi - \tan^{-1}\left(\frac{4}{3}\right) \qquad (\because L < R)$$

Example 51. Tangents PQ, PR are drawn to the circle $x^2+y^2=36$ from the point $P(-8,2)$ touching the circle at Q, R respectively. Find the equation of the circumcircle of ΔPQR.

Sol. Here, $P \equiv (-8,2)$ and $O \equiv (0,0)$

$\therefore$ Equation of the required circle is

$$(x-(-8))(x-0)+(y-2)(y-0)=0$$

or $\quad x^2+y^2+8x-2y=0 \qquad (\because OP \text{ is the diameter})$

Example 52. Find the condition that chord of contact of any external point (h,k) to the circle $x^2+y^2=a^2$ should subtend right angle at the centre of the circle .

Sol. Equation of chord of contact AB is $hx+ky=a^2$

For equation of pair of tangents of OA and OB, make homogeneous $x^2+y^2=a^2$ with the help of $hx+ky=a^2$ or

$$\frac{hx+ky}{a^2}=1$$

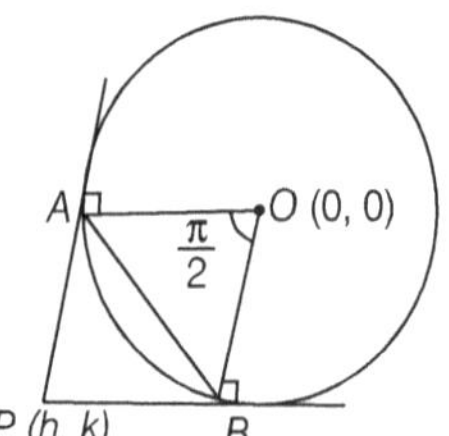

then, $\quad x^2+y^2 = a^2\left(\dfrac{hx+ky}{a^2}\right)^2$

or $\quad a^2(x^2+y^2) = (hx+ky)^2$

or $\quad x^2(a^2-h^2) - 2hkxy + y^2(a^2-k^2) = 0$

but $\quad \angle AOB = \dfrac{\pi}{2}$

$\therefore$ Coefficient of x^2 + Coefficient of $y^2 = 0$

$\Rightarrow \quad a^2-h^2+a^2-k^2=0$ or $h^2+k^2=2a^2$

Example 53. The chord of contact of tangents drawn from a point on the circle $x^2+y^2=a^2$ to the circle $x^2+y^2=b^2$ touches the circle $x^2+y^2=c^2$. Show that a, b, c are in GP.

Sol. Let $P(a\cos\theta, a\sin\theta)$ be a point on the circle $x^2+y^2=a^2$.

Then, equation of chord of contact of tangents drawn from $P(a\cos\theta, a\sin\theta)$ to the circle $x^2+y^2=b^2$ is

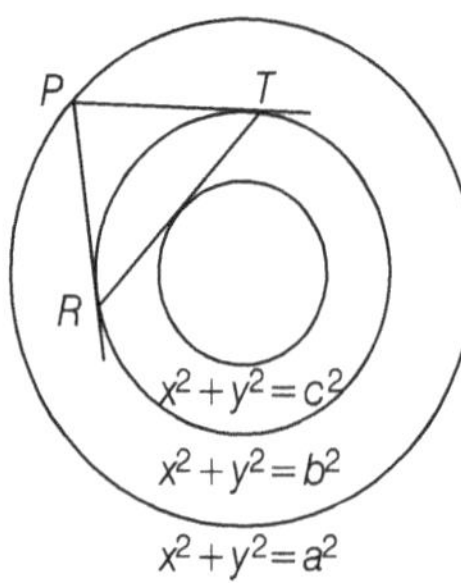

$$ax\cos\theta + ay\sin\theta = b^2 \qquad \text{...(i)}$$

This touches the circle $\quad x^2+y^2=c^2 \qquad$ ...(ii)

$\therefore$ Length of perpendicular from (0, 0) to Eq. (i) = radius of Eq. (ii)

$$\therefore \quad \frac{|0+0-b^2|}{\sqrt{(a^2\cos^2\theta + a^2\sin^2\theta)}} = c$$

or $\quad b^2 = ac$

$\Rightarrow \quad a, b, c$ are in GP.

Chord Bisected at a Given Point

Theorem : The equation of the chord of the circle $x^2+y^2=a^2$ bisected at the point (x_1, y_1) is given by

$$xx_1+yy_1-a^2=x_1^2+y_1^2-a^2$$

or $$T=S_1$$

Proof : Let any chord AB of the circle $x^2+y^2=a^2$ be bisected at $D(x_1, y_1)$.

If centre of circle is represented by C

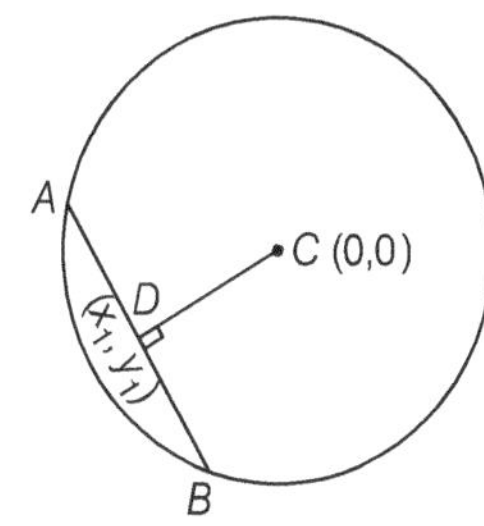

then, slope of $DC=\frac{0-y_1}{0-x_1}=\frac{y_1}{x_1}$

$\therefore$ Slope of the chord AB is $-\frac{x_1}{y_1}$

then, equation of AB is $y-y_1=-\frac{x_1}{y_1}(x-x_1)$

or $$yy_1-y_1^2=-xx_1+x_1^2$$

or $$xx_1+yy_1=x_1^2+y_1^2$$

or $$\boldsymbol{xx_1+yy_1-a^2=x_1^2+y_1^2-a^2} \text{ or } \boldsymbol{T=S_1}$$

Remarks

1. The equation of chord of the circle $x^2+y^2+2gx+2fy+c=0$, which is bisected at (x_1, y_1) ; is $T=S_1$
   where, $T=xx_1+yy_1+g(x+x_1)+f(y+y_1)+c$
   and $S_1=x_1^2+y_1^2+2gx_1+2fy_1+c$
2. The chord bisected at point (x_1, y_1) is the farthest from the centre among all the chords passing through the point (x_1, y_1). Also, for such chord, the length of the chord is minimum.

Example 54. Find the equation of the chord of $x^2+y^2-6x+10y-9=0$ which is bisected at $(-2,4)$.

Sol. The equation of the required chord is

$$-2x+4y-3(x-2)+5(y+4)-9$$
$$=4+16+12+40-9$$
$$\Rightarrow \quad -5x+9y-46=0$$
or $$5x-9y+46=0$$

Example 55. Find the middle point of the chord intercepted on line $lx+my+n=0$ by the circle $x^2+y^2=a^2$.

Sol. Let (x_1, y_1) be the middle point of the chord intercepted by the circle $x^2+y^2=a^2$ on the line $lx+my+n=0$. Then, equation of the chord of the circle $x^2+y^2=a^2$, whose middle points is (x_1, y_1), is

$$xx_1+yy_1-a^2=x_1^2+y_1^2-a^2$$

or $$xx_1+yy_1=x_1^2+y_1^2 \quad \text{...(i)}$$

Clearly, $lx+my+n=0$ and Eq. (i) represented the same line,

$$\frac{x_1}{l}=\frac{y_1}{m}=\frac{x_1^2+y_1^2}{-n}=\lambda \quad \text{(say)}$$

$$\therefore \quad \left.\begin{aligned}x_1&=l\lambda\\ y_1&=m\lambda\end{aligned}\right\} \quad \text{...(ii)}$$

and $$x_1^2+y_1^2=-n\lambda$$

or $$l^2\lambda^2+m^2\lambda^2=-n\lambda \quad \text{[from (ii)]}$$

$$\therefore \quad \lambda=-\frac{n}{l^2+m^2}$$

So, from Eq. (ii), $x_1=-\frac{nl}{l^2+m^2}, y_1=-\frac{mn}{l^2+m^2}$

Hence, the required point is $\left(-\frac{nl}{l^2+m^2}, -\frac{nm}{l^2+m^2}\right)$.

Example 56. Through a fixed point (h, k), secants are drawn to the circle $x^2+y^2=r^2$. Show that the locus of mid-point of the portions of secants intercepted by the circle is $x^2+y^2=hx+ky$.

Sol. Let $P(x_1, y_1)$ be the middle point of any chord AB, which passes through the point $C(h, k)$.

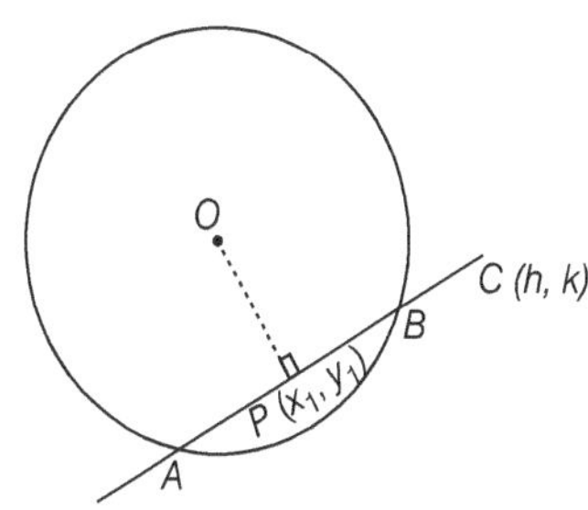

Equation of chord AB is $T=S_1$

$$\therefore \quad xx_1+yy_1-r^2=x_1^2+y_1^2-r^2$$

or $$x_1^2+y_1^2=xx_1+yy_1$$

But since AB passes through $C(h, k)$, then

$$x_1^2+y_1^2=hx_1+ky_1$$

$\therefore$ Locus of $P(x_1, y_1)$ is $x^2+y^2=hx+ky$

Example 57. Find the locus of middle points of chords of the circle $x^2 + y^2 = a^2$, which subtend right angle at the point $(c, 0)$.

Sol. Let $N(h, k)$ be the middle point of any chord AB, which subtend a right angle at $P(c, 0)$.

Since, $\angle APB = 90^\circ$

$\therefore \quad NA = NB = NP$

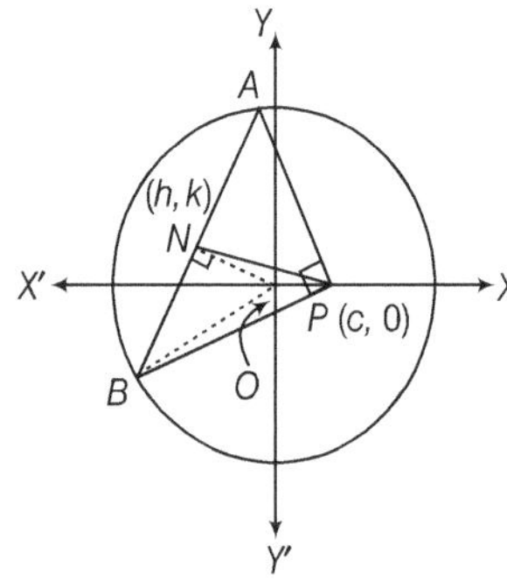

(since distance of the vertices from middle point of the hypotenuse are equal)

or $\quad (NA)^2 = (NB)^2 = (h - c)^2 + (k - 0)^2 \quad$ ...(i)

But also $\quad \angle BNO = 90^\circ$

$\therefore \quad (OB)^2 = (ON)^2 + (NB)^2$

$\Rightarrow \quad -(NB)^2 = (ON)^2 - (OB)^2$

$\Rightarrow \quad -[(h - c)^2 + (k - 0)^2] = (h^2 + k^2) - a^2$

or $\quad 2(h^2 + k^2) - 2ch + c^2 - a^2 = 0$

$\therefore$ Locus of $N(h, k)$ is

$$2(x^2 + y^2) - 2cx + c^2 - a^2 = 0$$

Example 58. Find the equation of the chord of the circle $x^2 + y^2 = r^2$ passing through the point $(2, 3)$ farthest from the centre.

Sol. Let $P \equiv (2, 3)$ be the given point and M be the middle point of chord of circle $x^2 + y^2 = r^2$ through P.

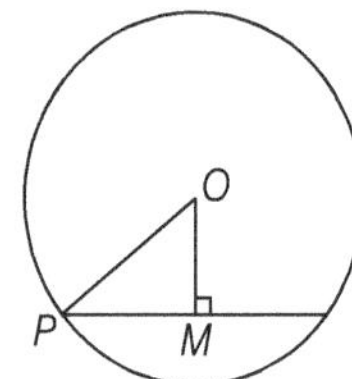

Then, $\quad (OM)^2 = (OP)^2 - (PM)^2$

If OM maximum, then PM is minimum. i.e. P coincides with M, which is middle point of the chord.

Hence, the equation of the chord is

$$T = S_1$$

i.e. $\quad 2x + 3y - r^2 = 2^2 + 3^2 - r^2$

or $\quad 2x + 3y = 13$

Pair of Tangents

Theorem : The combined equation of the pair of tangents drawn from a point $P(x_1, y_1)$ to the circle $x^2 + y^2 = a^2$ is

$$(x^2 + y^2 - a^2)(x_1^2 + y_1^2 - a^2) = (xx_1 + yy_1 - a^2)^2$$

or $\quad SS_1 = T^2$

where, $\quad S = x^2 + y^2 - a^2, S_1 = x_1^2 + y_1^2 - a^2$

and $\quad T = xx_1 + yy_1 - a^2$

Proof : The given circle is $x^2 + y^2 = a^2$

Its centre and radius are $C(0, 0)$ and a respectively. Given external point be $P(x_1, y_1)$.

From point $P(x_1, y_1)$ two tangents PT and PR be drawn to the circle, touching circle at T and R respectively.

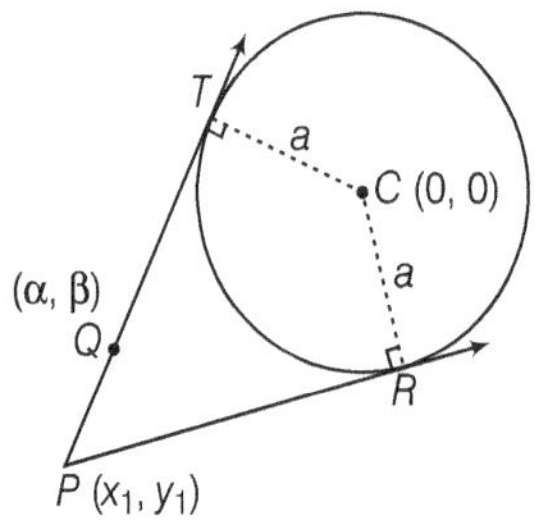

Let $Q(\alpha, \beta)$ on PT, then equation of PQ is

$$y - y_1 = \frac{\beta - y_1}{\alpha - x_1}(x - x_1)$$

or $\quad y(\alpha - x_1) - x(\beta - y_1) - \alpha y_1 + \beta x_1 = 0$

Length of perpendicular from $C(0, 0)$ on $PT = a$ (radius)

$$\Rightarrow \quad \frac{|\beta x_1 - \alpha y_1|}{\sqrt{(\alpha - x_1)^2 + (\beta - y_1)^2}} = a$$

or $\quad (\beta x_1 - \alpha y_1)^2 = a^2\{(\alpha - x_1)^2 + (\beta - y_1)^2\}$

$\therefore$ Locus of $Q(\alpha, \beta)$ is

$$(yx_1 - xy_1)^2 = a^2\{(x - x_1)^2 + (y - y_1)^2\}$$

$\Rightarrow \quad y^2x_1^2 + x^2y_1^2 - 2xy\,x_1y_1 = a^2 \{x^2 + x_1^2 - 2xx_1 + y^2 + y_1^2 - 2yy_1\}$

$\Rightarrow y^2(x_1^2 - a^2) + x^2(y_1^2 - a^2) - a^2(x_1^2 + y_1^2) = 2xyx_1y_1 - 2a^2xx_1 - 2a^2yy_1$

On adding both sides, $(x^2x_1^2 + y^2y_1^2 + a^4)$, then

$$y^2(x_1^2 + y_1^2 - a^2) + x^2(x_1^2 + y_1^2 - a^2) - a^2(x_1^2 + y_1^2 - a^2) = (xx_1 + yy_1 - a^2)^2$$

$\Rightarrow$ $(x^2+y^2-a^2)(x_1^2+y_1^2-a^2)=(xx_1+yy_1-a^2)^2$

This is the required equation of pair of tangents drawn from (x_1, y_1) to circle $x^2+y^2=a^2$.

Aliter : Let circle be $x^2+y^2=a^2$ with centre $C(0,0)$ and radius a. Length of tangents from $P(x_1, y_1)$ and $Q(\alpha, \beta)$ are

$$PT=\sqrt{x_1^2+y_1^2-a^2}$$

and $$QT=\sqrt{\alpha^2+\beta^2-a^2}$$

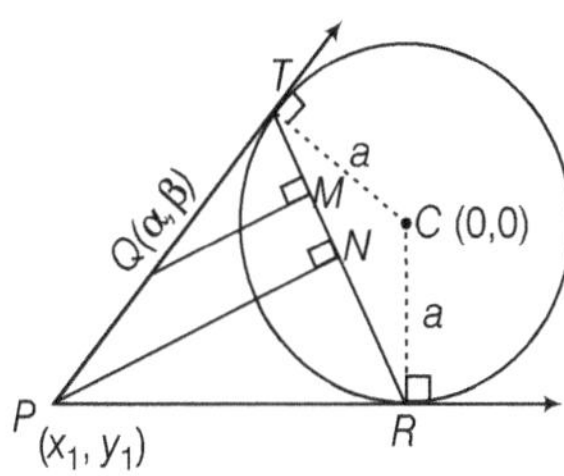

Now, equation of TR (chord of contact is)

$$xx_1+yy_1-a^2=0$$

$\therefore$ $$PN=\frac{|x_1^2+y_1^2-a^2|}{\sqrt{(x_1^2+y_1^2)}} \text{ and } QM=\frac{|\alpha x_1+\beta y_1-a^2|}{\sqrt{(x_1^2+y_1^2)}}$$

But from similar Δ^s PNT and QMT,

$$\frac{PN}{QM}=\frac{PT}{QT} \Rightarrow \frac{(PN)^2}{(QM)^2}=\frac{(PT)^2}{(QT)^2}$$

$$\Rightarrow \frac{\dfrac{(x_1^2+y_1^2-a^2)^2}{(x_1^2+y_1^2)}}{\dfrac{(\alpha x_1+\beta y_1-a^2)^2}{(x_1^2+y_1^2)}}=\frac{x_1^2+y_1^2-a^2}{\alpha^2+\beta^2-a^2}$$

$$\Rightarrow (x_1^2+y_1^2-a^2)(\alpha^2+\beta^2-a^2)=(\alpha x_1+\beta y_1-a^2)^2$$

$\therefore$ Locus of $Q(\alpha, \beta)$ is

$$(x^2+y^2-a^2)(x_1^2+y_1^2-a^2)$$
$$=(xx_1+yy_1-a^2)^2$$

This is the required equation of pair of tangents drawn from (x_1, y_1) to circle $x^2+y^2=a^2$.

Corollary : The angle between the two tangents from (x_1, y_1) to the circle $x^2+y^2=a^2$ is $2\tan^{-1}\left(\dfrac{a}{\sqrt{S_1}}\right)$, where $S_1=x_1^2+y_1^2-a^2$.

Remarks

1. Equation of pair of tangents in notation form is $SS_1=T^2$

where, $S \equiv x^2+y^2-a^2$

$S_1 \equiv x_1^2+y_1^2-a^2, T \equiv xx_1+yy_1-a^2$

2. When circle is $x^2+y^2+2gx+2fy+c=0$ and tangents are drawn from (x_1, y_1), then pair of tangents is

$(x^2+y^2+2gx+2fy+c)(x_1^2+y_1^2+2gx_1+2fy_1+c)$

$=[xx_1+yy_1+g(x+x_1)+f(y+y_1)+c]^2$

where, $S \equiv x^2+y^2+2gx+2fy+c$,

$S_1 \equiv x_1^2+y_1^2+2gx_1+2fy_1+c$,

and $T \equiv xx_1+yy_1+g(x+x_1)+f(y+y_1)+c$

Advised for Students

Students are advised that, if they do not want to use the formula ($SS_1=T^2$), then use the following method :

Let $y-y_1=m(x-x_1)$ be any line through $P(x_1, y_1)$.

Then, use condition of tangency $p=r$ i.e.

Length of perpendicular from the centre of circle or this line = radius of the circle.

Gives the values of m. In such away, we can find the equations of tangents from P.

Example 59. Find the equations of the tangents from the point $A(3,2)$ to the circle $x^2+y^2+4x+6y+8=0$.

Sol. Combined equation of the pair of tangents drawn from $A(3,2)$ to the given circle $x^2+y^2+4x+6y+8=0$ can be written in the usual notation.

$$T^2=SS_1 \text{ namely}$$

$$\Rightarrow [3x+2y+2(x+3)+3(y+2)+8]^2$$
$$=[x^2+y^2+4x+6y+8][9+4+12+12+8]$$

$$\Rightarrow (5x+5y+20)^2=45(x^2+y^2+4x+6y+8)$$

$$\Rightarrow 5(x+y+4)^2=9(x^2+y^2+4x+6y+8)$$

$$\Rightarrow 5(x^2+y^2+2xy+8x+8y+16)$$
$$=9(x^2+y^2+4x+6y+8)$$

$$\Rightarrow 4x^2+4y^2-10xy-4x+14y-8=0$$

or $$2x^2+2y^2-5xy-2x+7y-4=0$$

or $$(2x-y-4)(x-2y+1)=0$$

Hence, the required tangents to the circle from $A(3,2)$ are

$$2x-y-4=0 \quad \text{and} \quad x-2y+1=0$$

Aliter : Let $S \equiv x^2+y^2+4x+6y+8=0$

Centre $C(-2,-3)$ and radius $=\sqrt{5}$

Let the slope of a tangent from A to '$S=0$' be m, then equation of tangent is

$$y - 2 = m(x - 3)$$

or $$mx - y + 2 - 3m = 0 \quad \text{...(i)}$$

Length of perpendicular from $C(-2, -3)$ on Eq. (i) = radius of circle.

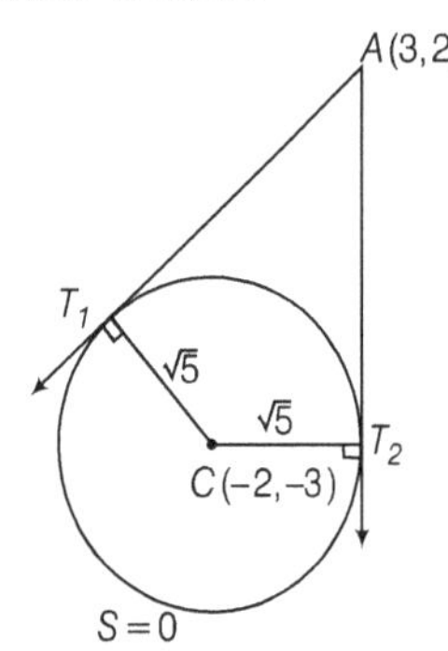

$$\Rightarrow \quad \frac{|-2m + 3 + 2 - 3m|}{\sqrt{(m^2 + 1)}} = \sqrt{5}$$

or $$(5m - 5)^2 = 5(m^2 + 1)$$

$$\Rightarrow \quad 25m^2 - 50m + 25 = 5m^2 + 5$$

$$\Rightarrow \quad 20m^2 - 50m + 20 = 0$$

or $$2m^2 - 5m + 2 = 0$$

or $$(2m - 1)(m - 2) = 0$$

$$\therefore \quad m = \frac{1}{2} \text{ or } m = 2$$

Substituting these values of m in Eq. (i), we get the equations of two tangents are $x - 2y + 1 = 0$ and $2x - y - 4 = 0$.

Director Circle

Director circle : The locus of the point of intersection of two perpendicular tangents to a given circle is known as its director circle.

Theorem : The equation of the director circle of the circle $x^2 + y^2 = a^2$ is

$$x^2 + y^2 = 2a^2$$

Proof : The equation of any tangent to the circle $x^2 + y^2 = a^2$

is $$y = mx + a\sqrt{(1 + m^2)} \quad \text{...(i)}$$

Let $P(h, k)$ be the point of intersection of tangents, then $P(h, k)$ lies on Eq. (i)

$$\therefore \quad k = mh + a\sqrt{(1 + m^2)}$$

or $$(k - mh)^2 = a^2(1 + m^2)q$$

or $$m^2(h^2 - a^2) - 2mkh + k^2 - a^2 = 0$$

This is quadratic equation in m, let two roots are m_1 and m_2.

But tangents are perpendiculars, then

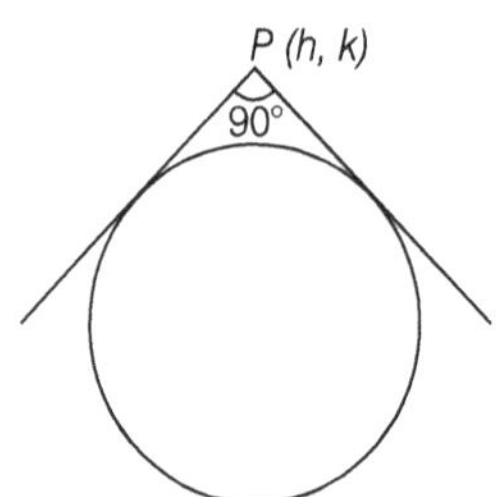

$$m_1 m_2 = -1$$

$$\Rightarrow \quad \frac{k^2 - a^2}{h^2 - a^2} = -1 \text{ or } k^2 - a^2 = -h^2 + a^2$$

or $$h^2 + k^2 = 2a^2$$

Hence, locus of $P(h, k)$ is $\mathbf{x^2 + y^2 = 2a^2}$

Aliter : The combined equation of the pair of tangents drawn from (h, k) to $x^2 + y^2 = a^2$ is

$$SS_1 = T^2$$

where, $$S = x^2 + y^2 - a^2$$

$$S_1 = h^2 + k^2 - a^2$$

and $$T = hx + ky - a^2$$

$$\therefore \quad (x^2 + y^2 - a^2)(h^2 + k^2 - a^2) = (hx + ky - a^2)^2$$

This equation will represent a pair of perpendicular lines if, coefficient of x^2 + coefficient of $y^2 = 0$

$$\Rightarrow \quad h^2 + k^2 - a^2 - h^2 + h^2 + k^2 - a^2 - k^2 = 0$$

$$\Rightarrow \quad h^2 + k^2 - 2a^2 = 0 \text{ or } h^2 + k^2 = 2a^2$$

Hence, the locus of (h, k) is $\mathbf{x^2 + y^2 = 2a^2}$

Remarks

1. The equation of the director circle of the circle $(x - h)^2 + (y - k)^2 = a^2$ is $(x - h)^2 + (y - k)^2 = 2a^2$
2. The equation of the director circle of the circle $x^2 + y^2 + 2gx + 2fy + c = 0$ is $x^2 + y^2 + 2gx + 2fy + c = g^2 + f^2 - c$
3. If two tangents are drawn from a point on the director circle to the circle, then angle between tangents is 90°.

Example 60. If two tangents are drawn from a point on the circle $x^2 + y^2 = 50$ to the circle $x^2 + y^2 = 25$, then find the angle between the tangents.

Sol. $\because x^2 + y^2 = 50$ is the director circle of $x^2 + y^2 = 25$

Hence, angle between tangents = 90°

Exercise for Session 5

1. If the tangent at the point P on the circle $x^2+y^2+6x+6y=2$ meets the straight line $5x-2y+6=0$ at a point Q on the Y-axis, then the length PQ is

(a) 4 (b) $2\sqrt{5}$ (c) 5 (d) $3\sqrt{5}$

2. If the circle $x^2+y^2+2gx+2fy+c=0$ is touched by $y=x$ at P such that $OP=6\sqrt{2}$, where O is origin, then the value of c is

(a) 36 (b) 72 (c) 144 (d) 288

3. The chord of contact of tangents from a point P to a circle passes through Q. If l_1 and l_2 are the lengths of tangents from P and Q to the circle, then PQ is equal to

(a) $\frac{l_1+l_2}{2}$ (b) $\frac{l_1-l_2}{2}$ (c) $\sqrt{(l_1^2+l_2^2)}$ (d) $\sqrt{(l_1^2-l_2^2)}$

4. If the chord of contact of tangents from a point (x_1, y_1) to the circle $x^2+y^2=a^2$ touches the circle $(x-a)^2+y^2=a^2$, then the locus of (x_1, y_1) is

(a) a circle (b) a parabola (c) an ellipse (d) a hyperbola

5. The locus of the mid-points of a chord of the circle $x^2+y^2=4$, which subtends a right angle at the origin is

(a) $x+y=1$ (b) $x^2+y^2=1$ (c) $x+y=2$ (d) $x^2+y^2=2$

6. The length of tangents from $P(1,-1)$ and $Q(3,3)$ to a circle are $\sqrt{2}$ and $\sqrt{6}$ respectively, then the length of tangent from $R(-2,-7)$ to the same circle is

(a) $\sqrt{41}$ (b) $\sqrt{51}$ (c) $\sqrt{61}$ (d) $\sqrt{71}$

7. If the angle between the tangents drawn to $x^2+y^2+2gx+2fy+c=0$ from $(0,0)$ is $\frac{\pi}{2}$, then

(a) $g^2+f^2=3c$ (b) $g^2+f^2=2c$ (c) $g^2+f^2=5c$ (d) $g^2+f^2=4c$

8. The chords of contact of the pair of tangents drawn from each point on the line $2x+y=4$ to the circle $x^2+y^2=1$ pass through a fixed point

(a) (2, 4) (b) $\left(-\frac{1}{2},-\frac{1}{4}\right)$ (c) $\left(\frac{1}{2},\frac{1}{4}\right)$ (d) $(-2,-4)$

9. The length of tangent from (0, 0) to the circle $2(x^2+y^2)+x-y+5=0$ is

(a) $\sqrt{5}$ (b) $\sqrt{\left(\frac{5}{2}\right)}$ (c) $\frac{\sqrt{5}}{2}$ (d) $\sqrt{2}$

10. The perpendicular tangents to the circle $x^2+y^2=a^2$ meet at P. Then, the locus of P has the equation

(a) $x^2+y^2=2a^2$ (b) $x^2+y^2=3a^2$ (c) $x^2+y^2=4a^2$ (d) $x^2+y^2=5a^2$

11. The tangents to $x^2+y^2=a^2$ having inclinations α and β intersect at P. If $\cot\alpha+\cot\beta=0$, then the locus of P is

(a) $x+y=0$ (b) $x-y=0$ (c) $xy=0$ (d) $xy=1$

12. The exhaustive range of values of a such that the angle between the pair of tangents drawn from (a,a) to the circle $x^2+y^2-2x-2y-6=0$ lies in the range $\left(\frac{\pi}{3},\pi\right)$ is

(a) $(-1, 3)$ (b) $(-5,-3)\cup(3, 5)$ (c) $(-3, 5)$ (d) $(-3,-1)\cup(3, 5)$

13. Distances from the origin to the centres of the three circles $x^2+y^2-2\lambda x=c^2$, where c is a constant and λ is available, are in GP. Prove that the lengths of tangents drawn from any point on the circle $x^2+y^2=c^2$ to the three circles are also in GP.

14. Find the area of the quadrilateral formed by a pair of tangents from the point (4, 5) to the circle $x^2+y^2-4x-2y-11=0$ and a pair of its radii.

15. If the length of the tangent from a point (f, g) to the circle $x^2+y^2=4$ be four times the length of the tangent from it to the circle $x^2+y^2=4x$, show that $15f^2+15g^2-64f+4=0$.

16. Find the equation of that chord of the circle $x^2+y^2=15$ which is bisected at (3, 2).

17. The chords of contact of the pair of tangents to the circle $x^2+y^2=1$ drawn from any point on the line $2x+y=4$ pass through the point (α,β), then find $\alpha^2+\beta^2$.

Session 6

Diameter of a Circle, Two Circles Touching Each Other, Common Tangents to Two Circles, Common Chord of Two Circles, Family of Circles

Diameter of a Circle

The locus of the middle points of a system of parallel chords of a circle is called a diameter of the circle.

Let the circle be $x^2 + y^2 = a^2$ and equation of parallel chord is

$$y = mx + c$$

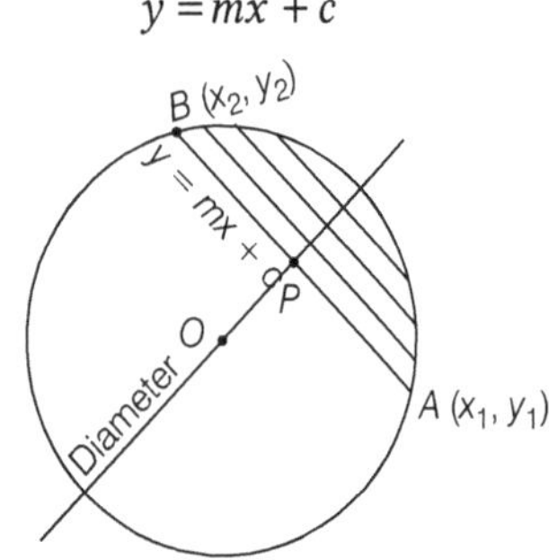

Let $P(h, k)$ be the middle point of the chord $y = mx + c$. Since, P is the mid-point of $A(x_1\ y_1)$ and $B(x_2, y_2)$, then

$$\frac{x_1 + x_2}{2} = h \quad \text{and} \quad \frac{y_1 + y_2}{2} = k$$

or $\quad x_1 + x_2 = 2h \quad \text{and} \quad y_1 + y_2 = 2k \quad$ ...(i)

$\because \quad P(h, k)$ lie on $y = mx + c$

then, $\quad k = mh + c$

or $\quad k - mh = c \quad$ ...(ii)

Substituting $y = mx + c$ in $x^2 + y^2 = a^2$

then, $\quad x^2 + (mx + c)^2 = a^2$

or $\quad (1 + m^2)x^2 + 2mcx + c^2 - a^2 = 0 \quad$ ...(iii)

Let x_1, x_2 are roots of Eq. (iii), then

$$x_1 + x_2 = -\frac{2mc}{1 + m^2}$$

$\Rightarrow \quad 2h = -\frac{2m}{(1 + m^2)}(k - mh) \quad$ [from Eq. (i) and Eq. (ii)]

$\Rightarrow \quad h + m^2h = -mk + m^2h \Rightarrow h + mk = 0$

Hence, locus of (h, k) is $x + my = 0$

Aliter : Let (h, k) be the middle point of the chord $y = mx + c$ of the circle $x^2 + y^2 = a^2$

then, $\quad T = S_1 \Rightarrow xh + ky = h^2 + k^2$

$$\text{slope} = -\frac{h}{k} = m \Rightarrow h + mk = 0$$

Hence, locus of mid-point is $x + my = 0$.

Remark

The diameter of circle always passes through the centre of the circle and perpendicular to the parallel chords.

Let circle is $x^2 + y^2 = a^2$ and parallel chord be $y = mx + c$, then equation of line $\perp$ to $y = mx + c$ is

$$my + x + \lambda = 0 \quad \text{...(i)}$$

which passes through origin (centre)

then, $\quad 0 + 0 + \lambda = 0 \quad \therefore \quad \lambda = 0$

Then, equation of diameter from Eq. (i) is $x + my = 0$.

Example 61. Find the equation of the diameter of the circle $x^2 + y^2 + 2gx + 2fy + c = 0$ which corresponds to the chord $ax + by + d = 0$.

Sol. The diameter of circle passes through the centre of the circle and perpendicular to the chord $ax + by + d = 0$ is

$$bx - ay + \lambda = 0 \quad \text{...(i)}$$

which passes through centre of circle i.e. $(-g, -f)$

Then, $\quad -bg + af + \lambda = 0$

$\therefore \quad \lambda = bg - af$

From Eq. (i), the equation of the diameter is

$$bx - ay + bg - af = 0$$

Two Circles Touching Each Other

1. When two circles touch each other externally

Then, distance between their centres = sum of their radii

i.e. $\quad |C_1C_2| = r_1 + r_2$

In such cases, the point of contact P divides the line joining C_1 and C_2 internally in the ratio $r_1 : r_2$

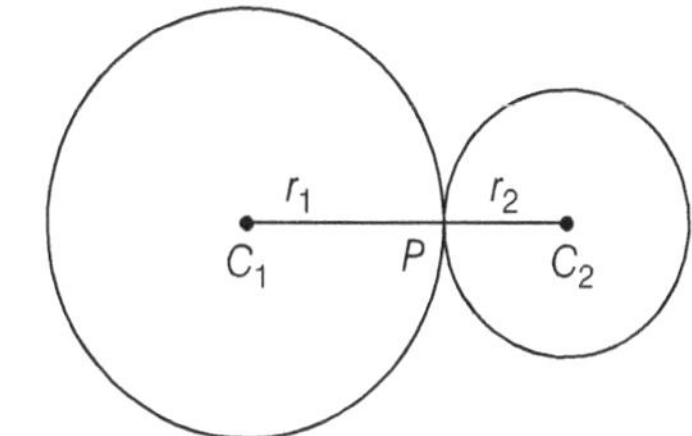

$$\Rightarrow \quad \frac{C_1P}{C_2P} = \frac{r_1}{r_2}$$

If $\quad C_1 \equiv (x_1, y_1)$ and $C_2 \equiv (x_2, y_2)$

then, coordinate of P is $\left(\frac{r_1x_2 + r_2x_1}{r_1 + r_2}, \frac{r_1y_2 + r_2y_1}{r_1 + r_2}\right)$

2. When two Circles Touch each other Internally

Then, distance between their centres =Difference of their radii

i.e. $\quad |C_1C_2| = |r_1 - r_2|$

In such cases, the point of contact P divides the line joining C_1 and C_2 externally in the ratio $r_1 : r_2$

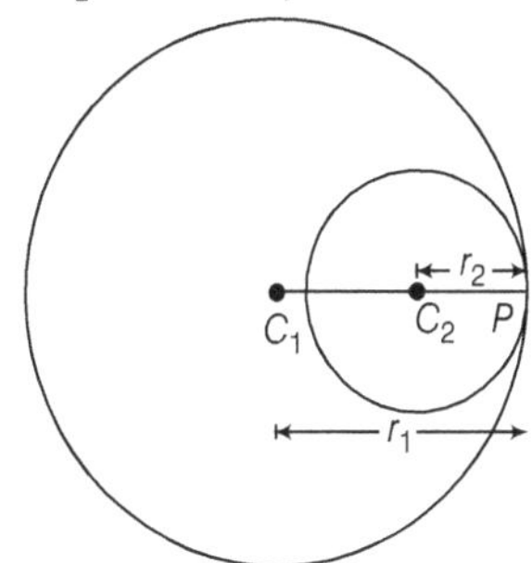

$$\Rightarrow \quad \frac{C_1P}{C_2P} = \frac{r_1}{r_2}$$

If $\quad C_1 \equiv (x_1, y_1)$ and $C_2 \equiv (x_2, y_2)$

then, coordinates of P is $\left(\frac{r_1x_2 - r_2x_1}{r_1 - r_2}, \frac{r_1y_2 - r_2y_1}{r_1 - r_2}\right)$

Example 62. Examine if the two circles $x^2 + y^2 - 2x - 4y = 0$ and $x^2 + y^2 - 8y - 4 = 0$ touch each other externally or internally.

Sol. Given circles are

$$x^2 + y^2 - 2x - 4y = 0 \qquad \text{...(i)}$$

and $$x^2 + y^2 - 8y - 4 = 0 \qquad \text{...(ii)}$$

Let centres and radii of circles Eqs. (i) and (ii) are represented by C_1, r_1 and C_2, r_2, respectively.

$\therefore \quad C_1 \equiv (1, 2), r_1 = \sqrt{(1 + 4)}$ or $r_1 = \sqrt{5}$

and $\quad C_2 \equiv (0, 4), r_2 = \sqrt{0 + 16 + 4}$ or $r_2 = 2\sqrt{5}$

Now, $C_1C_2 = \sqrt{(1 - 0)^2 + (2 - 4)^2}$

$C_1C_2 = \sqrt{5} = r_2 - r_1$

Hence, the two circles touch each other internally.

Example 63. Prove that the circles $x^2 + y^2 + 2ax + c^2 = 0$ and $x^2 + y^2 + 2by + c^2 = 0$ touch each other, if $\frac{1}{a^2} + \frac{1}{b^2} = \frac{1}{c^2}$.

Sol. Given circles are

$$x^2 + y^2 + 2ax + c^2 = 0 \qquad \text{...(i)}$$

and $$x^2 + y^2 + 2by + c^2 = 0 \qquad \text{...(ii)}$$

Let C_1 and C_2 be the centres of circles Eqs. (i) and (ii), respectively and r_1 and r_2 be their radii, then

$$C_1 = (-a, 0), C_2 = (0, -b),$$

$$r_1 = \sqrt{(a^2 - c^2)}, r_2 = \sqrt{(b^2 - c^2)}$$

Here, we do not find the two circles touch each other internally or externally.

For touch, $|C_1C_2| = |r_1 \pm r_2|$

or $\quad \sqrt{(a^2 + b^2)} = |\sqrt{(a^2 - c^2)} \pm \sqrt{(b^2 - c^2)}|$

On squaring

$$a^2 + b^2 = a^2 - c^2 + b^2 - c^2 \pm 2\sqrt{(a^2 - c^2)}\sqrt{(b^2 - c^2)}$$

or $$c^2 = \pm\sqrt{a^2b^2 - c^2(a^2 + b^2) + c^4}$$

Again, squaring,

$$c^4 = a^2b^2 - c^2(a^2 + b^2) + c^4$$

or $\quad c^2(a^2 + b^2) = a^2b^2$ or $\frac{1}{a^2} + \frac{1}{b^2} = \frac{1}{c^2}$

Common Tangents to Two Circles

Different Cases of Intersection of Two Circles :

Let the two circles be

$$(x - x_1)^2 + (y - y_1)^2 = r_1^2 \qquad \text{...(i)}$$

and $$(x - x_2)^2 + (y - y_2)^2 = r_2^2 \qquad \text{...(ii)}$$

with centres $C_1(x_1, y_1)$ and $C_2(x_2, y_2)$ and radii r_1 and r_2 respectively. Then following cases may arise :

Case I : When $|C_1C_2| > r_1 + r_2$ i.e. the distance between the centres is greater than the sum of their radii.

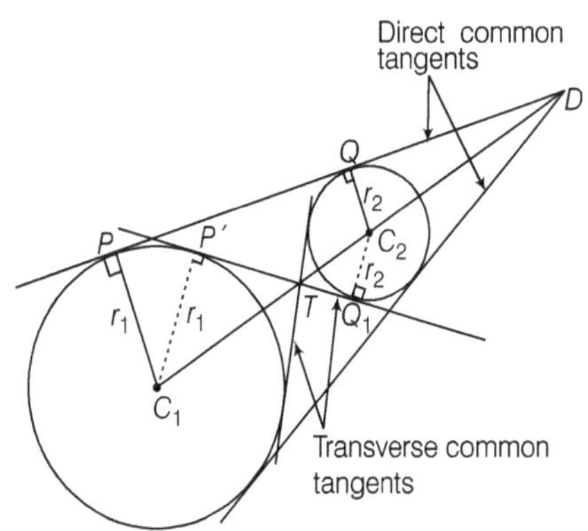

$\because \quad C_1 \equiv (x_1, y_1), C_2 \equiv (x_2, y_2)$

$$\therefore \quad D \equiv \left(\frac{r_1 x_2 - r_2 x_1}{r_1 - r_2}, \frac{r_1 y_2 - r_2 y_1}{r_1 - r_2} \right) \equiv (\alpha, \beta) \text{ (say)}$$

$$\text{and} \quad T \equiv \left(\frac{r_1 x_2 + r_2 x_1}{r_1 + r_2}, \frac{r_1 y_2 + r_2 y_1}{r_1 + r_2} \right) \equiv (\gamma, \delta) \text{ (say)}$$

How to find direct common tangents Let equation of common tangent through $D(\alpha, \beta)$ is

$$y - \beta = m(x - \alpha) \qquad \text{...(i)}$$

Now, length of $\perp$ from C_1 or C_2 on Eq. (i) $= r_1$ or r_2

Then, we get two values of m.

Substituting the values of m in Eq. (i), we get two direct common tangents.

How to find transverse common tangents Let equation of common tangent through $T(\gamma, \delta)$ is

$$y - \delta = M(x - \gamma) \qquad \text{...(ii)}$$

Now, length of $\perp$ from C_1 or C_2 on Eq. (i) $= r_1$ or r_2

then, we get two values of M.

Substituting the values of M in Eq. (i), we get two transverse common tangents.

Remark

In this case circles neither cut nor touch i.e. Number of solutions of two circles is zero.

Case II : When $|C_1C_2| = r_1 + r_2$

i.e. the distance between the centres is equal to the sum of their radii.

In this case two direct common tangents are real and distinct while the transverse tangents are coincident.

How to find transverse common tangent

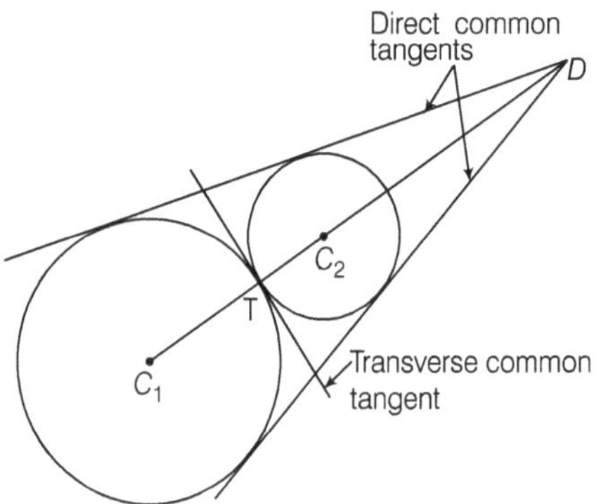

$\because$ Equation of circles are

$$S_1 \equiv (x - x_1)^2 + (y - y_1)^2 - r_1^2 = 0$$

$$\text{and} \quad S_2 \equiv (x - x_2)^2 + (y - y_2)^2 - r_2^2 = 0$$

then, equation of common tangent is

$$S_1 - S_2 = 0$$

which is same as equation of common chord.

Remark

In this case circles touch at one point i.e. Number of solutions of two circles is one.

Case III : When $|r_1 - r_2| < |C_1C_2| < r_1 + r_2$

i.e. the distance between the centres is less than sum of their radii and greater than difference of their radii.

In this case two direct common tangents are real and distinct while the transverse tangents are imaginary.

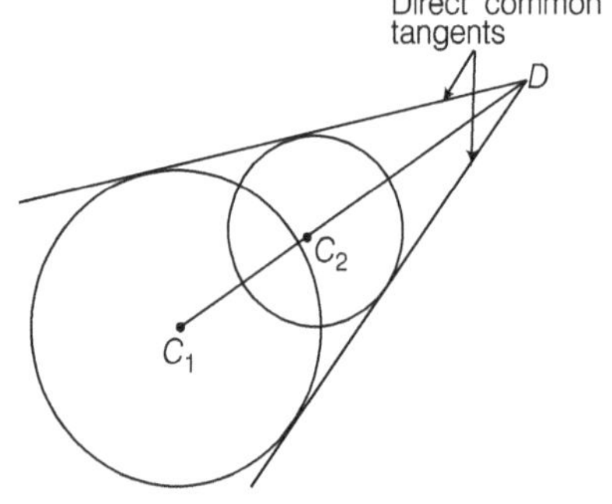

Remark

In this case circles cuts at two points i.e. Number of solutions of two circles is two.

Case IV : When $|C_1C_2| = |r_1 - r_2|$, i.e. the distance between the centres is equal to the difference of their radii.

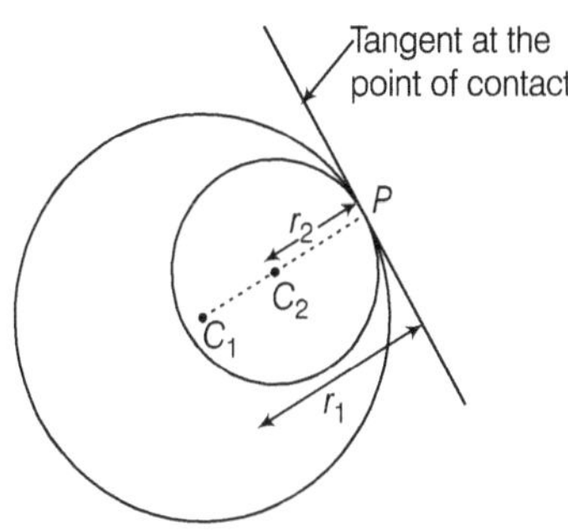

In this case two tangents are real and coincident while the other two tangents are imaginary.

If circles are represented by $S_1 = 0$ and $S_2 = 0$, then equation of common tangent is $S_1 - S_2 = 0$.

Remark

If circles touch each other externally, i.e. $|C_1C_2| = r_1 + r_2$, then equation of tangent at the point of contact is

$$S_1 - S_2 = 0$$

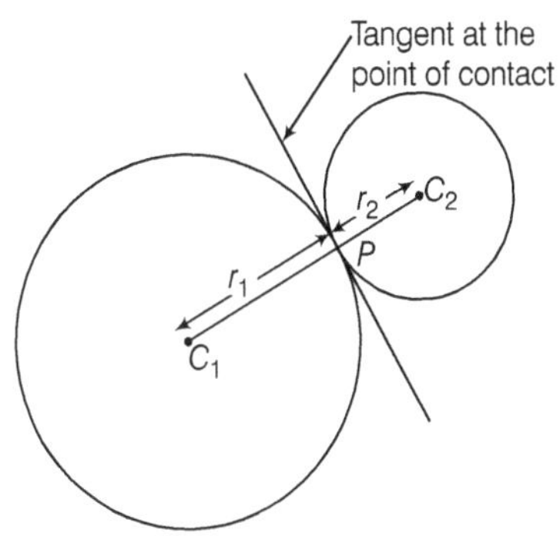

In this case circles touch at one point.
i.e. Number of solutions of two circles is one.

Case V : When $|C_1C_2| < |r_1 - r_2|$, i.e. the distance between the centres is less than the difference of their radii.

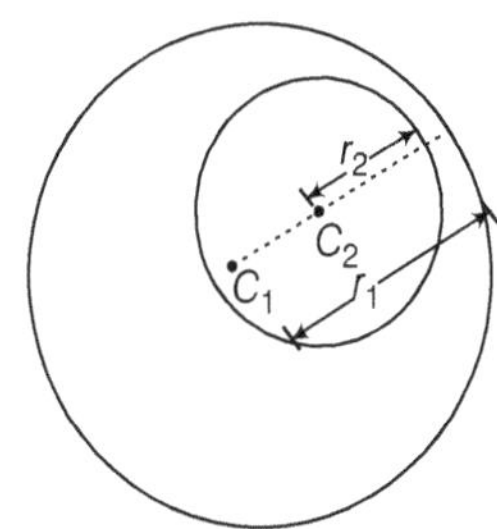

In this case, all the four common tangents are imaginary.

Remark

In this case circles neither cut nor touch each other i.e. Number of solution of two circles is zero.

Common Tangents to two Circles

If two circles with centres C_1 and C_2 and their radii are r_1 and r_2, then

	Condition	Figure	Number of common tangents
(i)	$\|C_1C_2\| > r_1 + r_2$		4
(ii)	$\|C_1C_2\| = r_1 + r_2$		3
(iii)	$\|r_1 - r_2\| < \|C_1C_2\| < r_1 + r_2$		2
(iv)	$\|C_1C_2\| = \|r_1 - r_2\|$		1
(v)	$\|C_1C_2\| < \|r_1 - r_2\|$		0

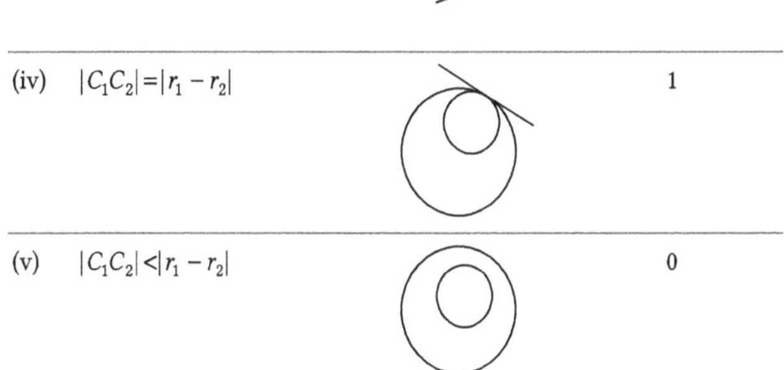

Length of External Common Tangent and Internal Common Tangent to Two Circles

Length of external common tangent $L_{ex} = \sqrt{d^2 - (r_1 - r_2)^2}$ and length of internal common tangent

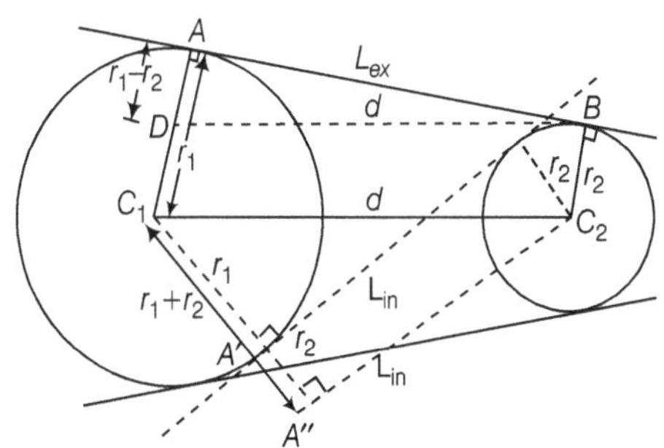

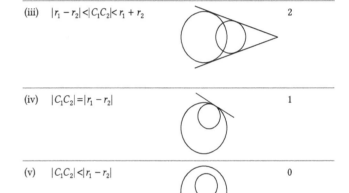

$L_{in} = \sqrt{d^2 - (r_1 + r_2)^2}$ (Applicable only when $d > r_1 + r_2$)

where, d is the distance between the centres of two circles and r_1, r_2 are the radii of two circles, when $|C_1C_2| = d$.

Angle between Direct Common Tangents (DCT) and Transverse Common Tangents (TCT)

Case I : If $d > r_1 + r_2$, then

Angle between DCT $= 2\sin^{-1}\left(\frac{|r_1 - r_2|}{d}\right)$

And angle between TCT $= 2\sin^{-1}\left(\frac{r_1 + r_2}{d}\right)$

Case II : If $d = r_1 + r_2$, then

angle between DCT $= 2\sin^{-1}\left(\frac{|r_1 - r_2|}{r_1 + r_2}\right)$

and angle between TCT $= \pi$

Case III : If $|r_1 - r_2| < d < r_1 + r_2$, then

angle between DCT $= 2\sin^{-1}\left(\frac{|r_1 - r_2|}{d}\right)$

Here, transverse common tangents are not possible .

Case IV : If $d = |r_1 - r_2|$

Angle between DCT $= \pi$

Here, transverse common tangents are not possible.

Case V : If $d < |r_1 - r_2|$

Here, tangents are not possible.

Example 64. Find all the common tangents to the circles
$x^2 + y^2 - 2x - 6y + 9 = 0$ and $x^2 + y^2 + 6x - 2y + 1 = 0.$

Sol. The given circles are

$$x^2 + y^2 - 2x - 6x + 9 = 0$$

$$\Rightarrow \quad (x-1)^2 + (y-3)^2 = 1 \quad \text{...(i)}$$

and $$x^2 + y^2 + 6x - 2y + 1 = 0$$

$$\Rightarrow \quad (x+3)^2 + (y-1)^2 = 9 \quad \text{...(ii)}$$

Centres and radii of circles Eq. (i) and Eq. (ii) are

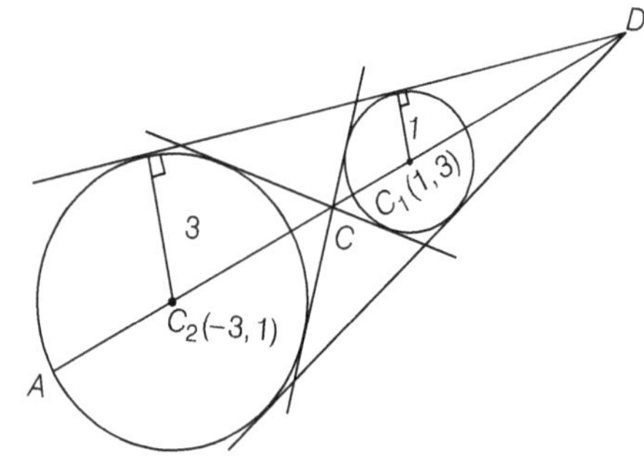

$C_1(1, 3), r_1 = 1$

and $C_2(-3, 1), r_2 = 3$ respectively.

$\therefore \quad C_1C_2 = \sqrt{(16+4)} = 2\sqrt{5}$

$\therefore \quad C_1C_2 > r_1 + r_2$

Hence, the circles do not intersect to each other.

The direct common tangents meet AB produced at D, then point D will divide C_2C_1 in the ratio 3 : 1 (externally).

Coordinates of D are $\left(\frac{3(1) - 1(-3)}{3-1}, \frac{3(3) - 1(1)}{3-1}\right)$ or (3, 4)

and the point C divide C_2C_1 in the ratio 3 : 1 (internally)

then coordinates of C are $\left(\frac{3(1) + 1(-3)}{3+1}, \frac{3(3) + 1(1)}{3+1}\right)$ or (0, 5/2)

Direct tangents : Any line through (3, 4) is

$$y - 4 = m(x - 3)$$

$$\Rightarrow \quad mx - y + 4 - 3m = 0 \quad \text{...(i)}$$

Apply the usual condition of tangency to any of the circle

$$\frac{m - 3 + 4 - 3m}{\sqrt{m^2 + 1}} = \pm 1$$

$$\Rightarrow \quad (-2m + 1)^2 = m^2 + 1$$

$$\Rightarrow \quad 3m^2 - 4m = 0$$

$$\Rightarrow \quad m = 0, m = 4/3$$

$\therefore$ Equations of direct common tangents are

$$y = 4 \quad \text{and} \quad 4x - 3y = 0$$

Transverse tangents : Any line through C (0, 5/2) is

$$y - 5/2 = mx$$

or $$mx - y + 5/2 = 0 \quad \text{...(ii)}$$

Apply the usual condition of tangency to any of the circle

$$\therefore \quad \frac{m \cdot 1 - 3 + 5/2}{\sqrt{m^2 + 1}} = \pm 1$$

$$\Rightarrow \quad m^2 + \frac{1}{4} - m = m^2 + 1$$

$$\Rightarrow \quad 0 \cdot m^2 - m - \frac{3}{4} = 0$$

$$\therefore \quad m = \infty \quad \text{and} \quad m = -3/4$$

Hence, equations of transverse tangents are

$$x = 0 \quad \text{and} \quad 3x + 4y - 10 = 0$$

Example 65. Show that the common tangents to the circles $x^2 + y^2 - 6x = 0$ and $x^2 + y^2 + 2x = 0$ form an equilateral triangle.

Sol. The given circles are

$$x^2 + y^2 - 6x = 0$$

or $$(x-3)^2 + (y-0)^2 = 9 \quad \text{...(i)}$$

and $$x^2 + y^2 + 2x = 0$$

or $$(x+1)^2 + (y-0)^2 = 1 \quad \text{...(ii)}$$

Centres and radii of circles Eqs. (i) and (ii) are $C_1(3, 0), r_1 = 3$ and $C_2(-1, 0), r_2 = 1$, respectively.

$\because \quad C_1C_2 = \sqrt{[3 - (-1)]^2 + 0} = 4$

$\therefore \quad C_1C_2 = r_1 + r_2$

Hence, the two circles touch each other externally, therefore, there will be three common tangents. Equation of the common tangent at the point of contact is $S_1 - S_2 = 0$

$\Rightarrow \quad (x^2 + y^2 - 6x) - (x^2 + y^2 + 2x) = 0$

$\Rightarrow \quad -8x = 0$

$\therefore \quad x = 0$

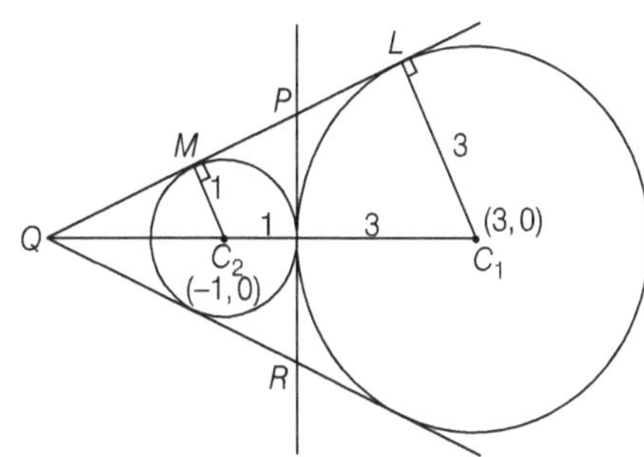

Let the coordinates of Q be (h, k), then

$$\frac{QC_2}{QC_1} = \frac{C_2M}{C_1L} = \frac{1}{3}$$

$\therefore \quad QC_2 : QC_1 = 1 : 3$

$\therefore \quad h = \dfrac{1\cdot(3) - 3\cdot(-1)}{1-3} = -3$ and $k = 0$

$\therefore \quad Q \equiv (-3, 0)$

Equation of line passing through $Q(-3, 0)$ is

$$y - 0 = m(x + 3)$$

or $\quad mx - y + 3m = 0 \quad$ ...(iii)

where, m is the slope of direct tangents since Eq. (iii) is the common tangent (direct) of the circles Eqs. (i) and (ii), then

Length of perpendicular from centre of Eq. (ii) i.e. $(-1, 0)$ to the Eq. (iii) = radius of circle Eq. (ii)

$\Rightarrow \quad \dfrac{|-m - 0 + 3m|}{\sqrt{m^2 + 1}} = 1$ or $4m^2 = m^2 + 1$

$\Rightarrow \quad 3m^2 = 1$

$\therefore \quad m = \pm \dfrac{1}{\sqrt{3}}$

From Eq. (iii), common tangents are (direct)

$$y = \frac{x}{\sqrt{3}} + \sqrt{3} \quad \text{and} \quad y = -\frac{x}{\sqrt{3}} - \sqrt{3}$$

Hence, all common tangents are $\quad x = 0 \quad$ ...(iv)

$y = \dfrac{x}{\sqrt{3}} + \sqrt{3} \quad$ ...(v)

and $\quad y = -\dfrac{x}{\sqrt{3}} - \sqrt{3} \quad$ ...(vi)

Let P, Q, R be the point of intersection of lines Eqs.(iv), (v); (v), (vi) and (iv), (vi) respectively, then

$$P \equiv (0, \sqrt{3}); Q \equiv (-3, 0) \quad \text{and} \quad R \equiv (0, -\sqrt{3})$$

Now, $PQ = QR = RP = 2\sqrt{3}$

Hence, ΔPQR is an equilateral triangle thus common tangents form an equilateral triangle.

Example 66. Find the number of common tangents to the circles $x^2 + y^2 - 8x + 2y + 8 = 0$ and $x^2 + y^2 - 2x - 6y - 15 = 0$.

Sol. For $x^2 + y^2 - 8x + 2y + 8 = 0$

$$C_1 \equiv (4, -1), r_1 = \sqrt{(16 + 1 - 8)} = 3$$

and for $x^2 + y^2 - 2x - 6y - 15 = 0$

$$C_2 \equiv (1, 3), r_2 = \sqrt{(1 + 9 + 15)} = 5$$

Now, $|C_1C_2|$ = Distance between centres

$$= \sqrt{(4-1)^2 + (-1-3)^2} = 5$$

and $\quad r_1 + r_2 = 3 + 5 = 8$

$\quad |r_1 - r_2| = |3 - 5| = 2$

or $\quad |r_1 - r_2| < |C_1C_2| < r_1 + r_2$

Hence, the two circles intersect at two distinct points. Therefore, two tangents can be drawn.

Example 67. Find the lengths of external and internal common tangents and also find the angle between external common tangents and internal common tangents of the circles $x^2 + y^2 + 2x - 8y + 13 = 0$ and $x^2 + y^2 - 8x - 2y + 8 = 0$.

Sol. The given circles are $x^2 + y^2 + 2x - 8y + 13 = 0$

$\Rightarrow \quad (x + 1)^2 + (y - 4)^2 = 2^2 \quad$ ...(i)

and $\quad x^2 + y^2 - 8x - 2y + 8 = 0$

$\Rightarrow \quad (x - 4)^2 + (y - 1)^2 = 3^2 \quad$ ...(ii)

Centres and radii of circles Eqs. (i) and (ii) are $C_1(-1, 4)$, $r_1 = 2$ and $C_2(4, 1)$, $r_2 = 3$ respectively.

$\therefore \quad |C_1C_2| = d = \sqrt{(25 + 9)} = \sqrt{34}$

$\Rightarrow \quad d > r_1 + r_2$

Hence, the circles do not intersect to each other.

$\therefore \quad L_{ex} = \sqrt{d^2 - (r_1 - r_2)^2} = \sqrt{34 - 1} = \sqrt{33}$

and $\quad L_{in} = \sqrt{d^2 - (r_1 + r_2)^2} = \sqrt{(34 - 25)} = 3$

Angle between external common tangents

$$= 2\sin^{-1}\left(\frac{|r_1 - r_2|}{d}\right) = 2\sin^{-1}\left(\frac{1}{\sqrt{33}}\right)$$

and angle between internal common tangent

$$= 2\sin^{-1}\left(\frac{r_1 + r_2}{d}\right) = 2\sin^{-1}\left(\frac{5}{\sqrt{33}}\right)$$

Common Chord of Two Circles

The chord joining the points of intersection of two given circles is called their common chord.

Theorem : The equation of common chord of two circles

$$S \equiv x^2 + y^2 + 2gx + 2fy + c = 0$$

and $S' \equiv x^2 + y^2 + 2g'x + 2f'y + c' = 0$

is $2x(g - g') + 2y(f - f') + c - c' = 0$

i.e. $S - S' = 0$

Proof : $\because$ $S = 0$ and $S' = 0$ be two intersecting circles.

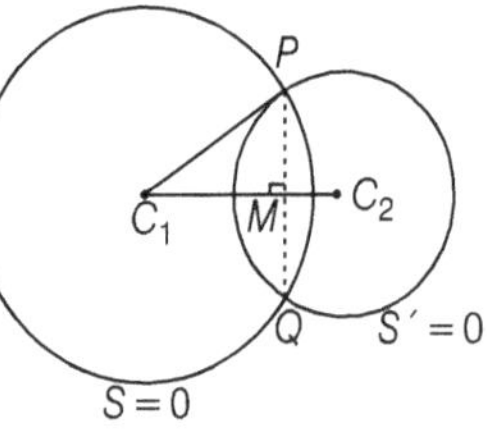

Then, $S - S' = 0$ or

$2x(g - g') + 2y(f - f') + c - c' = 0$

is a first degree equation in x and y.

So, it represent a straight line. Also, this equation satisfied by the intersecting points of two given circles $S = 0$ and $S' = 0$.

Hence, $S - S' = 0$ represents the common chord of circles $S = 0$ and $S' = 0$

Length of common chord :

We have, $PQ = 2(PM)$ ($\because M$ is mid-point of PQ)

$$= 2\sqrt{\{(C_1P)^2 - (C_1M)^2\}}$$

where, C_1P = radius of the circle ($S = 0$)

and C_1M = length of perpendicular from C_1 on common chord PQ.

Corollary 1 : The common chord PQ of two circles becomes of the maximum length when it is a diameter of the smaller one between them.

Corollary 2 : Circle on the common chord a diameter, then centre of the circle passing through P and Q lie on the common chord of two circles i.e.

$$S - S' = 0$$

Corollary 3 : If the length of common chord is zero, then the two circles touch each other and the common chord becomes the common tangent to the two circles at the common point of contact.

Example 68. Prove that the length of the common chord of the two circles :

$$(x - a)^2 + (y - b)^2 = c^2$$

and $(x - b)^2 + (y - a)^2 = c^2$ is $\sqrt{4c^2 - 2(a - b)^2}$.

Find also the condition when the given circles touch.

Sol. The equation of circles are

$$S_1 \equiv (x - a)^2 + (y - b)^2 - c^2 = 0 \quad \text{...(i)}$$

and $$S_2 \equiv (x - b)^2 + (y - a)^2 - c^2 = 0 \quad \text{...(ii)}$$

then equation of common chord is $S_1 - S_2 = 0$

$\Rightarrow$ $(x - a)^2 - (x - b)^2 + (y - b)^2 - (y - a)^2 = 0$

or $(2x - a - b)(-a + b) + (2y - b - a)(-b + a) = 0$

$\Rightarrow$ $2x - a - b - 2y + b + a = 0$

$\Rightarrow$ $x - y = 0$

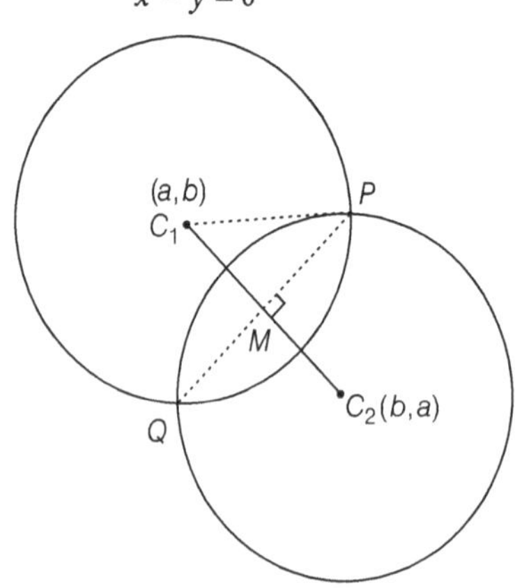

Now, C_1M = Length of perpendicular from C_1 (a, b) on $PQ(x - y = 0) = \dfrac{|a - b|}{\sqrt{2}}$

and C_1P = radius of the circle Eq. (i) = c

$\therefore$ In ΔPC_1M, $PM = \sqrt{(PC_1)^2 - (C_1M)^2}$

$$= \sqrt{c^2 - \frac{(a - b)^2}{2}}$$

$\therefore$ $$PQ = 2PM = 2\sqrt{c^2 - \frac{(a - b)^2}{2}}$$

$$= \sqrt{4c^2 - 2(a - b)^2}$$

Also, when the circles touch, then chord PQ becomes the tangent and $PQ = 0$.

$\therefore$ The condition of tangency is $4c^2 - 2(a - b)^2 = 0$.

i.e. $2c^2 = (a - b)^2$

Family of Circles

1. The equation of the family of circles passing through the point of intersection of two given circles $S = 0$ and $S' = 0$ is given as

$$S + \lambda S' = 0 \quad \text{(where, } \lambda \text{ is a parameter, } \lambda \neq -1\text{)}$$

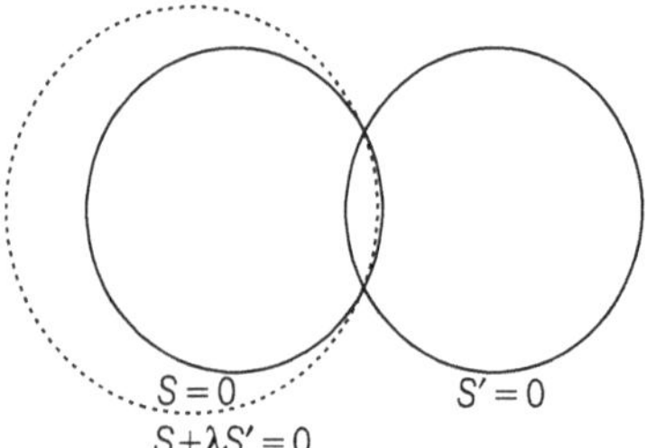

2. The equation of the family of circles passing through the point of intersection of circle $S=0$ and a line $L=0$ is given as

$$S+\lambda L = 0 \qquad \text{(where, } \lambda \text{ is a parameter)}$$

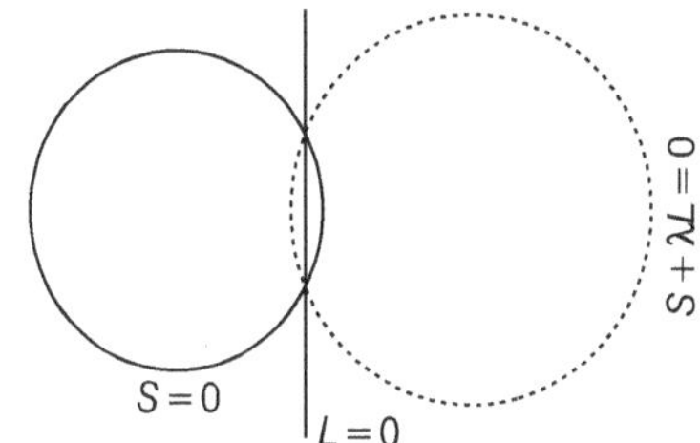

3. The equation of the family of circles touching the circle $S=0$ and the line $L=0$ at their point of contact P is

$$S+\lambda L=0 \qquad \text{(where, } \lambda \text{ is a parameter)}$$

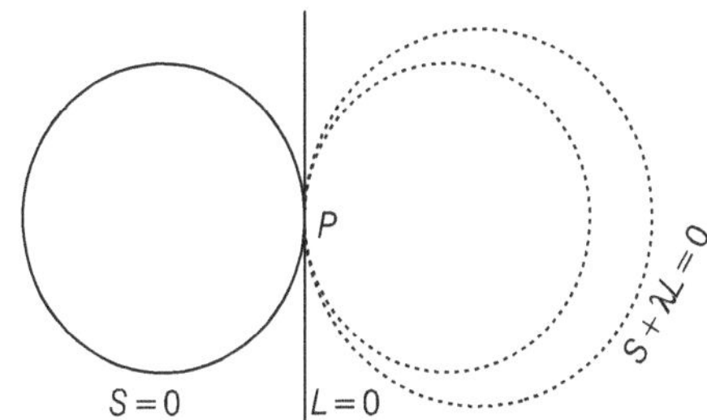

4. The equation of a family of circles passing through two given points $P(x_1, y_1)$ and $Q(x_2, y_2)$ can be written in the form

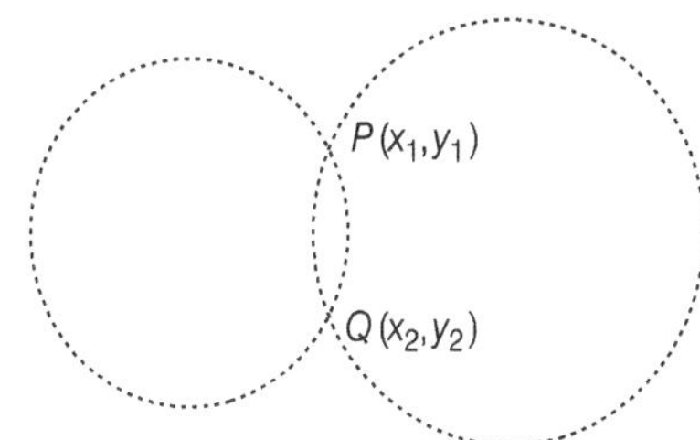

$$(x-x_1)(x-x_2)+(y-y_1)(y-y_2) + \lambda \begin{vmatrix} x & y & 1 \\ x_1 & y_1 & 1 \\ x_2 & y_2 & 1 \end{vmatrix} = 0$$

(where, λ is a parameter)

5. The equation of family of circles which touch $y-y_1 = m(x-x_1)$ at (x_1, y_1) for any finite m is

$$(x-x_1)^2 + (y-y_1)^2 + \lambda\{(y-y_1) - m(x-x_1)\} = 0$$

and if m is infinite, the family of circles is

$$(x-x_1)^2 + (y-y_1)^2 + \lambda(x-x_1) = 0$$

(where, λ is a parameter)

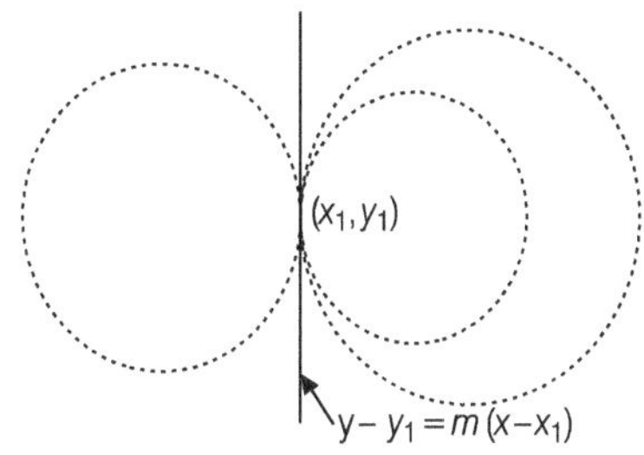

6. Equation of the circles given in diagram are

$$(x-x_1)(x-x_2)+(y-y_1)(y-y_2) \pm \cot\theta\,\{(x-x_1)(y-y_2)-(x-x_2)(y-y_1)\} = 0$$

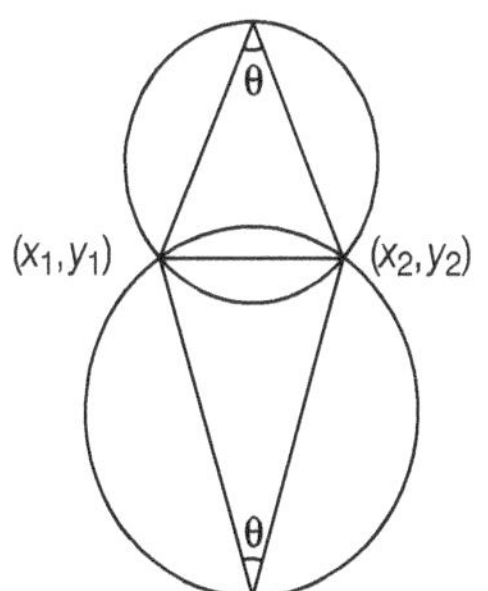

Example 69. Find the equation of the circle passing through (1, 1) and the points of intersection of the circles $x^2+y^2+13x-3y=0$ and $2x^2+2y^2+4x-7y-25=0$.

Sol. The given circles are

$$x^2+y^2+13x-3y=0 \qquad \text{...(i)}$$

and $\quad 2x^2+2y^2+4x-7y-25=0$

or $$x^2+y^2+2x-\frac{7}{2}y-\frac{25}{2}=0 \qquad \text{...(ii)}$$

Equation of any circle passing through the point of intersection of the circles Eqs. (i) and (ii) is

$$(x^2+y^2+13x-3y)+\lambda\left(x^2+y^2+2x-\frac{7}{2}y-\frac{25}{2}\right)=0 \quad \text{...(iii)}$$

Its passes through (1, 1), then

$$(1+1+13-3)+\lambda\left(1+1+2-\frac{7}{2}-\frac{25}{2}\right)=0$$

$\Rightarrow \quad 12+\lambda(-12)=0 \therefore \lambda=1$

Substituting the value of λ in Eq. (iii), the required equation is

$$x^2+y^2+13x-3y+x^2+y^2+2x-\frac{7}{2}y-\frac{25}{2}=0$$

$$\Rightarrow \quad 2x^2+2y^2+15x-\frac{13}{2}y-\frac{25}{2}=0$$

$$\Rightarrow \quad 4x^2+4y^2+30x-13y-25=0$$

Example 70. Find the equation of the circle passing through the point of intersection of the circles $x^2+y^2-6x+2y+4=0$, $x^2+y^2+2x-4y-6=0$ and with its centre on the line $y=x$.

Sol. Equation of any circle through the points of intersection of given circles is

$$(x^2+y^2-6x+2y+4)+\lambda(x^2+y^2+2x-4y-6)=0$$

$$\Rightarrow \quad x^2(1+\lambda)+y^2(1+\lambda)-2x(3-\lambda)+2y(1-2\lambda)+(4-6\lambda)=0$$

$$\text{or} \quad x^2+y^2-\frac{2x(3-\lambda)}{(1+\lambda)}+\frac{2y(1-2\lambda)}{(1+\lambda)}+\frac{(4-6\lambda)}{(1+\lambda)}=0 \quad \text{...(i)}$$

Its centre $\left\{\frac{3-\lambda}{1+\lambda}, \frac{2\lambda-1}{1+\lambda}\right\}$ lies on the line $y=x$

then $\quad \frac{2\lambda-1}{1+\lambda}=\frac{3-\lambda}{1+\lambda} \Rightarrow \lambda \neq -1$

$\therefore \quad 2\lambda-1=3-\lambda$ or $3\lambda=4$

$\therefore \quad \lambda=4/3$

$\therefore$ Substituting the value of $\lambda=4/3$ in Eq. (i), we get the required equation is

$$7x^2+7y^2-10x-10y-12=0$$

Example 71. Find the equation of the circle passing through the points of intersection of the circles $x^2+y^2-2x-4y-4=0$ and $x^2+y^2-10x-12y+40=0$ and whose radius is 4.

Sol. Equation of the any circle through the points of intersection of given circles is

$$(x^2+y^2-2x-4y-4)+\lambda(x^2+y^2-10x-12y+40)=0$$

$$\Rightarrow \quad x^2(1+\lambda)+y^2(1+\lambda)-2x(1+5\lambda)-2y(2+6\lambda)-4+40\lambda=0$$

$$\text{or} \quad x^2+y^2-2x\frac{(1+5\lambda)}{(1+\lambda)}-2y\frac{(2+6\lambda)}{(1+\lambda)}+\frac{(40\lambda-4)}{(1+\lambda)}=0 \quad \text{...(i)}$$

Its radius

$$\sqrt{\left(\frac{1+5\lambda}{1+\lambda}\right)^2+\left(\frac{2+6\lambda}{1+\lambda}\right)^2-\left(\frac{40\lambda-4}{1+\lambda}\right)}=4 \quad \text{(given)}$$

$$\Rightarrow \quad \frac{(1+5\lambda)^2+(2+6\lambda)^2-(40\lambda-4)(1+\lambda)}{(1+\lambda)^2}=16$$

$$\Rightarrow \quad 5\lambda^2-34\lambda-7=0$$

$$\text{or} \quad (\lambda-7)(5\lambda+1)=0$$

$$\therefore \quad \lambda=7 \quad \text{or} \quad \lambda=-\frac{1}{5}$$

Substituting the values of λ in Eq. (i), the required circles are

$$2x^2+2y^2-18x-22y+69=0$$

and $\quad x^2+y^2-2y-15=0$

Example 72. Find the equation of the circle passing through points of intersection of the circle $x^2+y^2-2x-4y+4=0$ and the line $x+2y=4$ which touches the line $x+2y=0$.

Sol. Equation of any circle through points of intersection of the given circle and the line is

$$(x^2+y^2-2x-4y+4)+\lambda(x+2y-4)=0$$

$$\text{or} \quad x^2+y^2+(\lambda-2)x+(2\lambda-4)y+4(1-\lambda)=0 \quad \text{...(i)}$$

It will touch the line $x+2y=0$, then solution of Eq. (i) and $x=-2y$ be unique.

Hence, the roots of the equation

$$(-2y)^2+y^2+(\lambda-2)(-2y)+(2\lambda-4)y+4(1-\lambda)=0$$

$$\text{or} \quad 5y^2+4(1-\lambda)=0$$

must be equal.

Then, $0-4\cdot5\cdot4(1-\lambda)=0$ or $1-\lambda=0$ or $\lambda=1$

From Eq. (i), the required circle is $x^2+y^2-x-2y=0$

Example 73. Find the circle whose diameter is the common chord of the circles $x^2+y^2+2x+3y+1=0$ and $x^2+y^2+4x+3y+2=0$.

Sol. Given circles are

$$S \equiv x^2+y^2+2x+3y+1=0$$

and $\quad S' \equiv x^2+y^2+4x+3y+2=0$

Hence, their common chord is $S-S'=0$

$$\Rightarrow \quad -2x-1=0 \quad \text{or} \quad 2x+1=0 \quad \text{...(i)}$$

Now, the required circle must pass through the point of intersection of S and S'.

Hence, its equation is $\quad S+\lambda S'=0$

$$\Rightarrow \quad (x^2+y^2+2x+3y+1)+\lambda(x^2+y^2+4x+3y+2)=0$$

$$\Rightarrow \quad x^2(1+\lambda)+y^2(1+\lambda)+2x(1+2\lambda)+3y(1+\lambda)+(1+2\lambda)=0$$

$$\text{or} \quad x^2+y^2+2x\frac{(1+2\lambda)}{(1+\lambda)}+3y+\frac{(1+2\lambda)}{(1+\lambda)}=0 \quad \text{...(ii)}$$

Its centre is $\left(-\frac{1+2\lambda}{1+\lambda}, -\frac{3}{2}\right)$

But from Eq. (i), $2x+1=0$ is a diameter of this circle. Hence, its centre must lie on this line

$$\therefore \quad -2\left(\frac{1+2\lambda}{1+\lambda}\right)+1=0$$

$$\Rightarrow \quad -2-4\lambda+1+\lambda=0$$

$$\Rightarrow \quad -1-3\lambda=0$$

$$\therefore \quad \lambda=-\frac{1}{3}$$

Hence, from Eq. (ii), the required circle is

$$2x^2+2y^2+2x+6y+1=0$$

Example 74. If two curves, whose equations are $ax^2+2hxy+by^2+2gx+2fy+c=0$ and $a'x^2+2h'xy+b'y^2+2g'x+2f'y+c'=0$ intersect in four concyclic points, prove that $\frac{a-b}{h}=\frac{a'-b'}{h'}$

Sol. The equation of family of curves passing through the points of intersection of two curves is

$$(ax^2+2hxy+by^2+2gx+2fy+c)$$
$$+\lambda(a'x^2+2h'xy+b'y^2+2g'x+2f'y+c')=0$$

or $$(a+\lambda a')x^2+2xy(h+h'\lambda)+(b+\lambda b')y^2$$
$$+2x(g+\lambda g')+2y(f+\lambda f')+(c+\lambda c')=0 \quad \text{...(i)}$$

Four concyclic points lie on a circle, then Eq. (i) represents a circle. Then,

coefficient of x^2 = coefficient of y^2 and coefficient of $xy=0$

$\Rightarrow$ $$a+\lambda a'=b+\lambda b'$$

or $$(a-b)=-\lambda(a'-b') \quad \text{...(ii)}$$

and $$2(h+h'\lambda)=0$$

or $$\lambda=-\frac{h}{h'} \quad \text{...(iii)}$$

Substituting the value of λ from Eq. (iii) in Eq. (ii), then

$$\frac{a-b}{h}=\frac{a'-b'}{h'}$$

Exercise for Session 6

1. Circles $x^2+y^2-2x-4y=0$ and $x^2+y^2-8y-4=0$
   (a) touch each other internally
   (b) touch each other externally
   (c) cuts each other at two points
   (d) None of these

2. The number of common tangents that can be drawn to the circles $x^2+y^2-4x-6y-3=0$ and $x^2+y^2+2x+2y+1=0$ is
   (a) 1 (b) 2 (c) 3 (d) 4

3. If one of the circles $x^2+y^2+2ax+c=0$ and $x^2+y^2+2bx+c=0$ lies within the other, then
   (a) $ab>0, c>0$
   (b) $ab>0,\ c<0$
   (c) $ab<0,\ c>0$
   (d) $ab<0,\ c<0$

4. The condition that the circle $(x-3)^2+(y-4)^2=r^2$ lies entirely within the circle $x^2+y^2=R^2$ is
   (a) $R+r\le 7$
   (b) $R^2+r^2<49$
   (c) $R^2-r^2<25$
   (d) $R-r>5$

5. The circles whose equations are $x^2+y^2+c^2=2ax$ and $x^2+y^2+c^2-2by=0$ will touch one another externally, if
   (a) $\frac{1}{b^2}+\frac{1}{c^2}=\frac{1}{a^2}$
   (b) $\frac{1}{c^2}+\frac{1}{a^2}=\frac{1}{b^2}$
   (c) $\frac{1}{a^2}+\frac{1}{b^2}=\frac{1}{c^2}$
   (d) $\frac{1}{b^2}+\frac{1}{c^2}=\frac{2}{a^2}$

6. Two circles with radii r_1 and r_2, $r_1>r_2\ge 2$, touch each other externally. If θ be the angle between the direct common tangents, then
   (a) $\theta=\sin^{-1}\left(\frac{r_1+r_2}{r_1-r_2}\right)$
   (b) $\theta=2\sin^{-1}\left(\frac{r_1-r_2}{r_1+r_2}\right)$
   (c) $\theta=\sin^{-1}\left(\frac{r_1-r_2}{r_1+r_2}\right)$
   (d) None of these

7. The circles $x^2+y^2-10x+16=0$ and $x^2+y^2=r^2$ intersect each other in two distinct points if
   (a) $r<2$ (b) $r>8$ (c) $2<r<8$ (d) $2\le r\le 8$

8. If the circle $x^2+y^2+4x+22y+c=0$ bisects the circumference of the circle $x^2+y^2-2x+8y-d=0$, then $c+d$ is equal to
   (a) 40 (b) 50 (c) 60 (d) 70

9. Two circles $x^2 + y^2 = 6$ and $x^2 + y^2 - 6x + 8 = 0$ are given. Then, the equation of the circle through their points of intersection and the point (1, 1) is

(a) $x^2 + y^2 - 6x + 4 = 0$
(b) $x^2 + y^2 - 3x + 1 = 0$
(c) $x^2 + y^2 - 4x + 2 = 0$
(d) $x^2 + y^2 - 2x + 1 = 0$

10. The equation of the circle described on the common chord of the circles $x^2 + y^2 + 2x = 0$ and $x^2 + y^2 + 2y = 0$ as diameter is

(a) $x^2 + y^2 + x - y = 0$
(b) $x^2 + y^2 - x + y = 0$
(c) $x^2 + y^2 - x - y = 0$
(d) $x^2 + y^2 + x + y = 0$

11. The equation of the diameter of the circle $3(x^2 + y^2) - 2x + 6y - 9 = 0$ which is perpendicular to the line $2x + 3y = 12$ is

(a) $3x - 2y + 3 = 0$
(b) $3x - 2y - 3 = 0$
(c) $3x - 2y + 1 = 0$
(d) $3x - 2y - 1 = 0$

12. If the curves $ax^2 + 4xy + 2y^2 + x + y + 5 = 0$ and $ax^2 + 6xy + 5y^2 + 2x + 3y + 8 = 0$ intersect at four concyclic points, then the value of a is

(a) –6
(b) –4
(c) 4
(d) 6

13. Find the equation of the circle passing through the points of intersection of $x^2 + y^2 + 13x - 3y = 0$ and $2x^2 + 2y^2 + 4x - 7y - 25 = 0$ and the point (1, 1).

14. Show that the common chord of the circles $x^2 + y^2 - 6x - 4y + 9 = 0$ and $x^2 + y^2 - 8x - 6y + 23 = 0$ pass through the centre of the second circle and find its length.

15. Prove that the circles $x^2 + y^2 + 2ax + 2by = 0$ and $x^2 + y^2 + 2a_1x + 2b_1y = 0$ touch each other, if $ab_1 = a_1 b$.

16. Find the equations of common tangents to the circles $x^2 + y^2 - 24x + 2y + 120 = 0$ and $x^2 + y^2 + 20x - 6y - 116 = 0$.

Session 7

Angle of Intersection of Two Circles, Radical Axis, Radical Centre, Co-axial System of Circles, Limiting Point, Image of the Circle by the Line Mirror

Angle of Intersection of Two Circles

Let the two circles

$$S \equiv x^2 + y^2 + 2gx + 2fy + c = 0$$

and $\quad S' \equiv x^2 + y^2 + 2g_1x + 2f_1y + c_1 = 0$

intersect each other at the points P and Q. The angle θ between two circles $S = 0$ and $S' = 0$ is defined as the angle between the tangents to the two circles at the point of intersection.

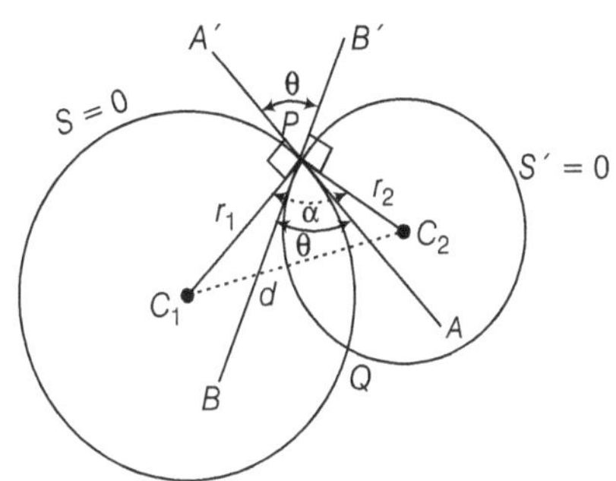

C_1 and C_2 are the centres of circles

$S = 0$ and $S' = 0$, then

$$C_1 \equiv (-g, -f) \quad \text{and} \quad C_2 \equiv (-g_1, -f_1)$$

and radii of circles $S = 0$ and $S' = 0$ are

$$r_1 = \sqrt{(g^2 + f^2 - c)} \text{ and } r_2 = \sqrt{(g_1^2 + f_1^2 - c_1)}$$

Let $\quad d = |C_1C_2| =$ Distance between their centres

$$= \sqrt{(-g + g_1)^2 + (-f + f_1)^2}$$

$$= \sqrt{(g^2 + f^2 + g_1^2 + f_1^2 - 2gg_1 - 2ff_1)}$$

Now, in ΔC_1PC_2, $\cos\alpha = \left(\dfrac{r_1^2 + r_2^2 - d^2}{2r_1r_2}\right) \left(\because \alpha + \theta + 90^\circ + 90^\circ = 360^\circ\right)$

or $\quad \cos(180^\circ - \theta) = \left(\dfrac{r_1^2 + r_2^2 - d^2}{2r_1r_2}\right) \quad (\therefore \alpha = 180^\circ - \theta)$

$\therefore \quad \cos\theta = \left|\dfrac{r_1^2 + r_2^2 - d^2}{2r_1r_2}\right| \quad$ ...(i)

Orthogonal Intersection of Circles

If the angle between the circles is 90°, i.e. $\theta = 90^\circ$, then the circles are said to be **orthogonal circles** or we say that the circles cut each other **orthogonally**.

Then, from Eq. (i), $0 = \dfrac{r_1^2 + r_2^2 - d^2}{2r_1r_2}$

or $\quad r_1^2 + r_2^2 - d^2 = 0$ or $r_1^2 + r_2^2 = d^2$

$$\Rightarrow \quad g^2 + f^2 - c + g_1^2 + f_1^2 - c_1 = g^2 + f^2 + g_1^2 + f_1^2 - 2gg_1 - 2ff_1$$

or $\quad 2gg_1 + 2ff_1 = c + c_1$

Remark

Equation of a circle cutting the three circles $x^2 + y^2 + 2g_ix + 2f_iy + c_i = 0$ $(i = 1, 2, 3)$ orthogonally is

$$\begin{vmatrix} x^2 + y^2 & x & y & 1 \\ -c_1 & g_1 & f_1 & -1 \\ -c_2 & g_2 & f_2 & -1 \\ -c_3 & g_3 & f_3 & -1 \end{vmatrix}$$

| Example 75. Find the angle between the circles

$$S : x^2 + y^2 - 4x + 6y + 11 = 0$$

and $\quad S' : x^2 + y^2 - 2x + 8y + 13 = 0$

Sol. Centres and radii of circles S and S' are

$$C_1(2, -3),\ r_1 = \sqrt{2},\ C_2(1, -4),\ r_2 = 2.$$

Distance between centres, $d = |C_1C_2|$

$$= \sqrt{(2-1)^2 + (-3+4)^2} = \sqrt{2}$$

If angle between the circles is θ, then

$$\cos\theta = \left|\frac{r_1^2 + r_2^2 - d^2}{2r_1 r_2}\right|$$

$$\cos\theta = \left|\frac{2+4-2}{2\cdot\sqrt{2}\cdot 2}\right| = \frac{1}{\sqrt{2}}$$

$\therefore \quad \theta = 45^\circ$

Example 76. Show that the circles $x^2 + y^2 - 6x + 4y + 4 = 0$ and $x^2 + y^2 + x + 4y + 1 = 0$ cut orthogonally.

Sol. Comparing the given circles by general equation of circles

$$x^2 + y^2 + 2gx + 2fy + c = 0$$

and $\quad x^2 + y^2 + 2g_1x + 2f_1y + c_1 = 0$

then, $\quad g = -3, f = 2, c = 4$

and $\quad g_1 = \frac{1}{2}, f_1 = 2, c_1 = 1$

Then, given circles cut orthogonally, if

$$2gg_1 + 2ff_1 = c + c_1$$

We have, $\quad 2\times(-3)\times\frac{1}{2} + 2\times 2\times 2 = 4 + 1$

$\Rightarrow \quad -3 + 8 = 5$ or $5 = 5.$

Hence, the given circles cut each other orthogonally.

Example 77. Find the equation of the circle which cuts the circle $x^2 + y^2 + 5x + 7y - 4 = 0$ orthogonally, has its centre on the line $x = 2$ and passes through the point $(4, -1)$.

Sol. Let the required circle be

$$x^2 + y^2 + 2gx + 2fy + c = 0 \quad \text{...(i)}$$

Since, $(4, -1)$ lie on Eq. (i), then

$$17 + 8g - 2f + c = 0 \quad \text{...(ii)}$$

Centre of Eq. (i) is $(-g, -f)$

Since, centre lie on $x = 2$ then $-g = 2$

$\therefore \quad g = -2 \quad$ ...(iii)

From Eq. (ii), $1 - 2f + c = 0 \quad$ ...(iv)

and given circle is

$$x^2 + y^2 + 5x + 7y - 4 = 0 \quad \text{...(v)}$$

Given the circles Eqs. (i) and (v) cut each other orthogonally,

$\therefore \quad 2g\times\frac{5}{2} + 2f\times\frac{7}{2} = c - 4$

or $\quad 5g + 7f = c - 4$

$\quad -10 + 7f = c - 4 \quad$ [from Eq. (iii)]

or $\quad -6 + 7f - c = 0 \quad$ ...(vi)

Solving Eqs. (iv) and (vi), we get

$$f = 1 \quad \text{and} \quad c = 1$$

Substituting the values of g, f, c in Eq. (i), we get

$$x^2 + y^2 - 4x + 2y + 1 = 0$$

Example 78. Find the equations of the two circles which intersect the circles $x^2 + y^2 - 6y + 1 = 0$ and $x^2 + y^2 - 4y + 1 = 0$ orthogonally and touch the line $3x + 4y + 5 = 0$.

Sol. Let the required circle be

$$x^2 + y^2 + 2gx + 2fy + c = 0 \quad \text{...(i)}$$

and given circles are $x^2 + y^2 - 6y + 1 = 0 \quad$ ...(ii)

and $\quad x^2 + y^2 - 4y + 1 = 0 \quad$ ...(iii)

Since, Eq. (i) cuts Eq. (ii) and Eq. (iii) orthogonally

$\therefore \quad 2g\times 0 + 2f\times(-3) = c + 1$

or $\quad -6f = c + 1 \quad$ ...(iv)

and $\quad 2g\times 0 + 2f\times(-2) = c + 1$

or $\quad -4f = c + 1 \quad$ ...(v)

Solving, Eqs. (iv) and (v), we get

$$f = 0 \quad \text{and} \quad c = -1$$

From Eq. (i), $\quad x^2 + y^2 + 2gx - 1 = 0 \quad$ ...(vi)

centre and radius of Eq. (vi) are $(-g, 0)$ and $\sqrt{(g^2 + 1)}$, respectively.

Since, $3x + 4y + 5 = 0$ is tangent of Eq. (vi), then length of perpendicular from $(-g, 0)$ to this line = radius of circle

or $\quad \frac{|-3g + 0 + 5|}{\sqrt{(9 + 16)}} = \sqrt{(g^2 + 1)}$

$$|-3g + 5| = 5\sqrt{(g^2 + 1)}$$

or $\quad (-3g + 5)^2 = 25(g^2 + 1)$

or $\quad 9g^2 + 25 - 30g = 25g^2 + 25$

or $\quad 16g^2 + 30g = 0$

$\therefore \quad g = 0$ and $g = -\frac{15}{8}$

Equations of circles are from Eq. (vi),

$$x^2 + y^2 - 1 = 0 \quad \text{and} \quad x^2 + y^2 - \frac{15}{4}x - 1 = 0$$

or $\quad x^2 + y^2 - 1 = 0$ and $4x^2 + 4y^2 - 15x - 4 = 0.$

Example 79. Prove that the two circles, which pass through $(0, a)$ and $(0, -a)$ and touch the line $y = mx + c$, will cut orthogonally, if $c^2 = a^2(2 + m^2)$

Sol. Let the equation of the circles be

$$x^2 + y^2 + 2gx + 2fy + d = 0 \quad \text{...(i)}$$

Since, these circles pass through $(0, a)$ and $(0, -a)$, then

$$a^2 + 2fa + d = 0 \quad \text{...(ii)}$$

and $\quad a^2 - 2fa + d = 0 \quad$ ...(iii)

Solving, Eq. (ii) and Eq. (iii), we get $f = 0$ and $d = -a^2$.

Substituting these values of f and d in Eq. (i), we obtain

$$x^2 + y^2 + 2gx - a^2 = 0 \quad \text{...(iv)}$$

Now, $y = mx + c$ touch this circle, therefore, length of the perpendicular from the centre = radius

$$\frac{|-mg - 0 + c|}{\sqrt{1+m^2}} = \sqrt{(g^2 + a^2)}$$

$$(c - mg)^2 = (1 + m^2)(g^2 + a^2)$$

or $\quad g^2 + 2mcg + a^2(1 + m^2) - c^2 = 0$

Let g_1, g_2 are the roots of this equation

$\therefore \quad g_1 g_2 = a^2(1 + m^2) - c^2 \quad$ ...(v)

Now, the equations of the two circles represented by Eq. (iv) are

$$x^2 + y^2 + 2g_1 x - a^2 = 0$$

and $\quad x^2 + y^2 + 2g_2 x - a^2 = 0.$

These two circles will be cuts orthogonal, if

$$2g_1 g_2 + 0 = -a^2 - a^2$$

or $\quad g_1 g_2 = -a^2 \quad$ ...(vi)

From Eqs. (v) and (vi),

$$-a^2 = a^2(1 + m^2) - c^2$$

or $\quad c^2 = a^2(2 + m^2)$

which is the required condition.

Example 80. Find the equation of the circle which cuts orthogonally each of the three circles given below :

$x^2 + y^2 - 2x + 3y - 7 = 0$, $x^2 + y^2 + 5x - 5y + 9 = 0$ and $x^2 + y^2 + 7x - 9x + 29 = 0$.

Sol. Let the required circle be

$x^2 + y^2 + 2gx + 2fy + c = 0 \quad$ ...(i)

Since, it is orthogonal to three given circles respectively, therefore

$$2g \times (-1) + 2f \times \frac{3}{2} = c - 7$$

or $\quad -2g + 3f = c - 7 \quad$ ...(ii)

$$2g \times \frac{5}{2} + 2f \times \left(-\frac{5}{2}\right) = c + 9$$

or $\quad 5g - 5f = c + 9 \quad$ ...(iii)

and $\quad 2g \times \frac{7}{2} + 2f \times \left(-\frac{9}{2}\right) = c + 29$

or $\quad 7g - 9f = c + 29 \quad$ ...(iv)

Subtracting, Eq. (ii) from Eq. (iii),

$7g - 8f = 16 \quad$ ...(v)

and subtracting Eq. (iii) from Eq. (iv),

$2g - 4f = 20 \quad$ ...(vi)

Solving Eq. (v) and Eq. (vi), we get

$$g = -8 \quad \text{and} \quad f = -9$$

Putting the values of g and f in Eq. (iii)

$$-40 + 45 = c + 9$$

$\Rightarrow \quad 5 = c + 9$

or $\quad c = -4$

Substituting the values of g, f, c in Eq. (i), then required circle is

$$x^2 + y^2 - 16x - 18y - 4 = 0$$

Radical Axis

The radical axis of two circles is the locus of a point which moves such that the lengths of the tangents drawn from it to the two circles are equal.

Consider, $\quad S \equiv x^2 + y^2 + 2gx + 2fy + c = 0 \quad$ ...(i)

and $\quad S' \equiv x^2 + y^2 + 2g_1 x + 2f_1 y + c_1 = 0 \quad$ ...(ii)

Let $P(x_1, y_1)$ be a point such that

$$|PA| = |PB|$$

$$\Rightarrow \quad \sqrt{(x_1^2 + y_1^2 + 2gx_1 + 2fy_1 + c)} = \sqrt{(x_1^2 + y_1^2 + 2g_1 x_1 + 2f_1 y_1 + c_1)}$$

On squaring, $\quad x_1^2 + y_1^2 + 2gx_1 + 2fy_1 + c = x_1^2 + y_1^2 + 2g_1 x_1 + 2f_1 y_1 + c_1$

$$\Rightarrow \quad 2(g - g_1)x_1 + 2(f - f_1)y_1 + c - c_1 = 0$$

$\therefore$ Locus of $P(x_1, y_1)$ is

$$2(g - g_1)x + 2(f - f_1)y + c - c_1 = 0$$

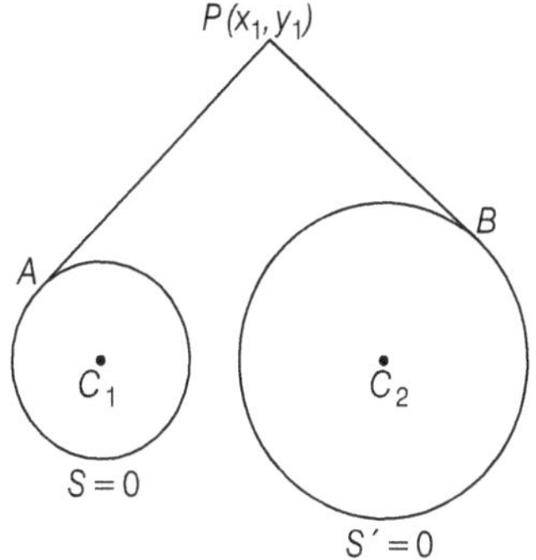

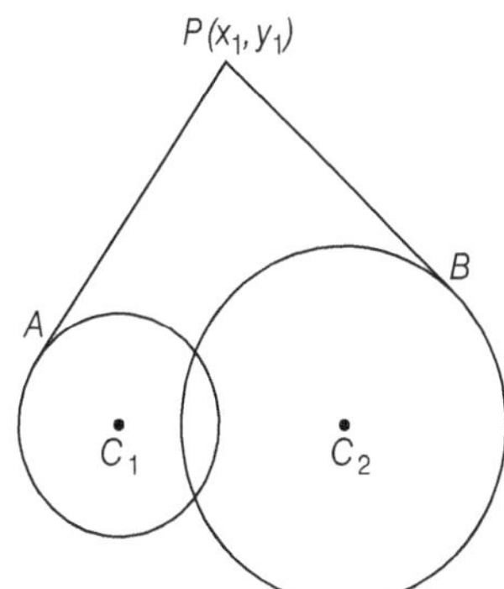

which is the required equation of radical axis of the given circles. Clearly this is a straight line.

Some Properties of the Radical Axis

(i) **The radical axis and common chord are identical :** Since, the radical axis and common chord of two circles $S=0$ and $S'=0$ are the same straight line $S-S'=0$, they are identical. The only difference is that the common chord exists only if the circles intersect in two real points, while the radical axis exists for all pair of circles irrespective of their position.

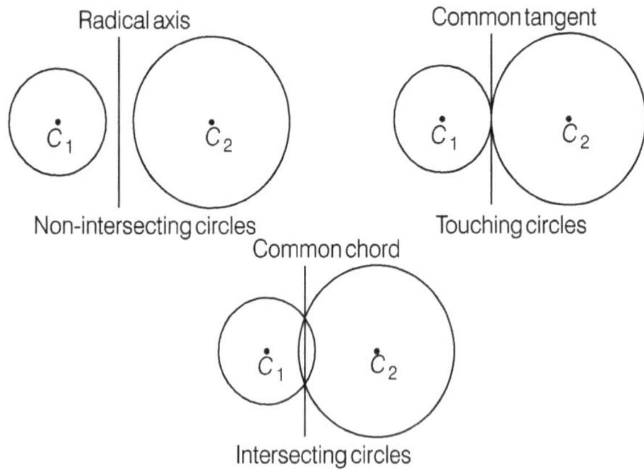

The position of the radical axis of the two circles geometrically is shown below:

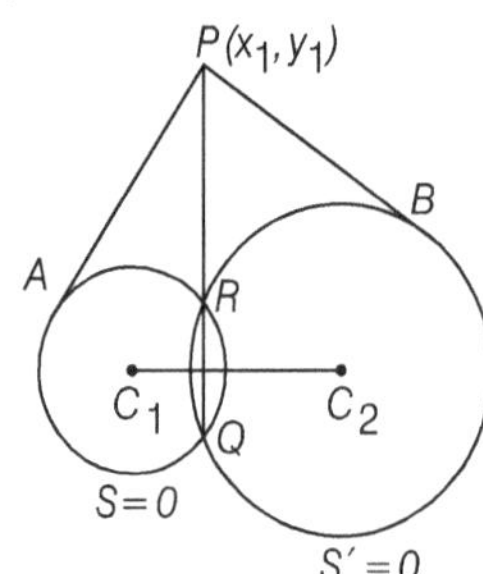

From Euclidian geometry

$$(PA)^2 = PR \cdot PQ = (PB)^2$$

(ii) **The radical axis is perpendicular to the straight line which joins the centres of the circles :**

Consider, $S \equiv x^2 + y^2 + 2gx + 2fy + c = 0$ ...(i)

and $S_1 \equiv x^2 + y^2 + 2g_1x + 2f_1y + c_1 = 0$ ...(ii)

Since, $C_1 \equiv (-g, -f)$ and $C_2 \equiv (-g_1, -f_1)$ are the centres of the circles Eqs. (i) and (ii), then slope of

$$C_1C_2 = \frac{-f_1 + f}{-g_1 + g} = \frac{f - f_1}{g - g_1} = m_1 \quad \text{(say)}$$

Equation of the radical axis is

$$2(g - g_1)x + 2(f - f_1)y + c - c_1 = 0$$

Slope of radical axis is $-\dfrac{(g - g_1)}{f - f_1} = m_2$ (say)

$$\therefore \quad m_1m_2 = -1$$

Hence, C_1C_2 and radical axis are perpendicular to each other.

(iii) **The radical axis bisects common tangents of two circles :** Let AB be the common tangent. If it meets the radical axis LM in M, then MA and MB are two tangents to the circles. Hence, $MA = MB$ since lengths of tangents are equal from any point on radical axis. Hence, radical axis bisects the common tangent AB.

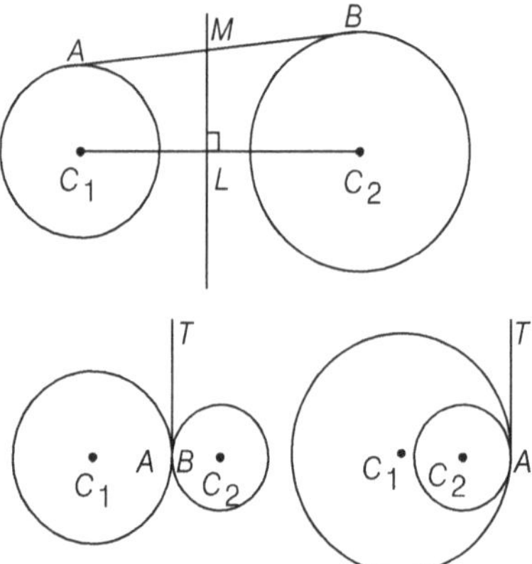

If the two circles touch each other externally or internally, then A and B coincide. In this case the common tangent itself becomes the radical axis.

(iv) **The radical axis of three circles taken in pairs are concurrent :** Let the equations of three circles be

$$S_1 \equiv x^2 + y^2 + 2g_1x + 2f_1y + c_1 = 0 \quad \text{...(i)}$$

$$S_2 \equiv x^2 + y^2 + 2g_2x + 2f_2y + c_2 = 0 \quad \text{...(ii)}$$

$$S_3 \equiv x^2 + y^2 + 2g_3x + 2f_3y + c_3 = 0 \quad \text{...(iii)}$$

The radical axis of the above three circles taken in pairs are given by

$$S_1 - S_2 \equiv 2x(g_1 - g_2) + 2y(f_1 - f_2) + c_1 - c_2 = 0 \quad \text{...(iv)}$$

$$S_2 - S_3 \equiv 2x(g_2 - g_3) + 2y(f_2 - f_3) + c_2 - c_3 = 0 \quad \text{...(v)}$$

$$S_3 - S_1 \equiv 2x(g_3 - g_1) + 2y(f_3 - f_1) + c_3 - c_1 = 0 \quad \text{...(vi)}$$

Adding Eqs. (iv), (v) and (vi), we find LHS vanished identically. Thus, the three lines are concurrent.

(v) **If two circles cut a third circle orthogonally, the radical axis of the two circles will pass through the centre of the third circle.**

OR

The locus of the centre of a circle cutting two given circles orthogonally is the radical axis of the two circles.

Let $S_1 \equiv x^2 + y^2 + 2g_1x + 2f_1y + c_1 = 0$ ...(i)

$S_2 \equiv x^2 + y^2 + 2g_2x + 2f_2y + c_2 = 0$ ...(ii)

$S_3 \equiv x^2 + y^2 + 2g_3x + 2f_3y + c_3 = 0$ ...(iii)

Since, Eqs. (i) and (ii) both cut Eq. (iii) orthogonally

$\therefore \quad 2g_1g_3 + 2f_1f_3 = c_1 + c_3$

and $\quad 2g_2g_3 + 2f_2f_3 = c_2 + c_3$

Subtracting, we get

$$2g_3(g_1 - g_2) + 2f_3(f_1 - f_2) = c_1 - c_2 \quad \text{...(iv)}$$

Now, radical axis of Eqs. (i) and (ii) is

$$S_1 - S_2 = 0$$

or $\quad 2x(g_1 - g_2) + 2y(f_1 - f_2) + c_1 - c_2 = 0$

Since, it will pass through the centre of Eq. (iii) circle

$\therefore -2g_3(g_1 - g_2) - 2f_3(f_1 - f_2) + c_1 - c_2 = 0$

or $2g_3(g_1 - g_2) + 2f_3(f_1 - f_2) = c_1 - c_2$ ...(v)

which is true by Eq. (iv),

Remark

Radical axis need not always pass through the mid-point of the line joining the centres of the two circles.

Example 81. If two circles $x^2 + y^2 + 2gx + 2fy = 0$ and $x^2 + y^2 + 2g'x + 2f'y = 0$ touch each other, then $f'g = fg'$.

Sol. If two circles touch each other, then their radical axis is their common tangent.

$\therefore$ Radical axis of two circles is

$$(x^2 + y^2 + 2gx + 2fy) - (x^2 + y^2 + 2g'x + 2f'y) = 0$$

or $\quad 2x(g - g') + 2y(f - f') = 0$

or $\quad x(g - g') + y(f - f') = 0$ ...(i)

If this touches the circle $x^2 + y^2 + 2gx + 2fy = 0$, then the length of perpendicular from its centre $(-g, -f)$ to (i) =radius $\sqrt{(g^2 + f^2)}$ of the circle

i.e. $$\frac{|-g(g - g') - f(f - f')|}{\sqrt{(g - g')^2 + (f - f')^2}} = \sqrt{g^2 + f^2}$$

or $\quad \{(-(g^2 + f^2) + gg' + ff')\}^2$

$$= (g^2 + f^2)\{(g - g')^2 + (f + f')^2\}$$

or $\quad (g^2 + f^2)^2 + (gg' + ff')^2 - 2(g^2 + f^2)(gg' + ff')$

$$= (g^2 + f^2)\{(g^2 + f^2) + (g'^2 + f'^2) - 2(gg' + ff')\}$$

or $(gg' + ff')^2 = (g^2 + f^2)(g'^2 + f'^2)$

On simplifying, $\quad 2gg'ff' = g^2f'^2 + f^2g'^2$

or $\quad (gf' - g'f)^2 = 0$

or $\quad gf' = g'f$

Aliter : If two circles touch each other, then distance between their centres = sum or difference of their radii

$$\sqrt{(g - g')^2 + (f - f')^2} = \sqrt{(g^2 + f^2)} \pm \sqrt{(g'^2 + f'^2)}$$

or $\quad \sqrt{(g^2 + f^2 + g'^2 + f'^2 - 2gg' - 2ff')}$

$$= \sqrt{(g^2 + f^2)} \pm \sqrt{(g'^2 + f'^2)}$$

On squaring, we have

$g^2 + f^2 + g'^2 + f'^2 - 2gg' - 2ff'$

$$= g^2 + f^2 + g'^2 + f'^2 \pm 2\sqrt{(g^2 + f^2)}\sqrt{(g'^2 + f'^2)}$$

or $(gg' + ff') = \pm\sqrt{(g^2 + f^2)(g'^2 + f'^2)}$

Again, on squaring both sides, we get

$$g^2g'^2 + f^2f'^2 + 2gg'ff' = g^2g'^2 + g^2f'^2 + f^2g'^2 + f^2f'^2$$

or $\quad g^2f'^2 + f^2g'^2 - 2gg'ff' = 0$

or $\quad (gf' - g'f)^2 = 0$

or $\quad gf' - g'f = 0$

or $\quad gf' = g'f$

Example 82. A and B are two fixed points and P moves so that $PA = nPB$. Show that locus of P is a circle and for different values of n all the circles have a common radical axis.

Sol. Let $A \equiv (a, 0)$, $B \equiv (-a, 0)$ and $P \equiv (h, k)$

$\therefore \quad PA = \sqrt{(h - a)^2 + k^2}$

$\quad PB = \sqrt{(h + a)^2 + k^2}$

Since, $\quad PA = nPB$

or $\quad (PA)^2 = n^2(PB)^2$

$\Rightarrow \quad \{(h - a)^2 + k^2\} = n^2\{(h + a)^2 + k^2\}$

$\Rightarrow \quad (h^2 + k^2 - 2ah + a^2) = n^2(h^2 + k^2 + 2ah + a^2)$

$\Rightarrow \quad (1 - n^2)h^2 + (1 - n^2)k^2 - 2ah(1 + n^2) + (1 - n^2)a^2 = 0$

or $\quad h^2 + k^2 - 2ah\dfrac{(1 + n^2)}{(1 - n^2)} + a^2 = 0$

$\therefore$ Locus of P is $\quad x^2 + y^2 - \left(\dfrac{1 + n^2}{1 - n^2}\right)2ax + a^2 = 0$

which is a circle. For different values of n.

If two different values of n are n_1 and n_2, then circles are

$$x^2 + y^2 - \left(\frac{1 + n_1^2}{1 - n_1^2}\right)2ax + a^2 = 0 \quad \text{...(i)}$$

and $$x^2 + y^2 - \left(\frac{1 + n_2^2}{1 - n_2^2}\right)2ax + a^2 = 0 \quad \text{...(ii)}$$

$\therefore$ Radical axis of Eqs. (i) and (ii) is

$$2ax\left\{\frac{1+n_2^2}{1-n_2^2}-\frac{1+n_1^2}{1-n_1^2}\right\}=0$$

or $\quad x=0$ or Y-axis.

Hence, for different values of n the circles have a common radical axis.

Example 83. Show that the difference of the squares of the tangents to two coplanar circles from any point P in the plane of the circles varies as the perpendicular from P on their radical axis. Also, prove that the locus of a point such that the difference of the squares of the tangents from it to two given circles is constant is a line parallel to their radical axis.

Sol. Let the two circles be

$$S_1 \equiv x^2+y^2+2g_1x+2f_1y+c_1=0 \quad \text{...(i)}$$

and $$S_2 \equiv x^2+y^2+2g_2x+2f_2y+c_2=0 \quad \text{...(ii)}$$

and let $P=(h,k)$

$\therefore$ Radical axis of Eqs. (i) and (ii) is

$$2(g_1-g_2)x+2(f_1-f_2)y+c_1-c_2=0 \quad \text{...(iii)}$$

Let length of tangents from $P(h,k)$ on Eqs. (i) and (ii) are l_1 and l_2, then

$$l_1=\sqrt{S_1}=\sqrt{(h^2+k^2+2g_1h+2f_1k+c_1)}$$

and $$l_2=\sqrt{S_2}=\sqrt{(h^2+k^2+2g_2h+2f_2k+c_2)}$$

According to the question,

$$l_1^2-l_2^2=2(g_1-g_2)h+2(f_1-f_2)k+c_1-c_2 \quad \text{...(iv)}$$

Let p be the perpendicular distance from $P(h,k)$ on Eq. (iii),

$$\therefore \quad p=\frac{|2(g_1-g_2)h+2(f_1-f_2)k+c_1-c_2|}{\sqrt{4(g_1-g_2)^2+4(f_1-f_2)^2}} \quad \text{...(v)}$$

From Eqs. (iv) and (v), we get

$$p=\frac{|l_1^2-l_2^2|}{2\sqrt{(g_1-g_2)^2+(f_1-f_2)^2}}$$

or $$\frac{|l_1^2-l_2^2|}{p}=2\sqrt{(g_1-g_2)^2+(f_1-f_2)^2}=\text{constant}$$

$$\therefore \quad |l_1^2-l_2^2| \propto p$$

Locus of $P(h,k)$ in Eq. (iv) is

$$2(g_1-g_2)x+2(f_1-f_2)y+c_1-c_2=(l_1^2-l_2^2)$$

a line which is parallel to Eq. (iii).

Radical Centre

The radical axes of three circles, taken in pairs, meet in a point, which is called their radical centre. Let the three circles be

$$S_1=0 \quad \text{...(i)}$$
$$S_2=0 \quad \text{...(ii)}$$
$$S_3=0 \quad \text{...(iii)}$$

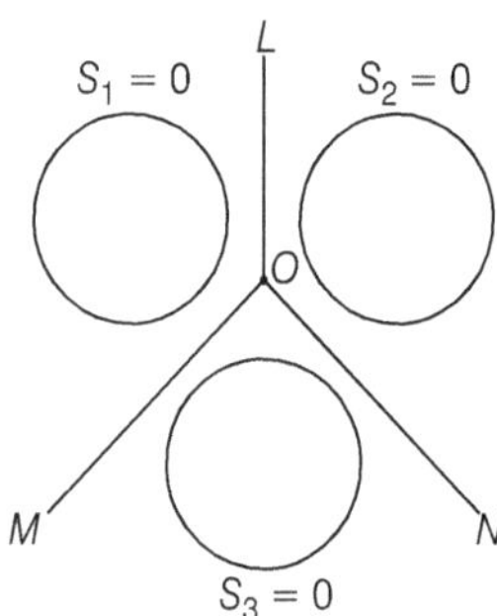

Let OL, OM and ON be radical axes of the pair sets of circles

$$\{S_1=0, S_2=0\}, \{S_3=0, S_1=0\}$$

and $\{S_2=0, S_3=0\}$ respectively.

Equations of OL, OM and ON are respectively

$$S_1-S_2=0 \quad \text{...(iv)}$$
$$S_3-S_1=0 \quad \text{...(v)}$$
$$S_2-S_3=0 \quad \text{...(vi)}$$

Let the straight lines Eqs. (iv) and (v) i.e. OL and OM meet in O. The equation of any straight line passing through O is

$$(S_1-S_2)+\lambda(S_3-S_1)=0$$

where λ is any constant.

For $\lambda=1$ this equation becomes

$$S_2-S_3=0$$

which is, by Eq. (vi), equation of ON.

Thus, the third radical axis also passes through the point where the Eqs. (iv) and (v) meet. In the above figure O is the **radical centre.**

Properties of Radical Centre

1. Coordinates of radical centre can be found by solving the equations

$$S_1=S_2=S_3=0$$

2. **The radical centre of three circles described on the sides of a triangle as diameters is the orthocentre of the triangle :**

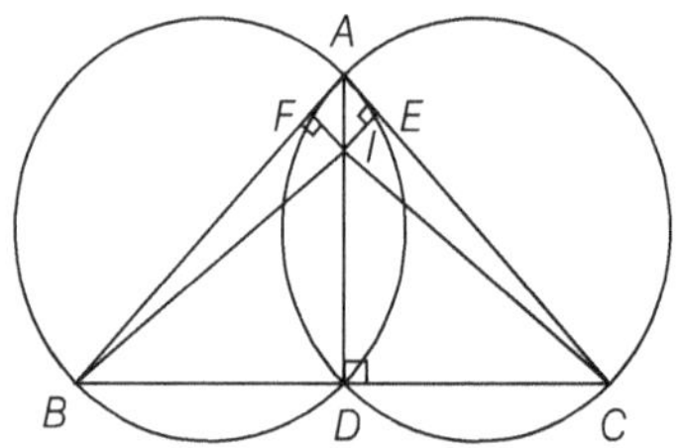

Draw perpendicular from A on BC.

$\therefore \quad \angle ADB = \angle ADC = \pi/2$

Therefore, the circles whose diameters are AB and AC passes through D and A. Hence, AD is their radical axis. Similarly, the radical axis of the circles on AB and BC as diameters is the perpendicular line from B on CA and radical axis of the circles on BC and CA as diameters is the perpendicular line from C on AB. Hence, the radial axis of three circles meet in a point. This point I is radical centre but here radical centre is the point of intersection of altitudes i.e. AD, BE and CF. Hence, radical centre = orthocentre.

3. The radical centre of three given circles will be the centre of a fourth circle which cuts all the three circles orthogonally and the radius of the fourth circle is the length of tangent drawn from radical centre of the three given circles to any of these circles.

   Let the fourth circle be $(x-h)^2+(y-k)^2=r^2$, where (h, k) is centre of this circle and r be the radius. The centre of circle is the radical centre of the given circles and r is the length of tangent from (h, k) to any of the given three circles.

Example 84. Find the radical centre of circles $x^2+y^2+3x+2y+1=0$, $x^2+y^2-x+6y+5=0$ and $x^2+y^2+5x-8y+15=0$. Also, find the equation of the circle cutting them orthogonally.

Sol. : Given circles are

$$S_1 \equiv x^2+y^2+3x+2y+1=0$$
$$S_2 \equiv x^2+y^2-x+6y+5=0$$
$$S_3 \equiv x^2+y^2+5x-8y+15=0$$

Equations of two radical axes are

$$S_1 - S_2 \equiv 4x-4y-4=0 \quad \text{or} \quad x-y-1=0$$
and $$S_2 - S_3 \equiv -6x+14y-10=0 \quad \text{or} \quad 3x-7x+5=0$$

Solving them the radical centre is (3, 2) also, if r is the length of the tangent drawn from the radical centre (3, 2) to any one of the given circles, say S_1, we have

$$r = \sqrt{S_1} = \sqrt{3^2+2^2+3\cdot3+2\cdot2+1} = \sqrt{27}$$

Hence, (3, 2) is the centre and $\sqrt{27}$ is the radius of the circle intersecting them orthogonally.

$\therefore$ Its equation is

$$(x-3)^2+(y-2)^2=r^2=27 \text{ or } x^2+y^2-6x-4y-14=0$$

Aliter : Let $x^2+y^2+2gx+2fy+c=0$ be the equation of the circle cutting the given circles orthogonally.

$$\therefore \quad 2g\left(\frac{3}{2}\right)+2f(1)=c+1$$

or $$3g+2f=c+1 \qquad \text{...(i)}$$

$$2g\left(-\frac{1}{2}\right)+2f(3)=c+5$$

or $$-g+6f=c+5 \qquad \text{...(ii)}$$

and $$2g\left(\frac{5}{2}\right)+2f(-4)=c+15$$

or $$5g-8f=c+15 \qquad \text{...(iii)}$$

Solving, Eqs. (i), (ii) and (iii), we get

$$g=-3,\ f=-2 \text{ and } c=-14$$

$\therefore$ Equation of required circle is

$$x^2+y^2-6x-4y-14=0$$

Example 85. Find the radical centre of three circles described on the three sides $4x-7y+10=0$, $x+y-5=0$ and $7x+4y-15=0$ of a triangle as diameters.

Sol. Since, the radical centre of three circles described on the sides of a triangle as diameters is the orthocentre of the triangle.

$\therefore \quad$ Radical centre = orthocentre

Given sides are

$$4x-7y+10=0 \qquad \text{...(i)}$$
$$x+y-5=0 \qquad \text{...(ii)}$$
$$7x+4y-15=0 \qquad \text{...(iii)}$$

Since, lines Eqs. (i) and (iii) are perpendiculars the point of intersection of Eqs. (i) and (iii) is (1, 2), the orthocentre of the triangle. Hence, radical centre is (1, 2).

Example 86. Prove that if the four points of intersection of the circles $x^2+y^2+ax+by+c=0$ and $x^2+y^2+a'x+b'y+c'=0$ by the lines $Ax+By+C=0$ and $A'x+B'y+C'=0$ respectively are concyclic, then

$$\begin{vmatrix} a-a' & b-b' & c-c' \\ A & B & C \\ A' & B' & C' \end{vmatrix} = 0$$

Sol. The given circles and given lines are

$$S_1 \equiv x^2+y^2+ax+by+c=0$$
$$S_2 \equiv x^2+y^2+a'x+b'y+c'=0$$
$$L_1 \equiv Ax+By+C=0$$
$$L_2 \equiv A'x+B'y+C'=0$$

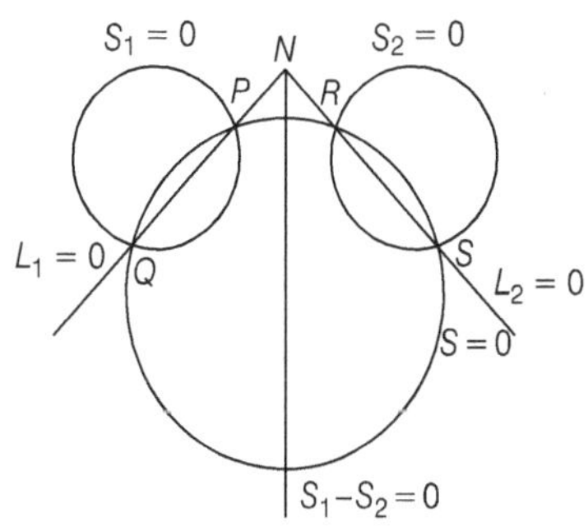

Let $S_1 = 0$ meet $L_1 = 0$ at two points P and Q and $S_2 = 0$ meet $L_2 = 0$ at two points R and S.

Further P, Q, R and S are given to be concyclic. Let the circle through them is

$$x^2 + y^2 + 2gx + 2fy + \lambda = 0 \quad \text{...(i)}$$

Radical axis of $S_1 = 0$ and $S_2 = 0$ is

$$S_1 - S_2 = 0$$

$$\Rightarrow \quad (a - a')x + (b - b')y + c - c' = 0 \quad \text{...(ii)}$$

The radical axis of $S_1 = 0$ and $S = 0$ is $L_1 = 0$

or $\quad Ax + By + C = 0 \quad$ ...(iii)

and $\quad$ radical axis of $S_2 = 0$ and $S = 0$ is $L_2 = 0$

or $\quad A'x + B'y + C' = 0 \quad$ ...(iv)

Since, the radical axes of any three circles taken in pairs are concurrent. (i.e. lines Eqs. (ii), (iii) and (iv) are concurrent).

we have $\begin{vmatrix} a - a' & b - b' & c - c' \\ A & B & C \\ A' & B' & C' \end{vmatrix} = 0$

Co-axial System of Circles

A system (or a family) of circles, every pair of which have the same radical axis, are called co-axial circles.

(1) The equation of a system of co-axial circles, when the equation of the radical axis and of one circle of the system are

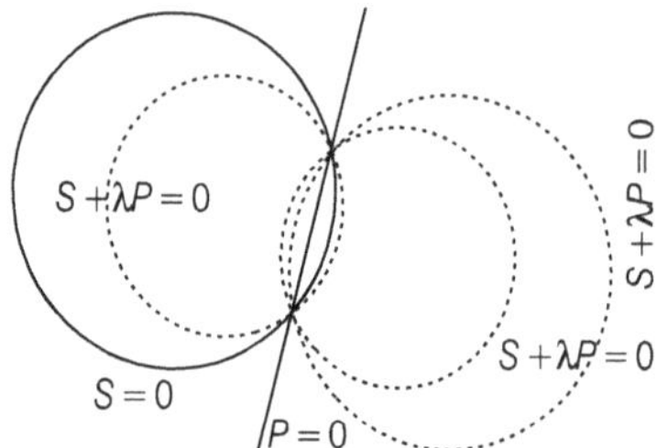

$$P \equiv lx + my + n = 0$$

and $\quad S \equiv x^2 + y^2 + 2gx + 2fy + c = 0$

respectively, is

$$S + \lambda P = 0 \ (\lambda \text{ is an arbitrary constant})$$

(2) The equation of a co-axial system of circles, where the equation of any two circles of the system are

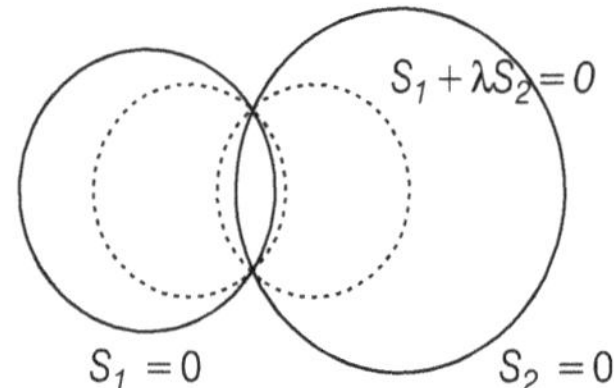

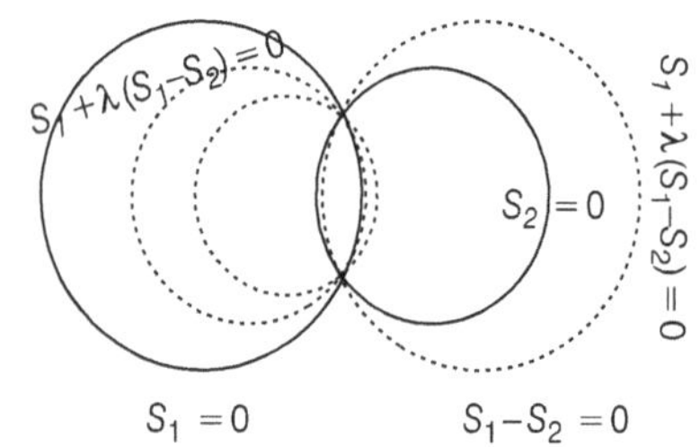

$$S_1 \equiv x^2 + y^2 + 2g_1x + 2f_1y + c_1 = 0$$

and $\quad S_2 \equiv x^2 + y^2 + 2g_2x + 2f_2y + c_2 = 0$

respectively is

$$S_1 + \lambda(S_1 - S_2) = 0 \quad (\lambda \neq -1)$$

or $\quad S_2 + \lambda_1(S_1 - S_2) = 0 \quad (\lambda_1 \neq -1)$

Other form $S_1 + \lambda S_2 = 0 \quad (\lambda \neq -1)$

(3) The equation of a system of co-axial circles in the simplest form is

$$x^2 + y^2 + 2gx + c = 0$$

where, g is variable and c, a constant.

The common radical axis is the Y-axis (since centre on X-axis) and the equation of a system of other co-axial circles in the simplest form is

$$x^2 + y^2 + 2fy + c = 0$$

where, f is variable and c, a constant (since centre on Y-axis). The common radical axis is the X-axis.

Example 87. Find the equation of the system of circles co-axial with the circles

$$x^2 + y^2 + 4x + 2y + 1 = 0$$

and $x^2 + y^2 - 2x + 6y - 6 = 0$

Also, find the equation of that particular circle whose centre lies on the radical axis.

Sol. Given circles are

$$S_1 \equiv x^2 + y^2 + 4x + 2y + 1 = 0$$

and $\quad S_2 \equiv x^2 + y^2 - 2x + 6y - 6 = 0$

$\therefore$ Radical axis is $\quad S_1 - S_2 = 0$

i.e. $\quad 6x - 4y + 7 = 0 \quad$ ...(i)

Now, system of co-axial circle is

$$S_1 + \lambda(S_1 - S_2) = 0$$

$$\Rightarrow \quad (x^2 + y^2 + 4x + 2y + 1) + \lambda(6x - 4y + 7) = 0$$

$$\Rightarrow \quad x^2 + y^2 + 2x(2 + 3\lambda) + 2y(1 - 2\lambda) + 1 + 7\lambda = 0 \quad \text{...(ii)}$$

Its centre $[-(2 + 3\lambda), -(1 - 2\lambda)]$ lies on Eq. (i)

$$\therefore \quad 6 \times -(2 + 3\lambda) - 4 \times -(1 - 2\lambda) + 7 = 0$$

or $\quad -12 - 18\lambda + 4 - 8\lambda + 7 = 0$

or $\quad -26\lambda - 1 = 0$

$\therefore \quad \lambda = -\frac{1}{26}$

Substituting the value of λ in Eq. (ii), the equation of circle is

$$x^2 + y^2 + 2x\left(2 - \frac{3}{26}\right) + 2y\left(1 + \frac{2}{26}\right) + 1 - \frac{7}{26} = 0$$

$\Rightarrow \quad 26(x^2 + y^2) + 98x + 56y + 9 = 0$

Example 88. Prove that the tangents from any point of a fixed circle of co-axial system to two other fixed circles of the system are in a constant ratio.

Sol. Let the equations of the circles be $x^2 + y^2 + 2g_i x + c = 0$, $i = 1,2,3$. Since, all the three circles are fixed g_1, g_2 and g_3 are constants.

Let $P(h, k)$ be any point on the first circle, so that

$$h^2 + k^2 + 2g_1 h + c = 0 \quad \text{...(i)}$$

Let PQ and PR be the tangents from P on the other two circles

$\therefore \quad PQ = \sqrt{(h^2 + k^2 + 2g_2 h + c)}$

and $\quad PR = \sqrt{(h^2 + k^2 + 2g_3 h + c)}$

$$\therefore \quad \frac{(PQ)^2}{(PR)^2} = \frac{h^2 + k^2 + 2g_2 h + c}{h^2 + k^2 + 2g_3 h + c}$$

$$= \frac{-2g_1 h + 2g_2 h}{-2g_1 h + 2g_3 h} \quad \text{[from Eq. (i)]}$$

$$= \frac{g_2 - g_1}{g_3 - g_1} = \text{constant}$$

because g_1, g_2, g_3 are constants.

Example 89. If A, B, C be the centres of three co-axial circles and t_1, t_2, t_3 be the lengths of the tangents to them from any point, prove that

$$\overline{BC} \cdot t_1^2 + \overline{CA} \cdot t_2^2 + \overline{AB}\ t_3^2 = 0$$

Sol. Let the equations of three circles are $x^2 + y^2 + 2g_i x + c = 0$, $i = 1, 2, 3$, .

According to the question

$$A \equiv (-g_1, 0), B \equiv (-g_2, 0), C \equiv (-g_3, 0)$$

Let any point be $P(h, k)$

$\therefore \quad t_1 = \sqrt{h^2 + k^2 + 2g_1 h + c}$

$t_2 = \sqrt{h^2 + k^2 + 2g_2 h + c}$

$t_3 = \sqrt{h^2 + k^2 + 2g_3 h + c}$

and $\quad \overline{AB} = (g_1 - g_2)$

$\overline{BC} = (g_2 - g_3)$

and $\quad \overline{CA} = (g_3 - g_1)$

Now, $\overline{BC} \cdot t_1^2 + \overline{CA} \cdot t_2^2 + \overline{AB}\ t_3^2$

$$= \Sigma (g_2 - g_3)(h^2 + k^2 + 2g_1 h + c)$$

$$= (h^2 + k^2 + c)\ \Sigma (g_2 - g_3) + 2h \Sigma g_1 (g_2 - g_3)$$

$$= (h^2 + k^2 + c)(g_2 - g_3 + g_3 - g_1 + g_1 - g_2)$$

$$+ 2h\ \{g_1(g_2 - g_3) + g_2(g_3 - g_1) + g_3(g_1 - g_2)\}$$

$$= (h^2 + k^2 + c)(0) + 2h(0) = 0$$

which proves the result.

Limiting Point

Limiting points of system of co-axial circles are the centres of the point circles belonging to the family (Circles whose radii are zero are called **point circles).**

1. Limiting points of the co-axial system

Let the circle is

$$x^2 + y^2 + 2gx + c = 0 \quad \text{...(i)}$$

where, g is variable and c is constant.

$\therefore$ Centre and the radius of Eq. (i) are $(-g, 0)$ and $\sqrt{(g^2 - c)}$, respectively. Let

$$\sqrt{g^2 - c} = 0$$

$\therefore \quad g = \pm\sqrt{c}$

Thus, we get the two limiting points of the given co-axial system as

$$(\sqrt{c}, 0) \text{ and } (-\sqrt{c}, 0)$$

Clearly the above limiting points are real and distinct, real and coincident or imaginary according as $c >, =, < 0$

2. System of co-axial circles whose two limiting point are given :

Let (α, β) and (γ, δ) be the two given limiting points. Then, the corresponding point circles with zero radii are

$$(x - \alpha)^2 + (y - \beta)^2 = 0$$

and $\quad (x - \gamma)^2 + (y - \delta)^2 = 0$

or $\quad x^2 + y^2 - 2\alpha x - 2\beta y + \alpha^2 + \beta^2 = 0$

and $\quad x^2 + y^2 - 2\gamma x - 2\delta y + \gamma^2 + \delta^2 = 0$

The equation of co-axial system is

$$(x^2 + y^2 - 2\alpha x - 2\beta y + \alpha^2 + \beta^2)$$
$$+ \lambda(x^2 + y^2 - 2\gamma x - 2\delta y + \gamma^2 + \delta^2) = 0$$

where, $\lambda \neq -1$ is a variable parameter.

$$\Rightarrow x^2(1+\lambda)+y^2(1+\lambda)-2x(\alpha+\gamma\lambda)$$
$$-2y(\beta+\delta\lambda)+(\alpha^2+\beta^2)+\lambda(\gamma^2+\delta^2)=0$$

or $$x^2+y^2-\frac{2(\alpha+\gamma\lambda)}{(1+\lambda)}x-2\frac{(\beta+\delta\lambda)}{(1+\lambda)}y$$
$$+\frac{(\alpha^2+\beta^2)+\lambda(\gamma^2+\delta^2)}{(1+\lambda)}=0$$

Centre of this circle is $\left(\frac{(\alpha+\gamma\lambda)}{(1+\lambda)},\frac{(\beta+\delta\lambda)}{(1+\lambda)}\right)$ ...(i)

For limiting point,

Radius

$$=\sqrt{\frac{(\alpha+\gamma\lambda)^2}{(1+\lambda)^2}+\frac{(\beta+\delta\lambda)^2}{(1+\lambda)^2}-\frac{(\alpha^2+\beta^2)+\lambda(\gamma^2+\delta^2)}{(1+\lambda)}}=0$$

After solving, find λ. Substituting value of λ in Eq. (i), we get the limiting point of co-axial system.

Example 90. Find the coordinates of the limiting points of the system of circles determined by the two circles

$$x^2+y^2+5x+y+4=0 \text{ and } x^2+y^2+10x-4y-1=0$$

Sol. The given circles are

$$S_1 \equiv x^2+y^2+5x+y+4=0$$

and $$S_2 \equiv x^2+y^2+10x-4y-1=0$$

$\therefore$ Equation of the co-axial system of circles is $S_1+\lambda S_2=0$

or $$(x^2+y^2+5x+y+4)$$
$$+\lambda(x^2+y^2+10x-4y-1)=0$$

or $$x^2(1+\lambda)+y^2(1+\lambda)+5x(1+2\lambda)$$
$$+y(1-4\lambda)+(4-\lambda)=0$$

or $$x^2+y^2+\frac{5(1+2\lambda)}{(1+\lambda)}x+\frac{(1-4\lambda)}{(1+\lambda)}y+\frac{(4-\lambda)}{(1+\lambda)}=0$$

The centre of this circles is

$$\left(\frac{-5(1+2\lambda)}{2(1+\lambda)},-\frac{(1-4\lambda)}{2(1+\lambda)}\right) \quad ...(i)$$

$$\text{Radius}=\sqrt{\frac{25(1+2\lambda)^2}{4(1+\lambda)^2}+\frac{(1-4\lambda)^2}{4(1+\lambda)^2}-\frac{(4-\lambda)}{(1+\lambda)}}=0$$

or $25(1+2\lambda)^2+(1-4\lambda)^2-4(4-\lambda)(1+\lambda)=0$

or $25(4\lambda^2+4\lambda+1)+(16\lambda^2-8\lambda+1)-4(-\lambda^2+3\lambda+4)=0$

or $120\lambda^2+80\lambda+10=0$ or $12\lambda^2+8\lambda+1=0$

or $(6\lambda+1)(2\lambda+1)=0$

i.e. $$\lambda=-\frac{1}{6} \text{ and } -\frac{1}{2}$$

Substituting these values of λ in Eq. (i), we get the points $(-2,-1)$ and $(0,-3)$ which are the required limiting points.

Example 91. If the origin be one limiting point of a system of co-axial circles of which $x^2+y^2+3x+4y+25=0$ is a member, find the other limiting point.

Sol. Equation of circle with origin as limiting point is

$$(x-0)^2+(y-0)^2=0 \quad \text{or } x^2+y^2=0$$

belongs to the system of co-axial circles of which one member is

$$x^2+y^2+3x+4y+25=0$$

Hence, the equation of the whole system is

$$(x^2+y^2+3x+4y+25)+\lambda(x^2+y^2)=0$$

or $$x^2(1+\lambda)+y^2(1+\lambda)+3x+4y+25=0$$

or $$x^2+y^2+\frac{3}{(1+\lambda)}x+\frac{4}{(1+\lambda)}y+\frac{25}{(1+\lambda)}=0 \quad ...(i)$$

$\therefore$ $$\text{Its centre}=\left(-\frac{3}{2(1+\lambda)},-\frac{2}{(1+\lambda)}\right) \quad ...(ii)$$

Radius of Eq. (i) can be zero for limiting point, then

$$\frac{9}{4(1+\lambda)^2}+\frac{4}{(1+\lambda)^2}-\frac{25}{(1+\lambda)}=0$$

$$9+16-100(1+\lambda)=0$$

$\Rightarrow$ $$1+\lambda=\frac{1}{4} \text{ or } \lambda=-\frac{3}{4}$$

From Eq. (ii), $$\left(\frac{-3}{2(1-3/4)},\frac{-2}{(1-3/4)}\right)$$

or $(-6,-8)$ is the other limiting point of the system.

Example 92. Prove that the limiting points of the system

$$x^2+y^2+2gx+c+\lambda(x^2+y^2+2fx+k)=0$$

subtend a right angle at the origin, if $\frac{c}{g^2}+\frac{k}{f^2}=2$.

Sol. The given circle is

$$x^2+y^2+2gx+c+\lambda(x^2+y^2+2fy+k)=0$$

or $(1+\lambda)x^2+(1+\lambda)y^2+2gx+2fy\lambda+c+k\lambda=0$

or $$x^2+y^2+\frac{2g}{(1+\lambda)}x+\frac{2f\lambda}{(1+\lambda)}y+\frac{c+k\lambda}{(1+\lambda)}=0 \quad ...(i)$$

Its centre is $\left(\frac{-g}{1+\lambda},\frac{-f\lambda}{1+\lambda}\right)$ ...(ii)

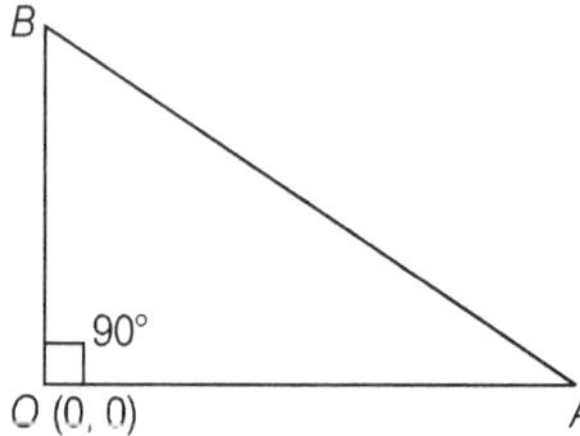

Radius of circle Eq. (i) is =0

$$\Rightarrow \sqrt{\frac{g^2}{(1+\lambda)^2}+\frac{f^2\lambda^2}{(1+\lambda)^2}-\frac{(c+k\lambda)}{(1+\lambda)}}=0$$

or $\lambda^2(f^2-k)-\lambda(k+c)+g^2-c=0$

which is a quadratic in λ. Let roots be λ_1 and λ_2.

$$\therefore \quad \lambda_1+\lambda_2=\frac{k+c}{f^2-k} \text{ and } \lambda_1\lambda_2=\frac{g^2-c}{f^2-k}$$

then limiting points are [from Eq. (ii)]

$$A\left(\frac{-g}{1+\lambda_1},\frac{-f\lambda_1}{1+\lambda_1}\right) \text{ and } B\left(\frac{-g}{1+\lambda_2},\frac{-f\lambda_2}{1+\lambda_2}\right)$$

But given that AB subtend a right angle at the origin.

$\therefore$ Slope of OA $\times$ Slope of $OB = -1$

$$\Rightarrow \left(\frac{\frac{-f\lambda_1}{1+\lambda_1}}{\frac{-g}{1+\lambda_1}}\right)\times\left(\frac{\frac{-f\lambda_2}{1+\lambda_2}}{\frac{-g}{1+\lambda_2}}\right)=-1$$

or $$\frac{f\lambda_1}{g}\times\frac{f\lambda_2}{g}=-1$$

or $$f^2\lambda_1\lambda_2+g^2=0$$

or $$f^2\frac{(g^2-c)}{(f^2-k)}+g^2=0$$

or $$2g^2f^2-cf^2-kg^2=0$$

or $$2=\frac{c}{g^2}+\frac{k}{f^2}$$

Example 93. Find the radical axis of co-axial system of circles whose limiting points are (–1,2) and (2, 3).

Sol. Equations of circles with limiting points are (–1, 2) and (2,3) are

$$(x+1)^2+(y-2)^2=0$$

or $$x^2+y^2+2x-4y+5=0 \quad \text{...(i)}$$

and $$(x-2)^2+(y-3)^2=0$$

or $$x^2+y^2-4x-6y+13=0 \quad \text{...(ii)}$$

respectively.

$\therefore$ Radical axis of circles Eqs. (i) and (ii) is

$$(x^2+y^2+2x-4y+5)-(x^2+y^2-4x-6y+13)=0$$

or $$6x+2y-8=0$$

or $$3x+y-4=0$$

Example 94. Find the equation of the circle which passes through the origin and belongs to the co-axial of circles whose limiting points are (1,2) and (4,3).

Sol. Equations of circles whose limiting points are (1,2) and (4,3) are

$$(x-1)^2+(y-2)^2=0$$

or $$x^2+y^2-2x-4y+5=0 \quad \text{...(i)}$$

and $$(x-4)^2+(y-3)^2=0$$

or $$x^2+y^2-8x-6y+25=0 \quad \text{...(ii)}$$

Therefore, the corresponding system of co-axial circles is

$$(x^2+y^2-2x-4y+5)+\lambda(x^2+y^2-8x-6y+25)=0 \quad \text{...(iii)}$$

It passes through origin, then

$$5+25\lambda=0$$

$$\therefore \quad \lambda=-\frac{1}{5}$$

Substituting the value of λ in Eq. (iii), the required circle is

$$5(x^2+y^2-2x-4y+5)-(x^2+y^2-8x-6y+25)=0$$

or $$4x^2+4y^2-2x-14y=0$$

or $$2x^2+2y^2-x-7y=0$$

Image of the Circle by the Line Mirror

Let the circle be $x^2+y^2+2gx+2fy+c=0$ and line mirror is $lx+my+n=0$ in this condition, radius of circle remains unchanged but centres changes. Let the centre of imaged circle be (x_1, y_1).

Then, $$\frac{x_1-(-g)}{l}=\frac{y_1-(-f)}{m}=\frac{-2(-lg-mf+c)}{(l^2+m^2)}$$

we get, $$x_1=\frac{(l^2g-m^2g+2mlf-2nl)}{(l^2+m^2)}$$

and $$y_1=\frac{(m^2f-l^2f+2mlg-2mn)}{(l^2+m^2)}$$

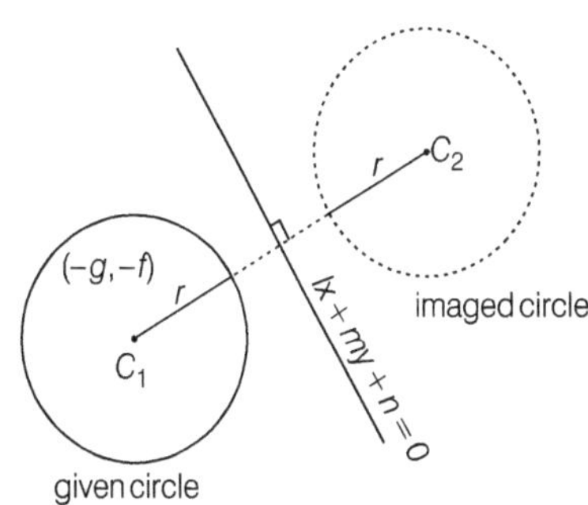

$\therefore$ Required imaged circle is $(x-x_1)^2+(y-y_1)^2=r^2$

where, $r=\sqrt{(g^2+f^2-c)}$

Example 95. Find the equation of the image of the circle $x^2+y^2+16x-24y+183=0$ by the line mirror $4x+7y+13=0$.

Sol. The given circle and line are

$$x^2+y^2+16x-24y+183=0 \quad \ldots\text{(i)}$$

and
$$4x+7y+13=0 \quad \ldots\text{(ii)}$$

Centre and radius of circle Eq. (i) are (–8,12) and 5, respectively. Let the centre of the imaged circle be (x_1,y_1).

Hence, (x_1,y_1) be the image of the point $(-8, 12)$ with respect to the line $4x+7y+13=0$, then

$$\frac{x_1-(-8)}{4}=\frac{y_1-12}{7}=\frac{-2(4(-8)+7(12)+13)}{(4^2+7^2)}$$

$$\Rightarrow \quad \frac{x_1+8}{4}=\frac{y_1-12}{7}=-2$$

$\therefore$ $x_1=-16, y_1=-2$

$\therefore$ Equation of the imaged circle is $(x+16)^2+(y+2)^2=5^2$

or
$$x^2+y^2+32x+4y+235=0$$

Exercise for Session 7

1. The circles $x^2+y^2+x+y=0$ and $x^2+y^2+x-y=0$ intersect at an angle of
   (a) $\pi/6$ (b) $\pi/4$ (c) $\pi/3$ (d) $\pi/2$

2. If the circles of same radius a and centres at (2, 3) and (5, 6) cut orthogonally, then a equals to
   (a) 1 (b) 2 (c) 3 (d) 4

3. If the circles $x^2+y^2+2x+2ky+6=0$ and $x^2+y^2+2ky+k=0$ intersect orthogonally, k is
   (a) 2 or $-\frac{3}{2}$ (b) -2 or $-\frac{3}{2}$ (c) 2 or $\frac{3}{2}$ (d) -2 or $\frac{3}{2}$

4. If a circle passes through the point (a,b) and cuts the circle $x^2+y^2=4$ orthogonally, then the locus of its centre is
   (a) $2ax+2by+(a^2+b^2+4)=0$ (b) $2ax+2by-(a^2+b^2+4)=0$
   (c) $2ax-2by+(a^2+b^2+4)=0$ (d) $2ax-2by-(a^2+b^2+4)=0$

5. The locus of the centre of the circle which cuts orthogonally the circle $x^2+y^2-20x+4=0$ and which touches $x=2$ is
   (a) $x^2=16y$ (b) $x^2=16y+4$
   (c) $y^2=16x$ (d) $y^2=16x+4$

6. The equation of a circle which cuts the three circles $x^2+y^2-3x-6y+14=0$, $x^2+y^2-x-4y+8=0$ and $x^2+y^2+2x-6y+9=0$ orthogonally is
   (a) $x^2+y^2-2x-4y+1=0$ (b) $x^2+y^2+2x+4y+1=0$
   (c) $x^2+y^2-2x+4y+1=0$ (d) $x^2+y^2-2x-4y-1=0$

7. The equation of radical axis of the circles $x^2+y^2+x-y+2=0$ and $3x^2+3y^2-4x-12=0$ is
   (a) $2x^2+2y^2-5x+y-14=0$ (b) $7x-3y+18=0$
   (c) $5x-y+14=0$ (d) None of these

8. The radical centre of the circles $x^2+y^2=1$, $x^2+y^2+10y+24=0$ and $x^2+y^2-8x+15=0$ is
   (a) $(2, 5/2)$ (b) $(-2, 5/2)$
   (c) $(-2, -5/2)$ (d) $(2, -5/2)$

9. If (1,2) is a limiting point of the co-axial system of circles containing the circle $x^2+y^2+x-5y+9=0$, then the equation of the radical axis is
   (a) $x-9y+4=0$ (b) $3x-y+4=0$
   (c) $x+3y-4=0$ (d) $9x+y-4=0$

10. The limiting points of the system of circles represented by the equation $2(x^2+y^2)+\lambda x+\frac{9}{2}=0$ are

(a) $\left(\pm\frac{3}{2},0\right)$ (b) $(0,0)$ and $\left(\frac{9}{2},0\right)$

(c) $\left(\pm\frac{9}{2},0\right)$ (d) $(\pm 3, 0)$

11. One of the limiting points of the co-axial system of circles containing the circles $x^2+y^2-4=0$ and $x^2+y^2-x-y=0$ is

(a) $(\sqrt{2},\sqrt{2})$ (b) $(-\sqrt{2},\sqrt{2})$

(c) $(-\sqrt{2},-\sqrt{2})$ (d) None of these

12. The point (2, 3) is a limiting point of a co-axial system of circles of which $x^2+y^2=9$ is a member. The coordinates of the other limiting point is given by

(a) $\left(\frac{18}{13},\frac{27}{13}\right)$ (b) $\left(\frac{9}{13},\frac{6}{13}\right)$

(c) $\left(\frac{18}{13},-\frac{27}{13}\right)$ (d) $\left(-\frac{18}{13},-\frac{9}{13}\right)$

13. Two circles are drawn through the points $(a,5a)$ and $(4a,a)$ to touch the Y-axis. Prove that they intersect at angle $\tan^{-1}\left(\frac{40}{9}\right)$.

14. Find the equation of the circle which cuts orthogonally the circle $x^2+y^2-6x+4y-3=0$, passes through (3,0) and touches the axis of y.

15. Tangents are drawn to the circles $x^2+y^2+4x+6y-19=0$, $x^2+y^2=9$ from any point on the line $2x+3y=5$. Prove that their lengths are equal.

16. Find the coordinates of the point from which the lengths of the tangents to the following three circles be equal $3x^2+3y^2+4x-6y-1=0$, $2x^2+2y^2-3x-2y-4=0$ and $2x^2+2y^2-x+y-1=0$

17. Find the equation of a circle which is co-axial with the circles $x^2+y^2+4x+2y+1=0$ and $x^2+y^2-x+3y-\frac{3}{2}=0$ and having its centre on the radical axis of these circles.

18. Find the radical axis of a co-axial system of circles whose limiting points are (1, 2) and (3 , 4).

Shortcuts and Important Results to Remember

1. If the lines $a_1x + b_1y + c_1 = 0$ and $a_2x + b_2y + c_2 = 0$ cut the X-axis and Y-axis in four concyclic points, then $a_1a_2 = b_1b_2$.

2. If two conic sections $a_1x^2 + 2h_1xy + b_1y^2 + 2g_1x + 2f_1y + c_1 = 0$ and $a_2x^2 + 2h_2xy + b_2y^2 + 2g_2x + 2f_2y + c_2 = 0$ will intersect each other in four concyclic points, if $\dfrac{a_1 - b_1}{a_2 - b_2} = \dfrac{h_1}{h_2}$.

3. If the circle $S_1 = 0$, bisects the circumference of the circle $S_2 = 0$, then their common chord will be the diameter of the circle $S_2 = 0$.

4. The radius of the director circle of a given circle is $\sqrt{2}$ times the radius of the given circle.

5. The point of intersection of the tangents at the points $P(a\cos\alpha, a\sin\alpha)$ and $Q(a\cos\beta, a\sin\beta)$ on the circle $x^2 + y^2 = a^2$ is

$$\left(\frac{a\cos\left(\frac{\alpha+\beta}{2}\right)}{\cos\left(\frac{\alpha-\beta}{2}\right)}, \frac{a\sin\left(\frac{\alpha+\beta}{2}\right)}{\cos\left(\frac{\alpha-\beta}{2}\right)}\right)$$

6. If the tangent to the circle $x^2 + y^2 = r^2$ at the point (a, b) meets the coordinates axes at the points A and B and O is the origin, then the area of the ΔOAB is $\dfrac{r^4}{2ab}$.

7. The length of the common chord of the circles $x^2 + y^2 + ax + by + c = 0$ and $x^2 + y^2 + bx + ay + c = 0$ is $\sqrt{\frac{1}{2}(a+b)^2 - 4c}$.

8. The length of the common chord of the circles $(x-a)^2 + y^2 = a^2$ and $x^2 + (y-b)^2 = b^2$ is $\dfrac{2ab}{\sqrt{a^2+b^2}}$.

9. Family of circles circumscribing a triangle whose sides are given by $L_1 = 0, L_2 = 0$ and $L_3 = 0$ is given by $L_1L_2 + \lambda L_2L_3 + \mu L_3L_1 = 0$ provided coefficient of $xy = 0$ and coefficient of x^2 = coefficient of y^2.

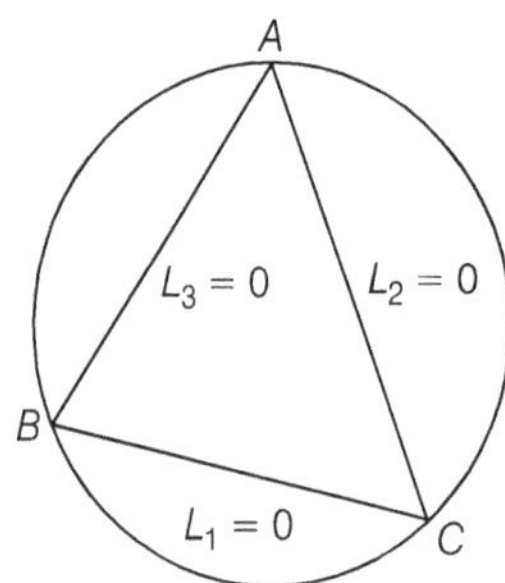

Remark

Equation of the circle circumscribing the triangle formed by the lines $a_rx + b_ry + c_r = 0$, where $r = 1, 2, 3$, is :

$$\begin{vmatrix} \dfrac{a_1^2 + b_1^2}{a_1x + b_1y + c_1} & a_1 & b_1 \\ \dfrac{a_2^2 + b_2^2}{a_2x + b_2y + c_2} & a_2 & b_2 \\ \dfrac{a_3^2 + b_3^2}{a_3x + b_3y + c_3} & a_3 & b_3 \end{vmatrix} = 0$$

10. Equation of circle circumscribing a quadrilateral whose sides in order are represented by the lines $L_1 = 0, L_2 = 0, L_3 = 0$ and $L_4 = 0$ is given by $L_1L_3 + \lambda L_2L_4 = 0$

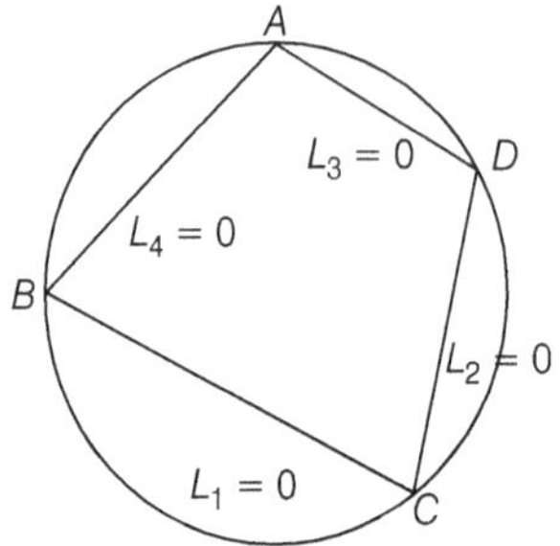

provided coefficient of x^2 = coefficient of y^2 and coefficient of $xy = 0$.

11. The locus of the middle point of a chord of a circle subtending a right angle at a given point will be a circle.

12. The length of an equilateral triangle inscribed in the circle $x^2 + y^2 = a^2$ is $a\sqrt{3}$.

13. The distance between the chord of contact of tangents to $x^2 + y^2 + 2gx + 2fy + c = 0$ from the origin and the point (g, f) is $\dfrac{|g^2 + f^2 - c|}{2\sqrt{(g^2 + f^2)}}$.

14. The shortest chord of a circle passing through a point P inside the circle is the chord whose middle point is P.

15. The length of transverse common tangent $<$ the length of direct common tangent.

JEE Type Solved Examples : Single Option Correct Type Questions

- This section contains **10 multiple choice examples.** Each example has four choices (a), (b), (c) and (d) out of which **ONLY ONE** is correct.

Ex. 1 *Two distinct chords drawn from the point (p,q) on the circle $x^2+y^2=px+qy$, where $pq\neq 0$, are bisected by the X-axis. Then,*

(a) $|p|=|q|$ (b) $p^2=8q^2$ (c) $p^2<8q^2$ (d) $p^2>8q^2$

Sol. (d)

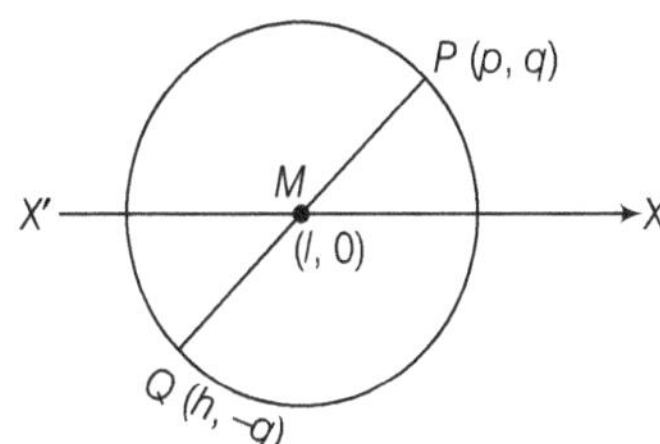

Suppose chord bisect at $M(\lambda,0)$, then other end point of chord is $(h,-q)$

where, $\lambda=\frac{p+h}{2}$

which lie on $x^2+y^2=px+qy$

or $h^2+q^2=ph-q^2$

$\Rightarrow h^2-ph+2q^2=0$

for two distinct chords, $B^2-4AC>0$

or $p^2-4\cdot1\cdot2q^2>0$

or $p^2>8q^2$

Ex. 2 *The values of λ for which the circle $x^2+y^2+6x+5+\lambda(x^2+y^2-8x+7)=0$ dwindles into a point are*

(a) $1\pm\frac{\sqrt{2}}{3}$ (b) $2\pm\frac{2\sqrt{2}}{3}$ (c) $2\pm\frac{4\sqrt{2}}{3}$ (d) $1\pm\frac{4\sqrt{2}}{3}$

Sol. (c) The given circle is

$$x^2+y^2+6x+5+\lambda(x^2+y^2-8x+7)=0$$

or $x^2(1+\lambda)+y^2(1-\lambda)+(6-8\lambda)x+(5+7\lambda)=0$

$$\Rightarrow x^2+y^2+\left(\frac{6-8\lambda}{1+\lambda}\right)x+\left(\frac{5+7\lambda}{1+\lambda}\right)=0$$

This will dwindle into a point circle, then radius of the circle $=0$

$$\sqrt{\left(\frac{3-4\lambda}{1+\lambda}\right)^2+0-\left(\frac{5+7\lambda}{1+\lambda}\right)}=0$$

$\Rightarrow (3-4\lambda)^2-(5+7\lambda)(1+\lambda)=0$

$\Rightarrow 9-16\lambda^2-24\lambda-5-5\lambda-7\lambda-7\lambda^2=0$

$\Rightarrow 9\lambda^2-36\lambda+4=0$

$$\lambda=\frac{36\pm\sqrt{(36)^2-4.9.4}}{2.9}$$

$\therefore \lambda=2\pm\frac{4\sqrt{2}}{3}$

Ex. 3 *If $f(x+y)=f(x)\cdot f(y)$ for all x and y, $f(1)=2$ and $\alpha_n=f(n), n\in N$, then the equation of the circle having (α_1,α_2) and (α_3,α_4) as the ends of its one diameter is*

(a) $(x-2)(x-8)+(y-4)(y-16)=0$
(b) $(x-4)(x-8)+(y-2)(y-16)=0$
(c) $(x-2)(x-16)+(y-4)(y-8)=0$
(d) $(x-6)(x-8)+(y-5)(y-6)=0$

Sol. (a) $\because f(x+y)=f(x).f(y)$ ...(i)

$\because f(1)=2$

In Eq. (i), Put $x=y=1$,

then $f(2)=f(1).f(1)=2^2$

Now, in Eq. (i), $x=1, y=2$, then

$$f(3)=f(1)f(2)=2.2^2=2^3$$

Hence, $f(n)=2^n$

$\therefore \alpha_n=f(n)=2^n\,\forall n\in N$

$(\alpha_1,\alpha_2)\equiv(2,4)$

and $(\alpha_3,\alpha_4)\equiv(8,16)$

Equation of circle in diametric form is

$(x-2)(x-8)+(y-4)(y-16)=0$

Ex. 4 *Two circles of radii a and b touching each other externally, are inscribed in the area bounded by $y=\sqrt{(1-x^2)}$ and the X-axis. If $b=\frac{1}{2}$, then a is equal to*

(a) $\frac{1}{4}$ (b) $\frac{1}{8}$
(c) $\frac{1}{2}$ (d) $\frac{1}{\sqrt{2}}$

Sol. (a) Let the centres of circles be C_1 and C_2, then

$C_1\equiv(\sqrt{(1-2a)},a)$

and $C_2\equiv(\sqrt{(1-2b)},b)$

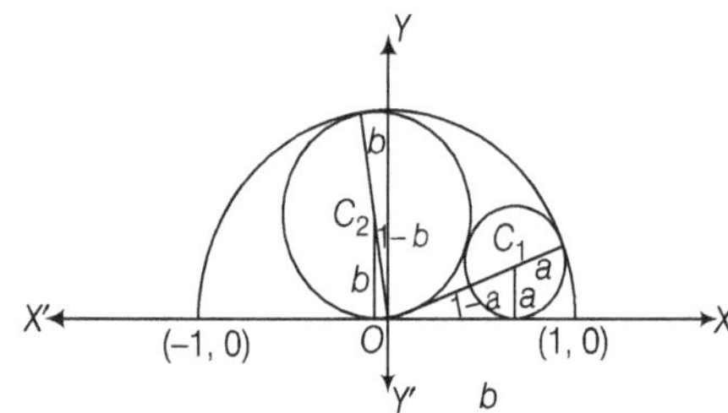

Now, $C_1C_2 = a + b$

$$\Rightarrow \quad \left((\sqrt{(1-2a)})^2 + \left(a - \frac{1}{2}\right)^2\right) = \left(a + \frac{1}{2}\right)^2 \qquad \left[\because b = \frac{1}{2}\right]$$

or $$1 - 2a + \left(a - \frac{1}{2}\right)^2 = \left(a + \frac{1}{2}\right)^2$$

or $$1 - 2a + a^2 + \frac{1}{4} - a = a^2 + \frac{1}{4} + a$$

or $$a = \frac{1}{4}$$

Ex. 5 *There are two circles whose equations are $x^2 + y^2 = 9$ and $x^2 + y^2 - 8x - 6y + n^2 = 0, n \in I$. If the two circles having exactly two common tangents, then the number of possible values of n is*

(a) 2 (b) 7 (c) 8 (d) 9

Sol. (d) Given circles are $S_1 : x^2 + y^2 - 9 = 0$

Its centre $C_1 : (0,0)$ and radius $r_1 = 3$

and $S_2 : x^2 + y^2 - 8x - 6y + n^2 = 0$

Its centre $C_2 : (4,3)$ and radius $r_2 = \sqrt{(25 - n^2)}$

Here, $25 - n^2 > 0 \Rightarrow -5 < n < 5$ ...(i)

For exactly two common tangents,

$$r_1 + r_2 > C_1C_2$$

$$\Rightarrow \quad 3 + \sqrt{(25 - n^2)} > \sqrt{(4^2 + 3^2)}$$

$$\Rightarrow \quad \sqrt{(25 - n^2)} > 2$$

$$\Rightarrow \quad 25 - n^2 > 4$$

or $$n^2 < 21$$

or $$-\sqrt{21} < n < \sqrt{21} \qquad \text{...(ii)}$$

From Eqs. (i) and (ii), we get

$$-\sqrt{21} < n < \sqrt{21}$$

But $n \in I$. So, $n = -4, -3, -2, -1, 0, 1, 2, 3, 4$

Hence, number of possible values of n is 9.

Ex. 6 *Suppose $f(x, y) = 0$ is the equation of a circle such that $f(x, 1) = 0$ has equal roots (each equal to 2) and $f(1, x) = 0$ also has equal roots (each equal to zero). The equation of circle is*

(a) $x^2 + y^2 + 4x + 3 = 0$ (b) $x^2 + y^2 + 4y + 3 = 0$

(c) $x^2 + y^2 + 4x - 3 = 0$ (d) $x^2 + y^2 - 4x + 3 = 0$

Sol. (d) Let $f(x, y) = x^2 + y^2 + 2gx + 2fy + c$

$$\Rightarrow \quad f(x, 1) = x^2 + 1 + 2gx + 2f + c \equiv (x - 2)^2 \qquad \text{(given)}$$

then, $g = -2,\ 2f + c = 3$ ...(i)

Also, $f(1, x) = 1 + x^2 + 2g + 2fx + c \equiv (x - 0)^2$ (given)

then, $f = 0,\ 2g + c = -1$ ...(ii)

From Eqs. (i) and (ii), we get

$$g = -2, f = 0, c = 3$$

Thus, equation of circle is

$$x^2 + y^2 - 4x + 3 = 0$$

Ex. 7 *A variable circle C has the equation $x^2 + y^2 - 2(t^2 - 3t + 1)x - 2(t^2 + 2t)y + t = 0$, where t is a parameter. If the power of point (a, b) w.r.t. the circle C is constant, then the ordered pair (a, b) is*

(a) $\left(\frac{1}{10}, -\frac{1}{10}\right)$ (b) $\left(\frac{1}{10}, \frac{1}{10}\right)$

(c) $\left(-\frac{1}{10}, \frac{1}{10}\right)$ (d) $\left(-\frac{1}{10}, -\frac{1}{10}\right)$

Sol. (c) $\because C : x^2 + y^2 - 2(t^2 - 3t + 1)x - 2(t^2 + 2t)y + t = 0$

given power of circle = constant

$$\therefore \quad a^2 + b^2 - 2(t^2 - 3t + 1)a - 2(t^2 + 2t)b + t = \text{constant}$$

$$\Rightarrow \quad -2(a + b)t^2 + (6a - 4b + 1)t + (a^2 + b^2 - 2a) = \text{constant}$$

$\because$ Power of circle is constant, then

$a + b = 0$ and $6a - 4b + 1 = 0$

or $b = -a$, then $6a + 4a + 1 = 0$

$$\therefore \quad a = -\frac{1}{10}, b = \frac{1}{10}$$

Hence, required ordered pair is $\left(-\frac{1}{10}, \frac{1}{10}\right)$

Ex. 8 *If the radii of the circles $(x - 1)^2 + (y - 2)^2 = 1$ and $(x - 7)^2 + (y - 10)^2 = 4$ are increasing uniformly w.r.t. time as 0.3 unit/s and 0.4 unit/s respectively, then they will touch each other at t equals to*

(a) 45 s (b) 90 s

(c) 11 s (d) 135 s

Sol. (b) Given circles are $S_1 : (x - 1)^2 + (y - 2)^2 = 1$

Its centre $C_1 : (1,2)$ and radius $r_1 = 1$

and $S_2 : (x - 7)^2 + (y - 10)^2 = 4$

Its centre $C_2 : (7,10)$ and radius $r_2 = 2$

$\because \quad C_1C_2 = 10 > r_1 + r_2$

Hence, the two circles are separated.

The radii of the two circles at time t are $(1 + 0.3t)$ and $(2 + 0.4t)$

For the two circles touch each other, then

$$C_1C_2 = |(1+0.3t) \pm (2+0.4t)|$$

$\Rightarrow$ $10 = |3+0.7t|$ or $10 = |-1-0.1t|$

$\Rightarrow$ $0.7t + 3 = \pm 10$ or $-1-0.1t = \pm 10$

$\Rightarrow$ $t = 10$ or $t = 90$ $[\because t > 0]$

Ex. 9 *A light ray gets reflected from $x = -2$. If the reflected ray touches the circle $x^2 + y^2 = 4$ and the point of incident is $(-2, -4)$, then the equation of the incident ray is*

(a) $4y + 3x + 22 = 0$ (b) $3y + 4x + 20 = 0$
(c) $4y + 2x + 20 = 0$ (d) $y + x + 6 = 0$

Sol. (a) Any tangent of $x^2 + y^2 = 4$ is $y = mx \pm 2\sqrt{(1+m^2)}$.

If it passes through $(-2, -4)$, then $-4 = -2m \pm 2\sqrt{(1+m^2)}$

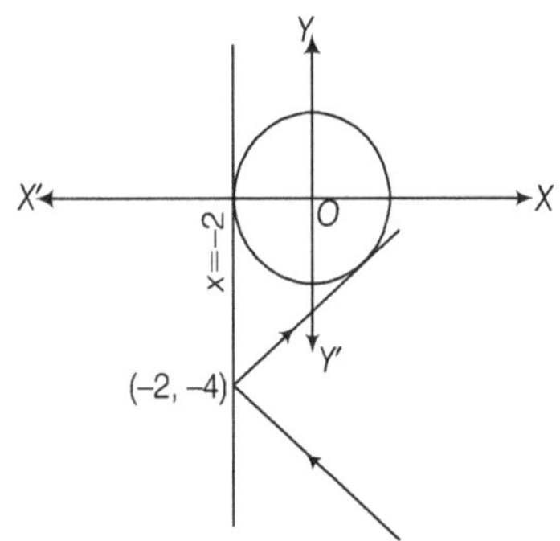

or $(m-2)^2 = 1 + m^2$

or $m = \infty, m = 3/4$

Hence, the slope of the reflected ray is 3/4.

Thus, the equation of the incident ray is

$$y + 4 = -\frac{3}{4}(x+2)$$

i.e. $4y + 3x + 22 = 0$

Ex. 10 *If a circle having centre at (α, β) radius r completely lies with in two lines $x + y = 2$ and $x + y = -2$, then,* $\min.(|\alpha + \beta + 2|, |\alpha + \beta - 2|)$ *is*

(a) greater than $\sqrt{2}r$
(b) less than $\sqrt{2}r$
(c) greater than $2r$
(d) less than $2r$

Sol. (a) Minimum distance of the centre from line > radius of circle i.e. $\min.\left\{\frac{|\alpha+\beta+2|}{\sqrt{2}}, \frac{|\alpha+\beta-2|}{\sqrt{2}}\right\} > r$

or $\min.\{|\alpha+\beta+2|, |\alpha+\beta-2|\} > \sqrt{2}r$

JEE Type Solved Examples : More than One Correct Option Type Questions

- This section contains **5 multiple choice examples.** Each example has four choices (a), (b), (c) and (d) out of which MORE THAN ONE may be correct.

Ex. 11 *If point $P(x, y)$ is called a lattice point, if $x, y \in I$. Then, the total number of lattice points in the interior of the circle $x^2 + y^2 = a^2, a \neq 0$ cannot be*

(a) 202 (b) 203 (c) 204 (d) 205

Sol. (a, b, c) Given circle is $x^2 + y^2 = a^2$ ...(i)

Clearly (0, 0) will belong the interior of circle Eq. (i). Also, other points interior to circle Eq. (i) will have the coordinates of the form

$$(\pm\lambda, 0), (0, \pm\lambda), \text{ where } \lambda^2 < a^2$$

and $(\pm\lambda, \pm\mu)$ and $(\pm\mu, \pm\lambda)$, where $\lambda^2 + \mu^2 < a^2$ and $\lambda, \mu \in I$

$\therefore$ Number of lattice points in the interior of the circle will be of the form $1 + 4r + 8t$, where $r, t = 0, 1, 2, \ldots$

$\therefore$ Number of such points must be of the form $4n + 1$, where $n = 0, 1, 2, \ldots$

Ex. 12 *Let x, y be real variable satisfying $x^2 + y^2 + 8x - 10y - 40 = 0$. Let $a = \max.\{\sqrt{(x+2)^2 + (y-3)^2}\}$ and $b = \min.\{\sqrt{(x+2)^2 + (y-3)^2}\}$, then*

(a) $a + b = 18$ (b) $a - b = 4\sqrt{2}$
(c) $a + b = 4\sqrt{2}$ (d) $a \cdot b = 73$

Sol. (a, b, d) Given circle is

$$x^2 + y^2 + 8x - 10y - 40 = 0$$

The centre and radius of the circle are $(-4, 5)$ and 9, respectively.

Distance of the centre $(-4, 5)$ from $(-2, 3)$ is

$$\sqrt{(4+4)} = 2\sqrt{2}.$$

Therefore, $a = 2\sqrt{2} + 9$

and $b = -2\sqrt{2} + 9$

$\therefore$ $a + b = 18, a - b = 4\sqrt{2}, ab = 73$

Ex. 13 *The equation of the tangents drawn from the origin to the circle $x^2+y^2-2rx-2hy+h^2=0$, are*

(a) $x=0$

(b) $y=0$

(c) $(h^2-r^2)x-2rhy=0$

(d) $(h^2-r^2)x+2rhy=0$

Sol. (a, c) The given equation is $(x-r)^2+(y-h)^2=r^2$

tangents are $x=0$

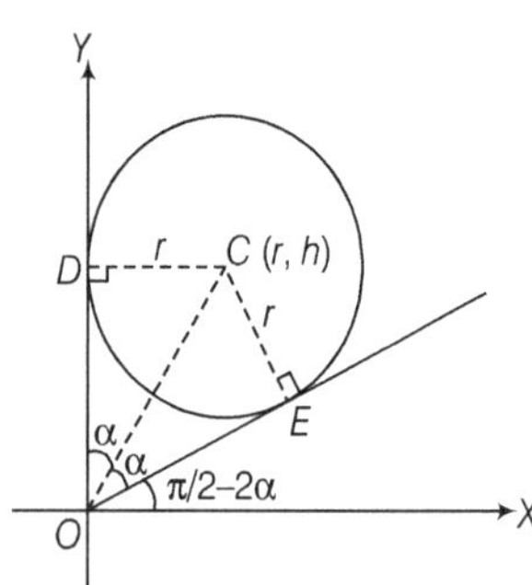

and $\quad y = x\tan\left(\frac{\pi}{2}-2\alpha\right) = x\cot 2\alpha$

$$= \frac{x(1-\tan^2\alpha)}{2\tan\alpha}$$

$$y = \frac{x\left(1-\frac{r^2}{h^2}\right)}{2\left(\frac{r}{h}\right)} \qquad \left(\because \text{in } \Delta ODC, \tan\alpha = \frac{r}{h}\right)$$

or $\quad (h^2-r^2)x-2rhy=0$

Ex. 14 *Point M moved on the circle $(x-4)^2+(y-8)^2=20$. Then it broke away from it and moving along a tangent to the circle cut the X-axis at point $(-2, 0)$. The coordinates of the point on the circle at which the moving point broke away is*

(a) $\left(\frac{42}{5},\frac{36}{5}\right)$ (b) $\left(-\frac{2}{5},\frac{44}{5}\right)$

(c) $(6, 4)$ (d) $(2, 4)$

Sol. (b, c) Given circle is

$$(x-4)^2+(y-8)^2=20$$

or $\quad x^2+y^2-8x-16y+60=0 \quad$ ...(i)

Equation of chord of contact from $(-2, 0)$ is

$$-2\cdot x+0\cdot y-4(x-2)-8(y+0)+60=0$$

or $\quad 3x+4y-34=0 \quad$ ...(ii)

Solving Eqs. (i) and (ii), we get

$$x^2+\left(\frac{34-3x}{4}\right)^2-8x-16\left(\frac{34-3x}{4}\right)+60=0$$

or $\quad 5x^2-28x-12=0$

or $\quad (x-6)(5x+2)=0$

or $\quad x=6, -\frac{2}{5}$

Therefore, the points are $(6, 4)$ and $\left(-\frac{2}{5},\frac{44}{5}\right)$.

Ex. 15 *The equations of four circles are $(x\pm a)^2+(y\pm a)^2=a^2$. The radius of a circle touching all the four circles is*

(a) $(\sqrt{2}-1)a$ (b) $2\sqrt{2}a$

(c) $(\sqrt{2}+1)a$ (d) $(2+\sqrt{2})a$

Sol. (a, c) Radius of inner circle $= OR-a$

$$=\sqrt{(a^2+a^2)}-a$$

$$=a(\sqrt{2}-1)$$

Radius of outer circle $= OR+RQ$

$$=a\sqrt{2}+a=a(\sqrt{2}+1)$$

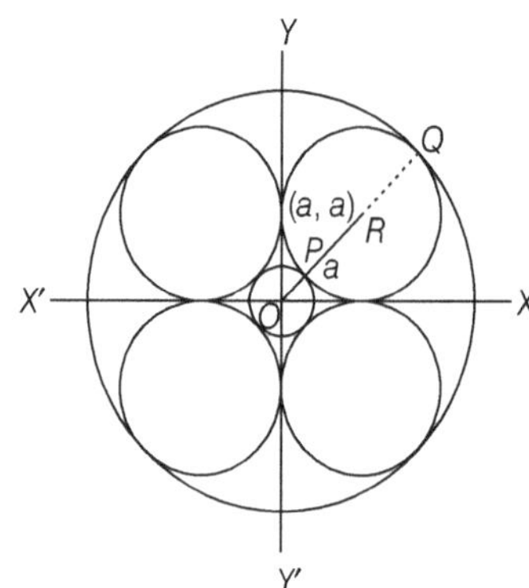

JEE Type Solved Examples :
Paragraph Based Questions

- This section contains **2 solved paragraphs** based upon each of the paragraph **3 multiple choice** questions have to be answered. Each of these questions has four choices (a), (b), (c) and (d) out of which **ONLY ONE** is correct.

Paragraph I
(Q. Nos. 16 to 18)

Consider the relation $4l^2 - 5m^2 + 6l + 1 = 0$, where $l, m \in R$.

16. The line $lx + my + 1 = 0$ touches a fixed circle whose equation is

(a) $x^2 + y^2 - 4x - 5 = 0$ (b) $x^2 + y^2 + 6x + 6 = 0$

(c) $x^2 + y^2 - 6x + 4 = 0$ (d) $x^2 + y^2 + 4x - 4 = 0$

17. Tangents PA and PB are drawn to the above fixed circle from the point P on the line $x + y - 1 = 0$. Then, the chord of contact AB passes through the fixed point

(a) $\left(\frac{1}{2}, -\frac{5}{2}\right)$ (b) $\left(\frac{1}{3}, \frac{4}{3}\right)$ (c) $\left(-\frac{1}{2}, \frac{3}{2}\right)$ (d) $\left(\frac{1}{2}, \frac{5}{2}\right)$

18. The number of tangents which can be drawn from the point $(2, -3)$ are

(a) 0 (b) 1 (c) 2 (d) 1 or 2

Sol.

16. (c) Let the equation of the circle be

$$x^2 + y^2 + 2gx + 2fy + c = 0 \quad \text{...(i)}$$

The line $lx + my + 1 = 0$ touch circle Eq. (i), then

$$\frac{|-lg - mf + 1|}{\sqrt{(l^2 + m^2)}} = \sqrt{(g^2 + f^2 - c)}$$

$$\Rightarrow \quad (lg + mf - 1)^2 = (l^2 + m^2)(g^2 + f^2 - c)$$

or $(f^2 - c)l^2 + (g^2 - c)m^2 - 2gflm + 2gl + 2fm - 1 = 0$ ...(ii)

But the given condition is

$$4l^2 - 5m^2 + 6l + 1 = 0 \quad \text{...(iii)}$$

Comparing Eqs. (ii) and (iii), we get

$$\frac{f^2 - c}{4} = \frac{g^2 - c}{-5} = \frac{-2gf}{0} = \frac{g}{3} = \frac{2f}{0} = \frac{-1}{1}$$

Then, we get $g = -3, f = 0, c = 4$

Substituting these values in Eq. (i), the equation of the circle is

$$x^2 + y^2 - 6x + 4 = 0$$

17. (a) Let any point on the line $x + y - 1 = 0$ is

$$P(\lambda, 1 - \lambda), \lambda \in R.$$

Then, equation of AB is

$$\lambda x + (1 - \lambda)y - 3(x + \lambda) + 4 = 0$$

$$\Rightarrow \quad (-3x + y + 4) + \lambda(x - y - 3) = 0$$

for fixed point $-3x + y + 4 = 0, x - y - 3 = 0$

$$\therefore \quad x = \frac{1}{2}, y = -\frac{5}{2}$$

$\therefore$ Fixed point is $\left(\frac{1}{2}, \frac{-5}{2}\right)$

18. (c) Let $S \equiv x^2 + y^2 - 6x + 4 = 0$.

$$\therefore \quad S_1 = (2)^2 + (-3)^2 - 6(2) + 4$$
$$= 4 + 9 - 12 - 4$$
$$= 5 > 0$$

Therefore, point $(2, -3)$ lies outside the circle from which two tangents can be drawn.

Paragraph II
(Q. Nos. 19 to 21)

If α- chord of a circle be that chord which subtends an angle α at the centre of the circle.

19. If $x + y = 1$ is α-chord of $x^2 + y^2 = 1$, then α is equal to

(a) $\frac{\pi}{6}$ (b) $\frac{\pi}{4}$ (c) $\frac{\pi}{2}$ (d) $\frac{3\pi}{4}$

20. If slope of a $\frac{\pi}{3}$-chord of $x^2 + y^2 = 4$ is 1, then its equation is

(a) $x - y + \sqrt{6} = 0$ (b) $x - y + \sqrt{3} = 0$

(c) $x - y - \sqrt{3} = 0$ (d) $x - y - 2\sqrt{3} = 0$

21. Distance of $\frac{2\pi}{3}$ — chord of $x^2 + y^2 + 2x + 4y + 1 = 0$ from the centre is

(a) $\frac{1}{\sqrt{2}}$ (b) 1 (c) $\sqrt{2}$ (d) 2

Sol.

19. (c) From figure

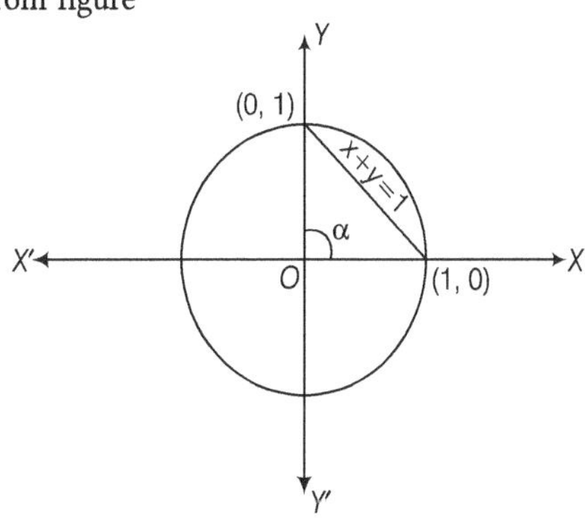

$$\alpha = \frac{\pi}{2}$$

20. (a) $\because$ Slope of chord is 1.

Let the equation of chord be $x - y + \lambda = 0$.

$$\because \quad OM = 2\cos\left(\frac{\pi}{6}\right) = \sqrt{3}$$

$$\therefore \quad \frac{|0 - 0 + \lambda|}{\sqrt{2}} = \sqrt{3}$$

$$\Rightarrow \quad \lambda = \pm\sqrt{6}$$

Hence, equation of chords are

$$x - y \pm \sqrt{6} = 0.$$

21. (b) From figure,

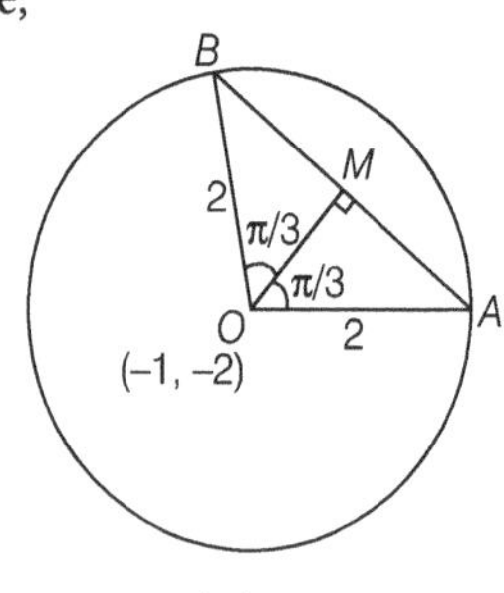

$$OM = 2\cos\left(\frac{\pi}{3}\right) = 1$$

JEE Type Solved Examples : Single Integer Answer Type Questions

- This section contains **2 examples.** The answer to each example is a **single digit integer,** ranging from 0 to 9 (both inclusive).

Ex. 22 *A circle with centre in the first quadrant is tangent to $y = x + 10$, $y = x - 6$ and the Y-axis. Let (p, q) be the centre of the circle. If the value of $(p + q) = a + b\sqrt{a}$, when $a, b \in Q$, then the value of $|a - b|$ is*

Sol. (6) $\because \quad CP = CR$

$$\Rightarrow \quad \frac{|p - q + 10|}{\sqrt{2}} = p$$

or $\quad p - q + 10 = p\sqrt{2}$ ...(i)

and $\quad CP = CQ$

$$\frac{p - q + 10}{\sqrt{2}} = -\left(\frac{p - q - 6}{\sqrt{2}}\right) \text{ or } p - q = -2 \qquad \text{...(ii)}$$

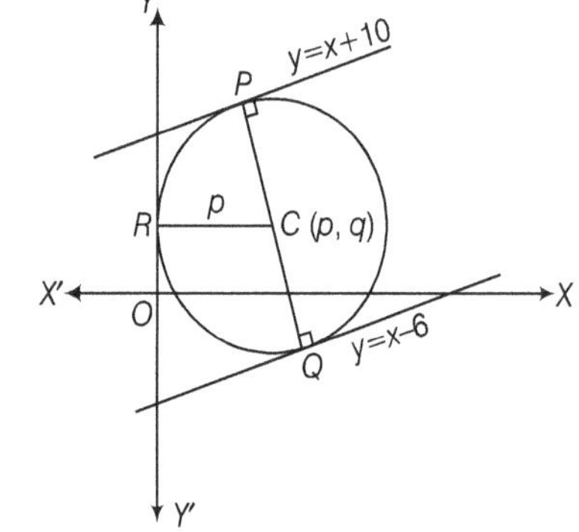

From Eqs. (i) and (ii), we get

$$p = 4\sqrt{2} \text{ and } q = 4\sqrt{2} + 2$$

Now, $\quad p + q = 2 + 8\sqrt{2} = a + b\sqrt{2}$ (given)

$\therefore \quad a = 2, b = 8$

Hence, $|a - b| = |2 - 8| = 6$

Ex. 23 *If the circles $x^2 + y^2 + (3 + \sin\theta)x + 2\cos\phi y = 0$ and $x^2 + y^2 + (2\cos\phi)x + 2\lambda y = 0$ touch each other, then the maximum value of λ is*

Sol. (1) Since, both the circles are passing through the origin (0, 0), the equation of tangent at (0,0) of first circle will be same as that of the tangent at (0, 0) of second circle.

Equation of tangent at (0, 0) of first circle is

$$(3 + \sin\theta)x + (2\cos\phi)y = 0 \qquad \text{...(i)}$$

Equaton of tangent at (0, 0) of second circle is

$$(2\cos\phi)x + 2\lambda y = 0 \qquad \text{...(ii)}$$

Therefore, Eqs. (i) and (ii) must be identical, then

$$\frac{3 + \sin\theta}{2\cos\phi} = \frac{2\cos\phi}{2\lambda}$$

or $$\lambda = \frac{2\cos^2\phi}{(3 + \sin\theta)}$$

or $$\lambda_{max} = 1 \qquad (\text{when } \sin\theta = -1 \text{ and } \cos\phi = 1)$$

JEE Type Solved Examples : Matching Type Questions

- This section contains **2 examples.** Examples 24 and 25 have four statements (A, B, C and D) given in **Column I** and four statements (p, q, r and s) in **Column II.** Any given statement in **Column I** can have correct matching with one or more statement(s) given in **Column II.**

Ex. 24. *Consider the circles C_1 of radius a and C_2 of radius b, b > a both lying the first quadrant and touching the coordinate axes.*

	Column I		Column II
(A)	C_1 and C_2 touch each other and $\frac{b}{a} = \lambda + \sqrt{\mu}$, $\lambda \in$ prime number and $\mu \in$ whole number, then	(p)	$\lambda + \mu$ is a prime number
(B)	C_1 and C_2 cut orthogonally and $\frac{b}{a} = \lambda + \sqrt{\mu}$, $\lambda \in$ prime number and $\mu \in$ whole number, then	(q)	$\lambda + \mu$ is a composite number
(C)	C_1 and C_2 intersect so that the common chord is longest and $\frac{b}{a} = \lambda + \sqrt{\mu}$, $\lambda \in$ prime number and $\mu \in$ whole number, then	(r)	$2\lambda + \mu$ is a perfect number
(D)	C_2 passes through the centre of C_1 and $\frac{b}{a} = \lambda + \sqrt{\mu}$, $\lambda \in$ prime number and $\mu \in$ whole number, then	(s)	$\lvert \lambda - \mu \rvert$ is a prime number

Sol. (A)→ (p, s); (B) → (p); (C) → (p, r, s); (D) → (q, r)

$\because \quad C_1 : x^2 + y^2 - 2ax - 2ay + a^2 = 0$

Centre : (a, a) and radius : a

and $\quad C_2 : x^2 + y^2 - 2bx - 2by + b^2 = 0$

Centre : (b, b) and radius : b

(A) $\because C_1$ and C_2 touch each other, then

$$\sqrt{2}(b-a) = b + a \Rightarrow \frac{b}{a} = (\sqrt{2}+1)^2 = 3 + \sqrt{8}$$

$\Rightarrow \quad \lambda = 3, \mu = 8$

(B) $\because C_1$ and C_2 intersect orthogonally, then

$$2(b-a)^2 = b^2 + a^2$$

$\Rightarrow \quad a^2 + b^2 - 4ab = 0$

or $\quad \left(\frac{b}{a}\right)^2 - 4\left(\frac{b}{a}\right) + 1 = 0$

$\therefore \quad \frac{b}{a} = \frac{4 \pm \sqrt{(16-4)}}{2} = 2 + \sqrt{3}$

$\Rightarrow \quad \lambda = 2, \mu = 3]$

(C) $\because C_1$ and C_2 intersect, the common chord is

$$2(b-a)(x+y) = b^2 - a^2$$

given common chord is longest, then passes through (a, a)

$\Rightarrow \quad 2(b-a)(2a) = b^2 - a^2$

or $\quad (b-3a)(b-a) = 0$

$\because \quad b - a \neq 0 \quad [b > a]$

$\therefore \quad b - 3a = 0$

or $\quad \frac{b}{a} = 3 \Rightarrow \lambda = 3, \mu = 0$

(D) $\because C_2$ passes through (a, a), then $a^2 + a^2 - 2ab - 2ab + b^2 = 0$

or $b^2 - 4ab + 2a^2 = 0$

or $\quad \left(\frac{b}{a}\right)^2 - 4\left(\frac{b}{a}\right) + 2 = 0$

or $\quad \frac{b}{a} = \frac{4 \pm \sqrt{(16-8)}}{2} = 2 + \sqrt{2}$

$\Rightarrow \quad \lambda = 2, \mu = 2$

Ex. 25. *Match the following*

	Column I		Column II
(A)	The circles $x^2 + y^2 + 2x + c = 0$ $(c > 0)$ and $x^2 + y^2 + 2y + c = 0$ touch each other, then the value of $2c$ is	(p)	1
(B)	The circles $x^2 + y^2 + 2x + 3y + c = 0$ $(c > 0)$ and $x^2 + y^2 - x + 2y + c = 0$ intersect orthogonally, then the value of $2c$ is	(q)	2
(C)	The circle $x^2 + y^2 = 9$ is contains the circle $x^2 + y^2 - 2x + 1 - c^2 = 0$ $(c > 0)$, then $2c$ can be	(r)	3
(D)	The circle $x^2 + y^2 = 9$ is contains in the circle $x^2 + y^2 - 2x + 1 - \frac{c^2}{4} = 0$ $(c > 0)$, then $(c - 6)$ can be	(s)	4

Sol. (A) → (p); (B) → (q); (C) → (p, q, r); (D) → (r, s)

(A) The circles

$$S_1 : (x+1)^2 + y^2 = (\sqrt{(1-c)})^2$$

Centre $C_1 : (-1, 0)$, radius $r_1 : \sqrt{(1-c)}$

and $\quad S_2 : x^2 + (y+1)^2 = (\sqrt{(1-c)})^2$

Centre $C_2 : (0, -1)$, radius : $r_2 = \sqrt{(1-c)}$

Now, $\quad C_1C_2 = \sqrt{2}$ and $r_1 = r_2$

$\therefore$ The circles will touch externally only and $C_1C_2 = r_1 + r_2$

$\Rightarrow \quad \sqrt{2} = 2\sqrt{(1-c)}$ or $2c = 1$

(B) The circles $S_1:(x+1)^2+\left(y+\frac{3}{2}\right)^2=\left(\sqrt{\left(\frac{13}{4}-c\right)}\right)^2$

Centre $C_1:\left(-1,-\frac{3}{2}\right)$, radius $r_1:\sqrt{\left(\frac{13}{4}-c\right)}$

and $\quad S_2:\left(x-\frac{1}{2}\right)^2+(y+1)^2=\left(\sqrt{\left(\frac{5}{4}-c\right)}\right)^2$

Centre $C_2:\left(\frac{1}{2},-1\right)$, radius $r_2:\sqrt{\left(\frac{5}{4}-c\right)}$

For intersect orthogonally

$$(C_1C_2)^2=r_1^2+r_2^2$$

$$\Rightarrow \quad \left(\frac{3}{2}\right)^2+\left(\frac{1}{2}\right)^2=\frac{13}{4}-c+\frac{5}{4}-c$$

or $\quad 2c=2$

(C) The circles

$$S_1:x^2+y^2=3^2$$

Centre $C_1:(0,0)$, radius $r_1:3$

and $\quad S_2:(x-1)^2+y^2=c^2$

Centre $C_2:(1,0)$, radius $r_2:c$

Now, S_2 will be contained in S_1, then

$$C_1C_2<r_1-r_2$$

or $\quad 1<3-c$ or $c<2\Rightarrow 2c<4$

(D) The circles

$$S_1:x^2+y^2=9$$

Centre $C_1:(0,0)$, radius $r_1:3$ and

$$S_2:(x-1)^2+y^2=\left(\frac{c}{2}\right)^2$$

Centre $C_2:(1,0)$, radius $r_2:\frac{c}{2}$

Now, S_1 will be contained in S_2,

then, $\quad r_2-r_1>C_1C_2$

$$\Rightarrow \quad \frac{c}{2}-3>1 \text{ or } c>8$$

$$\therefore \quad (c-6)>2$$

JEE Type Solved Examples :
Statement I and II Type Questions

- **Directions** (Ex. Nos. 26 and 27) are Assertion-Reason Type examples. Each of these examples contains two statements :
Statement I (Assertion) and **Statement II** (Reason)

Each of these examples also has four alternative choices only one of which is the correct answer. You have to select the correct choice as given below :

(a) Statement I is true, Statement II is true; Statement II is a correct explanation for Statement I
(b) Statement I is true, Statement II is true; Statement II is not a correct explanation for Statement I
(c) Statement I is true, Statement II is false
(d) Statement I is false, Statement II is true

● **Ex. 26** *C_1 is a circle of radius 2 touching X-axis and Y-axis. C_2 is another circle of radius greater than 2 and touching the axes as well as the circle C_1.*

Statement I *Radius of Circle $C_2=\sqrt{2}(\sqrt{2}+1)(\sqrt{2}+2)$*

Statement II *Centres of both circles always lie on the line $y=x$.*

Sol. (c) $C_1:(x-2)^2+(y-2)^2=2^2$

$$C_2:(x-r)^2+(y-r)^2=r^2 \qquad (r>2)$$

According to question,

$$\sqrt{(r-2)^2+(r-2)^2}=r+2$$

$$(r-2)^2+(r-2)^2=(r+2)^2$$

$$r^2-12r+4=0$$

$$r=\frac{12\pm\sqrt{(144-16)}}{2}$$

$$=6\pm4\sqrt{2}$$

$$\therefore \quad r=6+4\sqrt{2} \qquad [\because r>2]$$

$$=2(\sqrt{2}+1)^2$$

$$=\sqrt{2}(\sqrt{2}+1)(2+\sqrt{2})$$

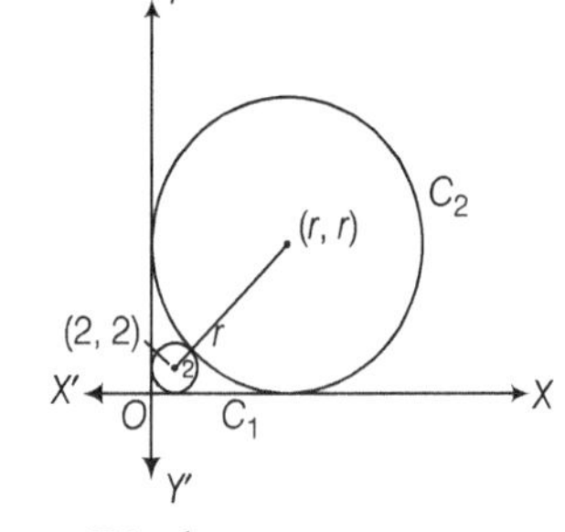

$\therefore$Statement I is true and Statement II is always not true (where circles in II or IV quadrants)

● **Ex. 27** *From the point $P(\sqrt{2},\sqrt{6})$ tangents PA and PB are drawn to the circle $x^2+y^2=4$*

Statement I *Area of the quadrilateral OAPB (O being origin) is 4.*

Statement II *Tangents PA and PB are perpendicular to each other and therefore quadrilateral OAPB is a square.*

Sol. (a) Clearly, $P(\sqrt{2},\sqrt{6})$ lies on $x^2+y^2=8$, which is the director circle of $x^2+y^2=4$.

Therefore, tangents PA and PB are perpendicular to each other. So, $OAPB$ is a square.

Hence, area of $OAPB=(\sqrt{S_1})^2=S_1$

$$=(\sqrt{2})^2+(\sqrt{6})^2-4=4$$

$\therefore$Both statements are true and statement II is correct explanation of statement I.

Subjective Type Examples

- In this section, there are **16 subjective solved examples.**

Ex. 28 *Find the equation of a circle having the lines $x^2+2xy+3x+6y=0$ as its normals and having size just sufficient to contain the circle*

$$x(x-4)+y(y-3)=0.$$

Sol. Given pair of normals is $\quad x^2+2xy+3x+6y=0$

or $\quad (x+2y)(x+3)=0$

$\therefore$ Normals are $x+2y=0$ and $x+3=0$ the point of intersection of normals $x+2y=0$ and $x+3=0$ is the centre of required circle, we get centre $C_1\equiv(-3,3/2)$ and other circle is

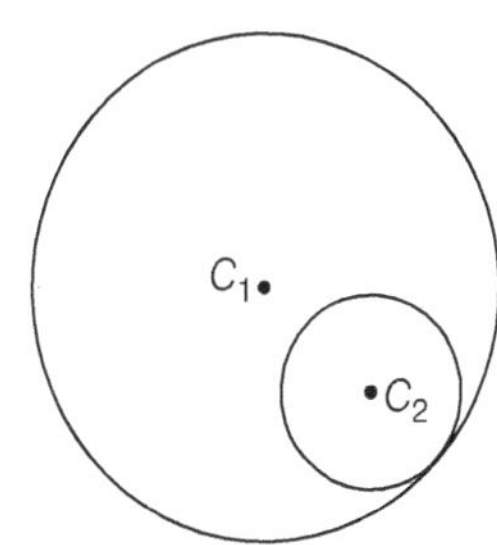

$$x(x-4)+y(y-3)=0$$

or $\quad x^2+y^2-4x-3y=0 \quad$ ...(i)

its centre $C_2\equiv(2,3/2)$ and radius $r=\sqrt{4+\frac{9}{4}}=\frac{5}{2}$

Since, the required circle just contains the given circle(i), the given circle should touch the required circle internally from inside.

$\Rightarrow$ radius of the required circle $=|C_1-C_2|+r$

$$=\sqrt{(-3-2)^2+\left(\frac{3}{2}-\frac{3}{2}\right)^2}+\frac{5}{2}$$

$$=5+\frac{5}{2}=\frac{15}{2}$$

Hence, equation of required circle is

$$(x+3)^2+(y-3/2)^2=\left(\frac{15}{2}\right)^2$$

or $\quad x^2+y^2+6x-3y-54=0$

Ex. 29 *Let a circle be given by*

$$2x(x-a)+y(2y-b)=0 \qquad (a\neq 0, b\neq 0)$$

Find the condition on a and b if two chords, each bisected by the X-axis, can be drawn to the circle from $(a, b/2)$.

Sol. The given circle is $\quad 2x(x-a)+y(2y-b)=0$

or $\quad x^2+y^2-ax-by/2=0$

Let AB be the chord which is bisected by X-axis at a point M. Let its coordinates be $M(h,0)$

and let $\quad S\equiv x^2+y^2-ax-by/2=0$

$\therefore$ Equation of chord AB is $T=S_1$

$$hx+0-\frac{a}{2}(x+h)-\frac{b}{4}(y+0)=h^2+0-ah-0$$

Since, its passes through $(a, b/2)$ we have

$$ah-\frac{a}{2}(a+h)-\frac{b^2}{8}=h^2-ah$$

$$\Rightarrow \quad h^2-\frac{3ah}{2}+\frac{a^2}{2}+\frac{b^2}{8}=0$$

Now, there are two chords bisected by the X-axis, so there must be two distinct real roots of h.

$$\therefore \quad B^2-4AC>0$$

$$\Rightarrow \quad \left(\frac{-3a}{2}\right)^2-4\cdot1\cdot\left(\frac{a^2}{2}+\frac{b^2}{8}\right)>0$$

$$\Rightarrow \quad a^2>2b^2.$$

Aliter : Given circle is

$$2x(x-a)+y(2y-b)=0$$

or $\quad x^2+y^2-ax-\frac{by}{2}=0 \quad$ ...(i)

Let chords bisected at $M(h,0)$ but given chords can be drawn $A\left(a,\frac{b}{2}\right)$ then chord cut the circle at $B(\lambda,-b/2)$

$\because$ Mid-point of ordinates of A and B is origin.

$\therefore$ $B(\lambda, b/2)$ lies on Eq. (i)

$$\therefore \quad \lambda^2+\frac{b^2}{4}-a\lambda+\frac{b^2}{4}=0$$

or $\quad \lambda^2-a\lambda+\frac{b^2}{2}=0$

$\because \quad \lambda$ is real

$$\therefore \quad B^2-4AC>0 \text{ or } a^2-4\cdot\frac{b^2}{2}>0 \text{ or } a^2>2b^2$$

Ex. 30 *Let C_1 and C_2 be two circles with C_2 lying inside C_1. A circle C lying inside C_1 touches C_1 internally and C_2 externally. Identify the locus of the centre of C.*

Sol. Let the given circles C_1 and C_2 have centres O_1 and O_2 with radii r_1 and r_2, respectively. Let centre of circle C is at O radius is r.

$$\because \quad OO_2=r+r_2$$

$$OO_1=r_1-r$$

$$\Rightarrow \quad OO_1+OO_2=r_1+r_2$$

which is greater than O_1O_2 as $O_1O_2<r_1+r_2$.

$\therefore$ Locus of O is an ellipse with foci O_1 and O_2.

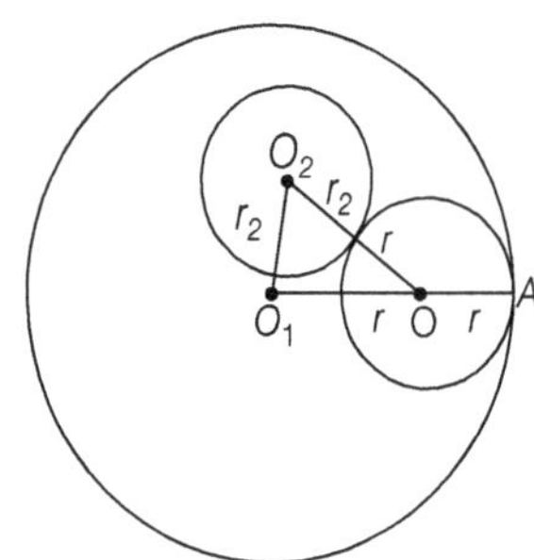

Aliter :

Let $O_1 \equiv (0, 0)$, $O_2 \equiv (a, b)$ and $O \equiv (h, k)$

$\therefore \quad C_1 : x^2 + y^2 = r_1^2$

$C_2 : (x-a)^2 + (y-b)^2 = r_2^2$

$C : (x-h)^2 + (y-k)^2 = r^2$

$\Rightarrow \quad OO_2 = r + r_2$

$\Rightarrow \quad \sqrt{(h-a)^2 + (k-b)^2} = r + r_2 \quad$ ...(i)

and $\quad OO_1 = r_1 - r$

$\Rightarrow \quad \sqrt{(h^2 + k^2)} = r_1 - r \quad$ ...(ii)

On adding Eqs. (i) and (ii) we get

$$\sqrt{(h-a)^2 + (k-b)^2} + \sqrt{(h^2 + k^2)} = r_1 + r_2$$

$\therefore$ Locus of O is $\sqrt{(x-a)^2 + (y-b)^2} + \sqrt{(x^2 + y^2)} = r_1 + r_2$

which represents an ellipse with foci are at (a, b) and $(0, 0)$.

Ex. 31 *A circle of constant radius r passes through the origin O, and cuts the axes at A and B. Show that the locus of the foot of the perpendicular from O to AB is*

$$(x^2 + y^2)^2 (x^{-2} + y^{-2}) = 4r^2$$

Sol. Let the coordinates of A and B are $(a, 0)$ and $(0, b)$.

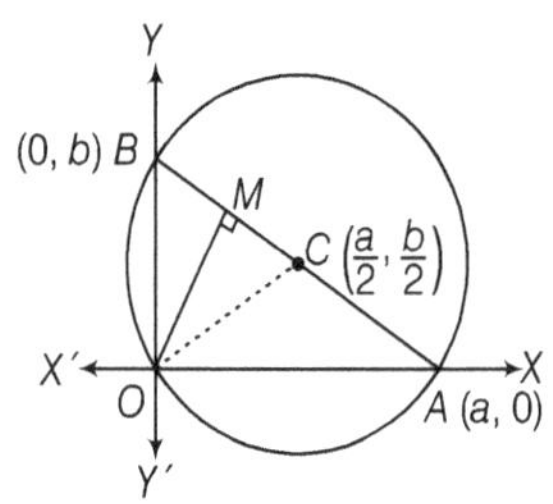

$\therefore$ Equation of AB is $\quad \dfrac{x}{a} + \dfrac{y}{b} = 1 \quad$ ...(i)

Centre of circle lie on line AB, since AB is diameter of the circle ($\because \angle AOB = \pi/2$)

$\therefore$ Coordinate of centre C is $C \equiv \left(\dfrac{a}{2}, \dfrac{b}{2}\right)$

Since, the radius of circle $= r$

$\therefore \quad r = AC = CB = OC$

$$= \sqrt{\left(0 - \frac{a}{2}\right)^2 + \left(0 - \frac{b}{2}\right)^2} = \sqrt{\frac{a^2 + b^2}{4}}$$

$\therefore \quad a^2 + b^2 = 4r^2 \quad$ ...(ii)

Equation of OM which is $\perp$ to AB is

$$ax - by = \lambda$$

It passes through (0, 0)

$\therefore \quad 0 = \lambda$

$\therefore$ Equation of OM is

$$ax - by = 0 \quad \text{...(iii)}$$

On solving Eq. (i) and Eq. (iii), we get

$$a = \frac{x^2 + y^2}{x} \text{ and } b = \frac{x^2 + y^2}{y}$$

Substituting the values of a and b in Eq. (ii), we get

$$(x^2 + y^2)^2 \left(\frac{1}{x^2} + \frac{1}{y^2}\right) = 4r^2$$

or $\quad (x^2 + y^2)^2 (x^{-2} + y^{-2}) = 4r^2$

which is the required locus.

Aliter :

$\because$ AB is the diameter of circle. If $\angle OAB = \alpha$, then

$$OA = 2r \cos \alpha, OB = 2r \sin \alpha$$

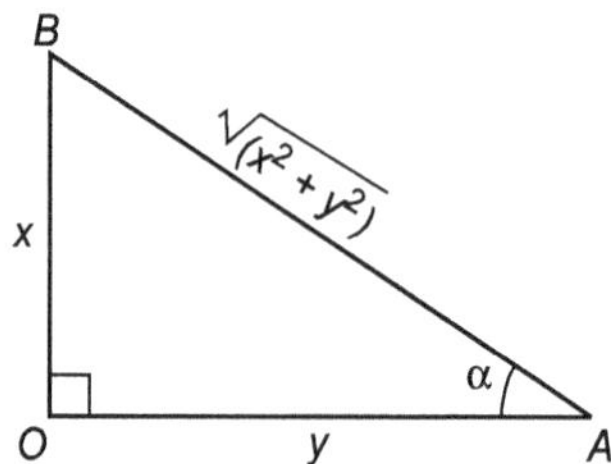

Equation of AB is

$$\frac{x}{2r \cos \alpha} + \frac{y}{2r \sin \alpha} = 1$$

$\Rightarrow \quad \dfrac{x}{\cos \alpha} + \dfrac{y}{\sin \alpha} = 2r \quad$ ...(i)

and equation of OM is $y = x \tan (90° - \alpha)$

$\Rightarrow \quad \cot \alpha = \dfrac{y}{x}$

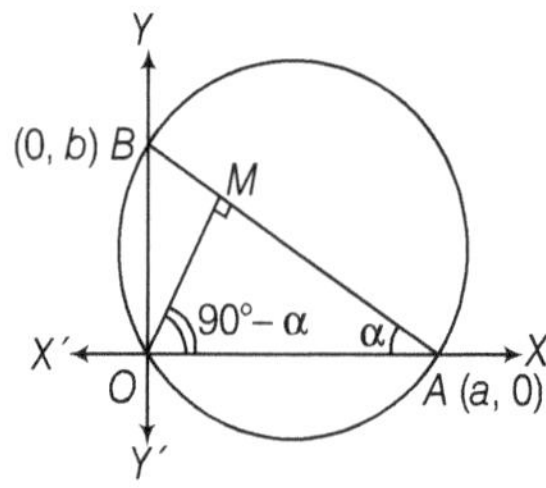

$\therefore \quad \sin \alpha = \dfrac{x}{\sqrt{(x^2 + y^2)}}$

and $\quad \cos \alpha = \dfrac{y}{\sqrt{(x^2 + y^2)}}$

Then, from Eq. (i),

$$\frac{x}{y}\sqrt{(x^2+y^2)}+\frac{y}{x}\sqrt{(x^2+y^2)}=2r$$

$$\Rightarrow \quad \frac{(x^2+y^2)\sqrt{(x^2+y^2)}}{xy}=2r$$

On squaring, we have $(x^2+y^2)^2\,\dfrac{(x^2+y^2)}{x^2\,y^2}=4r^2$

$$\Rightarrow \quad (x^2+y^2)^2\,(x^{-2}+y^{-2})=4r^2$$

Ex. 32 *The circle $x^2+y^2-4x-4y+4=0$ is inscribed in a triangle which has two of its sides along the coordinate axes. The locus of the circumcentre of the triangle is $x+y-xy+k(x^2+y^2)^{1/2}=0$. Find k.*

Sol. The given circle is $x^2+y^2-4x-4y+4=0$. This can be re-written as $(x-2)^2+(y-2)^2=4$ which has centre $C(2,2)$ and radius 2.

Let the equation of third side is

$$\frac{x}{a}+\frac{y}{b}=1 \quad \text{(equation of } AB)$$

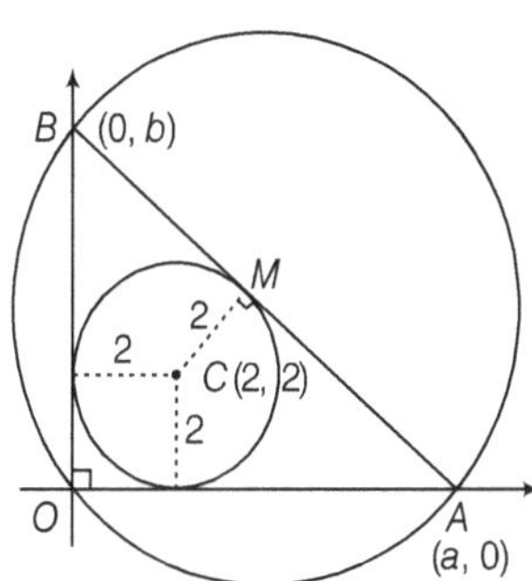

Length of perpendicular from (2, 2) on $AB=$ radius $=CM$

$$\therefore \quad \frac{\left|\dfrac{2}{a}+\dfrac{2}{b}-1\right|}{\sqrt{\left(\dfrac{1}{a^2}+\dfrac{1}{b^2}\right)}}=2$$

Since, origin and (2, 2) lie on the same side of AB

$$\therefore \quad -\frac{\left(\dfrac{2}{a}+\dfrac{2}{b}-1\right)}{\sqrt{\left(\dfrac{1}{a^2}+\dfrac{1}{b^2}\right)}}=2$$

or $$\frac{2}{a}+\frac{2}{b}-1=-2\sqrt{\left(\frac{1}{a^2}+\frac{1}{b^2}\right)} \quad \text{...(i)}$$

Since, $\angle AOB=\dfrac{\pi}{2}$

Hence, AB is the diameter of the circle passing through ΔOAB, mid-point of AB is the centre of the circle i.e. $\left(\dfrac{a}{2},\dfrac{b}{2}\right)$.

Let centre be $(h,k)\equiv\left(\dfrac{a}{2},\dfrac{b}{2}\right)$ then $a=2h$ and $b=2k$.

Substituting the values of a and b in Eq. (i), then

$$\frac{2}{2h}+\frac{2}{2k}-1=-2\sqrt{\left(\frac{1}{4h^2}+\frac{1}{4k^2}\right)}$$

$$\Rightarrow \quad \frac{1}{h}+\frac{1}{k}-1=-\sqrt{\left(\frac{1}{h^2}+\frac{1}{k^2}\right)}$$

or $$h+k-hk+\sqrt{(h^2+k^2)}=0$$

$\therefore$ Locus of $M(h,k)$ is

$$x+y-xy+\sqrt{(x^2+y^2)}=0$$

Hence, the required value of k is 1.

Ex. 33 *P is a variable on the line $y=4$. Tangents are drawn to the circle $x^2+y^2=4$ from P to touch it at A and B. The parallelogram PAQB is completed. Find the equation of the locus of Q.*

Sol. Let $P(h,4)$ be a variable point. Given circle is

$$x^2+y^2=4 \quad \text{...(i)}$$

Draw tangents from $P(h,4)$ and complete parallelogram $PAQB$.

Equation of the diagonal AB which is chord of contact of $x^2+y^2=4$ is $hx+4y=4$ ...(ii)

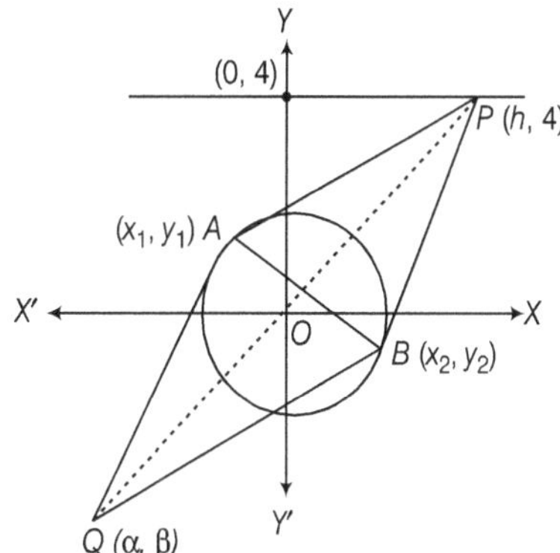

Let coordinates of A and B are (x_1,y_1) and (x_2,y_2), respectively.

Since, $A(x_1,y_1)$ and $B(x_2,y_2)$ lies on Eq. (ii)

$\therefore \quad hx_1+4y_1=4$ and $hx_2+4y_2=4$

$\therefore \quad h(x_1+x_2)+4(y_1+y_2)=8$ ...(iii)

Since, $PAQB$ is parallelogram

$\therefore$ Mid-point of AB = Mid-point of PQ

$$\Rightarrow \quad \frac{x_1+x_2}{2}=\frac{\alpha+h}{2}$$

and $$\frac{y_1+y_2}{2}=\frac{\beta+4}{2} \quad \text{...(iv)}$$

Eliminating x from Eqs. (i) and (ii), then

$$\left(\frac{4-4y}{h}\right)^2 + y^2 = 4$$

$$\Rightarrow \quad 16 + 16y^2 - 32y + h^2y^2 = 4h^2$$

$$\Rightarrow \quad (16 + h^2)\,y^2 - 32y + 16 - 4h^2 = 0$$

$$\therefore \quad y_1 + y_2 = \frac{32}{16 + h^2} \quad \text{...(v)}$$

From Eqs. (iii) and (v), we get

$$x_1 + x_2 = \frac{8h}{16 + h^2} \quad \text{...(vi)}$$

From Eqs. (iv) and (vi)

$$\beta + 4 = \frac{32}{16 + h^2}$$

$$\text{or} \quad (16 + h^2)(\beta + 4) = 32 \quad \text{...(vii)}$$

From Eqs. (iv) and (vi)

$$\alpha + h = \frac{8h}{16 + h^2}$$

$$\text{or} \quad (16 + h^2)(\alpha + h) = 8h \quad \text{...(viii)}$$

Dividing Eq. (viii) by Eq. (vii), then

$$\frac{\alpha + h}{\beta + 4} = \frac{h}{4} \quad \text{or} \quad h = \frac{4\alpha}{\beta}$$

Substituting the value of h in Eq. (vii) then

$$\left(16 + \frac{16\alpha^2}{\beta^2}\right)(\beta + 4) = 32$$

$$\Rightarrow \quad (\alpha^2 + \beta^2)(\beta + 4) = 2\beta^2$$

Hence, locus of $Q\,(\alpha, \beta)$ is $(x^2 + y^2)(y + 4) = 2y^2$

Ex. 34 *Show that the circumcircle of the triangle formed by the lines $ax + by + c = 0$; $bx + cy + a = 0$ and $cx + ay + b = 0$ passes through the origin if $(b^2 + c^2)(c^2 + a^2)(a^2 + b^2) = abc\,(b + c)(c + a)(a + b)$.*

Sol. Equation of conic is

$$(bx + cy + a)(cx + ay + b) + \lambda\,(cx + ay + b)(ax + by + c) + \mu\,(ax + by + c)(bx + cy + a) = 0 \quad \text{...(i)}$$

where, λ and μ are constants.

Eq. (i) represents a circle if the coefficient of x^2 and y^2 are equal and the coefficient of xy is zero such that

$$bc + \lambda ca + \mu ab = ca + \lambda ab + \mu bc$$

$$\text{or} \quad (a - b)\,c + \lambda\,(b - c)\,a + \mu\,(c - a)\,b = 0 \quad \text{...(ii)}$$

$$\text{and} \quad (c^2 + ab) + \lambda\,(a^2 + bc) + \mu\,(b^2 + ac) = 0 \quad \text{...(iii)}$$

on solving Eq. (ii) and Eq. (iii) by cross multiplication rule, we get

$$\frac{1}{(c^2 - ab)(a^2 + b^2)} = \frac{\lambda}{(a^2 - bc)(b^2 + c^2)} = \frac{\mu}{(b^2 - ac)(c^2 + a^2)}$$

$$\therefore \quad \lambda = \frac{(a^2 - bc)(b^2 + c^2)}{(c^2 - ab)(a^2 + b^2)}$$

$$\text{and} \quad \mu = \frac{(b^2 - ac)(c^2 + a^2)}{(c^2 - ab)(a^2 + b^2)} \quad \text{...(iv)}$$

and given, Eq. (i) passes through the origin then

$$ab + bc\lambda + ca\,\mu = 0 \quad \text{...(v)}$$

From Eqs. (iv) and (v), we get

$$ab + \frac{bc\,(a^2 - bc)(b^2 + c^2)}{(c^2 - ab)(a^2 + b^2)} + \frac{ca\,(b^2 - ac)(c^2 + a^2)}{(c^2 - ab)(a^2 + b^2)} = 0$$

$$\Rightarrow \quad (c^2 - ab)(a^2 + b^2)\,ab + (a^2 - bc)(b^2 + c^2)bc + (b^2 - ca)(c^2 + a^2)\,ca = 0$$

$$\Rightarrow \quad abc^2\,(a^2 + b^2) + a^2bc\,(b^2 + c^2) + b^2ca\,(c^2 + a^2) = a^2b^2\,(a^2 + b^2) + b^2c^2\,(b^2 + c^2) + c^2a^2\,(c^2 + a^2)$$

$$\Rightarrow \quad abc\,\{c\,(a^2 + b^2) + a\,(b^2 + c^2) + b\,(c^2 + a^2)\} = a^2b^2\,(a^2 + b^2) + b^2c^2\,(b^2 + c^2) + c^2a^2\,(c^2 + a^2)$$

$$\Rightarrow \quad abc\,\{(a + b)(b + c)(c + a) - 2abc\} = a^2b^2\,(a^2 + b^2) + b^2c^2\,(b^2 + c^2) + c^2a^2\,(c^2 + a^2)$$

$$\Rightarrow \quad abc\,(a + b)(b + c)(c + a) = 2a^2b^2c^2 + a^2b^2\,(a^2 + b^2) + b^2c^2\,(b^2 + c^2) + c^2a^2\,(c^2 + a^2)$$

$$\Rightarrow \quad abc\,(a + b)(b + c)(c + a) = (a^2 + b^2)(b^2 + c^2)(c^2 + a^2)$$

Hence, $(a^2 + b^2)(b^2 + c^2)(c^2 + a^2) = abc\,(a + b)(b + c)(c + a)$

Ex. 35 *If four points P, Q, R, S in the plane be taken and the square of the length of the tangents from P to the circle on QR as diameter be denoted by $\{P, QR\}$, show that*

$$\{P, RS\} - \{P, QS\} + \{Q, PR\} - \{Q, RS\} = 0$$

Sol. Let $P \equiv (x_1, y_1)$, $Q \equiv (x_2, y_2)$, $R \equiv (x_3, y_3)$ and $S \equiv (x_4, y_4)$.

Equation of circle with RS as diameter is

$$(x - x_3)(x - x_4) + (y - y_3)(y - y_4) = 0$$

$$\therefore \quad \{P, RS\} = (x_1 - x_3)(x_1 - x_4) + (y_1 - y_3)(y_1 - y_4)$$

Now, equation of circle with QS as diameter is

$$(x - x_2)(x - x_4) + (y - y_2)(y - y_4) = 0$$

$$\therefore \quad \{P, QS\} = (x_1 - x_2)(x_1 - x_4) + (y_1 - y_2)(y_1 - y_4)$$

Equation of circle with PR as diameter is

$$(x-x_1)(x-x_3)+(y-y_1)(y-y_3)=0$$

$\therefore \quad \{Q, PR\} = (x_2-x_1)(x_2-x_3)+(y_2-y_1)(y_2-y_3)$

Equation of circle with RS as diameter is

$$(x-x_3)(x-x_4)+(y-y_3)(y-y_4)=0$$

$\therefore \quad \{Q, RS\} = (x_2-x_3)(x_2-x_4)+(y_2-y_3)(y_2-y_4)$

Hence, $\{P, RS\} - \{P, QS\} + \{Q, PR\} - \{Q, RS\} = 0$

Ex. 36 *Let T_1, T_2 be two tangents drawn from $(-2,0)$ on the circle $C: x^2+y^2=1$. Determine the circles touching C and having T_1, T_2 as their pair of tangents. Further, find the equations of all possible common tangents to these circles when taken two at a time.*

Sol. In figure $OS = 1$, $OP = 2$

$$\therefore \quad \sin \angle SPO = \frac{1}{2} = \sin 30°$$

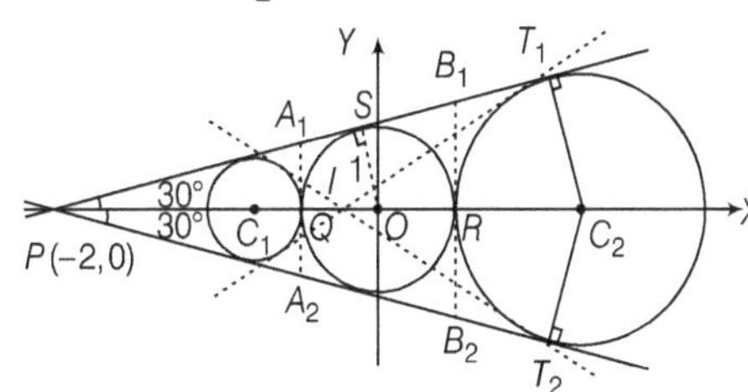

$\therefore \quad \angle SPO = 30°$

$\because \quad PA_1 = PA_2 \Rightarrow \angle PA_1A_2 = \angle PA_2A_1$

$\Rightarrow \quad \Delta PA_1A_2$ is an equilateral triangle.

Therefore, centre C_1 is centroid of $\Delta PA_1A_2, C_1$ divides PQ in the ratio 2 : 1.

$$\therefore \quad C_1 \equiv \left(-\frac{4}{3}, 0\right) \text{ and its radius} = C_1Q = \frac{1}{3}$$

$$\Rightarrow \quad C_1 : (x+4/3)^2 + y^2 = \left(\frac{1}{3}\right)^2 \quad \text{...(i)}$$

The other circle C_2 touches the equilateral triangle PB_1B_2 externally.

its radius is given by $= \dfrac{\Delta}{s-a}$, where $B_1B_2 = a$

$$= \frac{\frac{\sqrt{3}}{4}a^2}{\frac{3a}{2}-a} = \frac{\sqrt{3}}{2}a$$

but $\quad \tan 30° = \dfrac{a/2}{3} \Rightarrow a = \dfrac{6}{\sqrt{3}}$

$$\therefore \quad \text{Radius} = \frac{\sqrt{3}}{2} \cdot \frac{6}{\sqrt{3}} = 3$$

$\Rightarrow$ coordinates of C_2 are (4, 0)

$\therefore$ Equation of $C_2 : (x-4)^2 + y^2 = 3^2 \quad$ ...(ii)

Equations of common tangents to circle (i) and circle C are

$$x = -1, y = \pm \frac{1}{\sqrt{3}}(x+2), \{T_1 \text{ and } T_2\}$$

and equations of common tangents to circle (ii) and circle C are

$$x = 1, y = \pm \frac{1}{\sqrt{3}}(x+2) (\{T_1 \text{ and } T_2\}$$

To find the remaining two transverse common tangents to Eqs. (i) and (ii). If I divides C_1 and C_2 in the ratio $r_1 : r_2 = 1/3 : 3 = 1 : 9$.

Therefore coordinates of I are $(-4/5, 0)$.

Equation of any line through I is $y - 0 = m(x + 4/5)$. If it will touch Eq. (ii)

then $\quad \dfrac{|m(4+4/5)-0|}{\sqrt{(1+m^2)}} = 3$

$$\Rightarrow \quad \left(\frac{24}{5}\right)^2 m^2 = 9(1+m^2)$$

$$\Rightarrow \quad 64m^2 = 25 + 25m^2$$

$$\Rightarrow \quad 39m^2 = 25 \Rightarrow m = \pm \frac{5}{\sqrt{39}}$$

Therefore, equations of transverse common tangents are

$$y = \pm \frac{5}{\sqrt{39}}(x + 4/5)$$

Ex. 37 *Find the equation of the circle of minimum radius which contains the three circles*

$$x^2 - y^2 - 4y - 5 = 0$$

$$x^2 + y^2 + 12x + 4y + 31 = 0$$

and $\quad x^2 + y^2 + 6x + 12y + 36 = 0$

Sol. The coordinates of the centres and radii of three given circles are as given below :

$$C_1 \equiv (0, 2) ; r_1 = 3$$

$$C_2 \equiv (-6, -2) ; r_2 = 3$$

and $\quad C_3 \equiv (-3, -6) ; r_3 = 3$

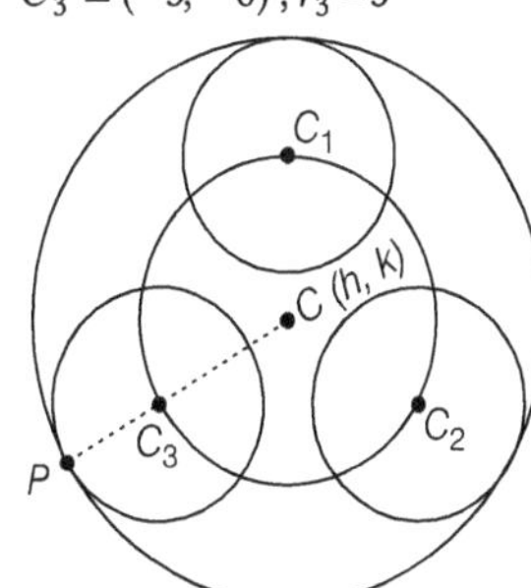

Let $C \equiv (h, k)$ be the centre of the circle passing through the centres $C_1(0, 2)$, $C_2(-6, -2)$ and $C_3(-3, -6)$.

Then, $\quad CC_1 = CC_2 = CC_3$

$$\Rightarrow \quad (CC_1)^2 = (CC_2)^2 = (CC_3)^2$$

$$\Rightarrow \quad (h-0)^2+(k-2)^2=(h+6)^2+(k+2)^2$$
$$=(h+3)^2+(k+6)^2$$
$$\Rightarrow \quad -4k+4=12h+4k+40=6h+12k+45$$
$$\Rightarrow \quad 12h+8k+36=0$$
or $$3h+2k+9=0 \quad \text{...(i)}$$
and $$6h-8k-5=0 \quad \text{...(ii)}$$

On solving Eqs. (i) and (ii), we get $h=-\frac{31}{18}, k=-\frac{23}{12}$

Now, $CP=CC_3+C_3P=CC_3+3$

$$=\sqrt{\left(-3+\frac{31}{18}\right)^2+\left(-6+\frac{23}{12}\right)^2}+3=\left(\frac{5}{36}\sqrt{(949)}+3\right)$$

Hence, equation of required circle is

$$\left(x+\frac{31}{18}\right)^2+\left(y+\frac{23}{12}\right)^2=\left(3+\frac{5}{\sqrt{36}}\sqrt{949}\right)^2$$

Remark

If radii of three given circles are distinct say $r_1<r_2<r_3$ then the radius of the required circle will be equal to (CC_1 or CC_2 or CC_3) + r_3 ($\because CC_1=CC_2=CC_3$)

Ex. 38 *Find the point P on the circle $x^2+y^2-4x-6y+9=0$ such that*

(i) $\angle POX$ is minimum,

(ii) *OP is maximum, when O is the origin and OX is the X-axis.*

Sol. Given circle is

$$x^2+y^2-4x-6y+9=0$$
or $$(x-2)^2+(y-3)^2=2^2 \quad \text{.... (i)}$$

Its centre is $C\equiv(2,3)$ and radius $r=2$

Eq. (i) Let OP and ON be the two tangents from O to the circle Eq. (i), then $OP=ON=3$

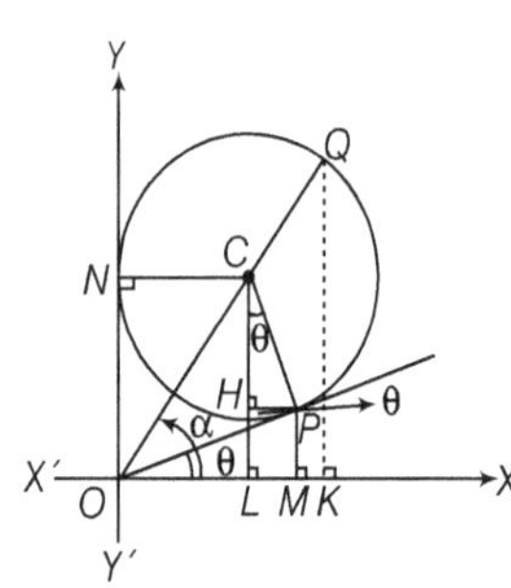

then $\angle POX$ is minimum when OP is tangent to the circle Eq. (i) at P

Let $\angle POX=\theta$

$\therefore \quad P\equiv(OP\cos\theta, OP\sin\theta)$

i.e. $\quad P\equiv(3\cos\theta, 3\sin\theta) \quad$ ...(ii)

From figure, $OM=OL+LM=NC+HP=NC+CP\sin\theta$

$$\Rightarrow \quad OP\cos\theta=NC+CP\sin\theta$$
$$\Rightarrow \quad 3\cos\theta=2+2\sin\theta$$
$$\Rightarrow \quad 9(1-\sin^2\theta)=4(1+\sin\theta)^2$$
$$\Rightarrow \quad 9(1-\sin\theta)=4(1+\sin\theta) \qquad (\because \sin\theta\neq-1)$$
$$\therefore \quad \sin\theta=\frac{5}{13} \text{ and } \cos\theta=\frac{12}{13}$$

From Eq. (ii), $P\equiv\left(3\times\frac{12}{13}, 3\times\frac{5}{13}\right)$ i.e. $P\equiv\left(\frac{36}{13},\frac{15}{13}\right)$

Eq. (ii) OP will be maximum, if P becomes the point extended part of OC cuts the circle. Let this point be Q

then maximum value of $OP=OQ=OC+CQ=(\sqrt{13}+2)$

Let $\quad \angle COX=\alpha$

then, $Q\equiv(OQ\cos\alpha, OQ\sin\alpha)$

$$\equiv((2+\sqrt{13})\cos\alpha, (2+\sqrt{13})\sin\alpha) \quad \text{... (iii)}$$

Now, in ΔCOL, $\quad \cos\alpha=\frac{OL}{OC}=\frac{NC}{OC}=\frac{2}{\sqrt{13}}$

$$\therefore \quad \sin\alpha=\frac{3}{\sqrt{13}}$$

Now, from Eq. (iii), $Q\equiv\left(2+\frac{4}{\sqrt{13}}, 3+\frac{6}{\sqrt{13}}\right)$

Ex. 39 *The circle $x^2+y^2-4x-8y+16=0$ rolls up the tangent to it at $(2+\sqrt{3},3)$ by 2 units, assuming the X-axis as horizontal, find the equation of the circle in the new position.*

Sol. Given circle is

$$x^2+y^2-4x-8y+16=0 \quad \text{...(i)}$$

Let $\quad P\equiv(2+\sqrt{3},3)$

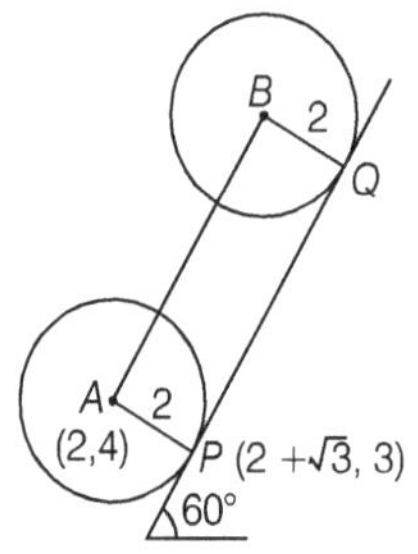

Equation of tangent to the circle Eq. (i) at $P(2+\sqrt{3},3)$ is

$$(2+\sqrt{3})x+3y-2(x+2+\sqrt{3})-4(y+3)+16=0$$
or $$\sqrt{3}x-y-2\sqrt{3}=0 \quad \text{...(ii)}$$

Let A and B be the centres of the circles in old and new positions, then

$$B\equiv(2+2\cos60^\circ, 4+2\sin60^\circ)$$
($\because AB$ makes an angle 60° with X-axis)

or $\quad B\equiv(3, 4+\sqrt{3})$

and $\quad$ radius $= \sqrt{2^2 + 4^2 - 16} = 2$

$\therefore$ Equation of the required circle is

$$(x-3)^2 + (y - 4 - \sqrt{3})^2 = 2^2$$

or $\quad x^2 + y^2 - 6x - 2(4 + \sqrt{3})\,y + 24 + 8\sqrt{3} = 0$

Ex. 40 *Find the intervals of the values of 'a' for which the line $y + x = 0$ bisects two chords drawn from a point $\left(\frac{1+\sqrt{2}a}{2}, \frac{1-\sqrt{2}a}{2}\right)$ to the circle*

$$2x^2 + 2y^2 - (1+\sqrt{2}\,a)x - (1-\sqrt{2}a)y = 0.$$

Sol. The point $A\left(\frac{1+\sqrt{2}a}{2}, \frac{1-\sqrt{2}a}{2}\right)$ lies on the given circle as its coordinate satisfy the equation of the circle. Let AB and AC are two chords drawn from A. Let M and N are the mid-points of AB and AC.

Let coordinate of M be $(h, -h)$ and coordinate of B is (α, β), then

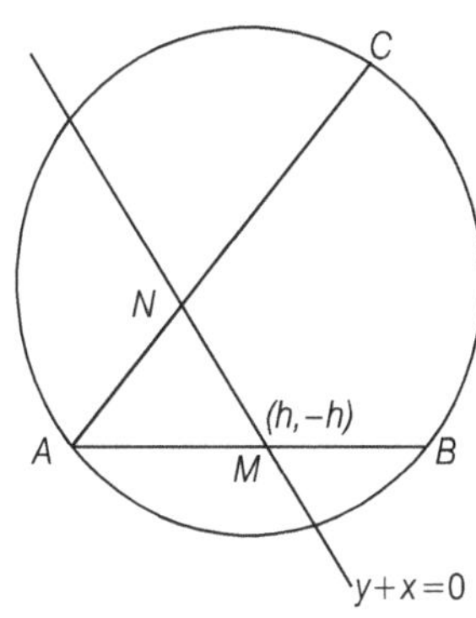

$$h = \frac{\alpha + \frac{1+\sqrt{2}a}{2}}{2}$$

and $$-h = \frac{\beta + \frac{1-\sqrt{2}a}{2}}{2}$$

$\therefore$ $$\alpha = 2h - \frac{1-\sqrt{2}a}{2}$$

and $$\beta = -2h - \frac{1-\sqrt{2}a}{2}$$

Since, $B(\alpha, \beta)$ lies on the given circle, we have

$$\Rightarrow \quad 2\left[2h - \frac{1+\sqrt{2}a}{2}\right]^2 + 2\left[-2h - \frac{1-\sqrt{2}a}{2}\right]^2 - (1+\sqrt{2}a)\left[2h - \frac{1+\sqrt{2}a}{2}\right] - (1-\sqrt{2}a)\left[-2h - \frac{1-\sqrt{2}a}{2}\right] = 0$$

$$\Rightarrow \quad 16h^2 - 4h(1+\sqrt{2}a) + 4h(1-\sqrt{2}a) + \frac{(1+\sqrt{2}a)^2}{2} + \frac{(1-\sqrt{2}a)^2}{2} - 2h(1+\sqrt{2}a) + \frac{(1+\sqrt{2}a)^2}{2} + 2h(1-\sqrt{2}a) + \frac{(1-\sqrt{2}a)^2}{2} = 0$$

$$\Rightarrow \quad 16h^2 - 12\sqrt{2}\,ah + (1+\sqrt{2}a)^2 + (1-\sqrt{2}a)^2 = 0$$

$$\Rightarrow \quad 16h^2 - 12\sqrt{2}\,ah + 2 + 4a^2 = 0$$

or $$8h^2 - 6\sqrt{2}\,ah + 1 + 2a^2 = 0$$

Hence, for two real and different values of h, we must have

\+ $\quad -2 \quad - \quad 2 \quad$ +

$$(-6\sqrt{2}a)^2 - 4\cdot 8(1 + 2a^2) > 0$$

or $$72a^2 - 32(1+2a^2) > 0$$

$$\Rightarrow \quad 8a^2 - 32 > 0$$

$$\Rightarrow \quad a^2 - 4 > 0$$

$$(a+2)(a-2) > 0$$

Hence, the required value of a (from wavy curve)

$$a \in (-\infty, -2) \cup (2, \infty)$$

Aliter : Equation of chord AB whose mid-point is $(h, -h)$ is

$$T = S_1$$

$$2xh - 2yh - (1+\sqrt{2}a)\left(\frac{x+h}{2}\right) - (1-\sqrt{2}a)\left(\frac{y-h}{2}\right) = 2h^2 + 2h^2 - (1+\sqrt{2}a)\,h + (1-\sqrt{2}a)\,h$$

$$\Rightarrow \quad 4xh - 4yh - (1+\sqrt{2}a)(x+h) - (1-\sqrt{2}a)(y-h) = 8h^2 - 2(1+\sqrt{2}a)\,h + 2(1-\sqrt{2}a)\,h$$

$$\Rightarrow \quad x[4h - (1+\sqrt{2}a)] - y[4h + (1-\sqrt{2}a)] - h(1+\sqrt{2}a) + h(1-\sqrt{2}a) = 8h^2 - 2(1+\sqrt{2}a)\,h + 2(1-\sqrt{2}a)\,h$$

or $$8h^2 - (1+\sqrt{2}a)\,h + (1-\sqrt{2}a)\,h - x[4h - (1+\sqrt{2}a)] + y[4h + (1-\sqrt{2}a)] = 0$$

It passes through $A\left(\frac{1+\sqrt{2}a}{2}, \frac{1-\sqrt{2}a}{2}\right)$, then

$$8h^2 - 2\sqrt{2}ah - \left(\frac{1+\sqrt{2}a}{2}\right)[4h - (1+\sqrt{2}a)] + \left(\frac{1-\sqrt{2}a}{2}\right)[4h + (1-\sqrt{2}a)] = 0$$

or $$8h^2 - 2\sqrt{2}ah - 2h(1+\sqrt{2}a) + \frac{(1+\sqrt{2}a)^2}{2} + 2h(1-\sqrt{2}a) + \frac{(1-\sqrt{2}a)^2}{2} = 0$$

or $$8h^2 - 6\sqrt{2}ah + 1 + 2a^2 = 0$$

Hence, for two real and different values of h, we must have

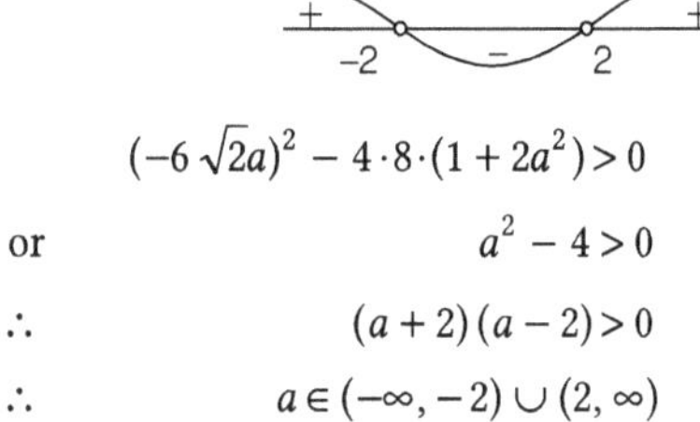

$$(-6\sqrt{2}a)^2 - 4\cdot 8\cdot(1+2a^2) > 0$$

or $$a^2 - 4 > 0$$

$\therefore$ $$(a+2)(a-2) > 0$$

$\therefore$ $$a \in (-\infty, -2) \cup (2, \infty)$$

Ex. 41 *A ball moving around the circle $x^2 + y^2 - 2x - 4y - 20 = 0$ in anti-clockwise direction leaves it tangentially at the point $P(-2, -2)$. After getting reflected from a straight line, it passes through the centre of the circle. Find the equation of the straight line if its perpendicular distance from P is 5/2. You can assume that the angle of incidence is equal to the angle of reflection.*

Sol. Radius of the circle $= CP = \sqrt{9+16} = 5$

Let the equation is of surface is $y = mx + c$

given $$PQ = \frac{5}{2}$$

$\therefore$ $$\frac{-2m + 2 + c}{\sqrt{(1+m^2)}} = \pm\frac{5}{2} \qquad \text{...(i)}$$

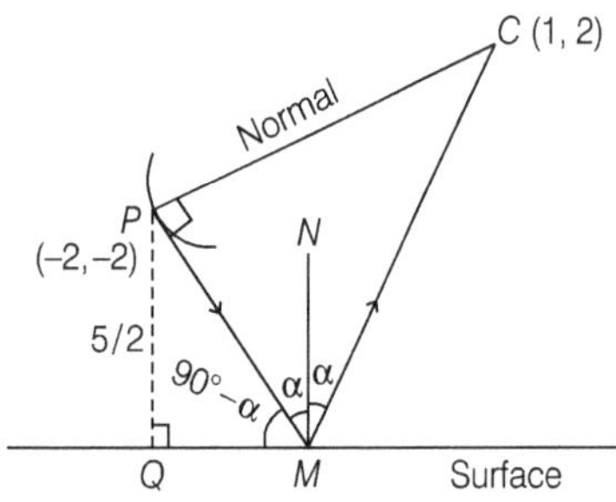

Tangent at P strikes it at the point M and after reflection passes through the centre $C(1, 2)$.

Let MN be the normal at M.

$$\angle PMN = \angle NMC = \alpha$$

In ΔPCM, $$\tan 2\alpha = \frac{PC}{PM}$$

$\Rightarrow$ $$\tan 2\alpha = \frac{5}{PM}$$

$\Rightarrow$ $$PM = 5\cot 2\alpha \qquad \text{...(ii)}$$

and in ΔPQM

$$\sin(90° - \alpha) = \frac{5/2}{PM}$$

$\therefore$ $$PM = \frac{5}{2\cos\alpha} \qquad \text{...(iii)}$$

From Eqs. (ii) and (iii), $5\cot 2\alpha = \dfrac{5}{2\cos\alpha}$

$\Rightarrow$ $$2\cot 2\alpha \cos\alpha = 1$$

$\Rightarrow$ $$\frac{2\cos 2\alpha}{\sin 2\alpha}.\cos\alpha = 1$$

$\Rightarrow$ $$\frac{2(1-2\sin^2\alpha)\cos\alpha}{2\sin\alpha\cos\alpha} = 1$$

$\Rightarrow$ $$1 - 2\sin^2\alpha = \sin\alpha$$

$\Rightarrow$ $$2\sin^2\alpha + \sin\alpha - 1 = 0$$

$\Rightarrow$ $$(2\sin\alpha - 1)(\sin\alpha + 1) = 0$$

$\Rightarrow$ $$\sin\alpha \neq -1$$

$\therefore$ $$\sin\alpha = \frac{1}{2}$$

$\therefore$ $$\alpha = 30°$$

Tangent at $P(-2, -2)$ is

$$-2x - 2y - (x-2) - 2(y-2) - 20 = 0$$

$\Rightarrow$ $$3x + 4y + 14 = 0$$

Slope of $PM = -3/4$

$\because$ $\angle PMQ = 90° - \alpha = 90° - 30° = 60°$

$\therefore$ $$\tan 60° = \left|\frac{m + 3/4}{1 - 3m/4}\right|, \quad \sqrt{3} = \frac{4m+3}{4-3m}$$

$\therefore$ $$m = \frac{4\sqrt{3} - 3}{4 + 3\sqrt{3}}$$

From Eq. (i) $$\pm\frac{5}{2} = \frac{2(1-m) + c}{\sqrt{1+m^2}}$$

we get $$c = \frac{11 + 2\sqrt{3}}{4 + 3\sqrt{3}} \quad \text{or} \quad \frac{-39 + 2\sqrt{3}}{4 + 3\sqrt{3}}$$

c being intercept on Y-axis made by surface is clearly–ve. Hence, the required line is

$$y = \left(\frac{4\sqrt{3} - 3}{4 + 3\sqrt{3}}\right)x + \left(\frac{-39 + 2\sqrt{3}}{4 + 3\sqrt{3}}\right)$$

$\Rightarrow$ $$(4\sqrt{3} - 3)x - (4 + 3\sqrt{3})y - (39 - 2\sqrt{3}) = 0.$$

Ex. 42 *Find the limiting points of the circles $(x^2 + y^2 + 2gx + c) + \lambda(x^2 + y^2 + 2fy + d) = 0$ and show that the square of the distance between them is*

$$\frac{(c-d)^2 - 4f^2g^2 + 4cf^2 + 4dg^2}{f^2 + g^2}$$

Sol. The given circles are

$$(x^2 + y^2 + 2gx + c) + \lambda(x^2 + y^2 + 2fy + d) = 0$$

$\Rightarrow$ $$x^2 + y^2 + \frac{2g}{1+\lambda}x + \frac{2f\lambda}{1+\lambda}y + \frac{(c + \lambda d)}{1+\lambda} = 0$$

Centre of the circle $\left(\dfrac{-g}{1+\lambda}, \dfrac{-f\lambda}{1+\lambda}\right)$

Equating the radius of this circle to zero, we get

$$\frac{g^2}{(1+\lambda)^2} + \frac{f^2\lambda^2}{(1+\lambda)^2} - \frac{(c + \lambda d)}{(1+\lambda)} = 0$$

$\Rightarrow \quad g^2 + f^2\lambda^2 - (c + \lambda d)(1 + \lambda) = 0$

$\Rightarrow \quad (f^2 - d)\lambda^2 - (c + d)\lambda + g^2 - c = 0$

Let the roots be λ_1 and λ_2

then $\quad \lambda_1 + \lambda_2 = \dfrac{(c + d)}{(f^2 - d)}, \lambda_1\lambda_2 = \dfrac{g^2 - c}{f^2 - d}$

$$\therefore \quad (\lambda_1 - \lambda_2) = \sqrt{(\lambda_1 + \lambda_2)^2 - 4\lambda_1\lambda_2}$$

$$= \sqrt{\frac{(c + d)^2}{(f^2 - d)^2} - \frac{4(g^2 - c)}{(f^2 - d)}}$$

$$= \frac{\sqrt{(c + d)^2 - 4f^2g^2 + 4cf^2 + 4dg^2}}{(f^2 - d)} \quad \text{...(i)}$$

$$\therefore \quad \lambda_1 = \frac{(c + d) + \sqrt{(c - d)^2 - 4f^2g^2 + 4cf^2 + 4dg^2}}{2(f^2 - d)} \quad \text{...(ii)}$$

$$\text{and } \lambda_2 = \frac{(c + d) - \sqrt{\{(c - d)^2 - 4f^2g^2 + 4cf^2 + 4dg^2\}}}{2(f^2 - d)} \quad \text{...(iii)}$$

Hence, limiting points are

$$\left(\frac{-g}{1 + \lambda_1}, \frac{-f\lambda_1}{1 + \lambda_1}\right) \text{ and } \left(\frac{-g}{1 + \lambda_2}, \frac{-f\lambda_2}{1 + \lambda_2}\right)$$

Substituting the values of λ_1 and λ_2 from Eqs. (ii) and (iii) square of the distance between limiting points

$$= \left(\frac{-g}{1 + \lambda_1} + \frac{g}{1 + \lambda_2}\right)^2 + \left(\frac{-f\lambda_1}{1 + \lambda_1} + \frac{f\lambda_2}{1 + \lambda_2}\right)^2$$

$$= \frac{(g^2 + f^2)(\lambda_1 - \lambda_2)^2}{[1 + (\lambda_1 + \lambda_2) + \lambda_1\lambda_2]^2}$$

$$= \frac{(g^2 + f^2)\dfrac{\{(c - d)^2 - 4f^2g^2 + 4cf^2 + 4dg^2\}}{(f^2 - d)^2}}{\left(\dfrac{g^2 + f^2}{f^2 - d}\right)^2}$$

$$\Rightarrow \quad \frac{[(c - d)^2 - 4f^2g^2 + 4cf^2 + 4dg^2]}{(g^2 + f^2)}$$

Ex. 43 *One vertex of a triangle of given species is fixed and another moves along circumference of a fixed circle. Prove that the locus of the remaining vertex is a circle and find its radius.*

Sol. Let OPQ be a triangle of given species. Then the angles α, β, γ will be fixed.

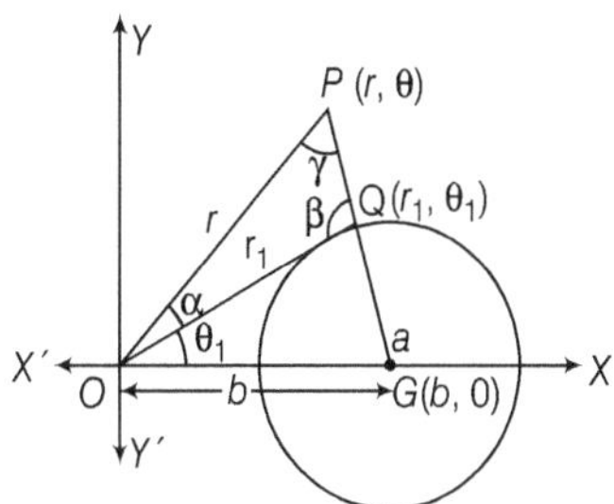

Let the polar coordinates of Q be (r_1, θ_1), we have to find the locus of $P(r, \theta)$. In $\angle OCQ$

$$\cos\theta_1 = \frac{r_1^2 + b^2 - a^2}{2r_1 b} \quad \text{...(i)}$$

$$\because \quad \theta = \alpha + \theta_1, \quad \therefore \theta_1 = \theta - \alpha \quad \text{...(ii)}$$

using sine rule in ΔOPQ

$$\frac{r}{\sin\beta} = \frac{r_1}{\sin\gamma}$$

$$\therefore \quad r_1 = \frac{r\sin\gamma}{\sin\beta} \quad \text{...(iii)}$$

Substituting the values of θ_1 and r_1 from Eqs. (ii)and (iii) in Eq. (i)

$$2b\frac{r\sin\gamma}{\sin\beta}\cos(\theta - \alpha) = \frac{r^2\sin^2\gamma}{\sin^2\beta} + b^2 - a^2$$

$$\Rightarrow \quad \frac{a^2\sin^2\beta}{\sin^2\gamma} = r^2 + \frac{b^2\sin^2\beta}{\sin^2\gamma} - 2b\frac{r\sin\beta}{\sin\gamma}\cos(\theta - \alpha)$$

This is an equation of circle in polar form with radius $\dfrac{\sin\beta}{\sin\gamma}$.

Circle Exercise 1 : Single Option Correct Type Questions

- This section contains **30 multiple choice questions.** Each question has four choices (a), (b), (c) and (d) out of which **ONLY ONE** is correct

1. The sum of the square of the length of the chord intercepted by the line $x+y=n, n \in N$ on the circle $x^2+y^2=4$ is

(a) 11 (b) 22
(c) 33 (d) None of these

2. Tangents are drawn to the circle $x^2+y^2=50$ from a point 'P' lying on the X-axis. These tangents meet the Y-axis at points 'P_1' and 'P_2'. Possible coordinates of 'P' so that area of triangle PP_1P_2 is minimum, is

(a) $(10,0)$ (b) $(10\sqrt{2},0)$ (c) $(-10\sqrt{2},0)$ (d) $(10\sqrt{3},0)$

3. Equation of chord AB of circle $x^2+y^2=2$ passing through $P(2,2)$ such that $\frac{PB}{PA}=3$, is given by

(a) $x=3y$ (b) $x=y$
(c) $y-2=\sqrt{3}(x-2)$ (d) $y-3=\sqrt{3}(x-1)$

4. If r_1 and r_2 are the radii of smallest and largest circles which passes through (5, 6) and touches the circle $(x-2)^2+y^2=4$, then r_1r_2 is

(a) $\frac{4}{41}$ (b) $\frac{41}{4}$ (c) $\frac{5}{41}$ (d) $\frac{41}{5}$

5. Equation of circle $S(x,y)=0$, $(S(2,3)=16)$ which touches the line $3x+4y-7=0$ at $(1,1)$ is given by

(a) $x^2+y^2+x+2y-5=0$
(b) $x^2+y^2+2x+2y-7=0$
(c) $x^2+y^2+4x-6y+13=0$
(d) $x^2+y^2-4x+6y-7=0$

6. If $P(2,8)$ is an interior point of a circle $x^2+y^2-2x+4y-\lambda=0$ which neither touches nor intersects the axes, then set for λ is

(a) $(-\infty,-1)$ (b) $(-\infty,-4)$
(c) $(96,\infty)$ (d) ϕ

7. The difference between the radii of the largest and smallest circles which have their centre on the circumference of the circle $x^2+y^2+2x+4y-4=0$ and pass through the point (a,b) lying outside the given circle is

(a) 6 (b) $\sqrt{(a+1)^2+(b+2)^2}$
(c) 3 (d) $\sqrt{(a+1)^2+(b+2)^2}-3$

8. The number of rational point(s) (a point (a,b) is rational, if a and b both are rational numbers) on the circumference of a circle having centre (π, e) is

(a) atmost one (b) atleast two
(c) exactly two (d) infinite

9. Three sides of a triangle have the equations $L_r \equiv y-m_rx-c_r=0; r=1,2,3$. Then $\lambda L_2L_3+\mu L_3L_1+\nu L_1L_2=0$, where $\lambda\neq 0, \mu\neq 0, \nu\neq 0$ is the equation of circumcircle of triangle, if

(a) $\lambda(m_2+m_3)+\mu(m_3+m_1)+\nu(m_1+m_2)=0$
(b) $\lambda(m_2m_3-1)+\mu(m_3m_1-1)+\nu(m_1m_2-1)=0$
(c) Both (a) and (b)
(d) None of the above

10. $f(x,y)\equiv x^2+y^2+2ax+2by+c=0$ represent a circle. If $f(x,0)=0$ has equal roots, each being 2 and $f(0,y)=0$ has 2 and 3 as its roots, then the centre of the circle is

(a) $\left(2,\frac{5}{2}\right)$ (b) Data are not consistent
(c) $\left(-2,-\frac{5}{2}\right)$ (d) Data are inconsistent

11. If $(1+\alpha x)^n=1+8x+24x^2+\ldots$ and a line through $P(\alpha,n)$ cuts the circle $x^2+y^2=4$ in A and B, then $PA.PB$ is equal to

(a) 4 (b) 8 (c) 16 (d) 32

12. A region in the xy-plane is bounded by the curve $y=\sqrt{(25-x^2)}$ and the line $y=0$. If the point $(a,a+1)$ lies in the interior of the region, then

(a) $a\in(-4,3)$ (b) $a\in(-\infty,-1)\cup(3,\infty)$
(c) $a\in(-1,3)$ (d) None of these

13. $S(x,y)=0$ represents a circle. The equation $S(x,2)=0$ gives two identical solutions $x=1$ and the equation $S(1,y)=0$ gives two distinct solutions $y=0,2$, then the equation of the circle is

(a) $x^2+y^2+2x-2y+1=0$ (b) $x^2+y^2-2x+2y+1=0$
(c) $x^2+y^2-2x-2y-1=0$ (d) $x^2+y^2-2x-2y+1=0$

14. Let $0<\alpha<\frac{\pi}{2}$ be a fixed angle. If $P=(\cos\theta,\sin\theta)$ and $Q=(\cos(\alpha-\theta),\sin(\alpha-\theta))$, then Q is obtained from P by

(a) clockwise rotation around origin through an angle α
(b) anti-clockwise rotation around origin through an angle α
(c) reflection in the line through origin with slope $\tan\alpha$
(d) reflection in the line through origin with slope $\tan\left(\frac{\alpha}{2}\right)$

15. The number of points (x, y) having integral coordinates satisfying the condition $x^2 + y^2 < 25$ is

(a) 69 (b) 80 (c) 81 (d) 77

16. The point $([P+1], [P])$, (where $[.]$ denotes the greatest integer function) lying inside the region bounded by the circle $x^2 + y^2 - 2x - 15 = 0$ and $x^2 + y^2 - 2x - 7 = 0$, then

(a) $P \in [-1, 0) \cup [0, 1) \cup [1, 2)$ (b) $P \in [-1, 2) - \{0, 1\}$
(c) $P \in (-1, 2)$ (d) None of these

17. A point P lies inside the circles $x^2 + y^2 - 4 = 0$ and $x^2 + y^2 - 8x + 7 = 0$. The point P starts moving under the conditions that its path encloses greatest possible area and it is at a fixed distance from any arbitrarily chosen fixed point in its region. The locus of P is

(a) $4x^2 + 4y^2 - 12x + 1 = 0$ (b) $4x^2 + 4y^2 + 12x - 1 = 0$
(c) $x^2 + y^2 - 3x - 2 = 0$ (d) $x^2 + y^2 - 3x + 2 = 0$

18. The set of values of 'c' so that the equations $y = |x| + c$ and $x^2 + y^2 - 8|x| - 9 = 0$ have no solution is

(a) $(-\infty, -3) \cup (3, \infty)$ (b) $(-3, 3)$
(c) $(-\infty, -5\sqrt{2}) \cup (5\sqrt{2}, \infty)$ (d) $(5\sqrt{2} - 4, \infty)$

19. If a line segment $AM = a$ moves in the plane XOY remaining parallel to OX so that the left end point A slides along the circle $x^2 + y^2 = a^2$, the locus of M is

(a) $x^2 + y^2 = 4a^2$ (b) $x^2 + y^2 = 2ax$
(c) $x^2 + y^2 = 2ay$ (d) $x^2 + y^2 - 2ax - 2ay = 0$

20. The four points of intersection of the lines $(2x - y + 1)(x - 2y + 3) = 0$ with the axes lie on a circle whose centre is at the point

(a) $\left(-\frac{7}{4}, \frac{5}{4}\right)$ (b) $\left(\frac{3}{4}, \frac{5}{4}\right)$ (c) $\left(\frac{9}{4}, \frac{5}{4}\right)$ (d) $\left(0, \frac{5}{4}\right)$

21. The number of integral values of λ for which $x^2 + y^2 + \lambda x + (1 - \lambda)y + 5 = 0$ is the equation of a circle whose radius cannot exceed 5, is

(a) 14 (b) 18 (c) 16 (d) None of these

22. Let $\phi(x, y) = 0$ be the equation of a circle. If $\phi(0, \lambda) = 0$ has equal roots $\lambda = 2, 2$ and $\phi(\lambda, 0) = 0$ has roots $\lambda = \frac{4}{5}, 5$, then the centre of the circle is

(a) $\left(2, \frac{29}{10}\right)$ (b) $\left(\frac{29}{10}, 2\right)$ (c) $\left(-2, \frac{29}{10}\right)$ (d) None of these

23. The locus of the point of intersection of the tangents to the circle $x = r\cos\theta, y = r\sin\theta$ at points whose parametric angles differ by $\frac{\pi}{3}$ is

(a) $x^2 + y^2 = 4(2 - \sqrt{3})r^2$ (b) $3(x^2 + y^2) = 1$
(c) $x^2 + y^2 = (2 - \sqrt{3})r^2$ (d) $3(x^2 + y^2) = 4r^2$

24. One of the diameter of the circle circumscribing the rectangle $ABCD$ is $4y = x + 7$. If A and B are the points $(-3, 4)$ and $(5, 4)$ respectively, then the area of the rectangle is

(a) 16 sq units (b) 24 sq units
(c) 32 sq units (d) None of these

25. A, B, C and D are the points of intersection with the coordinate axes of the lines $ax + by = ab$ and $bx + ay = ab$, then

(a) A, B, C, D are concyclic
(b) A, B, C, D form a parallelogram
(c) A, B, C, D form a rhombus
(d) None of the above

26. α, β and γ are parametric angles of three points P, Q and R respectively, on the circle $x^2 + y^2 = 1$ and A is the point $(-1, 0)$. If the lengths of the chords AP, AQ and AR are in GP, then $\cos\left(\frac{\alpha}{2}\right)$, $\cos\left(\frac{\beta}{2}\right)$ and $\cos\left(\frac{\gamma}{2}\right)$ are in

(a) AP (b) GP
(c) HP (d) None of these

27. The equation of the circle passing through (2, 0) and (0, 4) and having the minimum radius is

(a) $x^2 + y^2 = 20$
(b) $x^2 + y^2 - 2x - 4y = 0$
(c) $(x^2 + y^2 - 4) + \lambda(x^2 + y^2 - 16) = 0$
(d) None of the above

28. A circle of radius unity is centred at the origin. Two particles start moving at the same time from the point (1, 0) and move around the circle in opposite direction. One of the particle moves anticlockwise with constant speed v and the other moves clockwise with constant speed $3v$. After leaving (1, 0), the two particles meet first at a point P and continue until they meet next at point Q. The coordinates of the point Q are

(a) (1, 0) (b) (0, 1) (c) (−1, 0) (d) (0, −1)

29. The circle $x^2 + y^2 = 4$ cuts the line joining the points $A(1, 0)$ and $B(3, 4)$ in two points P and Q. Let $\frac{BP}{PA} = \alpha$ and $\frac{BQ}{QA} = \beta$, then α and β are roots of the quadratic equation

(a) $x^2 + 2x + 7 = 0$ (b) $3x^2 + 2x - 21 = 0$
(c) $2x^2 + 3x - 27 = 0$ (d) None of these

30. The locus of the mid-points of the chords of the circle $x^2 + y^2 + 4x - 6y - 12 = 0$ which subtend an angle of $\frac{\pi}{3}$ radians at its circumference is

(a) $(x + 2)^2 + (y - 3)^2 = 6.25$ (b) $(x - 2)^2 + (y + 3)^2 = 6.25$
(c) $(x + 2)^2 + (y - 3)^2 = 18.75$ (d) $(x + 2)^2 + (y + 3)^2 = 18.75$

Circle Exercise 2 :
More than One Correct Option Type Questions

This section contains **15 multiple choice questions**. Each question has four choices (a), (b), (c) and (d) out of which **MORE THAN ONE** may be correct.

31. If OA and OB are two perpendicular chords of the circle $r = a\cos\theta + b\sin\theta$ passing through origin, then the locus of the mid-point of AB is

(a) $x^2 + y^2 = a + b$ (b) $x = \frac{a}{2}$

(c) $x^2 - y^2 = a^2 - b^2$ (d) $y = \frac{b}{2}$

32. If A and B are two points on the circle $x^2 + y^2 - 4x + 6y - 3 = 0$ which are farthest and nearest respectively, from the point (7, 2), then

(a) $A \equiv (2 - 2\sqrt{2}, -3 - 2\sqrt{2})$

(b) $A \equiv (2 + 2\sqrt{2}, -3 + 2\sqrt{2})$

(c) $B \equiv (2 + 2\sqrt{2}, -3 + 2\sqrt{2})$

(d) $B \equiv (2 - 2\sqrt{2}, -3 - 2\sqrt{2})$

33. If the circle $x^2 + y^2 + 2gx + 2fy + c = 0$ cuts each of the circles $x^2 + y^2 - 4 = 0$, $x^2 + y^2 - 6x - 8y + 10 = 0$ and $x^2 + y^2 + 2x - 4y - 2 = 0$ at the extremities of a diameter, then

(a) $c = -4$ (b) $g + f = c - 1$

(c) $g^2 + f^2 - c = 17$ (d) $gf = 6$

34. The possible value of $\lambda (\lambda > 0)$ such that the angle between the pair of tangents from point $(\lambda, 0)$ to the circle $x^2 + y^2 = 4$ lies in interval $\left(\frac{\pi}{2}, \frac{2\pi}{3}\right)$ is

(a) $\left(\frac{4}{\sqrt{3}}, 2\sqrt{2}\right)$ (b) $(0, \sqrt{2})$

(c) $(1, 2)$ (d) $\left(\frac{4}{\sqrt{3}}, \frac{4}{\sqrt{3}}\right)$

35. If a chord of the circle $x^2 + y^2 - 4x - 2y - c = 0$ is trisected at the points $\left(\frac{1}{3}, \frac{1}{3}\right)$ and $\left(\frac{8}{3}, \frac{8}{3}\right)$, then

(a) $c = 10$ (b) $c = 20$

(c) $c = 15$ (d) $c^2 - 40c + 400 = 0$

36. From the point $A(0, 3)$ on $x^2 + 4x + (y - 3)^2 = 0$, a chord AB is drawn and extended to a point M, such that $AM = 2AB$. An equation of the locus of M is

(a) $x^2 + 6x + (y - 2)^2 = 0$

(b) $x^2 + 8x + (y - 3)^2 = 0$

(c) $x^2 + y^2 + 8x - 6y + 9 = 0$

(d) $x^2 + y^2 + 6x - 4y + 4 = 0$

37. An equation of a circle touching the axes of coordinates and the line $x\cos\alpha + y\sin\alpha = 2$ can be

(a) $x^2 + y^2 - 2gx - 2gy + g^2 = 0$, where $g = \frac{2}{(\cos\alpha + \sin\alpha + 1)}$

(b) $x^2 + y^2 - 2gx - 2gy + g^2 = 0$, where $g = \frac{2}{(\cos\alpha + \sin\alpha - 1)}$

(c) $x^2 + y^2 - 2gx + 2gy + g^2 = 0$, where $g = \frac{2}{(\cos\alpha - \sin\alpha + 1)}$

(d) $x^2 + y^2 - 2gx + 2gy + g^2 = 0$, where $g = \frac{2}{(\cos\alpha - \sin\alpha - 1)}$

38. If α is the angle subtended at $P(x_1, y_1)$ by the circle $S \equiv x^2 + y^2 + 2gx + 2fy + c = 0$, then

(a) $\cot\alpha = \frac{\sqrt{S_1}}{\sqrt{(g^2 + f^2 - c)}}$ (b) $\cot\frac{\alpha}{2} = \frac{\sqrt{S_1}}{\sqrt{(g^2 + f^2 - c)}}$

(c) $\tan\alpha = \frac{2\sqrt{(g^2 + f^2 - c)}}{\sqrt{S_1}}$ (d) $\alpha = 2\tan^{-1}\left(\frac{\sqrt{(g^2 + f^2 - c)}}{\sqrt{S_1}}\right)$

39. The equation of the circle which touches the axis of coordinates and the line $\frac{x}{3} + \frac{y}{4} = 1$ and whose centre lies in the first quadrant is $x^2 + y^2 - 2\lambda x - 2\lambda y + \lambda^2 = 0$, then λ is equal to

(a) 1 (b) 2

(c) 3 (d) 6

40. If P is a point on the circle $x^2 + y^2 = 9$, Q is a point on the line $7x + y + 3 = 0$, and the line $x - y + 1 = 0$, is the perpendicular bisector of PQ, then the coordinates of P are

(a) (3, 0) (b) $\left(\frac{72}{25}, -\frac{21}{25}\right)$

(c) (0, 3) (d) $\left(-\frac{72}{25}, \frac{21}{25}\right)$

41. If a circle passes through the point $\left(3, \sqrt{\frac{7}{2}}\right)$ and touches $x + y = 1$ and $x - y = 1$, then the centre of the circle is

(a) (4, 0) (b) (4, 2) (c) (6, 0) (d) (7, 9)

42. The equation of a circle C_1 is $x^2 + y^2 = 4$. The locus of the intersection of orthogonal tangents to the circle is the curve C_2 and the locus of the intersection of perpendicular tangents to the curve C_2 is the curve C_3. Then,

(a) C_3 is a circle

(b) the area enclosed by the curve C_3 is 8π

(c) C_2 and C_3 are circles with the same centre

(d) None of the above

43. The equation of a tangent to the circle $x^2+y^2=25$ passing through $(-2,11)$ is

(a) $4x+3y=25$ (b) $3x+4y=38$
(c) $24x-7y+125=0$ (d) $7x+24y=230$

44. Consider the circles
$C_1 \equiv x^2+y^2-2x-4y-4=0$ and
$C_2 \equiv x^2+y^2+2x+4y+4=0$
and the line $L \equiv x+2y+2=0$, then

(a) L is the radical axis of C_1 and C_2
(b) L is the common tangent of C_1 and C_2
(c) L is the common chord of C_1 and C_2
(d) L is perpendicular to the line joining centres of C_1 and C_2

45. A square is inscribed in the circle $x^2+y^2-10x-6y+30=0$. One side of the square is parallel to $y=x+3$, then one vertex of the square is

(a) (3, 3) (b) (7,3)
(c) $(6,3-\sqrt{3})$ (d) $(6,3+\sqrt{3})$

Circle Exercise 3 :
Paragraph Based Questions

This section contains **7 paragraphs** based upon each of the paragraph **3 multiple choice questions** have to be answered. Each of these questions has four choices (a), (b), (c) and (d) out of which **ONLY ONE** is correct.

Paragraph I
(Q. Nos. 46 to 48)

Consider the circle $S: x^2+y^2-4x-1=0$ and the line $L: y=3x-1$. If the line L cuts the circle at A and B.

46. Length of the chord AB is

(a) $\sqrt{5}$ (b) $\sqrt{10}$ (c) $2\sqrt{5}$ (d) $5\sqrt{2}$

47. The angle subtended by the chord AB is the minor arc of S is

(a) $\frac{\pi}{4}$ (b) $\frac{2\pi}{3}$ (c) $\frac{3\pi}{4}$ (d) $\frac{5\pi}{6}$

48. Acute angle between the line L and the circle S is

(a) $\frac{\pi}{6}$ (b) $\frac{\pi}{4}$ (c) $\frac{\pi}{3}$ (d) $\frac{\pi}{2}$

Paragraph II
(Q. Nos. 49 to 51)

P is a variable point on the line $L=0$. Tangents are drawn to the circle $x^2+y^2=4$ from P to touch it at Q and R. The parallelogram PQSR is completed.

49. If $L \equiv 2x+y-6=0$, then the locus of the circumcenter of ΔPQR is

(a) $2x-y=4$ (b) $2x+y=3$
(c) $x-2y=4$ (d) $x+2y=3$

50. If $P \equiv (6,8)$, then area of ΔQRS is $\frac{192}{25}\sqrt{\lambda}$ sq units. The value of λ is

(a) 2 (b) 3 (c) 5 (d) 6

51. If $P \equiv (3,4)$, then the coordinates of S are

(a) $\left(-\frac{46}{25},\frac{63}{25}\right)$ (b) $\left(-\frac{51}{25},-\frac{68}{25}\right)$
(c) $\left(-\frac{46}{25},\frac{68}{25}\right)$ (d) $\left(-\frac{68}{25},\frac{51}{25}\right)$

Paragraph III
(Q. Nos. 52 to 54)

Equation of the circumcircle of a triangle formed by the lines $L_1=0$, $L_2=0$ and $L_3=0$ can be written as $L_1L_2+\lambda L_2L_3+\mu L_3L_1=0$, where λ and μ are such that coefficient of x^2 = coefficient of y^2 and coefficient of $xy=0$.

52. $L_1L_2^2+\lambda L_2L_3^2+\mu L_3L_1^2=0$ represents

(a) a curve passing through point of intersection of $L_1=0$, $L_2=0$ and $L_3=0$
(b) a circle is coefficient of x^2 = coefficient of y^2 and coefficient of $xy=0$
(c) a parabola
(d) pair of straight lines

53. $L_1=0$, $L_2=0$ be the distinct parallel lines, $L_3=0$, $L_4=0$ be two other distinct parallel lines which are not parallel to $L_1=0$. The equation of a circle passing through the vertices of the parallelogram formed must be of the form

(a) $\lambda L_1L_4+\mu L_2L_3=0$ (b) $\lambda L_1L_3+\mu L_2L_4=0$
(c) $\lambda L_1L_2+\mu L_3L_4=0$ (d) $\lambda L_1^2L_3+\mu L_2^2L_4=0$

54. If $L_1L_2+\lambda L_2L_3+\mu L_3L_1=0$ is such that $\mu=0$ and λ is non-zero, then it represents

(a) a parabola
(b) a pair of straight lines
(c) a circle
(d) an ellipse

Paragraph IV

(Q. Nos. 55 to 57)

Given two circles intersecting orthogonally having the length of common chord $\frac{24}{5}$ unit. The radius of one of the circles is 3 units.

55. If radius of other circle is λ units, then λ is
(a) 2 (b) 4 (c) 5 (d) 6

56. If angle between direct common tangents is 2θ, then $\sin 2\theta$ is
(a) $\frac{4}{5}$ (b) $\frac{4\sqrt{6}}{25}$ (c) $\frac{12}{25}$ (d) $\frac{24}{25}$

57. If length of direct common tangent is λ units, then λ^2 is
(a) 12 (b) 24 (c) 36 (d) 48

Paragraph V

(Q. Nos. 58 to 60)

Consider the two circles $C_1 : x^2 + y^2 = a^2$ and $C_2 : x^2 + y^2 = b^2$ $(a > b)$. Let A be a fixed point on the circle C_1, say $A(a, 0)$ and B be a variable point on the circle C_2. The line BA meets the circle C_2 again at C. 'O' being the origin.

58. If $(OA)^2 + (OB)^2 + (BC)^2 = \lambda$, then $\lambda \in$
(a) $[5b^2 - 3a^2, 5b^2 + a^2]$ (b) $[4b^2, 4b^2 + a^2]$
(c) $[4a^2, 4b^2]$ (d) $[5b^2 - 3a^2, 5b^2 + 3a^2]$

59. The locus of the mid-point of AB is
(a) $\left(x - \frac{a}{2}\right)^2 + y^2 = \frac{b^2}{4}$ (b) $\left(x - \frac{a}{2}\right)^2 + y^2 = \frac{a^2}{4}$
(c) $\left(x - \frac{b}{2}\right)^2 + y^2 = \frac{a^2}{4}$ (d) $\left(x - \frac{b}{2}\right)^2 + y^2 = \frac{b^2}{4}$

60. If $(BC)^2$ is maximum, then the locus of the mid-point of AB is
(a) $x^2 + y^2 = b^2$ (b) $x^2 + y^2 = (a + b)^2$
(c) $x^2 + y^2 = (a - b)^2$ (d) None of these

Paragraph VI

(Q. Nos. 61 to 63)

Two variable chords AB and BC of a circle $x^2 + y^2 = a^2$ are such that $AB = BC = a$, M and N are the mid-points of AB and BC respectively such that line joining MN intersect the circle at P and Q, where P is closer to AB and O is the centre of the circle.

61. $\angle OAB$ is
(a) 15° (b) 30°
(c) 45° (d) 60°

62. Angle between tangents at A and C is
(a) 60° (b) 90°
(c) 120° (d) 150°

63. Locus of point of intersection of tangents at A and C is
(a) $x^2 + y^2 = a^2$ (b) $x^2 + y^2 = 2a^2$
(c) $x^2 + y^2 = 4a^2$ (d) $x^2 + y^2 = 8a^2$

Paragraph VII

(Q. Nos. 64 to 66)

t_1, t_2, t_3 are lengths of tangents drawn from a point (h, k) to the circles $x^2 + y^2 = 4$, $x^2 + y^2 - 4x = 0$ and $x^2 + y^2 - 4y = 0$ respectively further, $t_1^4 = t_2^2 t_3^2 + 16$. Locus of the point (h, k) consist of a straight line L_1 and a circle C_1 passing through origin. A circle C_2, which is equal to circle C_1 is drawn touching the line L_1 and the circle C_1 externally.

64. Equation of L_1 is
(a) $x + y = 0$ (b) $x - y = 0$
(c) $2x + y = 0$ (d) $x + 2y = 0$

65. Equation of C_1 is
(a) $x^2 + y^2 - x - y = 0$ (b) $x^2 + y^2 - 2x + y = 0$
(c) $x^2 + y^2 - x + 2y = 0$ (d) $x^2 + y^2 - 2x - 2y = 0$

66. The distance between the centres of C_1 and C_2 is
(a) $\sqrt{2}$ (b) 2
(c) $2\sqrt{2}$ (d) 4

Circle Exercise 4 :
Single Integer Answer Type Questions

- This section contains **10 questions**. The answer to each question is a **single digit integer**, ranging from 0 to 9 (both inclusive).

67. The point (1, 4) lies inside the circle $x^2 + y^2 - 6x - 10y + \lambda = 0$. If the circle neither touches nor cuts the axes, then the difference between the maximum and the minimum possible values of λ is

68. Consider the family of circles $x^2 + y^2 - 2x - 2\lambda y - 8 = 0$ passing through two fixed points A and B. Then the distance between the points A and B is

69. If $C_1 : x^2 + y^2 = (3 + 2\sqrt{2})^2$ be a circle and PA and PB are pair of tangents on C_1, where P is any point on the director circle of C_1, then the radius of the smallest circle which touches C_1 externally and also the two tangents PA and PB, is

70. If a circle $S(x, y) = 0$ touches the point $(2, 3)$ of the line $x + y = 5$ and $S(1, 2) = 0$, then radius of such circle is $\frac{1}{\sqrt{\lambda}}$ units, then the value of λ^2 is.

71. If real numbers x and y satisfy $(x+5)^2 + (y-12)^2 = 196$, then the maximum value of $(x^2 + y^2)^{\frac{1}{3}}$ is

72. If the equation of circle circumscribing the quadrilateral formed by the lines in order are
$2x + 3y = 2$, $3x - 2y = 3$, $x + 2y = 3$ and $2x - y = 1$ is given by $x^2 + y^2 + \lambda x + \mu y + v = 0$. Then the value of $|\lambda + 2\mu + v|$ is

73. A circle $x^2 + y^2 + 4x - 2\sqrt{2}y + c = 0$ is the director circle of the circle C_1 and C_1 is the director circle of circle C_2 and so on. If the sum of radii of all these circles is 2 and if $c = \lambda\sqrt{2}$, then the value of λ is

74. If the area bounded by the circles $x^2 + y^2 = r^2$, $r = 1, 2$ and the rays given by $2x^2 - 3xy - 2y^2 = 0$, $y > 0$ is $\frac{\lambda\pi}{4}$ sq units, then the value of λ is

75. The length of a common internal tangent of two circles is 5 and that of a common external tangent is 13. If the product of the radii of two circles is λ, then the value of $\frac{\lambda}{4}$ is

76. Consider a circles S with centre at the origin and radius 4. Four circles A, B, C and D each with radius unity and centres $(-3, 0)$, $(-1, 0)$, $(1, 0)$ and $(3, 0)$ respectively are drawn. A chord PQ of the circle S touches the circle B and passes through the centre of the circle C. If the length of this chord can be expressed as $\sqrt{\lambda}$, then the value of $\frac{\lambda}{9}$ is

Circle Exercise 5 : Matching Type Questions

- This section contains **4 questions**. Questions 77 and 78 have four statements (A, B, C and D) given in **Column I** and four statements (p, q, r and s) in **Column II**, and questions 79 and 80 have three statements (A, B and C) given in **Column I** and five statements (p, q, r, s and t) in **Column II**. Any given statement in **Column I** can have correct matching with one or more statement(s) given in **Column II**.

77. Consider the circles $S_1 : x^2 + y^2 - 4x - 6y + 12 = 0$ and $S_2 : (x-5)^2 + (y-6)^2 = r^2 > 1$

	Column I		Column II
(A)	S_1 and S_2 touch internally, then $(r-1)^2$ is divisible by	(p)	3
(B)	S_1 and S_2 touch externally, then $r^2 + 2r + 3$ is divisible by	(q)	4
(C)	S_1 and S_2 intersect orthogonally, then $r^2 - 1$ is divisible by	(r)	5
(D)	S_1 and S_2 intersect so that the common chord is longest, then $r^2 + 5$ is divisible by	(s)	6

78. Match the following

	Column I		Column II
(A)	If $ax + by - 5 = 0$ is the equation of the chord of the circle $(x-3)^2 + (y-4)^2 = 4$, which passes through $(2, 3)$ and at the greatest distance from the centre of the circle, then	(p)	$a + b = 1$
(B)	Let O be the origin and P be a variable point on the circle $x^2 + y^2 + 2x + 2y = 0$. If the locus of mid-point of OP is $x^2 + y^2 + 2ax + 2by = 0$, then	(q)	$a + b = 2$
(C)	If (a, b) be coordinates of the centre of the smallest circle which cuts the circle $x^2 + y^2 - 2x - 4y - 4 = 0$ and $x^2 + y^2 - 10x + 12y + 52 = 0$ orthogonally, then	(r)	$a^2 + b^2 = 2$
(D)	If a and b are the slope of tangents which are drawn to the circle $x^2 + y^2 - 6\sqrt{3}x - 6y + 27 = 0$ from the origin, then	(s)	$a^2 + b^2 = 3$

79. Match the following

	Column I		Column I
(A)	If the shortest and largest distance from the point (10,7) to the circle $x^2+y^2-4x-2y-20=0$ are L and M respectively, then	(p)	$M+L=10$
(B)	If the shortest and largest distance from the point (3, −6) to the circle $x^2+y^2-16x-12y-125=0$ are L and M respectively, then	(q)	$M+L=20$
(C)	If the shortest and largest distance from the point (6, −6) to the circle $x^2+y^2-4x+6y-12=0$ are L and M respectively, then	(r)	$M+L=30$
		(s)	$M-L=10$
		(t)	$M-L=26$

80. Match the following

	Column I		Column II
(A)	If the straight lines $y=a_1x+b$ and $y=a_2x+b\ (a_1 \neq a_2)$ and $b \in R$ meet the coordinate axes in concyclic points, then	(p)	$a_1^2+a_2^2=4$
(B)	If the chord of contact of the tangents drawn to $x^2+y^2=b^2$ and $b \in R$ from any point on $x^2+y^2=a_1^2$, touches the circle $x^2+y^2=a_2^2$ $(a_1 \neq a_2)$, then	(q)	$a_1+a_2=3$
(C)	If the circle $x^2+y^2+2a_1x+b=0$ and $x^2+y^2+2a_2x+b=0 (a_1 \neq a_2)$ and $b \in R$ cuts orthogonally, then	(r)	$a_1a_2=b$
		(s)	$a_1a_2=1$
		(t)	$a_1a_2=b^2$

Circle Exercise 6 : Statement I and II Type Questions

- **Directions** (Q. Nos. 81 to 88) are Assertion-Reason type questions. Each of these questions contains two statements:
Statement I (Assertion) and **Statement II** (Reason)
Each of these questions also has four alternative choices, only one of which is the correct answer. You have to select the correct choice as given below :

(a) Statement I is true, Statement II is true; Statement II is a correct explanation for Statement I
(b) Statement I is true, Statement II is true; Statement II is not a correct explanation for Statement I
(c) Statement I is true, Statement II is false
(d) Statement I is false, Statement II is true

81. Statement I Only one tangent can be drawn from the point (1, 3) to the circle $x^2+y^2=1$

Statement II Solving $\dfrac{|3-m|}{\sqrt{(1+m^2)}}=1$, we get only one real value of m

82. Statement I Tangents cannot be drawn from the point $(1,\lambda)$ to the circle $x^2+y^2+2x-4y=0$

Statement II $(1+1)^2+(\lambda+2)^2<1^2+2^2$

83. Statement I Number of circles passing through (1, 4), (2, 3), (−1, 6) is one

Statement II Every triangle has one circumcircle

84. Statement I Two tangents are drawn from a point on the circle $x^2+y^2=50$ to the circle $x^2+y^2=25$, then angle between tangents is $\dfrac{\pi}{3}$

Statement II $x^2+y^2=50$ is the director circle of $x^2+y^2=25$.

85. Statement I Circles $x^2+y^2=4$ and $x^2+y^2-6x+5=0$ intersect each other at two distinct points

Statement II Circles with centres C_1, C_2 and radii r_1, r_2 intersect at two distinct points if $|C_1C_2|<r_1+r_2$

86. Statement I The line $3x-4y=7$ is a diameter of the circle $x^2+y^2-2x+2y-47=0$

Statement II Normal of a circle always pass through centre of circle

87. Statement I A ray of light incident at the point (−3, −1) gets reflected from the tangent at $(0,-1)$ to the circle $x^2+y^2=1$. If the reflected ray touches the circle, then equation of the reflected ray is $4y-3x=5$

Statement I The angle of incidence = angle of reflection i.e. $\angle i=\angle r$

88. Statement I The chord of contact of the circle $x^2+y^2=1$ w.r.t. the points (2,3), (3,5) and (1,1) are concurrent.

Statement II Points (1, 1), (2, 3) and (3,5) are collinear.

Circle Exercise 7 :
Subjective Type Questions

- In this section, there are **16 subjective questions**.

89. Find the equation of the circle passing through (1, 0) and (0, 1) and having the smallest possible radius.

90. Find the equation of the circle which touches the circle $x^2 + y^2 - 6x + 6y + 17 = 0$ externally and to which the lines $x^2 - 3xy - 3x + 9y = 0$ are normals.

91. A line meets the coordinate axes at A and B. A circle is circumscribed about the triangle OAB. If the distance of the points A and B from the tangent at O, the origin, to the circle are m and n respectively, find the equation of the circle.

92. Find the equation of a circle which passes through the point (2 , 0) and whose centre is the limit of the point of intersection of the lines $3x + 5y = 1$ and $(2 + c)\,x + 5c^2 y = 1$ as $c \to 1$.

93. Tangents are drawn from $P(6, 8)$ to the circle $x^2 + y^2 = r^2$. Find the radius of the circle such that the area of the Δ formed by tangents and chord of contact is maximum.

94. $2x - y + 4 = 0$ is a diameter of the circle which circumscribed a rectangle $ABCD$. If the coordinates of A and B are $A(4, 6)$ and $B(1, 9)$, find the area of rectangle $ABCD$.

95. Find the radius of smaller circle which touches the straight line $3x - y = 6$ at $(1, -3)$ and also touches the line $y = x$.

96. If the circle C_1, $x^2 + y^2 = 16$ intersects another circle C_2 of radius 5 in such a manner that the common chord is of maximum length and has a slope equal to (3/4), find the coordinates of centre C_2.

97. Let $2x^2 + y^2 - 3xy = 0$ be the equation of a pair of tangents drawn from the origin O to a circle of radius 3 with centre in the first quadrant. If A is one of the points of contact, find the length of OA.

98. The circle $x^2 + y^2 = 1$ cuts the X-axis at P and Q. another circle with centre at Q and variable radius intersects the first circle at R above the X-axis and the line segment PQ at S. Find the maximum area of the ΔQSR.

99. If the two lines $a_1 x + b_1 y + c_1 = 0$ and $a_2 x + b_2 y + c_2 = 0$ cut the coordinate axes in concyclic points, prove that $a_1 a_2 = b_1 b_2$ and find the equation of the circle.

100. The centre of the circle $S = 0$ lie on the line $2x - 2y + 9 = 0$ and $S = 0$ cuts orthogonally the circle $x^2 + y^2 = 4$. Show that circle $S = 0$ passes through two fixed points and find their coordinates.

101. Find the condition on a , b , c such that two chords of the circle
$$x^2 + y^2 - 2ax - 2by + a^2 + b^2 - c^2 = 0$$
passing through the point $(a, b + c)$ are bisected by the line $y = x$.

102. Two straight lines rotate about two fixed points. If they start from their position of coincidence such that one rotates at the rate double that of the other. Prove that the locus of their point of intersection is a circle.

103. The base AB of a triangle is fixed and its vertex C moves such that $\sin A = k \sin B\,(k \neq 1)$. Show that the locus of C is a circle whose centre lies on the line AB and whose radius is equal to $\dfrac{ak}{(1 - k^2)}$, a being the length of the base AB.

104. Consider a curve $ax^2 + 2hxy + by^2 = 1$ and a point P not on the curve. A line drawn from the point P intersects the curve at points Q and R. If the product $PQ \cdot PR$ is independent of the slope of the line, then show that the curve is a circle.

Circle Exercise 8 :
Questions Asked in Previous 13 Year's Exams

- This section contains questions asked in **IIT-JEE, AIEEE, JEE Main & JEE Advanced** from year **2005** to **2017**.

105. A circle is given by $x^2+(y-1)^2=1$, another circle C touches it externally and also the X-axis, then the locus of its centre is **[IIT-JEE 2005, 3M]**

(a) $\{(x,y): x^2=4y\} \cup \{(x,y): y \le 0\}$
(b) $\{(x,y): x^2+(y-1)^2=4\} \cup \{(x,y): y \le 0\}$
(c) $\{(x,y): x^2=y\} \cup \{(0,y): y \le 0\}$
(d) $\{(x,y): x^2=4y\} \cup \{(0,y): y \le 0\}$

106. If the circles $x^2+y^2+2ax+cy+a=0$ and $x^2+y^2-3ax+dy-1=0$ intersect in two distinct points P and Q, then the line $5x+by-a=0$ passes through P and Q for **[AIEEE 2005, 6M]**

(a) exactly one value of a (b) no value of a
(c) infinitely many values of a (d) exactly two values of a

107. A circle touches the X-axis and also touches the circle with centre at (0, 3) and radius 2. The locus of the centre of the circle is **[AIEEE 2005, 3M]**

(a) an ellipse (b) a circle
(c) a hyperbola (d) a parabola

108. If a circle passes through the point (a, b) and cuts the circle $x^2+y^2=p^2$ orthogonally, then the equation of the locus of its centre is **[AIEEE 2005, 3M]**

(a) $x^2+y^2-3ax-4by+(a^2+b^2-p^2)=0$
(b) $2ax+2by-(a^2-b^2+p^2)=0$
(c) $x^2+y^2-2ax-3by+(a^2-b^2-p^2)=0$
(d) $2ax+2by-(a^2+b^2+p^2)=0$

Paragraph

(Q. Nos. 109 to 111)

ABCD is a square of side length 2 units. C_1 is the circle touching all the sides of the square ABCD and C_2 is the circumcircle of square ABCD. L is a fixed line in the same plane and R is a fixed point.

109. If P is any point of C_1 and Q is another point on C_2, then $\dfrac{PA^2+PB^2+PC^2+PD^2}{QA^2+QB^2+QC^2+QD^2}$ is equal to

(a) 0.75 (b) 1.25 (c) 1 (d) 0.5

110. If a circle is such that it touches the line L and the circle C_1 externally, such that both the circles are on the same side of the line, then the locus of centre of the circle is

(a) ellipse (b) hyperbola
(c) parabola (d) pair of straight line

111. A line L' through A is drawn parallel to BD. Point S moves such that its distances from the line BD and the vertex A are equal. If locus of S cuts L' at T_2 and T_3 and AC at T_1, then area of $\Delta T_1T_2T_3$ is **[IIT-JEE 2006, 5+5+5 M]**

(a) $\frac{1}{2}$ sq units (b) $\frac{2}{3}$ sq units
(c) 1 sq units (d) 2 sq units

112. If the lines $3x-4y-7=0$ and $2x-3y-5=0$ are two diameters of a circle of area 49π square units, the equation of the circle is **[AIEEE 2006, 6M]**

(a) $x^2+y^2+2x-2y-47=0$
(b) $x^2+y^2+2x-2y-62=0$
(c) $x^2+y^2-2x+2y-62=0$
(d) $x^2+y^2-2x+2y-47=0$

113. Let C be the circle with centre (0, 0) and radius 3 units. The equation of the locus of the mid-points of the chords of the circle C that subtend an angle of $\frac{2\pi}{3}$ at its centre is **[AIEEE 2006, 6M]**

(a) $x^2+y^2=\frac{3}{2}$ (b) $x^2+y^2=1$
(c) $x^2+y^2=\frac{27}{4}$ (d) $x^2+y^2=\frac{9}{4}$

114. Tangents are drawn from the point (17, 7) to the circle $x^2+y^2=169$.

Statement I The tangents are mutually perpendicular. because

Statement II The locus of the points from which mutually perpendicular tangents can be drawn to the given circle is $x^2+y^2=338$. **[IIT-JEE 2007, 3M]**

(a) Statement I is True, statement II is True; statement II is a correct explanation for statement I
(b) Statement I is True, statement II is True; statement II is not a correct explanation for statement I
(c) Statement I is True, statement II is False
(d) Statement I is False, statement II is True

115. Consider a family of circles which are passing through the point $(-1,1)$ and are tangent to X-axis. If (h,k) are the coordinate of the centre of the circles, then the set of values of k is given by the interval **[AIEEE 2007, 3M]**

(a) $-\frac{1}{2} \le k \le \frac{1}{2}$ (b) $k \le \frac{1}{2}$
(c) $0 \le k \le \frac{1}{2}$ (d) $k \ge \frac{1}{2}$

Paragraph

(Q. Nos. 116 to 118)

A circle C of radius 1 is inscribed in an equilateral triangle PQR. The points of contact of C with the sides PQ, QR, RP are D, E, F, respectively. The line PQ is given by the equation $\sqrt{3}x + y - 6 = 0$ and the point D is $\left(\frac{3\sqrt{3}}{2}, \frac{3}{2}\right)$. Further, it is given that the origin and the centre of C are on the same side of the line PQ.

116. The equation of circle C is

(a) $(x-2\sqrt{3})^2 + (y-1)^2 = 1$ (b) $(x-2\sqrt{3})^2 + \left(y+\frac{1}{2}\right)^2 = 1$

(c) $(x-\sqrt{3})^2 + (y+1)^2 = 1$ (d) $(x-\sqrt{3})^2 + (y-1)^2 = 1$

117. Points E and F are given by

(a) $\left(\frac{\sqrt{3}}{2}, \frac{3}{2}\right), (\sqrt{3}, 0)$ (b) $\left(\frac{\sqrt{3}}{2}, \frac{1}{2}\right), (\sqrt{3}, 0)$

(c) $\left(\frac{\sqrt{3}}{2}, \frac{3}{2}\right), \left(\frac{\sqrt{3}}{2}, \frac{1}{2}\right)$ (d) $\left(\frac{3}{2}, \frac{\sqrt{3}}{2}\right), \left(\frac{\sqrt{3}}{2}, \frac{1}{2}\right)$

118. Equations of the sides QR, RP are **[IIT-JEE 2008, (4 + 4 + 4) M]**

(a) $y = \frac{2}{\sqrt{3}}x + 1,\ y = -\frac{2}{\sqrt{3}}x - 1$ (b) $y = \frac{1}{\sqrt{3}}x,\ y = 0$

(c) $y = \frac{\sqrt{3}}{2}x + 1,\ y = -\frac{\sqrt{3}}{2}x - 1$ (d) $y = \sqrt{3}x,\ y = 0$

119. Consider $L_1: 2x + 3y + p - 3 = 0$; $L_2: 2x + 3y + p + 3 = 0$ where, p is a real number, and $C: x^2 + y^2 + 6x - 10y + 30 = 0$

Statement I If line L_1 is a chord of circle C, then line L_2 is not always a diameter of circle C and

Statement II If line L_1 is a diameter of circle C, then line L_2 is not a chord of circle C. **[IIT-JEE 2008, 3M]**

(a) Statement I is True, statement II is True; statement II is a correct explanation for statement I

(b) Statement I is True, statement II is True; statement II is not a correct explanation for statement I

(c) Statement I is True, statement II is False

(d) Statement I is False, statement II is True

120. The point diametrically opposite to the point $P(1, 0)$ on the circle $x^2 + y^2 + 2x + 4y - 3 = 0$ is **[AIEEE 2008, 3M]**

(a) $(3, -4)$ (b) $(-3, 4)$ (c) $(-3, -4)$ (d) $(3, 4)$

121. Tangents drawn from the point $P(1, 8)$ to the circle $x^2 + y^2 - 6x - 4y - 11 = 0$ touch the circle at the points A and B. The equation of the circumcircle of the triangle PAB is **[IIT-JEE 2009, 3M]**

(a) $x^2 + y^2 + 4x - 6y + 19 = 0$ (b) $x^2 + y^2 - 4x - 10y + 19 = 0$

(c) $x^2 + y^2 - 2x + 6y - 29 = 0$ (d) $x^2 + y^2 - 6x - 4y + 19 = 0$

122. The centres of two circles C_1 and C_2 each of unit radius are at a distance of 6 units from each other. Let P be the mid point of the line segment joining the centres of C_1 and C_2 and C be a circle touching circles C_1 and C_2 externally. If a common tangent to C_1 and C passing through P is also a common tangent to C_2 and C, then the radius of the circle C is **[IIT-JEE 2009, 4M]**

123. If P and Q are the points of intersection of the circles $x^2 + y^2 + 3x + 7y + 2p - 5 = 0$ and $x^2 + y^2 + 2x + 2y - p^2 = 0$ then there is a circle passing through P, Q and $(1, 1)$ for : **[AIEEE 2009, 4M]**

(a) all except one value of p

(b) all except two values of p

(c) exactly one value of p

(d) all values of p

124. The circle $x^2 + y^{2d} = 4x + 8y + 5$ intersects the line $3x - 4y = m$ at two distinct points if **[AIEEE 2010, 4M]**

(a) $-35 < m < 15$ (b) $15 < m < 65$

(c) $35 < m < 85$ (d) $-85 < m < -35$

125. The circle passing through the point $(-1, 0)$ and touching the Y-axis at $(0, 2)$ also passes through the point. **[IIT-JEE 2011, 3M]**

(a) $\left(-\frac{3}{2}, 0\right)$ (b) $\left(-\frac{5}{2}, 2\right)$

(c) $\left(-\frac{3}{2}, \frac{5}{2}\right)$ (d) $(-4, 0)$

126. The straight line $2x - 3y = 1$ divides the circular region $x^2 + y^2 \le 6$ into two parts.

If $S = \left\{\left(2, \frac{3}{4}\right), \left(\frac{5}{2}, \frac{3}{4}\right), \left(\frac{1}{4}, -\frac{1}{4}\right), \left(\frac{1}{8}, \frac{1}{4}\right)\right\}$ then the number of point(s) in S lying inside the smaller part is **[IIT-JEE 2011, 4M]**

127. The two circles $x^2 + y^2 = ax$ and $x^2 + y^2 = c^2 (c > 0)$ touch each other if **[AIEEE 2011, 4M]**

(a) $|a| = c$ (b) $a = 2c$

(c) $|a| = 2c$ (d) $2|a| = c$

128. The locus of the mid-point of the chord of contact of tangents drawn from points lying on the straight line $4x - 5y = 20$ to the circle $x^2 + y^2 = 9$ is **[IIT-JEE 2012, 3M]**

(a) $20(x^2 + y^2) - 36x + 45y = 0$

(b) $20(x^2 + y^2) + 36x - 45y = 0$

(c) $36(x^2 + y^2) - 20x + 45y = 0$

(d) $36(x^2 + y^2) + 20x - 45y = 0$

Paragraph

(Q. Nos. 129 and 130)

A tangent PT is drawn to the circle $x^2 + y^2 = 4$ at the point $P(\sqrt{3}, 1)$. A straight line L, perpendicular to PT is a tangent to the circle $(x-3)^2 + y^2 = 1$.

129. A possible equation of L is

(a) $x - \sqrt{3}y = 1$ (b) $x + \sqrt{3}y = 1$

(c) $x - \sqrt{3}y = -1$ (d) $x + \sqrt{3}y = 5$

130. A common tangent of the two circles is **[IIT-JEE 2012, (3 + 3) M]**

(a) $x = 4$ (b) $y = 2$

(c) $x + \sqrt{3}y = 4$ (d) $x + 2\sqrt{2}y = 6$

131. The length of the diameter of the circle which touches the X-axis at the point (1, 0) and passes through the point (2, 3) is **[AIEEE 2012, 4M]**

(a) $\frac{10}{3}$ (b) $\frac{3}{5}$

(c) $\frac{6}{5}$ (d) $\frac{5}{3}$

132. The circle passing through $(1, -2)$ and touching the axis of x at (3, 0) also passes through the point **[JEE Main 2013, 4M]**

(a) $(-5, 2)$ (b) $(2, -5)$

(c) $(5, -2)$ (d) $(-2, 5)$

133. Circle(s) touching X-axis at a distance 3 from the origin and having an intercept of length $2\sqrt{7}$ on Y-axis is (are) **[JEE Advanced 2013, 3M]**

(a) $x^2 + y^2 - 6x + 8y + 9 = 0$

(b) $x^2 + y^2 - 6x + 7y + 9 = 0$

(c) $x^2 + y^2 - 6x - 8y + 9 = 0$

(d) $x^2 + y^2 - 6x - 7y + 9 = 0$

134. Let C be the circle with centre at $(1, 1)$ and radius = 1. If T is the circle centred at $(0, y)$, passing through origin and touching the circle C externally, then the radius of T is equal to **[JEE Main 2014, 4M]**

(a) $\frac{1}{2}$ (b) $\frac{1}{4}$

(c) $\frac{\sqrt{3}}{\sqrt{2}}$ (d) $\frac{\sqrt{3}}{2}$

135. A circle S passes through the point (0, 1) and is orthogonal to the circles $(x-1)^2 + y^2 = 16$ and $x^2 + y^2 = 1$. Then **[JEE Advanced 2014, 3M]**

(a) radius of S is 8 (b) radius of S is 7

(c) centre of S is $(-7, 1)$ (d) centre of S is $(-8, 1)$

136. Locus of the image of the point (2, 3) in the line $(2x - 3y + 4) + k(x - 2y + 3) = 0$, $k \in R$, is a **[JEE Main 2015, 4M]**

(a) circle of radius $\sqrt{2}$

(b) circle of radius $\sqrt{3}$

(c) straight line parallel to X-axis

(d) straight line parallel to Y-axis

137. The number of common tangents to the circles $x^2 + y^2 - 4x - 6x - 12 = 0$ and $x^2 + y^2 + 6x + 18y + 26 = 0$, is **[JEE Main 2015, 4M]**

(a) 3 (b) 4

(c) 1 (d) 2

138. The centres of those circles which touch the circle, $x^2 + y^2 - 8x - 8y - 4 = 0$, externally and also touch the X-axis, lie on **[JEE Main 2016, 4M]**

(a) a hyperbola

(b) a parabola

(c) a circle

(d) an ellipse which is not a circle

139. If one of the diameters of the circle, given by the equation, $x^2 + y^2 - 4x + 6y - 12 = 0$, is a chord of a circle S, whose centre is at $(-3, 2)$, then the radius of S is **[JEE Main 2016, 4M]**

(a) 5 (b) 10

(c) $5\sqrt{2}$ (d) $5\sqrt{3}$

140. Let RS be the diameter of the circle $x^2 + y^2 = 1$, where S is the point (1, 0). Let P be a variable point (other than R and S) on the circle and tangents to the circle at S and P meet at the point Q. The normal to the circle at P intersects a line drawn through Q parallel to RS at point E. Then the locus of E passes through the point(s) **[JEE Advanced 2016, 4M]**

(a) $\left(\frac{1}{3}, \frac{1}{\sqrt{3}}\right)$ (b) $\left(\frac{1}{4}, \frac{1}{2}\right)$

(c) $\left(\frac{1}{3}, -\frac{1}{\sqrt{3}}\right)$ (d) $\left(\frac{1}{4}, -\frac{1}{2}\right)$

141. For how many values of p, the circle $x^2 + y^2 + 2x + 4y - p = 0$ and the co-ordinate axes have exactly three common points? **[JEE Advanced 2017, 3M]**

Answers

Exercise for Session 1

1. (d) 2. (b) 3. (b) 4. (b) 5. (a)
6. (c) 7. (d) 8. (a) 9. (c) 10. (c)
11. (b) 12. (a) 13. $\left(\frac{-2}{5}, \frac{4}{5}\right)$; 2

15. $x^2 + y^2 - 2x - 4y - 4 = 0$

16. $x^2 + y^2 - 2x - 8y + 15 = 0$

18. $(x+1)^2 + (y-3)^2 = 4$; $(-1, 3)$; 2

Exercise for Session 2

1. (c) 2. (b) 3. (b) 4. (c) 5. (a)
6. (a) 7. (c) 8. (b) 9. (d) 10. (c)
11. (c) 12. (a) 13. $x^2 + y^2 - y - 16 = 0$; $\left(0, \frac{1}{2}\right)$; $\frac{\sqrt{65}}{2}$

14. $(-2, -7)$ 15. $x^2 + y^2 - 2x - 3y - 18 = 0$

16. $(x^2 + y^2 - 4x - 2y + 4) = 0$

17. $x^2 + y^2 - 6x + 2y - 15 = 0$

Exercise for Session 3

1. (d) 2. (a) 3. (a) 4. (d) 5. (d)
6. (c) 7. (a) 8. (a) 9. (d) 10. (b)
11. (a) 12. (c) 13. $x^2 + y^2 \pm 10x - 6y + 9 = 0$

15. $\lambda \in (-1, 4)$ 16. $x^2 + y^2 - 4x - 6y = 0$

Exercise for Session 4

1. (c) 2. (c) 3. (c) 4. (d) 5. (b)
6. (b) 7. (b) 8. (a) 9. (d) 10. (b)
11. (d) 12. (a)

14. (i) $3x - 4y + 20 = 0$ and $3x - 4y - 10 = 0$ (ii) $4x + 3y + 5 = 0$ and $4x + 3y - 25 = 0$,

15. centre of the circle $(0, 1, \pm r\sqrt{2})$, where r is radius

16. 15, − 35

Exercise for Session 5

1. (c) 2. (b) 3. (c) 4. (b) 5. (d)
6. (d) 7. (b) 8. (c) 9. (b) 10. (a)
11. (c) 12. (d) 14. 8 sq units

16. $3x + 2y - 13 = 0$ 17. $\left(\frac{5}{16}\right)$

Exercise for Session 6

1. (a) 2. (c) 3. (a) 4. (d) 5. (c) 6. (b)
7. (c) 8. (b) 9. (b) 10. (d) 11. (b) 12. (b)

13. $4x^2 + 4y^2 + 30x - 13y - 25 = 0$ 14. $2\sqrt{2}$

16. Direct common tangents are $3x + 4y = 57$, $7x - 24y = 233$, Transverse common tangents are $4x - 3y = 26$, $24x + 7y = 156$

Exercise for Session 7

1. (d) 2. (c) 3. (a) 4. (b) 5. (c)
6. (a) 7. (b) 8. (d) 9. (b) 10. (a) 11. (d)
12. (a) 14. $x^2 + y^2 - 6x - 6y + 9 = 0$ 16. $\left(\frac{-16}{21}, \frac{-31}{63}\right)$

17. $4x^2 + 4y^2 + 6x + 10y - 1 = 0$ 18. $x + y - 5 = 0$

Chapter Exercises

1. (b) 2. (a) 3. (b) 4. (b) 5. (a) 6. (d)
7. (a) 8. (a) 9. (c) 10. (b) 11. (c) 12. (c)
13. (d) 14. (d) 15. (a) 16. (d) 17. (d) 18. (d)
19. (b) 20. (a) 21. (c) 22. (b) 23. (d) 24. (c)
25. (a) 26. (b) 27. (b) 28. (c) 29. (b) 30. (a)
31. (b,d) 32. (b,d) 33. (a,b,c,d) 34. (a,d) 35. (b,d)
36. (b,c) 37. (a,b,c,d) 38. (b,d) 39. (a,d) 40. (a,d)
41. (a,c) 42. (a,c) 43. (a,c) 44. (a,c,d) 45. (a,b) 46. (b)
47. (c) 48. (b) 49. (b) 50. (d) 51. (b) 52. (a)
53. (c) 54. (b) 55. (b) 56. (b) 57. (b) 58. (a)
59. (a) 60. (d) 61. (d) 62. (a) 63. (c) 64. (a)
65. (d) 66. (c) 67. (4) 68. (6) 69. (1) 70. (4)
71. (9) 72. (3) 73. (4) 74. (3) 75. (9) 76. (7)

77. (A) → (p, s); (B) → (q, r); (C) → (q); (D) → (p, q, s)

78. (A) → (q, r) ; (B) → (p); (C) → (p) (D) → (s)

79. (A) → (q, s); (B) → (r,t); (C) → (p,s)

80. (A) → (p, q, s); (B) → (p, q, s, t); (C) → (p, q, r, s)

81. (d) 82. (a) 83. (d) 84. (d) 85. (c) 86. (b)
87. (b) 88. (a) 89. $(x^2 + y^2 - x - y) = 0$

90. $x^2 + y^2 - 6x - 2y + 1 = 0$

91. $x^2 + y^2 \pm \sqrt{m(m+n)}\,x \pm \sqrt{n(m+n)}\,y = 0$

92. $25x^2 + 25y^2 - 20x + 2y - 60 = 0$

93. (5) 94. 18 sq units

95. 1.5 units 96. $\left(\frac{9}{5}, \frac{-12}{5}\right)$ or $\left(\frac{-9}{5}, \frac{12}{5}\right)$

97. $3(3 + \sqrt{10})$ 98. $\frac{4\sqrt{3}}{9}$ sq units

99. $a_1 a_2 (x^2 + y^2) + (a_1 c_2 + a_2 c_1)x + (b_1 c_2 + b_2 c_1)y = 0$

100. $(-4, 4)$ or $\left(\frac{-1}{2}, \frac{1}{2}\right)$

101. $4a^2 + 4b^2 - c^2 - 8ab + 4bc - 4ca < 0$

105. (d) 106. (b) 107. (d) 108. (d) 109. (a) 110. (b)
111. (c) 112. (d) 113. (d) 114. (a) 115. (d) 116. (d)
117. (a) 118. (d) 119. (c) 120. (c) 121. (b) 122. (8)
123. (a) 124. (a) 125. (d) 126. (2) 127. (a) 128. (a)
129. (a) 130. (d) 131. (a) 132. (c) 133. (a,c) 134. (b)
135. (b,c) 136. (a) 137. (a) 138. (b) 139. (d) 140. (a,c)
141. (2)

Solutions

1. $AB^2 = 4AM^2 = 4\left(4 - \frac{n^2}{2}\right) = 2(8 - n^2)$

Hence, required sum $= 2(8 - 1^2 + 8 - 2^2) = 22$

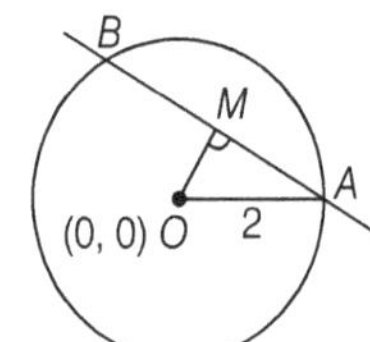

2. Tangent at $(5\sqrt{2}\cos\theta, 5\sqrt{2}\sin\theta)$ is

$$x\cos\theta + y\sin\theta = 5\sqrt{2}$$

$\therefore$ $OP = 5\sqrt{2}\sec\theta, OP_1 = 5\sqrt{2}\operatorname{cosec}\theta$

$\therefore$ Area $(\Delta PP_1P_2) = 2 \times$ area of ΔOPP_1

$$= 2 \times \frac{1}{2} \times 5\sqrt{2}\sec\theta \times 5\sqrt{2}\operatorname{cosec}\theta$$

$$= \frac{100}{\sin 2\theta},$$

Area $(\Delta PP_1P_2)_{\min} = 100$

$\Rightarrow$ $\theta = \frac{\pi}{4} \Rightarrow OP = 10$

$\Rightarrow$ $P \equiv (10, 0), (-10, 0)$

3. Let $S \equiv x^2 + y^2 - 2 = 0, P \equiv (2, 2)$

$\therefore$ $S_1 = 2^2 + 2^2 - 2 = 6 > 0$

$\Rightarrow P$ lies outside the circle

$$PA.PB = (PT)^2 = S_1 = 6 \quad \text{...(i)}$$

given $\frac{PB}{PA} = 3$ ...(ii)

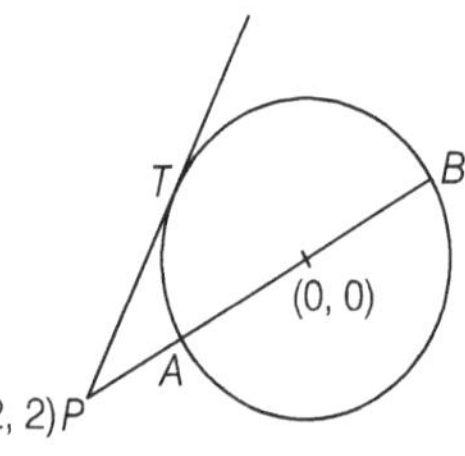

From Eqs. (i) and (ii), we get

$$PA = \sqrt{2}, PB = 3\sqrt{2}$$

$\Rightarrow$ $AB = PB - PA = 2\sqrt{2} =$ Diameter of circle

Hence, chord AB passes through the centre $(0, 0)$, $y = x$

4. Let $S \equiv (x - 2)^2 + y^2 - 4 = 0$

Its centre $C \equiv (2, 0)$ and radius $r = 2$

Distance between $C \equiv (2, 0)$ and (5, 6) is $\sqrt{(2-5)^2 + (0-6)^2}$

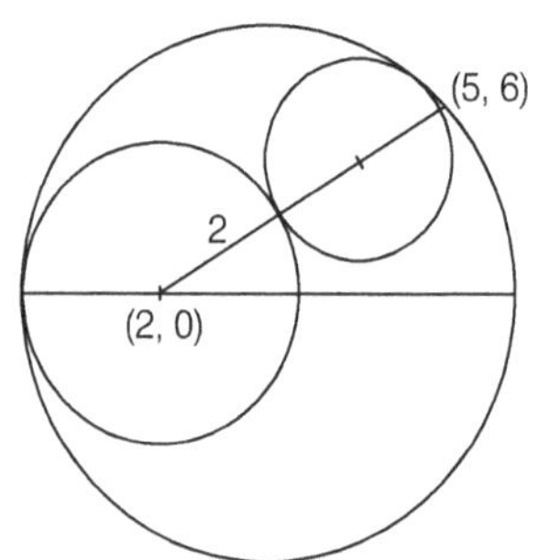

i.e. $3\sqrt{5}$

$\therefore$ $r_1r_2 = \left(\frac{3\sqrt{5} - 2}{2}\right) \cdot \left(\frac{3\sqrt{5} + 2}{2}\right)$

$$= \frac{41}{4}$$

5. Any circle which touches $3x + 4y - 7 = 0$ at (1, 1) will be of the form

$$S(x, y) \equiv (x - 1)^2 + (y - 1)^2 + \lambda(3x + 4y - 7) = 0$$

Since, $S(2, 3) = 16 \Rightarrow 1 + 4 + \lambda(11) = 16$

$\therefore$ $\lambda = 1$

So, required circle will be $x^2 + y^2 + x + 2y - 5 = 0$

6. Let $S \equiv x^2 + y^2 - 2x + 4y - \lambda = 0$

for interval point $P(2, 8)$,

$$4 + 64 - 4 + 32 - \lambda < 0$$

$\Rightarrow$ $\lambda > 96$ ...(i)

and x-intercept $= 2\sqrt{(1 + \lambda)}$ and y-intercept $= 2\sqrt{(4 + \lambda)}$

given $2\sqrt{(1 + \lambda)} < 0 \Rightarrow \lambda < -1$ ...(ii)

and $2\sqrt{(4 + \lambda)} < 0 \Rightarrow \lambda < -4$ ...(iii)

from Eqs. (i), (ii) and (iii), we get

$$\lambda \in \phi$$

7. Let $S \equiv x^2 + y^2 + 2x + 4y - 4 = 0$

Its centre $C \equiv (-1, -2)$ and radius $r = 3$. The points on the circle which are nearest and farthest to the point $P(a, b)$ are Q and R respectively. Thus, the circle centred at Q having radius PQ will be the smallest circle while the circle centred at R having radius PR will be the largest required circle.

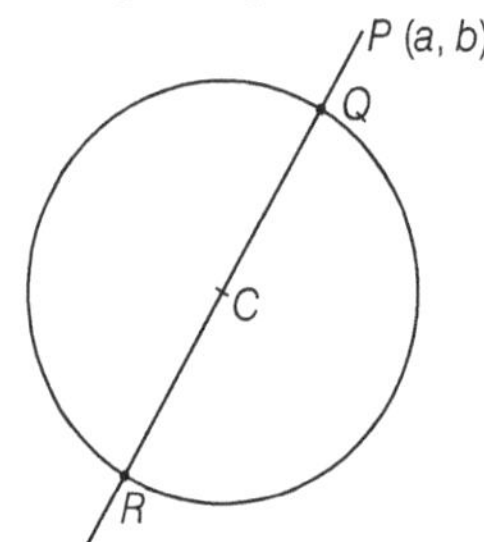

Hence, the difference between their radii is

$$PR - PQ = QR = 2 \times 3 = 6$$

8. Radius $= \sqrt{(a - \pi)^2 + (b - e)^2}$

$$= \text{irrational} = k$$

$\therefore$ Circle $(x - \pi)^2 + (y - e)^2 = k^2$

9. Given $\lambda L_2L_3 + \mu L_3L_1 + v L_1L_2 = 0$

$$\Rightarrow \lambda(y - m_2x - c_2)(y - m_3x - c_3) + \mu(y - m_3x - c_3)(y - m_1x - c_1) + v(y - m_1x - c_1)(y - m_2x - c_2) = 0$$

for circle coefficient of x^2 = coefficient of y^2 and coefficient of $xy = 0$,

then, $\lambda(m_2m_3 - 1) + \mu(m_3m_1 - 1) + v(m_1m_2 - 1) = 0$

and $(m_2 + m_3)\lambda + (m_3 + m_1)\mu + (m_1 + m_2)v = 0$

10. $\because f(x,y) \equiv x^2 + y^2 + 2ax + 2by + c = 0$

$\Rightarrow \quad f(x,0) = 0 \Rightarrow x^2 + 2ax + c = (x-2)^2$

$\therefore \quad a = -2, c = 4$

and $\quad f(0,y) = 0 \Rightarrow y^2 + 2by + c = (y-2)(y-3)$

$\therefore \quad 2b = -5, c = 6$

or $\quad b = -\dfrac{5}{2}, c = 6$

Clearly, that data are not consistent.

11. Given, $(1 + \alpha x)^n = 1 + 8x + 24x^2 + \dots$

$$\Rightarrow \quad 1 + n(\alpha x) + \frac{n(n-1)}{1.2}(\alpha x)^2 + \dots = 1 + 8x + 24x^2 + \dots$$

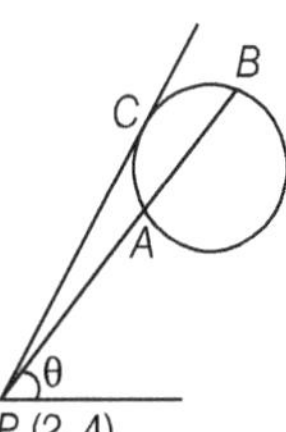

Equating the coefficients of x and x^2, we get

$$n\alpha = 8, \frac{n\alpha(n\alpha - \alpha)}{1.2} = 24$$

or $\quad \dfrac{8(8-\alpha)}{2} = 24 \Rightarrow 8 - \alpha = 6$

$\therefore \quad \alpha = 2$ and $n = 4$

Equation of line is $\dfrac{x-2}{\cos\theta} = \dfrac{y-4}{\sin\theta} = r$, then point $(2 + r\cos\theta, 4 + r\sin\theta)$ lies on the circle $x^2 + y^2 = 4$,

then, $\quad (2 + r\cos\theta)^2 + (4 + r\sin\theta)^2 = 4$

or $\quad r^2 + 4r(\cos\theta + 2\sin\theta) + 16 = 0$

$\therefore \quad PA \cdot PB = r_1r_2 = \dfrac{16}{1} = 16$

Aliter : $\quad PA \cdot PB = (PC)^2 = 2^2 + 4^2 - 4 = 16$

12. For interior point $OP < 5$

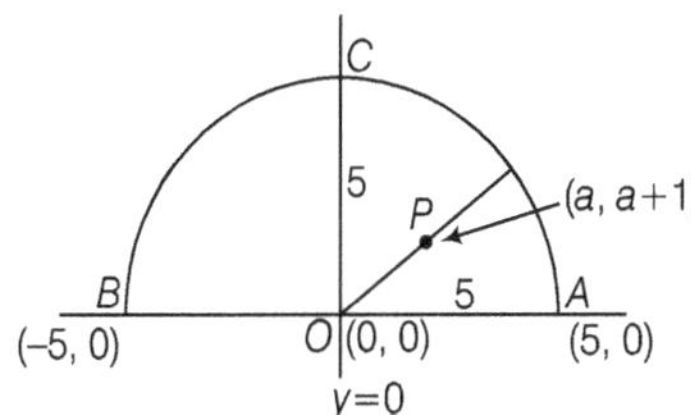

$\Rightarrow \quad \sqrt{a^2 + (a+1)^2} < 5$

$\Rightarrow \quad 2a^2 + 2a - 24 < 0$

$\therefore \quad a^2 + a - 12 < 0$

$(a+4)(a-3) < 0$

$\Rightarrow -4 < a < 3$ and for I and II quadrant

$a + 1 > 0$

$\therefore \quad a > -1$

Hence, $-1 < a < 3$

13. Let $S(x,y) \equiv x^2 + y^2 + 2gx + 2fy + c = 0$

$\Rightarrow \quad S(x,2) = 0$

$\Rightarrow \quad x^2 + 4 + 2gx + 4f + c = (x-1)^2$

$\therefore \quad g = -1, 3 + 4f + c = 0 \quad$ ...(i)

and $\quad S(1,y) = 0 \Rightarrow 1 + y^2 + 2g + 2fy + c = (y-0)(y-2)$

$\therefore \quad f = -1, 1 + 2g + c = 0 \quad$ ...(ii)

From Eqs. (i) and (ii), we get

$$g = -1, f = -1, c = 1$$

$\therefore$ Equation of required circle is

$$x^2 + y^2 - 2x - 2y + 1 = 0$$

14. See the diagram. Since, there is no condition on θ, Q can be placed either at Q_1 or Q_2 for a particular position of P. So option (a) and (b) cannot be definitely true.

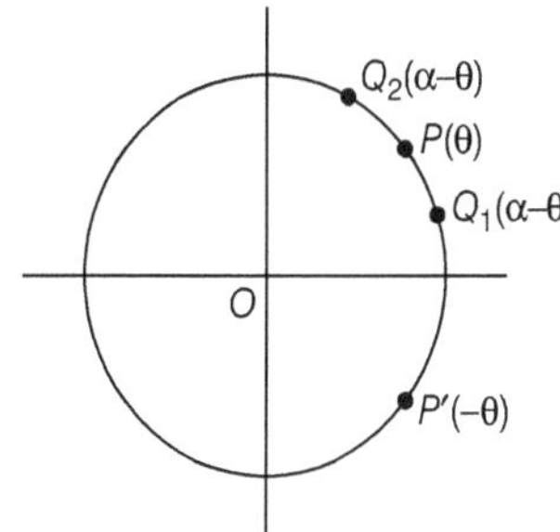

Consider a line through origin $y = mx$. If Q and P are reflection of each other with line mirror $y = mx$

(Slope of PQ) $\times m = -1$

or $\quad m\left(\dfrac{\sin\theta - \sin(\alpha - \theta)}{\cos\theta - \cos(\alpha - \theta)}\right) = -1$

$$m\left(\frac{2\cos\left(\frac{\alpha}{2}\right).\sin\left(\frac{2\theta - \alpha}{2}\right)}{2\sin\left(\frac{\alpha}{2}\right).\sin\left(\frac{\alpha - 2\theta}{2}\right)}\right) = -1$$

or $\quad m\left(-\cot\dfrac{\alpha}{2}\right) = -1$

or $\quad m = \tan\left(\dfrac{\alpha}{2}\right)$

15. Since, $x^2 + y^2 < 25$ and x and y are integers, the possible values of x and $y \in (0, \pm 1, \pm 2, \pm 3, \pm 4)$. Thus, x and y can be chosen in $9 \times 9 = 81$ ways. However, we have to exclude cases (3, 4), (4,3) and (4, 4) i.e. $3 \times 4 = 12$ cases. Hence, the number of permissible values

$$= 81 - 12 = 69$$

16. $\because$ The point $([P+1],[P])$ lies inside the circle $x^2+y^2-2x-15=0$, then

$$[P+1]^2+[P]^2-2[P+1]-15<0$$

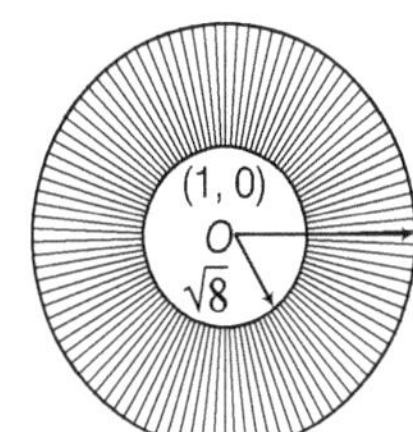

$$\Rightarrow \quad ([P]+1)^2+[P]^2-2([P]+1)-15<0$$

$$\Rightarrow \quad 2[P]^2-16<0 \Rightarrow [P]^2<8 \quad \text{...(i)}$$

$\because$ Circles are concentric

$\therefore$ point $([P+1],[P])$ out side the circle

$$x^2+y^2-2x-7=0$$

$$\therefore \quad ([P]+1)^2+[P]^2-2([P+1])-7>0$$

$$\Rightarrow \quad ([P]+1)^2+[P]^2-2([P]+1)-7>0$$

$$\Rightarrow \quad 2[P]^2-8>0$$

$$\therefore \quad [P]^2>4 \quad \text{...(ii)}$$

From Eqs. (i) and (ii), we get

$4<[P]^2<8$ which is impossible

$\therefore$ For no value of 'P' the point will be within the region.

17. The circles are $x^2+y^2=2^2$ and $(x-4)^2+(y-0)^2=3^2$

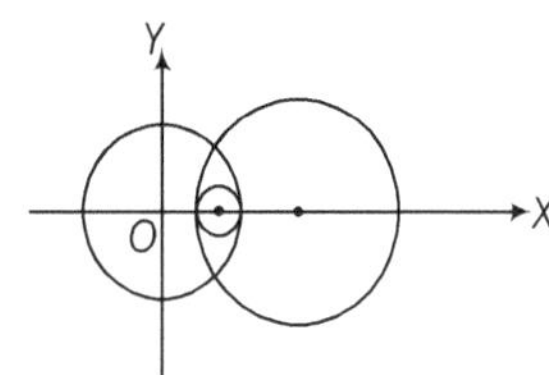

For the point P to enclose greatest area, the arbitrarily chosen point should be $\left(\frac{3}{2},0\right)$ and P should move in a circle of radius $\frac{1}{2}$

The locus of P is $\left(x-\frac{3}{2}\right)^2+(y-0)^2=\left(\frac{1}{2}\right)^2$

$$\Rightarrow \quad x^2+y^2-3x+2=0.$$

18. Since, $y=|x|+c$ and $x^2+y^2-8|x|-9=0$ both are symmetrical about Y-axis for $x>0$, $y=x+c$.

Equation of tangent to circle $x^2+y^2-8x-9=0$

Parallel to $y=x+c$ is $y=(x-4)+5\sqrt{(1+1)}$

$$\Rightarrow \quad y=x+(5\sqrt{2}-4)$$

for no solution $c>5\sqrt{2}-4$,

$$\therefore \quad c\in(5\sqrt{2}-4,\infty)$$

19. Let $\angle AOL=\theta$

$$\therefore \quad A\equiv(a\cos\theta, a\sin\theta)$$

$$\therefore \quad M\equiv(a+a\cos\theta, a\sin\theta)$$

$$x=a+a\cos\theta$$

$$\Rightarrow \quad (x-a)=a\cos\theta \quad \text{...(i)}$$

and $\quad y=a\sin\theta$

From Eqs. (i) and (ii), we get

$$(x-a)^2+y^2=a^2$$

$$\Rightarrow \quad x^2+y^2-2ax=0$$

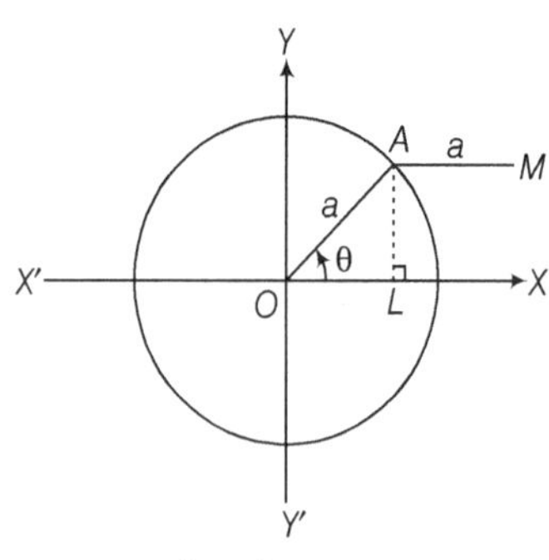

$$\Rightarrow \quad x^2+y^2=2ax$$

20. Equation of circle is $(2x-y+1)(x-2y+3)+\lambda xy=0$

for circle coefficient of $xy=0$

i.e. $\quad -5+\lambda=0,$

$$\therefore \quad \lambda=5$$

$\therefore$ Circle is $2x^2+2y^2+7x-5y+3=0$

$$\Rightarrow \quad x^2+y^2+\frac{7}{2}x-\frac{5}{2}y+\frac{3}{2}=0$$

$\therefore$ Centre is $\left(-\frac{7}{4},\frac{5}{4}\right)$

21. $\sqrt{\left\{\frac{\lambda^2}{4}+\frac{(1-\lambda)^2}{4}-5\right\}}\le 5$

$$\Rightarrow \quad \lambda^2+(1-\lambda)^2-20\le 100$$

$$\Rightarrow \quad 2\lambda^2-2\lambda-119\le 0$$

$$\therefore \quad \frac{1-\sqrt{239}}{2}\le\lambda\le\frac{1+\sqrt{239}}{2}$$

$$\Rightarrow \quad -7.2\le\lambda\le 8.2 \quad \text{(approx.)}$$

$$\therefore \quad \lambda=-7,-6,-5,\ldots,7,8$$

22. Let $\phi(x,y)\equiv x^2+y^2+2gx+2fy+c=0$

$$\therefore \quad \phi(0,\lambda)=0+\lambda^2+0+2f\lambda+c=0$$

have equal roots,

Then, $2+2=-\frac{2f}{1}$ and $2.2=\frac{c}{1}$

$$\therefore \quad f=-2 \text{ and } c=4$$

and $\phi(\lambda,0)\equiv\lambda^2+0+2g\lambda+0+c=0$

$$\therefore \quad \lambda^2+2g\lambda+c=0$$

Here, $c=4$

$$\therefore \quad \lambda^2+2g\lambda+4=0$$

have roots 4/5, 5

$$\therefore \quad \frac{4}{5}+5=-2g$$

$$\Rightarrow \quad g=-\frac{29}{10}$$

$$\therefore \quad \text{Centre} \equiv (-g,-f)-\left(\frac{29}{10},2\right)$$

23. Circle is $x^2+y^2=r^2\cos^2\theta+r^2\sin^2\theta$

$$x^2+y^2=r^2$$

Equation of tangent at θ is

$$x\cos\theta+y\sin\theta=r \quad ...(i)$$

and at $\left(\theta+\frac{\pi}{3}\right)$ is $x\cos\left(\theta+\frac{\pi}{3}\right)+y\sin\left(\theta+\frac{\pi}{3}\right)=r$

$$\Rightarrow x\left(\frac{1}{2}\cos\theta-\frac{\sqrt{3}}{2}\sin\theta\right)+y\left(\frac{1}{2}\sin\theta+\frac{\sqrt{3}}{2}\cos\theta\right)=r$$

$$\Rightarrow x\cos\theta+y\sin\theta-x\sqrt{3}\sin\theta+y\sqrt{3}\cos\theta=2r$$

$$\Rightarrow r-\sqrt{3}(x\sin\theta-y\cos\theta)=2r$$

or $$x\sin\theta-y\cos\theta=-\frac{r}{\sqrt{3}} \quad ...(ii)$$

Squaring and adding Eqs. (i) and (ii), then we get

$$x^2+y^2=\frac{4r^2}{3}\Rightarrow 3(x^2+y^2)=4r^2$$

24. Let MN be the diameter of the circle whose equation is

$$4y=x+7 \quad ...(i)$$

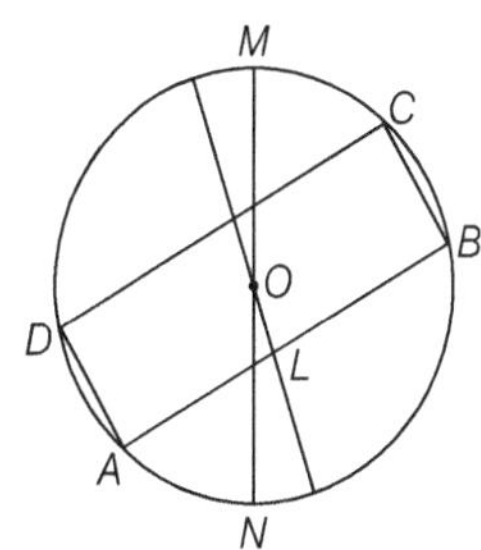

and coordinates of A and B are $(-3,4)$ and $(5,4)$ respectively.
Equation of $\perp$ bisector of AB is $[L\equiv(1,4)]$

$$y-4=-\frac{1}{0}(x-1) \quad (\because \text{slope of } AB=0)$$

$$\therefore \quad x=1 \quad ...(ii)$$

Solving Eqs. (i) and (ii), we get the coordinates of the centre of the circle as (1, 2)

$$\therefore \quad OL=\sqrt{(1-1)^2+(4-2)^2}=2$$

$$\therefore \quad BC=2OL=4 \text{ unit}$$

$$AB=8 \text{ unit}$$

$\therefore$ Area of rectangle $ABCD=4\times8$

$$=32 \text{ sq units.}$$

25. $\because OC\cdot OA=ab=OB\cdot OD$

$\therefore A, B, C, D$ are concyclic.

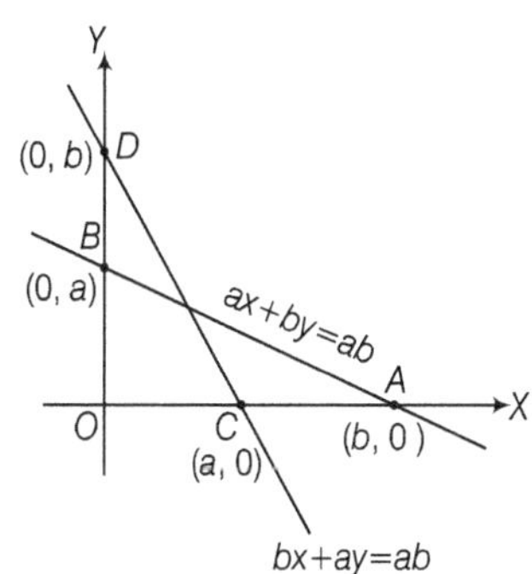

26. Coordinates of P, Q, R are $(\cos\alpha,\sin\alpha),(\cos\beta,\sin\beta)$ and $(\cos\gamma,\sin\gamma)$ respectively.

and $\quad A\equiv(-1,0)$

$$\therefore \quad AP=\sqrt{((1+\cos\alpha)^2+\sin^2\alpha)}=2\cos\left(\frac{\alpha}{2}\right)$$

$$AQ=\sqrt{((1+\cos\beta)^2+\sin^2\beta)}=2\cos\left(\frac{\beta}{2}\right)$$

$$AR=\sqrt{((1+\cos\gamma)^2+\sin^2\gamma)}=2\cos\left(\frac{\gamma}{2}\right)$$

$\because AP, AQ, AR$ are in GP, then

$\cos\left(\frac{\alpha}{2}\right),\cos\left(\frac{\beta}{2}\right),\cos\left(\frac{\gamma}{2}\right)$ are also in GP.

27. Let equation of circle be

$$x^2+y^2+2gx+2fy+c=0$$

It pass through (2, 0) and (0, 4), then $4+0+4g+0+c=0$

$$\Rightarrow \quad g=-\frac{(c+4)}{4} \text{ and } 0+16+0+8f+c=0$$

$$\Rightarrow \quad f=-\frac{(c+16)}{8}$$

$$\because \quad \text{Radius } r=\sqrt{(g^2+f^2-c)}$$

$$=\sqrt{\left\{\frac{(c+4)^2}{16}+\frac{(c+16)^2}{64}-c\right\}}$$

$$=\sqrt{\left\{\frac{4\{c^2+8c+16\}+\{c^2+32c+256\}-64c}{64}\right\}}$$

$$=\sqrt{\left(\frac{5c^2+320}{64}\right)}$$

For minimum radius $c=0$

$$\therefore \quad g=-1, f=-2$$

Required circle is $x^2+y^2-2x-4y=0$

28. The particle which moves clockwise is moving three times as fast as the particle moving anticlockwise ($\because$ speed in clockwise $3v$ and in anticlockwise v).

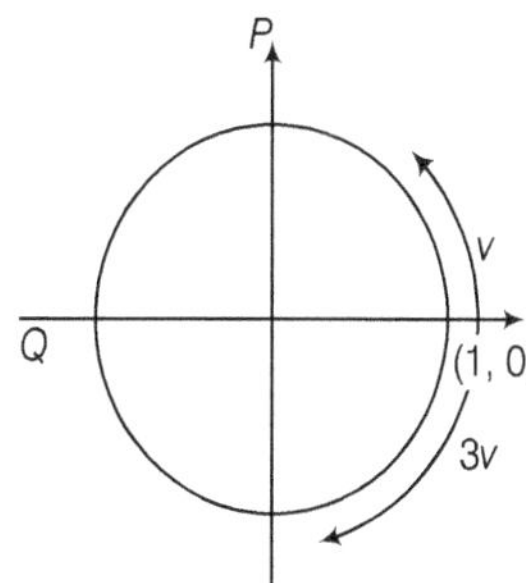

This mean the clockwise particle travels $\left(\frac{3}{4}\right)$th of the way around the circle, the anticlockwise particle will travel $\left(\frac{1}{4}\right)$th of the way around the circle. So, the second particle will meet at $P(0,1)$.

Using the same logic, they will meet at $Q(-1,0)$, when they meet the second time.

29. $\because \dfrac{BP}{PA} = \alpha$

$BP : PA = \alpha : 1$

$\therefore$ Coordinates of P is $\left(\dfrac{3+\alpha}{1+\alpha}, \dfrac{4}{\alpha+1}\right)$, P lie on $x^2 + y^2 = 4$

$\Rightarrow \quad (\alpha+3)^2 + 16 = 4(\alpha+1)^2$

$\Rightarrow \quad 3\alpha^2 + 2\alpha - 21 = 0 \quad \text{...(i)}$

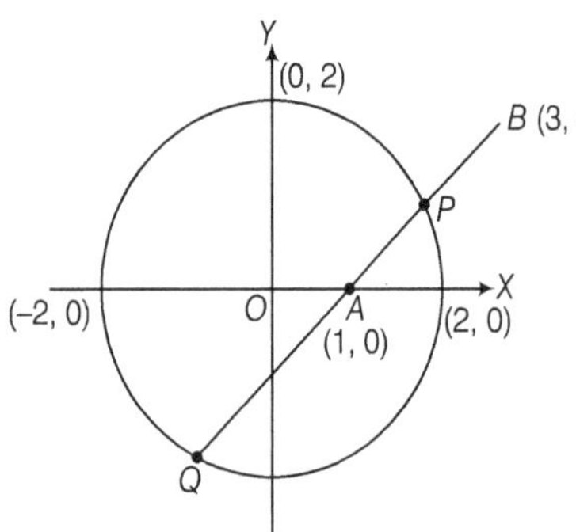

and $\quad \dfrac{BQ}{QA} = \dfrac{\beta}{1}$

$BQ : QA = \beta : 1$ or $\dfrac{BQ}{QA} - 1 = \beta - 1$

$\dfrac{AB}{QA} = \dfrac{(\beta-1)}{1}$

$AB : QA = (\beta - 1) : 1$

$\therefore$ Coordinates of Q is $\left(\dfrac{\beta-3}{\beta-1}, \dfrac{-4}{\beta-1}\right)$

Q lie on $x^2 + y^2 = 4$

$\therefore \quad (\beta-3)^2 + 16 = 4(\beta-1)^2$

$\Rightarrow \quad 3\beta^2 - 21\beta - 21 = 0$

Hence, α is a root of $3x^2 + 2x - 21 = 0$

and β is a root of $3x^2 - 2x - 21 = 0$

30. $\because \angle ACB = \dfrac{\pi}{3}$ (given)

$\therefore \angle AOB = \dfrac{2\pi}{3}$

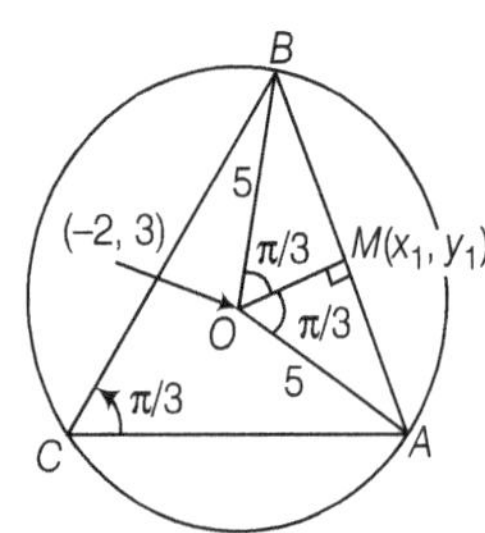

$\Rightarrow \quad \angle AOM = \angle BOM = \dfrac{\pi}{3}$

Let mid-point of chord AB is (x_1, y_1)

$\therefore$ In ΔAOM,

$$\cos\frac{\pi}{3} = \frac{OM}{OA} = \frac{\sqrt{(x_1+2)^2 + (y_1-3)^2}}{5}$$

or $\quad \left(\dfrac{5}{2}\right)^2 = (x_1+2)^2 + (y_1-3)^2$

$\Rightarrow \quad \dfrac{25}{4} = x_1^2 + y_1^2 + 4x_1 - 6y_1 + 13$

$4x_1^2 + 4y_1^2 + 16x_1 - 24y_1 + 27 = 0$

$\therefore$ Locus of mid-point is

$$x^2 + y^2 + 4x - 6y + \frac{27}{4} = 0$$

$\Rightarrow \quad (x+2)^2 + (y-3)^2 = 6.25$

31. $\because r = a\cos\theta + b\sin\theta$

$\Rightarrow \quad r^2 = a(r\cos\theta) + b(r\sin\theta)$

or $\quad x^2 + y^2 = ax + by \quad (\because x = r\cos\theta, y = r\sin\theta)$

or $\quad x^2 + y^2 - ax - by = 0 \quad \text{...(i)}$

Circle pass through O (origin)

given $\quad \angle AOB = 90°$

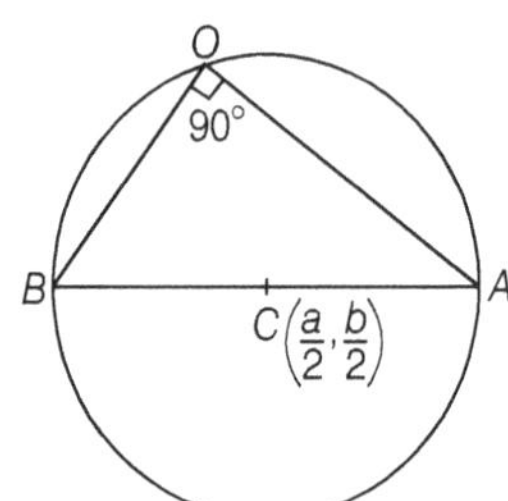

$\therefore AB$ is Diameter of circle Eq. (i), Centre is $\left(\dfrac{a}{2}, \dfrac{b}{2}\right)$

$\therefore$ Locus of mid point AB ($\because$ mid-point of AB is C)

$$x = \frac{a}{2}, y = \frac{b}{2}$$

32. Slope of $PC = \dfrac{-3-2}{2-7} = 1$

If $\tan\theta = 1$

$\therefore \quad \theta = 45°$

Equation of PA is $\dfrac{x-7}{\frac{1}{\sqrt{2}}} = \dfrac{y-2}{\frac{1}{\sqrt{2}}} = r$

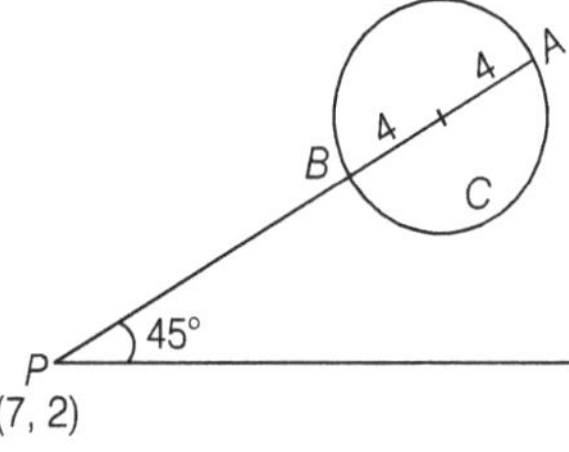

$\therefore \quad \left(7 + \dfrac{r}{\sqrt{2}}, 2 + \dfrac{r}{\sqrt{2}}\right)$ lie on circle,

then, $\left(7 + \dfrac{r}{\sqrt{2}}\right)^2 + \left(2 + \dfrac{r}{\sqrt{2}}\right)^2 - 4\left(7 + \dfrac{r}{\sqrt{2}}\right) + 6\left(2 + \dfrac{r}{\sqrt{2}}\right) - 3 = 0$

$\therefore \quad r^2 = -5\sqrt{2} \pm 4$

$\therefore \quad r = -5\sqrt{2} \pm 4$

$\therefore$ Points $\left(7+\frac{-5\sqrt{2}\pm4}{\sqrt{2}}, 2+\frac{-5\sqrt{2}\pm4}{\sqrt{2}}\right)$

$\Rightarrow (2\pm2\sqrt{2}, -3\pm2\sqrt{2})$

Taking + ve sign for A, –ve sign for B.

33. Let $S \equiv x^2+y^2+2gx+2fy+c=0$

$$S_1 \equiv x^2+y^2-4=0$$
$$S_2 \equiv x^2+y^2-6x-8y+10=0$$
$$S_3 \equiv x^2+y^2+2x-4y-2=0$$

$\therefore$ Common chords are

$$S-S_1 \equiv 2gx+2fy+c+4=0 \quad \text{...(i)}$$
$$S-S_2 \equiv (2g+6)x+(2f+8)y+c-10=0 \quad \text{...(ii)}$$
$$S-S_3 \equiv (2g-2)x+(2f+4)y+c+2=0 \quad \text{...(iii)}$$

For cutting the extremities of diameter, chords Eqs. (i), (ii) and (iii) pass through the centres of S_1, S_2 and S_3 respectively, then

$\therefore \quad c+4=0, (2g+6)3+(2f+8)4+c-10=0$

and $(2g-2)(-1)+(2f+4)(2)+c+2=0$

after solving $c=-4$, $g=-2$, $f=-3$

34.

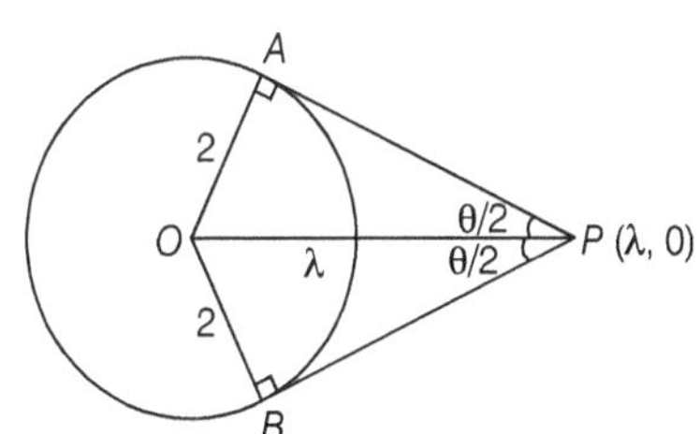

$\because \quad \frac{\pi}{2}<\theta<\frac{2\pi}{3} \Rightarrow \frac{\pi}{4}<\frac{\theta}{2}<\frac{\pi}{3}$

$\Rightarrow \quad \frac{1}{\sqrt{2}}<\sin\left(\frac{\theta}{2}\right)<\frac{\sqrt{3}}{2}$

$\Rightarrow \quad \frac{1}{\sqrt{2}}<\frac{2}{\lambda}<\frac{\sqrt{3}}{2}$ or $\sqrt{2}>\frac{\lambda}{2}>\frac{2}{\sqrt{3}}$

or $\quad 2\sqrt{2}>\lambda>\frac{4}{\sqrt{3}}$ or $\frac{4}{\sqrt{3}}<\lambda<2\sqrt{2}$

35. It is clear that N is the mid-point of M and P

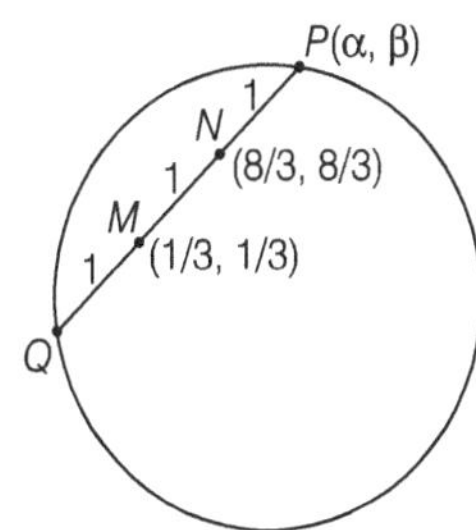

$\therefore \quad \alpha=\frac{16}{3}-\frac{1}{3}=5$ and $\beta=\frac{16}{3}-\frac{1}{3}=5$

$(\alpha,\beta)\equiv(5,5)$ lie on the circle

$\therefore \quad 5^2+5^2-4\times5-2\times5-c=0$

$$c=20$$

or $\quad c^2-40c+400=0$

36. Let $M(\alpha,\beta)$

$\because \quad AM=2AB \Rightarrow AB+BM=2AB$

$\therefore \quad AB=BM$

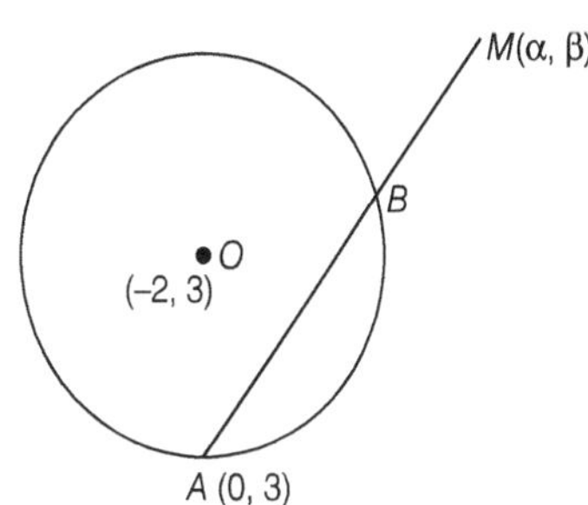

$\therefore B$ is the mid point of AM.

$\therefore$ Coordinates of B are $\left(\frac{\alpha}{2}, \frac{3+\beta}{2}\right)$ which lie on

$$x^2+4x+(y-3)^2=0$$
$$\frac{\alpha^2}{4}+4\times\frac{\alpha}{2}+\left(\frac{3+\beta}{2}-3\right)^2=0$$
$$\alpha^2+8\alpha+(\beta-3)^2=0$$

$\therefore$ Requires locus is

$$x^2+8x+(y-3)^2=0$$

or $\quad x^2+y^2+8x-6y+9=0$

37. $x\cos\alpha+y\sin\alpha=2$ or $\frac{x}{2\sec\alpha}+\frac{y}{2\operatorname{cosec}\alpha}=1$

$$2\sec\alpha = +\text{ ve in IV}$$

and $\quad 2\operatorname{cosec}\alpha = -\text{ve in IV}$

value of g in I quadrant

$$g=\left(\frac{g\cos\alpha+g\sin\alpha-2}{\sqrt{1}}\right)$$

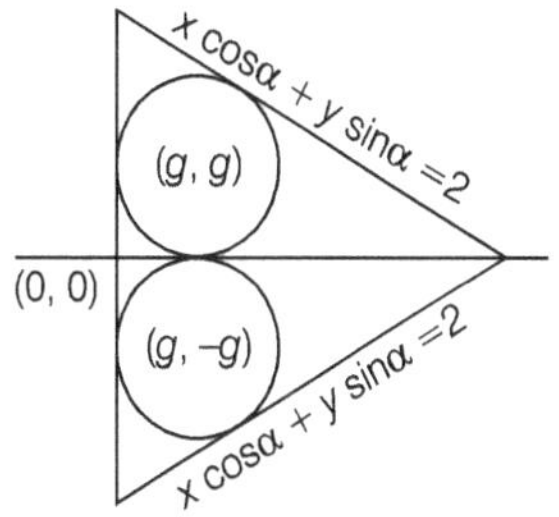

$\therefore \quad g=\frac{2}{\cos\alpha+\sin\alpha\pm1}$

and value g of in IV quadrant

$$g=\left|\frac{g\cos\alpha-g\sin\alpha-2}{1}\right|$$

$\Rightarrow \quad \pm g=g(\cos\alpha-\sin\alpha)-2$

$$g=\frac{2}{\cos\alpha-\sin\alpha\pm1}$$

Equation of circles in I quadrant

$$(x-g)^2+(y-g)^2=g^2$$

And in IV quadrant is $(x-g)^2+(y-g)^2=g^2$

38. $\therefore \quad \cot\left(\frac{\alpha}{2}\right) = \frac{\sqrt{S_1}}{\sqrt{(g^2+f^2-c)}}$

$\therefore \quad \tan\left(\frac{\alpha}{2}\right) = \frac{\sqrt{(g^2+f^2-c)}}{\sqrt{S_1}}$

$\therefore \quad \alpha = 2\tan^{-1}\left(\frac{\sqrt{(g^2+f^2-c)}}{\sqrt{S_1}}\right)$

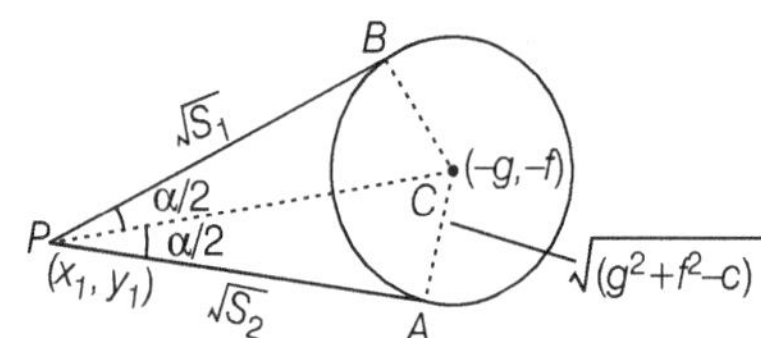

39. For condition of tangency

$$\frac{|4\lambda+3\lambda-12|}{5} = \lambda \Rightarrow \quad 7\lambda - 12 = \pm 5\lambda$$

$\therefore \quad \lambda = 1, 6$

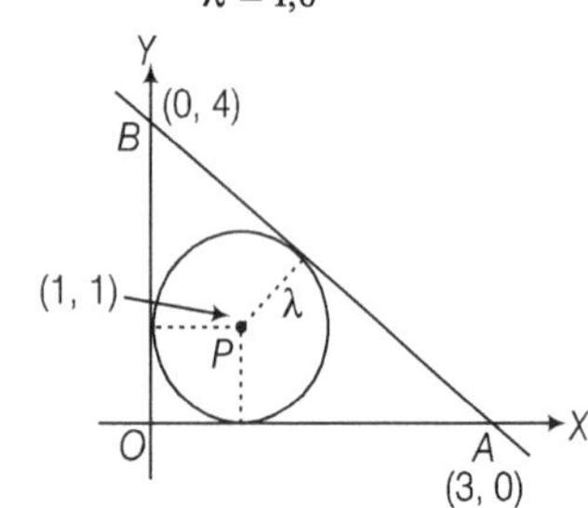

40. Let coordinates of $P \equiv (3\cos\alpha, 3\sin\alpha)$

Let x-coordinate of Q is x_1, then

y-coordinate of Q is $-7x_1 - 3$

$\therefore \quad Q \equiv (x_1, -7x_1 - 3)$

$\because x - y + 1 = 0$ is the perpendicular bisector of PQ, then mid-point of PQ lie on $x - y + 1 = 0$

$\Rightarrow \quad \frac{3\cos\alpha + x_1}{2} - \frac{3\sin\alpha - 7x_1 - 3}{2} + 1 = 0$

$\Rightarrow \quad 8x_1 + 3\cos\alpha - 3\sin\alpha + 5 = 0$

$\Rightarrow \quad 24x_1 + 9\cos\alpha - 9\sin\alpha + 15 = 0 \quad$ ...(i)

and slope of $(x - y + 1 = 0) \times$ slope of $PQ = -1$

$\Rightarrow \quad 1 \times \frac{3\sin\alpha + 7x_1 + 3}{3\cos\alpha - x_1} = -1$

$\Rightarrow \quad 3\sin\alpha + 7x_1 + 3 = -3\cos\alpha + x_1$

$\Rightarrow \quad 6x_1 + 3\sin\alpha + 3\cos\alpha + 3 = 0$

$\Rightarrow \quad 24x_1 + 12\sin\alpha + 12\cos\alpha + 12 = 0 \quad$ ...(ii)

Subtracting Eqs. (i) and (ii), we obtain

$-3\cos\alpha - 21\sin\alpha + 3 = 0$

$\Rightarrow \quad (1 - \cos\alpha) = 7\sin\alpha$

$\Rightarrow \quad (1-\cos\alpha)^2 = 49(1 - \cos^2\alpha)$

$\Rightarrow \quad (1-\cos\alpha)^2 = 49(1+\cos\alpha)(1-\cos\alpha)$

$\Rightarrow \quad (1-\cos\alpha)(1 - \cos\alpha - 49 - 49\cos\alpha) = 0$

$\therefore \quad \cos\alpha = 1$ and $\cos\alpha = -\frac{24}{25}$

$\therefore$ Coordinates of P are (3, 0) and $\left(-\frac{72}{25}, \frac{21}{25}\right)$.

41. Circle possible in I region and centre of circle on X-axis.

If centre is $(h, 0)$, then

$$\frac{|h-0-1|}{\sqrt{2}} = \sqrt{(h-3)^3 + \frac{7}{2}}$$

$\therefore \quad h = 6, 4$

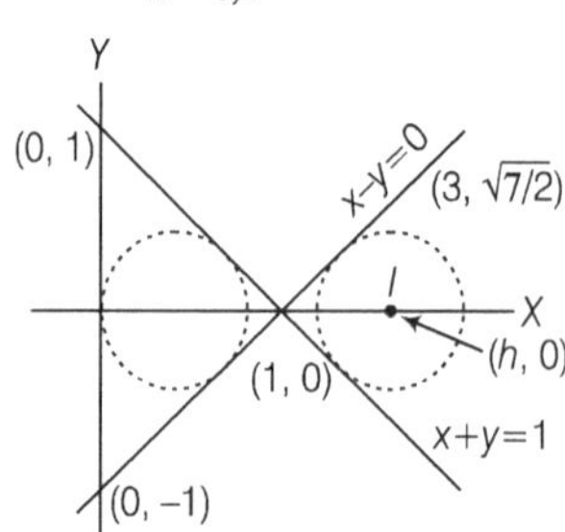

Then, centres are (6, 0) and (4, 0)

42. $\because C_2$ is the director circle of C_1

$\therefore$ Equation of C_2 is

$$x^2 + y^2 = 2(2)^2 = 8$$

Again C_3 is the director circle of C_2. Hence, the equation of C_3 is

$$x^2 + y^2 = 2(8) = 16$$

43. The equation of tangent in terms of slope of $x^2 + y^2 = 25$ is

$$y = mx \pm 5\sqrt{(1+m^2)} \quad \text{...(i)}$$

Given Eq. (i), pass through $(-2, 11)$, then

$$11 = -2m \pm 5\sqrt{(1+m^2)}$$

squaring both sides, then we get

$$21m^2 - 44m - 96 = 0$$

$\Rightarrow \quad (7m - 24)(3m + 4) = 0$

$\therefore \quad m = -\frac{4}{3}, \frac{24}{7}$

There from Eq. (i) we get required tangents are

$$24x - 7y \pm 125 = 0 \text{ and } 4x + 3y = \pm 25$$

Hence, tangents are $24x - 7y + 125 = 0$ and $4x + 3y = 25$

44. $C_1 \equiv x^2 + y^2 - 2x - 4y - 4 = 0 \quad$ ...(i)

and $\quad C_2 \equiv x^2 + y^2 + 2x + 4y + 4 = 0 \quad$ ...(ii)

$\therefore$ Radical axis is $C_1 - C_2 = 0$

$\Rightarrow \quad -4x - 8y - 8 = 0$

or $x + 2y + 2 = 0$ which is $L = 0$

(a) Option is correct.

Centre and radius of $C_1 = 0$ are (1, 2) and 3.

$\because$ Length of $\perp$ from (1, 2) on $L = 0$

is $\frac{|1+4+2|}{\sqrt{1+4}} = \frac{7}{\sqrt{5}} \neq$ radius

$\therefore$ **(b) Option is wrong.**

L is also the common chord of C_1 and C_2.

$\therefore$ **(c) Option is correct.**

$\because$ Centres of $C_1 = 0$ and $C_2 = 0$ are (1, 2) and $(-1, -2)$

$\therefore$ Slope of Line joining centres of circles $C_1 = 0$ and $C_2 = 0$ is

$$\frac{-2-2}{-1-1} = \frac{4}{2} = 2 = m_1 \quad \text{(say)}$$

and slope of $L = 0$ is $-\frac{1}{2} = m_2$ (say)

$\therefore \quad m_1 m_2 = -1$

Hence, L is perpendicular to the line joining centres of C_1 and C_2.

$\therefore$ **(d) Option is correct.**

45. Let slope of OA is m,

Then, $\left|\frac{m-1}{1+m}\right| = \tan 45°$

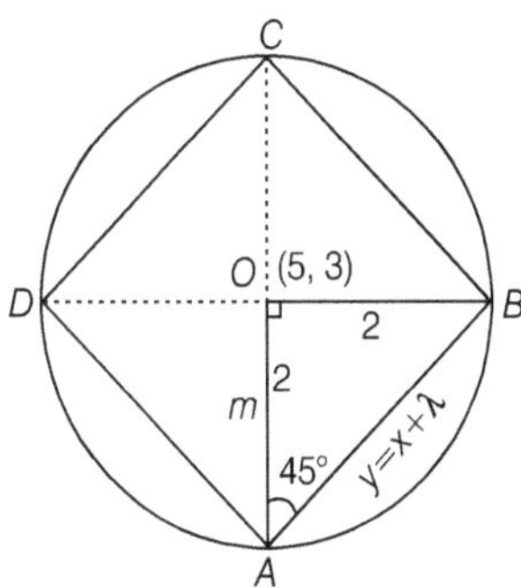

$\Rightarrow \quad \frac{m-1}{1+m} = \pm 1 \quad \text{or} \quad \frac{m-1}{m+1} = -1$

$\Rightarrow \quad m - 1 = -m - 1$

$\therefore \quad m = 0$

$\therefore$ Equation of OA is $y = 3$

Solving $y = 3$ and $x^2 + y^2 - 10x - 6y + 30 = 0$

$\Rightarrow \quad x^2 + 9 - 10x - 18 + 30 = 0$

$\Rightarrow \quad x^2 - 10x + 21 = 0$

$\Rightarrow \quad (x-7)(x-3) = 0$

or $\quad x = 3, 7$

$\therefore$ Two vertices are (3, 3) and (7, 3) and other diagonal is $\perp$ to $y = 3$ and through centre (5, 3) is $x = 5$.

Now, solving $x = 5$ and $x^2 + y^2 - 10x - 6y + 30 = 0$

$\Rightarrow \quad 25 + y^2 - 50 - 6y + 30 = 0$

$\Rightarrow \quad y^2 - 6y + 5 = 0$

$\Rightarrow \quad (y-1)(y-5) = 0 \text{ or } y = 1, 5$

$\therefore$ Other two vertices are (5, 1) and (5, 5).

Sol. (Q. Nos. 46 to 48)

$S : x^2 + y^2 - 4x - 1 = 0$ ...(i)

$L : y = 3x - 1$ ...(ii)

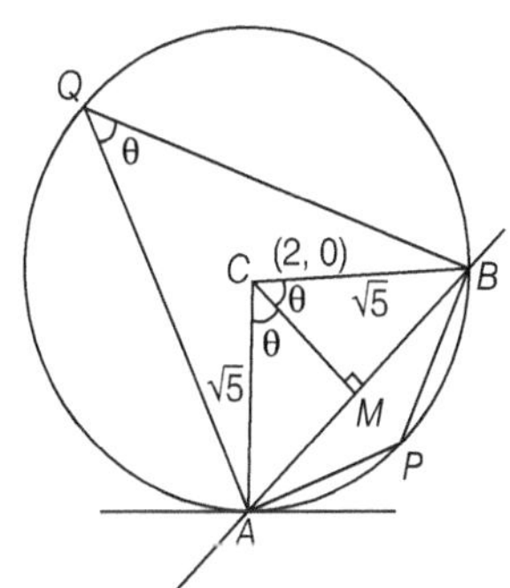

From Eqs. (i) and (ii), we get $x^2 + (3x-1)^2 - 4x - 1 = 0$

or $\quad 10x^2 - 10x = 0$

$\therefore \quad x = 0$ and $x = 1$

From Eq. (ii), $y = -1$ and $y = 2$

$\therefore \quad A \equiv (0, -1)$ and $B \equiv (1, 2)$

46. $AB = \sqrt{(0-1)^2 + (-1-2)^2} = \sqrt{10}$

47. Let $\angle ACB = 2\theta$

$\therefore \quad CM = \frac{5}{\sqrt{10}} = \sqrt{\frac{5}{2}}$

$\Rightarrow \quad \cos\theta = \frac{CM}{\sqrt{5}} = \frac{1}{\sqrt{2}}$

$\therefore \quad \theta = \frac{\pi}{4}$

Required angle $= \angle APB = \pi - \theta = \pi - \frac{\pi}{4} = \frac{3\pi}{4}$

48. Equation of tangent at $A(0, -1)$ to the circle S is

$0.x + (-1).y - 2(x + 0) - 1 = 0$

or $\quad 2x + y + 1 = 0$

$\therefore$ Slope $(m_1) = -2$

and slope of line L is $m_2 = 3$

If θ be the angle between L and S, then $\tan\theta = \left|\frac{-2-3}{1+(-2)(3)}\right| = 1$

$\therefore \quad \theta = \frac{\pi}{4}$

Sol. (Q. Nos. 49 to 51)

$\because \quad PQ = PR,$

parallelogram $PQRS$ is a rhombus.

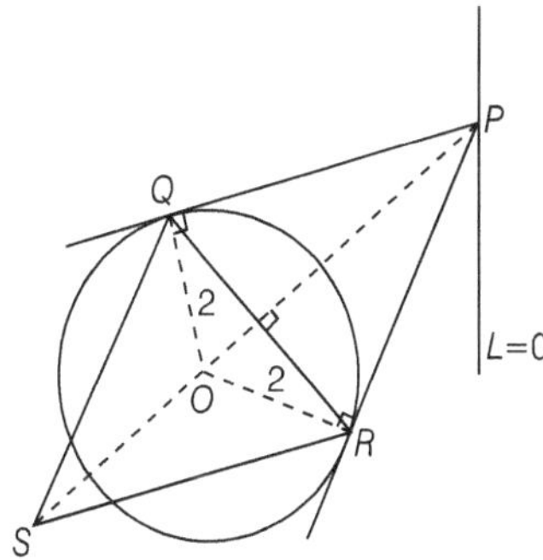

$\therefore$ Mid-point of QR = mid point of PS and $QR \perp PS$

Therefore, S in the mirror image of P w.r.t. QR.

49. Let $P(\lambda, 6 - 2\lambda)$ be any point on $L = 0$

$\because$ Circumcircle of ΔPQR always pass through O

$\therefore OP$ is diameter of circle.

Then, centre is $\left(\frac{\lambda}{2}, 3 - \lambda\right)$ So,

$x = \frac{\lambda}{2}$ and $y = 3 - \lambda$

or $2x + y = 3$ is the locus of the circumcenter of ΔPQR.

50. Area of ΔQRS = Area of $\Delta PQR = \dfrac{RL^3}{R^2+L^2}$ ...(i)

Here, $R = 2, L = \sqrt{S_1} = \sqrt{(6^2+8^2-4)} = \sqrt{96}$

From Eq. (i),

Area of $\Delta QRS = \dfrac{2\times 96\times\sqrt{96}}{4+96} = \dfrac{192\sqrt{6}}{25} = \dfrac{192\sqrt{\lambda}}{25}$ (given)

$\therefore \quad \lambda = 6$

51. Let $S \equiv (\alpha, \beta)$

$\because S$ is the mirror image of P w.r.t. QR.

Eq. (i) of QR is $3x + 4y = 4$, then

$$\frac{\alpha-3}{3} = \frac{\beta-4}{4} = \frac{-2(3.3+4.4-4)}{3^2+4^2}$$

$$= -\frac{42}{25}$$

$\therefore \quad \alpha = -\dfrac{51}{25}$ and $\beta = -\dfrac{68}{25}$

Hence, $\quad S \equiv \left(-\dfrac{51}{25}, -\dfrac{68}{25}\right)$

Sol. (Q. Nos. 52 to 54)

52. This is third degree equation which satisfy the point of intersection of $L_1 = 0$, $L_2 = 0$ and $L_3 = 0$.

53. $\lambda L_1L_2 + \mu L_3L_4 = 0$ will always pass through the vertices of the parallelogram for all $\lambda, \mu \in R \sim \{0\}$

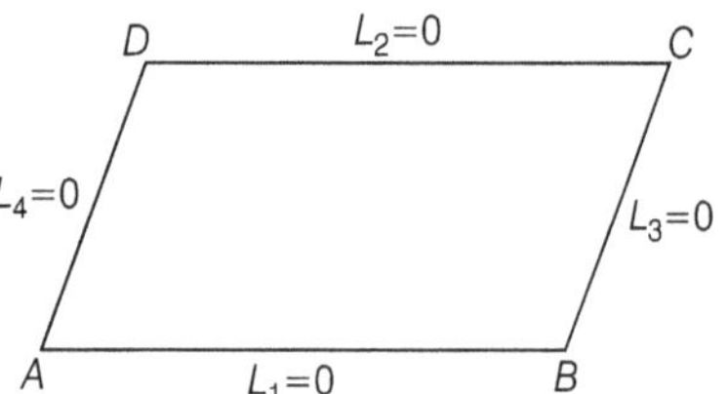

54. Since, $\mu = 0$

So, $\quad L_1L_2 + \lambda L_2L_3 = 0$

$\Rightarrow \quad L_2(L_1 + \lambda L_3) = 0$

This is the equation of pair of straight lines.

Sol. (Q. Nos. 55 to 57)

Let $2d$ = length of common chord and $\angle PC_1C_2 = \phi$, then

$\sin\phi = \dfrac{d}{3}$

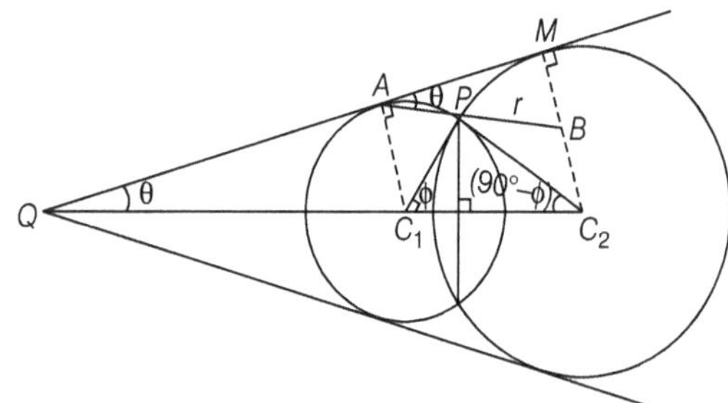

and $\quad \sin(90°-\phi) = \dfrac{d}{r}$ or $\cos\phi = \dfrac{d}{r}$

$$1 = \frac{d^2}{9} + \frac{d^2}{r^2}$$

$\Rightarrow \quad d = \dfrac{3r}{\sqrt{9+r^2}} = \dfrac{1}{2}\left(\dfrac{24}{5}\right)$ (given)

$\Rightarrow \quad \dfrac{r}{\sqrt{(9-r^2)}} = \dfrac{4}{5}$

$\therefore \quad r = 4$

55. $\lambda = r = 4$

56. $\because (C_1C_2)^2 = r^2 + 3^2 = 16 + 9 = 25$

$\therefore \quad C_1C_2 = 5$

In ΔABM, $\quad \sin\theta = \dfrac{BM}{AB} = \dfrac{4-3}{C_1C_2} = \dfrac{1}{5}$

$\therefore \quad \sin 2\theta = 2\sin\theta\cos\theta = 2\times\dfrac{1}{5}\times\sqrt{1-\left(\dfrac{1}{5}\right)^2} = \dfrac{4\sqrt{6}}{25}$

57. Length of direct common tangent $= \sqrt{(C_1C_2)^2 - (r-3)^2}$

$= \sqrt{(5)^2 - (1)^2}$

$= \sqrt{24} = \lambda$ (given)

$\therefore \quad \lambda^2 = 24$

Sol. (Q. Nos. 58 to 60)

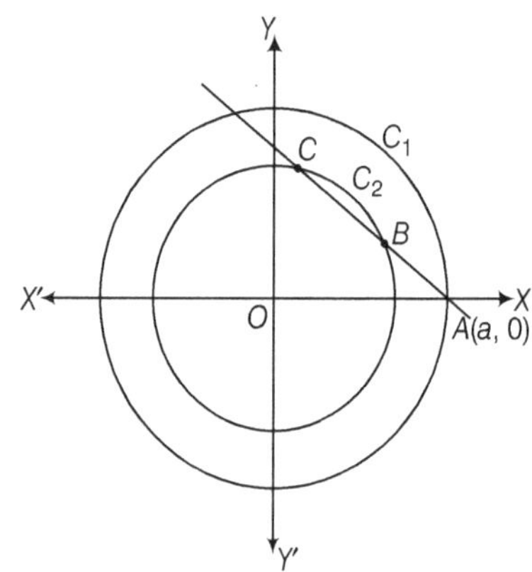

Let equation of line AB be

$$\frac{x-a}{\cos\theta} = \frac{y-0}{\sin\theta} = r$$

Coordinates of any point on the line AB is $(a + r\cos\theta, r\sin\theta)$, then

$B \equiv (a + r_1\cos\theta, r_1\sin\theta)$

and $\quad C \equiv (a + r_2\cos\theta, r_2\sin\theta)$

58. $\lambda = (OA)^2 + (OB)^2 + (BC)^2$

$= a^2 + b^2 + (r_1 - r_2)^2\cos^2\theta + (r_1 - r_2)^2\sin^2\theta$

$= (a^2 + b^2) + (r_1 - r_2)^2$

$= (a^2 + b^2) + 4a^2\cos^2\theta - 4(a^2 - b^2)$

($\because B$ and C lie on $x^2 + y^2 = b^2$

$\therefore \quad (a + r\cos\theta)^2 + (r\sin\theta)^2 = b^2$

or $\quad r^2 + 2ar\cos\theta + a^2 - b^2 = 0$

$\therefore \quad r_1 - r_2 = \sqrt{4a^2\cos^2\theta - 4(a^2 - b^2)}$

$\Rightarrow \quad \lambda = 5b^2 - 3a^2 + 4a^2\cos^2\theta$

$\because \quad 0 \le \cos^2\theta \le 1$

$\therefore \quad \lambda \in [5b^2 - 3a^2, 5b^2 + a^2]$

59. Let (h,k) be the mid-point of AB and let (α,β) be the coordinates of B, then

$$\frac{a+\alpha}{2}=h \text{ and } \frac{0+\beta}{2}=k$$

$\Rightarrow$ $\alpha=2h-a$ and $\beta=2k$

Since, (α,β) lies on $x^2+y^2=b^2$

$\Rightarrow$ $(2h-a)^2+(2k)^2=b^2$

or $\left(h-\frac{a}{2}\right)^2+k^2=\frac{b^2}{4}$

Hence, locus of (h,k) is

$$\left(x-\frac{a}{2}\right)^2+y^2=\frac{b^2}{4}$$

60. The locus of mid-point of AB, when BC is maximum is a fixed point M on X-axis.

Sol. (Q. Nos. 61 to 63)

61. From the figure $OA=OB=AB=a$

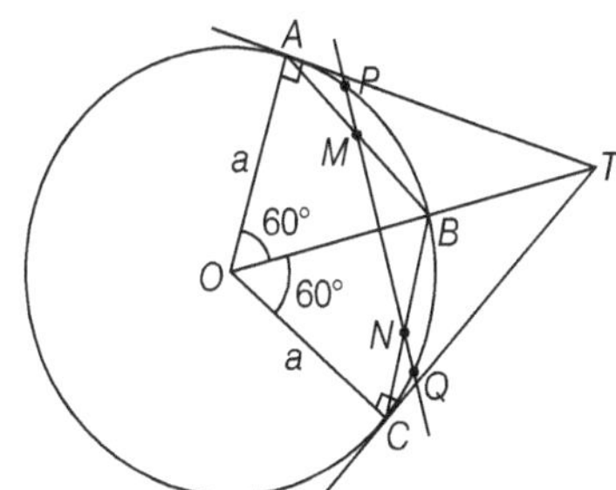

$\therefore$ $\angle OAB=60°$

62. Let T be the point of intersection of tangents.

$\because$ $\angle AOC=120°$

$\therefore$ $\angle ATC=180°-120°=60°$

63. Locus of point of intersection of tangents at A and C is

$$x^2+y^2=\frac{a^2}{\sin^2\left(\frac{\alpha}{2}\right)}$$

$$=\frac{a^2}{\sin^2(30°)}=4a^2 \qquad (\text{Here, } \alpha=60°)$$

Hence, $x^2+y^2=4a^2$

Sol. (Q. Nos. 64 to 66)

Here, $t_1^2=h^2+k^2-4,$

$t_2^2=h^2+k^2-4h,$

$t_3^2=h^2+k^2-4k$

given $t_1^4=t_2^2t_3^2+16$

or $(h^2+k^2-4)^2=(h^2+k^2-4h)(h^2+k^2-4k)+16$

or $(h^2+k^2)^2-8(h^2+k^2)+16=(h^2+k^2)^2-4(h^2+k^2)(h+k)+16hk+16$

or $(h^2+k^2)(h+k)-2(h^2+k^2)-4hk=0$

or $(h^2+k^2)(h+k)-2(h+k)^2=0$

or $(h+k)(h^2+k^2-2(h+k))=0$

or $h+k=0$ ...(i)

and $h^2+k^2-2h-2k=0$ ...(ii)

64. Locus of (h,k) is [From Eq. (i)]

$$L_1: x+y=0$$

65. Locus of (h,k) is [From Eq. (ii)]

$$C_1: x^2+y^2-2x-2y=0$$

66. $\because$ Circle C_2 is equal to circle C_1

$\therefore$ Radius of circle C_2 = radius of circle $C_1=\sqrt{2}$

$\therefore$ Distance between the centres of C_1 and C_2

$=\sqrt{2}+\sqrt{2}$

$=2\sqrt{2}$ ($\because$ circles C_1 and C_2 touch externally)

67. The given circle is

$$S:(x-3)^2+(y-5)^2=(\sqrt{(34-\lambda)})^2$$

Since, point $P(1,4)$ lies inside the circle

$\therefore$ $S_1<0$

$\Rightarrow$ $1+16-6-40+\lambda<0$

or $\lambda<29$ ...(i)

Also, circle neither touches nor cuts the axes, then

$3>\sqrt{(34-\lambda)}$ or $\lambda>25$ ...(ii)

and $5>\sqrt{(34-\lambda)}$ or $\lambda>9$ ...(iii)

From Eqs. (i), (ii) and (iii), we get

$25<\lambda<29$

Hence, difference $=29-25=4$

68. $x^2+y^2-2x-2\lambda y-8=0$

or $(x^2+y^2-2x-8)-2\lambda y=0$

which is of the form $S+\lambda L=0$

All the circles pass through the point of intersection of the circle $x^2+y^2-2x-8=0$ and $y=0$

Solving, we get

$x^2-2x-8=0$

or $(x-4)(x+2)=0$

$\therefore$ $A\equiv(-2,0)$

and $B\equiv(4,0)$

Hence, $|AB|=6$

69. $\because AQ=BQ=3+2\sqrt{2}$

and PQ = radius of director circle of C_1

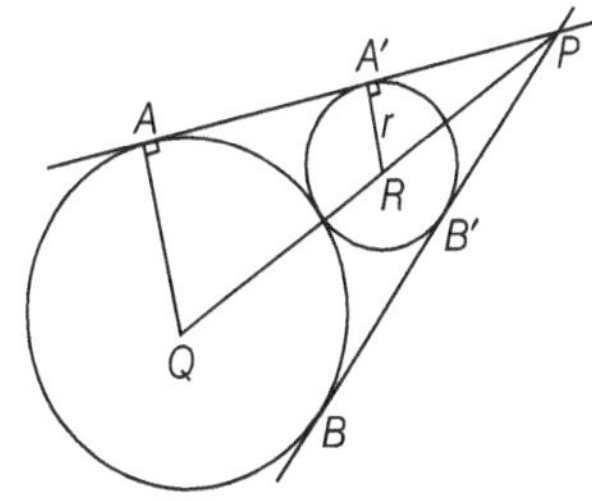

$=\sqrt{2}(3+2\sqrt{2})=3\sqrt{2}+4$

Let 'r' be required radius

$\therefore$ $3\sqrt{2}+4=3+2\sqrt{2}+r+r\sqrt{2}$ $\left(\because \frac{PR}{PQ}=\frac{A'R}{AQ}\right)$

$\Rightarrow$ $r=\frac{(\sqrt{2}+1)}{(\sqrt{2}+1)}=1$

70. Since, **A.** $x+y-5=0$ is a tangent to the circle at $P(2,3)$, so the centre of the circle lies on $x-y+1=0$. Now $Q(1,2)$ lies on the circle.

Equation of right bisector of PQ is $x+y-4=0$

$\therefore$ Centre of circle is point of intersection of $x-y+1=0$ and $x+y-4=0$ which is $\left(\frac{3}{2},\frac{5}{2}\right)$

$\therefore$ Radius $\frac{1}{\sqrt{\lambda}}=\frac{\left|\frac{3}{2}+\frac{5}{2}-5\right|}{\sqrt{2}}=\frac{1}{\sqrt{2}}$

$\therefore \quad \lambda=2$

Hence, $\quad \lambda^2=4$

71. Since, given circle is $(x+5)^2+(y-12)^2=(14)^2$

or $\quad \left(\frac{x+5}{14}\right)^2+\left(\frac{y-12}{14}\right)^2=1$

Let, $\quad \frac{x+5}{14}=\cos\theta$ and $\frac{y-12}{14}=\sin\theta$

or $\quad x=14\cos\theta-5$ and $y=14\sin\theta+12$

$$\therefore \quad x^2+y^2=(14\cos\theta-5)^2+(14\sin\theta+12)^2$$
$$=196+25+144+28(12\sin\theta-5\cos\theta)$$
$$=365+28(12\sin\theta-5\cos\theta)$$

Maximum value of $(x^2+y^2)=365+28\times 13=729$

$(\because -13\le 12\sin\theta-5\cos\theta\le 13)$

or maximum value of $(x^2+y^2)^{\frac{1}{3}}=9$

72. Let the given lines are represented by L_1, L_2, L_3 and L_4, then

$$L_1\equiv 2x+3y-2=0 \quad L_2\equiv 3x-2y-3=0$$
$$L_3\equiv x+2y-3=0 \quad L_4\equiv 2x-y-1=0$$

Equation of second degree conic circumscribing a quadrilateral whose sides are $L_1=0$, $L_2=0$, $L_3=0$ and $L_4=0$ is

$$L_1L_3+kL_2L_4=0$$

or $(2x+3y-2)(x+2y-3)+k(3x-2y-3)(2x-y-1)=0$ ...(i)

For circle, coefficient of x^2 = coefficient of y^2

or $\quad 2+6k=6+2k$

$\therefore \quad k=1$

From, Eq. (i), required circle is

$$8x^2+8y^2-17x-8y+9=0$$

or $\quad x^2+y^2-\left(\frac{17}{8}\right)x-y+\left(\frac{9}{8}\right)=0$

Here, $\quad \lambda=-\frac{17}{8}, \mu=-1, \nu=\frac{9}{8}$

then, $\quad |\lambda+2\mu+\nu|=3$

73. Let radius of given circle is a

$\therefore \quad a=\sqrt{(4+2-c)}=\sqrt{(6-c)}$ ...(i)

Now, radius of circle $C_1=\frac{a}{\sqrt{2}}$ and radius of circle $C_2=\frac{a}{(\sqrt{2})^2}$ and so on.

Also, $\quad a+\frac{a}{\sqrt{2}}+\frac{a}{(\sqrt{2})^2}+\ldots\infty=2$ (given)

Then, $\quad \frac{a}{1-\frac{1}{\sqrt{2}}}=2$

or $\quad a=2-\sqrt{2}=\sqrt{6-c}$ [From Eq. (i)]

or $\quad 4+2-4\sqrt{2}=6-c$

$\therefore \quad c=4\sqrt{2}$

Hence, $\lambda=4$

74. The rays are given as $2x^2-3xy-2y^2=0$ i.e. $(2x+y)(x-2y)=0$

$\Rightarrow y=\frac{x}{2}$ or $y=-2x$ which are perpendicular.

$\therefore$ Required area

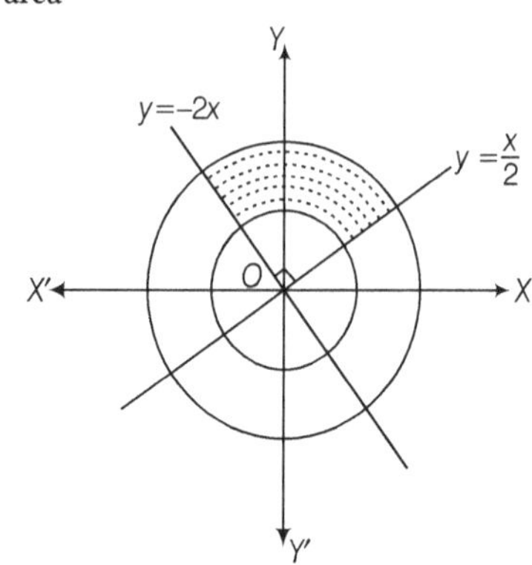

$$=\frac{1}{4}(\pi(2)^2-\pi(1)^2)$$
$$=\frac{3\pi}{4}=\frac{\lambda\pi}{4} \quad \text{(given)}$$

$\therefore \quad \lambda=3$

75. Let radii of circles be r_1 and r_2 and distance between centres is d, then

$\sqrt{d^2-(r_1+r_2)^2}=5$ ...(i)

and $\quad \sqrt{d^2-(r_1-r_2)^2}=13$ ...(ii)

From Eqs. (i) and (ii), we get

$$(r_1+r_2)^2-(r_1-r_2)^2=(13)^2-(5)^2$$

$\Rightarrow \quad 4r_1r_2=144$ or $\lambda=36$ $(\because r_1r_2=\lambda)$

$\therefore \quad \frac{\lambda}{4}=9$

76. Let $ax+by=1$ ...(i)

be a chord PQ.

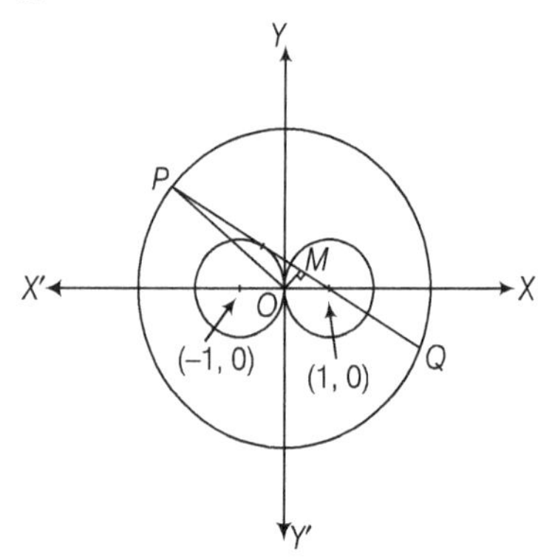

which pass through (1, 0), then $a + 0 = 1$

$\therefore \quad a = 1$

and touch circle B with centre $(-1, 0)$ and radius 1, then

$$\frac{|-a+0-1|}{\sqrt{a^2+b^2}} = 1$$

or $\quad a^2 + b^2 = (a+1)^2$

or $\quad b^2 = 2a + 1 = 3$

$\therefore \quad b = \sqrt{3}$

From Eq. (i), Equation of chord is $x + \sqrt{3}\, y = 4$

$\therefore \quad OM = \frac{1}{2}$ and $OP = 4$

$\therefore \quad PQ = 2PM = 2\sqrt{(OP)^2 - (OM)^2}$

$$= 2\sqrt{\left(16 - \frac{1}{4}\right)} = \sqrt{63} = \sqrt{\lambda}$$

$\therefore \quad \lambda = 63$

Hence, $\quad \frac{\lambda}{9} = 7$

77. $\because \; S_1 : (x-2)^2 + (y-3)^2 = 1$

Centre $C_1 : (2,3)$ and radius $r_1 : 1$ and $S_2 : (x-5)^2 + (y-6)^2 = r^2$

Centre $C_2 : (5,6)$ and radius $r_2 : r$

$\Rightarrow \quad C_1C_2 = 3\sqrt{2}$

(A) $\because S_1$ and S_2 touch internally, then

$$C_1C_2 = r_2 - r_1$$

or $\quad 3\sqrt{2} = r - 1$

or $\quad (r-1)^2 = 18$

(B) $\because S_1$ and S_2 touch externally, then

$$C_1C_2 = r_2 + r_1$$

or $\quad 3\sqrt{2} = r + 1$

or $\quad r^2 + 2r + 3 = (r+1)^2 + 2 = 18 + 2 = 20$

(C) $\because S_1$ and S_2 intersect orthogonally, then

$$(C_1C_2)^2 = r_1^2 + r_2^2$$

$\Rightarrow \quad 18 = r^2 + 1$

or $\quad r^2 - 1 = 16$

(D) $\because S_1$ and S_2 intersect, the common chord is $S_1 - S_2 = 0$

i.e. $\quad 6x + 6y + r^2 - 49 = 0$

Given, common chord is longest, then passes through (2, 3)

$\Rightarrow \quad 12 + 18 + r^2 - 49 = 0$

or $\quad r^2 = 19$

$\therefore \quad r^2 + 5 = 24$

78. **(A)** Since (2, 3) lies on $ax + by - 5 = 0$

$\therefore \quad 2a + 3b - 5 = 0 \quad$ ...(i)

Since, line is at greatest distance from centre

$\Rightarrow \quad \left(\frac{4-3}{3-2}\right)\left(-\frac{a}{b}\right) = -1$ i.e. $a = b$

From Eq. (i), $a = b = 1$

$\therefore \quad a + b = 2$ and $a^2 + b^2 = 2$

(B) Let P be the point (h,k), then $h^2 + k^2 + 2h + 2k = 0$ ...(i)

mid-point of OP is $\left(\frac{h}{2}, \frac{k}{2}\right)$

Let $\quad x = \frac{h}{2}, y = \frac{k}{2}$

or $\quad h = 2x, k = 2y$

From Eq. (i), $4x^2 + 4y^2 + 4x + 4y = 0$

or $\quad x^2 + y^2 + x + y = 0$

On comparing, we get

$$2a = 1, 2b = 1$$

or $\quad a = b = \frac{1}{2}$

$\therefore \quad a + b = 1$

(C) Centre of circles are $C_1 : (1,2)$ and $C_2 : (5,-6)$

Equation of C_1C_2 is $y - 2 = \frac{-6-2}{5-1}(x-1)$

or $\quad 2x + y - 4 = 0 \quad$ ...(i)

Equation of radical axis is $8x - 16y - 56 = 0$

or $\quad x - 2y - 7 = 0 \quad$ ...(ii)

Point of intersection of Eqs. (i) and (ii) are (3, –2)

$\therefore \quad a = 3, b = -2$

or $\quad a + b = 1$

(D) Let $S \equiv x^2 + y^2 - 6\sqrt{3}x - 6y + 27 = 0$

$$S_1 = 0^2 + 0^2 - 0 - 0 + 27 = 27$$

$$T = 0.x + 0.y - 3\sqrt{3}(x+0) - 3(y+0) + 27$$

$$= -3\sqrt{3}x - 3y + 27$$

Eq. of the pair of tangents is given by

$$SS_1 = T^2$$

$\Rightarrow \quad 27(x^2 + y^2 - 6\sqrt{3}x - 6y + 27) = (-3\sqrt{3}x - 3y + 27)^2$

or $\quad 3(x^2 + y^2 - 6\sqrt{3}x - 6y + 27) = (\sqrt{3}x + y - 9)^2$

or $\quad 18y^2 - 18\sqrt{3}xy = 0$

or $\quad 18y(y - \sqrt{3}x) = 0$

the tangents are $y = 0, y = \sqrt{3}x$

$\therefore \quad a = 0, b = \sqrt{3}$

then, $\quad a^2 + b^2 = 3$

79. **(A)** $\because \; P \equiv (10,7)$

and $\quad S = x^2 + y^2 - 4x - 2y - 20$

$\therefore \quad S_1 = 100 + 49 - 40 - 14 - 20 > 0$

$\therefore P$ outside the circle, radius $r = \sqrt{4 + 1 + 20} = 5$

centre $C \equiv (2,1)$

$\therefore$ Shortest distance $L = CP - r$

$$= \sqrt{(10-2)^2 + (7-1)^2} - 5$$

$$= \sqrt{(64+36)} - 5 = 10 - 5 = 5$$

And largest distance $M = CP + r$

$$= 10 + 5 = 15$$

$$M + L = 20, M - L = 10$$

(B) $\because$ $P \equiv (3,-6)$

and $S \equiv x^2 + y^2 - 16x - 12y - 125$

$\therefore$ $S_1 = 9 + 36 - 48 + 72 - 125 < 0$

$\therefore$ P inside the circle radius $r = \sqrt{(64+36+125)} = 15$

centre $C \equiv (8,6)$

$\therefore$ Shortest distance $L = r - CP$

$$= 15 - \sqrt{(8-3)^2 + (6+6)^2}$$

$$= 15 - 13 = 2$$

And largest distance $M = r + CP$

$$= 15 + 13 = 28$$

$$M + L = 30,$$

$$M - L = 26$$

(C) $P \equiv (6,-6)$

and $S \equiv x^2 + y^2 - 4x + 6y - 12$

$\therefore$ $S_1 = (6)^2 + (-6)^2 - 24 - 36 - 12 = 0$

P on the circle

$\therefore$ radius $r = \sqrt{(4+9+12)} = 5$

$\therefore$ Shortest distance $L = 0$

and largest distance $M = 2r = 10$

$$M + L = 10, M - L = 10$$

80. (A) Equation of conic

$(y - a_1x - b)(y - a_2x - b) + \lambda xy = 0$ represent a circle. If coefficient of x^2 = coefficient of y^2

$\therefore$ $a_1a_2 = 1$

$\because$ $AM > GM$

$\therefore$ $\dfrac{a_1 + a_2}{2} > \sqrt{a_1a_2} = 1$

$\Rightarrow$ $a_1 + a_2 > 2$

and $\dfrac{a_1^2 + a_2^2}{2} > \sqrt{a_1^2 . a_2^2} = |a_1a_2| = 1$

$\therefore$ $a_1^2 + a_2^2 > 2$

(B) Let $(a_1 \cos\theta, a_1 \sin\theta)$ be any point on $x^2 + y^2 = a_1^2$, then chord of contact is

$$x(a_1 \cos\theta) + y(a_1 \sin\theta) = b^2$$

which is tangent of $x^2 + y^2 = a_2^2$

$\therefore$ $\dfrac{|0 + 0 - b^2|}{\sqrt{\{(a_1\cos\theta)^2 + (a_1\sin\theta)^2\}}} = a_2$ or $b^2 = a_1a_2$

for $b = 1, a_1a_2 = 1$

$AM > GM$

$\Rightarrow$ $\dfrac{a_1 + a_2}{2} > \sqrt{a_1a_2} = |b|$

$\therefore$ $a_1 + a_2 > 2|b|,$

for $b = 1, a_1 + a_2 > 2$

and then, $a_1^2 + a_2^2 > 2$

(C) $2gg_1 + 2ff_1 = c + c_1$

$\Rightarrow$ $2 \times a_1 \times a_2 + 0 = b + b$

$\therefore$ $a_1a_2 = b$ for $b = 1, a_1a_2 = 1$

and then, $a_1 + a_2 > 2$

Also, $a_1^2 + a_2^2 > 2$

81. Let $S \equiv x^2 + y^2 - 1 = 0$

$\therefore$ $S(1,3) = 1^2 + 3^2 - 1 = 9 > 0$

$\Rightarrow$ Point (1, 3) outside the circle $x^2 + y^2 = 1$

$\therefore$ Two tangents can be drawn from (1, 3) to circle $x^2 + y^2 = 1$

$\Rightarrow$ Statement I is false

Also, $\dfrac{|3 - m|}{\sqrt{(1 + m^2)}} = 1$

Squaring both sides, we get

$$9 + m^2 - 6m = 1 + m^2$$

or $6m = 8 \Rightarrow m = \dfrac{4}{3}$

$\Rightarrow$ Statement II is true.

82. $\because x^2 + y^2 + 2x - 4y = 0$

$\Rightarrow$ $(x+1)^2 + (y-2)^2 = 1^2 + 2^2$

Let $S \equiv (x+1)^2 + (y-2)^2 - 1^2 - 2^2$

Value of $S(1, \lambda) = (1+1)^2 + (\lambda - 2)^2 - 1^2 - 2^2 < 0$

or $(1+1)^2 + (\lambda - 2)^2 < 1^2 + 2^2$

$\therefore$ Points $(1, \lambda)$ inside the circle.

$\Rightarrow$ No tangents can be drawn from the point $(1, \lambda)$ to the circle

$$x^2 + y^2 + 2x - 4y = 0$$

and $(1+1)^2 + (\lambda - 2)^2 < 1^2 + 2^2$

$\Rightarrow$ $(\lambda - 2)^2 < 1$

or $-1 < \lambda - 2 < 1$

or $1 < \lambda < 3$

$\therefore$ Statement II and Statement II are both true and statement II is correct explanation for statement I.

83. Let $A \equiv (1,4)$, $B \equiv (2,3)$ and $C \equiv (-1,6)$

$\therefore$ Area of $\Delta ABC = \dfrac{1}{2}\begin{vmatrix} 1 & 4 & 1 \\ 2 & 3 & 1 \\ -1 & 6 & 1 \end{vmatrix} = 0$

$\Rightarrow A, B, C$ are collinear

i.e. no circle is drawn.

Hence, Statement I is false and through three non-collinear points in a plane only one circle can be drawn.

$\therefore$ Statement II is true.

84. $\because$ Locus of point of intersection of perpendicular tangents is director circle.

$\because x^2 + y^2 = 50$ is director circle of $x^2 + y^2 = 25$

$\Rightarrow$ Statement I is false and statement II is true.

85. Here, $C_1 \equiv (0,0), r_1 = 2$

and $C_2 \equiv (3,0), r_2 = 2$

$\therefore$ $|C_1C_2| = 3$ and $r_1 + r_2 = 4$

and $|r_1 - r_2| = 0$

$\Rightarrow$ $|r_1 - r_2| < |C_1C_2| < r_1 + r_2$

Hence, circles $x^2 + y^2 = 4$ and $x^2 + y^2 - 6x + 5 = 0$ intersect each other at two distinct points.

$\Rightarrow$ Statement I is true and Statement II is false.

86. $\because$ Centre of circle $(1, -1)$ lies on $3x - 4y = 7$

$\therefore$ $3x - 4y = 7$ is a diameter of circle

$$x^2 + y^2 - 2x + 2y - 47 = 0$$

$\therefore$ Statement I is true.

Statement II is always true but Statement I is not a correct explanation of Statement I.

87. Statement I is true, line $4y - 3x - 5 = 0$ passes through $A(-3, -1)$ and its distance from $O(0,0)$ is 1 unit = radius of circle

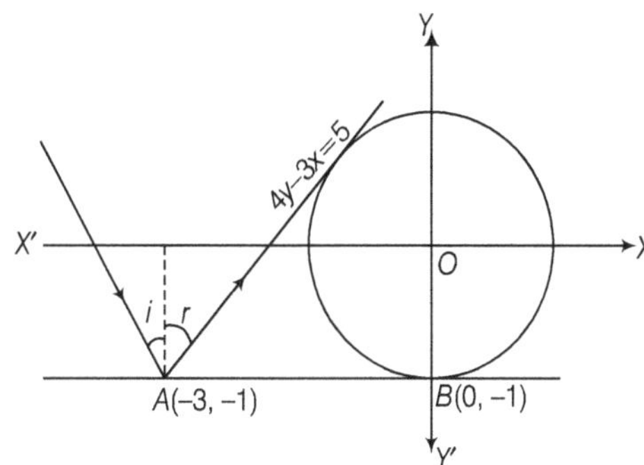

The tangent at $B(0, -1)$ is $y = -1$ and normal at A to line AB is $x = -3$

$\therefore$ Equation of incident ray is $y + 1 = \left(-\frac{4}{3}\right)(x + 3)$

$\Rightarrow$ $$4x + 3y + 15 = 0$$

Statement II is obviously true.

Hence, both statements are true and but Statement II is not correct explanation of Statement I.

88. The given points are $A(1,1)$, $B(2,3)$ and $C(3,5)$ which are collinear as

Slope of AB = Slope of $BC = 2$

Hence, Statement II is true

The chords of contact are concurrent, then,

$$\begin{vmatrix} x_1 & y_1 & 1 \\ x_2 & y_2 & 1 \\ x_3 & y_3 & 1 \end{vmatrix} = 0$$

Hence, points (x_1, y_1), (x_2, y_2) and (x_3, y_3) are collinear.

Therefore, Both statements are true and statement II is correct explanation of statement I.

89. Let the equation of circle be

$$x^2 + y^2 + 2gx + 2fy + c = 0 \quad \text{...(i)}$$

Since, circle Eq. (i) passes through (1,0) and (0,1) then

$$1 + 2g + c = 0 \Rightarrow g = -\frac{(1 + c)}{2} \quad \text{...(ii)}$$

and $$1 + 2f + c = 0 \Rightarrow f = -\frac{(1 + c)}{2} \quad \text{...(iii)}$$

Radius of the circle Eq. (ii) $= \sqrt{(g^2 + f^2 - c)}$

$$= \sqrt{\frac{(1 + c)^2}{4} + \frac{(1 + c)^2}{4} - c} = \sqrt{\left(\frac{1 + c^2}{2}\right)}$$

For minimum radius, c must be equal to zero, then from Eqs. (ii) and (iii),

$$g = -\frac{1}{2} \text{ and } f = -\frac{1}{2}$$

Equation of required circle, from Eq. (i), is

$$x^2 + y^2 - x - y = 0$$

90. The given circle is

$$x^2 + y^2 - 6x + 6y + 17 = 0$$

Centre and radius of this circle are $(3, -3)$ and $\sqrt{9 + 9 - 17} = 1$ respectively. But given the required circle has normals

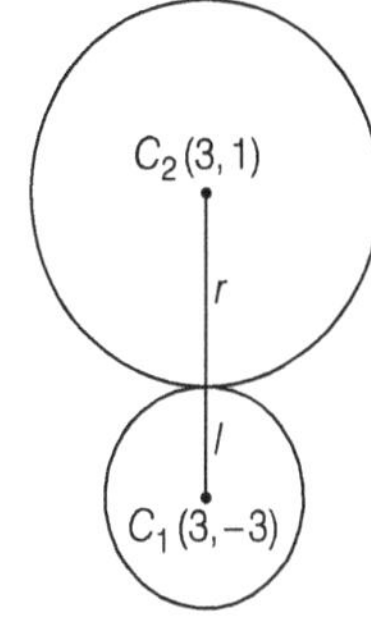

$$x^2 - 3xy - 3x + 9y = 0$$

or $$(x - 3)(x - 3y) = 0$$

or $$x = 3 \text{ and } x - 3y = 0 \quad \text{...(i)}$$

but point of intersection of normals is the centre of the circle. Point of intersection of normals represented by Eq. (i) is (3, 1) which is centre of the required circle. Since, given circle and required circle touch each other externally, then (if radius of required circles is r)

Sum of radii = Distance between the centres

$$r + 1 = \sqrt{(3 - 3)^2 + (-3 - 1)^2} = 4$$

$\therefore$ $$r = 3$$

$\therefore$ Equation of required circle is

$$(x - 3)^2 + (y - 1)^2 = 3^2$$

or $$x^2 + y^2 - 6x - 2y + 1 = 0$$

91. Let $OA = a$ and $OB = b$ then the coordinates of A and B are $(a, 0)$ and $(0, b)$ respectively.

Since, $\angle AOB = \pi / 2$

Hence, AB is the diameter of the required circle whose equation is

$$(x - a)(x - 0) + (y - 0)(y - b) = 0$$

or $$x^2 + y^2 - ax - by = 0 \quad \text{... (i)}$$

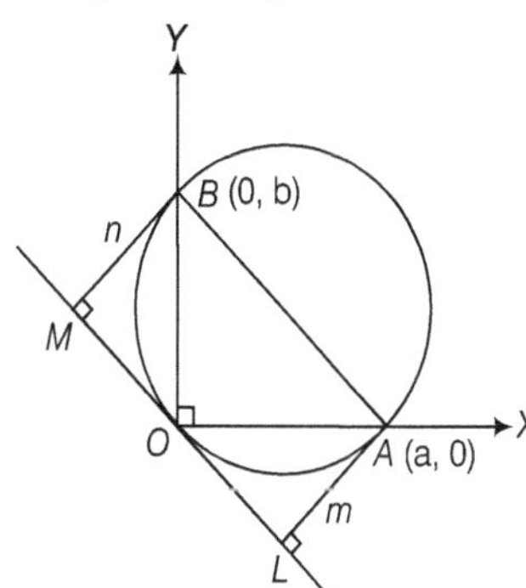

Equation of tangent at (0,0) of Eq. (i) is

$$0\cdot x+0\cdot y-\frac{a}{2}(x+0)-\frac{b}{2}(0+y)=0$$

or $$ax+by=0$$

$\therefore$ $$m=AL=\frac{a\cdot a+0}{\sqrt{a^2+b^2}}$$

or $$m=\frac{a^2}{\sqrt{a^2+b^2}} \qquad \text{...(ii)}$$

and $$n=BM=\frac{a\cdot 0+b\cdot b}{\sqrt{a^2+b^2}}$$

$\therefore$ $$n=\frac{b^2}{\sqrt{a^2+b^2}} \qquad \text{...(iii)}$$

Adding Eqs. (ii) and (iii), we get

$$m+n=\sqrt{(a^2+b^2)}$$

From Eqs. (ii) and (iii), we get

$$a=\pm\sqrt{m(m+n)} \quad \text{and} \quad b=\pm\sqrt{n(m+n)}$$

From Eq. (i), equation of required circle is

$$x^2+y^2\pm\sqrt{m(m+n)}x\pm\sqrt{n(m+n)}\,y=0$$

92. Solving the equations

$$(2+c)\,x+5c^2y=1 \quad \text{and} \quad 3x+5y=1$$

then $$(2+c)\,x+5c^2\left(\frac{1-3x}{5}\right)=1$$

or $$(2+c)\,x+c^2(1-3x)=1$$

$\therefore$ $$x=\frac{1-c^2}{2+c-3c^2}$$

or $$x=\frac{(1+c)(1-c)}{(3c+2)(1-c)}=\frac{1+c}{3c+2}$$

$\therefore$ $$x=\lim_{c\to 1}\frac{1+c}{3c+2}$$

$$x=\frac{2}{5}$$

$\therefore$ $$y=\frac{1-3x}{5}=\frac{1-\frac{6}{5}}{5}=-\frac{1}{25}$$

Therefore, the centre of the required circle is $\left(\frac{2}{5},-\frac{1}{25}\right)$ but circle passes through (2, 0)

$\therefore$ Radius of the required circle $=\sqrt{\left(\frac{2}{5}-2\right)^2+\left(-\frac{1}{25}-0\right)^2}$

$$=\sqrt{\frac{64}{25}+\frac{1}{625}}=\sqrt{\frac{1601}{625}}$$

Hence, the required equation of the circle is

$$\left(x-\frac{2}{5}\right)^2+\left(y+\frac{1}{25}\right)^2=\frac{1601}{625}$$

or $$25x^2+25y^2-20x+2y-60=0$$

93. Equation of chord of contact (QR) is $6x+8y-r^2=0$

$\therefore$ $$PM=\frac{|6\cdot 6+8\cdot 8-r^2|}{\sqrt{(6^2+8^2)}}=\frac{|100-r^2|}{10}$$

and $$OM=\frac{|0+0-r^2|}{\sqrt{(6^2+8^2)}}=\frac{r^2}{10}$$

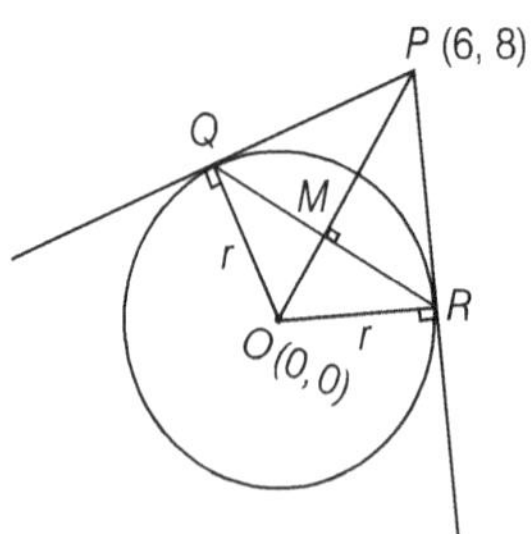

then $$QR=2\cdot QM=2\sqrt{\{(OQ)^2-(OM)^2\}}$$

$$=2\sqrt{\left(r^2-\frac{r^4}{100}\right)}$$

$\therefore$ Area of $\Delta QPR=\frac{1}{2}\cdot QR\cdot PM$

$$\Delta\,(\text{say})=\frac{1}{2}\cdot 2\sqrt{\left(r^2-\frac{r^4}{100}\right)}\cdot\frac{|100-r^2|}{10}$$

$\therefore$ $$\Delta^2=\frac{r^2(100-r^2)^3}{1000}=z \qquad \text{(say)}$$

$\therefore$ $$\frac{dz}{dr}=\frac{1}{1000}\{r^2\,.\,3\,(100-r^2)^2\,.\,(-2r)+(100-r^2)^3\cdot 2r\}$$

$$=\frac{2r\,(100-r^2)^2}{1000}\{100-r^2-3r^2\}$$

For maximum or minimum $\frac{dz}{dr}=0$, then we get $r=5$, ($r\neq 10$ as P is outside the circle)

and $$\left.\frac{d^2z}{dr^2}\right|_{r=5}=-\text{ve}$$

$\therefore$ Δ is also maximum at $r=5$.

94. Since, A (4, 6) and B (1, 9) do not lie on $2x-y+4=0$.

Let M be the mid-point of AB, then coordinates of M is $\left(\frac{5}{2},\frac{15}{2}\right)$

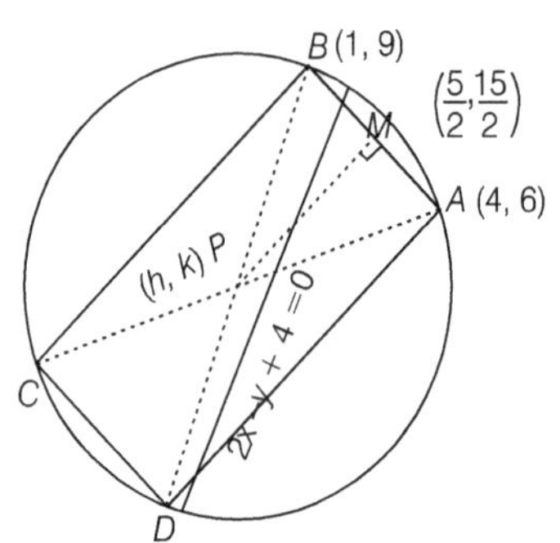

Slope of $AB = \frac{9-6}{1-4} = -1$

$\therefore$ Slope of $PM = 1$

Equation of PM is, $y - \frac{15}{2} = 1 \cdot \left(x - \frac{5}{2}\right)$

which passes through $P(h, k)$, then

$$k - \frac{15}{2} = h - \frac{5}{2} \quad \text{or} \quad k - h = 5 \quad \text{...(i)}$$

and (h, k) lie on $2x - y + 4 = 0$

$$\therefore \quad 2h - k + 4 = 0 \quad \text{...(ii)}$$

Solving Eqs. (i) and (ii), we get

$$h = 1 \quad \text{and} \quad k = 6$$

Now, $AD = 2PM = 2\sqrt{\left(1 - \frac{5}{2}\right)^2 + \left(6 - \frac{15}{2}\right)^2}$

$$= 2\sqrt{\frac{9}{4} + \frac{9}{4}} = 3\sqrt{2}$$

and $AB = \sqrt{(4-1)^2 + (6-9)^2} = 3\sqrt{2}$

$\therefore$ Area of rectangle

$$ABCD = AB \times AD = 3\sqrt{2} \times 3\sqrt{2} = 18 \text{ sq units.}$$

95. Let $C(h, k)$ be the centre of the circle. Let AB and $C'D$ be the lines represented by

$3x - y = 6$ and $y = x$ respectively.

Clearly, the circle touches AB at $A(1, -3)$.

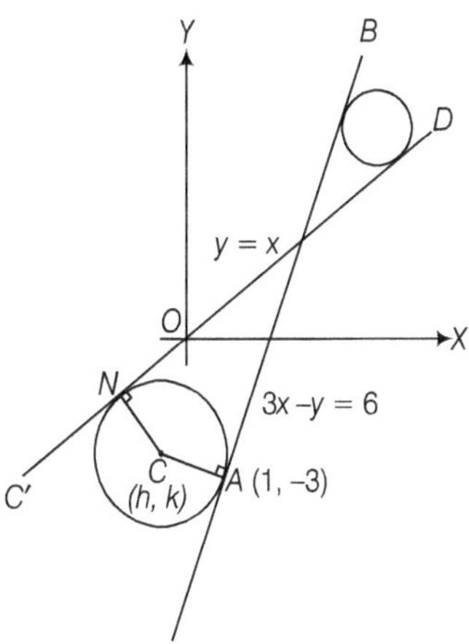

Equation of line $\perp$ to $3x - y = 6$ is $x + 3y = \lambda$ which passes through $(1, -3)$.

then $1 - 9 = \lambda$

$\therefore \quad \lambda = -8$

$\therefore \perp$ line is $x + 3y + 8 = 0$

which passes through $C(h, k)$

then $$h + 3k + 8 = 0 \quad \text{...(i)}$$

Now, centre $C(h, k) \equiv C(-3k - 8, k)$

Radius $CN = \frac{|-3k - 8 - k|}{\sqrt{1+1}} = CA$

$$= \sqrt{(-3k - 8 - 1)^2 + (k+3)^2}$$

$$\Rightarrow \quad \frac{4|k+2|}{\sqrt{2}} = |k+3|\sqrt{10} \quad \text{...(ii)}$$

$$\Rightarrow \quad 4|k+2| = 2\sqrt{5}|k+3|$$

$$\Rightarrow \quad 2|k+2| = \sqrt{5}|k+3|$$

$$\therefore \quad k + 2 = \pm \frac{\sqrt{5}}{2}(k+3)$$

$\therefore \quad k = -7 - 2\sqrt{5}$ or $k = -7 + 2\sqrt{5}$

Since, radius from Eq. (ii),

$$r = \frac{4|k+2|}{\sqrt{2}}$$

$$(\text{radius})_{\text{at } k = -7 - 2\sqrt{5}} = \frac{4|-7 - 2\sqrt{5} + 2|}{\sqrt{2}}$$

$$= 10\sqrt{2} + 4\sqrt{10} = 26.79$$

$$(\text{radius})_{\text{at } k = -7 + 2\sqrt{5}} = \frac{4|-7 + 2\sqrt{5} + 2|}{\sqrt{2}}$$

$$= 10\sqrt{2} - 4\sqrt{10} = 1.5$$

Hence, radius of smaller circle is 1.5 units.

96. Let the centre of the circle C_2 is $Q(h, k)$, equation of the circle C_2 is

$$(x-h)^2 + (y-k)^2 = 5^2$$

or $x^2 + y^2 - 2xh - 2yk + h^2 + k^2 - 25 = 0$

$$C_2 \equiv x^2 + y^2 - 2xh - 2yk + h^2 + k^2 - 25 = 0$$

and equation of circle $C_1 \equiv x^2 + y^2 - 16 = 0$

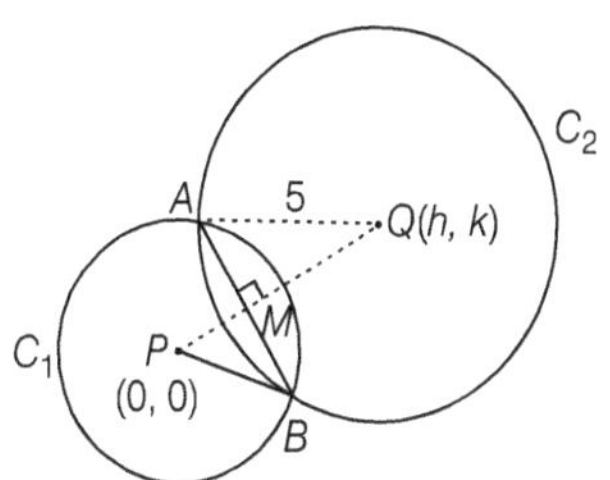

$\therefore$ Equation of common chord is

$$C_1 - C_2 = 0$$

$$\Rightarrow \quad -2xh - 2yk + h^2 + k^2 - 9 = 0$$

$$\text{or} \quad 2hx + 2ky - (h^2 + k^2 - 9) = 0 \quad \text{...(i)}$$

Slope of this line $= -h/k$

But, it is given that its slope $= 3/4$

$$\therefore \quad -\frac{h}{k} = \frac{3}{4}$$

$$\text{or} \quad 3k + 4h = 0 \quad \text{...(ii)}$$

Let p be the length perpendicular from $P(0, 0)$ on chord (1), then

$$p = \frac{h^2 + k^2 - 9}{\sqrt{(4h^2 + 4k^2)}}$$

$$\text{or} \quad p = \frac{(h^2 + k^2 - 9)}{2\sqrt{(h^2 + k^2)}} \quad \text{...(iii)}$$

Length of this chord $AB = 2AM$

$$= 2\sqrt{(16 - p^2)}$$

This chord has maximum length, then $p = 0$, then from Eq. (iii),

$$h^2 + k^2 - 9 = 0 \quad \text{...(iv)}$$

On solving Eqs. (ii) and (iv) we get

$$h = \mp\frac{9}{5}, k = \pm\frac{12}{5}$$

$\therefore$ Centre of C_2 is $\left(\frac{9}{5}, -\frac{12}{5}\right)$ or $\left(-\frac{9}{5}, \frac{12}{5}\right)$

97. $\because 2x^2 + y^2 - 3xy = 0$

$$\Rightarrow \quad (2x - y)(x - y) = 0$$

$$\Rightarrow \quad y = 2x, y = x$$

are the equations of straight lines passing through origin.

Now, let the angle between tangents is 2α,

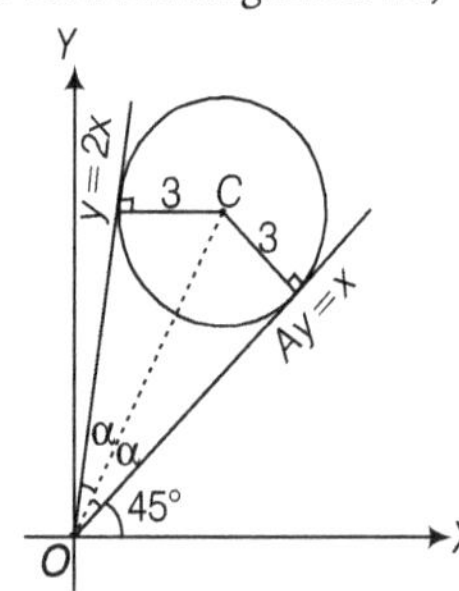

then, $\tan(45° + 2\alpha) = 2$

$$\Rightarrow \quad \frac{\tan 45° + \tan 2\alpha}{1 - \tan 45° \tan 2\alpha} = 2$$

$$\Rightarrow \quad \frac{1 + \tan 2\alpha}{1 - \tan 2\alpha} = \frac{2}{1} \Rightarrow \frac{2\tan 2\alpha}{2} = \frac{1}{3}$$

(By componendo and dividendo rule)

$$\Rightarrow \quad \frac{2\tan\alpha}{1 - \tan^2\alpha} = \frac{1}{3}$$

$$\Rightarrow \quad \tan^2\alpha + 6\tan\alpha - 1 = 0$$

$$\therefore \quad \tan\alpha = \frac{-6 \pm \sqrt{(36 + 4)}}{2} = -3 \pm \sqrt{10}$$

$$= -3 + \sqrt{10} \qquad \left(\because 0 < \alpha < \frac{\pi}{4}\right)$$

Now, in ΔOAC, $\tan\alpha = \frac{3}{OA} = (\sqrt{10} - 3)$

$$\therefore \quad OA = \frac{3}{(\sqrt{10} - 3)} \frac{(\sqrt{10} + 3)}{(\sqrt{10} + 3)} = 3(3 + \sqrt{10})$$

98. The given circle is $x^2 + y^2 = 1$ ...(i)

with centre at $O(0,0)$ and radius 1. It cuts X-axis at the points when $y = 0$ then $x = \pm 1$ i.e., *at* $P(-1, 0)$ and $Q(1, 0)$.

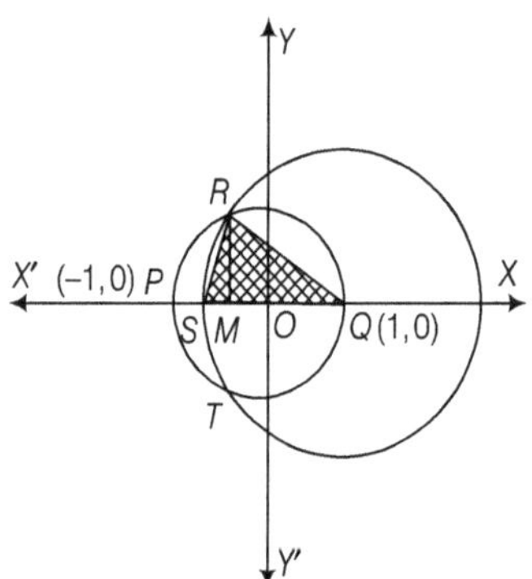

Equation of circle with centre at $Q(1, 0)$ and radius r is

$$(x - 1)^2 + (y - 0)^2 = r^2 \qquad \text{...(ii)}$$

$$(0 < r < 2)$$

Solving Eqs. (i) and (ii), we get

$$x = \frac{2 - r^2}{2} \quad \text{and} \quad y = \pm\frac{r\sqrt{4 - r^2}}{2}$$

but R above the X-axis.

$$\therefore \quad R \equiv \left(\frac{2 - r^2}{2}, \frac{r\sqrt{4 - r^2}}{2}\right)$$

So, $SQ = r$ and $MR = \frac{r\sqrt{4 - r^2}}{2}$

$\therefore$ Area of $\Delta QSR = \frac{1}{2} \cdot QS \cdot MR$

$$\Delta = \frac{1}{2} \cdot r \cdot \frac{r\sqrt{4 - r^2}}{2}$$

$$\Delta \text{ (say)} = \frac{r^2\sqrt{(4 - r^2)}}{4}$$

$$\Delta^2 = \frac{r^4}{16}(4 - r^2) = A \qquad \text{(say)}$$

$$\therefore \quad A = \frac{1}{16}(4r^4 - r^6)$$

$$\therefore \quad \frac{dA}{dr} = \frac{1}{16}(16r^3 - 6r^5) \text{ and } \frac{d^2A}{dr^2} = \frac{1}{16}(48r^2 - 30r^4)$$

For maximum and minimum area, $\frac{dA}{dr} = 0$

$$r^2 = \frac{8}{3}$$

$$\therefore \quad \left(\frac{d^2A}{dr^2}\right)_{r = \sqrt{\frac{8}{3}}} = \frac{1}{16}\left(48 \times \frac{8}{3} - 30 \times \frac{64}{9}\right) < 0$$

$\therefore$ A is maximum. Hence, Δ is also maximum.

$\therefore$ Maximum value of $\Delta = \frac{1}{2} \times \frac{8}{3} \times \frac{1}{2}\sqrt{\left(4 - \frac{8}{3}\right)}$

$$= \frac{2}{3} \times \frac{2}{\sqrt{3}}$$

$$= \frac{4\sqrt{3}}{9} \text{ sq units.}$$

99. The equation of any curve passing through

$$a_1x + b_1y + c_1 = 0$$

$$a_2x + b_2y + c_2 = 0$$

$$y = 0 \quad \text{and} \quad x = 0 \text{ is}$$

$$(a_1x + b_1y + c_1)(a_2x + b_2y + c_2) + \lambda xy = 0 \qquad \text{...(i)}$$

where, λ is a parameter.

This curve will represent a circle. If the coefficient of x^2 = coefficient of y^2,

i.e. $a_1a_2 = b_1b_2$ ...(ii)

and if the coefficient of $xy = 0$

then $a_1b_2 + a_2b_1 + \lambda = 0$

$$\therefore \quad \lambda = -(a_1b_2 + a_2b_1)$$

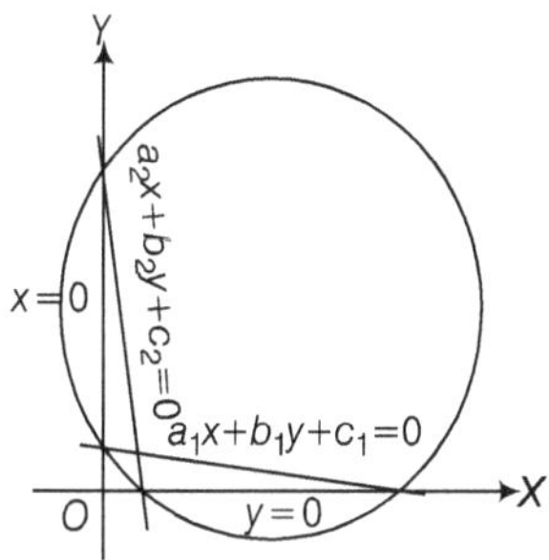

Substituting the value of λ in Eq. (i) then

$$(a_1x + b_1y + c_1)(a_2x + b_2y + c_2) - (a_1b_2 + a_2b_1)xy = 0$$

$$\Rightarrow a_1a_2x^2 + b_1b_2y^2 + (a_1c_2 + a_2c_1)x + (b_1c_2 + b_2c_1)y = 0$$

From Eq. (ii), $b_1b_2 = a_1a_2$

$\therefore$ Equation of required circle is

$$a_1a_2(x^2 + y^2) + (a_1c_2 + a_2c_1)x + (b_1c_2 + b_2c_1)y = 0$$

100. Let circle be

$$S \equiv x^2 + y^2 + 2gx + 2fy + c = 0 \quad \ldots\text{(i)}$$

Since, centre of this circle $(-g, -f)$ lie on $2x - 2y + 9 = 0$

$$\therefore \quad -2g + 2f + 9 = 0 \quad \ldots\text{(ii)}$$

and the circle $S = 0$ and $x^2 + y^2 - 4 = 0$ cuts orthogonally.

$$\therefore \quad 2g \times 0 + 2f \times 0 = c - 4$$

$$\therefore \quad c = 4 \quad \ldots\text{(iii)}$$

Substituting the values of g and c from Eqs. (ii) and (iii) in Eq. (i), then

$$x^2 + y^2 + (2f + 9)x + 2fy + 4 = 0$$

or $$(x^2 + y^2 + 9x + 4) + 2f(x + y) = 0$$

Hence, the circle $S = 0$ passes through fixed point

($\because$ form $S' + \lambda P = 0$)

$\therefore$ $x^2 + y^2 + 9x + 4 = 0$ and $x + y = 0$

After solving we get $(-4, 4)$ or $\left(-\frac{1}{2}, \frac{1}{2}\right)$.

101. Chords are bisected on the line $y = x$. Let (x_1, x_1) be the mid-point of the chord, then equation of the chord is $T = S_1$

$$\therefore \quad xx_1 + yx_1 - a(x + x_1) - b(y + x_1) + a^2 + b^2 - c^2$$
$$= x_1^2 + x_1^2 - 2ax_1 - 2bx_1 + a^2 + b^2 - c^2$$

$$\Rightarrow (x_1 - a)x + (x_1 - b)y + ax_1 + bx_1 - 2x_1^2 = 0$$

This chord passes through $(a, b + c)$

$$\Rightarrow (x_1 - a)a + (x_1 - b)(b + c) + ax_1 + bx_1 - 2x_1^2 = 0$$

$$\Rightarrow \quad 2x_1^2 - (2a + 2b + c)x_1 + a^2 + b^2 + bc = 0$$

which is quadratic in x_1. Since, it is given that two chords are bisected on the line $y = x$, then x_1 must have two real roots,

$$B^2 - 4AC > 0$$

$$\Rightarrow (2a + 2b + c)^2 - 4 \cdot 2(a^2 + b^2 + bc) > 0$$

$$\Rightarrow 4a^2 + 4b^2 + c^2 + 8ab + 4bc + 4ac - 8a^2 - 8b^2$$
$$- 8b^2 - 8bc > 0$$

$$\Rightarrow 4a^2 + 4b^2 - 8ab + 4bc - 4ac - c^2 < 0$$

Hence, the condition on a, b, c is

$$4a^2 + 4b^2 - c^2 - 8ab + 4bc - 4ca < 0$$

102. Let $A \equiv (-a, 0)$ and $B \equiv (a, 0)$ be two fixed points.

Let one line which rotates about B an angle θ with the X-axis at any time t and at that time the second line which rotates about A make an angle 2θ with X-axis.

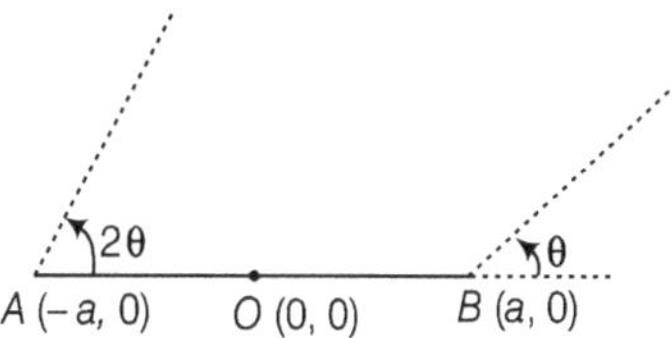

Now, equation of lines through B and A are respectively

$$y - 0 = \tan\theta(x - a) \quad \ldots\text{(i)}$$

and $$y - 0 = \tan 2\theta(x + a) \quad \ldots\text{(ii)}$$

From Eq. (ii), $y = \dfrac{2\tan\theta}{1 - \tan^2\theta}(x + a)$

$$= \left\{\frac{\dfrac{2y}{(x - a)}}{1 - \dfrac{y^2}{(x - a)^2}}\right\}(x + a) \quad \text{[from Eq. (i)]}$$

$$\Rightarrow \quad y = \frac{2y(x - a)(x + a)}{(x - a)^2 - y^2}$$

$$\Rightarrow (x - a)^2 - y^2 = 2(x^2 - a^2)$$

or $x^2 + y^2 + 2ax - 3a^2 = 0$ which is the required locus.

103. Let the coordinate of C is (x_1, y_1)

and let the coordinates of A and B are $(0, 0)$ and $(a, 0)$

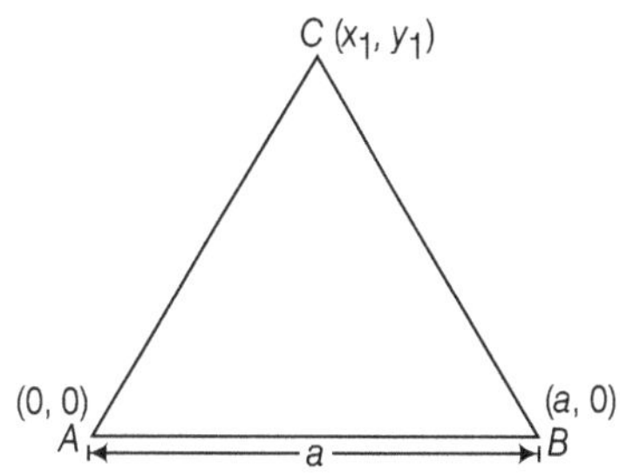

given $$k = \frac{\sin A}{\sin B} = \frac{BC}{AC}$$

$$\Rightarrow \quad (BC)^2 = k^2(AC)^2$$

$$\Rightarrow \quad (x_1 - a)^2 + y_1^2 = k^2(x_1^2 + y_1^2)$$

$$\Rightarrow (1 - k^2)x_1^2 + (1 - k^2)y_1^2 - 2ax_1 + a^2 = 0 \quad (\because k \neq 1)$$

$$\Rightarrow \quad x_1^2 + y_1^2 - \frac{2ax_1}{1 - k^2} + \frac{a^2}{1 - k^2} = 0$$

Hence, locus of C is

$$x^2 + y^2 - \frac{2ax}{1 - k^2} + \frac{a^2}{1 - k^2} = 0$$

This is a circle whose centre is

$$\left(\frac{a}{1 - k^2}, 0\right)$$

and $$\text{radius} = \sqrt{\frac{a^2}{(1 - k^2)^2} - \frac{a^2}{(1 - k^2)}} = \frac{ak}{(1 - k^2)}$$

104. Let P be (x_1, y_1) and line through $P\ (x_1, y_1)$ makes an angle θ with X-axis, then

$$\frac{x - x_1}{\cos\theta} = \frac{y - y_1}{\sin\theta} = r$$

Coordinates of any point on the curve is $(x_1 + r\cos\theta, y_1 + r\sin\theta)$. This point must lie on $ax^2 + 2hxy + by^2 = 1$

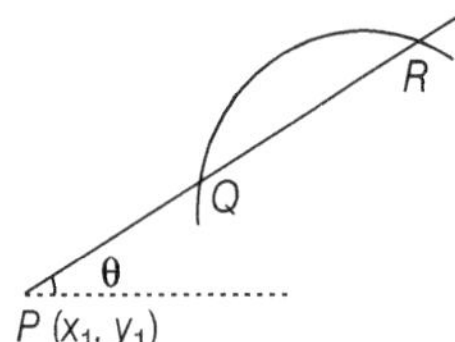

$$\therefore\ a(x_1 + r\cos\theta)^2 + 2h(x_1 + r\cos\theta)(y_1 + r\sin\theta) + b(y_1 + r\sin\theta)^2 = 1$$

$$\therefore\ (a\cos^2\theta + h\sin 2\theta + b\sin^2\theta)\,r^2 + 2(ax_1\cos\theta + hx_1\sin\theta + hy_1\cos\theta)\,r + ax_1^2 + 2hx_1y_1 + by_1^2 = 0$$

It is quadratic equation in r. Let roots of this equation are r_1 and r_2 then

$$r_1r_2 = \frac{ax_1^2 + 2hx_1y_1 + by_1^2}{(a\cos^2\theta + h\sin 2\theta + b\sin^2\theta)}$$

$$\therefore\quad PQ\cdot PR = \frac{ax_1^2 + 2hx_1y_1 + by_1^2}{a\cos^2\theta + h\sin 2\theta + b\sin^2\theta}\ \text{for } a = b, h = 0$$

$$\therefore\quad PQ\cdot PR = \frac{ax_1^2 + 0 + ay_1^2}{a\cos^2\theta + 0 + a\sin^2\theta} = x_1^2 + y_1^2$$

which is independent of θ.

Then curve $ax^2 + 2hxy + by^2 = 1$ becomes $ax^2 + 0 + ay^2 = 1$

$$\Rightarrow\quad x^2 + y^2 = \frac{1}{a}$$

is a circle with centre (0, 0) and radius $\frac{1}{\sqrt{a}}$.

105. Let the centre of circle C be (h,k). Then as this circle touches axis of x, its radius $=|k|$

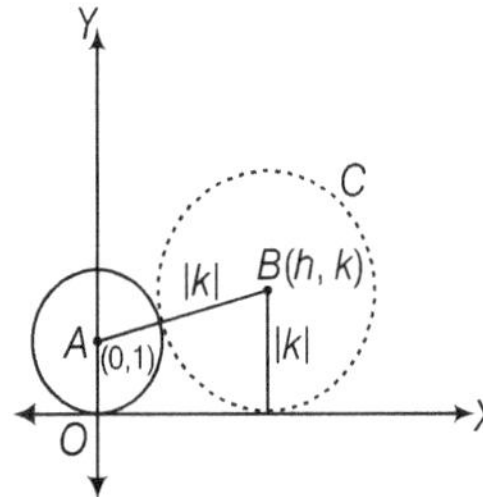

Also, it touches the given circle $x^2 + (y-1)^2 = 1$, centre (0, 1) radius 1, externally

Therefore, the distance between centres = sum of radii

$$\Rightarrow\quad \sqrt{(h-0)^2 + (k-1)^2} = 1 + |k|$$

$$\Rightarrow\quad h^2 + k^2 - 2k + 1 = (1 + |k|)^2$$

$$\Rightarrow\quad h^2 + k^2 - 2k + 1 = 1 + 2|k| + k^2$$

$$\Rightarrow\quad h^2 = 2k + 2|k|$$

$\therefore$ Locus of (h,k) is, $x^2 = 2y + 2|y|$

Now if $y > 0$, it becomes $x^2 = 4y$

and if $y \le 0$, it becomes $x = 0$

$\therefore$ Combining the two, the required locus is

$$\{(x,y) : x^2 = 4y\} \cup \{(0,y) : y \le 0\}$$

106. $s_1 = x^2 + y^2 + 2ax + cy + a = 0$

$$s_2 = x^2 + y^2 - 3ax + dy - 1 = 0$$

Equation of common chord of circles s_1 and s_2 is given by $s_1 - s_2 = 0$

$$\Rightarrow\quad 5ax + (c-d)y + a + 1 = 0$$

Given, that $5x + by - a = 0$ passes through P and Q

$\therefore$ The two equations should represent the same line

$$\Rightarrow\quad \frac{a}{1} = \frac{c-d}{b} = \frac{a+1}{-a}$$

$$\Rightarrow\quad a + 1 = -a^2$$

$$a^2 + a + 1 = 0$$

No real value of a.

107. Equation of circle with centre (0, 3) and radius 2 is

$$x^2 + (y-3)^2 = 4$$

Let centre of the variable circle is (α,β)

$\because$ It touches X-axis.

$\therefore$ It's equation is $(x-\alpha)^2 + (y+\beta)^2 = \beta^2$

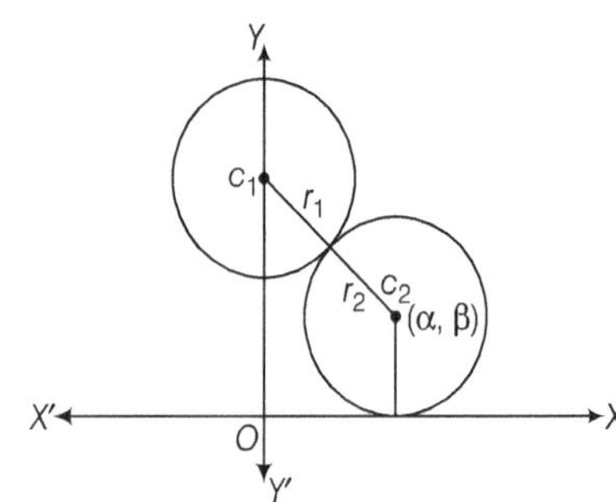

Circle touch externally

$$\Rightarrow\quad c_1c_2 = r_1 + r_2$$

$$\therefore\quad \sqrt{\alpha^2 + (\beta-3)^2} = 2 + \beta$$

$$\alpha^2 + (\beta-3)^2 = \beta^2 + 4 + 4\beta$$

$$\Rightarrow\quad \alpha^2 = 10(\beta - 1/2)$$

$\therefore$ Locus is $x^2 = 10\left(y - \frac{1}{2}\right)$ which is a parabola.

108. Let the centre be (α,β)

$\because$ It cuts the circle $x^2 + y^2 = p^2$ orthogonally

$\therefore$ Using $2g_1g_2 + 2f_1f_2 = c_1 + c_2$, we get

$$2(-\alpha)\times 0 + 2(-\beta)\times 0 = c_1 - p^2$$

$$\Rightarrow\quad c_1 = p^2$$

Let equation of circle is

$$x^2 + y^2 - 2\alpha x - 2\beta y + p^2 = 0$$

It passes through

$$(a,b) \Rightarrow a^2 + b^2 - 2\alpha a - 2\beta b + p^2 = 0$$

$\therefore$ Locus of (α, β) is

$$\therefore \quad 2ax + 2by - (a^2 + b^2 + p^2) = 0$$

109. Without loss of generally it we can assume the square $ABCD$ with its vertices $A(1,1)$, $B(-1,1)$, $C(-1,-1)$, $D(1,-1)$

P to be the point $(0,1)$ and Q as $(\sqrt{2}, 0)$.

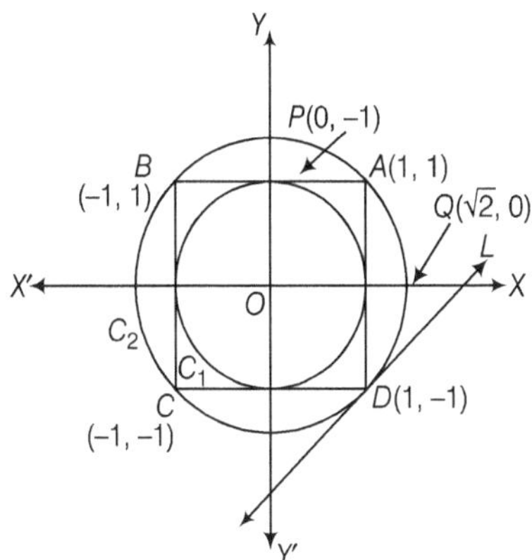

Then, $\dfrac{PA^2 + PB^2 + PC^2 + PD^2}{QA^2 + QB^2 + QC^2 + QD^2}$

$$= \frac{1+1+5+5}{2[(\sqrt{2}-1)^2 + 1] + 2((\sqrt{2}+1)^2 + 1)}$$

$$= \frac{12}{16} = 0.75$$

110. Let C' be the circle touching circle C_1 and L, so that C_1 and C' are on the same side of L. Let us draw a line T parallel to L at a distance equal to the radius of circle C_1, on opposite side of L.

Then, the centre of C' is equidistant from the centre of C_1 and from line T.

$\Rightarrow$ locus of centre of C' is a parabola.

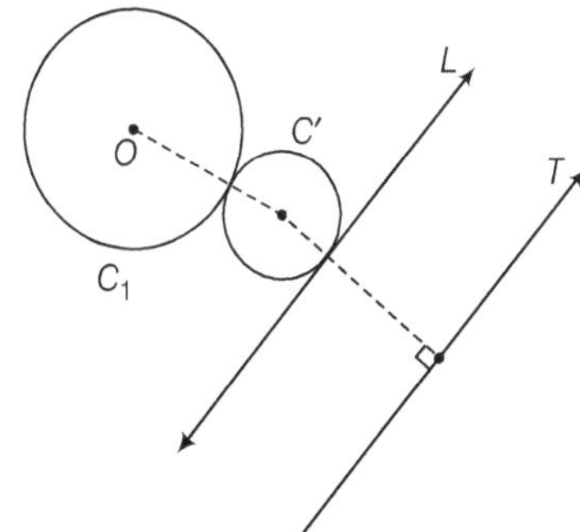

111. Since, S is equidistant from A and line BD, it traces a parabola. Clearly, AC is the axis, $A(1,1)$ is the focus and $T_1\left(\frac{1}{2}, \frac{1}{2}\right)$ is the vertex of parabola.

$$AT_1 = \frac{1}{\sqrt{2}}.$$

T_2T_3 = latusrectum of parabola

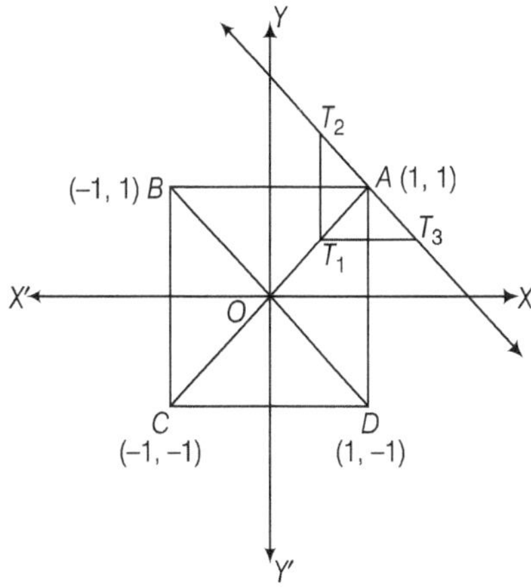

$$= 4 \times \frac{1}{\sqrt{2}} = 2\sqrt{2}$$

$\therefore$ Area $(\Delta T_1T_2T_3) = \dfrac{1}{2} \times \dfrac{1}{\sqrt{2}} \times 2\sqrt{2} = \dfrac{1}{2} = 1$ sq units.

112. Point of intersection of $3x - 47 - 7 = 0$ and $2x - 3y - 5 = 0$ is $(1, -1)$ which is the centre of the circle and radius $= 7$

$\therefore$Equation is $(x-1)^2 + (y+1)^2 = 49$

$$\Rightarrow \quad x^2 + y^2 - 2x + 2y - 47 = 0$$

113. Let $M(h,k)$ be the mid-point of chord AB where

$$\angle AOB = \frac{2\pi}{3}$$

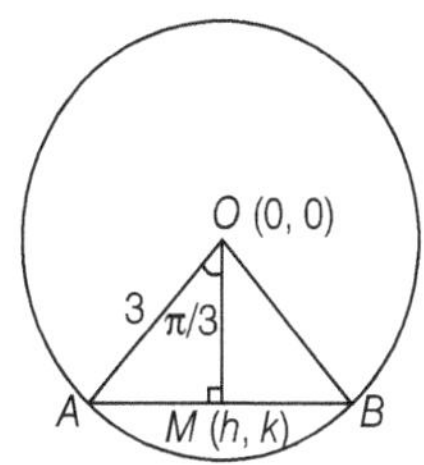

$$\therefore \quad \angle AOM = \frac{\pi}{3}.$$

Also, $\quad OM = 3\cos\dfrac{\pi}{3} = \dfrac{3}{2}$

$$\Rightarrow \quad \sqrt{h^2 + k^2} = \frac{3}{2}$$

$$\Rightarrow \quad h^2 + k^2 = \frac{9}{4}$$

$\therefore$ Locus of (h,k) is $x^2 + y^2 = \dfrac{9}{4}$

114. Equation of director circle of the given circle $x^2 + y^2 = 169$ is $x^2 + y^2 = 2 \times 169 = 338$.

We know from every point on director circle, the tangents drawn to given circle are perpendicular to each other.

Here, (17, 7) lies on director circle.

$\therefore$ The tangent from (17, 7) to given circle are mutually perpendicular.

115. Equation of circle whose centre is (h,k)

$$(x-h)^2+(y-k)^2=k^2$$

(radius of circle $= k$ because circle is tangent to x-axis)

Equation of circle passing through $(-1,+1)$

$\therefore \quad (-1-h)^2+(1-k)^2=k^2$

$\Rightarrow \quad 1+h^2+2h+1+k^2-2k=k^2$

$\Rightarrow \quad h^2+2h-2k+2=0 \quad D \geq 0$

$\therefore \quad (2)^2-4\times 1.(-2K+2)\geq 0$

$\Rightarrow \quad 4-4(-2k+2)\geq 0$

$\Rightarrow \quad 1+2k-2\geq 0 \Rightarrow k\geq \dfrac{1}{2}$

116. Slope of $CD = \dfrac{1}{\sqrt{3}}$

$\therefore$ Parametric equation of CD is

$$\frac{x-\frac{3\sqrt{3}}{2}}{\frac{\sqrt{3}}{2}}=\frac{y-\frac{3}{2}}{\frac{1}{2}}=\pm 1$$

$\therefore$ Two possible coordinates of C are

$$\left(\frac{\sqrt{3}}{2}+\frac{3\sqrt{3}}{2},\frac{1}{2}+\frac{3}{2}\right) \text{ or } \left(\frac{-\sqrt{3}}{2}+\frac{3\sqrt{3}}{2},-\frac{1}{2}+\frac{3}{2}\right)$$

i.e. $(2\sqrt{3},2)$ or $(\sqrt{3},1)$

As (0, 0) and C lie on the same side of PQ

$\therefore (\sqrt{3},1)$ should be the coordinates of C.

Remark : Remember (x_1,y_1) and (x_2,y_2) lie on the same or opposite side of a line $ax+by+c=0$ according as $\dfrac{ax_1+by_1+c}{ax_2+by_2+c}>0$ or <0. $\therefore$ Equation of the circle is

$(x-\sqrt{3})^2+(y-1)^2=1$

117. ΔPQR is an equilateral triangle, the incentre C must coincide with centroid of ΔPQR and D, E, F must coincide with the mid points of sides PQ, QR and RP respectively.

Also, $\quad \angle CPD = 30^\circ \Rightarrow PD=\sqrt{3}$

Writing the equation of side PQ in symmetric form we get,

$$\frac{x-\frac{3\sqrt{3}}{2}}{-\frac{1}{2}}=\frac{y-\frac{3}{2}}{\frac{\sqrt{3}}{2}}=\mp\sqrt{3}$$

$\therefore$ Coordinates of $P=\left(\dfrac{\sqrt{3}}{2}+\dfrac{3\sqrt{3}}{2},\dfrac{-3}{2}+\dfrac{3}{2}\right)=(2\sqrt{3},0)$

and coordinates of $Q=\left(\dfrac{-\sqrt{3}}{2}+\dfrac{3\sqrt{3}}{2},\dfrac{3}{2}+\dfrac{3}{2}\right)=(\sqrt{3},3)$

Let coordinates of R be (α,β), then using the formula for centriod of Δ we get

$$\frac{\sqrt{3}+2\sqrt{3}+\alpha}{3}=\sqrt{3} \text{ and } \frac{3+0+\beta}{3}=1$$

$\Rightarrow \quad \alpha=0$ and $\beta=0$

$\therefore$ Coordinates of $R=(0,0)$

Now, coordinates of $E=$ mid point of $QR=\left(\dfrac{\sqrt{3}}{2},\dfrac{3}{2}\right)$ and coordinates of $F=$ mid-point of $PR=(\sqrt{3},0)$

118. Equation of side QR is $y=\sqrt{3}x$ and equation of side RP is $y=0$

119. The given circle is $x^2+y^2+6x-10y+30=0$ Centre $(-3,5)$, radius $=2$

$$L_1: 2x+3y+(p-3)=0;$$
$$L_2: 2x+3y+p+3=0$$

Clearly, $L_1 || L_2$

Distance between L_1 and L_2

$$=\left|\frac{p+3-p+3}{\sqrt{2^2+3^2}}\right|=\frac{6}{\sqrt{13}}<2$$

$\Rightarrow$ If one line is a chord of the given circle, other line may or may not the diameter of the circle.

Statement I is true and statement II is false.

120. The given circle is $x^2+y^2+2x+4y-3=0$

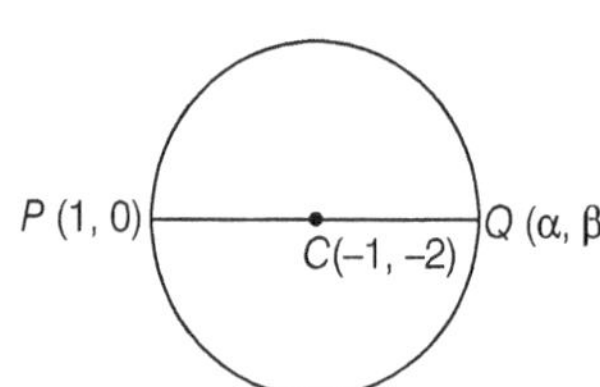

Centre $(-1,-2)$

Let $Q(\alpha,\beta)$ be the point diametrically opposite to the point $P(1,0)$,

then, $\dfrac{1+\alpha}{2}=-1$ and $\dfrac{0+\beta}{2}=-2$

$\Rightarrow \quad \alpha=-3, \beta=-4$, So, Q is $(-3,-4)$

121. Tangents PA and PB are drawn from the point $P(1,3)$ to circle $x^2+y^2-6x-4y-11=0$ with centre $C(3,2)$

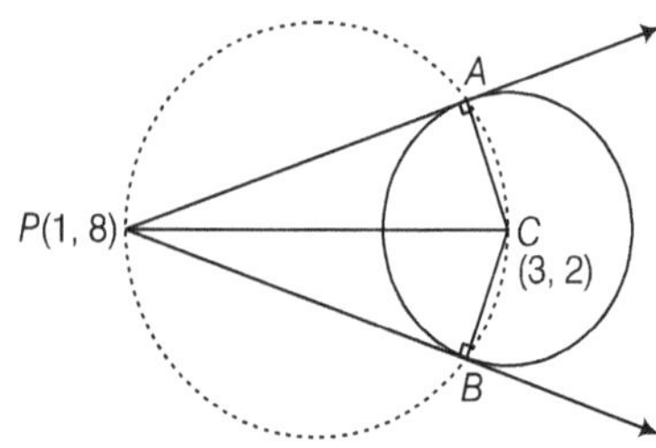

Clearly the circumcircle of ΔPAB will pass through C and as $\angle A=90^\circ$, PC must be a diameter of the circle.

$\therefore$ Equation of required circle is

$$(x-1)(x-3)+(y-2)=0$$

$\Rightarrow \quad x^2+y^2-4x-10y+19=0$

122. Let r be the radius of required circle.

Clearly, in $\Delta C_1CC_2, C_1C = C_2C = r+1$ and P is mid-point of C_1C_2

$\therefore \quad CP \perp C_1C_2$

Also, $\quad PM \perp CC_1$

Now, $\Delta PMC_1 \sim \Delta CPC_1$ (by AA similarity)

$$\therefore \quad \frac{MC_1}{PC_1} = \frac{PC_1}{CC_1}$$

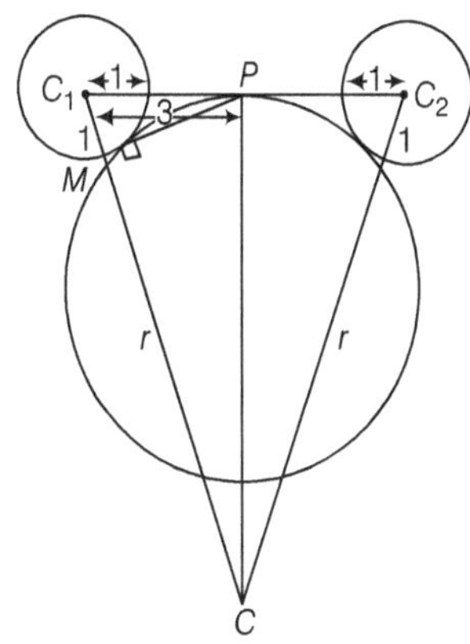

$$\Rightarrow \quad \frac{1}{3} = \frac{3}{r+1} \Rightarrow r+1 = 9 \Rightarrow r = 8.$$

123. The given circles are

$$S_1 \equiv x^2 + y^2 + 3x + 7y + 2p - 5 = 0 \quad \text{...(i)}$$

$$S_2 \equiv x^2 + y^2 + 2x + 2y - p^2 = 0 \quad \text{...(ii)}$$

$\therefore$ Equation of common chord PQ is $S_1 - S_2 = 0$

$$\Rightarrow \quad L \equiv x + 5y + p^2 + 2p - 5 = 0$$

$\Rightarrow$ Equation of circle passing through P and Q is $S_1 + \lambda L = 0$

$$\Rightarrow (x^2 + y^2 + 3x + 7y + 2p - 5) + \lambda(x + 5y + p^2 + 2p - 5) = 0$$

As it passes through (1, 1), therefore

$$\Rightarrow \quad (7 + 2p) + \lambda(2p + p^2 + 1) = 0$$

$$\Rightarrow \quad \lambda = -\frac{2p+7}{(p+1)^2}$$

which does not exist for $p = -1$

124. Circle $x^2 + y^2 - 4x - 8y - 5 = 0$

Centre = (2, 4)

Radius = $\sqrt{4+16+5} = 5$

If circle is intersecting line $3x - 4y = m$, at two distinct points.

$\Rightarrow$ length of perpendicular from centre to the line < radius

$$\Rightarrow \quad \frac{|6 - 16 - m|}{5} < 5$$

$$\Rightarrow \quad |10 + m| < 25$$

$$\Rightarrow \quad -25 < m + 10 < 25$$

$$\Rightarrow \quad -35 < m < 15$$

125. Let centre of the circle be $(h, 2)$ then radius $= |h|$

$\therefore$ Equation of circle becomes $(x-h)^2 + (y-2)^2 = h^2$

As it passes through (–1, 0)

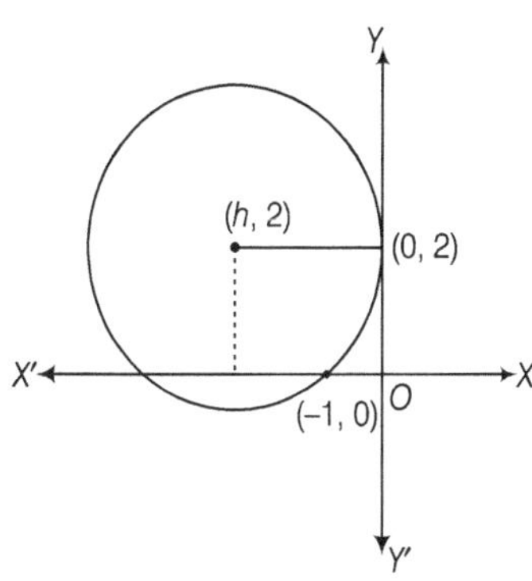

$$\Rightarrow \quad (-1-h)^2 + 4 = h^2 \Rightarrow h = \frac{-5}{2}$$

$$\therefore \quad \text{Centre} \left(\frac{-5}{2}, 2\right) \text{ and } r = \frac{5}{2}$$

Distance of centre from (–4, 0) is $\frac{5}{2}$

$\therefore$ It lies on the circle.

126. The smaller region of circle is the region given by

$$x^2 + y^2 \le 6 \quad \text{...(i)}$$

and $\quad 2x - 3y \ge 1 \quad$ ...(ii)

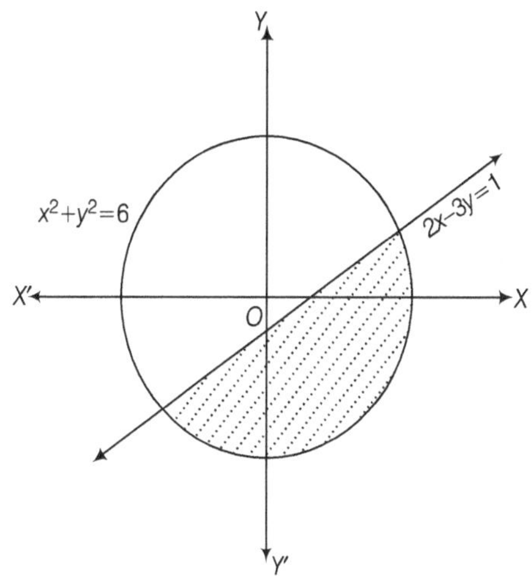

We observe that only two points $\left(2, \frac{3}{4}\right)$ and $\left(\frac{1}{4}, -\frac{1}{4}\right)$ satisfy both the inequations Eqs. (i) and (ii), we get

$\therefore$ 2 points in S lie inside the smaller part.

127. As centre of one circle is (0, 0) and other circle passes through (0, 0), therefore

Aslo, $\quad C_1\left(\frac{a}{2}, 0\right) C_2(0, 0)$

$$r_1 = \frac{|a|}{2} \; r_2 = C$$

$$C_1C_2 = r_1 - r_2 = \frac{|a|}{2}$$

$$\Rightarrow \quad c - \frac{|a|}{2} = \frac{|a|}{2} \Rightarrow c = |a|$$

If the two circles touch each other, then they must touch each other internally.

128. Any point P on line $4x-5y=20$ is $\left(\alpha, \frac{4\alpha-20}{5}\right)$.

Equation of chord of contact AB to the circle $x^2+y^2=9$

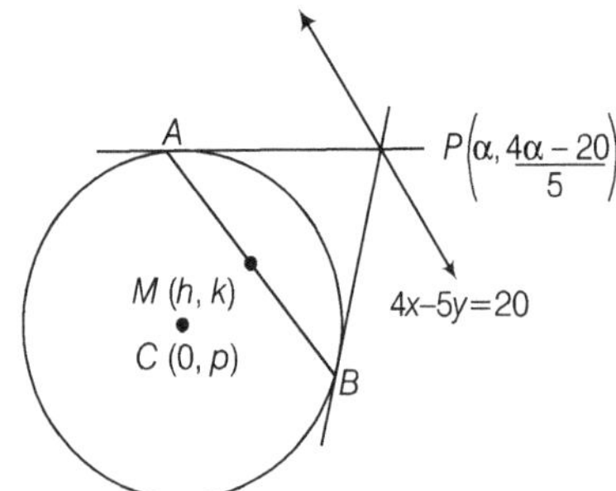

drawn from point $P\left(\alpha, \frac{4\alpha-20}{5}\right)$ is

$$x.\alpha + y.\left(\frac{4\alpha-20}{5}\right) = 9 \quad \text{...(i)}$$

Also, the equation of chord AB whose mid-point is (h,k) is

$$hx+ky=h^2+k^2 \quad \text{...(ii)}$$

$\because$ Eqs. (i) and (ii) represent the same line, therefore

$$\frac{h}{\alpha}=\frac{k}{\frac{4\alpha-20}{5}}=\frac{h^2+k^2}{9}$$

$\Rightarrow \quad 5k\alpha = 4h\alpha - 20h$

and $\quad 9h = \alpha(h^2+k^2)$

$\Rightarrow \quad \alpha = \frac{20h}{4h-5k}$ and $\alpha = \frac{9h}{h^2+k^2}$

$\Rightarrow \quad \frac{20h}{4h-5k} = \frac{9h}{h^2+k^2}$

$\Rightarrow \quad 20(h^2+k^2) = 9(4h-5k)$

$\therefore$ Locus of (h,k) is $20(x^2+y^2)-36x+45y=0$

Sol. (Q. Nos. 129 to 130)

Equation of tangent PT to the circle $x^2+y^2=4$ at the point $P(\sqrt{3},1)$ is $x\sqrt{3}+y=4$

Let the line L, perpendicular to tangent PT be

$$x-y\sqrt{3}+\lambda=0 \quad \text{...(i)}$$

As it is tangent to the circle $(x-3)^2+y^2=1$

$\therefore$ length of perpendicular from centre of circle to the tangent = radius of circle.

$\Rightarrow \quad \left|\frac{3+\lambda}{2}\right| = 1 \Rightarrow \lambda = -1$ or -5

129. From Eq. (i)

Equation of L can be

$$x-\sqrt{3}y=1$$

or $\quad x-\sqrt{3}y=5$

130.

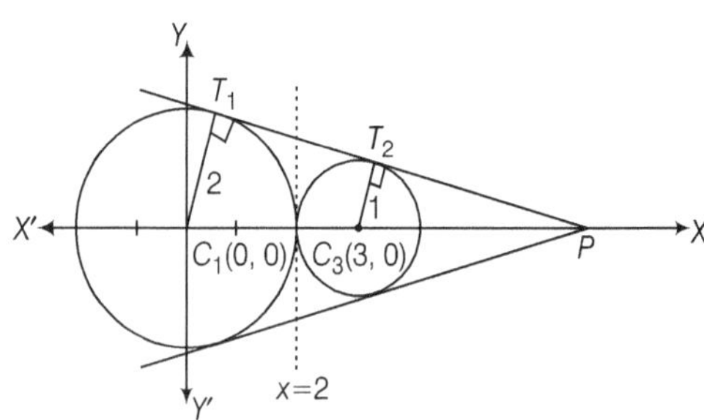

From the figure it is clear that the intersection point of two direct common tangents lies on X-axis.

Aslo $\quad \Delta PT_1C_1 \sim \Delta PT_2C_2$

$\Rightarrow \quad PC_1 : PC_2 = 2:1$

or P divides C_1C_2 in the ratio 2:1 externally

$\therefore$ Coordinates of P are $(6,0)$

Let the equation of tangent through P be

$$y=m(x-6)$$

As it touches $x^2+y^2=4$

$\therefore \quad \left|\frac{6m}{\sqrt{m^2+1}}\right| = 2$

$\Rightarrow \quad 36m^2 = 4(m^2+1)$

$\Rightarrow \quad m = \pm\frac{1}{2\sqrt{2}}$

$\therefore$ Equations of common tangents are $y=\pm\frac{1}{2\sqrt{2}}(x-6)$

Also $x=2$ is the common tangent to the two circles.

131. Let centre of the circle ne $(1,4)$

[$\because$ circle touches x-axis at (1, 0)]

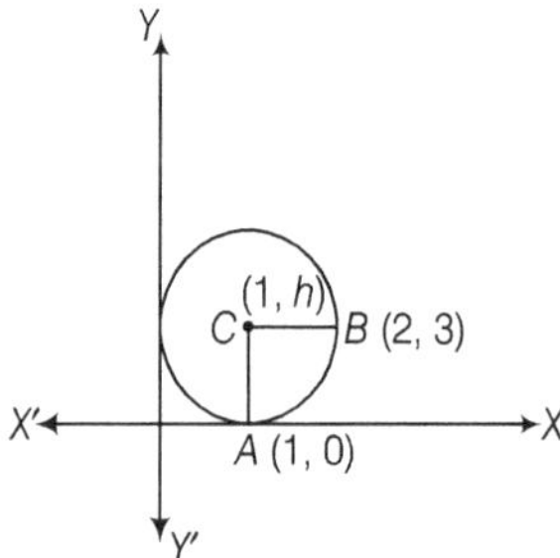

Let the circle passes through the point $B(2,3)$

$\therefore \quad CA = CB \quad$ (radius)

$\Rightarrow \quad CA^2 = CB^2$

$\Rightarrow \quad (1-1)^2+(h-0)^2 = (1-2)^2+(h-3)^2$

$\Rightarrow \quad h^2 = 1+h^2+9-6h$

$\Rightarrow \quad h = \frac{10}{6} = \frac{5}{3}$

Thus, diameter is $2h = \frac{10}{3}$.

132. Since, circle touches X-axis at (3, 0)

$\therefore$ The equation of circle be

$$(x-3)^2+(y-0)^2+\lambda y=0$$

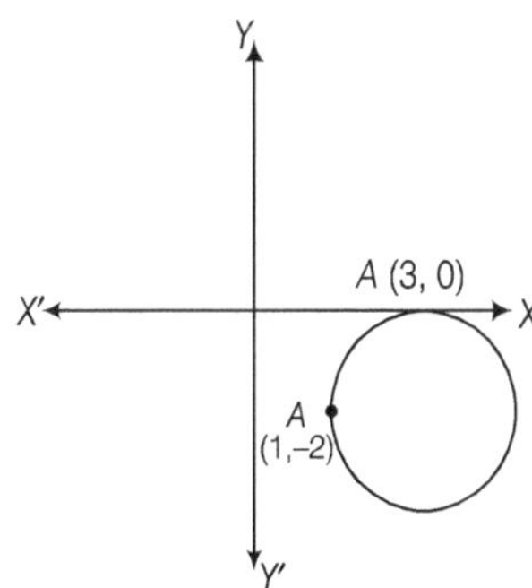

As it passes through (1, −2)

$\therefore$ Put $x=1, y=-2$

$\Rightarrow \quad (1-3)^2+(-2)^2+\lambda(-2)=0 \Rightarrow \lambda=4$

$\therefore$ Equation of circle is $(x-3)^2+y^2-8=0$

Now, from the options (5, −2) satisfies equation of circle.

133. There can be two possibilities for the given circle as shown in the figure

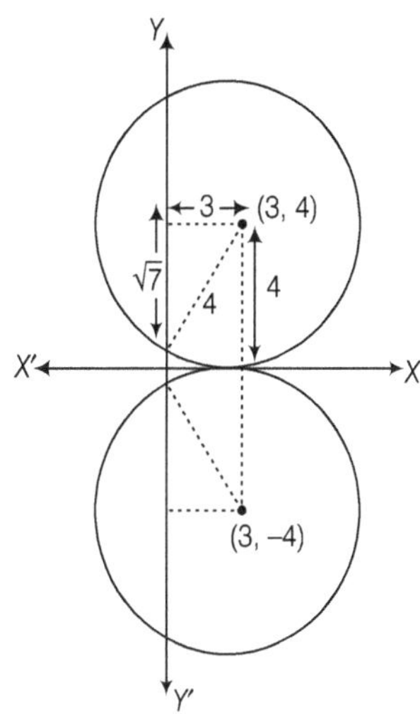

$\therefore$ The equations of circle can be

$$(x-3)^2+(y-4)^2=4^2$$

or $\quad (x-3)^2+(y+4)^2=4^2$

i.e. $\quad x^2+y^2-6x+8y+9=0$

or $\quad x^2+y^2-6x+8y+9=0$

134.

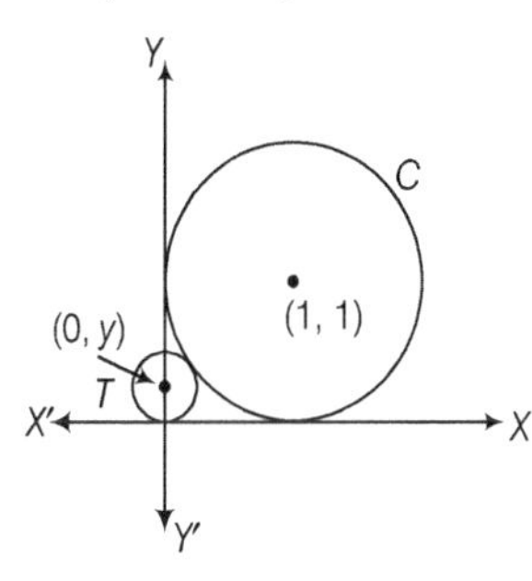

Equation of circle $C \equiv (x-1)^2+(y-1)^2=1$

Radius of $T=|y|$

T touches C externally

therefore,

Distance between the centres = sum of their radii

$\Rightarrow \quad \sqrt{(0-1)^2+(y-1)^2}=1+|y|$

$\Rightarrow \quad (0-1)^2+(y-1)^2=(1+|y|)^2$

$\Rightarrow \quad 1+y^2+1-2y=1+y^2+2|y|$

$$2|y|=1-2y$$

If $y>0$ then, $2y=1-2y \Rightarrow y=\frac{1}{4}$

If $y<0$ then, $-2y=1-2y \Rightarrow 0=1$ (not possible)

$\therefore \quad y=\frac{1}{4}$

135. Let the equation of circle be

$$x^2+y^2+2gx+2fy+c=0$$

It passes through (0, 1)

$\therefore \quad 1+2f+c=0 \quad$ ...(i)

This circle is orthogonal to $(x-1)^2+y^2=16$

i.e. $\quad x^2+y^2-2x-15=0$

and $\quad x^2+y^2-1=0$

$\therefore$ We should have

$$2g(-1)+2f(0)=c-15$$

or $\quad 2g+c-15=0 \quad$ ...(ii)

and $\quad 2g(0)+2f(0)=c-1$ or $c=1$

Solving Eqs. (i), (ii) and (iii), we get

$$c=1, g=7, f=-1$$

$\therefore$ Required circle is

$$x^2+y^2+14x-2y+1=0$$

With centre $(-7,1)$ and radius $=7$

136. Intersection point of $2x-3y+4=0$ and $x-2y+3=0$ is (1, 2)

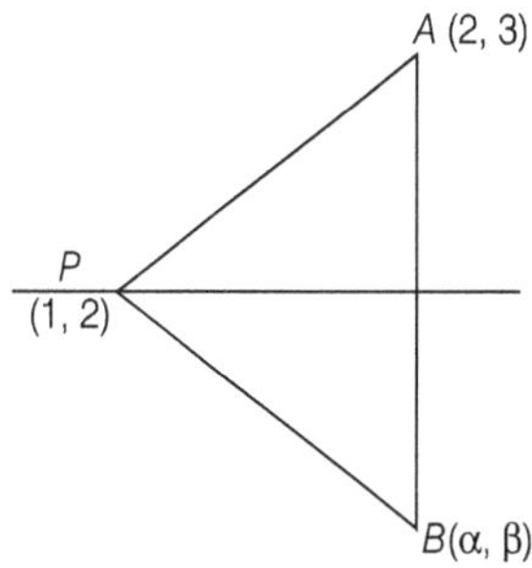

Since, P is the fixed point for given family of lines

So, $PB=PA$

$$(\alpha-1)^2+(\beta-2)^2=(2-1)^2+(3-2)^2$$

$$(\alpha-1)^2+(\beta-2)^2=1+1=2$$

$$(x-1)^2+(y-2)^2=(\sqrt{2})^2$$

$(x-a)^2+(y-b)^2=r^2$

Therefore, given locus is a circle with centre $(1,2)$ and radius $\sqrt{2}$.

137. $x^2+y^2-4x-6y-12=0$ ...(i)

Centre $C_1=(2,3)$ and Radius, $r_1=5$ units

$$x^2+y^2+6x+18y+26=0 \quad ...(ii)$$

Centre, $C_2=(-3,-9)$

and radius, $r_2=8$ units

$$|C_1C_2|=\sqrt{(2+3)^2+(3+9)^2}=13 \text{ units}$$

$$r_1+r_2=5+8=13$$

$\therefore$ $|C_1C_2|=r_1+r_2$

Therefore, there are three common tangents.

138. For the given circle, centre : (4, 4), radius =6

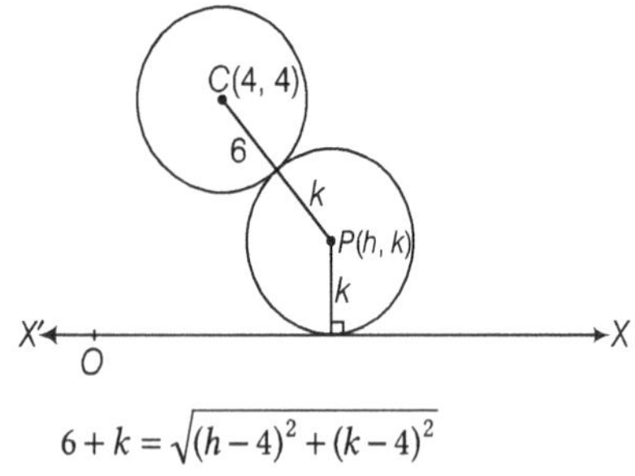

$$6+k=\sqrt{(h-4)^2+(k-4)^2}$$

$$(h-4)^2=20k+20$$

$\therefore$ locus of (h, k) is $(x-4)^2=20(y+1)$, which is parabola.

139. Centre of $S:O(-3,2)$ and centre of given circle is $A(2,-3)$

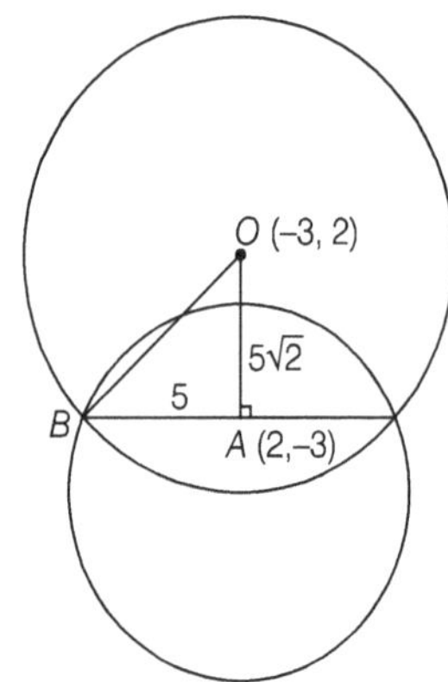

$\Rightarrow$ $OA=5\sqrt{2}$

Also, $AB=5$ ($\because AB=$ radius of the given circle)

Now, in ΔOAB,

$$(OB)^2=(AB)^2+(OA)^2=25+50=75$$

$\therefore$ $OB=5\sqrt{3}$

140. Circle : $x^2+y^2=1$

Equation of tangent at $P(\cos\theta, \sin\theta)$

$$x\cos\theta+y\sin\theta=1 \quad ...(i)$$

Equation of normal at P

$$y=x\tan\theta \quad ...(ii)$$

Equation of tangent at S is $x=1$

$$\therefore \quad Q\left(1,\frac{1-\cos\theta}{\sin\theta}\right)=Q\left(1,\tan\frac{\theta}{2}\right)$$

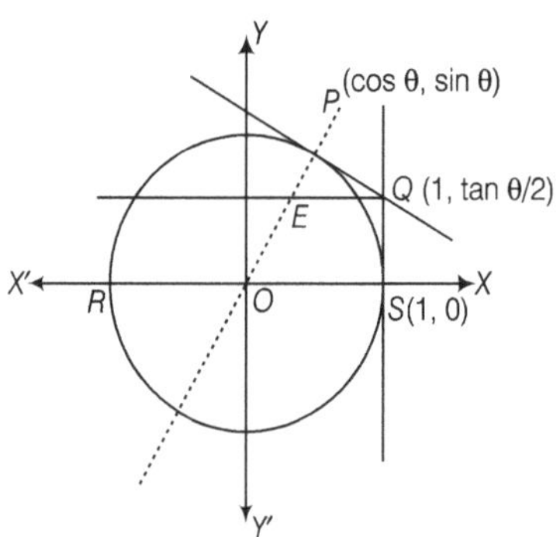

$\therefore$ Equation of line through Q and parallel to RS is $y=\tan\frac{\theta}{2}$

$\therefore$ Intersection point E of normal and $y=\tan\frac{\theta}{2}$

$$\tan\frac{\theta}{2}=x\tan\theta$$

$$\Rightarrow \quad x=\frac{1-\tan^2\frac{\theta}{2}}{2}$$

$\therefore$ Locus of $E: x=\frac{1-y^2}{2}$ or $y^2=1-2x$

It is satisfied by the points $\left(\frac{1}{3},\frac{1}{\sqrt{3}}\right)$ and $\left(\frac{1}{3},\frac{-1}{\sqrt{3}}\right)$.

141. (2) Equation of circle can be written as

$(x+1)^2+(y+2)^2=p+5$ ...(i)

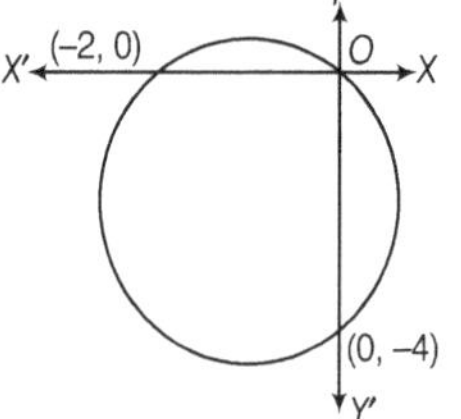

Case I. For $p=0$, circle passes through origin and cuts x-axis and y-axis at $(-2, 0)$ and $(0, -4)$ respectively.

Case II. If circle touch X-axis, then

$$(1)^2=-p \Rightarrow p=-1$$

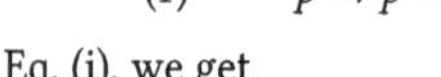

From Eq. (i), we get

$$(x+1)^2+(y+2)^2=2^2$$

Cut off Y-axis at (put $x=0$)

$$(y+2)^2=3$$

$\Rightarrow$ $y=-2\pm\sqrt{3}$

or $(0, -2\pm\sqrt{3})$

Case III. If circle touch Y-axis, then

$$(2)^2=-p$$

$\Rightarrow$ $p=-4$

From Eq. (i), we get

$$(x+1)^2+(y+2)^2=1$$

Cut off X-axis at (put $y=0$)

$$(x+1)^2=-3 \text{ (impossible)}$$

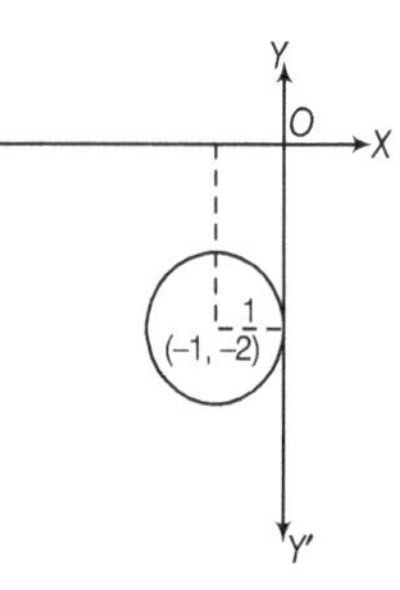

CHAPTER

05

Parabola

Learning Part

Session 1

- Introduction
- Section of a Right Circular Cone by Different Planes
- Equation of Conic Section
- How to Find the Centre of Conics
- Standard Equation of Parabola
- Other forms of Parabola with Latusrectum $4a$
- General Equation of a Parabola
- The Generalised form $(y-k)^2 = 4a(x-h)$
- Conic Section
- Conic Section : Definition
- Recognisation of Conics
- Parabola : Definition
- Some Terms Related to Parabola
- Smart Table
- Equation of Parabola if Equation of axis, Tangent at Vertex and Latusrectum are given
- Parabolic Curve

Session 2

- Position of a Point (x_1, y_1) with respect to a Parabola $y^2 = 4ax$
- Intersection of a Line and a Parabola
- Point of Intersection of Tangents at any Two Points on the Parabola
- Point of Intersection of Normals at any Two Points on the Parabola
- Co-normal Points
- Parametric Relation between the Coordinates of the Ends of a Focal Chord of a Parabola
- Equation of Tangent in Different Forms
- Equation of Normals in Different Forms
- Relation Between 't_1' and 't_2' if Normal at 't_1' meets the Parabola Again at 't_2'
- Circle Through Co-normal Points

Session 3

- Pair of Tangents $SS_1 = T^2$
- Equation of the Chord Bisected at a Given Point
- Lengths of Tangent, Subtangent, Normal and Subnormal
- Reflection Property of a Parabola
- Chord of Contact
- Diameter
- Some Standard Properties of the Parabola
- Study of Parabola of the Form $(\alpha x + \beta y)^2 + 2gx + 2fy + c = 0$

Practice Part

- JEE Type Examples
- Chapter Exercises

Arihant on Your Mobile !

Exercises with the symbol can be practised on your mobile. See inside cover page to activate for free.

Session 1

Introduction, Conic Section, Section of a Right Circular Cone by Different Planes, Conic Section : Definition, Equation of Conic Section, Recognisation of Conics, How to Find the Centre of Conics, Parabola : Definition, Other forms of Parabola with Latusrectum 4a, General Equation of a Parabola, The Generalised form $(y-k)^2 = 4a(x-h)$, Parabolic Curve

Introduction

The famous Greek mathematician Euclid, the father of creative Geometry, near about 300 BC considering various plane sections of a right circular cone found many curves, which are called conics or conic sections.

Conic Section

Let l_1 be a fixed vertical line and l_2 be another line intersecting it at a fixed point V and inclined to it at an angle α.

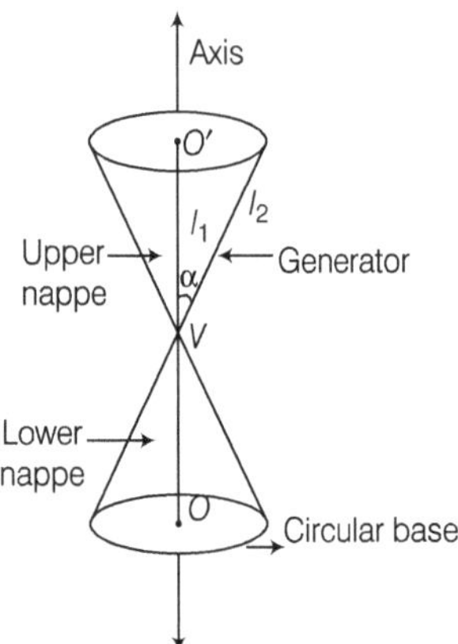

Suppose we rotate the line l_2 around the line l_1 in such a way the angle remains constant then, the surface generated is a double-napped right circular hollow cone.

The point V is called the vertex, the line l_1 is the axis of the cone. The rotating line l_2 is called a generator of the cone. The vertex separates the cone into two parts called nappes. The constant angle α is called the semi-vertical angle of the cone.

Section of a Right Circular Cone by Different Planes

1. Section of a right circular cone by a plane which is passing through its vertex is a pair of straight lines, lines always passes through the vertex of the cone.

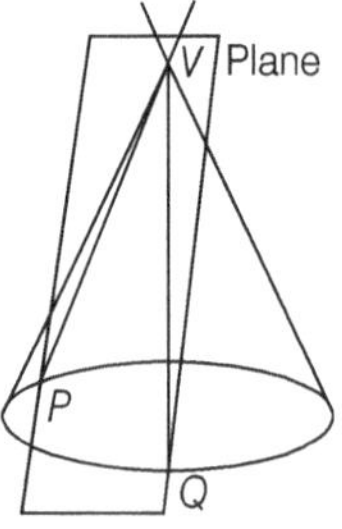

2. Section of a right circular cone by a plane which parallel to its base is a circle.

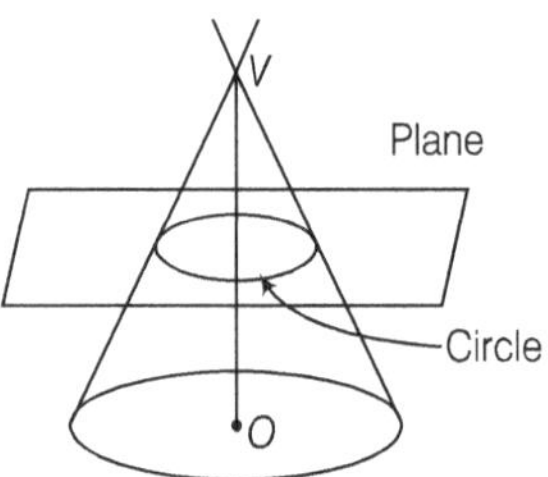

3. Section of a right circular cone by a plane which is parallel to a generator of the cone is a parabola.

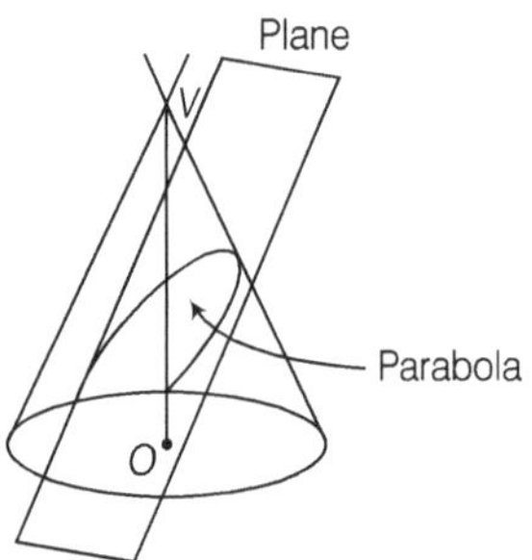

4. Section of a right circular cone by a plane which is not parallel to any generator and not parallel or perpendicular to the axis of the cone is an ellipse.

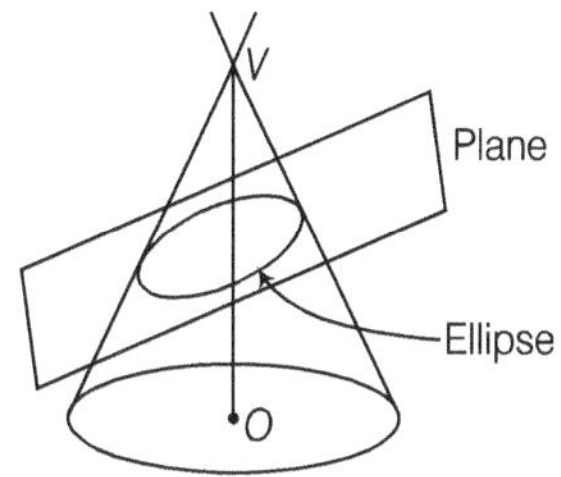

5. Section of a right circular cone by a plane which is parallel to the axis of the cone is a hyperbola.

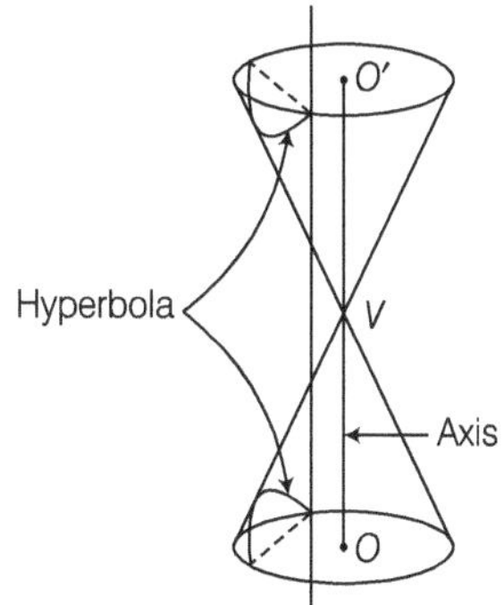

3D View

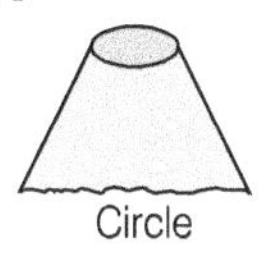

Circle

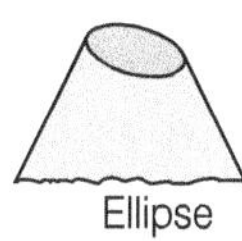

Ellipse

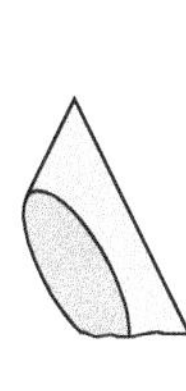

Parabola

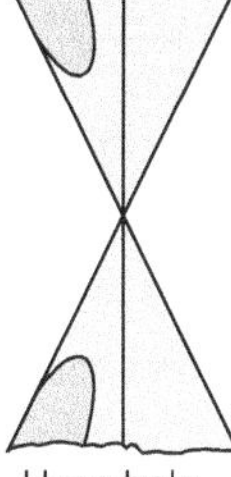

Hyperbola

Conic Section : Definition

The locus of a point which moves in a plane such that the ratio of its distance from a fixed point to its perpendicular distance from a fixed straight line is always constant, is known as a **conic section** or **a conic.**

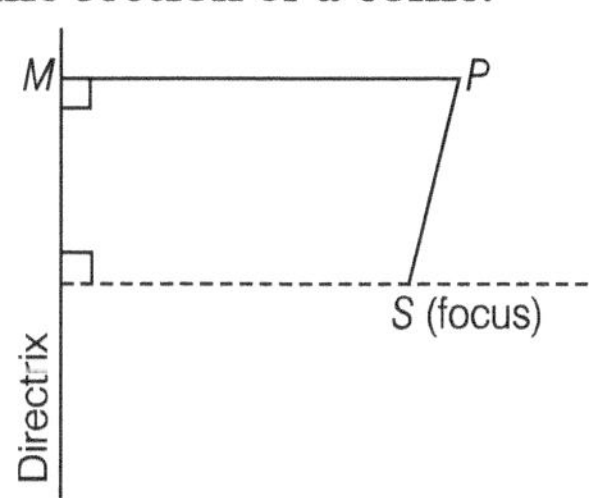

The fixed point is called the **focus** of the conic and this fixed line is called the **directrix** of the conic. Also, this constant ratio is called the **eccentricity** of the conic and is denoted by *e*.

In the figure, $\dfrac{SP}{PM} = \text{constant} = e$

$\Rightarrow \qquad SP = e\,PM$

Equation of Conic Section

If the focus is (α, β) and the directrix is $ax + by + c = 0$, then the equation of the conic section whose eccentricity $= e$ is $SP = e\,PM$

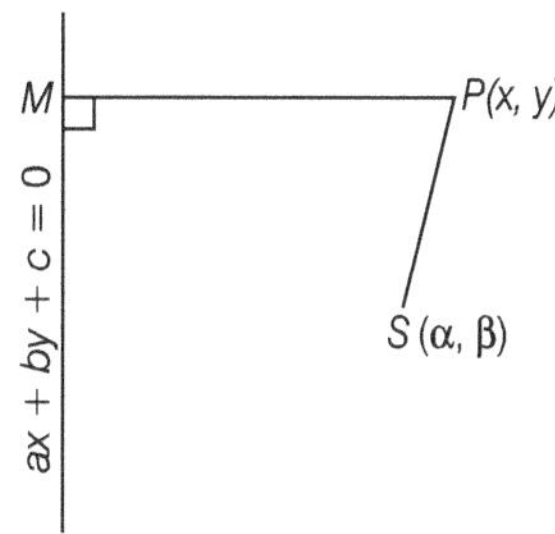

$$\Rightarrow \quad \sqrt{(x-\alpha)^2 + (y-\beta)^2} = e \cdot \frac{|ax + by + c|}{\sqrt{(a^2 + b^2)}}$$

$$\Rightarrow \quad (x-\alpha)^2 + (y-\beta)^2 = e^2 \cdot \frac{(ax + by + c)^2}{(a^2 + b^2)}.$$

Important Terms

Axis The straight line passing through the focus and perpendicular to the directrix is called the axis of the conic section.

Vertex The points of intersection of the conic section and the axis is (are) called vertex (vertices) of the conic section.

Focal Chord Any chord passing through the focus is called focal chord of the conic section.

Double Ordinate A straight line drawn perpendicular to the axis and terminated at both end of the curve is a double ordinate of the conic section.

Latusrectum The double ordinate passing through the focus is called the latusrectum of the conic section.

Centre The point which bisects every chord of the conic passing through it, is called the centre of the conic section.

Remark

Parabola has no centre but circle, ellipse and hyperbola have centre.

Example 1 Find the locus of a point, which moves such that its distance from the point (0, –1) is twice its distance from the line $3x+4y+1=0$.

Sol. Let $P(x_1, y_1)$ be the point, whose locus is required.

Its distance from $(0, -1) = 2\times$ its distance from the line $3x+4y+1=0$.

$$\Rightarrow \quad \sqrt{(x_1-0)^2+(y_1+1)^2} = 2\times\frac{|3x_1+4y_1+1|}{\sqrt{(3^2+4^2)}}$$

$$\Rightarrow \quad 5\sqrt{x_1^2+(y_1+1)^2} = 2|3x_1+4y_1+1|$$

Squaring and simplifying, we have

$$25(x_1^2+y_1^2+2y_1+1) = 4(9x_1^2+16y_1^2+24x_1y_1+6x_1+8y_1+1)$$

or $11x_1^2+39y_1^2+96x_1y_1+24x_1-18y_1-21=0$

Hence, the locus of (x_1, y_1) is

$$11x^2+39y^2+96xy+24x-18y-21=0$$

Example 2 What conic does the equation $25(x^2+y^2-2x+1)=(4x-3y+1)^2$ represent ?

Sol. Given equation is

$$25(x^2+y^2-2x+1)=(4x-3y+1)^2 \quad ...(i)$$

Write the right hand side of this equation, so that it appears in perpendicular distance form, then

$$(4x-3y+1)^2 = 25\left(\frac{4x-3y+1}{\sqrt{(4^2+3^2)}}\right)^2$$

then, Eq. (i) can be re-written as

$$25[(x-1)^2+(y-0)^2] = 25\left[\frac{4x-3y+1}{\sqrt{(4^2+3^2)}}\right]^2$$

or $$\sqrt{(x-1)^2+(y-0)^2} = \frac{|4x-3y+1|}{\sqrt{(4^2+3^2)}}$$

Here, $e=1$

Thus, the given equation represents a parabola. It may noted that (1,0) is the focus and $4x-3y+1=0$ is the directrix of the parabola.

Recognisation of Conics

The equation of conics represented by the general equation of second degree

$$ax^2+2hxy+by^2+2gx+2fy+c=0 \quad ...(i)$$

can be recognised easily by the condition given in the tabular form. For this, first we have to find discriminant of the equation. We know that the discriminant of above equation is represented by Δ, where

$$\Delta = abc+2fgh-af^2-bg^2-ch^2$$

The nature of the conic section depends upon the position of the focus S with respect to the directrix and also upon the value of the eccentricity e. Two different cases arise.

***Case* I (When the focus lies on the directrix)**

In this case Eq. (i) represents the **Degenerate conic** whose nature is given in the following table :

Condition	Nature of Conic
$e>1$; $\Delta=0$, $h^2>ab$	The lines will be real and distinct intersecting at S.
$e=1$; $\Delta=0$, $h^2=ab$	The lines will coincident
$e<1$; $\Delta=0$, $h^2<ab$	The lines will be imaginary.

***Case* II (When the focus does not lie on the directrix)**

In this case Eq. (i) represents the **Non-degenerate conic** whose nature is given in the following table :

Condition	Nature of Conic
$e=1$; $\Delta\neq0$, $h^2=ab$	a parabola
$0<e<1$; $\Delta\neq0$, $h^2<ab$	an ellipse
$e>1$; $\Delta\neq0$, $h^2>ab$	a hyperbola
$e>1$; $\Delta\neq0$, $h^2>ab$; $a+b=0$	rectangular hyperbola

Remark

1. If conic represents an empty set, then $\Delta\neq0$, $h^2<ab$.
2. If conic represents a single point, the $\Delta=0$, $h^2<ab$.

Example 3 What conic does $13x^2-18xy+37y^2+2x+14y-2=0$ represent?

Sol. Compare the given equation with

$$ax^2+2hxy+by^2+2gx+2fy+c=0$$

$\therefore \quad a=13, h=-9, b=37, g=1, f=7, c=-2,$

then, $\Delta = abc+2fgh-af^2-bg^2-ch^2$

$= (13)(37)(-2)+2(7)(1)(-9) - 13(7)^2-37(1)^2+2(-9)^2$

$= -962-126-637-37+162 = -1600\neq0$

and also $h^2=(-9)^2=81$ and $ab=13\times37=481$

Here, $h^2<ab$

So, we have $h^2<ab$ and $\Delta\neq0$.

Hence, the given equation represents an ellipse.

Example 4 What conic is represented by the equation $\sqrt{ax}+\sqrt{by}=1$?

Sol. Given conic is $\sqrt{ax}+\sqrt{by}=1$

On squaring both sides, we get

$$ax+by+2\sqrt{abxy}=1$$

$$\Rightarrow \quad ax+by-1=-2\sqrt{abxy}$$

Again, on squaring both sides, then

$$(ax + by - 1)^2 = 4abxy$$

$\Rightarrow \quad a^2x^2 + b^2y^2 + 1 + 2abxy - 2by - 2ax = 4abxy$

$\Rightarrow \quad a^2x^2 + b^2y^2 - 2abxy - 2ax - 2by + 1 = 0$

$\Rightarrow \quad a^2x^2 - 2abxy + b^2y^2 - 2ax - 2by + 1 = 0 \quad \ldots(i)$

Comparing the Eq. (i) with the equation

$$Ax^2 + 2Hxy + By^2 + 2Gx + 2Fy + C = 0$$

$\therefore \quad A = a^2, H = -ab, B = b^2, G = -a, F = -b, C = 1$

then, $\Delta = ABC + 2FGH - AF^2 - BG^2 - CH^2$

$= a^2b^2 - 2a^2b^2 - a^2b^2 - a^2b^2 - a^2b^2$

$= -4a^2b^2 \neq 0$ and $H^2 = a^2b^2 = AB$

So, we have $\Delta \neq 0$ and $H^2 = AB$.

Hence, the given equation represents a parabola.

Example 5 If the equation $x^2 - y^2 - 2x + 2y + \lambda = 0$ represents a degenerate conic, find the value of λ.

Sol. For degenerate conic $\Delta = 0$

Comparing the given equation of conic with

$$ax^2 + 2hxy + by^2 + 2gx + 2fy + c = 0$$

$\therefore \quad a = 1, b = -1, h = 0, g = -1, f = 1, c = \lambda$

$\therefore \quad \Delta = abc + 2fgh - af^2 - bg^2 - ch^2 = 0$

$\Rightarrow (1)(-1)(\lambda) + 0 - 1 \times (1)^2 + 1 \times (-1)^2 - \lambda (0)^2 = 0$

$\Rightarrow \quad -\lambda - 1 + 1 = 0 \Rightarrow \lambda = 0$

Example 6 If the equation $x^2 + y^2 - 2x - 2y + c = 0$ represents an empty set, then find the value of c.

Sol. For empty set $\Delta \neq 0$ and $h^2 < ab$.

Now, comparing the given equation of conic with

$$ax^2 + 2hxy + by^2 + 2gx + 2fy + c' = 0$$

then $a = 1, h = 0, b = 1, g = -1, f = -1, c' = c$

$\because \quad h^2 < ab$

$\therefore \quad 0 < 1$ which is true

and $\quad \Delta = abc' + 2fgh - af^2 - bg^2 - c'h^2 \neq 0$

$\Rightarrow \quad (1)(1)(c) + 0 - 1 \times (-1)^2 - 1 \times (-1)^2 - 0 \neq 0$

$\Rightarrow \quad c - 2 \neq 0$

$\therefore \quad c \neq 2$

Hence, $\quad c \in R \sim (2)$

Example 7 If the equation of conic $2x^2 + xy + 3y^2 - 3x + 5y + \lambda = 0$ represent a single point, then find the value of λ.

Sol. For single point,

$$h^2 < ab \text{ and } \Delta = 0$$

Comparing the given equation with

$$ax^2 + 2hxy + by^2 + 2gx + 2fy + c = 0$$

then, $a = 2, h = \frac{1}{2}, b = 3, g = -\frac{3}{2}, f = \frac{5}{2}, c = \lambda.$

$\because \quad h^2 = \frac{1}{4}, ab = 6$

$\therefore \quad h^2 < ab$

and $\quad \Delta = abc + 2fgh - af^2 - bg^2 - ch^2$

$= (2)(3)(\lambda) + 2 \times \frac{5}{2} \times -\frac{3}{2} \times \frac{1}{2} - 2 \times \frac{25}{4} - 3 \times \frac{9}{4} - \lambda \times \frac{1}{4}$

$= 6\lambda - \frac{15}{4} - \frac{25}{2} - \frac{27}{4} - \frac{\lambda}{4}$

$= \frac{23\lambda}{4} - 23 = 0$

$\therefore \quad \lambda = 4$

Example 8 For what value of λ the equation of conic $2xy + 4x - 6y + \lambda = 0$ represents two intersecting straight lines, if $\lambda = 17$, then this equation represents?

Sol. Comparing the given equation of conic with

$$ax^2 + 2hxy + by^2 + 2gx + 2fy + c = 0$$

$\therefore \quad a = 0, b = 0, h = 1, g = 2, f = -3, c = \lambda$

For two intersecting lines,

$$h^2 > ab, \Delta = 0$$

$\because \quad ab = 0, h = 1$

$\therefore \quad h^2 > ab$

and $\quad \Delta = abc + 2fgh - af^2 - bg^2 - ch^2$

$= 0 + 2 \times -3 \times 2 \times 1 - 0 - 0 - \lambda (1)^2$

$= -12 - \lambda = 0$

$\therefore \quad \lambda = -12$

For $\lambda = 17$, then the given equation of conic $2xy + 4x - 6y + 17 = 0$ according to the first system but here $c = 17$.

$\therefore \quad a = 0, b = 0, h = 1, g = 2, f = -3, c = 17,$

$\therefore \quad \Delta = abc + 2f\,gh - af^2 - bg^2 - ch^2$

$= 0 + 2 \times -3 \times 2 \times 1 - 0 - 0 - 17 \times (1)^2$

$= -12 - 17 = -29 \neq 0$

$\therefore \quad \Delta \neq 0$ and $h^2 > ab$

So, we have $\Delta \neq 0$ and $h^2 > ab$.

Hence, the given equation represents a hyperbola.

How to Find the Centre of Conics

If $S \equiv ax^2 + 2hxy + by^2 + 2gx + 2fy + c = 0$.

Partially differentiating w.r.t. x and y, we get

$$\frac{\partial S}{\partial x} = 2ax + 2hy + 2g; \quad \frac{\partial S}{\partial y} = 2hx + 2by + 2f$$

(Treating y as constant) (Treating x as constant)

For centre, $\frac{\partial S}{\partial x}=0$ and $\frac{\partial S}{\partial y}=0$

$\therefore$ $2ax+2hy+2g=0$ and $2hx+2by+2f=0$

$\Rightarrow$ $ax+hy+g=0$ and $hx+by+f=0$

Solving these equations we get the centre

$$(x,y)=\left(\frac{hf-bg}{ab-h^2},\frac{gh-af}{ab-h^2}\right).$$

Remembering Method

Since, $\Delta=\begin{vmatrix} a & h & g \\ h & b & f \\ g & f & c \end{vmatrix}$

Write first two rows,

i.e. $\begin{matrix} a & h & g & a \\ h & b & f & h \end{matrix}$ (Repeat Ist member)

$\therefore$ $ab-h^2, hf-bg, gh-af$

or points $\left(\frac{hf-bg}{ab-h^2},\frac{gh-af}{ab-h^2}\right)$ or $\left(\frac{C_{13}}{C_{33}},\frac{C_{23}}{C_{33}}\right)$.

OR

According to first two rows,

$$ax+hy+g=0 \text{ and } hx+by+f=0.$$

After solving we get find the centre of conic.

Example 9 Find the centre of the conic $14x^2-4xy+11y^2-44x-58y+71=0$

Sol. Let $f(x,y)\equiv 14x^2-4xy+11y^2-44x-58y+71=0$

Differentiating partially w.r.t. x and y, then

$\frac{\partial f}{\partial x}=28x-4y-44$ and $\frac{\partial f}{\partial y}=-4x+22y-58$

For centre, $\frac{\partial f}{\partial x}=0$ and $\frac{\partial f}{\partial y}=0,$

$\therefore$ $28x-4y-44=0$

or $7x-y-11=0$ ...(i)

and $-4x+22y-58=0$

or $-2x+11y=29$ ...(ii)

On solving Eqs. (i) and (ii) we get,

$x=2$ and $y=3$

$\therefore$ Centre is (2, 3).

Aliter : Comparing the given conic with

$$ax^2+2hxy+by^2+2gx+2fy+c=0$$

$\therefore$ $a=14, h=-2, b=11, g=-22, f=-29, c=71$

$\therefore$ Centre $\left(\frac{hf-bg}{ab-h^2},\frac{gh-af}{ab-h^2}\right)$

or $=\left(\frac{(-2)(-29)-(11)(-22)}{(14)(11)-(-2)^2},\frac{(-22)(-2)-(14)(-29)}{(14)(11)-(-2)^2}\right)$

or $=(2, 3)$

Parabola : Definition

A parabola is the locus of a point which moves in a plane such that its distance from a fixed point (i.e. focus) is always equal to its distance from a fixed straight line (i.e., directrix).

Standard Equation of Parabola

Let S be the focus and ZM be the directrix of the parabola. Draw SZ perpendicular to ZM, let A be the mid point of SZ, then as $AS=AZ$

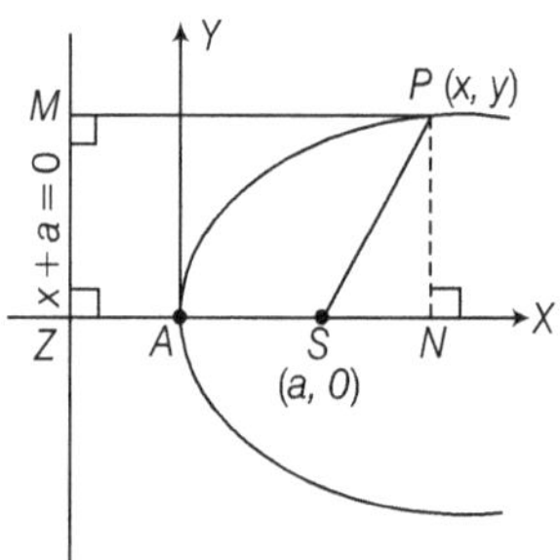

So, A lies on the parabola. Take A as the origin and a line AY through A perpendicular to AX as Y-axis.

Let $AS=AZ=a>0$

then, coordinate of S is $(a,0)$ and the equation of ZM is

$$x=-a \text{ or } x+a=0$$

Now, take $P(x,y)$ be any point on the parabola. Join SP and from P draw PM perpendicular to the directrix ZM.

Then, $SP=\sqrt{(x-a)^2+(y-0)^2}=\sqrt{(x-a)^2+y^2}$

and $PM=ZN=AZ+AN=a+x$

Now, for the parabola $SP=PM$

$\Rightarrow$ $(SP)^2=(PM)^2 \Rightarrow (x-a)^2+y^2=(a+x)^2$

$\Rightarrow$ $y^2=(a+x)^2-(x-a)^2=4ax$

$\therefore$ $y^2=4ax,$

which is required equation of the parabola.

Remark

A parabola has two real foci situated on its axis one of which is the focus S and the other lies at infinity. the corresponding directrix is also at infinity.

Some Terms Related to Parabola

1. **Axis** The axis of the parabola is the straight line which is passes through focus and perpendicular to the directrix of the parabola.

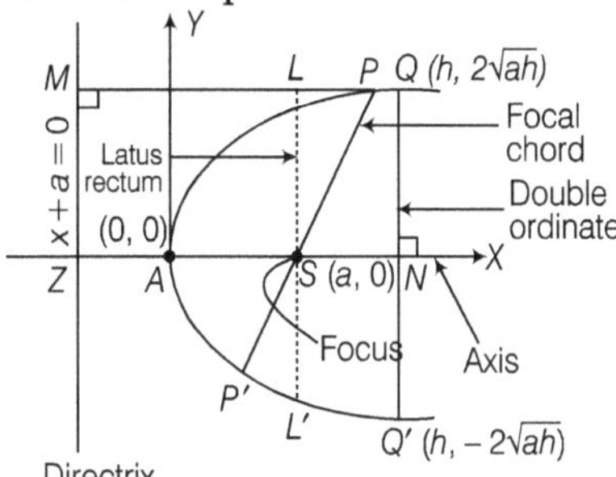

For the parabola $y^2 = 4ax$, X-axis is the **axis**.

Here, all powers of y are even in $y^2 = 4ax$ then, parabola $y^2 = 4ax$ is symmetrical about its axis (i.e. X-axis).

or

If the point (x, y) lie on the parabola $y^2 = 4ax$, then the point $(x, -y)$ also lies on it. Hence, the parabola is symmetrical about X-axis (i.e. axis of parabola).

2. **Vertex** The point of intersection of the parabola and its axis is called the vertex of the parabola. For the parabola $y^2 = 4ax$.
$A(0, 0)$ i.e. the origin is the vertex.

3. **Double ordinate** If Q be the point on the parabola, draw QN perpendicular to the axis of parabola and produced to meet the curve again at Q', then QQ' is called a double ordinate.
If abscissa of Q is h, then ordinate of Q,
$$y^2 = 4ah \quad \text{or } y = 2\sqrt{ah} \quad \text{(for first quadrant)}$$
and ordinate of Q' is $y = -2\sqrt{ah}$ (for fourth quadrant)
Hence, coordinates of Q and Q' are $(h, 2\sqrt{ah})$ and $(h, -2\sqrt{ah})$, respectively.

4. **Latusrectum** The double ordinate LL' passes through the focus is called the latusrectum of the parabola.
Since focus $S(a, 0)$ the equation of the latusrectum of the parabola is $x = a$, then solving
$$x = a \quad \text{and} \quad y^2 = 4ax$$
then, we get $\quad y = \pm 2a$
Hence, the coordinates of the extremities of the latusrectum are $L(a, 2a)$ and $L'(a, -2a)$, respectively.
Since, $\quad LS = L'S = 2a$
$\therefore$ Length of latusrectum $LL' = 2(LS) = 2(L'S) = 4a$.

5. **Focal chord** A chord of a parabola which is passing through the focus is called a focal chord of the parabola. In the given figure, PP' and LL' are the focal chords.

Remarks

1. In objective questions use LL' as focal chord and in subjective questions use PP' as focal chord.
2. Length of smallest focal chord of the parabola $4a$. Hence, the latusrectum of a parabola is the smallest focal chord.

6. **Focal distance** The focal distance of any point P on the parabola is its distance from the focus S i.e. SP
Also, $SP = PM =$ Distance of P from the directrix.
If $\quad P \equiv (x, y)$
then, $\quad SP = PM = x + a$

7. **Parametric equations** From the equation of the parabola $y^2 = 4ax$, we can write $\frac{y}{2a} = \frac{2x}{y} = t$
where 't' is a parameter.
Then, $\quad y = 2at \quad$ and $\quad x = at^2$
The equations $x = at^2$ and $y = 2at$ are called parametric equations. The point $(at^2, 2at)$ is also referred to as the point 't'.

Remarks

1. Coordinates of any point on the parabola $y^2 = 4ax$, may be taken as $(at^2, 2at)$.
2. Equation of chord joining t_1 and t_2 is $2x - (t_1 + t_2)y + 2at_1t_2 = 0$.
3. If the chord joining t_1, t_2 and t_3, t_4 pass through a point $(c, 0)$ on the axis, then $t_1t_2 = t_3t_4 = -\frac{c}{a}$.

Other forms of Parabola with Latusrectum $4a$

(1) Parabola opening to left (i.e. $y^2 = -4ax$) : $(a > 0)$

(i) Vertex is $A(0, 0)$.
(ii) Focus is $S(-a, 0)$.
(iii) Equation of the directrix MZ is $x - a = 0$.
(iv) Equation of the axis is $y = 0$ i.e. X-axis.
(v) Equation of the tangent at the vertex is $x = 0$ i.e. Y-axis.

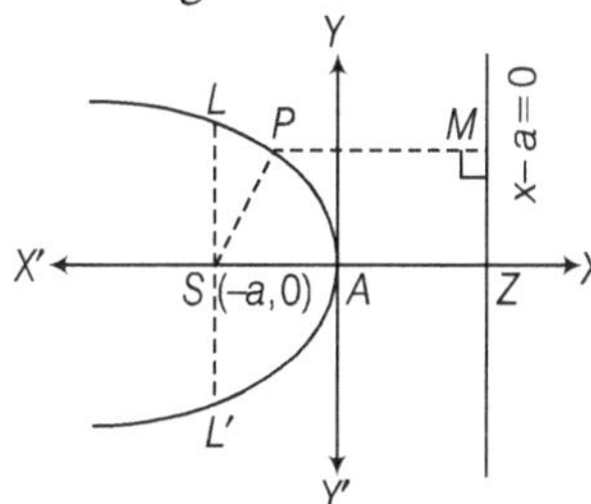

(vi) Length of latusrectum $= LL' = 4a$.

(vii) Ends of latusrectum are $L(-a, 2a)$ and $L'(-a, -2a)$.
(viii) Equation of latusrectum is $x = -a$ i.e. $x + a = 0$.
(ix) Parametric coordinates is $(-at^2, 2at)$.

(2) Parabola opening upwards (i.e. $x^2 = 4ay$) :($a > 0$)

(i) Vertex is $A(0, 0)$.
(ii) Focus is $S(0, a)$.
(iii) Equation of the directrix MZ is $y + a = 0$.

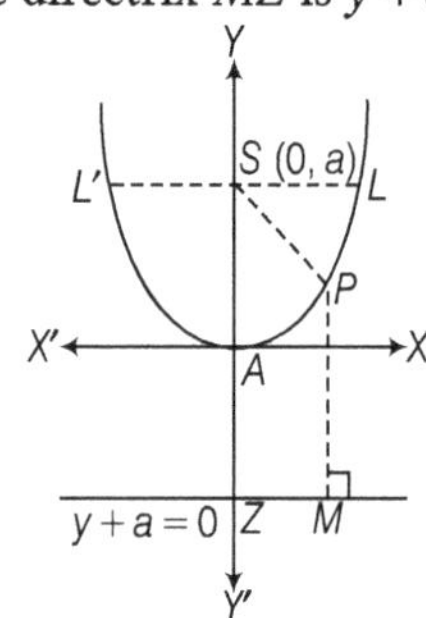

(iv) Equations of the axis is $x = 0$ i.e. Y-axis.
(v) Equation of the tangent at the vertex is $y = 0$ i.e. X-axis.
(vi) Ends of latusrectum are $L(2a, a)$ and $L'(-2a, a)$.
(vii) Length of latusrectum $= LL' = 4a$.
(viii) Equation of latusrectum is $y = a$ i.e. $y - a = 0$.
(ix) Parametric coordinates is $(2at, at^2)$.

(3) Parabola opening downwards (i.e. $x^2 = -4ay$): ($a > 0$)

(i) Vertex is $A(0, 0)$. (ii) Focus is $S(0, -a)$.
(iii) Equation of the directrix MZ is $y - a = 0$.
(iv) Equation of the axis is $x = 0$ i.e. Y-axis.
(v) Equation of the tangent at the vertex is $y = 0$ i.e. X-axis.

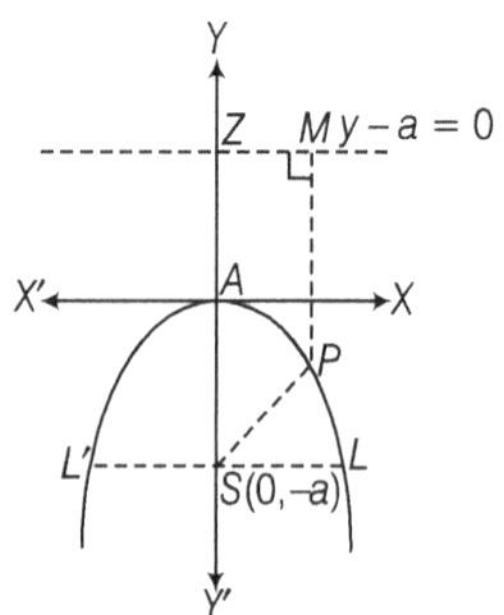

(vi) Length of latusrectum $= LL' = 4a$
(vii) Ends of latusrectum are $L(2a, -a)$ and $L'(-2a, -a)$
(viii) Equation of latusrectum is $y = -a$ i.e. $y + a = 0$.
(ix) Parametric coordinates are $(2at, -at^2)$.

Smart Table : The Study of Standard Parabolas

Equation and Graph of the parabola	$y^2 = 4ax, a > 0$	$y^2 = -4ax, a > 0$	$x^2 = 4ay, a > 0$	$x^2 = -4ay, a > 0$
Vertex	$(0, 0)$	$(0, 0)$	$(0, 0)$	$(0, 0)$
Focus	$(a, 0)$	$(-a, 0)$	$(0, a)$	$(0, -a)$
Equation of the axis	$y = 0$	$y = 0$	$x = 0$	$x = 0$
Equation of tangent at vertex	$x = 0$	$x = 0$	$y = 0$	$y = 0$
Equation of directrix	$x + a = 0$	$x - a = 0$	$y + a = 0$	$y - a = 0$
Length of latusrectum	$4a$	$4a$	$4a$	$4a$
Ends points of latusrectum	$(a, \pm 2a)$	$(-a, \pm 2a)$	$(\pm 2a, a)$	$(\pm 2a, -a)$
Equation of latusrectum	$x - a = 0$	$x + a = 0$	$y - a = 0$	$y + a = 0$
Focal distance of a point $P(x, y)$	$x + a$	$a - x$	$y + a$	$a - y$
Parametric coordinates	$(at^2, 2at)$	$(-at^2, 2at)$	$(2at, at^2)$	$(2at, -at^2)$
Eccentricity (e)	1	1	1	1

General Equation of a Parabola

Let $S(a,b)$ be the focus, and $lx+my+n=0$ is the equation of the directrix. Let $P(x,y)$ be any point on the parabola. Then by definition $SP = PM$

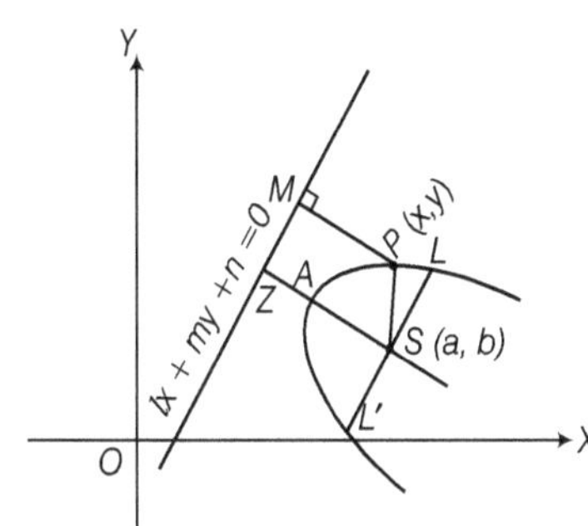

$$\Rightarrow \sqrt{(x-a)^2+(y-b)^2} = \frac{|lx+my+n|}{\sqrt{(l^2+m^2)}}$$

$$\Rightarrow (x-a)^2+(y-b)^2 = \frac{(lx+my+n)^2}{(l^2+m^2)}$$

$$\Rightarrow m^2x^2+l^2y^2-2lmxy+x \text{ term}+y\text{ term}+\text{constant}=0$$

This is of the form $(mx-ly)^2+2gx+2fy+c=0$.

This equation is the general equation of parabola.

Remark

Second degree terms in the general equation of a parabola forms a perfect square.

Example 10 Find the equation of the parabola whose focus is at (–1,–2) and the directrix is the straight line $x-2y+3=0$.

Sol. Let $P(x,y)$ be any point on the parabola whose focus is $S(-1,-2)$ and the directrix $x-2y+3=0$. Draw PM perpendicular from $P(x,y)$ on the directrix $x-2y+3=0$.

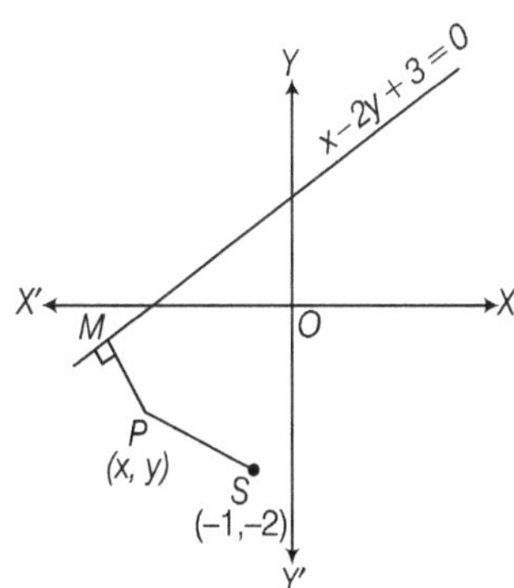

Then, by definition

$$SP = PM$$

$$\Rightarrow (SP)^2 = (PM)^2$$

$$\Rightarrow (x+1)^2+(y+2)^2 = \left(\frac{|x-2y+3|}{\sqrt{(1)^2+(-2)^2}}\right)^2$$

$$\Rightarrow 5(x^2+y^2+2x+4y+5)$$
$$= (x^2+4y^2-4xy+6x-12y+9)$$

$$\therefore 4x^2+y^2+4xy+4x+32y+16=0$$

Example 11 Find the equation of the parabola whose focus is (4, – 3) and vertex is (4, – 1).

Sol. Let $A(4,-1)$ be the vertex and $S(4,-3)$ be the focus.

$$\therefore \text{Slope of } AS = \frac{-3+1}{4-4} = \infty$$

which is parallel to Y-axis.

$\therefore$ Directrix parallel to X-axis.

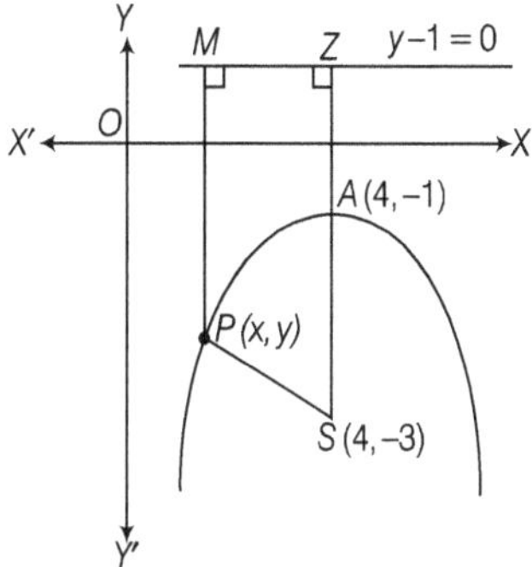

Let $Z(x_1,y_1)$ be any point on the directrix, then A is the mid-point of SZ.

$$\therefore 4 = \frac{x_1+4}{2} \Rightarrow x_1 = 4$$

and $$-1 = \frac{y_1-3}{2} \Rightarrow y_1 = 1$$

$$\therefore Z = (4,1)$$

Also, directrix is parallel to X-axis and passes through $Z(4,1)$, so equation of directrix is

$$y = 1 \text{ or } y-1=0$$

Now, let $P(x,y)$ be any point on the parabola. Join SP and draw PM perpendicular to the directrix. Then, by definition

$$SP = PM$$

$$\Rightarrow (SP)^2 = (PM)^2$$

$$\Rightarrow (x-4)^2+(y+3)^2 = \left(\frac{|y-1|}{\sqrt{1^2}}\right)^2$$

$$\Rightarrow (x-4)^2+(y+3)^2 = (y-1)^2$$

$$\therefore x^2-8x+8y+24=0$$

Aliter :

Here $a = AS = 2$

$\therefore$ Length of latusrectum $= 4a = 8$

Equation of parabola with vertex (0, 0) and open downward is $x^2 = -8y$.

Shifting (4, – 1) on (0, 0), we get required parabola

$$(x-4)^2 = -8(y+1)$$

$$\therefore x^2-8x+8y+24=0$$

Example 12 The focal distance of a point on a parabola $y^2 = 8x$ is 8. Find it.

Sol. Comparing $y^2 = 8x$ with $y^2 = 4ax$

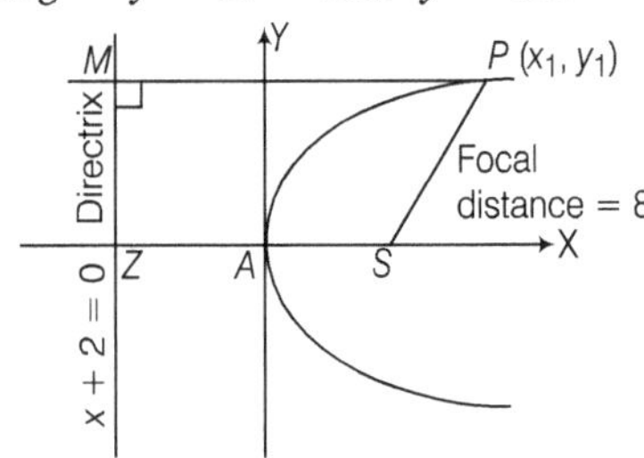

$\therefore \quad 4a = 8 \Rightarrow a = 2$

$\therefore$ Equation of directrix is $x + 2 = 0$.

Let $P(x_1, y_1)$ on the parabola

$$y^2 = 8x$$

$$\therefore \quad y_1^2 = 8x_1 \quad \text{...(i)}$$

$$\because \quad SP = 8$$

$$\Rightarrow \quad PM = 8 \quad [\because SP = PM]$$

$$\Rightarrow \quad x_1 + 2 = 8$$

or $x_1 = 6$

From Eq. (i), $y_1^2 = 8 \times 6$

$$\therefore \quad y_1 = \pm 4\sqrt{3}$$

$\therefore$ The required points are $(6, 4\sqrt{3})$ and $(6, -4\sqrt{3})$.

Example 13 QQ' is a double ordinate of a parabola $y^2 = 4ax$. Find the locus of its point of trisection.

Sol. Let the double ordinate QQ' meet the axis of the parabola

$$y^2 = 4ax \quad \text{...(i)}$$

Let coordinates of Q be (x_1, y_1), then coordinates of Q' be $(x_1 - y_1)$ since, Q and Q' lies on Eq. (i), then

$$y_1^2 = 4ax_1 \quad \text{...(ii)}$$

Let R and T be the points of trisection of QQ'. Then, the coordinates of R and T are

$$\left(\frac{1 \cdot x_1 + 2 \cdot x_1}{1+2}, \frac{1 \cdot (-y_1) + 2 \cdot y_1}{1+2}\right) \text{ or } \left(x_1, \frac{y_1}{3}\right)$$

and $$\left(\frac{2 \cdot x_1 + 1 \cdot x_1}{2+1}, \frac{2 \cdot (-y_1) + 1 \cdot y_1}{2+1}\right) \text{ or } \left(x_1, -\frac{y_1}{3}\right)$$

respectively.

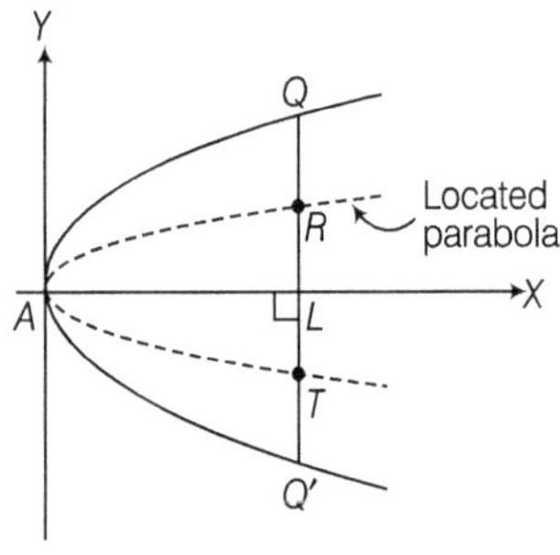

Since, R divide QQ' in 1 : 2 (internally)
and T divide QQ' in 2 : 1 (internally).

For locus, let $R(h,k)$, then

$$x_1 = h \quad \text{and} \quad \frac{y_1}{3} = k \quad \text{or} \quad y_1 = 3k$$

On substituting the values of x_1 and y_1 in Eq. (ii), then

$$(3k)^2 = 4a(h) \quad \text{or} \quad 9k^2 = 4ah$$

$\therefore$ The required locus is $9y^2 = 4ax$ similarly, let $T(h', k')$

then, $x_1 = h'$ and $-\frac{y_1}{3} = k'$

or $y_1 = -3k'$

On substituting the values of x_1 and y_1 in Eq. (ii), then

$$(-3k')^2 = 4a(h')$$

or $9k'^2 = 4ah'$

$\therefore$ The required locus is $9y^2 = 4ax$.

Hence, the locus of point of trisection is

$$9y^2 = 4ax.$$

Aliter : Let R and T be the points of trisection of double ordinates QQ'. Let (h, k) be the coordinates of R,

then, $AL = h$ and $RL = k$

$$RT = RL + LT = k + k = 2k.$$

Since, $RQ = TR = Q'T = 2k$

$$\therefore \quad LQ = LR + RQ = k + 2k = 3k$$

Thus, the coordinates of Q are $(h, 3k)$.

Since, $(h, 3k)$ lies on $y^2 = 4ax$

$$\Rightarrow \quad 9k^2 = 4ah$$

Hence, the locus of (h, k) is $9y^2 = 4ax$.

Example 14 Prove that the area of the triangle inscribed in the parabola $y^2 = 4ax$ is $\frac{1}{8a}(y_1 \sim y_2)(y_2 \sim y_3)(y_3 \sim y_1)$, where y_1, y_2, y_3 are the ordinates of the vertices.

Sol. Let the vertices of the triangle be $(x_1, y_1), (x_2, y_2)$ and (x_3, y_3).

$\because$ (x_1, y_1) is a point on the parabola $y^2 = 4ax$.

$$\therefore \quad y_1^2 = 4ax_1$$

$$\therefore \quad x_1 = \frac{y_1^2}{4a}$$

Similarly, $$x_2 = \frac{y_2^2}{4a}$$

and $$x_3 = \frac{y_3^2}{4a}$$

Now, vertices of triangle are

$$\left(\frac{y_1^2}{4a}, y_1\right), \left(\frac{y_2^2}{4a}, y_2\right) \text{ and } \left(\frac{y_3^2}{4a}, y_3\right).$$

$$\therefore \text{ Required area of the triangle} = \frac{1}{2}\left\|\begin{matrix} \frac{y_1^2}{4a} & y_1 & 1 \\ \frac{y_2^2}{4a} & y_2 & 1 \\ \frac{y_3^2}{4a} & y_3 & 1 \end{matrix}\right\|$$

$$= \frac{1}{8a}\left\|\begin{matrix} y_1^2 & y_1 & 1 \\ y_2^2 & y_2 & 1 \\ y_3^2 & y_3 & 1 \end{matrix}\right\| = \frac{1}{8a}(y_1 \sim y_2)(y_2 \sim y_3)(y_3 \sim y_1)$$

Example 15 Find the length of the side of an equilateral triangle inscribed in the parabola $y^2 = 4ax$, so that one angular point is at the vertex.

Sol. Let ABC be the inscribed equilateral triangle, with one angular point at the vertex A of the parabola

$$y^2 = 4ax \quad \text{...(i)}$$

Let the length of the side of equilateral triangle $= l$

$$\therefore \quad AB = BC = CA = l$$

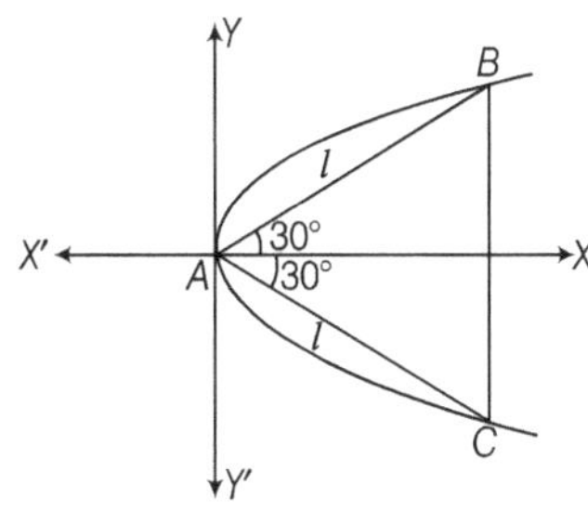

$\therefore$ The coordinates of B is $(l \cos 30°, l \sin 30°)$

i.e., $\left(\frac{l\sqrt{3}}{2}, \frac{l}{2}\right)$.

Since, B lies on Eq. (i), then $\left(\frac{l}{2}\right)^2 = 4a\left(\frac{l\sqrt{3}}{2}\right)$ or $l = 8a\sqrt{3}$

Example 16 Prove that the equation of the parabola whose focus is (0,0) and tangent at the vertex is $x - y + 1 = 0$ is $x^2 + y^2 + 2xy - 4x + 4y - 4 = 0$.

Sol. Let focus is $S(0, 0)$ and A is the vertex of the parabola take any point Z such that $AS = AZ$ given tangent at vertex is $x - y + 1 = 0$, since directrix is parallel to the tangent at the vertex.

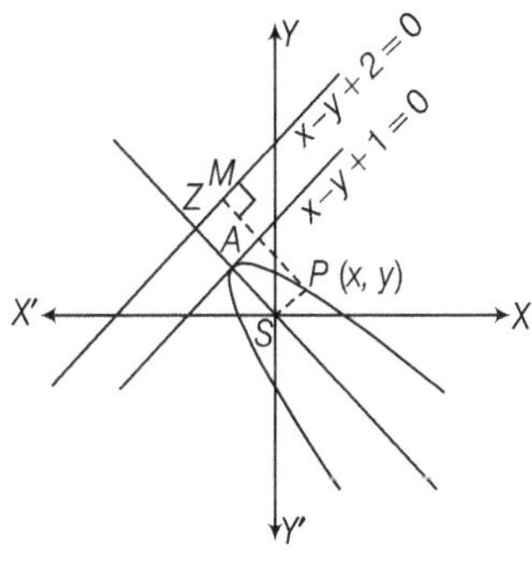

$\therefore$ Equation of directrix is $x - y + \lambda = 0$

where, λ is constant.

$\because A$ is the mid-point of SZ.

$$\therefore \quad SZ = 2SA$$

$$\Rightarrow \quad \frac{|0 - 0 + \lambda|}{\sqrt{(1^2 + (-1)^2)}} = 2 \times \frac{|0 - 0 + 1|}{\sqrt{(1^2 + (-1)^2)}}$$

$$\Rightarrow \quad \frac{|\lambda|}{\sqrt{2}} = \frac{2}{\sqrt{2}}$$

$$\therefore \quad \lambda = \pm 2$$

$$\Rightarrow \quad \lambda = 2$$

[$\because \lambda$ is positive since directrix in this case always lies in II quadrant]

$\therefore$ Equation of directrix is $x - y + 2 = 0$.

Now, take $P(x, y)$ be any point on the parabola, draw $PM \perp ZM$, then from definition,

$$SP = PM$$

$$\Rightarrow \quad (SP)^2 = (PM)^2$$

$$\Rightarrow \quad (x - 0)^2 + (y - 0)^2 = \left(\frac{|x - y + 2|}{\sqrt{2}}\right)^2$$

$$\Rightarrow \quad 2(x^2 + y^2) = (x - y + 2)^2$$

$$\Rightarrow \quad 2x^2 + 2y^2 = x^2 + y^2 - 2xy + 4x - 4y + 4$$

$$\therefore \quad x^2 + y^2 + 2xy - 4x + 4y - 4 = 0$$

Equation of Parabola if Equation of axis, Tangent at Vertex and Latusrectum are given

Let equation of axis is $ax + by + c = 0$ and equation of tangent at vertex is $bx - ay + d = 0$.

Equation of parabola is

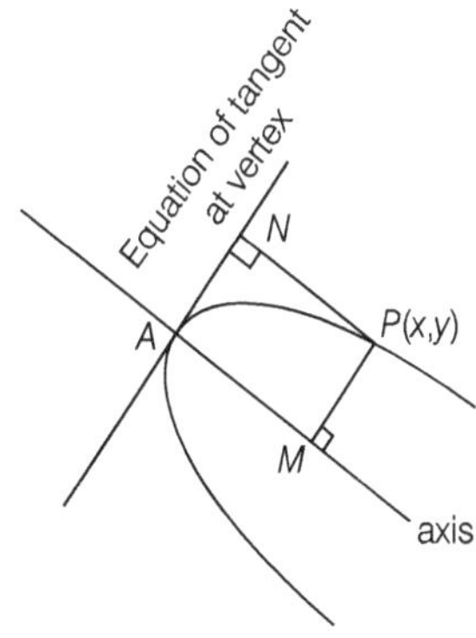

$$(PM)^2 = (\text{Latusrectum})\ (PN)$$

$$\Rightarrow \left(\frac{ax + by + c}{\sqrt{(a^2 + b^2)}}\right)^2 = (\text{Latusrectum})\left(\frac{bx - ay + d}{\sqrt{(b^2 + a^2)}}\right)$$

Example 17 Find the equation of the parabola whose latusrectum is 4 units, axis is the line $3x+4y-4=0$ and the tangent at the vertex is the line $4x-3y+7=0$.

Sol. Let $P(x, y)$ be any point on the parabola and let PM and PN are perpendiculars from P on the axis and tangent at the vertex respectively, then

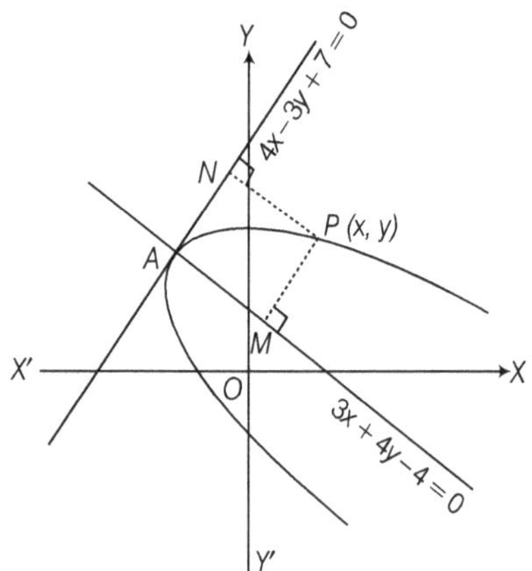

$$(PM)^2 = (\text{latusrectum})(PN)$$

$$\Rightarrow \left(\frac{3x+4y-4}{\sqrt{3^2+4^2}}\right)^2 = 4\left(\frac{4x-3y+7}{\sqrt{4^2+(-3)^2}}\right)$$

$$\therefore \quad (3x+4y-4)^2 = 20(4x-3y+7)$$

which is required parabola.

The Generalised form $(y-k)^2 = 4a(x-h)$

The parabola

$$y^2 = 4ax \qquad \text{...(i)}$$

can be written as $(y-0)^2 = 4a(x-0)$.

The vertex of this parabola is $A(0,0)$

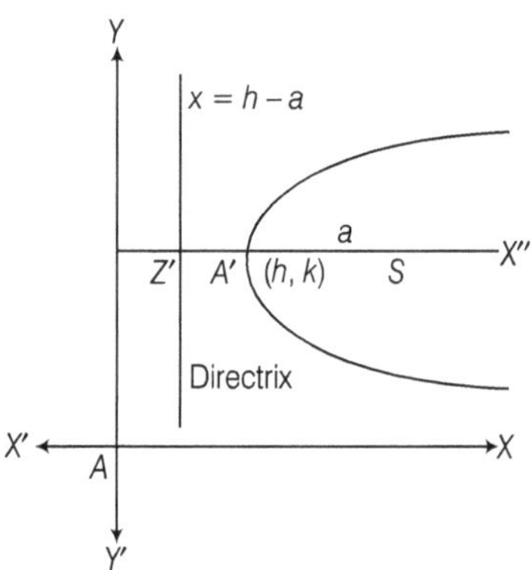

Now, when origin is shifted at $A'(h,k)$ without changing the direction of axes, its equation becomes

$$(y-k)^2 = 4a(x-h) \qquad \text{...(ii)}$$

This is called generalised form of the parabola Eq. (i) and axis $A'X''\|AX$ with its vertex at $A'(h,k)$. Its focus is at $(a+h,k)$ and length of latusrectum $= 4a$, the equation of the directrix is

$$x = h-a \Rightarrow x+a-h=0$$

Another form is $(x-h)^2 = 4a(y-k)$ axis parallel to

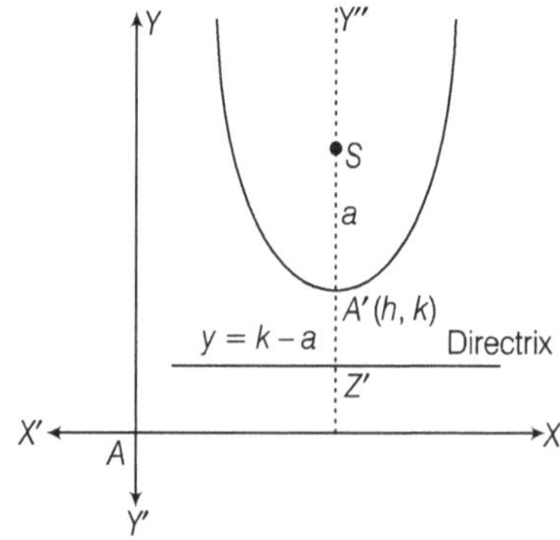

Y-axis with its vertex (h,k) its focus is at $(h,a+k)$ and length of latusrectum $= 4a$, the equation of the directrix is

$$y = k-a \Rightarrow y+a-k=0.$$

Remark

The parametric equation of $(y-k)^2 = 4a(x-h)$ are $x = h+at^2$ and $y = k+2at$.

Parabolic Curve

The equations $y = Ax^2+Bx+C$ and $x = Ay^2+By+C$ are always represents parabolas generally called parabolic curve.

Now, $\quad y = Ax^2+Bx+C$

$$= A\left\{x^2+\frac{B}{A}x+\frac{C}{A}\right\}$$

$$= A\left\{\left(x+\frac{B}{2A}\right)^2 - \frac{B^2}{4A^2}+\frac{C}{A}\right\}$$

$$= A\left\{\left(x+\frac{B}{2A}\right)^2 - \frac{(B^2-4AC)}{4A^2}\right\}$$

or $\quad \left(x+\frac{B}{2A}\right)^2 = \frac{1}{A}\left(y+\frac{B^2-4AC}{4A}\right)$

Comparing it with $(x-h)^2 = 4a(y-k)$ it represent a parabola with vertex at $(h,k) = \left(-\frac{B}{2A}, -\frac{B^2-4AC}{4A}\right)$

and axis parallel to Y-axis and latusrectum $= \dfrac{1}{|A|}$

and the curve opening upwards and downwards depending upon the sign of A and B.

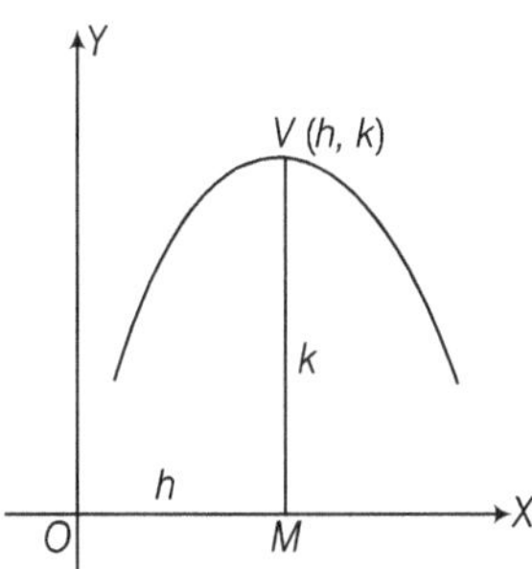

The optimum distance of its vertex V from OX is

$$\left|-\frac{B^2-4AC}{4A}\right|$$

and $\quad x = Ay^2 + By + C$

$$= A\left\{y^2 + \frac{B}{A}y + \frac{C}{A}\right\}$$

$$= A\left\{\left(y+\frac{B}{2A}\right)^2 - \frac{B^2}{4A^2} + \frac{C}{A}\right\}$$

$$= A\left\{\left(y+\frac{B}{2A}\right)^2 - \frac{B^2-4AC}{4A^2}\right\}$$

$$\Rightarrow \left(y+\frac{B}{2A}\right)^2 = \frac{1}{A}\left(x+\frac{B^2-4AC}{4A}\right)$$

Comparing it with $(y-k)^2 = 4a(x-h)$, it represent a parabola with vertex at

$$(h,k) = \left(-\frac{B^2-4AC}{4A}, -\frac{B}{2A}\right)$$

and axis parallel to X-axis and latusrectum $= \dfrac{1}{|A|}$

and the curve opening left and right depending upon the sign of A and B.

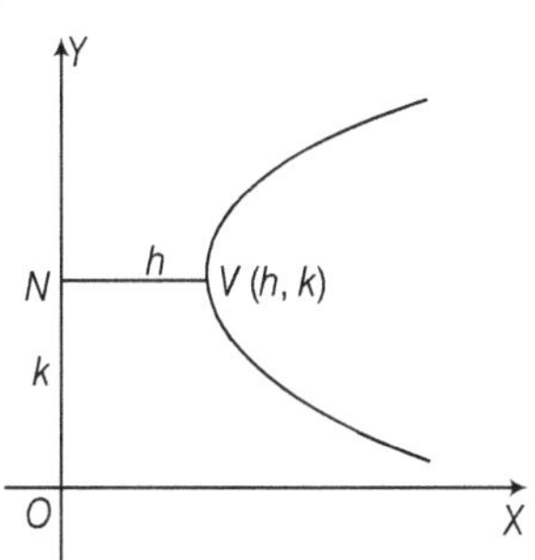

The optimum distance of its vertex V from OY is

$$\left|-\frac{B^2-4AC}{4A}\right|.$$

Remarks

1. The optimum distance of vertex from OX or OY can be easily obtained using calculus Method.
2. Equation of the parabola with axis parallel to the X-axis is of the form $x = Ay^2 + By + C$.
3. Equation of the parabola with axis parallel to the Y-axis is of the form $\quad y = Ax^2 + Bx + C$.

Method to Make Perfect Square

If $\quad x = \alpha y^2 \pm \beta y + \gamma$

first make the coefficient of y^2 is unity

i.e., $\quad x = \alpha\left\{y^2 \pm \frac{\beta}{\alpha}y + \frac{\gamma}{\alpha}\right\}$

Now, in braces write y and put the sign after y which between y^2 and y i.e. $\pm$ and after this sign write the half the coefficient of y i.e. $\dfrac{\beta}{2\alpha}$.

Now, write in braces $\left(y \pm \dfrac{\beta}{2\alpha}\right)^2$

and always subtract $\left(\dfrac{\beta}{2\alpha}\right)^2 = \dfrac{\beta^2}{4\alpha^2}$

$$\therefore \quad x = \alpha\left\{\left(y \pm \frac{\beta}{2\alpha}\right)^2 - \frac{\beta^2}{4\alpha^2} + \frac{\gamma}{\alpha}\right\}$$

$$= \alpha\left\{\left(y \pm \frac{\beta}{2\alpha}\right)^2 - \frac{(\beta^2 - 4\gamma\alpha)}{4\alpha^2}\right\}$$

Example 18 Find the vertex, focus, latusrectum, axis and the directrix of the parabola $x^2 + 8x + 12y + 4 = 0$.

Sol. The equation of parabola is

$$x^2 + 8x + 12y + 4 = 0 \quad \text{...(i)}$$

$$\Rightarrow \quad (x+4)^2 - 16 + 12y + 4 = 0$$

$$\Rightarrow \quad (x+4)^2 - 12 + 12y = 0$$

$$\Rightarrow \quad (x+4)^2 = -12y + 12$$

$$\Rightarrow \quad (x+4)^2 = -12(y-1)$$

Let $\quad x + 4 = X, y - 1 = Y \quad$ ...(ii)

$\therefore \quad X^2 = -12Y \quad$ ...(iii)

Comparing it with $\quad X^2 = -4aY$

$\therefore \quad a = 3$

$\therefore$ Vertex of Eq. (iii) is (0, 0)

i.e. $\quad X = 0, Y = 0$

From Eq. (ii),

$$x+4=0, y-1=0$$

$\therefore$ $x=-4, y=1$

$\therefore$ Vertex of Eq. (i) is $(-4, 1)$.

Foucs of Eq. (iii) is $(0, -3)$

i.e. $X=0, Y=-3$

From Eq. (ii),

$$x+4=0, y-1=-3$$

$\therefore$ $x=-4, y=-2$

$\therefore$ Focus of Eq. (i) is $(-4, -2)$.

and latusrectum $= 4a = 12$.

Equation of axis of Eq. (iii) is $X=0$

$\therefore$ Equation of axis of Eq. (i) is $x+4=0$

Equation of directrix of Eq. (iii) is

$$Y=3 \text{ or } y-1=3$$

$\therefore$ $y-4=0$

$\therefore$ Equation of directrix of Eq. (i) is

$$y-4=0.$$

Example 19 Prove that the equation $y^2+2ax+2by+c=0$ represents a parabola whose axis is parallel to the axis of x. Find its vertex.

Sol. The equation of parabola is

$$y^2+2ax+2by+c=0$$

$$(y+b)^2-b^2+2ax+c=0$$

$$\Rightarrow \quad (y+b)^2=-2ax+b^2-c$$

$$\Rightarrow \quad (y+b)^2=-2a\left(x-\frac{b^2-c}{2a}\right) \quad \text{...(i)}$$

Let $y+b=Y, x-\dfrac{b^2-c}{2a}=X$

From Eq. (i),

$$Y^2=-2aX \quad \text{...(ii)}$$

axis of its parabola is $Y=0$

or $y+b=0$,

which is parallel to X-axis

and vertex of Eq. (ii) is $X=0, Y=0$

$$\Rightarrow \quad x-\frac{b^2-c}{2a}=0, \quad y+b=0$$

$$\Rightarrow \quad x=\frac{b^2-c}{2a}, \quad y=-b$$

$\therefore$ Vertex of given parabola is $\left(\dfrac{b^2-c}{2a}, -b\right)$.

Example 20 Find the equation of the parabola with its vertex at (3, 2) and its focus at (5, 2).

Sol. Let Vertex $A(3,2)$ and focus is $S(5,2)$

Slope of $AS=\dfrac{2-2}{5-3}=0$, which is parallel to X-axis.

Hence, axis of parabola parallel to X-axis.

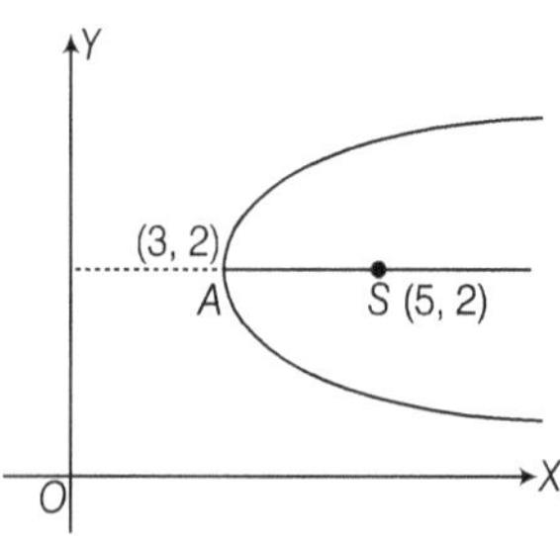

The equation is of the form

$$(y-k)^2=4a(x-h)$$

or $$(y-2)^2=4a(x-3)$$

as (h,k) is the vertex $(3,2)$

$a=$ distance between the focus and the vertex

$$=\sqrt{(5-3)^2+(2-2)^2}=2$$

Hence, the required equation is

$$(y-2)^2=8(x-3)$$

or $$y^2-8x-4y-28=0.$$

Example 21 Find the equation of the parabola with latusrectum joining the points (3, 6) and (3, −2).

Sol. Slope of (3,6) and (3, −2) is $\dfrac{-2-6}{3-3}=\infty$, since latusrectum is perpendicular to axis. Hence, axis parallel to X-axis. The equation of the two possible parabolas will be of the form

$$(y-k)^2=\pm 4a(x-h) \quad \text{...(i)}$$

Since, latusrectum $=\sqrt{(3-3)^2+(6+2)^2}=8$

$\therefore$ $4a=8$

$\Rightarrow$ $a=2$

$\therefore$ From Eq. (i),

$$(y-k)^2=\pm 8(x-h)$$

Since, (3,6) and (3, −2) lie on the parabola, then

$$(6-k)^2=\pm 8(3-h) \quad \text{...(ii)}$$

and $$(-2-k)^2=\pm 8(3-h) \quad \text{...(iii)}$$

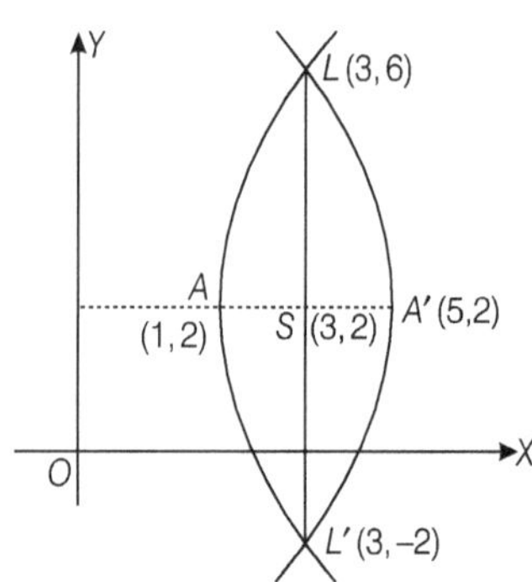

On solving Eqs. (ii) and (iii), we get

$$k=2$$

From Eq. (ii),

$$16 = \pm 8(3-h),$$

$\therefore$ $h = 3 \pm 2$

$\therefore$ $h = 5, 1$

Hence, values of (h, k) are (5,2) and (1, 2).

The required parabolas are

$$(y-2)^2 = 8(x-5)$$

and $(y-2)^2 = -8(x-1)$.

Example 22 Find the equation to the parabola whose axis parallel to the Y-axis and which passes through the points (0, 4) (1, 9) and (4, 5) and determine its latusrectum .

Sol. The equation of parabola parallel to Y-axis is

$$y = Ax^2 + Bx + C \quad \text{...(i)}$$

The points (0,4) , (1,9) and (4,5) lie on Eq. (i), then

$$4 = 0 + 0 + C \Rightarrow C = 4 \quad \text{...(ii)}$$

$\Rightarrow$ $9 = A + B + C$

$\Rightarrow$ $9 = A + B + 4$ $[\because C = 4]$

$\therefore$ $A + B = 5$ ...(iii)

and $5 = 16A + 4B + C$ $[\because C = 4]$

$\Rightarrow$ $5 = 16A + 4B + 4$

$\therefore$ $16A + 4B = 1$

$\Rightarrow$ $4A + B = \frac{1}{4}$ ...(iv)

On solving Eqs. (iii) and (iv), we get

$$A = -\frac{19}{12}, B = \frac{79}{12} \quad \text{...(v)}$$

On substituting the values of A, B and C from Eqs. (ii) and Eq. (v) in Eq. (i), then equation of parabola is

$$y = -\frac{19}{12}x^2 + \frac{79}{12}x + 4$$

Hence, length of latusrectum $= \frac{1}{\left|-\frac{19}{12}\right|} = \frac{12}{19}$.

Exercise for Session 1

1. The vertex of the parabola $y^2 + 6x - 2y + 13 = 0$ is
   (a) (–2, 1) (b) (2, – 1)
   (c) (1, 1) (d) (1 , –1)

2. If the parabola $y^2 = 4ax$ passes through (3, 2), then the length of latusrectum is
   (a) $\frac{1}{3}$ (b) $\frac{2}{3}$
   (c) 1 (d) $\frac{4}{3}$

3. The value of p such that the vertex of $y = x^2 + 2px + 13$ is 4 units above the X-axis is
   (a) ± 2 (b) 4
   (c) ± 3 (d) 5

4. The length of the latusrectum of the parabola whose focus is (3,3) and directrix is $3x - 4y - 2 = 0$, is
   (a) 1 (b) 2
   (c) 4 (d) 8

5. If the vertex and focus of a parabola are (3,3) and (–3, 3) respectively , then its equation is
   (a) $x^2 - 6x + 24y - 63 = 0$ (b) $x^2 - 6x + 24y + 81 = 0$
   (c) $y^2 - 6y + 24x - 63 = 0$ (d) $y^2 - 6y - 24x + 81 = 0$

6. If the vertex of the parabola $y = x^2 - 8x + c$ lies on X-axis, then the value of c is
   (a) 4 (b) – 4
   (c) 16 (d) –16

7. The parabola having its focus at (3,2) and directrix along the Y-axis has its vertex at
   (a) $\left(\frac{3}{2}, 1\right)$ (b) $\left(\frac{3}{2}, 2\right)$
   (c) $\left(\frac{3}{2}, \frac{1}{2}\right)$ (d) $\left(\frac{3}{2}, -\frac{1}{2}\right)$

8. The directrix of the parabola $x^2 - 4x - 8y + 12 = 0$ is

(a) $y = 0$ (b) $x = 1$
(c) $y = -1$ (d) $x = -1$

9. The equation of the latusrectum of the parabola $x^2 + 4x + 2y = 0$ is

(a) $3y - 2 = 0$ (b) $3y + 2 = 0$
(c) $2y - 3 = 0$ (d) $2y + 3 = 0$

10. The focus of the parabola $x^2 - 8x + 2y + 7 = 0$ is

(a) $\left(0, -\frac{1}{2}\right)$ (b) $(4,4)$
(c) $\left(4, \frac{9}{2}\right)$ (d) $\left(-4, -\frac{9}{2}\right)$

11. The equation of the parabola with the focus $(3,0)$ and directrix $x + 3 = 0$ is

(a) $y^2 = 2x$ (b) $y^2 = 3x$
(c) $y^2 = 6x$ (d) $y^2 = 12x$

12. Equation of the parabola whose axis is parallel to Y-axis and which passes through the points $(1,0)$, $(0,0)$ and $(-2,4)$, is

(a) $2x^2 + 2x = 3y$ (b) $2x^2 - 2x = 3y$
(c) $2x^2 + 2x = y$ (d) $2x^2 - 2x = y$

13. Find the equation of the parabola whose focus is $(5,3)$ and directrix is the line $3x - 4y + 1 = 0$.

14. Find the equation of the parabola is focus is at $(-6, -6)$ and vertex is at $(-2, 2)$.

15. Find the vertex, focus, axis, directrix and latusrectum of the parabola $4y^2 + 12x - 20y + 67 = 0$.

16. Find the name of the conic represented by $\sqrt{\left(\frac{x}{a}\right)} + \sqrt{\left(\frac{y}{b}\right)} = 1$.

17. Determine the name of the curve described parametrically by the equations
$x = t^2 + t + 1, y = t^2 - t + 1$.

18. Prove that the equation of the parabola whose vertex and focus are on the X-axis at a distance a and a' from the origin respectively is $y^2 = 4(a' - a)(x - a)$.

19. Find the equation of the parabola whose axis is parallel to X-axis and which passes through the points $(0, 4)$, $(1, 9)$ and $(-2, 6)$. Also, find its latusrectum.

20. The equation $ax^2 + 4xy + y^2 + ax + 3y + 2 = 0$ represents a parabola, then find the value of a.

Session 2

Position of a Point (x_1, y_1) with respect to a Parabola $y^2 = 4ax$, Parametric Relation between the Coordinates of the Ends of a Focal Chord of a Parabola, Intersection of a Line and a Parabola, Equation of Tangent in Different Forms, Point of Intersection of Tangents at any Two Points on the Parabola, Equation of Normals in Different Forms, Point of Intersection of Normals at any Two Points on the Parabola, Circle Through Co-normal Points

Position of a Point (x_1, y_1) with Respect to a Parabola $y^2 = 4ax$

Theorem The point (x_1, y_1) lies outside, on or inside the parabola $y^2 = 4ax$ according as

$$y_1^2 - 4ax_1 >, =, \text{or} < 0.$$

Proof Let $P(x_1, y_1)$ be a point. From P draw $PM \perp AX$ (on the axis of parabola) meeting the parabola $y^2 = 4ax$ at Q let the coordinate of Q be (x_1, y_2).

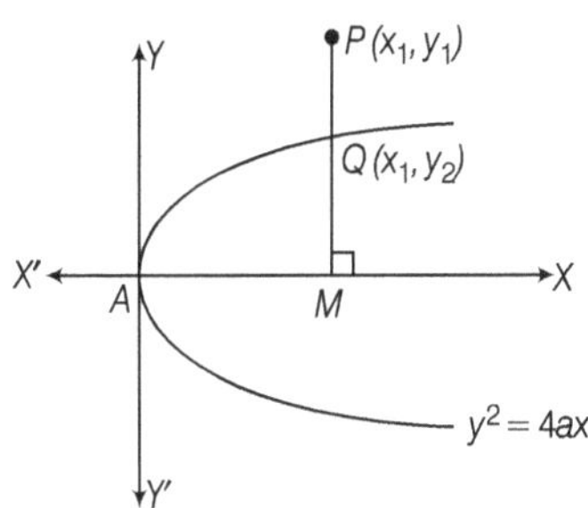

Since, $Q(x_1, y_2)$ lies on the parabola

$$y_1^2 = 4ax$$

then, $$y_2^2 = 4ax_1 \quad \ldots\text{(i)}$$

Now, P will be outside, on or inside the parabola $y^2 = 4ax$ according as

$$PM >, =, \text{or} < QM$$

$\Rightarrow$ $$(PM)^2 >, =, \text{or} < (QM)^2$$

$\Rightarrow$ $$y_1^2 >, =, \text{or} < y_2^2$$

$\Rightarrow$ $$y_1^2 >, =, \text{or} < 4ax_1 \quad \text{[from Eq. (i)]}$$

Hence, $y_1^2 - 4ax_1 >, =, \text{or} < 0$

Remarks

1. The point (x_1, y_1) lies inside, on or outside $y^2 = -4ax$ according as $y_1^2 + 4ax_1 <, =, \text{or} > 0$
2. The point (x_1, y_1) lies inside, on or outside $x^2 = 4ay$ according as $x_1^2 - 4ay_1 <, =, \text{or} > 0$
3. The point (x_1, y_1) lies inside, on or outside $x^2 = -4ay$ according as $x_1^2 + 4ay_1 <, =, \text{or} > 0$

Example 23 Show that the point (2, 3) lies outside the parabola $y^2 = 3x$.

Sol. Let the point $(h, k) = (2, 3)$

We have, $k^2 - 3h = 3^2 - 3.2 = 9 - 6 = 3 > 0$

$\therefore$ $$k^2 - 3h > 0$$

This shows that (2,3) lies outside the parabola $y^2 = 3x$.

Example 24 Find the position of the point $(-2, 2)$ with respect to the parabola $y^2 - 4y + 9x + 13 = 0$.

Sol. Let the point $(h, k) = (-2, 2)$

We have, $k^2 - 4k + 9h + 13 = (2)^2 - 4(2) + 9(-2) + 13 = 4 - 8 - 18 + 13 = -9 < 0$

Hence, $$k^2 - 4k + 9h + 13 < 0$$

Therefore, the point $(-2, 2)$ lies inside the parabola

$$y^2 - 4y + 9x + 13 = 0.$$

Parameteric Relation between the Coordinates of the Ends of a Focal Chord of a Parabola

Let $y^2 = 4ax$ be a parabola, if PQ be a focal chord.

Then, $P \equiv (at_1^2, 2at_1)$ and $Q \equiv (at_2^2, 2at_2)$

Since, PQ passes through the focus $S(a, 0)$.

$\therefore$ Q, S, P are collinear.

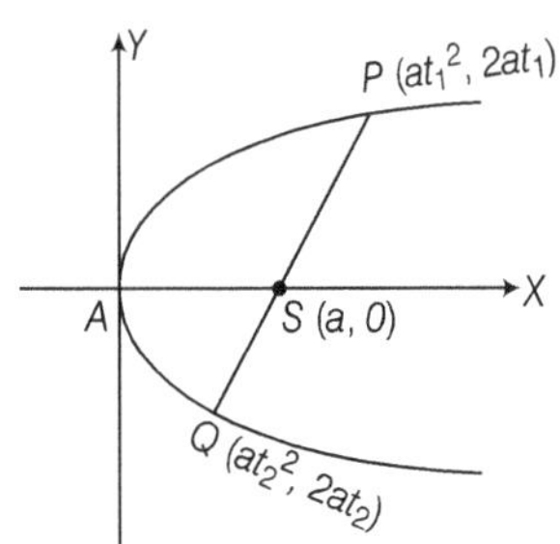

$\therefore$ Slope of PS = Slope of QS

$$\Rightarrow \quad \frac{2at_1 - 0}{at_1^2 - a} = \frac{0 - 2at_2}{a - at_2^2} \Rightarrow \frac{2t_1}{t_1^2 - 1} = \frac{2t_2}{t_2^2 - 1}$$

$$\Rightarrow \quad t_1 (t_2^2 - 1) = t_2 (t_1^2 - 1)$$

$$\Rightarrow \quad t_1 t_2 (t_2 - t_1) + (t_2 - t_1) = 0$$

$$\Rightarrow \quad t_2 - t_1 \neq 0 \quad \text{or} \quad t_1 t_2 + 1 = 0$$

$$\Rightarrow \quad t_1 t_2 = -1 \quad \text{or} \quad t_2 = -\frac{1}{t_1}, \qquad \text{...(i)}$$

which is required relation.

Remark

If one extremity of a focal chord is $(at_1^2, 2at_1)$ then the other extremity $(at_2^2, 2at_2)$ becomes $\left(\frac{a}{t_1^2}, -\frac{2a}{t_1}\right)$ by virtue of relation Eq. (i).

Example 25 If the point $(at^2, 2at)$ be the extremity of a focal chord of parabola $y^2 = 4ax$ then show that the length of the focal chord is $a\left(t + \frac{1}{t}\right)^2$.

Sol. Since, one extremity of focal chord is $P(at^2, 2at)$, then the other extremity is $Q\left(\frac{a}{t^2}, -\frac{2a}{t}\right)$ [Replacing t by $-1/t$]

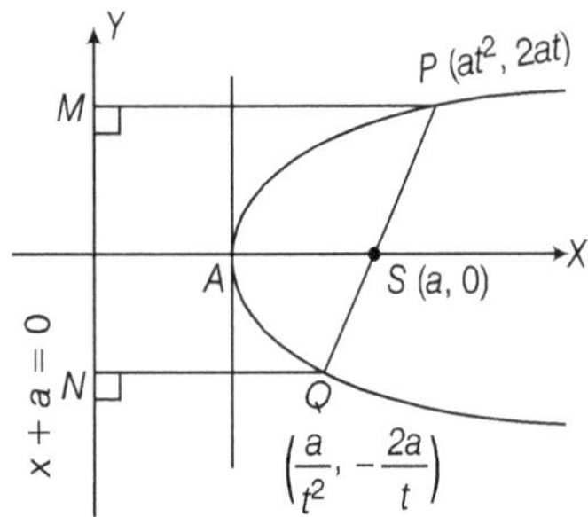

$\therefore$ Length of focal chord $= PQ$

$$= SP + SQ \qquad [\because SP = PM \text{ and } SQ = QN]$$

$$= PM + QN$$

$$= at^2 + a + \frac{a}{t^2} + a$$

$$= a\left(t^2 + \frac{1}{t^2} + 2\right) = a\left(t + \frac{1}{t}\right)^2$$

Remark

$$\because \quad \left|t + \frac{1}{t}\right| \geq 2 \text{ for all } t \neq 0 \qquad [\because \text{AM} \geq \text{GM}]$$

$$\therefore \quad a\left(t + \frac{1}{t}\right)^2 \geq 4a$$

$\Rightarrow$ Length of focal chord $\geq$ latusrectum i.e. The length of smallest focal chord of the parabola is $4a$. Hence, the latusrectum of a parabola is the smallest focal chord.

Example 26 Prove that the semi-latusrectum of the parabola $y^2 = 4ax$ is the harmonic mean between the segments of any focal chord of the parabola.

Sol. Let parabola be $y^2 = 4ax$

If PQ be the focal chord, if

$$P \equiv (at^2, 2at), \text{ then } Q \equiv \left(\frac{a}{t^2}, \frac{-2a}{t}\right)$$

$\therefore$ Length of latusrectum $LL' = 4a$.

$\therefore$ Semi-latusrectum $= \frac{1}{2}(4a) = 2a$.

If sections of focal chord are k_1 and k_2,

then, $k_1 = SP = PM = a + at^2 = a(1 + t^2)$

and $k_2 = SQ = QN = a + \frac{a}{t^2} = \frac{a(1 + t^2)}{t^2}$

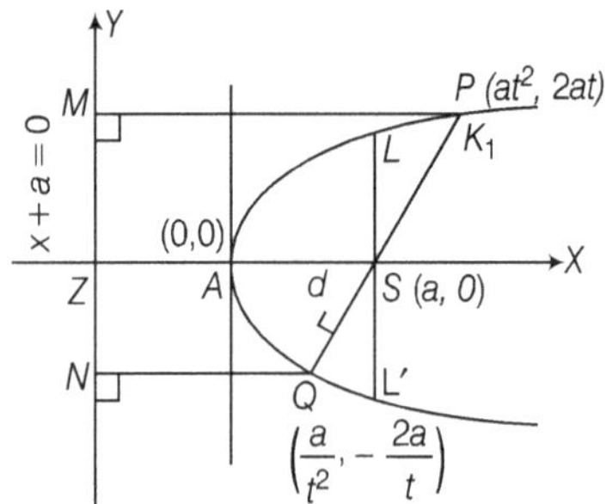

$\therefore$ Harmonic mean of k_1

and $k_2 = \frac{2k_1k_2}{k_1 + k_2}$

$$= \frac{2}{\frac{1}{k_2} + \frac{1}{k_1}} = \frac{2}{\frac{t^2}{a(1+t^2)} + \frac{1}{a(1+t^2)}}$$

$$= \frac{2}{\frac{1}{a}} = 2a = \text{Semi-latusrectum.}$$

Remarks

1. The length of focal chord having parameters t_1 and t_2 for its end points is $a(t_2 - t_1)^2$.
2. If l_1 and l_2 are the length of segments of a focal chord of a parabola, then its latusrectum is $\frac{4l_1l_2}{l_1 + l_2}$.

Example 27. Show that the focal chord of parabola $y^2 = 4ax$ makes an angle α with the X-axis is of length $4a \operatorname{cosec}^2\alpha$.

Sol. Let $P(at_1^2, 2at_1)$ and $Q(at_2^2, 2at_2)$ be the end points of a focal chord PQ which makes an angle α with the axis of the parabola. Then,

$$PQ = a(t_2 - t_1)^2$$
$$= a[(t_2 + t_1)^2 - 4t_1t_2] \quad \text{...(i)}$$
$$= a[(t_2 + t_1)^2 + 4] \quad [\because t_1t_2 = -1]$$

$$\therefore \quad \tan\alpha = \text{slope of } PQ = \frac{2at_2 - 2at_1}{at_2^2 - at_1^2}$$

$$\Rightarrow \quad \tan\alpha = \frac{2}{t_2 + t_1}$$

$$\Rightarrow \quad t_2 + t_1 = 2\cot\alpha \quad \text{...(ii)}$$

On substituting the value of $t_2 + t_1$ from Eq. (ii) in Eq. (i), then

$$PQ = a(4\cot^2\alpha + 4)$$
$$= 4a \operatorname{cosec}^2\alpha.$$

Example 28 Prove that the length of a focal chord of a parabola varies inversly as the square of its distance from the vertex.

Sol. Let $P(at^2, 2at)$ be one end of a focal chord of the parabola $y^2 = 4ax$. The focus of its parabola is $S(a,0)$.

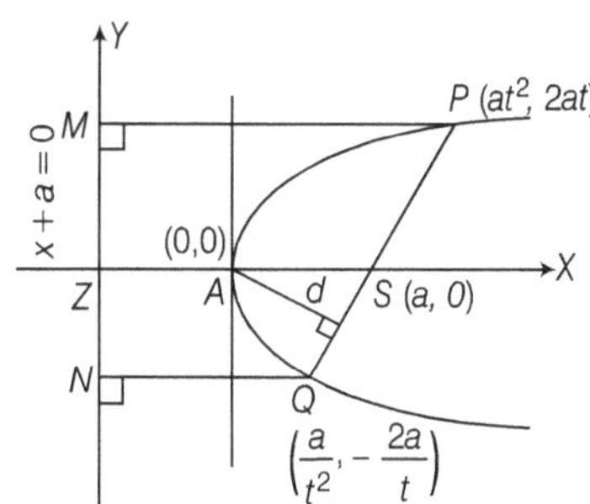

$\therefore$ Equation of focal chord is (i.e. equation of PS)

$$y - 0 = \frac{2at - 0}{at^2 - a}(x - a)$$

$$\Rightarrow \quad y = \frac{2t}{(t^2 - 1)}(x - a)$$

$$\Rightarrow \quad (t^2 - 1)y = 2tx - 2at$$

$$\Rightarrow \quad 2tx - (t^2 - 1)y - 2at = 0$$

If d be the distance of this focal chord from the vertex (0,0) of the parabola $y^2 = 4ax$, then

$$d = \frac{|0 - 0 - 2at|}{\sqrt{(2t)^2 + (t^2 - 1)^2}}$$

$$= \frac{|2at|}{(t^2 + 1)} = \frac{2a}{\left|t + \frac{1}{t}\right|}$$

$$\Rightarrow \quad d^2 = \frac{4a^2}{\left(t + \frac{1}{t}\right)^2} \quad \text{...(i)}$$

The other end of the focal chord is $Q\left(\frac{a}{t^2}, -\frac{2a}{t}\right)$

If length of focal chord $= PQ = (l \text{ say})$

$$\therefore \quad l = PQ = PS + SQ = PM + QN$$

$$\therefore \quad l = at^2 + a + \frac{a}{t^2} + a$$

$$\Rightarrow \quad l = a\left(t^2 + \frac{1}{t^2} + 2\right) \Rightarrow l = a\left(t + \frac{1}{t}\right)^2$$

$$\Rightarrow \quad \frac{l}{a} = \left(t + \frac{1}{t}\right)^2 \quad \text{...(ii)}$$

From Eqs. (i) and (ii), $d^2 = \frac{4a^2}{(l/a)} = \frac{4a^3}{l}$

$$\therefore \quad l = \frac{4a^3}{d^2} \Rightarrow l \propto \frac{1}{d^2}$$

i.e. the length of the focal chord varies inversely as the square of its distance from vertex.

Intersection of a Line and a Parabola

Let the parabola be $\quad y^2 = 4ax \quad$ ...(i)

and the given line be $\quad y = mx + c \quad$ ...(ii)

On eliminating x from Eqs. (i) and (ii), then

$$y^2 = 4a\left(\frac{y - c}{m}\right)$$

$$\Rightarrow \quad my^2 - 4ay + 4ac = 0 \quad \text{...(iii)}$$

This equation being quadratic in y, gives two values of y, shows that every straight line will cut the parabola in two points may be real, coincident or imaginary according as discriminant of Eq. (iii) $>, =, < 0$

i.e. $(-4a)^2 - 4 \cdot m \cdot 4ac >, =, < 0$ or $a - mc >, =, < 0$

or $\quad a >, =, < mc \quad$ ...(iv)

Condition of tangency

If the line Eq. (ii) touches the parabola Eq. (i), then Eq. (iii) has equal roots

$\therefore$ Discriminant of Eq. (iii) $= 0$

$$\Rightarrow \quad (-4a)^2 - 4m \cdot 4ac = 0$$

$\Rightarrow \quad c = \dfrac{a}{m}, m \neq 0$ ...(v)

So, the line $y = mx + c$ touches the parabola $y^2 = 4ax$ if $c = \dfrac{a}{m}$ (which is condition of tangency).

Substituting the value of c from Eq. (v) in Eq. (ii), then

$$y = mx + \frac{a}{m}, m \neq 0$$

Hence, the line $y = mx + \dfrac{a}{m}$ will always be a tangent to the parabola $y^2 = 4ax$.

The point of contact Substituting $c = \dfrac{a}{m}$ in Eq. (iii), then

$$my^2 - 4ay + 4a\left(\frac{a}{m}\right) = 0$$

$\Rightarrow \quad m^2y^2 - 4amy + 4a^2 = 0$

$\Rightarrow \quad (my - 2a)^2 = 0$

$\Rightarrow \quad my - 2a = 0$

or $\quad y = \dfrac{2a}{m}$

Substituting this value of y in $y = mx + \dfrac{a}{m}$

$\therefore \quad \dfrac{2a}{m} = mx + \dfrac{a}{m}$

$\Rightarrow \quad mx = \dfrac{a}{m}$ or $x = \dfrac{a}{m^2}$

Hence, the point of contact is $\left(\dfrac{a}{m^2}, \dfrac{2a}{m}\right), (m \neq 0)$ this known as ***m*-point** on the parabola.

Remark

If $m = 0$, then Eq. (iii) gives

$$0 - 4ay + 4ac = 0$$

$\Rightarrow \quad y = c$

which gives only one value of y and so every line parallel to X-axis cuts the parabola only in one real point.

Example 29 Prove that the straight line $lx + my + n = 0$ touches the parabola $y^2 = 4ax$, if $ln = am^2$.

Sol. The given line is $lx + my + n = 0$

or $\quad y = -\dfrac{l}{m}x - \dfrac{n}{m}$ ...(i)

Comparing this line with $y = Mx + c$

$\therefore \quad M = -\dfrac{l}{m}$ and $c = -\dfrac{n}{m}$

The line Eq. (i) will touch the parabola $y^2 = 4ax$, if

$$c = \frac{a}{M} \Rightarrow cM = a$$

$\Rightarrow \quad \left(-\dfrac{n}{m}\right)\left(-\dfrac{l}{m}\right) = a$

$\therefore \quad ln = am^2$

Aliter :

Given line $\quad lx + my + n = 0$ ...(i)

and the parabola $\quad y^2 = 4ax$ ...(ii)

Substituting the value of x from Eq. (i) i.e. $x = -\dfrac{n + my}{l}$ in Eq. (ii), then

(we should not substituting the value of y from Eq. (i), in Eq. (ii) since y is quadratic, substituting the value of x since x is linear).

$$y^2 = 4a\left(-\frac{n + my}{l}\right)$$

$\Rightarrow \quad ly^2 + 4amy + 4an = 0$ ...(iii)

Since, Eq. (i) touches the parabola Eq. (ii), then roots of Eq. (iii) must be coincident and condition for the same is $B^2 = 4AC$,

i.e., $\quad (4am)^2 = 4 \cdot l4an$

$\Rightarrow \quad am^2 = ln$

$\therefore \quad ln = am^2$

Example 30 Show that the line $x\cos\alpha + y\sin\alpha = p$ touches the parabola $y^2 = 4ax$, if $p\cos\alpha + a\sin^2\alpha = 0$ and that the point of contact is $(a\tan^2\alpha, -2a\tan\alpha)$.

Sol. The given line is

$$x\cos\alpha + y\sin\alpha = p$$

$\Rightarrow \quad y = -x\cot\alpha + p\,\text{cosec}\alpha$

Comparing this line with $y = mx + c$.

$\therefore \quad m = -\cot\alpha$ and $c = p\,\text{cosec}\alpha$

since, the given line touches the parabola

$\therefore \quad c = \dfrac{a}{m}$ or $cm = a$

$\Rightarrow \quad (p\,\text{cosec}\alpha)(-\cot\alpha) = a$

$\Rightarrow \quad a\sin^2\alpha + p\cos\alpha = 0$

and point of contact is $\left(\dfrac{a}{m^2}, \dfrac{2a}{m}\right)$

i.e. $\quad \left(\dfrac{a}{\cot^2\alpha}, -\dfrac{2a}{\cot\alpha}\right)$

or $\quad (a\tan^2\alpha, -2a\tan\alpha)$

Example 31 Prove that the line $\frac{x}{l}+\frac{y}{m}=1$ touches the parabola $y^2=4a(x+b)$, if $m^2(l+b)+al^2=0$.

Sol. The given parabola is

$$y^2 = 4a(x+b) \quad \text{...(i)}$$

Vertex of this parabola is $(-b, 0)$.
Now, shifting $(0, 0)$ at $(-b, 0)$,
then, $x = X + (-b)$ and $y = Y + 0$
or $x + b = X$ and $y = Y$ ...(ii)
From Eq. (i), $Y^2 = 4aX$ ...(iii)

and the line $\frac{x}{l}+\frac{y}{m}=1$

reduces to $\frac{X-b}{l}+\frac{Y}{m}=1$

$$Y = m\left(1-\frac{X-b}{l}\right)$$

$$\Rightarrow \quad Y = \left(-\frac{m}{l}\right)X + m\left(1+\frac{b}{l}\right) \quad \text{...(iv)}$$

The line Eq. (iv) will touch the parabola Eq. (iii), if

$$m\left(1+\frac{b}{l}\right) = \frac{a}{\left(-\frac{m}{l}\right)}$$

$$\Rightarrow \quad \frac{m^2}{l}\left(1+\frac{b}{l}\right) = -a$$

$$\therefore \quad m^2(l+b) + al^2 = 0$$

Aliter :
The given line and parabola are

$$\frac{x}{l}+\frac{y}{m}=1 \quad \text{...(i)}$$

and $$y^2 = 4a(x+b) \quad \text{...(ii)}$$

respectively substituting the value of x from Eq. (i)

$$x = l\left(1-\frac{y}{m}\right)$$

in Eq. (ii), then $$y^2 = 4a\left\{l\left(1-\frac{y}{m}\right)+b\right\}$$

or $$y^2 + \frac{4al}{m}y - 4a(l+b) = 0 \quad \text{...(iii)}$$

Since, the line Eq. (i) touches the parabola Eq. (ii), then the roots of Eq. (iii) are equal.

$$\therefore \quad \left(\frac{4al}{m}\right)^2 - 4\cdot 1\{-4a(l+b)\} = 0$$

$$\Rightarrow \quad \frac{al^2}{m^2} + (l+b) = 0$$

$$\Rightarrow \quad al^2 + m^2(l+b) = 0$$

$$\Rightarrow \quad m^2(l+b) + al^2 = 0$$

Example 32 Find the equations of the straight lines touching both $x^2+y^2=2a^2$ and $y^2=8ax$.

Sol. The given curves are

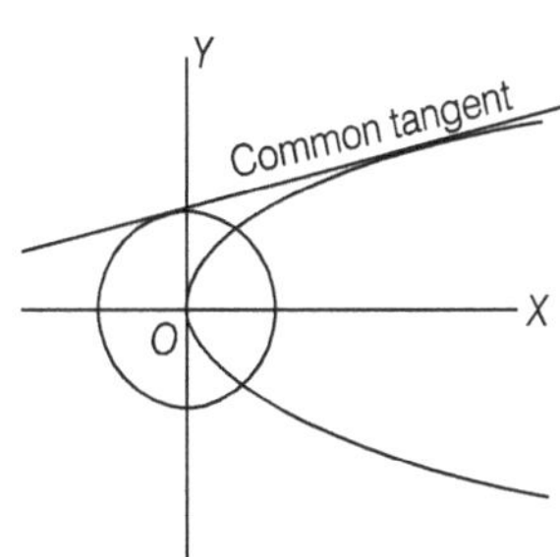

$$x^2 + y^2 = 2a^2 \quad \text{...(i)}$$

and $$y^2 = 8ax \quad \text{...(ii)}$$

The parabola Eq. (ii) is $y^2 = 8ax$

or $$y^2 = 4(2a)x$$

$\therefore$ Equation of tangent of Eq. (ii) is

$$y = mx + \frac{2a}{m}$$

or $$m^2x - my + 2a = 0 \quad \text{...(iii)}$$

It is also tangent of Eq. (i), then the length of perpendicular from centre of Eq. (i) i.e. $(0, 0)$ to Eq. (iii) must be equal to the radius of Eq. (i) i.e. $a\sqrt{2}$.

$$\therefore \quad \frac{|0-0+2a|}{\sqrt{(m^2)^2+(-m)^2}} = a\sqrt{2} \Rightarrow \frac{4a^2}{m^4+m^2} = 2a^2$$

$$\Rightarrow \quad m^4 + m^2 - 2 = 0$$

$$\Rightarrow \quad (m^2+2)(m^2-1) = 0$$

$$\because \quad m^2 + 2 \neq 0 \quad \text{[gives the imaginary values]}$$

$$\therefore \quad m^2 - 1 = 0$$

$$\Rightarrow \quad m = \pm 1$$

Hence, from Eq. (iii) the required tangents are

$$x \pm y + 2a = 0.$$

Equation of Tangent in Different Forms

1. Point Form :

To find the equation of the tangent to the parabola $y^2 = 4ax$ at the point (x_1, y_1).

(First Principal Method) Equation of parabola is

$$y^2 = 4ax \quad \text{...(i)}$$

Let $P \equiv (x_1, y_1)$ and $Q \equiv (x_2, y_2)$ be any two points on parabola (i), then

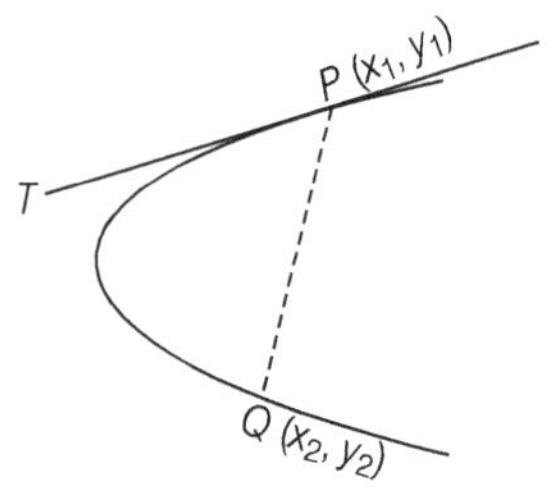

$$y_1^2 = 4ax_1 \quad \text{...(ii)}$$

and $$y_2^2 = 4ax_2 \quad \text{...(iii)}$$

Subtracting Eq. (ii) from Eq. (iii), then

$$y_2^2 - y_1^2 = 4a(x_2 - x_1)$$

$$\Rightarrow \quad \frac{y_2 - y_1}{x_2 - x_1} = \frac{4a}{y_2 + y_1} \quad \text{...(iv)}$$

Equation of PQ is

$$y - y_1 = \frac{y_2 - y_1}{x_2 - x_1}(x - x_1) \quad \text{...(v)}$$

From Eqs. (iv) and (v), then

$$y - y_1 = \frac{4a}{y_2 + y_1}(x - x_1) \quad \text{...(vi)}$$

Now, for tangent at $P, Q \to P$, i.e. $x_2 \to x_1$ and $y_2 \to y_1$, then Eq. (vi) becomes

$$y - y_1 = \frac{4a}{2y_1}(x - x_1) \Rightarrow yy_1 - y_1^2 = 2ax - 2ax_1$$

$$\Rightarrow \quad yy_1 = 2ax + y_1^2 - 2ax_1$$

$$\Rightarrow \quad yy_1 = 2ax + 4ax_1 - 2ax_1 \quad \text{[from Eq. (ii)]}$$

$$\Rightarrow \quad yy_1 = 2ax + 2ax_1$$

$$\therefore \quad yy_1 = 2a(x + x_1),$$

which is the required equation of tangent at (x_1, y_1).

Remarks

1. The equation of tangent at (x_1, y_1) can also be obtained by replacing x^2 by xx_1, y^2 by yy_1, x by $\frac{x + x_1}{2}$, y by $\frac{y + y_1}{2}$ and xy by $\frac{xy_1 + x_1y}{2}$ and without changing the constant (if any) in the equation of curve. This method is apply only when the equations of parabola is polynomial of second degree in x and y.
2. Equation of tangents of all standard parabolas at (x_1, y_1).

Equations of Parabolas	Tangent at(x_1, y_1)
$y^2 = 4ax$	$yy_1 = 2a(x + x_1)$
$y^2 = -4ax$	$yy_1 = -2a(x + x_1)$
$x^2 = 4ay$	$xx_1 = 2a(y + y_1)$
$x^2 = -4ay$	$xx_1 = -2a(y + y_1)$

2. Parametric Form :

To find the equation of tangent to the parabola $y^2 = 4ax$ at the point $(at^2, 2at)$ or 't'.

Since, the equation of tangent of the parabola $y^2 = 4ax$ at (x_1, y_1) is $yy_1 = 2a(x + x_1)$ ...(i)

replacing x_1 by at^2 and y_1 by $2at$, then Eq. (i) becomes

$$y(2at) = 2a(x + at^2) \Rightarrow ty = x + at^2$$

Remark

The equations of tangent of all standard parabolas at 't'.

Equations of Parabolas	Parametric coordinates 't'	Tangent at 't'
$y^2 = 4ax$	$(at^2, 2at)$	$ty = x + at^2$
$y^2 = -4ax$	$(-at^2, 2at)$	$ty = -x + at^2$
$x^2 = 4ay$	$(2at, at^2)$	$tx = y + at^2$
$x^2 = -4ay$	$(2at, -at^2)$	$tx = -y + at^2$

3. Slope Form :

To find the equation of tangent and point of contact in terms of m(slope) to the parabola $y^2 = 4ax$.

The equation of tangent to the parabola $y^2 = 4ax$ at (x_1, y_1) is $yy_1 = 2a(x + x_1)$. ...(i)

Since, m is the slope of the tangent, then

$$m = \frac{2a}{y_1} \Rightarrow y_1 = \frac{2a}{m}$$

Since, (x_1, y_1) lies on $y^2 = 4ax$, therefore

$$y_1^2 = 4ax_1 \Rightarrow \frac{4a^2}{m^2} = 4ax_1$$

$$\therefore \quad x_1 = \frac{a}{m^2}$$

Substituting the values of x_1 and y_1 in Eq. (i), we get

$$y = mx + \frac{a}{m} \quad \text{...(ii)}$$

Thus, $y = mx + \frac{a}{m}$ is a tangent to the parabola $y^2 = 4ax$, where, m is the slope of the tangent.

The coordinates of the point of contact are $\left(\frac{a}{m^2}, \frac{2a}{m}\right)$.

Comparing Eq. (ii) with $y = mx + c$,

$$c = \frac{a}{m}$$

which is condition of tangency.

when, $y = mx + c$ is the tangent of $y^2 = 4ax$.

Remark

The equation of tangent, condition of tangency and point of contact in terms of slope (m) of all standard parabolas.

Equation of parabolas	Point of contact in terms of slope (m)	Equation of tangent in terms of slope (m)	Condition of tangency
$y^2 = 4ax$	$\left(\frac{a}{m^2}, \frac{2a}{m}\right)$	$y = mx + \frac{a}{m}$	$c = \frac{a}{m}$
$y^2 = -4ax$	$\left(-\frac{a}{m^2}, \frac{2a}{m}\right)$	$y = mx - \frac{a}{m}$	$c = -\frac{a}{m}$
$x^2 = 4ay$	$(2am, am^2)$	$y = mx - am^2$	$c = -am^2$
$x^2 = -4ay$	$(2am, -am^2)$	$y = mx + am^2$	$c = am^2$
$(y-k)^2 = 4a(x-h)$	$\left(h + \frac{a}{m^2}, k + \frac{2a}{m}\right)$	$y = mx - mh + k + \frac{a}{m}$	$c + mh = k + \frac{a}{m}$
$(y-k)^2 = -4a(x-h)$	$\left(h - \frac{a}{m^2}, k + \frac{2a}{m}\right)$	$y = mx - mh + k - \frac{a}{m}$	$c + mh = k - \frac{a}{m}$
$(x-h)^2 = 4a(y-k)$	$(h + 2am, k + am^2)$	$y = mx - mh + k - am^2$	$c + mh = k - am^2$
$(x-h)^2 = -4a(y-k)$	$(h + 2am, k - am^2)$	$y = mx - mh + k + am^2$	$c + mh = k + am^2$

Point of Intersection of Tangents at any two Points on the Parabola

Let the parabola be $y^2 = 4ax$

let two points on the parabola are

$$P \equiv (at_1^2, 2at_1) \text{ and } Q \equiv (at_2^2, 2at_2).$$

Equation of tangents at $P(at_1^2, 2at_1)$

and $Q(at_2^2, 2at_2)$

are $t_1 y = x + at_1^2$ ...(i)

and $t_2 y = x + at_2^2$ ...(ii)

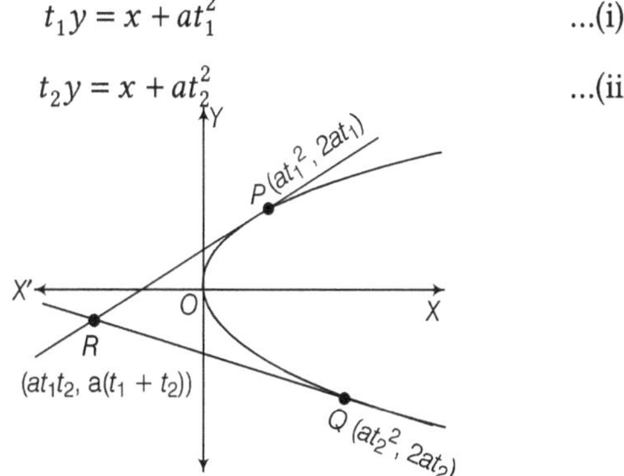

On solving these equations, we get $x = at_1t_2, y = a(t_1 + t_2)$

Thus, the coordinates of the point of intersection of tangents at

$$(at_1^2, 2at_1) \text{ and } (at_2^2, 2at_2) \text{ are } (at_1t_2, a(t_1 + t_2)).$$

Remarks

1. The geometric mean of the x-coordinates of P and Q (i.e. $\sqrt{at_1^2 \times at_2^2} = at_1t_2$) is the x-coordinate of the point of intersection of tangents at P and Q on the parabola. If P and Q are the ends points of focal chord, then x-coordinate of point of intersection of tangents at P and Q is $(-at_1t_2)$.
2. The arithmetic mean of the y-coordinates of P and Q $\left(\text{i.e. } \frac{2at_1 + 2at_2}{2} = a(t_1 + t_2)\right)$ is the y-coordinate of the point of intersection of tangents at P and Q on the parabola.

Remembering Method :

G O A [GOA rule]

GM of at_1^2 and at_2^2 , AM of $2at_1$ and $2at_2$

i.e. at_1t_2 i.e. $\frac{2at_1 + 2at_2}{2} = a(t_1 + t_2)$

Example 33 Find the equation of the common tangents to the parabola $y^2 = 4ax$ and $x^2 = 4by$.

Sol. The equation of any tangent in terms of slope (m) to the parabola $y^2 = 4ax$ is

$$y = mx + \frac{a}{m} \quad \text{...(i)}$$

If this line is also tangent to the parabola $x^2 = 4ay$, then Eq. (i) meets $x^2 = 4by$ in two coincident points.

Substituting the value of y from Eq. (i) in $x^2 = 4by$, we get

$$x^2 = 4b\left(mx + \frac{a}{m}\right)$$

$$\Rightarrow \quad x^2 - 4bmx - \frac{4ab}{m} = 0$$

The roots of this quadratic are equal provided

$$B^2 = 4AC$$

i.e., $$(-4bm)^2 = 4 \cdot 1\left(\frac{-4ab}{m}\right)$$

$$\Rightarrow \quad 16b^2m^3 + 16ab = 0, m \neq 0$$

or $$m^3 = -a/b$$

$$\therefore \quad m = -a^{1/3}/b^{1/3}$$

Substituting the value of m in Eq. (i) the required equation is

$$y = -\frac{a^{1/3}}{b^{1/3}}x - \frac{ab^{1/3}}{a^{1/3}}$$

$$\Rightarrow \quad y = -\frac{a^{1/3}}{b^{1/3}}x - a^{2/3}b^{1/3}$$

$$\therefore \quad a^{1/3}x + b^{1/3}y + a^{2/3}b^{2/3} = 0$$

Example 34 The tangents to the parabola $y^2 = 4ax$ make angle θ_1 and θ_2 with X-axis. Find the locus of their point of intersection, if $\cot\theta_1 + \cot\theta_2 = c$.

Sol. Let the equation of any tangent to the parabola $y^2 = 4ax$ is

$$y = mx + (a/m) \quad \text{...(i)}$$

Let (x_1, y_1) be the point of intersection of the tangents to $y^2 = 4ax$, then Eq. (i) passes through (x_1, y_1).

$$\therefore \quad y_1 = mx_1 + (a/m)$$

or $$m^2x_1 - my_1 + a = 0$$

Let m_1 and m_2 be the roots of this quadratic equation, then

$$m_1 + m_2 = y_1/x_1 \quad \text{and} \quad m_1m_2 = a/x_1$$

or $$\tan\theta_1 + \tan\theta_2 = y_1/x_1$$

and $$\tan\theta_1 \tan\theta_2 = a/x_1 \quad \text{...(ii)}$$

Now, $$\cot\theta_1 + \cot\theta_2 = c \quad \text{(given)}$$

$$\Rightarrow \quad \frac{1}{\tan\theta_1} + \frac{1}{\tan\theta_2} = c$$

$$\Rightarrow \quad \frac{\tan\theta_1 + \tan\theta_2}{\tan\theta_1 \tan\theta_2} = c \quad \text{[from Eq. (ii)]}$$

$$\Rightarrow \quad \frac{y_1/x_1}{a/x_1} = c$$

$$\Rightarrow \quad y_1 = ac$$

The required locus is $y = ac$, which is a line parallel to X-axis.

Example 35. Show that the locus of the points of intersection of the mutually perpendicular tangents to a parabola is the directrix of the parabola.

Sol. Let the points $P(at_1^2, 2at_1)$ and $Q(at_2^2, 2at_2)$ on the parabola $y^2 = 4ax$ tangents at P and Q are

$$t_1y = x + at_1^2 \quad \text{...(i)}$$

and $$t_2y = x + at_2^2 \quad \text{...(ii)}$$

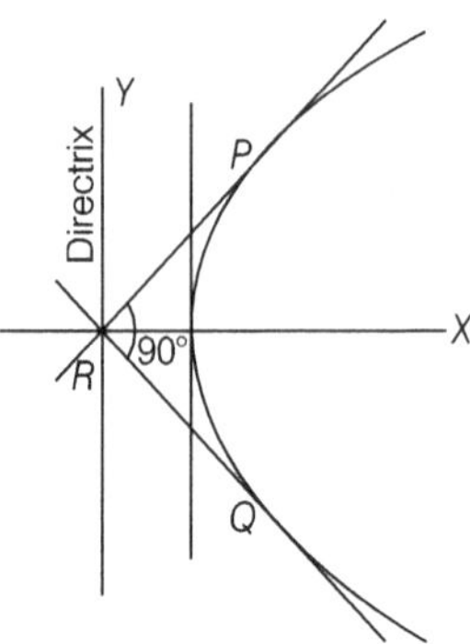

$\because$ Point of intersection of these tangents is $(at_1t_2, a(t_1 + t_2))$

Let this point is (h, k),

then, $$h = at_1t_2 \quad \text{...(iii)}$$

and $$k = a(t_1 + t_2) \quad \text{...(iv)}$$

Slope of tangents Eqs. (i) and (ii) are $\frac{1}{t_1}$ and $\frac{1}{t_2}$, respectively.

Since, tangents are perpendicular, then

$$\frac{1}{t_1} \times \frac{1}{t_2} = -1$$

or $$t_1t_2 = -1 \quad \text{...(v)}$$

From Eqs. (iii) and (v), we get

$$h = -a \quad \text{or} \quad h + a = 0$$

$\therefore$ Locus of the point of intersection of tangents is

$$x + a = 0$$

which is directrix of $y^2 = 4ax$.

Aliter :

Let the equation of any tangent to the parabola $y^2 = 4ax$ is

$$y = mx + a/m \quad \text{...(i)}$$

Let the point of intersection of the tangents to $y^2 = 4ax$ then, Eq (i) passes through (x_1, y_1).

$$\therefore \quad y_1 = mx_1 + a/m$$

or $$m^2x_1 - my_1 + a = 0$$

Let m_1, m_2 be the roots of this quadratic equation then

$$m_1m_2 = a/x_1 = -1$$

[since, tangents are perpendiculars]

$$\Rightarrow \quad a + x_1 = 0$$

$\therefore$ Locus of the point of intersection of tangents is $x + a = 0$ which is directrix of $y^2 = 4ax$.

Remark

Locus of the point of intersection of the perpendicular tangents to the parabola $y^2 = 4ax$ is called the director circle. Its equation is $x + a = 0$, which is parabola's own directrix.

Example 36 The tangents to the parabola $y^2 = 4ax$ at $P(at_1^2, 2at_1)$ and $Q(at_2^2, 2at_2)$ intersect at R. Prove that the area of the ΔPQR is $\frac{1}{2}a^2|(t_1 - t_2)|^3$.

Sol. Equations of tangents at $P(at_1^2, 2at_1)$ and $Q(at_2^2, 2at_2)$ are

$$t_1 y = x + at_1^2 \quad \text{...(i)}$$

and $$t_2 y = x + at_2^2 \quad \text{...(ii)}$$

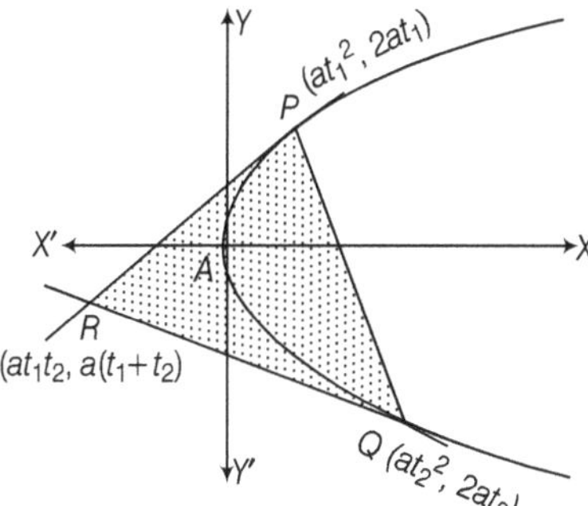

Since, point of intersect of Eqs. (i) and (ii) is $R(at_1t_2, a(t_1 + t_2))$.

$$\therefore \text{ Area of } \Delta PQR = \frac{1}{2}\begin{vmatrix} at_1^2 & 2at_1 & 1 \\ at_2^2 & 2at_2 & 1 \\ at_1t_2 & a(t_1+t_2) & 1 \end{vmatrix}$$

Applying $R_2 \to R_2 - R_1$ and $R_3 \to R_3 - R_1$

$$= \frac{1}{2}\begin{vmatrix} at_1^2 & 2at_1 & 1 \\ a(t_2^2 - t_1^2) & 2a(t_2 - t_1) & 0 \\ at_1(t_2 - t_1) & a(t_2 - t_1) & 0 \end{vmatrix}$$

Expanding with respect to first row

$$= \frac{1}{2}\begin{vmatrix} a(t_2^2 - t_1^2) & 2a(t_2 - t_1) \\ at_1(t_2 - t_1) & a(t_2 - t_1) \end{vmatrix}$$

$$= \frac{1}{2}a^2(t_2 - t_1)^2\begin{vmatrix} t_2 + t_1 & 2 \\ t_1 & 1 \end{vmatrix}$$

$$= \frac{1}{2}a^2(t_1 - t_2)^2|(t_2 - t_1)|$$

$$= \frac{1}{2}a^2(t_1 - t_2)^2|(t_1 - t_2)|$$

$$= \frac{1}{2}a^2|(t_1 - t_2)^3|.$$

Equations of Normals in Different Forms

1. Point Form: To find the equation of the normal to the parabola $y^2 = 4ax$ at the point (x_1, y_1).

Since, the equation of the tangent to the parabola $y^2 = 4ax$ at (x_1, y_1) is

$$yy_1 = 2a(x + x_1)$$

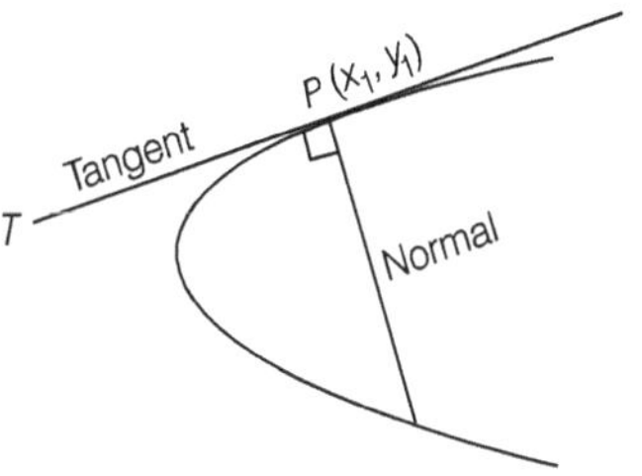

The slope of the tangent at $(x_1, y_1) = 2a/y_1$

Since, the normal at (x_1, y_1) is perpendicular to the tangent at (x_1, y_1).

$\therefore$ Slope of normal at $(x_1, y_1) = -y_1/2a$

Hence, the equation of normal at (x_1, y_1) is

$$y - y_1 = -\frac{y_1}{2a}(x - x_1).$$

Remarks

1. The equation of normal at (x_1, y_1) can also be obtained by this method

$$\frac{x - x_1}{a'x_1 + hy_1 + g} = \frac{y - y_1}{hx_1 + by_1 + f} \quad \text{...(i)}$$

a', b, g, f, h are obtained by comparing the given parabola with

$$a'x^2 + 2hxy + by^2 + 2gx + 2fy + c = 0 \quad \text{...(ii)}$$

and denominators of Eq. (i) can easily remembered by the first two rows of this determinant

i.e. $$\begin{vmatrix} a' & h & g \\ h & b & f \\ g & f & c \end{vmatrix}$$

Since, first row $a'(x_1) + h(y_1) + g(1)$

and second row, $h(x_1) + b(y_1) + f(1)$

Here, parabola $y^2 = 4ax$

or $$y^2 - 4ax = 0 \quad \text{...(iii)}$$

Comparing Eqs. (ii) and (iii), then we get

$a' = 0, b = 1, g = -2a, h = 0, f = 0$

From Eq. (i), equation of normal of Eq. (iii) is

$$\frac{x - x_1}{0 + 0 - 2a} = \frac{y - y_1}{0 + y_1 + 0}$$

or $$y - y_1 = -\frac{y_1}{2a}(x - x_1)$$

2. Equations of normals of all standard parabolas at (x_1, y_1).

Equations of Parabola	Normal at (x_1, y_1)
$y^2 = 4ax$	$y - y_1 = -\frac{y_1}{2a}(x - x_1)$
$y^2 = -4ax$	$y - y_1 = \frac{y_1}{2a}(x - x_1)$
$x^2 = 4ay$	$y - y_1 = -\frac{2a}{x_1}(x - x_1)$
$x^2 = 4ay$	$y - y_1 = \frac{2a}{x_1}(x - x_1)$

2. Parametric form :

To find the equation of normal to the parabola $y^2 = 4ax$ at the point $(at^2, 2at)$ or '*t*'.

Since, the equation of normal of the parabola $y^2 = 4ax$ at (x_1, y_1) is

$$y - y_1 = -\frac{y_1}{2a}(x - x_1) \quad \text{...(i)}$$

Replacing x_1 by at^2 and y_1 by $2at$, then Eq. (i) becomes

$$y - 2at = -t(x - at^2)$$

or $\quad \boldsymbol{y + tx = 2at + at^3}$

Remark

The equations of normals of all standard parabolas at '*t*'

Equations of Parabolas	Parametric coordinates '*t*'	Normals at '*t*'
$y^2 = 4ax$	$(at^2, 2at)$	$y + tx = 2at + at^3$
$y^2 = -4ax$	$(-at^2, 2at)$	$y - tx = 2at + at^3$
$x^2 = 4ay$	$(2at, at^2)$	$x + ty = 2at + at^3$
$x^2 = -4ay$	$(2at, -at^2)$	$x - ty = 2at + at^3$

3. Slope form :

To find the Equation of normal, condition for normality and point of contact in terms of *m* (slope) to the parabola $y^2 = 4ax$

The equation of normal to the parabola $y^2 = 4ax$ at (x_1, y_1) is

$$y - y_1 = -\frac{y_1}{2a}(x - x_1) \quad \text{...(i)}$$

Since, *m* is the slope of the normal,

then, $\quad m = -\frac{y_1}{2a} \Rightarrow y_1 = -2am$

Since, (x_1, y_1) lies on $y^2 = 4ax$, therefore

$$y_1^2 = 4ax_1$$

$$\Rightarrow \quad 4a^2m^2 = 4ax_1$$

$$\therefore \quad x_1 = am^2$$

On substituting the values of x_1 and y_1 in Eq. (i) we get

$$y + 2am = m(x - am^2)$$

$$\therefore \quad y = mx - 2am - am^3 \quad \text{...(ii)}$$

Thus, $y = mx - 2am - am^3$ is a normal to the parabola $y^2 = 4ax$, where *m* is the slope of the normal. The coordinates of the point of contact are $(am^2, -2am)$

On comparing Eq. (ii) with

$$y = mx + c$$

$$\therefore \quad c = -2am - am^3$$

which is condition of normality when $y = mx + c$ is the normal of $y^2 = 4ax$.

Remark

The equations of normals, point of contact and condition of normality in terms of slope (*m*) of all standard parabolas.

Equation of parabolas	Point of contact in terms of slope (*m*)	Equation of normals in terms of slope (*m*)	Condition of normality
$y^2 = 4ax$	$(am^2, -2am)$	$y = mx - 2am - am^3$	$c = -2am - am^3$
$y^2 = -4ax$	$(-am^2, 2am)$	$y = mx + 2am + am^3$	$c = 2am + am^3$
$x^2 = 4ay$	$\left(-\frac{2a}{m}, \frac{a}{m^2}\right)$	$y = mx + 2a + \frac{a}{m^2}$	$c = 2a + \frac{a}{m^2}$
$x^2 = -4ay$	$\left(\frac{2a}{m}, -\frac{a}{m^2}\right)$	$y = mx - 2a - \frac{a}{m^2}$	$c = -2a - \frac{a}{m^2}$
$(y-k)^2 = 4a(x-h)$	$(h + am^2, k - 2am)$	$y - k = m(x-h) - 2am - am^3$	$c = k - mh - 2am - am^3$
$(y-k)^2 = -4a(x-h)$	$(h - am^2, k + 2am)$	$y - k = m(x-h) + 2am + am^3$	$c = k - mh + 2am + am^3$
$(x-h)^2 = 4a(y-k)$	$\left(h - \frac{2a}{m}, k + \frac{a}{m^2}\right)$	$y - k = m(x-h) + 2a + \frac{a}{m^2}$	$c = k - mh + 2a + \frac{a}{m^2}$

Point of Intersection of Normals at any Two Points on the Parabola

Let the parabola be $y^2 = 4ax$.

Let the points on the parabola are

$$P \equiv (at_1^2, 2at_1) \quad \text{and} \quad Q = (at_2^2, 2at_2).$$

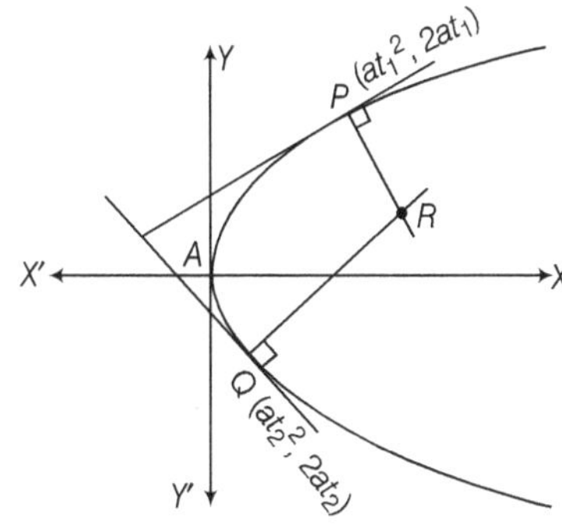

Equations of normals at $P(at_1^2, 2at_1)$ and $Q(at_2^2, 2at_2)$ are

$$y = -t_1 x + 2at_1 + at_1^3 \quad \text{...(i)}$$

and $$y = -t_2 x + 2at_2 + at_2^3 \quad \text{...(ii)}$$

On solving Eqs. (i) and (ii), we get

$$x = 2a + a(t_1^2 + t_2^2 + t_1 t_2) \text{ and } y = -at_1 t_2 (t_1 + t_2)$$

If R is the point of intersection, then

$$\boldsymbol{R \equiv [2a + a(t_1^2 + t_2^2 + t_1 t_2), -at_1 t_2 (t_1 + t_2)]}$$

(Remember)

Point of intersection of normals at t_1 and t_2

Parabola	Equation of normal at any point 't'	Point of intersection of normals at t_1 and t_2
$y^2 = 4ax$	$y + tx = 2at + at^3$	$(2a + a(t_1^2 + t_1t_2 + t_2^2), -at_1t_2(t_1 + t_2))$
$y^2 = -4ax$	$y - tx = 2at + at^3$	$(-2a - a(t_1^2 + t_1t_2 + t_2^2), at_1t_2(t_1 + t_2))$
$x^2 = 4ay$	$x + ty = 2at + at^3$	$(-at_1t_2(t_1 + t_2), 2a + a(t_1^2 + t_1t_2 + t_2^2))$
$x^2 = -4ay$	$x - ty = 2at + at^3$	$(at_1t_2(t_1 + t_2), -2a - a(t_1^2 + t_1t_2 + t_2^2))$

Relation between 't_1' and 't_2' if Normal at 't_1' meets the Parabola Again at 't_2'

Let the parabola be $y^2 = 4ax$, equation of normal at $P(at_1^2, 2at_1)$ is

$$y = -t_1 x + 2at_1 + at_1^3 \quad \text{...(i)}$$

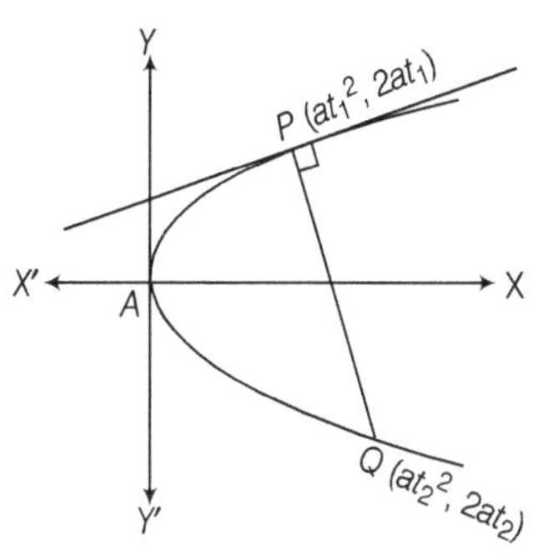

Since, it meet the parabola again at $Q(at_2^2, 2at_2)$, then Eq. (i) passes through $Q(at_2^2, 2at_2)$.

$\therefore \quad 2at_2 = -at_1 t_2^2 + 2at_1 + at_1^3$

$\Rightarrow \quad 2a(t_2 - t_1) + at_1(t_2^2 - t_1^2) = 0$

$\Rightarrow \quad a(t_2 - t_1)[2 + t_1(t_2 + t_1)] = 0$

$\because \quad a(t_2 - t_1) \neq 0$

[$\because t_1$ and t_2 are different]

$\therefore \quad 2 + t_1(t_2 + t_1) = 0$

$\therefore \quad \boldsymbol{t_2 = -t_1 - \frac{2}{t_1}}$

Remarks

1. If normals at 't_1' and 't_2' meets the parabola $y^2 = 4ax$ at same point, then $t_1 t_2 = 2$.

   Proof Suppose normals meet at 'T', then

   $$T = -t_1 - \frac{2}{t_1} = -t_2 - \frac{2}{t_2}$$

   $$\Rightarrow \quad (t_1 - t_2) = 2\left(\frac{1}{t_2} - \frac{1}{t_1}\right)$$

   or $\quad t_1 t_2 = 2 \quad [\because t_1 \neq t_2]$

2. If the normals to the parabola $y^2 = 4ax$ at the points t_1 and t_2 intersect again on the parabola at the point t_3, then $t_3 = -(t_1 + t_2)$ and the line joining t_1 and t_2 passes through a fixed point $(-2a, 0)$.

Example 37 Show that normal to the parabola $y^2 = 8x$ at the point (2, 4) meets it again at (18, –12). Find also the length of the normal chord.

Sol. Comparing the given parabola (i.e. $y^2 = 8x$) with $y^2 = 4ax$.

$\therefore \quad 4a = 8 \Rightarrow a = 2$

Since, normal at (x_1, y_1) to the parabola $y^2 = 4ax$ is

$$y - y_1 = -\frac{y_1}{2a}(x - x_1)$$

Here, $x_1 = 2$ and $y_1 = 4$.

$\therefore$ Equation of normal is

$$y - 4 = -\frac{4}{4}(x - 2)$$

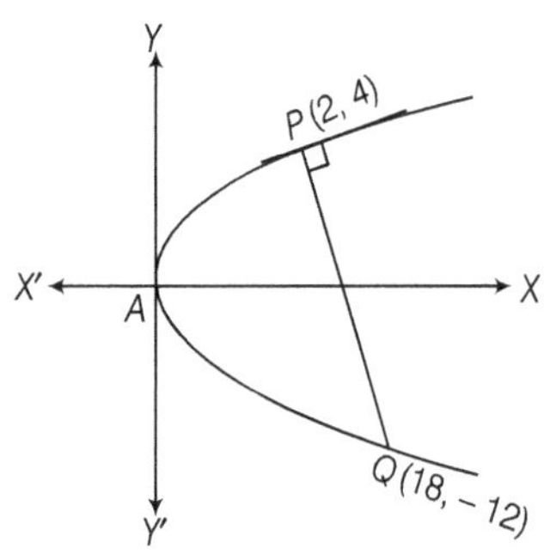

$$\Rightarrow \quad y - 4 = -x + 2$$

$$\Rightarrow \quad x + y - 6 = 0 \qquad \text{...(i)}$$

On solving Eq. (i) and $y^2 = 8x$,

then, $\quad y^2 = 8(6 - y)$

$$\Rightarrow \quad y^2 + 8y - 48 = 0$$

$$\Rightarrow \quad (y + 12)(y - 4) = 0$$

$$\therefore \quad y = -12 \quad \text{and} \quad y = 4$$

then, $x = 18$ and $x = 2$.

Hence, the point of intersection of normal and parabola are $(18, -12)$ and $(2, 4)$, therefore normal meets the parabola at $(18, -12)$ and length of normal chord is distance between their points

$$= PQ = \sqrt{(18-2)^2 + (-12-4)^2} = 16\sqrt{2}$$

Example 38 Prove that the chord $y - x\sqrt{2} + 4a\sqrt{2} = 0$ is a normal chord of the parabola $y^2 = 4ax$. Also, find the point on the parabola when the given chord is normal to the parabola.

Sol. We have, $\quad y - x\sqrt{2} + 4a\sqrt{2} = 0$

i.e., $\quad y = x\sqrt{2} - 4a\sqrt{2} \qquad \text{...(i)}$

Comparing the Eq. (i) with the equation $y = mx + c$, then

$$m = \sqrt{2}, c = -4a\sqrt{2}$$

Since, $\quad -2am - am^3 = -2a\sqrt{2} - a(\sqrt{2})^3$

$$= -2a\sqrt{2} - 2a\sqrt{2} = -4a\sqrt{2} = c$$

Hence, the given chord is normal to the parabola $y^2 = 4ax$.

The coordinates of the points are $(am^2, -2am)$ i.e. $(2a, -2\sqrt{2}a)$.

Example 39 If the normal to a parabola $y^2 = 4ax$, makes an angle ϕ with the axis. Show that it will cut the curve again at an angle $\tan^{-1}\left(\frac{1}{2}\tan\phi\right)$.

Sol. Let the normal at $P(at_1^2, 2at_1)$ be

$$y = -t_1 x + 2at_1 + at_1^3.$$

$\therefore \quad \tan\phi = -t_1 =$ slope of the normal, $\qquad$ ...(i)

it meet the curve again Q say $(at_2^2, 2at_2)$.

$$\therefore \quad t_2 = -t_1 - \frac{2}{t_1} \qquad \text{...(ii)}$$

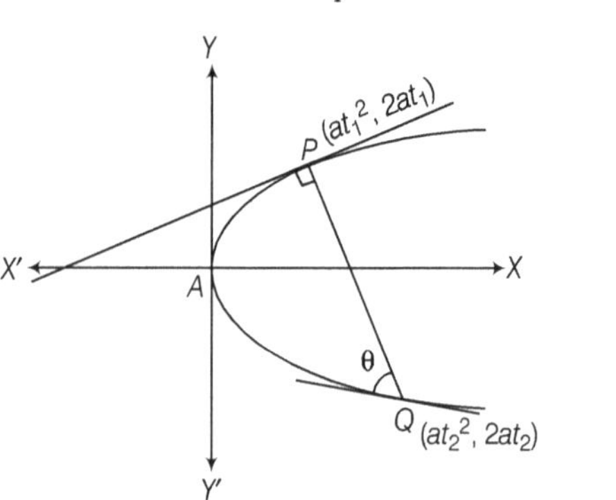

Now, angle between the normal and parabola
= Angle between the normal and tangent at Q
(i.e. $t_2 y = x + at_2^2$)

If θ be the angle, then

$$\tan\theta = \frac{m_1 - m_2}{1 + m_1 m_2} = \frac{-t_1 - \frac{1}{t_2}}{1 + (-t_1)\left(\frac{1}{t_2}\right)} = -\frac{t_1 t_2 + 1}{t_2 - t_1}$$

$$= -\frac{t_1\left(-t_1 - \frac{2}{t_1}\right) + 1}{-t_1 - \frac{2}{t_1} - t_1} \qquad \text{[from Eq. (ii)]}$$

$$= -\frac{-t_1^2 - 1}{-2\left(\frac{1 + t_1^2}{t_1}\right)} = -\frac{t_1}{2}$$

$$= \frac{\tan\phi}{2} \qquad \text{[from Eq. (i)]}$$

$$\therefore \quad \theta = \tan^{-1}\left(\frac{1}{2}\tan\phi\right)$$

Example 40 Prove that the normal chord to a parabola $y^2 = 4ax$ at the point whose ordinate is equal to abscissa subtends a right angle at the focus.

Sol. Let the normal at $P(at_1^2, 2at_1)$ meet the curve at $Q(at_2^2, 2at_2)$.

$\therefore$ PQ is a normal chord

and $\quad t_2 = -t_1 - \frac{2}{t_1}. \qquad$ ...(i)

By given condition, $2at_1 = at_1^2$

$\therefore$ $t_1 = 2$ from Eq. (i), $t_2 = -3$

then, $P(4a, 4a)$ and $Q(9a, -6a)$

but focus $S(a, 0)$.

$$\therefore \quad \text{Slope of } SP = \frac{4a - 0}{4a - a} = \frac{4a}{3a} = \frac{4}{3}$$

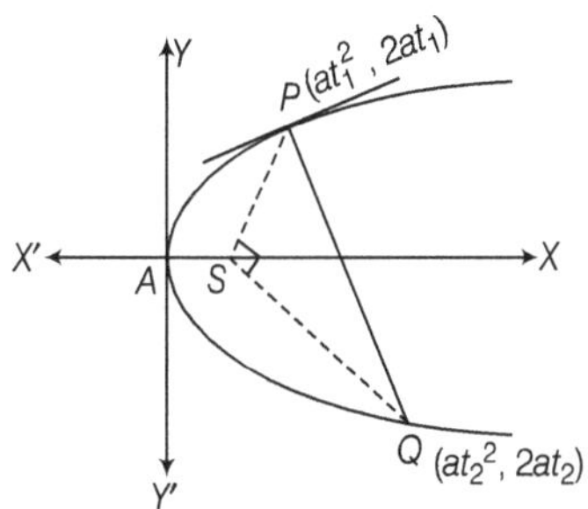

and slope of $SQ = \frac{-6a - 0}{9a - a} = -\frac{6a}{8a} = -\frac{3}{4}$

$\because$ Slope of $SP \times$ Slope of $SQ = \frac{4}{3} \times -\frac{3}{4} = -1$

$\therefore \quad \angle PSQ = \pi / 2$

i.e. PQ subtends a right angle at the focus S.

Example 41 If the normal to the parabola $y^2 = 4ax$ at point t_1 cuts the parabola again at point t_2, prove that $t_2^2 = 8$.

Sol. A normal at point t_1 cuts the parabola again at t_2. Then,

$$t_2 = -t_1 - \frac{2}{t_1} \Rightarrow t_1^2 + t_1t_2 + 2 = 0$$

Since, t_1 is real , so $(t_2)^2 - 4 \cdot 1 \cdot 2 \geq 0$

$\Rightarrow \quad t_2^2 \geq 8$

Co-normal Points

In general three normals can be drawn from a point to a parabola and their feet, points where they meet the parabola are called conormal points.

Let $P(h, k)$ be any given point and $y^2 = 4ax$ be a parabola.

The equation of any normal to $y^2 = 4ax$ is

$$y = mx - 2am - am^3$$

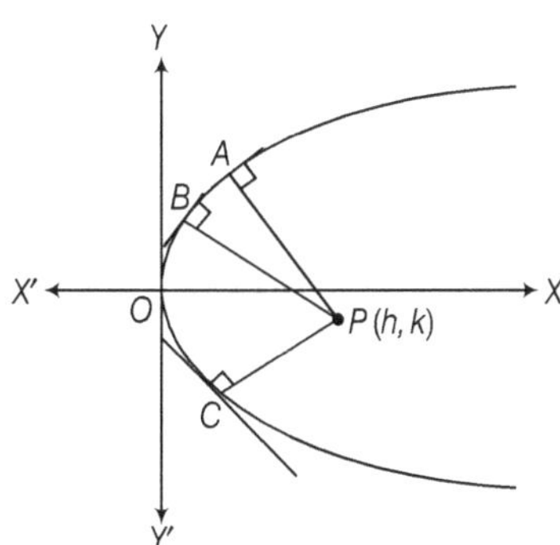

If it passes through (h, k), then

$$k = mh - 2am - am^3$$

$$\Rightarrow am^3 + m(2a - h) + k = 0 \quad \text{...(i)}$$

This is a cubic equation in m, so it has three roots, say m_1, m_2 and m_3.

$$\therefore \quad m_1 + m_2 + m_3 = 0,$$

$$m_1m_2 + m_2m_3 + m_3m_1 = \frac{(2a - h)}{a},$$

$$m_1m_2m_3 = -\frac{k}{a} \quad \text{...(ii)}$$

Hence, for any given point $P(h, k)$, Eq. (i) has three real or imaginary roots. Corresponding to each of these three roots, we have one normal passing through $P(h, k)$. Hence, in total, we have three normals PA, PB and PC drawn through P to the parabola.

Points A, B, C in which the three normals from $P(h, k)$ meet the parabola are **called co-normal points.**

Corollary 1 *The algebraic sum of the slopes of three concurrent normals is zero. This follows from Eq.* (ii).

Corollary 2 *The algebraic sum of ordinates of the feets of three normals drawn to a parabola from a given point is zero.*

Let the ordinates of A, B, C be y_1, y_2, y_3 respectively, then

$$y_1 = -2am_1, y_2 = -2am_2 \text{ and } y_3 = -2am_3$$

$\therefore$ Algebraic sum of these ordinates is

$$y_1 + y_2 + y_3 = -2am_1 - 2am_2 - 2am_3$$
$$= -2a(m_1 + m_2 + m_3)$$
$$= -2a \times 0 \quad \text{[from Eq. (ii)]}$$
$$= 0$$

Corollary 3 *If three normals drawn to any parabola $y^2 = 4ax$ from a given point (h, k) be real then $h > 2a$.*

When normals are real, then all the three roots of Eq. (i) are real and in that case

$$m_1^2 + m_2^2 + m_3^2 > 0 \quad \text{(for any values of } m_1, m_2, m_3)$$

$$\Rightarrow (m_1 + m_2 + m_3)^2 - 2(m_1m_2 + m_2m_3 + m_3m_1) > 0$$

$$\Rightarrow (0)^2 - \frac{2(2a - h)}{a} > 0 \Rightarrow h - 2a > 0$$

$$\therefore \quad h > 2a$$

Remark

For $a = 1$ normals drawn to the parabola $y^2 = 4x$ from any point (h, k) are real, if $h > 2$.

Corollary 4 *If three normals drawn to any parabola $y^2 = 4ax$ from a given point (h, k) be real and distinct, then $27ak^2 < 4(h - 2a)^3$*

Let $\quad f(m) = am^3 + m(2a - h) + k$

$\therefore \quad f'(m) = 3am^2 + (2a - h)$

Two distinct roots of $f'(m) = 0$ are

$$\alpha = \sqrt{\left(\frac{h-2a}{3a}\right)} \quad \text{and} \quad \beta = -\sqrt{\left(\frac{h-2a}{3a}\right)},$$

Now, $\quad f(\alpha)\, f(\beta) < 0 \Rightarrow f(\alpha)\, f(-\alpha) < 0$

$\Rightarrow \quad (a\alpha^3 + \alpha(2a-h) + k)(-a\alpha^3 - \alpha(2a-h) + k) < 0$

$\Rightarrow \quad k^2 - (a\alpha^2 + (2a-h))^2 \alpha^2 < 0$

$\Rightarrow \quad k^2 - \left(\frac{h-2a}{3} + (2a-h)\right)^2 \frac{(h-2a)}{3a} < 0$

$\Rightarrow \quad k^2 - \left(\frac{4a-2h}{3}\right)^2 \left(\frac{h-2a}{3a}\right) < 0$

$\Rightarrow \quad k^2 - \frac{4(h-2a)^3}{27a} < 0 \Rightarrow 27ak^2 - 4(h-2a)^3 < 0$

$\therefore \quad 27ak^2 < 4(h-2a)^3$

Corollary 5 *The centroid of the triangle formed by the feet of the three normals lies on the axis of the parabola.*

If $A(x_1, y_1)$, $B(x_2, y_2)$ and $C(x_3, y_3)$ be vertices of ΔABC, then its centroid is

$$\left(\frac{x_1 + x_2 + x_3}{3}, \frac{y_1 + y_2 + y_3}{3}\right) = \left(\frac{x_1 + x_2 + x_3}{3}, 0\right).$$

Since, $y_1 + y_2 + y_3 = 0$ (from corollary 2). Hence, the centroid lies on the X-axis OX, which is the axis of the parabola also.

Now, $\frac{x_1 + x_2 + x_3}{3} = \frac{1}{3}(am_1^2 + am_2^2 + am_3^2)$

$$= \frac{a}{3}(m_1^2 + m_2^2 + m_3^2)$$

$$= \frac{a}{3}\{(m_1 + m_2 + m_3)^2 - 2(m_1m_2 + m_2m_3 + m_3m_1)\}$$

$$= \frac{a}{3}\left[(0)^2 - 2\left\{\frac{2a-h}{a}\right\}\right] = \frac{2h-4a}{3}$$

$\therefore$ Centroid of ΔABC is $\left(\frac{2h-4a}{3}, 0\right)$.

Example 42 Show that the locus of points such that two of the three normals drawn from them to the parabola $y^2 = 4ax$ coincide is $27ay^2 = 4(x-2a)^3$.

Sol. Let (h, k) be the point of intersection of three normals to the parabola $y^2 = 4ax$. The equation of any normal to $y^2 = 4ax$ is

$$y = mx - 2am - am^3$$

If it passes through (h, k), then

$$k = mh - 2am - am^3$$

$\Rightarrow \quad am^3 + m(2a - h) + k = 0 \quad \text{...(i)}$

Let the roots of Eq. (i) be m_1, m_2 and m_3.

Then, from Eq. (i), $\quad m_1 + m_2 + m_3 = 0 \quad \text{...(ii)}$

$$m_1m_2 + m_2m_3 + m_3m_1 = \frac{(2a-h)}{a} \quad \text{...(iii)}$$

and $\quad m_1m_2m_3 = -\frac{k}{a} \quad \text{...(iv)}$

But here, two of the three normals are given to be coincident i.e. $m_1 = m_2$.

Putting $m_1 = m_2$ in Eqs. (ii) and (iv), we get

$$2m_1 + m_3 = 0 \quad \text{...(v)}$$

and $\quad m_1^2 m_3 = -\frac{k}{a} \quad \text{...(vi)}$

Putting $m_3 = -2m_1$ from Eq. (v) in Eq. (vi), we get

$$-2m_1^3 = -\frac{k}{a}$$

$\Rightarrow \quad m_1^3 = \frac{k}{2a}$

Since, m_1 is a root of Eq. (i).

$\therefore \quad am_1^3 + m_1(2a-h) + k = 0$

$\Rightarrow \quad a\left(\frac{k}{2a}\right) + \left(\frac{k}{2a}\right)^{1/3}(2a-h) + k = 0$

$$\left[\text{putting } m_1 = \left(\frac{k}{2a}\right)^{1/3}\right]$$

$\Rightarrow \quad \left(\frac{k}{2a}\right)^{1/3}(2a-h) = -\frac{3k}{2}$

$\Rightarrow \quad \frac{k}{2a}(2a-h)^3 = -\frac{27k^3}{8}$

$\Rightarrow \quad 27ak^2 = 4(h-2a)^3$

Hence, the locus of (h, k) is

$$27ay^2 = 4(x-2a)^3.$$

Example 43 Find the locus of the point through which pass three normals to the parabola $y^2 = 4ax$ such that two of them make angles α and β respectively with the axis such that $\tan\alpha \tan\beta = 2$.

Sol. Let (h, k) be the point of intersection of three normals to the parabola $y^2 = 4ax$.

The equation of any normal to $y^2 = 4ax$ is

$$y = mx - 2am - am^3$$

If it passes through (h_1, k), then

$$k = mh - 2am - am^3$$

$\Rightarrow \quad am^3 + m(2a-h) + k = 0 \quad \text{...(i)}$

Let roots of Eq. (i) be m_1, m_2, m_3 then from Eq. (i)

$$m_1m_2m_3 = -\frac{k}{a} \quad \text{...(ii)}$$

Also $m_1 = \tan\alpha$, $m_2 = \tan\beta$ and $\tan\alpha \tan\beta = 2$

$$\therefore \quad m_1m_2 = 2 \quad \text{...(iii)}$$

From Eqs. (ii) and (iii), $2m_3 = -\frac{k}{a}$

or $$m_3 = -\frac{k}{2a}$$

Which being a root of Eq. (i) must satisfy it

i.e. $$am_3^3 + m_3(2a - h) + k = 0$$

$$\Rightarrow \quad a\left(-\frac{k}{2a}\right)^3 - \frac{k}{2a}(2a - h) + k = 0$$

$$\Rightarrow \quad -\frac{k^3}{8a^2} - k + \frac{kh}{2a} + k = 0$$

$$\Rightarrow \quad k^2 - 4ah = 0$$

$\therefore$ Required locus of (h, k) is $y^2 - 4ax = 0$.

Example 44 If the three normals from a point to the parabola $y^2 = 4ax$ cut the axis in points whose distance from the vertex are in AP, show that the point lies on the curve $27ay^2 = 2(x - 2a)^3$.

Sol. Let (h, k) be the point of intersection of three normals to the parabola $y^2 = 4ax$. The equation of any normal to $y^2 = 4ax$ is $y = mx - 2am - am^3$ ...(i)

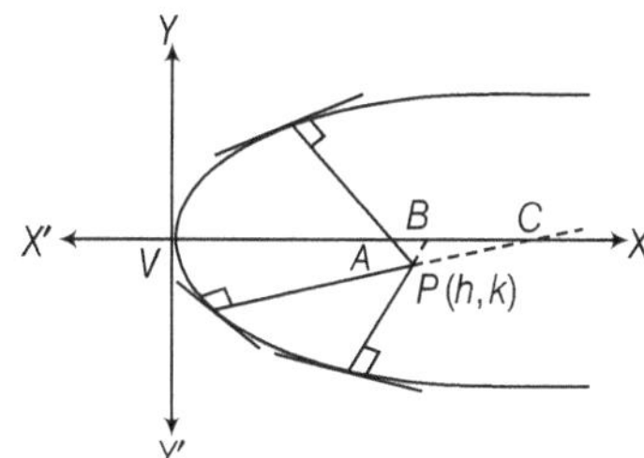

If it passes through (h, k) then

$$k = mh - 2am - am^3$$

$$\Rightarrow \quad am^3 + m(2a - h) + k = 0 \quad \text{...(ii)}$$

Let roots of Eq. (ii) be m_1, m_2, m_3 then from Eq. (ii)

$$m_1 + m_2 + m_3 = 0 \quad \text{...(iii)}$$

$$m_1m_2 + m_2m_3 + m_3m_1 = \frac{(2a - h)}{a} \quad \text{...(iv)}$$

and $$m_1m_2m_3 = -\frac{k}{a} \quad \text{...(v)}$$

Since, Eq. (i) cuts the axis of parabola *viz.* $y = 0$ at $(2a + am^2, 0)$.

$\therefore$ The normal through (h, k) cut the axis at $A\,(2a + am_1^2, 0)$, $B\,(2a + am_2^2, 0)$ and $C\,(2a + am_3^2, 0)$ and let $V\,(0, 0)$ be the vertex of the parabola $y^2 = 4ax$.

Then, $VA = 2a + am_1^2$, $VB = 2a + am_2^2$ and $VC = 2a + am_3^2$.

Given, VA, VB and VC are in AP.

$$\therefore \quad 2VB = VA + VC$$

$$\Rightarrow \quad 4a + 2am_2^2 = 2a + am_1^2 + 2a + am_3^2$$

$$\Rightarrow \quad 2m_2^2 = m_1^2 + m_3^2$$

$$\Rightarrow \quad 2m_2^2 = (m_1 + m_3)^2 - 2m_1m_3$$

$$\Rightarrow \quad 2m_2^2 = (m_1 + m_2 + m_3 - m_2)^2 - \frac{2m_1m_2m_3}{m_2}$$

$$\Rightarrow \quad 2m_2^2 = (0 - m_2)^2 - \frac{2}{m_2}\left(-\frac{k}{a}\right)$$

[from Eqs. (iii) and (v)]

$$\Rightarrow \quad m_2^3 = \frac{2k}{a} \quad \text{...(vi)}$$

Now, from Eq. (iv), $m_2(m_1 + m_3) + m_3m_1 = \frac{(2a - h)}{a}$

$$\Rightarrow m_2(m_1 + m_2 + m_3 - m_2) + \frac{m_1m_2m_3}{m_2} = \frac{(2a - h)}{a}$$

$$\Rightarrow \quad m_2(0 - m_2) - \frac{k}{am_2} = \frac{(2a - h)}{a}$$

$$\Rightarrow \quad -am_2^3 - k = m_2(2a - h)$$

$$\Rightarrow \quad (-am_2^3 - k)^3 = m_2^3(2a - h)^3$$

$$\Rightarrow \quad (-2k - k)^3 = \frac{2k}{a}(2a - h)^3 \quad \text{[from Eq. (vi)]}$$

$$\Rightarrow \quad -27k^3 = -\frac{2k}{a}(h - 2a)^3$$

$$\Rightarrow \quad 27ak^2 = 2(h - 2a)^3$$

Hence, locus of (h, k) is

$$27ay^2 = 2(x - 2a)^3.$$

Example 45 The normals at P, Q, R on the parabola $y^2 = 4ax$ meet in a point on the line $y = k$. Prove that the sides of the ΔPQR touch the parabola $x^2 - 2ky = 0$.

Sol. Any normal to the parabola $y^2 = 4ax$ is

$$y = mx - 2am - am^3 \quad \text{...(i)}$$

Also, any point on the line $y = k$ is (x_1, k).

If Eq. (i) passes through (x_1, k) then $k = mx_1 - 2am - am^3$

or $$am^3 + m(2a - x_1) + k = 0$$

If the roots of this equation are m_1, m_2, m_3 then we get

$$m_1 + m_2 + m_3 = 0 \quad \text{...(ii)}$$

$$m_1m_2 + m_2m_3 + m_3m_1 = \frac{(2a - x_1)}{a} \quad \text{...(iii)}$$

and $$m_1m_2m_3 = -\frac{k}{a} \quad \text{...(iv)}$$

Also, coordinates of three points P, Q and R are $(am_1^2, -2am_1)(am_2^2, -2am_2)$ and $(am_3^2, -2am_3)$, respectively.

$\therefore$ The equation of the line PQ is

$$y-(-2am_1)=\frac{(-2am_2)-(-2am_1)}{am_2^2-am_1^2}(x-am_1^2)$$

$$\Rightarrow \quad y+2am_1=-\frac{2}{(m_2+m_1)}(x-am_1^2)$$

$$\Rightarrow \quad y(m_1+m_2)+2am_1(m_1+m_2)=-2x+2am_1^2$$

$$\Rightarrow \quad y(m_1+m_2)+2am_1m_2=-2x$$

$$\Rightarrow \quad y(m_1+m_2+m_3-m_3)+\frac{2am_1m_2m_3}{m_3}=-2x$$

$$\Rightarrow \quad y(0-m_3)-\frac{2k}{m_3}=-2x \qquad \text{[from Eqs. (ii) and (iv)]}$$

$$\Rightarrow \quad -ym_3^2-2k=-2m_3x$$

$$\Rightarrow \quad ym_3^2-2m_3x+2k=0,$$

which is a quadratic in m_3.

Since, PQ will touch it, then

$$B^2-4AC=0$$

$$\Rightarrow \quad (-2x)^2-4\cdot y\cdot 2k=0$$

$$\therefore \quad x^2-2ky=0$$

Example 46 Find the point on the axis of the parabola $3y^2+4y-6x+8=0$ from when three distinct normals can be drawn.

Sol. Given, parabola is $3y^2+4y-6x+8=0$

$$\Rightarrow \quad 3\left(y^2+\frac{4}{3}y\right)=6x-8$$

$$\Rightarrow \quad 3\left\{\left(y+\frac{2}{3}\right)^2-\frac{4}{9}\right\}=6x-8$$

$$\Rightarrow \quad 3\left(y+\frac{2}{3}\right)^2=\left(6x-8+\frac{4}{3}\right)$$

$$\therefore \quad \left(y+\frac{2}{3}\right)^2=2\left(x-\frac{10}{9}\right)$$

Let $\quad y+\frac{2}{3}=Y,\ x-\frac{10}{9}=X$

Then, $\quad Y^2=2X$

Comparing with $\quad Y^2=4aX$

$$\therefore \quad a=\frac{1}{2}$$

any point on the axis of parabola is $\left(x, -\frac{2}{3}\right)$

and $\quad X>2a \Rightarrow x-\frac{10}{9}>1$

$$\Rightarrow \quad x>\frac{19}{9}$$

Circle Through Co-normal Points

To find the equation of the circle passing through the three (conormal) points on the parabola, normals at which pass through a given point (α, β).

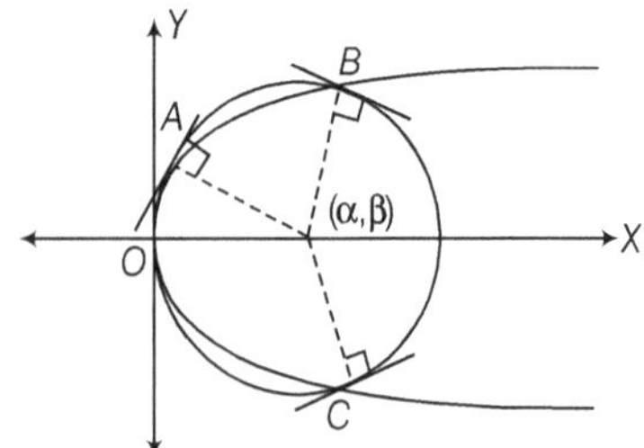

Let $A(am_1^2, -2am_1)$, $B(am_2^2, -2am_2)$ and $C(am_3^2, -2am_3)$ be the three points on the parabola

$$y^2=4ax$$

Since, point of intersection of normals is (α, β), then

$$am^3+(2a-\alpha)m+\beta=0 \qquad \text{...(E)}$$

$$\therefore \quad m_1+m_2+m_3=0 \qquad \text{...(i)}$$

$$m_1m_2+m_2m_3+m_3m_1=\frac{(2a-\alpha)}{a} \qquad \text{... (ii)}$$

and $$m_1m_2m_3=-\frac{\beta}{a} \qquad \text{...(iii)}$$

Let the equation of the circle through A, B, C be

$$x^2+y^2+2gx+2fy+c=0 \qquad \text{...(iv)}$$

If the point $(am^2, -2am)$ lies on it, then

$$(am^2)^2+(-2am)^2+2g(am^2)+2f(-2am)+c=0$$

$$\Rightarrow \quad a^2m^4+(4a^2+2ag)m^2-4afm+c=0 \qquad \text{...(v)}$$

This is a biquadratic equation in m. Hence, there are four values of m, say m_1, m_2, m_3 and m_4 such that the circle pass through the points.

$A(am_1^2, -2am_1), B(am_2^2, -2am_2), C(am_3^2, -2am_3)$ and $D(am_4^2, -2am_4)$.

$$\therefore \quad m_1+m_2+m_3+m_4=0 \qquad \text{...(F)}$$

$$\Rightarrow \quad 0+m_4=0 \qquad \text{[from Eq. (i)]}$$

$$\Rightarrow \quad m_4=0$$

$$\therefore \quad (am_4^2, -2am_4)=(0,0)$$

Thus, the circle passes through the vertex of the parabola $y^2=4ax$ from Eq. (iv),

$$0+0+0+0+c=0$$

$$\therefore \quad c=0$$

From Eq. (v), $a^2m^4+(4a^2+2ag)m^2-4afm=0$

$$\Rightarrow \quad am^3+(4a+2g)m-4f=0 \qquad \text{...(vi)}$$

Now, Eqs. (E) and (vi) are identical.

$$\therefore \quad 1 = \frac{4a + 2g}{2a - \alpha} = -\frac{4f}{\beta}$$

$$\therefore \quad 2g = -(2a + \alpha), 2f = -\beta/2$$

$\therefore$ The equation of the required circle is

$$x^2 + y^2 - (2a + \alpha)x - \frac{\beta}{2}y = 0$$

[from Eq. (iv)]

Corollary 1. *The algebraic sum of the ordinates of the four points of intersection of a circle and a parabola is zero.*

Sum of ordinates

$$= -2am_1 - 2am_2 - 2am_3 - 2am_4$$
$$= -2a(m_1 + m_2 + m_3 + m_4) \quad \text{[from Eq. (F)]}$$
$$= -2a \times 0 = 0$$

Corollary 2. *The common chords of a circle and a parabola are in pairs equally inclined to the axis of the parabola.*

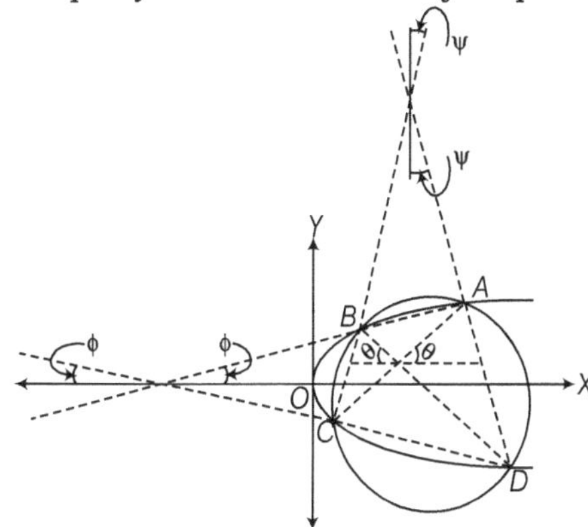

Let A, B, C, D be the points of intersection of the circle and the parabola with $A(am_1^2, -2am_1)$, $B(am_2^2, -2am_2)$ $C(am_3^2, -2am_3)$ and $D(am_4^2, -2am_4)$ then equation of AC and BD are

$$y(m_1 + m_3) = -2x - 2am_1m_3$$

and $\quad y(m_2 + m_4) = -2x - 2am_2m_4$, respectively.

$\therefore$ Slopes of the chords AC and BD are

$$-\frac{2}{m_1 + m_3} \text{ and } -\frac{2}{m_2 + m_4}, \text{ respectively.}$$

$$\therefore \quad \text{Slope of } AC = -\frac{2}{m_1 + m_3}$$
$$= \frac{2}{m_2 + m_4} \quad [\because m_1 + m_2 + m_3 + m_4 = 0]$$
$$= -\left(-\frac{2}{m_2 + m_4}\right) = -\text{ Slope of } BD$$

$\therefore$ Their slopes are equal in magnitude and opposite in sign.

$\therefore$ The chords of AC and BD are equally inclined to the axis.

Remark

This is likewise true for the pairs of chords AB, CD and AD, BC.

Corollary 3. *The circle through conormal point passes through the vertex $(0, 0)$ of the parabola.*

Corollary 4. *The centroid of four points; in which a circle intersects a parabola, lies on the axis of the parabola.*

$$\text{Centroid} = \left(\frac{\sum_{i=1}^{4} am_i^2}{4}, \frac{\sum_{i=1}^{4}(-2am_i)}{4}\right)$$

$$= \left(\frac{a}{4}\{(\Sigma m_1)^2 - 2\Sigma m_1m_2\}, -\frac{a}{2}(\Sigma m_1)\right)$$

$$= \left(\frac{a}{4}\left(0 - \frac{2(4a^2 + 2ag)}{a^2}\right), 0\right)$$

$$= (-2a - g, 0)$$

Here $y = 0$, which is axis of the parabola $y^2 = 4ax$.

Example 47 A circle cuts the parabola $y^2 = 4ax$ at right angles and passes through the focus, show that its centre lies on the curve $y^2(a + 2x) = a(a + 3x)^2$.

Sol. Let the circle $x^2 + y^2 + 2gx + 2fy + c = 0$ ...(i)

meet the parabola $y^2 = 4ax$ at any point $P(at^2, 2at)$ cutting it at right angles.

We have to find locus of centre of circle Eq. (i),

i.e. $\quad (-g, -f)$

But given circle Eq. (i) passes through the focus $(a, 0)$, then

$$a^2 + 0 + 2ga + 0 + c = 0$$

$$\Rightarrow \quad c = -a^2 - 2ag \quad \text{...(ii)}$$

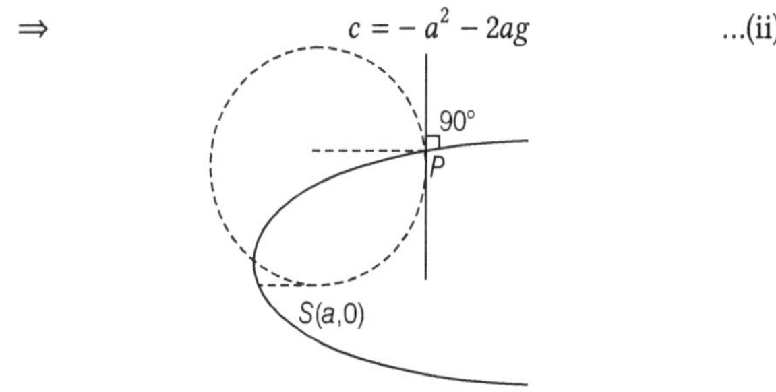

Now, the circle and parabola intersect at $P(at^2, 2at)$ at right angles.

Since, tangent at $P(at^2, 2at)$ to the parabola $y^2 = 4ax$ is

$$ty = x + at^2$$

Hence, this tangent must pass through the centre $(-g, -f)$ of the circle

$$\therefore \quad -ft = -g + at^2$$

$$\Rightarrow \quad ft = g - at^2 \quad \text{...(iii)}$$

Also the point $P(at^2, 2at)$ lies on the circle (i), then

$$a^2t^4 + 4a^2t^2 + 2agt^2 + 4aft + c = 0$$

Hence, from Eqs. (ii) and (iii) when we put values for c and ft.

$$\therefore \quad a^2t^4 + 4a^2t^2 + 2agt^2 + 4ag - 4a^2t^2 - a^2 - 2ag = 0$$

$$\Rightarrow \quad a^2t^4 + 2agt^2 + 2ag - a^2 = 0$$

$$\Rightarrow \quad at^4 + 2gt^2 + 2g - a = 0$$

$$\Rightarrow \quad a(t^4 - 1) + 2g(t^2 + 1) = 0$$

$$\Rightarrow \quad (t^2 + 1)[a(t^2 - 1) + 2g] = 0 \quad \text{But } t^2 + 1 \neq 0$$

$$\Rightarrow \quad a(t^2 - 1) + 2g = 0 \Rightarrow t^2 = \frac{a - 2g}{a}$$

Hence, from Eq. (iii),

$$f\sqrt{\left(\frac{a-2g}{a}\right)} = g - a\left(\frac{a-2g}{a}\right)$$

$$\Rightarrow \quad f\sqrt{\left(\frac{a-2g}{a}\right)} = (3g - a)$$

$$\Rightarrow \quad f^2(a - 2g) = a(3g - a)^2$$

$$\Rightarrow \quad (-f)^2[a + 2(-g)] = a(a - 3g)^2$$

$$\Rightarrow \quad (-f)^2[a + 2(-g)] = a[a + 3(-g)]^2$$

Hence, locus of the centre $(-g, -f)$ is the curve

$$y^2(a + 2x) = a(a + 3x)^2.$$

Exercise for Session 2

1. If $2x + y + \lambda = 0$ is a normal to the parabola $y^2 = -8x$, then the value of λ is

(a) -24 (b) -16 (c) -8 (d) 24

2. The slope of a chord of the parabola $y^2 = 4ax$ which is normal at one end and which subtends a right angle at the origin is

(a) $\frac{1}{\sqrt{2}}$ (b) $\sqrt{2}$ (c) $-\frac{1}{\sqrt{2}}$ (d) $-\sqrt{2}$

3. The common tangent to the parabola $y^2 = 4ax$ and $x^2 = 4ay$ is

(a) $x + y + a = 0$ (b) $x + y - a = 0$ (c) $x - y + a = 0$ (d) $x - y - a = 0$

4. The circle $x^2 + y^2 + 4\lambda x = 0$ which $\lambda \in R$ touches the parabola $y^2 = 8x$. The value of λ is given by

(a) $\lambda \in (0, \infty)$ (b) $\lambda \in (-\infty, 0)$ (c) $\lambda \in (1 \infty)$ (d) $\lambda \in (-\infty, 1)$

5. If the normals at two points P and Q of a parabola $y^2 = 4ax$ intersect at a third point R on the curve, then the product of ordinates of P and Q is

(a) $4a^2$ (b) $2a^2$ (c) $-4a^2$ (d) $8a^2$

6. The normals at three points P, Q, R of the parabola $y^2 = 4ax$ meet in (h, k). The centroid of ΔPQR lies on

(a) $x = 0$ (b) $y = 0$ (c) $x = -a$ (d) $y = a$

7. The set of points on the axis of the parabola $y^2 - 4x - 2y + 5 = 0$ from which all the three normals to the parabola are real, is

(a) $(\lambda, 0); \lambda > 1$ (b) $(\lambda, 1); \lambda > 3$ (c) $(\lambda, 2); \lambda > 6$ (d) $(\lambda, 3); \lambda > 8$

8. Prove that any three tangents to a parabola whose slopes are in harmonic progression enclose a triangle of constant area.

9. A chord of parabola $y^2 = 4ax$ subtends a right angle at the vertex. Find the locus of the point of intersection of tangents at its extremities.

10. Find the equation of the normal to the parabola $y^2 = 4x$ which is

(a) parallel to the line $y = 2x - 5$. (b) perpendicular to the line $2x + 6y + 5 = 0$.

11. The ordinates of points P and Q on the parabola $y^2 = 12x$ are in the ratio 1 : 2. Find the locus of the point of intersection of the normals to the parabola at P and Q.

12. The normals at P, Q, R on the parabola $y^2 = 4ax$ meet in a point on the line $y = c$. Prove that the sides of the ΔPQR touch the parabola $x^2 = 2cy$.

13. The normals are drawn from $(2\lambda, 0)$ to the parabola $y^2 = 4x$. Show that λ must be greater than 1. One normal is always the X-axis. Find λ for which the other two normals are perpendicular to each other.

Session 3

Pair of Tangents $SS_1 = T^2$, Chord of Contact, Equation of the Chord Bisected at a Given Point, Diameter, Lengths of Tangent, Subtangent, Normal and Subnormal, Some Standard Properties of the Parabola, Reflection Property of a Parabola, Study of Parabola of the Form $(\alpha x^2 + \beta y)^2 + 2gx + 2fy + c = 0$

Pair of Tangents $SS_1 = T^2$

If $y_1^2 - 4ax_1 > 0$, then any point $P(x_1, y_1)$ lies outside the parabola and a pair of tangents PQ, PR can be drawn to it from P. We find their equation as follows.

Let $T(h, k)$ be any point on the pair of tangents PQ or PR drawn from any external point $P(x_1, y_1)$ to the parabola $y^2 = 4ax$.

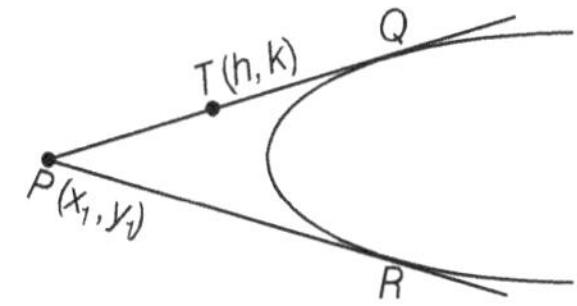

Equation of PT is

$$y - y_1 = \frac{k - y_1}{h - x_1}(x - x_1)$$

$$\Rightarrow \quad y = \left(\frac{k - y_1}{h - x_1}\right)x + \left(\frac{hy_1 - kx_1}{h - x_1}\right)$$

which is tangent to the parabola

$$y^2 = 4ax$$

$$\therefore \quad c = \frac{a}{m}$$

$$\Rightarrow \quad cm = a \quad \Rightarrow \quad \left(\frac{hy_1 - kx_1}{h - x_1}\right)\left(\frac{k - y_1}{h - x_1}\right) = a$$

$$\Rightarrow \quad (k - y_1)(hy_1 - kx_1) = a(h - x_1)^2$$

$\therefore$ Locus of (h, k), equation of pair of tangents is

$$(y - y_1)(xy_1 - x_1y) = a(x - x_1)^2$$

$$\Rightarrow (y^2 - 4ax)(y_1^2 - 4ax_1) = \{yy_1 - 2a(x + x_1)\}^2$$

$$\therefore \quad SS_1 = T^2$$

where $\quad S = y^2 - 4ax, S_1 = y_1^2 - 4ax_1$

and $\quad T = yy_1 - 2a(x + x_1)$.

Aliter :

Let the parabola be $y^2 = 4ax$ ...(i)

Let $P(x_1, y_1)$ be any point outside the parabola. Let a chord of the parabola through the point $P(x_1, y_1)$ cut the parabola at Q and let $R(h, k)$ be any arbitrary point on the line PQ (R inside or outside).

Let Q divide PR in the ratio $\lambda : 1$, then coordinates of Q are

$$\left(\frac{\lambda h + x_1}{\lambda + 1}, \frac{\lambda k + y_1}{\lambda + 1}\right) \qquad [\because PQ : QR = \lambda : 1]$$

Since, Q lies on parabola Eq. (i), then

$$\left(\frac{\lambda k + y_1}{\lambda + 1}\right)^2 = 4a\left(\frac{\lambda h + x_1}{\lambda + 1}\right)$$

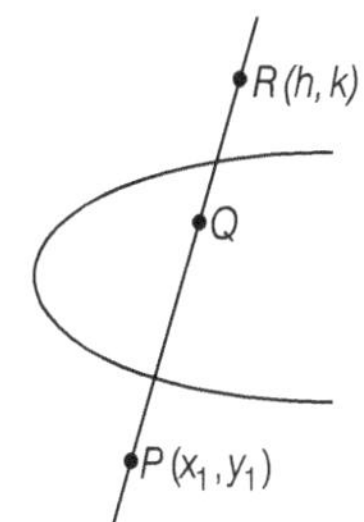

$$\Rightarrow \quad (\lambda k + y_1)^2 - 4a(\lambda h + x_1)(\lambda + 1) = 0$$

$$\Rightarrow \quad (k^2 - 4ah)\lambda^2 + 2[ky_1 - 2a(h + x_1)]\lambda + (y_1^2 - 4ax_1) = 0 \quad \text{...(ii)}$$

Line PR will become tangent to parabola Eq. (i), then roots of Eq. (ii) are equal

$$\therefore \quad 4[ky_1 - 2a(h + x_1)]^2 - 4(k^2 - 4ah)(y_1^2 - 4ax_1) = 0$$

or $\quad \{ky_1 - 2a(h + x_1)\}^2 = (k^2 - 4ah)(y_1^2 - 4ax_1)$

Hence, locus of $R(h, k)$ i.e. equation of pair of tangents from $P(x_1, y_1)$ is

$$\{yy_1 - 2a(x + x_1)\}^2 = (y^2 - 4ax)(y_1^2 - 4ax_1)$$

i.e. $\quad T^2 = SS_1 \quad$ or $\quad SS_1 = T^2$

Remark

$S = 0$ is the equation of the curve, S_1 is obtained from S by replacing x by x_1 and y by y_1 and $T = 0$ is the equation tangent at (x_1, y_1) to $S = 0$.

Chord of Contact

The chord joining the points of contact of two tangents drawn from an external point to a parabola is known as the chord of contact of tangents drawn from external point.

Theorem The chord of contact of tangents drawn from a point (x_1, y_1) to the parabola $y^2 = 4ax$ is

$$yy_1 = 2a(x + x_1).$$

Proof Let PQ and PR be tangents to the parabola $y^2 = 4ax$ drawn from any external point $P(x_1, y_1)$, then QR is called **chord of contact** of the parabola $y^2 = 4ax$.

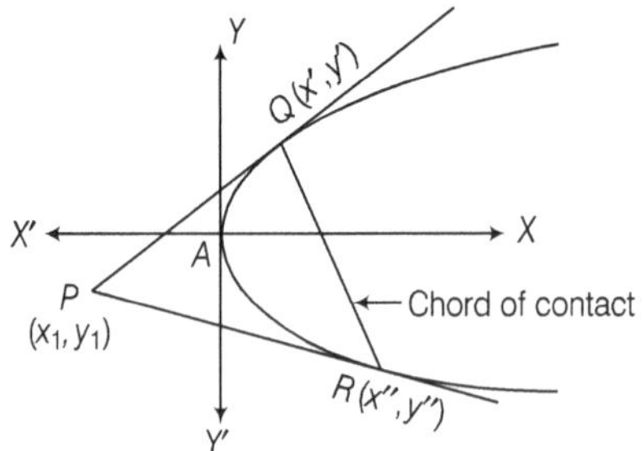

Let $\quad Q \equiv (x', y')$ and $R \equiv (x'', y'')$

Equation of tangent PQ is

$$yy' = 2a(x + x') \quad \text{...(i)}$$

and equation of tangent PR is

$$yy'' = 2a(x + x'') \quad \text{...(ii)}$$

Since, lines Eqs. (i) and (ii) pass through (x_1, y_1), then

$$y_1y' = 2a(x_1 + x') \text{ and } y_1y'' = 2a(x_1 + x'')$$

Hence, it is clear $Q(x', y')$ and $R(x'', y'')$ lie on

$$yy_1 = 2a(x + x_1)$$

which is **chord of contact** QR.

Example 48 Tangents are drawn from the point (x_1, y_1) to the parabola $y^2 = 4ax$, show that the length of their chord of contact is $\dfrac{1}{|a|}\sqrt{(y_1^2 - 4ax_1)(y_1^2 + 4a^2)}$.

Sol. Given parabola is

$$y^2 = 4ax \quad \text{...(i)}$$

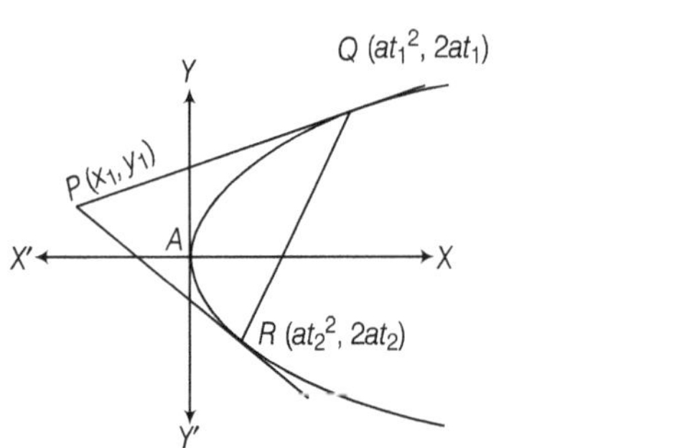

Let $\quad P \equiv (x_1, y_1)$

and the tangents from P touch the parabola at $Q(at_1^2, 2at_1)$ and $R(at_2^2, 2at_2)$ then P is the point of intersection of tangents.

$\therefore \quad x_1 = at_1t_2$ and $y_1 = a(t_1 + t_2)$

$\Rightarrow \quad t_1t_2 = \dfrac{x_1}{a}$ and $t_1 + t_2 = \dfrac{y_1}{a}$ ...(ii)

Now, $\quad QR = \sqrt{(at_1^2 - at_2^2)^2 + (2at_1 - 2at_2)^2}$

$$= \sqrt{a^2(t_1 - t_2)^2 [(t_1 + t_2)^2 + 4]}$$

$$= |a||t_1 - t_2|\sqrt{\{(t_1 + t_2)^2 + 4\}}$$

$$= |a|\sqrt{\{(t_1 + t_2)^2 - 4t_1t_2\}}\sqrt{\{(t_1 + t_2)^2 + 4\}}$$

$$= |a|\sqrt{\left(\frac{y_1^2}{a^2} - \frac{4x_1}{a}\right)} \cdot \sqrt{\left(\frac{y_1^2}{a^2} + 4\right)}$$

[from Eq. (ii)]

$$= |a|\frac{\sqrt{(y_1^2 - 4ax_1)}}{|a|} \cdot \frac{\sqrt{(y_1^2 + 4a^2)}}{|a|}$$

$$= \frac{1}{|a|}\sqrt{(y_1^2 - 4ax_1)(y_1^2 + 4a^2)}$$

Aliter :

Equation of QR is $\quad yy_1 = 2a(x + x_1)$

$$\Rightarrow \quad x = \frac{yy_1 - 2ax_1}{2a}$$

The ordinates of Q and R are the roots of the equation

$$y^2 = 4a\left(\frac{yy_1 - 2ax_1}{2a}\right)$$

$$\Rightarrow \quad y^2 = 2(yy_1 - 2ax_1) \quad \text{... (i)}$$

$$\Rightarrow \quad y^2 - 2yy_1 + 4ax_1 = 0$$

$\therefore \quad k_1 + k_2 = 2y_1$ and $k_1k = 4ax_1$

$\therefore \quad (k_2 - k_1) = \sqrt{(k_1 + k_2)^2 - 4k_1k_2}$

$$= \sqrt{(4y_1^2 - 16ax_1)} = 2\sqrt{(y_1^2 - 4ax_1)} \quad \text{...(ii)}$$

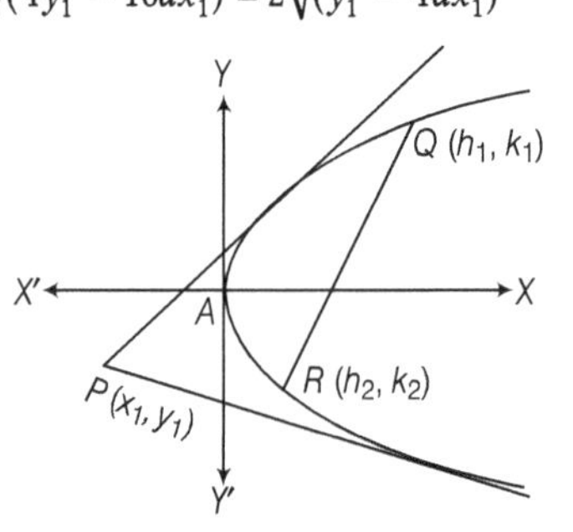

Since, $Q(h_1, k_1)$ and $R(h_2, k_2)$ lie on the parabola $y^2 = 4ax$, therefore

$$k_1^2 = 4ah_1 \text{ and } k_2^2 = 4ah_2$$

$$\Rightarrow \quad k_2^2 - k_1^2 = 4a(h_2 - h_1)$$

$$(k_2 + k_1)(k_2 - k_1) = 4a(h_2 - h_1)$$

$$\Rightarrow \quad 2y_1(k_2 - k_1) = 4a(h_2 - h_1)$$

$$\Rightarrow \quad (h_2 - h_1) = \frac{y_1(k_2 - k_1)}{2a} \quad \text{...(iii)}$$

Now, $QR = \sqrt{(k_2 - k_1)^2 + (h_2 - h_1)^2}$

$$= \sqrt{(k_2 - k_1)^2 + \frac{y_1^2(k_2 - k_1)^2}{4a^2}} \quad \text{[from Eq. (iii)]}$$

$$= \frac{(k_2 - k_1)}{2|a|}\sqrt{(y_1^2 + 4a^2)}$$

$$= \frac{2\sqrt{(y_1^2 - 4ax_1)}}{2|a|}\sqrt{(y_1^2 + 4a^2)} \quad \text{[from Eq. (ii)]}$$

$$= \frac{1}{|a|}\sqrt{(y_1^2 - 4ax_1)(y_1^2 + 4a^2)}$$

Example 49 Prove that the area of the triangle formed by the tangents drawn from (x_1, y_1) to $y^2 = 4ax$ and their chord of contact is $(y_1^2 - 4ax_1)^{3/2}/2a$.

Sol. Equation of QR (chord of contact) is

$$yy_1 = 2a(x + x_1)$$

$$\Rightarrow \quad yy_1 - 2a(x + x_1) = 0$$

$\because$ PM = Length of perpendicular from $P(x_1, y_1)$ on QR

$$= \frac{|y_1y_1 - 2a(x_1 + x_1)|}{\sqrt{(y_1^2 + 4a^2)}} = \frac{|(y_1^2 - 4ax_1)|}{\sqrt{(y_1^2 + 4a^2)}}$$

[Since, $P(x_1, y_1)$ lies outside the parabola. So, $y_1^2 - 4ax_1 > 0$]

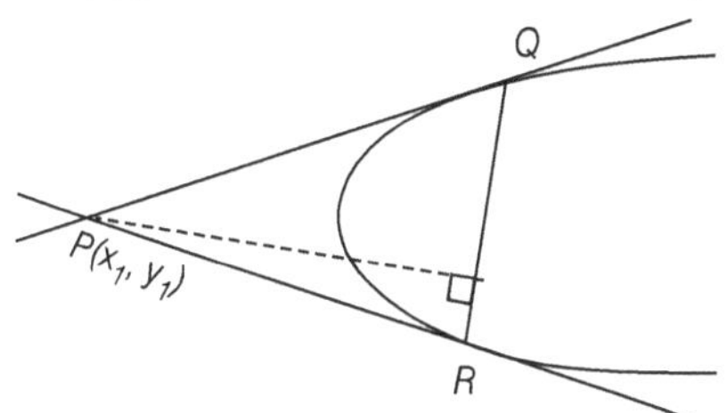

Now, area of $\Delta PQR = \frac{1}{2} QR \cdot PM$

$$= \frac{1}{2}\frac{1}{|a|}\sqrt{(y_1^2 - 4ax_1)(y_1^2 + 4a^2)}\,\frac{(y_1^2 - 4ax_1)}{\sqrt{(y_1^2 + 4a^2)}}$$

$$= (y_1^2 - 4ax_1)^{3/2}/2a, \text{ if } a > 0$$

Equation of the Chord Bisected at a Given Point

Theorem The equation of the chord of the parabola $y^2 = 4ax$ which is bisected at (x_1, y_1) is

$$yy_1 - 2a(x + x_1) = y_1^2 - 4ax_1$$

or $$T = S_1,$$

where, $T = yy_1 - 2a(x + x_1)$ and $S_1 = y_1^2 - 4ax_1$.

Proof Since, equation of the parabola is

$$y^2 = 4ax \quad \text{...(i)}$$

Let QR be the chord of the parabola whose mid-point is $P(x_1, y_1)$.

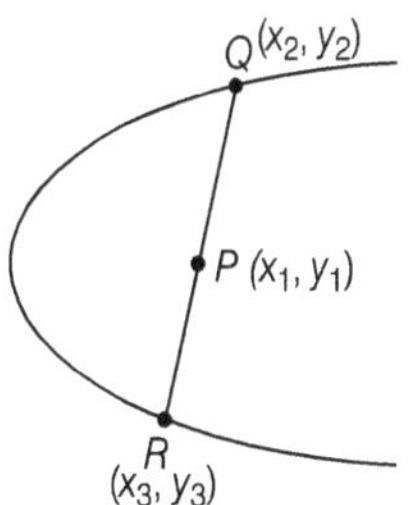

Since, Q and R lie on parabola (i),

$$y_2^2 = 4ax_2 \text{ and } y_3^2 = 4ax_3$$

$$\therefore \quad y_3^2 - y_2^2 = 4a(x_3 - x_2)$$

$$\Rightarrow \quad \frac{y_3 - y_2}{x_3 - x_2} = \frac{4a}{y_3 + y_2}$$

$$= \frac{4a}{2y_1} \quad [\because P(x_1, y_1) \text{ is mid-point of } QR]$$

$$\therefore \quad \frac{y_3 - y_2}{x_3 - x_2} = \frac{2a}{y_1} = \text{Slope of } QR$$

Equation of QR is $y - y_1 = \frac{2a}{y_1}(x - x_1)$

$$\Rightarrow \quad yy_1 - y_1^2 = 2ax - 2ax_1$$

$$\Rightarrow \quad yy_1 - 2a(x + x_1) = y_1^2 - 4ax_1$$

[subtracting $2ax_1$ from both sides]

$$\therefore \quad T = S_1,$$

where $T = yy_1 - 2a(x + x_1)$ and $S_1 = y_1^2 - 4ax_1$.

Example 50 Find the locus of the mid-points of the chords of the parabola $y^2 = 4ax$ which subtend a right angle at the vertex of the parabola.

Sol. Let $P(h, k)$ be the mid-point of a chord QR of the parabola $y^2 = 4ax$ then equation of chord QR is

$$T = S_1$$

or $$yk - 2a(x + h) = k^2 - 4ah$$

$$\Rightarrow \quad yk - 2ax = k^2 - 2ah \quad \text{...(i)}$$

If A is the vertex of the parabola. For combined equation of AQ and AR making homogeneous of $y^2 = 4ax$ with the help of Eq. (i).

$$\therefore \quad y^2 = 4ax$$

$$\Rightarrow \quad y^2 = 4ax\left(\frac{yk - 2ax}{k^2 - 2ah}\right)$$

$$\Rightarrow \quad y^2(k^2 - 2ah) - 4akxy + 8a^2x^2 = 0$$

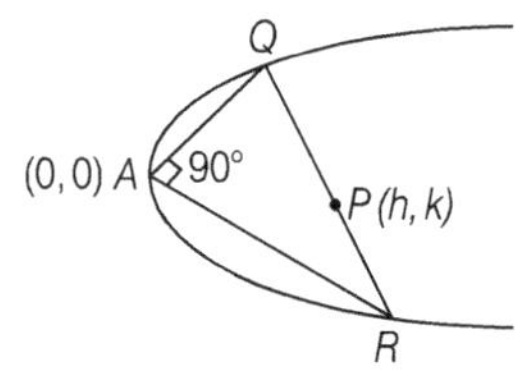

Since, $\angle QAR = 90^\circ$

$\therefore$ Coefficient of x^2 + Coefficient of $y^2 = 0$

$$k^2 - 2ah + 8a^2 = 0$$

Hence, the locus of $P(h, k)$ is $y^2 - 2ax + 8a^2 = 0$.

Example 51 Show that the locus of the middle points of normal chords of the parabola $y^2 = 4ax$ is

$$y^4 - 2a(x - 2a)y^2 + 8a^4 = 0.$$

Sol. Equation of the normal chord at any point $(at^2, 2at)$ of the parabola $y^2 = 4ax$ is

$$y + tx = 2at + at^3 \quad \text{...(i)}$$

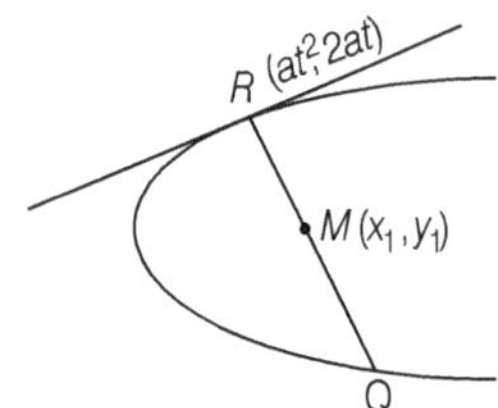

But if $M(x_1, y_1)$ be its middle point its equation must be also

$$T = S_1$$

$$\Rightarrow \quad yy_1 - 2a(x + x_1) = y_1^2 - 4ax_1$$

$$\Rightarrow \quad yy_1 - 2ax = y_1^2 - 2ax_1 \quad \text{...(ii)}$$

$\because$ From Eqs. (i) and (ii) are identical, comparing, them

$$\frac{1}{y_1} = \frac{t}{-2a} = \frac{2at + at^3}{y_1^2 - 2ax_1}$$

From first two relations, $t = -\dfrac{2a}{y_1}$ ...(iii)

From last two relations, $\dfrac{t}{-2a} = \dfrac{2at + at^3}{y_1^2 - 2ax_1}$

$$\Rightarrow \quad \frac{y_1^2 - 2ax_1}{-2a} = 2a + at^2$$

$$\Rightarrow \quad \frac{y_1^2 - 2ax_1}{-2a} = 2a + a\left(\frac{-2a}{y_1}\right)^2 \quad \text{[from Eq. (iii)]}$$

$$\Rightarrow \quad \frac{y_1^2 - 2ax_1}{-2a} = \frac{2ay_1^2 + 4a^3}{y_1^2}$$

$$\Rightarrow \quad y_1^4 - 2ax_1y_1^2 = -4a^2y_1^2 - 8a^4$$

$$\Rightarrow \quad y_1^4 - 2a(x_1 - 2a)y_1^2 + 8a^4 = 0$$

Hence, the locus of middle point (x_1, y_1) is

$$y^4 - 2a(x - 2a)y^2 + 8a^4 = 0.$$

Diameter

The locus of the middle points of a system of parallel chords is called a diameter and in case of a parabola this diameter is shown to be a straight line which is parallel to the axis of the parabola.

Theorem The equation of the diameter bisecting chords of slope m of the parabola $y^2 = 4ax$ is $y = \dfrac{2a}{m}$.

Proof Let $y = mx + c$ be system of parallel chords to $y^2 = 4ax$ for different chords c varies, m remains constant.

Let the extremities of any chord PQ of the set be $P(x_1, y_1)$ and $Q(x_2, y_2)$ and let its middle point be $M(h, k)$.

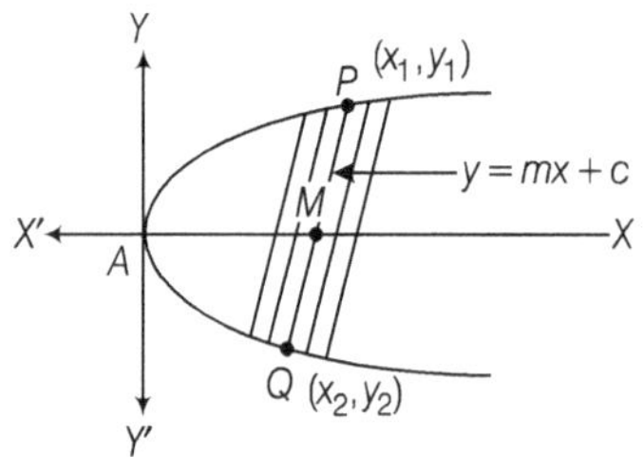

On solving equations

$$y^2 = 4ax \quad \text{and} \quad y = mx + c.$$

$$\therefore \quad y^2 = 4a\left(\frac{y - c}{m}\right)$$

$$\therefore \quad my^2 - 4ay + 4ac = 0$$

$$\therefore \quad y_1 + y_2 = \frac{4a}{m} \quad \text{or} \quad \frac{y_1 + y_2}{2} = \frac{2a}{m}$$

[$\because (h, k)$ is the mid-point of PQ]

Hence, locus of $M(h, k)$ is $y = \dfrac{2a}{m}$.

Aliter :

Let (h, k) be the middle point of the chord $y = mx + c$ of the parabola $y^2 = 4ax$ then

$$T = S_1 \Rightarrow ky - 2a(x + h) = k^2 - 4ah$$

$$\text{slope} = \frac{2a}{k} = m \Rightarrow k = \frac{2a}{m}$$

Hence, locus of the mid-point is $y = \dfrac{2a}{m}$.

Remarks

1. The point in which any diameter meets the curve is called the extremity of the diameter.
2. Any line which is parallel to the axis of the parabola drawn through any point on the parabola is called diameter and its equation is y-coordinate of that point.

   If point on diameter (x_1, y_1), then diameter is $y = y_1$.

Corollary 1. *The tangent at the extremity of a diameter of a parabola is parallel to the system of chords it bisects.*

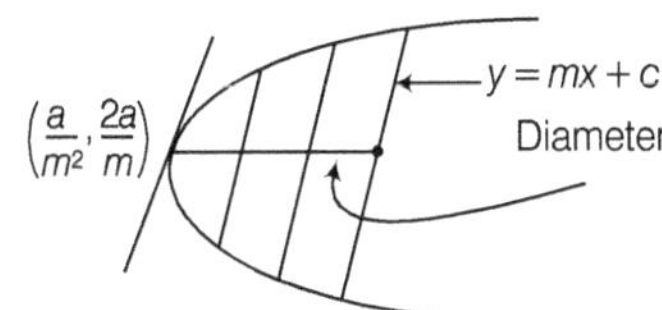

Let $y = mx + c$ (c variable) represents the system of parallel chords, then the equation of diameter of $y^2 = 4ax$ is $y = \frac{2a}{m}$.

The diameter meets the parabola $y^2 = 4ax$ at $\left(\frac{a}{m^2}, \frac{2a}{m}\right)$

and tangent is $y = mx + \frac{a}{m}$ which is parallel to $y = mx + c$.

Corollary 2. *Tangents at the end of any chord meet on the diameter which bisects the chords.*

If extremities of the chord be $P(at_1^2, 2at_1)$ and $Q(at_2^2, 2at_2)$ then its slope

$$m = \frac{2at_2 - 2at_1}{at_2^2 - at_1^2} \Rightarrow m = \frac{2}{(t_2 + t_1)}.$$

$\therefore$ Equation of diameter is

$$y = 2a/m \Rightarrow y = a(t_1 + t_2) \qquad \text{...(i)}$$

Now, tangents at $P(at_1^2, 2at_1)$ and $Q(at_2^2, 2at_2)$ meet at a point $[at_1t_2, a(t_1 + t_2)]$ which lies on Eq. (i).

Aliter

Let equation of any chord PQ be $y = mx + c$.

If tangents at P and Q meet at $R(x_1, y_1)$, then PQ is the chord of contact with respect to $R(x_1, y_1)$.

$\therefore$ Equation of PQ is

$$yy_1 = 2x(x + x_1) \quad \text{or} \quad y = \frac{2a}{y_1}x + \frac{2ax_1}{y_1}$$

which is identical to $y = mx + c$

$$m = \frac{2a}{y_1} \quad \text{or} \quad y_1 = \frac{2a}{m}.$$

Hence, locus of $R(x_1, y_1)$ is $y = \frac{2a}{m}$, which bisects the chord PQ.

Corollary 3. *To find the equation of a parabola when the axes are any diameter and the tangent to the parabola at the point where this diameter meets the curve.*

Let the equation of the parabola be

$$y^2 = 4ax \qquad \text{...(i)}$$

Let AB be the diameter of the parabola Eq. (i), then its equation is $y = \frac{2a}{m}$

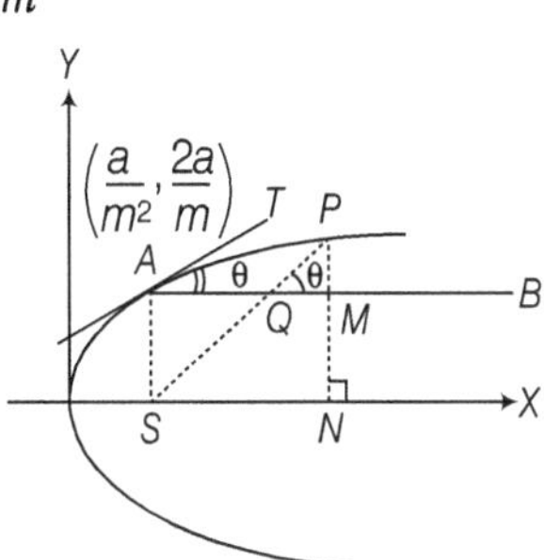

Since, A is the extremity of the diameter

$\therefore$ Coordinates of A is $\left(\frac{a}{m^2}, \frac{2a}{m}\right)$

where, $m = \tan\theta$

then, the equation of tangent AT at A is

$$y = mx + \frac{a}{m}.$$

Now, let P be any point on the parabola Eq. (i), whose coordinates referred to Vx and Vy are (x, y) and referred to diameter AB and tangent AT are (X, Y).

then $\quad X = AQ$ and $Y = QP \qquad$ [since, $PQ \| AT$]

Now, $\quad VN = VL + LN = VL + AM = VL + AQ + QM$

$$= \frac{a}{m^2} + X + QP\cos\theta$$

or

$$x = \frac{a}{m^2} + X + Y\cos\theta \qquad \text{...(ii)}$$

and $\quad PN = PM + MN = PM + AL$

$$= QP\sin\theta + \frac{2a}{m}$$

$\therefore$

$$y = Y\sin\theta + \frac{2a}{m} \qquad \text{... (iii)}$$

From Eqs. (ii) and (iii) coordinates of P are

$$\left(\frac{a}{m^2} + X + Y\cos\theta, Y\sin\theta + \frac{2a}{m}\right)$$

Now, P lies on Eq. (i).

$\therefore$

$$\left(Y\sin\theta + \frac{2a}{m}\right)^2 = 4a\left(\frac{a}{m^2} + X + Y\cos\theta\right)$$

$$\Rightarrow \quad Y^2\sin^2\theta + \frac{4a^2}{m^2} + \frac{4a}{m}Y\sin\theta = \frac{4a^2}{m^2} + 4aX + 4aY\cos\theta$$

$$\Rightarrow \quad Y^2\sin^2\theta + 4a^2\cot^2\theta + 4a\cos\theta Y = 4a^2\cot^2\theta + 4aX + 4aY\cos\theta \quad [\because m = \tan\theta]$$

$$\Rightarrow Y^2\sin^2\theta = 4aX$$

$$\therefore \quad Y^2 = (4a\,\text{cosec}^2\theta)\,X,$$

which is the required parabola referred to diameter and tangent at the extremity of the diameter as axes.

Remark

The quantity $4a\text{cosec}^2\theta$ is called the parameter of the diameter AQ. It is equal to length of the chord which is parallel to AT and passes through the focus.

i.e. $a\,\text{cosec}^2\theta = a(1+\cot^2\theta) = a + a\cot^2\theta$

$$= a + \frac{a}{m^2}$$

$$= a + VL = SP$$

But length of focal chord if $P(at^2, 2at)$ is $[\because S(a, 0)]\ a\left(t+\frac{1}{t}\right)^2$.

$$\therefore \quad \tan\theta = \frac{2at-0}{at^2-a} = \frac{2t}{t^2-1} \text{ or } t - \frac{1}{t} = 2\cot\theta$$

$$\therefore \quad a\left(t+\frac{1}{t}\right)^2 = a\left\{\left(t-\frac{1}{t}\right)^2 + 4\right\}$$

$$= a\{(2\cot\theta)^2 + 4\}$$

$$= 4a\,\text{cosec}^2\theta = 4 \cdot SP$$

Example 52 If the diameter through any point P of a parabola meets any chord in A and the tangent at the end of the chord meets the diameter in B and C, then prove that $PA^2 = PB \cdot PC$.

Sol. The equation of the parabola referred to the diameter through P and tangent at P as axes is

$$y^2 = 4\lambda x \quad \text{...(i)}$$

where, $\lambda = a\,\text{cosec}^2\theta$ [from previous corollary]

Let QR be any chord of the parabola Eq. (i). Let the extremities Q and R be $(\lambda t_1^2, 2\lambda t_1)$ and $(\lambda t_2^2, 2\lambda t_2)$.

Then, the equation of QR is

$$y(t_1+t_2) - 2x - 2\lambda t_1 t_2 = 0 \quad \text{... (ii)}$$

It meets the diameter through P i.e. X-axis or $y = 0$, then Eq. (ii) reduces

$$0 - 2x - 2\lambda\, t_1 t_2 = 0$$

$$\Rightarrow \quad x = -\lambda t_1 t_2 = PA$$

Now, tangent at Q is $\quad t_1 y = x + \lambda t_1^2 \quad$ ...(iii)

It meets the diameter through P i.e. X-axis or $y = 0$, then Eq. (iii) reduces

$$0 = x + \lambda t_1^2$$

$$\Rightarrow \quad x = -\lambda t_1^2 = PB \quad \text{...(iv)}$$

Similarly, $-\lambda t_2^2 = PC$ ...(v)

$$\therefore \quad (PA)^2 = (-\lambda t_1 t_2)^2 = \lambda^2 t_1^2 t_2^2$$

$$= (-\lambda t_1^2)(-\lambda t_2^2) \quad \text{[from Eqs. (iv) and (v)]}$$

$$= PB \cdot PC$$

Lengths of Tangent, Subtangent, Normal and Subnormal

Let the parabola $y^2 = 4ax$. Let the tangent and normal at $P(x, y)$ meet the axis of parabola at T and G respectively and let tangent at $P(x, y)$ makes angle ψ with the positive direction of X-axis.

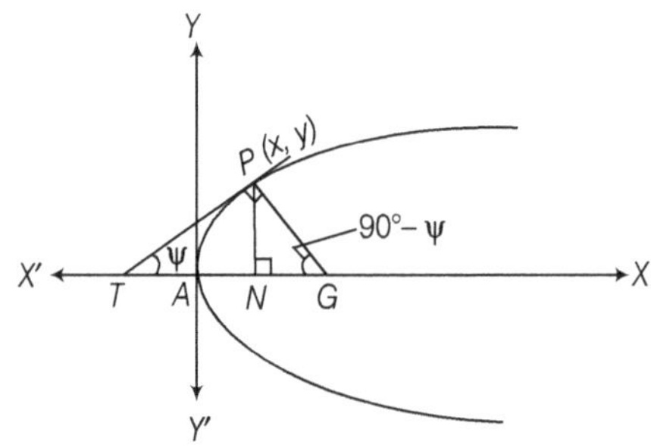

Then, PT = Length of Tangent

PG = Length of Normal

TN = Length of Subtangent

and NG = Length of Subnormal

If $A(0, 0)$ is the vertex of the parabola.

$$\because \quad PN = y$$

$$\therefore \quad PT = PN\,\text{cosec}\,\psi = y\,\text{cosec}\,\psi$$

$$PG = PN\,\text{cosec}\,(90^\circ - \psi) = y\sec\psi$$

$$TN = PN\cot\psi = y\cot\psi$$

and $\quad NG = PN\cot(90^\circ - \psi) = y\tan\psi$

where, $\tan\psi = \dfrac{2a}{y} = m$ [slope of tangent at $P(x, y)$]

Example 53 Find the length of tangent, subtangent, normal and subnormal to $y^2 = 4ax$ at $(at^2, 2at)$.

Sol. $\because$ Equation of tangent of $(at^2, 2at)$ of parabola $y^2 = 4ax$ is

$$ty = x + at^2$$

Slope of this tangent $m = \dfrac{1}{t}$

Let tangent makes angle ψ with positive direction of X-axis

$$\tan\psi = \frac{1}{t}$$

then $t = \cot\psi$

$\therefore$ Length of tangent at

$$(at^2, 2at) = 2at \operatorname{cosec}\psi$$
$$= 2at\sqrt{(1+\cot^2\psi)} = 2at\sqrt{(1+t^2)}$$

Length of normals at

$$(at^2, 2at) = 2at \sec\psi = 2at\sqrt{(1+\tan^2\psi)}$$
$$= 2a\sqrt{(t^2 + t^2\tan^2\psi)} = 2a\sqrt{(t^2+1)}$$

Length of subtangent at $(at^2, 2at) = 2at \cot\psi$

$$= 2at^2$$

Length of subnormal at $(at^2, 2at) = 2at \tan\psi$

$$= 2a$$

Some Standard Properties of the Parabola

(1) The tangents at the extremities of a focal chord intersect at right angles on the directrix.

The extremities of a focal chord PQ are

$$P \equiv (at^2, 2at) \text{ and } Q \equiv \left(\frac{a}{t^2}, -\frac{2a}{t}\right)$$

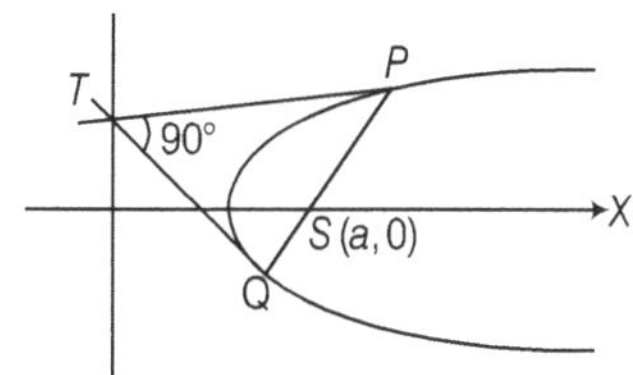

Let parabola is $y^2 = 4ax$

$\therefore$ Tangent at $P(at^2, 2at)$ is

$$ty = x + at^2 \qquad \text{...(i)}$$

Its slope $\frac{1}{t} = m_1$ (say)

and tangent at $Q\left(\frac{a}{t^2}, -\frac{2a}{t}\right)$ is

$$-\frac{y}{t} = x + \frac{a}{t^2} \qquad \text{...(ii)}$$

$\Rightarrow$ $-ty = xt^2 + a$

Its slope $-t = m_2$ (say)

$\because$ $m_1 m_2 = -1$

$\therefore$ $\angle PTQ = 90°$

and adding Eqs. (i) and (ii), we get

$$(x+a)(1+t^2) = 0 \Rightarrow 1+t^2 \neq 0$$

$\therefore$ $x + a = 0$, which is directrix.

(2) The portion of a tangent to a parabola intercepted between the directrix and the curve subtends a right angle at the focus.

The equation of the tangent to the parabola $y^2 = 4ax$ at $P(at^2, 2at)$ is

$$ty = x + at^2 \qquad \text{...(i)}$$

Let Eq. (i) meet the directrix $x + a = 0$ at Q,

then coordinates of Q are $\left(-a, \frac{at^2 - a}{t}\right)$, also focus S is $(a, 0)$.

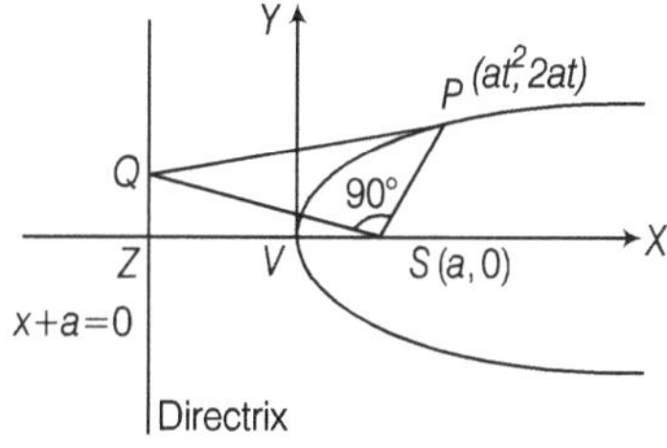

$\therefore$ Slope of $SP = \frac{2at - 0}{at^2 - a}$

$$= \frac{2t}{t^2 - 1} = m_1 \qquad \text{(say)}$$

and slope of $SQ = \frac{\frac{at^2-a}{t} - 0}{-a-a} = \frac{t^2-1}{-2t} = m_2$ (say)

$\therefore$ $m_1 m_2 = -1$

i.e. SP is perpendicular to SQ i.e. $\angle PSQ = 90°$

(3) The tangent at any point P of a parabola bisects the angle between the focal chord through P and the perpendicular from P to the directrix.

Let the tangent at $P(at^2, 2at)$ to the parabola $y^2 = 4ax$ meets the axis of the parabola i.e. X-axis or $y = 0$ at T. The equation of tangent to the parabola $y^2 = 4ax$ at $P(at^2, 2at)$ is

$$ty = x + at^2$$

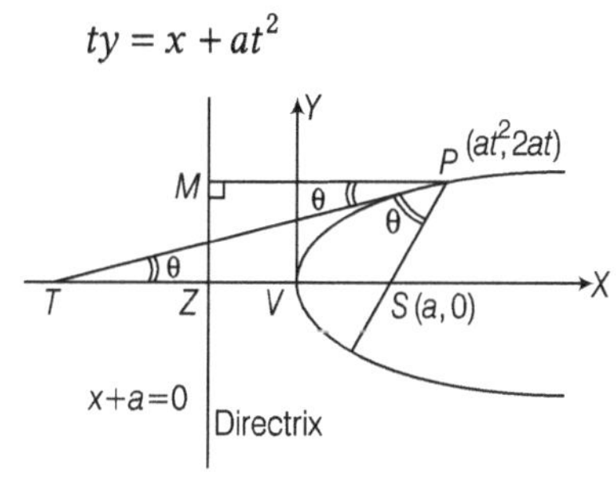

For coordinates of T solve it with $y = 0$.

$\therefore \quad T(-at^2, 0)$

$\therefore \quad ST = SV + VT = a + at^2 = a(1 + t^2)$

Also, $\quad SP = PM = a + at^2 = a(1 + t^2)$

$\therefore \quad SP = ST$, i.e. $\angle STP = \angle SPT$

But $\quad \angle STP = \angle MPT$ [alternate angles]

$\angle SPT = \angle MPT$

(4) The foot of the perpendicular from the focus on any tangent to a parabola lies on the tangent at the vertex.

Equation of tangent at $P(at^2, 2at)$

On the parabola $y^2 = 4ax$

is $\quad ty = x + at^2$

$\Rightarrow \quad x - ty + at^2 = 0$ ...(i)

Now, the equation of line through $S(a, 0)$ and perpendicular to Eq. (i) is

$$tx + y = \lambda$$

Since, it passes through $(a, 0)$.

$\therefore \quad ta + 0 = \lambda$

$\therefore$ Equation $tx + y = ta$ or $t^2x + ty - at^2 = 0$ ...(ii)

By adding Eqs. (i) and (ii), we get

$$x(1 + t^2) = 0$$

$\Rightarrow \quad x = 0 \quad [\because 1 + t^2 \neq 0]$

Hence, the point of intersection of Eq. (i) and (ii) lies on $x = 0$ i.e. on Y-axis (which is tangent at the vertex of a parabola).

(5) If S be the focus of the parabola and tangent and normal at any point P meet its axis in T and G respectively then $ST = SG = SP$.

Let $P(at^2, 2at)$ be any point on the parabola $y^2 = 4ax$, then equation of tangent and normal at $P(at^2, 2at)$ are

$ty = x + at^2$ and $y = -tx + 2at + at^2$, respectively.

Since, tangent and normal meet its axis in T and G.

$\therefore$ Coordinates of T' and G are $(-at^2, 0)$ and $(2a + at^2, 0)$ respectively.

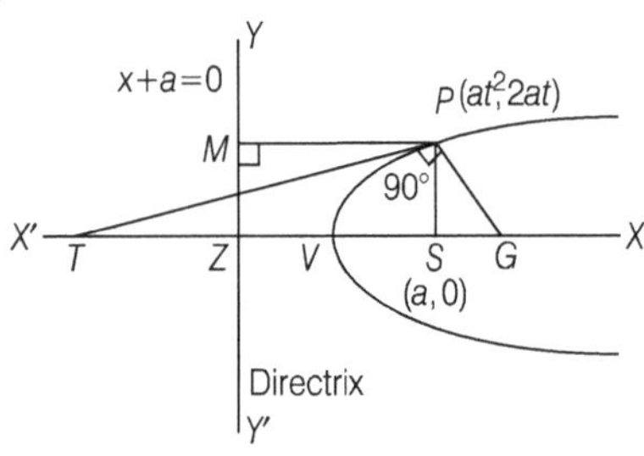

$\therefore \quad SP = PM = a + at^2$

$SG = VG - VS = 2a + at^2 - a$

$= a + at^2$

and $\quad ST = VS + VT = a + at^2$

Hence, $SP = SG = ST$

(6) If S be the focus and SH be perpendicular to the tangent at P, then H lies on the tangent at the vertex and $SH^2 = OS \cdot SP$, where O is the vertex of the parabola.

Let $P(at^2, 2at)$ be any point on the parabola

$$y^2 = 4ax \quad \text{... (i)}$$

then, tangent at $P(at^2, 2at)$ to the parabola Eq. (i) is

$$ty = x + at^2$$

It meets the tangent at the vertex i.e. $x = 0$.

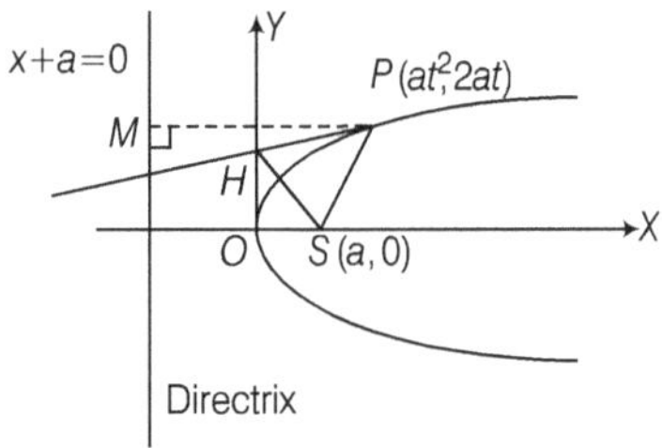

$\therefore$ Coordinates of H is $(0, at)$

and $\quad SP = PM = a + at^2 \Rightarrow OS = a$

and $\quad SH = \sqrt{(a - 0)^2 + (0 - at)^2} = \sqrt{a^2 + a^2t^2}$

or $(SH)^2 = a\{a(1 + t^2)\} = OS \cdot SP$.

Reflection Property of Parabola

The tangent (PT) and normal (PN) of the parabola

$$y^2 = 4ax$$

at P are the internal and external bisectors of $\angle SPM$ and BP is parallel to the axis of the parabola and $\angle BPN = \angle SPN$.

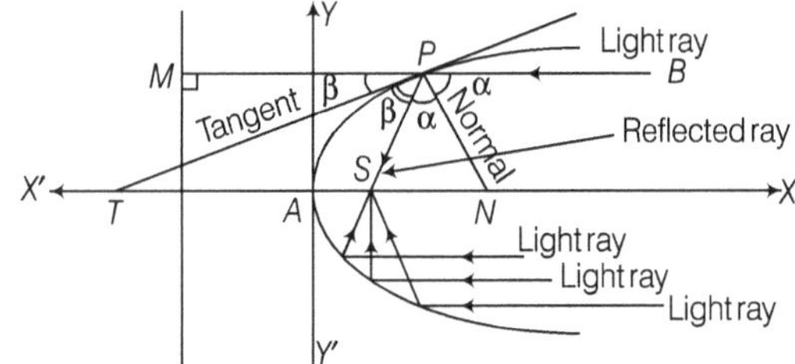

All rays of light coming from the positive direction of X-axis and parallel to the axis of the parabola after reflection pass through the focus of the parabola.

Example 54 A ray of light is coming along the line $y = b$ from the positive direction of X-axis and strikes a concave mirror whose intersection with the xy-plane is a parabola $y^2 = 4ax$. Find the equation of the reflected ray and show that it passes through the focus of the parabola. Both a and b are positive.

Sol. Given parabola is $y^2 = 4ax$

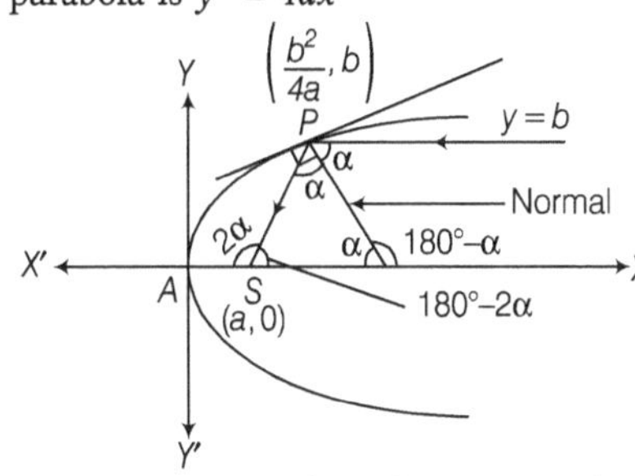

Equation of tangent at $P\left(\frac{b^2}{4a}, b\right)$ is $yb = 2a\left(x + \frac{b^2}{4a}\right)$,

Slope of tangent is $\frac{2a}{b}$.

Hence, slope of normal $= -\frac{b}{2a} = \tan(180° - \alpha)$.

$$\therefore \quad \tan\alpha = \frac{b}{2a}$$

$\therefore$ Slope of reflected ray $= \tan(180° - 2\alpha)$

$$= -\tan 2\alpha$$

$$= -\left\{\frac{2\tan\alpha}{1-\tan^2\alpha}\right\} = -\left\{\frac{2\cdot\frac{b}{2a}}{1-\frac{b^2}{4a^2}}\right\} = -\frac{4ab}{(4a^2 - b^2)}$$

Hence, equation of reflected ray is

$$y - b = -\frac{4ab}{(4a^2 - b^2)}\left(x - \frac{b^2}{4a}\right)$$

$$\Rightarrow \quad (y - b)(4a^2 - b^2) = -(4ax - b^2)$$

which obviously passes through the focus $S(a, 0)$.

Study of Parabola of the Form $(\alpha x + \beta y)^2 + 2gx + 2fy + c = 0$

Given equation can be written as

$$(\alpha x + \beta y)^2 = -2gx - 2fy - c$$

Now, add an arbitrary constant λ in the square root of the second degree terms. Then the equation will be of the form

i.e. $$(\alpha x + \beta y + \lambda)^2 = xf_1(\lambda) + yf_2(\lambda) + f_3(\lambda) \quad \text{...(i)}$$

Now, choose λ such that the lines

$\alpha x + \beta y + \lambda = 0$ and $xf_1(\lambda) + yf_2(\lambda) + f_3(\lambda) = 0$

are perpendicular

i.e. (slope of $\alpha x + \beta y + \lambda = 0$) $\times$ (slope of $xf_1(\lambda) + yf_2(\lambda) + f_3(\lambda) = 0$) $= -1$

$$\Rightarrow \quad -\frac{\alpha}{\beta} \times -\frac{f_1(\lambda)}{f_2(\lambda)} = -1$$

$$\Rightarrow \quad \alpha f_1(\lambda) + \beta f_2(\lambda) = 0 \quad \text{...(ii)}$$

Now, substitute the value of λ in Eq. (i) from Eq. (ii).

Multiply and divide $(\alpha^2 + \beta^2)$ in LHS of Eq. (i)

i.e. $$(\alpha x + \beta y + \lambda)^2 = (\alpha^2 + \beta^2)\left(\frac{\alpha x + \beta y + \lambda}{\sqrt{\alpha^2 + \beta^2}}\right)^2$$

and RHS of Eq. (i) by $\sqrt{(\alpha^2 + \beta^2)}$

i.e. $$xf_1(\lambda) + yf_2(\lambda) + f_3(\lambda)$$

$$= \sqrt{(\alpha^2 + \beta^2)}\left(\frac{xf_1(\lambda) + yf_2(\lambda) + f_3(\lambda)}{\sqrt{(\alpha^2 + \beta^2)}}\right)$$

Then, Eq. (i) reduce in the form

$$\left(\frac{\alpha x + \beta y + \lambda}{\sqrt{\alpha^2 + \beta^2}}\right)^2 = 4\rho\left(\frac{\beta x - \alpha y + \mu}{\sqrt{(\alpha^2 + \beta^2)}}\right)$$

which is of the form $Y^2 = 4\rho X$

$$Y = \frac{\alpha x + \beta y + \lambda}{\sqrt{(\alpha^2 + \beta^2)}}, X = \frac{\beta x - \alpha y + \mu}{\sqrt{(\alpha^2 + \beta^2)}} \text{ and } 4\rho = \frac{1}{\sqrt{(\alpha^2 + \beta^2)}}.$$

Latusrectum is $4\rho = \frac{1}{\sqrt{(\alpha^2 + \beta^2)}}$.

Axis is $Y = 0$ or $\alpha x + \beta y + \lambda = 0$.

Equation of tangent at vertex is

$$X = 0 \text{ or } \beta x - \alpha y + \mu = 0.$$

Vertex is the point of intersection of

$$X = 0 \text{ and } Y = 0$$

i.e. $\beta x - \alpha y + \mu = 0$ and $\alpha x + \beta y + \lambda = 0$.

Equation of directrix is $X + \rho = 0$.

Equation of latusrectum is $X - \rho = 0$.

Focus Since, axis and latusrectum intersect at the focus S its coordinates are detained by solving

$$X - \rho = 0 \text{ and } Y = 0.$$

Example 55. Find the length of latusrectum of the parabola $(a^2 + b^2)(x^2 + y^2) = (bx + ay - ab)^2$.

Sol. Given equation may be written as

$$a^2x^2 + a^2y^2 + b^2x^2 + b^2y^2 = b^2x^2 + a^2y^2 + a^2b^2 + 2abxy - 2a^2by - 2ab^2x$$

$$\Rightarrow \quad a^2x^2 - 2abxy + b^2y^2 = -2ab^2x - 2a^2by + a^2b^2$$

$$\Rightarrow \quad (ax - by)^2 = -2ab\left(bx + ay - \frac{ab}{2}\right)$$

Since, $ax - by = 0$ and $bx + ay - \frac{ab}{2} = 0$ are perpendicular.

$$\therefore (a^2 + b^2)\left(\frac{ax - by}{\sqrt{a^2 + b^2}}\right)^2 = -2ab\sqrt{(a^2 + b^2)}\left(\frac{bx + ay - \frac{ab}{2}}{\sqrt{(a^2 + b^2)}}\right)$$

$$\Rightarrow \quad \left(\frac{ax - by}{\sqrt{a^2 + b^2}}\right)^2 = \frac{-2ab}{\sqrt{(a^2 + b^2)}}\left(\frac{bx + ay - \frac{ab}{2}}{\sqrt{(a^2 + b^2)}}\right)$$

which is of the form $Y^2 = -4\rho X$.

Therefore, the latusrectum $= 4\rho = \dfrac{2ab}{\sqrt{(a^2 + b^2)}}$.

Aliter :

Given equation may be written as

$$x^2 + y^2 = \frac{(bx + ay - ab)^2}{(a^2 + b^2)}$$

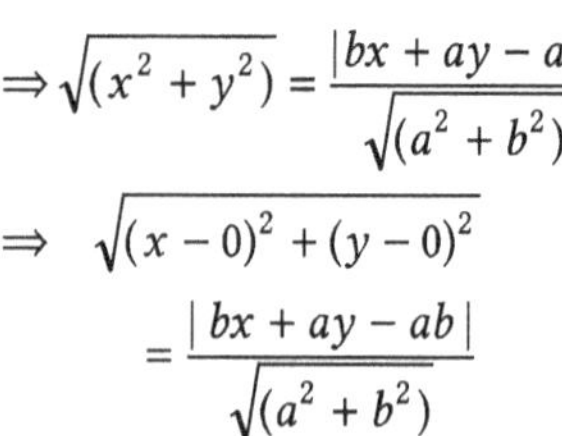

$$\Rightarrow \sqrt{(x^2 + y^2)} = \frac{|bx + ay - ab|}{\sqrt{(a^2 + b^2)}}$$

$$\Rightarrow \quad \sqrt{(x - 0)^2 + (y - 0)^2} = \frac{|bx + ay - ab|}{\sqrt{(a^2 + b^2)}}$$

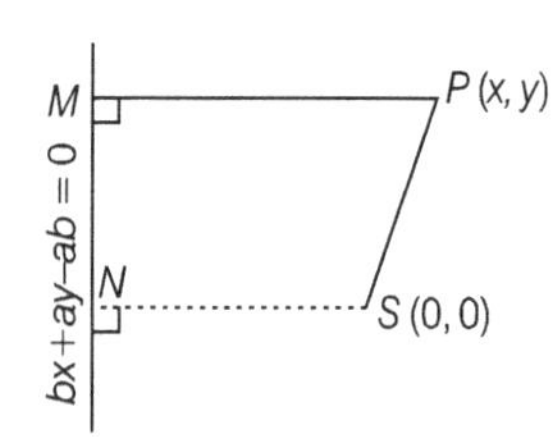

which is of the form $SP = PM$.

Since, distance from focus S to ($bx + ay - ab = 0$) $= \frac{1}{2}(4\rho)$

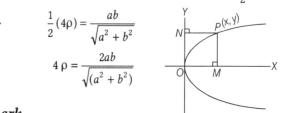

$$\Rightarrow \quad \frac{1}{2}(4\rho) = \frac{ab}{\sqrt{a^2 + b^2}}$$

$$\therefore \quad 4\rho = \frac{2ab}{\sqrt{(a^2 + b^2)}}$$

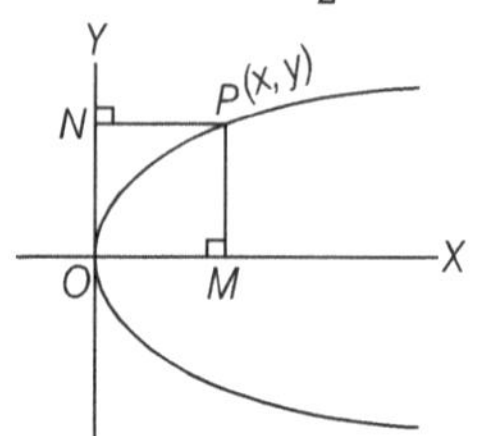

Remark

Consider the equation of parabola is $y^2 = 4ax$.

i.e. $(MP)^2 =$ (Latusrectum) NP.

i.e. if P is any point on the given parabola, then

(the distance of P from its axis)^2 = (Latusrectum)

(The distance of P from the tangent at its vertex).

Exercise for Session 3

1. If m_1, m_2 are slopes of the two tangents that are drawn from (2, 3) to the parabola $y^2 = 4x$, then the value of $\frac{1}{m_1} + \frac{1}{m_2}$ is

(a) −3 (b) 3 (c) $\frac{2}{3}$ (d) $\frac{3}{2}$

2. The angle between the tangents drawn from the origin to the parabola $y^2 = 4a(x - a)$ is

(a) 90° (b) 30° (c) $\tan^{-1}\left(\frac{1}{2}\right)$ (d) 45°

3. If (a, b) is the mid-point of chord passing through the vertex of the parabola $y^2 = 4x$, then

(a) $a = 2b$ (b) $2a = b$ (c) $a^2 = 2b$ (d) $2a = b^2$

4. The diameter of the parabola $y^2 = 6x$ corresponding to the system of parallel chords $3x - y + c = 0$ is

(a) $y - 1 = 0$ (b) $y - 2 = 0$ (c) $y + 1 = 0$ (d) $y + 2 = 0$

5. From the point $(-1, 2)$ tangent lines are drawn to the parabola $y^2 = 4x$, the area of triangle formed by chord of contact and the tangents is given by

(a) 8 (b) $8\sqrt{3}$ (c) $8\sqrt{2}$ (d) None of these

6. For parabola $x^2 + y^2 + 2xy - 6x - 2y + 3 = 0$, the focus is

(a) $(1, -1)$ (b) $(-1, 1)$ (c) $(3, 1)$ (d) None of these

7. The locus of the mid-point of that chord of parabola which subtends right angle on the vertex will be

(a) $y^2 - 2ax + 8a^2 = 0$ (b) $y^2 = a(x - 4a)$ (c) $y^2 = 4a(x - 4a)$ (d) $y^2 + 3ax + 4a^2 = 0$

8. A ray of light moving parallel to the X-axis gets reflected from a parabolic mirror whose equation is $(y-2)^2 = 4(x+1)$. After reflection, the ray must pass through the point

(a) $(-2, 0)$ (b) $(-1, 2)$ (c) $(0, 2)$ (d) $(2, 0)$

9. Prove that the locus of the point of intersection of tangents to the parabola $y^2 = 4ax$ which meet at an angle α is $(x+a)^2 \tan^2 \alpha = y^2 - 4ax$.

10. Find the locus of the middle points of the chords of the parabola $y^2 = 4ax$ which pass through the focus.

11. From the point $P(-1, 2)$ tangents are drawn to the parabola $y^2 = 4x$. Find the equation of the chord of contact. Also, find the area of the triangle formed by the chord of contact and the tangents.

Shortcuts and Important Results to Remember

1 Second degree terms in the equation of a parabola should make perfect squares.

2 If l_1 and l_2 are the lengths of segments of a focal chord then the latusrectum of the parabola is $\frac{4l_1l_2}{l_1+l_2}$.

3 If α be the inclination of a focal chord with axis of the parabola then its length is $4a\operatorname{cosec}^2\alpha$.

4 If tangents of $y^2 = 4ax$ at $P(t_1)$ and $Q(t_2)$ meets at R, then area of ΔPQR is $\frac{1}{2}a^2(t_1 - t_2)^3$.

5 The foot of the perpendicular from the focus on any tangent to a parabola lies on the tangent at the vertex.

6 The area of the triangle formed by three points on a parabola is twice the area of the triangle formed by the tangents, at these points.

7 The equation of the common tangent to the parabolas $x^2 = 4ay$ and $y^2 = 4ax$ is $x + y + a = 0$.

8 If the chord joining t_1, t_2 and t_3, t_4 pass through a point $(c, 0)$ on the axis, then

$$t_1t_2 = t_3t_4 = -c / a.$$

9 If the normals to the parabola $y^2 = 4ax$ at the points t_1 and t_2 intersect again on the parabola at the point 't_3', then $t_1t_2 = 2; t_3 = -(t_1 + t_2)$ and the line joining t_1 and t_2 passes through a fixed point $(-2a, 0)$.

10 If the length of a focal chord of $y^2 = 4ax$ at a distance b from the vertex is c then $b^2c = 4a^3$.

11 From an external point only one normal can be drawn.

12 If a normal to $y^2 = 4ax$ makes an angle θ with the axis of $y^2 = 4ax$ then it will cut the curve again at an angle of $\tan^{-1}\left(\frac{\tan\theta}{2}\right)$.

13 The orthocentre of any triangle formed by the three tangents to a parabola $y^2 = 4ax$ 't_1', 't_2' and 't_3' lies on the directrix and has the coordinates $(-a, a(t_1 + t_2 + t_3 + t_1t_2t_3))$.

14 Normals at the end points of the latusrectum of a parabola $y^2 = 4ax$ intersect at right angle on the axis of the parabola and their point of intersection is $(3a, 0)$.

15 A line ray parallel to axis of the parabola after reflection passes through the focus.

JEE Type Solved Examples :
Single Option Correct Type Questions

- This section contains **10 multiple choice examples.** Each example has four choices (a), (b), (c) and (d) out of which **ONLY ONE** is correct.

Ex. 1 *A ray of light travels along a line $y = 4$ and strikes the surface of curves $y^2 = 4(x + y)$, then the equation of the line along which the reflected ray travels is*

(a) $x = 0$ (b) $x = 2$

(c) $x + y = 4$ (d) $2x + y = 4$

Sol. (a) The given curve is $(y-2)^2 = 4(x+1)$

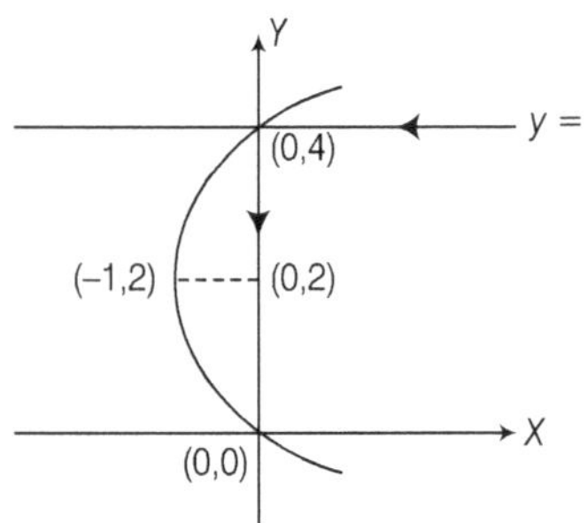

The focus is $(0, 2)$.

The point of intersection of the curve and $y = 4$ is $(0, 4)$. From the reflection property of parabola the reflected ray passes through the focus.

Therefore, $x = 0$ is the reflected ray.

Ex. 2 *A parabola is drawn with focus at $(3, 4)$ and vertex at the focus of the parabola $y^2 - 12x - 4y + 4 = 0$. The equation of the parabola is*

(a) $x^2 - 6x - 8y + 25 = 0$ (b) $y^2 - 8x - 6y + 25 = 0$

(c) $x^2 - 6x + 8y - 25 = 0$ (d) $x^2 + 6x - 8y - 25 = 0$

Sol. (a) $y^2 - 12x - 4y + 4 = 0 \Rightarrow (y-2)^2 = 12x$

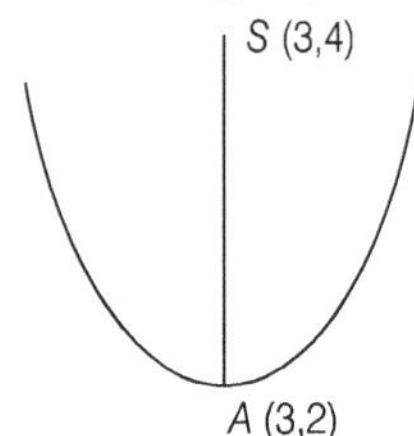

Its vertex is $(0, 2)$ and $a = 3$,

its focus $= (3, 2)$.

Hence, for the required parabola; focus is $(3, 4)$, vertex $= (3, 2)$ and $a = 2$,

Hence, the equation of the parabola is

$$(x-3)^2 = 4(2)(y-2)$$

or $\quad x^2 - 6x - 8y + 25 = 0$

Ex. 3 *Two parabolas have the same focus. If their directrices are the X-axis and the Y-axis, respectively, then the slope of their common chord is*

(a) ± 1 (b) $\frac{4}{3}$ (c) $\frac{3}{4}$ (d) None of these

Sol. (a) Let the focus be (a, b)

Then, equations are $(x-a)^2 + (y-b)^2 = y^2$ and

$$(x-a)^2 + (y-b)^2 = x^2$$

If $\quad S_1 \equiv (x-a)^2 + (y-b)^2 - y^2 = 0$

and $\quad S_2 \equiv (x-a)^2 + (y-b)^2 - x^2 = 0$

$\therefore$ Equation of common chord $S_1 - S_2 = 0$ gives

$$x^2 - y^2 = 0 \quad \text{or} \quad y = \pm x$$

Hence, slope of common chord is ± 1.

Ex. 4 *Let us define a region R in xy-plane as a set of points (x, y) satisfying $[x^2] = [y]$ (where $[x]$ denotes greatest integer $\leq x$), then the region R defines*

(a) a parabola whose axis is horizontal

(b) a parabola whose axis is vertical

(c) integer point of the parabola $y = x^2$

(d) None of the above

Sol. (d) $\because [x^2] = [y]$

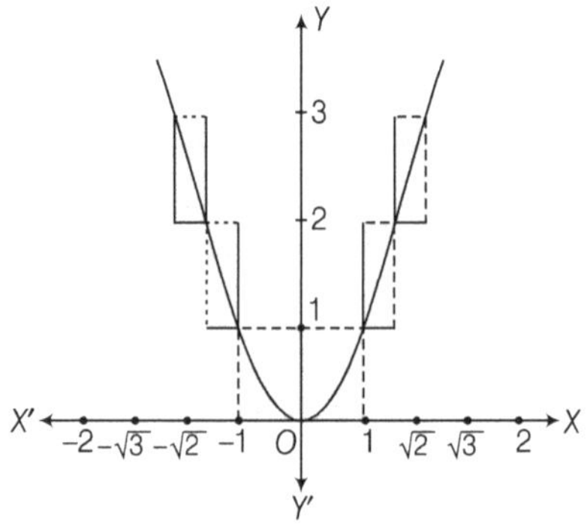

If $\quad 0 \leq y < 1$,

then, $[y] = 0$

$\therefore \quad [x^2] = 0$

$\quad 0 \leq x^2 < 1$

$\Rightarrow \quad x \in (-1, 1)$

for $\quad 1 \leq y < 2$,

then $[y] = 1$

$\therefore \quad [x^2] = 1$

$\Rightarrow \quad 1 \leq x^2 < 2$

$\Rightarrow \quad x \in (-\sqrt{2}, -1] \cup [1, \sqrt{2})$

for $\quad 2 \leq y < 3$, then $[y] = 2$

then, $[x^2] = 2 \Rightarrow 2 \leq x^2 < 3$

$\therefore \quad x \in (-\sqrt{3}, -\sqrt{2}] \cup [\sqrt{2}, \sqrt{3})$

The graph of the region will not only contain of the parabola $y = x^2$ but $[x^2] = [y]$ contain points within the rectangles of side $1, 2, ; 1, \sqrt{2} - 1; 1, \sqrt{3} - \sqrt{2}$ etc.

Hence, a, b, c are incorrects.

Ex. 5 *The minimum area of circle which touches the parabolas $y = x^2 + 1$ and $x = y^2 + 1$ is*

(a) $\frac{9\pi}{16}$ sq units (b) $\frac{9\pi}{32}$ sq units

(c) $\frac{9\pi}{8}$ sq units (d) $\frac{9\pi}{4}$ sq units

Sol. (b) The parabolas $y = x^2 + 1$ and $x = y^2 + 1$ are symmetrical about $y = x$.

Therefore, the tangent at point A is parallel to $y = x$

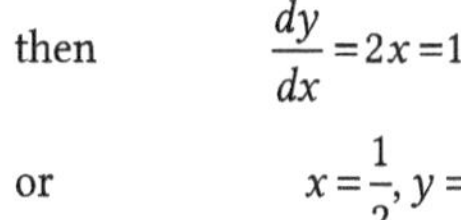

then $\frac{dy}{dx} = 2x = 1$

or $x = \frac{1}{2}, y = \frac{5}{4}$

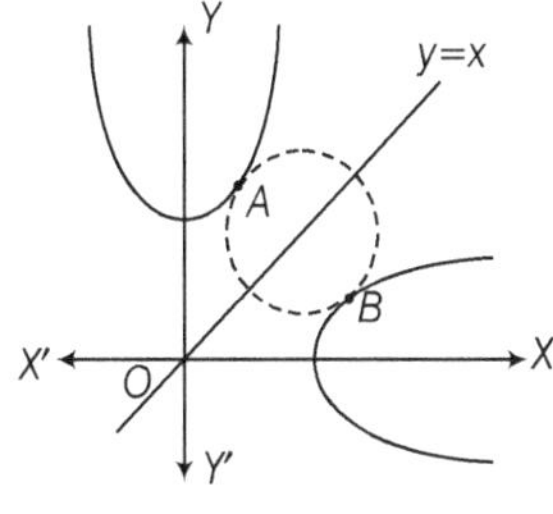

$\therefore \quad A \equiv \left(\frac{1}{2}, \frac{5}{4}\right)$

and $B \equiv \left(\frac{5}{4}, \frac{1}{2}\right)$

Hence, Radius $(r) = \frac{1}{2} AB = \frac{1}{2}\sqrt{\left(\frac{1}{2} - \frac{5}{4}\right)^2 + \left(\frac{5}{4} - \frac{1}{2}\right)^2} = \frac{3\sqrt{2}}{8}$

$\therefore \quad \text{Area} = \pi r^2 = \frac{9\pi}{32}$ sq units

Ex. 6 *Let the line $lx + my = 1$ cut the parabola $y^2 = 4ax$ in the points A and B. Normals at A and B meet at point C. Normal from C other than these two meet the parabola at D, then the coordinate of D are*

(a) $(a, 2a)$ (b) $\left(\frac{4am}{l^2}, \frac{4a}{l}\right)$

(c) $\left(\frac{2am^2}{l^2}, \frac{2a}{l}\right)$ (d) $\left(\frac{4am^2}{l^2}, \frac{4am}{l}\right)$

Sol. (d) Let $A \equiv (am_1^2, -2am_1)$ and $B \equiv (am_2^2, -2am_2)$

Now, A and B lie on $lx + my = 1$

$\Rightarrow \quad l(am_1^2) + m(-2am_1) = 1 \quad ...(i)$

and $\quad l(am_2^2) + m(-2am_2) = 1 \quad ...(ii)$

Subtracting Eq. (ii) from Eq. (i), then

$$la(m_1^2 - m_2^2) - 2am(m_1 - m_2) = 0$$

$\Rightarrow \quad a(m_1 - m_2) \neq 0$

$\therefore \quad l(m_1 + m_2) - 2m = 0$

$\Rightarrow \quad m_1 + m_2 = \frac{2m}{l} \quad ...(iii)$

Let $\quad D \equiv (am_3^2, -2am_3)$ and $C \equiv (h, k)$

$\therefore$ Equation of normal in terms of slope

$$y = Mx - 2aM - aM^3$$

then $\quad aM^3 - (h - 2a)M + k = 0$

$\therefore \quad m_1 + m_2 + m_3 = 0$

$\Rightarrow \quad \frac{2m}{l} + m_3 = 0$

$\therefore \quad m_3 = -\frac{2m}{l}$

$\therefore \quad D \equiv \left(a\left(\frac{-2m}{l}\right)^2, -2a\left(\frac{-2m}{l}\right)\right)$

$\Rightarrow \quad D \equiv \left(\frac{4am^2}{l^2}, \frac{4am}{l}\right)$

Ex. 7 *If d is the distance between the parallel tangents with positive slope to $y^2 = 4x$ and $x^2 + y^2 - 2x + 4y - 11 = 0$, then*

(a) $10 < d < 20$ (b) $4 < d < 6$

(c) $d < 4$ (d) None of these

Sol. (c) Tangent to the parabola $y^2 = 4x$ having slope m is

$$y = mx + \frac{1}{m}$$

and tangent to the circle $(x-1)^2 + (y+2)^2 = 4^2$ having slope m is

$$y + 2 = m(x - 1) + 4\sqrt{(1 + m^2)}$$

$\therefore$ Distance between tangents $(d) = \left|\frac{4\sqrt{(1+m^2)} - m - 2 - \frac{1}{m}}{\sqrt{(1+m^2)}}\right|$

$$= \left|4 - \frac{2}{\sqrt{(1+m^2)}} - \frac{\sqrt{(1+m^2)}}{m}\right|$$

As $\quad m > 0 \quad$ (given)

we get $\quad d < 4$

Ex. 8 *Two parabolas C and D intersect at two different points, where C is $y = x^2 - 3$ and D is $y = kx^2$. The intersection at which the x value is positive is designated point A, and $x = a$ at this intersection the tangent line l at A to the curve D intersects curve C at point B, other than A. If x-value of point B is 1, then a is equal to*

(a) 1 (b) 2 (c) 3 (d) 4

Sol. (c) $C: y = x^2 - 3$ and $D: y = kx^2$

Solving C and D, then

$kx^2 = x^2 - 3 \quad ...(i)$

or $\quad x^2 = \frac{3}{1-k},$

then, $\quad y = \frac{3k}{1-k}$

$\therefore \quad A \equiv \left(\sqrt{\frac{3}{1-k}}, \frac{3k}{1-k}\right)$ (given x-value of A is positive)

and $\quad a = \sqrt{\left(\frac{3}{1-k}\right)}$

then $\quad A \equiv (a, ka^2) \equiv (a, a^2 - 3) \quad$ [from Eq. (i)]

tangent 'l' at A to the curve D is

$$\frac{y+a^2-3}{2}=kx\cdot a$$

$$\Rightarrow \quad y+a^2-3=2ax\left(1-\frac{3}{a^2}\right) \quad \text{[from Eq. (i)] ...(ii)}$$

$\therefore \quad B\equiv(1,-2)\ (a\neq 1)$

From Eq. (ii), $-2+a^2-3=2a\left(1-\frac{3}{a^2}\right)$

$$\Rightarrow \quad a^3-5a=2a^2-6$$

$$\Rightarrow \quad a^3-2a^2-5a+6=0$$

$$\Rightarrow \quad (a-1)(a+2)(a-3)=0$$

$$\therefore \quad a=3 \quad (\because a\neq 1, a\neq -2)$$

Ex. 9 *$\min[(x_1-x_2)^2+(3+\sqrt{(1-x_1^2)}-\sqrt{4x_2})^2], \forall$ $x_1, x_2 \in R$, is*

(a) $4\sqrt{5}+1$ (b) $3-2\sqrt{2}$ (c) $\sqrt{5}+1$ (d) $\sqrt{5}-1$

Sol. (b) Let $y_1=3+\sqrt{(1-x_1^2)}$ and $y_2=\sqrt{4x_2}$

or $x_1^2+(y_1-3)^2=1$ and $y_2^2=4x_2$

Thus, (x_1, y_1) lies on the circle $x^2+(y-3)^2=1$ and (x_2, y_2) lies on the parabola $y^2=4x$.

Thus, the given expression is the shortest distance between the curve $x^2+(y-3)^2=1$ and $y^2=4x$.

Now, the shortest distance always occurs along the common normal to the curves and normal to the circle passes through the centre of the circle.

Normal to parabola $y^2=4x$ is $y=mx-2m-m^3$. It passes through centre of circle $(0,3)$.

Therefore, $3=-2m-m^3 \Rightarrow m^3+2m+3=0$ which has only one real value $m=-1$.

Hence, the corresponding point on the parabola is $(1,2)$

$$\therefore \sqrt{(x_1-x_2)^2+(3+\sqrt{(1-x_1^2)}-\sqrt{4x_2})^2}=\sqrt{(x_1-x_2)^2+(y_1-y_2)^2}$$

$=$ Distance between $(1,2)$ and $(0,3)$ − radius

$$=\sqrt{(1+1)}-1=(\sqrt{2}-1)$$

or $\quad (x_1-x_2)^2+(3+\sqrt{(1-x_1^2)}-\sqrt{4x_2})^2=(\sqrt{2}-1)^2$

$$\therefore \quad \min\cdot[(x_1-x_2)^2+(3+\sqrt{(1-x_1^2)}-\sqrt{4x_2})^2]=3-2\sqrt{2}$$

Ex. 10 *The condition that the parabolas $y^2=4c(x-d)$ and $y^2=4ax$ have a common normal other than X-axis $(a>0, c>0)$ is*

(a) $2a<2c+d$ (b) $2c<2a+d$

(c) $2d<2a+c$ (d) $2d<2c+a$

Sol. (a) Normals of parabolas $y^2=4ax$ and $y^2=4c(x-d)$ in terms of slope are

$$y=mx-2am-am^3 \quad \text{...(i)}$$

and

$$y=m(x-d)-2cm-cm^3 \quad \text{...(ii)}$$

Subtracting Eqs. (ii) from (i), then

$$md-2am-am^3+2cm+cm^3=0$$

$$m\neq 0$$

$$\therefore \quad d-2a-am^2+2c+cm^2=0$$

$$\Rightarrow \quad (a-c)m^2=d-2a+2c$$

$$\Rightarrow \quad m^2=\frac{d-2a+2c}{(a-c)}$$

$$\Rightarrow \quad \frac{d}{a-c}-2>0$$

$$\Rightarrow \quad d>2a-2c$$

$$\Rightarrow \quad 2a<2c+d$$

JEE Type Solved Examples : More than One Correct Option Type Questions

- This section contains **5 multiple choice examples.** Each example has four choices (a), (b), (c) and (d) out of **which MORE THAN ONE** may be correct.

Ex. 11 *The locus of the mid-point of the focal radii of a variable point moving on the parabola $y^2=4ax$ is a parabola whose*

(a) latusrectum is half the latusrectum of the original parabola

(b) vertex is $\left(\frac{a}{2}, 0\right)$

(c) directrix is Y-axls

(d) focus has the coordinates $(a, 0)$

Sol. (a, b, c, d) Let $P(at^2, 2at)$ be a point on the parabola $y^2=4ax$ with focus $S(a, 0)$

Now, mid-point of focal radii SP is $M\left(\frac{a}{2}(t^2+1), at\right)$.

Let $\quad x=\frac{a}{2}(t^2+1)$ and $y=at$

or $\quad x=\frac{a}{2}\left(\frac{y^2}{a^2}+1\right)$

$$\Rightarrow \quad y^2=2ax-a^2 \quad \text{or} \quad y^2=2a\left(x-\frac{a}{2}\right)$$

which is a parabola with vertex $\left(\frac{a}{2}, 0\right)$ and latusrectum is $2a$,

directrix is $x-\frac{a}{2}=\frac{a}{2}$ i.e. $x=0$ (Y) and focus $\left(\frac{a}{2}+\frac{a}{2}, 0\right)$ i.e. $(a, 0)$.

Ex. 12 *If P_1P_2 and Q_1Q_2, two focal chords of a parabola $y^2 = 4ax$ at right angles, then*

(a) area of the quadrilateral $P_1Q_1P_2Q_2$ is minimum when the chords are inclined at an angle $\pi/4$ to the axis of the parabola.
(b) minimum area is twice the area of the square on the latusrectum of the parabola.
(c) minimum area of quadrilateral $P_1Q_1P_2Q_2$ cannot be found.
(d) minimum area is thrice the area of the square on the latusrectum of the parabola.

Sol. (a, b) Let coordinates of P_1 are $(at^2, 2at)$, then coordinates of P_2 are $\left(\frac{a}{t^2}, -\frac{2a}{t}\right)$.

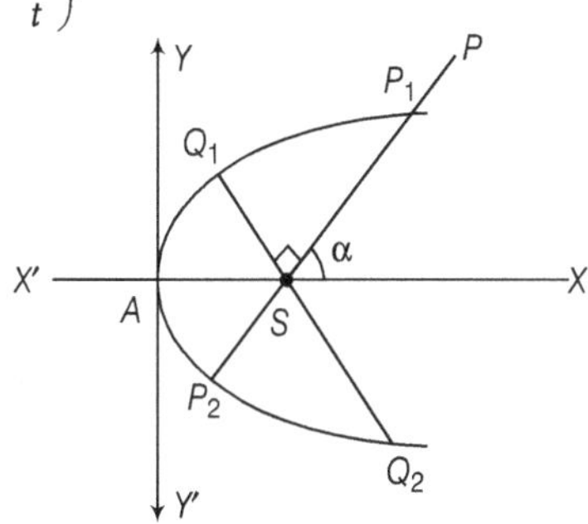

Let focal chord P_1P_2 makes an angle α with X-axis, then

$$\tan\alpha = \frac{2at - \left(-\frac{2a}{t}\right)}{at^2 - \frac{a}{t^2}} = \frac{2}{t - \frac{1}{t}}$$

$$\Rightarrow \quad t - \frac{1}{t} = 2\cot\alpha \qquad \text{... (i)}$$

Now, $$P_1P_2 = a\left(t + \frac{1}{t}\right)^2 = a\left\{\left(t - \frac{1}{t}\right)^2 + 4\right\}$$

$$= a\{4\cot^2\alpha + 4\} = 4a\operatorname{cosec}^2\alpha \quad \text{[from Eq. (i)]}$$

Similarly, $$Q_1Q_2 = 4a\operatorname{cosec}^2(90 - \alpha) = 4a\sec^2\alpha$$

$\therefore$ Area of quadrilateral $P_1Q_1P_2Q_2 = \frac{1}{2}(P_1P_2)(Q_1Q_2)$

$$= 8a^2\sec^2\alpha\operatorname{cosec}^2\alpha = 32a^2\operatorname{cosec}^2\alpha$$

$\therefore$ Minimum area $= 32a^2 = 2(\text{latusrectum})^2$ and is inclined at

$$\alpha = \pi/4 \qquad (\because \operatorname{cosec} 2\alpha = 1)$$

Ex. 13 *The equation of the line that touches the curves $y = x|x|$ and $x^2 + (y-2)^2 = 4$, where $x \neq 0$, is*

(a) $y = 4\sqrt{5}x + 20$ (b) $y = 4\sqrt{3}x - 12$
(c) $y = 0$ (d) $y = -4\sqrt{5}x - 20$

Sol. (a, b, c) $\because y = x|x| = \begin{cases} x^2, & x \geq 0 \\ -x^2, & x < 0 \end{cases}$

$\because$ Equation of tangent in terms of slope (m) of $x^2 = 4ay$ is

$$y = mx - am^2 \qquad \text{... (i)}$$

Also, line (i) touches the circle $x^2 + (y-2)^2 = 4$, then

$$\frac{|2 + am^2|}{\sqrt{(1 + m^2)}} = 2$$

$$\Rightarrow \quad 4 + a^2m^4 + 4am^2 = 4 + 4m^2$$

$$\therefore \quad m^2 = \frac{4 - 4a}{a^2} \text{ and } m^2 = 0$$

Put $4a = 1$ for $y = x^2, x \geq 0$, then $m^2 = 48$

and put $4a = -1$ for $y = -x^2, x < 0$, then $m^2 = 80$

$\therefore$ Common tangents are

$$y = 0, y = 4\sqrt{3}x - 12 \text{ and } y = 4\sqrt{5}x + 20$$

Ex. 14 *Let V be the vertex and L be the latusrectum of the parabola $x^2 = 2y + 4x - 4$. Then, the equation of the parabola whose vertex is at V, latusrectum $L/2$ and axis is perpendicular to the axis of the given parabola.*

(a) $y^2 = x - 2$ (b) $y^2 = x - 4$
(c) $y^2 = 2 - x$ (d) $y^2 = 4 - x$

Sol. (a, c) Given parabola is $x^2 = 2y + 4x - 4$

$$\Rightarrow \quad (x-2)^2 = 2y$$

Vertex of the parabola is (2, 0) and length of latusrectum $= 2$

$$\therefore \quad V(2, 0) \text{ and } L = 2$$

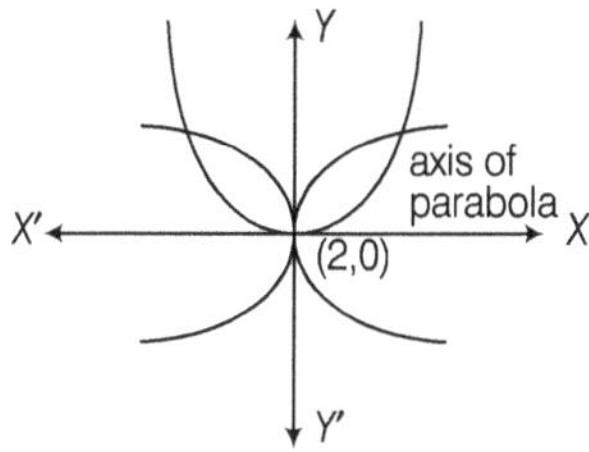

Length of latusrectum of required parabola $= L/2 = 1$

$\therefore$ Equation of the required parabola is $(y - 0)^2 = \pm 1(x - 2)$

$$\Rightarrow \quad y^2 = x - 2 \text{ or } y^2 = -x + 2$$

Ex. 15 *Consider a circle with its centre lying on the focus of the parabola $y^2 = 2ax$ such that it touches the directrix of the parabola. Then a point of intersection of the circle and the parabola is*

(a) $\left(\frac{a}{2}, a\right)$ (b) $\left(\frac{a}{2}, -a\right)$
(c) $\left(-\frac{a}{2}, a\right)$ (d) $\left(-\frac{a}{2}, -a\right)$

Sol. (a, b) Given parabola is $y^2 = 2ax$ ...(i)

$\therefore$ Focus and equation of directrix are $S\left(\frac{a}{2}, 0\right)$ and $x = -\frac{a}{2}$ respectively.

$\therefore$ Equation of circle is $\left(x - \frac{a}{2}\right)^2 + (y - 0)^2 = a^2$ ... (ii)

($\because$ radius = distance between focus and directrix)

From Eqs. (i) and (ii),

$$\left(x-\frac{a}{2}\right)^2+2ax=a^2 \Rightarrow x^2+ax-\frac{3a^2}{4}=0$$

or $$x=\frac{a}{2}, x\neq -\frac{3a}{2} \quad \left(\because \text{for } x=-\frac{3a}{2}, y=\text{imaginary}\right)$$

From Eq. (i),

$$y^2=a^2$$

$$\therefore \quad y=\pm a$$

Hence, required point of intersection are $\left(\frac{a}{2}, \pm a\right)$.

JEE Type Solved Examples : Paragraph Based Questions

- This section contains **2 Solved Paragraphs** based upon each of the paragraph **3 multiple choice question.** Each of these questions has four choices (a), (b), (c) and (d) out of which **ONLY ONE** is correct.

Paragraph I

(Q. Nos. 16 to 18)

Tangents are drawn to the parabola $y^2=4x$ at the point P which is the upper end of latusrectum.

16. Image of the parabola $y^2=4x$ in the tangent line at the point P is

(a) $(x+4)^2=16y$ (b) $(x+2)^2=8(y-2)$

(c) $(x+1)^2=4(y-1)$ (d) $(x-2)^2=2(y-2)$

17. Radius of the circle touching the parabola $y^2=4x$ at the point P and passing through its focus is

(a) 1 (b) $\sqrt{2}$ (c) $\sqrt{3}$ (d) 2

18. Area enclosed by the tangent line at P, X-axis and the parabola is

(a) $\frac{2}{3}$ sq units (b) $\frac{4}{3}$ sq units

(c) $\frac{14}{3}$ sq units (d) $\frac{16}{3}$ sq units

Sol. Upper end of latusrectum is $P(1,2)$

$\therefore$ The equation of tangent at $P(1,2)$ is

$$y\cdot 2=2(x+1) \Rightarrow x-y+1=0$$

16. (c) Any point on the given parabola is $(t^2, 2t)$. The image of (h,k) of the point $(t^2, 2t)$ on $x-y+1=0$ is given by

$$\frac{h-t^2}{1}=\frac{k-2t}{-1}=\frac{-2(t^2-2t+1)}{1+1}$$

$$\Rightarrow \quad h=2t-1 \text{ and } k=t^2+1$$

or $$k=\left(\frac{h+1}{2}\right)^2+1 \Rightarrow (h+1)^2=4(k-1)$$

The required equation of image is $(x+1)^2=4(y-1)$.

17. (c) $\because$ Focus is $S(1,0)$ and P is $(1,2)$.

Equation of circle touching the parabola at (1, 2) is $(x-1)^2+(y-2)^2+\lambda(x-y+1)=0$ it passes through (1, 0).

Therefore, $4+2\lambda=0$ or $\lambda=-2$

Thus, the required circle is

$$(x-1)^2+(y-2)^2-2(x-y+1)=0$$

or $$x^2+y^2-4x-2y+3=0$$

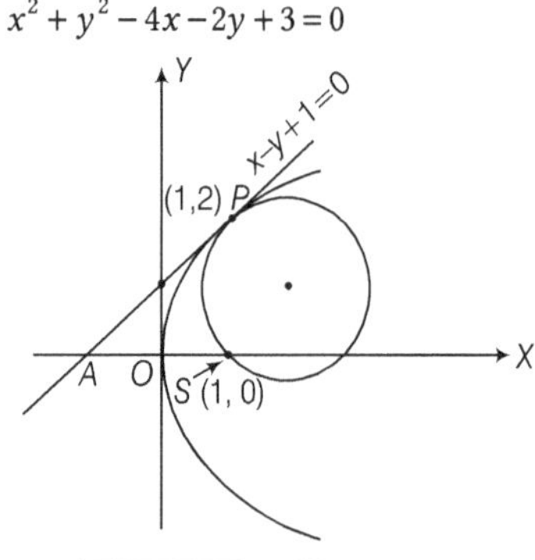

Its radius is $\sqrt{(4+1-3)}=\sqrt{2}$.

18. (a) Area bounded by $AOPA$ = Area of ΔAOB + Area of $OPBO$

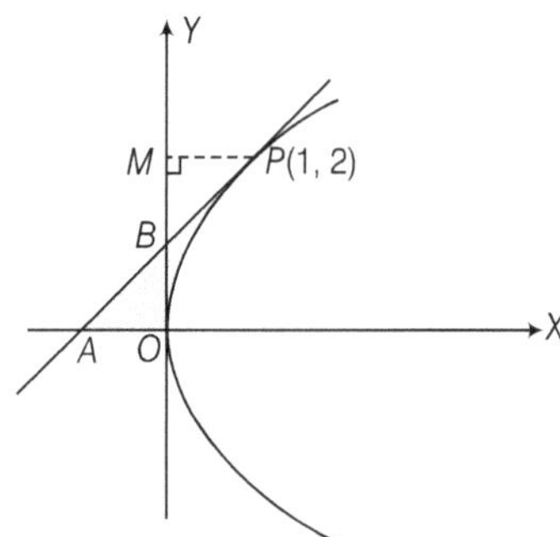

$$=\frac{1}{2}\times 1\times 1+\int_0^2 \frac{y^2}{4}dy-\frac{1}{2}\times 1\times 1=\left[\frac{y^3}{12}\right]_0^2=\frac{8}{12}=\frac{2}{3} \text{ sq unit}$$

Paragraph II

(Q. Nos. 19 to 21)

Let C_1 and C_2 be respectively, the parabolas $x^2=y-1$ and $y^2=x-1$. Let P be any point on C_1 and Q be any point on C_2. Let P_1 and Q_1 be the reflections of P and Q, respectively with respect to the line $y=x$.

19. P_1 and Q_1 lie on

(a) C_1 and C_2 respectively (b) C_2 and C_1 respectively

(c) Cannot be determined (d) None of these

20. If the point $P(\lambda, \lambda^2+1)$ and $Q(\mu^2+1, \mu)$, then P_1 and Q_1 are

(a) (λ^2+1, λ) and (μ^2+1, μ) (b) (λ^2+1, λ) and (μ, μ^2+1)
(c) (λ, λ^2+1) and (μ, μ^2+1) (d) (λ, λ^2+1) and (μ^2+1, μ)

21. Arithmetic mean of PP_1 and QQ_1 is always less than

(a) PQ (b) $\frac{1}{2}PQ$ (c) $2PQ$ (d) $\frac{3}{2}PQ$

Sol. Since, the reflection of a point (p, q) with respect to line $y = x$ is (q, p).

Let $P(\lambda, \lambda^2+1)$ and $Q(\mu^2+1, \mu)$ be points on C_1 and C_2, respectively.

$\therefore$ Reflection of $P(\lambda, \lambda^2+1)$ with respect to line $y = x$ is $P_1(\lambda^2+1, \lambda)$ and reflection of $Q(\mu^2+1, \mu)$ with respect to line $y = x$ is $Q_1(\mu, \mu^2+1)$.

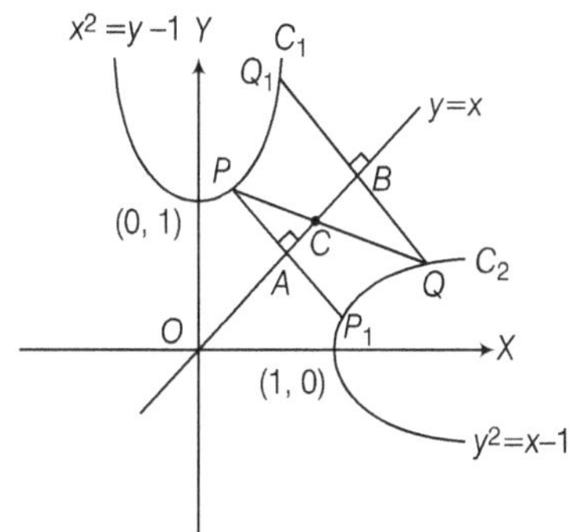

$\therefore$ P_1 and Q_1 are (λ^2+1, λ)

and (μ, μ^2+1) (**Ans.** 20(b))

Also, P_1 and Q_1 lie on $y^2 = x - 1$

and $x^2 = y - 1$.

Hence, P_1 and Q_1 lie on C_2 and C_1, respectively. (**Ans.** 19(b))

21. (a) $\because$ A is mid-point of PP_1 and B is mid-point of QQ_1.

$\therefore$ $PA = \frac{1}{2}PP_1$

and $QB = \frac{1}{2}QQ_1$ ...(i)

$\Rightarrow$ $PC \geq PA$ ...(ii)

and $QC \geq QB$ ...(iii)

On adding Eqs. (ii) and (iii), then

$$PC + QC \geq PA + QB$$

$$= \frac{1}{2}PP_1 + \frac{1}{2}QQ_1 \quad \text{[from Eq. (i)]}$$

$$= \left(\frac{PP_1 + QQ_1}{2}\right)$$

$\therefore$ $PC + QC \geq \left(\frac{PP_1 + QQ_1}{2}\right)$

$\Rightarrow$ $PQ \geq$ (AM of PP_1 and QQ_1)

JEE Type Solved Examples :
Single Integer Answer Type Questions

- This section contains **2 solved examples.** The answer to each example is **a single digit integer,** ranging from 0 to 9 (both inclusive).

Ex. 22 *Points A, B, C lie on the parabola $y^2 = 4ax$. The tangents to the parabola at A, B, C taken in pairs intersect at points P, Q, R, then, the ratio of the areas of the ΔABC and ΔPQR is*

Sol. (2) Let $(at_1^2, 2at_1)$, $(at_2^2, 2at_2)$ and $(at_3^2, 2at_3)$ be the points A, B and C respectively.

$$\therefore \text{Area of } \Delta ABC = \frac{1}{2}\left\|\begin{matrix} at_1^2 & 2at_1 & 1 \\ at_2^2 & 2at_2 & 1 \\ at_3^2 & 2at_3 & 1 \end{matrix}\right\| = a^2 \left\|\begin{matrix} 1 & t_1 & t_1^2 \\ 1 & t_2 & t_2^2 \\ 1 & t_3 & t_3^2 \end{matrix}\right\|$$

$$= a^2 |(t_1 - t_2)(t_2 - t_3)(t_3 - t_1)|$$

Coordinates of P, Q and R are $(at_2t_3, a(t_2+t_3))$, $(at_3t_1, a(t_3+t_1))$, $(at_1t_2, a(t_1+t_2))$ respectively, then

$$\text{Area of } \Delta PQR = \frac{1}{2}\left\|\begin{matrix} at_2t_3 & a(t_2+t_3) & 1 \\ at_3t_1 & a(t_3+t_1) & 1 \\ at_1t_2 & a(t_1+t_2) & 1 \end{matrix}\right\| = \frac{a^2}{2}\left\|\begin{matrix} t_2t_3 & t_2+t_3 & 1 \\ t_3t_1 & t_3+t_1 & 1 \\ t_1t_2 & t_1+t_2 & 1 \end{matrix}\right\|$$

$$= \frac{a^2}{2}|\Sigma t_2t_3(t_3 - t_2)|$$

$$= \frac{a^2}{2}|(t_1 - t_2)(t_2 - t_3)(t_3 - t_1)|$$

$$= \frac{1}{2} \times \text{Area of } \Delta ABC$$

$$\therefore \quad \frac{\text{Area of } \Delta ABC}{\text{Area of } \Delta PQR} = 2$$

Ex. 23 *If the orthocentre of the triangle formed by the points t_1, t_2, t_3 on the parabola $y^2 = 4ax$ is the focus, the value of $|t_1t_2 + t_2t_3 + t_3t_1|$ is*

Sol. (5) $\because SA$ is perpendicular to BC[S is focus $(a, 0)$]

$$\Rightarrow \quad \left(\frac{2at_1 - 0}{at_1^2 - a}\right)\left(\frac{2at_3 - 2at_2}{at_3^2 - at_2^2}\right) = -1$$

$$\Rightarrow \quad \left(\frac{2t_1}{t_1^2 - 1}\right)\left(\frac{2}{t_3 + t_2}\right) = -1$$

$$\Rightarrow \quad 4t_1 + t_1^2(t_2 + t_3) = t_2 + t_3 \qquad \text{...(i)}$$

Similarly, $\quad 4t_2 + t_2^2(t_3 + t_1) = t_3 + t_1 \qquad$ ...(ii)

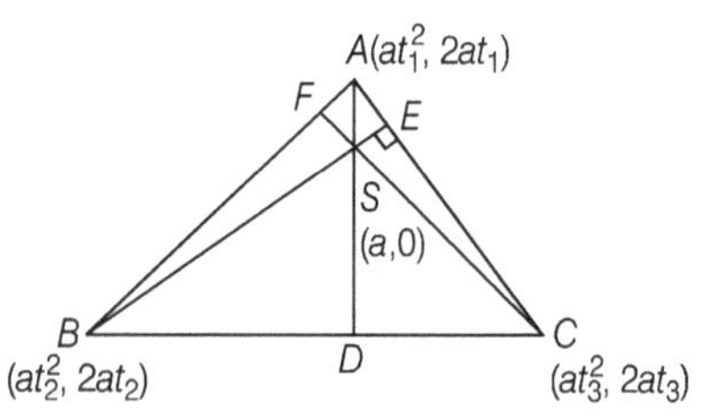

On subtracting Eq. (ii) from Eq. (i), then

$$4 + (t_1t_2 + t_2t_3 + t_3t_1) = -1 \Rightarrow t_1t_2 + t_2t_3 + t_3t_1 = -5$$

$$\therefore \quad |t_1t_2 + t_2t_3 + t_3t_1| = 5$$

JEE Type Solved Examples : Matching Type Questions

- This section contains **one solved example.** Example 24 has three statements (A, B and C) given in **Column I** and five statements (p, q, r, s and t) in **Column II.** Any given statement in **Column I** can have correct matching with one or more statement(s) given in **Column II.**

Ex. 24 *Match the following.*

Column I	Column II
(A) If PQ is any focal chord of the parabola $y^2 = 32x$ and length of PQ can never be less than λ units, then λ is divisible by	(p) 2
(B) A tangent is drawn to the parabola $y^2 = 4x$ at the point 'P' whose abscissa lies in the interval $[1, 4]$. If maximum possible area of the triangle formed by the tangent at 'P', ordinate of the point 'P' and the X-axis is λ sq units, then λ is divisible by	(q) 3
(C) The normal at the ends of the latusrectum of the parabola $y^2 = 4x$ meet the parabola again at A and A'. If length $AA' = \lambda$ unit, then λ is divisible by	(r) 4
	(s) 6
	(t) 8

Sol. (A) $\rightarrow$ (p, r, t); (B) $\rightarrow$ (p, r, t); (C) $\rightarrow$ (p, q, r, s)

(A) Let $P(at^2, 2at)$ be any point on the parabola $y^2 = 4ax$ and $S(a, 0)$ be the focus, then the other end of focal chord through P will be $Q\left(\frac{a}{t^2}, -\frac{2a}{t}\right)$.

Then, length of focal chord $PQ = a\left(t + \frac{1}{t}\right)^2$

$$\because \quad t + \frac{1}{t} \geq 2 \Rightarrow a\left(t + \frac{1}{t}\right)^2 \geq 4a$$

or $\quad PQ \geq 32 \qquad [\because 4a = 32]$

$$\therefore \quad \lambda = 32$$

(B) Equation of tangent to parabola $y^2 = 4x$ at $P(t^2, 2t)$ is

$$ty = x + t^2$$

Given $\quad t^2 \in [1, 4]$

$\therefore$ Area of $\Delta APN = \frac{1}{2}(AN)(PN)$

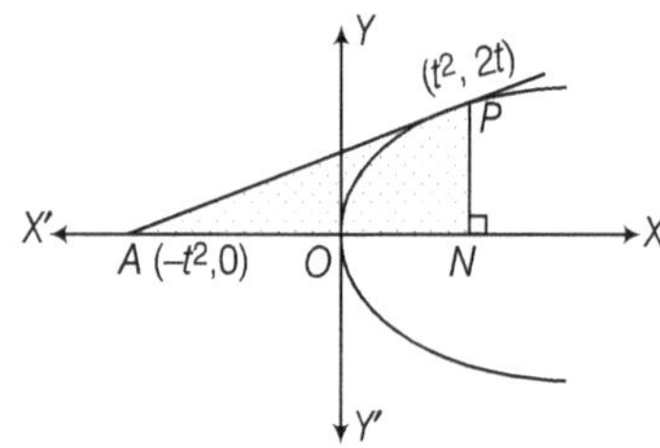

$$= \frac{1}{2}(2t^2)(2t)$$

$$\Rightarrow \quad \Delta = 2t^3 = 2(t^2)^{\frac{3}{2}}$$

$$\because \quad t^2 \in [1, 4]$$

$\Rightarrow \quad \Delta_{max}$ occurs, when $t^2 = 4$

$$\Rightarrow \quad \Delta_{max} = 2(4)^{\frac{3}{2}} = 16 \text{ sq units}$$

$$\therefore \quad \lambda = 16$$

(C) Given parabola $y^2 = 4x$. Now, the ends of latusrectum are $P(1, 2)$ and $Q(1, -2)$ or $P(t^2, 2t)$ and $Q(t_1^2, 2t_1)$, where $t = 1, t_1 = -1$.

We know that the other end of normal is given by $t_2 = -t - \frac{2}{t}$

$$\Rightarrow \quad A(t_2^2, 2t_2) \text{ and } A'(t_3^2, 2t_3),$$

where $\quad t_2 = -3, t_3 = 3$

or $\quad A(9, -6)$ and $A'(9, 6)$

$\therefore \quad AA' = 12$ units

$$\therefore \quad \lambda = 12$$

JEE Type Solved Examples :
Statement I and II Type Questions

- **Directions** (Ex. Nos. 25 and 26) are Assertion-Reason type questions. Each of these question contains two statements :
Statement I (Assertion) and
Statement II (Reason)
Each of these examples also has four alternative choices, only one of which is the correct answer.
You have to select the correct choice
(a) Statement I is true, Statement II is true; Statement II is a correct explanation for statement I.
(b) Statement I is true, Statement II is true; Statement II is not a correct explanation for Statement I.
(c) Statement I is true, Statement II is false.
(d) Statement I is false, Statement II is true.

Ex. 25 Statement I *Through the point $(\lambda, \lambda+1), \lambda<2$, there cannot be more than one normal to the parabola $y^2=4x$.*

Statement II *The point $(\lambda, \lambda+1)$ cannot lie inside the parabola $y^2=4x$.*

Sol. (b) Let $S=y^2-4x$

$$\therefore \quad S_1=(\lambda+1)^2-4\lambda=(\lambda-1)^2 \geq 0$$

$\therefore$ Point $(\lambda, \lambda+1)$ cannot lie inside the parabola $y^2=4x$.

$\therefore$ Statement II is true.

Now, equation of normal at $(t^2, 2t)$ is $y+tx=2t+t^3$ passes through $(\lambda, \lambda+1)$.

$$\Rightarrow \quad \lambda+1+t\lambda=2t+t^3$$

$$\Rightarrow \quad t^3+(2-\lambda)t-(\lambda+1)=0 \quad \text{...(i)}$$

On differentiating w.r.t. t, we get

$$3t^2+(2-\lambda)>0, \text{ for } \lambda<2$$

The cubic Eq. (i) has only one real root.

$\therefore$ Statement I is true.

Hence, both statements are true but Statement II is not correct explanation for Statement I.

Ex. 26 Statement I *If there exist points on the circle $x^2+y^2=\lambda^2$ from which two perpendicular tangents can be drawn to the parabola $y^2=2x$, then $\lambda \geq \frac{1}{2}$.*

Statement II *Perpendicular tangents to the parabola meet at the directrix.*

Sol. (a) Statement II is true as it is property of parabola. Equation of directrix of parabola $y^2=2x$ is $x=-\frac{1}{2}$.

Any point on directrix is $\left(-\frac{1}{2}, y\right)$, now this point exists on the circle, then

$$\frac{1}{4}+y^2=\lambda^2$$

$$\Rightarrow \quad y^2=\lambda^2-\frac{1}{4} \geq 0$$

$$\therefore \quad \lambda \geq \frac{1}{2}$$

Hence, both statements are true and Statement II is correct explanation for Statement I.

Subjective Type Examples

- In this section, there are **16 subjective solved examples.**

Ex. 27 *The two parabolas $y^2=4a(x-l)$ and $x^2=4a(y-l_1)$ always touch one another, l and l_1 being variable parameters. Prove that the point of contact lies on the curve $xy=4a^2$.*

Sol. Let (h, k) be the common point and if the parabolas touch each other, then the tangents at (h, k) should be identical. Their equations are

$$ky=2a(x-l+h)$$

$$\Rightarrow \quad 2ax-ky=2a(l-h) \quad \text{...(i)}$$

and

$$hx=2a(y-l_1+k)$$

$$\Rightarrow \quad hx-2ay=2a(k-l_1) \quad \text{...(ii)}$$

On comparing the coefficients of x and y in Eq. (i) and (ii), we get

$$\frac{2a}{h}=\frac{k}{2a}$$

$$\Rightarrow \quad hk=4a^2$$

Hence, the locus is $xy=4a^2$, which is independent of l and l_1.

Ex. 28 *Show that the area formed by the normals to $y^2=4ax$ at the points t_1, t_2, t_3 is $\frac{1}{2}a^2|(t_1-t_2)(t_2-t_3)(t_3-t_1)|\lambda^2$, where $\lambda=(t_1+t_2+t_3)$.*

Sol. Equation of normals at P, Q, R are

$$y=-t_1x+2at_1+at_1^3$$

$y=-t_2x+2at_2+at_2^3,\ y=-t_3x+2at_3+at_3^3,$ respectively.

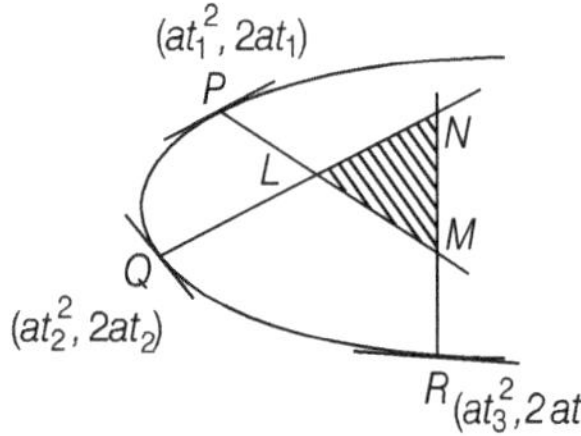

Subtracting them two by two, coordinates of L, M and N are

$$L \equiv \{2a+a(t_1^2+t_1t_2+t_2^2), -at_1t_2(t_1+t_2)\}$$
$$M \equiv \{2a+a(t_1^2+t_1t_3+t_3^2), -at_1t_3(t_1+t_3)\}$$
$$N \equiv \{2a+a(t_2^2+t_2t_3+t_3^2), -at_2t_3(t_2+t_3)\}$$

$\therefore$ Area of ΔLMN

$$=\frac{1}{2}\left|\begin{vmatrix} 2a+a(t_1^2+t_1t_2+t_2^2) & -at_1t_2(t_1+t_2) & 1 \\ 2a+a(t_1^2+t_1t_3+t_3^2) & -at_1t_3(t_1+t_3) & 1 \\ 2a+a(t_2^2+t_2t_3+t_3^2) & -at_2t_3(t_2+t_3) & 1 \end{vmatrix}\right|$$

On applying $R_2 \to R_2 - R_1$ and $R_3 \to R_3 - R_1$

$$=\frac{a^2}{2}\left|\begin{vmatrix} 2+(t_1^2+t_1t_2+t_2^2) & -t_1t_2(t_1+t_2) & 1 \\ (t_3-t_2)(t_1+t_2+t_3) & t_1(t_3-t_2)(t_1+t_2+t_3) & 0 \\ (t_3-t_1)(t_1+t_2+t_3) & t_2(t_3-t_1)(t_1+t_2+t_3) & 0 \end{vmatrix}\right|$$

Expanding by last column

$$=\frac{a^2}{2}|(t_3-t_1)(t_3-t_2)|(t_1+t_2+t_3)^2\left|\begin{vmatrix} 1 & t_1 \\ 1 & t_2 \end{vmatrix}\right|$$
$$=\frac{1}{2}a^2|(t_1-t_2)(t_2-t_3)(t_3-t_1)|(t_1+t_2+t_3)^2$$
$$=\frac{1}{2}a^2|(t_1-t_2)(t_2-t_3)(t_3-t_1)|\lambda^2$$

Aliter

Equations of sides of ΔLMN formed by the normals are

$$y+t_1x-(2at_1+at_1^3)=0$$
$$y+t_2x-(2at_2+at_2^3)=0$$
$$y+t_3x-(2at_3+at_3^3)=0$$

$$\therefore \text{ Required area} = \frac{1}{2|C_1C_2C_3|}\begin{vmatrix} t_1 & 1 & -(2at_1+at_1^3) \\ t_2 & 1 & -(2at_2+at_2^3) \\ t_3 & 1 & -(2at_3+at_3^3) \end{vmatrix}^2$$

$$=\frac{a^2}{|2(t_2-t_3)(t_3-t_1)(t_1-t_2)|}\begin{vmatrix} t_1 & 1 & 2t_1+t_1^3 \\ t_2 & 1 & 2t_2+t_2^3 \\ t_3 & 1 & 2t_3+t_3^3 \end{vmatrix}^2$$

$$=\frac{a^2}{2|(t_2-t_3)(t_3-t_1)(t_1-t_2)|}\left\{\begin{vmatrix} t_1 & 1 & 2t_1 \\ t_2 & 1 & 2t_2 \\ t_3 & 1 & 2t_3 \end{vmatrix}+\begin{vmatrix} t_1 & 1 & t_1^3 \\ t_2 & 1 & t_2^3 \\ t_3 & 1 & t_3^3 \end{vmatrix}\right\}^2$$

$$=\frac{a^2}{2|(t_2-t_3)(t_3-t_1)(t_1-t_2)|}\{0-(t_1-t_2)(t_2-t_3)(t_3-t_1)(t_1+t_2+t_3)\}^2$$

$$=\frac{1}{2}a^2|(t_1-t_2)(t_2-t_3)(t_3-t_1)|(t_1+t_2+t_3)^2$$
$$=\frac{1}{2}a^2|(t_1-t_2)(t_2-t_3)(t_3-t_1)|\lambda^2.$$

Ex. 29 *Prove that the two parabolas $y^2=4ax$ and $y^2=4c(x-b)$ cannot have common normal, other than the axis unless $b/(a-c)>2$.*

Sol. Given parabolas $y^2=4ax$ and $y^2=4c(x-b)$ have common normals. Then equation of normals in terms of slopes are

$$y=mx-2am-am^3$$

and $$y=m(x-b)-2cm-cm^3$$

respectively then normals must be identical, compare the coefficients

$$1=\frac{2am+am^3}{mb+2cm+cm^3}$$

$\Rightarrow$ $m[(c-a)m^2+(b+2c-2a)]=0,$

$m \neq 0$ [$\because$ other than axis]

and $m^2=\dfrac{2a-2c-b}{c-a},$

$$m=\pm\sqrt{\frac{2(a-c)-b}{c-a}}$$

$\Rightarrow$ $m=\pm\sqrt{\left(-2-\dfrac{b}{c-a}\right)}$

$\therefore$ $-2-\dfrac{b}{c-a}>0$

$\Rightarrow$ $-2+\dfrac{b}{a-c}>0$

$\Rightarrow$ $\dfrac{b}{a-c}>2$

Ex. 30 *If on a given base BC, a triangle is described such that the sum of the tangents of the base angles is m, then prove that the locus of the opposite vertex A is a parabola.*

Sol. Let the given point B and C be $(0, 0)$ and $(a, 0)$, respectively.

Given, $\tan\alpha+\tan\beta=m$ (constant)

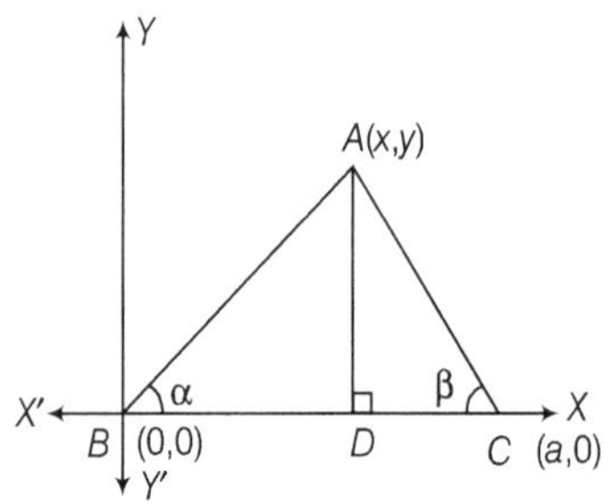

$\Rightarrow$ $\dfrac{y}{x}+\dfrac{y}{a-x}=m$

$\Rightarrow$ $\dfrac{ay}{x(a-x)}=m$

$\therefore$ $ay=amx-mx^2$

which is the equation of parabola.

Ex. 31 *A parabolic mirror is kept along $y^2 = 4x$ and two light rays parallel to its axis are reflected along one straight line. If one of the incident rays is at 3 units distance from the axis, then find the distance of the other incident ray from the axis.*

Sol. Let the incident rays be PA and QB.

After reflection, both rays passes through the focus $S(1, 0)$.

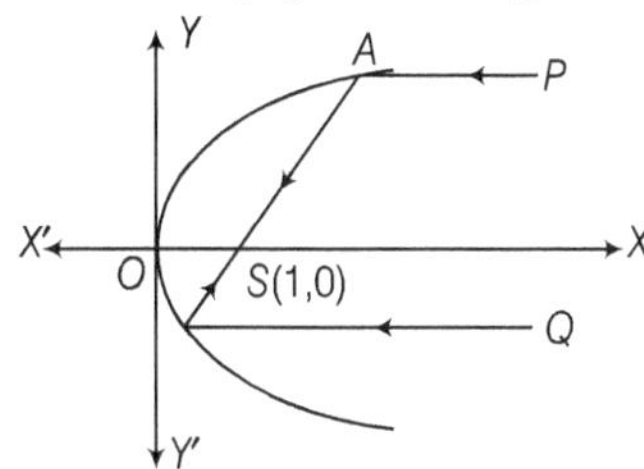

Therefore, AB is a focal chord.

Let A be $(t^2, 2t)$, then B be $\left(\frac{1}{t^2}, \frac{-2}{t}\right)$.

Given, $2t = 3 \therefore t = 3/2$

Hence, distance of B from the axis of parabola is $\left|-\frac{2}{t}\right| = \frac{4}{3}$ units.

Ex. 32 *Prove that the length of the intercept on the normal at the point $P(at^2, 2at)$ of a parabola $y^2 = 4ax$ made by the circle on the line joining the focus and point P as diameter is $a\sqrt{(1+t^2)}$.*

Sol. Let the normal at $P(at^2, 2at)$ cut the circle in K and the axis of parabola at G then PK is required intercept.

$$SP = PM = a + at^2$$

Directrix (x+a=0)

Since angle in a semi-circle being right angle.

$\therefore \quad \angle SKP = 90°$

and normal at $P(at^2, 2at)$ is

$$y = -tx + 2at + at^3$$

$$\Rightarrow \quad tx + y - 2at - at^3 = 0 \quad \text{...(i)}$$

$\therefore$ SK is the perpendicular distance from $S(a, 0)$ to the normal (i),

then $SK = \frac{|at + 0 - 2at - at^3|}{\sqrt{t^2+1}} = a|t|\sqrt{1+t^2}$

$\therefore$ In ΔSPK, $(Pk)^2 = (SP)^2 - (SK)^2$

$$= a^2(1+t^2)^2 - a^2t^2(1+t^2) = a^2(1+t^2)$$

$$\therefore \quad PK = a\sqrt{(1+t^2)}$$

Ex. 33 *A parabola of latusrectum 4a, touches a fixed equal parabola, the axes of the two curves being parallel; prove that the locus of the vertex of the moving curve is a parabola of latusrectum 8a.*

Sol. Let the given parabola is

$$y^2 = 4ax \quad \text{...(i)}$$

If the vertex of moving parabola is (α, β), then equation of moving parabola is

$$(y-\beta)^2 = -4a(x-\alpha) \quad \text{...(ii)}$$

On substituting the value of i.e. $x = \frac{y^2}{4a}$ in Eq. (ii),

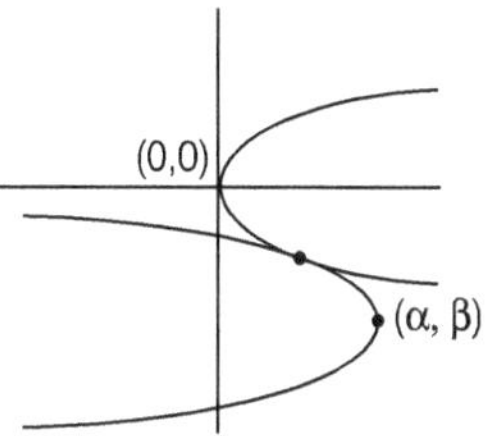

then $\quad (y-\beta)^2 = -4a\left(\frac{y^2}{4a} - \alpha\right)$

$$\Rightarrow \quad y^2 - 2\beta y + \beta^2 = -y^2 + 4a\alpha$$

$$2y^2 - 2\beta y + \beta^2 - 4a\alpha = 0 \quad \text{...(iii)}$$

Since, two parabolas (i) and (ii) touch each other.

Hence, roots of Eq. (iii) are equal i.e. Discriminant = 0

$\Rightarrow \quad$ "$B^2 - 4AC = 0$"

$\therefore \quad (-2\beta)^2 = 4 \cdot 2 \cdot (\beta^2 - 4a\alpha)$

$\Rightarrow \quad 4\beta^2 = 32a\alpha$

or $\quad \beta^2 = 8a\alpha$

the required locus is $\quad y^2 = 8ax$

which has latusrectum double that of given parabola.

Ex. 34 *The normal at point P on a given parabola meet the axis of parabola at Q. Then prove that a line through Q and perpendicular to this normal always touches a fixed parabola whose length of latusrectum is same as that of given parabola.*

Sol. Let the equation of parabola is

$$y^2 = 4ax. \quad \text{...(i)}$$

Let $P(at^2, 2at)$

Normal at P is $\quad y + tx = 2at + at^3$

$\because$ Normal meet the axis of parabola (i.e. X-axis), then $Q(2a + at^2, 0)$.

Now, equation of the line through Q and perpendicular to the normal is

$$y - 0 = \frac{1}{t}(x - 2a - at^2)$$

$$\Rightarrow \quad ty = x - 2a - at^2$$

$$\Rightarrow \quad ty = (x - 2a) - at^2$$

which is clearly tangent to the parabola

$$y^2 = 4a(2a - x).$$

Ex. 35 *TP and TQ are any two tangents to a parabola and the tangent at a third point R cuts them in P′ and Q′, prove that* $\frac{TP'}{TP} + \frac{TQ'}{TQ} = 1.$

Sol. Let parabola be $y^2 = 4ax$ and coordinates of P and Q on this parabola are $P \equiv (at_1^2, 2at_1)$ and $Q \equiv (at_2^2, 2at_2)$; T is the point of intersection of tangents at t_1 and t_2.

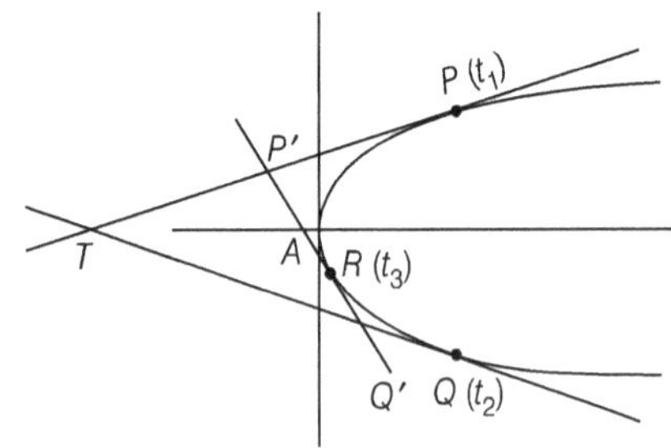

$\therefore$ Coordinates of $T \equiv \{at_1 t_2, a(t_1 + t_2)\}$

Similarly $\quad P' \equiv \{at_3 t_1, a(t_3 + t_1)\}$

$\quad Q' \equiv \{at_2 t_3, a(t_2 + t_3)\}$

Let $\quad TP' : TP = \lambda : 1$

$$\therefore \quad \lambda = \frac{t_3 - t_2}{t_1 - t_2} \quad \Rightarrow \quad \frac{TP'}{TP} = \frac{t_3 - t_2}{t_1 - t_2}$$

Similarly, $\quad \frac{TQ'}{TQ} = \frac{t_1 - t_3}{t_1 - t_2}$

$$\therefore \quad \frac{TP'}{TP} + \frac{TQ'}{TQ} = 1$$

Ex. 36 *Prove that on the axis of any parabola there is a certain point 'K' which has the property that, if a chord PQ of parabola be drawn through it, then* $\frac{1}{PK^2} + \frac{1}{QK^2}$ *is the same for all positions of the chord.*

Sol. Any line passing through K is $\frac{x - d}{\cos\theta} = \frac{y - 0}{\sin\theta} = r$

$\therefore$ Coordinates of P and Q are

$$(d + KP\cos\theta, KP\sin\theta)$$

and $\quad (d - KQ\cos\theta, -KQ\sin\theta).$

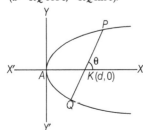

Points P and Q lie on $y^2 = 4ax$ then

$$(KP)^2 \sin^2\theta = 4a(d + KP\cos\theta) \quad \text{...(i)}$$

and $\quad (KQ)^2 \sin^2\theta = 4a(d - KQ\cos\theta) \quad$ ...(ii)

From Eq. (i), $\quad KP = \dfrac{4a\cos\theta + \sqrt{(16a^2\cos^2\theta + 16ad\sin^2\theta)}}{2\sin^2\theta}$

From Eq. (ii), $\quad KQ = \dfrac{-4a\cos\theta + \sqrt{(16a^2\cos^2\theta + 16ad\sin^2\theta)}}{2\sin^2\theta}$

$$\therefore \quad \frac{1}{(KP)^2} + \frac{1}{(KQ)^2} = \frac{2a\cos^2\theta + d\sin^2\theta}{2ad^2}$$

For $d = 2a$

$$\therefore \quad \frac{1}{(KP)^2} + \frac{1}{(KQ)^2} = \frac{1}{d^2}$$

$$= \frac{1}{4a^2}, \text{ which is independent of } \theta.$$

Ex. 37 *If the distribution of weight is uniform, then the rope of the suspended bridge takes the form of parabola. The height of the supporting towers is 20 m, the distance between these towers is 150 m and the height of the lowest point of the rope from the road is 3 m. Find the equation of the parabolic shape of the rope considering the floor of the bridge as X-axis and the axis of the parabola as Y-axis. Find the height of that tower which supports the rope and is at a distance of 30 m from the centre of the road.*

Sol. Here MZ is the road let V is lowest point of the rope given $VZ = 3$ m.

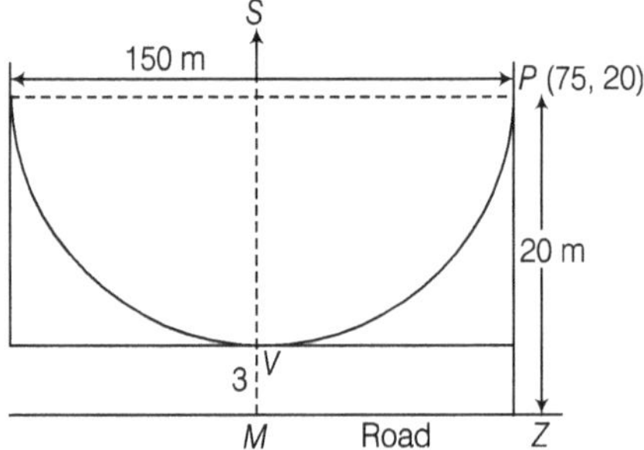

Let MZ is X-axis and let MVS is Y-axis.

Taking X and Y-axes as shown in the given figure, the equation of parabola is of the form

$$x^2 = 4ay$$

if V is origin

Coordinates of P is $\left\{\frac{1}{2}(150), 20 - 3\right\}$ i.e. $(75, 17)$ P lies on Eq. (i), then

$$(75)^2 = 4a(17)$$

or $\quad 4a = \dfrac{5625}{17}$

From Eq. (i), $\quad x^2 = \dfrac{5625}{17} y$

Now, shifting the origin (0, 0) to $M(0, -3)$, then equation of parabola in new form is

$$x^2 = \frac{5625}{17}(y-3) \quad \text{...(ii)}$$

Again, let the required height of supporting tower at a distance of 30 m from the centre of road be h metres, then the coordinates of the top of this tower are $(30, h)$ referred to given axes

from Eq. (ii), $(30)^2 = \frac{5625}{17}(h-3)$

$$\therefore \quad h = \left(\frac{900 \times 17}{5625}\right) + 3 = 5.72 \text{ m}$$

Ex. 38 *Tangent is drawn at any point (x_1, y_1) on the parabola $y^2 = 4ax$. Now tangents are drawn from any point on this tangent to the circle $x^2 + y^2 = a^2$ such that all the chords of contact pass through a fixed point (x_2, y_2). Prove that $4\left(\frac{x_1}{x_2}\right) + \left(\frac{y_1}{y_2}\right)^2 = 0$.*

Sol. Tangent at (x_1, y_1) on the parabola $y^2 = 4ax$

$$\therefore \quad yy_1 = 2a(x + x_1)$$

Any point on this tangent will be $\left(x', \frac{2a(x' + x_1)}{y_1}\right)$

Equation of chord of contact of the point $\left(x', \frac{2a(x' + x_1)}{y_1}\right)$ w.r.t. circle $x^2 + y^2 = a^2$ is $xx' + y \cdot \frac{2a(x' + x_1)}{y_1} = a^2$

$$\Rightarrow \quad xx'y_1 + 2ayx' + 2ayx_1 = a^2y_1$$

$$\Rightarrow \quad (2ayx_1 - a^2y_1) + x'(xy_1 + 2ay) = 0$$

which is family of straight lines passing through point of intersection of

$$2ayx_1 - a^2y_1 = 0 \quad \text{and} \quad xy_1 + 2ay = 0$$

$$\therefore \quad y = \frac{ay_1}{2x_1}$$

and
$$x = -\frac{2ay}{y_1} = \left(-\frac{2a}{y_1}\right)\left(\frac{ay_1}{2x_1}\right)$$

$$x = -\frac{a^2}{x_1}$$

The fixed point is (x_2, y_2).

$$\therefore \quad x_2 = -\frac{a^2}{x_1} \quad \text{and} \quad y_2 = \frac{ay_1}{2x_1}$$

$$\therefore \quad 4\left(\frac{x_1}{x_2}\right) + \left(\frac{y_1}{y_2}\right)^2 = 4\left(\frac{x_1}{-a^2/x_1}\right) + \left(\frac{y_1}{ay_1/2x_1}\right)^2$$

$$= -\frac{4x_1^2}{a^2} + \frac{4x_1^2}{a^2} = 0$$

Hence, $4\left(\frac{x_1}{x_2}\right) + \left(\frac{y_1}{y_2}\right)^2 = 0.$

Ex. 39 *A variable chord PQ of the parabola $y = 4x^2$ subtends a right angle at the vertex. Find the locus of the points of intersection of the normals at P and Q.*

Sol. Parametric point on the parabola

$$y = 4x^2 \text{ is } (t, 4t^2)$$

Let $P(t_1, 4t_1^2)$ and $Q(t_2, 4t_2^2)$,

if A is vertex of the parabola, then

Slope of $AP \times$ Slope of $AQ = -1$ $\quad [\because AP \perp AQ]$

$$\therefore \quad 4t_1 \times 4t_2 = -1$$

$$\therefore \quad t_1t_2 = -\frac{1}{16}$$

Equations of normals at P and Q are

$$x + 4t_1y = t_1 + 16t_1^3 \quad \text{...(i)}$$

and
$$x + 4t_2y = t_2 + 16t_2^3 \quad \text{...(ii)}$$

Let the normals (i) and (ii) intersect at (h, k), then on solving Eqs. (i) and (ii), then we get

$$k = \frac{1 + 16(t_1^2 + t_2^2 + t_1t_2)}{4}$$

$$\Rightarrow \quad k = \frac{1 + 16(t_1^2 + t_2^2) + 16t_1t_2}{4}$$

$$= \frac{1 + 16((t_1 + t_2)^2 - 2t_1t_2) - 1}{4} \quad [\because 16t_1t_2 = -1]$$

$$= 4\left\{(t_1 + t_2)^2 + \frac{1}{8}\right\}$$

$$k = 4(t_1 + t_2)^2 + \frac{1}{2} \quad \text{...(iii)}$$

Again $\quad h = -16t_1t_2(t_1 + t_2)$

$$\Rightarrow \quad h = t_1 + t_2 \quad \text{...(iv)}$$

On eliminating t_1 and t_2 from Eqs. (iii) and (iv), we get

$$k = 4h^2 + \frac{1}{2}$$

$$\Rightarrow \quad 2k = 8h^2 + 1$$

Hence, locus of (h, k) is $2y = 8x^2 + 1$.

Ex. 40 *Equilateral triangles are circumscribed to the parabola $y^2 = 4ax$. Prove that their angular points lie on the conic $(3x + a)(x + 3a) = y^2$.*

Sol. Let coordinates of P and Q are $(at_1^2, 2at_1)$ and $(at_2^2, 2at_2)$, respectively.

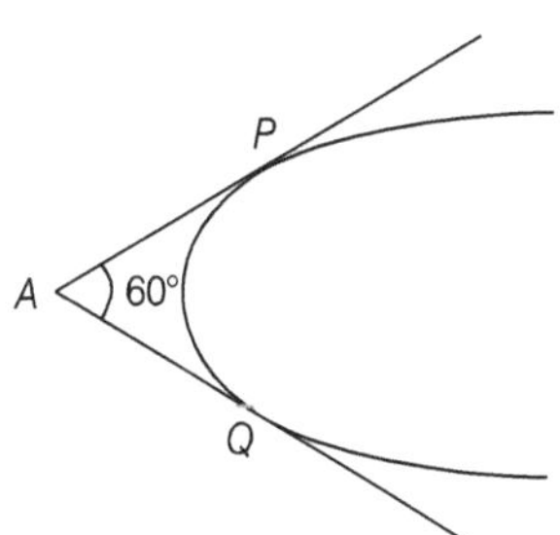

Tangents at P and Q are $t_1y = x + at_1^2$ and $t_2y = x + at_2^2$, respectively.

Slope of tangents at P and Q are $\frac{1}{t_1}$ and $\frac{1}{t_2}$, respectively.

Let one angular point of equilateral triangle is A.

$\therefore \quad A \equiv (at_1t_2, a(t_1 + t_2))$

Given, $\tan 60° = \left| \dfrac{\frac{1}{t_1} - \frac{1}{t_2}}{1 + \frac{1}{t_1} \cdot \frac{1}{t_2}} \right| = \left| \dfrac{t_2 - t_1}{1 + t_1t_2} \right|$

$\Rightarrow \quad (\sqrt{3})^2 (1 + t_1t_2)^2 = (t_2 - t_1)^2$

$\Rightarrow \quad 3(1 + t_1t_2)^2 = (t_1 + t_2)^2 - 4t_1t_2$

For locus of A, put $at_1t_2 = x$ and $a(t_1 + t_2) = y$, then

$$3\left(1 + \frac{x}{a}\right)^2 = \left(\frac{y}{a}\right)^2 - 4\frac{x}{a}$$

$\Rightarrow \quad y^2 = 3x^2 + 10ax + 3a^2$

$\therefore \quad (3x + a)(x + 3a) = y^2$

Ex. 41 *A parabola is drawn to pass through A and B, the ends of diameter of a given circle of radius a and to have a directrix a tangent to a concentric circle of radius b, the axes being AB and the perpendicular diameter. Prove that the locus of the focus of the parabola is* $\dfrac{x^2}{b^2} + \dfrac{y^2}{b^2 - a^2} = 1.$

Sol. Let AB be taken along X-axis, it mid-point O as origin and a line through O perpendicular to AB as Y-axis.

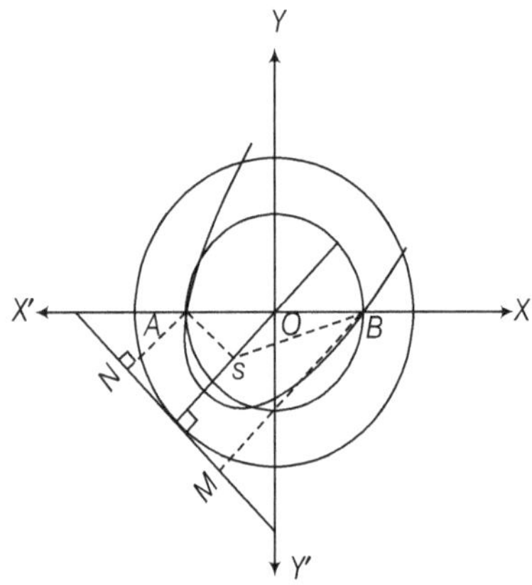

Equation of circle on AB as diameter is

$$x^2 + y^2 = a^2 \quad \text{...(i)}$$

The equation of a circle of radius b and concentric to circle (i) is

$$x^2 + y^2 = b^2 \quad \text{...(ii)}$$

Let $S(h, k)$ be the focus of the parabola which passes through $A(-a, 0)$ and $B(a, 0)$.

Let equation of tangent to circle (ii) be

$$x\cos\theta + y\sin\theta = 6. \quad \text{...(iii)}$$

This is taken as directrix, then

$$SP = PM$$

$\Rightarrow \quad BS = BM \Rightarrow (h - a)^2 + (k - 0)^2 = (a\cos\theta - b)^2 \quad \text{...(iv)}$

and $\quad AS = AN$

$\Rightarrow \quad (h + a)^2 + (k - 0)^2 = (a\cos\theta + b)^2 \quad \text{...(v)}$

On adding Eqs. (iv) and (v), then

$$a^2\cos^2\theta + b^2 = h^2 + k^2 + a^2 \quad \text{...(vi)}$$

On subtracting Eq. (iv) from Eq. (v), then

$$4ab\cos\theta = 4ah \text{ or } \cos\theta = \frac{h}{b} \quad \text{...(vii)}$$

From Eqs. (vi) and (vii), we get

$$\frac{a^2h^2}{b^2} + b^2 = h^2 + k^2 + a^2$$

$\Rightarrow \quad h^2\dfrac{(b^2 - a^2)}{a^2} + k^2 = b^2 - a^2$

$\Rightarrow \quad \dfrac{h^2}{a^2} + \dfrac{k^2}{b^2 - a^2} = 1$

Hence, the locus of $S(h, k)$ is

$$\frac{x^2}{a^2} + \frac{y^2}{b^2 - a^2} = 1.$$

Ex. 42 *Two straight lines are at right angles to one another and one of them touches* $y^2 = 4a(x + a)$ *and the other* $y^2 = 4b(x + b)$. *Prove that the point of intersection of the lines lies on the line* $x + a + b = 0$.

Sol. We know that any tangent in terms of slope (m) of the parabola $y^2 = 4ax$ is $y = mx + \frac{a}{m}$.

Replacing x by $x + a$, we get

$$y = m(x + a) + \frac{a}{m} \text{ which is tangent to}$$

$$y^2 = 4a(x + a) \quad \text{...(i)}$$

Similarly, tangent in terms of slope of $y^2 = 4b(x + b)$ is

$$y = m_1(x + b) + \frac{b}{m_1} \quad \text{...(ii)}$$

Given tangents are perpendicular, we have

$$mm_1 = -1 \quad \text{or} \quad m_1 = -\frac{1}{m}$$

then Eq. (ii) becomes $y = -\dfrac{(x + b)}{m} - bm$

On subtracting Eqs. (i) and (ii), then

$$0 = (x + a + b)\left(m + \frac{1}{m}\right)$$

$\Rightarrow \quad m + \dfrac{1}{m} \neq 0$

Hence, $\quad x + a + b = 0$

Parabola Exercise 1 :
Single Option Correct Type Questions

- This section contains **30 multiple choice questions.** Each question has four choices (a), (b), (c) and (d) out of which **ONLY ONE** is correct

1. A common tangent is drawn to the circle $x^2+y^2=a^2$ and the parabola $y^2=4bx$. If the angle which this tangent makes with the axis of x is $\frac{\pi}{4}$, then the relationship between a and b is $(a, b>0)$
(a) $b=\sqrt{2}a$ (b) $a=b\sqrt{2}$ (c) $c=2a$ (d) $a=2c$

2. The equation of parabola whose vertex and focus lie on the axis of x at distances a and a_1 from the origin respectively, is
(a) $y^2=4(a_1-a)x$ (b) $y^2=4(a_1-a)(x-a)$
(c) $y^2=4(a_1-a)(x-a_1)$ (d) $y^2=4aa_1x$

3. If parabolas $y^2=ax$ and $25[(x-3)^2+(y+2)^2]=(3x-4y-2)^2$ are equal, then the value of a is
(a) 3 (b) 6 (c) 7 (d) 9

4. $ABCD$ and $EFGC$ are squares and the curve $y=\lambda\sqrt{x}$ passes through the origin D and the points B and F. The ratio $\frac{FG}{BC}$ is

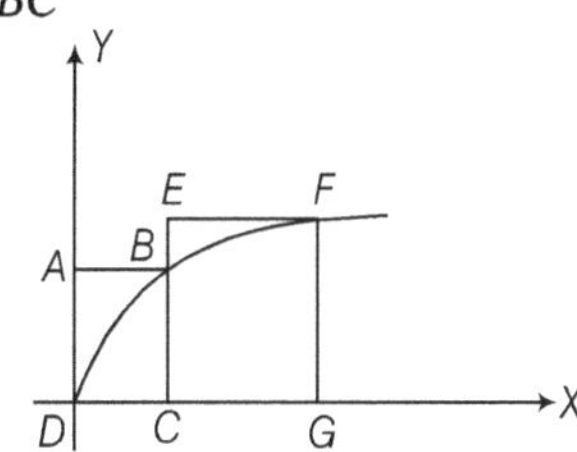

(a) $\frac{\sqrt{3}+1}{4}$ (b) $\frac{\sqrt{3}+1}{2}$ (c) $\frac{\sqrt{5}+1}{4}$ (d) $\frac{\sqrt{5}+1}{2}$

5. Let A and B be two points on a parabola $y^2=x$ with vertex V such that VA is perpendicular to VB and θ is the angle between the chord VA and the axis of the parabola. The value of $\frac{|VA|}{|VB|}$ is
(a) $\tan\theta$ (b) $\cot^2\theta$ (c) $\tan^3\theta$ (d) $\cot^3\theta$

6. The vertex of the parabola whose parametric equation is $x=t^2-t+1, y=t^2+t+1, t\in R$, is
(a) (1, 1) (b) (2, 2) (c) (3, 3) (d) $\left(\frac{1}{2},\frac{1}{2}\right)$

7. The circle $x^2+y^2+2px=0, p\in R$, touches the parabola $y^2=4x$ externally, then
(a) $p>0$ (b) $p<0$ (c) $p>1$ (d) $p>2$

8. If $a\neq 0$ and the line $2bx+3cy+4d=0$ passes through the points of intersection of the parabolas $y^2=4ax$ and $x^2=4ay$, then
(a) $d^2+(2b+3c)^2=0$ (b) $d^2+(3b+2c)^2=a^2$
(c) $d^2+(2b-3c)^2=0$ (d) $d^2+(2b+3c)^2=a^2$

9. A parabola $y=ax^2+bx+c$ crosses the X-axis at $(\alpha, 0)$ and $(\beta, 0)$ both to the right of the origin. A circle also passes through these two points. The length of a tangent from the origin to the circle is
(a) $\sqrt{\frac{bc}{a}}$ (b) ac^2 (c) $\frac{b}{a}$ (d) $\sqrt{\frac{c}{a}}$

10. Two mutually perpendicular tangent of the parabola $y^2=4ax$ meet the axis at P_1 and P_2. It S is the focus of the parabola, then $\frac{1}{SP_1}+\frac{1}{SP_2}$ is equal to
(a) $\frac{1}{4a}$ (b) $\frac{1}{a}$ (c) $\frac{2}{a}$ (d) $\frac{4}{a}$

11. If the normal to the parabola $y^2=4ax$ at P meets the curve again at Q and if PQ and the normal at Q make angles α and β respectively with the X-axis, then $\tan\alpha(\tan\alpha+\tan\beta)$ has the value equal to
(a) -2 (b) -1 (c) $-\frac{1}{2}$ (d) 0

12. If the normals to the parabola $y^2=4ax$ at three points P, Q and R meet at A and S is the focus, then $SP\cdot SQ\cdot SR$ is equal to
(a) $(SA)^2$ (b) $(SA)^3$ (c) $a(SA)^2$ (d) $a(SA)^3$

13. The length of the shortest normal chord of the parabola $y^2=4ax$ is
(a) $2a\sqrt{27}$ (b) $9a$ (c) $a\sqrt{54}$ (d) $18a$

14. The largest value of a for which the circle $x^2+y^2=a^2$ falls totally in the interior of the parabola $y^2=4(x+4)$ is
(a) $4\sqrt{3}$ (b) 4 (c) $\frac{4\sqrt{6}}{7}$ (d) $2\sqrt{3}$

15. From a point $(\sin\theta, \cos\theta)$, if three normals can be drawn to the parabola $y^2=4ax$, then the value of a is
(a) $\left(\frac{1}{2},1\right)$ (b) $\left[-\frac{1}{2},0\right)$
(c) $\left[\frac{1}{2},1\right]$ (d) $\left(\frac{-1}{2},0\right)\cup\left(0,\frac{1}{2}\right)$

16. If two different tangents of $y^2 = 4x$ are the normals to $x^2 = 4$ by, then

(a) $|b| < \frac{1}{2\sqrt{2}}$ (b) $|b| < \frac{1}{\sqrt{2}}$

(c) $|b| > \frac{1}{2\sqrt{2}}$ (d) $|b| > \frac{1}{\sqrt{2}}$

17. The shortest distance between the parabolas $2y^2 = 2x - 1$ and $2x^2 = 2y - 1$ is

(a) $\frac{1}{2\sqrt{2}}$ (b) $\frac{1}{2}$ (c) $2\sqrt{2}$ (d) 4

18. Normals at two points (x_1, y_1) and (x_2, y_2) of the parabola $y^2 = 4x$ meet again on the parabola, where $x_1 + x_2 = 4$, then $|y_1 + y_2|$ is equal to

(a) $\sqrt{2}$ (b) $2\sqrt{2}$ (c) $4\sqrt{2}$ (d) $8\sqrt{2}$

19. A line is drawn from $A(-2, 0)$ to intersect the curve $y^2 = 4x$ at P and Q in the first quadrant such that $\frac{1}{AP} + \frac{1}{AQ} < \frac{1}{4}$. Then the slope of the line is always

(a) $< \frac{1}{\sqrt{3}}$ (b) $> \frac{1}{\sqrt{3}}$ (c) $> \sqrt{2}$ (d) $> \sqrt{3}$

20. An equilateral triangle SAB is inscribed in the parabola $y^2 = 4ax$ having its focus at S. If chord AB lies towards the left of S, then the side length of this triangle is

(a) $a(2 - \sqrt{3})$ (b) $2a(2 - \sqrt{3})$

(c) $4a(2 - \sqrt{3})$ (d) $8a(2 - \sqrt{3})$

21. Let C be a circle with centre (0, 1) and radius unity. P is the parabola $y = ax^2$. The set of values of a for which they meet at a point other than origin is

(a) $(0, \infty)$ (b) $\left(0, \frac{1}{2}\right)$ (c) $\left(\frac{1}{4}, \frac{1}{2}\right)$ (d) $\left(\frac{1}{2}, \infty\right)$

22. Let S be the focus of $y^2 = 4x$ and a point P be moving on the curve such that its abscissa is increasing at the rate of 4 units/s. Then the rate of increase of the projection of SP on $x + y = 1$ when p is at (4, 4) is

(a) $-\sqrt{2}$ (b) $-\frac{3}{\sqrt{2}}$ (c) -1 (d) $\sqrt{2}$

23. If P is a point on the parabola $y^2 = 3(2x - 3)$ and M is the foot of perpendicular drawn from P on the directrix of the parabola, then the length of each side of the equilateral triangle SMP, where S is the focus of the parabola, is

(a) 2 (b) 4 (c) 6 (d) 8

24. Consider the parabola $y^2 = 4x$. Let $A \equiv (4, -4)$ and $B \equiv (9, 6)$ be two fixed points on the parabola. Let C be a moving point on the parabola between A and B such that the area of the triangle ABC is maximum. Then the coordinates of C are

(a) $\left(\frac{1}{4}, 1\right)$ (b) $(3, -2\sqrt{3})$

(c) $(3, 2\sqrt{3})$ (d) $(4, 4)$

25. Through the vertex O of the parabola $y^2 = 4ax$, two chords OP and OQ are drawn and the circles on OP and OQ as diameters intersect at R. If θ_1, θ_2 and ϕ are the angles made with the axis by the tangents at P and Q on the parabola and by OR, then the value of $\cot\theta_1 + \cot\theta_2$ is

(a) $-2\tan\phi$ (b) $2\tan\phi$

(c) 0 (d) $2\cot\phi$

26. AB is a double ordinate of the parabola $y^2 = 4ax$. Tangents drawn to the parabola at A and B meet the Y-axis at A_1 and B_1 respectively. If the area of trapezium AA_1B_1B is equal to $24a^2$, then the angle subtended by A_1B_1 at the focus of the parabola is equal to

(a) $\tan^{-1} 2$ (b) $\tan^{-1} 3$ (c) $2\tan^{-1} 2$ (d) $2\tan^{-1} 3$

27. If the 4th term in the expansion of $\left(px + \frac{1}{x}\right)^n$, $n \in N$ is $\frac{5}{2}$ and three normals to the parabola $y^2 = x$ are drawn through a point $(q, 0)$, then

(a) $q = p$ (b) $q > p$ (c) $q < p$ (d) $pq = 1$

28. The set of points on the axis of the parabola $y^2 - 4x - 2y + 5 = 0$ from which all the three normals to the parabola are real is

(a) $(k, 0); k > 1$ (b) $(k, 1); k > 3$

(c) $(k, 2); k > 6$ (d) $(k, 3); k > 8$

29. The triangle formed by the tangent to the parabola $y = x^2$ at the point whose abscissa is x_0 $(x_0 \in [1, 2])$, the Y-axis and the straight line $y = x_0^2$ has the greatest area if x_0 is equal to

(a) 0 (b) 1 (c) 2 (d) 3

30. The set of points (x, y) whose distance from the line $y = 2x + 2$ is the same as the distance from (2, 0) is a parabola. This parabola is congruent to the parabola in standard from $y = kx^2$ for some k which is equal to

(a) $\frac{4}{\sqrt{5}}$ (b) $\frac{12}{\sqrt{5}}$ (c) $\frac{\sqrt{5}}{4}$ (d) $\frac{\sqrt{5}}{12}$

Parabola Exercise 2 :
More than One Correct Option Type Questions

- This section contains **15 multiple choice questions**. Each question has four choices (a), (b), (c) and (d) out of which **MORE THAN ONE** may be correct.

31. Equation of the common tangent to the circle $x^2 + y^2 = 50$ and the parabola $y^2 = 40x$ can be

(a) $x + y - 10 = 0$ (b) $x - y + 10 = 0$
(c) $x + y + 10 = 0$ (d) $x - y - 10 = 0$

32. Let PQ be a chord of the parabola $y^2 = 4x$. A circle drawn with PQ as a diameter passes through the vertex V of the parabola. If area of $\Delta PVQ = 20$ unit^2, then the coordinates of P are

(a) $(16, 8)$ (b) $(16, -8)$
(c) $(-16, 8)$ (d) $(-16, -8)$

33. Let $y^2 = 4ax$ be a parabola and $x^2 + y^2 + 2bx = 0$ be a circle. If parabola and circle touch each other externally, then

(a) $a > 0, b < 0$ (b) $a > 0, b > 0$
(c) $a < 0, b > 0$ (d) $a < 0, b < 0$

34. Tangent is drawn at any point (x_1, y_1) other than the vertex on the parabola $y^2 = 4ax$. If tangents are drawn from any point on this tangent to the circle $x^2 + y^2 = a^2$ such that all the chords of chords of contact pass through a fixed point (x_2, y_2), then

(a) x_1, a, x_2 are in GP (b) $\frac{y_1}{2}, a, y_2$ are in GP
(c) $-4, \frac{y_1}{y_2}, \frac{x_1}{x_2}$ are in GP (d) $x_1x_2 + y_1y_2 = a^2$

35. Let P, Q and R are three co-normal points on the parabola $y^2 = 4ax$. Then the correct statement(s) is/at

(a) algebraic sum of the slopes of the normals at P, Q and R vanishes
(b) algebraic sum of the ordinates of the points P, Q and R vanishes
(c) centroid of the triangle PQR lies on the axis of the parabola
(d) Circle circumscribing the triangle PQR passes through the vertex of the parabola

36. Let P be a point whose coordinates differ by unity and the point does not lie on any of the axes of reference. If the parabola $y^2 = 4x + 1$ passes through P, then the ordinate of P may be

(a) 3 (b) -1
(c) 5 (d) 1

37. If a point P on $y^2 = 4x$, the foot of the perpendicular from P on the directrix and the focus form an equilateral triangle, then the coordinates of P may be

(a) $(3, -2\sqrt{3})$ (b) $(-3, 2\sqrt{3})$
(c) $(3, 2\sqrt{3})$ (d) $(-3, -2\sqrt{3})$

38. The locus of the foot of the perpendicular from the focus on a tangent to the parabola $y^2 = 4ax$ is

(a) the directrix (b) the tangent at the vertex
(c) $x = a$ (d) $x = 0$

39. The extremities of latusrectum of a parabola are (1, 1) and (1, −1). Then the equation of the parabola can be

(a) $y^2 = 2x - 1$ (b) $y^2 = 1 - 2x$
(c) $y^2 = 2x - 3$ (d) $y^2 = 2x - 4$

40. If from the vertex of a parabola $y^2 = 4ax$ a pair of chords be drawn at right angles to one another and with these chords as adjacent sides a rectangle be made, then the locus of the further angle of the rectangle is

(a) an equal parabola
(b) a parabola with focus at $(8a, 0)$
(c) a parabola with directrix as $x - 7a = 0$
(d) not a parabola

41. If two chords drawn from the point (4, 4) to the parabola $x^2 = 4y$ are divided by the line $y = mx$ in the ratio 1 : 2, then

(a) $m \in (-\infty, -\sqrt{3})$ (b) $m \in (-\infty, -\sqrt{3} - 1)$
(c) $m \in (\sqrt{3}, \infty)$ (d) $m \in (\sqrt{3} - 1, \infty)$

42. Through a point $P(-2, 0)$, tangents PQ and PR are drawn to the parabola $y^2 = 8x$. Two circles each passing through the focus of the parabola and one touching at Q and the other at R are drawn. Which of the following point (s) with respect to the triangle PQR lie (s) on the common chord of the two circles?

(a) centroid (b) orthocentre
(c) incentre (d) circumcentre

43. The set of points on the axis of the parabola $(y - 2)^2 = 4\left(x - \frac{1}{2}\right)$ from which three distinct normals can be drawn to the parabola are

(a) (3, 2) (b) (1, 2)
(c) (4, 2) (d) (5, 2)

44. Three normals are drawn from the point (14, 7) to the curve $y^2 - 16x - 8y = 0$. Then the coordinates of the feet of the normals are

(a) (3, – 4)
(b) (8, 16)
(c) (0, 0)
(d) (2, 2)

45. A quadrilateral is inscribed in a parabola, then

(a) the quadrilateral may be cyclic
(b) diagonals of the quadrilateral may be equal
(c) all possible pairs of adjacent sides may be perpendicular
(d) None of the above

Parabola Exercise 3 : Paragraph Based Questions

- This section contains **8 paragraphs** based upon each of the paragraph **3 multiple choice questions** have to be answered. Each of these questions has four choices (a), (b), (c) and (d) out of which **ONLY ONE** is correct.

Paragraph I

(Q. Nos. 46 to 48)

Consider a parabola P touches coordinate axes at $(4, 0)$ and $(0, 3)$.

46. If focus of parabola P is (a, b), then the value of $b - a$ is

(a) $\frac{1}{25}$ (b) $\frac{3}{25}$ (c) $\frac{4}{25}$ (d) $\frac{12}{25}$

47. Length of latus rectum of parabola P is

(a) $\frac{72}{125}$
(b) $\frac{144}{125}$
(c) $\frac{288}{125}$
(d) $\frac{576}{125}$

48. Equation of directrix of parabola P is

(a) $4x + 3y = 0$
(b) $3x + 4y = 12$
(c) $3x + 4y = 0$
(d) $4x + 3y = 12$

Paragraph II

(Q. Nos. 49 to 51)

Let C be the locus of the circumcentre of a variable triangle having sides Y-axis, $y = 2$ and $ax + by = 1$, where (a, b) lies on the parabola $y^2 = 4\lambda x$.

49. For $\lambda = 2$, the product of coordinates of the vertex of the curve C is

(a) – 8 (b) – 6 (c) 6 (d) 8

50. For $\lambda = \frac{1}{32}$, the length of smallest focal chord of the curve C is

(a) $\frac{8}{3}$ (b) 2 (c) 4 (d) 8

51. The curve C is symmetrical about the line

(a) $x = -\frac{3}{2}$
(b) $y = -\frac{3}{2}$
(c) $x = \frac{3}{2}$
(d) $y = \frac{3}{2}$

Paragraph III

(Q. Nos. 52 to 54)

Consider a parabola (P) $x^2 - 4xy + 4y^2 - 32x + 4y + 16 = 0$.

52. The focus of the parabola (P) is

(a) (2, 1) (b) (– 2, 1) (c) (– 2, – 1) (d) (2, – 1)

53. Length of latusrectum of the parabola (P) is

(a) $\frac{3}{\sqrt{5}}$ (b) $\frac{6}{\sqrt{5}}$ (c) $\frac{12}{\sqrt{5}}$ (d) $\frac{24}{\sqrt{5}}$

54. Equation of directrix of parabola (P) is

(a) $x - 2y - 4 = 0$
(b) $2x + y - 3 = 0$
(c) $x - 2y + 4 = 0$
(d) $2x + y + 3 = 0$

Paragraph IV

(Q. Nos. 55 to 57)

If l and m are variable real numbers such that $5l^2 - 4lm + 6m^2 + 3l = 0$, then the variable line $lx + my = 1$ always touches a fixed parabola, whose axis is parallel to the X-axis.

55. If (a, b) is the vertex of the parabola, then the value of $|a - b|$ is

(a) 2
(b) 3
(c) 4
(d) 5

56. If (c, d) is the focus of the parabola, then the value of $2^{|d - c|}$ is

(a) 1 (b) 2 (c) 4 (d) 8

57. If $ex + f = 0$ is directrix of the parabola and e, f are prime numbers, then the value of $|e - f|$ is

(a) 2
(b) 4
(c) 6
(d) 8

Paragraph V

(Q. Nos. 58 to 60)

C_1 is a curve $y^2 = 4x$, C_2 is curve obtained by rotating C_1, 120° in anti-clockwise direction C_3 is reflection of C_2 with respect to $y = x$ and S_1, S_2, S_3 are focii of C_1, C_2 and C_3, respectively, where O is origin.

58. If $(t^2, 2t)$ are parametric form of curve C_1, then the parametric form of curve C_2 is

(a) $\left(\frac{1}{2}(t^2 + 2\sqrt{3}t), \frac{1}{2}(\sqrt{3}t^2 + 2t)\right)$

(b) $\left(\frac{1}{2}(-t^2 + 2\sqrt{3}t), \frac{1}{2}(\sqrt{3}t^2 + 2t)\right)$

(c) $\left(\frac{1}{2}(-t^2 + 2\sqrt{3}t), \frac{1}{2}(-\sqrt{3}t^2 + 2t)\right)$

(d) $\left(\frac{1}{2}(-t^2 + 2\sqrt{3}t), \frac{1}{2}(-\sqrt{3}t^2 - 2t)\right)$

59. Area of ΔOS_2S_3 is

(a) $\frac{1}{8}$ (b) $\frac{1}{4}$

(c) $\frac{1}{2}$ (d) 1

60. If $S_1(x_1, y_1)$, $S_2(x_2, y_2)$ and $S_3(x_3, y_3)$, then the value of $\Sigma x_1^2 + \Sigma y_1^2$ is

(a) 2 (b) 3

(c) 4 (d) 5

Paragraph VI

(Q. Nos. 61 to 63)

Tangent to the parabola $y = x^2 + ax + 1$ at the point of intersection of the Y-axis also touches the circle $x^2 + y^2 = c^2$. It is known that no point of the parabola is below X-axis.

61. The value of $5c^2$ when a attains its maximum value is

(a) 1 (b) 3

(c) 5 (d) 7

62. The slope of the tangent when C is maximum, is

(a) -1 (b) 0 (c) 1 (d) 2

63. Let Δ be the minimum area bounded by the tangent and the coordinate axes, then the value of 8Δ is

(a) 1 (b) 2 (c) 4 (d) 8

Paragraph VII

(Q. Nos. 64 to 66)

A parabola (P) touches the conic

$$x^2 + xy + y^2 - 2x - 2y + 1 = 0$$

at the points when it is cut by the line $x + y + 1 = 0$.

64. If equation of parabola (P) is $ax^2 + 2hxy + by^2 + 2gx + 2fy + c = 0$, then the value of $|a + b + c + f + g + h|$ is

(a) 8 (b) 10 (c) 12 (d) 14

65. The length of latusrectum of parabola (P) is

(a) $\sqrt{2}$ (b) $3\sqrt{2}$ (c) $5\sqrt{2}$ (d) $7\sqrt{2}$

66. If (a, b) is the vertex of the parabola (P), then the value of $|a - b|$ is

(a) 0 (b) $\frac{1}{2}$ (c) 1 (d) $\frac{3}{2}$

Paragraph VIII

(Q. Nos. 67 to 69)

$y = 3x$ is tangent to the parabola $2y = ax^2 + b$.

67. The minimum value of $a + b$ is

(a) 2 (b) 4 (c) 6 (d) 8

68. If $(2, 6)$ is the point of contact, then the value of $2a$ is

(a) 2 (b) 3 (c) 4 (d) 5

69. If $b = 18$, then the point of contact is

(a) $(1, 3)$ (b) $(2, 6)$

(c) $(3, 9)$ (d) $(6, 18)$

Parabola Exercise 4 :
Single Integer Answer Type Questions

- This section contains **10 questions**. The answer to each question is a **single digit integer**, ranging from 0 to 9 (both inclusive).

70. Two tangents are drawn from the point $(-2, -1)$ to the parabola $y^2 = 4x$. If θ is the angle between these tangents, then the value of $\tan\theta$ is

71. If the distances of two points P and Q from the focus of a parabola $y^2 = 4x$ are 4 and 9 respectively, the distance of the point of intersection of tangents at P and Q from the focus is

72. The tangents and normals are drawn at the extremities of the latusrectum of the parabola $y^2 = 4x$. The area of quadrilateral so formed is λ sq units, the value of λ is

73. Three normals are drawn from the point $(a, 0)$ to the parabola $y^2 = x$. One normal is the X-axis. If other two normals are perpendicular to each other, then the value of $4a$ is

74. AB is the chord of the parabola $y^2 = 6x$ with the vertex at A. BC is drawn perpendicular to AB meeting the axis at C. The projection of BC on the axis is λ units, then the value of λ is

75. The parabolas $y = x^2 - 9$ and $y = \lambda x^2$ intersect at points A and B. If length of AB is equal to $2a$ and if $\lambda a^2 + \mu = a^2$, then the value of μ is

76. Let n be the number of integral points lying inside the parabola $y^2 = 8x$ and circle $x^2 + y^2 = 16$, then the sum of the digits of number n is

77. Radius of the largest circle which passes through the focus of the parabola $y^2 = 4x$ and contained in it, is

78. If the circle $(x-6)^2 + y^2 = r^2$ and the parabola $y^2 = 4x$ have maximum number of common chords, then the least integral value of r is

79. The slope of the line which belongs to the family of lines $(1+a)x + (a-1)y + 2(1-a) = 0$ and makes shortest intercept on $x^2 - 4y + 4 = 0$ is

Parabola Exercise 5 : Matching Type Questions

- This section contains **3 questions.** Each question has four statements (A, B, C and D) given in **Column** I and four statements (p, q, r and s) in **Column** II. Any given statement in **Column** I can have correct matching with one or more statement(s) given in **Column** II.

80. Match the following.

	Column I		Column II
(A)	The number of common chords of the parabola $x = y^2 - 6y + 11$ and $y = x^2 - 6x + 11$ is	(p)	Prime number
(B)	AB is a chord of the parabola $y^2 = 4x$ with vertex A, BC is drawn perpendicular to AB meeting the axis at C. The projection of BC on the axis of the parabola is	(q)	Composite number
(C)	The maximum number of common normals of $y^2 = 4ax$ and $x^2 = 4by$ is	(r)	Perfect number
(D)	If the locus of the middle of point of contact of tangents drawn to the parabola $y^2 = 8x$ and the foot of perpendicular drawn from its focus to the tangents is a conic, then the length of latusrectum of this conic is	(s)	Even number

81. Match the following.

	Column I		Column II
(A)	If the parabola $x^2 = ay$ makes an intercept of length $\sqrt{40}$ on the line $y - 2x = 1$, then the values of a are	(p)	-2
(B)	If the tangents drawn from the point $(0, 2)$ to the parabola $y^2 = 4ax$ are inclined at an angle $\frac{3\pi}{4}$, then the values of a are	(q)	1
(C)	If two distinct chords of a parabola $y^2 = 4ax$ passing through $(a, 2a)$ are bisected on the line $x + y = 1$, then the length of latusrectum can be	(r)	2
(D)	If the focus of the parabola $x^2 - ay + 3 = 0$ is $(0, 2)$ and if two values of a are a_1, a_2 such that $a_1 > a_2$, then the value of $\frac{a_1}{a_2}$ is	(s)	3

82. Match the following.

	Column I		Column II
(A)	The common chord of the circle $x^2 + y^2 = 5$ and the parabola $6y = 5x^2 + 7x$ will passes through the point (s)	(p)	$(1, 2)$
(B)	Tangents are drawn from point $(2, 3)$ to the parabola $y^2 = 4x$. Then, the points of contact are	(q)	$(4, 4)$
(C)	From a point P on the circle $x^2 + y^2 = 5$, the equation of chord of contact to the parabola $y^2 = 4x$ is $y = 2(x-2)$. Then, the coordinates of point P will be	(r)	$(-2, 1)$
(D)	$P(4, -4)$ and Q are points on the parabola $y^2 = 4x$ such that the area of ΔPOQ is 6 sq units, where O is the vertex. Then, the coordinates of Q may be	(s)	$(9, -6)$

Parabola Exercise 6 :
Statement I and II Type Questions

- **Directions** (Q. Nos. 83 to 90) are Assertion-Reason type questions. Each of these questions contains two statements:
Statement I (Assertion) and
Statement II (Reason)
Each of these questions also has four alternative choices, only one of which is the correct answer. You have to select the correct choice as given below :
(a) Statement I is true, Statement II is true; Statement II is a correct explanation for Statement I
(b) Statement I is true, Statement II is true; Statement II is not a correct explanation for Statement I
(c) Statement I is true, Statement II is false
(d) Statement I is false, Statement II is true

83. **Statement I** The equation of the common tangent to the parabolas $y^2 = 4x$ and $x^2 = 4y$ is $x + y + 1 = 0$.

Statement II Both the parabolas are reflected to each other about the line $y = x$.

84. **Statement I** Two perpendicular normals can be drawn from the point $\left(\frac{5}{2}, -2\right)$ to the parabola $(y+2)^2 = 2(x-1)$.

Statement II Two perpendicular normals can be drawn from the point $(3a, 0)$ to the parabola $y^2 = 4ax$.

85. **Statement I** The line $y = mx + \frac{a}{m}$ is tangent to the parabola $y^2 = 4ax$ for all values of m.

Statement II A straight line $y = mx + c$ that intersects the parabola $y^2 = 4ax$ one point is a tangent line.

86. **Statement I** The conic $\sqrt{ax} + \sqrt{by} = 1$ represents a parabola.

Statement II Conic $ax^2 + 2hxy + by^2 + 2gx + 2fy + c = 0$ represents a parabola, if $h^2 = ab$.

87. **Statement I** The lines from the vertex to the two extremities of a focal chord of the parabola $y^2 = 4ax$ are perpendicular to each other.

Statement II If extremities of focal chord of a parabola are $(at_1^2, 2at_1)$ and $(at_2^2, 2at_2)$, then $t_1t_2 = -1$.

88. **Statement I** Length of focal chord of a parabola $y^2 = 8x$ making an angle of 60° with X-axis is 32/3.

Statement II Length of focal chord of a parabola $y^2 = 4ax$ making an angle α with X-axis is $4a\sec^2(\alpha/2)$.

89. **Statement I** Straight line $x + y = \lambda$ touch the parabola $y = x - x^2$, if $k = 1$.

Statement II Discriminant of $(x-1)^2 = x - x^2$ is zero.

90. **Statement I** Length of latusrectum of parabola $(3x + 4y + 5)^2 = 4(4x + 3y + 2)$ is 4.

Statement II Length of latusrectum of parabola $y^2 = 4ax$ is $4a$.

Parabola Exercise 7 :
Subjective Type Questions

- In this section, there are **15 subjective questions**.

91. If the tangent to the parabola $y^2 = 4ax$ meets the axis in T and tangent at the vertex A in Y and the rectangle $TAYG$ is completed, show that the locus of G is $y^2 + ax = 0$.

92. If incident ray from point $(-1, 2)$ parallel to the axis of the parabola $y^2 = 4x$ strikes the parabola, find the equation of the reflected ray.

93. Prove that the normal chord to a parabola at the point whose ordinate is equal to the abscissa subtends a right angle at the focus.

94. Find the shortest distance between the parabola $y^2 = 4x$ and circle $x^2 + y^2 - 24y + 128 = 0$.

95. Show that the locus of a point that divides a chord of slope 2 of the parabola $y^2 = 4x$ internally in the ratio 1 : 2 is a parabola. Find the vertex of this parabola.

96. Show that the locus of the points of intersection of tangents to $y^2 = 4ax$, which intercept a constant length d on the directrix is $(y^2 - 4ax)(x + a)^2 = d^2x^2$.

97. Through the vertex O of the parabola $y^2 = 4ax$ two chords OP and OQ are drawn and the circle on OP and OQ as diameters intersect in R. If θ_1 and θ_2 are the angles made with the axes by the tangents at P and Q to the parabola and ϕ is the angle made by OR with the axis of the parabola, then prove that $\cot\theta_1 + \cot\theta_2 + 2\tan\phi = 0$.

98. Three normals with slopes m_1, m_2 and m_3 are drawn from a point P not on the axis of the parabola $y^2 = 4x$. If $m_1m_2 = \alpha$, results in the locus of P being a part of the parabola, find the value of α.

99. Find the locus of centres of a family of circles passing through the vertex of the parabola $y^2 = 4ax$ and cutting the parabola orthogonally at the other point of intersection.

100. TP and TQ are tangents to the parabola $y^2 = 4ax$. The normals at P and Q intersect at R on the curve. Prove that the circle circumscribing the ΔTPQ lies on the parabola $2y^2 = a(x - a)$.

101. A family of chords of the parabola $y^2 = 4ax$ is drawn so that their projections on a straight line inclined equally to both the axes are all of a constant length c; prove that the locus of their middle points is the curve $(y^2 - 4ax)(y + 2a)^2 + 2a^2c^2 = 0$.

102. The normals at P, Q, R are concurrent and PQ meets the diameter through R on the directrix $x = -a$. Prove that PQ touches [or PQ envelopes] the parabola $y^2 + 16a(x + a) = 0$.

103. If the normals to the parabola $y^2 = 4ax$ at three points P, Q and R meet at A and S be the focus, prove that $SP \cdot SQ \cdot SR = a(SA)^2$.

104. From a point A common tangents are drawn to the circle $x^2 + y^2 = (a^2/2)$ and the parabola $y^2 = 4ax$. Find the area of the quadrilateral formed by the common tangents, the chords of contact of the point A, with respect to the circle and the parabola.

105. Prove that the any three tangents to a parabola whose slopes are in harmonic progression enclose a triangle of constant area.

Parabola Exercise 8 : Questions Asked in Previous 13 Year's Exams

- This section contains questions asked in **IIT-JEE, AIEEE, JEE Main & JEE Advanced** from year **2005** to **2017**.

106. Tangent to the curve $y = x^2 + 6$ at a point (1, 7) touches the circle $x^2 + y^2 + 16x + 12y + c = 0$ at a point Q. Then the coordinates of Q are **[IIT-JEE 2005, 3M]**

(a) (− 6, − 11) (b) (− 9, − 13)
(c) (− 10, − 15) (d) (− 6, − 7)

107. Let P be a point (1, 0) and Q a point on the locus $y^2 = 8x$. The locus of mid-point of PQ is **[AIEEE 2005, 3M]**

(a) $x^2 - 4y + 2 = 0$ (b) $x^2 + 4y + 2 = 0$
(c) $y^2 + 4x + 2 = 0$ (d) $y^2 - 4x + 2 = 0$

108. The axis of a parabola is along the line $y = x$ and the distance of its vertex from origin is $\sqrt{2}$ and that from its focus is $2\sqrt{2}$. If vertex and focus both lie in the first quadrant, the equation of the parabola is **[IIT-JEE 2006, 3M]**

(a) $(x + y)^2 = (x - y - 2)$ (b) $(x - y)^2 = (x + y + 2)$
(c) $(x - y)^2 = 4(x + y - 2)$ (d) $(x - y)^2 = 8(x + y - 2)$

109. The equations of the common tangents to the parabolas $y = x^2$ and $y = -(x - 2)^2$ is/are **[IIT-JEE 2006, 5M]**

(a) $y = 4(x - 1)$ (b) $y = 0$
(c) $y = -4(x - 1)$ (d) $y = -30x - 50$

110. The locus of the vertices of the family of parabolas $y = \dfrac{a^3x^2}{3} + \dfrac{a^2x}{2} - 2a$ is **[AIEEE 2006, 4.5 *M*]**

(a) $xy = \dfrac{105}{64}$ (b) $xy = \dfrac{3}{4}$
(c) $xy = \dfrac{35}{16}$ (d) $xy = \dfrac{64}{105}$

111. Angle between the tangents to the curve $y = x^2 - 5x + 6$ at the points (2, 0) and (3, 0) is **[AIEEE 2006, 4.5 *M*]**

(a) $\pi/3$ (b) $\pi/2$
(c) $\pi/6$ (d) $\pi/4$

112. Consider the circle $x^2 + y^2 = 9$ and the parabola $y^2 = 8x$. They intersect at P and Q in the first and fourth quadrants, respectively. Tangents to the circle at P and Q intersect the X-axis at R and tangents to the parabola at P and Q intersect the X-axis at S.

(i) The ratio of the areas of the ΔPQS and ΔPQR is

(a) $1:\sqrt{2}$ (b) $1:2$

(c) $1:4$ (d) $1:8$

(ii) The radius of the circumcircle of the ΔPRS is

(a) 5 (b) $3\sqrt{3}$

(c) $3\sqrt{2}$ (d) $2\sqrt{3}$

(iii) The radius of the incircle of the ΔPQR is **[IIT-JEE 2007, (4 + 4 + 4) M]**

(a) 4 (b) 3

(c) 8/3 (d) 2

113. Statement I The curve $y = -\frac{x^2}{2} + x + 1$ is symmetric with respect to the line $x = 1$ because

Statement II A parabola is symmetric about its axis. **[IIT-JEE 2007, 3M]**

(a) Statement I is true, Statement II is true; Statement II is a correct explanation for Statement I

(b) Statement I is true, Statement II is true; Statement II is not a correct explanation for Statement I

(c) Statement I is true, Statement II is false

(d) Statement I is false, Statement II is true

114. The equation of a tangent to the parabola $y^2 = 8x$ is $y = x + 2$. The point on this line from which the other tangent to the parabola is perpendicular to the given tangent is **[AIEEE 2007, 3M]**

(a) $(-1, 1)$ (b) $(0, 2)$

(c) $(2, 4)$ (d) $(-2, 0)$

115. Consider the two curves $C_1 : y^2 = 4x$, $C_2 : x^2 + y^2 - 6x + 1 = 0$, then **[IIT-JEE 2008, 3M]**

(a) C_1 and C_2 touch each other only at one point

(b) C_1 and C_2 touch each other exactly at two points

(c) C_1 and C_2 intersect (but do not touch) at exactly two points

(d) C_1 and C_2 neither intersect nor touch each other

116. A parabola has the origin as its focus and the line $x = 2$ as the directrix. The vertex of the parabola is at **[AIEEE 2008, 3M]**

(a) $(0, 2)$ (b) $(1, 0)$

(c) $(0, 1)$ (d) $(2, 0)$

117. The tangent PT and the normal PN to the parabola $y^2 = 4ax$ at a point P on it meet its axis at points T and N, respectively. The locus of the centroid of the ΔPTN is a parabola whose **[IIT-JEE 2009, 4M]**

(a) vertex is $\left(\frac{2a}{3}, 0\right)$ (b) directrix is at $x = 0$

(c) latusrectum is $\frac{2a}{3}$ (d) focus is $(a, 0)$

118. Let A and B be two distinct points on the parabola $y^2 = 4x$. If the axis of the parabola touches a circle of radius r having AB as its diameter, The slope of the line joining A and B can be **[IIT-JEE 2010, 3M]**

(a) $-\frac{1}{r}$ (b) $\frac{1}{r}$ (c) $\frac{2}{r}$ (d) $-\frac{2}{r}$

119. If two tangents drawn from a point P to the parabola $y^2 = 4x$ are at right angles, the locus of P is **[AIEEE 2010, 4M]**

(a) $2x + 1 = 0$ (b) $x = -1$

(c) $2x - 1 = 0$ (d) $x = 1$

120. Consider the parabola $y^2 = 8x$. Let Δ_1 be the area of the triangle formed by the end points of its latusrectum and the point $P\left(\frac{1}{2}, 2\right)$ on the parabola and Δ_2 be the area of the triangle formed by drawing tangent at P and at the end points of the latusrectum. Then, $\frac{\Delta_1}{\Delta_2}$ is **[IIT-JEE 2011, 4M]**

121. Let (x, y) be any point on the parabola $y^2 = 4x$. Let P be the point that divides the line segment from $(0, 0)$ to (x, y) in the ratio $1 : 3$. Then, the locus of P is **[IIT-JEE 2011, 3M]**

(a) $x^2 = y$ (b) $y^2 = 2x$

(c) $y^2 = x$ (d) $x^2 = 2y$

122. Let L be a normal to the parabola $y^2 = 4x$. If L passes through the point $(9, 6)$, then L is given by **[IIT-JEE 2011, 4M]**

(a) $y - x + 3 = 0$ (b) $y + 3x - 33 = 0$

(c) $y + x - 15 = 0$ (d) $y - 2x + 12 = 0$

123. The shortest distance between line $y - x = 1$ and curve $x = y^2$ is **[AIEEE 2011, 4M]**

(a) $\frac{3\sqrt{2}}{8}$ (b) $\frac{8}{3\sqrt{2}}$

(c) $\frac{4}{\sqrt{3}}$ (d) $\frac{\sqrt{3}}{4}$

124. Let S be the focus of the parabola $y^2 = 8x$ and let PQ be the common chord of the circle $x^2 + y^2 - 2x - 4y = 0$ and the given parabola. The area of the ΔPQS is **[IIT-JEE 2012, 4M]**

Paragraph

(Q. Nos. 125 and 126)

Let PQ be a focal chord of the parabola $y^2 = 4ax$. The tangent to the parabola at P and Q meet at a point lying on the line $y = 2x + a, a > 0$. **[JEE Advanced 2013, 3+3 M]**

125. If chord PQ subtends an angle θ at the vertex of $y^2 = 4ax$, them $\tan\theta$ is equal to

(a) $\frac{2}{3}\sqrt{7}$ (b) $-\frac{2}{3}\sqrt{7}$ (c) $\frac{2}{3}\sqrt{5}$ (d) $-\frac{2}{3}\sqrt{5}$

126. Length of chord PQ is

(a) $7a$ (b) $5a$ (c) $2a$ (d) $3a$

127. The slope of the line touching the parabolas $y^2 = 4x$ and $x^2 = -32y$ is **[JEE Main 2014, 4M]**

(a) 1/8 (b) 2/3
(c) 1/2 (d) 3/2

128. The common tangent to the circle $x^2 + y^2 = 2$ and the parabola $y^2 = 8x$ touch the circle at the points P, Q and the parabola at the points R, S. Then, the area of the quadrilateral $PQRS$ is **[JEE Advanced 2014, 3 M]**

(a) 3 (b) 6 (c) 9 (d) 15

Paragraph

(Q. Nos. 129 and 130)

Let a, r, s and t be non-zero real numbers. Let $P(at^2\ 2at)$, $Q\left(\frac{a}{t^2}, \frac{-2a}{t}\right)$, $R(ar^2, 2ar)$ and $S(as^2, 2as)$ be distinct points on the parabola $y^2 = 4ax$. Suppose that PQ is the focal chord and lines QR and PK are parallel, where K is the point $(2a, 0)$. **[JEE Advanced 2014, (3 + 3) M]**

129. The value of r is

(a) $-\frac{1}{t}$ (b) $\frac{t^2+1}{t}$ (c) $\frac{1}{t}$ (d) $\frac{t^2-1}{t}$

130. If $st = 1$, then the tangent at P and the normal at S to the parabola meet at a point whose ordinate is

(a) $\frac{(t^2+1)^2}{2t^3}$ (b) $\frac{a(t^2+1)^2}{2t^3}$
(c) $\frac{a(t^2+1)^2}{t^3}$ (d) $\frac{a(t^2+2)^2}{t^3}$

131. Let O be the vertex and Q be any point on the parabola $x^2 = 8y$. If the point P divides the line segment OQ internally in the ratio 1 : 3, then the locus of P is **[JEE Main 2015, 4M]**

(a) $x^2 = y$ (b) $y^2 = x$
(c) $y^2 = 2x$ (d) $x^2 = 2y$

132. If the normals of the parabola $y^2 = 4x$ drawn at the end points of its latusrectum are tangents to the circle $(x-3)^2 + (y+2)^2 = r^2$, then the value of r^2 is **[JEE Advanced 2015, 4M]**

133. Let the curve C be the mirror image of the parabola $y^2 = 4x$ with respect to the line $x + y + 4 = 0$. If A and B are the points of intersection of C with the line $y = -5$, the distance between A and B is **[JEE Advanced 2015, 4M]**

134. Let P and Q be distinct points on the parabola $y^2 = 2x$ such that a circle with PQ as diameter passes through the vertex O of the parabola. If P lies in the first quadrant and the area of the ΔOPQ is $3\sqrt{2}$, then which of the following is (are) the coordinates of P? **[JEE Advanced 2015, 4M]**

(a) $(4, 2\sqrt{2})$ (b) $(9, 3\sqrt{2})$
(c) $\left(\frac{1}{4}, \frac{1}{\sqrt{2}}\right)$ (d) $(1, \sqrt{2})$

135. Let P be the point on the parabola $y^2 = 8x$, which is at a minimum distance from the centre C of the circle $x^2 + (y+6)^2 = 1$, the equation of the circle passing through C and having its centre at P, is **[JEE Main 2016, 4M]**

(a) $x^2 + y^2 - 4x + 8y + 12 = 0$
(b) $x^2 + y^2 - x + 4y - 12 = 0$
(c) $x^2 + y^2 - \frac{x}{4} + 2y - 24 = 0$
(d) $x^2 + y^2 - 4x + 9y + 18 = 0$

136. The circle $C_1 : x^2 + y^2 = 3$ with centre at O, intersects the parabola $x^2 = 2y$ at the point P in the first quadrant. Let the tangent to the circle C_1 at P touches other two circles C_2 and C_3 at R_2 and R_3, respectively. Suppose C_2 and C_3 have equal radii $2\sqrt{3}$ and centres Q_2 and Q_3, respectively. If Q_2 and Q_3 lie on the Y-axis, then **[JEE Advanced 2016, 4M]**

(a) $Q_2Q_3 = 12$
(b) $R_2R_3 = 4\sqrt{6}$
(c) area of ΔOR_2R_3 is $6\sqrt{2}$
(d) area of ΔPQ_2Q_3 is $4\sqrt{2}$

137. Let P be the point on the parabola $y^2 = 4x$ which is at the shortest distance from the centre S of the circle $x^2 + y^2 - 4x - 16y + 64 = 0$. Let Q be the point on the circle dividing the line segment SP internally. Then,

(a) $SP = 2\sqrt{5}$ **[JEE Advanced 2016, 4M]**

(b) $SQ : QP = (\sqrt{5} + 1) : 2$

(c) the x-intercept of the normal to the parabola at P is 6

(d) the slope of the tangent to the circle at Q is $\frac{1}{2}$

138. The radius of a circle, having minimum area, which touches the curve $y = 4 - x^2$ and the lines, $y = |x|$ is **[JEE Main 2017, 4M]**

(a) $4(\sqrt{2} + 1)$
(b) $2(\sqrt{2} + 1)$
(c) $2(\sqrt{2} - 1)$
(d) $4(\sqrt{2} - 1)$

139. If a chord, which is not a tangent of the parabola $y^2 = 16x$ has the equation $2x + y = p$, and mid-point (h, k), then which of the following is (are) possible value(s) of p, h and k? **[JEE Advanced 2017, 4M]**

(a) $p = 2, h = 3, k = -4$
(b) $p = -1, h = 1, k = -3$
(c) $p = -2, h = 2, k = -4$
(d) $p = 5, h = 4, k = -3$

Answers

Exercise for Session 1

1. (a) **2.** (d) **3.** (c) **4.** (b) **5.** (c) **6.** (c)
7. (b) **8.** (c) **9.** (c) **10.** (b) **11.** (d) **12.** (b)
13. $16x^2 + 9y^2 + 24xy - 256x - 142y + 849 = 0$
14. $4x^2 + y^2 - 4xy + 104x + 148y - 124 = 0$
15. $\left(\frac{-7}{2}, \frac{5}{2}\right); \left(\frac{-17}{2}, \frac{5}{2}\right); y = \frac{5}{2}; x + \frac{11}{4} = 0; 3$
16. Parabola **17.** Parabola
19. $x = \frac{2}{5}y^2 - 5y + \frac{68}{5}; \frac{5}{2}$ **20.** 4

Exercise for Session 2

1. (d) **2.** (b, d) **3.** (a) **4.** (a) **5.** (d) **6.** (d)
7. (b) **9.** $x + 4a = 0$ **10.** (a) $y = 2x - 12$ (b) $y = 3x - 33$
11. $y^2 = \frac{12}{343}(x-6)^2$ **13.** $\lambda = \frac{3}{2}$

Exercise for Session 3

1. (b) **2.** (a) **3.** (d) **4.** (a) **5.** (c) **6.** (c)
7. (a) **8.** (c) **10.** $y^2 = 2a(x - a)$ **11.** $y = x - 1, 8\sqrt{2}$ sq units

Chapter Exercise

1. (a) **2.** (b) **3.** (b) **4.** (d) **5.** (d) **6.** (a)
7. (a) **8.** (a) **9.** (d) **10.** (b) **11.** (a) **12.** (c)
13. (a) **14.** (d) **15.** (d) **16.** (a) **17.** (a) **18.** (c)
19. (d) **20.** (c) **21.** (d) **22.** (a) **23.** (c) **24.** (a)
25. (a) **26.** (c) **27.** (b) **28.** (b) **29.** (c) **30.** (d)
31. (b,c) **32.** (a,b) **33.** (b,d) **34.** (b,c,d) **35.** (a,b,c, d) **36.** (a, c)
37. (a,c) **38.** (b,d) **39.** (a,c) **40.** (a,c) **41.** (b,c,d) **42.** (a,b,c,d)
43. (a,c,d) **44.** (a,b,c) **45.** (a,b) **46.** (d) **47.** (d) **48.** (c)
49. (b) **50.** (c) **51.** (d) **52.** (d) **53.** (c) **54.** (d)
55. (b) **56.** (b) **57.** (d) **58.** (d) **59.** (b) **60.** (b)
61. (a) **62.** (b) **63.** (b) **64.** (c) **65.** (d) **66.** (a)
67. (c) **68.** (b) **69.** (d) **70.** (3) **71.** (6) **72.** (8)
73. (3) **74.** (6) **75.** (9) **76.** (8) **77.** (4) **78.** (5)
79. (0)
80. (A) → (q,r,s); (B) → (q,s); (C) → (p); (D) → (q)
81. (A) → (p,q); (B) → (p,r); (C) → (q,r,s); (D) → (s)
82. (A) → (p,r); (B) → (p,q); (C) → (r); (D) → (p,s)
83. (a) **84.** (a) **85.** (a) **88.** (c) **87.** (d) **88.** (c)
89. (c) **90.** (d) **92.** $x = 1$
94. $4(\sqrt{5} - 1)$ **95.** $\left(\frac{8}{9}, \frac{2}{9}\right)$ **98.** (2)
99. $2y^2(2y^2 + x^2 - 12ax) = ax(3x - 4a)^2$
104. $\frac{15a^2}{4}$ sq units **106.** (d) **107.** (d) **108.** (d) **109.** (a, b)
110. (a) **111.** (b) **112.** [i] (c) [ii] (b) [iii] (d) **113.** (a)
114. (d) **115.** (b) **116.** (b) **117.** (a,d) **118.** (c,d) **119.** (b)
120. (2) **121.** (c) **122.** (a,b,d) **123.** (a) **124.** 4 sq units
125. (d) **126.** (b) **127.** (c) **128.** (d) **129.** (d) **130.** (b)
131. (d) **132.** (2) **133.** (4) **134.** (a,d)
135. (a) **136.** (a,b,c) **137.** (a,c,d) **138.** (d) **139.** (a)

Solutions

1. Equation of tangent of $y^2 = 4bx$ is

$$y = mx + \frac{b}{m} \qquad \text{...(i)}$$

Here, $m = \tan\frac{\pi}{4} = 1$

From Eq. (i), $y = x + b$

For common tangent $y = x + b$ is also tangent of circle $x^2 + y^2 = a^2$, then

$$\frac{|0 - 0 + b|}{\sqrt{1+1}} = a$$

$$\Rightarrow \quad b = a\sqrt{2} \qquad [\because a > 0, b > 0]$$

2. The coordinates of vertex and focus of required parabola are $(a, 0)$ and $(a_1, 0)$ respectively. Therefore, the distance between the vertex and the focus is $AS = a_1 - a$. So, the length of latusrectum is $4(a_1 - a)$. Thus, the equation of the required parabola is

$$(y - 0)^2 = 4(a_1 - a)(x - a)$$

or $\quad y^2 = 4(a_1 - a)(x - a)$.

3. The parabolas are equal if the lengths of their latusrectum are equal.

The length of latusrectum of $y^2 = ax$ is a

The equation of second parabola can be written as

$$\sqrt{(x-3)^2 + (y+2)^2} = \left(\frac{3x - 4y - 2}{5}\right)$$

Here, focus is $(3, -2)$ and the equation of directrix is $3x - 4y - 2 = 0$.

$\therefore$ Length of latusrectum $= 2 \times$ Distance between focus and directrix

$$= 2\left|\frac{9 - 4 \times -2 - 2}{\sqrt{(9+16)}}\right| = 6$$

Thus, the two parabolas are equal if $a = 6$.

4. Let $DC = CB = BA = AD = k$

$\therefore$ Coordinates of B are (k, k), which lie on $y = \lambda\sqrt{x}$

$\therefore \quad k = \lambda\sqrt{k}$

$\therefore \quad k = \lambda^2$

$\therefore \quad BC = k = \lambda^2 \qquad \text{...(i)}$

Also, let $\quad CG = GF = FE = EC = k_1$

$\therefore$ Coordinates of F are $(\lambda^2 + k_1, k_1)$, which lie on $y = \lambda\sqrt{x}$

Then $\quad k_1 = \lambda\sqrt{(\lambda^2 + k_1)}$

$\Rightarrow \quad k_1^2 = \lambda^4 + \lambda^2 k_1$

or $\quad k_1^2 - \lambda^2 k_1 - \lambda^4 = 0$

$$\therefore \quad k_1 = \frac{\lambda^2 \pm \sqrt{(\lambda^4 + 4\lambda^4)}}{2} \qquad [\because k_1 > 0]$$

or $\quad \dfrac{k_1}{\lambda^2} = \dfrac{1 + \sqrt{5}}{2}$

or $\quad \dfrac{FG}{BC} = \dfrac{\sqrt{5} + 1}{2}$

5. Coordinates of A and B are $(VA\cos\theta, VA\sin\theta)$ and $(VB\sin\theta, -VB\cos\theta)$ respectively

$\because A$ and B lie on $y^2 = x$, then $(VA\sin\theta)^2 = VA\cos\theta$

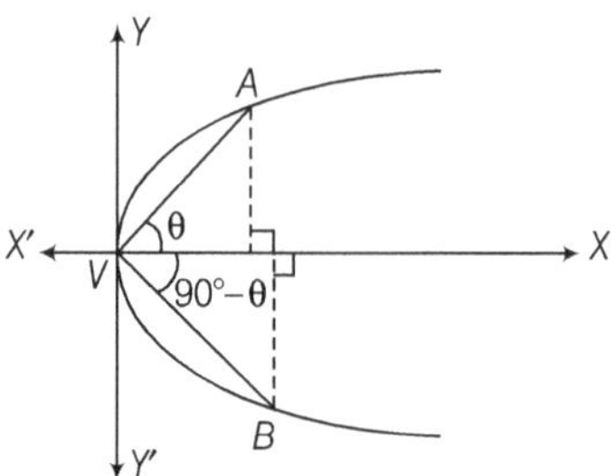

$$\Rightarrow \quad VA = \frac{\cos\theta}{\sin^2\theta}$$

Similarly, $\quad VB = \dfrac{\sin\theta}{\cos^2\theta}$

$$\therefore \quad \frac{|VA|}{|VB|} = \cot^3\theta$$

6. $\because \quad x = t^2 - t + 1, y = t^2 + t + 1$

$\therefore \quad x + y = 2t^2 + 2$ and $y - x = 2t$

or $\quad 2(x + y - 2) = 4t^2 = (2t)^2 = (y - x)^2$

or $\quad (x - y)^2 = 2(x + y - 2)$

or $\quad \left(\dfrac{x - y}{\sqrt{2}}\right)^2 = \sqrt{2}\left(\dfrac{x + y - 2}{\sqrt{2}}\right)$

For vertex, $\quad \dfrac{x - y}{\sqrt{2}} = 0$ and $\dfrac{x + y - 2}{\sqrt{2}} = 0$

or $\quad x = y$ and $x + y = 2$

$\therefore \quad x = y = 1$

Hence, vertex is $(1, 1)$.

7. It is clear from figure

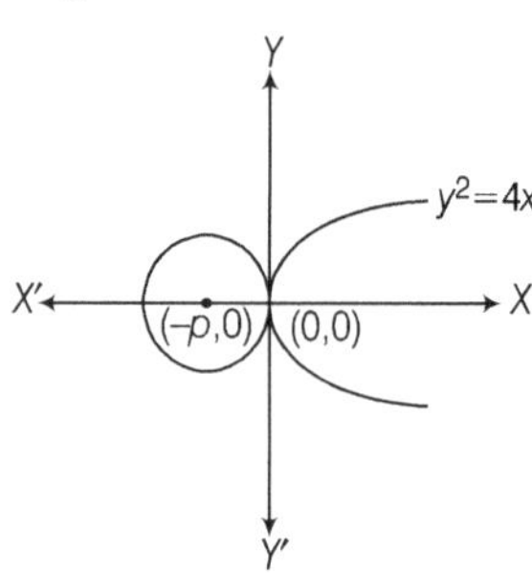

$$-p < 0 \quad \text{or} \quad p > 0$$

8. The point of intersection of the parabolas $y^2 = 4ax$ and $x^2 = 4ay$ are $(0, 0)$ and $(4a, 4a)$ but $a \neq 0$.

Now, $2bx + 3cy + 4d = 0$ passes through $(0, 0)$ and $(4a, 4a)$.

Therefore, $d = 0$ and $2b(4a) + 3c(4a) = 0$ i.e.,

$$2b + 3c = 0 \quad [\because a \neq 0]$$

or $$d^2 + (2b + 3c)^2 = 0$$

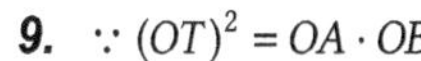

9. $\because (OT)^2 = OA \cdot OB$

$$= \alpha \cdot \beta$$

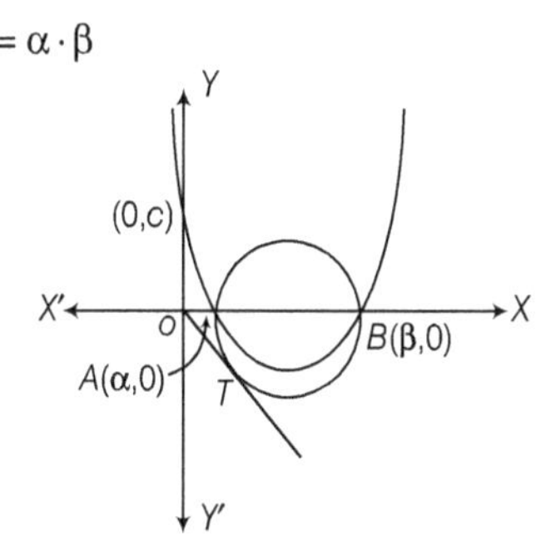

or $$OT = \sqrt{\alpha\beta} \quad \text{...(i)}$$

Parabola cuts X-axis at α and β.

$\therefore \alpha, \beta$ are the roots of $ax^2 + bx + c = 0$

$$\therefore \quad \alpha\beta = \frac{c}{a} \quad \text{...(ii)}$$

From Eqs. (i) and (ii), we get

$$OT = \sqrt{\frac{c}{a}}$$

10. $\because$ Two perpendicular tangents meet a point on directrix.

Now, equations of tangents at $(at_1^2, 2at_1)$ and $(at_2^2, 2at_2)$ are $t_1 y = x + at_1^2$ and $t_2 y = x + at_2^2$, respectively.

$$\therefore \quad P_1 \equiv (-at_1^2, 0), P_2 \equiv (-at_2^2, 0)$$

$\Rightarrow SP_1 = a(1 + t_1^2), SP_2 = a(1 + t_2^2)$ and $t_1 t_2 = -1$

$$\therefore \quad \frac{1}{SP_1} + \frac{1}{SP_2} = \frac{1}{a(1 + t_1^2)} + \frac{1}{a(1 + t_2^2)}$$

$$= \frac{1}{a(1 + t_1^2)} + \frac{1}{a\left(1 + \frac{1}{t_1^2}\right)} \quad \left[\therefore t_2 = -\frac{1}{t_1}\right]$$

$$= \frac{1}{a(1 + t_1^2)} + \frac{t_1^2}{a(1 + t_1^2)} = \frac{1}{a}$$

11. Let $P \equiv (at_1^2, 2at_1)$ and $Q \equiv (at_2^2, 2at_2)$

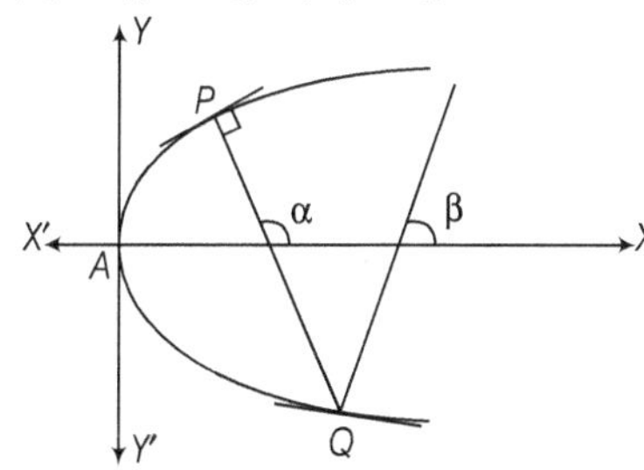

Equation of normal at P is

$$y + t_1 x = 2at_1 + at_1^3$$

meet the curve again at Q, then

$$t_2 = -t_1 - \frac{2}{t_1} \quad \text{...(i)}$$

Here $\tan\alpha = -t_1$ and $\tan\beta = -t_2$, from Eq. (i)

$$\therefore \quad -\tan\beta = \tan\alpha + \frac{2}{\tan\alpha}$$

$$\Rightarrow \quad \tan\alpha(\tan\alpha + \tan\beta) = -2$$

12. Let $A \equiv (\alpha, \beta)$

The equation of normal at $(at^2, 2at)$

$$y + tx = 2at + at^3 \quad \text{...(i)}$$

(α, β) lie on Eq. (i), then

$$at^3 + (2a - \alpha)t - \beta = 0 \quad \text{...(ii)}$$

Let t_1, t_2 and t_3 be the roots of Eq. (ii), then

$$at^3 + (2a - \alpha)t - \beta = a(t - t_1)(t - t_2)(t - t_3) \quad \text{...(iii)}$$

Let $P \equiv (at_1^2, 2at_1)$, $Q \equiv (at_2^2, 2at_2)$ and $R \equiv (at_3^2, 2at_3)$

Since, the focus is $S(a, 0)$

$$\therefore \quad SP = a(1 + t_1^2), SQ = a(1 + t_2^2)$$

and $$SR = a(1 + t_3^2)$$

On putting $t = i = \sqrt{-1}$ in Eq. (iii), we get

$$-ai + (2a - \alpha)i - \beta$$

$$= a(i - t_1)(i - t_2)(i - t_3)$$

or $|(a - \alpha)i - \beta| = a|i - t_1||i - t_2|i - t_3|$

$$\Rightarrow \quad \sqrt{(a - \alpha)^2 + \beta^2}$$

$$= a\sqrt{(1 + t_1^2)}\sqrt{(1 + t_2^2)}\sqrt{(1 + t_3^2)}$$

or $a((a - \alpha)^2 + \beta^2) = a(1 + t_1^2) \cdot a(1 + t_2^2) \cdot a(1 + t_3^2)$

$$a(SA)^2 = SP \cdot SQ \cdot SR$$

or $$SP \cdot SQ \cdot SR = a(SA)^2$$

13. Let AB be a normal chord, where $A \equiv (at_1^2, 2at_1)$ and $B \equiv (at_2^2, 2at_2)$, we have $t_2 = -t_1 - \dfrac{2}{t_1}$

Now, $$AB = \sqrt{(at_1^2 - at_2^2)^2 + (2at_1 - 2at_2)^2}$$

$$= a|t_1 - t_2|\sqrt{(t_1 + t_2)^2 + 4}$$

$$= a\left|2\left(t_1 + \frac{1}{t_1}\right)\right|\sqrt{\left(\frac{4}{t_1^2} + 4\right)}$$

$$= 4a\sqrt{\frac{(t_1^2 + 1)^3}{t_1^4}}$$

$$(AB)^2 = 16a^2\frac{(t_1^2 + 1)^3}{t_1^4}$$

$$\frac{d(AB)^2}{dt_1} = 16a^2\left\{\frac{(1 + t_1^2)^2}{t_1^5}(t_1^2 - 2)\right\}$$

For $$\frac{d(AB)^2}{dt_1} = 0 \Rightarrow t_1 = \sqrt{2}$$

For which $(AB)^2$ is minimum, thus

$$AB_{\min} = \sqrt{\frac{16a^2(2 + 1)^3}{4}} = 2a\sqrt{27}$$

14. On solving

$$x^2 + y^2 = a^2 \text{ and } y^2 = 4(x+4)$$

$\Rightarrow$ $x^2 + 4(x+4) = a^2$

or $x^2 + 4x + 16 - a^2 = 0$

If the circle and parabola touch each other, then

$$D = 0 \Rightarrow 16 - 4\cdot 1\cdot(16 - a^2) = 0$$

$\Rightarrow$ $a^2 = 12$ or $a = 2\sqrt{3}$

15. $\sin\theta > |2a|$ $[\because h > 2a]$

$\Rightarrow$ $0 < |2a| < 1$ or $0 < |a| < \frac{1}{2}$

$\therefore$ $a \in \left(-\frac{1}{2}, 0\right) \cup \left(0, \frac{1}{2}\right)$

16. Tangent to $y^2 = 4x$ in terms of m is

$$y = mx + \frac{1}{m} \quad \text{...(i)}$$

and normal to $x^2 = 4by$ in terms of m is

$$y = mx + 2b + \frac{b}{m^2} \quad \text{...(ii)}$$

$\because$ Eqs. (i) and (ii) are same, then

$$\frac{1}{m} = 2b + \frac{b}{m^2}$$

$\Rightarrow$ $2bm^2 - m + b = 0$

For two different tangents

$\therefore$ $D > 0 \Rightarrow 1 - 8b^3 > 0$

or $|b| < \frac{1}{2\sqrt{2}}$

17. The given parabolas $2y^2 = 2x - 1$ and $2x^2 = 2y - 1$ are symmetrical about the line $y = x$. The shortest distance occurs along the common normal which is perpendicular to the line $y = x$.

Therefore, the tangent at point A on $2y^2 = 2x - 1$ is parallel to $y = x$. Therefore,

$$4y\frac{dy}{dx} = 2 \Rightarrow \frac{dy}{dx} = \frac{1}{2y} = 1$$

or $y = \frac{1}{2}$ and $x = \frac{3}{4}$

$\therefore$ $A \equiv \left(\frac{3}{4}, \frac{1}{2}\right)$, then coordinates of B on $2x^2 = 2y - 1$ is

$B \equiv \left(\frac{1}{2}, \frac{3}{4}\right)$

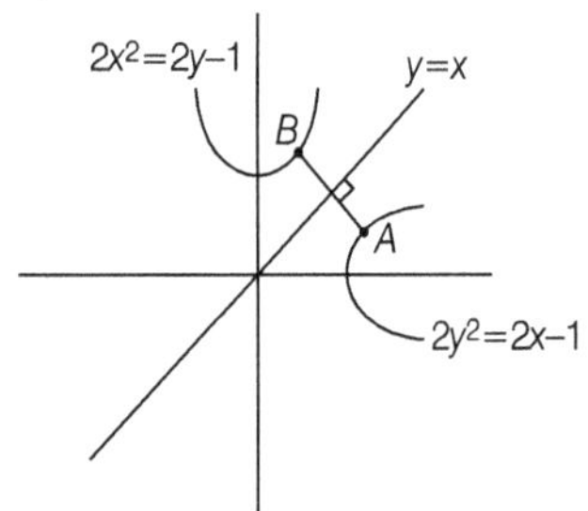

$\therefore$ Shortest distance $= AB$

$$= \sqrt{\left(\frac{3}{4} - \frac{1}{2}\right)^2 + \left(\frac{1}{2} - \frac{3}{4}\right)^2}$$

$$= \sqrt{\left(\frac{1}{16} + \frac{1}{16}\right)} = \frac{1}{\sqrt{8}} = \frac{1}{2\sqrt{2}}$$

18. We know that normals at $(at_1^2, 2at_1)$ and $(at_2^2, 2at_2)$ meet again on the parabola. Then $t_1t_2 = 2$

Here, $a = 1$

and $x_1 = at_1^2 = t_1^2$ and $y_1 = 2at_1 = 2t_1$

$x_2 = at_2^2 = t_2^2$ and $y_2 = 2at_2 = 2t_2$

Given $x_1 + x_2 = 4 \Rightarrow t_1^2 + t_2^2 = 4$

or $(t_1 + t_2)^2 - 2t_1t_2 = 4$

$\Rightarrow$ $(t_1 + t_2)^2 = 8$ $[\because t_1t_2 = 2]$

or $|t_1 + t_2| = \sqrt{8}$

or $|2t_1 + 2t_2| = 2\sqrt{8}$

or $|y_1 + y_2| = 2\sqrt{8} = 4\sqrt{2}$

19. Let any point at distance r from A on the parabola is

$$(-2 + r\cos\theta, r\sin\theta),$$

then $r^2\sin^2\theta = 4(-2 + r\cos\theta)$

or $r^2\sin^2\theta - 4r\cos\theta + 8 = 0$

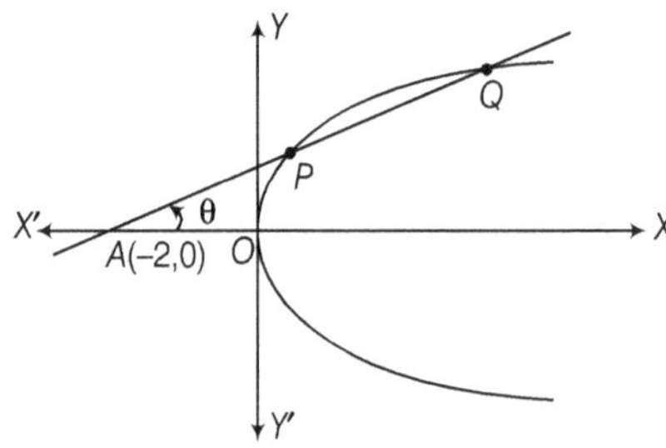

Let P and Q are distances r_1 and r_2 from A, then

$$r_1 + r_2 = \frac{4\cos\theta}{\sin^2\theta}$$

and $r_1r_2 = \frac{8}{\sin^2\theta}$

Now, $\frac{1}{AP} + \frac{1}{AQ} = \frac{1}{r_1} + \frac{1}{r_2} = \frac{r_1 + r_2}{r_1r_2} = \frac{\cos\theta}{2}$

given that $\frac{1}{AP} + \frac{1}{AQ} < \frac{1}{4}$

$\Rightarrow$ $\frac{\cos\theta}{2} < \frac{1}{4}$

or $\cos\theta < \frac{1}{2}$

or $\tan\theta > \sqrt{3}$

[$\because$ $\cos\theta$ is decreasing and $\tan\theta$ is increasing in $\left(0, \frac{\pi}{2}\right)$]

$\therefore$ Slope $(m) > \sqrt{3}$

20. Coordinates of A are $(a - l\cos 30°, l\sin 30°)$

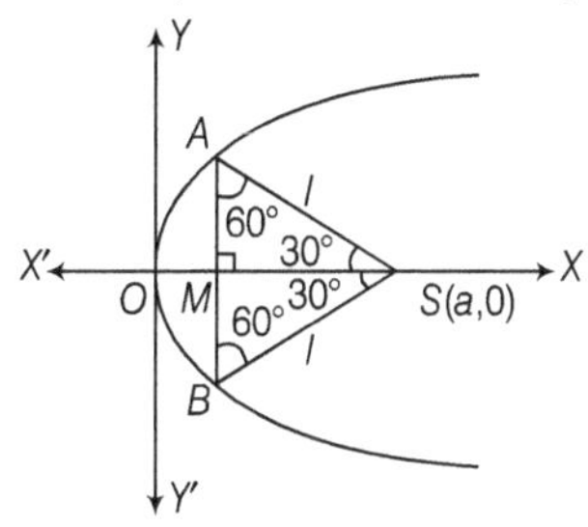

or $$A \equiv \left(a - \frac{l\sqrt{3}}{2}, \frac{l}{2}\right)$$

which lies on $y^2 = 4ax$, then

$$\frac{l^2}{4} = 4a\left(a - \frac{l\sqrt{3}}{2}\right) \Rightarrow l^2 + 8a\sqrt{3}l - 16a^2 = 0$$

$$\therefore \quad l = \frac{-8a\sqrt{3} \pm \sqrt{(192a^2 + 64a^2)}}{2}$$

$$= \frac{-8a\sqrt{3} \pm 16a}{2}$$

$$= 4a(2 - \sqrt{3}) \quad \text{[taking +ve sign]}$$

Aliter :

Let $A \equiv (at_1^2, 2at_1)$ and $B \equiv (at_1^2 - 2at_1)$.

Slope of $SA = \tan(180° - 30°)$

$$\frac{2at_1}{at_1^2 - a} = -\tan 30°$$

$$\frac{2t_1}{t_1^2 - 1} = -\frac{1}{\sqrt{3}}$$

or $t_1^2 + 2\sqrt{3}t_1 - 1 = 0'$ or $t_1 = -\sqrt{3} \pm 2$

Thus, $t_1 = 2 - \sqrt{3}$ [$\because t_1 = -2 - \sqrt{3}$ rejected]

Here, $AB = 4at_1 = 4a(2 - \sqrt{3})$

21. $C : x^2 + (y-1)^2 = 1$ and $P : y = ax^2$

Putting $x^2 = \frac{y}{a}$ in $x^2 + (y-1)^2 = 1$

or $$\frac{y}{a} + (y-1)^2 = 1$$

or $$y^2 - 2y + \frac{y}{a} = 0$$

$$\therefore \quad y = 0 \text{ or } y = 2 - \frac{1}{a}$$

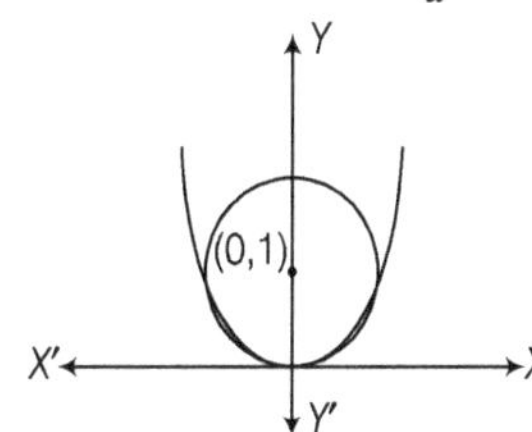

On substituting $y = 2 - \frac{1}{a}$ in $y = ax^2$, then

$$ax^2 = 2 - \frac{1}{a}$$

or $$x^2 = \frac{2a-1}{a^2} > 0$$

or $$2a - 1 > 0$$

$$\therefore \quad a > \frac{1}{2}$$

or $$a \in \left(\frac{1}{2}, \infty\right)$$

22. $\vec{\mathbf{V}} = (\lambda^2 - 1)\hat{\mathbf{i}} + (2\lambda - 0)\hat{\mathbf{j}}$

$\vec{\mathbf{V}} = (\lambda^2 - 1)\hat{\mathbf{i}} + (2\lambda)\hat{\mathbf{j}}$ ...(i)

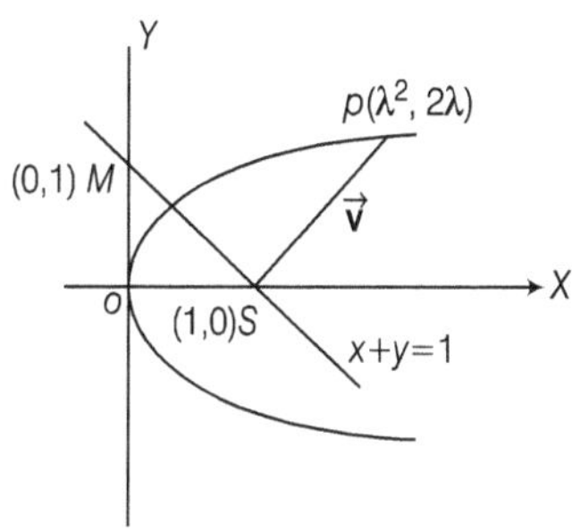

and $$\vec{\mathbf{n}} = (0-1)\hat{\mathbf{i}} + (1-0)\hat{\mathbf{j}}$$

$$= -\hat{\mathbf{i}} + \hat{\mathbf{j}}$$

The projection of $\vec{\mathbf{V}}$ on $\vec{\mathbf{n}} = y$ [given]

$$\therefore \quad y = \frac{\vec{\mathbf{V}} \cdot \vec{\mathbf{n}}}{|\vec{\mathbf{n}}|} = \frac{-(\lambda^2 - 1) + 2\lambda}{\sqrt{2}} \quad \text{...(ii)}$$

Given, $$\frac{dx}{dt} = 4$$

$$\Rightarrow \quad \frac{d}{dt}(\lambda^2 - 1) = 4 \Rightarrow 2\lambda\frac{d\lambda}{dt} = 4$$

When $P \equiv (4, 4)$,

We have $\lambda = 2$, therefore

$$\frac{d\lambda}{dt} = 1 \quad \text{...(iii)}$$

From Eq. (ii),

$$\frac{dy}{dt} = \frac{(2 - 2\lambda)\frac{d\lambda}{dt}}{\sqrt{2}} \quad \text{[from Eq. (ii)]}$$

$$= \frac{(2-4) \times 1}{\sqrt{2}} = -\sqrt{2}$$

23. Given parabola is

$$y^2 = 6\left(x - \frac{3}{2}\right)$$

The equation of directrix is $x - \frac{3}{2} + \frac{6}{4} = 0$

i.e. $x = 0$

Let the coordinates of P be $\left(\frac{3}{2} + \frac{3}{2}t^2, 3t\right)$

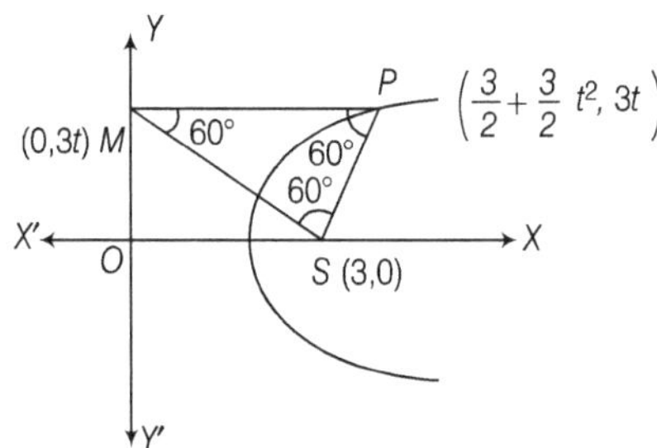

Therefore, $MS = MP$

$$\sqrt{(9+9t^2)} = \frac{3}{2} + \frac{3}{2}t^2$$

or $$9 + 9t^2 = \frac{9}{4}(1+t^2)^2$$

or $$1 + t^2 = 4$$

$\therefore$ Length of each side $= MS$

$$= \sqrt{9(1+t^2)} = \sqrt{36} = 6$$

24. The area of ΔABC is maximum if CD is maximum, because AB is fixed.

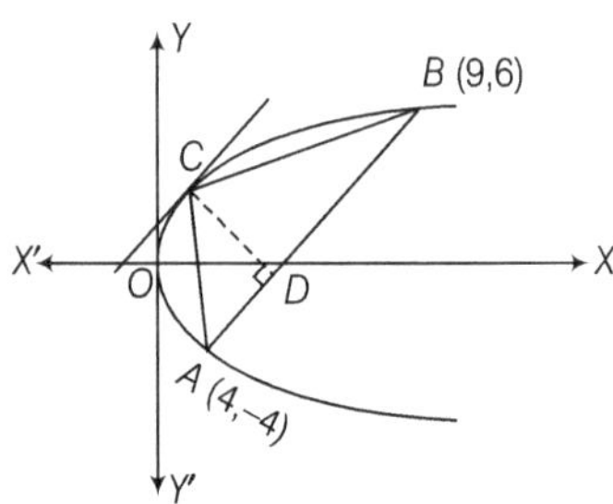

It is clear that tangent drawn to the parabola at C should be parallel to AB.

For $$y^2 = 4x$$

$\therefore$ $$2y\frac{dy}{dx} = 4 \quad \text{or} \quad \frac{dy}{dx} = \frac{2}{y} = \text{slope of } AB$$

$\Rightarrow$ $$\frac{2}{y} = \frac{6+4}{9-4} = 2 \quad \text{or} \quad y = 1, \text{ then } x = \frac{1}{4}$$

Hence, coordinates of C are $\left(\frac{1}{4}, 1\right)$.

25. $\because$ Tangent at $P(at_1^2, 2at_1)$ is $t_1 y = x + at_1^2$.

$\therefore$ $$\tan\theta_1 = \frac{1}{t_1}$$

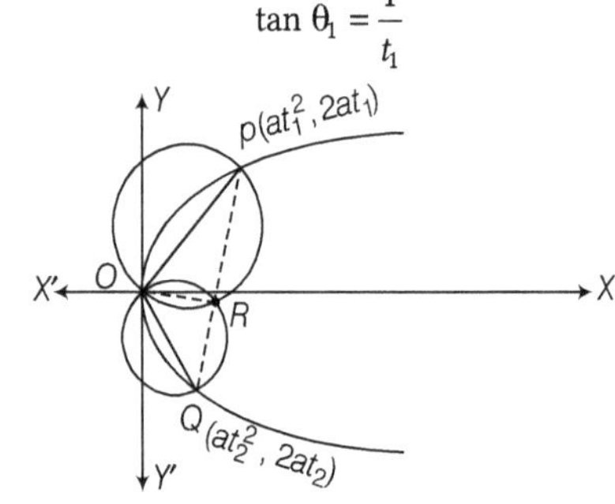

Similarly, $$\tan\theta_2 = \frac{1}{t_2}$$

$\because$ Angle in a semicircle is 90°.

$\therefore$ $$\angle ORP = \angle ORQ = 90^\circ$$

$\Rightarrow$ P, R, Q are collinear.

$$\text{Slope of } PQ = \frac{2}{t_1 + t_2} \qquad [\because OR \perp PQ]$$

$\therefore$ $$\text{Slope of } OR = -\frac{(t_1+t_2)}{2} = \tan\phi$$

or $$t_1 + t_2 = -2\tan\phi$$

$\Rightarrow$ $$\cot\theta_1 + \cot\theta_2 = -2\tan\phi$$

26. Let $A \equiv (at^2, 2at)$ and $B \equiv (at^2, -2at)$

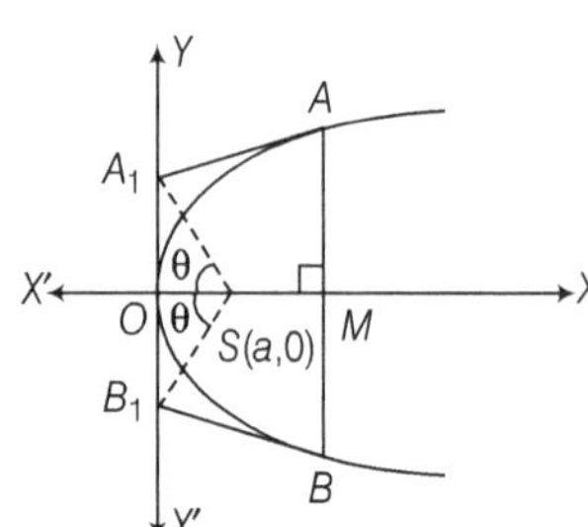

The equations of tangents at A and B are

$$ty = x + at^2 \text{ and } -ty = x + at^2.$$

These tangents meet the Y-axis at $A_1(0, at)$ and $B_1(0, -at)$ respectively.

Area of trapezium

$$AA_1B_1B = \frac{1}{2}(AB + A_1B_1) \times OM$$

$$24a^2 = \frac{1}{2}(4at + 2at) \times at^2$$

$$24a^2 = 3a^2t^3 \Rightarrow t^3 = 8$$

$\therefore$ $$t = 2$$

$\therefore$ Coordinates of A_1 and B_1 are $(0, 2a)$ and $(0, -2a)$ respectively.

If $\angle OSA_1 = \angle OSB_1 = \theta$, then

$\therefore$ $$\tan\theta = \frac{2a}{a} = 2$$

$\Rightarrow$ $$\theta = \tan^{-1} 2$$

Hence, subtended angle $= 2\theta = 2\tan^{-1} 2$

27. Given, $$\frac{5}{2} = {}^nC_3(px)^{n-3}\left(\frac{1}{x}\right)^3 = {}^nC_3 \cdot p^{n-3} x^{n-6} \qquad \text{...(i)}$$

Since, LHS of Eq. (i) is independent of x

$\therefore$ $$n - 6 = 0 \Rightarrow n = 6$$

From Eq. (i),

$$\frac{5}{2} = {}^6C_3 p^3 = 20p^3$$

$\Rightarrow$ $$p^3 = \left(\frac{1}{2}\right)^3 \Rightarrow p = \frac{1}{2}$$

Given, parabola is $y^2 = x$

Here, $$4a = 1$$

$\Rightarrow$ $$a = \frac{1}{4}$$

Since, three normals are drawn from point $(q, 0)$,

$\therefore$ $$q > 2a \text{ or } q > \frac{1}{2} \text{ or } q > p \qquad \left[\because p = \frac{1}{2}\right]$$

28. $y^2 - 4x - 2y + 5 = 0$

$\Rightarrow \quad (y-1)^2 - 4x + 4 = 0$

$\Rightarrow \quad (y-1)^2 = 4(x-1)$

Let $y - 1 = Y$ and $x - 1 = X$

then, $y^2 = 4X$ comparing with $Y^2 = 4ax$

$\therefore \quad a = 1$

$\because$ All three normals to the parabola are real and meet on the axis of parabola, then

$X > 2a$ and $Y = 0$

i.e., $x - 1 > 2$ and $y - 1 = 0$

$\therefore \quad x > 3$ and $y = 1$

or $(k, 1); k > 3$

29. Let $P(x_0, x_0^2)$ be any point on the parabola $y = x^2$

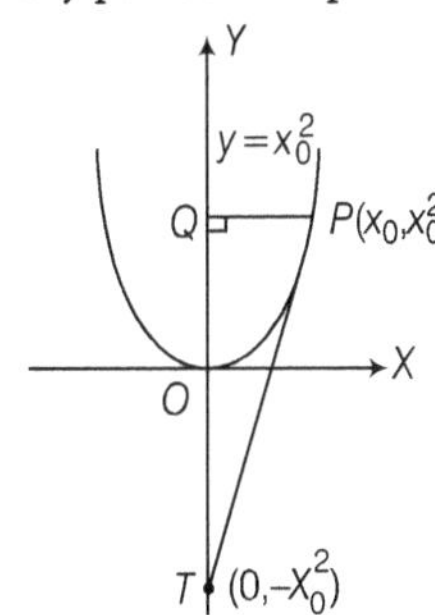

Equation of tangent at $P(x_0, x_0^2)$ is

$$xx_0 = \frac{1}{2}(y + x_0^2)$$

$\Rightarrow \quad 2xx_0 - y - x_0^2 = 0$

Tangent meets the Y-axis at $T(0, -x_0^2)$.

Hence, the area of the triangle $\Delta PTQ = \frac{1}{2} \times PQ \times QT$

$$= \frac{1}{2} \times x_0 \times 2x_0^2 = x_0^3$$

which increases in the interval $[1, 2]$ and hence is greatest when $x_0 = 2$.

30. $\left(\frac{2x - y + 2}{\sqrt{5}}\right) = \sqrt{(x-2)^2 + (y-0)^2}$ [given]

$\Rightarrow \quad (2x - y + 2)^2 = 5(x^2 + y^2 - 4x + 4)$

or $\quad x^2 + 4y^2 + 4xy = 28x - 4y - 16$

$\Rightarrow \quad (x + 2y)^2 = 4(7x - y - 4)$

$\because \quad x + 2y = 0$ and $7x - y - 4 = 0$ and are not perpendicular.

$\therefore \quad (x + 2y + \lambda)^2 = (2\lambda + 28)x + (4\lambda - 4)y + \lambda^2 - 16$ ...(i)

Now, (slope of $x + 2y + \lambda = 0$) $\times$ (slope of $(2\lambda + 28)x + (4\lambda - 4)y + \lambda^2 - 16 = 0$) $= -1$

$\therefore \quad -\frac{1}{2} \times -\frac{(2\lambda + 28)}{(4\lambda - 4)} = -1$

$\Rightarrow \quad 2\lambda + 28 = -8\lambda + 8$

or $\quad 10\lambda = -20$

$\therefore \quad \lambda = -2$

From Eq. (i),

$$(x + 2y - 2)^2 = (24x - 12y - 12)$$

$\Rightarrow \quad \left(\frac{x + 2y - 2}{\sqrt{5}}\right)^2 = \frac{12}{\sqrt{5}}\left(\frac{2x - y - 1}{\sqrt{5}}\right)$

Let $\quad \frac{x + 2y - 2}{\sqrt{5}} = X, \frac{2x - y - 1}{\sqrt{5}} = Y$

or $\quad X^2 = \frac{12}{\sqrt{5}} Y$ or $Y = \frac{\sqrt{5}}{12} X^2$

$\therefore \quad k = \frac{\sqrt{5}}{12}$

31. Equation of tangent of parabola

$y^2 = 40x$ is $y = mx + \frac{10}{m}$ ... (i)

which is also tangent of circle $x^2 + y^2 = 50$, then

$$\frac{\left|\frac{10}{m}\right|}{\sqrt{(m^2 + 1)}} = 5\sqrt{2}$$

$\Rightarrow \quad m^4 + m^2 - 2 = 0$

$\Rightarrow \quad (m^2 + 2)(m^2 - 1) = 0$

$\therefore \quad m^2 = 1, m^2 + 2 \neq 0$ or $m = \pm 1$

From Eq. (i), common tangents are

$y = x + 10$ and $y = -x - 10$

or $\quad x - y + 10 = 0$ and $x + y + 10 = 0$

32. Let coordinates of P be $(t^2, 2t)$

$\therefore$ Slope of $PV = \frac{2t - 0}{t^2 - 0} = \frac{2}{t}$

$\Rightarrow$ Slope of QV is $-\frac{t}{2}$

$\therefore$ Equation of QV is $y = \frac{-t}{2}x$

Solving it with $y^2 = 4x$, we get $Q\left(\frac{16}{t^2}, \frac{-8}{t}\right)$

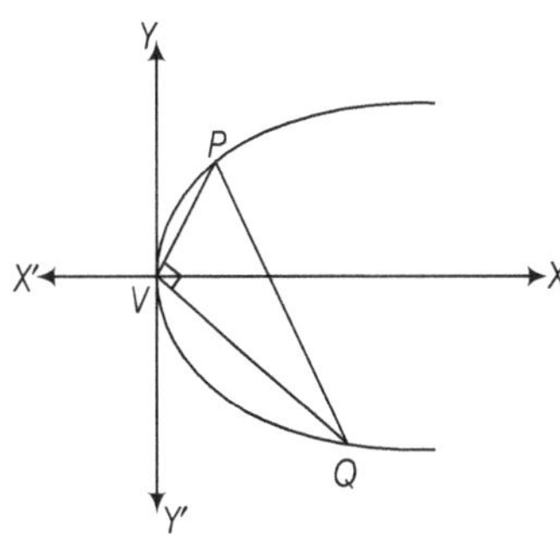

Area of $\Delta PVQ = 20$ (given)

$\Rightarrow \quad \frac{1}{2}\left|\begin{vmatrix} t^2 & 2t \\ \frac{16}{t^2} & \frac{-8}{t} \end{vmatrix}\right| = 20$

$\Rightarrow \quad t + \frac{4}{t} = \pm 5$

$\Rightarrow \quad t^2 - 5t + 4 = 0$ or $t^2 + 5t + 4 = 0$

$\therefore \quad t = 1, 4$ or $t = -1, -4$

Hence coordinates of P are $(1, 2), (16, 8), (1 - 2), (16, -8)$

33. Parabola is $y^2 = 4ax$ and circle is $(x + b)^2 + (y - 0)^2 = b^2$

If parabola and circle touch each other externally, then

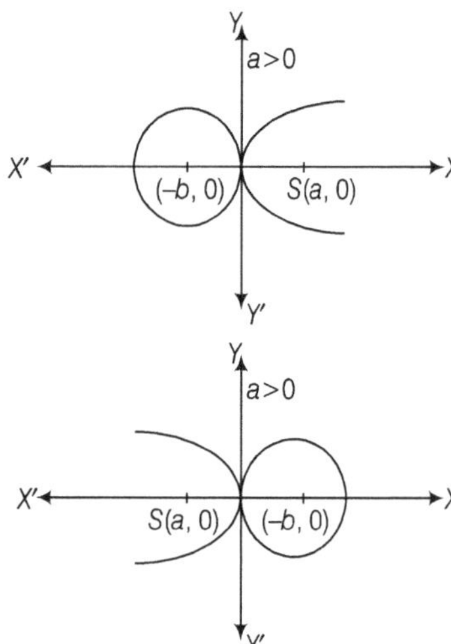

If $a > 0, -b < 0$ and if $a < 0, -b > 0$

or $a > 0, b > 0$ and $a < 0, b < 0$

34. Let $(x_1, y_1) \equiv (at^2, 2at)$

Equation of tangent at $(at^2, 2at)$ is $ty = x + at^2$

Let any point on this tangent is $\left(\lambda, \frac{\lambda + at^2}{t}\right)$

The chord of contact of this point w.r.t the circle $x^2 + y^2 = a^2$ is

$$x \cdot \lambda + y \cdot \left(\frac{\lambda + at^2}{t}\right) = a^2$$

$$\Rightarrow \quad (aty - a^2) + \lambda \cdot \left(x + \frac{y}{t}\right) = 0$$

which is family of straight lines passing through the point of intersection of

$$aty - a^2 = 0 \text{ and } x + \frac{y}{t} = 0$$

So, the fixed point is $\left(\frac{-a}{t^2}, \frac{a}{t}\right)$, therefore

$$x_2 = -\frac{a}{t^2} \quad , \quad y_2 = \frac{a}{t}$$

Clearly, $\quad x_1x_2 = -a^2 \quad , \quad y_1y_2 = 2a^2$

$\Rightarrow \quad x_1x_2 + y_1y_2 = a^2$

Also, $\quad \frac{x_1}{x_2} = -t^4 \quad , \quad \frac{y_1}{y_2} = 2t^2$

or $\quad \left(\frac{y_1}{y_2}\right)^2 + 4\left(\frac{x_1}{x_2}\right) = 0$

$\Rightarrow \; -4, \frac{y_1}{y_2}, \frac{x_1}{x_2}$ are in G.P.

Also, $y_1y_2 = 2a^2 \Rightarrow \frac{y_1}{2}, a, y_2$ are in G.P.

35. Equation of normal in slope form is

$$y = mx - 2am - am^3,$$

if normals meet at (h, k), then

$$am^3 - (h - 2a)m + k = 0 \quad \text{...(i)}$$

Let $\quad P \equiv (am_1^2, -2am_1), Q = (am_2^2, -2am_2)$

and $\quad R \equiv (am_3^2, -2am_3)$

$\Rightarrow \quad m_1, m_2, m_3$ are the roots of Eq. (i), then

$$m_1 + m_2 + m_3 = 0 \quad \text{...(ii)}$$

i.e. algebraic sum of the slopes of the normals at P, Q and R vanishes.

From Eq. (ii)

$$-2am_1 - 2am_2 - 2am_3 = 0$$

i.e. algebraic sum of the ordinates of the points P, Q and R vanishes.

Also, $\quad y$-coordinate of centroid of ΔPQR is zero

$\therefore$ centroid lies on X-axis

and circle circumscribing the triangle PQR always passes through the vertex of the parabola.

36. Let $P \equiv (\lambda, \lambda + 1)$, where $\lambda \neq 0, -1$

or $P \equiv (\lambda, \lambda - 1)$, where $\lambda \neq 0, 1$

The point $(\lambda, \lambda + 1)$ is on $y^2 = 4x + 1$, therefore

$$(\lambda + 1)^2 = 4\lambda + 1$$

$\Rightarrow \quad \lambda^2 - 2\lambda = 0$

$\therefore \quad \lambda = 2$

Therefore, the ordinate of P is 3

and the point $(\lambda, \lambda - 1)$ is on $y^2 = 4x + 1$, therefore

$$(\lambda - 1)^2 = 4(\lambda) + 1$$

$\Rightarrow \quad \lambda^2 - 6\lambda = 0$

$\therefore \quad \lambda = 6$

Therefore, the ordinate of P is 5,

37. From figure,

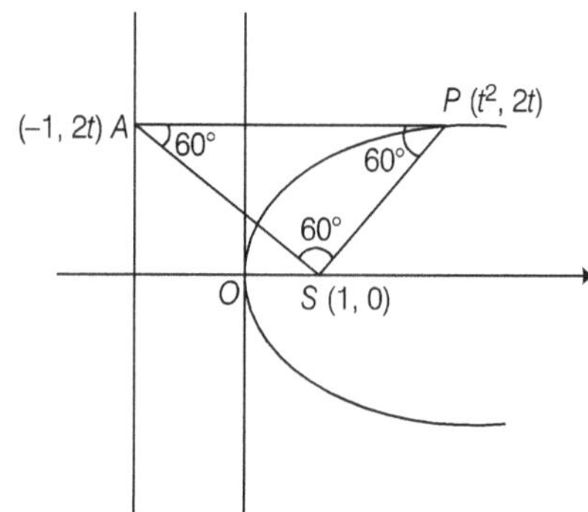

Slope of $AP = 0$ and slope of $AS = -t$

$\therefore \quad \tan 60^\circ = \left|\frac{0 - (-t)}{1 + 0}\right|$

$\Rightarrow \quad \sqrt{3} = |t|$

$\Rightarrow \quad t = \pm\sqrt{3}$

$\therefore$ Coordinates of P are $(3, \pm 2\sqrt{3})$

38. Let $M(\alpha, \beta)$ be the foot of the perpendicular from the focus $S(a, 0)$ on any tangent to the parabola at $P(at^2, 2at)$.

i.e. $\quad ty + x + at^2$

$\Rightarrow \quad \alpha - t\beta + at^2 = 0 \quad$ ...(i)

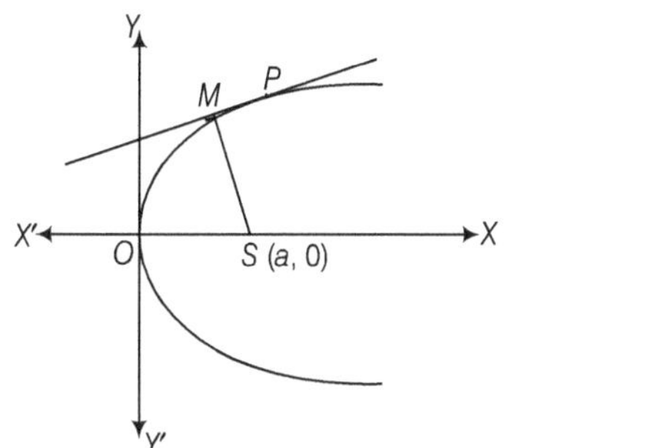

Since, SM is perpendicular to the tangent

$\therefore \quad \frac{1}{t} \times \frac{\beta - 0}{\alpha - a} = -1$

$\Rightarrow \quad \alpha t + \beta - at = 0 \quad$ ...(ii)

On solving Eqs. (i) and (ii), we get

$$\alpha = 0$$

The locus of $M(\alpha, \beta)$ is the tangent at the vertex.

i.e. $\quad x = 0$

39. Given that the extremities of the latusrectum are (1, 1) and (1, – 1), then $4a = 2$ or $a = \frac{1}{2}$

So, the focus of the parabola is (1, 0).

Hence, the vertex can be $\left(\frac{1}{2}, 0\right)$ or $\left(\frac{3}{2}, 0\right)$.

Therefore, the equations of the parabola can be $y^2 = 2\left(x - \frac{1}{2}\right)$

or $y^2 = 2\left(x - \frac{3}{2}\right)$

$\Rightarrow y^2 = 2x - 1$ or $y^2 = 2x - 3$.

40. Let $\quad P \equiv (at^2, 2at)$ and $R \equiv (at_1^2, 2at_1)$

$\because \quad OP \perp OR$

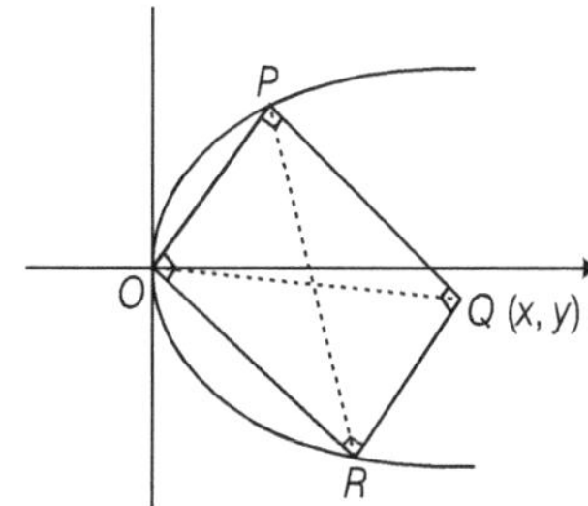

$\therefore$ Slope of OP × Slope of $OR = -1$

$\Rightarrow \quad \frac{2}{t} \times \frac{2}{t_1} = -1$

$\therefore \quad t_1 = -\frac{4}{t}$

Now, coordinates of R are $\left(\frac{16a}{t^2}, \frac{-8a}{t}\right)$

$\because OPQR$ is a rectangle.

$\therefore$ Mid-point of OQ = mid-point of PR

$\Rightarrow \quad x = at^2 + \frac{16a}{t^2} \quad \Rightarrow \quad \frac{x}{a} = t^2 + \frac{16}{t^2} \quad$ ... (i)

and $\quad y = 2at - \frac{8a}{t} \quad \Rightarrow \quad \frac{y}{2a} = t - \frac{4}{t} \quad$ ... (ii)

From Eqs. (i) and (ii), we get

$$\left(\frac{y}{2a}\right)^2 = t^2 + \frac{16}{t^2} - 8 = \frac{x}{a} - 8$$

$\Rightarrow \quad y^2 = 4ax - 32a^2$

or $\quad y^2 = 4a(x - 8a)$

which is equal parabola and focus $(9a, 0)$ and directrix

$$x - 8a = -a$$

or $\quad x - 7a = 0.$

41. Let point of intersection of the line $y = mx$ with the chord be $(\lambda, m\lambda)$, then

$$\lambda = \frac{1.4 + 2.x_1}{1 + 2} \quad \Rightarrow \quad x_1 = \frac{3\lambda - 4}{2}$$

and $\quad m\lambda = \frac{1.4 + 2.y_1}{1 + 2} \quad \Rightarrow \quad y_1 = \frac{3m\lambda - 4}{2}$

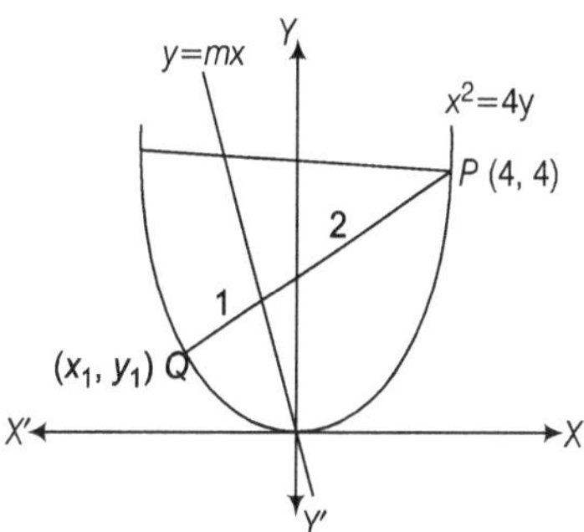

$\because Q(x_1, y_1)$ lies on the parabola $x^2 = 4y$, then

$$\left(\frac{3\lambda - 4}{2}\right)^2 = 4\left(\frac{3m\lambda - 4}{2}\right)$$

$\Rightarrow \quad 9\lambda^2 - 24\lambda(1 + m) + 48 = 0$

For two distinct chords $\quad D > 0$

$\Rightarrow \quad (24)^2 (1 + m)^2 - 4 \cdot 9 \cdot 48 > 0$

or $\quad (1 + m)^2 > 3$

$\Rightarrow \quad 1 + m < -\sqrt{3}$

or $\quad 1 + m > \sqrt{3}$

$\therefore \quad m < -\sqrt{3} - 1$

or $\quad m > \sqrt{3} - 1$

Hence , $m \in (-\infty, -\sqrt{3} - 1) \cup (\sqrt{3} - 1, \infty)$

42. The given parabola is $y^2 = 4(2)x$

$\Rightarrow \quad a = 2$

Since, $P(-2, 0)$ lies on the directrix and the axis.

$\Rightarrow$ The tangents will have slope $m = \pm 1$ and the equations are $y = x + 2$ and $y = -x - 2$.

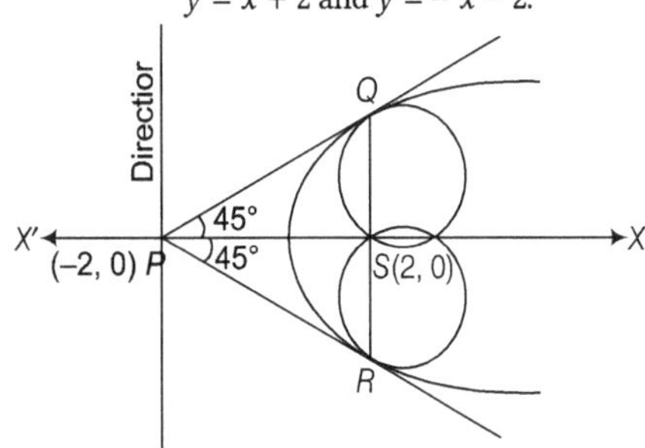

The chord of contact of tangents is QR as $x = 2$ (i.e. L.R.)

$\because$ Common chord of two circles is X-axis.

$\because \quad \angle QPR = 90°$

$\therefore$ Circumcentre is $S(2, 0)$ on X-axis and orthocentre is $P(-2, 0)$ on X-axis.

Centroid and incentre also lies on X-axis,

($\because$ orthocentre, centroid, circumcentre and incentre are collinear).

43. Given parabola is $(y-2)^2 = 4\left(x - \frac{1}{2}\right)$

Let $\quad x - \frac{1}{2} = X, y - 2 = Y$

$\therefore$ Parabola is $Y^2 = 4X$

Any point on axis of parabola is $(x, 2)$ for three distinct normals $X > 2.1$

$$\Rightarrow \quad x - \frac{1}{2} > 2 \text{ or } x > \frac{5}{2}$$

$\therefore \quad x = 3, 4, 5$

Hence, points are (3, 2), (4, 2) and (5, 2).

44. The given parabola is $y^2 - 16x - 8y = 0$

$$\Rightarrow \quad (y-4)^2 = 16(x+1)$$

Shifting the origin to the point $(-1, 4)$ the equation of parabola becomes $y^2 = 16x$

then the coordinates of the point (14, 7) becomes (15, 3).

$\therefore$ Equation of any normal to the parabola is $Y + tX = 8t + 4t^3$.

Since, it passes through (15, 3)

$$\therefore \quad 3 + 15t = 8t + 4t^3 \Rightarrow 4t^3 - 7t - 3 = 0$$

or $\quad (t+1)(2t-3)(2t+1) = 0 \Rightarrow t = -1, \frac{3}{2}, -\frac{1}{2}$

$\therefore$ Corresponding points are $(4, -8)$, $(9, 12)$ and $(1, -4)$. Hence, the coordinates of the feet of the normals w.r.t. the original system of coordinates are $(3, -4)$, $(8, 16)$ and $(0, 0)$.

45. As a circle can intersect a parabola at four points, the quadrilateral may be cyclic.

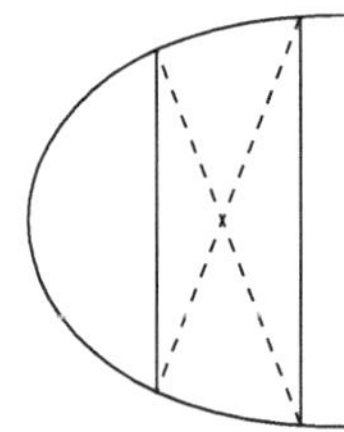

The diagonals of the quadrilateral may be equal as the quadrilateral may be an isosceles trapezium.

A rectangle cannot be inscribed in a parabola.

Sol. (Q. Nos. 46 to 48)

Let $A \equiv (4, 0)$ and $B \equiv (0, 3)$.

$\because$ OA and OB are mutually perpendicular tangents to the parabola. Therefore, O will lie on the directrix of the parabola.

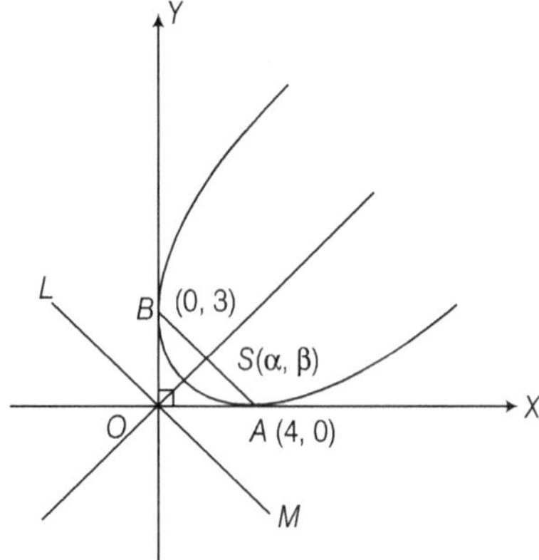

Let $S(\alpha, \beta)$ be the focus of the parabola.

$\because$ Portion of a tangent to a parabola intercepted between the directrix and point of contact subtends a right angle at the focus.

$$\therefore \quad \angle OSA = \angle OSB = \frac{\pi}{2}$$

Now, $OS \perp SA \Rightarrow$ Slope of $OS \times$ Slope of $SA = -1$

$$\Rightarrow \quad \left(\frac{\beta - 0}{\alpha - 0}\right) \times \left(\frac{\beta - 0}{\alpha - 4}\right) = -1$$

$$\Rightarrow \quad \alpha^2 + \beta^2 - 4\alpha = 0 \quad \text{...(i)}$$

Again, $OS \perp SB \Rightarrow$ Slope of $OS \times$ Slope of $SB = -1$

$$\Rightarrow \quad \left(\frac{\beta - 0}{\alpha - 0}\right) \times \left(\frac{\beta - 3}{\alpha - 0}\right) = -1$$

$$\Rightarrow \quad \alpha^2 + \beta^2 - 3\beta = 0 \quad \text{...(ii)}$$

From Eqs. (i) and (ii), we get

$$4\alpha = 3\beta \quad \text{...(iii)}$$

Since, tangents AO and BO at A and B to parabola are at right angles, therefore AB will be a focal chord of the parabola.

Equation of AB is

$$\frac{x}{4} + \frac{y}{3} = 1 \Rightarrow \frac{\alpha}{4} + \frac{\beta}{3} = 1$$

$$\Rightarrow \quad 3\alpha + 4\beta = 12 \quad \text{...(iv)}$$

From Eqs. (iii) and (iv), we get

$$\alpha = \frac{36}{25} \text{ and } \beta = \frac{48}{25}$$

$\therefore$ Focus of parabola is $\left(\frac{36}{25}, \frac{48}{25}\right)$.

46. $\because$ Focus is (a, b).

$$\therefore \quad b - a = \beta - \alpha = \frac{12}{25}$$

47. $\because \quad AS = \sqrt{\left(4 - \frac{36}{25}\right)^2 + \left(0 - \frac{48}{25}\right)^2} = \frac{16}{5}$

and $\quad BS = \sqrt{\left(0 - \frac{36}{25}\right)^2 + \left(3 - \frac{48}{25}\right)^2} = \frac{9}{5}$

If l be the semi-latusrectum, then l = HM of AS and BS

$\therefore \quad \frac{2}{l} = \frac{5}{16} + \frac{5}{9} = \frac{125}{144}$

$\Rightarrow \quad l = \frac{288}{125}$

$\therefore \quad 2l = \frac{576}{125}$

48. $\because \quad$ Slope of $OS = \frac{\beta}{\alpha} = \frac{4}{3}$

$\therefore \quad$ Slope of directrix $LM = -\frac{3}{4}$

$\therefore$ Equation of directrix is $y = -\frac{3}{4}x$

$\Rightarrow \quad 3x + 4y = 0.$

Sol. (Q. Nos. 49 to 51)

Since, (a, b) lies on parabola, $y^2 = 4\lambda x$

$\therefore \quad b^2 = 4a\lambda \quad$ ...(i)

It is clear that ΔPQR is right angled at $P(0, 2)$.

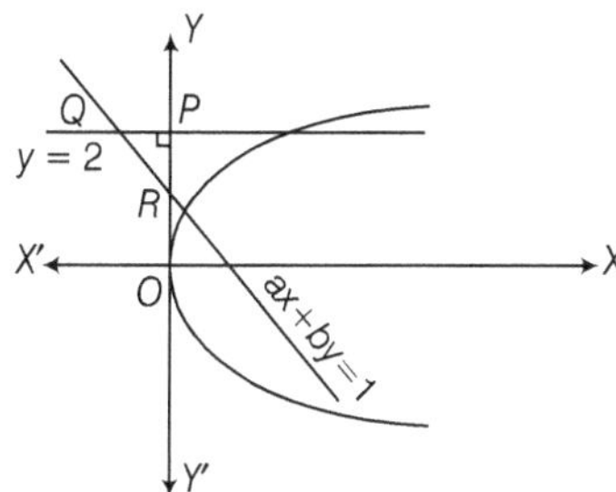

So, its circumcentre is the mid-point of Q and R, where

$$Q \equiv \left(\frac{1-2b}{a}, 2\right) \text{ and } R \equiv \left(0, \frac{1}{b}\right).$$

$\therefore$ Circumcentre $\equiv \left(\frac{1-2b}{2a}, 1 + \frac{1}{2b}\right)$

$\therefore \quad x = \frac{1-2b}{2ab}, y = 1 + \frac{1}{2b}$

$\Rightarrow \quad 2b = \frac{1}{y-1}$ and $2a = \frac{(y-2)}{x(y-1)} \quad$ ...(ii)

From Eqs. (i) and (ii), we get

$(y-1)(y-2) = \frac{x}{8\lambda}$

$\Rightarrow \quad \left(y - \frac{3}{2}\right)^2 = \frac{1}{8\lambda}(x + 2\lambda)$

$\therefore$ Vertex is $\left(-2\lambda, \frac{3}{2}\right)$

and length of latusrectum is $\frac{1}{8\lambda}$.

49. Product of coordinates of vertex $= -2\lambda \times \frac{3}{2} = -3\lambda$

$= -3 \times 2 \quad [\because \lambda = 2]$

$= -6$

50. Length of smallest focal chord = Length of latusrectum

$= \frac{1}{8\lambda}$

$= \frac{1}{8 \times \left(\frac{1}{32}\right)} = 4 \quad \left[\because \lambda = \frac{1}{32}\right]$

51. Let $y - \frac{3}{2} = Y, x + 2\lambda = X$

$\therefore \quad Y^2 = \frac{1}{8\lambda}X$

Curve is symmetrical about $Y = 0$

$\Rightarrow \quad y - \frac{3}{2} = 0$

$\therefore \quad y = \frac{3}{2}$

Sol. (Q. Nos. 52 to 54)

Given parabola (P) can be written as

$$(x - 2y)^2 = 32x - 4y - 16$$

On adding $2(x-2y)\lambda + \lambda^2$ both sides, it becomes

$$(x - 2y + \lambda)^2 = 32x - 4y - 16 + 2(x-2y)\lambda + \lambda^2$$
$$= 2(\lambda + 16)x - 4(\lambda + 1)y + \lambda^2 - 16 \quad \text{...(i)}$$

We choose λ such that lines

$$x - 2y + \lambda = 0 \text{ and } 2(\lambda + 16)x - 4(\lambda + 1)y + \lambda^2 - 16 = 0$$

are perpendicular to each other. It requires

$$\frac{1}{2} \times \frac{2(\lambda + 16)}{4(\lambda + 1)} = -1$$

$\Rightarrow \quad \lambda + 16 = -4\lambda - 4$

$\Rightarrow \quad \lambda = -4$

Hence, Eq. (i) becomes

$$(x - 2y - 4)^2 = 24x + 12y = 12(2x + y)$$

$\Rightarrow \quad \left(\frac{x - 2y - 4}{\sqrt{5}}\right)^2 = \frac{12}{\sqrt{5}}\left(\frac{2x + y}{\sqrt{5}}\right) \Rightarrow Y^2 = 4\rho X$

where, $\quad X = \frac{2x + y}{\sqrt{5}}, Y = \frac{x - 2y - 4}{\sqrt{5}}$

and $\quad 4\rho = \frac{12}{\sqrt{5}} \Rightarrow \rho = \frac{3}{\sqrt{5}}.$

52. $\because$ Equation of axis is $Y = 0$

$\Rightarrow \quad x - 2y - 4 = 0 \quad$ ...(i)

and equation of latusrectum is $X = \rho$

$\Rightarrow \quad \frac{2x + y}{\sqrt{5}} = \frac{3}{\sqrt{5}}$

$\Rightarrow \quad 2x + y - 3 = 0 \quad$ ...(ii)

On solving Eqs. (i) and (ii),

focus is $\quad (x, y) = (2, -1).$

53. Length of latusrectum $= 4\rho = \dfrac{12}{\sqrt{5}}$

54. Equation of directrix is $X + \rho = 0$

$$\Rightarrow \quad \frac{2x+y}{\sqrt{5}} + \frac{3}{\sqrt{5}} = 0$$

$$\therefore \quad 2x + y + 3 = 0$$

Sol. (Q. Nos. 55 to 57)

Any parabola whose axis is parallel to the X-axis will be of the form

$$(y-q)^2 = 4\lambda(x-p) \qquad \text{...(i)}$$

Now, $lx + my = 1$ can be written as

$$(y-q) = -\frac{l}{m}(x-p) + \left(\frac{1-mq-lp}{m}\right) \qquad \text{...(ii)}$$

Eq. (ii) will touch Eq. (i), then

$$\frac{1-mq-lp}{m} = \frac{\lambda}{-\dfrac{l}{m}}$$

$$\Rightarrow \quad -l + mlq + l^2p = m^2\lambda$$

$$\Rightarrow \quad pl^2 + qlm - \lambda m^2 - l = 0 \qquad \text{...(iii)}$$

But given that

$$5l^2 - 4lm + 6m^2 + 3l = 0 \qquad \text{...(iv)}$$

On comparing Eqs. (iii) and (iv), we get

$$\frac{p}{5} = \frac{q}{-4} = \frac{-\lambda}{6} = \frac{-1}{3}$$

$$\Rightarrow \quad p = -\frac{5}{3}, q = \frac{4}{3}, \lambda = 2$$

So, the parabola is

$$\left(y - \frac{4}{3}\right)^2 = 8\left(x + \frac{5}{3}\right).$$

55. $\because$ Vertex is $\left(-\dfrac{5}{3}, \dfrac{4}{3}\right)$.

Here, $a = -\dfrac{5}{3}$ and $b = \dfrac{4}{3}$

$$\therefore \quad a - b = -3$$

$$\Rightarrow \quad |a-b| = 3$$

56. For focus,

$$x + \frac{5}{3} = 2 \text{ and } y - \frac{4}{3} = 0$$

$\therefore$ Coordinates of focus are $\left(\dfrac{1}{3}, \dfrac{4}{3}\right)$.

Here, $c = \dfrac{1}{3}$ and $d = \dfrac{4}{3}$

$$\therefore \quad d - c = 1$$

$$\Rightarrow \quad 2^{|d-c|} = 2$$

57. For directrix $\left(x + \dfrac{5}{3}\right) + 2 = 0$

$\Rightarrow 3x + 11 = 0$ given $ex + f = 0$

$$\therefore \quad e = 3, f = 11$$

Now, $\quad |e - f| = |3 - 11| = 8$

Sol. (Q. Nos. 58 to 60)

$$\because \quad C_1 : y^2 = 4x$$

$$\therefore \quad S_1 : (1, 0)$$

Let $z = x + iy$ and $z_1 = x_1 + iy_1$

If z_1 is obtained by rotating z, 120° in anti-clockwise direction, then

$$z_1 = ze^{2\pi i/3} = (x+iy)\left(-\frac{1}{2} + \frac{i\sqrt{3}}{2}\right)$$

$$= \left(-\frac{x}{2} - \frac{\sqrt{3}y}{2}\right) + i\left(\frac{\sqrt{3}}{2}x - \frac{y}{2}\right)$$

$\therefore$ Equation of curve C_2 is

$$\left(\frac{\sqrt{3}}{2}x - \frac{y}{2}\right)^2 = 4\left(-\frac{x}{2} - \frac{\sqrt{3}}{2}y\right) \qquad \text{...(i)}$$

For focus $-\dfrac{x}{2} - \dfrac{\sqrt{3}}{2}y = 1$ and $\dfrac{\sqrt{3}}{2}x - \dfrac{y}{2} = 0$.

$$\therefore \quad x = -\frac{1}{2}, y = -\frac{\sqrt{3}}{2}$$

$$\Rightarrow \quad S_2 : \left(-\frac{1}{2}, -\frac{\sqrt{3}}{2}\right)$$

$\because$ C_3 is reflection of C_2 with respect to $y = x$.

$$\therefore \quad S_3 : \left(-\frac{\sqrt{3}}{2}, -\frac{1}{2}\right).$$

58. $\because (t^2, 2t)$ are parametric form of curve C_1.

$\therefore$ From Eq. (i),

$$\frac{\sqrt{3}}{2}x - \frac{y}{2} = 2t \text{ and } -\frac{x}{2} - \frac{\sqrt{3}}{2}y = t^2,$$

we get $x = \dfrac{1}{2}(-t^2 + 2\sqrt{3}t), y = \dfrac{1}{2}(-\sqrt{3}t^2 - 2t)$

$\therefore$ Parametric coordinates of C_2 are

$$\left(\frac{1}{2}(-t^2 + 2\sqrt{3}t), \frac{1}{2}(-\sqrt{3}t^2 - 2t)\right).$$

59. Area of ΔOS_2S_3

$$= \frac{1}{2}\left|\begin{vmatrix} -\dfrac{1}{2} & -\dfrac{\sqrt{3}}{2} \\ -\dfrac{\sqrt{3}}{2} & -\dfrac{1}{2} \end{vmatrix}\right|$$

$$= \frac{1}{2}\left|\frac{1}{4} - \frac{3}{4}\right| = \frac{1}{4} \text{ sq unit}$$

60. $$\Sigma x_1^2 + \Sigma y_1^2 = (1)^2 + \left(-\frac{1}{2}\right)^2 + \left(-\frac{\sqrt{3}}{2}\right)^2 + (0)^2 + \left(-\frac{\sqrt{3}}{2}\right)^2 + \left(-\frac{1}{2}\right)^2$$

$$= 1 + \frac{1}{4} + \frac{3}{4} + 0 + \frac{3}{4} + \frac{1}{4} = 3$$

Sol. (Q. Nos. 61 to 63)

Since, no point of the parabola $y = x^2 + ax + 1$ is below the X-axis.

$$\therefore \quad D \le 0$$

$$\Rightarrow \quad a^2 - 4 \le 0$$

$$\Rightarrow \quad -2 \le a \le 2$$

61. The maximum value of a is 2.

The equation of the parabola is $y = x^2 + 2x + 1$.

It intersect the Y-axis at (0, 1).

$\therefore$ Equation of tangent at (0, 1) is

$$\frac{y+1}{2} = 0 \cdot x + (x+0) + 1$$

$$\Rightarrow \quad y = 2x + 1$$

$$\Rightarrow \quad 2x - y + 1 = 0$$

Since, $2x - y + 1 = 0$ touches the circle $x^2 + y^2 = c^2$, then

$$\frac{0 - 0 + 1}{\sqrt{4+1}} = c \qquad [\because c > 0]$$

$$\Rightarrow \quad c = \frac{1}{\sqrt{5}}$$

$$\therefore \quad 5c^2 = 1$$

62. Equation of the tangent at (0, 1) to the parabola

$y = x^2 + ax + 1$ is

$$\Rightarrow \quad \frac{y+1}{2} = 0 \cdot x + \frac{a}{2}(x+0) + 1$$

$$\Rightarrow \quad y = ax + 1$$

$$\Rightarrow \quad ax - y + 1 = 0$$

As it touches the circle $x^2 + y^2 = c^2$, then

$$\frac{1}{\sqrt{(a^2+1)}} = c$$

i.e. c is maximum, when $a = 0$.

Therefore, the equation of the tangent is $y = 1$.

$\therefore$ Slope of the tangent is 0.

63. Equation of tangent is

$$y = ax + 1$$

$$\Rightarrow \quad ax - y = -1$$

$$\Rightarrow \quad \frac{x}{\left(-\frac{1}{a}\right)} + \frac{y}{(1)} = 1$$

Therefore, the area of the triangle bounded by the tangent and the axes is

$$\frac{1}{2}\left|-\frac{1}{a}\right||1| = \frac{1}{2|a|}$$

$$\therefore \quad \Delta = \frac{1}{4} \qquad [\text{for minimum area } a = 2]$$

$$\Rightarrow \quad 8\Delta = 2$$

Sol. (Q. Nos. 64 to 66)

The conic is $S \equiv x^2 + xy + y^2 - 2x - 2y + 1 = 0$

and the line is $L \equiv x + y + 1 = 0$

It is required to find equation of the parabola (P) which touches the conic $S = 0$ at those (two) points, where the line $L = 0$ intersect the conic. Obviously at these points the parabola is in double contact with the conic.

$\therefore$ The equation of any such conic is $\phi \equiv S + \lambda L^2 = 0$

$$\Rightarrow (x^2 + xy + y^2 - 2x - 2y + 1) + \lambda(x + y + 1)^2 = 0 \qquad \text{...(i)}$$

$$\Rightarrow (1+\lambda)x^2 + (1+2\lambda)xy + (1+\lambda)y^2 + 2(\lambda-1)x + 2(\lambda-1)y + \lambda + 1 = 0$$

It will be a parabola, if $h^2 = ab$

$$\Rightarrow \quad \frac{1}{4}(1+2\lambda)^2 = (1+\lambda)^2$$

$$\Rightarrow \quad 1 + 4\lambda + 4\lambda^2 = 4 + 8\lambda + 4\lambda^2$$

$$\therefore \quad \lambda = -\frac{3}{4}$$

Hence, from Eq. (i), the required parabola is

$$(x^2 + xy + y^2 - 2x - 2y + 1) - \frac{3}{4}(x + y + 1)^2 = 0$$

$$\Rightarrow \quad x^2 - 2xy + y^2 - 14x - 14y + 1 = 0 \qquad \text{...(ii)}$$

64. Comparing parabola (ii) with

$$ax^2 + 2hxy + by^2 + 2gx + 2fy + c = 0$$

$\therefore a = 1, h = -1, b = 1, g = -7, f = -7, c = 1$

Now, $|a + b + c + f + g + h| = |1 + 1 + 1 - 7 - 7 - 1| = 12$

65. The parabola (P) can be written as

$$(x-y)^2 = (14x + 14y - 1)$$

$$\Rightarrow \quad \left(\frac{x-y}{\sqrt{2}}\right)^2 = 7\sqrt{2}\left(\frac{14x + 14y - 1}{\sqrt{(14)^2 + (14)^2}}\right) \qquad \text{...(iii)}$$

$\therefore$ Length of latusrectum is $7\sqrt{2}$.

66. For vertex,

$$\frac{x-y}{\sqrt{2}} = 0, \frac{14x + 14y - 1}{\sqrt{(14)^2 + (14)^2}} = 0 \qquad [\text{from Eq. (iii)}]$$

$$\Rightarrow \quad x = y, 14x + 14y = 1$$

$$\therefore \quad x = y = \frac{1}{28}$$

$$\text{Vertex is } \left(\frac{1}{28}, \frac{1}{28}\right) = (a, b) \qquad [\text{given}]$$

$$\therefore \quad |a - b| = 0$$

Sol. (Q. Nos. 67 to 69)

$\because$ $y = 3x$ is tangent to the parabola

$$2y = ax^2 + b \qquad \text{...(i)}$$

$$\therefore \quad 2(3x) = ax^2 + b$$

[substitute the value of $y = 3x$ in $2y = ax^2 + b$]

$$\Rightarrow \quad ax^2 - 6x + b = 0$$

$$D = 0$$

[$\because y = 3x$ is tangent to $2y = ax^2 + b$]

$$\therefore \quad 36 - 4ab = 0$$

$$\Rightarrow \quad ab = 9 \qquad \text{...(ii)}$$

From Eqs. (i) and (ii), we get

$$2y = ax^2 + \frac{9}{a} \qquad \text{...(iii)}$$

67. $\because \quad \dfrac{a+b}{2} \geq \sqrt{ab} = 3 \qquad [\text{from Eq. (ii)}]$

$$\Rightarrow \quad a + b \geq 6$$

$\therefore$ Minimum value of $a + b$ is 6.

68. $\because (2, 6)$ is the point of contact.

From Eq. (iii), we get

$$12 = 4a + \frac{9}{a}$$

$$\Rightarrow \quad 4a^2 - 12a + 9 = 0$$

$$\Rightarrow \quad (2a - 3)^2 = 0$$

$$\therefore \quad 2a = 3$$

69. For $b = 18$

From Eq. (ii), $a = \frac{1}{2}$

From Eq. (iii), $2y = \frac{x^2}{2} + 18$ ...(iv)

On solving $y = 3x$ and Eq. (iv), we get

$$6x = \frac{x^2}{2} + 18$$

$$\Rightarrow \quad x^2 - 12x + 36 = 0$$

$$\Rightarrow \quad (x - 6)^2 = 0$$

$$\therefore \quad x = 6, \text{ then } y = 3x = 18$$

$\therefore$ Point of contact is (6, 18).

70. Equation of tangent in terms of slope (m) of the parabola $y^2 = 4x$ is $y = mx + \frac{1}{m}$.

$\because$ Point of intersection of tangents is $(-2, -1)$, then

$$-1 = -2m + \frac{1}{m}$$

$$\Rightarrow \quad 2m^2 - m - 1 = 0$$

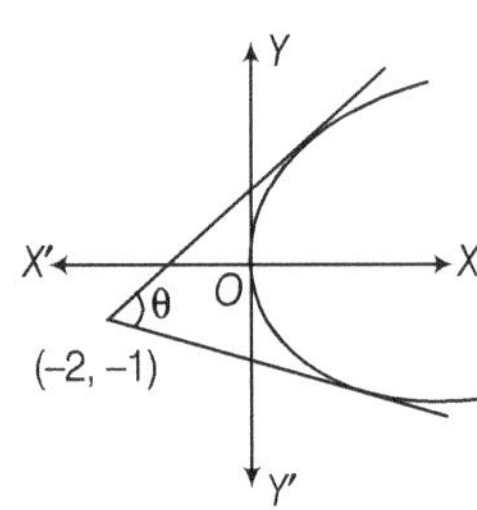

Let m_1, m_2 be slopes of the tangents, then

$$m_1 - m_2 = \frac{\sqrt{D}}{a} = \frac{\sqrt{(1+8)}}{2} = \frac{3}{2}$$

and $\quad m_1 m_2 = -\frac{1}{2}$

$$\therefore \quad \tan\theta = \left|\frac{m_1 - m_2}{1 + m_1 m_2}\right| = \left|\frac{3/2}{1 - 1/2}\right| = 3$$

71. Let S be the focus and point of intersection of tangents at P and Q is R.

$$\because \quad (SR)^2 = SP \cdot SQ = 4 \times 9 = 36$$

$$\therefore \quad SR = 6$$

72. The four lines form a square. The tangents at $L(1, 2)$ and $L'(1, -2)$ are $x - y + 1 = 0$ and $x + y + 1 = 0$. They intersect at $M(-1, 0)$.

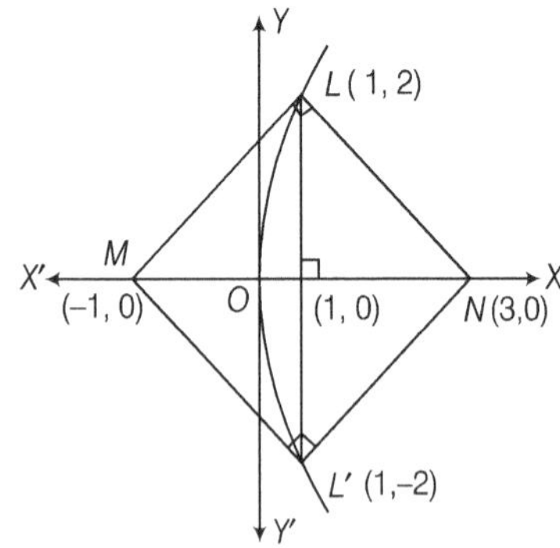

The area of the square

$MLNL'$ is $(ML)^2 = (1 + 1)^2 + (2 - 0)^2 = 8$ sq units

$$\therefore \quad \lambda = 8$$

73. Parabola is $y^2 = x$

$$\therefore \quad a = \frac{1}{4}$$

The normal at t is

$$tx + y = \frac{t^3}{4} + \frac{t}{2}$$

It passes through $(a, 0)$.

$$\therefore \quad ta = \frac{t^3}{4} + \frac{t}{2}$$

$$\Rightarrow \quad t^2 = 4\left(a - \frac{1}{2}\right) \Rightarrow a > \frac{1}{2}$$

$$\therefore \quad t_1 = 2\sqrt{\left(a - \frac{1}{2}\right)}, t_2 = -2\sqrt{\left(a - \frac{1}{2}\right)}$$

The normals are perpendicular $\Rightarrow t_1 t_2 = -1$

$$\Rightarrow \quad -4\left(a - \frac{1}{2}\right) = -1$$

$$\therefore \quad 4a = 3$$

74. Let B as $\left(\frac{3}{2}t^2, 3t\right)$ $\left[\text{Here, } a = \frac{3}{2}\right]$

and let $BD \perp AC$ and $\angle DAB = \theta$

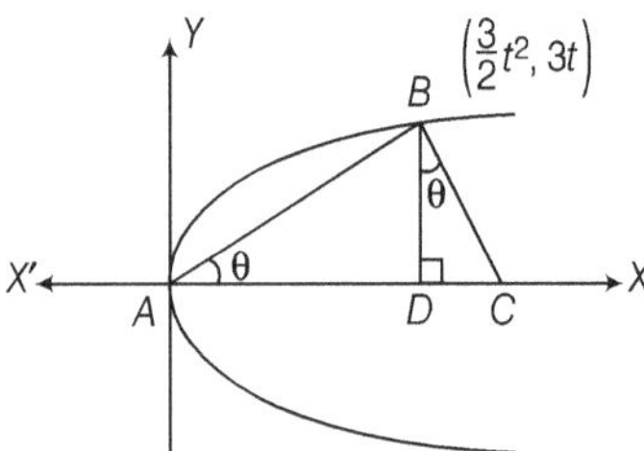

$$\Rightarrow \quad \tan\theta = \frac{BD}{AD} = \frac{3t}{\frac{3}{2}t^2} = \frac{2}{t}$$

$\therefore$ Projection of BC on the axis $= DC$

$$= BD\tan\theta = 3t\left(\frac{2}{t}\right) = 6 \text{ units}$$

$$\therefore \quad \lambda = 6$$

75. The parabolas are $y = x^2 - 9$ and $y = \lambda x^2$.

$\Rightarrow \quad x^2 - 9 = \lambda x^2 \Rightarrow \quad x^2(1-\lambda) = 9$

$\Rightarrow \quad x^2 = \dfrac{9}{1-\lambda}$

$\therefore \quad x = \pm \dfrac{3}{\sqrt{(1-\lambda)}}$

Now, from the symmetry about Y-axis,

$$AB = 2a = \frac{6}{\sqrt{(1-\lambda)}} \Rightarrow a = \frac{3}{\sqrt{(1-\lambda)}}$$

$\Rightarrow \quad a^2(1-\lambda) = 9 \quad \Rightarrow \quad \lambda a^2 + 9 = a^2$

$\Rightarrow \quad a^2 + \mu = a^2$ [given]

$\therefore \quad \mu = 9$

76. Given, $y^2 - 8x < 0$, $x^2 + y^2 < 16$ and $x > 0$.

For $x = 1$,

$y^2 < 8$ and $y^2 < 15 \Rightarrow y^2 < 8$

$\therefore \quad y = 0, \pm 1, \pm 2$

$\therefore$ 5 points.

For $x = 2$,

$y^2 < 16, y^2 < 12 \Rightarrow y^2 < 12$

$\therefore \quad y = 0, \pm 1, \pm 2, \pm 3$

$\therefore$ 7 points

For $x = 3$,

$y^2 < 24, y^2 < 7 \Rightarrow y^2 < 7$

$\therefore \quad y = 0, \pm 1, \pm 2$

$\therefore$ 5 points

Hence, total points is 17.

$\therefore \quad n = 17$

Sum of digits of n is 8.

77. Focus of the parabola $y^2 = 4x$ is $S(1, 0)$.

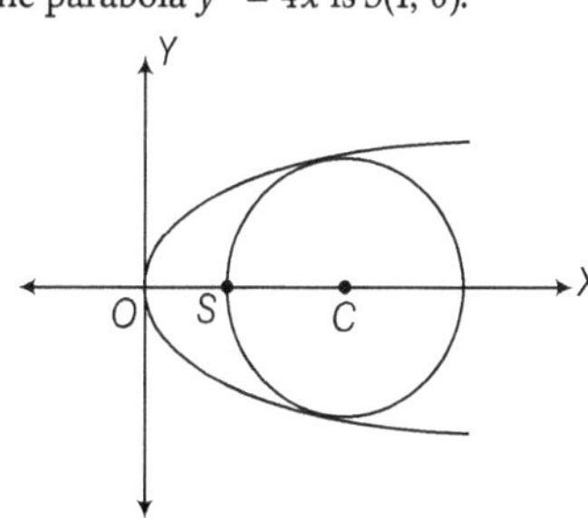

Let radius of circle be r.

$\therefore$ Centre of circle is $(1 + r, 0)$.

$\Rightarrow$ Equation of circle is $(x - 1 - r)^2 + y^2 = r^2$

$\Rightarrow \quad (x - 1 - r)^2 + 4x = r^2$ $[\because y^2 = 4x]$

$\Rightarrow \quad x^2 + 2(2 - 1 - r)x + 2r + 1 = 0$

$\Rightarrow \quad x^2 + 2(1 - r)x + 2r + 1 = 0$

It would have same roots due to symmetry.

$\therefore \quad D = 0$

$\Rightarrow \quad 4(1 - r)^2 - 4 \cdot 1 \cdot (2r + 1) = 0$

$\therefore \quad r = 0, 4$

Hence, $\quad r = 4$ $[\because r \neq 0]$

78. For maximum number of common chords, the circle and the parabola must intersect at four points.

Now, solving the given curves, we have

$$(x - 6)^2 + 4x = r^2$$

$\Rightarrow \quad x^2 - 8x + 36 - r^2 = 0$

The curves touch, if $\quad D = 0$

$\Rightarrow \quad 64 - 4 \cdot 1 \cdot (36 - r^2) = 0$

$\Rightarrow \quad r^2 = 20$

$\therefore \quad r = 2\sqrt{5}$

Hence, the least integral value of r for which the curves intersect is 5.

79. Given parabola is

$$x^2 = 4(y - 1)$$

$\therefore$ Focus is $(0, 2)$.

Now, the shortest intercept of the line on the parabola which passes through the focus is latusrectum. The axis of the given parabola is the Y-axis.

Therefore, the latusrectum is parallel to the X-axis.

$\therefore$ Slope = 0

80. (A) The given parabolas are symmetrical about the line $y = x$ as shown in the figure

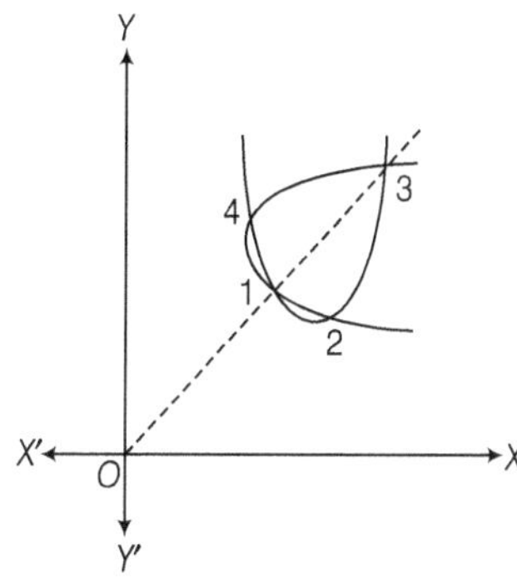

They intersect each other at four distinct points.

Hence, the number of common chords is

$${}^4C_2 = \frac{4 \cdot 3}{1 \cdot 2} = 6$$

Which is perfect number $[\because 1 \times 2 \times 3 = 1 + 2 + 3 = 6]$

(B) $\because \quad \tan\theta = \dfrac{y}{x}$ ...(i)

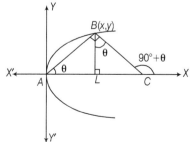

LC = Projection of BC on X-axis

$= BL \tan\theta = y \tan\theta$

$$= y \times \frac{y}{x} \quad \text{[from Eq. (i)]}$$

$$= \frac{y^2}{x}$$

$$= 4 \quad [\because y^2 = 4x]$$

(C) Normals to $y^2 = 4ax$ and $x^2 = 4by$ in terms of m are

$y = mx - 2am - am^3$ and $y = mx + 2b + \frac{b}{m^2}$.

For common normal,

$$2b + \frac{b}{m^2} = -2am - am^3$$

or $$am^5 + 2am^3 + 2bm^2 + b = 0$$

It is clear that at most five common normals.

(D) Let middle point of P and B be (h,k), then $2h = at^2$

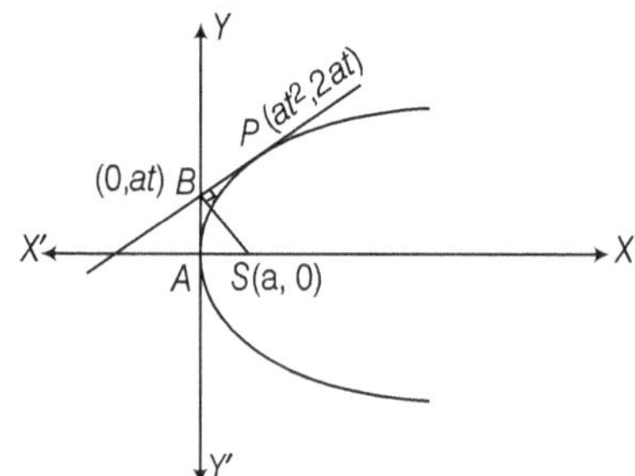

and $$2k = 3at$$

or $$2h = a\left(\frac{2k}{3a}\right)^2$$

or $$2k^2 = 9ah$$

$\therefore$ Locus of mid-point is

$$2y^2 = 9ax$$

$$\therefore \text{Length of latusrectum} = \frac{9a}{2}$$

$$= \frac{9}{2} \times 2 \quad [\because a = 2]$$

$$= 9$$

81. (A) Given parabola is $x^2 = ay$ ...(i)

and the given line is $y - 2x = 1$ ...(ii)

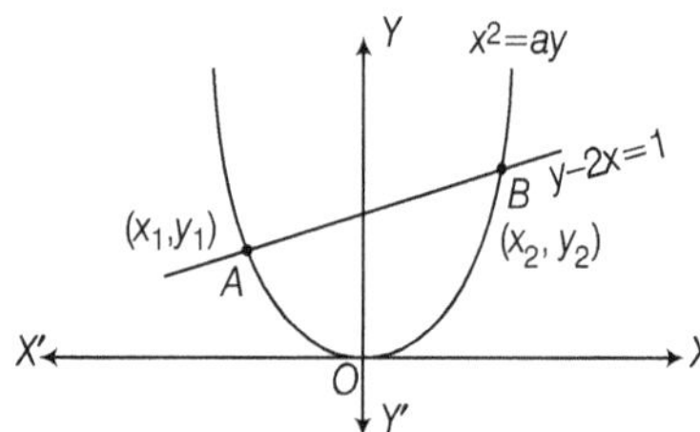

On solving Eqs. (i) and (ii), we get

$$x^2 = a(2x + 1) \Rightarrow x^2 - 2ax - a = 0$$

Let coordinates of A and B are (x_1, y_1) and (x_2, y_2) respectively, then

$$|x_1 - x_2| = \frac{\sqrt{D}}{a} = \frac{\sqrt{(4a^2 + 4a)}}{1} = 2\sqrt{(a^2 + a)} \quad \text{...(iii)}$$

Also A, B lie on $y - 2x = 1$

$\therefore$ $y_1 - 2x_1 = 1$ and $y_2 - 2x_2 = 1$

or $$y_2 - y_1 = 2(x_2 - x_1) \quad \text{...(iv)}$$

$$\therefore \text{Length of } AB = \sqrt{(x_2 - x_1)^2 + (y_2 - y_1)^2}$$

$$= \sqrt{5}\,|x_1 - x_2| \quad \text{[from Eq. (iv)]}$$

$$= 2\sqrt{5}\sqrt{(a^2 + a)} \quad \text{[from Eq. (iii)]}$$

Given, $2\sqrt{5}\sqrt{(a^2 + a)} = \sqrt{40}$

$$\Rightarrow a^2 + a = 2$$

$$\Rightarrow a^2 + a - 2 = 0$$

$$\Rightarrow (a + 2)(a - 1) = 0$$

$$\Rightarrow a = -2, 1$$

(B) If tangents are drawn from (x_1, y_1) to the parabola $y^2 = 4ax$ and angle between tangents is θ, then

$$|\tan\theta| = \frac{\sqrt{(y_1^2 - 4ax_1)}}{|x_1 + a|}$$

Here, $x_1 = 0, y_1 = 2, \theta = \frac{3\pi}{4}$, then

$$|-1| = \frac{2}{|0 + a|}$$

$$\Rightarrow |a| = 2$$

$$\therefore a = \pm 2$$

Aliter :

Observe that one tangent is the Y-axis, the other tangent is at $\theta = \frac{\pi}{4}$ and its equation is $ty = x + at^2$

for $t = 1$, we get $y = x + a$

$\Rightarrow a = 2$ from the symmetry $a = -2$ is also possible.

(C) Let the other end be at $(at^2, 2at)$

So, mid-point is $\left(\frac{at^2 + a}{2}, \frac{2at + 2a}{2}\right)$

which satisfy $x + y = 1$

or $$\frac{at^2 + a}{2} + at + a = 1$$

$$\Rightarrow at^2 + 2at + 3a - 2 = 0$$

Since, two distinct chords are possible, so $D > 0$.

$$\therefore 4a^2 - 4a(3a - 2) > 0$$

$$\Rightarrow -8a^2 + 8a > 0$$

$$\Rightarrow 8a(a - 1) < 0$$

$$\therefore 0 < a < 1$$

or $$0 < 4a < 4$$

or $0 <$ Length of latusrectum < 4

$\therefore$ Length of latusrectum can be 1 or 2 or 3 from the given values.

(D) The given parabola is

$$x^2 - ay + 3 = 0$$

or $$x^2 = a\left(y - \frac{3}{a}\right)$$

Let $\quad x = X, y - \frac{3}{a} = Y$

Then, the parabola is

$$X^2 = aY$$

For focus $X = 0, Y = \frac{a}{4}$

$\Rightarrow \quad x = 0, y - \frac{3}{a} = \frac{a}{4}$

$\therefore$ Focus is $\left(0, \frac{3}{a} + \frac{a}{4}\right)$ given focus is (0, 2)

$\therefore \quad \frac{3}{a} + \frac{a}{4} = 2$

$\Rightarrow \quad a^2 - 8a + 12 = 0$

$\Rightarrow \quad (a-6)(a-2) = 0$

$\therefore \quad a = 2, 6$

Here, $\quad a_1 = 6, a_2 = 2$

$\therefore \quad \frac{a_1}{a_2} = 3$

82. (A) Points (1, 2) and (– 2 , 1) satisfy both the curves.

(B) Equation of tangent at $(t^2, 2t)$ on $y^2 = 4x$ is

$$ty = x + t^2$$

It passes through the point (2, 3), then

$$3t = 2 + t^2$$

$\Rightarrow \quad t^2 - 3t + 2 = 0$

or $\quad (t-1)(t-2) = 0$

or $\quad t = 1$ or 2

The point of contact is (1, 2) or (4, 4).

(C) Let $P(\sqrt{5}\cos\theta, \sqrt{5}\sin\theta)$, then the chord of contact of the parabola $y^2 = 4x$ w.r.t. P is

$$y \cdot \sqrt{5}\sin\theta = 2(x + \sqrt{5}\cos\theta)$$

or $\quad y = \frac{2x}{\sqrt{5}\sin\theta} + 2\cot\theta$

On comparing with $y = 2(x-2)$, then

$$\sqrt{5}\sin\theta = 1 \text{ and } \cot\theta = -2$$

or $\quad \sqrt{5}\sin\theta = 1$ and $\sqrt{5}\cos\theta = -2$

Hence, coordinates of P are (– 2, 1).

(D) Let coordinates of Q be $(t^2, 2t)$.

Now, the area of ΔOPQ is

$$\frac{1}{2}\left|\begin{vmatrix} t^2 & 2t \\ 4 & -4 \end{vmatrix}\right| = 6 \quad \text{[given]}$$

$\Rightarrow \quad 2t^2 + 4t = \pm 6$

or $\quad t^2 + 2t \pm 3 = 0$

$\therefore \quad t^2 + 2t - 3 = 0 \quad [\because t^2 + 2t + 3 \neq 0]$

$\Rightarrow \quad (t+3)(t-1) = 0$

Then, $\quad t = 1$ or -3

Hence, the point Q are (1, 2) or (9, – 6).

83. Equation of tangent to $y^2 = 4x$ is

$$y = mx + \frac{1}{m}$$

it is also tangent to $x^2 = 4y$, then

$$x^2 = 4\left(mx + \frac{1}{m}\right)$$

$\Rightarrow \quad x^2 - 4mx - \frac{4}{m} = 0$

It discriminant = 0

$\Rightarrow \quad 16m^2 + \frac{16}{m} = 0$

$\Rightarrow \quad m^3 = -1$

$\therefore \quad m = -1$

$\therefore$ Equation of common tangent is $x + y + 1 = 0$.

Statement II is also true and it is correct explanation of Statement I.

84. The vertex of $(y+2)^2 = 2(x-1)$ is (1, – 2) and equation of axis is $y = -2$.

Here, $\quad 4a = 2$

$\therefore \quad a = \frac{1}{2} \Rightarrow 3a = \frac{3}{2}$

$\therefore$ Required point is $\left(1 + \frac{3}{2}, -2\right)$, i.e. $\left(\frac{5}{2}, -2\right)$.

Hence, both statements are true and Statement II is correct explanation for Statement I.

85. $\because \quad y = mx + c \quad$ ...(i)

and $\quad y^2 = 4ax \quad$ ...(ii)

From Eqs. (i) and (ii),

$$y^2 = 4a\left(\frac{y-c}{m}\right)$$

$\Rightarrow \quad my^2 - 4ay + 4ac = 0$

If line Eq. (i) intersect the parabola $y^2 = 4ax$ at one point, then

$$B^2 = 4AC$$

$\Rightarrow \quad (-4a)^2 = 4 \cdot m \cdot 4ac$

$\Rightarrow \quad c = \frac{a}{m}$

From Eq. (i), equation of tangent is

$$y = mx + \frac{a}{m}$$

$\therefore$ Statement I and Statement II are individual true and Statement II is correct explanation of Statement I.

86. $\because \quad \sqrt{ax} + \sqrt{by} = 1 \quad$ ...(i)

On squaring both sides, then

$$ax + by + 2\sqrt{abxy} = 1$$

$\Rightarrow \quad (ax + by - 1) = -2\sqrt{abxy}$

Again, on squaring both sides, we get

$$a^2x^2 + b^2y^2 + 1 + 2abxy - 2ax - 2by + 1 = 4abxy$$

$$\Rightarrow a^2x^2 - 2abxy + b^2y^2 - 2ax - 2by + 1 = 0$$

Now, comparing with

$$Ax^2 + 2Hxy + By^2 + 2Gx + 2Fy + C = 0$$

$\therefore \quad A = a^2, H = -ab, B = b^2, G = -a, F = -b, C = 1$

$\therefore \quad \Delta = ABC + 2FGH - AF^2 - BG^2 - CH^2$

$= a^2b^2 - 2a^2b^2 - a^2b^2 - a^2b^2 - a^2b^2$

$= -4a^2b^2 \neq 0$

and $H^2 = AB$

Hence, Eq. (i) represent a parabola.

$\therefore$ Statement I is true and Statement II is false.

87. $\because$ Slope of $AP = m_1 = \dfrac{2at_1 - 0}{at_1^2 - 0} = \dfrac{2}{t_1}$

and slope of $AQ = m_2 = \dfrac{2at_2 - 0}{at_2^2 - 0} = \dfrac{2}{t_2}$

$\because \quad m_1 m_2 = \dfrac{4}{t_1 t_2} \neq -1$

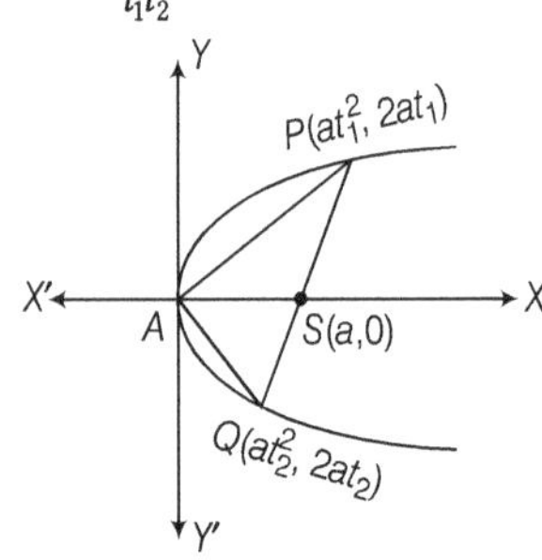

Also, P, S, Q are collinear, then

$$\frac{2at_1 - 0}{at_1^2 - a} = \frac{0 - 2at_2}{a - at_2^2}$$

$\Rightarrow \quad t_1 - t_1 t_2^2 = -t_1^2 t_2 + t_2$

$\Rightarrow \quad (t_1 - t_2) + t_1 t_2 (t_1 - t_2) = 0$

$\because \quad t_1 - t_2 \neq 0, 1 + t_1 t_2 = 0$

$\therefore \quad t_1 t_2 = -1$

Hence, Statement I is false and Statement II is true.

88. Length of focal chord $PQ = a\left(t + \dfrac{1}{t}\right)^2$ ...(i)

and $\tan\alpha = \dfrac{2at + \dfrac{2a}{t}}{at^2 - \dfrac{a}{t^2}} = \dfrac{2t}{t^2 - 1} = \dfrac{2\left(\dfrac{1}{t}\right)}{1 - \left(\dfrac{1}{t}\right)^2}$

$\therefore \quad \dfrac{1}{t} = \tan(\alpha/2)$

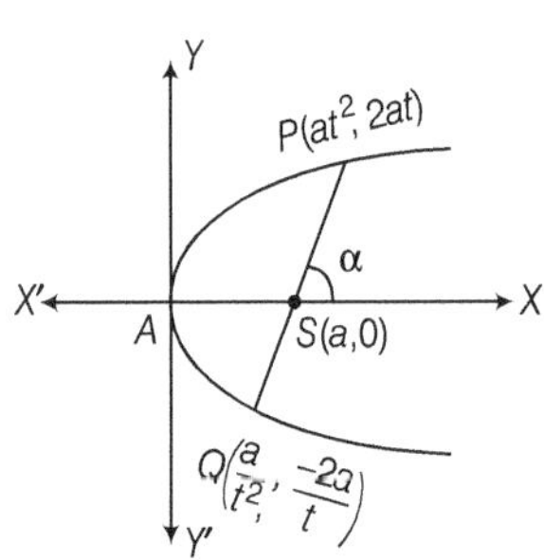

From Eq. (i)

$$PQ = a(\cot(\alpha/2) + \tan(\alpha/2))^2$$

$$= a\left(\frac{1}{\sin(\alpha/2)\cos(\alpha/2)}\right)^2$$

$$= a\left(\frac{2}{\sin\alpha}\right)^2 = 4a \operatorname{cosec}^2 \alpha$$

For $\alpha = 60°$, $4a = 8$ and

$$PQ = 8 \operatorname{cosec}^2 60° = 8\left(\frac{2}{\sqrt{3}}\right)^2 = 32/3$$

$\therefore$ Statement I is true and Statement II is false.

89. $\because \quad x + y = \lambda \Rightarrow y = \lambda - x$ ...(i)

and $\quad y = x - x^2$ ...(ii)

From Eqs. (i) and (ii), we get

$$\lambda - x = x - x^2$$

$\Rightarrow \quad x^2 - 2x + \lambda = 0$

$\because$ Eq. (i) touch the parabola Eq. (ii), then

$$B^2 - 4AC = 0$$

$\Rightarrow \quad (-2)^2 - 4 \cdot 1 \cdot \lambda = 0$

$\therefore \quad \lambda = 1$

$\Rightarrow$ Statement I is true.

From Statement II,

$$(x - 1)^2 = x - x^2$$

$\Rightarrow \quad 2x^2 - 3x + 1 = 0$

$\therefore$ Discriminant $= (-3)^2 - 4 \cdot 2 \cdot 1 = 1 \neq 0$

$\therefore$ Statement II is false.

90. $\because$ $3x + 4y + 5 = 0$ and $4x + 3y + 2 = 0$ are not perpendicular to each other.

$\therefore$ Latusrectum $\neq 4$

$\therefore$ Statement I is false and Statement II is true.

91. Let $P(at^2, 2at)$ be any point on the parabola $y^2 = 4ax$.

Then, tangent at $P(at^2, 2at)$ is $ty = x + at^2$.

Since, tangent meet the axis of parabola in T and tangent at the vertex in Y

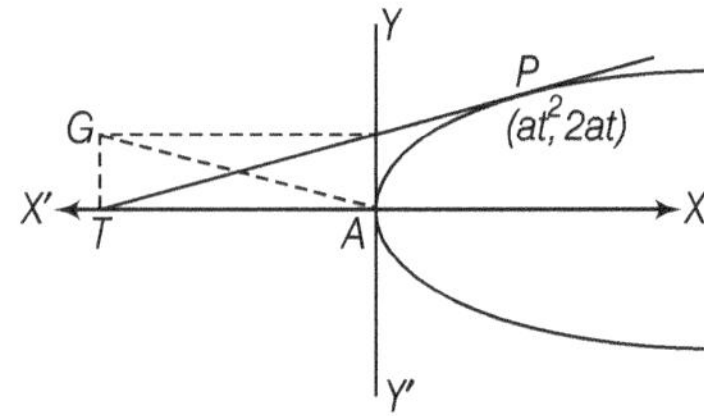

$\therefore$ Coordinates of T and Y are $(-at^2, 0)$ and $(0, at)$ respectively.

Let coordinates of G be (x_1, y_1).

Since, $TAYG$ is rectangle.

$\because$ Mid-points of diagonals TY and GA is same.

$\Rightarrow \quad \dfrac{x_1 + 0}{2} = \dfrac{-at^2 + 0}{2}$

$\Rightarrow \quad x_1 = -at^2$ ...(i)

and $\dfrac{y_1 + 0}{2} + \dfrac{0 + at}{2} \Rightarrow y_1 = at$ ...(ii)

Eliminating t from Eqs. (i) and (ii), we get

$$x_1 = -a\left(\frac{y_1}{a}\right)^2$$

$$\Rightarrow \quad y_1^2 = -ax_1$$

$$\Rightarrow \quad y_1^2 + ax_1 = 0$$

Hence, the locus of $G(x_1, y_1)$ is $y^2 + ax = 0$.

92. Equation of incident ray parallel to axis of parabola (X-axis) is $y = \lambda$, which pass through $(-1, 2)$, then $2 = \lambda$.

$\therefore$ Equation of incident ray is $y = 2$

Incident ray strikes the parabola $y^2 = 4x$ at (1, 2).

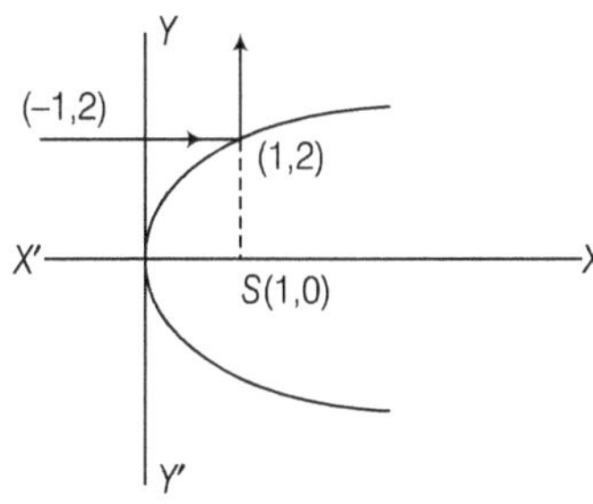

The reflected ray passes through the focus (1, 0).

Hence, the equation of the reflected ray is $x = 1$.

93. Let PQ be a normal chord to a parabola at $P(at^2, 2at)$.

Since, the ordinate and abscissa of P are equal.

$$\Rightarrow \quad at^2 = 2at, t \neq 0$$

$$\therefore \quad t = 2$$

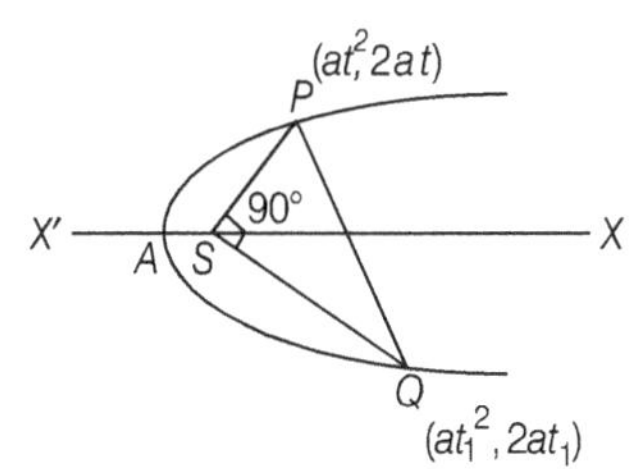

Since, normal at $P\,(at^2, 2at)$ meet the parabola at $Q\,(at_1^2, 2at_1)$.

$$\therefore \quad t_1 = -t - \frac{2}{t}$$

or $\quad t_1 = -2 - 1$

or $\quad t_1 = -3$

$\therefore$ Coordinates of P and Q are $(4a, 4a)$ and $(9a, -6a)$, respectively.

$\therefore$ Slope of $SP = \dfrac{4a - 0}{4a - a} = \dfrac{4}{3} = m_1$ (say)

and slope of $SQ = \dfrac{-6a - 0}{9a - a} = -\dfrac{3}{4} = m_2$ (say)

$$\therefore \quad m_1 m_2 = -1$$

Hence, SP and SQ are perpendicular to each other

i.e. $\quad \angle PSQ = 90°$

94. The centre and radius of the given circle are (0, 12) and 4, respectively.

Now, the shortest distance always occurs along the common normal.

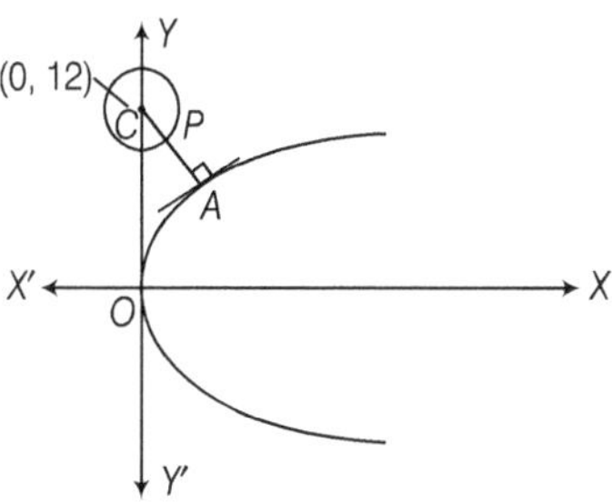

Let $\quad A \equiv (t^2, 2t)$

Equation of normal at A is $y + tx = 2t + t^3$,

which passes through (0, 12), then

$$12 + 0 = 2t + t^3 \Rightarrow t^3 + 2t - 12 = 0$$

or $\quad (t - 2)(t^2 + 2t + 6) = 0$

$\therefore \quad t = 2 \quad [\because t^2 + 2t + 6 \neq 0]$

Coordinates of A are (4, 4).

$\therefore$ Shortest distance $= AP = AC - CP = \sqrt{80} - 4 = 4(\sqrt{5} - 1)$

95. Let $P\,(t_1^2, 2t_1)$ and $Q\,(t_2^2, 2t_2)$ be extremities of the chord with slope 2.

$$\therefore \quad \frac{2t_1 - 2t_2}{t_1^2 - t_2^2} = 2$$

$\Rightarrow \quad t_1 + t_2 = 1$ ...(i)

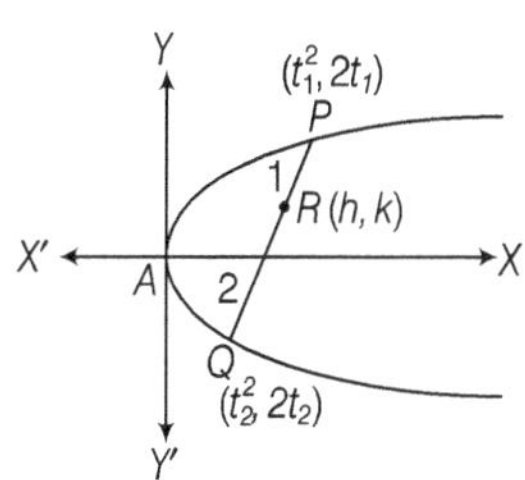

Let $R\,(h, k)$ be coordinates of the point which divides PQ in the ratio 1 : 2, then

$$h = \frac{2t_1^2 + t_2^2}{3}$$

and $\quad k = \dfrac{4t_1 + 2t_2}{3}$

$\Rightarrow \quad 3h = 2t_1^2 + (1 - t_1)^2$

and $\quad 3k = 4t_1 + 2(1 - t_1)$ [from Eq. (i)]

or $\quad 3h = 3t_1^2 - 2t_1 + 1$

and $\quad 3k = 2t_1 + 2$

Eliminating t_1

$$\therefore \quad 3h = 3\left(\frac{3k - 2}{2}\right)^2 - 2\left(\frac{3k - 2}{2}\right) + 1$$

$$\Rightarrow \quad 9k^2 - 16k - 4h + 8 = 0$$

$$\Rightarrow \quad k^2 - \frac{16k}{9} - \frac{4h}{9} + \frac{8}{9} = 0$$

$\Rightarrow \quad \left(k - \frac{8}{9}\right)^2 = \frac{4}{9}\left(h - \frac{2}{9}\right)$

$\therefore$ Locus of $R(h, k)$ is $\left(y - \frac{8}{9}\right)^2 = \frac{4}{9}\left(x - \frac{2}{9}\right)$,

which is a parabola with vertex $\left(\frac{8}{9}, \frac{2}{9}\right)$.

96. Let coordinates of P and Q on the parabola $y^2 = 4ax$ are $(at_1^2, 2at_1)$ and $(at_2^2, 2at_2)$.

Equation of tangents at P and Q are

$$t_1 y = x + at_1^2 \quad \text{and} \quad t_2 y = x + at_2^2$$

Let these tangents meet $x + a = 0$ at R and S, then coordinates of R and S' are $\left(-a, \frac{a(t_1^2 - 1)}{t_1}\right)$ and $\left(-a, \frac{a(t_2^2 - 1)}{t_2}\right)$, respectively.

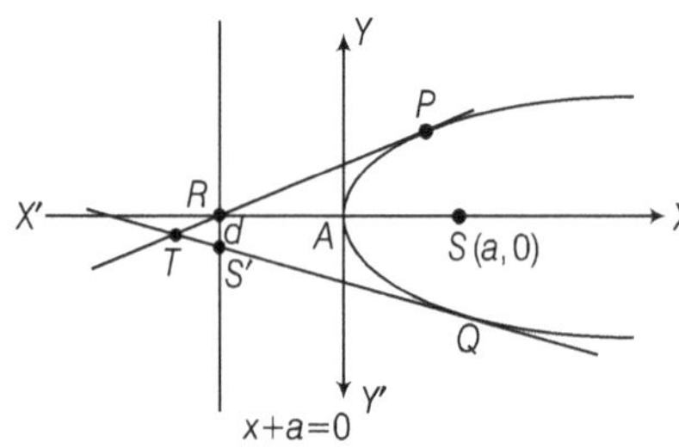

Given, $|RS'| = d$

$$\therefore \quad \left| a\left(\frac{t_1^2 - 1}{t_1}\right) - a\left(\frac{t_2^2 - 1}{t_2}\right) \right| = d$$

$$\Rightarrow \quad \left| \frac{a}{t_1 t_2} t_1^2 t_2 - t_2 - t_1 t_2^2 + t_1 \right| = d$$

$$\Rightarrow \quad \left| \frac{a}{t_1 t_2} ((t_1 - t_2)(1 + t_1 t_2)) \right| = d$$

$$\Rightarrow \quad \left| \frac{a\sqrt{\{(t_1 + t_2)^2 - 4t_1 t_2\}}\,(1 + t_1 t_2)}{t_1 t_2} \right| = d$$

Let the point of intersection of tangents at P at Q is T then

$$T = (at_1 t_2, a(t_1 + t_2))$$

Now, let $\quad T = (h, k)$

$$\therefore \quad h = at_1 t_2 \quad \text{and} \quad k = a(t_1 + t_2)$$

$$\therefore \quad t_1 t_2 = \frac{h}{a} \quad \text{and} \quad t_1 + t_2 = \frac{k}{a} \qquad \text{...(ii)}$$

From Eqs. (i) and (ii), we get

$$\left| \frac{a\sqrt{\left(\frac{k^2}{a^2} - \frac{4h}{a}\right)}\left(1 + \frac{h}{a}\right)}{\frac{h}{a}} \right| = d$$

$$\Rightarrow \quad (k^2 - 4ah)(h + a)^2 = h^2 d^2$$

Hence, required locus is

$$(y^2 - 4ax)(x + a)^2 = d^2 x^2.$$

Aliter :

Let point of intersection of tangents at P and Q is $T(h, k)$ then equation of pair of tangents TP and TQ is

$$SS_1 = T^2$$

$$\Rightarrow \quad (y^2 - 4ax)(k^2 - 4ah) = [ky - 2a(x + h)]^2 \qquad \text{...(i)}$$

Let the pair of tangents cut the directrix $x + a = 0$ are in R and S, then substitute $x = -a$ in Eq. (i), then we get

$$hy^2 - k(h - a)y + a\{(h + a)^2 - k^2\} = 0$$

Now let coordinates of R and S be

$$(-a, y_1) \quad \text{and} \quad (-a, y_2).$$

$$\therefore \quad y_1 + y_2 = \frac{k(h - a)}{h}$$

and $\quad y_1 y_2 = \dfrac{a\{(h + a)^2 - k^2\}}{h}$

but given $\quad |RS| = d$

$$\Rightarrow \quad (RS)^2 = d^2$$

$$\Rightarrow \quad (y_1 - y_2)^2 = d^2$$

$$\Rightarrow \quad (y_1 + y_2)^2 - 4y_1 y_2 = d^2$$

$$\Rightarrow \quad \frac{k^2}{h^2}(h - a)^2 - \frac{4a}{h}\{(h + a)^2 - k^2\} = d^2$$

$$\Rightarrow \quad k^2\{(h - a)^2 + 4ah\} - 4ah(h + a)^2 = d^2 h^2$$

$$\Rightarrow \quad (k^2 - 4ah)(h + a)^2 = d^2 h^2$$

Hence, locus of $T(h, k)$ is

$$(y^2 - 4ax)(x + a)^2 = d^2 x^2.$$

97. Let $P(at_1^2, 2at_1)$ and $Q(at_2^2, 2at_2)$ be two points on the parabola $y^2 = 4ax$

The equations of tangents at P and Q are

$$t_1 y = x + at_1^2$$

and $\quad t_2 y = x + at_2^2$

$$\therefore \quad \tan\theta_1 = \frac{1}{t_1}, \tan\theta_2 = \frac{1}{t_2}$$

Equations of circles with OP and OQ as diameters are

$$(x - 0)(x - at_1^2) + (y - 0)(y - 2at_1) = 0$$

and $\quad (x - 0)(x - at_2^2) + (y - 0)(y - 2at_2) = 0$ respectively.

i.e. $\quad x^2 + y^2 - axt_1^2 - 2at_1 y = 0$

and $\quad x^2 + y^2 - axt_2^2 - 2at_2 y = 0$

then, point of intersection of circles are $O(0, 0)$

and $\quad R\left(\dfrac{-4at_1 t_2}{(t_1 + t_2)^2 + 4}, \dfrac{2at_1 t_2(t_1 + t_2)}{(t_1 + t_2)^2 + 4}\right)$

Since, OR makes an angle ϕ with the X-axis. Therefore,

$$\tan\phi = -\left(\frac{t_1 + t_2}{2}\right)$$

Now, $\quad \cot\theta_1 + \cot\theta_2 + 2\tan\phi = t_1 + t_2 - (t_1 + t_2)$

$$= 0$$

98. Any normal of the parabola $y^2 = 4x$ with slope m is

$$y = mx - 2m - m^3$$

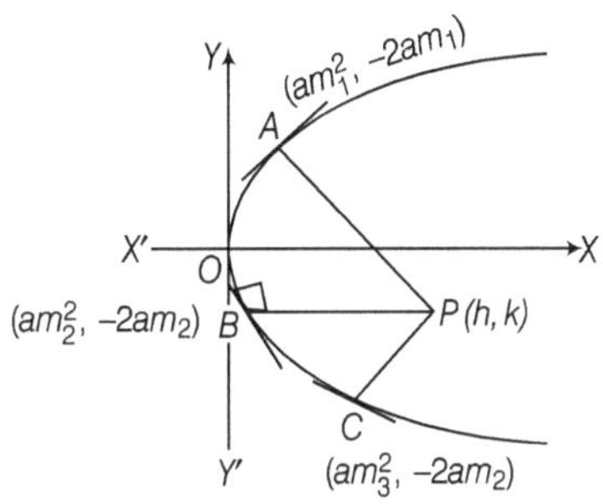

It passes through P, then

$$k = mh - 2m - m^3$$

$\Rightarrow m^3 + (2 - h)m + k = 0$ ...(i)

Thus, $m_1m_2m_3 = -k$

$\alpha m_3 = -k$ $(\because m_1m_2 = \alpha)$

$\Rightarrow m_3 = -\dfrac{k}{\alpha}$

$\because$ m_3 is a root of Eq. (i), then

$$-\frac{k^3}{\alpha^3} + (2-h)\left(-\frac{k}{\alpha}\right) + k = 0$$

$\Rightarrow k^3 + (2-h)k\alpha^2 - k\alpha^3 = 0$

$\therefore$ Locus of $P(h, k)$ is

$$y^3 + (2-x)y\alpha^2 - y\alpha^3 = 0$$

$\Rightarrow y^2 + (2-x)\alpha^2 - \alpha^3 = 0$ $[\because y \neq 0]$

(P does not lie on the axis of the parabola)

$\Rightarrow y^2 = \alpha^2 x - 2\alpha^2 + \alpha^3$

If it is a part of the parabola $y^2 = 4x$

then, $\alpha^2 = 4$

and $-2\alpha^2 + \alpha^3 = 0$

$\Rightarrow \alpha^2(\alpha - 2) = 0$

$\Rightarrow \alpha - 2 = 0, \alpha \neq 0$

$\therefore \alpha = 2$

99. Let $P(at^2, 2at)$ be any point on $y^2 = 4ax$. Then, vertex $A(0,0)$. The equation of tangent at P is

$ty = x + at^2$ ...(i)

Tangent at P will be normal to the circle, AP is a chord whose mid-point is $\left(\dfrac{at^2}{2}, at\right)$ and slope is $\dfrac{2}{t}$.

$\therefore$ Equation of the line passing through mid-point of AP and perpendicular to AP is

$$y - at = -\frac{t}{2}\left(x - \frac{at^2}{2}\right)$$

$\Rightarrow tx + 2y = \dfrac{ut^3}{2} + 2at$ ...(ii)

Eqs. (i) and (ii) both pass through (x_1, y_1) which is the centre of the circle

$ty_1 = x_1 + at^2$ ...(iii)

and $2tx_1 + 4y_1 = at^3 + 4at$ ...(iv)

Multiplying Eq. (iii) by t and subtracting Eq. (iv), we have

$t^2y_1 + t(4a - 3x_1) - 4y_1 = 0$ ...(v)

Also, from Eq. (iii), $at^2 - ty_1 + x_1 = 0$ ...(vi)

Eliminating t from Eqs. (v) and (vi), we get

$$\frac{t^2}{x_1(4a - 3x_1) - 4y_1^2} = \frac{t}{-4ay_1 - x_1y_1} = \frac{1}{-y_1^2 - a(4a - 3x_1)}$$

On simplyfying, we get

$$2y_1^2(2y_1^2 + x_1^2 - 12ax_1) = ax_1(3x_1 - 4a)^2$$

Hence, required locus is

$$2y^2(2y^2 + x^2 - 12ax) = ax(3x - 4a)^2.$$

100. Let $P(at_1^2, 2at_1)$ and $Q(at_2^2, 2at_2)$ be two points on the parabola $y^2 = 4ax$ such that the normals at P and Q intersect at a point $R(aT^2, 2aT)$ on the parabola $y^2 = 4ax$, then

$$T = -t_1 - \frac{2}{t_1} = -t_2 - \frac{2}{t_2}, \text{ then } t_1t_2 = 2$$

$\because$ Tangents at P and Q intersect at $T(at_1t_2, a(t_1 + t_2))$

i.e. $T(2a, a(t_1 + t_2))$.

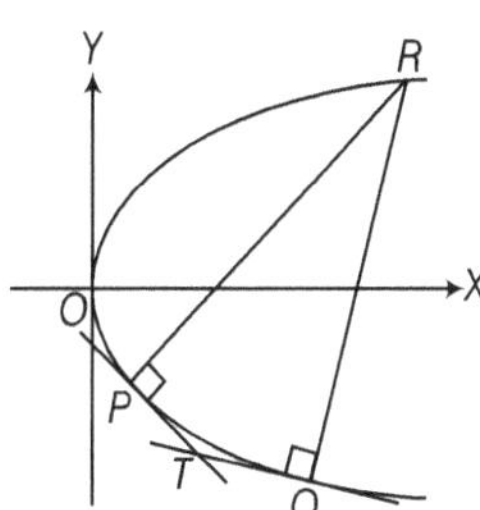

Also, the coordinates of R being the point of intersection of normals at P and Q are

$$(2a + a(t_1^2 + t_2^2 + t_1t_2), -at_1t_2(t_1 + t_2))$$

$\Rightarrow (4a + a(t_1^2 + t_2^2), -2a(t_1 + t_2))$

Now, $\angle TPR = \angle TQR = 90°$

$\Rightarrow \angle TPR + \angle TQR = 180°$

$\Rightarrow$ Quadrilateral $PTQR$ is a cyclic quadrilateral, therefore centre of the circle circumscribing the ΔTPQ is at the mid-point of TR.

Let its coordinates be (h, k), then

$$2h = 2a + 4a + a(t_1^2 + t_2^2)$$

$\Rightarrow \dfrac{2h - 6a}{a} = (t_1 + t_2)^2 - 2t_1t_2$

$\Rightarrow \dfrac{2h - 2a}{a} = (t_1 + t_2)^2$ $[\because t_1t_2 = 2]$ ...(i)

and $2k = a(t_1 + t_2) - 2a(t_1 + t_2)$

$\Rightarrow -\dfrac{2k}{a} = (t_1 + t_2)$ ...(ii)

From Eqs. (i) and (ii), then $\left(\frac{2h-2a}{a}\right)=\left(-\frac{2k}{a}\right)^2$

$\Rightarrow \quad 2k^2 = a(h-a)$

Hence, locus of (h, k) is $\quad 2y^2 = a(x-a)$.

101. Let the equation of straight line (h, k) as its mid-point,

then, $$\frac{x-h}{\cos\theta}=\frac{y-k}{\sin\theta}=r \qquad \text{...(i)}$$

Any point on the line Eq. (i) is $(h + r\cos\theta, k + r\sin\theta)$.

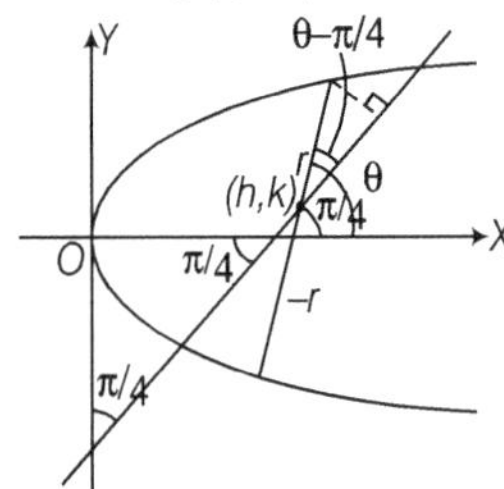

Solving with the equation of parabola

$y^2 = 4ax$, we get

$$(k + r\sin\theta)^2 = 4a(h + r\cos\theta)$$

$$\Rightarrow r^2\sin^2\theta + 2r(k\sin\theta - 2a\cos\theta) + k^2 - 4ah = 0 \qquad \text{...(ii)}$$

which is quadratic in r.

The roots of the quadratic equation will be equal but of opposite sign as (h, k) is the mid-point.

$$\text{Sum of roots} = -\frac{2(k\sin\theta - 2a\cos\theta)}{\sin^2\theta} = 0$$

$$\therefore \quad k\sin\theta - 2a\cos\theta = 0$$

$$\therefore \quad \tan\theta = \frac{2a}{k}$$

Now, from Eq. (ii),

$$r^2\sin^2\theta + (k^2 - 4ah) = 0$$

$$\Rightarrow \quad r^2 \cdot \frac{4a^2}{(4a^2+k^2)} + (k^2 - 4ah) = 0 \qquad \text{...(iii)}$$

Length of the chord will be $2r$. Angle between the two lines will be $(\theta - \pi/4)$ and the projection of the chord on the given line will be $2r\cos(\theta - \pi/4) = c$

$$\Rightarrow \quad \frac{2r}{\sqrt{2}}(\cos\theta + \sin\theta) = c$$

$$\Rightarrow \quad \frac{2r}{\sqrt{2}}\left(\frac{k+2a}{\sqrt{4a^2+k^2}}\right) = c$$

$$\Rightarrow \quad 2r^2(k+2a)^2 = c^2(4a^2+k^2)$$

$$\Rightarrow \quad \frac{2r^2}{(4a^2+k^2)} = \frac{c^2}{(k+2a)^2} \qquad \text{...(iv)}$$

From Eqs. (iii) and (iv), we get

$$\frac{2a^2c^2}{(k+2a)^2} + (k^2 - 4ah) = 0$$

$$\Rightarrow \quad (k^2 - 4ah)(k+2a)^2 + 2a^2c^2 = 0$$

Hence, the locus of the middle points is

$$(y^2 - 4ax)(y+2a)^2 + 2a^2c^2 = 0.$$

102. Equation of normal at $(am^2, -2am)$ is

$$y = mx - 2am - am^3$$

If the three normals of P, Q, R meet at (h, k), then

$$am^3 + m(2a-h) + k = 0$$

$$\therefore \quad \Sigma m_1 = 0$$

$$\Sigma m_1 m_2 = \frac{(2a-h)}{a},$$

$$m_1 m_2 m_3 = \frac{-k}{a}$$

$$P \equiv (am_1^2, -2am_1)$$

$$Q \equiv (am_2^2, -2am_2)$$

and $$R \equiv (am_3^2, -2am_3)$$

Equation of PQ is

$$-y(m_1 + m_2) = 2(x + am_1m_2) \qquad \text{...(i)}$$

and equation of diameter through R is

$$y = -2am_3 \qquad \text{...(ii)}$$

Point of intersection of Eqs. (i) and (ii) is on the directrix and hence it must be $(-a, -2am_3)$ and it satisfies Eq. (ii), then

$$2am_3(m_1 + m_2) = 2(-a + am_1m_2)$$

$$\Rightarrow \quad m_3(-m_3) = -1 + m_1m_2$$

$$\Rightarrow \quad m_1m_2 = 1 - m_3^2$$

$\therefore$ Equation of PQ becomes

$$-y(0 - m_3) = 2(x + a - am_3^2)$$

$$\Rightarrow \quad 2am_3^2 + m_3y - 2(x+a) = 0 \qquad [m_3 \text{ is parameter}]$$

Its envelope is given by the discriminant of this quadratic equated to zero.

$$\therefore \quad (y)^2 - 4\cdot 2a\cdot\{-2\cdot(x+a)\} = 0$$

$$\Rightarrow \quad y^2 + 16a(x+a) = 0$$

103. Equation of normal at 't' is $y = -tx + 2at + at^3$.

Let A be (h, k), then $k = -th + 2at + at^3$

or $$at^3 - t(h-2a) - k = 0 \qquad \text{...(i)}$$

Let the coordinates of P, Q, R are $(at_1^2, 2at_1), (at_2^2, 2at_2), (at_3^2, 2at_3)$ respectively, then from Eq. (i),

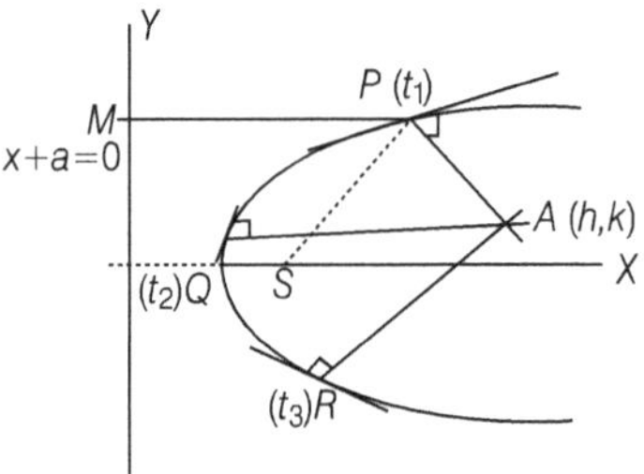

$$t_1 + t_2 + t_3 = 0$$

$$\Rightarrow \quad t_1t_2 + t_2t_3 + t_3t_1 = -\left(\frac{h-2a}{a}\right)$$

and $$t_1t_2t_3 = \frac{k}{a}$$

Since, $SP = PM = a + at_1^2$

Similarly, $SQ = a + at_2^2$

and $SR = a + at_3^2$

$\therefore \quad SP \cdot SQ \cdot SR = a(1 + t_1^2) \cdot a(1 + t_2^2) \cdot a(1 + t_3^2)$

$= a^3\{1 + (t_1^2 + t_2^2 + t_3^2) + (t_1^2 t_2^2 + t_2^2 t_3^2 + t_3^2 t_1^2) + (t_1^2 t_2^2 t_3^2)\}$

$= a^3\{1 + (t_1 + t_2 + t_3)^2 - 2(t_1t_2 + t_2t_3 + t_3t_1)$

$+ (t_1t_2 + t_2t_3 + t_3t_1)^2 - 2t_1t_2t_3(t_1 + t_2 + t_3) + (t_1t_2t_3)^2\}$

$= a^3\left\{1 + 0 + 2\left(\frac{h - 2a}{a}\right) + \left(\frac{h - 2a}{a}\right)^2 - 0 + \frac{k^2}{a^2}\right\}$

$= a^3\left\{\left(\frac{h - 2a}{a} + 1\right)^2 + \frac{k^2}{a^2}\right\}$

$= a\{(h - a)^2 + (k - 0)^2\} = a(SA)^2$

104. Equation of tangent at $P(at^2, 2at)$ is

$$ty = x + at^2 \Rightarrow x - ty + at^2 = 0 \quad \text{...(i)}$$

which is also tangent to the circle

$$x^2 + y^2 = a^2/2 \quad \text{...(ii)}$$

then, length of perpendicular from centre of Eq. (ii) to Eq. (i) radius of the circle

$\Rightarrow \quad \frac{|at^2|}{\sqrt{1 + t^2}} = \frac{a}{\sqrt{2}}$

$\Rightarrow \quad 2t^4 = (1 + t^2)$

$\Rightarrow \quad (t^2 - 1)(2t^2 + 1) = 0$

$\therefore \quad 2t^2 + 1 \neq 0 \quad \therefore \quad t^2 - 1 = 0$

then, $\quad t = \pm 1$

then, coordinates of P and Q are $(a, 2a)$ and $(a, -2a)$ respectively.

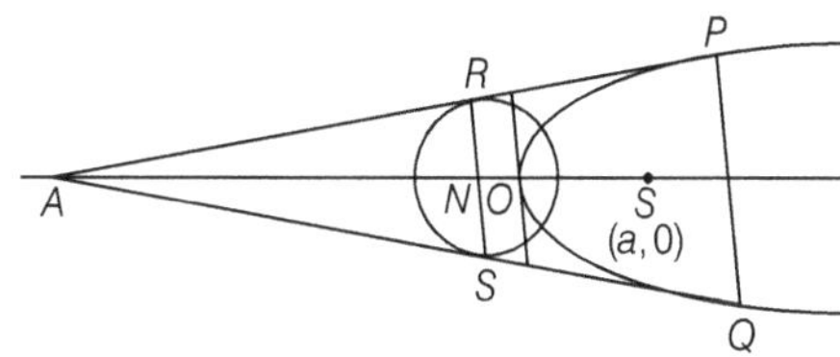

$\therefore \quad PQ = 4a$

$\therefore$ Equation of tangent at $P(a, 2a)$ is

$$x - y + a = 0 \quad \text{...(iii)}$$

[from Eq. (i)]

Let R be (x_1, y_1)

then, equation of tangent at $R(x_1, y_1)$ on Eq. (ii) is

$$xx_1 + yy_1 = \frac{a^2}{2} \quad \text{...(iv)}$$

Hence, Eqs. (iii) and (iv) are identical.

$\therefore \quad \frac{x_1}{1} = \frac{y_1}{-1} = -\frac{a}{2}$

$\therefore \quad (x_1, y_1) = \left(-\frac{a}{2}, \frac{a}{2}\right)$

Hence coordinates of S are $\left(-\frac{a}{2}, \frac{a}{2}\right)$.

$\therefore \quad RS' = a$

Hence, quadrilateral $PQRS'$ is trapezium whose area

$= \frac{1}{2}(PQ + RS') \times \left(a + \frac{a}{2}\right)$

$= \frac{1}{2} \times (4a + a) \times \frac{3a}{2} = \frac{15a^2}{4}$ sq units.

Aliter :

Here, centre of the circle is the vertex of the parabola and both circle and parabola are symmetrical about axis of parabola. In this case the point of intersection of common tangents must lie on the directrix and axis of the parabola.

i.e. $\quad A(-a, 0)$.

Chord of contact of circle w.r.t. $A(-a, 0)$ is

$$x(-a) + y \cdot 0 = \frac{a^2}{2}$$

$\therefore \quad x = -\frac{a}{2}$

$\therefore$ Coordinates of R are $\left(-\frac{a}{2}, \frac{a}{2}\right)$ and chord of contact of parabola w.r.t. $A(-a, 0)$ is

$$y \cdot 0 = 2a(x - a)$$

i.e. $\quad x = a$

$\therefore$ Coordinates of P is $(a, 2a)$

$\therefore$ Area of quadrilateral

$PQRS' = 2\{\text{Area of } \Delta PAS - \text{Area of } \Delta RAN\}$

$= 2\left\{\frac{1}{2} \cdot 2a \cdot 2a - \frac{1}{2} \cdot \frac{a}{2} \cdot \frac{a}{2}\right\}$

$= 4a^2 - \frac{a^2}{4} = \frac{15a^2}{4}$ sq units

105. Let parabola be $y^2 = 4ax$ and let $P(at_1^2, 2at_1)$, $Q(at_2^2, 2at_2)$ and $R(at_3^2, 2at_3)$ are three points on the parabola.

$\because$ Tangents at P, Q and R on parabola $y^2 = 4ax$

are $\quad t_1y = x + at_1^2, t_2y = x + at_2^2$

and $\quad t_3y = x + at_3^2$

Slopes of these tangents are $\frac{1}{t_1}, \frac{1}{t_2}, \frac{1}{t_3}$

but given slopes are in HP.

$\therefore$ t_1, t_2, t_3 are in AP if d is the common difference. Then,

$$t_2 - t_1 = d, t_3 - t_2 = d$$

and $\quad t_3 - t_1 = 2d \quad \text{...(i)}$

Let the tangents at Q and R meet at P', R and P meet at Q', P and Q meet at R'.

$\therefore \quad P' = \{at_2t_3, a(t_2 + t_3)\}$

$Q' = \{at_3t_1, a(t_3 + t_1)\}$

and $\quad R' = \{at_1t_2, a(t_1 + t_2)\}$

$$\therefore \text{ Area of } \Delta P'Q'R' = \frac{1}{2}\begin{vmatrix} at_2t_3 & a(t_2+t_3) & 1 \\ at_3t_1 & a(t_3+t_1) & 1 \\ at_1t_2 & a(t_1+t_2) & 1 \end{vmatrix}$$

$$= \frac{1}{2}\{at_2t_3\{a(t_3+t_1)-(t_1+t_2)\}+\ldots+\ldots\}$$

$$= \frac{1}{2}a^2\Sigma\, t_2t_3(t_3-t_2)$$

$$= \frac{1}{2}a^2(t_1-t_2)(t_2-t_3)(t_3-t_1)$$

$$= \frac{1}{2}a^2(-d)(-d)(2d) \qquad \text{[by using Eq. (i)]}$$

$= a^2d^3$, which is constant.

Remark

$\Sigma t_1^2(t_2-t_3) = \Sigma t_2t_3(t_3-t_2) = (t_1-t_2)(t_2-t_3)(t_3-t_1)$

Corollary Area of triangle of $P(at_1^2, 2at_1)$, $Q(at_2^2, 2at_2)$ and $R(at_3^2, 2at_3)$ is $a^2(t_1-t_2)(t_2-t_3)(t_3-t_1) = \Delta$ (say)

It is clear from just previous example the area of the triangle inscribed in a parabola is twice the area of the triangle formed by the tangents at the vertices.

106. Equation of tangent at (1, 7) to $y = x^2 + 6$

$$\Rightarrow \quad \frac{1}{2}(y+7) = x\cdot 1 + 6$$

$$\Rightarrow \quad y = 2x + 5 \qquad \ldots\text{(i)}$$

This tangent also touches the circle.

$$x^2 + y^2 + 16x + 12y + c = 0 \qquad \ldots\text{(ii)}$$

Now, solving Eqs. (i) and (ii), we get

$$x^2 + (2x+5)^2 + 16x + 12(2x+5) + c = 0$$

$$\Rightarrow \quad 5x^2 + 60x + 85 + c = 0$$

Since, roots are equal, so

$$B^2 - 4AC = 0$$

$$\Rightarrow \quad (60)^2 - 4\times 5\times(85+c) = 0$$

$$\Rightarrow \quad 85 + c = 180$$

$$\Rightarrow \quad 5x^2 + 60x + 180 = 0$$

$$\Rightarrow \quad x = -\frac{60}{10} = -6 \quad \Rightarrow \quad y = -7$$

Hence, point of contact is $(-6, -7)$.

107. $\because P \equiv (1,0)$, let $Q \equiv (h, k)$

such that $\quad k^2 = 8h \qquad \ldots\text{(i)}$

Let (α, β) be the mid-point of PQ.

$$\therefore \quad \alpha = \frac{h+1}{2}, \beta = \frac{k+0}{2}$$

$$\Rightarrow \quad h = 2\alpha - 1, k = 2\beta$$

From Eq. (i), we get

$$(2\beta)^2 = 8(2\alpha - 1)$$

$$\Rightarrow \quad \beta^2 = 4\alpha - 2$$

$$\Rightarrow \quad \beta^2 - 4\alpha + 2 = 0$$

$\therefore$ Required locus is $y^2 - 4x + 2 = 0$.

108. Coordinates of S are $(2\sqrt{2}\cos 45°, 2\sqrt{2}\sin 45°)$ i.e. (2, 2).

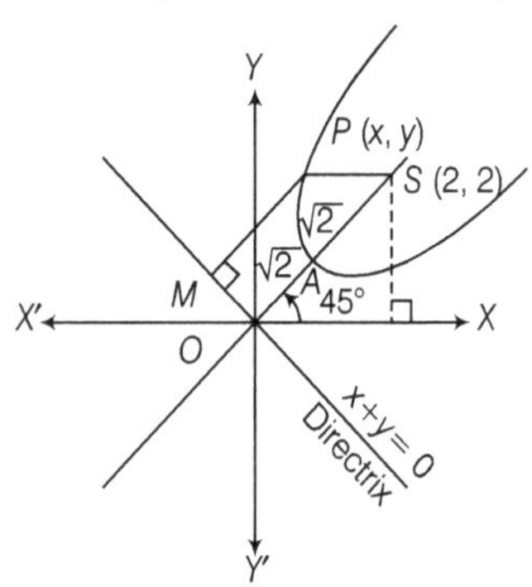

$$\therefore \quad SP = PM$$

$$\Rightarrow \quad (SP)^2 = (PM)^2$$

$$\Rightarrow \quad (x-2)^2 + (y-2)^2 = \left[\frac{(x+y)}{\sqrt{2}}\right]^2$$

$$\Rightarrow \quad 2(x^2 + y^2 - 4x - 4y + 8) = x^2 + y^2 + 2xy$$

$$\Rightarrow \quad x^2 + y^2 - 2xy - 8x - 8y + 16 = 0$$

$$\therefore \quad (x-y)^2 = 8(x + y - 2)$$

109. Equation of tangent to $y = x^2$ is

$$y = mx - \frac{1}{4}m^2 \qquad \ldots\text{(i)}$$

Equation of tangent to $(x-2)^2 = -y$ is

$$y = m(x-2) + \frac{1}{4}m^2 \qquad \ldots\text{(ii)}$$

$\because$ Eqs. (i) and (ii) are identical.

$$\Rightarrow \quad m = 0 \text{ or } 4$$

$\therefore$ Common tangents are $y = 0$ and $y = 4x - 4 = 4(x-1)$.

110. Given parabola is

$$y = \frac{a^3x^2}{3} + \frac{a^2x}{2} - 2a \qquad \ldots\text{(i)}$$

For vertex $\dfrac{dy}{dx} = 0 \Rightarrow x = -\dfrac{3}{4a}$

Substitute $x = -\dfrac{3}{4a}$ in Eq. (i), we get

$$y = -\frac{35a}{16}$$

$\therefore$ Coordinates of vertex are $\left(-\dfrac{3}{4a}, -\dfrac{35a}{16}\right)$.

For locus let $x = -\dfrac{3}{4a}$ and $y = -\dfrac{35a}{16}$.

$\therefore \quad xy = \dfrac{105}{64}$, which is the required locus.

111. $\because \quad y = x^2 - 5x + 6$

$\therefore$ Equation of tangent at (2, 0) is

$$\frac{y+0}{2} = x\cdot 2 - \frac{5}{2}(x+2) + 6$$

$$\Rightarrow \quad y = -x + 2 \qquad \ldots\text{(i)}$$

and equation of tangent at (3, 0) is

$\Rightarrow \quad y = x - 3 \quad$ ...(ii)

$\because$ Eqs. (i) and (ii) are perpendicular.

$\therefore$ Angle between tangents is $\pi / 2$.

112. (i) Coordinates of P and Q are $(1, 2\sqrt{2})$ and $(1, -2\sqrt{2})$.

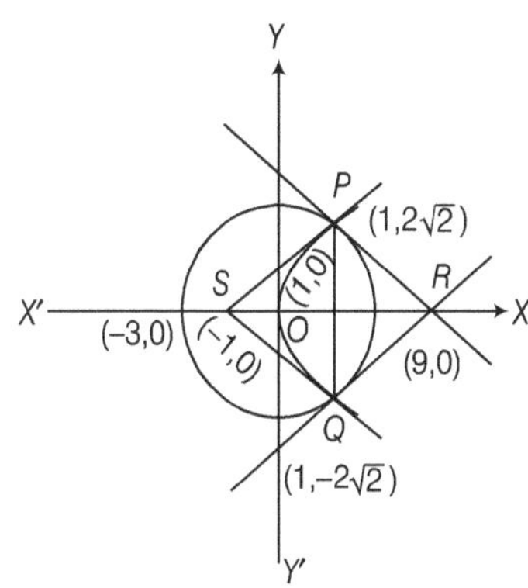

Area of $\Delta PQR = \frac{1}{2} \cdot 4\sqrt{2} \cdot 8 = 16\sqrt{2}$

Area of $\Delta PQS = \frac{1}{2} \cdot 4\sqrt{2} \cdot 2 = 4\sqrt{2}$

$\therefore$ Ratio of area of ΔPQS and ΔPQR is 1 : 4.

(ii) Equation of circumcircle of ΔPRS is

$$(x + 1)(x - 9) + y^2 + \lambda y = 0$$

It will pass through $(1, 2\sqrt{2})$, then

$$-16 + 8 + \lambda 2\sqrt{2} = 0 \Rightarrow \lambda = \frac{8}{2\sqrt{2}} = 2\sqrt{2}$$

Equation of circumcircle is

$$x^2 + y^2 - 8x + 2\sqrt{2}y - 9 = 0$$

Hence, radius is $3\sqrt{3}$.

Aliter :

Let $\angle PSR = \theta \Rightarrow \sin\theta = \frac{2\sqrt{2}}{2\sqrt{3}}$

$\Rightarrow \quad PR = 6\sqrt{2} = 2R \cdot \sin\theta \Rightarrow R = 3\sqrt{3}$.

(iii) Radius of incircle is $r = \frac{\Delta}{s}$.

As $\quad \Delta = 16\sqrt{2}$

$\therefore \quad s = \frac{6\sqrt{2} + 6\sqrt{2} + 4\sqrt{2}}{2} = 8\sqrt{2}$

$\therefore \quad r = \frac{16\sqrt{2}}{8\sqrt{2}} = 2$

113. $y = -\frac{x^2}{2} + x + 1 \Rightarrow y - \frac{3}{2} = -\frac{1}{2}(x - 1)^2$

$\Rightarrow$ It is symmetric about $x = 1$.

Hence, both statement are true and Statement II is correct explanation of Statement I.

114. $\because$ Point of intersection of two perpendicular tangents to the parabola lies on directrix of the parabola.

$\therefore$ Equation of directrix is $x + 2 = 0$.

So, point is $(-2, 0)$.

115. The circle and the parabola touch each other at $x = 1$, i.e. at the points (1, 2) and (1, – 2) as shown in figure.

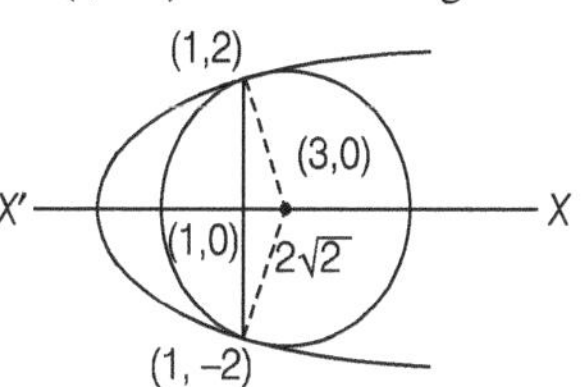

116. Vertex is (1,0).

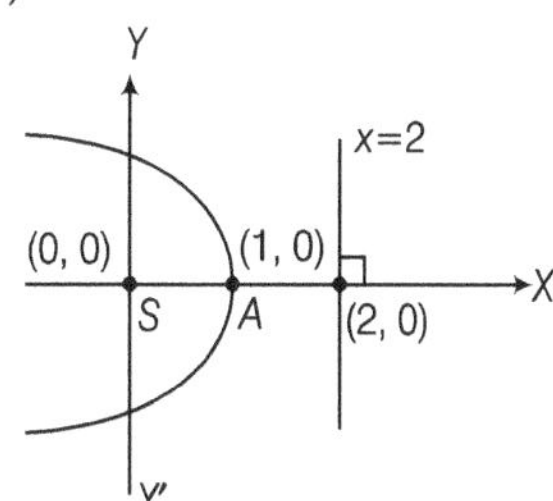

117. $\quad G \equiv (h, k)$

$\Rightarrow \quad h = \frac{2a + at^2}{3}, k = \frac{2at}{3}$

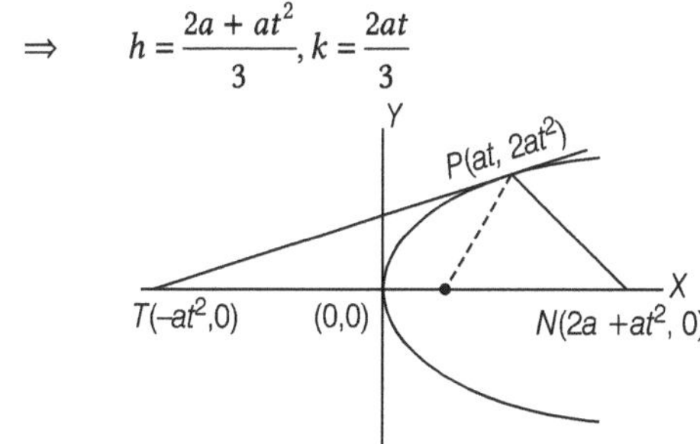

$\Rightarrow \quad \left(\frac{3h - 2a}{a}\right) = \frac{9k^2}{4a^2}$

$\therefore$ Required parabola is

$$\frac{9y^2}{4a^2} = \frac{(3x - 2a)}{a} = \frac{3}{a}\left(x - \frac{2a}{3}\right)$$

$\Rightarrow \quad y^2 = \frac{4a}{3}\left(x - \frac{2a}{3}\right)$

$\therefore$ Vertex $\equiv \left(\frac{2a}{3}, 0\right)$; Focus $\equiv (a, 0)$.

118. Slope of $AB = \frac{2t_2 - 2t_1}{(t_2^2 - t_1^2)} = \frac{2}{(t_2 + t_1)}$ ...(i)

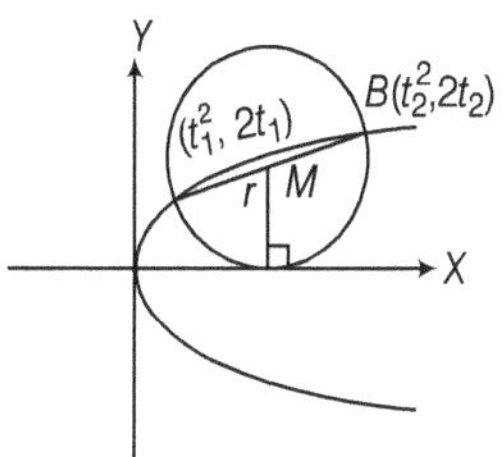

$M =$ Mid-point of $AB = \left(\frac{t_1^2 + t_2^2}{2}, t_1 + t_2\right)$

$\therefore \quad r = |t_1 + t_2| \Rightarrow t_1 + t_2 = \pm r$

Now, from Eq. (i),

$$\text{slope of } AB = \pm \frac{2}{r}.$$

119. The locus of perpendicular tangent is directrix, i.e., $x + 1 = 0$ or $x = -1$.

120. $\Delta_1 =$ Area of $\Delta PLL'$

$$= \frac{1}{2} \times 8 \times \left(2 - \frac{1}{2}\right) = 6 \text{ sq unitss}$$

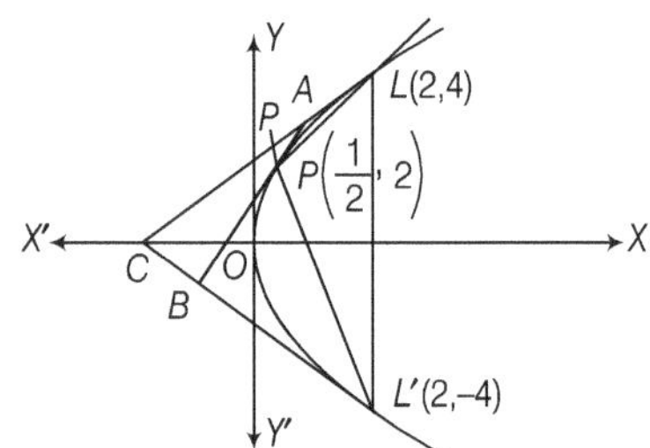

Now, equation of AB is $y = 2x + 1$,
equation of AC is $y = x + 2$ and
equation of BC is $y = -x - 2$
On solving above equations, we get
$A(1, 3)$, $B(-1, -1)$ and $C(-2, 0)$

$$\therefore \quad \Delta_2 = \frac{1}{2} \left\| \begin{matrix} 1+2 & 3-0 \\ -1+2 & -1-0 \end{matrix} \right\| = 3 \text{ sq units}$$

$$\therefore \quad \frac{\Delta_1}{\Delta_2} = 2$$

121. Let $A(x, y) = A(t^2, 2t)$ be any point on the parabola $y^2 = 4x$, then

$$x = \frac{t^2}{4} \quad \text{...(i)}$$

and

$$y = \frac{2t}{4} \quad \text{...(ii)}$$

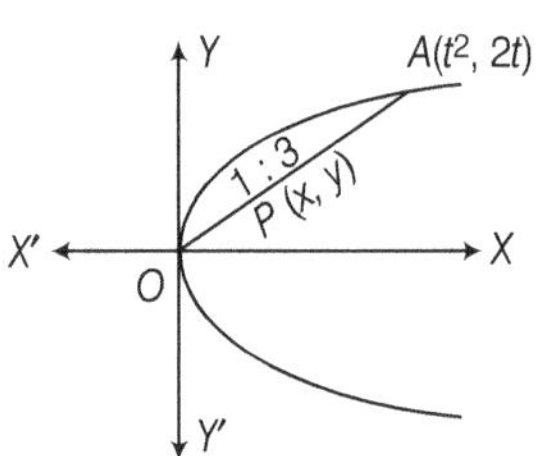

From Eqs. (i) and (ii), we get

$$x = y^2$$

122. The equation of normal to

$$y^2 = 4x \text{ is } y = mx - 2m - m^3 \quad \text{...(i)}$$

As it passes through (9, 6), then

$$6 = 9m - 2m - m^3$$

$$\Rightarrow \quad m^3 - 7m + 6 = 0$$

$$\Rightarrow (m-1)(m-2)(m+3) = 0$$

$$\Rightarrow \quad m = 1, 2, -3$$

From Eq. (i), equations of normals are

$$y = x - 3, y = 2x - 12, \ y = -3x + 33$$

$$\Rightarrow \ y - x + 3 = 0, y - 2x + 12 = 0, \ y + 3x - 33 = 0$$

123. The shortest distance between $y = x - 1$ and $y^2 = x$ is along the normal of $y^2 = x$.

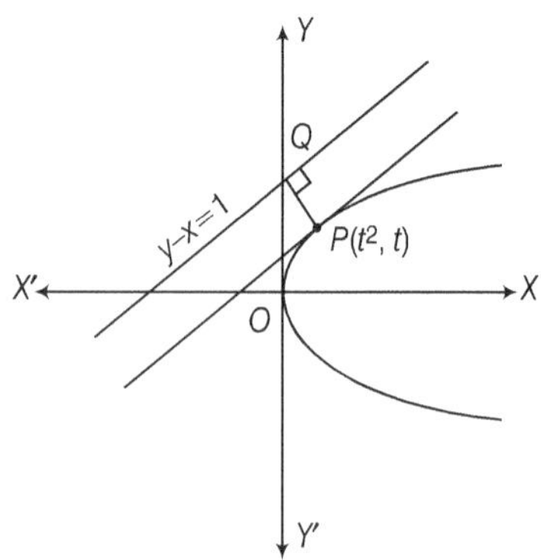

Let $P(t^2, t)$ be any point on $y^2 = x$.

$\therefore$ Tangent at P is $y = \frac{x}{2t} + \frac{t}{2}$.

$\therefore$ Slope of tangent $= \frac{1}{2t}$

and tangent at P is parallel to $y - x = 1$

$$\therefore \quad \frac{1}{2t} = 1 \Rightarrow t = \frac{1}{2} \Rightarrow P\left(\frac{1}{4}, \frac{1}{2}\right)$$

Hence, shortest distance $= PQ = \dfrac{\left|\frac{1}{2} - \frac{1}{4} - 1\right|}{\sqrt{(1+1)}} = \dfrac{3}{4\sqrt{2}} = \dfrac{3\sqrt{2}}{8}$

124. We observe that both parabola $y^2 = 8x$ and circle $x^2 + y^2 - 2x - 4y = 0$ pass through origin say $P(0, 0)$.

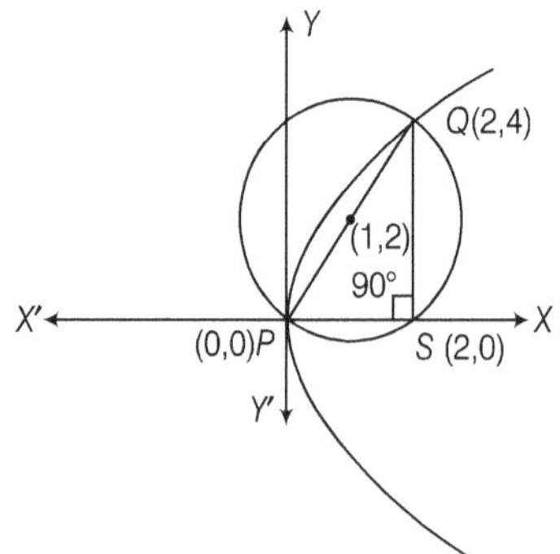

Let Q be the point $(2t^2, 4t)$, then it will satisfy the equation of circle.

$$\therefore \quad (2t^2)^2 + (4t)^2 - 2(2t^2) - 4(4t) = 0$$

$$\Rightarrow \quad 4t^4 + 12t^2 - 16t = 0$$

$$\Rightarrow \quad t(t-1)(t^2 + t - 4) = 0 \Rightarrow t = 0 \text{ or } 1$$

For $t = 0$, we get point P, therefore $t = 1$ gives point Q as (2, 4).
Here, $P(0, 0)$ and $Q(2, 4)$ are end points of diameter of the given circle and focus of the parabola is the point $S(2, 0)$.

$$\therefore \quad \angle PSQ = 90^\circ$$

Hence, area of $\Delta PQS = \frac{1}{2} \times 2 \times 4 = 4$ sq units.

Sol. (Q. Nos. 125 and 126)

$\because$ PQ is the focal chord of $y^2 = 4ax$.

$\therefore$ Coordinates of P and Q are $(at^2, 2at)$ and $\left(\frac{a}{t^2}, -\frac{2a}{t}\right)$.

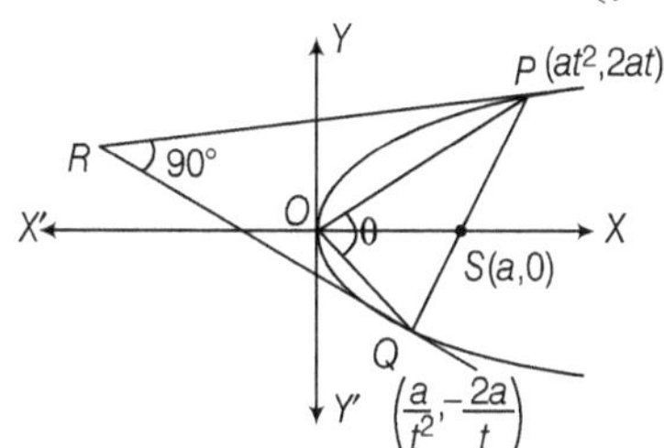

Tangents at P and Q are

$$ty = x + at^2 \text{ and } ty = xt^2 + a$$

which intersect each other at $R\left(-a, a\left(t - \frac{1}{t}\right)\right)$.

As R lies on the line $y = 2x + a, a > 0$

$$\therefore \quad a\left(t - \frac{1}{t}\right) = -2a + a$$

$$\Rightarrow \quad t - \frac{1}{t} = -1$$

125. $\because$ Slope of $OP = \frac{2}{t}$ and slope of $OQ = -2t$

$$\therefore \quad \tan\theta = \left|\frac{\frac{2}{t} + 2t}{1 - 4}\right| = \frac{2}{3}\left|t + \frac{1}{t}\right|$$

$$= \frac{2}{3}\sqrt{\left(t - \frac{1}{t}\right)^2 + 4} = \frac{2}{3}\sqrt{5} \quad \left[\because t - \frac{1}{t} = -1\right]$$

$$\because \quad \theta > 90^\circ$$

$$\therefore \quad \tan\theta = -\frac{2}{3}\sqrt{5}$$

126. $PQ = a\left(t + \frac{1}{t}\right)^2 = a\left\{\left(t - \frac{1}{t}\right)^2 + 4\right\}$

$$= a(1 + 4) = 5a \quad \left[\because t - \frac{1}{t} = -1\right]$$

127. Equation of tangent of $y^2 = 4x$ in terms of slope is

$$y = mx + \frac{1}{m} \quad \text{...(i)}$$

$\because$ Line Eq. (i) touches $x^2 = -32y$

$$\Rightarrow \quad x^2 = -32\left(mx + \frac{1}{m}\right)$$

$$\Rightarrow \quad x^2 + 32mx + \frac{32}{m} = 0 \quad \text{...(ii)}$$

For touching roots of Eq. (ii) are equal.

$$\therefore \quad D = 0$$

$$\Rightarrow \quad (32m)^2 = 4 \cdot 1 \cdot \left(\frac{32}{m}\right)$$

$$\Rightarrow \quad m^3 = \frac{1}{8}$$

$$\therefore \quad m = 1/2$$

128. Let the tangent to, $y^2 = 8x$ be $y = mx + \frac{2}{m}$.

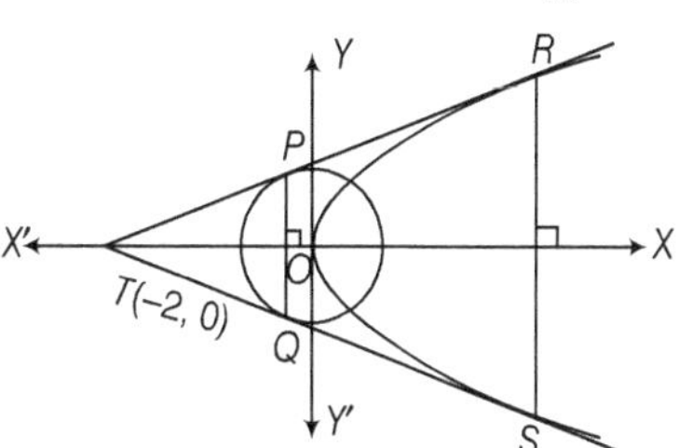

If it is common tangent to parabola and circle, then $y = mx + \frac{2}{m}$ is a tangent to $x^2 + y^2 = 2$.

$$\therefore \quad \frac{\frac{2}{m}}{\sqrt{(1 + m^2)}} = \sqrt{2}$$

$$\Rightarrow \quad \frac{4}{m^2(1 + m^2)} = 2$$

$$\Rightarrow \quad m^4 + m^2 - 2 = 0$$

$$\Rightarrow \quad (m^2 + 2)(m^2 - 1) = 0$$

$$\therefore \quad m = \pm 1$$

$\therefore$ Required tangents are $y = x + 2$ and $y = -x - 2$.

Their common point is $T(-2, 0)$.

Chord of contact PQ to circle is

$$x \cdot (-2) + y \cdot 0 = 2$$

$$\Rightarrow \quad x = -1$$

Hence, coordinates of P and Q are $(-1, 1)$ and $(-1, -1)$ and chord of contact RS to parabola is

$$y \cdot 0 = 4(x - 2)$$

$$\Rightarrow \quad x = 2$$

Hence, coordinates of R and S are $(2, 4)$ and $(2, -4)$.

$\therefore$ Area of trapezium $PQRS = \frac{1}{2}(2 + 8) \times 3 = 15$ sq units

Sol. (Q. Nos. 129 and 130)

$\because$ PQ is a focal chord, then $Q\left(\frac{a}{t^2}, \frac{-2a}{t}\right)$.

Also, $\quad QR \parallel PK \Rightarrow m_{QR} = m_{PK}$

$$\Rightarrow \quad \frac{2ar + \frac{2a}{t}}{ar^2 - \frac{a}{t^2}} = \frac{0 - 2at}{2a - at^2}$$

$$\Rightarrow \quad \frac{2}{r - \frac{1}{t}} = \frac{-2t}{2 - t^2}$$

$$\left[\because r + \frac{1}{t} \neq 0, \text{ otherwise } Q \text{ will coincide with } R\right]$$

$$\Rightarrow \quad 2 - t^2 = -rt + 1$$

$$\therefore \quad r = \frac{t^2 - 1}{t}$$

129. $r = \frac{t^2 - 1}{t}$

130. Tangent at P is $\quad ty = x + at^2 \quad$ ...(i)

Normal at S is $\quad y + sx = 2as + as^3 \quad$ ...(ii)

Putting the value of x from Eq. (i) in Eq. (ii), then

$$y + s(ty - at^2) = 2as + as^3$$

$$\Rightarrow \quad y + (st)y - a(st)t = 2as + as^3$$

$$\Rightarrow \quad y + y - at = \frac{2a}{t} + \frac{a}{t^3} \quad [\because st = 1]$$

$$\Rightarrow \quad 2y = a\left(t + \frac{2}{t} + \frac{1}{t^3}\right)$$

$$\therefore \quad y = \frac{a(t^2+1)^2}{2t^3}$$

131. Let any point Q on $x^2 = 8y$ is $(4t, 2t^2)$ and given $P(h, k)$ divides OQ in the ratio 1:3 (internally).

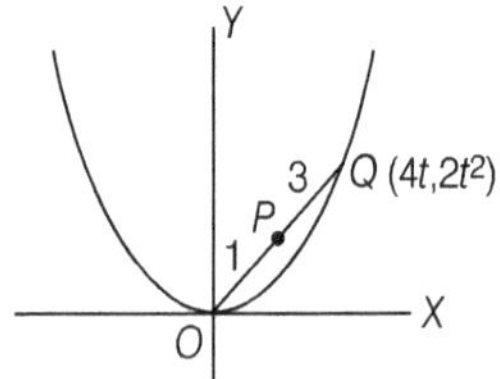

Then, $\quad h = \frac{4t}{4} = t$ and $k = \frac{2t^2}{4} \Rightarrow 2k = h^2$

$\therefore$ Required locus of P is $x^2 = 2y$.

132. End points of latusrectum of

$$y^2 = 4x \text{ are } (1, \pm 2).$$

Equation of normal to $y^2 = 4x$ at $(1, 2)$ is

$$y - 2 = -\frac{2}{2}(x - 1)$$

$$\Rightarrow \quad x + y - 3 = 0$$

As it is tangent to circle $(x-3)^2 + (y+2)^2 = r^2$

$$\therefore \quad \frac{|3 - 2 - 3|}{\sqrt{(1+1)}} = r \Rightarrow r^2 = 2$$

133. Let $(t^2, 2t)$ be any point on $y^2 = 4x$. Let (h, k) be image of $(t^2, 2t)$ with respect to the line $x + y + 4 = 0$, then

$$\frac{h - t^2}{1} = \frac{k - 2t}{1} = \frac{-2(t^2 + 2t + 4)}{1 + 1}$$

$$\Rightarrow \quad h = -(2t + 4) \text{ and } k = -(t^2 + 4)$$

$$\Rightarrow \quad (k + 4) = -\left(\frac{h+4}{-2}\right)^2$$

$$\Rightarrow \quad (h + 4)^2 = -4(k + 4)$$

Locus of (h, k) is $(x + 4)^2 = -4(y + 4)$.

$\therefore \quad$ Curve C is $(x+4)^2 = -4(y + 4)$

Now, intersection of C with $y = -5$, then

$$(x + 4)^2 = -4(-5 + 4) = 4$$

$$\therefore \quad x + 4 = \pm 2 \Rightarrow x = -6, -2$$

$\therefore \quad A(-6, -5)$ and $B(-2, -5)$

$$\therefore \quad AB = 4$$

134. Let $P\left(\frac{t_1^2}{2}, t_1\right)$ and $Q\left(\frac{t_2^2}{2}, t_2\right)$ such that $t_1 > 0$

[$\because$ P lies in first quadrant]

$\because$ Circle with PQ as diameter passes through the vertex $O(0, 0)$ of the parabola.

$$\therefore \quad \angle POQ = 90^\circ$$

$\Rightarrow$ Slope of $OP \times$ Slope of $OQ = -1$

$$\Rightarrow \quad \frac{2}{t_1} \times \frac{2}{t_2} = -1$$

$$\Rightarrow \quad t_1 t_2 = -4 \quad [\because t_2 < 0]$$

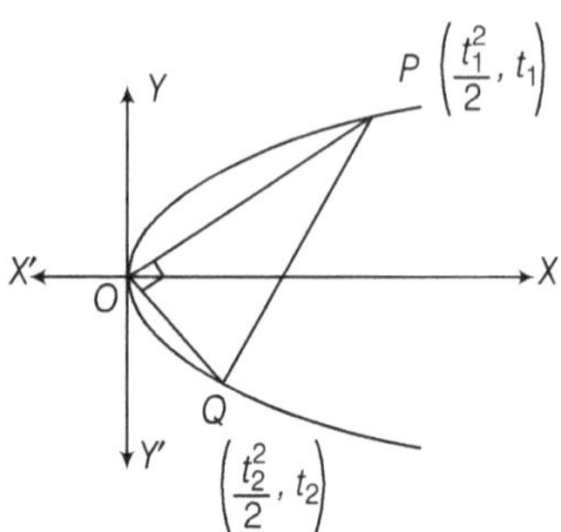

Now, area of $\Delta OPQ = 3\sqrt{2}$

$$\Rightarrow \quad \frac{1}{2}\begin{vmatrix} \frac{t_1^2}{2} & t_1 \\ \frac{t_2^2}{2} & t_2 \end{vmatrix} = 3\sqrt{2}$$

$$\Rightarrow \quad \frac{1}{4}t_1 t_2(t_1 - t_2) = \pm 3\sqrt{2}$$

$$\Rightarrow \quad t_1 - t_2 = \pm 3\sqrt{2} \quad [\because t_1 t_2 = -4]$$

$$\Rightarrow \quad t_1 + \frac{4}{t_1} = \pm 3\sqrt{2}$$

$$\text{or} \quad t_1 + \frac{4}{t_1} = 3\sqrt{2} \quad [\because t_1 > 0]$$

$$\Rightarrow \quad t_1^2 - 3\sqrt{2}t_1 + 4 = 0$$

$$\therefore \quad t_1 = \frac{3\sqrt{2} \pm \sqrt{2}}{2} = 2\sqrt{2}, \sqrt{2}.$$

$\therefore$ Point P can be $(4, 2\sqrt{2})$ or $(1, \sqrt{2})$.

135. Let $P(2t^2, 4t)$ and $C(0, -6)$.

$$\therefore \quad (CP)^2 = 4t^4 + (4t + 6)^2 = z \quad \text{(say)}$$

$$\therefore \quad \frac{dz}{dt} = 0$$

$$\Rightarrow \quad 16t^3 + 2(4t + 6)\cdot 4 = 0$$

$$\Rightarrow \quad t^3 + 2t + 3 = 0$$

$$\Rightarrow \quad (t + 1)(t^2 - t + 3) = 0$$

$$\therefore \quad t = -1$$

$$\Rightarrow \quad P(2, -4)$$

Equation of circle is

$$(x - 2)^2 + (y + 4)^2 = (2 - 0)^2 + (-4 + 6)^2$$

$$\Rightarrow \quad x^2 + y^2 - 4x + 8y + 12 = 0$$

136. $\because C_1 : x^2 + y^2 = 3$ and parabola $x^2 = 2y$, then

$$y^2 + 2y - 3 = 0 \Rightarrow y = 1, -3$$

$\therefore \quad P(\sqrt{2}, 1)$ [$\because P$ lies in first quadrant]

Now, tangent at $P(\sqrt{2}, 1)$ on the circle C_1 is

$$x\sqrt{2} + y = 3$$

Let Q_2 or $Q_3(0, \lambda)$

$$\therefore \quad \frac{|0 + \lambda - 3|}{\sqrt{(2+1)}} = 2\sqrt{3}$$

$$\Rightarrow \quad |\lambda - 3| = 6$$

$$\therefore \quad \lambda = 9 \text{ or } -3$$

$\Rightarrow Q_2(0, -3)$ and $Q_3(0, 9)$.

Alternate (a) $Q_2Q_3 = 12$

Alternate (b) R_2R_3 = Length of external common tangent

$$= \sqrt{(Q_2Q_3)^2 - (2\sqrt{3} + 2\sqrt{3})^2}$$

$$= \sqrt{(144 - 48)} = 4\sqrt{6}$$

Alternate (c) Area of $\Delta OR_2R_3 = \frac{1}{2} \times R_2R_3 \times \frac{|0 + 0 - 3|}{\sqrt{(2+1)}}$

$$= \frac{1}{2} \times 4\sqrt{6} \times \frac{3}{\sqrt{3}} = 6\sqrt{2}$$

Alternate (d) Area of $\Delta PQ_2Q_3 = \frac{1}{2} \times Q_2Q_3 \times \sqrt{2}$

$$= \frac{1}{2} \times 12 \times \sqrt{2} = 6\sqrt{2}$$

137. Let $P(t^2, 2t)$, $S(2, 8)$ and $r = \sqrt{(4 + 64 - 64)} = 2$

We know that, shortest distance between two curves lies along their common normal. The common normal will pass through centre of circle.

$\therefore$ Slope of PS = Slope of normal to the parabola $y^2 = 4x$ at $P(t^2, 2t)$

$$\Rightarrow \quad \frac{2t - 8}{t^2 - 2} = -t \text{ or } t^3 = 8 \Rightarrow t = 2$$

$\therefore P(4, 4)$

Alternate (a) $\quad SP = \sqrt{(2-4)^2 + (8-4)^2} = 2\sqrt{5}$

Alternate (b) $\quad SQ = r = 2$

$$\therefore \quad \frac{SQ}{QP} = \frac{SQ}{SP - SQ} = \frac{2}{2\sqrt{5} - 2}$$

$$= \frac{1}{(\sqrt{5} - 1)} \times \frac{(\sqrt{5} + 1)}{(\sqrt{5} + 1)} = \frac{\sqrt{5} + 1}{4}$$

$$\Rightarrow \quad SQ : QP = (\sqrt{5} + 1) : 4$$

Alternate (c) Equation of normal at $P(4, 4)$ is

$$y - 4 = -\frac{4}{2}(x - 4)$$

$$\Rightarrow \quad y - 4 = -2x + 8$$

$$\Rightarrow \quad 2x + y = 12$$

$\therefore$ Intercept on X-axis is 6.

Alternate (d) Slope of tangent at Q = Slope of tangent at $P = \frac{1}{2}$

138. Centre of circle

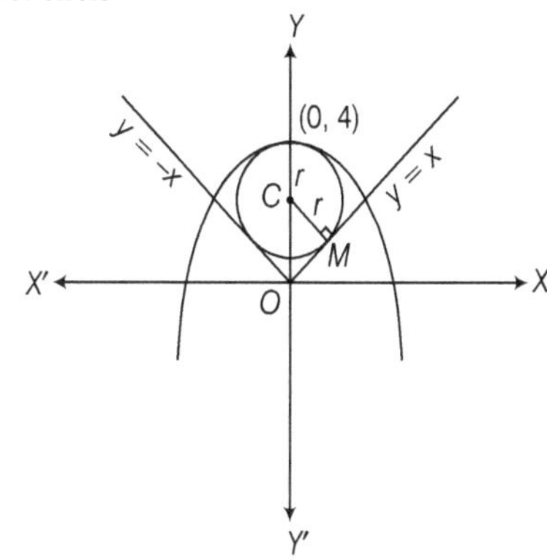

$$C \equiv (0, 4 - r)$$

$$\because \quad CM = r$$

$$\therefore \quad \frac{|10 - (4 - r)|}{\sqrt{2}} = r$$

$$\Rightarrow \quad 4 - r = r\sqrt{2}$$

$$\text{or} \quad r = \frac{4}{\sqrt{2} + 1} = 4(\sqrt{2} - 1)$$

139. (a) Equation of chord of parabola $y^2 = 16x$ whose mid-point (h, k) is

$$T = S_1$$

$$\text{or} \quad ky - 8(x + h) = k^2 - 16h$$

$$\text{or} \quad 8x - ky = 8h - k^2 \quad \text{...(i)}$$

Now comparing Eq. (i) and $2x + y = p$, then

$$\frac{8}{2} = \frac{-k}{1} = \frac{8h - k^2}{p}$$

$$\Rightarrow \quad k = -4 \text{ and } 4p = 8h - k^2$$

$$\text{or} \quad k = -4 \text{ and } p = 2h - 4$$

Hence, $\quad p = 2, h = 3, k = -4$

CHAPTER

06

Ellipse

Learning Part

Session 1

- Ellipse Definition
- The Foci and Two Directrices of an Ellipse
- Some Terms Related to an Ellipse
- The Shape of the Ellipse $\frac{x^2}{a^2}+\frac{y^2}{b^2}=1$, when $b > a$
- Standard Equation of Ellipse
- Tracing of the Ellipse
- Focal Distances of a Point
- Mechanical Construction of an Ellipse

Session 2

- Position of a Point with Respect to an Ellipse
- Equation of Tangent in Different Forms
- Properties of Eccentric Angles of the Co-normal Points
- Smart Table
- Intersection of a Line and an Ellipse
- Equations of Normals in Different Forms
- Co-normal Points Lie on a Fixed Curve

Session 3

- Pair of Tangents
- Chord Bisected at a Given Point
- Conjugate Diameters
- Director Circle
- Co+ncyclic Points
- Reflection Property of an Ellipse
- Equation of an Ellipse Referred to Two Perpendicular Lines
- Chord of Contact
- Diameter
- Equi-Conjugate Diameters
- Sub-Tangent and Sub-Normal
- Some Standard Properties of the Ellipse

Practice Part

- JEE Types Examples
- Chapter Exercises

Session 1

Ellipse Definition, Standard Equation of Ellipse, Tracing of the Ellipse, Focal Distances of a Point, The Shape of the Ellipse $x^2/a^2 + y^2/b^2 = 1$, When $b > a$, Mechanical Construction of an Ellipse,

Ellipse Definition

An ellipse is the locus of a point which moves in a plane such that its distance from a fixed point (i.e. focus) is a constant ratio from a fixed line (i.e. directrix).
This ratio is called eccentricity and is denoted by e.
For an ellipse $0 < e < 1$.

Standard Equation of Ellipse

Let S be the focus and ZM the directrix of the ellipse. Drow $SZ \perp ZM$. Divide SZ internally and externally in the ratio $e:1 (0 < e < 1)$ and let A and A' be these internal and external point of division

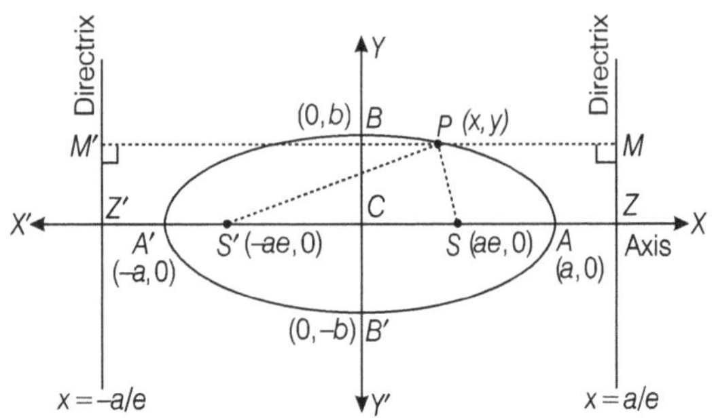

Then, $\quad SA = eAZ \quad$ ...(i)

and $\quad SA' = eA'Z \quad$ ...(ii)

Clearly A and A' will lie on the ellipse

Let $AA' = 2a$ and take C the mid point of AA' as origin

$\therefore \quad CA = CA' = a \quad$ ...(iii)

Let $P(x, y)$ by any point on the ellipse referred to CA and CB as co-ordinate axes

Then, adding Eqs. (i) and (ii),

$$SA + SA' = e(AZ + A'Z)$$

$$\Rightarrow \quad AA' = e(CZ - CA + CA' + CZ) \quad \text{(from figure)}$$

$$\Rightarrow \quad AA' = e(2CZ) \quad (\because CA = CA')$$

$$\Rightarrow \quad 2a = 2eCZ$$

$$\because \quad CZ = a/e$$

$\therefore$ The directrix MZ is $x = CZ = a/e$

$$\text{or} \quad \frac{a}{e} - x = 0 \quad \left(\because e < 1, \therefore \frac{a}{e} > 1\right)$$

and subtracting Eqs. (i) from (ii), then

$$SA' - SA = e(A'Z - AZ)$$

$$\Rightarrow \quad (CA' + CS) - (CA - CS) = e(AA')$$

$$\Rightarrow \quad 2CS = e(AA') \quad (\because CA = CA')$$

$$\Rightarrow \quad 2CS = e(2a)$$

$$\therefore \quad CS = ae$$

$\therefore$ The focus S is $(CS, 0)$ i.e. $(ae, 0)$

Now draw $PM \perp MZ$

$$\therefore \quad \frac{SP}{PM} = e \text{ or } (SP)^2 = e^2 (PM)^2$$

$$(x - ae)^2 + (y - 0)^2 = e^2 \left(\frac{a}{e} - x\right)^2$$

$$\Rightarrow \quad (x - ae)^2 + y^2 = (a - ex)^2$$

$$\Rightarrow \quad x^2 + a^2e^2 - 2aex + y^2 = a^2 - 2aex + e^2x^2$$

$$\Rightarrow \quad x^2 (1 - e^2) + y^2 = a^2 (1 - e^2)$$

$$\Rightarrow \quad \frac{x^2}{a^2} + \frac{y^2}{a^2 (1 - e^2)} = 1$$

or $$\frac{x^2}{a^2}+\frac{y^2}{b^2}=1$$

where, $$b^2=a^2(1-e^2)$$

This is the standard equation of an ellipse, AA' and BB' are called the major and minor axes of the ellipse. (Here $b<a$) and A and A' are the vertices of the ellipse.

Remark

Two ellipse are said to be similar if they have the same value of eccentricity.

Generally,

The equation to the ellipse, whose focus is the point (h,k) and directrix is $lx+my+n=0$ and whose eccentricity is e, is

$$(x-h)^2+(y-k)^2=e^2\cdot\frac{(lx+my+n)^2}{(l^2+m^2)}$$

The Foci and Two Directrices of an Ellipse

On the negative side of origin take a point S' which is such that

$$CS=CS'=ae$$

and another point Z', then

$$CZ=CZ'=\frac{a}{e}$$

$\therefore$ Coordinates of S' are $(-ae,0)$ and equation of second directrix (*i.e.*, $Z'M'$) is $x=-\frac{a}{e}$

Let $P(x,y)$ be any point on the ellipse, then

$$S'P=ePM'$$

or $$(S'P)^2=e^2(PM')^2$$

or $$(x+ae)^2+(y-0)^2=e^2\left(x+\frac{a}{e}\right)^2$$

or $$(x+ae)^2+y^2=(ex+a)^2$$

or $$x^2(1-e^2)+y^2=a^2(1-e^2)$$

or $$\frac{x^2}{a^2}+\frac{y^2}{a^2(1-e^2)}=1$$

or $$\frac{x^2}{a^2}+\frac{y^2}{b^2}=1,$$

where, $$b^2=a^2(1-e^2)$$

The equation being the same as that of the ellipse when $S(ae,0)$ is focus and MZ i.e. $x=a/e$ is directrix.

Hence, coordinates of foci are $(\pm ae,0)$ and equations of directrices are $x=\pm a/e$.

Remarks

1. Distance between foci $SS'=2ae$ and distance between directrices $ZZ'=2a/e$
2. If $e=0$
   then $$b^2=a^2(1-0)$$
   $\therefore$ $$b^2=a^2$$
   then equation of ellipse $\frac{x^2}{a^2}+\frac{y^2}{b^2}=1$ changes in circle
   i.e. $$x^2+y^2=a^2$$
3. Since, $\frac{x^2}{a^2}+\frac{y^2}{b^2}=1$
   $$\Rightarrow \frac{y^2}{b^2}=1-\frac{x^2}{a^2}=\frac{a^2-x^2}{a^2}$$
   $$\frac{y^2}{b^2}=\frac{(a+x)(a-x)}{a^2}$$

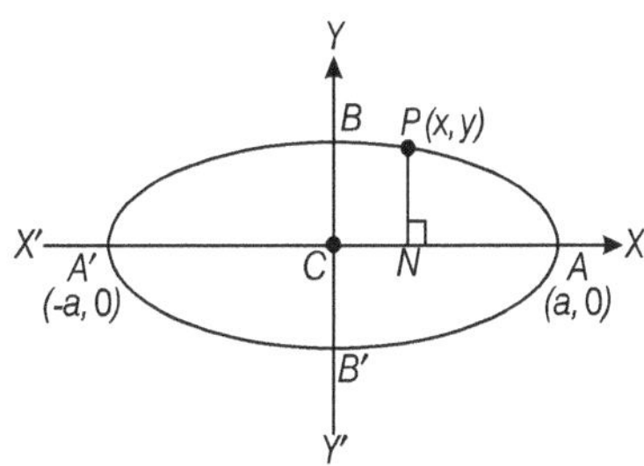

   or $$\frac{(PN)^2}{b^2}=\frac{A'N\cdot AN}{a^2}$$
   or $$\frac{(PN)^2}{AN\cdot A'N}=\frac{b^2}{a^2}=\frac{(BC)^2}{(AC)^2}$$
   i.e. $$(PN)^2:AN\cdot A'N::(BC)^2:(AC)^2$$
4. The distance of every focus from the extremity of minor axis is equal to a.
   i.e. $$\sqrt{(a^2e^2+b^2)}=\sqrt{(a^2-b^2+b^2)}=a$$

Tracing of the Ellipse

Equation of the ellipse is

$$\frac{x^2}{a^2}+\frac{y^2}{b^2}=1 \qquad \text{...(i)}$$

1. The ellipse (i) cuts X-axis at $A(a,0)$ and $A'(-a,0)$ and cuts Y-axis at $B(0,b)$ and $B'(0,-b)$.
2. The Eq. (i) does not change when y is replaced by $-y$ and x is replaced by $-x$, Hence ellipse (i) is symmetrical about both axes

3. The equation (i), may be written in either of the form

$$y = \pm b \sqrt{\left(1 - \frac{x^2}{a^2}\right)} \quad \text{...(ii)}$$

or $$x = \pm a \sqrt{\left(1 - \frac{y^2}{b^2}\right)} \quad \text{...(iii)}$$

From Eq. (ii), it follows that (y is real)

if $$1 - \frac{x^2}{a^2} \geq 0 \text{ or } a^2 - x^2 \geq 0$$

or $$x^2 \leq a^2 \text{ or } -a \leq x \leq a$$

Also from Eq. (iii), it follows that (x is real)

if $$1 - \frac{y^2}{b^2} \geq 0 \text{ or } b^2 - y^2 \geq 0 \text{ or } y^2 \leq b^2$$

$\therefore$ $$-b \leq y \leq b$$

Ellipse (i) is a closed curve lies entirely between the lines $x = a$ and $x = -a$ and the lines $y = b$ and $y = -b$.

Since, when x increases, then y decreases from Eq. (ii) and when y decreases, then x increases from Eq. (iii).

Remark

Area of the ellipse $\frac{x^2}{a^2} + \frac{y^2}{b^2} = 1$ is πab.

Some Terms Related to an Ellipse

Let the equation of the ellipse $\frac{x^2}{a^2} + \frac{y^2}{b^2} = 1$ $(a > b)$

1. **Centre :** All chords passing through C is bisected at C

   Here $C \equiv (0, 0)$

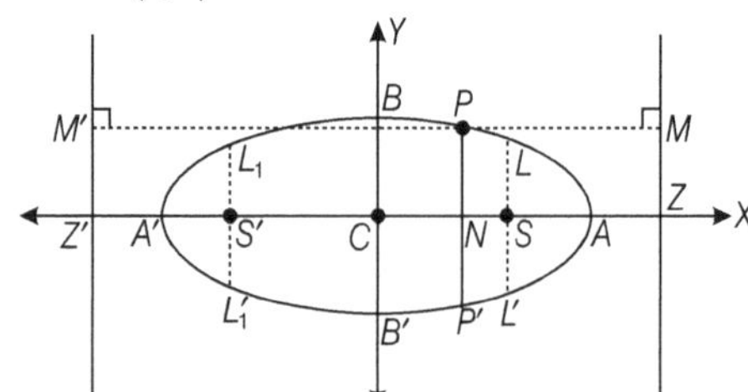

2. **Foci :** S and S' are two foci of the ellipse and their coordinates are $(ae, 0)$ and $(-ae, 0)$ respectively.
3. **Directrices :** ZM and $Z'M'$ are two directrices of the ellipse and their equation are $x = \frac{a}{e}$ and $x = -\frac{a}{e}$ respectively.
4. **Axes :** The lines AA' and BB' are called the **major** and **minor** axes of the ellipse

$\because$ $$0 < e < 1$$

or $$0 < e^2 < 1 \quad (\therefore 0 > -e^2 > -1)$$

or $$0 < 1 - e^2 < 1 \quad (\text{or } 1 > 1 - e^2 > 1 - 1)$$

or $$a^2 (1 - e^2) < a^2 \quad (\text{or } 0 < 1 - e^2 < 1)$$

or $$b^2 < a^2$$

i.e. $$b < a$$

Remark

The major and minor axis together are called **principal axes** of the ellipse.

5. **Double ordinates :** If P be a point on the ellipse draw PN perpendicular to the axis of the ellipse and produced to meet the curve again at P'. Then PP' is called a double ordinate.

   If abscissa of P is h, then ordinate of P,

$$\frac{y^2}{b^2} = 1 - \frac{h^2}{a^2}$$

$$y = \frac{b}{a} \sqrt{(a^2 - h^2)} \quad \text{(for first quadrant)}$$

and ordinate of P' is

$$y = -\frac{b}{a} \sqrt{(a^2 - h^2)} \quad \text{(for fourth quadrant)}$$

Hence, coordinates of P and P' are

$$\left(h, \frac{b}{a}\sqrt{(a^2 - h^2)}\right) \text{ and } \left(h, -\frac{b}{a}\sqrt{(a^2 - h^2)}\right)$$

respectively.

6. **Latusrectum** The double ordinates LL' and L_1L_1' are latusrectums of the ellipse. These line are perpendicular to major axis $A'A$ and through the foci S and S', respectively.

Length of the latusrectum

Now let $$LL' = 2k$$

then $$LS = L'S = k$$

Coordinates of L and L' are (ae, k) and $(ae, -k)$ lies on the ellipse

$$\frac{x^2}{a^2} + \frac{y^2}{b^2} = 1$$

$\therefore$ $$\frac{a^2e^2}{a^2} + \frac{k^2}{b^2} = 1 \text{ or } k^2 = b^2 (1 - e^2)$$

$$= b^2 \left(\frac{b^2}{a^2}\right) \quad [\because b^2 = a^2 (1 - e^2)]$$

$\therefore \quad k = \dfrac{b^2}{a} \quad (\because k > 0)$

$\therefore \quad 2k = \dfrac{2b^2}{a} = LL'$

$\therefore$ Length of latusrectum $LL' = L_1 L_1' = \dfrac{2b^2}{a}$ and end of points of latusrectum are

$$L \equiv \left(ae, \frac{b^2}{a}\right); L' \equiv \left(ae, -\frac{b^2}{a}\right)$$

$$L_1 \equiv \left(-ae, \frac{b^2}{a}\right); L_1' \equiv \left(-ae, -\frac{b^2}{a}\right)$$

respectively.

Remark

Latusrectum

$$= LL' = \frac{2b^2}{a} = \frac{(2b)^2}{(2a)} = \frac{(\text{Minor axis})^2}{(\text{Major axis})}$$

$$= 2a(1-e^2) = 2e\left(\frac{a}{e} - ae\right)$$

$= 2e$ (distance from focus to the corresponding directrix)

7. **Focal chord :** A chord of the ellipse passing through its focus is called a focal chord.

Remark

Semi latusrectum is the harmonic mean of the segments of focal chord or $\dfrac{1}{SP} + \dfrac{1}{SQ} = \dfrac{2a}{b^2}$, $(a > b)$, where PQ is the focal chord and S is the focus.

8. **Vertices :** The vertices of the ellipse are the points where the ellipse meets its major axis.

   Hence, A and A' are the vertices

   $\therefore \quad A \equiv (a, 0)$ and $A' \equiv (-a, 0)$

Example 1 If PSQ is a focal chord of the ellipse $16x^2 + 25y^2 = 400$, such that $SP = 8$, then find the length of SQ.

Sol. The given ellipse is $16x^2 + 25y^2 = 400$ or $\dfrac{x^2}{25} + \dfrac{y^2}{16} = 1$

$\because \quad \dfrac{1}{SP} + \dfrac{1}{SQ} = \dfrac{2a}{b^2}$

$\Rightarrow \quad \dfrac{1}{8} + \dfrac{1}{SQ} = \dfrac{2(5)}{16} = \dfrac{5}{8}$ or $\dfrac{1}{SQ} = \dfrac{1}{2}$

$\therefore \quad SQ = 2$

Example 2 If the latusrectum of an ellipse is equal to half of its minor-axis, then find its eccentricity.

Sol. $\because$ Latusrectum $= \dfrac{1}{2}$ (minor axis)

$\Rightarrow \quad \dfrac{2b^2}{a} = \dfrac{1}{2}(2b)$

or $\quad 2b = a$

or $\quad 4b^2 = a^2$

$\Rightarrow \quad 4a^2(1 - e^2) = a^2$

or $\quad 4e^2 = 3$

$\therefore \quad e = \dfrac{\sqrt{3}}{2}$

Example 3 If the distance between the directrices is thrice the distance between the foci, then find eccentricity of the ellipse.

Sol. Given, $\dfrac{2a}{e} = 3(2ae) \Rightarrow e^2 = \dfrac{1}{3}$

$\therefore \quad e = \dfrac{1}{\sqrt{3}}$

Example 4 If $P(x, y)$ be any point on the ellipse $16x^2 + 25y^2 = 400$ and $F_1 \equiv (3, 0), F_2 \equiv (-3, 0)$, then find the value of $PF_1 + PF_2$.

Sol. We have, $16x^2 + 25y^2 = 400$

$\Rightarrow \quad \dfrac{x^2}{5^2} + \dfrac{y^2}{4^2} = 1$

$\because$ Coordinates of foci an $(\pm ae, 0)$

or $\quad \left(\pm\sqrt{(a^2 - b^2)}, 0\right)$

i.e. $\quad (\pm\sqrt{(25 - 16)}, 0)$ or $(\pm 3, 0)$

Thus, F_1 and F_2 are foci of the ellipse.

$\therefore \quad PF_1 + PF_2 =$ Length of major axis

$= 2a = 2 \times 5 = 10$

9. **Parametric equation of the ellipse :** The circle described on the major-axis of an ellipse as diameter is called the **auxiliary circle** of the ellipse.

   Let the equation of ellipse be

$$\frac{x^2}{a^2} + \frac{y^2}{b^2} = 1$$

$\therefore$ Equation of its auxiliary circle is

$x^2 + y^2 = a^2$ ($\because AA'$ is diameter of the circle)

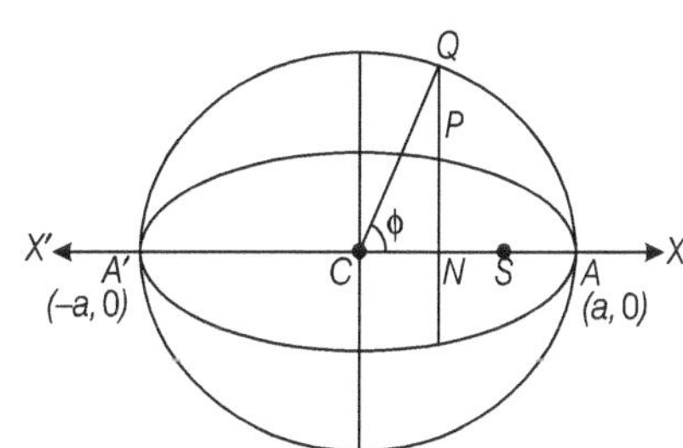

Let Q be a point on the auxiliary circle $x^2+y^2=a^2$ such that QP produced is perpendicular to the X-axis.

Then P and Q are the **corresponding points** on the ellipse and the auxiliary circle respectively.

Let $\angle QCA=\phi \qquad (0\le\phi<2\pi)$

i.e. the eccentric angle of P on an ellipse is the angle which the radius (or **radius vector)** through the corresponding point on the auxiliary circle makes with the major axis.

$\therefore \quad Q\equiv(a\cos\phi, a\sin\phi)$

$\therefore$ Now x-coordinate of P is $a\cos\phi$

Let y-coordinate of P is y, then $(a\cos\phi, y)$ lies on the ellipse

$$\frac{x^2}{a^2}+\frac{y^2}{b^2}=1$$

$$\frac{a^2\cos^2\phi}{a^2}+\frac{y^2}{b^2}=1$$

$$\Rightarrow \quad y^2=b^2\sin^2\phi$$

$$\therefore \quad y=\pm b\sin\phi$$

$\because$ P is in I quadrant

$$\therefore \quad y=b\sin\phi$$

Coordinates of P are $(a\cos\phi, b\sin\phi)$. We have $x=a\cos\phi$, $y=b\sin\phi$ are called parametric equations of the ellipse.

This point $(a\cos\phi, b\sin\phi)$ is also called the point 'ϕ'.

Remark

The equation of the chord joining the points

$P\equiv(a\cos\phi_1, b\sin\phi_1)$

and $Q\equiv(a\cos\phi_2, b\sin\phi_2)$ is

$$\frac{x}{a}\cos\left(\frac{\phi_1+\phi_2}{2}\right)+\frac{y}{b}\sin\left(\frac{\phi_1+\phi_2}{2}\right)=\cos\left(\frac{\phi_1-\phi_2}{2}\right)$$

If its focal chord, then it pass through $(ae,0)$ or $(-ae,0)$, then

$$\pm e\cos\left(\frac{\phi_1+\phi_2}{2}\right)+0=\cos\left(\frac{\phi_1-\phi_2}{2}\right)$$

$$\Rightarrow \quad \frac{\cos\left(\frac{\phi_1-\phi_2}{2}\right)}{\cos\left(\frac{\phi_1+\phi_2}{2}\right)}=\pm\frac{e}{1}$$

$$\Rightarrow \quad \frac{\cos\left(\frac{\phi_1-\phi_2}{2}\right)-\cos\left(\frac{\phi_1+\phi_2}{2}\right)}{\cos\left(\frac{\phi_1-\phi_2}{2}\right)+\cos\left(\frac{\phi_1+\phi_2}{2}\right)}=\left(\frac{\pm e-1}{\pm e+1}\right)$$

$$\Rightarrow \quad \tan\left(\frac{\phi_1}{2}\right)\tan\left(\frac{\phi_2}{2}\right)=\left(\frac{\pm e-1}{\pm e+1}\right)$$

if focal chord pass through $(ae,0)$, then

$$\tan\left(\frac{\phi_1}{2}\right)\tan\left(\frac{\phi_2}{2}\right)=\left(\frac{e-1}{e+1}\right)$$

and if focal chord pass through $(-ae,0)$, then

$$\tan\left(\frac{\phi_1}{2}\right)\tan\left(\frac{\phi_2}{2}\right)=\left(\frac{e+1}{e-1}\right)$$

or

$$\cot\left(\frac{\phi_1}{2}\right)\cot\left(\frac{\phi_2}{2}\right)=\left(\frac{e-1}{e+1}\right)$$

Remark

Circle described on focal length as diameter always touches the auxiliary circle.

Proof

Consider ellipse $\frac{x^2}{a^2}+\frac{y^2}{b^2}=1$

Let P be $(a\cos\theta, b\sin\theta)$

and S be $(ae,0)$

$$\therefore \quad SP=ePM=e\left(\frac{a}{e}-a\cos\theta\right)$$

$$=(a-ae\cos\theta)$$

The auxiliary circle $x^2+y^2=a^2$ having center $C_1(0,0)$ and radius $r_1=a$

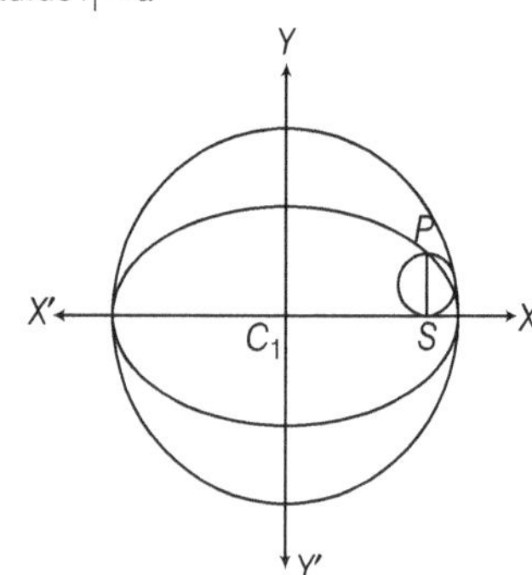

The circle having SP as the diameter has center

$$C_2\left(\frac{ae+a\cos\theta}{2}, \frac{b\sin\theta}{2}\right)$$

and radius $r_2=\frac{SP}{2}=\frac{a(1-e\cos\theta)}{2}$

$$\text{Now, } C_1C_2=\sqrt{\left(\frac{ae+a\cos\theta}{2}\right)^2+\left(\frac{b\sin\theta}{2}\right)^2}$$

$$=\frac{1}{2}\sqrt{a^2(e+\cos\theta)^2+a^2(1-e^2)\sin^2\theta}$$

$$=\frac{a}{2}\sqrt{(e^2+\cos^2\theta+2e\cos\theta+\sin^2\theta-e^2\sin^2\theta)}$$

$$=\frac{a}{2}\sqrt{(e^2\cos^2\theta+2e\cos\theta+1)}$$

$$=\frac{a}{2}(1+e\cos\theta)$$

$$=r_1-r_2$$

Hence, the circle on SP as diameter touches the auxiliary circle internally.

Example 5 Find the eccentric angle of a point on the ellipse $\frac{x^2}{6}+\frac{y^2}{2}=1$. Whose distance from the center of the ellipse is $\sqrt{5}$.

Sol. Any point on the ellipse is $P(\sqrt{6}\cos\theta, \sqrt{2}\sin\theta)$

Where, $0 \le \theta < 2\pi$ and $C(0,0)$ is center, given $CP = \sqrt{5}$

$$\Rightarrow \quad (CP)^2 = 5$$

$$\Rightarrow \quad 6\cos^2\theta + 2\sin^2\theta = 5$$

$$\Rightarrow \quad 6(1-\sin^2\theta) + 2\sin^2\theta = 5$$

$$\text{or} \quad \sin^2\theta = \frac{1}{4}$$

$$\text{or} \quad \sin\theta = \pm\frac{1}{2} = \pm\sin\frac{\pi}{6}$$

$$\therefore \quad \theta = \frac{\pi}{6}, \frac{5\pi}{6}, \frac{7\pi}{6}, \frac{11\pi}{6}$$

Focal Distances of a Point

The sum of focal distances of any point on the ellipse is equal to the major axis. The ellipse is

$$\frac{x^2}{a^2}+\frac{y^2}{b^2}=1 \qquad \text{...(i)}$$

The foci S and S' are $(ae, 0)$ and $(-ae, 0)$.

The equations of its directrices MZ and $M'Z'$ are $x = a/e$ and $x = -a/e$

Let $P(x_1, y_1)$ be any point on Eq. (i)

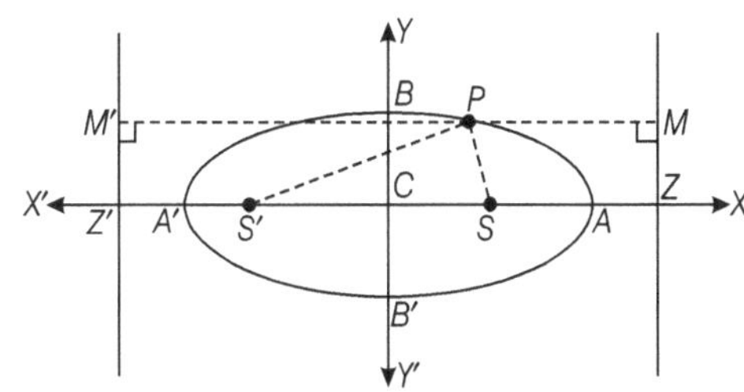

Now $\quad SP = ePM = e\left(\frac{a}{e} - x_1\right)$

$$= a - ex_1$$

and $\quad S'P = ePM' = e\left(\frac{a}{e} + x_1\right)$

$$= a + ex_1$$

$$SP + S'P = (a - ex_1) + (a + ex_1)$$

$$= 2a = AA' = \text{major axis}$$

Hence, the sum of the focal distances of a point on the ellipse is constant and is equal to the length of the major axis of the ellipse.

Another definition of ellipse : An ellipse is the locus of a point which moves in a plane such that the sum of its distances from two fixed points in the same plane is always constant.

Remark

SP and $S'P$ are also called focal radii of the ellipse

$\therefore \quad SP = a - ex_1$ and $S'P = a + ex_1$

Example 6 An ellipse having foci at (3, 3) and (−4, 4) and passing through the origin, then find eccentricity of the ellipse.

Sol. The ellipse is passing through $O(0,0)$ and has foci $P(3,3)$ and $Q(-4,4)$, then

$$OP + OQ = 2a \text{ and } PQ = 2ae$$

$$\therefore \quad e = \frac{PQ}{OP+OQ} = \frac{\sqrt{50}}{3\sqrt{2}+4\sqrt{2}} = \frac{5}{7}$$

The Shape of the Ellipse $\frac{x^2}{a^2}+\frac{y^2}{b^2}=1$, when $b > a$

In this case major and minor-axis of the ellipse along Y-axis and X-axis respectively.

then $\quad AA' = 2b$ and $BB' = 2a$

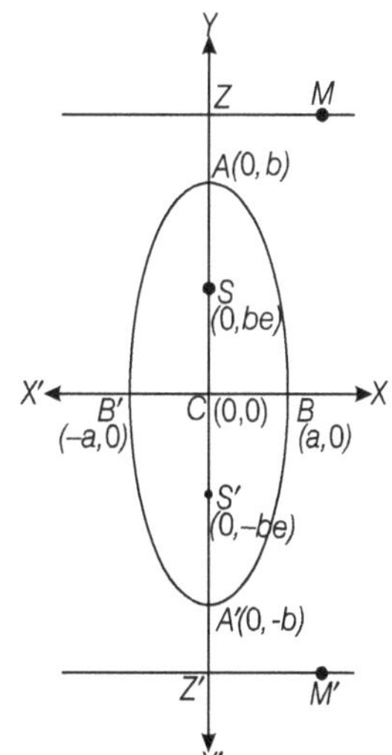

The foci S and S' are $(0, be)$ and $(0, -be)$ respectively

The directrices are MZ and $M'Z'$ are

$$y = \frac{b}{e} \text{ and } y = -\frac{b}{e}$$

are respectively,

Mechanical Construction of an Ellipse

Let S and S' be two drawing pins and let an inextensible string whose ends at S and S' and length is equal to sum of SP and $S'P$ i.e. $2a$, where P is point of pencil. The point of pencil move on paper and the fixed ends always tight. So as to satisfy these conditions it will trace out the curve on the paper. This curve is an ellipse. Hence the locus of the point of pencil is an ellipse.

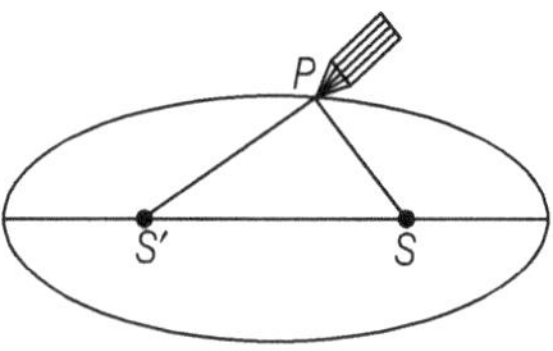

Smart Table : Difference between both (Horizontal and Vertical) Ellipses will be clear from the following table

Equation and graph of the ellipse → / Basic fundamentals ↓	Horizontal ellipse $\frac{x^2}{a^2}+\frac{y^2}{b^2}=1;a>b$	Vertical ellipse $\frac{x^2}{a^2}+\frac{y^2}{b^2}=1;a<b$
Centre	$(0, 0)$	$(0, 0)$
Vertices	$(\pm a, 0)$	$(0, \pm b)$
Length of major axis	$2a$	$2b$
Length of minor axis	$2b$	$2a$
Foci	$(\pm ae, 0)$ or $(\pm \sqrt{(a^2-b^2)}, 0)$	$(0, \pm be)$ or $(0, \pm \sqrt{(b^2-a^2)})$
Distance between foci	$2ae$ or $2\sqrt{(a^2-b^2)}$	$2be$ or $2\sqrt{(b^2-a^2)}$
Equation of directrices	$x = \pm \frac{a}{e}$	$y = \pm \frac{b}{e}$
Distance between directrices	$\frac{2a}{e}$	$\frac{2b}{e}$
Relation between a, b and e	$b^2 = a^2(1-e^2)$	$a^2 = b^2(1-e^2)$
Length of latusrectum	$\frac{2b^2}{a}$ or $2a(1-e^2)$	$\frac{2a^2}{b}$ or $2b(1-e^2)$
End points of latusrectum	$\left(\pm ae, \pm \frac{b^2}{a}\right)$	$\left(\pm \frac{a^2}{b}, \pm be\right)$
Focal radii	$SP = a - ex_1, S'P = a + ex_1$ and $SP + S'P = 2a$	$SP = b - ey_1, S'P = b + ey_1$ and $SP + S'P = 2b$
Parametric Coordinates	$(a\cos\theta, b\sin\theta), 0 \le \theta < 2\pi$	$(a\cos\theta, b\sin\theta), 0 \le \theta < 2\pi$
Tangents at the vertices	$x = \pm a$	$y = \pm b$

Example 7 Find the lengths of major and minor axes, the coordinates of foci, vertices and the eccentricity of the ellipse $3x^2 + 2y^2 = 6$. Also, find the equation of the directrices.

Sol. The equation of ellipse is

$$3x^2 + 2y^2 = 6$$

$$\Rightarrow \quad \frac{x^2}{2} + \frac{y^2}{3} = 1$$

$$\Rightarrow \quad \frac{x^2}{(\sqrt{2})^2} + \frac{y^2}{(\sqrt{3})^2} = 1$$

Comparing this equation with

$$\frac{x^2}{a^2} + \frac{y^2}{b^2} = 1$$

$$\therefore \quad a = \sqrt{2}, b = \sqrt{3} \qquad \text{(Here } b > a\text{)}$$

Length of major axis $= 2b = 2\sqrt{3}$

and Length of minor axis $= 2a = 2\sqrt{2}$

If e be the eccentricity, then $a^2 = b^2 (1 - e^2)$

$$\Rightarrow \quad 2 = 3(1 - e^2) \Rightarrow e^2 = \frac{1}{3}$$

$$\therefore \quad e = \frac{1}{\sqrt{3}}$$

Vertices $= (0, \pm b) = (0, \pm \sqrt{3})$

and foci are $(0, \pm be) = (0, \pm 1)$

and equation of the directrices are $y = \pm b/e$

$$y = \pm \frac{\sqrt{3}}{(1/\sqrt{3})}$$

$$\therefore \quad y = \pm 3$$

Example 8 Find the equation of an ellipse whose focus is (–1, 1), eccentricity is $\frac{1}{2}$ and the directrix is $x - y + 3 = 0$.

Sol. Let $P(x, y)$ be any point on the ellipse whose focus is $S(-1, 1)$ and the directrix is $x - y + 3 = 0$. Draw PM perpendicular from $P(x, y)$ on the directrix $x - y + 3 = 0$. Then by definition

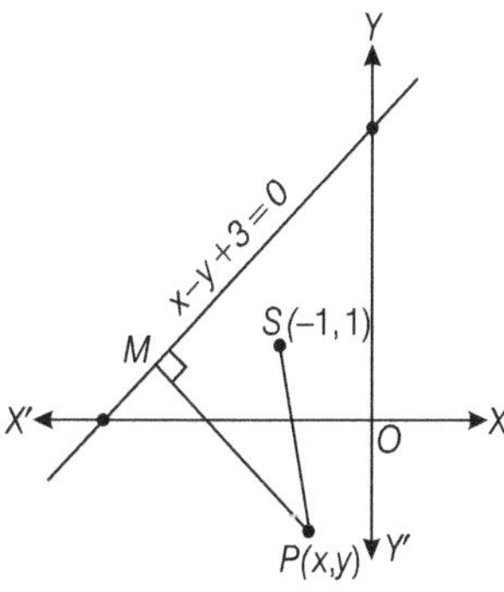

$$SP = ePM$$

$$\Rightarrow \quad (SP)^2 = e^2 (PM)^2$$

$$\Rightarrow \quad (x + 1)^2 + (y - 1)^2 = \frac{1}{4}\left\{\frac{x - y + 3}{\sqrt{2}}\right\}^2$$

$$\Rightarrow \quad 8(x^2 + y^2 + 2x - 2y + 2) = x^2 + y^2 + 9 - 2xy + 6x - 6y$$

$$\Rightarrow \quad 7x^2 + 7y^2 + 2xy + 10x - 10y + 7 = 0$$

which is the required equation of the ellipse.

Example 9 Show that the line $lx + my + n = 0$ will cut the ellipse $x^2/a^2 + y^2/b^2 = 1$ in points whose eccentric angles differ by $(\pi/2)$, if $a^2l^2 + b^2m^2 = 2n^2$.

Sol. Let eccentric angles are θ and ϕ, then

$$\theta - \phi = \frac{\pi}{2} \qquad \text{(given)}$$

$$\therefore \quad \theta = \frac{\pi}{2} + \phi$$

The line joining the point 'θ' and 'ϕ' is

$$\frac{x}{a}\cos\left(\frac{\theta + \phi}{2}\right) + \frac{y}{b}\sin\left(\frac{\theta + \phi}{2}\right) = \cos\left(\frac{\theta - \phi}{2}\right)$$

or $$\frac{x}{a}\cos\left(\frac{\pi}{4} + \phi\right) + \frac{y}{b}\sin\left(\frac{\pi}{4} + \phi\right) = \cos\frac{\pi}{4} \quad \left(\because \theta = \frac{\pi}{2} + \phi\right)$$

or $$\frac{x}{a}\cos\left(\frac{\pi}{4} + \phi\right) + \frac{y}{b}\sin\left(\frac{\pi}{4} + \phi\right) = \frac{1}{\sqrt{2}} \qquad \text{...(i)}$$

and the given line is $lx + my + n = 0$

or $$lx + my = -n \qquad \text{...(ii)}$$

Now, Eqs. (i) and (ii) represent the same line, so comparing them, we get

$$\frac{\cos\left(\frac{\pi}{4} + \phi\right)}{la} = \frac{\sin\left(\frac{\pi}{4} + \phi\right)}{mb} = -\frac{1}{n\sqrt{2}}$$

$$\therefore \quad \cos\left(\frac{\pi}{4} + \phi\right) = -\frac{la}{n\sqrt{2}} \qquad \text{...(iii)}$$

and $$\sin\left(\frac{\pi}{4} + \phi\right) = -\frac{mb}{n\sqrt{2}} \qquad \text{...(iv)}$$

Squaring and adding Eqs. (iii) and (iv), then

$$\frac{l^2a^2}{2n^2} + \frac{m^2b^2}{2n^2} = 1$$

$$l^2a^2 + m^2b^2 = 2n^2$$

Example 10 If a chord joining two points whose eccentric angles are α, β cut the major axis of an ellipse at a distance d from the centre. Show that $\tan(\alpha/2)\tan(\beta/2) = (d - a)/(d + a)$, where $2a$ is the length of major axis.

Sol. Let the equation of the ellipse be

$$\frac{x^2}{a^2}+\frac{y^2}{b^2}=1 \quad \text{...(i)}$$

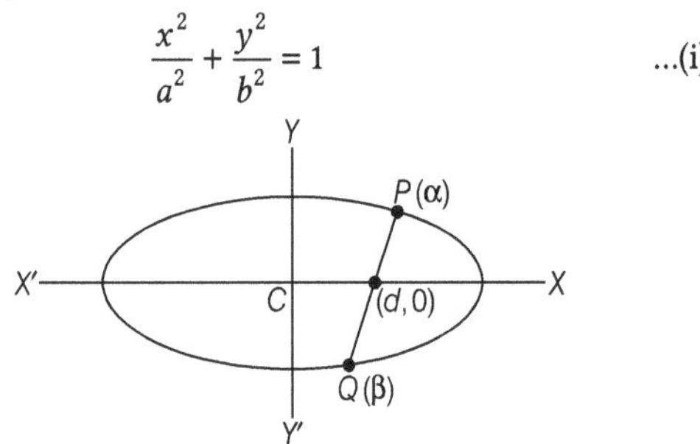

The equation of the line joining 'α' and 'β' on the ellipse Eq. (i) is

$$\frac{x}{a}\cos\left(\frac{\alpha+\beta}{2}\right)+\frac{y}{b}\sin\left(\frac{\alpha+\beta}{2}\right)=\cos\left(\frac{\alpha-\beta}{2}\right) \quad \text{...(ii)}$$

Since, it cuts the major axis of the ellipse at a distance d from the centre i.e. passes through the point $(d, 0)$, then

$$\frac{d}{a}\cos\left(\frac{\alpha+\beta}{2}\right)+0=\cos\left(\frac{\alpha-\beta}{2}\right)$$

or $$\frac{d}{a}=\frac{\cos\left(\frac{\alpha-\beta}{2}\right)}{\cos\left(\frac{\alpha+\beta}{2}\right)}$$

or $$\frac{d-a}{d+a}=\frac{\cos\left(\frac{\alpha-\beta}{2}\right)-\cos\left(\frac{\alpha+\beta}{2}\right)}{\cos\left(\frac{\alpha-\beta}{2}\right)+\cos\left(\frac{\alpha+\beta}{2}\right)}$$

(By componendo and dividendo)

$$=\frac{2\sin(\alpha/2)\sin(\beta/2)}{2\cos(\alpha/2)\cos(\beta/2)}$$

$$=\tan(\alpha/2)\tan(\beta/2)$$

$$\therefore \quad \tan(\alpha/2)\tan(\beta/2)=\frac{d-a}{d+a}$$

Example 11 If the angle between the straight lines joining foci and the ends of the minor axis of the ellipse $\frac{x^2}{a^2}+\frac{y^2}{b^2}=1$, is $90°$. Find its eccentricity.

Sol. The equation of the ellipse is $\frac{x^2}{a^2}+\frac{y^2}{b^2}=1$

Let $a > b$

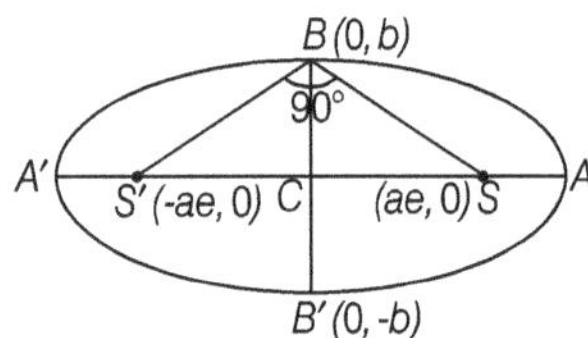

∴ The ends of minor axis are $B(0, b)$ and $B'(0, -b)$. If the eccentricity of the ellipse is e, then the foci are $S(ae, 0)$ and $S'(-ae, 0)$

$$\therefore \quad \text{Slope of } BS \text{ is } m_1=\frac{b-0}{0-ae}=-\frac{b}{ae}$$

and slope of BS' is $$m_2=\frac{b-0}{0+ae}=\frac{b}{ae}$$

∵ The angle between BS and BS' is 90°,

$$\therefore \quad m_1m_2=-1$$

$$\Rightarrow \quad -\frac{b}{ae}\times\frac{b}{ae}=-1$$

$$\Rightarrow \quad b^2=a^2e^2$$

$$a^2(1-e^2)=a^2e^2$$

$$\Rightarrow \quad 1-e^2=e^2$$

$$\Rightarrow \quad 2e^2=1$$

$$\therefore \quad e=\frac{1}{\sqrt{2}}$$

Example 12 Find the equation of the ellipse referred to its centre whose minor axis is equal to the distance between the foci and whose latusrectum is 10.

Sol. Let the equation of the ellipse is

$$\frac{x^2}{a^2}+\frac{y^2}{b^2}=1 \quad (\text{let } a > b)$$

Then, the foci are $S(ae, 0)$ and $S'(-ae, 0)$, length of minor axis $BB'=2b$ and length of latusrectum $=\frac{2b^2}{a}$

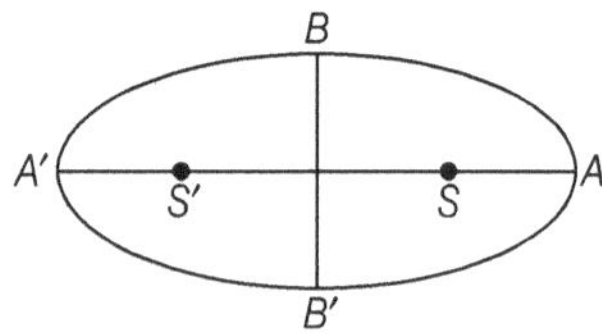

∴ According to the question

$$BB'=SS' \Rightarrow 2b=2ae$$

$$\Rightarrow \quad b=ae \quad \text{...(i)}$$

and $$\frac{2b^2}{a}=10$$

$$\Rightarrow \quad b^2=5a \quad \text{...(ii)}$$

also we have $b^2=a^2(1-e^2)$ ...(iii)

Putting the value of b from Eq. (i) in Eq. (iii), we have

$$a^2e^2=a^2(1-e^2)$$

$$\Rightarrow \quad e^2=1-e^2$$

$$\Rightarrow \quad 2e^2=1$$

$$\therefore \quad e=\frac{1}{\sqrt{2}}$$

From Eq. (i), we have

$$b=\frac{a}{\sqrt{2}}$$

$$\therefore \quad b^2=\frac{a^2}{2}$$

$$\Rightarrow \qquad 5a = \frac{a^2}{2} \qquad \text{[from Eq. (ii)]}$$

$$\Rightarrow \qquad a = 10$$

From Eq. (ii)

$$b^2 = 5 \times 10 = 50$$

Putting the values of a and b in $\frac{x^2}{a^2} + \frac{y^2}{b^2} = 1$, the equation of required ellipse is

$$\frac{x^2}{100} + \frac{y^2}{50} = 1$$

$$x^2 + 2y^2 = 100$$

Example 13 Prove that the ratio of area of any triangle PQR inscribed in the ellipse $\frac{x^2}{a^2} + \frac{y^2}{b^2} = 1$ and that of triangle formed by the corresponding points on the auxiliary circle is $\frac{b}{a}$.

Sol. Let the three points on the ellipse be $P(a\cos\alpha, b\sin\alpha)$, $Q(a\cos\beta, b\sin\beta)$ and $R(a\cos\gamma, b\sin\gamma)$.

Then, the corresponding points on the auxiliary circle are $A(a\cos\alpha, a\sin\alpha)$, $B(a\cos\beta, a\sin\beta)$ and $C(a\cos\gamma, a\sin\gamma)$, then

$$\frac{\text{Area of } \Delta PQR}{\text{Area of } \Delta ABC} = \frac{\frac{1}{2}\begin{vmatrix} a\cos\alpha & b\sin\alpha & 1 \\ a\cos\beta & b\sin\beta & 1 \\ a\cos\gamma & b\sin\gamma & 1 \end{vmatrix}}{\frac{1}{2}\begin{vmatrix} a\cos\alpha & a\sin\alpha & 1 \\ a\cos\beta & a\sin\beta & 1 \\ a\cos\gamma & a\sin\gamma & 1 \end{vmatrix}}$$

$$= \frac{ab\begin{vmatrix} \cos\alpha & \sin\alpha & 1 \\ \cos\beta & \sin\beta & 1 \\ \cos\gamma & \sin\gamma & 1 \end{vmatrix}}{a^2\begin{vmatrix} \cos\alpha & \sin\alpha & 1 \\ \cos\beta & \sin\beta & 1 \\ \cos\gamma & \sin\gamma & 1 \end{vmatrix}}$$

$$= \frac{b}{a}$$

Example 14 The extremities of a line segment of length l move in two fixed perpendicular straight lines. Find the locus of that point which divides this line segment in ratio 1 : 2.

Sol. Let $PA : PB = 1 : 2$

$$PA = \frac{l}{3} \quad \text{and} \quad PB = \frac{2l}{3}$$

$$k = \frac{l}{3}\sin\theta$$

or $\qquad 3k = l\sin\theta \qquad$ ...(i)

and $\qquad h = \frac{2l}{3}\cos\theta$

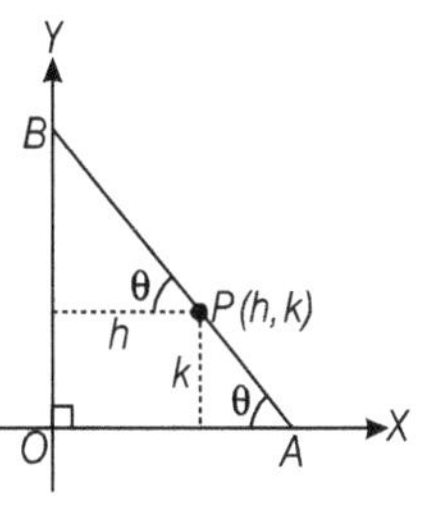

or $\qquad \frac{3h}{2} = l\cos\theta \qquad$ ...(ii)

Squaring and adding Eqs. (i) and (ii), then

$$9k^2 + \frac{9h^2}{4} = l^2$$

or $\qquad 9h^2 + 36k^2 = 4l^2$

$\therefore$ Locus of $P(h, k)$ is

$$9x^2 + 36y^2 = 4l^2$$

Aliter :

Let $A \equiv (a, 0)$ and $B \equiv (0, b)$

$\because \quad P(h, k)$ divide AB in the ratio $1 : 2$ (internally), then

$$h = \frac{1.0 + 2.a}{1 + 2} \Rightarrow a = \frac{3h}{2}$$

and $\qquad k = \frac{1.b + 2.0}{1 + 2} \Rightarrow b = 3k$

$\because \qquad a^2 + b^2 = l^2$

$\Rightarrow \qquad \frac{9h^2}{4} + 9k^2 = l^2$

or $\qquad 9h^2 + 36k^2 = 4l^2$

$\therefore$ Locus of $P(h, k)$ is

$$9x^2 + 36y^2 = 4l^2$$

Example 15 Find the lengths and equations of the focal radii drawn from the point $(4\sqrt{3}, 5)$ on the ellipse $25x^2 + 16y^2 = 1600$.

Sol. The equation of the ellipse is

$$25x^2 + 16y^2 = 1600$$

or $\qquad \frac{x^2}{64} + \frac{y^2}{100} = 1$

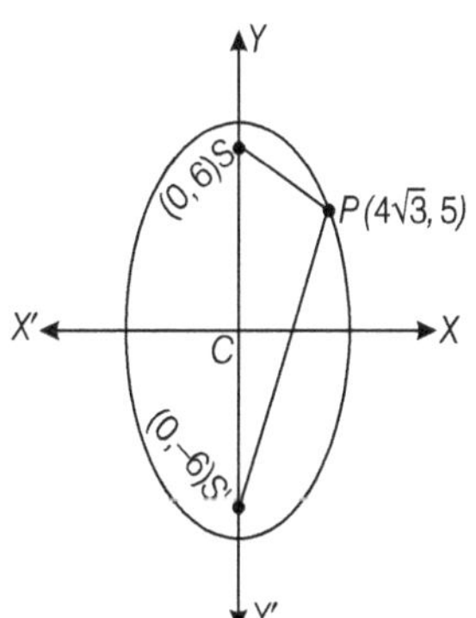

Here, $b > a$

$$a^2 = 64,\ b^2 = 100$$

$$a^2 = b^2(1 - e^2)$$

$$\therefore \quad 64 = 100(1 - e^2)$$

$$\Rightarrow \quad e = 3/5$$

Let $P(x_1, y_1) \equiv (4\sqrt{3}, 5)$

be a point on the ellipse, then SP and $S'P$ are the focal radii

$$\therefore \quad SP = b - ey_1 \text{ and } S'P = b + ey_1$$

$$\therefore \quad SP = 10 - \frac{3}{5} \times 5 \text{ and } S'P = 10 + \frac{3}{5} \times 5$$

$$\Rightarrow \quad SP = 7 \text{ and } S'P = 13$$

Also, S is $(0, be)$

i.e. $\left(0, 10 \times \frac{3}{5}\right)$ i.e. $(0, 6)$

and S' is $(0, -be)$

i.e. $\left(0, -10 \times \frac{3}{5}\right)$

i.e. $(0, -6)$

$\therefore$ Equation of SP is

$$y - 5 = \frac{6 - 5}{0 - 4\sqrt{3}}(x - 4\sqrt{3})$$

$$-4\sqrt{3}y + 20\sqrt{3} = x - 4\sqrt{3}$$

or $$x + 4\sqrt{3}y - 24\sqrt{3} = 0$$

and equation of $S'P$ is

$$\therefore \quad y - 5 = \frac{-6 - 5}{0 - 4\sqrt{3}}(x - 4\sqrt{3})$$

$$\Rightarrow \quad -4\sqrt{3}y + 20\sqrt{3} = -11x + 44\sqrt{3}$$

or $$11x - 4\sqrt{3}y - 24\sqrt{3} = 0$$

Exercise for Session 1

1. The length of the major axis of the ellipse $\frac{x^2}{a^2} + \frac{y^2}{b^2} = 1$, is three times the length of minor axis, it eccentricity is

(a) $\frac{1}{\sqrt{2}}$ (b) $\frac{1}{\sqrt{3}}$ (c) $\frac{2\sqrt{2}}{3}$ (d) $\frac{2\sqrt{2}}{5}$

2. The equation $\frac{x^2}{10 - a} + \frac{y^2}{4 - a} = 1$, represents an ellipse, if

(a) $a < 4$ (b) $a > 4$ (c) $4 < a < 10$ (d) $a > 10$

3. The eccentricity of an ellipse $\frac{x^2}{a^2} + \frac{y^2}{b^2} = 1$, whose latusrectum is half of its major axis, is

(a) $\frac{1}{\sqrt{3}}$ (b) $\frac{1}{\sqrt{2}}$ (c) $\frac{\sqrt{3}}{2}$ (d) $\sqrt{\left(\frac{2}{3}\right)}$

4. If the eccentricity of an ellipse is $\frac{1}{\sqrt{2}}$, then its latusrectum is equal to its

(a) minor axis (b) semi minor axis (c) major axis (d) semi major axis

5. If the distance between the foci of an ellipse is equal to its minor axis, then its eccentricity is

(a) $\frac{1}{2}$ (b) $\frac{1}{\sqrt{2}}$ (c) $\frac{1}{3}$ (d) $\frac{1}{\sqrt{3}}$

6. The eccentric angle of a point on the ellipse $\frac{x^2}{6} + \frac{y^2}{2} = 1$, whose distance from the centre of ellipse is 2, is

(a) $-\frac{\pi}{4}$ (b) $\frac{\pi}{4}$ (c) $\frac{3\pi}{2}$ (d) $\frac{5\pi}{3}$

7. If $\tan\alpha \tan\beta = -\frac{a^2}{b^2}$, then the chord joining two points α and β on the ellipse $\frac{x^2}{a^2} + \frac{y^2}{b^2} = 1$, will subtend a right angle at

(a) focus (b) centre (c) end of major axis (d) end of minor axis

8. If the eccentricity of the two ellipses $\frac{x^2}{169}+\frac{y^2}{25}=1$ and $\frac{x^2}{a^2}+\frac{y^2}{b^2}=1$ are equal, then the value of a/b is

(a) $\frac{5}{13}$ (b) $\frac{6}{13}$

(c) $\frac{13}{5}$ (d) $\frac{13}{6}$

9. The ratio of the areas of triangle inscribed in ellipse $\frac{x^2}{a^2}+\frac{y^2}{b^2}=1$, to that of triangle formed by the corresponding points on the auxiliary circle is $\frac{1}{2}$, then the eccentricity of the ellipse is

(a) $\frac{1}{2}$ (b) $\frac{\sqrt{3}}{2}$

(c) $\frac{1}{\sqrt{2}}$ (d) $\frac{1}{\sqrt{3}}$

10. If PSQ is a focal chord of the ellipse $16x^2+25y^2=400$ such that $SP=16$, then the length SQ is

(a) $\frac{2}{9}$ (b) $\frac{4}{9}$

(c) $\frac{8}{9}$ (d) $\frac{16}{9}$

11. Let P be a variable point on the ellipse $\frac{x^2}{25}+\frac{y^2}{16}=1$ with foci at S and S'. If A be the area of triangle PSS', then the maximum value of A is

(a) 12 sq units (b) 24 sq units

(c) 36 sq units (d) 48 sq units

12. If S and S' are the foci of an ellipse of major axis of length 10 units and P is any point on the ellipse such that the perimeter of triangle PSS' is 15 units, then the eccentricity of the ellipse is

(a) $\frac{1}{2}$ (b) $\frac{1}{4}$

(c) $\frac{7}{25}$ (d) $\frac{3}{4}$

13. Find the latusrectum, eccentricity, coordinates of the foci, coordinates of the vertices, the length of the axes and the centre of the ellipse

$4x^2+9y^2-8x-36y+4=0$

14. The distance between the foci of an ellipse is 10 and its latusrectum is 15 ; find its equation referred to its axes as axes of coordinates.

15. Find the equation of the ellipse whose axes are parallel to the coordinate axes having its centre at the point $(2,-3)$ one focus at $(3,-3)$ and one vertex at $(4,-3)$.

16. Find the equation of the ellipse whose foci are $(2,3)$, $(-2,3)$ and whose semi-minor axes is $\sqrt{5}$.

17. Show that the equation $(10x-5)^2+(10y-5)^2=(3x+4y-1)^2$ represents an ellipse, find the eccentricity of the ellipse.

18. Find the locus of the extremities of the latusrectum of the family of ellipses $b^2x^2+y^2=a^2b^2$ having a given major axes.

Session 2

Position of a Point with Respect to an Ellipse, Intersection of a Line and an Ellipse, Equation of Tangent in Different Forms, Equations of Normals in Different Forms, Properties of Eccentric Angles of the Co-normal Points, Co-normal Points Lie on a Fixed Curve

Position of a Point with Respect to an Ellipse

Theorem : Prove that the point $P(x_1, y_1)$ lies outside, on, or inside the ellipse $\frac{x^2}{a^2}+\frac{y^2}{b^2}=1$ according as

$$\frac{x_1^2}{a^2}+\frac{y_1^2}{b^2}-1 >, = \text{or}, < 0$$

Proof : From point $P(x_1, y_1)$ draw perpendicular PM on AA' to meet the ellipse at $Q(x_1, y_2)$.

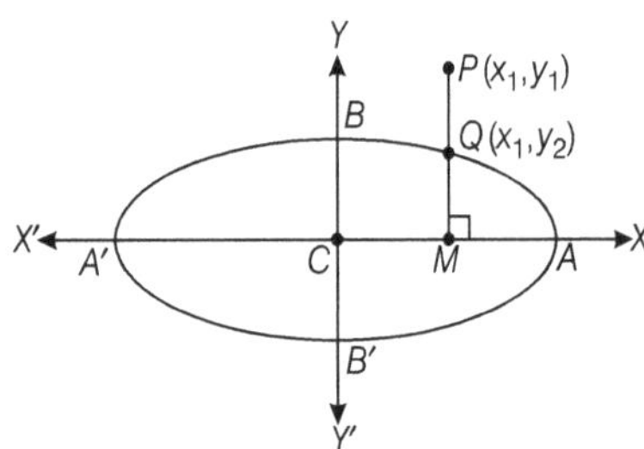

Since, $Q(x_1, y_2)$ lies on the ellipse

$$\frac{x^2}{a^2}+\frac{y^2}{b^2}=1$$

then, $$\frac{x_1^2}{a^2}+\frac{y_2^2}{b^2}=1$$

$$\Rightarrow \quad \frac{y_2^2}{b^2}=1-\frac{x_1^2}{a^2} \quad \text{...(i)}$$

Now, point P lies outside, on or inside the ellipse according as

$$PM >, = \text{or}, < QM$$

$$\Rightarrow \quad y_1 >, = \text{or}, < y_2$$

$$\Rightarrow \quad \frac{y_1^2}{b^2} >, = \text{or}, < \frac{y_2^2}{b^2}$$

$$\Rightarrow \quad \frac{y_1^2}{b^2} >, = \text{or}, < 1-\frac{x_1^2}{a^2} \quad \text{[from Eq. (i)]}$$

$$\Rightarrow \quad \frac{x_1^2}{a^2}+\frac{y_1^2}{b^2} >, = \text{or}, < 1,$$

or $$\frac{x_1^2}{a^2}+\frac{y_1^2}{b^2}-1 >, = \text{or}, < 0$$

Hence, the point $P(x_1, y_1)$ lies outside, on or inside the ellipse $\frac{x^2}{a^2}+\frac{y^2}{b^2}=1$ according as

$$\frac{x_1^2}{a^2}+\frac{y_1^2}{b^2}-1 > 0, = \text{or}, < 0$$

Remark

Let $S=\frac{x^2}{a^2}+\frac{y^2}{b^2}-1$, then $S_1=\frac{x_1^2}{a^2}+\frac{y_1^2}{b^2}-1$

The point (x_1, y_1) lies outside, on or inside the ellipse $S=0$ according as $S_1 >, = \text{or} < 0$.

Example 16 Find the position of the point $(4, -3)$ relative to the ellipse $5x^2+7y^2=140$.

Sol. The given ellipse can be written as $\frac{x^2}{28}+\frac{y^2}{20}-1=0$

Let $$S=\frac{x^2}{28}+\frac{y^2}{20}-1$$

$$\therefore \quad S_1=\frac{(4)^2}{28}+\frac{(-3)^2}{20}-1=\frac{3}{140}>0$$

So, the point $(4, -3)$ lies outside the ellipse $5x^2 + 7y^2 = 140$.

Example 17 Find the integral value of α for which the point $\left(7 - \frac{5\alpha}{4}, -\alpha\right)$ lies inside the ellipse $\frac{x^2}{25} + \frac{y^2}{16} = 1$.

Sol. Since, the point $\left(7 - \frac{5\alpha}{4}, -\alpha\right)$ lies inside the ellipse

$\frac{x^2}{25} + \frac{y^2}{16} = 1$, then $\frac{1}{25}\left(7 - \frac{5\alpha}{4}\right)^2 + \frac{1}{16}(-\alpha)^2 - 1 < 0$

$$\Rightarrow \quad (28 - 5\alpha)^2 + 25\alpha^2 - 400 < 0$$

$$\Rightarrow \quad 50\alpha^2 - 280\alpha + 384 < 0$$

$$\Rightarrow \quad 25\alpha^2 - 140\alpha + 192 < 0$$

$$\Rightarrow \quad (5\alpha - 12)(5\alpha - 16) < 0$$

$$\therefore \quad \frac{12}{5} < \alpha < \frac{16}{5}$$

Hence, integral value of α is 3

Intersection of a Line and an Ellipse

Let the ellipse be $\frac{x^2}{a^2} + \frac{y^2}{b^2} = 1$ ...(i)

and the given line be $y = mx + c$ ...(ii)

Eliminating y from Eqs. (i) and (ii), then

$$\frac{x^2}{a^2} + \frac{(mx + c)^2}{b^2} = 1$$

$$\Rightarrow \quad (a^2m^2 + b^2)x^2 + 2mca^2x + c^2a^2 - a^2b^2 = 0 \quad \text{...(iii)}$$

Above equation being a quadratic in x gives two values of x. Shows that every straight line will cut the ellipse in two points may be real, coincident or imaginary according as

Discriminant of Eq. (iii) $>, =, < 0$

i.e. $\quad 4m^2c^2a^4 - 4(a^2m^2 + b^2)(c^2a^2 - a^2b^2) >, =, < 0$

or $\quad -a^2b^2c^2 + a^4b^2m^2 + a^2b^4 >, =, < 0$

or $\quad a^2m^2 + b^2 >, =, < c^2$ ...(iv)

Condition of Tangency : If the line Eq. (ii) touches the ellipse Eq. (i), then Eq. (iii) has equal roots.

$\therefore$ Discriminant of Eq. (iii) $= 0$

$$\Rightarrow \quad c^2 = a^2m^2 + b^2 \quad \text{or} \quad c = \pm\sqrt{(a^2m^2 + b^2)} \quad \text{...(v)}$$

so, the line $y = mx + c$ touches the ellipse

$$\frac{x^2}{a^2} + \frac{y^2}{b^2} = 1 \quad \text{if} \quad c^2 = a^2m^2 + b^2$$

(which is condition of tangency)

Substituting the value of c from Eq. (v) in Eq. (ii), then

$$y = mx \pm \sqrt{(a^2m^2 + b^2)}$$

Hence, the lines $y = mx \pm \sqrt{(a^2m^2 + b^2)}$ will always tangents to the ellipse.

Point of contact : Substituting $c = \pm\sqrt{(a^2m^2 + b^2)}$ in Eq. (iii), then

$$(a^2m^2 + b^2)x^2 \pm 2ma^2x\sqrt{(a^2m^2 + b^2)} + (a^2m^2 + b^2)a^2 - a^2b^2 = 0$$

or $\quad (a^2m^2 + b^2)x^2 \pm 2ma^2x\sqrt{(a^2m^2 + b^2)} + a^4m^2 = 0$

or $\quad (x\sqrt{(a^2m^2 + b^2)} \pm a^2m)^2 = 0$

$$\therefore \quad x = \pm\frac{a^2m}{\sqrt{(a^2m^2 + b^2)}} = \pm\frac{a^2m}{c}$$

From Eq. (i), $\quad \frac{a^4m^2}{c^2} \cdot \frac{1}{a^2} + \frac{y^2}{b^2} = 1$

$$\Rightarrow \quad \frac{y^2}{b^2} = 1 - \frac{a^2m^2}{c^2} = \frac{c^2 - a^2m^2}{c^2} = \frac{b^2}{c^2}$$

$$y = \pm\frac{b^2}{c}$$

Hence, the point of contact is $\left(\pm\frac{a^2m}{c}, \pm\frac{b^2}{c}\right)$ this known as m-point on the ellipse.

Remark

If $m = 0$, then Eq. (iii) gives $b^2x^2 + c^2a^2 - a^2b^2 = 0$

or $\quad b^2x^2 + (a^2m^2 + b^2)a^2 - a^2b^2 = 0$

$$\therefore \quad x = \pm\frac{a^2m}{b}$$

which gives two values of x.

Example 18 Prove that the straight line $lx + my + n = 0$ touches the ellipse $\frac{x^2}{a^2} + \frac{y^2}{b^2} = 1$ if $a^2l^2 + b^2m^2 = n^2$.

Sol. The given line is

$$lx + my + n = 0$$

or $\quad y = -\frac{l}{m}x - \frac{n}{m}$ ...(i)

Comparing this line with $y = Mx + c$

$$\therefore \quad M = -\frac{l}{m} \quad \text{and} \quad c = -\frac{n}{m}$$

The line Eq. (i) will touch the ellipse $\frac{x^2}{a^2}+\frac{y^2}{b^2}=1$ if

$$c^2 = a^2M^2 + b^2$$

$$\frac{n^2}{m^2} = \frac{a^2l^2}{m^2} + b^2$$

$$a^2l^2 + b^2m^2 = n^2$$

Example 19 Show that the line $x\cos\alpha + y\sin\alpha = p$ touches the ellipse $\frac{x^2}{a^2}+\frac{y^2}{b^2}=1$ if $a^2\cos^2\alpha + b^2\sin^2\alpha = p^2$ and that point of contact is $\left(\frac{a^2\cos\alpha}{p}, \frac{b^2\sin\alpha}{p}\right)$.

Sol. The given line is $x\cos\alpha + y\sin\alpha = p$

$$y = -x\cot\alpha + p\operatorname{cosec}\alpha$$

Comparing this line with $y = mx + c$

$\therefore$ $m = -\cot\alpha$ and $c = p\operatorname{cosec}\alpha$

Hence, the given line touches the ellipse, then

$$c^2 = a^2m^2 + b^2$$

$\Rightarrow$ $p^2\operatorname{cosec}^2\alpha = a^2\cot^2\alpha + b^2$

$\Rightarrow$ $p^2 = a^2\cos^2\alpha + b^2\sin^2\alpha$

and point of contact is $\left(-\frac{a^2m}{c}, \frac{b^2}{c}\right)$

i.e. $\left(-\frac{a^2(-\cot\alpha)}{p\operatorname{cosec}\alpha}, \frac{b^2}{p\operatorname{cosec}\alpha}\right)$

i.e. $\left(\frac{a^2\cos\alpha}{p}, \frac{b^2\sin\alpha}{p}\right)$

Example 20 For what value of λ does the line $y = x + \lambda$ touches the ellipse $9x^2 + 16y^2 = 144$.

Sol. $\because$ Equation of ellipse is

$$9x^2 + 16y^2 = 144 \quad \text{or} \quad \frac{x^2}{16}+\frac{y^2}{9}=1$$

Comparing this with $\frac{x^2}{a^2}+\frac{y^2}{b^2}=1$

then, we get $a^2 = 16$ and $b^2 = 9$

and comparing the line $y = x + \lambda$ with $y = mx + c$

$\therefore$ $m = 1$

and $c = \lambda$

If the line $y = x + \lambda$ touches the ellipse

$$9x^2 + 16y^2 = 144$$

then $c^2 = a^2m^2 + b^2$

$\Rightarrow$ $\lambda^2 = 16 \times 1^2 + 9$

$\rightarrow$ $\lambda^2 - 25$

$\therefore$ $\lambda = \pm 5$

Equation of Tangent in Different Forms

1. Point Form

Theorem : The equation of tangent to the ellipse $\frac{x^2}{a^2}+\frac{y^2}{b^2}=1$ at the point (x_1, y_1) is $\frac{xx_1}{a^2}+\frac{yy_1}{b^2}=1$

Proof : (By first Principal Method)

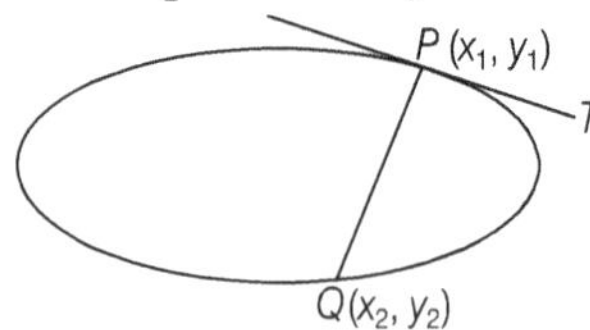

$\because$ Equation of ellipse is $\frac{x^2}{a^2}+\frac{y^2}{b^2}=1$ ...(i)

Let $P \equiv (x_1, y_1)$ and $Q \equiv (x_2, y_2)$ be any two point on Eq. (i), then

$$\frac{x_1^2}{a^2}+\frac{y_1^2}{b^2}=1 \quad \text{...(ii)}$$

and

$$\frac{x_2^2}{a^2}+\frac{y_2^2}{b^2}=1 \quad \text{...(iii)}$$

Subtracting Eqs. (ii) from (iii), then

$$\frac{1}{a^2}(x_2^2 - x_1^2) + \frac{1}{b^2}(y_2^2 - y_1^2) = 0$$

$$\Rightarrow \frac{(x_2+x_1)(x_2-x_1)}{a^2} + \frac{(y_2+y_1)(y_2-y_1)}{b^2} = 0$$

$$\Rightarrow \frac{y_2-y_1}{x_2-x_1} = -\frac{b^2(x_1+x_2)}{a^2(y_1+y_2)} \quad \text{...(iv)}$$

Equation of PQ is

$$y - y_1 = \frac{y_2-y_1}{x_2-x_1}(x - x_1) \quad \text{...(v)}$$

From Eqs. (iv) and (v), then

$$y - y_1 = -\frac{b^2(x_1+x_2)}{a^2(y_1+y_2)}(x - x_1) \quad \text{...(vi)}$$

Now, for tangent at $P, Q \to P$ i.e., $x_2 \to x_1$ and $y_2 \to y_1$, then Eq. (vi) becomes

$$y - y_1 = -\frac{b^2(2x_1)}{a^2(2y_1)}(x - x_1)$$

or

$$\frac{yy_1 - y_1^2}{b^2} = -\left(\frac{xx_1 - x_1^2}{a^2}\right)$$

or

$$\frac{xx_1}{a^2}+\frac{yy_1}{b^2} = \frac{x_1^2}{a^2}+\frac{y_1^2}{b^2} \text{ or } \frac{xx_1}{a^2}+\frac{yy_1}{b^2} = 1 \quad \text{[from (ii)]}$$

which is required equation of tangent at (x_1, y_1).

Remark

The equation of tangent at (x_1, y_1) can be obtained by replacing x^2 by xx_1, y^2 by yy_1, x by $\frac{x+x_1}{2}$, y by $\frac{y+y_1}{2}$ and xy by $\frac{xy_1+x_1y}{2}$.

This method is applicable only when the equation of ellipse is a polynomial of second degree in x and y.

2. Parametric form

Theorem : The equation of tangent to the ellipse $\frac{x^2}{a^2}+\frac{y^2}{b^2}=1$ at the point $(a\cos\phi, b\sin\phi)$ is

$$\frac{x}{a}\cos\phi+\frac{y}{b}\sin\phi=1$$

Proof : The equation of tangent to the ellipse $\frac{x^2}{a^2}+\frac{y^2}{b^2}=1$ at the point (x_1, y_1) is $\frac{xx_1}{a^2}+\frac{yy_1}{b^2}=1$ (by point form)

Replacing x_1 by $a\cos\phi$ and y_1 by $b\sin\phi$, then we get

$$\frac{x}{a}\cos\phi+\frac{y}{b}\sin\phi=1$$

Remark

Point of intersection of tangent at 'θ' and 'ϕ' on the ellipse $\frac{x^2}{a^2}+\frac{y^2}{b^2}=1$ is $\left(\frac{a\cos\left(\frac{\theta+\phi}{2}\right)}{\cos\left(\frac{\theta-\phi}{2}\right)}, \frac{b\sin\left(\frac{\theta+\phi}{2}\right)}{\cos\left(\frac{\theta-\phi}{2}\right)}\right)$

Remembering method : $\because$ Equation of chord joining $(a\cos\theta, b\sin\theta)$ and $(a\cos\phi, b\sin\phi)$ is

$$\frac{x}{a}\cos\left(\frac{\theta+\phi}{2}\right)+\frac{y}{b}\sin\left(\frac{\theta+\phi}{2}\right)=\cos\left(\frac{\theta-\phi}{2}\right)$$

$$\Rightarrow \quad \frac{x}{a}\left\{\frac{\cos\left(\frac{\theta+\phi}{2}\right)}{\cos\left(\frac{\theta-\phi}{2}\right)}\right\}+\frac{y}{b}\left\{\frac{\sin\left(\frac{\theta+\phi}{2}\right)}{\cos\left(\frac{\theta-\phi}{2}\right)}\right\}=1$$

$$\text{or} \quad \frac{x}{a^2}\left\{\frac{a\cos\left(\frac{\theta+\phi}{2}\right)}{\cos\left(\frac{\theta-\phi}{2}\right)}\right\}+\frac{y}{b^2}\left\{\frac{b\sin\left(\frac{\theta+\phi}{2}\right)}{\cos\left(\frac{\theta-\phi}{2}\right)}\right\}=1$$

3. Slope form

Theorem : The equations of tangents of slope m to ellipse $\frac{x^2}{a^2}+\frac{y^2}{b^2}=1$ are $y=mx\pm\sqrt{(a^2m^2+b^2)}$ and the coordinates of the points of contact are

$$\left(\mp\frac{a^2m}{\sqrt{(a^2m^2+b^2)}}, \pm\frac{b^2}{\sqrt{(a^2m^2+b^2)}}\right)$$

Proof : Let $y=mx+c$ be a tangent to the ellipse

$$\frac{x^2}{a^2}+\frac{y^2}{b^2}=1.$$

Then the equation $\frac{x^2}{a^2}+\frac{(mx+c)^2}{b^2}=1$

$$\Rightarrow \quad x^2(a^2m^2+b^2)+2a^2mcx+a^2(c^2-b^2)=0 \quad \text{...(i)}$$

must have equal roots

$$4a^4m^2c^2-4(a^2m^2+b^2)a^2(c^2-b^2)=0$$

$$\{\because B^2-4AC=0\}$$

$$\Rightarrow \quad a^2m^2c^2-(a^2m^2+b^2)(c^2-b^2)=0$$

$$\Rightarrow \quad a^2m^2c^2-a^2m^2c^2+a^2b^2m^2-b^2c^2+b^4=0$$

$$\Rightarrow \quad a^2b^2m^2-b^2c^2+b^4=0$$

$$\Rightarrow \quad c^2=a^2m^2+b^2$$

$$\therefore \quad c=\pm\sqrt{(a^2m^2+b^2)}$$

Substituting this value of c in $y=mx+c$, we get

$$y=mx\pm\sqrt{(a^2m^2+b^2)}$$

as the required equations of tangent of ellipse in terms of slope, putting $c=\pm\sqrt{(a^2m^2+b^2)}$ in (i), we get

$$x^2(a^2m^2+b^2)\pm2a^2m\sqrt{(a^2m^2+b^2)}\,x+a^4m^2=0$$

$$\Rightarrow \quad (\sqrt{(a^2m^2+b^2)}\,x\pm a^2m)^2=0$$

$$\Rightarrow \quad x=\mp\frac{a^2m}{\sqrt{(a^2m^2+b^2)}}$$

Substituting this value of x in

$$y=mx\pm\sqrt{a^2m^2+b^2}$$

we obtained $\quad y=\pm\frac{b^2}{\sqrt{(a^2m^2+b^2)}}$

Thus, the coordinates of the points of contact are

$$\left(\mp\frac{a^2m}{\sqrt{(a^2m^2+b^2)}}, \pm\frac{b^2}{\sqrt{(a^2m^2+b^2)}}\right)$$

Example 21 If the line $3x+4y=\sqrt{7}$ touches the ellipse $3x^2+4y^2=1$, then find the point of contact.

Sol. Let the given line touches the ellipse at point $P(x_1, y_1)$.

The equation of tangent at P is

$$3xx_1+4yy_1=1 \quad \text{...(i)}$$

Comparing Eq. (i) with the given equation of line $3x + 4y = \sqrt{7}$, we get

$$\frac{3x_1}{3} = \frac{4y_1}{4} = \frac{1}{\sqrt{7}}$$

$$\therefore \quad x_1 = y_1 = \frac{1}{\sqrt{7}}$$

Hence, point of contact (x_1, y_1) is $\left(\frac{1}{\sqrt{7}}, \frac{1}{\sqrt{7}}\right)$.

Example 22 Find the equations of the tangents to the ellipse $3x^2 + 4y^2 = 12$ which are perpendicular to the line $y + 2x = 4$.

Sol. Let m be the slope of the tangent, since the tangent is perpendicular to the line $y + 2x = 4$.

$$\therefore \quad m \times -2 = -1$$

$$\Rightarrow \quad m = \frac{1}{2}$$

Since $3x^2 + 4y^2 = 12$

or $\frac{x^2}{4} + \frac{y^2}{3} = 1$

Comparing this with $\frac{x^2}{a^2} + \frac{y^2}{b^2} = 1$

$\therefore \quad a^2 = 4$

and $\quad b^2 = 3$

So the equations of the tangents are

$$y = \frac{1}{2}x \pm \sqrt{4 \times \frac{1}{4} + 3}$$

$$\Rightarrow \quad y = \frac{1}{2}x \pm 2$$

or $\quad x - 2y \pm 4 = 0$

Example 23 Find the locus of the foot of the perpendicular drawn from centre upon any tangent to the ellipse $\frac{x^2}{a^2} + \frac{y^2}{b^2} = 1$.

Sol. Any tangent of $\frac{x^2}{a^2} + \frac{y^2}{b^2} = 1$ is

$$y = mx + \sqrt{(a^2m^2 + b^2)} \quad \text{...(i)}$$

Equation of the line perpendicular to Eq. (i) and passing through (0, 0) is

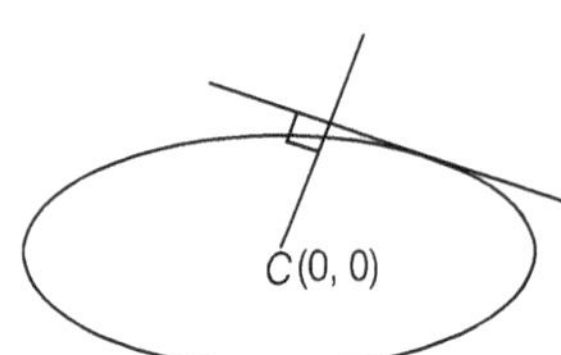

$$y = -\frac{1}{m}x \text{ or } m = -\frac{x}{y} \quad \text{...(ii)}$$

Substituting the value of m from Eq. (ii) in Eq. (i), then

$$y = -\frac{x^2}{y} + \sqrt{\left(a^2\frac{x^2}{y^2} + b^2\right)}$$

$$\Rightarrow \quad (x^2 + y^2)^2 = a^2x^2 + b^2y^2$$

or changing to polars by putting $x = r\cos\theta, y = r\sin\theta$ it becomes

$$r^2 = a^2\cos^2\theta + b^2\sin^2\theta$$

Example 24 Find the point on the ellipse $16x^2 + 11y^2 = 256$, where the common tangent to it and the circle $x^2 + y^2 - 2x = 15$ touch.

Sol. The given ellipse is $\frac{x^2}{16} + \frac{y^2}{(256/11)} = 1$

Equation of tangent to it at point $\left(4\cos\theta, \frac{16}{\sqrt{11}}\sin\theta\right)$ is

$$\frac{x}{4}\cos\theta + y\frac{\sqrt{11}}{16}\sin\theta = 1$$

It also touch the circle $(x-1)^2 + (y-0)^2 = 4^2$

Therefore,

$$\frac{\left|\frac{1}{4}\cos\theta - 1\right|}{\sqrt{\left(\frac{\cos^2\theta}{16} + \frac{11}{256}\sin^2\theta\right)}} = 4$$

$$\Rightarrow \quad |\cos\theta - 4| = \sqrt{(16\cos^2\theta + 11\sin^2\theta)}$$

or $\quad 4\cos^2\theta + 8\cos\theta - 5 = 0$

or $\quad (2\cos\theta - 1)(2\cos\theta + 5) = 0$

or $\quad \cos\theta = \frac{1}{2} \qquad \left(\because \cos\theta \neq -\frac{5}{2}\right)$

$$\therefore \quad \theta = \frac{\pi}{3}, \frac{5\pi}{3}$$

Therefore, points are $\left(2, \pm\frac{8\sqrt{3}}{11}\right)$.

Example 25 Find the maximum area of the ellipse $\frac{x^2}{a^2} + \frac{y^2}{b^2} = 1$ which touches the line $y = 3x + 2$.

Sol. $\because$ Line $y = 3x + 2$ touches ellipse $\frac{x^2}{a^2} + \frac{y^2}{b^2} = 1$

Here, $\quad m = 3$ and $c = 2$

Substituting in $c^2 = a^2m^2 + b^2$

or $\quad 4 = 9a^2 + b^2 \quad \text{...(i)}$

Now, $AM \geq GM$

$$\Rightarrow \quad \frac{9a^2 + b^2}{2} \geq \sqrt{(9a^2)\,b^2} \Rightarrow \frac{9a^2 + b^2}{2} \geq 3ab$$

$$\Rightarrow \quad 2 \geq 3ab \quad \text{[from Eq. (i)]}$$

or $$\frac{2\pi}{3} \geq \pi\, ab$$

or $$\frac{2\pi}{3} \geq \text{Area of ellipse}$$

Therefore, the maximum area of the ellipse is $\frac{2\pi}{3}$.

Example 26 A circle of radius r is concentric with the ellipse $\frac{x^2}{a^2} + \frac{y^2}{b^2} = 1$. Prove that the common tangent is inclined to the major axis at an angle $\tan^{-1}\sqrt{\left(\frac{r^2 - b^2}{a^2 - r^2}\right)}$.

Sol. Equation of the circle of radius r and concentric with ellipse $\frac{x^2}{a^2} + \frac{y^2}{b^2} = 1$ is

$$x^2 + y^2 = r^2 \quad \text{...(i)}$$

any tangent to ellipse $\frac{x^2}{a^2} + \frac{y^2}{b^2} = 1$ is

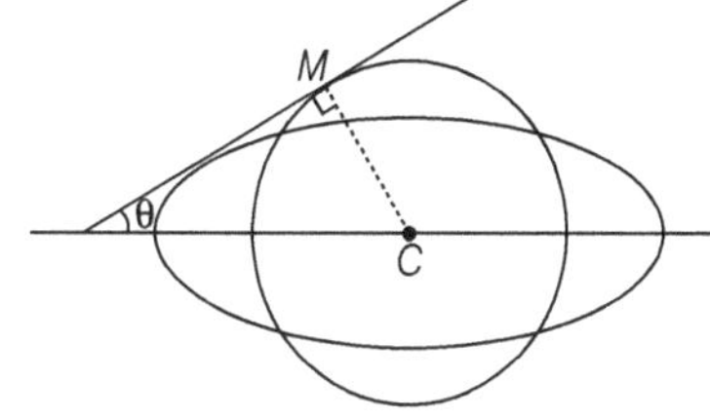

$$y = mx + \sqrt{(a^2m^2 + b^2)} \quad \text{(where } m = \tan\theta)$$

If it is a tangent to circle, then perpendicular from (0, 0) is equal to radius r,

$$\therefore \quad \frac{\sqrt{(a^2m^2 + b^2)}}{\sqrt{(m^2 + 1)}} = |r| \text{ or } a^2m^2 + b^2 = m^2r^2 + r^2$$

$$(a^2 - r^2)\,m^2 = r^2 - b^2$$

$$\therefore \quad m = \sqrt{\left(\frac{r^2 - b^2}{a^2 - r^2}\right)}$$

$$\tan\theta = \sqrt{\left(\frac{r^2 - b^2}{a^2 - r^2}\right)}$$

$$\theta = \tan^{-1}\sqrt{\left(\frac{r^2 - b^2}{a^2 - r^2}\right)}$$

Example 27 Show that the product of the perpendiculars from the foci of any tangent to an ellipse is equal to the square of the semi minor axis, and the feet of a these perpendiculars lie on the auxiliary circle.

Sol. Let equation of ellipse be

$$\frac{x^2}{a^2} + \frac{y^2}{b^2} = 1 \quad \text{... (i)}$$

Equation of any tangent in term of slope (m) of (i) is

$$y = mx + \sqrt{(a^2m^2 + b^2)}$$

or $$y - mx = \sqrt{a^2m^2 + b^2} \quad \text{...(ii)}$$

Equation of a line perpendicular to Eq. (ii) and passing through $S\,(ae, 0)$ is

$$y - 0 = -\frac{1}{m}(x - ae)$$

or $$x + my = ae \quad \text{...(iii)}$$

The lines Eq. (ii) and Eq. (iii) will meet at the foot of perpendicular whose locus is obtained by eliminating the variable m between Eq. (ii) and Eq. (iii), then squaring and adding Eq. (ii) and Eq. (iii), we get

$$(y - mx)^2 + (x + my)^2 = a^2m^2 + b^2 + a^2e^2$$

$$\Rightarrow \quad (1 + m^2)(x^2 + y^2) = a^2m^2 + b^2 + a^2 - b^2$$

$$\Rightarrow \quad (1 + m^2)(x^2 + y^2) = a^2\,(1 + m^2)$$

or $$x^2 + y^2 = a^2$$

which is auxiliary circle of ellipse, similarly we can show that the other foot drawn from second focus also lies on $x^2 + y^2 = a^2$.

Again if p_1 and p_2 be perpendiculars from foci $S(ae, 0)$ and $S'\,(-ae, 0)$ on (ii), then

$$p_1 = \frac{|\sqrt{(a^2m^2 + b^2)} + mae|}{\sqrt{(1 + m^2)}}$$

and $$p_2 = \frac{|\sqrt{(a^2m^2 + b^2)} - mae|}{\sqrt{(1 + m^2)}}$$

$$\therefore \quad p_1p_2 = \frac{|a^2m^2 + b^2 - a^2e^2m^2|}{(1 + m^2)}$$

$$= \frac{|a^2m^2 + b^2 - (a^2 - b^2)\,m^2|}{(1 + m^2)}$$

$$= \frac{b^2\,(1 + m^2)}{(1 + m^2)}$$

$$= b^2 = (\text{semi minor axis})^2$$

Example 28 Prove that the locus of mid-points of the portion of the tangents to the ellipse $\frac{x^2}{a^2}+\frac{y^2}{b^2}=1$ intercepted between the axes is $a^2y^2+b^2x^2=4x^2y^2$.

Sol. Let $P(x_1, y_1)$ be any point on the ellipse

$$\frac{x^2}{a^2}+\frac{y^2}{b^2}=1 \quad \text{...(i)}$$

$\therefore$ Equation of tangent at (x_1, y_1) to (i) is $\frac{xx_1}{a^2}+\frac{yy_1}{b^2}=1$

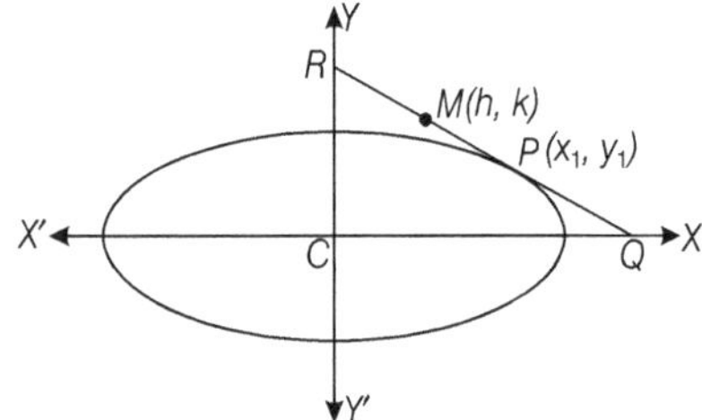

This meet the coordinate axes at

$$Q\left(\frac{a^2}{x_1}, 0\right) \text{ and } R\left(0, \frac{b^2}{y_1}\right)$$

Let $M(h, k)$ be the mid-point of QR then,

$$h=\frac{\frac{a^2}{x_1}+0}{2}, k=\frac{0+\frac{b^2}{y_1}}{2}$$

$$\Rightarrow \quad x_1=\frac{a^2}{2h}, y_1=\frac{b^2}{2k}$$

Since, (x_1, y_1) lies on Eq. (i)

$$\therefore \quad \frac{\left(\frac{a^2}{2h}\right)^2}{a^2}+\frac{\left(\frac{b^2}{2k}\right)^2}{b^2}=1$$

$$\Rightarrow \quad \frac{a^2}{4h^2}+\frac{b^2}{4k^2}=1$$

$$\Rightarrow \quad a^2k^2+b^2h^2=4h^2k^2$$

Hence, the locus of $M(h, k)$ is $a^2y^2+b^2x^2=4x^2y^2$

Example 29 Prove that the tangents at the extremities of latusrectum of an ellipse intersect on the corresponding directrix.

Sol. Let LSL' be a latusrectum of the ellipse $\frac{x^2}{a^2}+\frac{y^2}{b^2}=1$.

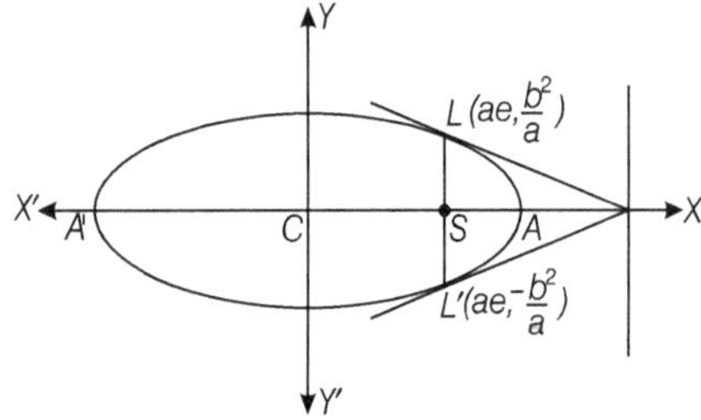

$\therefore$ The coordinates of L and L' are

$$\left(ae, \frac{b^2}{a}\right) \text{ and } \left(ae, -\frac{b^2}{a}\right) \text{ respectively}$$

$\therefore$ Equation of tangent at $L\left(ae, \frac{b^2}{a}\right)$ is

$$\Rightarrow \quad \frac{x(ae)}{a^2}+\frac{y\left(\frac{b^2}{a}\right)}{b^2}=1$$

$$\Rightarrow \quad xe+y=a \quad \text{...(i)}$$

The equation of the tangent at $L'\left(ae, -\frac{b^2}{a}\right)$ is

$$\frac{x(ae)}{a^2}+\frac{y\left(-\frac{b^2}{a}\right)}{b^2}=1$$

$$\Rightarrow \quad ex-y=a \quad \text{...(ii)}$$

Solving Eqs. (i) and (ii), we get

$$x=\frac{a}{e} \text{ and } y=0$$

Thus, the tangents at L and L' intersect at $(a/e, 0)$ which is a point lying on the corresponding directrix i.e. $x=\frac{a}{e}$.

Equations of Normals in Different Forms

1. Point form

Theorem : The equation of normal at (x_1, y_1) to the ellipse $\frac{x^2}{a^2}+\frac{y^2}{b^2}=1$ is

$$\frac{a^2x}{x_1}-\frac{b^2y}{y_1}=a^2-b^2$$

Proof : Since the equation of tangent to the ellipse $\frac{x^2}{a^2}+\frac{y^2}{b^2}=1$ at (x_1, y_1) is

$$\frac{xx_1}{a^2}+\frac{yy_1}{b^2}=1$$

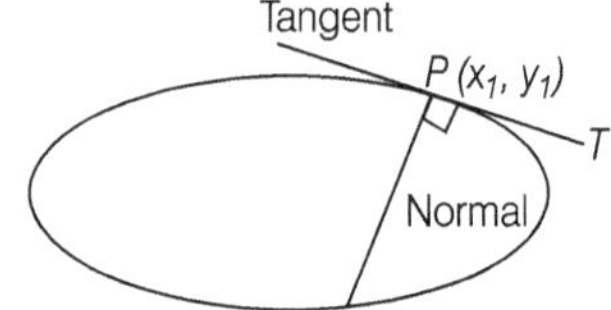

The slope of the tangent at $(x_1, y_1)=-\frac{b^2x_1}{a^2y_1}$

$\therefore$ Slope of Normals at $(x_1, y_1) = \dfrac{a^2 y_1}{b^2 x_1}$

Hence, the equation of normal at (x_1, y_1) is

$$y - y_1 = \frac{a^2 y_1}{b^2 x_1}(x - x_1)$$

or
$$\frac{a^2 x}{x_1} - \frac{b^2 y}{y_1} = a^2 - b^2$$

Remark

The equation of normal at (x_1, y_1) can also be obtained by this method

$$\frac{x - x_1}{a' x_1 + h y_1 + g} = \frac{y - y_1}{h x_1 + b' y_1 + f} \quad \text{...(i)}$$

a', b', g, f, h are obtained by comparing the given ellipse with

$$a' x^2 + 2hxy + b' y^2 + 2gx + 2fy + c = 0 \quad \text{...(ii)}$$

The denominors of (i) can easily remembered by the first two rows of this determinant

i.e.
$$\begin{vmatrix} a' & h & g \\ h & b' & f \\ g & f & c \end{vmatrix}$$

Since, first row, $a'(x_1) + h(y_1) + g(1)$

and second row, $h(x_1) + b'(y_1) + f(1)$

Here ellipse $\dfrac{x^2}{a^2} + \dfrac{y^2}{b^2} = 1$

or
$$\frac{x^2}{a^2} + \frac{y^2}{b^2} - 1 = 0 \quad \text{... (iii)}$$

Comparing Eqs. (ii) and (iii), then we get

$$a' = \frac{1}{a^2}, b' = \frac{1}{b^2}, g = 0, f = 0, h = 0$$

From, Eq. (i), equation of normal of Eq. (iii) at (x_1, y_1) is

$$\frac{x - x_1}{\frac{1}{a^2} x_1 + 0 + 0} = \frac{y - y_1}{0 + \frac{1}{b^2} y_1 + 0}$$

or
$$\frac{a^2 (x - x_1)}{x_1} = \frac{b^2 (y - y_1)}{y_1}$$

or
$$\frac{a^2 x}{x_1} - \frac{b^2 y}{y_1} = a^2 - b^2$$

2. Parametric form

Theorem : The equation of normal to the ellipse

$$\frac{x^2}{a^2} + \frac{y^2}{b^2} = 1 \text{ at } (a\cos\phi, b\sin\phi) \text{ is}$$

$$ax \sec\phi - by \operatorname{cosec}\phi = a^2 - b^2$$

Proof : Since, the equation of normal of the ellipse $\dfrac{x^2}{a^2} + \dfrac{y^2}{b^2} = 1$ at (x_1, y_1) is

$$\frac{a^2 x}{x_1} - \frac{b^2 y}{y_1} = a^2 - b^2 \quad \text{...(i)}$$

Replacing x_1 by $a\cos\phi$ and y_1 by $b\sin\phi$, then Eq.(i) becomes

$$\frac{a^2 x}{a\cos\phi} - \frac{b^2 y}{b\sin\phi} = a^2 - b^2$$

$$ax \sec\phi - by \operatorname{cosec}\phi = a^2 - b^2$$

is the equation of normal at $(a\cos\phi, b\sin\phi)$

3. Slope form

Theorem : The equations of the normals of slope m to the ellipse $\dfrac{x^2}{a^2} + \dfrac{y^2}{b^2} = 1$ are given by

$$y = mx \mp \frac{m(a^2 - b^2)}{\sqrt{(a^2 + b^2 m^2)}}$$

at the points $\left(\pm \dfrac{a^2}{\sqrt{(a^2 + b^2 m^2)}}, \pm \dfrac{mb^2}{\sqrt{(a^2 + b^2 m^2)}} \right)$.

Proof : The equation of normal to the ellipse $\dfrac{x^2}{a^2} + \dfrac{y^2}{b^2} = 1$

at (x_1, y_1) is

$$\frac{a^2 x}{x_1} - \frac{b^2 y}{y_1} = a^2 - b^2 \quad \text{...(i)}$$

Since, 'm' is the slope of the normal, then

$$m = \frac{a^2 y_1}{b^2 x_1}$$

$$y_1 = \frac{b^2 x_1 m}{a^2} \quad \text{...(ii)}$$

Since, (x_1, y_1) lies on $\dfrac{x^2}{a^2} + \dfrac{y^2}{b^2} = 1$

$\therefore$
$$\frac{x_1^2}{a^2} + \frac{y_1^2}{b^2} = 1$$

or
$$\frac{x_1^2}{a^2} + \frac{b^4 x_1^2 m^2}{a^4 b^2} = 1$$

or
$$\frac{x_1^2}{a^2} + \frac{b^2 x_1^2 m^2}{a^4} = 1 \text{ or } x_1^2 = \frac{a^4}{(a^2 + b^2 m^2)}$$

$\therefore$
$$x_1 = \pm \frac{a^2}{\sqrt{a^2 + b^2 m^2}}$$

From Eq. (ii),

$$y_1 = \pm \frac{mb^2}{\sqrt{(a^2 + b^2m^2)}}$$

$\therefore$ Equation of normal in terms of slope is

$$y - \left(\pm \frac{mb^2}{\sqrt{a^2 + b^2m^2}} \right) = m \left(x - \left(\pm \frac{a^2}{\sqrt{a^2 + b^2m^2}} \right) \right)$$

$$\Rightarrow \quad y = mx \mp \frac{m(a^2 - b^2)}{\sqrt{(a^2 + b^2m^2)}} \quad \text{...(iii)}$$

Thus $y = mx \pm \frac{m(a^2 - b^2)}{\sqrt{(a^2 + b^2m^2)}}$ is a normal to the ellipse $\frac{x^2}{a^2} + \frac{y^2}{b^2} = 1$, where m is the slope of the normal.

The coordinates of the point of contact are

$$\left(\pm \frac{a^2}{\sqrt{a^2 + b^2m^2}}, \pm \frac{mb^2}{\sqrt{a^2 + b^2m^2}} \right)$$

Comparing Eq. (iii) with,

$$y = mx + c$$

$$\therefore \quad c = \mp \frac{m(a^2 - b^2)}{\sqrt{(a^2 + b^2m^2)}}$$

or

$$c^2 = \frac{m^2(a^2 - b^2)^2}{(a^2 + b^2m^2)}$$

which is condition of normality, when $y = mx + c$ is the normal of

$$\frac{x^2}{a^2} + \frac{y^2}{b^2} = 1$$

Example 30 If the normal at an end of a latusrectum of an ellipse $\frac{x^2}{a^2} + \frac{y^2}{b^2} = 1$ passes through one extremity of the minor axis, show that the eccentricity of the ellipse is given by

$$e^4 + e^2 - 1 = 0 \text{ or } e^2 = \frac{\sqrt{5} - 1}{2}$$

Sol. The coordinates of an end of the latusrectum are $(ae, b^2/a)$. The equation of normal at $P(ae, b^2/a)$ is

$$\frac{a^2x}{ae} - \frac{b^2(y)}{b^2/a} = a^2 - b^2$$

or

$$\frac{ax}{e} - ay = a^2 - b^2$$

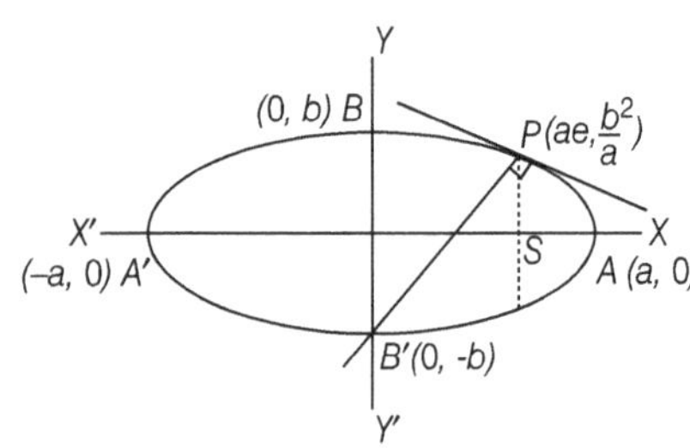

It passes through one extremity of the minor axis whose coordinates are $(0, -b)$

$$\therefore \quad 0 + ab = a^2 - b^2$$

or $\quad (a^2b^2) = (a^2 - b^2)^2$

or $\quad a^2a^2(1 - e^2) = (a^2e^2)^2$

or $\quad 1 - e^2 = e^4$

or $\quad e^4 + e^2 - 1 = 0$

or $\quad (e^2)^2 + e^2 - 1 = 0$

$$\therefore \quad e^2 = \frac{-1 \pm \sqrt{1 + 4}}{2}$$

$$\Rightarrow \quad e^2 = \frac{\sqrt{5} - 1}{2} \quad \text{(taking +ve sign)}$$

Example 31 Prove that the straight line $lx + my + n = 0$ is a normal to the ellipse $\frac{x^2}{a^2} + \frac{y^2}{b^2} = 1$ if $\frac{a^2}{l^2} + \frac{b^2}{m^2} = \frac{(a^2 - b^2)^2}{n^2}$.

Sol. The equation of any normal to $\frac{x^2}{a^2} + \frac{y^2}{b^2} = 1$ is

$$ax \sec \phi - by \operatorname{cosec} \phi = a^2 - b^2 \quad \text{... (i)}$$

The straight line $lx + my + n = 0$ will be a normal to the ellipse $\frac{x^2}{a^2} + \frac{y^2}{b^2} = 1$

Therefore, Eq. (i) and $lx + my + n = 0$ represent the same line

$$\frac{a \sec \phi}{l} = \frac{-b \operatorname{cosec} \phi}{m} = \frac{a^2 - b^2}{-n}$$

$$\cos \phi = \frac{-na}{l(a^2 - b^2)}$$

and $\quad \sin \phi = \frac{nb}{m(a^2 - b^2)}$

$$\because \quad \sin^2 \phi + \cos^2 \phi = 1$$

$$\therefore \quad \frac{n^2b^2}{m^2(a^2 - b^2)^2} + \frac{n^2a^2}{l^2(a^2 - b^2)^2} = 1$$

$$\Rightarrow \quad \frac{a^2}{l^2} + \frac{b^2}{m^2} = \frac{(a^2 - b^2)^2}{n^2}$$

Example 32 A normal inclined at an angle of 45° to x-axis of the ellipse $\frac{x^2}{a^2}+\frac{y^2}{b^2}=1$ is drawn. It meets the major and minor axes in P and Q respectively. If C is the centre of the ellipse, prove that area of ΔCPQ is $\frac{(a^2-b^2)^2}{2(a^2+b^2)}$ sq units.

Sol. Let $R(a\cos\phi, b\sin\phi)$ be any point on the ellipse, then equation of normal at R is

$$ax\sec\phi - by\operatorname{cosec}\phi = a^2-b^2$$

or $$\frac{x}{\frac{\cos\phi\,(a^2-b^2)}{a}}+\frac{y}{\frac{-\sin\phi\,(a^2-b^2)}{b}}=1$$

If meets the major and minor axes at $P\left(\frac{(a^2-b^2)}{a}\cos\phi, 0\right)$ and $Q\left(0, -\frac{(a^2-b^2)}{b}\sin\phi\right)$ are respectively

$$\therefore \quad CP=\left(\frac{a^2-b^2}{a}\right)|\cos\phi|$$

and $$CQ=\left(\frac{a^2-b^2}{b}\right)|\sin\phi|$$

$\therefore$ Area of $\Delta CPQ=\frac{1}{2}\times CP\times CQ$

$$=\frac{(a^2-b^2)^2|\sin\phi\cos\phi|}{2ab} \quad \text{... (i)}$$

But slope of normal $=\frac{a}{b}\tan\phi=\tan 45°$ (given)

$$\frac{a}{b}\tan\phi=1$$

$$\tan\phi=\frac{b}{a}$$

$$\therefore \quad \sin 2\phi=\frac{2\tan\phi}{1+\tan^2\phi}=\frac{2ab}{a^2+b^2}$$

$\therefore$ From Eq. (i), Area of $\Delta CPQ=\dfrac{(a^2-b^2)^2\left|\frac{\sin 2\phi}{2}\right|}{2ab}$

$$=\frac{(a^2-b^2)^2\,\frac{ab}{(a^2+b^2)}}{2ab}$$

$$=\frac{(a^2-b^2)^2}{2(a^2+b^2)}\text{ sq units.}$$

Example 33 Any ordinate MP of an ellipse meets the auxiliary circle in Q. Prove that the locus of the point of intersection of the normals at P and Q is the circle $x^2+y^2=(a^2+b^2)^2$.

Sol. Let equation of ellipse is $\frac{x^2}{a^2}+\frac{y^2}{b^2}=1$ its auxiliary circle is

$$x^2+y^2=a^2$$

Coordinates of P and Q are $(a\cos\phi, b\sin\phi)$ and $(a\cos\phi, a\sin\phi)$ respectively. Equation of normal at P to the ellipse $\frac{x^2}{a^2}+\frac{y^2}{b^2}=1$ is

$$ax\sec\phi - by\operatorname{cosec}\phi=a^2-b^2 \quad \text{...(i)}$$

and equation of normal at Q to the circle $x^2+y^2=a^2$ is

$$y=x\tan\phi \quad \text{...(ii)}$$

From Eq. (ii), $\tan\phi=\frac{y}{x}$

$$\therefore \quad \sin\phi=\frac{y}{\sqrt{(x^2+y^2)}} \text{ and } \cos\phi=\frac{x}{\sqrt{(x^2+y^2)}}$$

or $$\operatorname{cosec}\phi=\frac{\sqrt{(x^2+y^2)}}{y}$$

and $$\sec\phi=\frac{\sqrt{(x^2+y^2)}}{x} \quad \text{...(iii)}$$

Substituting the values of $\sec\phi$ and $\operatorname{cosec}\phi$ from Eq. (iii) in Eq. (i)

$$\therefore \quad ax\times\frac{\sqrt{(x^2+y^2)}}{x}-by\times\frac{\sqrt{(x^2+y^2)}}{y}=a^2-b^2$$

or $$(a-b)\sqrt{(x^2+y^2)}=(a+b)(a-b)$$

or $$\sqrt{x^2+y^2}=a+b$$

$$\therefore \quad x^2+y^2=(a+b)^2$$

which is required locus.

Properties of Eccentric Angles of the Co-normal Points

1. In general, four normals can be drawn to an ellipse from any point and if $\alpha, \beta, \gamma, \delta$ the eccentric angles of these four co-normal points, then $\alpha+\beta+\gamma+\delta$ is an odd multiple of π.

Let $Q(h, k)$ be any given point and let $P(a\cos\phi, b\sin\phi)$ be any point on the ellipse

$$\frac{x^2}{a^2}+\frac{y^2}{b^2}=1$$

Equation of normal at $P(a\cos\phi, b\sin\phi)$ is

$$ax\sec\phi-by\operatorname{cosec}\phi=a^2-b^2$$

it passes through $Q(h, k)$

$\therefore \quad ah\sec\phi - bk\operatorname{cosec}\phi = a^2 - b^2$

or
$$\frac{ah}{\cos\phi} - \frac{bk}{\sin\phi} = a^2 - b^2 \quad ...(i)$$

or
$$\frac{ah}{\left(\frac{1-\tan^2(\phi/2)}{1+\tan^2(\phi/2)}\right)} - \frac{bk}{\left(\frac{2\tan(\phi/2)}{1+\tan^2(\phi/2)}\right)} = a^2 - b^2 \quad ...(ii)$$

Let $\tan\phi/2 = t$

then, Eq. (ii) reduced to

$$bkt^4 + 2\{ah + (a^2 - b^2)\}t^3 + 2\{ah - (a^2 - b^2)\}t - bk = 0 \quad ...(iii)$$

Which is a fourth degree equation in t, hence four normals can be drawn to an ellipse from any point.

Consequently, it has four values of ϕ say $\alpha, \beta, \gamma, \delta$ ($\because t = \tan\phi/2$).

Now,
$$\tan\left(\frac{\alpha}{2}+\frac{\beta}{2}+\frac{\gamma}{2}+\frac{\delta}{2}\right) = \frac{S_1 - S_3}{1 - S_2 + S_4}$$

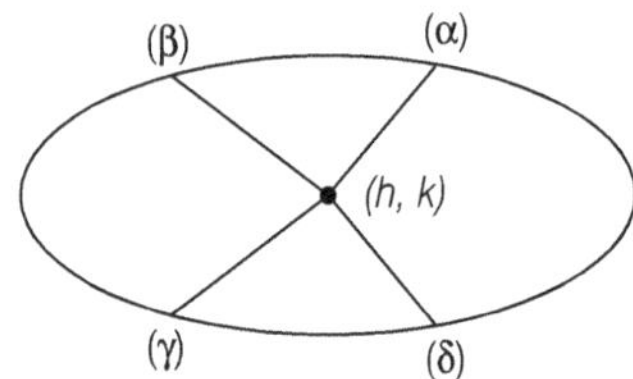

$$= \frac{\frac{-2\{ah + (a^2 - b^2)\}}{bk} + \frac{2\{(ah - (a^2 - b^2)\}}{bk}}{1 - 0 - 1}$$

$= \infty$ (From trigonometry) $(\because a \neq b)$

or
$$\cot\left(\frac{\alpha}{2}+\frac{\beta}{2}+\frac{\gamma}{2}+\frac{\delta}{2}\right) = 0$$

or
$$\frac{\alpha}{2}+\frac{\beta}{2}+\frac{\gamma}{2}+\frac{\delta}{2} = \text{an odd multiple of } \pi/2$$

$\Rightarrow \quad \alpha + \beta + \gamma + \delta = \text{an odd multiple of } \pi$

Aliter :

Let $\quad z = e^{i\phi} = \cos\phi + i\sin\phi$

$\therefore \quad \frac{1}{z} = e^{-i\phi} = \cos\phi - i\sin\phi$

$\therefore \quad \cos\phi = \frac{z + \frac{1}{z}}{2} = \frac{z^2+1}{2z}$

and $\quad \sin\phi = \frac{z - \frac{1}{z}}{2i} = \frac{z^2-1}{2iz}$

Now, Eq. (i), reduces to

$$\frac{ah}{\left(\frac{z^2+1}{2z}\right)} - \frac{bk}{\left(\frac{z^2-1}{2iz}\right)} = a^2 - b^2$$

$$\Rightarrow \quad (a^2 - b^2)z^4 - 2(ah - ibk)z^3 + 2(ah + ibk)z - (a^2 - b^2) = 0 \quad ...(iv)$$

Consequently $z = e^{i\phi}$

gives four values of ϕ, say $\alpha, \beta, \gamma, \delta$ (Here, sum of four angles)

$\therefore \quad z_1 . z_2 . z_3 . z_4 = -1$

$\Rightarrow \quad e^{i\alpha} \cdot e^{i\beta} \cdot e^{i\gamma} \cdot e^{i\delta} = -1$

$\Rightarrow \quad e^{i(\alpha+\beta+\gamma+\delta)} = -1$

$\cos(\alpha+\beta+\gamma+\delta) + i\sin(\alpha+\beta+\gamma+\delta) = -1$

or $\quad \cos(\alpha+\beta+\gamma+\delta) = -1$

and $\quad \sin(\alpha+\beta+\gamma+\delta) = 0$

$\alpha+\beta+\gamma+\delta = (2n+1)\pi$

and $\quad \alpha+\beta+\gamma+\delta = r\pi$

where, $n\ r, \in I$

Hence, $\alpha+\beta+\gamma+\delta$ = odd multiple of π

2. If α, β, γ are the eccentric angles of three points on the ellipse $\frac{x^2}{a^2} + \frac{y^2}{b^2} = 1$, the normals at which are concurrent, then

$\sin(\alpha+\beta) + \sin(\beta+\gamma) + \sin(\gamma+\alpha) = 0$

Here, in each term sum of two eccentric angles

$\therefore$ From Eq. (iv),

$$\Sigma z_1 z_2 = 0$$

or $\quad z_1z_2 + z_1z_3 + z_1z_4 + z_2z_3 + z_2z_4 + z_3z_4 = 0$

$$\Rightarrow \quad e^{i(\alpha+\beta)} + e^{i(\alpha+\gamma)} + e^{i(\alpha+\delta)} + e^{i(\beta+\gamma)} + e^{i(\beta+\delta)} + e^{i(\gamma+\delta)} = 0$$

$$\Rightarrow \quad [\cos(\alpha+\beta) + \cos(\alpha+\gamma) + \cos(\alpha+\delta) + \cos(\beta+\gamma) + \cos(\beta+\delta) + \cos(\gamma+\delta)] + i[(\sin(\alpha+\beta) + \sin(\alpha+\gamma) + \sin(\alpha+\delta) + \sin(\beta+\gamma) + \sin(\beta+\delta) + \sin(\gamma+\delta)] = 0$$

Comparing the imaginary part, then

$$\sin(\alpha+\beta) + \sin(\alpha+\gamma) + \sin(\alpha+\delta) + \sin(\beta+\gamma) + \sin(\beta+\delta) + \sin(\gamma+\delta) = 0 \quad ...(v)$$

Since, from property Eq. (i)

$\alpha+\beta+\gamma+\delta$ = odd multiple of π

$(\alpha+\delta)$ = odd multiple of $\pi - (\beta+\gamma)$

$(\beta+\delta)$ = odd multiple of $\pi - (\alpha+\gamma)$

$$(\gamma + \delta) = \text{odd multiple of } \pi - (\alpha + \beta)$$

$$\left.\begin{aligned}\sin(\alpha + \delta) &= \sin(\beta + \gamma)\\ \sin(\beta + \delta) &= \sin(\alpha + \gamma)\\ \sin(\gamma + \delta) &= \sin(\alpha + \beta)\end{aligned}\right\}$$

$$\{\because \sin(n\pi - \alpha) = \sin\alpha, \text{ if } n \text{ is integer}\} \quad \text{...(vi)}$$

From Eqs. (v) and (vi), we get

$$2\sin(\alpha + \beta) + 2\sin(\beta + \gamma) + 2\sin(\gamma + \alpha) = 0$$

Hence, $\sin(\alpha + \beta) + \sin(\beta + \gamma) + \sin(\gamma + \alpha) = 0$

Aliter :

From Eq. (iii), $\Sigma t_1 t_2 = 0$ ...(vii)

and $t_1 t_2 t_3 t_4 = -1$ ...(viii)

Now, $\Sigma t_1 t_2 = 0$

$\Rightarrow \quad t_1t_2 + t_2t_3 + t_3t_1 = -t_4(t_1 + t_2 + t_3)$

$\Rightarrow \quad t_1t_2 + t_2t_3 + t_3t_1 = \dfrac{t_1 + t_2 + t_3}{t_1t_2t_3}$ {from (viii)}

$\Rightarrow \quad t_1t_2 + t_2t_3 + t_3t_1 = \dfrac{1}{t_2t_3} + \dfrac{1}{t_3t_1} + \dfrac{1}{t_1t_2}$

$\Rightarrow \quad \tan\dfrac{\alpha}{2}\tan\dfrac{\beta}{2} + \tan\dfrac{\beta}{2}\tan\dfrac{\gamma}{2} + \tan\dfrac{\gamma}{2}\tan\dfrac{\alpha}{2}$

$$= \cot\frac{\beta}{2}\cot\frac{\gamma}{2} + \cot\frac{\gamma}{2}\cot\frac{\alpha}{2} + \cot\frac{\alpha}{2}\cot\frac{\beta}{2}$$

$\Rightarrow \sum\left(\tan\dfrac{\alpha}{2}\tan\dfrac{\beta}{2} - \cot\dfrac{\alpha}{2}\cot\dfrac{\beta}{2}\right) = 0$

$\Rightarrow \sum\left(\dfrac{\sin^2(\alpha/2)\sin^2(\beta/2) - \cos^2(\alpha/2)\cos^2(\beta/2)}{\sin(\alpha/2)\sin(\beta/2)\cos(\alpha/2)\cos(\beta/2)}\right) = 0$

$\Rightarrow \sum -4\left(\dfrac{\{\cos(\alpha/2)\cos(\beta/2) + \sin(\alpha/2)\sin(\beta/2)\}\{\cos(\alpha/2)\cos(\beta/2) - \sin(\alpha/2)\sin(\beta/2)\}}{\sin\alpha\sin\beta}\right) = 0$

$\Rightarrow \quad \sum -4\left(\dfrac{\cos\left(\dfrac{\alpha-\beta}{2}\right)\cos\left(\dfrac{\alpha+\beta}{2}\right)}{\sin\alpha\sin\beta}\right) = 0$

$\Rightarrow \quad \sum -2\dfrac{[\cos\alpha + \cos\beta]}{\sin\alpha\sin\beta} = 0$

$\Rightarrow \quad \sum \dfrac{\sin\gamma(\cos\alpha + \cos\beta)}{\sin\alpha\sin\beta\sin\gamma} = 0$

$\Rightarrow \quad \sum \sin\gamma(\cos\alpha + \cos\beta) = 0$

$\Rightarrow \quad \sin\gamma(\cos\alpha + \cos\beta) + \sin\alpha(\cos\beta + \cos\gamma) + \sin\beta(\cos\gamma + \cos\alpha) = 0$

$\Rightarrow \quad \sin(\alpha + \beta) + \sin(\beta + \gamma) + \sin(\gamma + \alpha) = 0$

Co-normal Points Lie on a Fixed Curve

Let $P(x_1, y_1), Q(x_2, y_2), R(x_3, y_3)$ and $T(x_4, y_4)$ be conormal points so that normal drawn from them meet in $T(h, k)$.

Then, equation of normal at $P(x_1, y_1)$ is

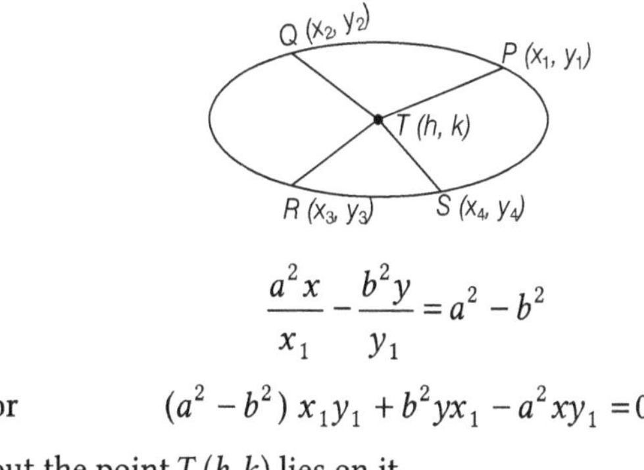

$$\frac{a^2x}{x_1} - \frac{b^2y}{y_1} = a^2 - b^2$$

or $\quad (a^2 - b^2)x_1y_1 + b^2yx_1 - a^2xy_1 = 0$

but the point $T(h, k)$ lies on it

$\therefore \quad (a^2 - b^2)x_1y_1 + b^2kx_1 - a^2hy_1 = 0$

Similarly, for points Q, R and S are

$$(a^2 - b^2)x_2y_2 + b^2kx_2 - a^2hy_2 = 0$$

$$(a^2 - b^2)x_3y_3 + b^2kx_3 - a^2hy_3 = 0$$

and $\quad (a^2 - b^2)x_4y_4 + b^2kx_4 - a^2hy_4 = 0$

Hence, P, Q, R, S all lie on the curve

$$(a^2 - b^2)xy + b^2kx - a^2hy = 0$$

This curve is called **Apollonian rectangular hyperbola**.

Remark

The feet of the normals from any fixed point to the ellipse lie at the intersections of the **Apollonian rectangular hyperbola** with the ellipse.

Exercise for Session 2

1. The number of values of c such that the straight line $y = 4x + c$ touches the curve $\frac{x^2}{4} + y^2 = 1$, is

(a) 0 (b) 1 (c) 2 (d) infinite

2. If any tangent to the ellipse $\frac{x^2}{a^2} + \frac{y^2}{b^2} = 1$ cuts off intercepts of length h and k on the axes, then $\frac{a^2}{h^2} + \frac{b^2}{k^2}$ is equal to

(a) -1 (b) 0 (c) 1 (d) None of these

3. The equations of the tangents to the ellipse $3x^2 + y^2 = 3$ making equal intercepts on the axes are

(a) $y = \pm x \pm 2$ (b) $y = \pm x \pm 4$ (c) $y = \pm x \pm \sqrt{30}$ (d) $y = \pm x \pm \sqrt{35}$

4. If $\frac{x}{a} + \frac{y}{b} = \sqrt{2}$ touches the ellipse $\frac{x^2}{a^2} + \frac{y^2}{b^2} = 1$, then its, eccentric angle θ is equal to

(a) 0 (b) 45° (c) 60° (d) 90°

5. The number of values of $\theta \in [0, 2\pi]$ for which the line $2x \cos\theta + 3y \sin\theta = 6$ touches the ellipse $4x^2 + 9y^2 = 36$ is

(a) 1 (b) 2 (c) 4 (d) infinite

6. The common tangent of $x^2 + y^2 = 4$ and $2x^2 + y^2 = 2$ is

(a) $x + y + 4 = 0$ (b) $x - y + 7 = 0$ (c) $2x + 3y + 8 = 0$ (d) None of these

7. If the normal at any point P on the ellipse $\frac{x^2}{a^2} + \frac{y^2}{b^2} = 1$ meets the axes in G and g respectively, then $PG \cdot Pg =$

(a) $a : b$ (b) $a^2 : b^2$ (c) $b : a$ (d) $b^2 : a^2$

8. Number of distinct normal lines that can be drawn to the ellipse $\frac{x^2}{169} + \frac{y^2}{25} = 1$, from the point $(0, 6)$ is

(a) one (b) two (c) three (d) four

9. If a tangent of slope 2 of the ellipse $\frac{x^2}{a^2} + \frac{y^2}{b^2} = 1$, is normal to the circle $x^2 + y^2 + 4x + 1 = 0$, then the maximum value of ab is

(a) 4 (b) 2 (c) 1 (d) None of these

10. If the normal at the point $P(\theta)$ to the ellipse $\frac{x^2}{14} + \frac{y^2}{5} = 1$, intersect it again at the point $Q(2\theta)$, then $\cos\theta$ is equal to

(a) $\frac{2}{3}$ (b) $-\frac{2}{3}$ (c) $\frac{3}{2}$ (d) $-\frac{3}{2}$

11. The line $5x - 3y = 8\sqrt{2}$ is a normal to the ellipse $\frac{x^2}{25} + \frac{y^2}{9} = 1$. If '$\theta$' be eccentric angle of the foot of this normal, then 'θ' is equal to

(a) $\frac{\pi}{6}$ (b) $\frac{\pi}{4}$ (c) $\frac{\pi}{3}$ (d) $\frac{\pi}{2}$

12. If the tangent drawn at point $(\lambda^2, 2\lambda)$ on the parabola $y^2 = 4x$ is same as the normal drawn at a point $(\sqrt{5}\cos\theta, 2\sin\theta)$ on the ellipse $4x^2 + 5y^2 = 20$. Find the values of λ and θ.

13. If the normal at any point P of the ellipse $\frac{x^2}{a^2} + \frac{y^2}{b^2} = 1$, meets the major and minor axes in G and H respectively and C in the centre of the ellipse, then prove that

$$a^2 (CG)^2 + b^2 (CH)^2 = (a^2 - b^2)^2$$

14. If the normal at the point $P(\theta)$ to the ellipse $5x^2 + 14y^2 = 70$ intersects it again at the point $Q(2\theta)$, show that $\cos\theta = -\frac{2}{3}$.

15. The tangent and normal at any point P of an ellipse $\frac{x^2}{a^2} + \frac{y^2}{b^2} = 1$ cut its major axis in point Q and R respectively. If $QR = a$ prove that the eccentric angle of the point P Is given by

$$e^2 \cos^2\phi + \cos\phi - 1 = 0$$

Session 3

Pair of Tangents, Chord of Contact, Chord Bisected at a Given Point, Diameter, Conjugate Diameters, Equi-Conjugate Diameters, Director Circle, Sub-Tangent and Sub-Normal, Concyclic Points, Some Standard Properties of the Ellipse, Reflection Property of an Ellipse, Equation of an Ellipse Referred to Two Perpendicular Lines

Pair of Tangents

Theorem : The combined equation of the pair of tangents drawn from a point (x_1, y_1) to the ellipse $\frac{x^2}{a^2}+\frac{y^2}{b^2}=1$ is

$$\left(\frac{x^2}{a^2}+\frac{y^2}{b^2}-1\right)\left(\frac{x_1^2}{a^2}+\frac{y_1^2}{b^2}-1\right)=\left(\frac{xx_1}{a^2}+\frac{yy_1}{b^2}-1\right)^2$$

or $\quad SS_1 = T^2$

where $\quad S=\frac{x^2}{a^2}+\frac{y^2}{b^2}-1;\ S_1=\frac{x_1^2}{a^2}+\frac{y_1^2}{b^2}-1$

and $\quad T=\frac{xx_1}{a^2}+\frac{yy_1}{b^2}-1$

Proof : Let $T(h, k)$ be any point on the pair of tangents PQ or PR drawn from any external point $P(x_1, y_1)$ to the ellipse $\quad \frac{x^2}{a^2}+\frac{y^2}{b^2}=1$

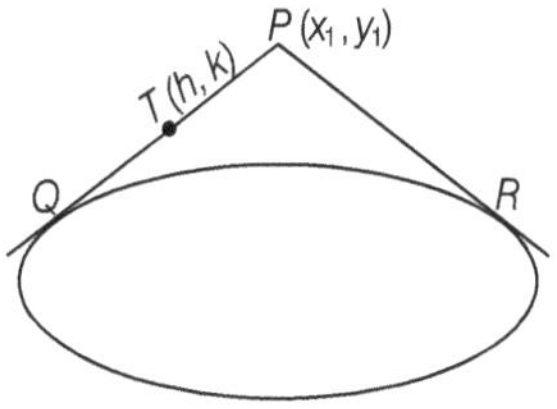

$\therefore$ Equation of PT is

$$y-y_1=\frac{k-y_1}{h-x_1}(x-x_1)$$

or $$y=\left(\frac{k-y_1}{h-x_1}\right)x+\left(\frac{hy_1-kx_1}{h-x_1}\right)$$

which is the tangent to the ellipse

$$\frac{x^2}{a^2}+\frac{y^2}{b^2}=1$$

$\therefore$ $$c^2=a^2m^2+b^2$$

or $$\left(\frac{hy_1-kx_1}{h-x_1}\right)^2=a^2\left(\frac{k-y_1}{h-x_1}\right)^2+b^2$$

$\Rightarrow$ $$(hy_1-kx_1)^2=a^2(k-y_1)^2+b^2(h-x_1)^2$$

Hence, locus of (h, k) is

$$(xy_1-x_1y)^2=a^2(y-y_1)^2+b^2(x-x_1)^2$$

or $$(xy_1-x_1y)^2=(b^2x^2+a^2y^2)+(b^2x_1^2+a^2y_1^2)-2(b^2xx_1+a^2yy_1)$$

or $$\left(\frac{xy_1-x_1y}{ab}\right)^2=\left(\frac{x^2}{a^2}+\frac{y^2}{b^2}\right)+\left(\frac{x_1^2}{a^2}+\frac{y_1^2}{b^2}\right)-2\left(\frac{xx_1}{a^2}+\frac{yy_1}{b^2}\right)$$

or $$\left(\frac{xy_1-x_1y}{ab}\right)^2-\left(\frac{x^2}{a^2}+\frac{y^2}{b^2}\right)-\left(\frac{x_1^2}{a^2}+\frac{y_1^2}{b^2}\right)+\left(\frac{xx_1}{a^2}+\frac{yy_1}{b^2}\right)^2$$

$$=\left(\frac{xx_1}{a^2}+\frac{yy_1}{b^2}\right)^2+1-2\left(\frac{xx_1}{a^2}+\frac{yy_1}{b^2}\right)$$

or $$\left(\frac{x^2}{a^2}+\frac{y^2}{b^2}-1\right)\left(\frac{x_1^2}{a^2}+\frac{y_1^2}{b^2}-1\right)=\left(\frac{xx_1}{a^2}+\frac{yy_1}{b^2}-1\right)^2$$

or $$SS_1=T^2$$

Aliter : Let the ellipse be $\frac{x^2}{a^2}+\frac{y^2}{b^2}=1$ ...(i)

Let $P(x_1, y_1)$ be any point outside the ellipse let a chord of the ellipse through the point $P(x_1, y_1)$ cut the ellipse at Q and let $R(h, k)$ be any arbitrary point on the line PQ (R inside or outside). Let Q divides PR in the ratio $\lambda : 1$ then coordinates of Q is

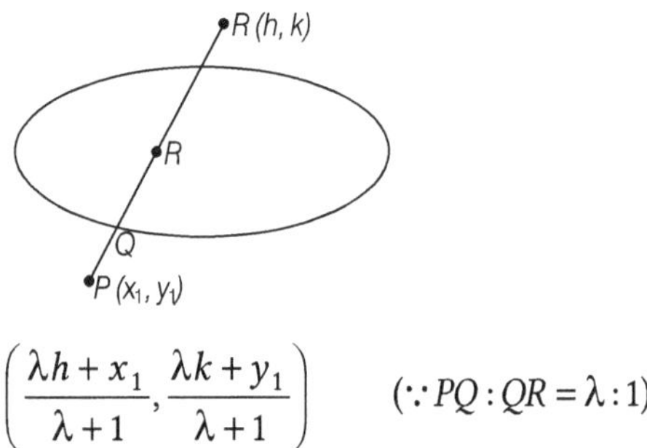

$$\left(\frac{\lambda h+x_1}{\lambda+1}, \frac{\lambda k+y_1}{\lambda+1}\right) \quad (\because PQ:QR=\lambda:1)$$

since Q lies on ellipse Eq. (i), then

$$\frac{1}{a^2}\left(\frac{\lambda h+x_1}{\lambda+1}\right)^2+\frac{1}{b^2}\left(\frac{\lambda k+y_1}{\lambda+1}\right)^2=1$$

$$\Rightarrow \quad b^2(\lambda h+x_1)^2+a^2(\lambda k+y_1)^2=a^2b^2(\lambda+1)^2$$

$$\Rightarrow \quad (a^2k^2+b^2h^2-a^2b^2)\lambda^2+2$$

$$(hx_1b^2+ky_1a^2-a^2b^2)\lambda+(b^2x_1^2+a^2y_1^2-a^2b^2)=0 \quad ...(ii)$$

Line PR will become tangent to ellipse Eq. (i) then roots of Eq. (ii) are equal

$$\therefore \quad 4(hx_1b^2+ky_1a^2-a^2b^2)^2$$

$$-4(a^2k^2+b^2h^2-a^2b^2)(b^2x_1^2+a^2y_1^2-a^2b^2)=0$$

Dividing by $4a^4b^4$

$$\therefore \quad \left(\frac{hx_1}{a^2}+\frac{ky_1}{b^2}-1\right)^2=\left(\frac{k^2}{b^2}+\frac{h^2}{a^2}-1\right)\left(\frac{x_1^2}{a^2}+\frac{y_1^2}{b^2}-1\right)$$

Hence, locus of $R(h, k)$ i.e. equation of pair of tangents from $P(x_1, y_1)$ is

$$\left(\frac{xx_1}{a^2}+\frac{yy_1}{b^2}-1\right)^2=\left(\frac{x^2}{a^2}+\frac{y^2}{b^2}-1\right)\left(\frac{x_1^2}{a^2}+\frac{y_1^2}{b^2}-1\right)$$

i.e. $$T^2=SS_1 \text{ or } SS_1=T^2$$

Remark

$S=0$ is the equation of the curve, S_1 is obtained from S by replacing x by x_1 and y by y_1 and $T=0$ is the equation of tangent at (x_1, y_1) to $S=0$

Chord of Contact

Theorem : The equation of chord of contact of tangents drawn from a point (x_1, y_1) to the ellipse $\frac{x^2}{a^2}+\frac{y^2}{b^2}=1$ is $\frac{xx_1}{a^2}+\frac{yy_1}{b^2}=1$

Proof : Let PQ and PR be the tangents drawn from a point $P(x_1, y_1)$ to the ellipse $\frac{x^2}{a^2}+\frac{y^2}{b^2}=1$ such that

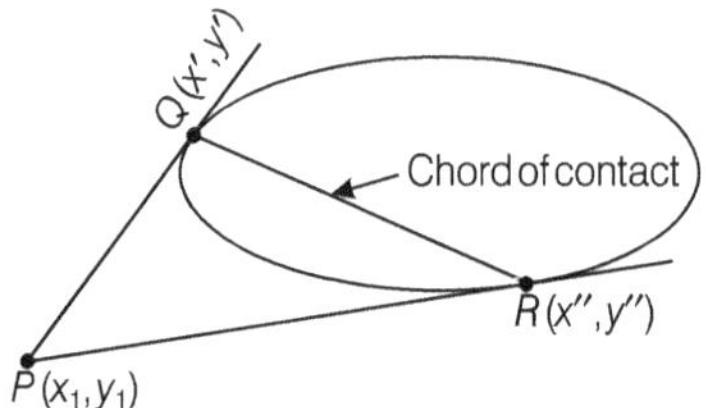

$$Q\equiv(x', y') \quad \text{and} \quad R\equiv(x'', y'')$$

are the points of contacts of these tangents the chord QR is called chord of contact of the ellipse

$$\frac{x^2}{a^2}+\frac{y^2}{b^2}=1$$

Equations of tangents at $Q(x', y')$ and $R(x'', y'')$ are

$$\frac{xx'}{a^2}+\frac{yy'}{b^2}=1$$

and $$\frac{xx''}{a^2}+\frac{yy''}{b^2}=1, \text{ respectively}$$

These tangents pass through $P(x_1, y_1)$ therefore,

$$\frac{x'x_1}{a^2}+\frac{y'y_1}{b^2}=1 \quad \text{and} \quad \frac{x''x_1}{a^2}+\frac{y''y_1}{b^2}=1$$

$$\Rightarrow \quad (x', y') \text{ and } (x'', y'') \text{ lie on } \frac{xx_1}{a^2}+\frac{yy_1}{b^2}=1$$

Hence, the equation QR is $\frac{xx_1}{a^2}+\frac{yy_1}{b^2}=1$

which is same as the equation of tangent but position of point differ.

Example 34 Find the locus of the points of the intersection of tangents to ellipse $\frac{x^2}{a^2}+\frac{y^2}{b^2}=1$ which make an angle θ .

Sol. Given ellipse is $\frac{x^2}{a^2}+\frac{y^2}{b^2}=1$ ...(i)

Equation of any tangent to ellipse Eq. (i) in terms of slope (m) is $y = mx + \sqrt{(a^2m^2+b^2)}$

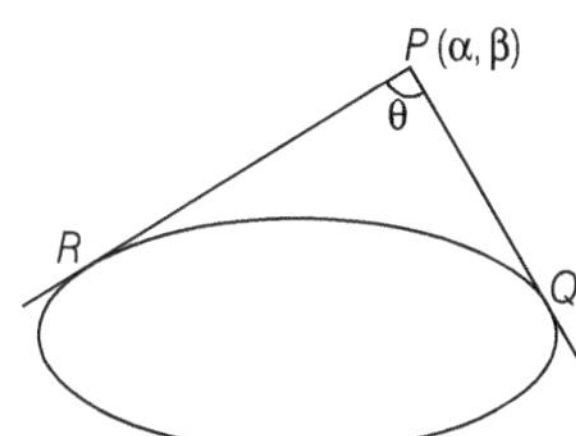

Since, its passes through $P(\alpha, \beta)$ then

$$\beta = m\alpha + \sqrt{(a^2m^2+b^2)}$$

$$\Rightarrow \quad (\beta - m\alpha) = \sqrt{(a^2m^2+b^2)}$$

$$\Rightarrow \quad (\beta - m\alpha)^2 = a^2m^2+b^2$$

$$\Rightarrow \quad m^2(a^2-\alpha^2)+2\alpha\beta m+(b^2-\beta^2)=0 \quad \text{...(ii)}$$

Eq. (ii) being a quadratic equation in m.
Let roots of Eq. (ii) are m_1 and m_2, then

$$\therefore \quad m_1+m_2 = -\frac{2\alpha\beta}{(a^2-\alpha^2)},\ m_1m_2 = \frac{b^2-\beta^2}{a^2-\alpha^2}$$

$$\therefore \quad (m_1-m_2) = \sqrt{(m_1+m_2)^2-4m_1m_2}$$

$$= \sqrt{\frac{4\alpha^2\beta^2}{(a^2-\alpha^2)^2} - \frac{4(b^2-\beta^2)}{(a^2-\alpha^2)}}$$

$$= \sqrt{\frac{4\alpha^2\beta^2 - 4(b^2-\beta^2)(a^2-\alpha^2)}{(a^2-\alpha^2)^2}}$$

$$= \sqrt{\frac{4\{\alpha^2\beta^2 - a^2b^2 + b^2\alpha^2 + a^2\beta^2 - \alpha^2\beta^2\}}{(a^2-\alpha^2)^2}}$$

$$= \frac{2}{|(a^2-\alpha^2)|}\sqrt{(a^2\beta^2+b^2\alpha^2-a^2b^2)}$$

$\because$ θ be the angle between these two tangents, then

$$\tan\theta = \left|\frac{m_1-m_2}{1+m_1m_2}\right|$$

$$= \left|\frac{\frac{2}{(a^2-\alpha^2)}\sqrt{(a^2\beta^2+b^2\alpha^2-a^2b^2)}}{\left(1+\frac{b^2-\beta^2}{a^2-\alpha^2}\right)}\right|$$

$$\tan\theta = \left|\frac{2\sqrt{(a^2\beta^2+b^2\alpha^2-a^2b^2)}}{a^2+b^2-\alpha^2-\beta^2}\right|$$

or $\quad (a^2+b^2-\alpha^2-\beta^2)^2\tan^2\theta = 4\ (a^2\beta^2+b^2\alpha^2-a^2b^2)$

$\Rightarrow \quad (\alpha^2+\beta^2-a^2-b^2)^2\tan^2\theta = 4\ (b^2\alpha^2+a^2\beta^2-a^2b^2)$

$\therefore$ Locus of $P(\alpha, \beta)$ is

$$(x^2+y^2-a^2-b^2)^2\tan^2\theta = 4\ (b^2x^2+a^2y^2-a^2b^2)$$

Example 35 Prove that the chord of contact of tangents drawn from the point (h, k) to the ellipse $\frac{x^2}{a^2}+\frac{y^2}{b^2}=1$ will subtend a right angle at the centre, if $\frac{h^2}{a^4}+\frac{k^2}{b^4}=\frac{1}{a^2}+\frac{1}{b^2}$. Also, find the locus of (h, k).

Sol. The equation of chord of contact of tangents drawn from $P(h, k)$ to the ellipse $\frac{x^2}{a^2}+\frac{y^2}{b^2}=1$ is $\frac{hx}{a^2}+\frac{ky}{b^2}=1$ ...(i)

The equation of the straight lines CA and CB is obtained by making homogeneous ellipse $\frac{x^2}{a^2}+\frac{y^2}{b^2}=1$ with the help of Eq. (i)

$$\therefore \quad \frac{x^2}{a^2}+\frac{y^2}{b^2} = \left(\frac{hx}{a^2}+\frac{ky}{b^2}\right)^2$$

$$\Rightarrow \quad \left(\frac{k^2}{a^4}-\frac{1}{a^2}\right)x^2 + \left(\frac{k^2}{b^4}-\frac{1}{b^2}\right)y^2 + \frac{2hk}{a^2b^2}xy = 0 \quad \text{...(ii)}$$

But given $\angle ACB = 90°$

$\therefore$ Coefficient of x^2 + Coefficient of $y^2 = 0$

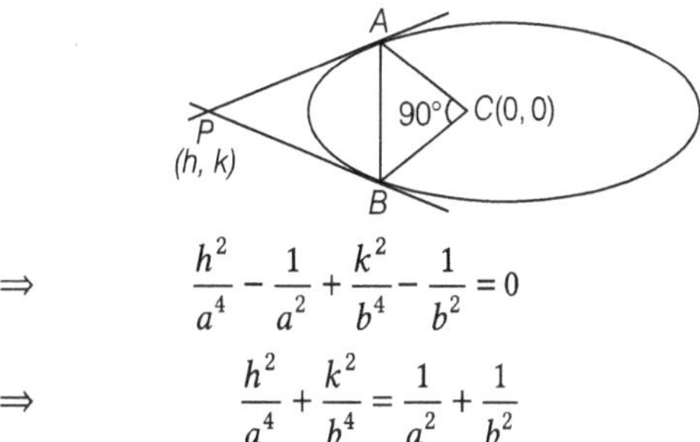

$$\Rightarrow \quad \frac{h^2}{a^4}-\frac{1}{a^2}+\frac{k^2}{b^4}-\frac{1}{b^2}=0$$

$$\Rightarrow \quad \frac{h^2}{a^4}+\frac{k^2}{b^4}=\frac{1}{a^2}+\frac{1}{b^2}$$

Hence, locus of (h, k) is

$$\frac{x^2}{a^4}+\frac{y^2}{b^4}=\frac{1}{a^2}+\frac{1}{b^2}$$

Chord Bisected at a Given Point

Theorem : The equation of a chord of the ellipse

$$\frac{x^2}{a^2}+\frac{y^2}{b^2}=1$$

bisected at the point (x_1, y_1) is given by

$$\frac{xx_1}{a^2}+\frac{yy_1}{b^2}-1=\frac{x_1^2}{a^2}+\frac{y_1^2}{b^2}-1$$

or $\quad T = S_1$

Proof : Let $Q \equiv (x_2, y_2)$ and $R \equiv (x_3, y_3)$ be the end points of a chord QR of the ellipse $\frac{x^2}{a^2}+\frac{y^2}{b^2}=1$ and let $P \equiv (x_1, y_1)$ be its mid point.

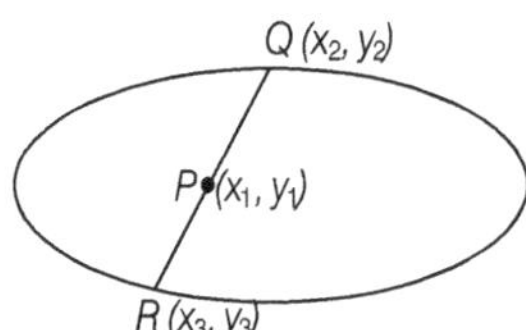

Now, $Q \equiv (x_2, y_2)$ and $R \equiv (x_3, y_3)$ lie on $\frac{x^2}{a^2} + \frac{y^2}{b^2} = 1$, then

$$\frac{x_2^2}{a^2} + \frac{y_2^2}{b^2} = 1 \quad \text{...(i)}$$

and
$$\frac{x_3^2}{a^2} + \frac{y_3^2}{b^2} = 1 \quad \text{...(ii)}$$

Subtracting Eq. (ii) from Eq. (i),

$$\therefore \quad \frac{1}{a^2}(x_2^2 - x_3^2) + \frac{1}{b^2}(y_2^2 - y_3^2) = 0$$

$$\Rightarrow \quad \frac{(x_2 + x_3)(x_2 - x_3)}{a^2} + \frac{(y_2 + y_3)(y_2 - y_3)}{b^2} = 0$$

$$\Rightarrow \quad \frac{y_2 - y_3}{x_2 - x_3} = -\frac{b^2 (x_2 + x_3)}{a^2 (y_2 + y_3)} = -\frac{b^2}{a^2} \cdot \frac{2x_1}{2y_1}$$

$$\left(\because x_1 = \frac{x_2 + x_3}{2} \text{ and } y_1 = \frac{y_2 + y_3}{2}\right)$$

$$= -\frac{b^2 x_1}{a^2 y_1} \quad \text{...(iii)}$$

$\therefore$ Equation of QR is

$$y - y_1 = \frac{y_2 - y_3}{x_2 - x_3}(x - x_1)$$

$$\Rightarrow \quad y - y_1 = -\frac{b^2 x_1}{a^2 y_1}(x - x_1) \quad \text{[from Eq. (iii)]}$$

$$\Rightarrow \quad \frac{yy_1}{b^2} - \frac{y_1^2}{b^2} = -\frac{xx_1}{a^2} + \frac{x_1^2}{a^2}$$

$$\Rightarrow \quad \frac{xx_1}{a^2} + \frac{yy_1}{b^2} - 1 = \frac{x_1^2}{a^2} + \frac{y_1^2}{b^2} - 1 \text{ or } T = S_1$$

where,
$$T = \frac{xx_1}{a^2} + \frac{yy_1}{b^2} - 1$$

and
$$S_1 = \frac{x_1^2}{a^2} + \frac{y_1^2}{b^2} - 1$$

Example 36 Prove that the locus of the middle points of normal chords of the ellipse $\frac{x^2}{a^2} + \frac{y^2}{b^2} = 1$ is the curve $\left(\frac{x^2}{a^2} + \frac{y^2}{b^2}\right)^2 \left(\frac{a^6}{x^2} + \frac{b^6}{y^2}\right) = (a^2 - b^2)^2$.

Sol. Let (h, k) be the middle point of any chord of an ellipse, then its equation is $T = S_1$

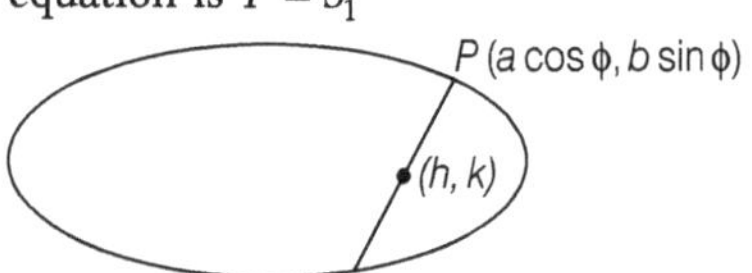

$$\text{or} \quad \frac{xh}{a^2} + \frac{yk}{b^2} - 1 = \frac{h^2}{a^2} + \frac{k^2}{b^2} - 1 \text{ or } \frac{xh}{a^2} + \frac{yk}{b^2} = \frac{h^2}{a^2} + \frac{k^2}{b^2} \quad \text{...(i)}$$

If Eq. (i) is a normal chords, then it must be of the form

$$ax \sec \phi - by \operatorname{cosec} \phi = a^2 - b^2 \quad \text{...(ii)}$$

Thus, the Eqs. (i) and (ii) represents the same normal chord of the ellipse with its middle point (h, k).

Hence, they are identical and comparing their co-efficients,

$$\text{we get} \quad \frac{h/a^2}{a \sec \phi} = \frac{k/b^2}{-b \operatorname{cosec} \phi} = \frac{\frac{h^2}{a^2} + \frac{k^2}{b^2}}{(a^2 - b^2)}$$

$$\Rightarrow \quad \cos \phi = \frac{a^3}{h} \frac{\left(\frac{h^2}{a^2} + \frac{k^2}{b^2}\right)}{(a^2 - b^2)} \quad \text{...(iii)}$$

$$\text{and} \quad \sin \phi = -\frac{b^3}{k} \frac{\left(\frac{h^2}{a^2} + \frac{k^2}{b^2}\right)}{(a^2 - b^2)} \quad \text{...(iv)}$$

Squaring and adding Eqs. (iii) and (iv), then

$$\cos^2 \phi + \sin^2 \phi = \frac{\left(\frac{a^6}{h^2} + \frac{b^6}{k^2}\right)\left(\frac{h^2}{a^2} + \frac{k^2}{b^2}\right)^2}{(a^2 - b^2)^2}$$

$$\Rightarrow \quad 1 = \frac{\left(\frac{a^6}{h^2} + \frac{b^6}{k^2}\right)\left(\frac{h^2}{a^2} + \frac{k^2}{b^2}\right)^2}{(a^2 - b^2)^2}$$

$$\Rightarrow \quad \left(\frac{h^2}{a^2} + \frac{k^2}{b^2}\right)^2 \left(\frac{a^6}{h^2} + \frac{b^6}{k^2}\right) = (a^2 - b^2)^2$$

Hence, locus of (h, k) is $\left(\frac{x^2}{a^2} + \frac{y^2}{b^2}\right)^2 \left(\frac{a^6}{x^2} + \frac{b^6}{y^2}\right) = (a^2 - b^2)^2$

Example 37 Show that the locus of the middle points of chords of an ellipse which pass through a fixed point, is another ellipse

Sol. Let $P(x_1, y_1)$ be the middle point of any chord AB of the ellipse $\frac{x^2}{a^2} + \frac{y^2}{b^2} = 1$, then equation of chord AB is

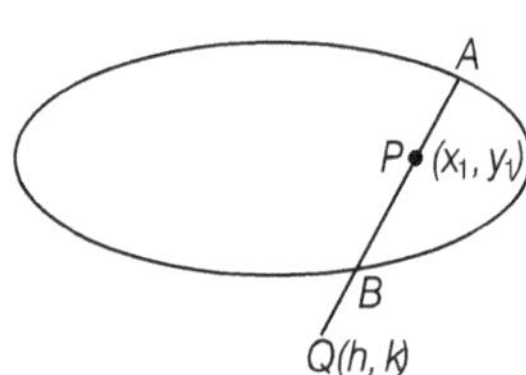

$$T = S_1$$

$$\Rightarrow \quad \frac{xx_1}{a^2} + \frac{yy_1}{b^2} - 1 = \frac{x_1^2}{a^2} + \frac{y_1^2}{b^2} - 1$$

$$\Rightarrow \quad \frac{xx_1}{a^2} + \frac{yy_1}{b^2} = \frac{x_1^2}{a^2} + \frac{y_1^2}{b^2} \quad \text{... (i)}$$

But it passes through a fixed point $Q(h, k)$ its coordinates must satisfy Eq. (i),

$$\therefore \quad \frac{hx_1}{a^2} + \frac{ky_1}{b^2} = \frac{x_1^2}{a^2} + \frac{y_1^2}{b^2}$$

This can be re-written as

$$\frac{\left(x_1 - \frac{h}{2}\right)^2}{a^2} + \frac{\left(y_1 - \frac{k}{2}\right)^2}{b^2} = \frac{1}{4}\left(\frac{h^2}{a^2} + \frac{k^2}{b^2}\right)$$

Hence, locus of $P(x_1, y_1)$ is

$$\frac{\left(x - \frac{h}{2}\right)^2}{a^2} + \frac{\left(y - \frac{k}{2}\right)^2}{b^2} = \frac{1}{4}\left(\frac{h^2}{a^2} + \frac{k^2}{b^2}\right)$$

Its obviously an ellipse with centre at $\left(\frac{h}{2}, \frac{k}{2}\right)$ and axes parallel to coordinates axes.

Diameter

The locus of the middle points of a system of parallel chords of an ellipse is called a diameter and the point where the diameter intersects the ellipse is called the vertex of the diameter.

Let $y = mx + c$ be system of parallel chords to $\frac{x^2}{a^2} + \frac{y^2}{b^2} = 1$ for different chords c varies, m remains constant.

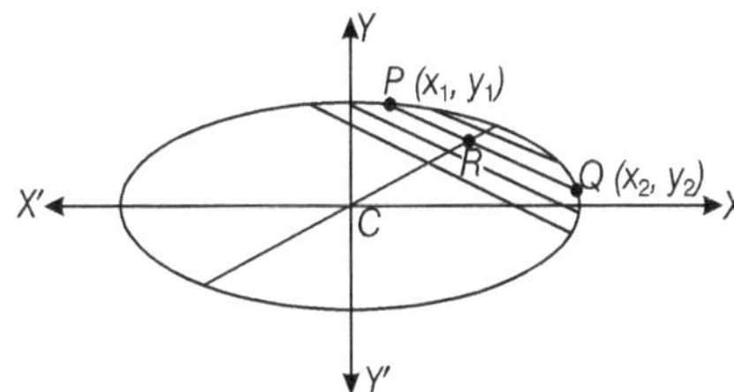

Let the extremities of any chord PQ of the set be $P(x_1, y_1)$ and $Q(x_2, y_2)$ and let its middle point be $R(h, k)$, then solving equations.

$$\frac{x^2}{a^2} + \frac{y^2}{b^2} = 1 \text{ and } y = mx + c$$

$$\therefore \quad \frac{x^2}{a^2} + \frac{(mx + c)^2}{b^2} = 1$$

$$\Rightarrow \quad (a^2m^2 + b^2)x^2 + 2mca^2x + a^2(c^2 - b^2) = 0$$

Since, x_1 and x_2 be the roots of this equation, then

$$x_1 + x_2 = -\frac{2mca^2}{a^2m^2 + b^2} \quad \text{...(i)}$$

Since, (h, k) be the middle point of QR, then

$$h = \frac{x_1 + x_2}{2}$$

then, from Eq. (i),

$$2h = -\frac{2mca^2}{a^2m^2 + b^2}$$

$$\Rightarrow \quad h = -\frac{mca^2}{a^2m^2 + b^2} \quad \text{...(ii)}$$

but (h, k) lies on $y = mx + c$

$$\therefore \quad k = mh + c, \; c = k - mh \quad \text{...(iii)}$$

From Eqs. (ii) and (iii), then, $h = -\frac{ma^2(k - mh)}{a^2m^2 + b^2}$

$$\Rightarrow \quad a^2m^2h + b^2h = -mka^2 + m^2a^2h$$

$$\Rightarrow \quad b^2h = -mka^2 \text{ or } k = -\frac{b^2h}{a^2m}$$

Hence, locus of $R(h, k)$ is $y = -\frac{b^2x}{a^2m}$

which is diameter of the ellipse passing through $(0, 0)$.

Aliter : Let (h, k) be the middle point of the chord $y = mx + c$ of the ellipse $\frac{x^2}{a^2} + \frac{y^2}{b^2} = 1$, then

$$T = S_1$$

$$\Rightarrow \quad \frac{xh}{a^2} + \frac{ky}{b^2} = \frac{h^2}{a^2} + \frac{k^2}{b^2}$$

$$\therefore \quad \text{Slope} = -\frac{b^2h}{a^2k} = m$$

$$\Rightarrow \quad k = -\frac{b^2h}{a^2m}$$

Hence, locus of the mid-point is

$$y = -\frac{b^2x}{a^2m}$$

Conjugate Diameters

Two diameters are said to be *conjugate* when each bisects all chords parallel to the other. If $y = mx$ and $y = m_1x$ be two conjugate diameters of an ellipse, then $mm_1 = \frac{b^2}{a^2}$.

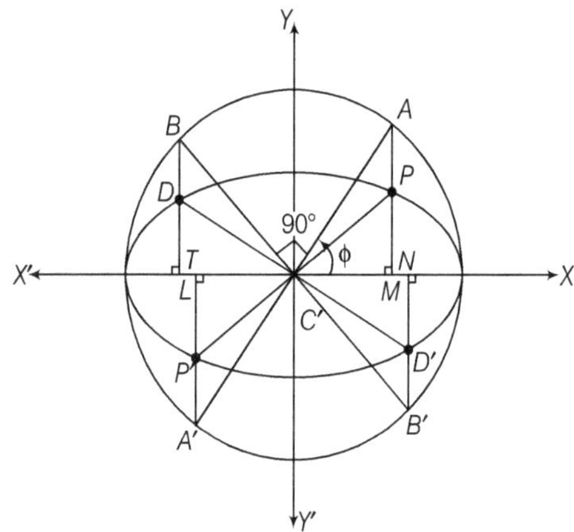

Conjugate diameters of circle i.e. AA' and BB' are perpendicular to each other. Hence, conjugate diameters of ellipse are PP' and DD'.

Hence, angle between conjugate diameters of ellipse $\neq 90°$.

Now the co-ordinates of the four extremities of two conjugate diameters are

$$P\,(a\cos\phi,\, b\sin\phi),\ P'\,(-a\cos\phi, -b\sin\phi),$$

$$D\,(-a\sin\phi,\, b\cos\phi),\ D'\,(a\sin\phi, -b\cos\phi)$$

Properties of Conjugate Diameters

Prop. 1 : *The eccentric angles of the ends of a pair of conjugate diameters of an ellipse differ by a right angle.*

Let PCP' and DCD' be two conjugate diameters of the ellipse $\frac{x^2}{a^2}+\frac{y^2}{b^2}=1$ and let the eccentric angles of the

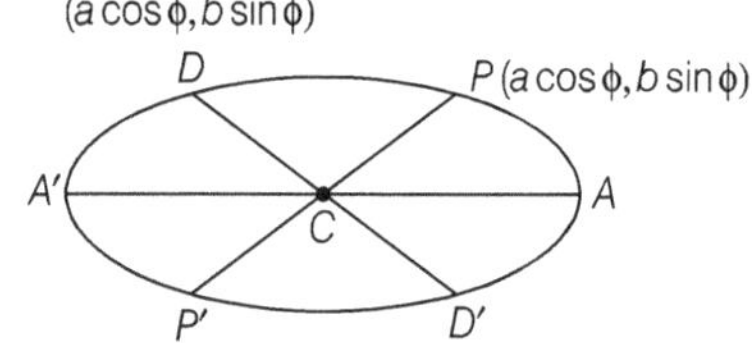

extremities P and D be ϕ and ϕ' respectively. Then, the co-ordinates of P and D are $(a\cos\phi, b\sin\phi)$ and $(a\cos\phi', b\sin\phi')$ respectively.

Now m_1 = slope of $CP = \frac{b}{a}\tan\phi$

and m_2 = slope of $CD = \frac{b}{a}\tan\phi'$

since, the diameters PCP' and DCD' are conjugate diameters.

$$\therefore \qquad m_1 m_2 = -\frac{b^2}{a^2}$$

$$\Rightarrow \qquad \frac{b^2}{a^2}\tan\phi\tan\phi' = -\frac{b^2}{a^2}$$

$$\Rightarrow \qquad \tan\phi\tan\phi' = -1$$

$$\Rightarrow \qquad \tan\phi = -\cot\phi' = \tan\left(\frac{\pi}{2}+\phi'\right)$$

$$\Rightarrow \qquad \phi = \frac{\pi}{2}+\phi' \Rightarrow \phi-\phi' = \frac{\pi}{2}$$

Prop. 2 : *The sum of the squares of any two conjugate semi diameters of an ellipse is constant and equal to the sum of the squares of the semi-axes of the ellipse* i.e.

$$CP^2 + CD^2 = a^2 + b^2$$

Let CP and CD be two conjugate semi-diameters of an ellipse $\frac{x^2}{a^2}+\frac{y^2}{b^2}=1$ and let eccentric angle of P is ϕ. The eccentric angle of D is $\frac{\pi}{2}+\phi$. So the coordinates of P and D are

$$(a\cos\phi, b\sin\phi) \quad \text{and} \quad \left(a\cos\left(\frac{\pi}{2}+\phi\right), b\sin\left(\frac{\pi}{2}+\phi\right)\right)$$

i.e. $(-a\sin\phi, b\cos\phi)$ respectively

$$\therefore \qquad CP^2 + CD^2 = (a^2\cos^2\phi + b^2\sin^2\phi) + (a^2\sin^2\phi + b^2\cos^2\phi)$$

$$= a^2 + b^2$$

Prop. 3 : *The product of the focal distances of a point on an ellipse is equal to the square of the semi diameter which is conjugate to the diameter through the point.*

Let PCP' and DCD' be the conjugate diameters of an ellipse and let the eccentric angle of P is ϕ then coordinates of P is $(a\cos\phi, b\sin\phi)$

$\therefore$ Coordinates of D is $(-a\sin\phi, b\cos\phi)$

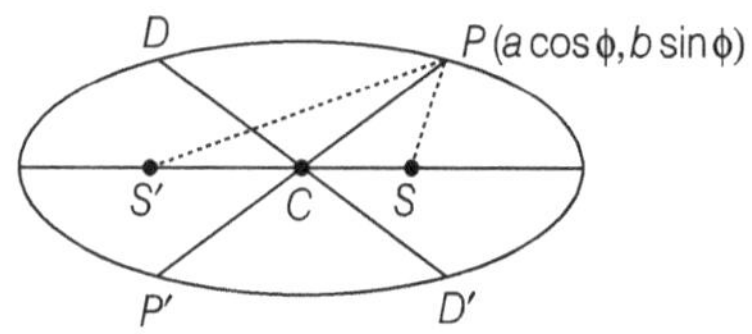

Let S and S' be two foci of the ellipse. Then

$$SP\cdot S'P = (a - ae\cos\phi)\cdot(a + ae\cos\phi)$$

$$= a^2 - a^2e^2\cos^2\phi$$

$$= a^2 - (a^2 - b^2)\cos^2\phi \quad \{\because b^2 = a^2(1-e^2)\}$$

$$= a^2\sin^2\phi + b^2\cos^2\phi = CD^2$$

$$\{\therefore a^2 - b^2 = a^2e^2\}$$

Prop. 4 : *The tangents at the extremities of a pair of conjugate diameters form a parallelogram whose area is constant and equal to product of the axes.*

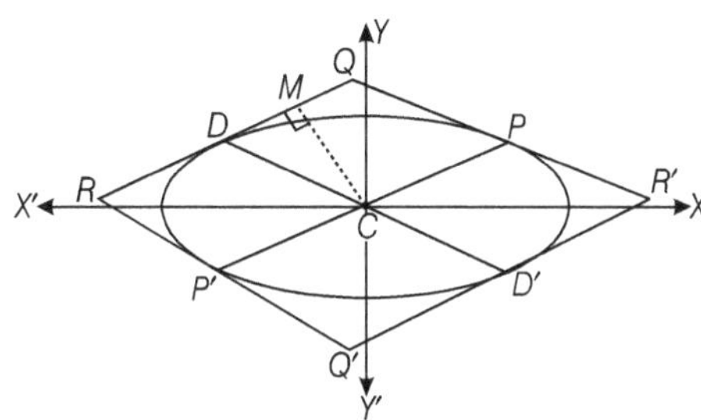

Let PCP' and DCD' be a pair of conjugate diameters of the ellipse $\frac{x^2}{a^2}+\frac{y^2}{b^2}=1$. Let the eccentric angle of P be ϕ. Then the eccentric angle of D is $\left(\frac{\pi}{2}+\phi\right)$ so the coordinates of P and D are

$$(a\cos\phi, b\sin\phi) \text{ and } \left(a\cos\left(\frac{\pi}{2}+\phi\right), b\sin\left(\frac{\pi}{2}+\phi\right)\right)$$

i.e. $(-a\sin\phi, b\cos\phi)$

Similarly the coordinates of P' and D' are

$(-a\cos\phi, -b\sin\phi)$ and $(a\sin\phi, -b\cos\phi)$ respectively.

Equation of tangents at P, D, P' and D' are respectively.

$$\frac{x}{a}\cos\phi+\frac{y}{b}\sin\phi=1, -\frac{x}{a}\sin\phi+\frac{y}{b}\cos\phi=1,$$

$$-\frac{x}{a}\cos\phi-\frac{y}{b}\sin\phi=1$$

and $\frac{x}{a}\sin\phi-\frac{y}{b}\cos\phi=1$

Clearly the tangents at P and P' are parallel. Also, the tangents at D and D' are parallel. Hence, the tangents at P, D, P', D' form a parallelogram.

Area of parallelogram $QRQ'R'=4$

(the area of parallelogram $QDCP$)

$$= 4\cdot|QD|\cdot\{\perp \text{ from } C \text{ on } QD\}$$

$$= 4\cdot|CP|\cdot\{\perp \text{ from } C \text{ on } QD\} \quad \text{...(i)}$$

Now $|CP|=\sqrt{(a^2\cos^2\phi+b^2\sin^2\phi)}$

$\because$ tangent at D is $-\frac{x}{a}\sin\phi+\frac{y}{b}\cos\phi=1$

$\therefore$ $\perp$ from C on

$$QD=\frac{1}{\sqrt{\frac{\sin^2\phi}{a^2}+\frac{\cos^2\phi}{b^2}}}=\frac{ab}{\sqrt{a^2\cos^2\phi+b^2\sin^2\phi}}$$

Now from Eq. (i),

Area of parallelogram $QRQ'R'$

$$= 4\times\sqrt{(a^2\cos^2\phi+b^2\sin^2\phi)}\times\frac{ab}{\sqrt{a^2\cos^2\phi+b^2\sin^2\phi)}}$$

$$= 4ab \,(= \text{constant}) = (2a)(2b)$$

= Area of rectangle contained under major and minor axes.

Prop. 5 : *The polar of any point with respect to ellipse is parallel to the diameter to the one on which the point lies. Hence obtain the equation of the chord whose mid-point is* (h, k).

Let (h, k) be the point on the diameter $y=m_1x$

$\therefore$ $m_1=k/h$

any diameter conjugate to it is $y=m_2x$

but $m_1m_2=-\frac{b^2}{a^2} \Rightarrow \frac{k}{h}m_2=-\frac{b^2}{a^2}$

$\therefore$ $m_2=-\frac{b^2h}{a^2k}$

Polar of (h, k) is $\frac{hx}{a^2}+\frac{ky}{b^2}=1$ ...(i)

Its slope is $-\frac{b^2h}{a^2k}=m_2$ and hence parallel.

Now, equation of chord parallel to the Eq. (i) is

$$\frac{hx}{a^2}+\frac{ky}{b^2}=\lambda \quad \text{...(ii)}$$

It is passes through points (h, k)

$$\therefore \quad \lambda=\frac{h^2}{a^2}+\frac{k^2}{b^2} \quad \text{... (iii)}$$

From Eqs. (ii) and (iii), $\frac{hx}{a^2}+\frac{ky}{b^2}=\frac{h^2}{a^2}+\frac{k^2}{b^2}$

i.e. $T=S_1$

which is the equation of chord of the ellipse, if mid-points is (h, k).

Equi-Conjugate Diameters

Two conjugate diameters are called *equi-conjugate* if their lengths are equal. In such cases therefore.

$$(CP)^2=(CD)^2$$

$\therefore$ $a^2\cos^2\phi+b^2\sin^2\phi=a^2\sin^2\phi+b^2\cos^2\phi$

$\Rightarrow$ $(a^2\cos^2\phi-\sin^2\phi)-b^2(\cos^2\phi-\sin^2\phi)=0$

$\Rightarrow \quad (a^2 - b^2)\cos 2\phi = 0$

$\because \quad (a^2 - b^2) \neq 0$

$\therefore \quad \cos 2\phi = 0$

$\therefore \quad \phi = \frac{\pi}{4}$ or $\frac{3\pi}{4}$

$\therefore \quad (CP) = (CD) = \sqrt{\frac{(a^2 + b^2)}{2}}$

Example 38 Show that the tangents at the ends of conjugate diameters of the ellipse $x^2/a^2 + y^2/b^2 = 1$ intersect on the ellipse $x^2/a^2 + y^2/b^2 = 2$.

Or

Prove that the locus of the poles of the line joining the extremities of two conjugate diameters is the ellipse $x^2/a^2 + y^2/b^2 = 2$.

Sol. Let CP and CD be two semi-conjugate diameters, so that if eccentric angle of P is ϕ then eccentric angle of D is $\frac{\pi}{2} + \phi$

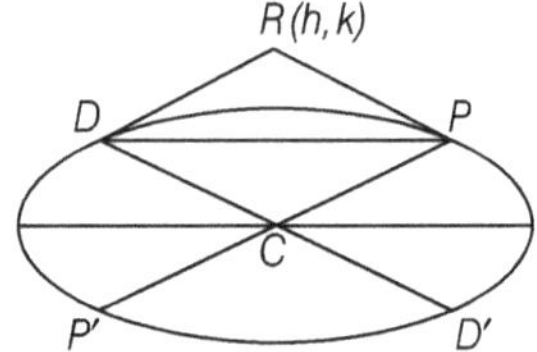

$\therefore$ Coordinates of P and D are

$(a\cos\phi, b\sin\phi)$ and $\left(a\cos\left(\frac{\pi}{2}+\phi\right), b\sin\left(\frac{\pi}{2}+\phi\right)\right)$

respectively

$\therefore$ Equation of (PD) is

$$\frac{x}{a}\cos\left(\frac{\phi + \frac{\pi}{2} + \phi}{2}\right) + \frac{y}{b}\sin\left(\frac{\phi + \frac{\pi}{2} + \phi}{2}\right) = \cos\left(\frac{\frac{\pi}{2} + \phi - \phi}{2}\right)$$

$$\Rightarrow \quad \frac{x}{a}\cos\left(\frac{\pi}{4}+\phi\right) + \frac{y}{b}\sin\left(\frac{\pi}{4}+\phi\right) = \frac{1}{\sqrt{2}} \quad \text{...(i)}$$

If its pole or point of intersection of tangents at its extremities be (h, k), then its equation is the same as that of the polar or the chord of contact of (h, k).

$$\text{i.e.} \quad \frac{hx}{a^2} + \frac{ky}{b^2} = 1 \quad \text{...(ii)}$$

Since, Eqs. (i) and (ii) are identical, comparing

$$\frac{h}{a\cos\left(\frac{\pi}{4}+\phi\right)} = \frac{k}{b\sin\left(\frac{\pi}{4}+\phi\right)} = \sqrt{2}$$

$$\text{or} \quad \sqrt{2}\cos\left(\frac{\pi}{4}+\phi\right) = \frac{h}{a} \quad \text{...(iii)}$$

$$\text{or} \quad \sqrt{2}\sin\left(\frac{\pi}{4}+\phi\right) = \frac{k}{b} \quad \text{...(iv)}$$

Squaring and adding Eqs. (iii) and (iv), then

$$\frac{h^2}{a^2} + \frac{k^2}{b^2} = 2\left(\cos^2\left(\frac{\pi}{4}+\phi\right) + \sin^2\left(\frac{\pi}{4}+\phi\right)\right)$$

$$\therefore \quad \frac{h^2}{a^2} + \frac{k^2}{b^2} = 2$$

Hence, locus of (h, k) is $\frac{x^2}{a^2} + \frac{y^2}{b^2} = 2$

Aliter : Equation of tangents at P and D are

$$\frac{x}{a}\cos\phi + \frac{y}{b}\sin\phi = 1 \quad \text{... (i)}$$

$$\text{and} \quad \frac{x}{a}\cos\left(\frac{\pi}{2}+\phi\right) + \frac{y}{b}\sin\left(\frac{\pi}{2}+\phi\right) = 1$$

$$\text{i.e.} \quad -\frac{x}{a}\sin\phi + \frac{y}{b}\cos\phi = 1 \quad \text{...(ii)}$$

Squaring and adding Eqs. (i) and (ii), we get

$$\frac{x^2}{a^2} + \frac{y^2}{b^2} = 2$$

which is required locus.

Example 39 If $x\cos\alpha + y\sin\alpha = p$ is a chord joining the ends P and D of conjugate semi-diameters, of the ellipse then prove that $a^2\cos^2\alpha + b^2\sin^2 a = 2p^2$ and hence or otherwise deduce that the line PD always touches a similar ellipse.

Sol. Let equation of ellipse be $\frac{x^2}{a^2} + \frac{y^2}{b^2} = 1$, eccentric angle of P is ϕ, then eccentric angle of D is $\frac{\pi}{2} + \phi$

$\therefore$ Coordinates of P and D are

$(a\cos\phi, b\sin\phi)$ and $\left(a\cos\left(\frac{\pi}{2}+\phi\right), b\sin\left(\frac{\pi}{2}+\phi\right)\right)$

$\therefore$ Equation of PD is

$$\frac{x}{a}\cos\left(\frac{\phi + \frac{\pi}{2} + \phi}{2}\right) + \frac{y}{b}\sin\left(\frac{\phi + \frac{\pi}{2} + \phi}{2}\right) = \cos\left(\frac{\frac{\pi}{2} + \phi - \phi}{2}\right)$$

$$\Rightarrow \quad \frac{x}{a}\cos\left(\frac{\pi}{4}+\phi\right) + \frac{y}{b}\sin\left(\frac{\pi}{4}+\phi\right) = \frac{1}{\sqrt{2}} \quad \text{...(i)}$$

If it is same as $x\cos\alpha + y\sin\alpha = p$ ...(ii)

then on comparing, we get

$$\frac{\cos\left(\frac{\pi}{4}+\phi\right)}{a\cos\alpha} = \frac{\sin\left(\frac{\pi}{4}+\phi\right)}{b\sin\alpha} = \frac{1}{p\sqrt{2}}$$

or $$a\cos\alpha = p\sqrt{2}\cos\left(\frac{\pi}{4}+\phi\right) \quad \text{...(iii)}$$

and $$b\sin\alpha = p\sqrt{2}\sin\left(\frac{\pi}{4}+\phi\right) \quad \text{...(iv)}$$

Squaring and adding Eq. (iii) and (iv), we get

$$a^2\cos^2\alpha + b^2\sin^2\alpha = (p\sqrt{2})^2$$
$$\left\{\cos^2\left(\frac{\pi}{4}+\phi\right)+\sin^2\left(\frac{\pi}{4}+\phi\right)\right\}$$

$\Rightarrow$ $$a^2\cos^2\alpha + b^2\sin^2\alpha = 2p^2$$

Again, line Eq. (i) can be written as

$$\frac{x}{a/\sqrt{2}}\cos\theta + \frac{y}{b/\sqrt{2}}\sin\theta = 1,$$

where $$\theta = \frac{\pi}{4}+\phi$$

which is clearly a tangent to the ellipse

$$\frac{x^2}{(a/\sqrt{2})^2}+\frac{y^2}{(b\sqrt{2})^2}=1 \text{ or } \frac{x^2}{a^2}+\frac{y^2}{b^2}=\frac{1}{2} \quad \text{...(v)}$$

If e' be its eccentricity, then

$$(b/\sqrt{2})^2 = (a/\sqrt{2})^2(1-e'^2)$$

$\Rightarrow$ $$b^2 = a^2(1-e'^2)$$

but $$b^2 = a^2(1-e^2)$$

$\therefore$ $$e = e'$$

Hence, ellipse (v) is a similar ellipse.

Director Circle

The locus of the point of intersection of the tangents to an ellipse $\frac{x^2}{a^2}+\frac{y^2}{b^2}=1$ which are perpendicular to each other is called director circle.

Let any tangent in terms of slope of ellipse $\frac{x^2}{a^2}+\frac{y^2}{b^2}=1$ is

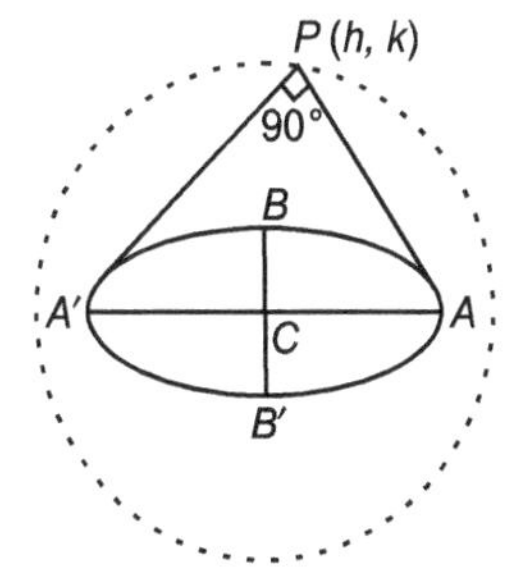

$$y = mx + \sqrt{(a^2m^2+b^2)}$$

It is passes through (h, k)

$\therefore$ $$k = mh + \sqrt{(a^2m^2+b^2)}$$

or $$(k-mh)^2 = a^2m^2+b^2$$

$\Rightarrow$ $$k^2 + m^2h^2 - 2mhk = a^2m^2 + b^2$$

$\Rightarrow$ $$m^2(h^2-a^2) - 2hkm + k^2 - b^2 = 0$$

It is quadratic equation in m let slope of two tangents are m_1 and m_2

$\therefore$ $$m_1m_2 = \frac{k^2-b^2}{h^2-a^2}$$
$$-1 = \frac{k^2-b^2}{h^2-a^2}$$

($\because$ tangents are perpendicular)

$\Rightarrow$ $$-h^2+a^2 = k^2-b^2$$

or $$h^2+k^2 = a^2+b^2$$

Hence, locus of $P(h, k)$ is

$$\boldsymbol{x^2+y^2 = a^2+b^2}$$

Aliter :

If any tangent $y = mx + \sqrt{(a^2m^2+b^2)}$ ...(i)

and $$y = -\frac{x}{m} + \sqrt{\left\{a^2\left(-\frac{1}{m}\right)^2 + b^2\right\}} \quad \text{...(ii)}$$

touch the ellipse and intersect at right angles.

From Eq. (i),

$$y - mx = \sqrt{(a^2m^2+b^2)} \quad \text{...(iii)}$$

Eq. (ii) can be re-written as

$$x + my = \sqrt{(a^2+b^2m^2)} \quad \text{...(iv)}$$

Squaring and adding Eqs. (iii) and (iv), then

$$(y-mx)^2 + (x+my)^2 = a^2m^2 + b^2 + a^2 + b^2m^2$$

$\Rightarrow$ $$(1+m^2)(x^2+y^2) = (1+m^2)(a^2+b^2)$$

Hence, $x^2+y^2 = a^2+b^2$ is the **director circle** of the ellipse.

Example 40 Tangents at right angles are drawn to the ellipse $\frac{x^2}{a^2}+\frac{y^2}{b^2}=1$. Show that the locus of the middle points of the chord of contact is the curve

$$\left(\frac{x^2}{a^2}+\frac{y^2}{b^2}\right)^2 = \frac{x^2+y^2}{a^2+b^2}$$

Sol. Let $Q(h, k)$ be the middle point of the chord of contact

$\therefore$ Equation of chord AB whose mid point $Q(h, k)$ is

$$T = S_1$$

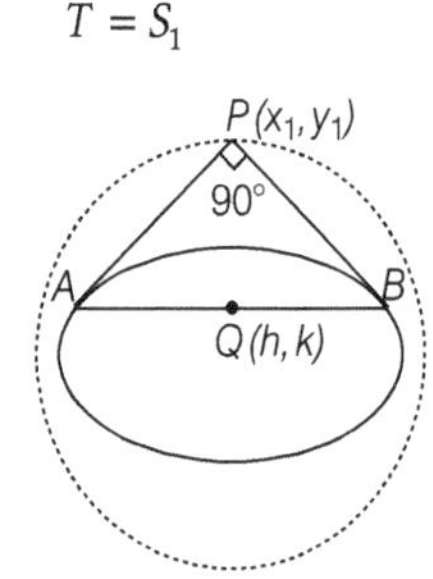

$$\frac{hx}{a^2} + \frac{ky}{b^2} = \frac{h^2}{a^2} + \frac{k^2}{b^2} \quad \text{...(i)}$$

and equation of chord of contact AB with respect to $P(x_1, y_1)$ is

$$\frac{xx_1}{a^2} + \frac{yy_1}{b^2} = 1 \quad \text{...(ii)}$$

the Eqs. (i) and (ii) are identical, hence comparing their coefficient, we get

$$\frac{x_1}{h} = \frac{y_1}{k} = \frac{1}{\left(\frac{h^2}{a^2} + \frac{k^2}{b^2}\right)}$$

$\therefore$
$$x_1 = \frac{h}{\left(\frac{h^2}{a^2} + \frac{k^2}{b^2}\right)} \quad \text{...(iii)}$$

and
$$y_1 = \frac{k}{\left(\frac{h^2}{a^2} + \frac{k^2}{b^2}\right)} \quad \text{...(iv)}$$

Since tangents are at right angles, then the point (x_1, y_1) must lie on the director circle $x^2 + y^2 = a^2 + b^2$ of the ellipse

$$x_1^2 + y_1^2 = a^2 + b^2$$

$$\frac{h^2}{\left(\frac{h^2}{a^2} + \frac{k^2}{b^2}\right)^2} + \frac{k^2}{\left(\frac{h^2}{a^2} + \frac{k^2}{b^2}\right)^2} = a^2 + b^2$$

[from Eqs. (iii) and (iv)]

$\therefore$
$$\left(\frac{h^2}{a^2} + \frac{k^2}{b^2}\right)^2 = \frac{h^2 + k^2}{a^2 + b^2}$$

Hence, locus of mid-point $Q(h, k)$ is $\left(\frac{x^2}{a^2} + \frac{y^2}{b^2}\right)^2 = \frac{x^2 + y^2}{a^2 + b^2}$

Sub-Tangent and Sub-Normal

Let the tangent and normal at $P(x_1, y_1)$ meet the axes at T and G respectively.

Equation of tangent at $P(x_1, y_1)$ to the ellipse $\frac{x^2}{a^2} + \frac{y^2}{b^2} = 1$ is

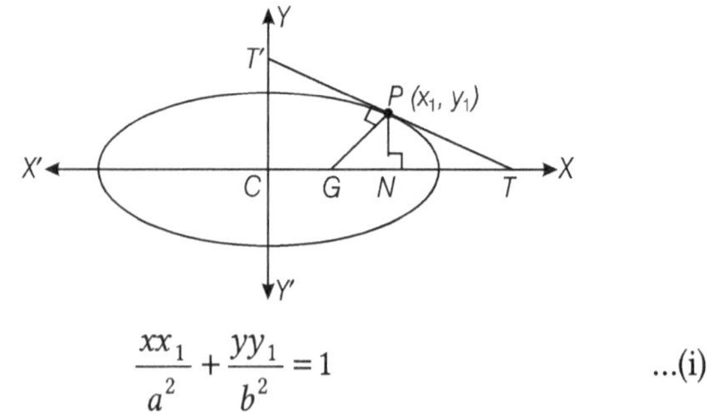

$$\frac{xx_1}{a^2} + \frac{yy_1}{b^2} = 1 \quad \text{...(i)}$$

$\because$ T lies on X-axis.

Put $y = 0$ in Eq. (i) $\Rightarrow x = CT$

$\therefore$ $CT = \frac{a^2}{x_1}$ and $CN = x_1$

and **length of sub-tangent** $NT = CT - CN = \frac{a^2}{x_1} - x_1$

Equation of normal at $P(x_1, y_1)$ to the ellipse

$$\frac{x^2}{a^2} + \frac{y^2}{b^2} = 1 \text{ is}$$

$$\frac{x - x_1}{x_1 / a^2} = \frac{y - y_1}{y_1 / b^2} \quad \text{...(ii)}$$

$\because$ G lies on X-axis. Put $y = 0$ in Eq. (ii)

$\Rightarrow$ $x = CG$

$\therefore$ $CG = x_1 - \frac{b^2}{a^2} x_1$

$\therefore$ **Length of sub-normal**

$$GN = CN - CG = x_1 - \left(x_1 - \frac{b^2}{a^2} x_1\right)$$

$$= \frac{b^2}{a^2} x_1 = (1 - e^2)\, x_1$$

Concyclic Points

Any circle intersects an ellipse in two or four real points. They are called concyclic points and the sum of their eccentric angles is an even multiple of π. If $\alpha, \beta, \gamma, \delta$ be the eccentric angles of the four concyclic points on an ellipse, then prove that $\alpha + \beta + \gamma + \delta = 2n\pi$ where n is any integer.

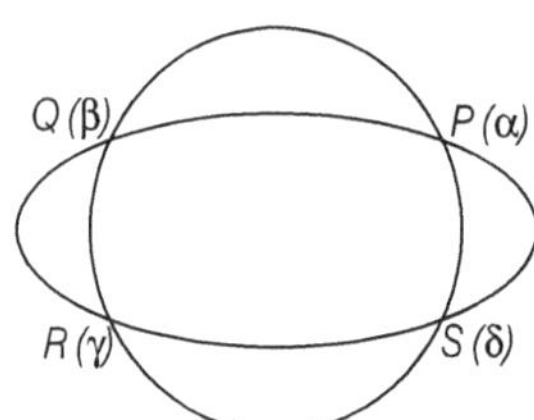

Let the given circle be

$$x^2+y^2+2gx+2fy+c=0 \quad \text{...(i)}$$

and the given ellipse be

$$\frac{x^2}{a^2}+\frac{y^2}{b^2}=1 \quad \text{...(ii)}$$

Let $(a\cos\phi, b\sin\phi)$ be a point of intersection of Eqs. (i) and (ii).

As it lies on the circle Eq. (i).

$$\therefore \quad a^2\cos^2\phi+b^2\sin^2\phi+2ga\cos\phi+2fb\sin\phi+c=0 \quad \text{...(iii)}$$

$$\text{or} \quad a^2\left(\frac{1-\tan^2(\phi/2)}{1+\tan^2(\phi/2)}\right)^2+b^2\left(\frac{2\tan(\phi/2)}{1+\tan^2(\phi/2)}\right)^2$$

$$+2ga\left(\frac{1-\tan^2(\phi/2)}{1+\tan^2(\phi/2)}\right)+2fb\left(\frac{2\tan(\phi/2)}{1+\tan^2(\phi/2)}\right)+c=0 \quad \text{...(iv)}$$

Put $\tan(\phi/2)=t$

$\therefore$ Eq. (iv) reduces to

$$a^2\left(\frac{1-t^2}{1+t^2}\right)^2+b^2\left(\frac{2t}{1+t^2}\right)^2+2ga\left(\frac{1-t^2}{1+t^2}\right)+2fb\left(\frac{2t}{1+t^2}\right)+c=0$$

$$\text{or} \quad (a^2-2ga+c)t^4+4bf\,t^3+(4b^2-2a^2+2c)\,t^2+4bft+(a^2+2ga+c)=0 \quad \text{...(v)}$$

which is biquadratic equation in t.

i.e. it has four values of t

$$t=\tan(\phi/2)$$

Since, four values of eccentric angles are $\alpha, \beta, \gamma, \delta$

$$\therefore \quad \tan\left(\frac{\alpha}{2}+\frac{\beta}{2}+\frac{\gamma}{2}+\frac{\delta}{2}\right)=\frac{S_1-S_3}{1-S_2+S_4}=\frac{\Sigma t_1-\Sigma t_1t_2t_3}{1-\Sigma t_1t_2+t_1t_2t_3t_4}=0$$

$$\Rightarrow \quad \frac{1}{2}(\alpha+\beta+\gamma+\delta)=n\pi$$

$\therefore \quad \alpha+\beta+\gamma+\delta=2n\pi$, when n is any integer.

Aliter : Let P, Q, R, S be four concyclic points on an ellipse, whose eccentric angles $\alpha, \beta, \gamma, \delta$ respectively.

Then equation of the chords PQ and RS are (Take any two chords)

$$\frac{x}{a}\cos\left(\frac{\alpha+\beta}{2}\right)+\frac{y}{b}\sin\left(\frac{\alpha+\beta}{2}\right)-\cos\left(\frac{\alpha-\beta}{2}\right)=0$$

$$\text{and} \quad \frac{x}{a}\cos\left(\frac{\gamma+\delta}{2}\right)+\frac{y}{b}\sin\left(\frac{\gamma+\delta}{2}\right)-\cos\left(\frac{\gamma-\delta}{2}\right)=0$$

Now, the equation of any curve passing through P, Q, R and S is given by

$$\left(\frac{x^2}{a^2}+\frac{y^2}{b^2}-1\right)+\lambda\left(\frac{x}{a}\cos\left(\frac{\alpha+\beta}{2}\right)+\frac{y}{b}\sin\left(\frac{\alpha+\beta}{2}\right)-\cos\left(\frac{\alpha-\beta}{2}\right)\right)$$

$$\times\left(\frac{x}{a}\cos\left(\frac{\gamma+\delta}{2}\right)+\frac{y}{b}\sin\left(\frac{\gamma+\delta}{2}\right)-\cos\left(\frac{\gamma-\delta}{2}\right)\right)=0$$

But the given points are concyclic. Hence this equation will represent a circle, if co-efficient of x^2 = co-efficient y^2. and co-efficient of $xy=0$

Now equation of the co-efficient of $xy=0$

$$\cos\left(\frac{\alpha+\beta}{2}\right)\sin\left(\frac{\gamma+\delta}{2}\right)+\sin\left(\frac{\alpha+\beta}{2}\right)\cos\left(\frac{\gamma+\delta}{2}\right)=0$$

$$\text{or} \quad \sin\left(\frac{\alpha+\beta+\gamma+\delta}{2}\right)=0=\sin n\pi$$

$$\therefore \quad \frac{1}{2}(\alpha+\beta+\gamma+\delta)=n\pi \quad \text{or} \quad \alpha+\beta+\gamma+\delta=2n\pi$$

where, n is any integer.

Hence, the sum of eccentric angles of four concylic points on an ellipse is always an even multiple of π

Corollary 1 : *Prove that the common chords of a circle and an ellipse are equally inclined to the axes of the ellipse.*

If the point of intersection of chords PQ and RS is T, then equation of chord PQ is

$$\frac{x}{a}\cos\left(\frac{\alpha+\beta}{2}\right)+\frac{y}{b}\sin\left(\frac{\alpha+\beta}{2}\right)=\cos\left(\frac{\alpha-\beta}{2}\right)$$

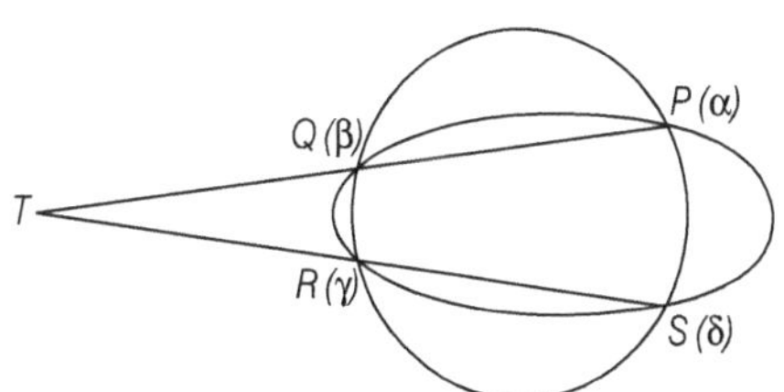

$$\therefore \text{ Slope of } PQ=-\frac{b}{a}\cot\left(\frac{\alpha+\beta}{2}\right)$$

$$=-\frac{b}{a}\cot\left(n\pi-\frac{\gamma+\delta}{2}\right)\quad(\because \alpha+\beta+\gamma+\delta=2n\pi)$$

$$=\frac{b}{a}\cot\left(\frac{\gamma+\delta}{2}\right)=-\text{(slope of } RS)$$

Hence, PQ and RS are equally inclined to the axis of x.

Corollary 2 : *Find the centre of the circle passing through the three points on an ellipse whose eccentric angles are* α, β, γ.

Let the point of intersection of ellipse

$$\frac{x^2}{a^2} + \frac{y^2}{b^2} = 1 \quad \text{...(i)}$$

and circle $x^2 + y^2 + 2gx + 2fy + c = 0$ ...(ii)

be $\alpha, \beta, \gamma, \delta$

$\therefore \quad \alpha + \beta + \gamma + \delta = 2n\pi$ (where n is an integer)

Let ϕ be any point on Eq. (i)

$\therefore \quad x = a\cos\phi, y = b\sin\phi$

This point also lie on Eq. (ii)

$\therefore \quad a^2\cos^2\phi + b^2\sin^2\phi + 2ga\cos\phi + 2fb\sin\phi + c = 0$...(iii)

$$\Rightarrow \{(a^2 - b^2)\cos^2\phi + 2ga\cos\phi + (b^2 + c)\}^2 = 4f^2b^2(1 - \cos^2\phi)$$

$$\Rightarrow (a^2 - b^2)^2\cos^4\phi + 4ga(a^2 - b)\cos^3\phi + \{2(a^2 - b^2)(b^2 + c) + 4g^2a^2 + 4f^2b^2\}\cos^2\phi + 4ga(b^2 + c)\cos\phi + \{b^2 + c^2 - 4f^2b^2\} = 0$$

This is a fourth degree equation in $\cos\phi$.

It has four roots (i.e. $\cos\alpha, \cos\beta, \cos\gamma, \cos\delta$)

$$\therefore \quad \cos\alpha + \cos\beta + \cos\gamma + \cos\delta = -\frac{4ga}{(a^2 - b^2)} \quad \text{...(iv)}$$

Similarly changing Eq. (iii) in $\sin\phi$, we get

$$\sin\alpha + \sin\beta + \sin\gamma + \sin\delta = -\frac{4fb}{b^2 - a^2} \quad \text{...(v)}$$

$\because \quad \alpha + \beta + \gamma + \delta = 2n\pi$

$\therefore \quad \delta = 2n\pi - (\alpha + \beta + \gamma)$

$\therefore \quad \sin\delta = -\{\sin(\alpha + \beta + \gamma)\}$ and $\cos\delta = \cos(\alpha + \beta + \gamma)$

then, from Eqs. (iv) and (v), we get

$$-g = \left(\frac{a^2 - b^2}{4a}\right)\{\cos\alpha + \cos\beta + \cos\gamma + \cos(\alpha + \beta + \gamma)\}$$

and $$-f = \left(\frac{b^2 - a^2}{4b}\right)\{\sin\alpha + \sin\beta + \sin\gamma - \sin(\alpha + \beta + \gamma)\}$$

which give co-ordinate of centre of circle through α, β and γ.

Corollary 3 : *$P'CP$ and $D'CD$ are conjugate diameters of an ellipse and α is the eccentric angle of P. Prove that the eccentric angle of the point where the circle through P, P′, D again cuts the ellipse is* $\frac{\pi}{2} - 3\alpha$.

The eccentric angles of P, P' and D are $\alpha, \pi + \alpha, \frac{\pi}{2} + \alpha$ respectively. Let β be the eccentric angle of the fourth point.

As above

$$\alpha + (\pi + \alpha) + \left(\frac{\pi}{2} + \alpha\right) + \beta = 2n\pi$$

$$\therefore \quad \beta = 2n\pi - \left(\frac{3\pi}{2} + 3\alpha\right) = \frac{\pi}{2} - 3\alpha \quad (\text{for } n = 1)$$

Note

Any other values of n gives the same point on the ellipse.

Some Standard Properties of the Ellipse

(i) If S be the focus and G be the point where the normal at P meets the axis of an ellipse, then $SG = e \cdot SP$ and the tangent and normal at P bisects the external and internal angles between the focal distances of P.

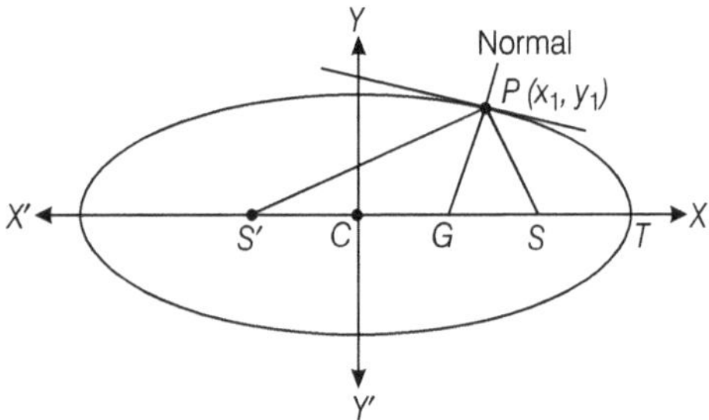

Let P be any point on the ellipse

$$\frac{x^2}{a^2} + \frac{y^2}{b^2} = 1$$

$\therefore$ Equation of normals PG is

$$(x - x_1)\frac{a^2}{x_1} = (y - y_1)\frac{b^2}{y_1}$$

Putting $y = 0$. For the point G, we have

$$(x - x_1)\frac{a^2}{x_1} = -b^2$$

$$\therefore x = CG = \left(\frac{a^2 - b^2}{a^2}\right)x_1 = \frac{a^2e^2}{a^2}x_1 = e^2x_1$$

$$\therefore \quad SG = CS - CG = ae - e^2x_1 = e(a - ex_1) = eSP$$

Similarly $S'G = eS'P$

$$\therefore \quad \frac{SG}{S'G} = \frac{eSP}{eS'P} = \frac{SP}{S'P}$$

$\therefore$ The normal PG bisects the internal $\angle SPS'$ between the focal distances but tangent and normal are at right angles, the tangent PT bisects the external angle SPL between them.

(ii) The locus of the feet of the perpendiculars from the foci on any tangent to an ellipse is the auxiliary circle.

The equation of any tangent in terms slope (m) of the ellipse $\frac{x^2}{a^2}+\frac{y^2}{b^2}=1$ is

$$y = mx + \sqrt{(a^2m^2+b^2)}$$

or $$y - mx = \sqrt{(a^2m^2+b^2)} \quad ...(i)$$

Equation of perpendicular line of Eq. (i) and passes through $(\pm ae, 0)$ is

$$my + x = \pm ae \quad ...(ii)$$

The locus of the point of intersection of the line given by Eqs. (i) and (ii) can be obtained by eliminating m between them, squaring and adding Eqs. (i) and (ii), we get

$$y^2(1+m^2)+x^2(1+m^2)=a^2m^2+b^2+a^2e^2$$

$$\Rightarrow \quad (1+m^2)(x^2+y^2)=a^2m^2+a^2$$

$$=a^2(1+m^2)$$

or $$x^2+y^2=a^2$$

which is the equation of the auxiliary circle of the ellipse $\frac{x^2}{a^2}+\frac{y^2}{b^2}=1.$

Reflection Property of an Ellipse

If an incoming light ray passes through on focus (S) strike the concave side of the ellipse, then it will get reflected towards other focus (S').

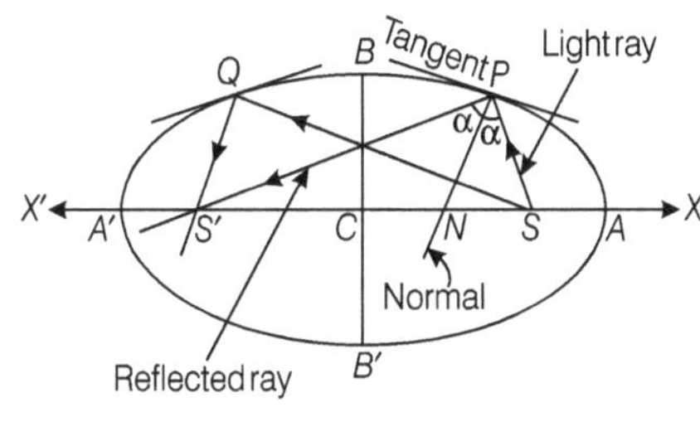

and $$\angle SPS' = \angle SQS'$$

Example 41 A ray emanating from the point $(-3, 0)$ is incident on the ellipse $16x^2+25y^2=400$ at the point P with ordinate 4. Find the equation of the reflected ray after first reflection.

Sol. For point P, y-coordinate $= 4$

$\because$ Given ellipse is $16x^2+25y^2=400$

$$16x^2+25(4)^2=400$$

Coordinate of P is $(0, 4)$

$$e^2 = 1-\frac{16}{25}=\frac{9}{25}$$

$$e=\frac{3}{5}$$

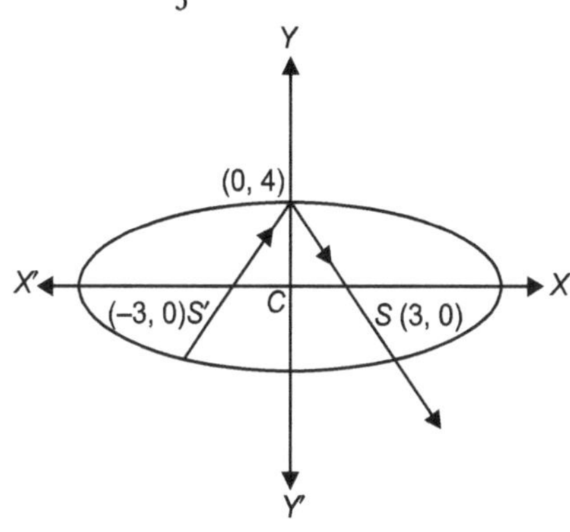

foci $(\pm ae, 0)$ i.e. $(\pm 3, 0)$

Equation of reflected ray (i.e. PS) is

$$\frac{x}{3}+\frac{y}{4}=1 \text{ or } 4x+3y=12.$$

Equation of an Ellipse Referred to Two Perpendicular Lines

Let $P(x, y)$ be any point on the ellipse $\frac{x^2}{a^2}+\frac{y^2}{b^2}=1$

then, $$y = PM, x = PN$$

$$\therefore \quad \frac{(PN)^2}{a^2}+\frac{(PM)^2}{b^2}=1$$

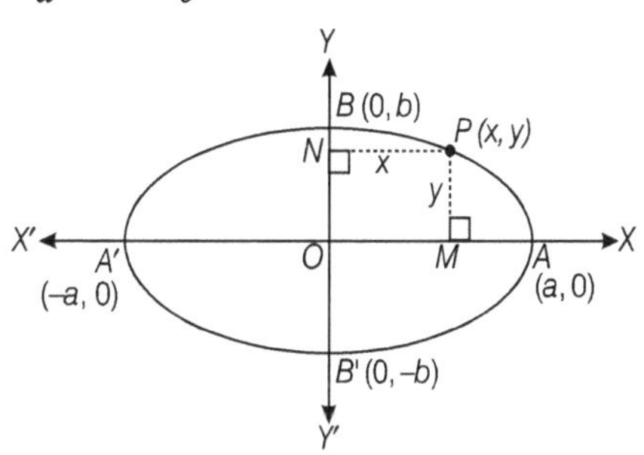

suppose if axes along the lines

$$a_1x + b_1y + c_1 = 0 \text{ and } b_1x - a_1y + c_2 = 0$$

then
$$PN = \frac{|a_1x + b_1y + c_1|}{\sqrt{(a_1^2 + b_1^2)}}$$

$$PM = \frac{|b_1x - a_1y + c_2|}{\sqrt{(b_1^2 + a_1^2)}}$$

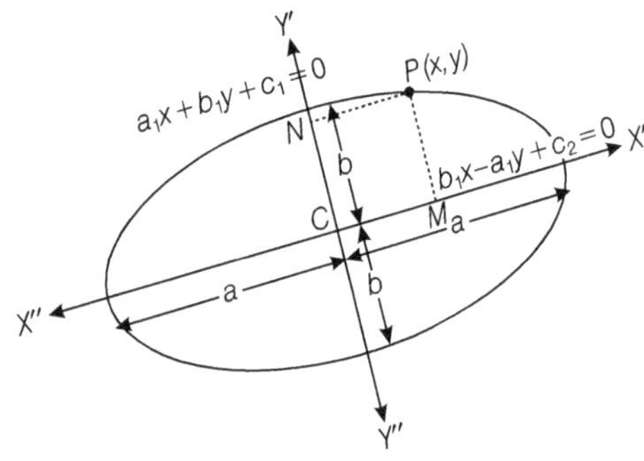

then, equation of ellipse is

$$\frac{\left\{\frac{a_1x + b_1y + c_1}{\sqrt{(a_1^2 + b_1^2)}}\right\}^2}{a^2} + \frac{\left\{\frac{b_1x - a_1y + c_2}{\sqrt{(b_1^2 + a_1^2)}}\right\}^2}{b^2} = 1$$

Centre : Is the point of intersection of $a_1x + b_1y + c_1 = 0$ and $b_1x - a_1y + c_2 = 0$

Equations of Major and Minor Axes :

(i) If $a > b$, then major axis lies along $b_1x - a_1y + c_2 = 0$ and minor axis lies along $a_1x + b_1y + c_1 = 0$.

(ii) If $a < b$, then major axis lies along $a_1x + b_1y + c_1 = 0$ and minor axis lies along $b_1x - a_1y + c_2 = 0$

Eccentricity :

(i) If $a > b$, $b^2 = a^2(1 - e^2)$ (ii) If $a < b$, $a^2 = b^2(1 - e^2)$

Foci :

(i) If $a > b$

$$\frac{a_1x + b_1y + c_1}{\sqrt{(a_1^2 + b_1^2)}} = \pm ae, \frac{b_1x - a_1y + c_2}{\sqrt{(b_1^2 + a_1^2}} = 0$$

we get after solving (x, y)

(ii) If $a < b$

$$\frac{a_1x + b_1y + c_1}{\sqrt{a_1^2 + b_1^2}} = 0, \frac{b_1x - a_1y + c_2}{\sqrt{b_1^2 + a_1^2}} = \pm be$$

we get after solving (x, y)

Directrices :

(i) If $a > b$,

$$\frac{a_1x + b_1y + c_1}{\sqrt{(a_1^2 + b_1^2)}} = \pm \frac{a}{e}$$

(ii) If $a < b$,

$$\frac{b_1x - a_1y + c_2}{\sqrt{(a_1^2 + b_1^2)}} = \pm \frac{b}{e}$$

Example 42 Determine the equations of major and minor axes of the ellipse

$$4(x - 2y + 1)^2 + 9(2x + y + 2)^2 = 25$$

Also, find its centre, length of the latusrectum and eccentricity.

Sol. The equation of the ellipse can be written as

$$4 \times 5\left(\frac{x - 2y + 1}{\sqrt{5}}\right)^2 + 9 \times 5\left(\frac{2x + y + 2}{\sqrt{5}}\right)^2 = 25$$

or
$$\frac{\left(\frac{x - 2y + 1}{\sqrt{5}}\right)^2}{(5/4)} + \frac{\left(\frac{2x + y + 2}{\sqrt{5}}\right)^2}{(5/9)} = 1$$

or
$$\frac{X^2}{a^2} + \frac{Y^2}{b^2} = 1$$

Here $a > b$

$\therefore$ **Equation of major axis is** $Y = 0$

i.e. $2x + y + 2 = 0$

and **Equation of minor axis is** $X = 0$

i.e. $x - 2y + 1 = 0$

Centre : $X = 0, Y = 0$

$\Rightarrow$ $x - 2y + 1 = 0, 2x + y + 2 = 0$

we get $x = -1, y = 0$

$\therefore$ Centre is $(-1, 0)$

Length of latusrectum $= \frac{2b^2}{a} = \frac{2 \times 5/9}{5/4} = \frac{8}{9}$

Eccentricity : $b^2 = a^2(1 - e^2)$

$$\Rightarrow \frac{5}{9} = \frac{5}{4}(1 - e^2)$$

$$\Rightarrow \frac{4}{9} = 1 - e^2$$

$$\Rightarrow e^2 = \frac{5}{9}$$

$$\therefore e = \frac{\sqrt{5}}{3}$$

Exercise for Session 3

1. The angle between the pair of tangents drawn from the point (1, 2) to the ellipse $3x^2 + 2y^2 = 5$ is

(a) $\tan^{-1}\left(\frac{12}{5}\right)$ (b) $\tan^{-1}\left(\frac{6}{\sqrt{5}}\right)$ (c) $\tan^{-1}\left(\frac{12}{\sqrt{5}}\right)$ (d) $\tan^{-1}(12\sqrt{5})$

2. If chords of contact of tangents from two points (x_1, y_1) and (x_2, y_2) to the ellipse $\frac{x^2}{a^2} + \frac{y^2}{b^2} = 1$ are at right angles, then $\frac{x_1x_2}{y_1y_2}$ is equal to

(a) $\frac{a^2}{b^2}$ (b) $-\frac{b^2}{a^2}$ (c) $-\frac{a^4}{b^4}$ (d) $-\frac{b^4}{a^4}$

3. From the point $(\lambda, 3)$ tangents are drawn to $\frac{x^2}{9} + \frac{y^2}{4} = 1$ and are perpendicular to each other than λ is

(a) ± 1 (b) ± 2 (c) ± 3 (d) ± 4

4. The eccentric angle of one end of a diameter of $x^2 + 3y^2 = 3$ is $\pi/6$, then the eccentric angle of the other end will be

(a) $\frac{5\pi}{6}$ (b) $-\frac{5\pi}{6}$ (c) $-\frac{2\pi}{3}$ (d) $\frac{2\pi}{3}$

5. The locus of the mid-points of a focal chord of the ellipse $\frac{x^2}{a^2} + \frac{y^2}{b^2} = 1$ is

(a) $\frac{x^2}{a^2} + \frac{y^2}{b^2} = \frac{ex}{a}$ (b) $\frac{x^2}{a^2} - \frac{y^2}{b^2} = \frac{ex}{a}$ (c) $x^2 + y^2 = a^2 + b^2$ (d) $x^2 - y^2 = a^2 + b^2$

6. The centre of the ellipse $\frac{(x + y - 2)^2}{9} + \frac{(x - y)^2}{16} = 1$ is

(a) (0, 0) (b) (1, 0) (c) (0, 1) (d) (1, 1)

7. The locus of the point of intersection of two perpendicular tangents of the ellipse $\frac{x^2}{9} + \frac{y^2}{4} = 1$ is

(a) $x^2 + y^2 = 4$ (b) $x^2 + y^2 = 9$ (c) $x^2 + y^2 = 13$ (d) $x^2 + y^2 = 5$

8. The area of the parallelogram inscribed in the ellipse $\frac{x^2}{a^2} + \frac{y^2}{b^2} = 1$ whose diagonals are the conjugate diameters of the ellipse is given by

(a) $2ab$ (b) $3ab$ (c) $4ab$ (d) $5ab$

9. Find the locus of the vertices of equilateral triangle circumscribing the ellipse $\frac{x^2}{a^2} + \frac{y^2}{b^2} = 1$.

10. A tangent to the ellipse $x^2 + 4y^2 = 4$ meets the ellipse $x^2 + 2y^2 = 6$ at P and Q. Prove that the tangents at P and Q of the ellipse $x^2 + 2y^2 = 6$ are at right angles.

11. Find the locus of the mid-point of chords of the ellipse $\frac{x^2}{a^2} + \frac{y^2}{b^2} = 1 (a > b)$ passing through the point $(2a, 0)$.

12. Find the locus of the point the chord of contact of tangents from which to the ellipse $\frac{x^2}{a^2} + \frac{y^2}{b^2} = 1$, touches the circle $x^2 + y^2 = c^2$.

13. Find the centre and eccentricity of the ellipse

$$4(x - 2y + 1)^2 + 9(2x + y + 2)^2 = 5$$

14. A ray emanating from the point $(0, -\sqrt{5})$ is incident on the ellipse $9x^2 + 4y^2 = 36$ at the point P with abscissa 2. Find the equation of the reflected ray after first reflection.

Shortcuts and Important Results to Remember

1 If S and S' are foci and P be a point, then

(a) If $|SP| + |S'P| > |SS'|$, then the locus of P is an ellipse.

(b) If $|SP| + |S'P| = |SS'|$, then the locus of P is a straight line.

(c) If $|SP| + |S'P| < |SS'|$, then the locus of P is an empty set.

2 If the ellipses $\frac{x^2}{a^2} + \frac{y^2}{b^2} = 1, \frac{x^2}{\alpha^2} + \frac{y^2}{\beta^2} = 1$ and $\frac{x^2}{\theta^2} + \frac{y^2}{\phi^2} = 1$ have a common tangent, then $\begin{vmatrix} a^2 & b^2 & 1 \\ \alpha^2 & \beta^2 & 1 \\ \theta^2 & \phi^2 & 1 \end{vmatrix} = 0$

3 Area of the quadrilateral formed by the common tangents of the circle $x^2 + y^2 = c^2$ and the ellipse $\frac{x^2}{a^2} + \frac{y^2}{b^2} = 1$; $c \in (a, b)$ is $\frac{2c^2|a^2 - b^2|}{\sqrt{(a^2 - c^2)(c^2 - b^2)}}$

4 The product of the two perpendicular distances from the foci on any tangent of an ellipse is b^2.

5 If the normals at the point $P(x_1, y_1); Q(x_2, y_2)$ and $R(x_3, y_3)$ on the ellipse $\frac{x^2}{a^2} + \frac{y^2}{b^2} = 1$ are concurrent, then

$\begin{vmatrix} x_1 & y_1 & x_1y_1 \\ x_2 & y_2 & x_2y_2 \\ x_3 & y_3 & x_3y_3 \end{vmatrix} = 0$ and if points $P(\alpha), Q(\beta)$ and $R(\gamma)$, then

$$\begin{vmatrix} \sec\alpha & \operatorname{cosec}\alpha & 1 \\ \sec\beta & \operatorname{cosec}\beta & 1 \\ \sec\gamma & \operatorname{cosec}\gamma & 1 \end{vmatrix} = 0$$

6 If ellipse $\frac{x^2}{a^2} + \frac{y^2}{b^2} = 1$, then

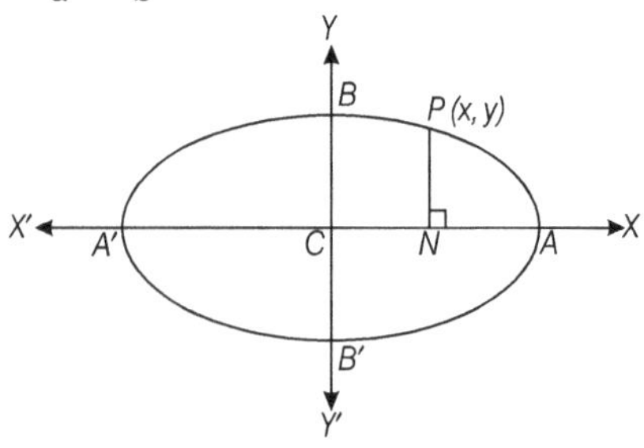

$$(PN)^2 : AN \cdot A'N = (BC)^2 : (AC)^2$$

7 If α and β are the eccentric angles of extremittes of a focal chord of the ellipse $\frac{x^2}{a^2} + \frac{y^2}{b^2} = 1$, then $\tan(\alpha/2).\tan(\beta/2) = \frac{e-1}{e+1}$ or $\frac{e+1}{e-1}$ according as focus $(ae, 0)$ or $(-ae, 0)$.

8 If the tangent at P on an ellipse meets the directrix in F; then the PF will subtend a right angle at the corresponding focus.

i.e. $\angle PSF = \pi/2$

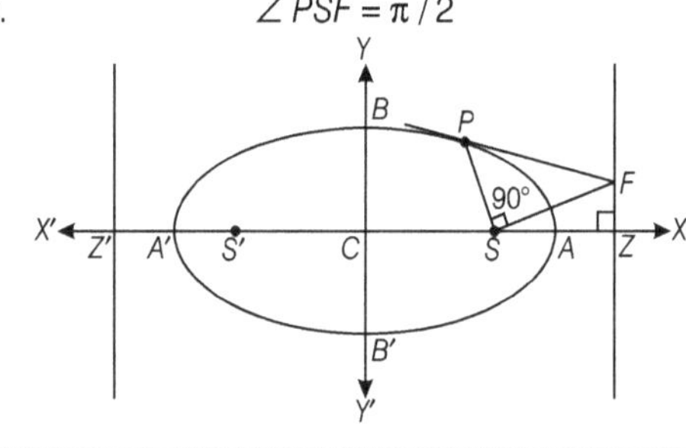

JEE Type Solved Examples : Single Option Correct Type Questions

- This section contains **10 multiple choice examples.** Each example has four choices (a), (b), (c) and (d) out of which **ONLY ONE** is correct.

Ex. 1 *Point 'O' is the centre of the ellipse with major axis AB and minor axis CD. Point F is one focus of the ellipse. If $OF = 6$ and the diameter of the inscribed circle of triangle OCF is 2, then the product $(AB)(CD)$ is equal to*

(a) 52 (b) 56 (c) 78 (d) None of these

Sol. (b) $\because$ Diameter of the inscribed circle of triangle OCF is 2.

$\therefore$ Radius $= 1$

Centre of the circle is (1, 1) and equation of CF is $\frac{x}{6} + \frac{y}{b} = 1$

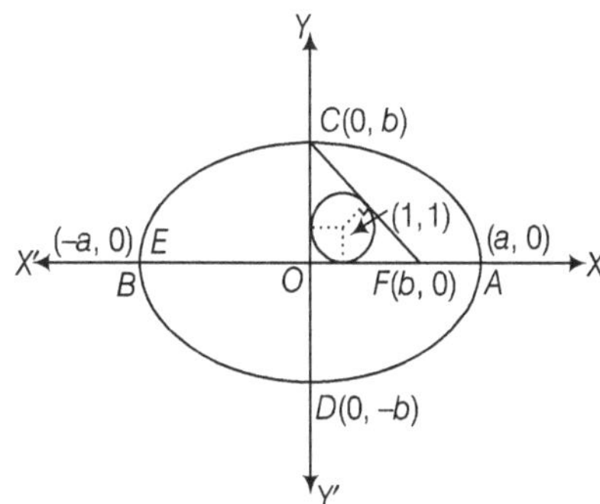

Now, length of perpendicular from (1, 1) on $CF = 1$ (radius)

$$\Rightarrow \quad \frac{\left|\frac{1}{6} + \frac{1}{b} - 1\right|}{\sqrt{\left(\frac{1}{36} + \frac{1}{b^2}\right)}} = 1 \text{ or } -\left(\frac{1}{b} - \frac{5}{6}\right) = \sqrt{\left(\frac{1}{36} + \frac{1}{b^2}\right)}$$

$$\Rightarrow \quad \left(\frac{5}{6} - \frac{1}{b}\right) = \sqrt{\left(\frac{1}{36} + \frac{1}{b^2}\right)}$$

On squaring both sides, then $\left(\frac{5}{6} - \frac{1}{b}\right)^2 = \frac{1}{36} + \frac{1}{b^2}$

$$\Rightarrow \quad \frac{25}{36} + \frac{1}{b^2} - \frac{5}{3b} = \frac{1}{36} + \frac{1}{b^2}$$

$$\Rightarrow \quad \frac{5}{3b} = \frac{24}{36} = \frac{2}{3}$$

$$\therefore \quad b = \frac{5}{2}$$

Also, $b^2 = a^2(1 - e^2)$

$$b^2 = a^2 - (ae)^2$$

$$\Rightarrow \quad a^2 = b^2 + (ae)^2 = \frac{25}{4} + 36 \quad [\because ae = 6]$$

$$\Rightarrow \quad a = \frac{13}{2}$$

Hence, $(AB)(CD) = (2a)(2b) = 13 \times 5 = 65$

Ex. 2 *Let P_i and P_i' be the feet of the perpendiculars drawn from the foci S and S' on a tangent T_i to an ellipse whose length of semi-major axis is 20. If $\sum_{i=1}^{10} (SP_i)(S'P_i') = 2560$, then the value of eccentricity is*

(a) $\frac{1}{5}$ (b) $\frac{2}{5}$

(c) $\frac{3}{5}$ (d) $\frac{4}{5}$

Sol. (c) $\therefore$ Product of length of perpendiculars from foci on a tangent to an ellipse $= b^2$

$$\therefore \quad (SP_1)(S'P_1) = (SP_2)(S'P_2) = \ldots = (SP_{10})(S'P_{10}') = b^2$$

Given $\sum_{i=1}^{10} (SP_i)(S'P_i') = 2560$

$$\Rightarrow \quad 10b^2 = 2560 \text{ or } b^2 = 256$$

or $\quad b = 16$

and $\quad b^2 = a^2(1 - e^2)$

$$\Rightarrow \quad (16)^2 = (20)^2(1 - e^2)$$

or $\quad 1 - e^2 = \frac{16}{25}$

or $\quad e^2 = \frac{9}{25}$ or $e = \frac{3}{5}$

Ex. 3 *Coordinates of the vertices B and C of a ΔABC are (2, 0) and (8, 0) respectively. The vertex A is varing in such a way that $4\tan\left(\frac{B}{2}\right).\tan\left(\frac{C}{2}\right) = 1$. Then, the locus of A is*

(a) $\frac{(x-5)^2}{25} + \frac{y^2}{16} = 1$ (b) $\frac{(x-5)^2}{16} + \frac{y^2}{9} = 1$

(c) $\frac{(x-5)^2}{25} + \frac{y^2}{9} = 1$ (d) $\frac{(x-5)^2}{16} + \frac{y^2}{25} = 1$

Sol. (a) $\because 4\tan\left(\frac{B}{2}\right) \cdot \tan\left(\frac{C}{2}\right) = 1$

$$\Rightarrow \quad 4 \times \sqrt{\frac{(s-c)(s-a)}{s(s-b)}} \times \sqrt{\frac{(s-a)(s-b)}{s(s-c)}} = 1$$

$$\Rightarrow \quad \frac{s-a}{s} = \frac{1}{4}$$

$$\Rightarrow \quad 3s = 4a$$

$$\Rightarrow \quad 3\left(\frac{a+b+c}{2}\right) = 4a$$

or $\quad b + c = \frac{5a}{3} = 10 = 2a_1$, $\quad [\because a = BC = 6]$

Since, the sum of distances of A from two given fixed points B and C is always 10.

Here, B and C are foci.

$\therefore$ Centre (5, 0) and distance between foci $=6$

$$\Rightarrow \quad 2a_1 e = 6$$

$$\Rightarrow \quad e = \frac{6}{10} = \frac{3}{5} \quad [\because a_1 = 5]$$

and $$b^2 = a_1^2(1-e^2) = 25\left(1 - \frac{9}{25}\right) = 16 \text{ or } b = 4$$

$\because$ A lies on the ellipse

$\therefore$ Locus of A is

$$\frac{(x-5)^2}{(5)^2} + \frac{(y-0)^2}{(4)^2} = 1$$

or $$\frac{(x-5)^2}{25} + \frac{y^2}{16} = 1$$

Ex. 4 *A ray emanating from the point (0, 6) is incident on the ellipse $25x^2 + 16y^2 = 1600$ at the point P with ordinate S. After reflection, ray cuts the Y-axis at B. The length of PB is*

(a) 5 (b) 7 (c) 12 (d) 13

Sol. (d) $\because$ Ellipse is $25x^2 + 16y^2 = 1600$

or $$\frac{x^2}{8^2} + \frac{y^2}{10^2} = 1$$

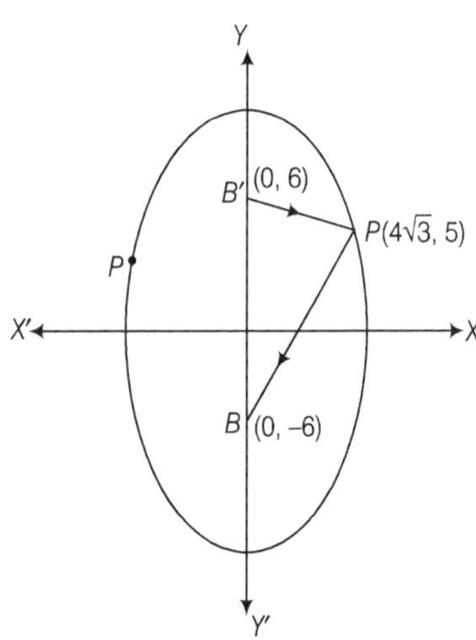

Coordinating foci an $\left(0, \pm\sqrt{(10^2 - 8^2)}\right)$

i.e. $(0, \pm 6)$

Let coordinates of P are $(\lambda, 5)$

$$\therefore \quad \frac{\lambda^2}{8^2} + \frac{5^2}{10^2} = 1$$

$$\Rightarrow \quad \lambda = \pm 4\sqrt{3}$$

$\therefore$ $P \equiv (\pm 4\sqrt{3}, 5)$ (lie in I or II quadrants)

According to reflection property, a ray passing through focus $B'(0, 6)$ will passing through $B(0, -6)$ (other focus). If P lies in I quadrant, then

$$PB = \sqrt{48 + (5+6)^2} = \sqrt{169} = 13$$

Ex. 5 *If the ellipse $\frac{x^2}{4} + y^2 = 1$ meets the ellipse $x^2 + \frac{y^2}{a^2} = 1$ in four distinct points and $a = b^2 - 5b + 7$, then b belongs to*

(a) (1, 4) (b) $(-\infty, 2) \cup (3, \infty)$

(c) (2, 3) (d) None of these

Sol. (b) The ellipse $\frac{x^2}{1^2} + \frac{y^2}{a^2} = 1$ will intersect in four distinct points with ellipse $\frac{x^2}{4} + \frac{y^2}{1} = 1$, where $a^2 > 1$

$$\Rightarrow \quad a > 1 \quad [\because \text{a always positive}]$$

Now, $$a = b^2 - 5b + 7$$

$$\Rightarrow \quad b^2 - 5b + 7 > 1$$

or $$b^2 - 5b + 6 > 0$$

or $$(b-2)(b-3) > 0$$

or $$b \in (-\infty, 2) \cup (3, \infty)$$

Ex. 6 *The normal at a variable point P on an ellipse $\frac{x^2}{a^2} + \frac{y^2}{b^2} = 1$ of eccentricity e meets the axes of the ellipse in Q and R, then the locus of the mid-point of QR is a conic with eccentricity e′ such that*

(a) e' is independent of e (b) $e' = 1$

(c) $e' = e$ (d) $e' = \frac{1}{e}$

Sol. (c) Normal at $P(a\cos\theta, b\sin\theta)$ is

$$ax\sec\theta - by\,\text{cosec}\,\theta = a^2 - b^2 \quad (\text{let } a > b)$$

It meets the axes at

$$Q\left(\frac{(a^2-b^2)}{a}\cos\theta, 0\right) \text{ and } R\left(0, -\frac{(a^2-b^2)}{b}\sin\theta\right)$$

Let mid-point of QR is $T(x, y)$, then

$$2x = \frac{(a^2-b^2)}{a}\cos\theta$$

or $$2ax = (a^2-b^2)\cos\theta \quad \text{...(i)}$$

and $$2y = -\frac{(a^2-b^2)}{b}\sin\theta$$

or $$2by = -(a^2-b^2)\sin\theta \quad \text{...(ii)}$$

On squaring and adding Eq. (i) and Eq.(ii), we get

$$4a^2x^2 + 4b^2y^2 = (a^2-b^2)^2$$

$$\Rightarrow \quad \frac{x^2}{\left(\frac{a^2-b^2}{2a}\right)^2} + \frac{y^2}{\left(\frac{a^2-b^2}{2b}\right)^2} = 1$$

which is an ellipse, having eccentricity e', then

Let $$A = \frac{a^2-b^2}{2a}, B = \frac{a^2-b^2}{2b}$$

$$A^2 = B^2(1-e'^2) \qquad [\because B > A]$$

$$\Rightarrow \quad e'^2 = 1 - \frac{A^2}{B^2} = 1 - \frac{b^2}{a^2} = e^2$$

$$\therefore \quad e' = e$$

Ex. 7 *If the curves* $\frac{x^2}{4} + y^2 = 1$ *and* $\frac{x^2}{a^2} + y^2 = 1$ *for a suitable value of a cut on four concyclic points, the equation of the circle passing through these four points is*

(a) $x^2 + y^2 = 8$ (b) $x^2 + y^2 = 4$

(c) $x^2 + y^2 = 2$ (d) $x^2 + y^2 = 1$

Sol. (d) The equation of conic through the point of intersection of given two ellipses is

$$\left(\frac{x^2}{4} + y^2 - 1\right) + \lambda\left(\frac{x^2}{a^2} + y^2 - 1\right) = 0$$

or $$x^2\left(\frac{1}{4} + \frac{\lambda}{a^2}\right) + y^2(1+\lambda) = (1+\lambda)$$

or $$x^2\left(\frac{a^2 + 4\lambda}{4a^2(1+\lambda)}\right) + y^2 = 1$$

for circle $$\frac{a^2 + 4\lambda}{4a^2(1+\lambda)} = 1$$

$$\Rightarrow \quad \lambda = -\frac{3a^2}{4(a^2-1)}$$

Therefore, the circle is $x^2 + y^2 = 1$

Ex. 8 *If p is the length of perpendicular drawn from the origin to any normal to the ellipse* $\frac{x^2}{25} + \frac{y^2}{16} = 1$, *then the maximum value of p is*

(a) 5 (b) 4

(c) 2 (d) 1

Sol. (d) The equation of any normal at $(5\cos\theta, 4\sin\theta)$ to the ellipse $\frac{x^2}{25} + \frac{y^2}{16} = 1$ is

$$5x\sec\theta - 4y\,\text{cosec}\,\theta = 9$$

$$\therefore \quad p = \frac{|0-0-9|}{\sqrt{(25\sec^2\theta + 16\,\text{cosec}^2\theta)}} = \frac{9}{\sqrt{(25\tan^2\theta + 16\cot^2\theta + 41)}}$$

Now, AM $\geq$ GM

$$\Rightarrow \quad \frac{25\tan^2\theta + 16\cot^2\theta}{2} \geq \sqrt{25 \times 16} = 20$$

$$\therefore \quad 25\tan^2\theta + 16\cot^2\theta \geq 40$$

$$\Rightarrow \quad 25\tan^2\theta + 16\cot^2\theta + 41 \geq 81$$

or $$\frac{9}{\sqrt{(25\tan^2\theta + 16\cot^2\theta + 41)}} \leq 1$$

$$\Rightarrow \quad p \leq 1$$

Thus, maximum value of p is 1.

Ex. 9 *If $f(x)$ is a decreasing function, then the set of values of 'k', for which the major axis of the ellipse* $\frac{x^2}{f(k^2+2k+5)} + \frac{y^2}{f(k+11)} = 1$ *is the X-axis, is*

(a) $k \in (-2, 3)$

(b) $k \in (-3, 2)$

(c) $k \in (-\infty, -3) \cup (2, \infty)$

(d) $k \in (-\infty, -2) \cup (3, \infty)$

Sol. (b) $\because$ $f(x)$ is a decreasing function and for major axis to be X-axis.

$$\therefore \quad f(k^2 + 2k + 5) > (f(k + 11)$$

$$\Rightarrow \quad k^2 + 2k + 5 < k + 11$$

or $$k^2 + k - 6 < 0$$

or $$(k+3)(k-2) < 0$$

or $$k \in (-3, 2)$$

Ex. 10 *If a tangent of slope 2 of the ellipse* $\frac{x^2}{a^2} + \frac{y^2}{b^2} = 1$ *is normal to the circle* $x^2 + y^2 + 4x + 1 = 0$, *then the maximum value of ab is*

(a) 1 (b) 2

(c) 4 (d) 8

Sol. (c) Equation of tangent is $y = 2x + \sqrt{(4a^2 + b^{2)}}$

This is normal to the circle

$$x^2 + y^2 + 4x + 1 = 0$$

This tangent passes through $(-2, 0)$, then

$$0 = -4 + \sqrt{(4a^2 + b^2)}$$

$$\Rightarrow \quad 4a^2 + b^2 = 16$$

$$\because \quad AM \geq GM$$

$$\therefore \quad \frac{4a^2 + b^2}{2} \quad \sqrt{(4a^2)(b^2)}$$

$$\Rightarrow \quad \frac{16}{2} \geq 2ab$$

or $$ab \leq 4$$

Hence, maximum value of ab is 4.

JEE Type Solved Examples : More than One Correct Option Type Questions

- This section contains **5 multiple choice examples.** Each example has four choices (a), (b), (c) and (d) out of which **MORE THAN ONE** may be correct.

Ex. 11 *Extremities of the latusrectum of the ellipse $\frac{x^2}{a^2}+\frac{y^2}{b^2}=1\,(a>b)$ having a given major axis 2a lies on*

(a) $x^2 = a(a-y)$ (b) $x^2 = a(a+y)$

(c) $y^2 = a(a+x)$ (d) $y^2 = a(a-x)$

Sol. (a, b) $\because$ Extremities of the latusrectum are $\left(ae, \pm\frac{b^2}{a}\right)$

Let $x = \pm ae$ and $y = \pm\frac{b^2}{a}$

or $\quad x^2 = a^2e^2$ and $b^2 = \pm ay$

or $\quad x^2 = a^2 - b^2$ and $b^2 = \pm ay$

$\therefore \quad x^2 = a^2 \pm ay$ or $x^2 = a(a \pm y)$

Ex. 12 *The locus of the image of the focus of the ellipse $\frac{x^2}{25}+\frac{y^2}{9}=1$, with respect to any of the tangent to the ellipse is*

(a) $(x+4)^2+y^2=100$ (b) $(x+2)^2+y^2=50$

(c) $(x-4)^2+y^2=100$ (d) $(x-2)^2+y^2=50$

Sol. (a, c) Let $M(h, k)$ be the image SM cuts a tangent at a point which lies on the auxiliary circle of the ellipse, therefore

$$\left(\frac{h\pm 4}{2}\right)^2+\frac{k^2}{4}=(5)^2 \quad [\because \text{foci of the given ellipse are } (\pm 4, 0)]$$

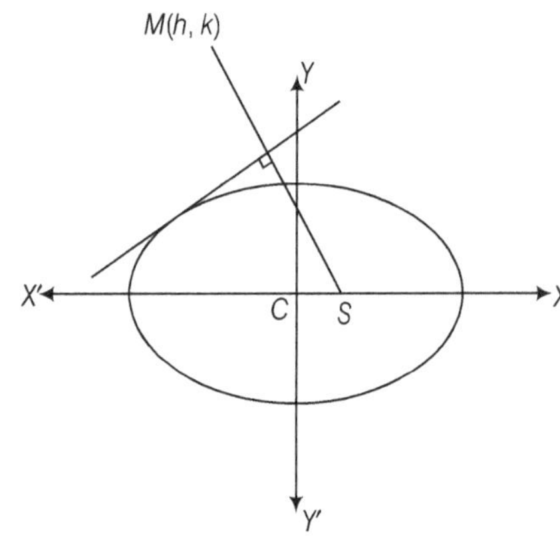

or $\quad (h\pm 4)^2+k^2=100$

Hence, the locus is $(x\pm 4)^2+y^2=100$

Ex. 13 *A tangent to the ellipse $4x^2+9y^2=36$ is cut by the tangent at the extremities of the major axis at T and T′. The circle TT′ as diameter passes through the point*

(a) $(-\sqrt{5}, 0)$ (b) $(\sqrt{5}, 0)$

(c) $(\sqrt{3}, 0)$ (d) $(-\sqrt{3}, 0)$

Sol. (a, b) Given equation of the ellipse is $4x^2+9y^2=36$

i.e., $$\frac{x^2}{9}+\frac{y^2}{4}=1 \quad \text{...(i)}$$

The equation of tangent at $(3\cos\theta, 2\sin\theta)$ is

$$\frac{x}{3}\cos\theta+\frac{y}{2}\sin\theta=1$$

which meets the tangent at $x=3$ and $x=-3$ at the extremities of major axis

$$T \equiv \left(3, \frac{2(1-\cos\theta)}{\sin\theta}\right)$$

and $$T' \equiv \left(-3, \frac{2(1+\cos\theta)}{\sin\theta}\right)$$

$\therefore$ Equation of circle on TT' as diameter is

$$(x-3)(x+3)+\left(y-\frac{2(1-\cos\theta)}{\sin\theta}\right)\left(y-\frac{2(1+\cos\theta)}{\sin\theta}\right)=0$$

$\Rightarrow$ $$x^2+y^2-\frac{4}{\sin\theta}\cdot y-5=0$$

or $$(x^2+y^2-5)-\frac{4}{\sin\theta}y=0 \quad \text{...(ii)}$$

Clearly Eq. (ii), passes through point of intersection of $x^2+y^2-5=0$ and $y=0$ i.e., $(\pm\sqrt{5}, 0)$

Ex. 14 *Consider the ellipse $\frac{x^2}{\tan^2\alpha}+\frac{y^2}{\sec^2\alpha}=1$, where $\alpha \in (0, \pi/2)$. Which of the following quantities would vary as α varies?*

(a) degree of flatness (b) ordinate of the vertex

(c) coordinate of the foci (d) length of latusrectum

Sol. (a, b, d) In $\alpha \in (0, \pi/2)$

$$\sec^2\alpha > \tan^2\alpha$$

$\therefore$ Coordinates of foci $(0, \pm\sqrt{(\sec^2\alpha+\tan^2\alpha)})$ i.e., $(0, \pm 1)$ which is independent of α.

Vertices are $(0, \pm\sec\alpha)$ and latusrectum

$$=\frac{2a^2}{b}=\frac{2\tan^2\alpha}{\sec\alpha}$$

$\because \quad \alpha \in (0, \pi/2)$

$\Rightarrow \quad \tan\alpha \in (0, \infty)$ and $\sec\alpha \in (1, \infty)$

Hence, $\alpha \propto$ degree of flatness.

Ex. 15 *Let $A(\theta)$ and $B(\phi)$ be the extremities of a chord of an ellipse. If the slope of AB is equal to the slope of the tangent at a point $C(\alpha)$ on the ellipse, then the value of α is*

(a) $\dfrac{\theta+\phi}{2}$ (b) $\dfrac{\theta-\phi}{2}$

(c) $\dfrac{\theta+\phi}{2}+\pi$ (d) $\dfrac{\theta+\phi}{2}-\pi$

Sol. (a. c) $\because$ Slope of AB = Slope of tangent at C

$$\Rightarrow \left(\frac{b\sin\phi - b\sin\theta}{a\cos\phi - a\cos\theta}\right) = -\frac{b\cos\alpha}{a\sin\alpha}$$

$$\Rightarrow \frac{b.2\cos\left(\frac{\theta+\phi}{2}\right).\sin\left(\frac{\phi-\theta}{2}\right)}{-a.2\sin\left(\frac{\theta+\phi}{2}\right).\sin\left(\frac{\phi-\theta}{2}\right)} = -\frac{b}{a}\cot\alpha$$

$$\therefore \tan\alpha = \tan\left(\frac{\theta+\phi}{2}\right)$$

$$\Rightarrow \alpha = n\pi + \left(\frac{\theta+\phi}{2}\right), n \in I$$

JEE Type Solved Examples : Paragraph Based Questions

- This section contains **2 solved Paragraphs** based upon each of the Paragraph **3 multiple choice** questions have to be answered. Each of these questions has four choices (a), (b), (c) and (d) out of which **ONLY ONE** is correct.

Paragraph I

(Q. Nos. 16 to 18)

A sequence of ellipses $E_1, E_2, E_3, \ldots, E_n$ is constructed as follows : Ellipse E_n is drawn so as to touch ellipse E_{n-1} as the extremities of the major axis of E_{n-1} and to have its foci at the extremities of the mirror axis of E_{n-1}.

16. If E_n is independent of n, then the eccentricity of ellipse E_{n-2} is

(a) $\left(\dfrac{3-\sqrt{5}}{2}\right)$ (b) $\left(\dfrac{\sqrt{5}-1}{2}\right)$

(c) $\left(\dfrac{2-\sqrt{3}}{2}\right)$ (d) $\left(\dfrac{\sqrt{3}-1}{2}\right)$

17. If eccentricity of ellipse E_n is e_n, then the locus of (e_n^2, e_{n-1}^2) is

(a) a parabola (b) an ellipse

(c) a hyperbola (d) a rectangular hyperbola

18. If equation of ellipse E_1 is $\dfrac{x^2}{9}+\dfrac{y^2}{16}=1$, then the equation of ellipse E_3 is

(a) $\dfrac{x^2}{9}+\dfrac{y^2}{16}=1$ (b) $\dfrac{x^2}{25}+\dfrac{y^2}{49}=1$

(c) $\dfrac{x^2}{25}+\dfrac{y^2}{41}=1$ (d) $\dfrac{x^2}{16}+\dfrac{y^2}{25}=1$

Sol.

16. (b) If $E_n : \dfrac{x^2}{a_n^2}+\dfrac{y^2}{b_n^2}=1$ and eccentricity of E_n is e_n

If $a_n > b_n$

Then, $b_n^2 = a_n^2(1-e_n^2)$ ...(i)

According to the question, $b_n = b_{n-1}$ ...(ii)

and $a_{n-1} = a_n e_n$ ...(iii)

For ellipse E_{n-1}, $a^2_{n-1} = b_{n-1}^2(1-e_{n-1}^2)$ ...(iv)

From Eqs. (i) and (ii), we get $b_{n-1}^2 = a_n^2(1-e_n^2)$ ...(v)

Substituting the values of a_{n-1} and b_{n-1}^2 from Eqs. (iii) and (v) in Eq. (iv), then

$$a_n^2 e_n^2 = a_n^2(1-e_n^2)(1-e_{n-1}^2)$$

$$\Rightarrow e_n^2 = (1-e_n^2)(1-e_{n-1}^2) \quad \text{...(vi)}$$

$\because$ E_n is independent of n

$\therefore$ $e_n = e_{n-1} = e$ [say]

From Eq. (vi), we get

$$e^2 = (1-e^2)^2$$

$$\Rightarrow e^4 - 3e^2 + 1 = 0$$

$$\therefore e^2 = \frac{3\pm\sqrt{5}}{2} = \frac{6\pm2\sqrt{5}}{4} = \left(\frac{\sqrt{5}\pm1}{2}\right)^2$$

$$\therefore e = \frac{\sqrt{5}-1}{2} \quad [\because 0<e<1]$$

17. (d) From Eq. (vi), $e_n^2 = (1-e_n^2)(1-e_{n-1}^2)$

Locus of (e_n^2, e_{n-1}^2) is

$$x = (1-x)(1-y)$$

$$\Rightarrow xy - 2x - y + 1 = 0$$

Here, $a=0, b=0, c=1,$

$$f = -\frac{1}{2}, g = -1, h = \frac{1}{2}$$

$$\therefore \Delta = 0 + 2\times-\frac{1}{2}\times-1\times\frac{1}{2} - 0 - 0 - 1\times\frac{1}{4} = \frac{1}{4} \neq 0$$

and $h^2 > ab, a+b=0$

$\Rightarrow$ rectangular hyperbola.

18. (c) From Eq. (vi), $e_n = \sqrt{\left(\dfrac{1-e_{n-1}^2}{2-e_{n-1}^2}\right)}$ ...(vii)

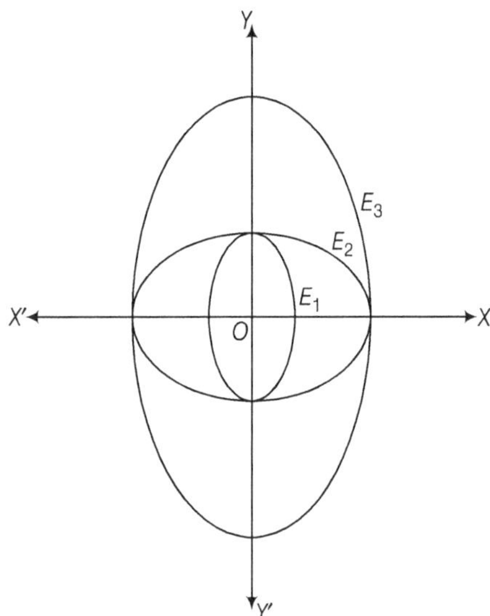

$\because \quad E_1 \equiv \dfrac{x^2}{9} + \dfrac{y^2}{16} = 1$

$\therefore \quad a_1 = 3, b_1 = 4$ and $9 = 16(1 - e_1^2)$

$\therefore \quad e_1 = \dfrac{\sqrt{7}}{4}$

From Eq. (vii), $e_2 = \sqrt{\left(\dfrac{1-e_1^2}{2-e_1^2}\right)} = \sqrt{\left(\dfrac{1-\dfrac{7}{16}}{2-\dfrac{7}{16}}\right)} = \dfrac{3}{5}$

and then, $e_3 = \sqrt{\left(\dfrac{1-\dfrac{9}{25}}{2-\dfrac{9}{25}}\right)} = \dfrac{4}{\sqrt{41}}$

Also, $a_1 = a_2 e_2$ and $b_1 = b_2$

$\therefore \quad b_2 = 4 = b_3 e_3 \Rightarrow b_3 = \sqrt{41}$

and $\quad a_3^2 = b_3^2(1 - e_3^2) = 41\left(1 - \dfrac{16}{41}\right) = 25$

$\therefore$ Ellipse E_3 is $\dfrac{x^2}{25} + \dfrac{y^2}{41} = 1$

Paragraph II

(Q. Nos. 19 to 21)

Consider an ellipse $E : \dfrac{x^2}{a^2} + \dfrac{y^2}{b^2} = 1$, centred at point 'O' and having AB and CD as its major and minor axes respectively if S_1 be one of the focus of the ellipse, radius of incircle of ΔOCS_1 be 1 unit and $OS_1 = 6$ units.

19. If area of ellipse (E) is Δ sq unit, then the value of 4Δ is

(a) 63π (b) 64π (c) 65π (d) 66π

20. If perimeter of ΔOCS_1 is p units, then the value of p is

(a) 10 (b) 15 (c) 20 (d) 25

21. The equation of the director circle of (E) is

(a) $x^2 + y^2 = 48.5$ (b) $x^2 + y^2 = 97$

(c) $x^2 + y^2 = \sqrt{48.5}$ (d) $x^2 + y^2 = \sqrt{97}$

Sol.

$\because \quad OS_1 = ae = 6,\ OC = b$

$\therefore \quad CS_1 = \sqrt{(OS_1)^2 + (OC)^2} = \sqrt{(a^2e^2 + b^2)} = a$

Area of $\Delta OCS_1 = \dfrac{1}{2} \times (OS_1) \times (OC) = \dfrac{1}{2} \times 6 \times b = 3b$

and semi-perimeter of $\Delta OCS_1 = \dfrac{1}{2}(OS_1 + OC + CS_1) = \dfrac{1}{2}(6 + a + b)$

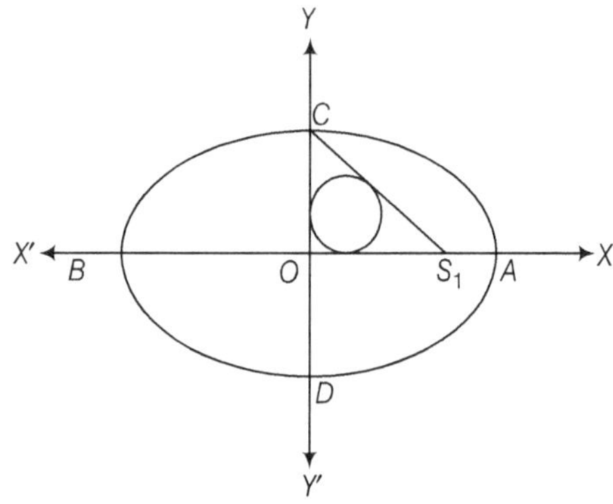

$\because$ In radius of $\Delta OCS_1 = 1$

$\therefore \quad \dfrac{3b}{\dfrac{1}{2}(6 + a + b)} = 1$

$\Rightarrow \quad b = \dfrac{1}{5}(6 + a)$ ...(i)

Also, $\quad b^2 = a^2(1 - e^2) = a^2 - 36$ ...(ii)

From Eqs. (i) and (ii), we get

$$\frac{1}{25}(6 + a)^2 = a^2 - 36$$

$\Rightarrow \quad 2a^2 - a - 78 = 0$

or $\quad a = \dfrac{13}{2}, -6$

19. (c) $\therefore \quad a = \dfrac{13}{2}$ and $b = \dfrac{5}{2}$ [from Eq. (i)]

$\because \quad \Delta = \pi ab = \pi \times \dfrac{13}{2} \times \dfrac{5}{2}$

$\therefore \quad 4\Delta = 65\pi$

20. (b) $p = (OS_1 + OC + CS_1) = 6 + b + a$

$$= 6 + \frac{5}{2} + \frac{13}{2} = 15$$

21. (a) Equation of director circle of E is

$$x^2 + y^2 = a^2 + b^2$$

$$= \frac{169 + 25}{4} = 48.5$$

JEE Type Solved Examples :
Single Integer Answer Type Questions

- This section contains **2 examples.** The answer to each example is a **single digit integer**, ranging from 0 to 9 (both inclusive).

Ex. 22 *If the normals at the four points $(x_1, y_1), (x_2, y_2), (x_3, y_3)$ and (x_4, y_4) on the ellipse $\frac{x^2}{a^2}+\frac{y^2}{b^2}=1$ are concurrent, then the value of $\left(\sum_{i=1}^{4} x_i\right)\left(\sum_{i=1}^{4}\frac{1}{x_i}\right)$ is*

Sol. (4) Let point of concurrent is (h, k).

Equation of normal at (x', y') is

$$\frac{x-x'}{x'a^2}=\frac{y-y'}{y'b^2}$$

It is passes through (h, k), then

$$y'^2\{a^2(h-x')+b^2x'^2\}=b^4k^2x'^2 \quad \text{...(i)}$$

But $$\frac{x'^2}{a^2}+\frac{y'^2}{b^2}=1 \text{ or } y'^2=\frac{b^2}{a^2}(a^2-x'^2) \quad \text{...(ii)}$$

Value of y'^2 from Eq. (ii), putting in Eq. (i), we get

$$\frac{b^2}{a^2}(a^2-x'^2)\{a^2h+(b^2-a^2)x'\}^2=b^4k^2x'^2$$

$$\Rightarrow \frac{b^2}{a^2}(a^2-x'^2)\{a^4h^2+(b^2-a^2)^2x'^2+2a^2hx'(b^2-a^2)\}$$
$$=b^4k^2x'^2$$

Arranging above as a fourth degree equation in x', we get

$$\Rightarrow -(a^2-b^2)^2x'^4+2ha^2(a^2-b^2)x'^3+x'^2(\dots)$$
$$-2a^4h(a^2-b^2)x'+a^6h^2=0$$

above equation being of fourth degree in x', therefore roots of the above equation are x_1, x_2, x_3, x_4, then

$$(x_1+x_2+x_3+x_4)=-\frac{2ha^2(a^2-b^2)}{-(a^2-b^2)^2}=\frac{2ha^2}{(a^2-b^2)} \quad \text{...(iii)}$$

$$\left(\frac{1}{x_1}+\frac{1}{x_2}+\frac{1}{x_3}+\frac{1}{x_4}\right)=\frac{\Sigma x_1x_2x_3}{x_1\cdot x_2\cdot x_3\cdot x_4}$$

$$=\frac{\dfrac{2a^4h(a^2-b^2)}{-(a^2-b^2)^2}}{\dfrac{a^6h^2}{-(a^2-b^2)^2}}=\frac{2(a^2-b^2)}{a^2h} \quad \text{...(iv)}$$

Multiplying Eqs. (iii) and (iv), we get

$$(x_1+x_2+x_3+x_4)\left(\frac{1}{x_1}+\frac{1}{x_2}+\frac{1}{x_3}+\frac{1}{x_4}\right)=4$$

or $$\left(\sum_{i=1}^{4}x_i\right)\left(\sum_{i=1}^{4}\frac{1}{x_i}\right)=4$$

Ex. 23 *If $x, y \in R$, satisfies the equation $\frac{(x-4)^2}{4}+\frac{y^2}{9}=1$, then the difference between the largest and the smallest value of the expression $\frac{x^2}{4}+\frac{y^2}{9}$ is*

Sol. (8) Parametric coordinates on $\frac{(x-4)^2}{4}+\frac{y^2}{9}=1$ are $(4+2\cos\theta, 3\sin\theta)$

Now, let $$E=\frac{x^2}{4}+\frac{y^2}{9}$$

$$=\frac{(4+2\cos\theta)^2}{4}+\frac{(3\sin\theta)^2}{9}$$

$$=(2+\cos\theta)^2+\sin^2\theta$$

$$=4+4\cos\theta+\cos^2\theta+\sin^2\theta$$

$$=5+4\cos\theta$$

$\therefore$ $E_{max}=5+4(1)=9$ $\quad (\because -1\le\cos\theta\le 1)$

and $E_{min}=5+4(-1)=1$

Hence, $E_{max}-E_{min}=9-1=8$

JEE Type Solved Examples : Matching Type Questions

- This section contains **only one example**. This example has four statements (A, B, C and D) given in **Column I** and four statements (p, q, r and s) in **Column II.** Any given statement in **Column I** can have correct matching with one or more statement(s) given in **Column II.**

Ex. 24 *Match the following*

	Column I	Column II
A.	Let $f(x)=\begin{cases} a^x, x<2 \\ 8, x=2 \\ \dfrac{b(x^2-b^2)}{(x-2)}, x>2 \end{cases}$ If f is continuous at $x=2$, then the locus of the pair of perpendicular tangents to the ellipse $\frac{x^2}{a^2}+\frac{y^2}{b^2}=1$ is $x^2+y^2=r^2$, then r^2 is divisible by	(p) 3
B.	If the ellipse $\frac{(x-h)^2}{M}+\frac{(y-k)^2}{N}=1$ has major axis on the line $y=2$, minor-axis on the line $x=-1$, major axis has length 10 and minor axis has length 4. Then, $h+k+M+N$ is divisible by	(q) 4
C.	If PQ is a focal chord of ellipse $\frac{x^2}{25}+\frac{y^2}{16}=1$, which passes through $S(3, 0)$ and $PS=2$, then length of PQ is divisible by	(r) 5
D.	A tangent to the ellipse $\frac{x^2}{27}+\frac{y^2}{48}=1$ having slope $\left(-\frac{4}{3}\right)$ cuts the x and y-axis at the points A and B respectively. If O is the origin, then area of ΔOAB is divisible by	(s) 6

Sol. (A) $\to$ (p, q, s); (B) $\to$ (p, r, s); (C) $\to$ (r); (D) $\to$ (p, q, s)

(A) $\lim_{x\to 2^-} f(x)=\lim_{x\to 2^+} f(x)=f(2)$

$$\Rightarrow \lim_{h\to 0} a^{2-h}=\lim_{h\to 0}\frac{b((2+h)^2-b^2)}{2+h-2}=8$$

$$\Rightarrow \quad a^2=b\lim_{h\to 0}\frac{(2+h)^2-b^2}{h}=8$$

at $h\to 0, (2+h)^2-b^2\to 0$

$\therefore \quad b^2=4$ and $a^2=8$

$\therefore$ Locus of the pair of perpendicular tangents to the ellipse

$$\frac{x^2}{a^2}+\frac{y^2}{b^2}=1$$

$\therefore$ Required locus is

$$x^2+y^2=a^2+b^2=8+`4=12$$

$$\Rightarrow \quad r^2=12$$

(B) $\because$ Major axis on the line $y=2$ and minor axis on the line $x=-1$

$\therefore$ Centre of ellipse is $(-1, 2)$

$$\Rightarrow \quad h=-1, k=2$$

Also, $2a=10$ and $2b=4$

$$\therefore \quad M=a^2=25$$

and $\quad N=b^2=4$

Now, $h+k+M+N=-1+2+25+4=30$

(C) Here, $a=5, b=4$

$$\because \quad b^2=a^2(1-e^2) \Rightarrow 16=25(1-e^2)$$

$$\therefore \quad e=\frac{3}{5}$$

Foci $(\pm 3, 0)$

Here, $SA=2$ [A and A' are vertices]

Also gives $PS=2$

$\therefore$ P coincides with A and Q coincides with A'

$\therefore$ $PQ=2a=10$

(D) Let $(\sqrt{27}\cos\theta, \sqrt{48}\sin\theta)$ be a point on the ellipse $\frac{x^2}{27}+\frac{y^2}{48}=1$

$\therefore$ Equation of tangent at $(\sqrt{27}\cos\theta, \sqrt{48}\sin\theta)$ is

$$\frac{x\cos\theta}{\sqrt{27}}+\frac{y\sin\theta}{\sqrt{48}}=1$$

$$\therefore \quad \text{slope}=-\frac{\sqrt{48}}{\sqrt{27}}\cdot\frac{\cos\theta}{\sin\theta}=-\frac{4}{3} \quad \text{[given]}$$

$$\therefore \quad \tan\theta=1$$

$$\Rightarrow \quad \theta=\frac{\pi}{4}$$

$\therefore$ Equation of tangent is $\frac{x}{\sqrt{54}}+\frac{y}{\sqrt{96}}=1$

$\therefore$ Area of triangle $=\frac{1}{2}\times 3\sqrt{6}\times 4\sqrt{6}=36$

JEE Type Solved Examples : Statement I and II Type Questions

- **Directions** (Ex. Nos. 25 and 26) are Assertion. Reason type examples. Each of these examples contains two statements.

  Statement I (Assertion) and **Statement II** (Reason)

  Each of these example also has four alternative choices, only one of which is the correct answer. You have to select the correct choice as given below.

  (a) Statement I is true, Statement II is true; Statement II is a correct explanation for statement I

  (b) Statement I is true, Statement II is true, Statement II is not a correct explanation for Statement I

  (c) Statement I is true, Statement II is flase

  (d) Statement I is false, Statement II is true

Ex. 25 **Statement I** *Feet of perpendiculars drawn from foci of an ellipse $4x^2 + y^2 = 16$ on the line $2\sqrt{3}x + y = 8$ lie on the circle $x^2 + y^2 = 16$.*

Statement II *If perpendiculars are drawn from foci of an ellipse to its any tangent, the feet of these perpendiculars lie on director circle of the ellipse.*

Sol. (c) Simultaneously solving the equations of ellipse and the given line, we get

$$4x^2 + (8 - 2\sqrt{3}x)^2 = 16$$

$$\Rightarrow \quad x^2 + (4 - \sqrt{3}x)^2 = 4$$

$$\Rightarrow \quad 4x^2 - 8\sqrt{3}\,x + 12 = 0$$

$$\text{or} \quad x^2 - 2\sqrt{3}x + 3 = 0$$

$$\text{or} \quad (x - \sqrt{3})^2 = 0$$

$\therefore$ $2\sqrt{3}x + y = 8$ is a tangent to the ellipse, the auxiliary circle is $x^2 + y^2 = 16$.

Hence, Statement I is true and Statement II is false.

Ex. 26 **Statement II** *The condition on a and b for which two distinct chords of the ellipse $\frac{x^2}{a^2} + \frac{y^2}{b^2} = 2$ passing through $(a, -b)$ are bisected by the line $x + y = b$ is $a^2 + 6ab - 7b^2 > 0$.*

Statement II *Equation of chord of the ellipse $\frac{x^2}{a^2} + \frac{y^2}{b^2} = 1$ whose mid-point (x_1, y_1) is $T = S_1$*

Sol. (a) Let $(\lambda, b - \lambda)$ is a point on the line $x + y = b$, then equation of chord whose mid-point $(\lambda, b - \lambda)$ is $T = S_1$

$$\text{or} \quad \frac{\lambda x}{2a^2} + \frac{(b-\lambda)y}{2b^2} - 1 = \frac{\lambda^2}{2a^2} + \frac{(b-\lambda)^2}{2b^2} - 1 \quad \text{...(i)}$$

$(a, -b)$ lies on Eq. (i), then

$$\frac{\lambda a}{2a^2} - \frac{b(b-\lambda)}{2b^2} = \frac{\lambda^2}{2a^2} + \frac{(b-\lambda)^2}{2b^2}$$

$$\Rightarrow \quad \lambda^2(a^2 + b^2) - ab\lambda(3a + b) + 2a^2b^2 = 0$$

For two distinct chords $D > 0$

$$\Rightarrow \quad a^2b^2(3a + b)^2 - 8a^2b^2(a^2 + b^2) > 0$$

$$\Rightarrow \quad a^2 + 6ab - 7b^2 > 0$$

Hence, both Statements are true and Statement II is correct explanation for Statement I.

Subjective Type Questions

- In this section, there are **12 subjective solved examples.**

Ex. 27 *Find the locus of the centroid of an equilateral triangle inscribed in the ellipse*

$$\frac{x^2}{a^2} + \frac{y^2}{b^2} = 1.$$

Sol. Let the vertices of the equilateral triangle P, Q and R and whose eccentric angles are α, β and γ.

Let the centroid of ΔPQR be (h, k) then

$$h = \frac{a}{3}(\cos\alpha + \cos\beta + \cos\gamma) \quad \text{...(i)}$$

$$\text{and} \quad k = \frac{b}{3}(\sin\alpha + \sin\beta + \sin\gamma) \quad \text{...(ii)}$$

$\because$ ΔPQR is equilateral.

$\therefore$ Centroid of the ΔPQR is same as the circumcentre.

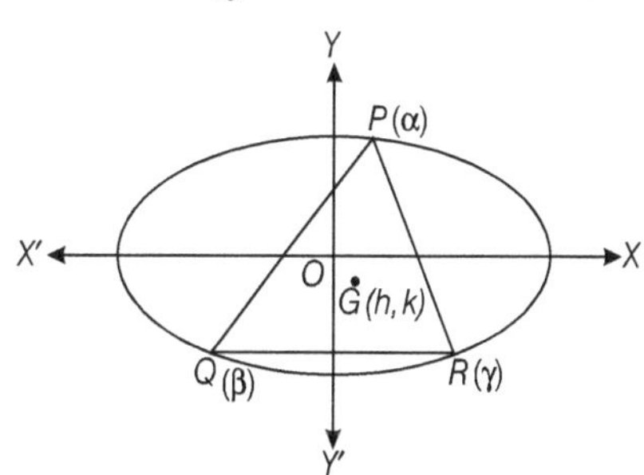

$\because$ Circumcentre of ΔPQR be

$$h = \frac{(a^2 - b^2)}{4a}\{\cos\alpha + \cos\beta + \cos\gamma + \cos(\alpha+\beta+\gamma)\}$$

$\left\{\begin{matrix}\text{Concyclic points}\\ \text{Coro : 2}\end{matrix}\right\}$

$$k = \frac{(b^2 - a^2)}{4b}\{\sin\alpha + \sin\beta + \sin\gamma - \sin(\alpha+\beta+\gamma)\}$$

Using Eqs. (i) and (ii), then

$$\cos(\alpha+\beta+\gamma) = h\left(\frac{4a}{a^2-b^2} - \frac{3}{a}\right) = \frac{h(a^2+3b^2)}{a(a^2-b^2)} \quad \text{...(iii)}$$

and $$\sin(\alpha+\beta+\gamma) = \frac{(3a^2+b^2)k}{b(a^2-b^2)} \quad \text{...(iv)}$$

Squaring and adding Eqs. (iii) and (iv), we get

$$\therefore \quad I = \frac{(a^2+3b^2)^2}{a^2(a^2-b^2)^2}h^2 + \frac{(3a^2+b^2)^2}{b^2(a^2-b^2)^2}k^2$$

Hence, locus of (h, k) is

$$\frac{(a^2+3b^2)^2}{a^2}x^2 + \frac{(3a^2+b^2)^2}{b^2}y^2 = (a^2-b^2)^2.$$

Ex. 28 *If the normals to $\frac{x^2}{a^2} + \frac{y^2}{b^2} = 1$ at the ends of the chords $lx + my = 1$ and $l'x + m'y = 1$ be concurrent; show that $a^2ll' = b^2mm' = -1$.*

Sol. Let these normals meet in (h, k), then their feet lie on the curve

$$b^2x(k-y) + a^2y(x-h) = 0$$

$$\Rightarrow \quad (a^2-b^2)xy + b^2kx - a^2hy = 0$$

$\therefore$ The locus passes through the points where the lines

$$lx + my - 1 = 0 \quad \text{and} \quad l'x + m'y - 1 = 0$$

meet the given ellipse,

$$\left(\frac{x^2}{a^2} + \frac{y^2}{b^2} - 1\right) - \lambda(lx + my - 1)(l'x + m'y - 1)$$

$$\equiv (a^2-b^2)xy + b^2kx - a^2hy$$

Comparing the co-efficients of x^2, y^2 and constant terms.

$$\frac{1}{a^2} - \lambda ll' = 0, \frac{1}{b^2} - \lambda mm' = 0, -1 - \lambda = 0$$

$$\therefore \quad \frac{1}{a^2} + ll' = 0 \quad \text{and} \quad \frac{1}{b^2} + mm' = 0 \quad (\because \lambda = -1)$$

$$\therefore \quad a^2ll' = b^2mm' = -1$$

Ex. 29 *An ellipse slides between two straight lines at right angles to each other. Show that the locus of its centre is a circle.*

Sol. Let the length of major and minor axes of an ellipse are $2a$ and $2b$ and if the centre of the ellipse be $C(h, k)$

If $S(x_1, y_1)$ and $S'(x_2, y_2)$ be two foci of the ellipse, then

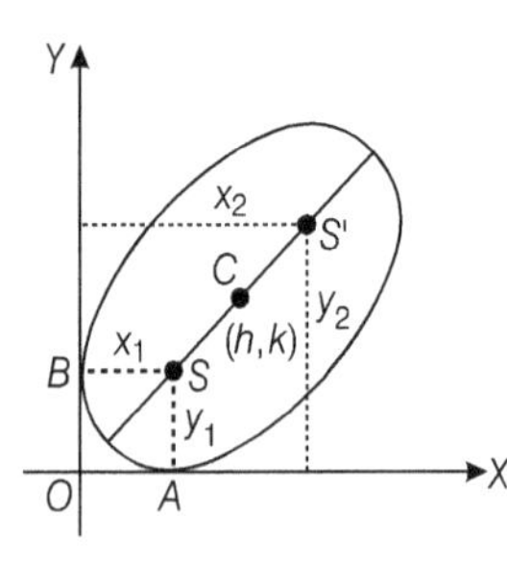

$$SS' = 2ae$$

$$\Rightarrow (x_1 - x_2)^2 + (y_1 - y_2)^2 = 4a^2e^2$$

$$\Rightarrow (x_1 + x_2)^2 - 4x_1x_2 + (y_1 + y_2)^2$$

$$- 4y_1y_2 = 4(a^2 - b^2)$$

$$\Rightarrow$$

$$(2h)^2 + (2k)^2 - 4(x_1x_2 + y_1y_2) = 4(a^2 - b^2) \quad \text{...(i)}$$

Since, the ellipse always slides between the two fixed lines OX and OY, they are always tangents to it. Therefore y_1, y_2 and x_1, x_2 are perpendicular distances of the foci from their tangents whose product are always b^2.

Hence, $$x_1x_2 = y_1y_2 = 6^2$$

$\Rightarrow$ Eq. (i) becomes

$$4h^2 + 4k^2 - 8b^2 = 4(a^2 - b^2)$$

$$\Rightarrow \quad h^2 + k^2 = a^2 + b^2$$

$\therefore$ Locus of the centre (h, k) is the circle

$$x^2 + y^2 = a^2 + b^2$$

Ex. 30 *Triangles are formed by pairs of tangents drawn from any point on the ellipse $a^2x^2 + b^2y^2 = (a^2 + b^2)^2$ to the ellipse $\frac{x^2}{a^2} + \frac{y^2}{b^2} = 1$, and the chord of contact. Show that the orthocentre of each such triangles lies on the ellipse.*

Sol. Let the coordinates of P and Q on the ellipse $\frac{x^2}{a^2} + \frac{y^2}{b^2} = 1$ are

$$P \equiv (a\cos\alpha, b\sin\alpha) \quad \text{and} \quad Q = (a\cos\beta, b\sin\beta)$$

Equation of tangents at P and Q are

$$\frac{x}{a}\cos\alpha + \frac{y}{b}\sin\alpha = 1 \quad \text{...(i)}$$

and $$\frac{x}{a}\cos\beta + \frac{y}{b}\sin\beta = 1 \quad \text{...(ii)}$$

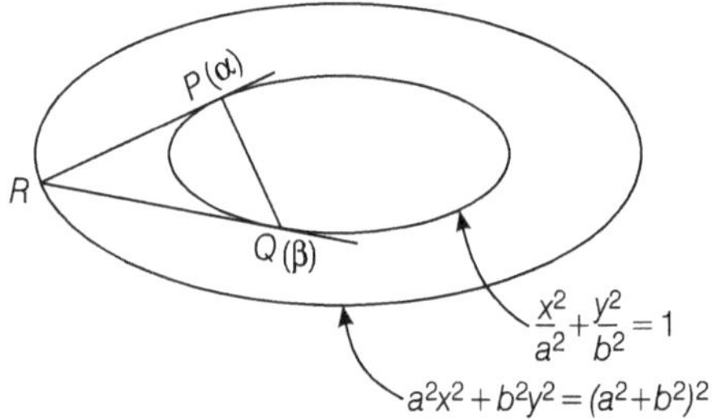

Point of intersection of Eqs. (i) and (ii) are

$$R\left\{a\frac{\cos\left(\frac{\alpha+\beta}{2}\right)}{\cos\left(\frac{\alpha-\beta}{2}\right)}, b\frac{\sin\left(\frac{\alpha+\beta}{2}\right)}{\cos\left(\frac{\alpha-\beta}{2}\right)}\right\}$$

This point R lies on the ellipse

$$a^2x^2 + b^2y^2 = (a^2 + b^2)^2$$

$$\Rightarrow \quad a^4 \cos^2\left(\frac{\alpha+\beta}{2}\right) + b^4 \sin^2\left(\frac{\alpha+\beta}{2}\right) = (a^2+b^2)^2 \cos^2\left(\frac{\alpha-\beta}{2}\right) \quad \text{...(iii)}$$

The equation of the line of perpendicular from Q on the tangent at P is

$$a \sin\alpha (x - a\cos\beta) - b\cos\alpha(y - b\sin\beta) = 0 \quad \text{...(iv)}$$

Similarly the equation to other perpendicular will be

$$a \sin\beta (x - a\cos\beta) - b\cos\beta(y - b\sin\alpha) = 0 \quad \text{...(v)}$$

On solving Eqs. (iv) and (v), we get

$$x = \frac{a^3}{a^2+b^2} \cdot \frac{\cos\left(\frac{\alpha+\beta}{2}\right)}{\cos\left(\frac{\alpha-\beta}{2}\right)} \quad \text{and} \quad y = \frac{b^3}{a^2+b^2} \cdot \frac{\sin\left(\frac{\alpha+\beta}{2}\right)}{\cos\left(\frac{\alpha-\beta}{2}\right)}$$

Since, this orthocentre lies on ellipse

$$\frac{x^2}{a^2} + \frac{y^2}{b^2} = 1$$

then, $$a^4 \cos^2\left(\frac{\alpha+\beta}{2}\right) + b^4 \sin^2\left(\frac{\alpha+\beta}{2}\right) = (a^2+b^2)^2 \cos^2\left(\frac{\alpha-\beta}{2}\right) \quad \text{...(vi)}$$

which is true by Eq. (iii).

Hence, the orthocentre of the triangle lies on the ellipse.

Ex. 31 *Show that the tangents drawn at those points of the ellipse $\frac{x^2}{a} + \frac{y^2}{b} = (a+b)$, where it is cut by any tangent to $\frac{x^2}{a^2} + \frac{y^2}{b^2} = 1$, intersect at right angles.*

Sol. The given ellipses, are

$$\frac{x^2}{a^2} + \frac{y^2}{b^2} = 1 \quad \text{...(i)}$$

$$\frac{x^2}{a(a+b)} + \frac{y^2}{b(a+b)} = 1 \quad \text{...(ii)}$$

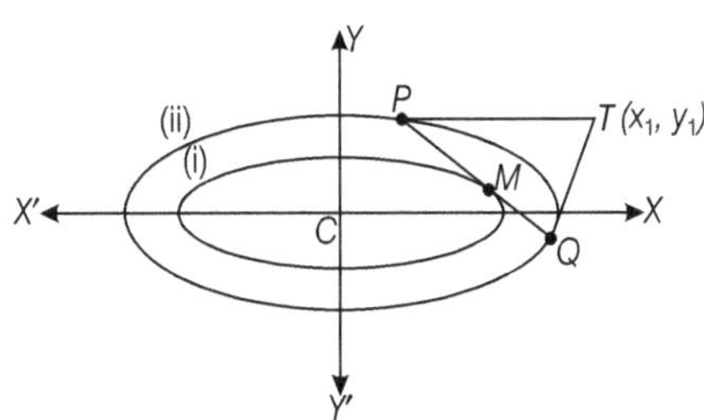

Chord of contact of (x_1, y_1) w.r.t ellipse (ii) is

$$\frac{xx_1}{a(a+b)} + \frac{yy_1}{b(a+b)} = 1 \quad \text{...(iii)}$$

or $$lx + my = n \quad \text{(say)}$$

If it touches $$\frac{x^2}{a^2} + \frac{y^2}{b^2} = 1$$

then $$a^2l^2 + b^2m^2 = n^2 \quad \text{[from corollary]}$$

$$\Rightarrow \quad \frac{a^2x_1^2}{a^2(a+b)^2} + \frac{b^2y_1^2}{b^2(a+b)^2} = 1$$

$$\Rightarrow \quad x_1^2 + y_1^2 = (a+b)^2$$

Locus of $T(x_1, y_1)$ is $x^2 + y^2 = (a+b)^2$

$$= a(a+b) + b(a+b)$$

which is the director circle of (ii).

Hence, PT and TQ are intersect at right angle.

Ex. 32 *From any point on the conic $\frac{x^2}{a^2} + \frac{y^2}{b^2} = 4$, tangents are drawn to the conic $\frac{x^2}{a^2} + \frac{y^2}{b^2} = 1$. Prove that the normals at the points of contact meet on the conic*

$$a^2x^2 + b^2y^2 = \frac{1}{4}(a^2 - b^2)^2.$$

Sol. Equations of concentric ellipses are

$$\frac{x^2}{a^2} + \frac{y^2}{b^2} = 4 \quad \text{...(i)}$$

$$\frac{x^2}{a^2} + \frac{y^2}{b^2} = 1 \quad \text{...(ii)}$$

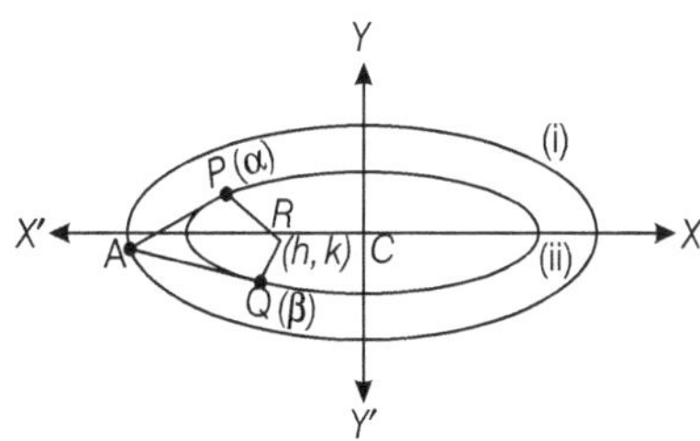

Let points $P(a\cos\alpha, b\sin\alpha)$ and $Q(a\cos\beta, b\sin\beta)$ on the ellipse (ii). Equation of tangents at P and Q are

$$\frac{x}{a}\cos\alpha + \frac{y}{b}\sin\alpha = 1 \quad \text{...(iii)}$$

and $$\frac{x}{a}\cos\beta + \frac{y}{b}\sin\beta = 1 \quad \text{...(iv)}$$

Point of intersection of Eqs. (iii) and (iv) is

$$A\left\{\frac{a\cos\left(\frac{\alpha+\beta}{2}\right)}{\cos\left(\frac{\alpha-\beta}{2}\right)}, \frac{b\sin\left(\frac{\alpha+\beta}{2}\right)}{\cos\left(\frac{\alpha-\beta}{2}\right)}\right\}$$

this point A satisfy Eq.(i)

$$\therefore \quad \frac{\cos^2\left(\frac{\alpha+\beta}{2}\right)}{\cos^2\left(\frac{\alpha-\beta}{2}\right)} + \frac{\sin^2\left(\frac{\alpha+\beta}{2}\right)}{\cos^2\left(\frac{\alpha-\beta}{2}\right)} = 4$$

$$\Rightarrow \quad 1 = 4\cos^2\left(\frac{\alpha-\beta}{2}\right)\cdot\frac{1}{2}$$

$$= 1 + \cos(\alpha - \beta)$$

$$\therefore \quad \cos(\alpha-\beta) = -\frac{1}{2} \quad \text{...(v)}$$

Equations of normals PR and QR are

$$ax \sec\alpha - by \operatorname{cosec}\alpha = a^2 - b^2$$

and
$$ax \sec\beta - by \operatorname{cosec}\beta = (a^2 - b^2)$$

or
$$ax \sin\alpha - by\cos\alpha = (a^2-b^2)\sin\alpha\cos\alpha \quad \text{...(vi)}$$

$$ax\sin\beta - by\cos\beta = (a^2-b^2)\sin\beta\cos\beta \quad \text{...(vii)}$$

Multiplying Eq. (vi) by $\cos\beta$ and (vii) by $\cos\alpha$ and subtracting, we get

$$ax\sin(\alpha-\beta) = (a^2-b^2)\cos\alpha\cos\beta(\sin\alpha - \sin\beta)$$

$$\frac{ax}{a^2-b^2} = \frac{\cos\alpha\cos\beta\cdot 2\cos\left(\frac{\alpha+\beta}{2}\right)\sin\left(\frac{\alpha-\beta}{2}\right)}{2\sin\left(\frac{\alpha-\beta}{2}\right)\cos\left(\frac{\alpha-\beta}{2}\right)}$$

$$= \frac{\cos\alpha\cos\beta\cos\left(\frac{\alpha+\beta}{2}\right)}{\cos\left(\frac{\alpha-\beta}{2}\right)}$$

$$= \pm 2\cos\alpha\cos\beta\cos\left(\frac{\alpha+\beta}{2}\right) \quad \text{[From (v)]}$$

$$= \pm\cos\left(\frac{\alpha+\beta}{2}\right)[\cos(\alpha+\beta)+\cos(\alpha-\beta)]$$

$$\frac{ax}{a^2-b^2} = \pm\cos\left(\frac{\alpha+\beta}{2}\right)\left\{\cos(\alpha+\beta) - \frac{1}{2}\right\} \quad \text{[Using (v)]}$$

$$\Rightarrow \quad \frac{a^2x^2}{(a^2-b^2)^2} = \cos^2\left(\frac{\alpha+\beta}{2}\right)\left[\cos(\alpha+\beta) - \frac{1}{2}\right]^2$$

Similarly,
$$\frac{b^2y^2}{(a^2-b^2)^2} = \sin^2\left(\frac{\alpha+\beta}{2}\right)\left[\cos(\alpha+\beta) + \frac{1}{2}\right]^2$$

$$\therefore \quad \frac{a^2x^2}{(a^2-b^2)^2} + \frac{b^2y^2}{(a^2-b^2)^2}$$

$$= \cos^2(\alpha+\beta) + \frac{1}{4} - \cos^2(\alpha+\beta)$$

Hence, required locus is

$$a^2x^2 + b^2y^2 = \frac{1}{4}(a^2-b^2)^2$$

Ex. 33 *A variable point P on an ellipse of eccentricity e, is joined to its foci S, S′ prove that the locus of the incentre of the triangle PSS′ is an ellipse whose eccentricity is* $\sqrt{\left(\frac{2e}{1+e}\right)}$.

Sol. Let the given ellipse be

$$\frac{x^2}{a^2} + \frac{y^2}{b^2} = 1$$

Let the coordinates of P are $(a\cos\phi, b\sin\phi)$

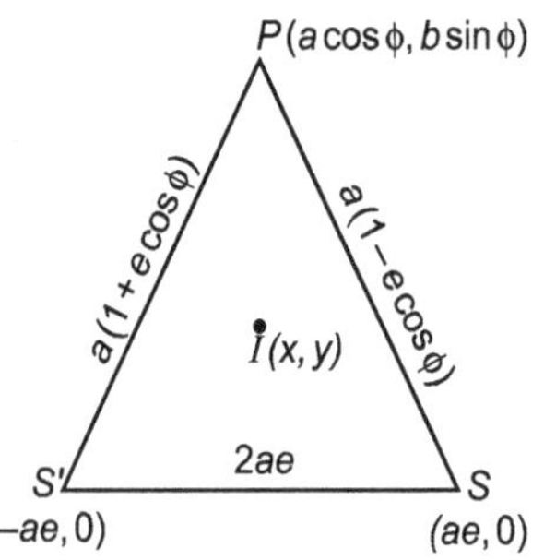

By hypothesis,

$$b^2 = a^2(1-e^2) \text{ and } S(ae, 0), S'(-ae, 0)$$

$\therefore \quad SP$ = focal distance of the point P

$$= a - ae\cos\phi \text{ and } S'P = a + ae\cos\phi$$

Also $SS' = 2ae$

If (x, y) be the incentre of the $\Delta PSS'$, then

$$\therefore \quad x = \frac{(2ae)\,a\cos\phi + a(1-e\cos\phi)(-ae) + 1(1+e\cos\phi)\,ae}{2ae + a(1-e\cos\phi) + a(1+e\cos\phi)}$$

$$x = ae\cos\phi \quad \text{...(i)}$$

and
$$y = \frac{2ae(b\sin\phi) + a(1+e\cos\phi)\cdot 0 + a(1-e\cos\phi)\cdot 0}{2ae + a(1-e\cos\phi) + a(1+e\cos\phi)},$$

$$\Rightarrow \quad y = \frac{eb\sin\phi}{(e+1)} \quad \text{...(ii)}$$

Eliminating ϕ from Eqs. (i) and (ii), we get

$$\frac{x^2}{a^2e^2} + \frac{y^2}{\left[\frac{be}{e+1}\right]^2} = 1$$

which represents an ellipse.

Let e_1 be its eccentricity.

$$\therefore \quad \frac{b^2e^2}{(e+1)^2} = a^2e^2(1-e_1^2) \Rightarrow e_1^2 = 1 - \frac{b^2}{a^2(e+1)^2}$$

$$= 1 - \frac{1-e^2}{(e+1)^2} = 1 - \frac{1-e}{1+e} = \frac{2e}{1+e} \Rightarrow e_1 = \sqrt{\left(\frac{2e}{1+e}\right)}$$

Ex. 34 *Prove that the eccentricity of the ellipse* $\frac{x^2}{a^2} + \frac{y^2}{b^2} = 1$ *is given by* $2\cot\omega = \frac{e^2\sin 2\theta}{\sqrt{(1-e^2)}}$ *where,* ω *is one of the angles between the normals at the points whose eccentric angles are* θ *and* $\frac{\pi}{2} + \theta$.

Sol. The equation of the normals at two given points θ and $\frac{\pi}{2} + \theta$ are

$$ax\sec\theta - by\operatorname{cosec}\theta = a^2 - b^2 \quad \text{...(i)}$$

and
$$ax\sec\left(\frac{\pi}{2}+\theta\right) - by\operatorname{cosec}\left(\frac{\pi}{2}+\theta\right) = a^2 - b^2 \quad \text{...(ii)}$$

their slopes are $m_1 = \frac{a}{b}\tan\theta$ and $m_2 = -\frac{a}{b}\cot\theta$

$$\therefore \quad \tan\omega = \frac{m_2 - m_1}{1 + m_2 m_1} = \frac{-\frac{a}{b}(\cot\theta + \tan\theta)}{\left(1 - \frac{a^2}{b^2}\right)} = \frac{2ab}{(a^2 - b^2)\sin 2\theta}$$

$$\Rightarrow \quad 2\cot\omega = \frac{(a^2 - b^2)\sin 2\theta}{ab} = \frac{a^2e^2}{a \cdot a\sqrt{1-e^2}}\sin 2\theta$$

$$\therefore \quad \frac{2\cot\omega}{\sin 2\theta} = \frac{e^2}{\sqrt{(1-e^2)}}$$

Ex. 35 *Show that the area of the triangle inscribed in an ellipse is*

$$\left[2ab\sin\left(\frac{\beta-\gamma}{2}\right)\sin\left(\frac{\gamma-\alpha}{2}\right)\sin\left(\frac{\alpha-\beta}{2}\right)\right],$$

where α, β, γ are the eccentric angles of the vertices and hence find the condition that the area of a triangle inscribed in an ellipse may be maximum.

Sol. The vertices of the triangle PQR are

$$P \equiv (a\cos\alpha, b\sin\alpha)$$
$$Q \equiv (a\cos\beta, b\sin\beta)$$
$$R \equiv (a\cos\gamma, b\sin\gamma)$$

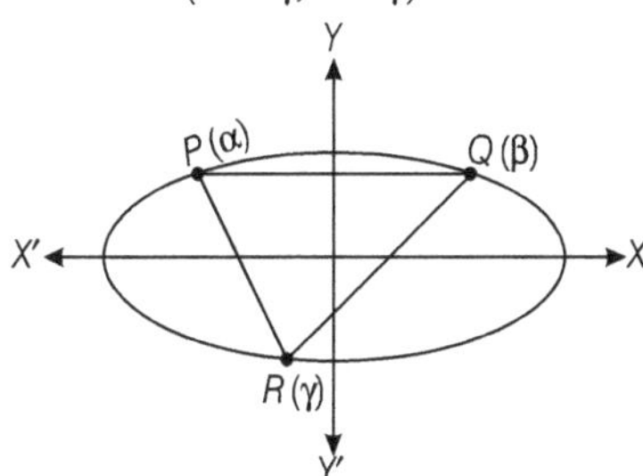

$$\therefore \text{ Area of } \Delta PQR = \frac{1}{2}\begin{vmatrix} a\cos\alpha & b\sin\alpha & 1 \\ a\cos\beta & b\sin\beta & 1 \\ a\cos\gamma & b\sin\gamma & 1 \end{vmatrix} = \frac{ab}{2}\begin{vmatrix} \cos\alpha & \sin\alpha & 1 \\ \cos\beta & \sin\beta & 1 \\ \cos\gamma & \sin\gamma & 1 \end{vmatrix}$$

$$= \frac{ab}{2}[\sin(\gamma - \beta) + \sin(\alpha - \gamma) + \sin(\beta - \alpha)]$$

$$= \frac{ab}{2}\left\{2\sin\left(\frac{\alpha-\beta}{2}\right)\cos\left(\frac{2\gamma-\alpha-\beta}{2}\right) - 2\sin\left(\frac{\alpha-\beta}{2}\right)\cos\left(\frac{\alpha-\beta}{2}\right)\right\}$$

$$= ab\sin\left(\frac{\alpha-\beta}{2}\right)\left[\cos\left(\frac{2\gamma-\alpha-\beta}{2}\right) - \cos\left(\frac{\alpha-\beta}{2}\right)\right]$$

$$= 2ab\sin\left(\frac{\alpha-\beta}{2}\right)\sin\left(\frac{\gamma-\beta}{2}\right)\sin\left(\frac{\alpha-\gamma}{2}\right)$$

$$\therefore \text{ Area of } \Delta PQR = 2ab\sin\left(\frac{\alpha-\beta}{2}\right)\sin\left(\frac{\beta-\gamma}{2}\right)\sin\left(\frac{\gamma-\alpha}{2}\right) \quad \text{...(i)}$$

If P_1, Q_1, R_1 be the points upon the auxiliary circle corresponding to points P, Q, R, then

$$\text{Area of } \Delta P_1Q_1R_1 = 2a^2\sin\left(\frac{\alpha-\beta}{2}\right)\sin\left(\frac{\beta-\gamma}{2}\right)\sin\left(\frac{\gamma-\alpha}{2}\right)$$

{taking $b = a$ in Eq. (i)}

$$\therefore \quad \frac{\text{Area of } \Delta PQR}{\text{Area of } \Delta P_1Q_1R_1} = \frac{b}{a}$$

$$\therefore \quad (\text{Area of } \Delta PQR) = \left(\frac{b}{a}\right)\text{Area of } (\Delta P_1Q_1R_1)$$

$\therefore$ Area of ΔPQR is the greatest when area of $\Delta P_1Q_1R_1$ be the greatest and hence $\Delta P_1Q_1R_1$ must be equilateral

$$\therefore \quad \alpha - \beta = \beta - \gamma = \gamma - \alpha = \frac{2\pi}{3}$$

$\therefore$ The eccentric angles of P, Q, R will be

$$\alpha, \alpha + \frac{2\pi}{3}, \alpha + \frac{4\pi}{3}$$

Ex. 36 *Let ABC be an equilateral triangle inscribed in the circle $x^2 + y^2 = a^2$ suppose perpendiculars form A, B, C to the major axis of the ellipse*

$$\frac{x^2}{a^2} + \frac{y^2}{b^2} = 1 \qquad (a > b)$$

meet the ellipse respectively at P, Q, R so that P, Q, R lie on the same side of the major axis as A, B, C respectively. Prove that the normal to the ellipse drawn at the points P, Q and R are concurrent.

Sol. Equation of normal at $P(a\cos\theta, b\sin\theta)$ is

$$ax\sec\theta - by\,\text{cosec}\,\theta = (a^2 - b^2)$$

or
$$ax\sin\theta - by\cos\theta = \frac{1}{2}(a^2 - b^2)\sin 2\theta \quad \text{...(i)}$$

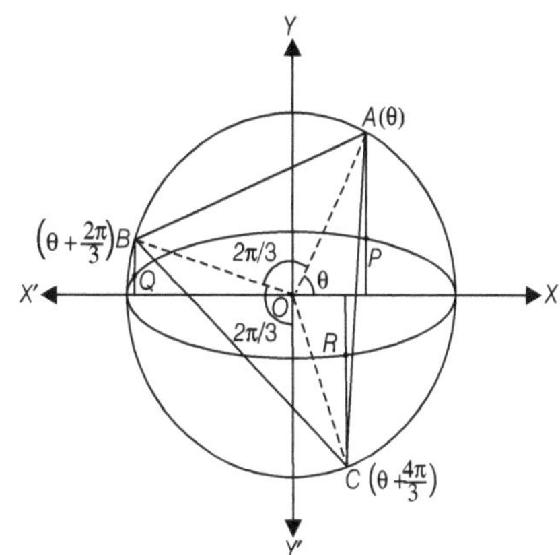

Similarly, the other normals

$$ax\sin\left(\theta + \frac{2\pi}{3}\right) - by\cos\left(\theta + \frac{2\pi}{3}\right)$$

$$= \frac{1}{2}(a^2 - b^2)\sin\left(2\theta + \frac{4\pi}{3}\right) \quad \text{...(ii)}$$

and
$$ax\sin\left(\theta + \frac{4\pi}{3}\right) - by\cos\left(\theta + \frac{4\pi}{3}\right)$$

$$= \frac{1}{2}(a^2 - b^2)\sin\left(2\theta + \frac{8\pi}{3}\right) \quad \text{...(iii)}$$

$$\because \quad \sin\left(\theta + \frac{4\pi}{3}\right) = \sin\left(\theta - \frac{2\pi}{3}\right), \cos\left(\theta + \frac{4\pi}{3}\right) = \cos\left(\theta - \frac{2\pi}{3}\right)$$

and
$$\sin\left(2\theta + \frac{8\pi}{3}\right) = \sin\left(2\theta - \frac{4\pi}{3}\right)$$

Further the three normals are concurrent, then

$$\begin{vmatrix} \sin\theta & \cos\theta & \sin 2\theta \\ \sin\left(\theta+\frac{2\pi}{3}\right) & \cos\left(\theta+\frac{2\pi}{3}\right) & \sin\left(2\theta+\frac{4\pi}{3}\right) \\ \sin\left(\theta-\frac{2\pi}{3}\right) & \cos\left(\theta-\frac{2\pi}{3}\right) & \sin\left(2\theta+\frac{8\pi}{3}\right) \end{vmatrix}=0$$

Applying $R_2 \to R_2 + R_3$, then

$$\text{LHS} = \begin{vmatrix} \sin\theta & \cos\theta & \sin 2\theta \\ 2\sin\theta\cos\frac{2\pi}{3} & 2\cos\theta\cos\frac{2\pi}{3} & 2\sin(2\theta+2\pi)\cos\frac{2\pi}{3} \\ \sin\left(\theta-\frac{2\pi}{3}\right) & \cos\left(\theta-\frac{2\pi}{3}\right) & \sin\left(2\theta+\frac{8\pi}{3}\right) \end{vmatrix}$$

$$= -\begin{vmatrix} \sin\theta & \cos\theta & \sin 2\theta \\ \sin\theta & \cos\theta & \sin 2\theta \\ \sin\left(\theta-\frac{2\pi}{3}\right) & \cos\left(\theta-\frac{2\pi}{3}\right) & \sin\left(2\theta+\frac{8\pi}{3}\right) \end{vmatrix}=0$$

$(\because R_1 = R_2)$

Ex. 37 *If two concentric ellipses be such that the foci of one be on the other and if e and e′ be their eccentricities. Prove that the angle between their axes is*

$$\cos^{-1}\left\{\frac{\sqrt{(e^2+e'^2-1)}}{ee'}\right\}$$

Sol. Let S and S' be the foci of one ellipse and H and H' be the other, C being their common centre. Then, $SHS'H'$ is a parallelogram and since

$$SH + S'H = HS' + H'S' = 2a$$

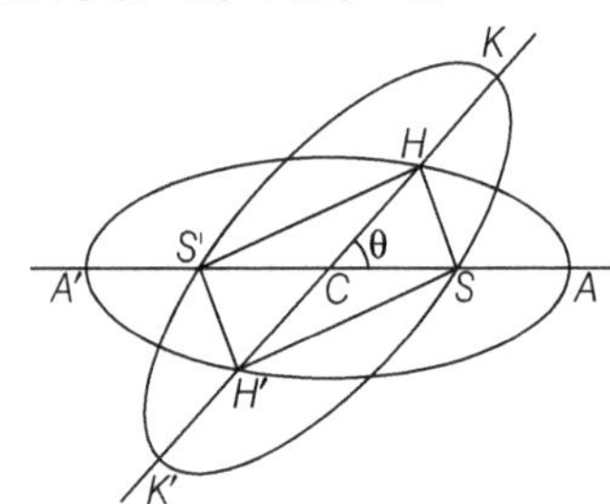

Since, the sum of the focal distances of any point on an ellipse is equal to its major axis which is $2a$.

Then $\quad CS = ae, CH = ae'$

Let θ be the angle between their axes.

then $\quad SH^2 = a^2e^2 + a^2e'^2 - 2a^2ee'\cos\theta$

$$HS'^2 = a^2e^2 + a^2e'^2 + 2a^2ee'\cos\theta$$

Now, $\quad 2a = SH + S'H$

Squaring both sides, then

$$4a^2 = (SH)^2 + (S'H)^2 + 2(SH)\cdot(S'H)$$

$$\Rightarrow \quad 4a^2 = 2a^2(e^2+e'^2) + 2\sqrt{(a^2e^2+a^2e'^2)^2 - 4a^4e^2e'^2\cos^2\theta}$$

$$\Rightarrow \quad (2-e^2-e'^2)^2 = (e^2+e'^2)^2 - 4e^2e'^2\cos^2\theta$$

$$\Rightarrow \quad 4+(e^2+e'^2)^2 - 4(e^2+e'^2) = (e^2+e'^2)^2 - 4e^2e'^2\cos^2\theta$$

$$\Rightarrow \quad 1-e^2-e'^2 = -e^2e'^2\cos^2\theta$$

$$\therefore \quad \cos\theta = \frac{\sqrt{e^2+e'^2-1}}{ee'}$$

$$\therefore \quad \theta = \cos^{-1}\left(\frac{\sqrt{(e^2+e'^2-1}}{ee'}\right)$$

Ex. 38 *If the normals at the four points* $(x_1, y_1), (x_2, y_2), (x_3, y_3)$ *and* (x_4, y_4) *on the ellipse* $\frac{x^2}{a^2}+\frac{y^2}{b^2}=1$ *are concurrent. Prove that*

$$(x_1+x_2+x_3+x_4)\left(\frac{1}{x_1}+\frac{1}{x_2}+\frac{1}{x_3}+\frac{1}{x_4}\right)=4$$

or $\quad (\Sigma\cos\alpha)(\Sigma\sec\alpha) = 4$

where, $\alpha, \beta, \gamma, \delta$ *are the eccentric angles of the points.*

Sol. Let point of concurrent is (h, k).

Equation of normal at (x', y') is

$$\frac{x-x'}{x'/a^2} = \frac{y_1-y'}{y'/b^2}$$

It is passes through (h, k) then

$$y'^2\{a^2(h-x') + b^2x'\}^2 = b^4k^2x'^2 \quad \text{...(i)}$$

But $\quad \frac{x'^2}{a^2}+\frac{y'^2}{b^2}=1 \quad$ or $\quad y'^2 = \frac{b^2}{a^2}(a^2-x'^2) \quad$ ...(ii)

Values of y'^2 from Eq. (ii), putting in Eq. (i) we get

$$\frac{b^2}{a^2}(a^2-x'^2)\{a^2h+(b^2-a^2)x'\}^2 = b^4k^2x'^2$$

$$\Rightarrow \frac{b^2}{a^2}(a^2-x'^2)\{a^4h^2+(b^2-a^2)^2x'^2+2a^2hx'(b^2-a^2)\} = b^4k^2x'^2$$

Arranging above as a fourth degree equation in x', we get

$$\Rightarrow \quad -(a^2-b^2)^2x'^4 + 2ha^2(a^2-b^2)x'^3 + x'^2(\ldots)$$

$$-2a^4h(a^2-b^2)x' + a^6h^2 = 0$$

above equation being of fourth degree in x', therefore roots of the above equation are x_1, x_2, x_3, x_4 then

$$(x_1+x_2+x_3+x_4) = -\frac{2ha^2(a^2-b^2)}{-(a^2-b^2)^2} = \frac{2ha^2}{(a^2-b^2)} \quad \text{...(iii)}$$

$$\left(\frac{1}{x_1}+\frac{1}{x_2}+\frac{1}{x_3}+\frac{1}{x_4}\right) = \frac{\Sigma x_1x_2x_3}{x_1\cdot x_2\cdot x_3\cdot x_4}$$

$$= \frac{\frac{2a^4h(a^2-b^2)}{-(a^2-b^2)^2}}{\frac{a^6h^2}{-(a^2-b^2)^2}} = \frac{2(a^2-b^2)}{a^2h} \quad \text{...(iv)}$$

Multiplying Eqs. (iii) and (iv), we get

$$(x_1+x_2+x_3+x_4)\left(\frac{1}{x_1}+\frac{1}{x_2}+\frac{1}{x_3}+\frac{1}{x_4}\right)=4$$

Replacing x_1 by $a\cos\alpha$, x_2 by $a\cos\beta$, ... etc, then, we get the second form

i.e. $\quad \Sigma\cos\alpha\,\Sigma\sec\alpha = 4.$

Ellipse Exercise 1 :
Single Option Correct Type Questions

- This section contains **30 multiple choice questions.** Each question has four choices (a), (b), (c) and (d) out of which **ONLY ONE** is correct.

1. Given f is increasing, the equation $\frac{x^2}{f(2a)}+\frac{y^2}{f(a^2-3)}=1$ represents an ellipse with X-axis as major axis if

(a) $[-1, 3]$ (b) $[1, 3]$ (c) $(-1, 3)$ (d) $(0, 5)$

2. If $\frac{x^2}{f(4a)}+\frac{y^2}{f(a^2-5)}$ represents an ellipse with major axis as Y-axis and f is a decreasing fucntion, then

(a) $a \in (-\infty, 1)$ (b) $a \in (5, \infty)$ (c) $a \in (1, 4)$ (d) $a \in (-1, 5)$

3. The curve represented by the equation $\frac{x^2}{\sin\sqrt{2}-\cos\sqrt{3}}+\frac{y^2}{\sin\sqrt{3}-\cos\sqrt{2}}=1$ is

(a) an ellipse with foci on X -axis
(b) an ellipse with foci on Y-axis
(c) a hyperbola with foci on X-axis
(d) a hyperbola with foci on Y-axis

4. The minimum distance of the centre of the ellipse $\frac{x^2}{16}+\frac{y^2}{9}=1$ from the chord of contact of mutually perpendicular tangents of the ellipse is

(a) $\frac{144}{5}$ (b) $\frac{16}{5}$ (c) $\frac{9}{5}$ (d) None of these

5. P and Q are the foci of the ellipse $\frac{x^2}{a^2}+\frac{y^2}{b^2}=1$ and B is an end of the minor axis. If PBQ, is an equilateral triangle, then the eccentricity of the ellipse is

(a) $\frac{1}{\sqrt{2}}$ (b) $\frac{1}{3}$
(c) $\frac{1}{2}$ (d) $\frac{\sqrt{3}}{2}$

6. A circle of radius $\frac{5}{\sqrt{2}}$ is concentric with the ellipse $\frac{x^2}{16}+\frac{y^2}{9}=1$, then the acute angle made by the common tangent with the line $\sqrt{3}x-y+6=0$ is

(a) $\frac{\pi}{3}$ (b) $\frac{\pi}{4}$
(c) $\frac{\pi}{6}$ (d) $\frac{\pi}{12}$

7. Consider the particle travelling clockwise on the elliptical path $\frac{x^2}{100}+\frac{y^2}{25}=1$. The particle leaves the orbit at the point $(-8, 3)$ and travels in a straight line tangent to the ellipse, then the point will the particle cross the Y-axis is

(a) $\left(0, -\frac{25}{3}\right)$ (b) $\left(0, \frac{7}{3}\right)$
(c) $\left(0, \frac{25}{3}\right)$ (d) $(0, 9)$

8. C is the centre of the ellipse $\frac{x^2}{16}+\frac{y^2}{9}=1$ and A and B are two points on the ellipse such that $\angle ACB = 90°$, then $\frac{1}{(CA)^2}+\frac{1}{(CB)^2}=$

(a) $\frac{7}{12}$ (b) $\frac{12}{7}$
(c) $\frac{25}{144}$ (d) $\frac{144}{25}$

9. Let (α, β) be a point from which two perpendicular tangents can be drawn to the ellipse $4x^2+5y^2=20$. If $F=4\alpha+3\beta$, then

(a) $-15 \le F \le 15$ (b) $F \ge 0$
(c) $-5 \le F \le 20$ (d) $F \le -5\sqrt{5}$ or $F \ge 5\sqrt{5}$

10. If $a=[t^2-3t+4]$ and $b=[3+5t]$, where $[\cdot]$ denotes the greatest integer function, then the latusrectum of the ellipse $\frac{x^2}{a^2}+\frac{y^2}{b^2}=1$ at $t=\frac{3}{2}$ is

(a) 20 (b) 10
(c) $\frac{1}{5}$ (d) $\frac{1}{10}$

11. If the line $x+2y+4=0$ cutting the ellipse $\frac{x^2}{a^2}+\frac{y^2}{b^2}=1$ in points whose eccentric angles are $30°$ and $60°$ subtends a right angle at the orgin, then its equation is

(a) $\frac{x^2}{8}+\frac{y^2}{4}=1$
(b) $\frac{x^2}{16}+\frac{y^2}{4}=1$
(c) $\frac{x^2}{4}+\frac{y^2}{16}=1$
(d) None of the above

12. An arc of a bridge is semi-elliptical with major axis horizontal. If the length of the base is 9 m and the highest part of the bridge is 3 m from the horizontal; the best approximation of the height of the arch 2 m from the centre of the base is

(a) $\frac{11}{4}$m (b) $\frac{8}{3}$m
(c) $\frac{7}{2}$m (d) 2m

13. A tangent to the ellipse $\frac{x^2}{25}+\frac{y^2}{16}=1$ at any point P meet the line $x=0$ at a point Q. Let R be the image of Q in the line $y=x$, then circle whose extremities of a diameter are Q and R passes through a fixed point. The fixed point is

(a) $(3, 0)$ (b) $(4, 0)$
(c) $(5, 0)$ (d) $(0, 0)$

14. If tangents PQ and PR are drawn from a point on the circle $x^2+y^2=25$ to the ellipse $\frac{x^2}{16}+\frac{y^2}{b^2}=1,(b<4)$, so that the fourth vertex S of parallelogram $PQSR$ lies on the circumcircle of triangle PQR, then the eccentricity of the ellipse is

(a) $\frac{\sqrt{5}}{4}$ (b) $\frac{\sqrt{5}}{3}$
(c) $\frac{\sqrt{7}}{4}$ (d) $\frac{\sqrt{7}}{3}$

15. The equation of the chord of contact of the pair of tangents drawn to the ellipse $4x^2+9y^2=36$ from the point (m, n), where $m\cdot n=m+n, m, n$ being non-zero positive integers is

(a) $2x+9y=18$ (b) $2x+2y=1$
(c) $4x+9y=18$ (d) $4x+2y=1$

16. $x-2y+4=0$ is a common tangent to $y^2=4x$ and $\frac{x^2}{4}+\frac{y^2}{b^2}=1$. Then, the value of b and the other common tangent are given by

(a) $b=\sqrt{3}$; $x+2y+4=0$
(b) $b=3$; $x+2y+4=0$
(c) $b=\sqrt{3}$; $x+2y-4=0$
(d) $b=\sqrt{3}$, $x-2y-4=0$

17. The point, at shortest distance from the line $x+y=7$ and lying on an ellipse $x^2+2y^2=6$, has coordinates

(a) $(\sqrt{2}, \sqrt{2})$ (b) $(0, \sqrt{3})$
(c) $(2, 1)$ (d) $\left(\sqrt{5}, \frac{1}{\sqrt{2}}\right)$

18. From a point on the axis of x common tangents are drawn to the parabola $y^2=4x$ and the ellipse $\frac{x^2}{a^2}+\frac{y^2}{b^2}=1(a>b>0)$. If these tangents form an equilateral triangle with their chord of contact w.r.t parabola, then set of exhaustive values of a is

(a) $(0, 3)$ (b) $\left(0, \frac{3}{2}\right)$
(c) $\left(\frac{3}{2}, 3\right)$ (d) $\left(1, \frac{3}{2}\right)$

19. If circumcentre of an equilateral triangle inscribed in $\frac{x^2}{a^2}+\frac{y^2}{b^2}=1$, with vertices having eccentric angle α, β, γ respectively is (h, k), then $\Sigma\cos(\alpha-\beta)=$

(a) $\frac{9h^2}{a^2}+\frac{9k^2}{b^2}+\frac{3}{2}$ (b) $9h^2-9k^2+a^2b^2$
(c) $\frac{9h^2}{a^2}+\frac{9k^2}{b^2}+3$ (b) $\frac{9h^2}{2a^2}+\frac{9k^2}{2b^2}-\frac{3}{2}$

20. A parabola is drawn with focus at one of the foci of the ellipse $\frac{x^2}{a^2}+\frac{y^2}{b^2}=1$, where $a>b$ and directrix passing through the other focus and perpendicular to the major axis of the ellipse. If the latusrectum of the ellipse and that of the parabola are some, then the eccentricity of the ellipse is

(a) $\sqrt{2}-1$ (b) $\sqrt{3}-1$
(c) $2\sqrt{2}-2$ (d) $3\sqrt{3}-5$

21. If the maximum distance of any point on the ellipse $x^2+2y^2+2xy=1$ from its center is r, then r is equal to

(a) $\frac{\sqrt{6}+1}{2}$ (b) $\frac{\sqrt{5}+1}{2}$
(c) $\frac{\sqrt{3}+1}{2}$ (d) $\frac{\sqrt{2}+2}{2}$

22. The length of the common chord of the ellipse $\frac{(x-1)^2}{9}+\frac{(y-2)^2}{4}=1$ and the circle $(x-1)^2+(y-2)^2=1$ is

(a) zero (b) one
(c) three (d) eight

23. The eccentricity of the ellipse $ax^2+by^2+2fx+2gy+c=0$ if axis of ellipse parallel to X-axis is

(a) $\sqrt{\left(\frac{b-a}{b}\right)}$ (b) $\sqrt{\left(\frac{a+b}{b}\right)}$
(c) $\sqrt{\left(\frac{a+b}{a}\right)}$ (d) None of these

24. A circle has the same center as an ellipse and passes through the foci F_1 and F_2 of the ellipse, such that two curves intersect at four points. Let P be any one of their point of intersection. If the major axis of the ellipse is 17 and the area of triangle PF_1F_2 is 30, then the distance between the foci is

(a) 13 (b) 11
(c) 9 (d) 7

25. The area of the rectangle formed by the perpendicular from the centre of the standard ellipse to the tangent and normal at its point whose eccentric angle is $\frac{\pi}{4}$, is

(a) $\frac{(a^2-b^2)\,ab}{a^2+b^2}$
(b) $\frac{(a^2-b^2)}{(a^2+b^2)\,ab}$
(c) $\frac{(a^2+b^2)\,ab}{(a^2-b^2)}$
(d) $\frac{(a^2+b^2)}{(a^2-b^2)\,ab}$

26. An ellipse is inscribed in a circle and a point within the circle is chosen at random. If the probability that this point lies outside the ellipse is 2/3, then the eccentricity of the ellipse is

(a) $\frac{2\sqrt{2}}{3}$ (b) $\frac{\sqrt{5}}{3}$
(c) $\frac{8}{9}$ (d) $\frac{2}{3}$

27. An ellipse slides between two perpendicular straight lines.
Then, the locus of its centre is a/an

(a) parabola (b) ellipse
(c) hyperbola (d) circle

28. The length of the chord of the ellipse $\frac{x^2}{25}+\frac{y^2}{16}=1$, where mid-point is $\left(\frac{1}{2},\frac{2}{3}\right)$ is

(a) $\frac{1}{10}$ (b) $\frac{\sqrt{8161}}{10}$
(c) $\frac{\sqrt{8061}}{10}$ (d) None of these

29. The equation of the locus of the middle point of the portion of the tangent to the ellipse $\frac{x^2}{16}+\frac{y^2}{9}=1$ include between the coordinate axes is the curve

(a) $9x^2+16y^2=4x^2y^2$ (b) $16x^2+9y^2=4x^2y^2$
(c) $3x^2+4y^2=4x^2y^2$ (d) $9x^2+16y^2=x^2y^2$

30. The tangent at the point 'θ' on the ellipse $\frac{x^2}{a^2}+\frac{y^2}{b^2}=1$ meets the auxilliary circle in two points which subtends a right angle at the centre, then the eccentricity 'e' of the ellipse is given by the equation

(a) $e^2(1+\cos^2\theta)=1$
(b) $e^2(\operatorname{cosec}^2\theta+1)=1$
(c) $e^2(1+\sin^2\theta)=1$
(d) $e^2(1+\tan^2\theta)=1$

Ellipse Exercise 2 :
More than One Correct Option Type Questions

- This section contains **15 multiple choice questions**. Each question has four choices (a), (b), (c) and (d) out of which **MORE THAN ONE** may be correct.

31. The locus extremities of the latusrectum of the family of ellipse $b^2x^2+y^2=a^2b^2$ is

(a) $x^2-ay=a^2$ (b) $x^2-ay=b^2$
(c) $x^2+ay=a^2$ (d) $x^2+ay=b^2$

32. The distance of a point on the ellipse $\frac{x^2}{6}+\frac{y^2}{2}=1$ from the centre is 2, then the eccentric angles are

(a) $\frac{\pi}{4}$ (b) $\frac{3\pi}{4}$ (c) $\frac{5\pi}{4}$ (d) $\frac{7\pi}{4}$

33. If the equation of family of ellipse is $x^2\sec^2\theta+y^2\operatorname{cosec}^2\theta=1$, where $\frac{\pi}{4}<\theta<\frac{\pi}{2}$, then the locus of extremities of the latusrectum is

(a) $2y^2(1+x^2)=(1-x^2)^2$ (b) $2x^2(1+y^2)=(1-y^2)^2$
(c) $2y(1-x^2)=1+x^2$ (d) $2y^2(1+x^2)=1+y^4-2x^2$

34. Let F_1, F_2 be two focii of the ellipse and PT and PN be the tangent and the normal respectively to the ellipse at point P. Then.

(a) PN bisects $\angle F_1PF_2$
(b) PT bisects $\angle F_1PF_2$
(c) PT bisects angle $(180^\circ - \angle F_1PF_2)$
(d) None of the above

35. $\dfrac{x^2}{(a^2-a-6)}+\dfrac{y^2}{(a^2-6a+5)}=1$ will represent an ellipse if a lies in the interval

(a) $(-\infty,-2)$ (b) $(1,\infty)$
(c) $(3,\infty)$ (d) $(5,\infty)$

36. A latusrectum of an ellipse is a line

(a) passing through a focus
(b) passing through the centre
(c) perpendicular to the major axis
(d) parallel to the minor axis

37. If the axes of an ellipse coincide with the coordinate axes and the ellipse passes through the point $(4,-1)$ and touches the line $x+4y-10=0$, then its equation is

(a) $x^2+64y^2=80$ (b) $x^2+4y^2=20$
(c) $x^2+20y^2=100$ (d) $x^2+8y^2=40$

38. If P is a point on the ellipse $\dfrac{x^2}{a^2}+\dfrac{y^2}{b^2}=1$, whose foci are S and S'. Let $\angle PSS'=\theta$ and $\angle PS'S=\phi$, then

(a) $SP+S'P=2a$, if $a>b$ (b) $SP+S'P=2b$, if $b>a$
(c) $\tan\left(\dfrac{\theta}{2}\right)\tan\left(\dfrac{\phi}{2}\right)=\dfrac{1-e}{1+e}$ (d) $\tan\left(\dfrac{\theta}{2}\right)\tan\left(\dfrac{\phi}{2}\right)=\dfrac{e-1}{e+1}$

39. If $(5,12)$ and $(24,7)$ are the focii of a conic passing through the origin, then the eccentricity of conic is

(a) $\dfrac{\sqrt{386}}{38}$ (b) $\dfrac{\sqrt{386}}{12}$
(c) $\dfrac{\sqrt{386}}{13}$ (d) $\dfrac{\sqrt{386}}{25}$

40. If a pair of variable straight lines $x^2+4y^2+axy=0$ (where a is a real parameter) cuts the ellipse $x^2+4y^2=4$ at two points A and B, then the locus of the point of intersection of tangents at A and B is

(a) $x-2y=0$ (b) $2x-y=0$
(c) $x+2y=0$ (d) $2x+y=0$

41. In the ellipse $25x^2+9y^2-150x-90y+225=0$

(a) foci are at (3, 1), (3, 9) (b) $e=\dfrac{4}{5}$
(c) centre is (5, 3) (d) major axis is 6

42. If the tangent to the ellipse $x^2+4y^2=16$ at the point $P(\theta)$ is a normal to the circle $x^2+y^2-8x-4y=0$, then θ equals

(a) $\dfrac{\pi}{2}$ (b) $\dfrac{\pi}{4}$
(c) 0 (d) $-\dfrac{\pi}{4}$

43. The product of eccentricties of two conics is unity, one of them can be a/an

(a) parabola (b) ellipse
(c) hyperbola (d) circle

44. The parametric angle α, where $-\pi<\alpha\le\pi$ of the point on the ellipse $\dfrac{x^2}{a^2}+\dfrac{y^2}{b^2}=1$ at which the tangent drawn cuts the intercept of minimum length on the coordinate axes, is/are

(a) $\tan^{-1}\sqrt{\left(\dfrac{b}{a}\right)}$ (b) $-\tan^{-1}\sqrt{\left(\dfrac{b}{a}\right)}$
(c) $\pi-\tan^{-1}\sqrt{\left(\dfrac{b}{a}\right)}$ (d) $\pi+\tan^{-1}\sqrt{\left(\dfrac{b}{a}\right)}$

45. If latusrectum of the ellipse $x^2\tan^2\alpha+y^2\sec^2\alpha=1$ is 1/2, then $\alpha(0<\alpha<\pi)$ is equal to

(a) $\pi/12$ (b) $\pi/6$
(c) $5\pi/12$ (d) $\pi/2$

Ellipse Exercise 3 : Paragraph Based Questions

- This section contains **5 paragraphs** based upon each paragraph **3 multiple choice question** have to be answered. Each of these questions has four choices (a), (b), (c) and (d) out of which **ONLY ONE** is correct.

Paragraph I

(Q. Nos. 46 to 48)

A conic is represented by

$$C\equiv 9x^2+4xy+6y^2-22x-16y+9=0$$

46. The centre of the conic C is

(a) (0, 0) (b) (1, 0) (c) (0, 1) (d) (1, 1)

47. The eccentricity of the conic C is

(a) $\dfrac{1}{2}$ (b) $\dfrac{1}{\sqrt{2}}$
(c) $\dfrac{2}{3}$ (d) $\dfrac{2}{\sqrt{5}}$

48. The lengths of axes of conic C are

(a) $2, 2\sqrt{2}$ (b) $4, 2\sqrt{3}$
(c) $6, 2\sqrt{5}$ (d) $5, 2\sqrt{6}$

Paragraph II

(Q. Nos. 49 to 51)

An ellipse E has its centre $C(3,1)$, focus at $(3,6)$ and passing through the point $P(7,4)$

49. The product of the lengths of the perpendicular segments from the focii on tangent at point P is

(a) 20 (b) 45
(c) 40 (d) 90

50. If F and F' are the foot of perpendiculars from focii S and S' on tangent at point P, then point of intersection of lines SF' and $S'F$ is

(a) $\left(5, \frac{5}{3}\right)$ (b) $\left(3, \frac{4}{3}\right)$
(c) $\left(5, \frac{10}{3}\right)$ (d) $\left(3, \frac{8}{3}\right)$

51. If the normal at a variable point on the ellipse (E) meets its axes in Q and R, then the locus of the mid-point of QR is a conic with eccentricity (e_1), then

(a) $e_1 = \frac{3}{\sqrt{5}}$ (b) $e_1 = \frac{\sqrt{5}}{3}$
(c) $e_1 = \frac{3}{\sqrt{10}}$ (d) $e_1 = \frac{\sqrt{10}}{3}$

Paragraph III

(Q. Nos. 52 to 54)

Curves $C_1 : x^2 + y^2 = r^2$ and $C_2 : \frac{x^2}{16} + \frac{y^2}{9} = 1$ intersect at four distinct points A, B, C and D. Their common tangents form a parallelogram PQRS.

52. If $ABCD$ is a square, then the value of $25r^2$ is

(a) 36 (b) 72
(c) 144 (d) 288

53. If $PQRS$ is a square, then the value of $2r^2$ is

(a) 12 (b) 15
(c) 20 (d) 25

54. If $PQRS$ is a square, then the ratio of the area of curve C_1 to the area of circumcircle of ΔPQR is

(a) 1 : 4 (b) 1 : 2
(c) 3 : 4 (d) 9 : 16

Paragraph IV

(Q. Nos. 55 to 57)

An ellipse whose distance between foci S and S′ is 4 units is inscribed in the ΔABC touching the sides AB, AC and BC at P, Q and R, respectively. If centre of ellipse is at origin and major axis along X-axis, $SP + S'P = 6$

55. Equation of the ellipse is

(a) $9x^2 + 5y^2 = 45$ (b) $4x^2 + 9y^2 = 36$
(c) $5x^2 + 9y^2 = 45$ (c) $9x^2 + 4y^2 = 36$

56. If $AB = BC$ and $\angle B = \pi / 2$, then locus of A is

(a) $(x^2 + y^2 - 14)^2 = 4(5x^2 + 9y^2 - 45)$
(b) $(x^2 + y^2 - 14)^2 = 4(5x^2 + 9y^2 - 54)$
(c) $(x^2 + y^2 - 14)^2 = 4(9x^2 + 5y^2 - 45)$
(d) $(x^2 + y^2 - 14)^2 = 4(9x^2 + 5y^2 - 54)$

57. If the difference of eccentric angles of P and Q is $\pi / 3$, then locus of A is

(a) $5x^2 + 9y^2 = 15$ (b) $5x^2 + 9y^2 = 60$
(c) $9x^2 + 5y^2 = 14$ (d) $9x^2 + 5y^2 = 144$

Paragraph V

(Q. Nos. 58 to 60)

The line $2px + y\sqrt{(1 - p^2)} = 1$ $(|p| < 1)$ for different values of p, touches a fixed ellipse whose axes are the coordinate axes.

58. The eccentricity of the ellipse is

(a) $\frac{1}{\sqrt{5}}$ (b) $\frac{1}{\sqrt{3}}$
(c) $\frac{\sqrt{3}}{2}$ (d) $\frac{2}{\sqrt{5}}$

59. The foci of the ellipse are

(a) $\left(\pm\frac{\sqrt{3}}{2}, 0\right)$ (b) $\left(0, \pm\frac{\sqrt{3}}{2}\right)$
(c) $(\pm\sqrt{3}, 0)$ (d) $(0, \pm\sqrt{3})$

60. The locus of the point of intersection of perpendicular tangents of ellipse is

(a) $x^2 + y^2 = 2$ (b) $x^2 + y^2 = \frac{3}{2}$
(c) $x^2 + y^2 = \frac{5}{4}$ (d) $x^2 + y^2 = \frac{1}{2}$

Ellipse Exercise 4 : Single Integer Answer Type Questions

- This section contains **10 questions**. The answer to each question is a **single digit integer**, ranging from 0 to 9 (both inclusive).

61. Two concentric ellipse be such that the foci of one be on the other and if 3/5 and 4/5 be their eccentricities. If θ be the angle between their axes, then the value of $2(1+\sin^2\theta+\sin^4\theta)$ must be

62. Rectangle $ABCD$ has area 200 unit^2. An ellipse with area 200π unit^2, passes through A and C and has foci at B and D. If the perimeter of the rectangle is P, then the value of $\sqrt{(P+1)}$ is

63. Number of points on the ellipse $2x^2+5y^2=100$ from which pair of perpendicular tangents may be drawn to the ellipse $9x^2+16y^2=144$ is

64. The length of sides of square which can be made by four perpendicular tangents to the ellipse $\frac{x^2}{7}+\frac{2y^2}{11}=1$ is

65. The length of the focal chord of the ellipse $\frac{x^2}{a^2}+\frac{y^2}{b^2}=1$ which makes an angle θ with the major axis is $\frac{\lambda ab^2}{a^2\sin^2\theta+b^2\cos^2\theta}$, then the value of λ is

66. Number of distinct normal lines that can be drawn to ellipse $\frac{x^2}{169}+\frac{y^2}{25}=1$ from the point $P(0,6)$ is n, then the value of 2^n is

67. If p is the length of the perpendicular from a focus upon the tangent at any point P of the ellipse $\frac{x^2}{a^2}+\frac{y^2}{b^2}=1$ and r is the distance of P from the focus, then the value of $\frac{2a}{r}-\frac{b^2}{p^2}$ is

68. An ellipse passing through the origin has its foci (3, 4) and (6, 8). The length of its semi-minor axis is b, then the value of $b/\sqrt{2}$ is

69. The maximum value of 5λ for which four normals can be drawn to ellipse $\frac{x^2}{25}+\frac{y^2}{16}=1$ through a point $(\lambda, 0)$ is

70. An ellipse with major and minor axis $6\sqrt{3}$ and 6 respectively, slides along the coordinate axes and always remains confined in the first quadrant. If the length of arc described by centre of ellipse is $\frac{\pi\lambda}{6}$, then the value of λ is

Ellipse Exercise 5 : Matching Type Questions

- This Section Contains **3 questions**. Each question has four statements (A,B,C and D) given in **Column** I and four statements (p,q,r and s) in **Column II**. Any given statement in **Column I** can have correct matching with one or more statement (s) given in **Column II.**

71. Match the following

	Column I		Column II
(A)	For the ellipse $\frac{x^2}{9}+\frac{y^2}{4}=1$ with vertices A and A', tangents drawn at the point P in the first quadrant meets the $y-$axis at Q and the chord $A'P$ meets the y-axis at M. If O is the origin, then OQ^2-MQ^2 is a	(p)	Natural number
(B)	If $y=x$ and $3y+2x=0$ are the equations of a pair of conjugate diameters of the ellipse $\frac{x^2}{a^2}+\frac{y^2}{b^2}=1$ and e be the eccentricity, then $4\,(1+e^2+e^4+\ldots+\infty)$ is a	(q)	Composite number
(C)	If the variable line $y=kx+2h$ is tangent to an ellipse $2x^2+3y^2=6$, then the locus of $P(h,k)$ is a conic C whose eccentricity is e, thus $3e^2$ is a	(r)	Prime number
(D)	If extremities of the latusrectum of the ellipse $\frac{x^2}{a^2}+\frac{y^2}{b^2}=1$, $(a>1)$ having positive ordinates lie on the parabola $x^2=-2(y-2)$, then a is a	(s)	Perfect number

72. Match the following

	Column I		Column II
(A)	An ellipse is sliding along the cordinate axes. If the foci of the ellipse are (1,1) and (3,3) if area of the director circle of the ellipse (in square units) is $\pi\lambda$, then λ is divisible by	(p)	3
(B)	If from a point $P\,(0,\lambda)$ two normals other then axes are drawn to the ellipse $\frac{x^2}{25}+\frac{y^2}{16}=1$, such that $\lvert\lambda\rvert<p$, then $4p$ is divisible by,	(q)	4
(C)	The orbit of the earth is an ellipse with eccentricity $\frac{1}{60}$ with the sun at one focus the major axis being approximately 186×10^6 miles in length. If the shortest and longest distances of the earth from the sun are $\lambda\times10^5$ miles and $\mu\times10^5$ miles, then $\mu-(\lambda+1)$ is divisible by	(r)	5
(D)	If the mid point of a chord of the ellipse $\frac{x^2}{16}+\frac{y^2}{25}=1$ is (0,3) and length of the chord is $\frac{4\lambda}{5}$, then λ is divisible by	(s)	6

73. Match the following

	Column I		Column II
(A)	The minimum and maximum distances of a point (2,6) from the ellipse $9x^2+8y^2-36x-16y-28=0$ are L and G, then	(p)	$L+G=10$
(B)	The minimum and maximum distances of a point (1,2) from the ellipse $4x^2+9y^2+8x-36y+4=0$ are L and G, then	(q)	$L+G=6$
(C)	The minimum and maximum distances of a point $\left(\frac{9}{5},\frac{12}{5}\right)$ from the ellipse $4(3x+4y)^2+9(4x-3y)^2=900$ are L and G, then	(r)	$G-L=8$
(D)	The minimum and maximum distances of a point (0,4) from the ellipse $25x^2+9y^2=225$ are L and G, then	(s)	$G-L=6$

Ellipse Exercise 6 :
Statement I and II Type Questions

- **Directions** (Q. Nos. 74 to 81) are Assertion-Reason type questions. Each of these qustions contains two statements :
Statement I (Assertion) and
Statement II (Reason)
Each of these questions also has four alternative choices, only one of which is the correct answer.
You have to select the correct choice as given below.
(a) Statement I is true, statement II is true; statement II is a correct explanation for statement I
(b) Statement I is true, statement II is true; statement II is not a correct explanation for statement I
(c) Statement I is true, statement II is false
(d) Statement I is false, statement II is true

74. Let the equation of ellipse be $\frac{x^2}{(a^2+1)} = \frac{y^2}{(a^2+2}) = 1$

Statement I If eccentricity of the ellipse be $\frac{1}{\sqrt{6}}$, then length of latusrectum is $\frac{10}{\sqrt{6}}$.

Statement II Length of latusrectum $= \frac{2(a^2+1)}{\sqrt{(a^2+2)}}$.

75. Statement I The area of the ellipse $2x^2 + 3y^2 = 6$ is more than the area of the circle $x^2 + y^2 - 2x + 4y + 4 = 0$.

Statement II The length of semi-major axis of an ellipse is more than the radius of the circle.

76. Statement I The equation of the director circle to the ellipse $4x^2 + 9y^2 = 36$ is $x^2 + y^2 = 13$

Statement II The locus of the point of intersection of perpendicular tangents to an ellipse is called the director circle.

77. Statement I In an ellipse the distance between foci is always less than the sum of focal distances of any point on it.

Statement II If e be the eccentricity of the ellipse, then $0 < e < 1$.

78. Statement I The sum of the focal distances of a point on the ellipse $4x^2 + 5y^2 - 16x - 30y + 41 = 0$ is $2\sqrt{5}$.

Statement II The equation $4x^2 + 5y^2 - 16x - 30y + 41 = 0$ can be expressed as $4(x-2)^2 + 5(y-3)^2 = 20$.

79. Statement I Locus of centre of a variable circle touching to circles $(x-1)^2 + (y-2)^2 = 25$ and $(x-2)^2 + (y-1)^2 = 16$ is an ellipse.

Statement II If a circle $S_2 = 0$ lies completely inside the circle $S_1 = 0$, then the locus of centre of a variable circle $S = 0$ which touches both the circles is an ellipse.

80. Statement I The tangent and normal at any point P on a ellipse bisect the external and internal angles between the focal distance of P.

Statement II The straight line joining the foci of the ellipse subtends of a right angle at P.

81. Statement I In a ΔABC, if base BC is fixed and perimeter of the triangle is also fixed, then vertex moves on an ellipse.

Statement II If sum of distances of a point P from two fixed points is constant, then locus of P is an ellipse.

Ellipse Exercise 7 :
Subjective Type Questions

- In this section, there are **12 subjective questions**.

82. If three of the sides of a quadrilateral inscribed in an ellipse are parallel respectively to three given straight lines. Show that fourth side will also be parallel to a fixed straight line.

83. If S and S' are the focii of an ellipse and P any point on the curve, show that

$$\tan\left(\frac{PSS'}{2}\right)\tan\left(\frac{PS'S}{2}\right)=\frac{1-e}{1+e}$$

Hence, or otherwise show that the locus of the centre of the circle inscribed in the triangle PSS' is another ellipse.

84. If the normal at any point P of the ellipse $\frac{x^2}{a^2}+\frac{y^2}{b^2}=1$ meets the major and minor axes in G and g respectively, and if CF is the perpendicular upon this normal from the centre C of the ellipse.

Show that $PF \cdot PG = b^2$

and $PF \cdot Pg = a^2$.

85. PQ is double ordinate of the ellipse $x^2/a^2+y^2/b^2=1$ and B an extremity of the minor axis. PB and QB meet the major axis in M and N. Show that M and N are inverse points with respect to the auxiliary circle of the ellipse.

86. Consider the family of circle $x^2+y^2=r^2, 2<r<5$. If in the first quadrant the common tangent to a circle of the family and the ellipse $4x^2+25y^2=100$ meets the coordinate axes at A and B, then find the equation of the locus of the mid-point of AB.

87. Prove that the normals at the four points, where the lines

$$\frac{lx}{a}+\frac{my}{b}=1$$

and $$\frac{x}{la}+\frac{y}{mb}=-1$$

cut the ellipse $\frac{x^2}{a^2}+\frac{y^2}{b^2}=1$ are concurrent.

88. The eccentric angle of any point P measured from the semi major axis CA is ϕ. If S be the focus nearest to A, and $\angle ASP=\theta$. Prove that

$$\tan\left(\frac{\theta}{2}\right)=\sqrt{\left(\frac{1+e}{1-e}\right)}\tan\left(\frac{\phi}{2}\right)$$

89. If θ is the difference of the eccentric angles of two points on an ellipse, the tangents at which are at right angles. Prove that $ab\sin\theta=d_1d_2$, where d_1, d_2 are the semi diameters parallel to the tangents at the points and a, b are the semi-axes of the ellipse.

90. A straight line PQ touches the ellipse $\frac{x^2}{a^2}+\frac{y^2}{b^2}=1$ and the circle $x^2+y^2=r^2\ (b<r<a)$. RS is a focal chord of the ellipse. If RS is parallel to PQ and meets the circle at points R and S. Find the length of RS.

91. Let d be the perpendicular distance from the centre of the ellipse to the tangent drawn at a point P on the ellipse. If F_1 and F_2 are two foci of the ellipse. Show that

$$(PF_1-PF_2)^2=4a^2\left(1-\frac{b^2}{d^2}\right).$$

92. TP and TQ are tangents drawn from an external point (x_1, y_1) to the ellipse $\frac{x^2}{a^2}+\frac{y^2}{b^2}=1$. Show that

(i) $\frac{ST^2}{SP\cdot SQ}=\frac{x_1^2}{a^2}+\frac{y_1^2}{b^2}$

(ii) $ST\cdot S'T\cos\theta=(CT)^2-a^2-b^2$

where, S and S' are the foci, C the centre and θ is the angle between the tangents.

93. If PSQ and PHR are focal chords of the ellipse $\frac{x^2}{a^2}+\frac{y^2}{b^2}=1$, where S and H are the foci. The tangents at Q and R meet at T. Show that the locus of T as P moves round the ellipse is

$$(1+e^2)^2\frac{x^2}{a^2}+(1-e^2)^2\frac{y^2}{b^2}=(1+e^2)^2$$

where, e is the eccentricity of the ellipse.

Ellipse Exercise 8 :
Questions Asked in Previous 13 Year's Exams

- This section contains questions asked in **IIT-JEE, AIEEE, JEE Main & JEE Advanced** from year **2005** to **2017**.

94. The minimum area of triangle formed by the tangent to the $\frac{x^2}{a^2}+\frac{y^2}{b^2}=1$ and coordinate axes is **[IIT-JEE 2003, 3M]**

(a) ab sq units (b) $\frac{a^2+b^2}{2}$ sq units

(c) $\frac{(a+b)^2}{2}$ sq units (d) $\frac{a^2+ab+b^2}{3}$ sq units

95. Find the equation of the common tangent in 1st quadrant to the circle $x^2+y^2=16$ and the ellipse $\frac{x^2}{25}+\frac{y^2}{4}=1$. Also find the length of the intercept of the tangent between the coordinate axes. **[IIT-JEE 2005, 4M]**

96. An ellipse has OB as semi minor axis, F and F' its focii and the angle FBF' is a right angle. Then, the eccentricity of the ellipse is **[AIEEE 2005, 3M]**

(a) $\frac{1}{\sqrt{2}}$ (b) $\frac{1}{2}$ (c) $\frac{1}{4}$ (d) $\frac{1}{\sqrt{3}}$

97. In an ellipse, the distance between its foci is 6 and minor axis is 8. Then, its eccentricity is **[AIEEE 2006, 4.5M]**

(a) $\frac{3}{5}$ (b) $\frac{1}{2}$

(c) $\frac{4}{5}$ (d) $\frac{1}{\sqrt{5}}$

98. Let $P(x_1, y_1)$ and $Q(x_2, y_2), y_1<0, y_2<0$ be the end points of the latusrectum of the, ellipse $x^2+4y^2=4$. The equations of parabolas with latusrectum PQ are **[IIT-JEE 2008, 4M]**

(a) $x^2+2\sqrt{3}y=3+\sqrt{3}$ (b) $x^2-2\sqrt{3}y=3+\sqrt{3}$

(c) $x^2+2\sqrt{3}y=3-\sqrt{3}$ (d) $x^2-2\sqrt{3}y=3-\sqrt{3}$

99. A focus of an ellipse is tat the origin. The directrix is the line $x=4$ and the eccentricity is $\frac{1}{2}$. Then, the length of the semi-major axis is **[AIEEE 2008, 3M]**

(a) $\frac{8}{3}$ (b) $\frac{2}{3}$

(c) $\frac{4}{3}$ (d) $\frac{5}{3}$

100. The line passing through the extermity A of the major axis and extremity B of the minor axis of the ellipse $x^2+9y^2=9$ meets its auxiliary circle at the point M. Then, the area of the triangle with vertices at A, M and the origin O is **[IIT-JEE 2009, 3M]**

(a) $\frac{31}{10}$ (b) $\frac{29}{10}$

(c) $\frac{21}{10}$ (d) $\frac{27}{10}$

101. The normal at a point P on the ellipse $x^2+4y^2=16$ meets the X-axis at Q. If M is the mid-point of the line segment PQ, then the locus of M intersects the latusrectum of the given ellipse at the points **[IIT-JEE 2009, 3M]**

(a) $\left(\pm\frac{3\sqrt{5}}{2},\pm\frac{2}{7}\right)$ (b) $\left(\pm\frac{3\sqrt{5}}{2},\pm\sqrt{\frac{19}{4}}\right)$

(c) $\left(\pm 2\sqrt{3},\pm\frac{1}{7}\right)$ (d) $\left(\pm 2\sqrt{3},\pm\frac{4\sqrt{3}}{7}\right)$

102. In a triangle ABC with fixed based BC, the vertex A moves such that

$$\cos B+\cos C=4\sin^2\frac{A}{2}$$

If a, b and c denote the lengths of the sides of the triangle opposite to the angles A, B and C, respectively, then **[IIT-JEE 2009, 4M]**

(a) $b+c=4a$
(b) $b+c=2a$
(c) locus of point A is an ellipse
(d) locus of point A is a pair of straight lines

103. The conic having parametric representation $x=\sqrt{3}\left(\frac{1-t^2}{1+t^2}\right), y=\frac{2t}{1+t^2}$ is **[IIT-JEE 2009, 2M]**

(a) a circle (b) a parabola

(c) an ellipse (d) a hyperbola

104. The ellipse $x^2+4y^2=4$ is inscribed in a rectangle aligned with the coordinate axes, which in turn is inscribed in another ellipse that passes through the point (4, 0). Then, the equation of the ellipse is **[AIEEE 2009, 4M]**

(a) $x^2+12y^2=16$ (b) $4x^2+48y^2=48$

(c) $4x^2+64y^2=48$ (d) $x^2+16y^2=16$

Paragraph

(Q. Nos. 105 to 107)

Tangents are drawn from the point $P(3,4)$ to the ellipse $\frac{x^2}{9}+\frac{y^2}{4}=1$ touching the ellipse at points A and B.

105. The coordinates of A and B are

(a) (3, 0) and (0, 2)

(b) $\left(-\frac{8}{5}, \frac{2\sqrt{161}}{15}\right)$ and $\left(-\frac{9}{5}, \frac{8}{5}\right)$

(c) $\left(-\frac{8}{5}, \frac{2\sqrt{161}}{15}\right)$ and (0, 2)

(d) (3, 0) and $\left(-\frac{9}{5}, \frac{8}{5}\right)$

106. The orthocenter of the triangle PAB is

(a) $\left(5, \frac{8}{7}\right)$ (b) $\left(\frac{7}{5}, \frac{25}{8}\right)$

(c) $\left(\frac{11}{5}, \frac{8}{5}\right)$ (d) $\left(\frac{8}{25}, \frac{7}{5}\right)$

107. The equation of the locus of the point whose distances from the point P and the line AB are equal, is **[IIT-JEE 2010, (3+3+3)M]**

(a) $9x^2+y^2-6xy-54x-62y+241=0$

(b) $x^2+9y^2+6xy-54x+62y-241=0$

(c) $9x^2+9y^2-6xy-54x-62y-241=0$

(d) $x^2+y^2-2xy+27x+31y-120=0$

108. Equation of the ellipse whose axes are the axes of coordinates an which passes through the point (–3, 1) and has eccentricity $\sqrt{\frac{2}{5}}$ is **[AIEEE 2011, 4M]**

(a) $5x^2+3y^2-48=0$ (b) $3x^2+5y^2-15=0$

(c) $5x^2+3y^2-32=0$ (d) $3x^2+5y^2-32=0$

109. The ellipse $E_1:\frac{x^2}{9}+\frac{y^2}{4}=1$ is inscribed in a rectangle R whose sides are parallel to the coordinate axes. Another ellipse E_2 passing through the point (0, 4) circumscribes the rectangle R. the eccentricity of the ellipse E_2 is **[IIT-JEE 2012, 4M]**

(a) $\frac{\sqrt{2}}{2}$ (b) $\frac{\sqrt{3}}{2}$

(c) $\frac{1}{2}$ (d) $\frac{3}{4}$

110. Statement I : An equation of a common tangent to the parabola $y^2=16\sqrt{3}x$ and the ellipse $2x^2+y^2=4$ is $y=2x+2\sqrt{3}$

Statement II : If the line $y=mx+\frac{4\sqrt{3}}{m},(m\neq 0)$ is a common tangent to the parabola $y^2=16\sqrt{3}x$ and the ellipse $2x^2+y^2=4$, then m satisfies $m^2+2m^2=24$ **[AIEEE 2012, 4M]**

(a) Statement I is false, statement-II is true

(b) Statement I is true, statementII is true; statement-II is a correct explanation for statement-I

(c) Statement I is true, statement II is true; statement II is not a correct explanation for statement I

(d) Statement I is true, statement II is false

111. An ellipse is drawn by taking a diameter of the circle $(x-1)^2+y^2=1$ as its semi-minor axis and diameter of the circle $x^2+(y-2)^2=4$ is semi-major axis. If the centre of the ellipse is at the origin and its axes are the coordinate axes, then the equation of the ellipse is **[AIEEE 2012, 4M]**

(a) $4x^2+y^2=4$ (b) $x^2+4y^2=8$

(c) $4x^2+y^2=8$ (d) $x^2+4y^2=16$

112. The equation of the circle passing through the foci of the ellipse $\frac{x^2}{16}+\frac{y^2}{9}=1$, and having centre at (0, 3) is **[JEE Main 2013, 4M]**

(a) $x^2+y^2-6y-7=0$ (b) $x^2+y^2-6y+7=0$

(c) $x^2+y^2-6y-5=0$ (d) $x^2+y^2-6y+5=0$

113. A vertical line passing through the point (h, 0) intersects the ellipse $\frac{x^2}{4}+\frac{y^2}{9}=1$ at the points P and Q. Let the tangents to the ellipse at P and Q meet at the point R. If $\Delta(h)$ = area of the triangle PQR, $\Delta_1=\frac{1}{2}\leq h\leq \max \Delta(h)$ and $\Delta_2=\frac{1}{2}\leq h\leq \min \Delta(h)$, then $\frac{8}{\sqrt{5}}\Delta_1-8\Delta_2=$ **[JEE Advanced 2013, 3M]**

114. The locus of the foot of perpendicular drawn from the centre of the ellipse $x^2+3y^2=6$ on any tangent to it is **[JEE Main 2014, 4M]**

(a) $(x^2+y^2)^2=6x^2+2y^2$ (b) $(x^2+y^2)^2=6x^2-2y^2$

(c) $(x^2-y^2)^2=6x^2+2y^2$ (d) $(x^2-y^2)^2=6x^2-2y^2$

115. The area (in sq units) of the quadrilateral formed by the tangents at the end points of the latus rectum to the ellipse $\frac{x^2}{9}+\frac{y^2}{5}=1$ is **[JEE Main 2015, 4M]**

(a) $\frac{27}{2}$ (b) 27

(c) $\frac{27}{4}$ (d) 18

116. Let E_1 and E_2 be two ellipses whose centers are at the origin. The major axes of E_1 and E_2 lie along the X-axis and the Y-axis, respectively. Let S be the circle $x^2+(y-1)^2=2$. The straight line $x+y=3$ touches the curves, S, E_1 and E_2 at P, Q and R respectively. Suppose that $PQ=PR=\frac{2\sqrt{2}}{3}$. If e_1 and e_2 are the eccentricities of E_1 and E_2, respectively, then the correct expression(s) is (are) **[JEE Advanced, 2015 4M]**

(a) $e_1^2+e_2^2=\frac{43}{40}$ (b) $e_1e_2=\frac{\sqrt{7}}{2\sqrt{10}}$

(c) $|e_1^2-e_2^2|=\frac{5}{8}$ (d) $e_1e_2=\frac{\sqrt{3}}{4}$

117. Suppose that the foci of the ellipse $\frac{x^2}{9}+\frac{y^2}{5}=1$ are $(f_1, 0)$ and $(f_2\ 0)$ where $f_1>0$ and $f_2>0$. Let P_1 and P_2 be two parabolas with a common vertex at (0, 0) and with foci at $(f_1, 0)$ and $(2f_2, 0)$, respectively. Let T_1 be a tangent to P_1 which passes through $(2f_2, 0)$ and T_2 be a tangent to P_2 which passes through $(f_1, 0)$. If m_1 is the slope of T_1 and m_2 is the slope of T_2, then the9 value of $\left(\frac{1}{m_1^2}+m_2^2\right)$ is **[JEE Advanced 2015, 4M]**

Paragraph

(Q. Nos. 118 and 119)

Let $F_1(x_1, 0)$ and $F_2(x_2, 0)$ for $x_1<0$ and $x_2>0$, be the foci of the ellipse $\frac{x^2}{9}+\frac{y^2}{8}=1$. Suppose a parabola having vertex at the origin and focus at F_2 intersects the ellipse at point M in the first quadrant and at point N in the fourth quadrant.

118. The orthocentre of the triangle F_1MN is

(a) $\left(-\frac{9}{10}, 0\right)$ (b) $\left(\frac{2}{3}, 0\right)$ (c) $\left(\frac{9}{10}, 0\right)$ (d) $\left(\frac{2}{3}, \sqrt{6}\right)$

119. If the tangents to the ellipse at M and N meet at R and the normal to the parabola at M meets the X-axis at Q, then the ratio of area of the triangle MQR to area of the quadrilateral MF_1NF_2 is **[JEE Advanced 2016, (3+3)M]**

(a) 3 : 4 (b) 4 : 5 (c) 5 : 8 (d) 2 : 3

120. The eccentricity of an ellipse whose centre is at the origin is 1/2. If one of its directices is $x=-4$, then the equation of the normal to it at (1, 3/2) is **[JEE Main 2017, 4M]**

(a) $x+2y=4$ (b) $2y-x=2$

(c) $4x-2y=1$ (d) $4x+2y=7$

Answers

Exercise for Session 1

1. (c) **2.** (a) **3.** (b) **4.** (d) **5.** (b)
6. (a,b) **7.** (b) **8.** (c) **9.** (b) **10.** (d)
11. (a) **12.** (a)
13. $\frac{8}{3}, \frac{\sqrt{5}}{3}$; $(1\pm\sqrt{5}, 2)$; (–2, 2) and (4, 2); 6 and 4; (1, 2)
14. $3x^2+4y^2=300$ **15.** $\frac{(x-2)^2}{4}+\frac{(y+3)^2}{3}=1$
16. $5x^2+9y^2-54y+36=0$ **17.** $\frac{1}{2}$
18. $x^2\pm ay=a^2$

Exercise for Session 2

1. (c) **2.** (c) **3.** (a) **4.** (b) **5.** (d)
6. (d) **7.** (d) **8.** (c) **9.** (a) **10.** (b)
11. (b) **12.** $\lambda=-\frac{1}{\sqrt{5}}$; $\theta=\cos^{-1}\left(-\frac{1}{\sqrt{5}}\right)$

Exercise for Session 3

1. (c) **2.** (c) **3.** (b) **4.** (b) **5.** (a) **6.** (d)
7. (b) **8.** (a)
9. $3(x^2+y^2-a^2-b^2)^2=4(b^2x^2+a^2y^2-a^2b^2)$
11. $\frac{(x-a)^2}{a^2}+\frac{y^2}{b^2}=1$ **12.** $b^4c^2x^2+a^2c^2y^2=a^4b^4$
13. $(-1, 0)$; $5\sqrt{3}$ **14.** $x\sqrt{5}+2y=2\sqrt{5}$

Chapter Exercises

1. (c) **2.** (d) **3.** (a) **4.** (b) **5.** (c) **6.** (d)
7. (a) **8.** (c) **9.** (a) **10.** (c) **11.** (b) **12.** (b)
13. (d) **14.** (c) **15.** (c) **16.** (a) **17.** (c) **18.** (c)
19. (d) **20.** (a) **21.** (b) **22.** (a) **23.** (a) **24.** (a)
25. (a) **26.** (a) **27.** (d) **28.** (d) **29.** (a) **30.** (c)
31. (a,c) **32.** (a,b,c,d) **33.** (b,d) **34.** (a,c) **35.** (a,d) **36.** (a, c)
37. (a,b) **38.** (a,b,c) **39.** (a,b) **40.** (a,c) **41.** (a,b) **42.** (a,c)
43. (a,b,c) **44.** (a,b,c) **45.** (a,c) **46.** (d) **47.** (b) **48.** (a)
49. (a) **50.** (c) **51.** (b) **52.** (d) **53.** (d) **54.** (b)
55. (c) **56.** (a) **57.** (b) **58.** (c) **59.** (b) **60.** (c)
61. (6) **62.** (9) **63.** (4) **64.** (5) **65.** (2) **66.** (8)
67. (1) **68.** (5) **69.** (9) **70.** (6)
71. (A) → (p,q); (B) → (p,q,s); (C) → (p,r); (D) → (p,r)
72. (A) → (q); (B) → (p); (C) → (p,r,s); (D) → (q)
73. (A) → (p,s); (B) → (q); (C) → (q,s); (D) → (p,r)
74. (a) **75.** (b) **76.** (a) **77.** (a) **78.** (b) **79.** (c)
80. (c) **81.** (a) **86.** $y=\pm\sqrt{\left(\frac{r^2-4}{(25-r^2)}\right)}x$ **90.** (2b)
94. (a) **95.** $\left(\frac{14}{\sqrt{3}}\right)$ **96.** (a) **97.** (a) **98.** (b,c) **99.** (a)
100. (d) **101.** (c) **102.** (b,c) **103.** (c) **104.** (a) **105.** (d)
106. (c) **107.** (a) **108.** (d) **109.** (c) **110.** (b) **111.** (d)
112. (a) **113.** (9) **114.** (a) **115.** (b) **116.** (a,b) **117.** (4)
118. (a) **119.** (c) **120.** (c)

Solutions

1. $\because$ Major axis on X-axis.

$$\therefore \quad f(2a) > f(a^2 - 3)$$
$$\Rightarrow \quad 2a > a^2 - 3 \quad [\because f \text{ is increasing}]$$
$$\Rightarrow \quad a^2 - 2a - 3 < 0 \text{ or } (a-3)(a+1) < 0$$
$$\text{or} \quad -1 < a < 3$$
$$\therefore \quad a \in (-1, 3)$$

2. $\because$ Major axis on Y-axis.

$$\therefore \quad f(a^2 - 5) > f(4a)$$
$$\Rightarrow \quad a^2 - 5 < 4a \quad [\because f \text{ is decreasing}]$$
$$\Rightarrow \quad a^2 - 4a - 5 < 0$$
$$\text{or} \quad (a-5)(a+1) < 0$$
$$\text{or} \quad -1 < a < 5$$
$$\therefore \quad a \in (-1, 5)$$

3. Let $a^2 = \sin\sqrt{2} - \cos\sqrt{3} = \sin\sqrt{2} - \sin\left(\frac{\pi}{2} - \sqrt{3}\right)$

$$= \sin\sqrt{2} + \sin\left(\sqrt{3} - \frac{\pi}{2}\right)$$
$$= \sin(1.41) + \sin(1.73 - 1.57)$$
$$= \sin(1.41) + \sin(0.16) > 0$$

and $b^2 = \sin\sqrt{3} - \cos\sqrt{2}$

$$= \sin\sqrt{3} - \sin\left(\frac{\pi}{2} - \sqrt{2}\right)$$
$$= \sin(1.73) - \sin(1.57 - 1.41)$$
$$= \sin(1.73) - \sin(0.36) > 0$$

Also, $a^2 > b^2$

Hence, curve represent an ellipse with foci on X-axis.

4. Mutually perpendicular tangents have been drawn by taking any point on the director circle of given ellipse. Any point on the director circle can be taken as $(5\cos\theta, 5\sin\theta)$. Equation of corresponding chord of contact is

$$\frac{5x}{16}\cos\theta + \frac{5y}{9}\sin\theta - 1 = 0$$

It's distance from the origin is equal to

$$\frac{1}{\sqrt{\left(\frac{25\cos^2\theta}{256} + \frac{25\sin^2\theta}{81}\right)}} = \frac{144}{5}$$

$$\Rightarrow \quad \frac{1}{\sqrt{(256 - 175\cos^2\theta)}} \le \frac{144}{5.9} = \frac{16}{5}$$

5. We have, $PQ = BP$

$$\Rightarrow \quad 2ae = \sqrt{(a^2e^2 + b^2)} = \sqrt{a^2} = a$$
$$\therefore \quad e = \frac{1}{2}$$

6. Any tangent to $\frac{x^2}{16} + \frac{y^2}{9} = 1$, is

$$y = mx + \sqrt{(16m^2 + 9)}$$

It is also tangent to the circle $x^2 + y^2 = \left(\frac{5}{\sqrt{2}}\right)^2$, then perpendicular distance from $(0, 0)$ is equal to $\frac{5}{\sqrt{2}}$

$$\therefore \quad \frac{\sqrt{(16m^2 + 9)}}{\sqrt{(m^2 + 1)}} = \frac{5}{\sqrt{2}}$$
$$\Rightarrow \quad 32m^2 + 18 = 25m^2 + 25$$
$$\text{or} \quad 7m^2 = 7 \Rightarrow m = \pm 1$$

for acute $m = 1$.

Now, let θ be the angle between common tangent and the line $\sqrt{3}x - y + 6 = 0$, then

$$\tan\theta = \left|\frac{\sqrt{3} - 1}{1 + \sqrt{3}}\right| = \frac{\sqrt{3} - 1}{\sqrt{3} + 1} = \tan\left(\frac{\pi}{12}\right)$$
$$\therefore \quad \theta = \frac{\pi}{12}$$

7. Tangent at $(-8, 3)$ is

$$\frac{x(-8)}{100} + \frac{y(3)}{25} = 1$$
$$\text{or} \quad 2x - 3y + 25 = 0$$

for Y-axis put $x = 0$, then $y = \frac{25}{3}$

Hence, required point is $\left(0, \frac{25}{3}\right)$.

8. Let $A \equiv (4\cos\theta, 3\sin\theta)$, then

$$B \equiv (-4\sin\theta, 3\cos\theta)$$
$$\therefore \quad (CA)^2 = 16\cos^2\theta + 9\sin^2\theta$$
$$\text{and } (CB)^2 = 16\sin^2\theta + 9\cos^2\theta$$

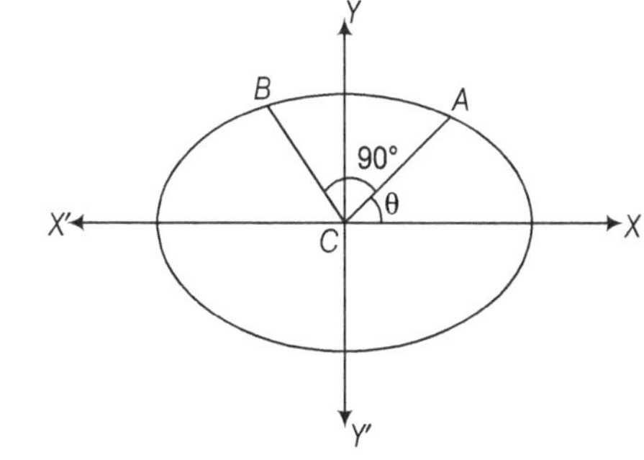

$$\therefore \frac{1}{(CA)^2} + \frac{1}{(CB)^2} = \frac{1}{16\cos^2\theta + 9\sin^2\theta} + \frac{1}{16\sin^2\theta + 9\cos^2\theta}$$
$$= \frac{25}{144(\sin^4\theta + \cos^4\theta) + 337\sin^2\theta\cos^2\theta}$$
$$= \frac{25}{144(1 - 2\sin^2\theta\cos^2\theta) + 337\sin^2\theta\cos^2\theta}$$
$$= \frac{25}{144 + 49\sin^2\theta\cos^2\theta} = \frac{25}{144} \quad (\text{for } \theta = 0)$$

9. (α, β) lies on the director circle of the ellipse i.e. on $x^2 + y^2 = 9$

So, we can assume

$$\alpha = 3\cos\theta, \beta = \sin\theta$$

$\therefore$ $F = 12\cos\theta + 9\sin\theta = 3(4\cos\theta + 3\sin\theta)$

$\Rightarrow$ $-15 \le F \le 15$

10. At, $t = \frac{3}{2}$, $b > a$

$\therefore$ Length of latusrectum $= \frac{2a^2}{b} = \frac{2[t^2 - 3t + 4]^2}{[3 + 5t]}$

$$= \frac{2\left[\frac{9}{4} - \frac{9}{2} + 4\right]^2}{\left[3 + \frac{15}{2}\right]} \quad \left[\text{at } t = \frac{3}{2}\right]$$

$$= \frac{2[1.75]^2}{[10.5]} = \frac{2(1)^2}{10} = \frac{1}{5}$$

11. Slope of line $= \frac{b}{a}\left(\frac{\sin 60° - \sin 30°}{\cos 60° - \cos 30°}\right) = -\frac{b}{a} = -\frac{1}{2}$ or $a = 2b$

Homogenizing the ellipse with $x + 2y + 4 = 0$, then

$$\frac{x^2}{4b^2} + \frac{y^2}{b^2} = \left(\frac{x + 2y}{-4}\right)^2$$

or $x^2\left(\frac{1}{4b^2} - \frac{1}{16}\right) + y^2\left(\frac{1}{b^2} - \frac{1}{4}\right) - \frac{xy}{4} = 0$

Now, coefficients of x^2 + coefficient of $y^2 = 0$

$\Rightarrow$ $\frac{1}{4b^2} - \frac{1}{16} + \frac{1}{b^2} - \frac{1}{4} = 0$

or $\frac{5}{4b^2} = \frac{5}{16}$

or $b^2 = 4$ then, $a^2 = 16$

$\therefore$ Ellipse is $\frac{x^2}{16} + \frac{y^2}{4} = 1$

12. Let the equation of the semi elliptical arch be

$$\frac{x^2}{a^2} + \frac{y^2}{b^2} = 1 \quad [y > 0]$$

Length of the major axis $= 2a = 9$

$\Rightarrow$ $a = \frac{9}{2}$

Length of the semi minor axis $b = 3$

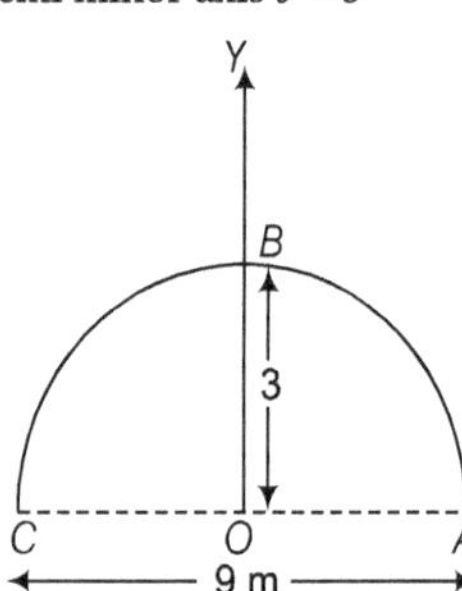

So, the equation of the arch becomes

$$\frac{4x^2}{81} + \frac{y^2}{9} = 1$$

If $x = 2$, then $y^2 = \frac{65}{9}$

$\Rightarrow$ $y = \frac{\sqrt{65}}{3} = \frac{8}{3}$ [approximately]

13. Equation of tangent of the ellipse at $P(5\cos\theta, 4\sin\theta)$ is

$$\frac{x}{5}\cos\theta + \frac{y}{4}\sin\theta = 1$$

It meets the line $x = 0$ at $Q(0, 4\operatorname{cosec}\theta)$ and image of Q in the line $y = x$ is $R(4\operatorname{cosec}\theta, 0)$.

$\therefore$ Equation of the circle is

$$(x - 0)(x - 4\operatorname{cosec}\theta) + (y - 4\operatorname{cosec}\theta)(y - 0) = 0$$

i.e. $x^2 + y^2 - 4(x + y)\operatorname{cosec}\theta = 0$

$\therefore$ Each member of the family passes through the intersection of

$$x^2 + y^2 = 0 \text{ and } x + y = 0$$

i.e. the point $(0, 0)$.

14. A cyclic parallelogram will be a rectangle or square.

So, $\angle QPR = 90°$

Therefore, P lies on the director circle of the ellipse

$$\frac{x^2}{16} + \frac{y^2}{b^2} = 1$$

Hence, $x^2 + y^2 = 25$ is the director circle of $\frac{x^2}{16} + \frac{y^2}{b^2} = 1$,

then $16 + b^2 = 25$ or $b^2 = 9$

$\Rightarrow$ $a^2(1 - e^2) = 9$

$\Rightarrow$ $16(1 - e^2) = 9$ $[\because a^2 = 16]$

$\Rightarrow$ $e^2 = 1 - \frac{9}{16} = \frac{7}{16}$

$\therefore$ $e = \frac{\sqrt{7}}{4}$

15. $\because m, n \in N$ and $m.n = m + n$

or $m(n - 1) = n$

n is divisible by $n - 1$. Therefore

$$n - 1 = 1$$

$\Rightarrow$ $n = 2, m = 2$

Hence, the chord of contact of tangents drawn from

$(2, 2)$ to $4x^2 + 9y^2 = 36$

is $4x \cdot 2 + 9y \cdot 2 = 36$

or $4x + 9y = 18$

16. $\because x - 2y + 4 = 0$ or $y = \frac{x}{2} + 2$

Condition of tangency

$$c^2 = a^2m^2 + b^2 \Rightarrow 4 = 4 \times \frac{1}{4} + b^2$$

$\therefore$ $b = \sqrt{3}$

Now, common tangent meet on X-axis at a point $(-4, 0)$.

According to symmetry other common tangent meet Y-axis at $(0, -2)$.

$\therefore$ Equation of other common tangent is

$$\frac{x}{-4} + \frac{y}{-2} = 1 \text{ or } x + 2y + 4 = 0$$

17. The tangent at the point of shortest distance from the line $x + y = 7$ parallel to the given line.

Any point on the given ellipse is

$$(\sqrt{6}\cos\theta, \sqrt{3}\sin\theta).$$

Equation of the tangent is

$$\frac{x\cos\theta}{\sqrt{6}} + \frac{y\sin\theta}{\sqrt{3}} = 1.$$

It is parallel to $x + y = 7$

$$\Rightarrow \quad \frac{\cos\theta}{\sqrt{6}} = \frac{\sin\theta}{\sqrt{3}}$$

$$\Rightarrow \quad \frac{\cos\theta}{\sqrt{2}} = \frac{\sin\theta}{1} = \frac{1}{\sqrt{3}}$$

The required point is (2, 1).

18. Let $y = mx + \frac{1}{m}$ be a tangent to the parabola, then for the required equilateral triangle.

$m = \pm\frac{1}{\sqrt{3}}$ and it is tangent to ellipse also, if

$$\left(\frac{1}{m}\right)^2 = a^2m^2 + b^2$$

$$\Rightarrow \quad 3 = \frac{a^2}{3} + b^2$$

$$\Rightarrow \quad 3 = \frac{a^2}{3} + a^2 - a^2e^2$$

$$\Rightarrow \quad a^2e^2 = \frac{4a^2}{3} - 3$$

$$\text{or} \quad e^2 = \frac{4}{3} - \frac{3}{a^2}$$

$$\text{Now,} \quad 0 < e^2 < 1$$

$$\Rightarrow \quad 0 < \frac{4}{3} - \frac{3}{a^2} < 1$$

$$\Rightarrow \quad \frac{3}{2} < a < 3$$

19. For equilateral triangle

Circumcentre = Centroid

$$\therefore \quad h = \frac{a\cos\alpha + a\cos\beta + a\cos\gamma}{3} \text{ or } \frac{3h}{a} = \Sigma\cos\alpha$$

$$\text{or} \quad \left(\frac{3h}{a}\right)^2 = (\Sigma\cos\alpha)^2 = \Sigma\cos^2\alpha + 2\,\Sigma\cos\alpha\cos\beta \quad \text{...(i)}$$

$$\text{and} \quad k = \frac{b\sin\alpha + b\sin\beta + b\sin\gamma}{3}$$

$$\text{or} \quad \frac{3k}{b} = \Sigma\sin\alpha$$

$$\text{or} \quad \left(\frac{3k}{b}\right)^2 = (\Sigma\sin\alpha)^2 = \Sigma\sin^2\alpha + 2\,\Sigma\sin\alpha\sin\beta \quad \text{...(ii)}$$

Adding Eqs. (i) and (ii), we get

$$\frac{9h^2}{a^2} + \frac{9k^2}{b^2} = 3 + 2\,\Sigma\cos(\alpha - \beta)$$

$$\text{or} \quad \Sigma\cos(\alpha - \beta) = \frac{9h^2}{2a^2} + \frac{9k^2}{2b^2} - \frac{3}{2}$$

20. $\because$ Latusrectum and parabola = $4(ae)$ ...(i)

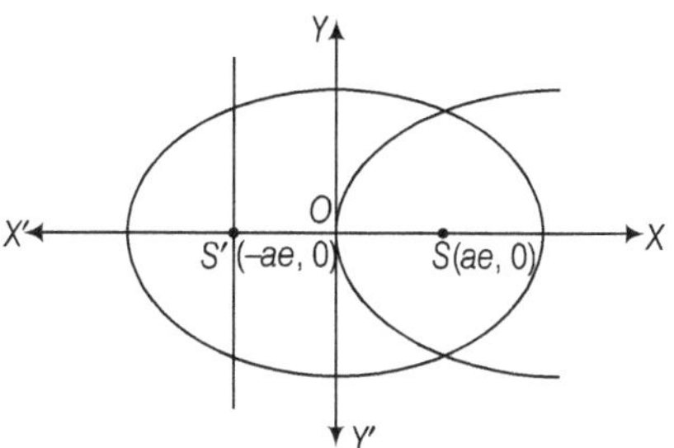

and latusrectum of ellipse $= \frac{2b^2}{a}$ ...(ii)

$\because$ Latusrectum and parabola and ellipse be equal

$$\therefore \quad \frac{2b^2}{a} = 4ae \quad \text{[from Eqs. (i) and (ii)]}$$

$$\Rightarrow \quad 2b^2 = 4a^2e$$

$$\text{or} \quad 2a^2(1 - e^2) = 4a^2e \quad \text{or } e^2 + 2e - 1 = 0$$

$$\text{Therefore, } e = \frac{-2 \pm \sqrt{(4 + 4)}}{2} = -1 \pm \sqrt{2}$$

$$\text{Hence,} \quad e = \sqrt{2} - 1$$

21. Here, the center of the ellipse is (0, 0)

Let $P(r\cos\theta, r\sin\theta)$ be any point on the given ellipse, then

$r^2\cos^2\theta + 2r^2\sin^2\theta + 2r^2\sin\theta\cos\theta = 1$

$$\text{or} \quad r^2 = \frac{1}{1 + \sin^2\theta + \sin 2\theta}$$

$$= \frac{2}{2 + (1 - \cos 2\theta) + 2\sin 2\theta} = \frac{2}{2\sin 2\theta - \cos 2\theta + 3}$$

$$\because \quad 3 - \sqrt{5} \le 2\sin 2\theta - \cos 2\theta + 3 \le 3 + \sqrt{5}$$

For r_{max}, $2\sin 2\theta - \cos 2\theta + 3 = 3 - \sqrt{5}$

$$\therefore \quad r_{max}^2 = \frac{2}{3 - \sqrt{5}} = \frac{2(3 + \sqrt{5})}{4} = \frac{6 + 2\sqrt{5}}{4} = \left(\frac{\sqrt{5} + 1}{2}\right)^2$$

$$\text{Hence,} \quad r_{max} = \frac{\sqrt{5} + 1}{2}$$

22. Centre of the ellipse if (1, 2) and length of major axis and minor axis are 6 and 4 respectively and centre and radius of the circle are (1, 2) and 1 respectively.

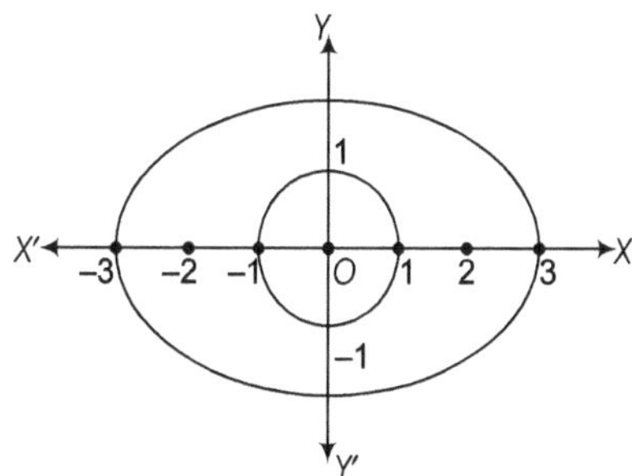

Hence, ellipse and circle do not touch or cut.

$\therefore$ Common chord impossible.

$\therefore$ Hence, length of common chord = 0

23. $ax^2 + by^2 + 2fx + 2gy + c = 0$

$$a\left\{x^2 + \frac{2fx}{a}\right\} + b\left\{y^2 + \frac{2gy}{b}\right\} + c = 0$$

$$\Rightarrow \quad a\left(x + \frac{f}{a}\right)^2 + b\left(y + \frac{g}{b}\right)^2 = \left(\frac{f^2}{a} + \frac{g^2}{b} - c\right)$$

$$\Rightarrow \quad \frac{(x + f/a)^2}{\left(\frac{f^2}{a} + \frac{g^2}{b} - c\right)/a} + \frac{(y + g/b)^2}{\left(\frac{f^2}{a} + \frac{g^2}{b} - c\right)/b} = 1$$

If e eccentricity, then

$$\frac{\left(\frac{f^2}{a} + \frac{g^2}{b} - c\right)}{b} = \frac{\left(\frac{f^2}{a} + \frac{g^2}{b} - c\right)}{a}(1 - e^2)$$

$$\Rightarrow \quad 1 - e^2 = \frac{a}{b}$$

$$\Rightarrow \quad e^2 = \frac{b - a}{b}$$

$$\therefore \quad e = \sqrt{\left(\frac{b - a}{b}\right)}$$

24. Let ellipse be $\frac{x^2}{a^2} + \frac{y^2}{b^2} = 1$ and the circle be $x^2 + y^2 = a^2e^2$, point of intersection of the circle and the ellipse is

$$P\left(\frac{a}{e}\sqrt{(2e^2 - 1)}, \frac{a}{e}(1 - e^2)\right)$$

Now, area of $\Delta\, PF_1F_2 = \left|\frac{1}{2} \times 2ae \times \frac{a}{e}(1 - e^2)\right|$

$$= a^2(1 - e^2) = 30 \qquad \text{[given]}$$

or $\quad a^2e^2 = a^2 - 30 = \left(\frac{17}{2}\right)^2 - 30 = \frac{169}{4}$

$$\therefore \quad ae = \frac{13}{2} \text{ or } 2ae = 13$$

25. Let standard ellipse is $\frac{x^2}{a^2} + \frac{y^2}{b^2} = 1 \qquad (a > b)$

Equations of tangent and normal at $\left(\frac{a}{\sqrt{2}}, \frac{b}{\sqrt{2}}\right)$

are $bx + ay - \sqrt{2}\,ab = 0$ and $ax - by - \frac{(a^2 - b^2)}{\sqrt{2}} = 0$

If sides of rectangles are p and q, then

$$p = \frac{|0 + 0 - \sqrt{2}\,ab|}{\sqrt{(a^2 + b^2)}} = \frac{\sqrt{2}\,ab}{\sqrt{(a^2 + b^2)}}$$

and
$$q = \left|\frac{0 - 0 - \frac{(a^2 - b^2)}{\sqrt{2}}}{\sqrt{(a^2 + b^2)}}\right|$$

$$= \frac{(a^2 - b^2)}{\sqrt{2}\sqrt{(a^2 + b^2)}}$$

$\therefore$ Area of rectangle $= pq = \frac{(a^2 - b^2)\,ab}{(a^2 + b^3)}$

26. Let equation of ellipse be $\frac{x^2}{a^2} + \frac{y^2}{b^2} = 1$

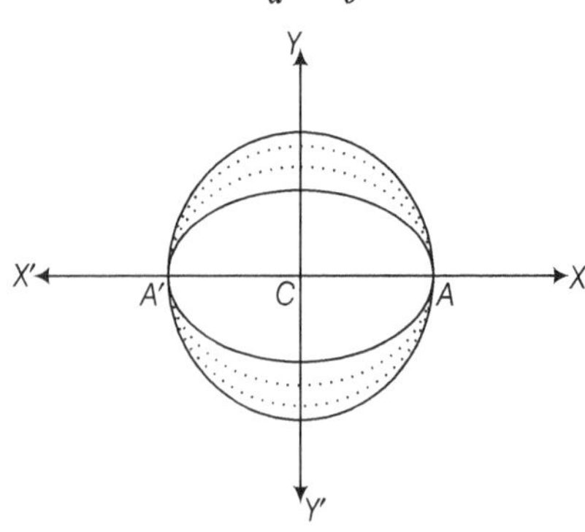

and equation of circle is $x^2 + y^2 = a^2$

$\therefore$ Area of ellipse $= \pi ab$

and Area of circle $= \pi a^2$

$$\therefore \quad \text{Probability} = \frac{\pi a^2 - \pi ab}{\pi a^2} = \frac{a - b}{a} = \frac{2}{3} \qquad \text{[given]}$$

$$\Rightarrow \quad 3a - 3b = 2a$$

or $\quad a = 3b$

or $\quad a^2 = 9b^2 = 9a^2(1 - e^2)$

$$\Rightarrow \quad 9e^2 = 8$$

$$\therefore \quad e = \frac{2\sqrt{2}}{3}$$

27. Let $S \equiv (x_1, y_1), S' \equiv (x_2, y_2)$

Let $C \equiv (h, k)$

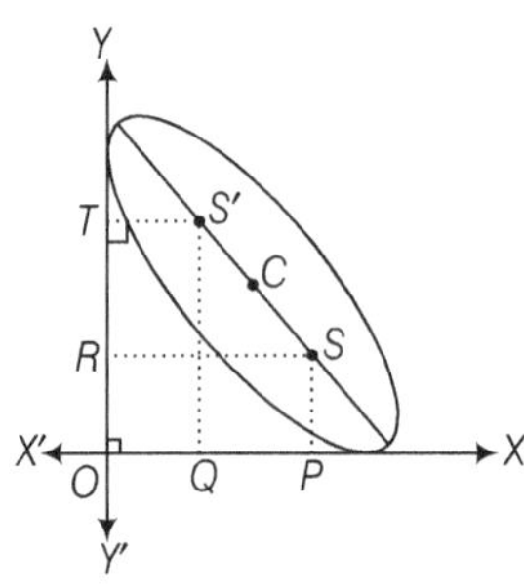

$$\therefore \quad \frac{x_1 + x_2}{2} = h$$

$$\Rightarrow \quad x_1 + x_2 = 2h$$

and $\quad y_1 + y_2 = 2k$

$\because \quad SP\, S'Q = b^2$

$\Rightarrow \quad y_1 y_2 = b^2$ and $SR \cdot S'T = b^2$

$$\Rightarrow \quad x_1 x_2 = b^2$$

Distance between foci $SS' = 2ae$

$$\Rightarrow \quad \sqrt{(x_1 - x_2)^2 + (y_1 - y_2)^2} = (2ae)$$

$$\Rightarrow \quad (x_1 - x_2)^2 + (y_1 - y_2)^2 = 4a^2e^2$$

$$\Rightarrow (x_1 + x_2)^2 - 4x_1x_2 + (y_1 + y_2)^2 - 4\,y_1y_2 = 4a^2e^2$$

$$\Rightarrow \quad 4h^2 - 4b^2 + 4k^2 - 4b^2 = 4(a^2 - b^2)$$

$$\Rightarrow \quad h^2 + k^2 - 2b^2 = a^2 - b^2$$

$$\therefore \quad h^2 + k^2 = a^2 + b^2$$

Locus of centre is $x^2 + y^2 = a^2 + b^2$ which is a circle.

28. If chord AB, then equation of AB, here mid-point of the chord is $\left(\frac{1}{2}, \frac{2}{3}\right)$

$$\therefore \quad T = S_1$$

$$\frac{x}{50} + \frac{y}{24} = \frac{1}{100} + \frac{1}{36} \quad \text{...(i)}$$

Let $A \equiv (x_1, y_1)$ and $B \equiv (x_2, y_2)$

$$\therefore \quad \frac{x_1}{50} + \frac{y_1}{24} = \frac{1}{100} + \frac{1}{36} \quad \text{...(ii)}$$

and $$\frac{x_2}{50} + \frac{y_2}{24} = \frac{1}{100} + \frac{1}{36} \quad \text{...(iii)}$$

$$\therefore \quad \frac{(x_2 - x_1)}{50} + \frac{(y_2 - y_1)}{24} = 0$$

$$\therefore \quad AB = \sqrt{(x_2 - x_1)^2 + (y_2 - y_1)^2}$$

$$= \sqrt{(x_2 - x_1)^2 + \left(\frac{24}{50}\right)^2 (x_2 - x_1)^2}$$

$$= \frac{|x_2 - x_1|}{25} \sqrt{769}$$

Now, solving $\frac{x}{50} + \frac{y}{24} = \frac{1}{100} + \frac{1}{36}$

and $$\frac{x^2}{25} + \frac{y^2}{16} = 1$$

then, $$x^2 - x - \frac{5336}{9} = 0$$

$$\therefore \quad |x_2 - x_1| = \frac{\sqrt{D}}{a} = \frac{\sqrt{21353}}{3}$$

$$\therefore \quad AB = \frac{\sqrt{21353}}{3 \times 25} \times \sqrt{769}$$

29. Equation of tangent at the point $P(4\cos\theta, 3\sin\theta)$ is

$$\frac{x}{4}\cos\theta + \frac{y}{3}\sin\theta = 1$$

or $$\frac{x}{4\sec\theta} + \frac{y}{3\operatorname{cosec}\theta} = 1$$

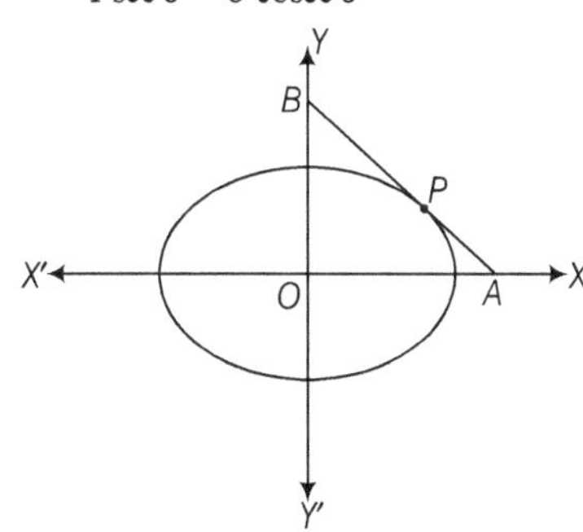

Coordinates of A and B are

$$A \equiv (4\sec\theta, 0) \text{ and } B \equiv (0, 3\operatorname{cosec}\theta)$$

Let middle point (h, k)

$$\therefore \quad h = 2\sec\theta, k = \frac{3}{2}\operatorname{cosec}\theta$$

$$\Rightarrow \quad \left(\frac{2}{h}\right)^2 + \left(\frac{3}{2k}\right)^2 = 1$$

$\therefore$ Locus is $9x^2 + 16y^2 = 4x^2y^2$

30. Equation of tangent at $(a\cos\alpha, b\sin\alpha)$ is

$$\frac{x}{a}\cos\alpha + \frac{y}{b}\sin\alpha = 1 \quad \text{...(i)}$$

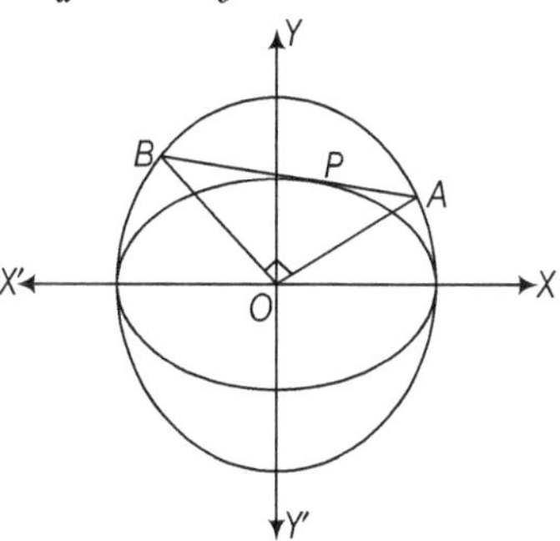

Equation of auxiliary circle is

$$x^2 + y^2 = a^2 \quad \text{...(ii)}$$

For combined equation of OA and OB, making homogeneous Eq. (ii) with the help of Eq. (i), then

$$x^2 + y^2 = a^2\left(\frac{x}{a}\cos\alpha + \frac{y}{b}\sin\alpha\right)^2$$

$$\Rightarrow \quad x^2\sin^2\alpha + y^2\left(1 - \frac{a^2}{b^2}\sin^2\alpha\right) - \frac{2axy}{b}\sin\alpha\cos\alpha = 0$$

$\because \quad \angle AOB = 90°$

$\therefore$ Coefficient of x^2 + Coefficient of $y^2 = 0$

$$\Rightarrow \quad \sin^2\alpha + 1 - \frac{a^2}{b^2}\sin^2\alpha = 0$$

$$\Rightarrow \quad 1 + \sin^2\alpha - \frac{a^2}{a^2(1 - e^2)}\sin^2\alpha = 0$$

$$\Rightarrow \quad (1 - e^2)(1 + \sin^2\alpha) - \sin^2\alpha = 0$$

$$\Rightarrow \quad 1 - e^2(1 + \sin^2\alpha) = 0$$

or $$e^2(1 + \sin^2\alpha) = 1$$

31. $\because b^2x^2 + y^2 = a^2b^2 \Rightarrow \frac{x^2}{a^2} + \frac{y^2}{a^2b^2} = 1$

Let $\quad a > ab,$

Then, $\quad (ab)^2 = a^2(1 - e^2)$

$$\Rightarrow \quad b^2 = 1 - e^2 \quad \text{...(i)}$$

$\therefore$ Extremities of the latusrectum $(\pm ae, \pm ab^2)$

Let $x_1 = \pm ae$ and $y_1 = \pm ab^2 = \pm a(1 - e^2)$

or $$y_1 = \pm(a - ae^2)$$

$$\Rightarrow \quad ay_1 = \pm(a^2 - a^2e^2)$$

$$= \pm(a^2 - x_1^2) \quad [\because x_1 = \pm ae]$$

or $$x_1^2 \pm ay_1 = a^2$$

$\therefore$ Required locus is $x^2 \pm ay = a^2$

32. Let $P \equiv (\sqrt{6}\cos\theta, \sqrt{2}\sin\theta)$ be any point on the ellipse

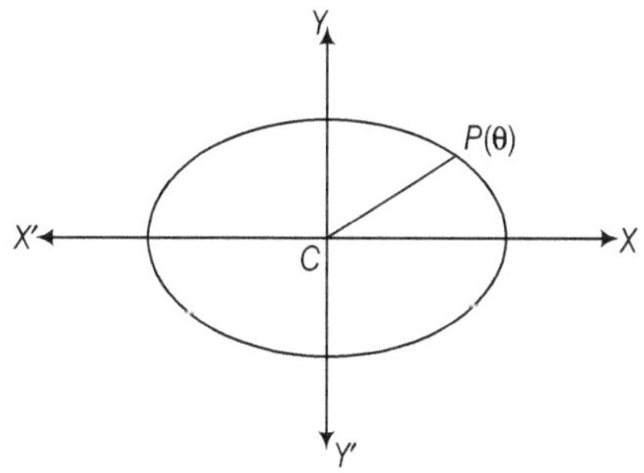

$$\frac{x^2}{6}+\frac{y^2}{2}=1$$

Given, $CP = 2 \Rightarrow (CP)^2 = 4$

$\Rightarrow \quad 6\cos^2\theta + 2\sin^2\theta = 4$

$\Rightarrow \quad 6\cos^2\theta + 2(1-\cos^2\theta) = 4$

or $\quad \cos^2\theta = \frac{1}{2} = \left(\frac{1}{\sqrt{2}}\right)^2 = \left(\cos\frac{\pi}{4}\right)^2$

$\therefore \quad \theta = n\pi \pm \frac{\pi}{4}, n \in I$

$\therefore \quad \theta = \frac{\pi}{4}, \frac{3\pi}{4}, \frac{5\pi}{4}, \frac{7\pi}{4}$

33. Here, $a = \cos\theta$ and $b = \sin\theta$

$\therefore \quad \frac{\pi}{4} < \theta < \frac{\pi}{2}$

$\therefore \quad a < b$

then, $\quad a^2 = b^2(1-e^2)$

$\Rightarrow \quad \cos^2\theta = \sin^2\theta(1-e^2)$

$\therefore \quad e^2 = 1 - \cot^2\theta$

or $\quad e = \sqrt{(1-\cot^2\theta)} \qquad \left(\because \frac{\pi}{4} < \theta < \frac{\pi}{2}\right)$

$\because$ Extremities of latusrectum are $\left(\pm\frac{a^2}{b}, \pm be\right)$

$\Rightarrow \quad x = \pm\frac{a^2}{b},\ y = \pm be$

or $\quad b^2x^2 = a^4$ and $y^2 = b^2e^2 = \sin^2\theta - \cos^2\theta$

or $\quad \sin^2\theta x^2 = \cos^4\theta$ and $y^2 = 1 - 2\cos^2\theta$

or $\quad (1-\cos^2\theta)x^2 = \cos^4\theta$ and $\cos^2\theta = \frac{1-y^2}{2}$

$\therefore \quad \left(1 - \frac{1-y^2}{2}\right)x^2 = \left(\frac{1-y^2}{2}\right)^2$

or $\quad 2x^2(1+y^2) = (1-y^2)^2$

or $\quad 2y^2(x^2+1) = 1 + y^4 - 2x^2$

34. $\because \frac{PF_1}{PF_2} = \frac{NF_1}{NF_2}$

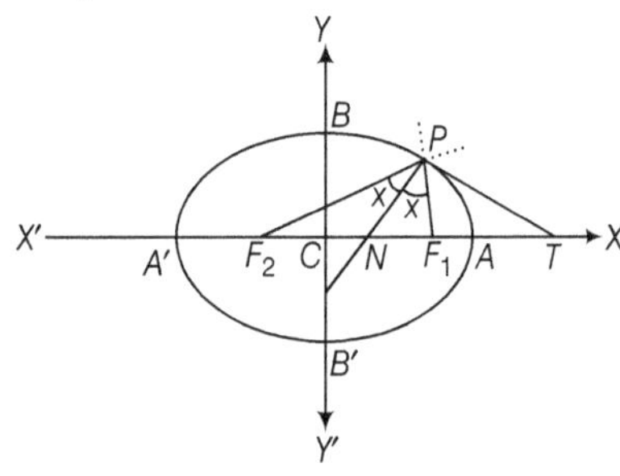

$\therefore$ PN bisects the $\angle F_1PF_2$

$\because$ Bisectors are perpendicular to each other.

$\therefore$ PT bisects the angle $(180° - \angle F_1PF_2)$

35. $\because a^2 - a - 6 > 0 \Rightarrow (a-3)(a+2) > 0$

$\therefore \quad a < -2$ or $a > 3 \quad$ ...(i)

and $\quad a^2 - 6a + 5 > 0 \Rightarrow (a-1)(a-5) > 0$

$\therefore \quad a < 1$ or $a > 5 \quad$ ...(ii)

Also $\quad a^2 - a - 6 \neq a^2 - 6a + 5$

or $\quad a \neq \frac{11}{5} \quad$ ...(iii)

From Eqs. (i), (ii) and (iii) we get

$$a \in (-\infty, -2) \cup (5, \infty)$$

36. $\because$ A latusrectum of an ellipse is a line passing through a focus, perpendicular to major axis i.e. parallel to minor axis.

37. Let the required equation be

$$\frac{x^2}{a^2}+\frac{y^2}{b^2}=1 \quad \text{...(i)}$$

Since, Eq. (i) passes through $(4, -1)$, then

$$\frac{16}{a^2}+\frac{1}{b^2}=1 \quad \text{...(ii)}$$

The equation of given line is $y = -\frac{x}{4} + \frac{10}{4}$

Which touches the ellipse Eq. (i),

$$\left(\frac{10}{4}\right)^2 = a^2\left(-\frac{1}{4}\right)^2 + b^2$$

$\Rightarrow \quad \frac{a^2}{16} + b^2 = \frac{25}{4} \quad$ ...(iii)

Solving, Eqs. (ii) and (iii), we get $a^2 = 20, b^2 = 5$

or $\quad a^2 = 80, b^2 = \frac{5}{4}$

Therefore, the required equation of ellipse will be

$$\frac{x^2}{20}+\frac{y^2}{5}=1 \text{ or } \frac{x^2}{80}+\frac{y^2}{5/4}=1$$

i.e. $\quad x^2 + 4y^2 = 20$ or $x^2 + 64y^2 = 80$

38. From focal property of ellipse

$SP + S'P = 2a$, if $a > b$

and $\quad SP + S'P = 2b$, if $b > a$

Also, $\quad PS\cos\theta + PS'\cos\phi = 2ae \quad$ ...(i)

$PS\sin\theta - PS'\sin\phi = 0 \quad$ ...(ii)

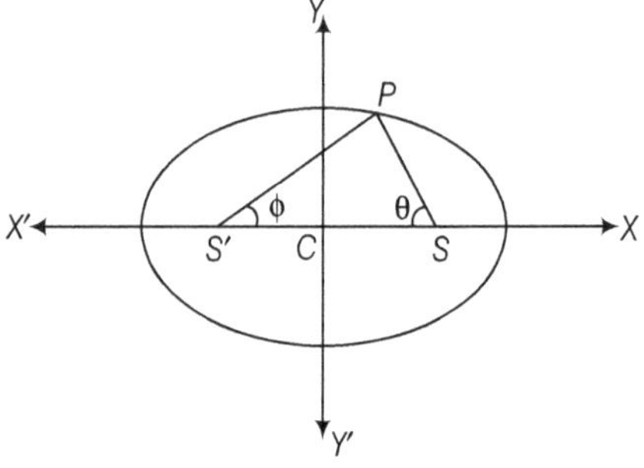

From Eqs. (i) and (ii), we get

$$PS = \frac{2ae\sin\phi}{\sin(\theta+\phi)},\ PS' = \frac{2ae\sin\theta}{\sin(\theta+\phi)}$$

$\because \quad SP + S'P = 2a$

$\therefore \quad e(\sin\theta + \sin\phi) = \sin(\theta+\phi)$

$\Rightarrow \quad e\cdot 2\sin\left(\frac{\theta+\phi}{2}\right)\cos\left(\frac{\theta-\phi}{2}\right) = 2\sin\left(\frac{\theta+\phi}{2}\right)\cos\left(\frac{\theta+\phi}{2}\right)$

or $\quad \frac{\cos\left(\frac{\theta-\phi}{2}\right)}{\cos\left(\frac{\theta+\phi}{2}\right)} = \frac{1}{e}$

or $$\frac{\cos\left(\frac{\theta-\phi}{2}\right)-\cos\left(\frac{\theta+\phi}{2}\right)}{\cos\left(\frac{\theta-\phi}{2}\right)+\cos\left(\frac{\theta+\phi}{2}\right)}=\frac{1-e}{1+e}$$

or $$\tan\left(\frac{\theta}{2}\right)\tan\left(\frac{\phi}{2}\right)=\frac{1-e}{1+e}$$

39. Let $S \equiv (5, 12)$, $S' \equiv (24, 7)$ and let $P \equiv (0, 0)$

Now, $$SS' = \sqrt{(24-5)^2+(7-12)^2} = \sqrt{(361+25)} = \sqrt{(386)}$$

For ellipse $SP + S'P = 2a$

$\Rightarrow$ $13 + 25 = 2a$

$\therefore$ $2a = 38$

$\because$ $SS' = 2ae \Rightarrow e = \frac{\sqrt{386}}{38}$

and for hyperbola $S'P - SP = 2a$

$\Rightarrow$ $25 - 13 = 2a \Rightarrow 2a = 12$

$\therefore$ $SS' = 2ae \Rightarrow e = \frac{\sqrt{386}}{12}$

40. Let the point of intersection of tangents at A and B be $P(x_1, y_1)$.

Then, equation of AB is

$$xx_1 + 4yy_1 = 4$$

or $$\frac{xx_1}{4} + yy_1 = 1 \quad \text{...(i)}$$

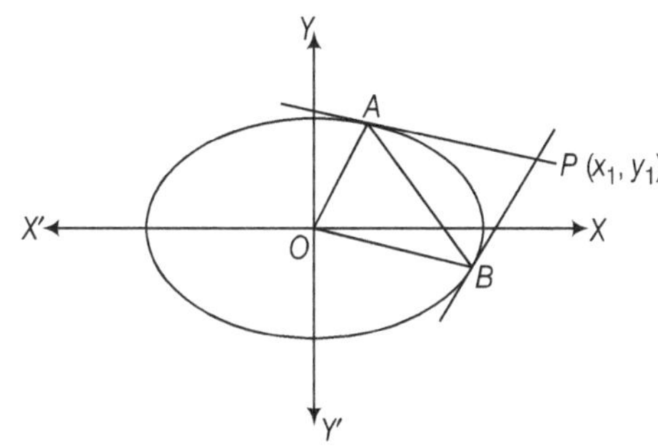

For point of OA and OB, homogenizing the equation of ellipse with the help of Eq. (i), then

$$x^2 + 4y^2 = 4\left(\frac{xx_1}{4} + yy_1\right)^2$$

or $$x^2\left(\frac{x_1^2}{4}-1\right) + y^2(4y_1^2 - 4) + 2xyx_1y_1 = 0 \quad \text{...(ii)}$$

But gives equation of OA and OB is

$$x^2 + 4y^2 + axy = 0 \quad \text{...(iii)}$$

Since, Eqs. (ii) and (iii) an identical, then

$$\frac{\frac{x_1^2}{4}-1}{1} = \frac{4y_1^2-4}{4} = \frac{2x_1y_1}{a}$$

or $x_1^2 - 4 = 4(y_1^2 - 1)$

or $x_1^2 - 4y_1^2 = 0$

Therefore, the locus is $x^2 - 4y^2 = 0$

or $(x + 2y)(x - 2y) = 0$

or $x + 2y = 0$ and $x - 2y = 0$

41. $\because$ $25x^2 + 9y^2 - 150x - 90y + 225 = 0$

$\Rightarrow$ $25(x^2 - 6x) + 9(y^2 - 10y) + 225 = 0$

$\Rightarrow$ $25\{(x-3)^2 - 9\} + 9\{(y-5)^2 - 25\} + 225 = 0$

$\Rightarrow$ $25(x-3)^2 + 9(y-5)^2 = 225$

$\Rightarrow$ $$\frac{(x-3)^2}{3^2} + \frac{(y-5)^2}{5^2} = 1 \quad \text{...(i)}$$

Let $x - 3 = X,\ y - 5 = Y$

Then, Eq. (i) becomes

$$\frac{X^2}{3^2} + \frac{Y^2}{5^2} = 1 \quad \text{...(ii)}$$

Now, comparing Eq. (ii) with

$$\frac{X^2}{a^2} + \frac{Y^2}{b^2} = 1$$

$\therefore$ $a = 3, b = 5$

$\Rightarrow$ $a^2 = b^2(1 - e^2)$

$\Rightarrow$ $9 = 25(1 - e^2)$

$\Rightarrow$ $e = \frac{4}{5}$

Centre : $X = 0,\ Y = 0$

$x - 3 = 0,\ y - 5 = 0$

$\therefore$ Centre $\equiv (3, 5)$

Foci : $X = 0, Y = \pm\, be$

$\Rightarrow$ $x - 3 = 0, y - 5 = \pm\, 4$

$\Rightarrow$ $y = 5 \pm 4$

$\therefore$ Foci (3, 1) and (3, 9)

Major axis $2b = 10$

42. $P(\theta)$ on the ellipse $x^2 + 4y^2 = 16$ is $(4\cos\theta, 2\sin\theta)$

Equation of tangent at P is

$$4\cos\theta\, x + 8\sin\theta\, y = 16$$

$\Rightarrow$ $x\cos\theta + 2y\sin\theta = 4$

It passes through centre (4, 2) of the given circle

$\therefore$ $4\cos\theta + 4\sin\theta = 4$

$\Rightarrow$ $\cos\theta + \sin\theta = 1,\ \theta = 0, \frac{\pi}{2}$

43. Since, the product of the two eccentricities e and e' is 1. Either $e = e' = 1$ in which case both the conics are parabolas or if $e > 1, e' < 1$ and *vice-versa.*

So, one of them is an ellipse and the other is a hyperbola.

44. Equation of tangent at 'α' is

$$\frac{x}{a}\cos\alpha + \frac{y}{b}\sin\alpha = 1$$

$\Rightarrow$ $$\frac{x}{a\sec\alpha} + \frac{y}{b\,\text{cosec}\,\alpha} = 1$$

Now, length of intercept,

$$z = \sqrt{(a^2\sec^2\alpha + b^2\,\text{cosec}^2\,\alpha)}$$

or $z^2 = a^2\sec^2\alpha + b^2\,\text{cosec}^2\,\alpha$

$\therefore$ $$\frac{d(z^2)}{d\alpha} = 2\left(\frac{a^2\sin\alpha}{\cos^3\alpha} - \frac{b^2\cos\alpha}{\sin^3\alpha}\right)$$

and $$\frac{d^2(z^2)}{d\alpha^2} > 0$$

For minimum of z, $\frac{d(z^2)}{d\alpha} = 0$

$\therefore \quad \tan^4 \alpha = \frac{b^2}{a^2}$

or $\quad \tan \alpha = \pm \sqrt{\left(\frac{b}{a}\right)}$

$\Rightarrow \quad \alpha = \tan^{-1} \sqrt{\left(\frac{b}{a}\right)}, \ \pi - \tan^{-1} \sqrt{\left(\frac{b}{a}\right)},$

$- \pi + \tan^{-1} \sqrt{\left(\frac{b}{a}\right)}, - \tan^{-1} \sqrt{\left(\frac{b}{a}\right)}$

45. $x^2 \tan^2 \alpha + y^2 \sec^2 \alpha = 1$

$\Rightarrow \quad \frac{x^2}{\cot^2 \alpha} + \frac{y^2}{\cos^2 \alpha} = 1$

$\because \quad \cos^2 \alpha = \cot^2 \alpha (1 - e^2)$

$\Rightarrow \quad \sin^2 \alpha = (1 - e^2)$

$\therefore \quad e^2 = \cos^2 \alpha \qquad (\alpha \neq 90^\circ)$

$e = \cos \alpha$

$\because \quad \text{Latusrectum} = \frac{1}{2} = \frac{2b^2}{a}$

$\Rightarrow \quad a = 4b^2 \qquad \Rightarrow \cot \alpha = 4 \cos^2 \alpha$

$\Rightarrow \quad \frac{1}{\sin \alpha} = 4 \cos \alpha \qquad \Rightarrow \sin 2\alpha = \frac{1}{2}$

$2\alpha = n\pi + (-1)^n \frac{\pi}{6} \qquad \Rightarrow \alpha = \frac{n\pi}{2} + (-1)^n \frac{\pi}{12}$

For $n = 0$

$\alpha = \frac{\pi}{12}$ and for $n = 1$

$\alpha = \frac{\pi}{2} - \frac{\pi}{12} = \frac{5\pi}{12}$

Sol. (Q. Nos. 46 to 48)

$\because \quad 9x^2 + 4xy + 6y^2 - 22x - 16y + 9 = 0$

or $\quad 2(2x + y - 3)^2 + (x - 2y + 1)^2 = 10$

or $\quad 2\left(\frac{2x + y - 3}{\sqrt{5}}\right)^2 + \left(\frac{x - 2y + 1}{\sqrt{5}}\right)^2 = 2$

or $\quad \frac{\left(\frac{2x + y - 3}{\sqrt{5}}\right)^2}{1} + \frac{\left(\frac{x - 2y + 1}{\sqrt{5}}\right)^2}{2} = 1$

or $\quad \frac{X^2}{a^2} + \frac{Y^2}{b^2} = 1$

Here, $b > a$

46. For centre: $X = 0, Y = 0$

$\Rightarrow \quad 2x + y - 3 = 0$

and $\quad x - 2y + 1 = 0$

we get, $\quad x = 1, y = 1$

$\therefore$ Centre is (1, 1).

47. For eccentricity: $a^2 = b^2(1 - e^2)$

$\Rightarrow \quad 1 = 2(1 - e^2)$ or $e^2 = \frac{1}{2}$

$\therefore \quad e = \frac{1}{\sqrt{2}}$

48. Lengths of axes are $2a$ and $2b$ i.e. 2 and $2\sqrt{2}$.

Sol. (Q. Nos. 49 to 51)

Here, $\quad b > a$

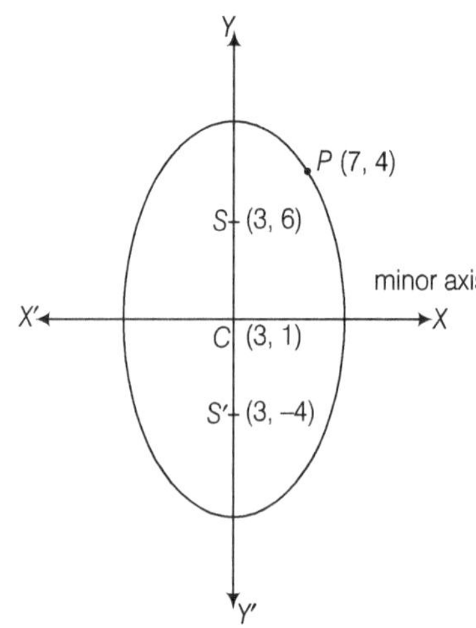

and $\quad CS = 5 = be \qquad$ ...(i)

Equation of ellipse is

$$\frac{(x-3)^2}{a^2} + \frac{(y-1)^2}{b^2} = 1 \qquad \text{...(ii)}$$

Which pass through $P(7, 4)$, then

$$\frac{16}{a^2} + \frac{9}{b^2} = 1$$

$\Rightarrow \quad \frac{16}{b^2 - 25} + \frac{9}{b^2} = 1 \quad [\because a^2 = b^2(1 - e^2) = b^2 - 25]$

$\Rightarrow \quad b^4 - 50b^2 + 225 = 0$

or $\quad (b^2 - 45)(b^2 - 5) = 0$

$\therefore \quad b = 3\sqrt{5} \qquad (b \neq \sqrt{5})$

From Eq. (i),

$e = \frac{\sqrt{5}}{3}$ and $a^2 = 45 - 25 = 20$

From Eq. (ii), ellipse (E) is

$$\frac{(x-3)^2}{20} + \frac{(y-1)^2}{45} = 1$$

49. Product of the lengths of the perpendicular segments from the foci on tangent at $P(7, 4)$ is equal to a^2 i.e. 20 ($\because b > a$)

50. $\because$ Lines SF' and $S'F$ meet the normal PG and bisects it.

$\therefore$ Required point is mid-point of PG.

$\because$ Equation of ellipse E is

$$\frac{(x-3)^2}{20} + \frac{(y-1)^2}{45} = 1$$

$\Rightarrow \quad \frac{2(x-3)}{20} + \frac{2(y-1)}{45} \frac{dy}{dx} = 0$

$\therefore \quad \left.\frac{dy}{dx}\right|_{(7,4)} = -3$

$\therefore$ Slope of normal $= \frac{1}{3}$

Equation of normal at $P(7, 4)$ is

$$y - 4 = \frac{1}{3}(x - 7)$$

$$\Rightarrow \quad x - 3y + 5 = 0$$

Which meet the major axis in $G\left(3, \frac{8}{3}\right)$.

Required point is mid-point of PG i.e. $\left(5, \frac{10}{3}\right)$.

51. Since locus of mid-point of QR is another ellipse having the same eccentricity as that of ellipse (E).

$$\Rightarrow e_1 = e = \sqrt{\left(1 - \frac{a^2}{b^2}\right)} = \sqrt{\left(1 - \frac{20}{45}\right)} = \sqrt{\left(1 - \frac{4}{9}\right)} = \frac{\sqrt{5}}{3}$$

Sol. (Q. Nos. 52 to 54)

52. Solving curves C_1 and C_2

$$x^2 + y^2 - r^2 = 0$$

and $$9x^2 + 16y^2 - 144 = 0$$

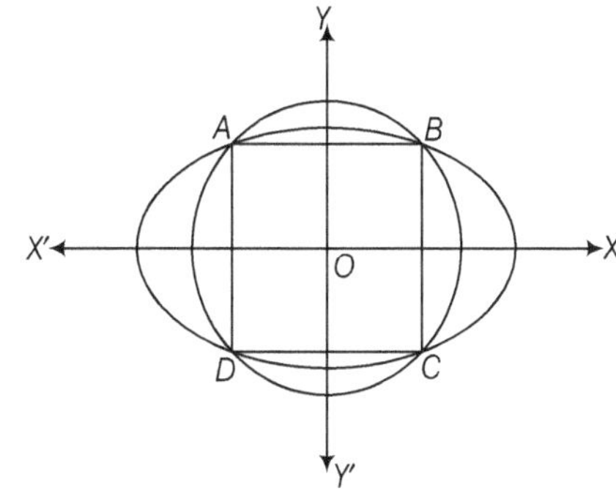

then,

x^2	y^2	1	x^2	y^2
1	1	$-r^2$	1	1
9	16	-144	9	16

$$\therefore \quad \frac{x^2}{16r^2 - 144} = \frac{y^2}{144 - 9r^2} = \frac{1}{7}$$

$$\therefore \quad x^2 = \frac{16r^2 - 144}{7} \text{ and } y^2 = \frac{144 - 9r^2}{7}$$

If $ABCD$ is a square, then $x^2 = y^2$

or $$\frac{16r^2 - 144}{7} = \frac{144 - 9r^2}{7} \Rightarrow 25r^2 = 288$$

53. Tangents of slope m to the circle and ellipse are respectively.

$$y = mx \pm r\sqrt{(m^2 + 1)} \text{ and } y = mx \pm \sqrt{(16m^2 + 9)}$$

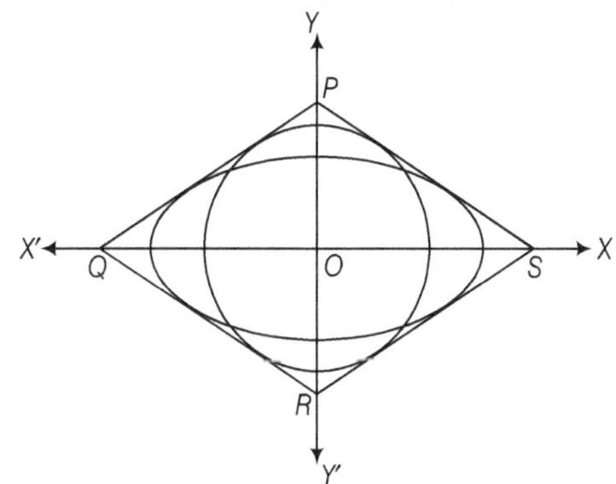

For common tangent, $r^2(m^2 + 1) = 16m^2 + 9$

$$\Rightarrow \quad r = \sqrt{\left(\frac{16m^2 + 9}{m^2 + 1}\right)}$$

If $PQRS$ is a square,

then, $\quad m = \pm 1$

or $\quad r\sqrt{2} = \sqrt{25}$

or $\quad 2r^2 = 25$

54. $\because$ $PQRS$ is a square, then $\angle PQR = 90°$

$\therefore$ PR is diameter of circle through P, Q, R

$\therefore$ Area of circumcircle of

$$\Delta PQR = \pi(OP)^2 = \pi(r\sqrt{2})^2 = 2\pi r^2$$

and area of circle C_1 is πr^2.

Hence, the required ratio is 1/2.

Sol. (Q. Nos. 55 to 57)

55. $\because$ Distance between foci S and S' is 4 units

$\therefore \quad SS' = 4$

$\Rightarrow \quad 2ae = 4$

$\therefore \quad ae = 2 \quad$ ...(i)

and given $SP + S'P = 6$

$\Rightarrow \quad 2a = 6$

$\because \quad a = 3 \quad$ ...(ii)

From Eqs. (i) and (ii), we get

$$e = \frac{2}{3}$$

and $$b^2 = a^2(1 - e^2) = a^2 - (ae)^2 = 9 - 4 = 5$$

$\therefore$ Equation of ellipse with centre (0, 0) is

$$\frac{x^2}{9} + \frac{y^2}{5} = 1 \Rightarrow 5x^2 + 9y^2 = 45$$

56. $\because$ $AB = AC$ and $\angle B = \pi/2$

$\because \quad \angle A = \angle C = \pi/4$

Now, if two tangents drawn from (x_1, y_1) on ellipse $\frac{x^2}{a^2} + \frac{y^2}{b^2} = 1$

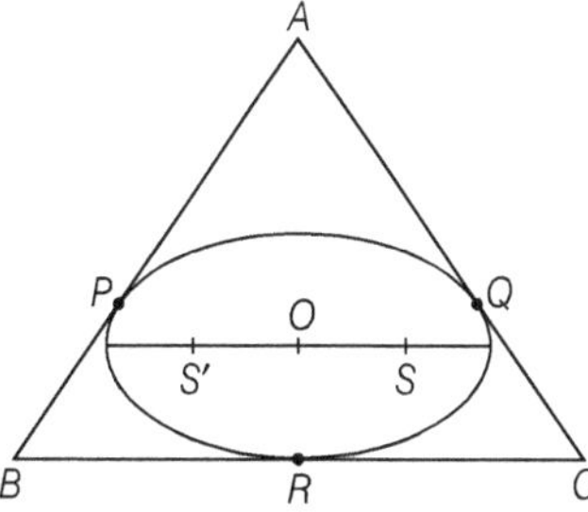

and angle between tangents is α, then

$$\tan\alpha = \frac{2ab\sqrt{\left(\frac{x_1^2}{a^2} + \frac{y_1^2}{b^2} - 1\right)}}{|x_1^2 + y_1^2 - a^2 - b^2|}$$

Let $A(x_1, y_1)$

Here, $\alpha = \frac{\pi}{4}$ and $a = 3, b = \sqrt{5}$

then, $$1 = \frac{6\sqrt{5}\sqrt{\left(\frac{x_1^2}{9} + \frac{y_1^2}{5} - 1\right)}}{(x_1^2 + y_1^2 - 9 - 5)}$$

or $$(x_1^2 + y_1^2 - 14)^2 = 180\left(\frac{x_1^2}{9} + \frac{y_1^2}{5} - 1\right)$$

$\therefore$ Required locus is

$$(x^2 + y^2 - 14)^2 = 4(5x^2 + 9y^2 - 45)$$

57. Let $P = (3\cos\theta, \sqrt{5}\sin\theta)$ and $Q \equiv (3\cos\phi, \sqrt{5}\sin\phi)$

Given, $\theta - \phi = \frac{\pi}{3}$

$\because$ A is the point of intersection of tangents at P and Q

$$\therefore \quad A \equiv \left(\frac{3\cos\left(\frac{\theta+\phi}{2}\right)}{\cos\left(\frac{\theta-\phi}{2}\right)}, \frac{\sqrt{5}\sin\left(\frac{\theta+\phi}{2}\right)}{\cos\left(\frac{\theta-\phi}{2}\right)}\right)$$

Let $$x = \frac{3\cos\left(\frac{\theta+\phi}{2}\right)}{\cos\left(\frac{\theta-\phi}{2}\right)} = \frac{3\cos\left(\frac{\theta+\phi}{2}\right)}{\cos\left(\frac{\pi}{6}\right)} = 2\sqrt{3}\cos\left(\frac{\theta+\phi}{2}\right) \quad \dots \text{(i)}$$

and $$y = \frac{\sqrt{5}\sin\left(\frac{\theta+\phi}{2}\right)}{\cos\left(\frac{\theta-\phi}{2}\right)} = \frac{2\sqrt{5}\sin\left(\frac{\theta+\phi}{2}\right)}{\sqrt{3}} \quad \dots \text{(ii)}$$

From Eqs. (i) and (ii), we get

$$\left(\frac{x}{\sqrt{3}}\right)^2 + \left(\frac{\sqrt{3}}{\sqrt{5}}y\right)^2 = 4 \text{ or } 5x^2 + 9y^2 = 60$$

which is required locus of A.

Sol. (Q. Nos. 58 to 60)

Given, line is

$$2px + y\sqrt{(1-p^2)} = 1$$

$$\Rightarrow \quad y = -\frac{2p}{\sqrt{(1-p^2)}}x + \frac{1}{\sqrt{(1-p^2)}}$$

$\because$ Equation of tangent in terms of slope (m) of ellipse $\frac{x^2}{a^2} + \frac{y^2}{b^2} = 1$ is $y = mx + \sqrt{(a^2m^2 + b^2)}$

$$\therefore \quad m = -\frac{2p}{\sqrt{(1-p^2)}}$$

and $$a^2m^2 + b^2 = \frac{1}{1-p^2}$$

or $$a^2m^2 + b^2 = \frac{1}{4}m^2 + 1 \qquad \left(\because p^2 = \frac{m^2}{m^2+4}\right)$$

$$\therefore \quad a^2 = \frac{1}{4} \text{ and } b^2 = 1$$

Equation of ellipse is $\frac{x^2}{1/4} + \frac{y^2}{1} = 1$

58. Here, $a^2 = \frac{1}{4}, b^2 = 1$

$\because \quad b > a$

$\therefore \quad a^2 = b^2(1-e^2) \Rightarrow \frac{1}{4} = 1 - e^2$

$\Rightarrow \quad e^2 = \frac{3}{4}$

$\therefore \quad e = \frac{\sqrt{3}}{2}$

59. Foci of ellipse are $(0, \pm\sqrt{(b^2 - a^2)})$

i.e. $\left(0, \pm\frac{\sqrt{3}}{2}\right)$

60. Required locus in the director circle of ellipse is

$$x^2 + y^2 = \frac{1}{4} + 1$$

i.e. $x^2 + y^2 = 5/4$

61. Let S and S' be the foci of one ellipse and H and H' be the other, C being their common centre. Then, $SHS'H'$ is a parallelogram and since

$$SH + S'H = HS' + H'S' = 2a$$

Since, the sum of the focal distances of any point on an ellipse is equal to its major axis which is $2a$.

Then, $CS = ae$, $CH = ae'$

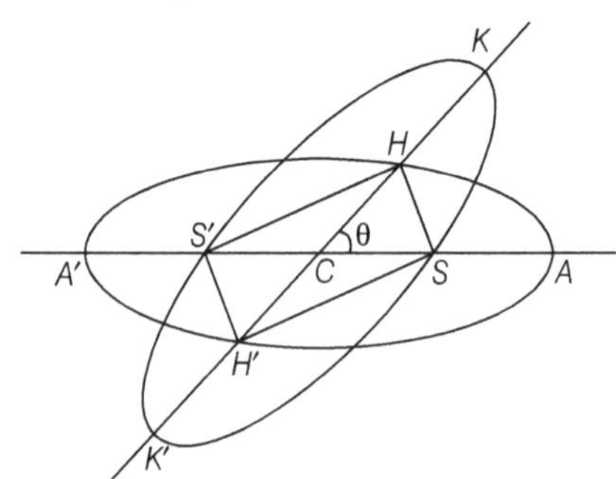

Let θ be the angle between their axes.

Then, $SH^2 = a^2e^2 + a^2e'^2 - 2a^2ee'\cos\theta$

$HS^2 = a^2e^2 + a^2e'^2 + 2a^2ee'\cos\theta$

Now, $2a = SH + S'H$

Squaring both sides, then

$$4a^2 = (SH)^2 + (S'H)^2 + 2(SH)\cdot(S'H)$$

$$\Rightarrow 4a^2 = 2a^2(e^2 + e'^2) + 2\sqrt{(a^2e^2 + a^2e'^2)^2 - 4a^4e^2e'^2\cos^2\theta}$$

$$\Rightarrow (2 - e^2 - e'^2)^2 = (e^2 + e'^2)^2 - 4e^2e'^2\cos^2\theta$$

$$\Rightarrow 4 + (e^2 + e'^2)^2 - 4(e^2 + e'^2) = (e^2 + e'^2)^2 - 4e^2e'^2\cos^2\theta$$

$$\Rightarrow 1 - e^2 - e'^2 = -e^2e'^2\cos^2\theta$$

$$\therefore \quad \cos\theta = \frac{\sqrt{e^2 + e'^2 - 1}}{ee'} = \frac{\sqrt{\left(\frac{9}{25} + \frac{16}{25} - 1\right)}}{12/25} = 0$$

$$\therefore \quad \theta = \frac{\pi}{2}$$

$$\sin\theta = 1$$

$$\therefore \quad 2(1 + \sin^2\theta + \sin^4\theta) = 2(1 + 1 + 1) = 6$$

62. Let the sides of the rectangle be p and q.

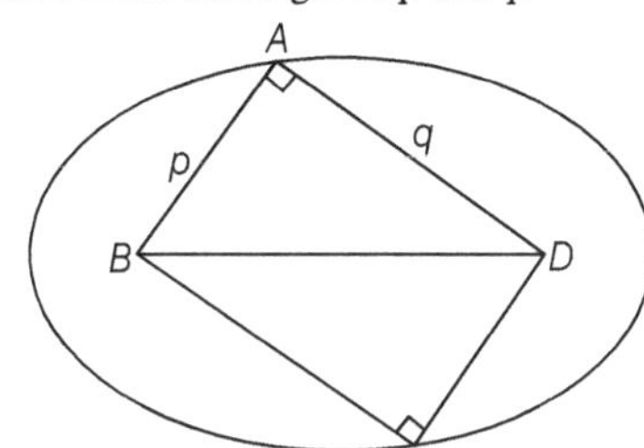

$\therefore$ Area of rectangle $= pq = 200$ ...(i)

and area of ellipse $= \pi ab = 200\pi$

$\therefore$ $ab = 200$ ...(ii)

Perimeter of rectangle $= 2(p + q)$ ...(iii)

In ΔABD,

Distance $BD = \sqrt{(p^2 + q^2)} =$ Distance between foci

$= 2ae$

or $p^2 + q^2 = 4a^2e^2 = 4(a^2 - b^2)$ ...(iv)

Also, $BA + DA = 2a$ $[\because SP + S'P = 2a]$

$\Rightarrow$ $p + q = 2a$ ...(v)

From Eq. (iv),

$$(p+q)^2 - 2pq = 4(a^2 - b^2)$$

$\Rightarrow$ $(2a)^2 - 2 \times 200 = 4(a^2 - b^2)$ [From Eqs. (i) and (v)]

or $b^2 = 100$ or $b = 10$

From Eq. (ii), $a = 20$

From Eq. (iii),

$$P = 2(p + q) = 2(2a) = 4a = 80$$

$\therefore$ $P + 1 = 81$

Hence, $\sqrt{(P + 1)} = 9$

63. For ellipse

$$9x^2 + 16y^2 = 144 \text{ or } \frac{x^2}{16} + \frac{y^2}{9} = 1$$

Equation of director circle is

$$x^2 + y^2 = 25$$

This director circle will cut the ellipse $\frac{x^2}{50} + \frac{y^2}{20} = 1$ at four points.

Hence, number of points = 4

64. $\because$ Perpendicular tangents meets on director circle of ellipse $\frac{x^2}{7} + \frac{y^2}{11/2} = 1$ is $x^2 + y^2 = 7 + \frac{11}{2}$

i.e., $$x^2 + y^2 = \left(\frac{5}{\sqrt{2}}\right)^2$$

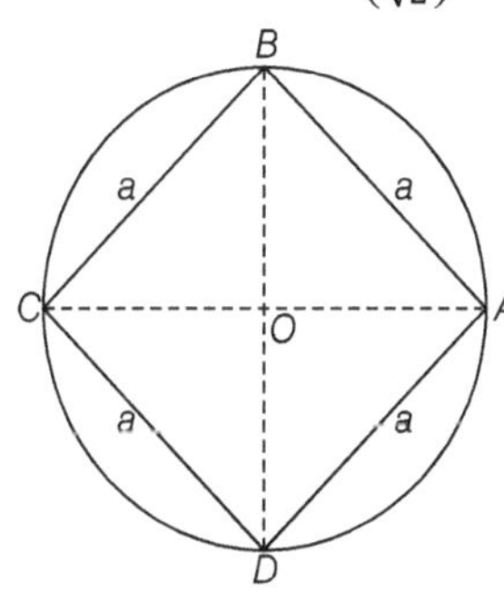

Let length of sides $= a$

$\therefore$ $OA = OB = OC = OD = \frac{a}{\sqrt{2}}$

Given $\frac{a}{\sqrt{2}} = \frac{5}{\sqrt{2}}$

$\therefore$ $a = 5$

65. We know that, for $\theta = \frac{\pi}{2}$ the focal chord will be latusrectum with length $\frac{2b^2}{a}$.

$$\Rightarrow \quad \frac{\lambda ab^2}{a^2 \sin^2\left(\frac{\pi}{2}\right) + b^2 \cos^2\left(\frac{\pi}{2}\right)} = \frac{2b^2}{a}$$

$$\Rightarrow \quad \frac{\lambda ab^2}{a^2 + 0} = \frac{2b^2}{a}$$

$\therefore$ $\lambda = 2$

66. Equation of normal at the point $(13\cos\theta, 5\sin\theta)$ is

$$y - 5\sin\theta = \frac{13}{5}\frac{\sin\theta}{\cos\theta}(x - 13\cos\theta)$$

or $5y\cos\theta - 25\sin\theta\cos\theta = 13x\sin\theta - 169\sin\theta\cos\theta$

It passes through (0, 6), then

$$30\cos\theta - 25\sin\theta\cos\theta = 0 - 169\sin\theta\cos\theta$$

$\Rightarrow$ $30\cos\theta + 144\sin\theta\cos\theta = 0$

or $6\cos\theta(5 + 24\sin\theta) = 0$

or $\cos\theta = 0,\ \sin\theta = -\frac{5}{24}$

$\therefore$ $\theta = \frac{\pi}{2},\ \theta = \pi + \sin^{-1}\left(\frac{5}{24}\right),$

$$\theta = 2\pi - \sin^{-1}\left(\frac{5}{24}\right)$$

Hence, three normals can be drawn.

i.e. $n = 3$

$\therefore$ $2^n = 2^3 = 8$

67. The equation of the tangent at $P(a\cos\theta, b\sin\theta)$ on the given ellipse $\frac{x^2}{a^2} + \frac{y^2}{b^2} = 1$ is $\frac{x}{a}\cos\theta + \frac{y}{b}\sin\theta = 1$

Length of the perpendicular from the focus $(ae, 0)$ on the ellipse is

$$p = \frac{|e\cos\theta - 1|}{\sqrt{\left(\frac{\cos^2\theta}{a^2} + \frac{\sin^2\theta}{b^2}\right)}}$$

$$= \frac{|ab(e\cos\theta - 1)|}{\sqrt{(b^2\cos^2\theta + a^2(1 - \cos^2\theta))}}$$

$$= \frac{ab(1 - e\cos\theta)}{\sqrt{a^2 - a^2e^2\cos^2\theta}} = b\sqrt{\left(\frac{1 - e\cos\theta}{1 + e\cos\theta}\right)}$$

$$\Rightarrow \quad \frac{b^2}{p^2} = \frac{1 + e\cos\theta}{1 - e\cos\theta}$$

Now, $r^2 = (ae - a\cos\theta)^2 + b^2\sin^2\theta$

$= a^2[(e - \cos\theta)^2 + (1 - e^2)\sin^2\theta]$

$$= a^2[e^2 \cos^2 \theta - 2e \cos \theta + 1]$$
$$= a^2(1 - e \cos \theta)^2$$
$$\Rightarrow \quad r = a(1 - e \cos \theta)$$
Now, $\dfrac{2a}{r} - \dfrac{b^2}{p^2} = \dfrac{2}{1 - e \cos \theta} - \dfrac{1 + e \cos \theta}{1 - e \cos \theta} = 1$

68. The points are $A(3, 4)$, $B(6, 8)$ and $O(0, 0)$.

$\because OA + OB = 2a$ (where, a is semi major axis)

$$\Rightarrow \quad 5 + 10 = 2a$$
$$\therefore \quad a = \frac{15}{2}$$
Now, $\quad AB = 2ae$
$$\Rightarrow \quad \sqrt{(6-3)^2 + (8-4)^2} = 2 \times \frac{15}{2} \times e$$
or $\quad 5 = 15e$
$$\therefore \quad e = \frac{1}{3}$$
$$\therefore \quad b^2 = a^2(1 - e^2) = \frac{225}{4}\left(1 - \frac{1}{9}\right) = 50$$
Hence, $\quad \left(\dfrac{b}{\sqrt{2}}\right) = 5$

69. For the ellipse $\dfrac{x^2}{25} + \dfrac{y^2}{16} = 1$, a normal at $P(5 \cos \theta, 4 \sin \theta)$ is
$$5x \sin \theta - 4y \cos \theta = 9 \sin \theta \cos \theta$$
Since, the normal pass through $(\lambda, 0)$, then
$$5\lambda \sin \theta - 0 = 9 \sin \theta \cos \theta$$
For, $\sin \theta \neq 0$ (i.e. $\theta \neq 0, \pi$), we get
$$5\lambda = 9 \cos \theta < 9 \qquad (\because \cos \theta < 1)$$
$$\therefore \quad 5\lambda < 9$$
Hence, maximum value of 5λ is 9.

70. Here, $a = 3\sqrt{3}, b = 3$

Since, axes are at 90° to each other.

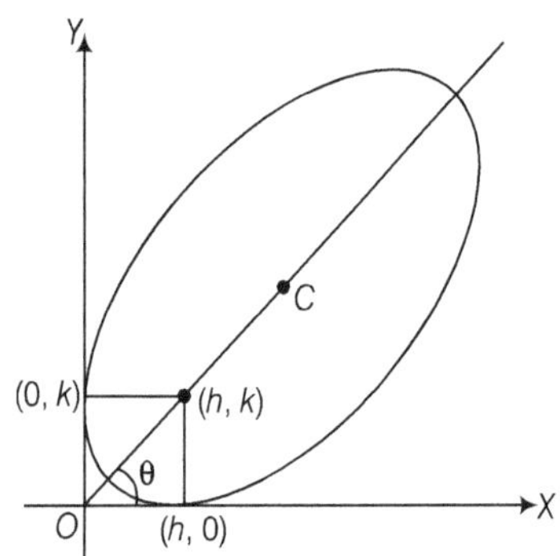

$\therefore O(0, 0)$ being the centre of arc and radius of arc is OC

$\Rightarrow \; OC = \sqrt{(27 + 9)} = 6$ units

The two extreme positions are horizontal and vertical orientation.

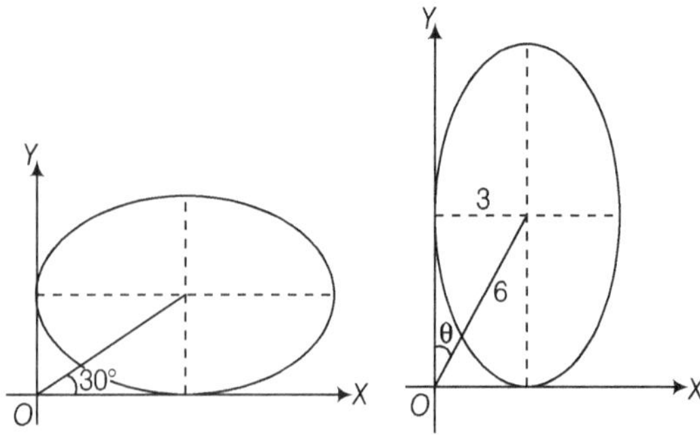

Hence, rotation 30° takes place in totality

$\Rightarrow$ Length of arc $= \dfrac{2\pi r}{12} = \dfrac{2\pi}{12} \times 6 = \pi = \dfrac{\pi\lambda}{6}$ [given]

$$\therefore \quad \lambda = 6$$

71. (A) Let point P be $(a \cos\theta, b \sin \theta)$. The equation of tangent at point P is $\dfrac{x}{a} \cos \theta + \dfrac{y}{b} \sin\theta = 1$

The point Q is $(0, b \operatorname{cosec} \theta)$.

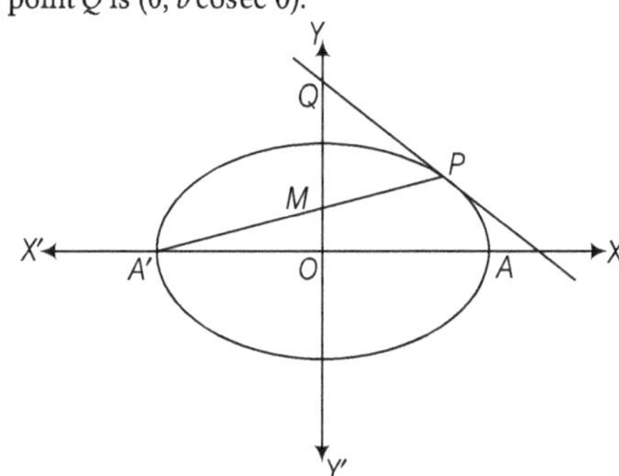

The equations of chord $A'P$ is
$$y - 0 = \frac{b \sin \theta - 0}{a \cos \theta + a}(x + a)$$
The point M is $\left(0, \dfrac{b \sin \theta}{1 + \cos\theta}\right)$

Then, $(OQ)^2 - (MQ)^2 = b^2 \operatorname{cosec}^2\theta - \left(b \operatorname{cosec} \theta - \dfrac{b \sin \theta}{1 + \cos \theta}\right)^2$
$$= \frac{2b^2}{1 + \cos\theta} - \frac{b^2 \sin^2 \theta}{(1 + \cos \theta)^2}$$
$$= \frac{2b^2}{1 + \cos\theta} - \frac{b^2(1 - \cos^2 \theta)}{(1 + \cos \theta)^2}$$
$$= \frac{2b^2}{(1 + \cos\theta)} - \frac{b^2(1 - \cos \theta)}{(1 + \cos\theta)}$$
$$= b^2 = 4$$

(B) We know that, two diameters $y = m_1 x$, $y = m_2 x$ are conjugate diameters of $\dfrac{x^2}{a^2} + \dfrac{y^2}{b^2} = 1$ if $m_1 m_2 = -\dfrac{b^2}{a^2}$
$$\Rightarrow \quad 1 \times -\frac{2}{3} = \frac{-b^2}{a^2}$$

or $$b^2 = \frac{2}{3}a^2$$

or $$a^2(1-e^2) = \frac{2}{3}a^2$$

or $$1-e^2 = \frac{2}{3} \text{ or } e^2 = \frac{1}{3}$$

Hence, $4(1+\frac{1}{3}+\frac{1}{9}+\ldots\infty) = 4\left(\frac{1}{1-\frac{1}{3}}\right) = 6$

(C) $\because\ 2x^2+3y^2=6 \Rightarrow \frac{x^2}{3}+\frac{y^2}{2}=1$

By using condition of tangency $(2h)^2 = 3\times(k)^2+2$

Therefore, the locus of $P(h,k)$ is

$$4x^2-3y^2=2 \quad \text{(which is hyperbola)}$$

or $$\frac{x^2}{1/2}-\frac{y^2}{2/3}=1$$

Hence, $$\frac{2}{3}=\frac{1}{2}(e^2-1)$$

$\Rightarrow$ $$e^2 = 1+\frac{4}{3} \text{ or } 3e^2=7$$

(D) $\left(\pm ae, \frac{b^2}{a}\right)$ are extremities of the latusrectum having positive ordinates, then,

$$a^2e^2 = -2\left(\frac{b^2}{a}-2\right) \quad \ldots\text{(i)}$$

But $$b^2 = a^2(1-e^2) \quad \ldots\text{(ii)}$$

From Eqs. (i) and (ii), we get

$$a^2e^2 = -2(a(1-e^2)-2)$$

$\Rightarrow$ $$a^2e^2-2ae^2+2a-4=0$$

$\Rightarrow$ $$ae^2(a-2)+2(a-2)=0$$

$\therefore$ $$(ae^2+2)(a-2)=0$$

Hence, $a=2$

72. (A) $\because$ (0, 0) lies on the director circle and mid-point of foci (2, 2) is the center of the circle.

Hence, radius of director circle $= OC$

$$r=\sqrt{(4+4)}=2\sqrt{2}$$

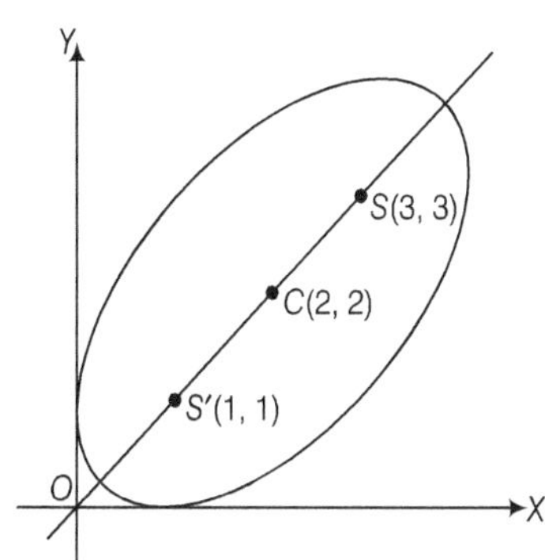

Therefore, the area is πr^2 i.e. $8\pi = \pi\lambda$ (given)

$\therefore$ $$\lambda = 8$$

(B) Equation of normal at $(5\cos\theta, 4\sin\theta)$ is $5x\sec\theta - 4y\,\text{cosec}\,\theta = 9$ and it passes through $P(0,\lambda)$.

Then, $$0-4\lambda\,\text{cosec}\,\theta = 9$$

or $$\lambda = -\frac{9}{4}\sin\theta$$

or $$|\lambda| = \frac{9}{4}|\sin\theta| < \frac{9}{4}$$

$\therefore$ $$p=\frac{9}{4} \Rightarrow 4p=9$$

(C) Let the orbit of the earth be the ellipse

$$\frac{x^2}{a^2}+\frac{y^2}{b^2}=1 \quad \ldots\text{(i)}$$

Its major axis $= 2a = 186\times10^6$ miles (given)

i.e. $a = 93\times10^6$ miles and $e = 1/60$ (given)

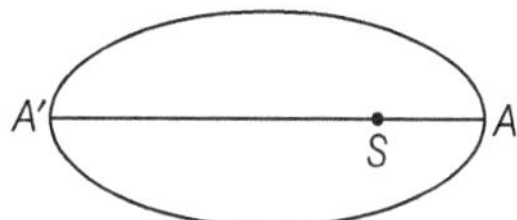

Let the Sun be at the focus $S(ae,0)$. Then, the Earth will be at shortest and longest distance from the Sun when the Earth is at the extremities of the major axis which are respectively nearest and farthest from this focus S.

$\therefore$ Shortest distance of the Earth from the Sun

$= SA$, where S is $(ae, 0)$ and A is $(a,0)$

$= a - ae = a(1-e)$

$= (93\times10^6)(1+(1/60))$

$= 91450000$ miles $= 914.5\times10^5$ miles and longest distance of Earth from the Sun

$= SA'$, where S is $(ae,0)$ and A' is $(-a,0)$

$= a+ae$

$= a(1+e)$

$= (93\times10^6)(1+(1/60))$

$= 94550000$ miles $= 945.5\times10^5$ miles

$\therefore\ \mu-\lambda+1 = 945.5-914.5-1 = 30$

(D) Equation of chord whose mid-point (0,3) is $T=S_1$

$\Rightarrow$ $$0+\frac{3.y}{25}-1 = 0+\frac{9}{25}-1$$

$\Rightarrow$ $$y=3$$

It intersects the ellipse $\frac{x^2}{16}+\frac{y^2}{25}=1$

at $$\frac{x^2}{16} = 1-\frac{3^2}{25} = \frac{16}{25}$$

or $$x = \pm\frac{16}{5}$$

$\therefore$ Length of chord $= \frac{32}{5} = \frac{4\lambda}{5}$ (given)

$\therefore$ $$\lambda = 8$$

73. (A) Let $S = 9x^2+8y^2-36x-16y-28$

$\therefore$ Value of S at (2,6)

$S_1 = 9(2)^2+8(6)^2-36(2)-16(6)-28$

$= 36+288-72-96-28$

$= 128 > 0$

$\therefore$ Point (2,6) lies outside the ellipse.

The equation of the given ellipse be rewritten as

$$9(x-2)^2+8(y-1)^2=72$$

$$\Rightarrow \quad \frac{(x-2)^2}{8}+\frac{(y-1)^2}{9}=1$$

Centre of ellipse is (2,1) and axis parallel to Y-axis

$\therefore$ Vertices are $x-2=0$

and $\quad y-1=\pm 3$

or $\quad$ (2,–2) and (2,4)

$\therefore$ Minimum distance

$$L=PA=2$$

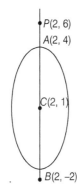

and maximum distance

$$G=PB=8$$

Then, $L+G=10, G-L=6$

(B) Let $\quad S=4x^2+9y^2+8x-36y+4$

$\therefore$ Value of S at (1,2) is

$$S_1=4(1)^2+9(2)^2+8(1)-36(2)+4$$
$$=4+36+8-72+4$$
$$=-20<0$$

$\therefore$ Point (1,2) lies inside the ellipse

The equation of the given ellipse be rewritten as

$$4(x+1)^2+9(y-2)^2=36$$

or $\quad \dfrac{(x+1)^2}{9}+\dfrac{(y-2)^2}{4}=1$

$\therefore$ Centre of ellipse is $(-1, 2)$ and axis parallel to X-axis.

$\therefore$ Vertices are $x+1=\pm 3$

and $\quad y-2=0$

or (-4,2) and (2,2)

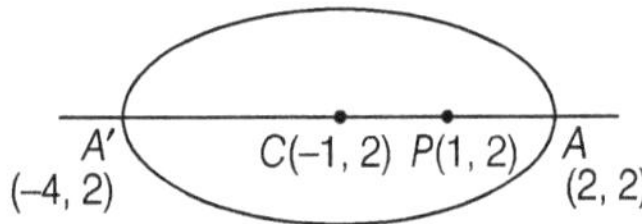

$\therefore$ Minimum distance $L=PA=1$

and Maximum distance

$$G=PA'=AA'-PA=6-1=5$$

$\therefore \quad L+G=6, G-L=4,$

(C) Here $3x+4y=0$ and $4x-3y=0$ are mutually perpendicular lines, then substituting

$$\frac{3x+4y}{\sqrt{(3^2+4^2)}}=X \text{ and } \frac{4x-3y}{\sqrt{((4)^2+(-3)^2)}}=Y$$

Then, the given equation can be written as

$$4X^2+9Y^2=36 \Rightarrow \frac{X^2}{9}+\frac{Y^2}{4}=1$$

$\therefore$ Vertices, $\quad X=\pm 3, Y=0$

or $\quad \dfrac{3x+4y}{5}=\pm 3, \dfrac{4x-3y}{5}=0$

or $\quad 3x+4y=\pm 15, y=\dfrac{4x}{3}$

Vertices are $\left(\dfrac{9}{5}, \dfrac{12}{5}\right)$ and $\left(-\dfrac{9}{5}, \dfrac{-12}{5}\right)$

$\because$ Given point is a vertex.

$\therefore$ Minimum distance $L=0$

and maximum distance G = Length of major axis $=2\times 3=6$

Then, $\quad L+G=6, G-L=6$

(D) Given ellipse is $25x^2+9y^2=225$

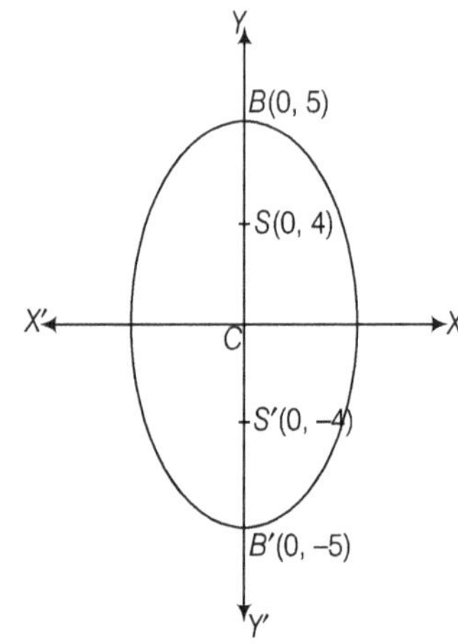

or $\quad \dfrac{x^2}{9}+\dfrac{y^2}{25}=1$

$\therefore$ focii $\quad (0, \pm\sqrt{(25-9)})$ or $(0, \pm 4)$

and vertices are B (0, 5) and B' (0, –5)

$\therefore$ Minimum distance $L=SB=1$

and maximum distance $G=SB'=4+5=9$

Then, $\quad L+G=10, G-L=8$

74. Here, $(a^2+1)<(a^2+2)$

$\therefore$ Length of latusrectum $=\dfrac{2(a^2+1)}{\sqrt{(a^2+2)}}=\dfrac{10}{\sqrt{6}}$

$$\Rightarrow \quad 6(a^2+1)^2=25(a^2+2)$$

or $\quad 6a^4-13a^2-44=0$

or $\quad (a^2-4)(6a^2+11)=0$

$\therefore \quad a^2=4,\ 6a^2+11\neq 0$

If e be the eccentricity, then

$$(a^2+1)=(a^2+2)(1-e^2)$$

$$\Rightarrow \quad e^2=1-\frac{5}{6}=\frac{1}{6}$$

$$\therefore \quad e=\frac{1}{\sqrt{6}}$$

Hence, both statements are true, statement II is correct explanation for statement I.

75. The given ellipse is $\frac{x^2}{3}+\frac{y^2}{2}=1$

$\therefore$ Area of ellipse $=\pi\sqrt{3}\sqrt{2}=\pi\sqrt{6}$

The circle is $x^2+y^2-2x+4y+4=0$

or $(x-1)^2+(y+2)^2=1$

Its area is π. Hence, statement I is true.

Also, statement II is true but it is not the correct explanation of statement I.

76. Given, ellipse is $4x^2+9y^2=36$

or $$\frac{x^2}{3^2}+\frac{y^2}{2^2}=1 \quad \text{...(i)}$$

Equation of tangents in terms of slope (m) are

$$y=mx\pm\sqrt{(9m^2+4)}$$

$\Rightarrow$ $(y-mx)^2=9m^2+4$

$\Rightarrow$ $m^2(x^2-9)-2mxy+y^2-4=0$

$\therefore$ $m_1m_2=-1 \Rightarrow \frac{y^2-4}{x^2-9}=-1$

$\Rightarrow x^2+y^2=13$, which is director circle of (i).

Hence, both statements are true and statement II is a correct explanation for statement I.

77. Distance between foci $=2ae$ and sum of focal distances from a point $=2a$

$\therefore$ $2ae<2a \Rightarrow e<1$

Both statements are true, statement II is correct explanation for statement I.

78. $4x^2+5y^2-16x-30y+41=0$ ...(i)

$\Rightarrow$ $4(x^2-4x)+5(y^2-6y)+41=0$

$\Rightarrow$ $4\{(x-2)^2-4\}+5\{(y-3)^2-9\}+41=0$

$\Rightarrow$ $4(x-2)^2+5(y-3)^2=20$

$\therefore$ statement II is true.

and $\frac{(x-2)^2}{5}+\frac{(y-3)^2}{4}=1$ or $\frac{(x-2)^2}{(\sqrt{5})^2}+\frac{(y-3)^2}{2^2}=1$

$\therefore$ Sum of focal distances of a point (P) on the ellipse (i) is $2\sqrt{5}$.

$\therefore$ Statement I is true, but statement II is not a correct explanation for statement I.

79. Let variable circle is $(x-h)^2+(y-k)^2=r^2$ ...(i)

$\therefore$ $C(h,k)$ and radius r and given circles

$$(x-1)^2+(y-2)^2=5^2 \quad \text{...(ii)}$$

$\therefore$ $C_1(1,2)$ and $r_1=5$

and $$(x-2)^2+(y-1)^2=4^2 \quad \text{...(iii)}$$

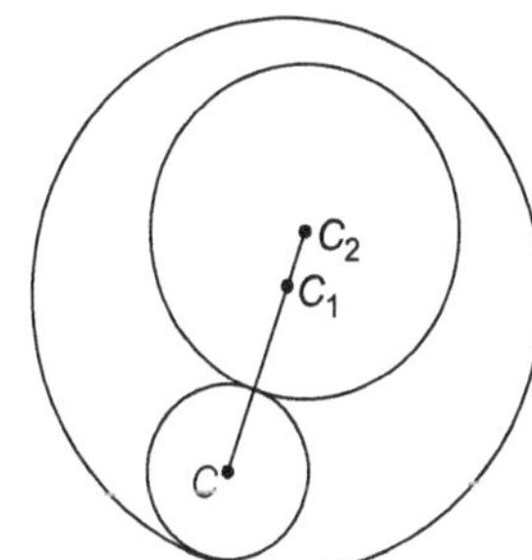

$\therefore$ $C_2(2,1)$ and $r_2=4$

$$|C_1C_2|=\sqrt{2}>|r_1-r_2|$$

$\therefore$ Circle (iii) lies completely inside the circle (ii)

$\because$ $CC_2=r+4$ and $CC_1=5-r$

$\Rightarrow$ $CC_1+CC_2=9=$ constant

$\therefore$ C lies on a ellipse.

Statement I is true and Statement II is false.

80. Statement I is obviously true since it is a theorem

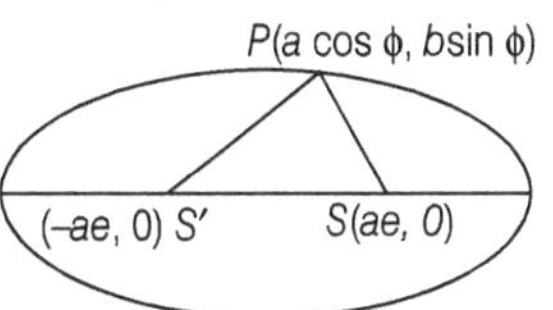

$\because$ (Slope of SP) $\times$ (Slope of $S'P$) $\neq -1$

$\therefore$ Statement II is false.

81. Given, $a=$ constant and $a+b+c=$ constant $=2s$.

Now, $BA+CA=c+b=2s-a=$ constant

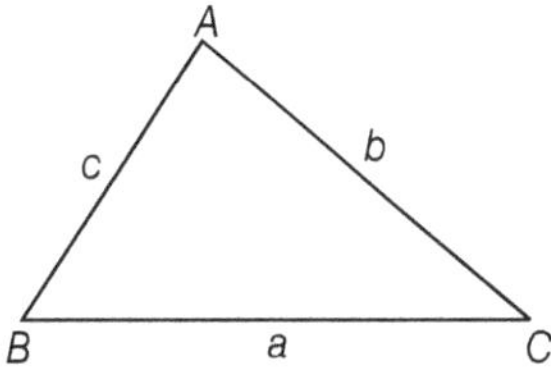

$\therefore$ Locus of A is an ellipse.

$\Rightarrow$ Both statements are true and statement II is a correct explanation for statement I.

82. Let $PQRS$ be a quadrilateral inscribed in the ellipse.

$$\frac{x^2}{a^2}+\frac{y^2}{b^2}=1$$

Let PQ, QR and RS be the three sides parallel to the given lines.

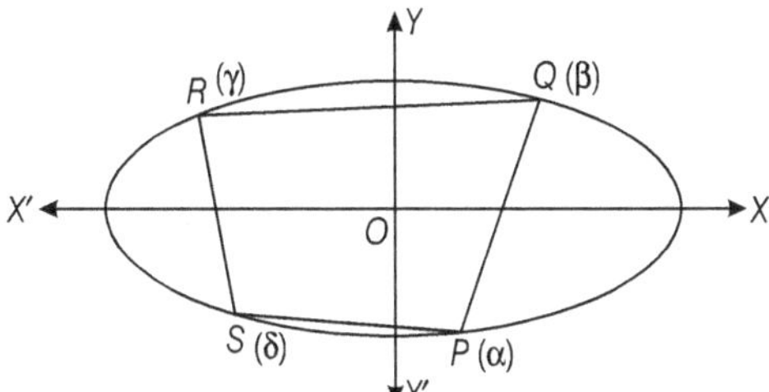

Equation of PQ is

$$\frac{x}{a}\cos\left(\frac{\alpha+\beta}{2}\right)+\frac{y}{b}\sin\left(\frac{\alpha+\beta}{2}\right)=\cos\left(\frac{\alpha-\beta}{2}\right)$$

Its slope is $-\frac{b}{a}\cot\left(\frac{\alpha+\beta}{2}\right)$ which is constant by hypothesis

$\therefore$ $\alpha+\beta=\text{constant}=2\lambda_1$ (say)

Similarly $\beta+\gamma=\text{constant}=2\lambda_2$ (say)

and $\gamma+\delta=\text{constant}=2\lambda_3$ (say)

Now the equation of SP is

$$\frac{x}{a}\cos\left(\frac{\alpha+\delta}{2}\right)+\frac{y}{b}\sin\left(\frac{\alpha+\delta}{2}\right)=\cos\left(\frac{\alpha-\delta}{2}\right)$$

Its slope $\quad m = -\dfrac{b}{a}\cot\left(\dfrac{\alpha+\delta}{2}\right)$

But $\quad \alpha + \delta = (\alpha+\beta) - (\beta+\gamma) + (\gamma+\delta)$

$$= 2\lambda_1 - 2\lambda_2 + 2\lambda_3$$

$$= \text{constant}$$

Hence, the slope of the fourth side PS is constant. Hence the fourth side is also parallel to a fixed straight line.

83. Let $\angle PSS' = \alpha$ and $\angle PS'S = \beta$

$\therefore \quad SS' = 2ae$

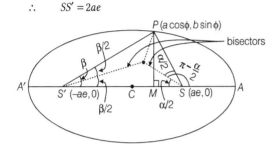

By sine rule in $\Delta PSS'$, then

$$\frac{SP}{\sin\beta} = \frac{S'P}{\sin\alpha} = \frac{SS'}{\sin\{\pi - (\alpha+\beta)\}}$$

$$\Rightarrow \quad \frac{SP}{\sin\beta} = \frac{S'P}{\sin\alpha} = \frac{SS'}{\sin(\alpha+\beta)}$$

or $$\frac{SP + S'P}{\sin\beta + \sin\alpha} = \frac{SS'}{(\sin\alpha + \beta)}$$

or $$\frac{2a}{\sin\beta + \sin\alpha} = \frac{2ae}{\sin(\alpha+\beta)} \qquad [\because SP + S'P = 2a]$$

or $$\frac{2a}{2ae} = \frac{\sin\beta + \sin\alpha}{\sin(\alpha+\beta)}$$

$$\Rightarrow \quad \frac{1}{e} = \frac{2\sin\left(\frac{\alpha+\beta}{2}\right)\cos\left(\frac{\alpha-\beta}{2}\right)}{2\sin\left(\frac{\alpha+\beta}{2}\right)\cos\left(\frac{\alpha+\beta}{2}\right)} \Rightarrow \frac{1}{e} = \frac{\cos\left(\frac{\alpha-\beta}{2}\right)}{\cos\left(\frac{\alpha+\beta}{2}\right)}$$

$$\frac{1-e}{1+e} = \frac{\cos\left(\frac{\alpha-\beta}{2}\right) - \cos\left(\frac{\alpha+\beta}{2}\right)}{\cos\left(\frac{\alpha-\beta}{2}\right) + \cos\left(\frac{\alpha+\beta}{2}\right)}$$

{By componendo and dividendo rule}

$$\Rightarrow \quad \frac{1-e}{1+e} = \tan(\alpha/2)\tan(\beta/2) \qquad \text{...(i)}$$

or $$\tan\left(\frac{PSS'}{2}\right)\tan\left(\frac{PS'S}{2}\right) = \frac{1-e}{1+e}$$

The centre of the circle inscribed in $\Delta\, PSS'$ will lie on the bisectors of angles α and β whose equations are

$$y = \tan\left(\frac{\beta}{2}\right)(x + ae)$$

and $y = \tan\left(\pi - \dfrac{\alpha}{2}\right)(x - ae)$ or $y = -\tan\left(\dfrac{\alpha}{2}\right)(x - ae)$

By multiplying we get

$$y^2 = -\tan\left(\frac{\alpha}{2}\right)\tan\left(\frac{\beta}{2}\right)(x^2 - a^2e^2)$$

$$y^2 = -\left(\frac{1-e}{1+e}\right)(x^2 - a^2e^2) \qquad \text{[From Eq. (i)]}$$

or $$y^2 + x^2\left(\frac{1-e}{1+e}\right) = a^2e^2\left(\frac{1-e}{1+e}\right)$$

or $$\frac{x^2}{a^2e^2} + \frac{y^2}{a^2e^2\left(\frac{1-e}{1+e}\right)} = 1$$

which is an ellipse.

84. Let P be $(a\cos\phi, b\sin\phi)$

$\therefore$ Equation of tangent at P is

$$\frac{x}{a}\cos\phi + \frac{y}{b}\sin\phi = 1 \qquad \text{...(i)}$$

and equation of normal at P is

$$ax\sec\phi - by\,\text{cosec}\,\phi = a^2 - b^2 \qquad \text{...(ii)}$$

It is clear from the figure $CFPQ$ is rectangle

$\therefore \quad PF = CQ$

{i.e. the perpendicular from $C(0, 0)$ on Eq. (i)}

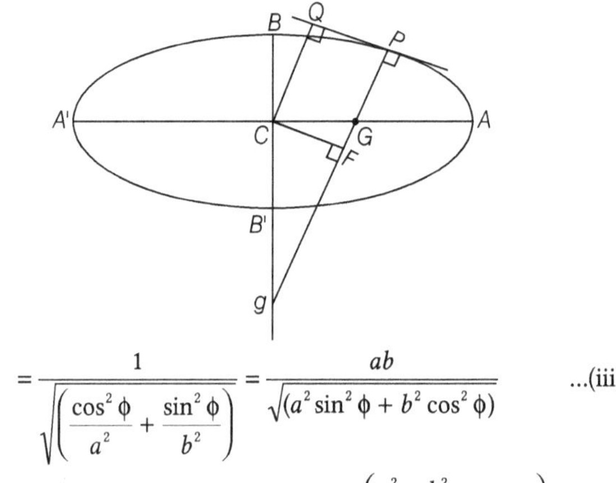

$$= \frac{1}{\sqrt{\left(\frac{\cos^2\phi}{a^2} + \frac{\sin^2\phi}{b^2}\right)}} = \frac{ab}{\sqrt{(a^2\sin^2\phi + b^2\cos^2\phi)}} \qquad \text{...(iii)}$$

Putting $y = 0$ in Eq. (ii), the point G is $\left(\dfrac{a^2-b^2}{a}\cos\phi, 0\right)$

and Putting $x = 0$ in Eq. (ii), the point g is

$$\left(0, -\frac{(a^2-b^2)}{b}\sin\phi\right)$$

$$\therefore \quad (PG)^2 = \left(a\cos\phi - \left(\frac{a^2-b^2}{2}\right)\cos\phi\right)^2 + (b\sin\phi - 0)^2$$

$$= \frac{b^4}{a^2}\cos^2\phi + b^2\sin^2\phi = \frac{b^2}{a^2}(b^2\cos^2\phi + a^2\sin^2\phi)$$

$$\therefore \quad PG = \frac{b}{a}\sqrt{(a^2\sin^2\phi + b^2\cos^2\phi)} \qquad \text{...(iv)}$$

and $$(Pg)^2 = (a\cos\phi - 0)^2 + \left(b\sin\phi + \frac{(a^2-b^2)}{b}\sin\phi\right)^2$$

$$= a^2\cos^2\phi + \frac{a^4}{b^2}\sin^2\phi = \frac{a^2}{b^2}(a^2\sin^2\phi + b^2\cos^2\phi)$$

$$\therefore \quad Pg = \frac{a}{b}\sqrt{(a^2\sin^2\phi + b^2\cos^2\phi)} \qquad \text{...(v)}$$

From Eqs. (iii) and (iv), $\quad PF \cdot PG = b^2$

and from Eqs. (iii) and (v), $PF \cdot Pg = a^2$.

85. Let the coordinates of P be (x_1, y_1) then Q is $(x_1, -y_1)$.
Also B is $(0, b)$

$\therefore$ Equation of PB is

$$y - y_1 = \frac{b - y_1}{0 - x_1}(x - x_1)$$

It meets major axis i.e. $y = 0$ in M

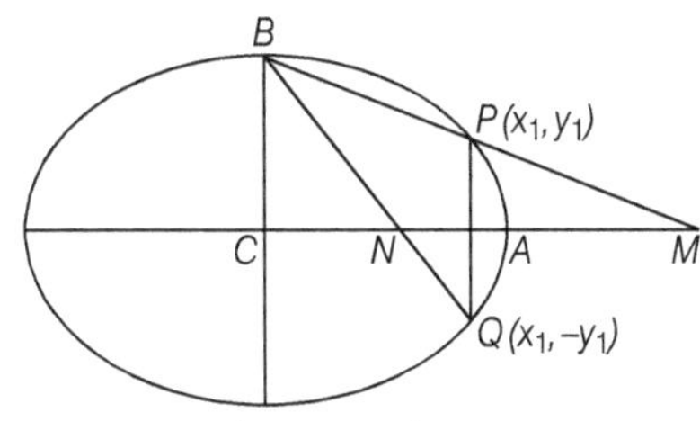

$\therefore$ $$M \text{ is } \left(\frac{bx_1}{(b - y_1)}, 0\right)$$

Also equation of BQ is $y + y_1 = \dfrac{b + y_1}{0 - x_1}(x - x_1)$

It meets the major axis *i.e.,* $y = 0$ in N.

$\therefore$ $$N \text{ is } \left(\frac{bx_1}{b + y_1}, 0\right)$$

Now the polar of M with respect to the auxiliary circle $x^2 + y^2 = a^2$ is

$$\frac{xbx_1}{b - y_1} + 0 \cdot y = a^2$$

or $$bxx_1 = a^2(b - y_1) \quad \text{...(i)}$$

If Eq. (i) passes through N, then

$$\frac{b^2x_1^2}{(b + y_1)} = a^2(b - y)$$

$\Rightarrow$ $$b^2x_1^2 = a^2(b^2 - y_1^2)$$

or $$\frac{x_1^2}{a^2} + \frac{y_1^2}{b^2} = 1 \text{ which is true.}$$

86. The equation of any tangent to the ellipse

$$4x^2 + 25y^2 = 100 \text{ or } \frac{x^2}{25} + \frac{y^2}{4} = 1 \text{ is}$$

$$y = mx + \sqrt{(25m^2 + 4)} \quad \text{...(i)}$$

It meets the coordinate of axes at

$$A\left(-\frac{\sqrt{(25m^2 + 4)}}{m}, 0\right) \text{ and } B\left(0, \sqrt{(25m^2 + 4}\right)$$

Let $P(h, k)$ be the mid-point of AB. Then

$$2h = -\frac{\sqrt{(25m^2 + 4)}}{m} \text{ and } 2k = \sqrt{(25m^2 + 4)}$$

$$\Rightarrow \frac{2k}{2h} = -m \Rightarrow m = -\frac{k}{h}$$

Since, Eq. (i) touches the circle $x^2 + y^2 = r^2$

Therefore, $$\frac{\sqrt{(25m^2 + 4)}}{\sqrt{(1 + m^2)}} = |r|$$

or $$\frac{25m^2 + 4}{1 + m^2} = r^2$$

or $$25\left(\frac{k^2}{h^2}\right) + 4 = r^2\left(1 + \frac{k^2}{h^2}\right) \quad \left(\because m = -\frac{k}{h}\right)$$

Hence the locus of $P(h, k)$ is

$$25y^2 + 4x^2 = r^2(x^2 + y^2)$$

or $$y = \pm\sqrt{\left(\frac{(r^2 - 4)}{(25 - r^2)}\right)}x$$

87. Let the normals at the points when the line, $\dfrac{lx}{a} + \dfrac{my}{b} = 1$ meet in $P(h, k)$

Let the line joining the feet of the other two normals from (h, k) have for its equation, $rx + sy = 1$

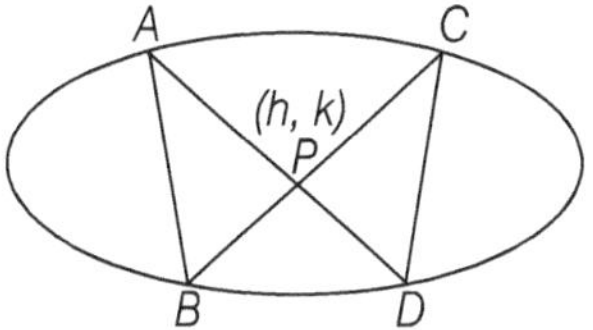

Then the general equation of a curve through the intersection of the ellipse and the two lines is

$$\left(\frac{x^2}{a^2} + \frac{y^2}{b^2} - 1\right) + \lambda\left(\frac{lx}{a} + \frac{my}{b} - 1\right) \times (rx + sy - 1) = 0 \quad \text{...(i)}$$

But the four points A, B, C, D also lie on the ellipse

$$(a^2 - b^2)xy + kb^2x - ha^2y = 0 \quad \text{...(ii)}$$

Curves Eqs. (i) and (ii) must be identical.

This is possible only one coefficient of x^2 and y^2 and the constant terms in Eq. (i) must vanish separately.

$$\frac{1}{a^2} + \frac{\lambda rl}{a} = 0, \text{ and } \frac{1}{b^2} + \frac{\lambda ms}{b} = 0, \lambda - 1 = 0$$

$\therefore$ $$\lambda = 1, 1 + arl = 0 = 1 + bms$$

$\therefore$ $$r = \frac{-1}{al} \text{ and } s = \frac{-1}{mb}$$

Therefore, the line $rx + sy = 1$ become

$$-\frac{x}{al} - \frac{y}{mb} = 1 \text{ or } \frac{x}{al} + \frac{y}{mb} = -1$$

88. $\therefore$ $$\tan\theta = \frac{b\sin\phi}{(a\cos\phi - ae)} = \frac{\left(\frac{b}{a}\right)\sin\phi}{(\cos\phi - e)}$$

$\because$ $$b^2 = a^2(1 - e^2)$$

$\therefore$ $$\frac{b}{a} = \sqrt{(1 - e^2)}$$

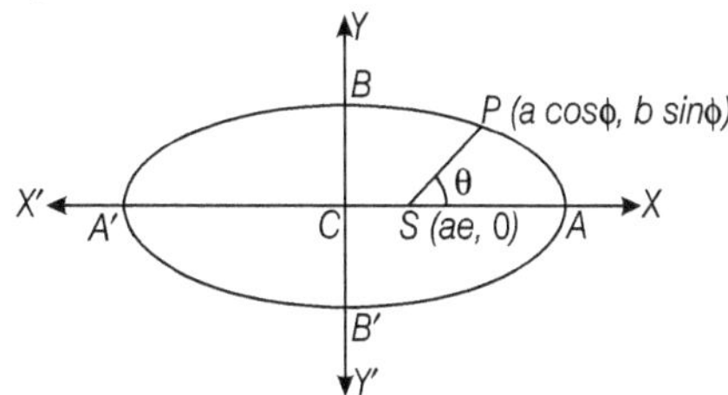

$$\Rightarrow \tan\theta = \frac{\sqrt{(1 - e^2)}\sin\phi}{(\cos\phi - e)}$$

$$\Rightarrow \sin\theta\cos\phi - e\sin\theta = \sqrt{(1 - e^2)}\sin\phi\cos\theta$$

$$\Rightarrow \frac{2\tan(\theta/2)}{1+\tan^2(\theta/2)}\cdot\frac{1-\tan^2(\phi/2)}{1+\tan^2(\phi/2)}-\frac{e(2\tan(\theta/2))}{(1+\tan^2(\theta/2))}$$

$$=\sqrt{(1-e^2)}\cdot\frac{2\tan(\phi/2)}{1+\tan^2(\phi/2)}\cdot\frac{1-\tan^2(\theta/2)}{1+\tan^2(\theta/2)}$$

$$\Rightarrow 2\tan(\theta/2)(1-\tan^2(\phi/2))-2e\tan(\theta/2)(1+\tan^2(\phi/2))$$
$$=2\sqrt{(1-e^2)}\cdot\tan(\phi/2)(1-\tan^2(\theta/2))$$

$$\Rightarrow (1-e)\tan(\theta/2)-(1+e)\tan(\theta/2)$$
$$\tan^2(\phi/2)-\sqrt{(1-e^2)}\tan(\phi/2)$$
$$+\sqrt{(1-e^2)}\tan^2(\theta/2)\tan(\phi/2)=0$$

$$\Rightarrow (1+e)\tan^2(\phi/2)+\sqrt{(1-e^2)}\tan(\phi/2)$$
$$(\cot(\theta/2)-\tan(\theta/2))-(1-e)=0$$

$$\Rightarrow \sqrt{(1+e)}\tan(\phi/2)\{\sqrt{(1+e)}\tan(\phi/2)-\sqrt{(1-e)}\tan(\theta/2)\}$$
$$+\sqrt{(1-e)}\cot(\theta/2)\{\sqrt{(1+e)}\tan(\phi/2)-\sqrt{(1-e)}\tan(\theta/2)\}=0$$

$$\Rightarrow (\sqrt{(1+e)}\tan(\phi/2)+\sqrt{(1-e)}\cot(\theta/2))$$
$$(\sqrt{(1+e)}\tan(\phi/2)-\sqrt{(1-e)}\tan(\theta/2))=0$$

But ϕ and θ lies between 0 and π

then $\tan(\phi/2)>0$ and $\tan(\theta/2)>0$

then $\sqrt{(1+e)}\tan(\phi/2)+\sqrt{(1-e)}\cot(\theta/2)\neq 0$

$\therefore \sqrt{(1+e)}\tan(\phi/2)-\sqrt{(1-e)}\tan(\theta/2)=0$

$$\tan(\theta/2)=\sqrt{\left(\frac{1+e}{1-e}\right)}\tan(\phi/2)$$

89. Let the given ellipse be

$$\frac{x^2}{a^2}+\frac{y^2}{b^2}=1 \quad \text{...(i)}$$

Let $P(\alpha)$ and $Q(\beta)$ be two points on Eq. (i) such that

$$\theta=\alpha-\beta \quad \text{...(ii)}$$

Given that tangents at P and Q are right angles.

$$\therefore \left(-\frac{b}{a}\cot\alpha\right)\left(-\frac{b}{a}\cot\beta\right)=-1$$

$$\Rightarrow a^2\sin\alpha\sin\beta+b^2\cos\alpha\cos\beta=0 \quad \text{...(iii)}$$

But the diameter parallel to the tangent at $P(\alpha)$ will be conjugate to the diameter CP, then its extremities will be

$(-a\sin\alpha, b\cos\alpha)$

$\therefore \quad d_1^2=a^2\sin^2\alpha+b^2\cos^2\alpha$

Similarly $\quad d_2^2=a^2\sin^2\beta+b^2\cos^2\beta$

$$\Rightarrow d_1^2d_2^2=(a^2\sin^2\alpha+b^2\cos^2\alpha)(a^2\sin^2\beta+b^2\cos^2\beta)$$
$$=(a^2\sin\alpha\sin\beta+b^2\cos\alpha\cos\beta)^2$$
$$+a^2b^2(\sin\alpha\cos\beta-\cos\alpha\sin\beta)^2$$
$$=0+a^2b^2\sin^2(\alpha-\beta) \quad \text{[from Eq. (iii)]}$$
$$=a^2b^2\sin^2\theta \quad \text{[from Eq. (ii)]}$$

$\therefore \quad ab\sin\theta=d_1d_2$

90. $y=mx+\sqrt{(a^2m^2+b^2)}$ is a tangent to the ellipse this tangent also touches the circle $x^2+y^2=r^2$

then $\quad \pm r=\dfrac{0-0+\sqrt{a^2m^2+b^2}}{\sqrt{1+m^2}}$

we get $\quad m=\sqrt{\left(\dfrac{r^2-b^2}{a^2-r^2}\right)} \quad (\because b<r<a)$

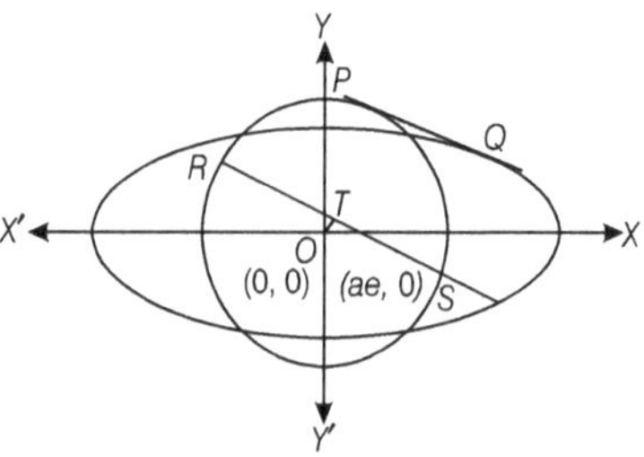

The line RS passes through $(ae, 0)$ and parallel to PQ is

$$y-0=m(x-ae)$$

$\Rightarrow mx-y-ame=0$

Let T be the feet of the perpendicular dropped from the origin on RS

$$\therefore \quad OT=\frac{ame}{\sqrt{1+m^2}}$$

$$(RT)^2=(OR)^2-(OT)^2$$
$$=r^2-\frac{a^2m^2e^2}{1+m^2}=r^2-(r^2-b^2)=b^2$$

$\therefore \quad RT=b,\ RS=2b$

91. Equation of the tangent at the point $P(a\cos\phi, b\sin\phi)$ on $\dfrac{x^2}{a^2}+\dfrac{y^2}{b^2}=1$ is

$$\frac{x}{a}\cos\phi+\frac{y}{b}\sin\phi=1 \quad \text{...(i)}$$

and foci $F_1\equiv(ae,0)\ F_2\equiv(-ae,0)$

$\therefore d=$ perpendicular distance of Eq. (i) form the centre (0, 0) of the ellipse

$$\therefore \quad d=\frac{1}{\sqrt{\dfrac{\cos^2\phi}{a^2}+\dfrac{\sin^2\phi}{b^2}}}=\frac{ab}{\sqrt{(a^2\sin^2\phi+b^2\cos^2\phi)}}$$

$$\therefore \quad 4a^2\left(1-\frac{b^2}{d^2}\right)=4a^2\left(1-\frac{b^2(a^2\sin^2\phi+b^2\cos^2\phi)}{a^2b^2}\right)$$
$$=4a^2\left(1-\sin^2\phi-\frac{b^2}{a^2}\cos^2\phi\right)$$
$$=4a^2\cos^2\phi\frac{(a^2-b^2)}{a^2}$$
$$=4\cos^2\phi(a^2-b^2)$$
$$=4a^2e^2\cos^2\phi=(2ae\cos\phi)^2$$
$$=[(a-ae\cos\phi)-(a+ae\cos\phi)]^2$$
$$=(PF_1-PF_2)^2$$

Hence $\quad (PF_1-PF_2)^2=4a^2\left(1-\dfrac{b^2}{d^2}\right).$

92. **(i)** Equation of ellipse is $\frac{x^2}{a^2} + \frac{y^2}{b^2} = 1$ ...(i)

PQ is the chord of contact.

Equation of chord of contact is $\frac{xx_1}{a^2} + \frac{yy_1}{b^2} = 1$ ...(ii)

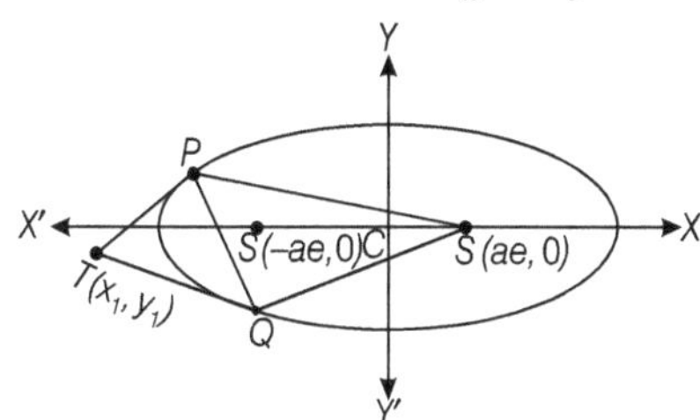

Eliminate y from Eqs. (i) and (ii), we get

$$x^2(a^2y_1^2 + b^2x_1^2) - 2a^2b^2xx_1 + a^4(b^2 - y_1^2) = 0$$

Let x' and x'' be it roots

$$\therefore \quad x' + x'' = \frac{2a^2b^2x_1}{(a^2y_1^2 + b^2x_1^2)}, x'x'' = \frac{a^4(b^2 - y_1^2)}{(a^2y_1^2 + b^2x_1^2)}$$

Now, $ST^2 = (x_1 - ae)^2 + y_1^2$

Also, $SP \cdot SQ = (a - ex')(a - ex'')$

$$= a^2 - ae(x' + x'') + e^2x'x''$$

$$= a^2 - \frac{ae \cdot (2a^2b^2x_1)}{(a^2y_1^2 + b^2x_1^2)} + \frac{e^2a^4(b^2 - y_1^2)}{(a^2y_1^2 + b^2x_1^2)}$$

$$= \frac{a^2}{(a^2y_1^2 + b^2x_1^2)}\{b^2(x_1 - ae)^2 + b^2y_1^2\}$$

$$= \frac{a^2b^2(ST)^2}{(a^2y_1^2 + b^2x_1^2)}$$

$$\therefore \quad \frac{(ST)^2}{SP \cdot SQ} = \frac{y_1^2}{b^2} + \frac{x_1^2}{a^2}$$

(ii) $ST \cdot S'T \cos\theta = (\sqrt{(x_1 - ae)^2 + y_1^2})(\sqrt{(x_1 + ae)^2 + y_1^2})\cos\theta$

$$= \sqrt{(x_1^2 + y_1^2 + a^2e^2)^2 - 4a^2e^2x_1^2}\cos\theta \quad ...(i)$$

Equation pair of tangents.

$$SS_1 = T^2$$

$$\left(\frac{x^2}{a^2} + \frac{y^2}{b^2} - 1\right)\left(\frac{x_1^2}{a^2} + \frac{y_1^2}{b^2} - 1\right) = \left(\frac{xx_1}{a^2} + \frac{yy_1}{b^2} - 1\right)^2$$

$$\therefore \quad \tan\theta = \frac{2ab\sqrt{\left(\frac{x_1^2}{a^2} + \frac{y_1^2}{b^2} - 1\right)}}{(x_1^2 + y_1^2 - a^2 - b^2)}$$

$$\therefore \quad \cos\theta = \frac{(x_1^2 + y_1^2 - a^2 - b^2)}{\sqrt{(x_1^2 + y_1^2 + a^2e^2)^2 - 4a^2e^2x_1^2}}$$

From Eq. (i), $ST \cdot S'T \cos\theta = x_1^2 + y_1^2 - a^2 - b^2$

Hence $ST \cdot S'T \cos\theta = (CT)^2 - a^2 - b^2$

93. Let coordinates of T be (x_1, y_1). Let eccentric angles of P, Q, R be ϕ, ϕ_1, ϕ_2

Thus equation of chords PSQ and PHR are

$$\frac{x}{a}\cos\left(\frac{\phi + \phi_1}{2}\right) + \frac{y}{b}\sin\left(\frac{\phi + \phi_1}{2}\right) = \cos\left(\frac{\phi - \phi_1}{2}\right) \quad ...(i)$$

and $$\frac{x}{a}\cos\left(\frac{\phi + \phi_2}{2}\right) + \frac{y}{b}\sin\left(\frac{\phi + \phi_2}{2}\right) = \cos\left(\frac{\phi - \phi_2}{2}\right) \quad ...(ii)$$

$\because$ Eqs. (i) and (ii) passes through $(ae, 0)$ and $(-ae, 0)$ then Eqs.(i) and (ii) becomes

$$e\cos\left(\frac{\phi + \phi_1}{2}\right) = \cos\left(\frac{\phi - \phi_1}{2}\right) \quad ...(iii)$$

and $$-e\cos\left(\frac{\phi + \phi_2}{2}\right) = \cos\left(\frac{\phi - \phi_2}{2}\right) \quad ...(iv)$$

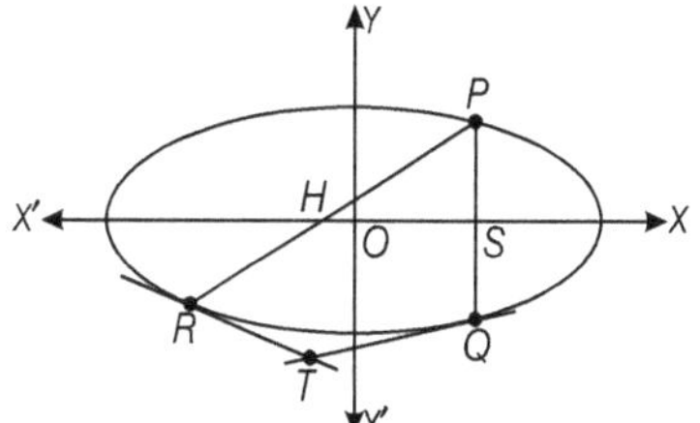

By componendo and dividendo

$$\frac{1 - e}{1 + e} = -\frac{2\cos(\phi/2)\cos(\phi_2/2)}{2\sin(\phi/2)\sin(\phi_2/2)}$$

or $$\frac{1 - e}{1 + e} = -\cot(\phi/2)\cot(\phi_2/2)$$

or $$\tan(\phi_2/2) = -\frac{(1 + e)}{(1 - e)}\cot(\phi/2)$$

Similarly, $\tan(\phi_1/2) = -\frac{(1 - e)}{(1 + e)}\cot(\phi/2)$

the equation of QR is

$$\frac{x}{a}\cos\left(\frac{\phi_1 + \phi_2}{2}\right) + \frac{y}{b}\sin\left(\frac{\phi_1 + \phi_2}{2}\right) = \cos\left(\frac{\phi_1 - \phi_2}{2}\right)$$

Dividing both sides by $\cos(\phi_1/2)\cos(\phi_2/2)$, we get

$$\Rightarrow \frac{x}{a}(1 - \tan(\phi_1/2)\tan(\phi_2/2)) + \frac{y}{b}(\tan(\phi_1/2) + \tan(\phi_2/2))$$

$$= 1 + \tan(\phi_1/2)\tan(\phi_2/2) \quad \text{or} \quad \frac{x}{a}(1 - \cot^2(\phi/2)) + \frac{y}{b}$$

$$\left\{-2\left(\frac{1 + e^2}{1 - e^2}\right)\cot(\phi/2)\right\} = 1 + \cot^2(\phi/2)$$

or $$\frac{x}{a}\frac{(1 - \cot^2(\phi/2))}{(1 + \cot^2(\phi/2))} - \frac{1 + e^2}{1 - e^2}\cdot\frac{2\cot\phi/2}{1 + \cot^2\phi/2}\cdot\frac{y}{b} = 1$$

or $$-\frac{x}{a}\cos\phi - \left(\frac{1 + e^2}{1 - e^2}\right)\sin\phi \cdot \frac{y}{b} = 1$$

or $$\frac{x}{a}(1 - e^2)\cos\phi + \frac{y}{b}(1 + e^2)\sin\phi = -(1 - e^2) \quad ...(v)$$

But QR is also chord of contact.

Thus equation of QR is

$$\frac{xx_1}{a^2} + \frac{yy_1}{b^2} = 1 \quad ...(vi)$$

Comparing the co-efficients of Eqs. (v) and (vi), we get

$$\frac{(1 - e^2)\cos\phi}{x_1/a} = \frac{(1 + e^2)\sin\phi}{y_1/b} = -(1 - e^2)$$

$$\Rightarrow \quad \cos^2\phi = \frac{x_1^2}{a^2} \text{ and } \sin^2\phi = \frac{y_1^2}{b^2}\frac{(1 - e^2)^2}{(1 + e^2)^2}$$

$$\because \quad \cos^2\phi + \sin^2\phi = 1$$

$$\therefore \quad \frac{x_1^2}{a^2} + \frac{y_1^2}{b^2}\cdot\frac{(1 - e^2)^2}{(1 + e^2)^2} = 1$$

Locus of (x_1, y_1) is $\frac{x^2}{a^2}(1 + e^2)^2 + (1 - e^2)^2\frac{y^2}{b^2} = (1 + e^2)^2$.

94. Any tangent to the ellipse $\frac{x^2}{a^2}+\frac{y^2}{b^2}=1$ at $P(a\cos\theta, b\sin\theta)$ is

$$\frac{x\cos\theta}{a}+\frac{y\sin\theta}{b}=1$$

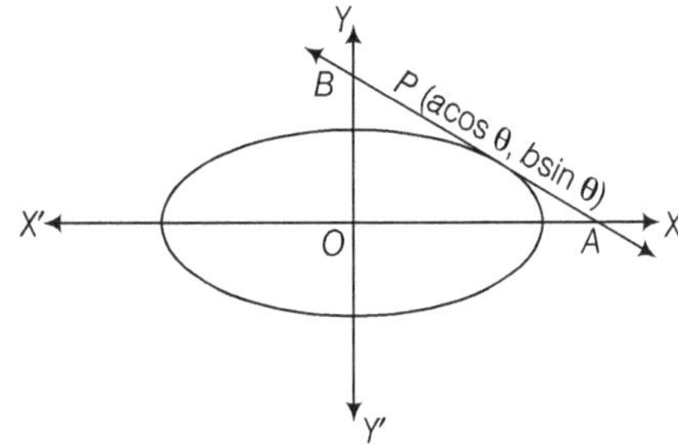

It meets coordinate axes at $A(a\sec\theta, 0)$ and $B(0, b\,\text{cosec}\theta)$.

$\therefore$ Area of $\Delta OAB=\frac{1}{2}\times a\sec\theta\times b\,\text{cosec}\theta$

$\Rightarrow \quad \Delta=\frac{ab}{\sin 2\theta}$

For Δ to be min, $\sin 2\theta$ should be max and we know max value of $\sin 2\theta=1$.

$\therefore \quad \Delta_{\max}=ab$ sq units.

95. Let the common tangent to circle $x^2+y^2=16$ and ellipse $x^2/25+y^2/4=1$ be

$$y=mx+\sqrt{25m^2+4} \quad \text{...(i)}$$

As it is tangent to circle $x^2+y^2=16$, we should have

$$\frac{\sqrt{25m^2+4}}{\sqrt{m^2+1}}=4 \quad \text{[Using: length of perpendicular from (0, 0) to (1) = 4]}$$

$\Rightarrow \quad 25m^2+4=16m^2+16$

$\Rightarrow \quad 9m^2=12$

$\Rightarrow \quad m=\frac{-2}{\sqrt{3}}$

[Leaving + ve sign to consider tangent in I quadrant]

$\therefore$Equation of common tangent is

$$y=-\frac{2}{\sqrt{3}}x+\sqrt{25\cdot\frac{4}{3}+4}$$

$\Rightarrow \quad y=-\frac{2}{\sqrt{3}}x+4\sqrt{\frac{7}{3}}$

This tangent meets the axes at $A(2\sqrt{7}, 0)$ and $B\left(0, 4\sqrt{\frac{7}{3}}\right)$.

$\therefore$Length of intercepted portion of tangent between axes

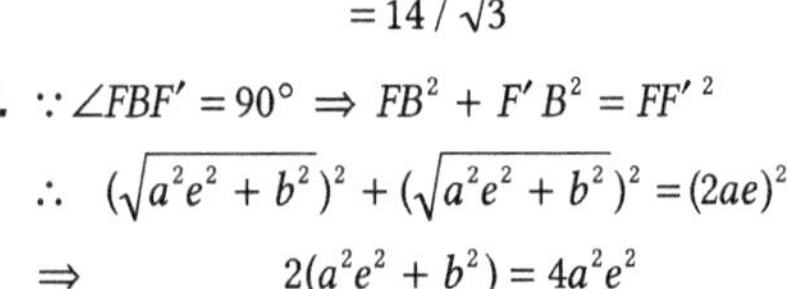

$$AB=\sqrt{(2\sqrt{7})+\left(4\sqrt{\frac{7}{3}}\right)^3}$$

$$=14/\sqrt{3}$$

96. $\because \angle FBF'=90^\circ \Rightarrow FB^2+F'B^2=FF'^2$

$\therefore \quad (\sqrt{a^2e^2+b^2})^2+(\sqrt{a^2e^2+b^2})^2=(2ae)^2$

$\Rightarrow \quad 2(a^2e^2+b^2)=4a^2e^2$

$\Rightarrow \quad e^2=\frac{b^2}{a^2}$

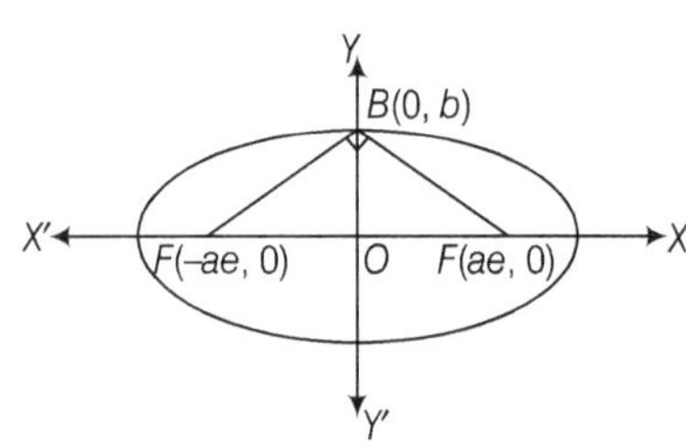

Also, $\quad e^2=1-b^2/a^2=1-e^2$

$\Rightarrow \quad 2e^2=1, e=\frac{1}{\sqrt{2}}$

97. $2ae=6 \Rightarrow ae=3; 2b=8$

$\Rightarrow \quad b=4$

$b^2=a^2(1-e^2); 16=a^2-a^2e^2$

$\Rightarrow \quad a^2=16+9=25 \Rightarrow a=5$

$\therefore \quad e=\frac{3}{a}=\frac{3}{5}$

98.

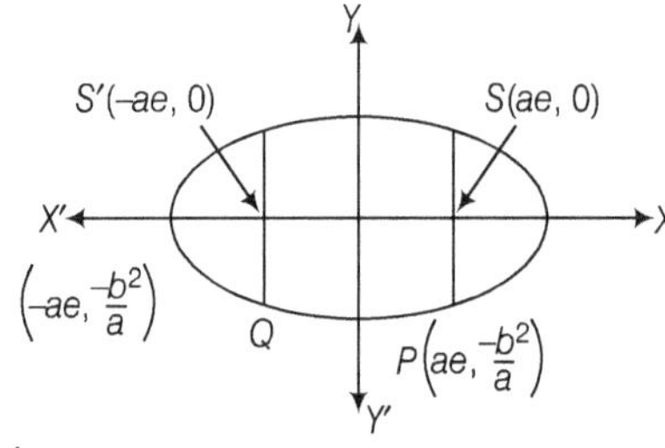

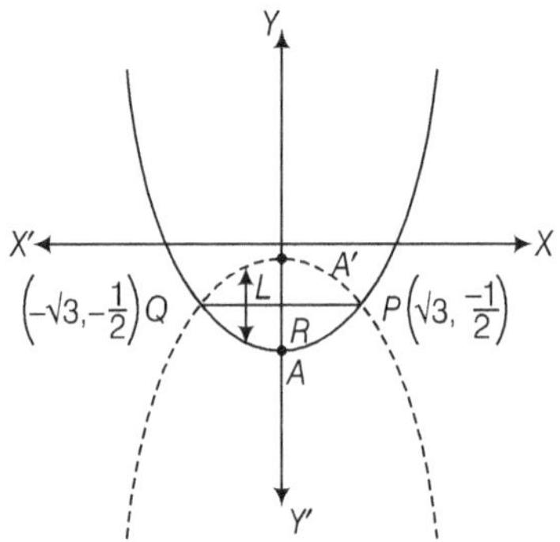

Given, ellipse is $x^2+4y^2=4$

or $\quad \frac{x^2}{2^2}+\frac{y^2}{1}=1 \Rightarrow a=2, b=1$

$\therefore \quad e=\sqrt{1-\frac{1}{4}}=\frac{\sqrt{3}}{2}$

$\therefore \quad ae=\sqrt{3}$

As per question $P\equiv(ae, -b^2/a)=\left(\sqrt{3}, -\frac{1}{2}\right)$

$$Q\equiv(-ae, -b^2/a)=\left(-\sqrt{3}, -\frac{1}{2}\right)$$

$\therefore \quad PQ=2\sqrt{3}$

Now, if PQ is the length of latusrectum to be found, then

$$PQ=4a=2\sqrt{3} \Rightarrow a=\frac{\sqrt{3}}{2}$$

Also, as PQ is horizontal, parabola with PQ as latusrectum can be upward parabola (with vertex at A) or down ward parabola (with vertex at A').

For upward parabola, $Ar = a = \frac{\sqrt{3}}{2}$

$\therefore$ Coordinates of $A = \left(0, -\left(\frac{\sqrt{3}+1}{2}\right)\right)$

So, Equation of upward parabola is given by

$$x^2 = 2\sqrt{3}\left(y + \frac{\sqrt{3}+1}{2}\right) \text{ or } x^2 - 2\sqrt{3}y = 3 + \sqrt{3} \quad \text{...(i)}$$

For downward parabola $A'R = a = \frac{\sqrt{3}}{2}$

$\therefore$ Coordinates of $A' = \left(0, -\left(\frac{1-\sqrt{3}}{2}\right)\right)$

So, equation of downward parabola is given by

$$x^2 = -2\sqrt{3}\left(y + \frac{1-\sqrt{3}}{2}\right)$$

or $$x^2 + 2\sqrt{3}y = 3 - \sqrt{3} \quad \text{...(ii)}$$

$\therefore$ Equation of required parabola is given by Eqs. (i) and (ii).

99. Perpendicular distance of directrix from focus

$$= \frac{a}{e} - ae = 4$$

$$\Rightarrow a\left(2 - \frac{1}{2}\right) = 4 \Rightarrow a = \frac{8}{3}$$

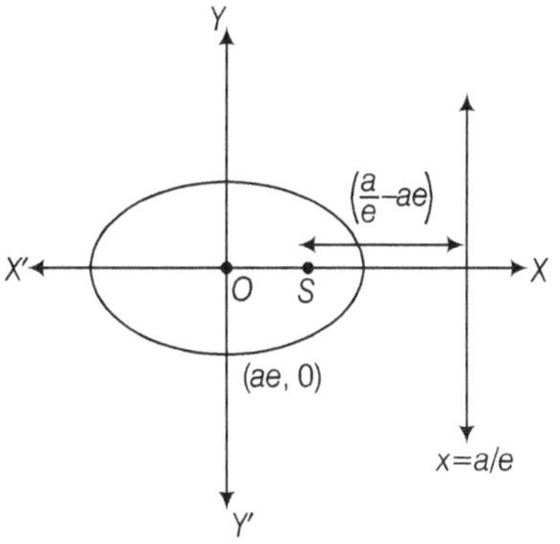

Y
X′ X
O S
(ae, 0)
$\left(\frac{a}{e} - ae\right)$
x=a/e
Y′

$\therefore$ Semi major axis = 8/3

100. The given ellipse is $x^2 + 9y^2 = 9$

or $$\frac{x^2}{3^2} + \frac{y^2}{1^2} = 1$$

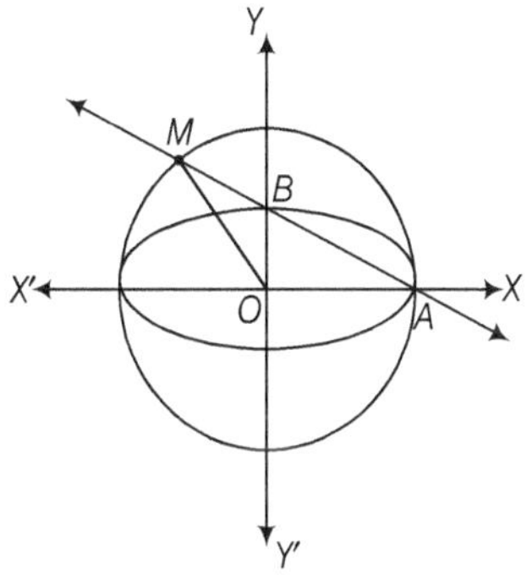

Y
M
B
X′ X
O A
Y′

So, the $A(3, 0)$ and $B(0, 1)$

$\therefore$ Equation of AB is $\frac{x}{3} + \frac{y}{1} = 1$ or $x + 3y - 3 = 0$ ...(i)

Also, auxillary circle of given ellipse is

$$x^2 + y^2 = 9 \quad \text{...(ii)}$$

Solving Eqs. (i) and (ii), we get the point M where line AB meets the auxillary circle.

Putting $x = 3 - 3y$ from Eqs. (i) and (ii)

we get $$(3-3y)^2 + y^2 = 9$$

$$\Rightarrow 9 - 18y + 9y^2 + y^2 = 9$$

$$\Rightarrow 10y^2 - 18y = 0$$

$$\Rightarrow y = 0, \frac{9}{5} \Rightarrow x = 3, \frac{-12}{5}$$

Clearly, $M\left(\frac{-12}{5}, \frac{9}{5}\right)$

$$\therefore \text{Area of } \Delta OAM = \frac{1}{2} \times \left| \begin{vmatrix} 0 & 0 & 1 \\ 3 & 0 & 1 \\ \frac{-12}{5} & \frac{9}{5} & 1 \end{vmatrix} \right| = \frac{27}{10}$$

101. The given ellipse is $\frac{x^2}{4^2} + \frac{y^2}{2^2} = 1$

such that $a^2 = 16$ and $b^2 = 4$

$$\therefore \quad e^2 = 1 - \frac{4}{16} = \frac{3}{4}$$

$$\Rightarrow \quad e = \frac{\sqrt{3}}{2}$$

Let $P(4\cos\theta, 2\sin\theta)$ be any point on the ellipse, then equation of normal at P is

$$4x\sin\theta - 2y\cos\theta = 12\sin\theta\cos\theta$$

$$\Rightarrow \frac{x}{3\cos\theta} - \frac{y}{6\sin\theta} = 1$$

$\therefore$ Q, the point where normal at P meets X-axis, has coordinates $(3\cos\theta, 0)$

$\therefore$ Mid-point of PQ is $M\left(\frac{7\cos\theta}{2}, \sin\theta\right)$

For locus of point M we consider

$$x = \frac{7\cos\theta}{2} \text{ and } y = \sin\theta$$

$$\Rightarrow \cos\theta = \frac{2x}{7} \text{ and } \sin\theta = y \Rightarrow \frac{4x^2}{49} + y^2 = 1 \quad \text{...(i)}$$

Also, the latusrectum of given ellipse is

$$x = \pm ae = \pm 4 \times \frac{\sqrt{3}}{2} = \pm 2\sqrt{3}$$

or $$x = \pm 2\sqrt{3} \quad \text{...(ii)}$$

Solving Eqs. (i) and (ii), we get

$$\frac{4 \times 12}{49} + y^2 = 1$$

$$\Rightarrow y^2 = \frac{1}{49} \text{ or } y = \pm\frac{1}{7}$$

$\therefore$ The required points are $\left(\pm 2\sqrt{3}, \pm\frac{1}{7}\right)$.

102. In ΔABC, given that $\cos B + \cos C = 4\sin^2 \frac{A}{2}$

$\Rightarrow 2\cos\frac{B+C}{2}\cos\frac{B-C}{2} - 4\sin^2\frac{A}{2} = 0$

$\Rightarrow \quad 2\sin\frac{A}{2}\left[\cos\frac{B-C}{2} - 2\sin\frac{A}{2}\right] = 0$

$\Rightarrow \sin\frac{A}{2} = 0$ or $\left(\cos\frac{B-C}{2} - 2\cos\frac{B+C}{2}\right) = 0$

$\left(\because \frac{A}{2} = 90^\circ - \left(\frac{B+C}{2}\right)\right)$

But in a triangle $\sin\frac{A}{2} \neq 0$

$$\cos\frac{B-C}{2} - 2\cos\frac{B+C}{2} = 0$$

$$\Rightarrow \quad \frac{\cos\left(\frac{B+C}{2}\right)}{\cos\left(\frac{B-C}{2}\right)} = \frac{1}{2}$$

Applying componendo and dividendo, we get

$$\frac{\cos\left(\frac{B+C}{2}\right) + \cos\left(\frac{B-C}{2}\right)}{\cos\left(\frac{B+C}{2}\right) - \cos\left(\frac{B-C}{2}\right)} = \frac{1+2}{1-2} = -3$$

$$\Rightarrow \quad -\frac{2\cos\frac{B}{2}\cos\frac{C}{2}}{2\sin\frac{B}{2}\sin\frac{C}{2}} = -3$$

$$\Rightarrow \quad \tan\frac{B}{2}\tan\frac{C}{2} = \frac{1}{3}$$

$$\Rightarrow \quad \sqrt{\frac{(s-a)(s-c)}{s(s-b)}}\sqrt{\frac{(s-a)(s-b)}{s(s-c)}} = \frac{1}{3}$$

$$\Rightarrow \quad \frac{s-a}{s} = \frac{1}{3}$$

or $\quad 2s = 3a$

$\Rightarrow \quad a + b + c = 3a$

or $\quad b + c = 2a$

i.e. $\quad AC + AB =$ constant

[$\because$ base $BC = a$ is given to be constant]

$\Rightarrow A$ moves on an ellipse.

103. $\left(\frac{x}{\sqrt{3}}\right)^2 + (y)^2 = \left(\frac{1-t^2}{1+t^2}\right)^2 + \left(\frac{2t}{1+t^2}\right)^2$

$$= \frac{(1+t^2)^2}{(1+t^2)^2} = 1$$

$\Rightarrow \quad \frac{x^2}{3} + y^2 = 1$

Which is an ellipse.

104. The given ellipse is $\frac{x^2}{4} + \frac{y^2}{1} = 1$

So, $A = (2, 0)$ and $B = (0,1)$

If $PQRS$ is the rectangle in which it is inscribed, then $P = (2, 1)$.

Let $\frac{x^2}{a^2} + \frac{y^2}{b^2} = 1$ be the ellipse circumscribing the rectangle $PQRS$. Then it passes through $P(2, 1)$

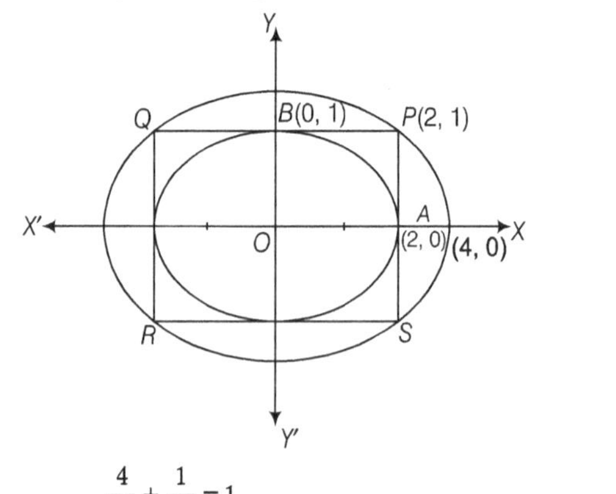

$\therefore \quad \frac{4}{a^2} + \frac{1}{b^2} = 1 \qquad$ ...(i)

Also, given that, it passes through (4, 0)

$\therefore \quad \frac{16}{a^2} + 0 = 1$

$\Rightarrow \quad a^2 = 16$

$\Rightarrow \quad b^2 = 4/3 \qquad$ [substituting $a^2 = 16$ in Eq. (i)]

$\therefore$ The required ellipse is $\frac{x^2}{16} + \frac{y^2}{4/3} = 1$

or $\quad x^2 + 12y^2 = 16$

105. Tangent to $\frac{x^2}{3^2} + \frac{y^2}{2^2} = 1$ at the point $(3\cos\theta, 2\sin\theta)$ is

$$\frac{x\cos\theta}{3} + \frac{y\sin\theta}{2} = 1$$

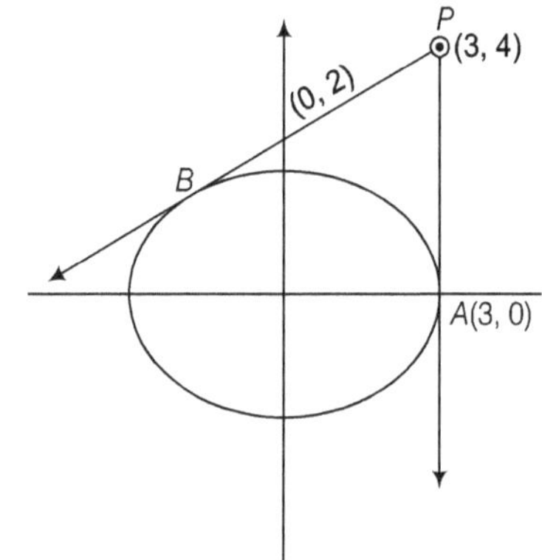

As it passes through (3, 4), we get

$$\cos\theta + 2\sin\theta = 1$$

$\Rightarrow \quad 4\sin^2\theta = 1 + \cos^2\theta - 2\cos\theta$

$\Rightarrow \quad 5\cos^2\theta - 2\cos\theta - 3 = 0$

$\Rightarrow \quad \cos\theta = 1, -\frac{3}{5}$

$\Rightarrow \quad \sin\theta = 0, \frac{4}{5}$

$\therefore$ Required points are $A(3, 0)$ and $B\left(\frac{9}{5}, \frac{8}{5}\right)$.

106. Let H be orthocentre of ΔPAB, then as $BH \perp AP$, BH is a horizontal line through B.

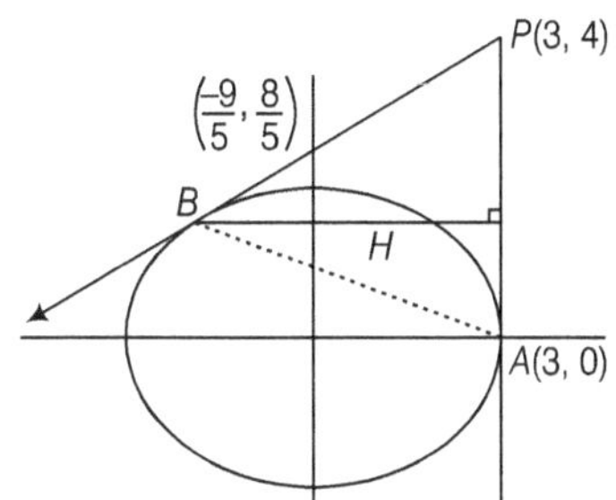

$\therefore y$-coordinate of $B = 8/5$

Let H has coordinate $(\alpha, 8/5)$

Then, slope of $PH = \dfrac{\frac{8}{5} - 4}{\alpha - 3} = \dfrac{-12}{5(\alpha - 3)}$

and s lope of $AB = \dfrac{\frac{8-0}{5}}{-\frac{9}{5-3}} = \dfrac{8}{-24} = \dfrac{-1}{3}$

But $PH \perp AB$

$\Rightarrow \quad \dfrac{-12}{5(\alpha - 3)} \times \left(\dfrac{-1}{3}\right) = -1$

$\Rightarrow \quad 4 = -5\alpha + 15$ or $\alpha = 11/5$

Hence $H\left(\dfrac{11}{5}, \dfrac{8}{5}\right)$.

107. Clearly, the moving point traces a parabola with focus at $P(3, 4)$ and directrix as

$$AB: \frac{y - 0}{x - 3} = \frac{-1}{3}$$

or $\quad x + 3y - 3 = 0$

$\therefore$ Equation of parabola is

$$(x - 3)^2 + (y - 4)^2 = \frac{(x + 3y - 3)^2}{10}$$

or $\quad 9x^2 + y^2 - 6xy - 54x - 62y + 241 = 0$

108. Let the ellipse be $\dfrac{x^2}{a^2} + \dfrac{y^2}{b^2} = 1$

It passes through $(-3, 1)$, so

$$\frac{9}{a^2} + \frac{1}{b^2} = 1 \quad \text{...(i)}$$

Also, $\quad b^2 = a^2(1 - 2/5)$

$\Rightarrow \quad 5b^2 = 3a^2 \quad$ ...(ii)

Solving Eqs. (i) and (ii), we get

$$a^2 = \frac{32}{3}, b^2 = \frac{32}{5}$$

So, the equation of the ellipse is $3x^2 + 5y^2 = 32$

109. As rectangle $ABCD$ circumscribed the ellipse

$$\frac{x^2}{9} + \frac{y^2}{4} = 1$$

$\therefore \quad A = (3, 2)$

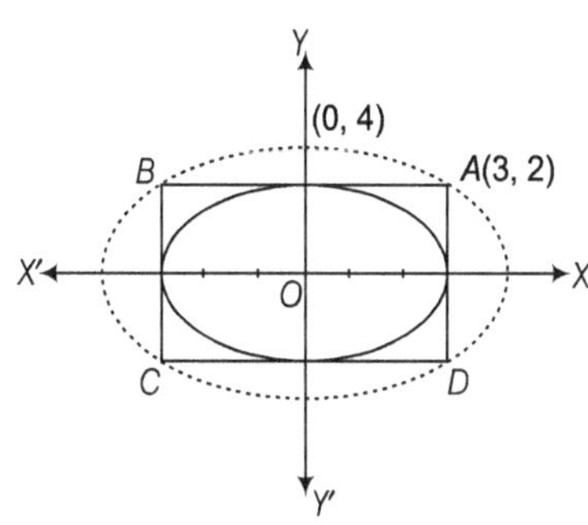

Let the ellipse circumscribing the rectangle $ABCD$ is

$$\frac{x^2}{a^2} + \frac{y^2}{b^2} = 1$$

Given that, it passes through (0, 4)

$\therefore \quad b^2 = 16$

Also, it passes through $A(3, 2)$

$\therefore \quad \dfrac{9}{a^2} + \dfrac{4}{16} = 1 \Rightarrow a^2 = 12$

$\therefore \quad e = \sqrt{1 - \dfrac{12}{16}} = \sqrt{\dfrac{1}{4}} = \dfrac{1}{2}$

110. Given, equation of ellipse is $2x^2 + y^2 = 4$

$\Rightarrow \quad \dfrac{2x^2}{4} + \dfrac{y^2}{4} = 1 \Rightarrow \dfrac{x^2}{2} + \dfrac{y^2}{4} = 1$

Equation of tangent to the ellipse $\dfrac{x^2}{2} + \dfrac{y^2}{4} = 1$ is

$$y = mx \pm \sqrt{2m^2 + 4} \quad \text{...(i)}$$

$\because$ equation of tangent to the ellipse $\dfrac{x^2}{a^2} + \dfrac{y^2}{b^2} = 1$

is $y = mx + c$, where $c = \pm\sqrt{a^2m^2 + b^2}$

Now, equation of tangent to the parabola

$\because \quad y^2 = 16\sqrt{3}x$ is $y = mx + \dfrac{4\sqrt{3}}{m}$ ...(ii)

($\because$ Equation of tangent to the parabola $y^2 = 4ax$ is $y = mx + \dfrac{a}{m}$)

On comparing Eqs. (i) and (ii), we get

$$\frac{4\sqrt{3}}{m} = \pm\sqrt{2m^2 + 4}$$

Squaring on both the sides, we get

$$16(3) = (2m^2 + 4)m^2$$

$\Rightarrow \quad 48 = m^2(2m^2 + 4)$

$\Rightarrow \quad 2m^2 + 4m^2 - 48 = 0$

$\Rightarrow \quad m^4 + 2m^2 - 24 = 0$

$\Rightarrow \quad (m^2 + 6)(m^2 - 4) = 0$

$\Rightarrow \quad m^2 = 4 \quad (\because m^2 \neq -6)$

$\Rightarrow \quad m = \pm 2$

$\Rightarrow$ Equation of common tangents are $y = \pm 2x \pm 2\sqrt{3}$

Thus, statement I is true.

statement II is obviously true.

111. Equation of circle is $(x-1)^2 + y^2 = 1$

$\Rightarrow$ Radius $= 1$ and Diameter $= 2$

$\therefore$ Length of semi-minor axis is 2.

Equation of circle is $x^2 + (y-2)^2 = 4 = (2)^2$

$\Rightarrow$ Radius $= 2$ and Diameter $= 4$

$\Rightarrow$ Length of semi-major axis is 4

We know, equation of ellipse is given by

$$\frac{x^2}{(\text{Major-axis})^2} + \frac{y^2}{(\text{Major-axis})^2} = 1$$

$$\Rightarrow \quad \frac{x^2}{(4)^2} + \frac{y^2}{(2)^2} = 1 \Rightarrow \frac{x^2}{16} + \frac{y^2}{4} = 1$$

$$\Rightarrow \quad x^2 + 4y^2 = 16$$

112. From the given equation of ellipse, we have

$$a = 4, b = 3e = \sqrt{1 - \frac{9}{16}}$$

$$\Rightarrow \quad e = \frac{\sqrt{7}}{4}$$

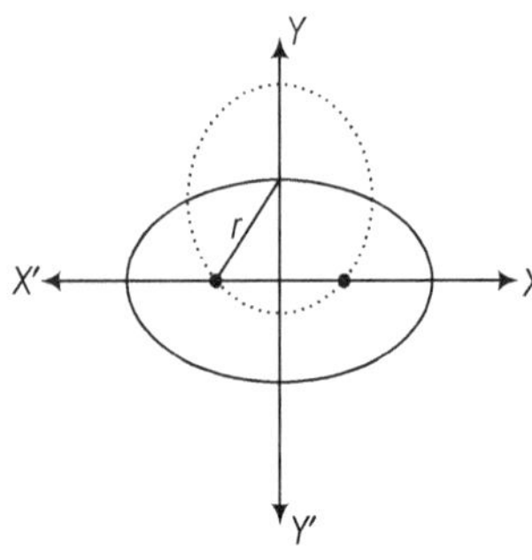

Now, radius of this circle $= a^2 = 16$

$$\Rightarrow \quad \text{Foci} = (\pm\sqrt{7}, 0)$$

Now, equation of circle is $(x-0)^2 + (y-3)^2 = 16$

$$x^2 + y^2 - 6y - 7 = 0$$

113. Vertical line $x = h$, meets the ellipse $\frac{x^2}{4} + \frac{y^2}{3} = 1$ at

$$P\left(h, \frac{\sqrt{3}}{2}\sqrt{(4-h^2)}\right) \text{ and } Q\left(h, \frac{-\sqrt{3}}{2}\sqrt{(4-h^2)}\right)$$

By symmetry, tangents at P and Q will meet each other at X-axis

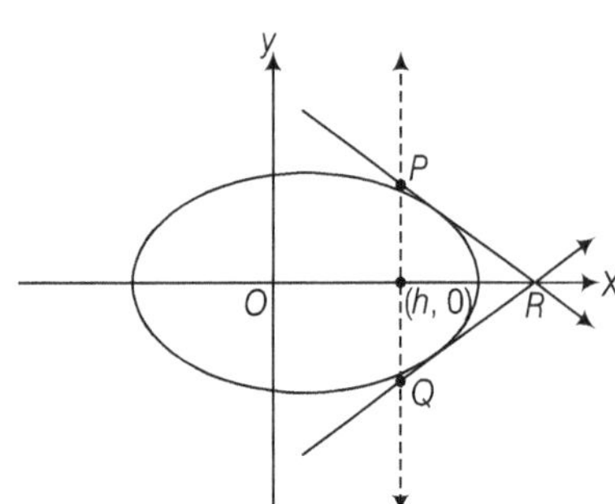

Tangent at P is $\frac{xh}{4} + \frac{y\sqrt{3}}{6}\sqrt{(4-h^2)} = 1$

Which meets X-axis at $R\left(\frac{4}{h}, 0\right)$

Area of $\Delta PQR = \frac{1}{2} \times \sqrt{3}\sqrt{(4-h^2)} \times \left(\frac{4}{h} - h\right)$

i.e. $$\Delta(h) = \frac{\sqrt{3}}{2}\frac{(4-h^2)^{3/2}}{h}$$

$$\frac{d\Delta}{dh} = -\sqrt{3}\left[\frac{\sqrt{(4-h^2)}(h^2+2)}{h^2}\right] < 0$$

$\therefore \Delta(h)$ is a decreasing function.

$$\therefore \quad \frac{1}{2} \le h \le 1$$

$$\Rightarrow \quad \Delta_{\max} = \Delta\left(\frac{1}{2}\right) \text{ and } \Delta_{\max} = \Delta(1)$$

$$\therefore \quad \Delta_1 = \frac{\sqrt{3}}{2}\left(\frac{\left(4 - \frac{1}{4}\right)^{3/2}}{\frac{1}{2}}\right) = \frac{45}{8}\sqrt{5}$$

$$\Delta_2 = \frac{\sqrt{3}}{2} \cdot \frac{3\sqrt{3}}{1} = \frac{9}{2}$$

$$\therefore \quad \frac{8}{\sqrt{5}}\Delta_1 - 8\Delta_2 = 45 - 36 = 9$$

114. Given, equation of ellipse can be written as

$$\frac{x^2}{6} + \frac{y^2}{2} = 1$$

$$\Rightarrow \quad a^2 = 6, b^2 = 2$$

Now, equation of any variable tangent is

$$y = mx \pm \sqrt{a^2m^2 + b^2} \qquad \text{...(i)}$$

where m is slope of the tangent

So, equation of perpendicular line drawn from centre to tangent is

$$y = \frac{-x}{m} \qquad \text{...(ii)}$$

Eliminating m, we get

$$(x^4 + y^4 + 2x^2y^2) = a^2x^2 + b^2y^2$$

$$\Rightarrow \quad (x^2 + y^2)^2 = a^2x^2 + b^2y^2$$

$$\Rightarrow \quad (x^2 + y^2)^2 = 6x^2 + 2y^2$$

115. The end point of latusrectum of ellipse

$\frac{x^2}{a^2} + \frac{y^2}{b^2} = 1$ in first quadrant is $\left(ae, \frac{b^2}{a}\right)$ and the tangent at this point intersects X-axis at $\left(\frac{a}{e}, 0\right)$ and Y- axis at $(0, a)$.

The given ellipse is $\frac{x^2}{9} + \frac{y^2}{5} = 1$

Then, $$a^2 = 9, b^2 = 5$$

$$\Rightarrow \quad e = \sqrt{\left(1 - \frac{5}{9}\right)} = \frac{2}{3}$$

$\therefore$ End point of latusrectum in first quadrant is $L(2, 5/3)$

Equation of tangent at L is $\frac{2x}{9} + \frac{y}{3} = 1$

It meets X-axis at $A\ (9/2, 0)$ and Y-axis at $B\ (0, 3)$

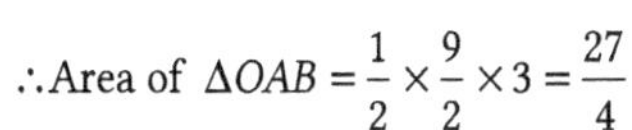

$\therefore$ Area of $\Delta OAB = \frac{1}{2} \times \frac{9}{2} \times 3 = \frac{27}{4}$

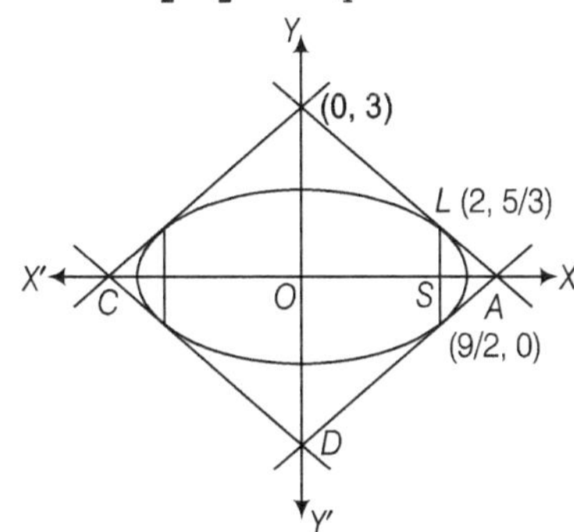

By symmetry area of quadrilateral

$$= 4 \times (\text{Area } \Delta OAB) = 4 \times \frac{27}{4} = 27 \text{ sq units}$$

116. Let $E_1: \frac{x^2}{a^2} + \frac{y^2}{b^2} = 1$, where $a > b$

and $E_2: \frac{x^2}{c^2} + \frac{y^2}{d^2} = 1$, where $c < d$

Also, $S: x^2 + (y-1)^2 = 2$

Tangent at $P(x_1, y_1)$ to S is $x + y = 3$

To find point of contact put $x = 3 - y$ in S, we get $P(1, 2)$

writing equation of tangent in parametric form

$$\frac{x-1}{\frac{-1}{\sqrt{2}}} = \frac{y-2}{\frac{1}{\sqrt{2}}} = \pm \frac{2\sqrt{2}}{3}$$

$$x = \frac{-2}{3} + 1 \text{ or } \frac{2}{3} + 1 \text{ and } y = \frac{2}{3} + 2 \text{ or } \frac{-2}{3} + 2$$

$\Rightarrow \quad x = \frac{1}{3} \text{ or } \frac{5}{3} \text{ and } y = \frac{8}{3} \text{ or } \frac{4}{3}$

$\therefore \quad Q\left(\frac{5}{3}, \frac{4}{3}\right)$ and $R\left(\frac{1}{3}, \frac{8}{3}\right)$

Equation of tangent to E_1 at Q is

$\frac{5x}{3a^2} + \frac{4y}{3b^2} = 1$ which is identical to $\frac{x}{3} + \frac{y}{3} = 1$

$\Rightarrow a^2 = 5$ and $b^2 = 4 \Rightarrow e_1^2 = 1 - \frac{4}{5} = \frac{1}{5}$

Equation of tangent to E_2 at R is

$\frac{x}{3c^2} + \frac{8y}{3d^2} = 1$ identical to $\frac{x}{3} + \frac{y}{3} = 1$

$\Rightarrow \quad c^2 = 1, d^2 = 8 \Rightarrow e_2^2 = 1 - \frac{1}{8} = \frac{7}{8}$

$\therefore \quad e_1^2 + e_2^2 = \frac{43}{40}, e_1 e_2 = \frac{\sqrt{7}}{2\sqrt{10}}, |e_1^2 - e_2^2| = \frac{27}{40}$

117. Ellipse $\frac{x^2}{9} + \frac{y^2}{5} = 1 \Rightarrow a = 3, b = \sqrt{5}$ and $e = \frac{2}{3}$

$\therefore \quad f_1 = 2$ and $f_2 = -2$

$$P_1: y^2 = 8x \quad \text{and} \quad P_2: y^2 = -16x$$

$$T_1: y = m_1 x + \frac{2}{m_1}$$

It passes through $(-4, 0)$,

$$0 = -4m_1 + \frac{2}{m_1} \Rightarrow m_1^2 = \frac{1}{2}$$

$$T_2: y = m_2 x - \frac{4}{m_2}$$

It passes through $(2, 0)$

$$0 = 2m_2 - \frac{4}{m_2} \Rightarrow m_2^2 = 2$$

$\therefore \quad \frac{1}{m_1^2} + m_2^2 = 4$

Sol. (Q. Nos. 118 & 119)

118. For ellipse $\frac{x^2}{9} + \frac{y^2}{8} = 1, e = \sqrt{\left(1 - \frac{8}{9}\right)} = \frac{1}{3}$

$\therefore \quad F_1(-1, 0)$ and $F_2(1, 0)$

Parabola with vertex at $(0, 0)$ and focus at F_2 $(1, 0)$ is $y^2 = 4x$.

Intersection points of ellipse and parabola are $M\left(\frac{3}{2}, \sqrt{6}\right)$ and $N\left(\frac{3}{2}, -\sqrt{6}\right)$.

For orthocentre of $\Delta F_1 MN$, clearly one altitude is X-axis i.e. $y = 0$ and altitude from M to $F_1 N$ is

$$y - \sqrt{6} = \frac{5}{2\sqrt{6}}\left(x - \frac{3}{2}\right)$$

Putting $y = 0$ in above equation, we get $x = -\frac{9}{10}$

Orthocentre $\left(-\frac{9}{10}, 0\right)$

119. Tangents to ellipse at M and N are

$$\frac{x}{6} + \frac{y\sqrt{6}}{8} = 1 \text{ and } \frac{x}{6} - \frac{y\sqrt{6}}{8} = 1$$

their intersection point is R $(6, 0)$

Also, normal to parabola at $M\left(\frac{3}{2}, \sqrt{6}\right)$ is

$$y - \sqrt{6} = -\frac{\sqrt{6}}{2}\left(x - \frac{3}{2}\right)$$

Its intersection with x-axis is $Q\left(\frac{7}{2}, 0\right)$

Now, $\quad \text{ar}(\Delta MQR) = \frac{1}{2} \times \frac{5}{2} \times \sqrt{6} = \frac{5\sqrt{6}}{4}$

Also, area $(MF_1NF_2) = 2 \times$ Area of(F_1MF_2)

$$= 2 \times \frac{1}{2} \times 2 \times \sqrt{6} = 2\sqrt{6}$$

$$\frac{\text{area}(\Delta MQR)}{\text{area}(MF_1NF_2)} = \frac{5\sqrt{6}}{4 \times 2\sqrt{6}} = 5:8$$

120. Here, $e = \frac{1}{2}$ and $x = -\frac{a}{e} = -4$

$\therefore \quad a = 2$

and $\quad b^2 = a^2(1 - e^2) = 4(1 - 1/4) = 3$

$\therefore$ Equation of ellipse is $\frac{x^2}{4} + \frac{y^2}{3} = 1$

$\Rightarrow$ Equation of normal at $(1, 3/2)$ is

$$\frac{4x}{1} - \frac{3y}{3/2} = 4 - 3$$

or $\quad 4x - 2y = 1$

CHAPTER

07

Hyperbola

Learning Part

Session 1

- Hyperbola : Definition
- The Foci and Two Directrices of a Hyperbola
- Some Terms Related to Hyperbola
- Conjugate Hyperbola
- Intersection of a Line and a Hyperbola
- Standard Equation of Hyperbola
- Tracing of the Hyperbola
- Focal Distances of a Point
- Position of a Point with Respect to a Hyperbola

Session 2

- Equations of Tangents in Different Forms
- Pair of Tangents
- Equation of the Chord Bisected at a Given Point
- Equations of Normals in Different Forms
- Chord of Contact

Session 3

- Diameter
- Properties of Hyperbola
- Director Circle
- Rectangular Hyperbola
- Study of Hyperbola $xy = c^2$
- Reflection Property of a Hyperbola
- Equation of a Hyperbola Referred to Two Perpendicular Lines
- Conjugate Diameters
- Intersection of Conjugate Diameters and Hyperbola
- Asymptotes
- The Rectangular Hyperbola $xy = c^2$
- Properties of Rectangular Hyperbola $xy = c^2$

Practice Part

- JEE Type Examples
- Chapter Exercises

Arihant on Your Mobile !

Exercises with the symbol can be practised on your mobile. See inside cover page to activate for free.

Session 1

Hyperbola : Definition, Standard Equation of Hyperbola, The Foci and Two Directrices of a Hyperbola, Tracing of the Hyperbola, Focal Distances of a Point, Conjugate Hyperbola, Position of a Point with Respect to a Hyperbola, Intersection of a Line and a Hyperbola

Hyperbola : Definition

The locus of a point which moves in a plane such that its distance from a fixed point (i.e. focus) is e times its distance from a fixed line (i.e. directrix) is known as hyperbola. For hyperbola $e > 1$.

Standard Equation of Hyperbola

Let S be the focus and ZM the directrix of the hyperbola. Draw $SZ \perp ZM$. Divide SZ internally and externally in the ratio $e:1 (e > 1)$ and let A and A' be their internal and external points of division.

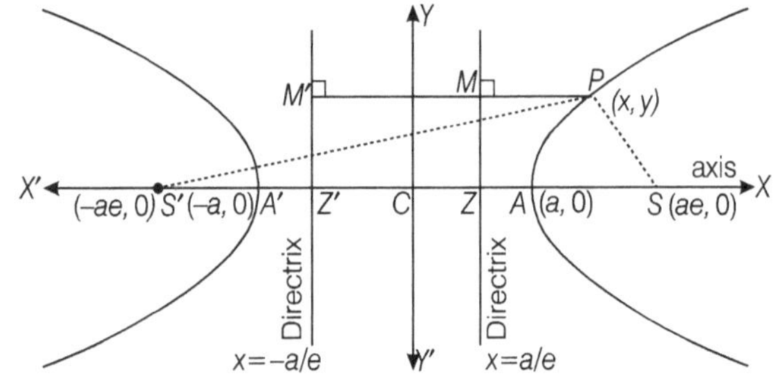

then $\qquad SA = e\,AZ \qquad$ ...(i)

and $\qquad SA' = e\,A'Z \qquad$ ...(ii)

Clearly A and A' will lie on the hyperbola. Let $AA' = 2a$ and take C the mid-point of AA' as origin

$\therefore \qquad CA = CA' = a$

Let $P(x, y)$ be any point on the hyperbola and CA as X-axis, the line through C perpendicular to CA as Y-axis.

Then adding Eqs. (i) and (ii)

$\therefore \qquad SA + SA' = e(AZ + A'Z)$

$\Rightarrow \qquad CS - CA + CS + CA' = e(AA')$

$\Rightarrow \qquad 2CS = e(2a) \qquad (\because CA = CA')$

$\therefore \qquad CS = ae$

$\therefore$ The focus S is $(CS, 0)$ i.e. $(ae, 0)$ and subtracting Eq. (i) from Eq. (ii), then

$$SA' - SA = e(A'Z - AZ)$$

$$AA' = e[(CA' + CZ) - (CA - CZ)]$$

$\Rightarrow \qquad AA' = e(2CZ) \qquad (\because CA = CA')$

$\Rightarrow \qquad 2a = e(2CZ)$

$\therefore \qquad CZ = a/e$

$\therefore$ The directrix MZ is $x = CZ = a/e$

or $\qquad x - a/e = 0 \qquad \left(\because e > 1, \therefore \dfrac{a}{e} < 1\right)$

Now, draw $PM \perp MZ$,

$\therefore \qquad \dfrac{SP}{PM} = e$ or $(SP)^2 = e^2 (PM)^2$

or $\qquad (x - ae)^2 + (y - 0)^2 = e^2\left(x - \dfrac{a}{e}\right)^2$

or $\qquad (x - ae)^2 + y^2 = (ex - a)^2$

$\Rightarrow \qquad x^2 + a^2e^2 - 2aex + y^2 = e^2x^2 - 2aex + a^2$

$\Rightarrow \qquad x^2(e^2 - 1) - y^2 = a^2(e^2 - 1)$

$\Rightarrow \qquad \dfrac{x^2}{a^2} - \dfrac{y^2}{a^2(e^2 - 1)} = 1$

or $\qquad \dfrac{x^2}{a^2} - \dfrac{y^2}{b^2} = 1$, where, $b^2 = a^2(e^2 - 1)$

This is the standard equation of the hyperbola.

Generally : The equation of the hyperbola whose focus is the point (h, k) and directrix is $lx + my + n = 0$ and whose eccentricity is e, is

$$(x - h)^2 + (y - k)^2 = e^2 \frac{(lx + my + n)^2}{(l^2 + m^2)}$$

The Foci and Two Directrices of a Hyperbola

On the negative side of origin take a point S' which is such that

$$CS = CS' = ae$$

and another point Z', then $CZ = CZ' = \frac{a}{e}$

$\therefore$ Coordinates of S' are $(-ae, 0)$ and equation of second directrix (i.e. $Z'M'$) is

$$x = -\frac{a}{e}$$

Let $P(x, y)$ be any point on the hyperbola, then

$$S'P = ePM' \text{ or } (S'P)^2 = e^2 (PM')^2$$

or $$(x + ae)^2 + (y - 0)^2 = e^2 \left(x + \frac{a}{e} \right)^2$$

or $$(x + ae)^2 + y^2 = (ex + a)^2$$

or $$x^2 + 2aex + a^2e^2 + y^2 = e^2x^2 + 2aex + a^2$$

or $$x^2 (e^2 - 1) - y^2 = a^2(e^2 - 1)$$

or $$\frac{x^2}{a^2} - \frac{y^2}{a^2 (e^2 - 1)} = 1$$

or $$\frac{x^2}{a^2} - \frac{y^2}{b^2} = 1, \text{ where, } b^2 = a^2 (e^2 - 1)$$

The equation being the same as that of hyperbola when $S(ae, 0)$ is focus and MZ i.e. $x = \frac{a}{e}$ is directrix.

Hence, coordinates of foci are $(\pm ae, 0)$ and equations of directrices are

$$x = \pm a/e$$

Remarks

1. Distance between foci $SS' = 2ae$ and distance between directrices $ZZ' = 2a/e$
2. Two hyperbolas are said to be similar if they have the same value of eccentricity.
3. Since, $\frac{x^2}{a^2} - \frac{y^2}{b^2} = 1$

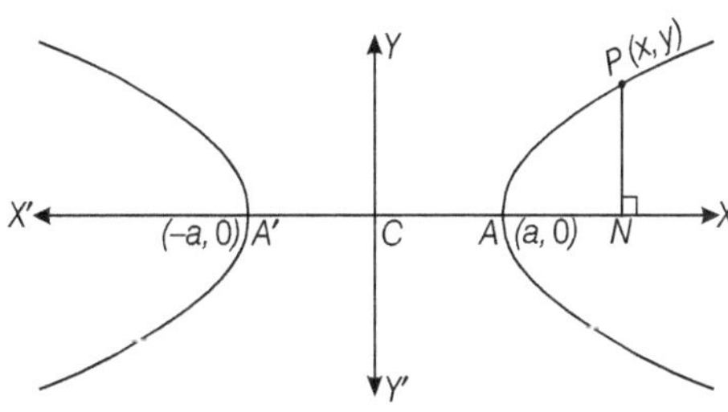

$$\Rightarrow \quad \frac{y^2}{b^2} = \frac{x^2}{a^2} - 1$$

$$\frac{y^2}{b^2} = \frac{(x - a)(x + a)}{a^2} \quad \text{...(i)}$$

$\because$ $AN = CN - CA = (x - a)$

and $A'N = CN + CA' = (x + a)$

and $PN = y$

$\therefore$ From Eq. (i), $\frac{(PN)^2}{AN \cdot A'N} = \frac{b^2}{a^2}$

Tracing of the Hyperbola

Equation of the hyperbola is

$$\frac{x^2}{a^2} - \frac{y^2}{b^2} = 1 \quad \text{...(i)}$$

(i) Since only even powers of x and y occur in this equation so it (hyperbola) is symmetrical about the both axes.

(ii) The hyperbola (i) does not cut Y-axis in real points where as it cuts X-axis at $(a, 0)$ and $(-a, 0)$.

(iii) The Eq. (i) may be written as

$$y = \pm \frac{b}{a}\sqrt{(x^2 - a^2)}$$

If follows that $x^2 - a^2 \geq 0$

$\therefore$ $x^2 \geq a^2$

$\Rightarrow$ $x \leq -a$ or $x \geq a$

Hence, $x \notin (-a, a)$

The curve does not exist in the region

$$x = -a \text{ to } x = a.$$

(iv) As x increases, y also increases i.e. the curve extends to infinity.

Some Terms Related to Hyperbola

Let the equation of hyperbola is $\frac{x^2}{a^2} - \frac{y^2}{b^2} = 1$

(1) Centre : All chords passing through C and bisected at C.

Here $C \equiv (0, 0)$

(2) Eccentricity : For the hyperbola $\frac{x^2}{a^2} - \frac{y^2}{b^2} = 1$ we have

$$b^2 = a^2 (e^2 - 1)$$

$$\Rightarrow \quad e^2 = \frac{a^2 + b^2}{a^2}$$

$$\Rightarrow \qquad e = \sqrt{1 + \left(\frac{b^2}{a^2}\right)} \Rightarrow e = \sqrt{\left\{1 + \frac{(2b)^2}{(2a)^2}\right\}}$$

$$\Rightarrow \qquad e = \sqrt{\left\{1 + \frac{(\text{conjugate axis})^2}{(\text{transverse axis})^2}\right\}}$$

(3) **Foci and directrices :** S and S' are the foci of the ellipse and their coordinates are $(ae, 0)$ and $(-ae, 0)$ respectively and ZM and $Z'M'$ are two directrices of the hyperbola and their equations are

$$x = \frac{a}{e} \text{ and } x = -\frac{a}{e} \text{ respectively.}$$

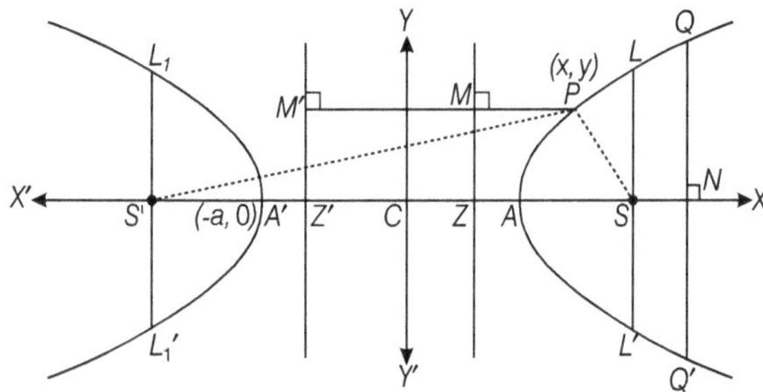

(4) **Axes :** The points $A(a, 0)$ and $A'(-a, 0)$ are called the vertices of the hyperbola and line AA' is called **transverse axis** and the line perpendicular to its through the centre $(0, 0)$ of the hyperbola is called **conjugate axis.**

The length of transverse and conjugate axes are taken as $2a$ and $2b$ respectively.

(5) **Double ordinates :** If Q be a point on the hyperbola draw QN perpendicular to the axis of the hyperbola and produced to meet the curve again at Q'. Then QQ' is called a double ordinate of Q.

If abscissa of Q is h, then ordinates of Q are

$$\frac{y^2}{b^2} = \frac{h^2}{a^2} - 1$$

$$\therefore \qquad y = \pm \frac{b}{a}\sqrt{(h^2 - a^2)}$$

$$\therefore \qquad y = \frac{b}{a}\sqrt{(h^2 - a^2)} \qquad \text{(for I quadrant)}$$

and ordinate of Q' is

$$y = -\frac{b}{a}\sqrt{(h^2 - a^2)} \qquad \text{(for IV quadrant)}$$

Hence, coordinates of Q and Q' are

$$\left(h, \frac{b}{a}\sqrt{(h^2 - a^2)}\right) \text{ and } \left(h, -\frac{b}{a}\sqrt{(h^2 - a^2)}\right)$$

respectively.

(6) **Latusrectum :** The double ordinates LL' and L_1L_1' are the latusrectums of the hyperbola. These lines are perpendicular to transverse axis AA' and through the foci S and S' respectively.

Length of latusrectum

Now, let $LL' = 2k$, then $LS = L'S = k$

Coordinates of L and L' are (ae, k) and $(ae, -k)$

lie on the hyperbola $\frac{x^2}{a^2} - \frac{y^2}{b^2} = 1$

$$\therefore \qquad \frac{a^2e^2}{a^2} - \frac{k^2}{b^2} = 1$$

or $\quad k^2 = b^2(e^2 - 1) = b^2\left(\frac{b^2}{a^2}\right) \qquad [\because b^2 = a^2(e^2 - 1)]$

$$\therefore \qquad k = \frac{b^2}{a} \qquad (\because k > 0)$$

$$\therefore \qquad 2k = \frac{2b^2}{a} = LL'$$

$\therefore$ Length of latusrectum $LL' = L_1L'_1 = \frac{2b^2}{a}$ and end points of latusrectums are

$$L \equiv \left(ae, \frac{b^2}{a}\right); L' \equiv \left(ae, -\frac{b^2}{a}\right);$$

$$L_1 \equiv \left(-ae, \frac{b^2}{a}\right); L_1' \equiv \left(-ae, -\frac{b^2}{a}\right) \text{ respectively.}$$

(7) **Focal chord :** A chord of hyperbola passing through its focus is called a focal chord.

(8) **Parametric equations of the hyperbola :** Let $\frac{x^2}{a^2} - \frac{y^2}{b^2} = 1$ be the hyperbola with centre C and transverse axis $A'A$. Therefore, circle drawn with centre C and segment $A'A$ as a diameter is called auxiliary circle of the hyperbola.

$$\frac{x^2}{a^2} - \frac{y^2}{b^2} = 1$$

$\therefore$ Equation of the auxiliary circle is $x^2 + y^2 = a^2$

Let $P(x, y)$ be any point on the hyperbola $\frac{x^2}{a^2} - \frac{y^2}{b^2} = 1$. Draw PN perpendicular to X-axis.

Let NQ be a tangent to the auxiliary circle $x^2 + y^2 = a^2$. Join CQ

Let $\quad \angle QCN = \phi$

Here, P and Q are the **corresponding points** of the hyperbola and the auxiliary circle. ϕ is the eccentric angle of $P \cdot (0 \le \phi < 2\pi)$

Since, $\quad Q \equiv (a\cos\phi, a\sin\phi)$

Now, $\quad x = CN = \frac{CN}{CQ} \cdot CQ = \sec\phi \cdot a$

$\therefore \quad x = CN = a\sec\phi$

$\therefore \quad P(x, y) \equiv (a\sec\phi, y)$

$\because$ P lies on $\quad \frac{x^2}{a^2} - \frac{y^2}{b^2} = 1$

$\therefore \quad \frac{a^2\sec^2\phi}{a^2} - \frac{y^2}{b^2} = 1$

or $\quad \frac{y^2}{b^2} = \sec^2\phi - 1 = \tan^2\phi$

$\therefore \quad y = \pm b\tan\phi$

$\therefore \quad y = b\tan\phi \qquad$ (P lies in I quadrant)

The equations of $x = a\sec\phi$ and $y = b\tan\phi$ are known as the parametric equations of the hyperbola

$$\frac{x^2}{a^2} - \frac{y^2}{b^2} = 1$$

Position of points Q an auxiliary circle and the corresponding point P which describes the hyperbola and $0 \le \phi < 2\pi$.

ϕ varies from	$Q(a\cos\phi, a\sin\phi)$	$P(a\sec\phi, b\tan\phi)$
0 to $\frac{\pi}{2}$	I	I
$\frac{\pi}{2}$ to π	II	III
π to $\frac{3\pi}{2}$	III	II
$\frac{3\pi}{2}$ to 2π	IV	IV

Remark

Equation of the chord joining the points $P \equiv (a\sec\phi_1, b\tan\phi_1)$ and $Q \equiv (a\sec\phi_2, b\tan\phi_2)$ is

$$\frac{x}{a}\cos\left(\frac{\phi_1 - \phi_2}{2}\right) - \frac{y}{b}\sin\left(\frac{\phi_1 + \phi_2}{2}\right) = \cos\left(\frac{\phi_1 + \phi_2}{2}\right)$$

If it is focal chord, then pass through $(ae, 0)$ or $(-ae, 0)$. Suppose it pass through $(ae, 0)$, then

$$e\cos\left(\frac{\phi_1 - \phi_2}{2}\right) - 0 = \cos\left(\frac{\phi_1 + \phi_2}{2}\right)$$

$$\Rightarrow \quad \frac{\cos\left(\frac{\phi_1 - \phi_2}{2}\right)}{\cos\left(\frac{\phi_1 + \phi_2}{2}\right)} = \frac{1}{e}$$

$$\Rightarrow \quad \frac{\cos\left(\frac{\phi_1 - \phi_2}{2}\right) - \cos\left(\frac{\phi_1 + \phi_2}{2}\right)}{\cos\left(\frac{\phi_1 - \phi_2}{2}\right) + \cos\left(\frac{\phi_1 + \phi_2}{2}\right)} = \frac{1 - e}{1 + e}$$

or $$\tan\left(\frac{\phi_1}{2}\right)\tan\left(\frac{\phi_2}{2}\right) = \frac{1 - e}{1 + e}$$

Hence, if ϕ_1 and ϕ_2 are the eccentric angles of extremities of a focal chord of the hyperbola $\frac{x^2}{a^2} - \frac{y^2}{b^2} = 1$, then

$$\tan\left(\frac{\phi_1}{2}\right)\tan\left(\frac{\phi_2}{2}\right) = \frac{1 - e}{1 + e} \text{ or } \frac{1 + e}{1 - e}$$

according as focus $(ae, 0)$ or $(-ae, 0)$.

Focal Distances of a Point

The difference of the focal distances of any point on the hyperbola is constant and equal to length of the transverse axis of the hyperbola.

The hyperbola is $\quad \frac{x^2}{a^2} - \frac{y^2}{b^2} = 1 \qquad$ ...(i)

The foci S and S' are $(ae, 0)$ and $(-ae, 0)$.

The equation of its directrices MZ and $M'Z'$ are

$$x = \frac{a}{e} \text{ and } x = -\frac{a}{e}$$

respectively.

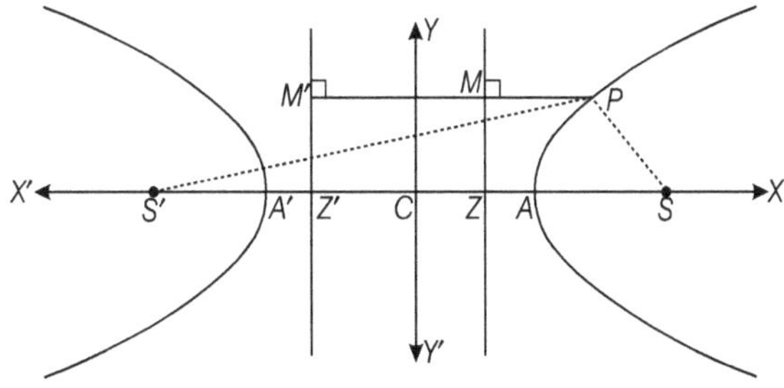

Let $P(x_1, y_1)$ be any point on Eq. (i).

Now $\quad SP = ePM = e\left(x_1 - \frac{a}{e}\right) = ex_1 - a$

and $\quad S'P' = ePM' = e\left(x_1 + \frac{a}{e}\right) = ex_1 + a$

$\therefore \quad S'P - SP = (ex_1 + a) - (ex_1 - a) = 2a = AA'$

$= \text{Transverse axis}$

A hyperbola is the locus of a point which moves in a plane such that the difference of its distances from two fixed point (foci) is always constant.

Example 1 To find the equation of the hyperbola from the definition that hyperbola is the locus of a point which moves such that the difference of its distances from two fixed points is constant with the fixed point as foci.

Sol. Let two fixed point be $S(ae, 0)$ and $S'(-ae, 0)$. Let $P(x, y)$ be a moving point such that

$$S'P - SP = \text{constant} = 2a \text{ (say)}$$

i.e. $\sqrt{(x+ae)^2+(y-0)^2} - \sqrt{(x-ae)^2+(y-0)^2} = 2a$

or $\sqrt{(x^2+y^2+2aex+a^2e^2)} - \sqrt{(x^2+y^2-2aex+a^2e^2)} = 2a$ ...(i)

Let $l = x^2+y^2+2aex+a^2e^2$ ...(ii)

and $m = x^2+y^2-2aex+a^2e^2$ ...(iii)

Eq. (i) can be re-written as

$\sqrt{l} - \sqrt{m} = 2a$ ...(iv)

From Eqs. (ii) and (iii),

$$l - m = 4aex$$

$\Rightarrow$ $(\sqrt{l}+\sqrt{m})(\sqrt{l}-\sqrt{m}) = 4aex$

$\Rightarrow$ $2a(\sqrt{l}+\sqrt{m}) = 4aex$ [from Eq. (iv)]

or $\sqrt{l}+\sqrt{m} = 2ex$ ...(v)

Adding Eqs. (iv) and (v), then

$$2\sqrt{l} = 2a + 2ex$$

$\Rightarrow$ $\sqrt{l} = a + ex \Rightarrow l = (a+ex)^2$

$$x^2+y^2+2aex+a^2e^2 = a^2+2aex+e^2x^2$$

or $x^2(e^2-1) - y^2 = a^2(e^2-1)$

or $\dfrac{x^2}{a^2} - \dfrac{y^2}{a^2(e^2-1)} = 1$

or $\dfrac{x^2}{a^2} - \dfrac{y^2}{b^2} = 1$, where $b^2 = a^2(e^2-1)$.

Conjugate Hyperbola

The hyperbola whose transverse and conjugate axes are respectively the conjugate and transverse axes of a given hyperbola is called the conjugate hyperbola of the given hyperbola.

The conjugate hyperbola of the hyperbola

$$\frac{x^2}{a^2} - \frac{y^2}{b^2} = 1 \text{ is } -\frac{x^2}{a^2} + \frac{y^2}{b^2} = 1$$

its shape is shown alongside.

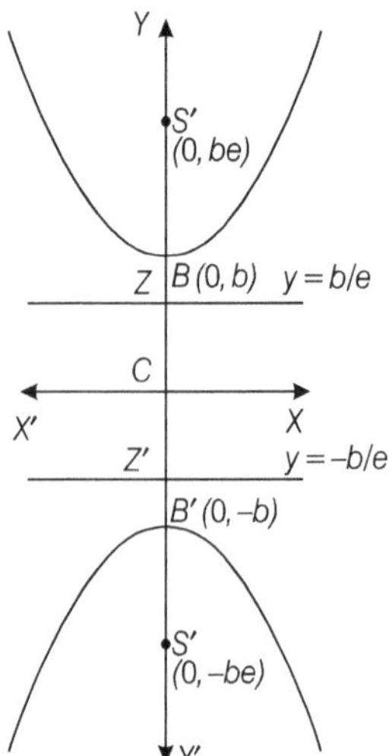

Various results related to hyperbola $\dfrac{x^2}{a^2} - \dfrac{y^2}{b^2} = 1$ and its conjugate

$$-\frac{x^2}{a^2} + \frac{y^2}{b^2} = 1 \quad \text{or} \quad \frac{x^2}{a^2} - \frac{y^2}{b^2} = -1$$

are given in the following table

Basic fundamentals \ Hyperbola	$\dfrac{x^2}{a^2} - \dfrac{y^2}{b^2} = 1$	$-\dfrac{x^2}{a^2} + \dfrac{y^2}{b^2} = 1$ or $\dfrac{x^2}{a^2} - \dfrac{y^2}{b^2} = -1$
Centre	$(0, 0)$	$(0, 0)$
Length of transverse axis	$2a$	$2b$
Length of conjugate axis	$2b$	$2a$
Foci	$(\pm ae, 0)$	$(0, \pm be)$
Equation of directrices	$x = \pm a/e$	$y = \pm b/e$
Eccentricity	$e = \sqrt{\left(\dfrac{a^2+b^2}{a^2}\right)}$	$e = \sqrt{\left(\dfrac{a^2+b^2}{b^2}\right)}$
Length of latusrectum	$\dfrac{2b^2}{a}$	$\dfrac{2a^2}{b}$
Parametric coordinates	$(a\sec\phi, b\tan\phi)$, $0 \le \phi < 2\pi$	$(a\tan\phi, b\sec\phi)$, $0 \le \phi < 2\pi$
Focal radii	$SP = ex_1 - a$ and $S'P = ex_1 + a$	$SP = ey_1 - b$ and $S'P = ey_1 + b$
Difference of focal radii ($S'P - SP$)	$2a$	$2b$
Tangents at the vertices	$x = -a, x = a$	$y = -b, y = b$
Equation of the transverse axis	$y = 0$	$x = 0$
Equation of the conjugate axis	$x = 0$	$y = 0$

Remarks

1. If the centre of hyperbola is (h,k) and axes are parallel to the coordinates axes, then its equation is
$$\frac{(x-h)^2}{a^2}-\frac{(y-k)^2}{b^2}=1.$$
By shifting the origin at (h, k) without rotating the coordinate axes, the above equation reduces to
$$\frac{X^2}{a^2}-\frac{Y^2}{b^2}=1$$
where, $\quad X = X + h, y = Y + k$
2. If e_1 and e_2 are the eccentricities of a hyperbola and its conjugate, respectively, then $e_1^2+e_2^2=1$.
Proof For hyperbola $b^2=a^2(e_1^2-1)$
or $$e_1^2=1+\frac{b^2}{a^2}=\frac{a^2+b^2}{a^2} \quad \dots \text{(i)}$$
and for conjugate hyperbola $a^2=b^2(e_2^2-1)$
or $$e_2^2=1+\frac{a^2}{b^2}=\frac{a^2+b^2}{b^2} \quad \dots \text{(ii)}$$
From Eqs. (i) and (ii), we get
$$\frac{1}{e_1^2}+\frac{1}{e_2^2}=1 \text{ or } e_1^{-2}+e_2^{-2}=1$$
3. The foci of a hyperbola and its conjugate are concyclic and form the vertices of a square.
4. A simple method to find the coordinates of the centre of the hyperbola expressed as a general equation of degree two should be remembered as :
Let $\phi(x, y)=0$ represents a hyperbola.
Find $\frac{\partial\phi}{\partial x}$ (differentiate w.r.t x keeping y as constant) and $\frac{\partial\phi}{\partial y}$ (differentiate w.r.t. y keeping x as constant).
Then the point of intersection of $\frac{\partial\phi}{\partial x}=0$ and $\frac{\partial\phi}{\partial y}=0$ gives the centre of the hyperbola.

Example 2 Find the equation of the hyperbola whose directrix is $2x + y = 1$, focus $(1, 2)$ and eccentricity $\sqrt{3}$.

Sol. Let $P(x, y)$ be any point on the hyperbola. Draw PM perpendicular from P on the directrix.

Then, by definition $\quad SP = e\, PM$

$$\Rightarrow \quad (SP)^2 = e^2 (PM)^2$$

$$\Rightarrow \quad (x-1)^2+(y-2)^2=3\left\{\frac{2x+y-1}{\sqrt{4+1}}\right\}^2$$

$$\Rightarrow \quad 5\{x^2+y^2-2x-4y+5\}$$
$$=3(4x^2+y^2+1+4xy-2y-4x)$$
$$\Rightarrow \quad 7x^2-2y^2+12xy-2x+14y-22=0$$

which is the required hyperbola.

Example 3 Find the lengths of transverse axis and conjugate axis, eccentricity, the coordinates of foci, vertices, lengths of the latusrectum and equations of the directrices of the following hyperbolas

(i) $9x^2-y^2=1$ $\quad$ (ii) $16x^2-9y^2=-144$

Sol. (i) The equation $9x^2-y^2=1$ can be written as
$$\frac{x^2}{(1/9)}-\frac{y^2}{1}=1.$$
This is of the form $\frac{x^2}{a^2}-\frac{y^2}{b^2}=1$
$$\therefore \quad a^2=\frac{1}{9}, b^2=1$$
$$\Rightarrow \quad a=\frac{1}{3}, b=1$$

Length of transverse axis : The length of transverse, axis $=2a=\frac{2}{3}$

Length of conjugate axis : The length of conjugate axis
$$=2b=2$$

Eccentricity : $e=\sqrt{\left(1+\frac{b^2}{a^2}\right)}=\sqrt{1+\frac{1}{(1/9)}}=\sqrt{10}$

Foci : The coordinates of the foci are $(\pm ae, 0)$ i.e. $\left(\pm\frac{\sqrt{10}}{3}, 0\right)$.

Vertices : The coordinates of the vertices are $(\pm a, 0)$ i.e. $\left(\pm\frac{1}{3}, 0\right)$.

Length of latusrectum : The length of latusrectum
$$=\frac{2b^2}{a}=\frac{2(1)^2}{1/3}=6$$

Equation of the directrices : The equations of the directrices are
$$x=\pm\frac{a}{e}$$
i.e. $$x=\pm\frac{1/3}{\sqrt{10}}$$
or $$x=\pm\frac{1}{3\sqrt{10}}$$

(ii) The equation $16x^2 - 9y^2 = -144$ can be written as

$$\frac{x^2}{9} - \frac{y^2}{16} = -1$$

This is of the form $\frac{x^2}{a^2} - \frac{y^2}{b^2} = -1$

$\therefore \quad a^2 = 9, b^2 = 16$

$\Rightarrow \quad a = 3, b = 4$

Length of transverse axis : The length of transverse axis $= 2b = 8$.

Length of conjugate axis : The length of conjugate axis $= 2a = 6$.

Eccentricity : $e = \sqrt{\left(1 + \frac{a^2}{b^2}\right)} = \sqrt{\left(1 + \frac{9}{16}\right)} = \frac{5}{4}$

Foci : The coordinates of the foci are $(0, \pm be)$ i.e. $(0, \pm 5)$

Vertices : The coordinates of the vertices are $(0, \pm b)$ i.e. $(0, \pm 4)$.

Length of latusrectum : The length of latusrectum $= \frac{2a^2}{b}$

$$= \frac{2(3)^2}{4} = \frac{9}{2}$$

Equation of directrices : The equation of directrices are

$$y = \pm \frac{b}{e}$$

$$y = \pm \frac{4}{(5/4)}$$

$$\Rightarrow \quad y = \pm \frac{16}{5}$$

Example 4 Find the eccentricity of the hyperbola whose latusrectum is half of its transverse axis.

Sol. Let the equation of hyperbola be

$$\frac{x^2}{a^2} - \frac{y^2}{b^2} = 1$$

Then, transverse axis $= 2a$ and latusrectum $= \frac{2b^2}{a}$

According to question $\frac{2b^2}{a} = \frac{1}{2}(2a)$

$$\Rightarrow \quad 2b^2 = a^2 \qquad (\because b^2 = a^2(e^2 - 1))$$

$$\Rightarrow \quad 2a^2(e^2 - 1) = a^2$$

$$\Rightarrow \quad 2e^2 - 2 = 1$$

$$\Rightarrow \quad e^2 = \frac{3}{2}$$

$$\therefore \quad e = \sqrt{\frac{3}{2}}$$

Hence, the required eccentricity is $\sqrt{\frac{3}{2}}$.

Example 5 Prove that the point $\left\{\frac{a}{2}\left(t + \frac{1}{t}\right), \frac{b}{2}\left(t - \frac{1}{t}\right)\right\}$ lies on the hyperbola for all values of t $(t \neq 0)$.

Sol. Let $x = \frac{a}{2}\left(t + \frac{1}{t}\right)$

or $\quad \frac{2x}{a} = t + \frac{1}{t}$

or $\quad \left(\frac{2x}{a}\right)^2 = t^2 + \frac{1}{t^2} + 2 \quad$ ...(i)

and let $\quad y = \frac{b}{2}\left(t - \frac{1}{t}\right)$

or $\quad \frac{2y}{b} = t - \frac{1}{t}$

or $\quad \left(\frac{2y}{b}\right)^2 = t^2 + \frac{1}{t^2} - 2 \quad$ ...(ii)

Subtracting Eqs. (ii) from (i),

$$\frac{4x^2}{a^2} - \frac{4y^2}{b^2} = 4$$

or $\quad \frac{x^2}{a^2} - \frac{y^2}{b^2} = 1$

which is hyperbola.

Example 6 Show that the equation $7y^2 - 9x^2 + 54x - 28y - 116 = 0$ represent a hyperbola. Find the coordinates of the centre, lengths of transverse and conjugate axes, eccentricity, latusrectum, coordinate of foci, vertices and equations of the directrices of the hyperbola.

Sol. We have, $7y^2 - 9x^2 + 54x - 28y - 116 = 0$

or $\quad 7(y^2 - 4y) - 9(x^2 - 6x) - 116 = 0$

or $\quad 7(y^2 - 4y + 4) - 9(x^2 - 6x + 9) = 116 + 28 - 81$

or $\quad 7(y - 2)^2 - 9(x - 3)^2 = 63$

or $\quad \frac{(y-2)^2}{9} - \frac{(x-3)^2}{7} = 1$

or $\quad \frac{Y^2}{9} - \frac{X^2}{7} = 1$

where $X = x - 3$ and $Y = y - 2$

This equation represents conjugate hyperbola. Comparing it with

$$\frac{Y^2}{b^2} - \frac{X^2}{a^2} = 1$$

we get, $\quad b^2 = 9$ and $a^2 = 7$

$\therefore \quad b = 3$ and $a = \sqrt{7}$

Centre : $\quad X = 0, Y = 0$

i.e. $\quad x - 3 = 0, y - 2 = 0$

$\therefore$ Centre is $(3, 2)$.

Length of transverse axis : Length of transverse axis

$$= 2b = 6.$$

Length of conjugate axis : Length of conjugate axis

$$= 2a = 2\sqrt{7}.$$

Eccentricity : The eccentricity e is given by

$$e = \sqrt{1 + \frac{a^2}{b^2}} = \sqrt{1 + \frac{7}{9}} = \frac{4}{3}$$

Length of latusrectum : The length of latusrectum

$$= \frac{2a^2}{b} = \frac{2(7)}{3} = \frac{14}{3}$$

Foci : The coordinates of foci are $(0, \pm be)$

$\therefore \quad X = 0, Y = \pm be$

$\Rightarrow \quad x - 3 = 0, y - 2 = \pm 3 \times \frac{4}{3}$

or $\quad (3, 2 \pm 4)$

i.e. $\quad (3, -2)$ and $(3, 6)$

Vertices : The coordinates of vertices are $(0, \pm b)$

or $\quad X = 0, Y = \pm b$

or $\quad x - 3 = 0, y - 2 = \pm 3$ or $(3, 2 \pm 3)$

or $\quad$ vertices are $(3, -1)$ and $(3, 5)$

Equation of directrices : The equation of directrices are

$$Y = \pm \frac{b}{e}$$

$\Rightarrow \quad y - 2 = \pm \frac{3}{4/3}$

$\Rightarrow \quad y = \left(2 \pm \frac{9}{4}\right)$

i.e. $\quad y = \frac{17}{4}$ and $y = -\frac{1}{4}$

Example 7 Find the equation of the hyperbola whose foci are (6, 4) and (–4, 4) and eccentricity is 2.

Sol. The centre of the hyperbola is the mid-point of the line joining the two foci. So, the coordinates of the centre are

$$\left(\frac{6-4}{2}, \frac{4+4}{2}\right) \text{ i.e. } (1, 4)$$

Let $2a$ and $2b$ be the lengths of transverse and conjugate axes and let e be the eccentricity. Then, equation of hyperbola is

$$\frac{(x-1)^2}{a^2} - \frac{(y-4)^2}{b^2} = 1$$

$\because \quad$ Distance between the foci $= 2ae$

$$\sqrt{(6+4)^2 + (4-4)^2} = 2a \times 2$$

$\Rightarrow \quad 10 = 4a$

$\therefore \quad a = 5/2$

$\therefore \quad b^2 = a^2(e^2 - 1) = \frac{25}{4}(4 - 1) = \frac{75}{4}$

Thus, the equation of the hyperbola is

$$\frac{(x-1)^2}{\left(\frac{25}{4}\right)} - \frac{(y-4)^2}{\left(\frac{75}{4}\right)} = 1$$

or $\quad 12(x-1)^2 - 4(y-4)^2 = 75$

or $\quad 12(x^2 - 2x + 1) - 4(y^2 - 8y + 16) = 75$

or $\quad 12x^2 - 4y^2 - 24x + 32y - 127 = 0$

Example 8 Obtain the equation of a hyperbola with coordinate axes as principal axes given that the distances of one of its vertices from the foci are 9 and 1 units.

Sol. Let equation of hyperbola is

$$\frac{x^2}{a^2} - \frac{y^2}{b^2} = 1 \quad \text{...(i)}$$

If vertices are $A(a, 0)$ and $A'(-a, 0)$ and foci are $S(ae, 0)$ and $S'(-ae, 0)$.

Given $\quad l(S'A) = 9$ and $l(SA) = 1$

$\Rightarrow \quad a + ae = 9$ and $ae - a = 1$

or $\quad a(1+e) = 9$ and $a(e-1) = 1$

$\therefore \quad \frac{a(1+e)}{a(e-1)} = \frac{9}{1}$

$\Rightarrow \quad 1 + e = 9e - 9 \Rightarrow e = \frac{5}{4}$

$\because \quad a(1+e) = 9$

$\therefore \quad a\left(1 + \frac{5}{4}\right) = 9 \Rightarrow a = 4$

$$b^2 = a^2(e^2 - 1) = 16\left(\frac{25}{16} - 1\right)$$

$\therefore \quad b^2 = 9$

From Eq. (i) equation of hyperbola is

$$\frac{x^2}{16} - \frac{y^2}{9} = 1$$

Example 9 The foci of a hyperbola coincide with the foci of the ellipse $\frac{x^2}{25} + \frac{y^2}{9} = 1$. Find the equation of the hyperbola if its eccentricity is 2.

Sol. The given ellipse is $\frac{x^2}{25} + \frac{y^2}{9} = 1$

Comparing with $\frac{x^2}{a^2} + \frac{y^2}{b^2} = 1$

$\therefore \quad a^2 = 25$ and $b^2 = 9$

then eccentricity $e = \sqrt{1 - \frac{b^2}{a^2}} = \sqrt{1 - \frac{9}{25}} = \frac{4}{5}$

$\therefore$ Foci of ellipse are $(\pm ae, 0)$ i.c. $(\pm 4, 0)$

So, the coordinates of foci of the hyperbola are $(\pm 4, 0)$.

Let e' be the eccentricity of the required hyperbola and its equation be

$$\frac{x^2}{A^2}-\frac{y^2}{B^2}=1 \quad \text{...(i)}$$

the coordinates of foci are $(\pm Ae', 0)$

$\therefore \quad Ae' = 4 \Rightarrow A \times 2 = 4 \Rightarrow A = 2$

Also $\quad B^2 = A^2(e'^2 - 1) \quad (\because \text{given } e' = 2)$

$= 4(4-1) = 12$

Substituting the values of A and B in Eq. (i), we get

$$\frac{x^2}{4}-\frac{y^2}{12}=1 \text{ or } 3x^2 - y^2 - 12 = 0$$

which is required hyperbola.

Example 10 If two points P and Q on the hyperbola $\frac{x^2}{a^2}-\frac{y^2}{b^2}=1$ whose centre is C, are such that CP is perpendicular to $CQ, a<b$, then prove that

$$\frac{1}{(CP)^2}+\frac{1}{(CQ)^2}=\frac{1}{a^2}-\frac{1}{b^2}.$$

Sol. Let $P(x, y)$ be any point on the given hyperbola. Let slope of CP is m, then equation of CP is $y = mx$.

Solving, $y = mx$ and $\frac{x^2}{a^2}-\frac{y^2}{b^2}=1$

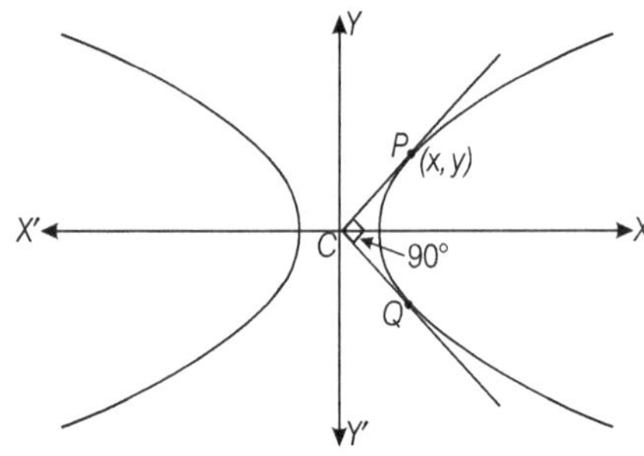

$$\frac{x^2}{a^2}-\frac{m^2x^2}{b^2}=1$$

$$\therefore \quad x^2 = \frac{a^2b^2}{(b^2-a^2m^2)}$$

and $$y^2 = m^2x^2 = \frac{a^2m^2b^2}{b^2-a^2m^2}$$

$$\therefore \quad x^2+y^2 = \frac{a^2b^2}{(b^2-a^2m^2)}(1+m^2)$$

$$\therefore \quad (CP)^2 = x^2+y^2 = \frac{a^2b^2(1+m^2)}{(b^2-a^2m^2)}$$

$$\Rightarrow \quad \frac{1}{(CP)^2} = \frac{b^2-a^2m^2}{a^2b^2(1+m^2)} \quad \text{...(i)}$$

and equation of CQ is $\quad y = -\frac{1}{m}x$

replacing m by $-\frac{1}{m}$ in Eq. (i)

then $$\frac{1}{(CQ)^2} = \frac{b^2 - a^2\left(-\frac{1}{m}\right)^2}{a^2b^2\left(1+\left(-\frac{1}{m}\right)^2\right)} = \frac{b^2m^2-a^2}{a^2b^2(1+m^2)} \quad \text{...(ii)}$$

Adding Eqs. (i) and (ii), then

$$\frac{1}{(CP)^2}+\frac{1}{(CQ)^2} = \frac{b^2(1+m^2)-a^2(1+m^2)}{a^2b^2(1+m^2)}$$

$$= \frac{b^2-a^2}{a^2b^2} = \frac{1}{a^2}-\frac{1}{b^2}$$

Position of a Point with Respect to a Hyperbola

Theorem : The point (x_1, y_1) lies outside, on or inside the hyperbola

$$\frac{x^2}{a^2}-\frac{y^2}{b^2}=1$$

according as $$\frac{x_1^2}{a^2}-\frac{y_1^2}{b^2}-1 <, = \text{ or } > 0$$

Proof : Let $P \equiv (x_1, y_1)$ then $Q \equiv (x_1, y_2)$

Draw PL perpendicular to X-axis

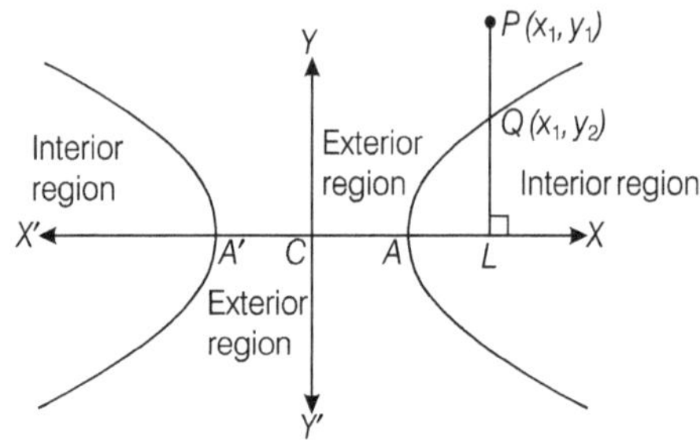

Clearly, $PL > QL$

$\Rightarrow \quad y_1 > y_2$

$\Rightarrow \quad \frac{y_1^2}{b^2} > \frac{y_2^2}{b^2}$

$\Rightarrow \quad -\frac{y_1^2}{b^2} < -\frac{y_2^2}{b^2}$

$\Rightarrow \quad \frac{x_1^2}{a^2}-\frac{y_1^2}{b^2} < \frac{x_1^2}{a^2}-\frac{y_2^2}{b^2}$

$\Rightarrow \quad \frac{x_1^2}{a^2}-\frac{y_1^2}{b^2} < 1 \quad \left(\because Q(x_1, y_2) \text{ lies on } \frac{x^2}{a^2}-\frac{y^2}{b^2}=1\right)$

$\Rightarrow \quad \frac{x_1^2}{a^2}-\frac{y_1^2}{b^2}-1 < 0$

Thus, the point $P(x_1, y_1)$ lies outside the hyperbola. Hence the point (x_1, y_1) lies outside, on or inside the hyperbola

$$\frac{x^2}{a^2} - \frac{y^2}{b^2} = 1$$

according as $\frac{x_1^2}{a^2} - \frac{y_1^2}{b^2} - 1 <, = \text{or} > 0.$

Example 11 Find the position of the point $(5, -4)$ relative to the hyperbola $9x^2 - y^2 = 1$.

Sol. Since, $9(5)^2 - (-4)^2 - 1 = 225 - 16 - 1 = 208 > 0,$

So, the point $(5, -4)$ inside the hyperbola $9x^2 - y^2 = 1$.

Intersection of a Line and a Hyperbola

Let the hyperbola be $\frac{x^2}{a^2} - \frac{y^2}{b^2} = 1$ ...(i)

and the given line be $y = mx + c$ ...(ii)

Eliminating y from Eqs. (i) and (ii),

$$\frac{x^2}{a^2} - \frac{(mx+c)^2}{b^2} = 1 \Rightarrow b^2x^2 - a^2(mx+c)^2 = a^2b^2$$

$$\Rightarrow \quad (a^2m^2 - b^2)x^2 + 2mca^2x + a^2(b^2 + c^2) = 0 \quad \text{...(iii)}$$

Above equation being a quadratic in x gives two values of x. It shows that every straight line will cut the hyperbola in two points, may be real, coincident or imaginary, according as discriminant of Eq. (iii) $>, =, < 0$

i.e. $4m^2c^2a^4 - 4(a^2m^2 - b^2)a^2(b^2 + c^2) >, =, < 0$

or $-a^2m^2 + b^2 + c^2 >, =, < 0$

or $c^2 >, =, < a^2m^2 - b^2$ ...(iv)

Condition of Tangency : If the line (ii) touches the hyperbola (i), then Eq. (iii) has equal roots.

$\therefore$ Discriminant of Eq. (iii) $= 0$

$$\Rightarrow \quad c^2 = a^2m^2 - b^2$$

$$\text{or} \quad c = \pm\sqrt{(a^2m^2 - b^2)} \quad \text{...(v)}$$

So, the line $y = mx + c$ touches the hyperbola

$$\frac{x^2}{a^2} - \frac{y^2}{b^2} = 1 \text{ if } c^2 = a^2m^2 - b^2$$

(which is condition of tangency)

Substituting the value of c from Eq. (v) in Eq. (ii)

$$\boldsymbol{y = mx \pm \sqrt{(a^2m^2 - b^2)}}$$

Hence, the line $y = mx \pm \sqrt{(a^2m^2 - b^2)}$ will always be tangent to the hyperbola.

Point of contact : Substituting $c = \pm\sqrt{(a^2m^2 - b^2)}$ in Eq. (iii)

$$(a^2m^2 - b^2)x^2 \pm 2ma^2\sqrt{(a^2m^2 - b^2)}\,x + a^4m^2 = 0$$

$$\text{or} \quad (x\sqrt{(a^2m^2 - b^2)} \pm a^2m)^2 = 0$$

$$\therefore \quad x = \pm\frac{a^2m}{\sqrt{(a^2m^2 - b^2)}} = \pm\frac{a^2m}{c}$$

From Eq. (i), $\frac{a^4m^2}{c^2} \cdot \frac{1}{a^2} - \frac{y^2}{b^2} = 1$

$$\Rightarrow \quad \frac{y^2}{b^2} = \frac{a^2m^2}{c^2} - 1 = -\frac{(c^2 - a^2m^2)}{c^2} = \frac{b^2}{c^2}$$

$$\therefore \quad y = \pm\frac{b^2}{c}$$

Hence, the point of contact is $\left(\pm\frac{a^2m}{c}, \pm\frac{b^2}{c}\right)$.

This is known as ***m*-point** on the hyperbola.

Remark

If $m = 0$, then Eq. (iii) gives $-b^2x^2 + a^2(b^2 + c^2) = 0$

$$x^2 = \frac{a^2(b^2 + c^2)}{b^2}$$

$$\therefore \quad x = \pm\frac{a}{b}\sqrt{(b^2 + c^2)}$$

which gives two values of x.

Example 12 Prove that the straight line $lx + my + n = 0$ touches the hyperbola $\frac{x^2}{a^2} - \frac{y^2}{b^2} = 1$ if $a^2l^2 - b^2m^2 = n^2$.

Sol. The given line is $lx + my + n = 0$ or $y = -\frac{l}{m}x - \frac{n}{m}$

Comparing this line with

$$y = Mx + c \quad \text{...(i)}$$

$$\therefore \quad M = -\frac{l}{m} \text{ and } c = -\frac{n}{m}$$

This line (i) will touch the hyperbola

$$\frac{x^2}{a^2} - \frac{y^2}{b^2} = 1 \text{ if } c^2 = a^2M^2 - b^2$$

$$\Rightarrow \quad \frac{n^2}{m^2} = \frac{a^2l^2}{m^2} - b^2 \text{ or } a^2l^2 - b^2m^2 = n^2$$

Example 13 Show that the line $x\cos\alpha + y\sin\alpha = p$ touches the hyperbola

$$\frac{x^2}{a^2}-\frac{y^2}{b^2}=1 \quad \text{if} \quad a^2\cos^2\alpha - b^2\sin^2\alpha = p^2.$$

Sol. The given line is

$$x\cos\alpha + y\sin\alpha = p$$

$\Rightarrow$ $y\sin\alpha = -x\cos\alpha + p$

$\Rightarrow$ $y = -x\cot x + p\operatorname{cosec}\alpha$

Comparing this line with $y = mx + c$

$\Rightarrow$ $m = -\cot\alpha, c = p\operatorname{cosec}\alpha$

Since, the given line touches the hyperbola

$$\frac{x^2}{a^2}-\frac{y^2}{b^2}=1, \text{ then } c^2 = a^2m^2 - b^2$$

$\Rightarrow$ $p^2\operatorname{cosec}^2\alpha = a^2\cot^2\alpha - b^2$

or $p^2 = a^2\cos^2\alpha - b^2\sin^2\alpha$

Example 14 For what value of λ does the line $y = 2x + \lambda$ touches the hyperbola $16x^2 - 9y^2 = 144$?

Sol. Equation of hyperbola is

$$16x^2 - 9y^2 = 144$$

or $$\frac{x^2}{9}-\frac{y^2}{16}=1$$

Comparing this with $\frac{x^2}{a^2}-\frac{y^2}{b^2}=1$, we get $a^2 = 9, b^2 = 16$

and comparing this line $y = 2x + \lambda$ with $y = mx + c$

$\therefore$ $m = 2$ and $c = \lambda$

If the line $y = 2x + \lambda$ touches the hyperbola

$$16x^2 - 9y^2 = 144$$

then $c^2 = a^2m^2 - b^2$

$\Rightarrow$ $\lambda^2 = 9(2)^2 - 16 = 36 - 16 = 20$

$\therefore$ $\lambda = \pm 2\sqrt{5}$

Example 15 If it possible to draw the tangent to the hyperbola $\frac{x^2}{a^2}-\frac{y^2}{b^2}=1$ having slope 2, then find its range of eccentricity.

Sol. Tangent having slope m is $y = mx \pm \sqrt{(a^2m^2 - b^2)}$

The tangent having slope 2 is $y = 2x \pm \sqrt{(4a^2 - b^2)}$, which is real if

$$4a^2 - b^2 \geq 0$$

or $\frac{b^2}{a^2} \leq 4$ or $e^2 - 1 \leq 4$ or $e^2 \leq 5$

or $1 < e \leq \sqrt{5}$ (for hyperbola $e > 1$)

Exercise for Session 1

1. The eccentricity of the conic represented by $x^2 - y^2 - 4x + 4y + 16 = 0$ is
   (a) 1 (b) $\frac{1}{2}$ (c) -1 (d) $\sqrt{2}$

2. If e_1 and e_2 are the eccentricities of the conic sections $16x^2 + 9y^2 = 144$ and $9x^2 - 16y^2 = 144$, then
   (a) $e_1^2 - e_2^2 = 1$ (b) $e_1^2 + e_2^2 < 3$ (c) $e_1^2 + e_2^2 = 3$ (d) $e_1^2 + e_2^2 > 3$

3. The transverse axis of a hyperbola is of length $2a$ and a vertex divides the segment of the axis between the centre and the corresponding focus in the ratio 2 : 1, then the equation of the hyperbola is
   (a) $4x^2 - 5y^2 = 4a^2$ (b) $4x^2 - 5y^2 = 5a^2$ (c) $5x^2 - 4y^2 = 4a^2$ (d) $5x^2 - 4y^2 = 5a^2$

4. The eccentricity of the hyperbola whose latusrectum is 8 and conjugate axis is equal to half of the distance between the foci, is
   (a) $\frac{2}{\sqrt{3}}$ (b) $\frac{3}{\sqrt{3}}$ (c) $\frac{4}{\sqrt{3}}$ (d) $\frac{5}{\sqrt{3}}$

5. The straight line $x + y = \sqrt{2}p$ will touch the hyperbola $4x^2 - 9y^2 = 36$, if
   (a) $p^2 = 2$ (b) $p^2 = 5$ (c) $5p^2 = 2$ (d) $2p^2 = 5$

6. The equation of the tangent, parallel to $y - x + 5 = 0$ drawn to $\frac{x^2}{3}-\frac{y^2}{2}=1$ is
   (a) $x - y - 1 = 0$ (b) $x - y + 2 = 0$ (c) $x + y - 1 = 0$ (d) $x + y + 2 = 0$

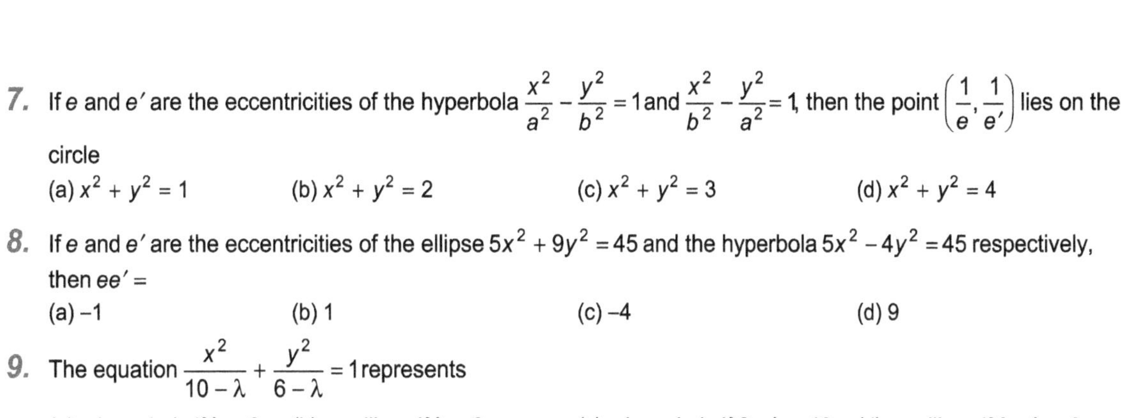

7. If e and e' are the eccentricities of the hyperbola $\frac{x^2}{a^2}-\frac{y^2}{b^2}=1$ and $\frac{x^2}{b^2}-\frac{y^2}{a^2}=1$, then the point $\left(\frac{1}{e},\frac{1}{e'}\right)$ lies on the circle

(a) $x^2+y^2=1$ (b) $x^2+y^2=2$ (c) $x^2+y^2=3$ (d) $x^2+y^2=4$

8. If e and e' are the eccentricities of the ellipse $5x^2+9y^2=45$ and the hyperbola $5x^2-4y^2=45$ respectively, then $ee'=$

(a) -1 (b) 1 (c) -4 (d) 9

9. The equation $\frac{x^2}{10-\lambda}+\frac{y^2}{6-\lambda}=1$ represents

(a) a hyperbola if $\lambda<6$ (b) an ellipse if $\lambda>6$ (c) a hyperbola if $6<\lambda<10$ (d) an ellipse if $0<\lambda<6$

10. The eccentricity of the hyperbola conjugate to $x^2-3y^2=2x+8$ is

(a) $\frac{2}{\sqrt{3}}$ (b) $\sqrt{3}$ (c) 2 (d) $\sqrt{2}$

11. For hyperbola $\frac{x^2}{\cos^2\alpha}-\frac{y^2}{\sin^2\alpha}=1$ which of the following remains constant with change in 'α'

(a) Abscissae of vertices (b) Abscissae of foci (c) Eccentricity (d) Directrix

12. If the foci of the ellipse $\frac{x^2}{16}+\frac{y^2}{b^2}=1$ and the hyperbola $\frac{x^2}{144}-\frac{y^2}{81}=\frac{1}{25}$ coincide, then the value of b^2 is

(a) 1 (b) 5 (c) 7 (d) 9

13. Find the equation of the hyperbola whose foci are $(0,\pm\sqrt{10})$ and which passes through the point $(2,3)$.

14. Find the equation of the hyperbola whose foci are $(10,5)$ and $(-2,5)$ and eccentricity 3.

15. Prove that the straight lines $\frac{x}{a}-\frac{y}{b}=m$ and $\frac{x}{a}+\frac{y}{b}=\frac{1}{m}$ always meet on a hyperbola.

16. Find the centre, eccentricity and length of axes of the hyperbola $3x^2-5y^2-6x+20y-32=0$.

17. Find the eccentricity of the hyperbola conjugate to the hyperbola $x^2-3y^2=1$.

18. For what value of λ, does the line $y=3x+\lambda$ touch the hyperbola $9x^2-5y^2=45$?

19. Find the equation of the tangent to the hyperbola $4x^2-9y^2=1$ which is parallel to the line $4y=5x+7$. Also find the point of contact.

Session 2

Equations of Tangents in Different Forms, Equations of Normals in Different Forms, Pair of Tangents, Chord of Contact, Equation of the Chord Bisected at a Given Point

Equations of Tangents in Different Forms

1. Point form (first principal method) :

Theorem : The equation of the tangent to the hyperbola

$$\frac{x^2}{a^2} - \frac{y^2}{b^2} = 1 \text{ at } (x_1, y_1) \text{ is}$$

$$\frac{xx_1}{a^2} - \frac{yy_1}{b^2} = 1.$$

Proof : Equation of hyperbola is

$$\frac{x^2}{a^2} - \frac{y^2}{b^2} = 1 \quad \text{...(i)}$$

Let $P \equiv (x_1, y_1)$ and $Q \equiv (x_2, y_2)$ be any two points in Eq. (i), then

$$\frac{x_1^2}{a^2} - \frac{y_1^2}{b^2} = 1 \quad \text{...(ii)}$$

and

$$\frac{x_2^2}{a^2} - \frac{y_2^2}{b^2} = 1 \quad \text{...(iii)}$$

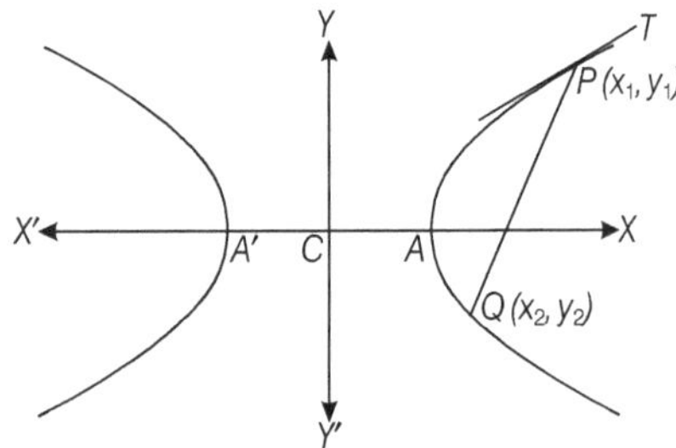

Subtracting Eq. (ii) from Eq. (iii), then

$$\frac{1}{a^2}(x_2^2 - x_1^2) - \frac{1}{b^2}(y_2^2 - y_1^2) = 0$$

$$\Rightarrow \quad \frac{(x_2 - x_1)(x_2 + x_1)}{a^2} - \frac{(y_2 - y_1)(y_2 + y_1)}{b^2} = 0$$

$$\Rightarrow \quad \frac{y_2 - y_1}{x_2 - x_1} = \frac{b^2}{a^2} \frac{(x_1 + x_2)}{(y_1 + y_2)} \quad \text{...(iv)}$$

Equation of PQ is

$$y - y_1 = \frac{y_2 - y_1}{x_2 - x_1}(x - x_1) \quad \text{...(v)}$$

From Eqs. (iv) and (v),

$$y - y_1 = \frac{b^2}{a^2} \cdot \frac{(x_1 + x_2)}{(y_1 + y_2)}(x - x_1) \quad \text{...(vi)}$$

Now, tangent at $P, Q \to P$

i.e. $x_2 \to x_1$ and $y_2 \to y_1$, then Eq. (vi) becomes

$$y - y_1 = \frac{b^2}{a^2} \cdot \frac{(2x_1)}{(2y_1)}(x - x_1)$$

or $\quad \dfrac{yy_1 - y_1^2}{b^2} = \dfrac{xx_1 - x_1^2}{a^2}$ or $\dfrac{xx_1}{a^2} - \dfrac{yy_1}{b^2} = \dfrac{x_1^2}{a^2} - \dfrac{y_1^2}{b^2}$

or $\quad \dfrac{xx_1}{a^2} - \dfrac{yy_1}{b^2} = 1 \quad$ [from Eq. (ii)]

which is the required equation of tangent at (x_1, y_1).

> ***Remark***
>
> The equation of tangent at (x_1, y_1) can be obtained by replacing x^2 by xx_1, y^2 by yy_1, x by $\frac{x + x_1}{2}$, y by $\frac{y + y_1}{2}$ and xy by $\frac{xy_1 + x_1y}{2}$. This method is applied only when the equation of conic is a polynomial of second degree in x and y.

2. Parametric form :

Theorem : The equation of tangent to the hyperbola

$$\frac{x^2}{a^2} - \frac{y^2}{b^2} = 1 \text{ at } (a \sec \phi, b \tan \phi) \text{ is}$$

$$\frac{x}{a} \sec \phi - \frac{y}{b} \tan \phi = 1$$

Proof : Since, equation of tangent at (x_1, y_1) is

$$\frac{xx_1}{a^2} - \frac{yy_1}{b^2} = 1$$

Now, replacing x_1 by $a \sec \phi$ and y_1 by $b \tan\phi$, we get

$$\frac{x}{a} \sec \phi - \frac{y}{b} \tan\phi = 1$$

Remark

The point of intersection of tangents at 'θ' and 'ϕ' on the hyperbola $\frac{x^2}{a^2} - \frac{y^2}{b^2} = 1$ is

$$\left(\frac{a\cos\left(\frac{\theta - \phi}{2}\right)}{\cos\left(\frac{\theta + \phi}{2}\right)}, \frac{b\sin\left(\frac{\theta + \phi}{2}\right)}{\cos\left(\frac{\theta + \phi}{2}\right)} \right)$$

Remembering method :

$\because$ Equations of chord joining 'θ' and 'ϕ' is

$$\frac{x}{a} \cos\left(\frac{\theta - \phi}{2}\right) - \frac{y}{b} \sin\left(\frac{\theta + \phi}{2}\right) = \cos\left(\frac{\theta + \phi}{2}\right)$$

or $$\frac{x}{a} \left\{ \frac{\cos\left(\frac{\theta - \phi}{2}\right)}{\cos\left(\frac{\theta + \phi}{2}\right)} \right\} - \frac{y}{b} \left\{ \frac{\sin\left(\frac{\theta + \phi}{2}\right)}{\cos\left(\frac{\theta + \phi}{2}\right)} \right\} = 1$$

or $$\frac{x}{a^2} \left\{ \frac{a\cos\left(\frac{\theta - \phi}{2}\right)}{\cos\left(\frac{\theta + \phi}{2}\right)} \right\} - \frac{y}{b^2} \left\{ \frac{b\sin\left(\frac{\theta + \phi}{2}\right)}{\cos\left(\frac{\theta + \phi}{2}\right)} \right\} = 1$$

i.e. $$\left\{ \frac{a\cos\left(\frac{\theta - \phi}{2}\right)}{\cos\left(\frac{\theta + \phi}{2}\right)}, \frac{b\sin\left(\frac{\theta + \phi}{2}\right)}{\cos\left(\frac{\theta + \phi}{2}\right)} \right\}$$

3. Slope form :

Theorem : The equations of tangents of slope m to the hyperbola $\frac{x^2}{a^2} - \frac{y^2}{b^2} = 1$ is given by

$$y = mx \pm \sqrt{(a^2m^2 - b^2)}$$

The coordinates of the points of contact are

$$\left(\pm \frac{a^2m}{\sqrt{(a^2m^2 - b^2}}, \pm \frac{b^2}{\sqrt{(a^2m^2 - b^2)}} \right)$$

Proof : Let $y = mx + c$ be a tangent to the hyperbola

$$\frac{x^2}{a^2} - \frac{y^2}{b^2} = 1 \quad \text{...(i)}$$

Substituting the value of $y = mx + c$ in Eq. (i), then

$$\frac{x^2}{a^2} - \frac{(mx + c)^2}{b^2} = 1$$

or $(a^2m^2 - b^2) x^2 + 2mca^2 x + a^2 (c^2 + b^2) = 0$

must have equal roots

$$\therefore \quad 4a^4m^2c^2 - 4(a^2m^2 - b^2) a^2 (c^2 + b^2) = 0$$

$$[\because B^2 - 4AC = 0]$$

$$\Rightarrow \quad a^2m^2c^2 - (a^2m^2 - b^2)(b^2 + c^2) = 0$$

$$\Rightarrow \quad a^2m^2c^2 - a^2b^2m^2 - a^2m^2c^2 + b^4 + b^2c^2 = 0$$

$$\Rightarrow \quad -a^2b^2m^2 + b^4 + b^2c^2 = 0 \Rightarrow c^2 = a^2m^2 - b^2$$

$$\therefore \quad c = \pm\sqrt{(a^2m^2 - b^2)}$$

Substituting this value of c in $y = mx + c$, we get

$$\boldsymbol{y = mx \pm \sqrt{(a^2m^2 - b^2)}} \quad \text{...(ii)}$$

as the required equation of tangents of hyperbola in terms of slope.

$\because$ Tangent at (x_1, y_1) to the hyperbola $\frac{x^2}{a^2} - \frac{y^2}{b^2} = 1$ is

$$\frac{xx_1}{a^2} - \frac{yy_1}{b^2} = 1 \quad \text{...(iii)}$$

On comparing Eqs. (ii) and (iii) we get

$$\frac{x_1/a^2}{m} = \frac{y_1/b^2}{1} = \pm \frac{1}{\sqrt{a^2m^2 - b^2}}$$

Thus, the coordinates of the points of contact are

$$\left(\frac{\pm a^2m}{\sqrt{(a^2m - b^2)}}, \pm \frac{b^2}{\sqrt{(a^2m - b^2)}} \right)$$

Remark

The equations of tangents of slope m to the hyperbola $-\frac{x^2}{a^2} + \frac{y^2}{b^2} = 1$ are given by $y = mx \pm \sqrt{(b^2 - a^2m^2)}$ and the coordinates of the points of contact are

$$\left(\mp \frac{a^2m}{\sqrt{(b^2 - a^2m^2)}}, \mp \frac{b^2}{\sqrt{(b^2 - a^2m^2)}} \right)$$

Example 16 Find the equation of the tangent to the hyperbola $x^2 - 4y^2 = 36$ which is perpendicular to the line $x - y + 4 = 0$.

Sol. Let m be the slope of the tangent. Since, the tangent is perpendicular to the line $x - y + 4 = 0$

$$\therefore \quad m \times 1 = -1$$

$$\Rightarrow \quad m = -1$$

Since $x^2 - 4y^2 = 36$ or $\frac{x^2}{36} - \frac{y^2}{9} = 1$

Comparing this with $\frac{x^2}{a^2} - \frac{y^2}{b^2} = 1$

$\therefore \quad a^2 = 36$ and $b^2 = 9$

So the equation of tangents are

$$y = (-1)\,x \pm \sqrt{36 \times (-1)^2 - 9}$$

$$\Rightarrow \quad y = -x \pm \sqrt{27}$$

$$\text{or} \quad x + y \pm 3\sqrt{3} = 0$$

Example 17 Find the equation and the length of the common tangents to hyperbola

$$\frac{x^2}{a^2} - \frac{y^2}{b^2} = 1 \text{ and } \frac{y^2}{a^2} - \frac{x^2}{b^2} = 1.$$

Sol. Tangent at $(a \sec\phi, b\tan\phi)$ on the 1st hyperbola is

$$\frac{x}{a}\sec\phi - \frac{y}{b}\tan\phi = 1 \quad \text{...(i)}$$

Similarly tangent at any point $(b\tan\theta, a\sec\theta)$ on 2nd hyperbola is

$$\frac{y}{a}\sec\theta - \frac{x}{b}\tan\theta = 1 \quad \text{...(ii)}$$

If Eqs. (i) and (ii) are common tangents then they should be identical. Comparing the coefficients of x and y

$$\Rightarrow \quad \frac{\sec\theta}{a} = -\frac{\tan\phi}{b}$$

$$\text{or} \quad \sec\theta = -\frac{a}{b}\tan\phi \quad \text{...(iii)}$$

$$\text{and} \quad -\frac{\tan\theta}{b} = \frac{\sec\phi}{a}$$

$$\text{or} \quad \tan\theta = -\frac{b}{a}\sec\phi \quad \text{...(iv)}$$

$$\because \quad \sec^2\theta - \tan^2\theta = 1$$

$$\Rightarrow \quad \frac{a^2}{b^2}\tan^2\phi - \frac{b^2}{a^2}\sec^2\phi = 1 \quad \text{[from Eqs. (iii) and (iv)]}$$

$$\text{or} \quad \frac{a^2}{b^2}\tan^2\phi - \frac{b^2}{a^2}(1 + \tan^2\phi) = 1$$

$$\text{or} \quad \left(\frac{a^2}{b^2} - \frac{b^2}{a^2}\right)\tan^2\phi = 1 + \frac{b^2}{a^2}$$

$$\therefore \quad \tan^2\phi = \frac{b^2}{a^2 - b^2}$$

$$\text{and} \quad \sec^2\phi = 1 + \tan^2\phi = \frac{a^2}{a^2 - b^2}$$

Hence, the points of contact are

$$\left\{\pm\frac{a^2}{\sqrt{(a^2 - b^2)}}, \pm\frac{b^2}{\sqrt{(a^2 - b^2)}}\right\}$$

$$\text{and} \quad \left\{\mp\frac{b^2}{\sqrt{(a^2 - b^2)}}, \mp\frac{a^2}{\sqrt{(a^2 - b^2)}}\right\} \quad \text{[from Eqs. (iii) and (iv)]}$$

Length of common tangent i.e. the distance between the above points is $\sqrt{2}\,\frac{(a^2 + b^2)}{\sqrt{(a^2 - b^2)}}$ and equation of common tangent on putting the values of $\sec\phi$ and $\tan\phi$ in Eqs. (i) is

$$\pm\frac{x}{\sqrt{(a^2 - b^2)}} \mp \frac{y}{\sqrt{(a^2 - b^2)}} = 1$$

$$\text{or} \quad x \mp y = \pm\sqrt{(a^2 - b^2)}$$

Aliter : The given two hyperbolas are

$$\frac{x^2}{a^2} - \frac{y^2}{b^2} = 1 \quad \text{...(i)}$$

$$\text{and} \quad \frac{x^2}{(-b^2)} - \frac{y^2}{(-a^2)} = 1 \quad \text{...(ii)}$$

we know that

$$y = mx \pm \sqrt{(a^2m^2 - b^2)} \quad \text{...(iii)}$$

is tangent to Eq. (i) for all m.

$$\text{Similarly } y = m_1x \pm \sqrt{(-b^2)\,m_1^2 - (-a^2)}$$

$$y = m_1x \pm \sqrt{(a^2 - b^2m_1^2)} \quad \text{...(iv)}$$

will be tangent to Eq. (ii)

For common tangents to Eqs. (i) and (ii), the lines (iii) and (iv) must be identical

i.e. $\quad m = m_1$ and $a^2m^2 - b^2 = a^2 - b^2m_1^2$

i.e. $\quad (a^2 + b^2)(m^2 - 1) = 0$

$\Rightarrow \quad m^2 = 1 \Rightarrow m = \pm 1$

$\therefore$ The equation of common tangent lines are

$$\boldsymbol{y = \pm x \pm \sqrt{(a^2 - b^2)}} \quad \text{[from Eq. (iii)]}$$

$$\text{or} \quad y \mp x = \pm\sqrt{(a^2 - b^2)} \quad \text{...(v)}$$

Equation of tangent to Eq. (i) at (x_1, y_1) is

$$\frac{xx_1}{a^2} - \frac{yy_1}{b^2} = 1 \quad \text{...(vi)}$$

On comparing Eqs.(v) and (vi), then

$$\frac{x_1/a^2}{\mp 1} = \frac{-y_1/b^2}{1} = \frac{1}{\pm\sqrt{(a^2 - b^2)}}$$

$$\text{i.e.} \quad \left(\mp\frac{a^2}{\sqrt{(a^2 - b^2)}}, \mp\frac{b^2}{\sqrt{(a^2 - b^2)}}\right)$$

and equation of tangent to Eq. (ii) at (x_2, y_2) is

$$\frac{xx_2}{(-b^2)} - \frac{yy_2}{(-a^2)} = 1 \quad \text{...(vii)}$$

On comparing Eqs. (v) and (vii), then

$$\frac{x_2/(-b^2)}{\mp 1} = \frac{y_2}{1} = \frac{1}{\pm\sqrt{(a^2 - b^2)}}$$

i.e. $$\left(\pm\frac{b^2}{\sqrt{(a^2-b^2)}}, \pm\frac{a^2}{\sqrt{(a^2-b^2)}}\right)$$

The points of contact are

$$\left(\pm\frac{a^2}{\sqrt{(a^2-b^2)}}, \pm\frac{b^2}{\sqrt{(a^2-b^2)}}\right)$$

and $$\left(\mp\frac{b^2}{\sqrt{(a^2-b^2)}}, \mp\frac{a^2}{\sqrt{(a^2-b^2)}}\right)$$

Hence, the length of common tangent is

$$\sqrt{2}\cdot\frac{(a^2+b^2)}{\sqrt{(a^2-b^2)}}$$

Example 18 PQ is the chord joining the points ϕ_1 and ϕ_2 on the hyperbola $\frac{x^2}{a^2}-\frac{y^2}{b^2}=1$. If $\phi_1-\phi_2=2\alpha$, where α is constant, prove that PQ touches the hyperbola

$$\frac{x^2}{a^2}\cos^2\alpha-\frac{y^2}{b^2}=1.$$

Sol. Given hyperbola is $$\frac{x^2}{a^2}-\frac{y^2}{b^2}=1 \quad \text{...(i)}$$

Equation of the chord PQ to the hyperbola (i) is

$$\frac{x}{a}\cos\left(\frac{\phi_1-\phi_2}{2}\right)-\frac{y}{b}\sin\left(\frac{\phi_1+\phi_2}{2}\right)=\cos\left(\frac{\phi_1+\phi_2}{2}\right)$$

$$\Rightarrow \quad \frac{x}{a}\cos\alpha-\frac{y}{b}\sin\left(\frac{\phi_1+\phi_2}{2}\right)=\cos\left(\frac{\phi_1+\phi_2}{2}\right)$$

(Given $\phi_1-\phi_2=2\alpha$)

i.e. $$y=\frac{b}{a}\frac{\cos\alpha}{\sin\left(\frac{\phi_1+\phi_2}{2}\right)}x+\frac{b\cos\left(\frac{\phi_1+\phi_2}{2}\right)}{\sin\left(\frac{\phi_1+\phi_2}{2}\right)} \quad \text{...(ii)}$$

Comparing this line with $y=mx+c$

$$\therefore \quad m=\frac{b}{a}\cdot\frac{\cos\alpha}{\sin\left(\frac{\phi_1+\phi_2}{2}\right)} \text{ and } c=\frac{b\cos\left(\frac{\phi_1+\phi_2}{2}\right)}{\sin\left(\frac{\phi_1+\phi_2}{2}\right)}$$

For line $y=mx+c$ to be a tangent on $\frac{x^2}{a^2}\cos^2\alpha-\frac{y^2}{b^2}=1$, we have

$$c^2=\frac{a^2}{\cos^2\alpha}m^2-b^2$$

$$\therefore \quad \text{LHS}=c^2=\frac{b^2\cos^2\left(\frac{\phi_1+\phi_2}{2}\right)}{\sin^2\left(\frac{\phi_1+\phi_2}{2}\right)}$$

and $$\text{RHS}=\frac{a^2}{\cos^2\alpha}m^2-b^2$$

$$=\frac{a^2}{\cos^2\alpha}\times\frac{b^2\cos^2\alpha}{a^2\sin^2\left(\frac{\phi_1+\phi_2}{2}\right)}-b^2$$

$$=\frac{b^2}{\sin^2\left(\frac{\phi_1+\phi_2}{2}\right)}-b^2$$

$$=\frac{b^2\cos^2\left(\frac{\phi_1+\phi_2}{2}\right)}{\sin\left(\frac{\phi_1+\phi_2}{2}\right)}$$

Hence proved.

Example 19 If the line $y=mx+\sqrt{(a^2m^2-b^2)}$ touches the hyperbola $\frac{x^2}{a^2}-\frac{y^2}{b^2}=1$ at the point $(a\sec\theta, b\tan\theta)$, show that $\theta=\sin^{-1}\left(\frac{b}{am}\right)$.

Sol. Since $(a\sec\theta, b\tan\theta)$ lies on

$$y=mx+\sqrt{(a^2m^2-b^2)}$$

$$\therefore \quad b\tan\theta=am\sec\theta+\sqrt{(a^2m^2-b^2)}$$

$$\Rightarrow \quad (b\tan\theta-am\sec\theta)^2=a^2m^2-b^2$$

$$\Rightarrow \quad b^2\tan^2\theta+a^2m^2\sec^2\theta-2abm\tan\theta\sec\theta=a^2m^2-b^2$$

$$\Rightarrow \quad a^2m^2\tan^2\theta-2abm\tan\theta\ \theta+b^2\sec^2\theta=0$$

or $$a^2m^2\sin^2\theta-2abm\sin\theta+b^2=0 \qquad (\because \cos\theta\neq 0)$$

$$\therefore \quad \sin\theta=\frac{2abm\pm\sqrt{4a^2b^2m^2-4a^2b^2m^2}}{2a^2m^2}=\left(\frac{b}{am}\right)$$

$$\therefore \quad \theta=\sin^{-1}\left(\frac{b}{am}\right)$$

Example 20 If SY and $S'Y'$ be drawn perpendiculars from foci to any tangent to a hyperbola. Prove that Y and Y' lie on the auxiliary circle and that product of these perpendiculars is constant.

Sol. Let hyperbola be

$$\frac{x^2}{a^2}-\frac{y^2}{b^2}=1 \quad \text{...(i)}$$

Tangent at $P(a\sec\phi, b\tan\phi)$ on Eq. (i) is

$$\frac{x}{a}\sec\phi-\frac{y}{b}\tan\phi=1 \quad \text{...(ii)}$$

Its slope is $$\frac{(b\sec\phi)}{(a\tan\phi)}$$

Equation of SY which is perpendicular to Eq. (i) and passes through focus S i.e. $(ae, 0)$ is

$$y - 0 = -\frac{a \tan \phi}{b \sec \phi}(x - ae)$$

or $$\frac{x}{b}\tan\phi + \frac{y}{a}\sec\phi = \frac{ae}{b}\tan\phi \quad \text{...(iii)}$$

$\because$ Lines (ii) and (iii) intersect at Y and in order to find its locus we have to eliminate ϕ between Eqs. (ii) and (iii), for which squaring and adding Eqs. (ii) and (iii) then, we get

$$(x^2 + y^2)\left(\frac{\sec^2\phi}{a^2} + \frac{\tan^2\phi}{b^2}\right) = 1 + \frac{a^2e^2}{b^2}\tan^2\phi$$

$$= 1 + \frac{a^2 + b^2}{b^2}\tan^2\phi = (1 + \tan^2\phi) + \frac{a^2}{b^2}\tan^2\phi$$

$$= \left(\sec^2\phi + \frac{a^2}{b^2}\tan^2\phi\right) = a^2\left(\frac{\sec^2\phi}{a^2} + \frac{\tan^2\phi}{b^2}\right)$$

$\therefore$ $x^2 + y^2 = a^2$ is the required locus.

Similarly the point Y' also lies on it. Again, if p_1 and p_2 be the length of perpendiculars from $S(ae, 0)$ and $S'(-ae, 0)$ on the tangent (ii), then

$$p_1p_2 = \frac{(e\sec\phi - 1)\cdot(e\sec\phi + 1)}{\sqrt{\left(\frac{\sec^2\phi}{a^2} + \frac{\tan^2\phi}{b^2}\right)}\sqrt{\left(\frac{\sec^2\phi}{a^2} + \frac{\tan^2\phi}{b^2}\right)}}$$

$$= \frac{a^2b^2(e^2\sec^2\phi - 1)}{b^2\sec^2\phi + a^2\tan^2\phi}$$

$$= \frac{a^2b^2(e^2\sec^2\phi - 1)}{a^2(e^2 - 1)\sec^2\phi + a^2\tan^2\phi}$$

$$= \frac{b^2(e^2\sec^2\phi - 1)}{(e^2\sec^2\phi - 1)} = b^2 \quad [(\because b^2 = a^2(e^2 - 1)]$$

Equations of Normals in Different Forms

1. Point form :

Theorem : The equation of the normal to the hyperbola $\frac{x^2}{a^2} - \frac{y^2}{b^2} = 1$ at (x_1, y_1) is $\frac{a^2x}{x_1} + \frac{b^2y}{y_1} = a^2 + b^2$

Proof : Since the equation of tangent to the hyperbola $\frac{x^2}{a^2} - \frac{y^2}{b^2} = 1$ at (x_1, y_1) is $\frac{xx_1}{a^2} - \frac{yy_1}{b^2} = 1$

The slope of tangent at $(x_1, y_1) = \frac{b^2x_1}{a^2y_1}$

$\therefore$ Slope of normal at $(x_1, y_1) = -\frac{a^2y_1}{b^2x_1}$

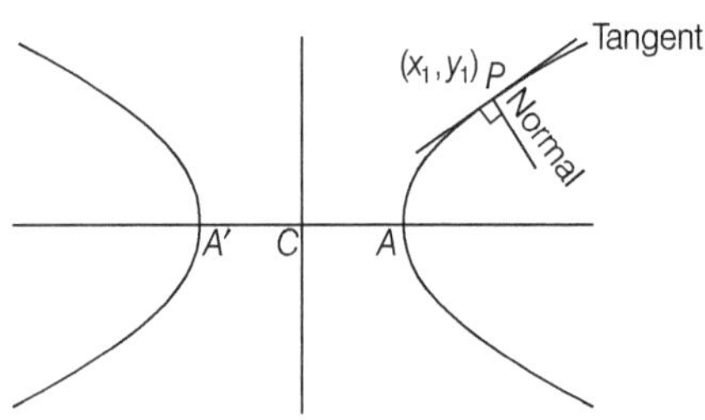

Hence, the equation of normal at (x_1, y_1)

$$y - y_1 = -\frac{a^2y_1}{b^2x_1}(x - x_1)$$

or $$\frac{a^2x}{x_1} + \frac{b^2y}{y_1} = a^2 + b^2$$

Remark

The equation of normal at (x_1, y_1) can also be obtained by this method

$$\frac{x - x_1}{a'x_1 + hy_1 + g} = \frac{y - y_1}{hx_1 + b'y_1 + f} \quad \text{...(i)}$$

a', b', g, f, h are obtained by comparing the given hyperbola with

$$a'x^2 + 2hxy + b'y^2 + 2gx + 2fy + c = 0 \quad \text{...(ii)}$$

The denominator of Eq. (i) can easily be remembered by the first two rows of this determinant

i.e. $$\begin{vmatrix} a' & h & g \\ h & b' & f \\ g & f & c \end{vmatrix}$$

Since first row is $a'(x_1) + h(y_1) + g(1)$

and second row i $h(x_1) + b'(y_1) + f(1)$

Here, hyperbola $\frac{x^2}{a^2} - \frac{y^2}{b^2} = 1$

or $$\frac{x^2}{a^2} - \frac{y^2}{b^2} - 1 = 0 \quad \text{...(iii)}$$

On comparing Eqs. (ii) and (iii), we get

$$a' = \frac{1}{a^2}, b' = -\frac{1}{b^2}, g = 0, f = 0, h = 0$$

From Eq. (i), equation of normal of (iii) at (x_1, y_1) is

$$\frac{x - x_1}{\frac{1}{a^2}x_1 + 0 + 0} = \frac{y - y_1}{0 - \frac{y_1}{b^2} + 0}$$

or $$\frac{a^2x}{x_1} - a^2 = -\frac{b^2y}{y_1} + b^2$$

or $$\frac{a^2x}{x_1} + \frac{b^2y}{y_1} = a^2 + b^2$$

2. Parametric form :

Theorem : The equation of normal at $(a\sec\phi, b\tan\phi)$ to the hyperbola $\frac{x^2}{a^2} - \frac{y^2}{b^2} = 1$ is $ax\cos\phi + by\cot\phi = a^2 + b^2$

Proof : Since the equation of normals of the hyperbola $\frac{x^2}{a^2}-\frac{y^2}{b^2}=1$ at (x_1, y_1) is

$$\frac{a^2x}{x_1}+\frac{b^2y}{y_1}=a^2+b^2 \qquad \text{...(i)}$$

Replacing x_1 by $a\sec\phi$ and y_1 by $b\tan\phi$, then Eq. (i) becomes

$$\frac{a^2x}{a\sec\phi}+\frac{b^2y}{b\tan\phi}=a^2+b^2$$

or $$ax\cos\phi+by\cot\phi=a^2+b^2$$

is equation of normal at $(a\sec\phi, b\tan\phi)$.

3. Slope form :

Theorem : The equations of normals of slope m to the hyperbola $\frac{x^2}{a^2}-\frac{y^2}{b^2}=1$ are given by

$$y=mx\mp\frac{m(a^2+b^2)}{\sqrt{(a^2-m^2b^2)}}$$

at the points $\left(\pm\frac{a^2}{\sqrt{(a^2-m^2b^2)}}, \mp\frac{mb^2}{\sqrt{(a^2-m^2b^2)}}\right)$

Proof : The equation of normal to the hyperbola $\frac{x^2}{a^2}-\frac{y^2}{b^2}=1$ at (x_1, y_1) is

$$\frac{a^2x}{x_1}+\frac{b^2y}{y_1}=a^2+b^2 \qquad \text{...(i)}$$

Since 'm' is the slope of the normal, then

$$m=-\frac{a^2y_1}{b^2x_1}$$

$$y_1=-\frac{b^2x_1m}{a^2} \qquad \text{...(ii)}$$

Since (x_1, y_1) lies on $\frac{x^2}{a^2}-\frac{y^2}{b^2}=1$

$\therefore$ $$\frac{x_1^2}{a^2}-\frac{y_1^2}{b^2}=1$$

or $$\frac{x_1^2}{a^2}-\frac{b^4x_1^2m^2}{a^4b^2}=1$$

or $$x_1^2=\frac{a^4}{a^2-b^2m^2}$$

$\therefore$ $$x_1=\pm\frac{a^2}{\sqrt{(a^2-b^2m^2)}}$$

From Eq. (ii), $$y_1=\mp\frac{mb^2}{\sqrt{(a^2-b^2m^2)}}$$

$\therefore$ Equation of normal in terms of slope is

$$y-\left(\mp\frac{mb^2}{\sqrt{(a^2-m^2b^2)}}\right)=m\left(x-\left(\pm\frac{a^2}{\sqrt{(a^2-m^2b^2)}}\right)\right)$$

$\Rightarrow$ $$\boldsymbol{y=mx\mp\frac{m(a^2+b^2)}{\sqrt{(a^2-m^2b^2)}}} \qquad \text{...(iii)}$$

Thus Eq. (iii) is a normal to the hyperbola

$$\frac{x^2}{a^2}-\frac{y^2}{b^2}=1$$

where m is the slope of the normal.

The coordinates of the point of contact are

$$\left(\pm\frac{a^2}{\sqrt{(a^2-b^2m^2)}}, \mp\frac{mb^2}{\sqrt{(a^2-b^2m^2)}}\right)$$

Comparing Eq. (iii) with $y=mx+c$

$\therefore$ $$c=\mp\frac{m(a^2+b^2)}{\sqrt{(a^2-m^2b^2)}}$$

or $$c^2=\frac{m^2(a^2+b^2)^2}{(a^2-m^2b^2)}$$

which is condition of normality, where $y=mx+c$ is the normal of

$$\frac{x^2}{a^2}-\frac{y^2}{b^2}=1$$

Remark

Normal other than transverse axis, never passes through the focus.

Example 21 A normal to the hyperbola $\frac{x^2}{a^2}-\frac{y^2}{b^2}=1$ meets the axes in M and N and lines MP and NP are drawn perpendiculars to the axes meeting at P. Prove that the locus of P is the hyperbola

$$a^2x^2-b^2y^2=(a^2+b^2)^2.$$

Sol. The equation of normal at the point $(a\sec\phi, b\tan\phi)$ to the hyperbola $\frac{x^2}{a^2}-\frac{y^2}{b^2}=1$ is

$$ax\cos\phi + by\cot\phi = a^2 + b^2 \quad \text{...(i)}$$

The normal (i) meets the X-axis in $M\left(\frac{a^2+b^2}{a}\sec\phi, 0\right)$ and Y-axis in $N\left(0, \frac{a^2+b^2}{b}\tan\phi\right)$

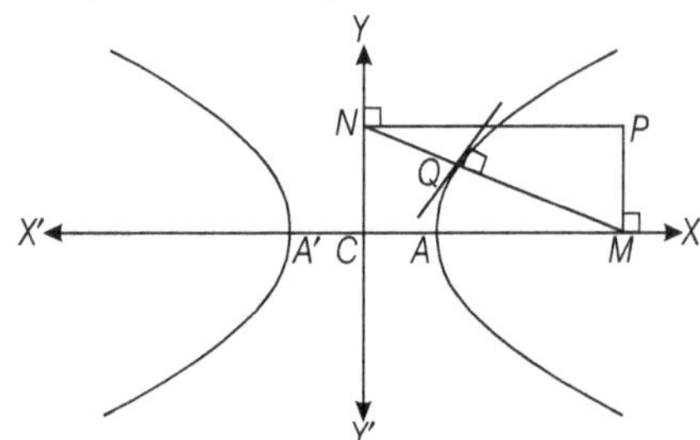

$\therefore$ Equation of MP, the line through M and perpendicular to X axis, is

$$x = \left(\frac{a^2+b^2}{a}\right)\sec\phi$$

or $$\sec\phi = \frac{ax}{(a^2+b^2)} \quad \text{...(ii)}$$

and the equation of NP, the line through N and perpendicular to the Y-axis, is

$$y = \left(\frac{a^2+b^2}{b}\right)\tan\phi$$

or $$\tan\phi = \frac{by}{(a^2+b^2)} \quad \text{...(iii)}$$

The locus of the point of intersection of MP and NP will be obtained by elminating ϕ from Eqs. (ii) and (iii), we have

$$\sec^2\phi - \tan^2\phi = 1$$

$$\Rightarrow \quad \frac{a^2x^2}{(a^2+b^2)^2} - \frac{b^2y^2}{(a^2+b^2)^2} = 1$$

or $$a^2x^2 - b^2y^2 = (a^2+b^2)^2$$

is the required locus of P.

Example 22 Prove that the line $lx + my - n = 0$ will be a normal to the hyperbola $\frac{x^2}{a^2} - \frac{y^2}{b^2} = 1$ if $\frac{a^2}{l^2} - \frac{b^2}{m^2} = \frac{(a^2+b^2)^2}{n^2}$.

Sol. The equation of any normal to $\frac{x^2}{a^2} - \frac{y^2}{b^2} = 1$ is

$$ax\cos\phi + by\cot\phi = a^2 + b^2$$

or $$ax\cos\phi + by\cot\phi - (a^2+b^2) = 0 \quad \text{...(i)}$$

The straight line $lx + my - n = 0$ will be a normal to the hyperbola $\frac{x^2}{a^2} - \frac{y^2}{b^2} = 1$, then Eq. (i) and $lx + my - n = 0$ represent the same line

$$\frac{a\cos\phi}{l} = \frac{b\cot\phi}{m} = \frac{(a^2+b^2)}{n}$$

or $$\sec\phi = \frac{na}{l(a^2+b^2)} \text{ and } \tan\phi = \frac{nb}{m(a^2+b^2)}$$

$\because$ $$\sec^2\phi - \tan^2\phi = 1$$

$\therefore$ $$\frac{n^2a^2}{l^2(a^2+b^2)^2} - \frac{n^2b^2}{m^2(a^2+b^2)^2} = 1$$

$\Rightarrow$ $$\frac{a^2}{l^2} - \frac{b^2}{m^2} = \frac{(a^2+b^2)^2}{n^2}$$

Example 23 If the normal at 'ϕ' on the hyperbola $\frac{x^2}{a^2} - \frac{y^2}{b^2} = 1$ meet transverse axis at G, prove that

$$AG \cdot A'G = a^2(e^4\sec^2\phi - 1).$$

where A and A' are the vertices of the hyperbola.

Sol. The equation of normal at $(a\sec\phi, b\tan\phi)$ to the given hyperbola is $ax\cos\phi + by\cot\phi = (a^2+b^2)$

This meets the transverse axis i.e. X-axis at G. So, the coordinates of G are $\left(\left(\frac{a^2+b^2}{a}\right)\sec\phi, 0\right)$ and the coordinates of the vertices A and A' are $A(a, 0)$ and $A'(-a, 0)$ respectively.

$$\therefore AG \cdot A'G = \left(-a + \left(\frac{a^2+b^2}{a}\right)\sec\phi\right)\left(a + \left(\frac{a^2+b^2}{a}\right)\sec\phi\right)$$

$$= \left(\frac{a^2+b^2}{a}\right)^2\sec^2\phi - a^2$$

$$= (ae^2)^2\sec^2\phi - a^2 = a^2(e^4\sec^2\phi - 1)$$

Example 24 Find the locus of the foot of perpendicular from the centre upon any normal to the hyperbola $\frac{x^2}{a^2} - \frac{y^2}{b^2} = 1$.

Sol. Normal at $P(a\sec\phi, b\tan\phi)$ is

$$ax\cos\phi + by\cot\phi = a^2 + b^2 \quad \text{...(i)}$$

and equation of line perpendicular to Eq. (i) and passing through origin is

$$bx - ay\sin\phi = 0 \quad \text{...(ii)}$$

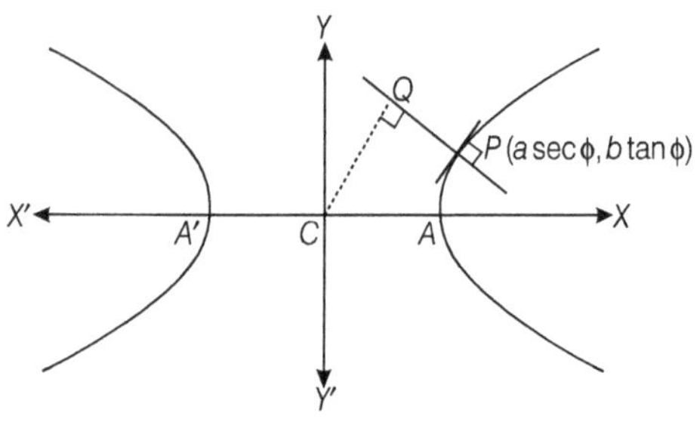

Eliminating ϕ from Eqs. (i) and (ii), we will get the equation of locus of Q, as from Eq. (ii),

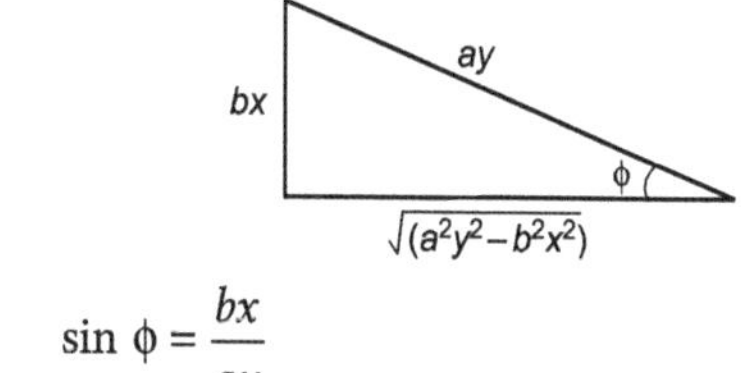

$$\sin\phi = \frac{bx}{ay}$$

$$\therefore \quad \cos\phi = \frac{\sqrt{(a^2y^2 - b^2x^2)}}{ay}$$

and $$\cot\phi = \frac{\sqrt{(a^2y^2 - b^2x^2)}}{bx}$$

From Eq. (i),

$$ax \times \frac{\sqrt{a^2y^2 - b^2x^2}}{ay} + by \times \frac{\sqrt{(a^2y^2 - b^2x^2)}}{bx} = a^2 + b^2$$

$$\Rightarrow \quad (x^2 + y^2)\sqrt{(a^2y^2 - b^2x^2)} = (a^2 + b^2)xy$$

or $$(x^2 + y^2)^2(a^2y^2 - b^2x^2) = (a^2 + b^2)^2x^2y^2$$

which is required locus.

Pair of Tangents

Theorem : The combined equation of the pair of tangents drawn from a point $P(x_1, y_1)$, lying outside the hyperbola $\frac{x^2}{a^2} - \frac{y^2}{b^2} = 1$ to the hyperbola $\frac{x^2}{a^2} - \frac{y^2}{b^2} = 1$ is

$$\left(\frac{x^2}{a^2} - \frac{y^2}{b^2} - 1\right)\left(\frac{x_1^2}{a^2} - \frac{y_1^2}{b^2} - 1\right) = \left(\frac{xx_1}{a^2} - \frac{yy_1}{b^2} - 1\right)^2$$

or $$SS_1 = T^2$$

where $$S = \frac{x^2}{a^2} - \frac{y^2}{b^2} - 1;$$

$$S_1 = \frac{x_1^2}{a^2} - \frac{y_1^2}{b^2} - 1 \text{ and } T = \frac{xx_1}{a^2} - \frac{yy_1}{b^2} - 1$$

Proof : Let $T(h, k)$ be any point on the pair of tangents PQ or PR drawn from any external point $P(x_1, y_1)$ to the hyperbola

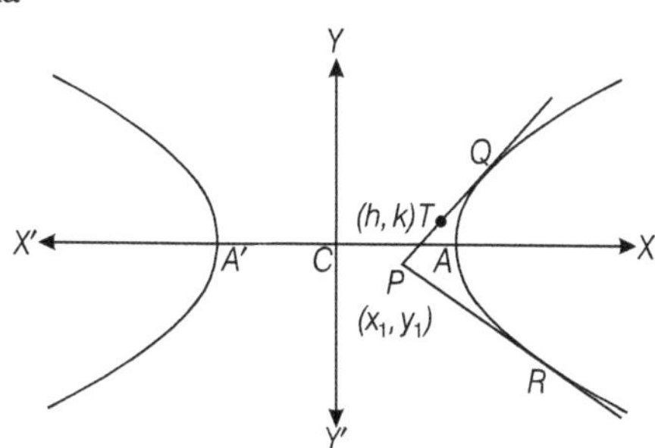

$$\frac{x^2}{a^2} - \frac{y^2}{b^2} = 1$$

$\therefore$ Equation of PT is $$y - y_1 = \frac{k - y_1}{h - x_1}(x - x_1)$$

or $$y = \left(\frac{k - y_1}{h - x_1}\right)x + \left(\frac{hy_1 - kx_1}{h - x_1}\right)$$

which is the tangent to the hyperbola

$$\frac{x^2}{a^2} - \frac{y^2}{b^2} = 1$$

$$\therefore \quad c^2 = a^2m^2 - b^2$$

or $$\left(\frac{hy_1 - kx_1}{h - x_1}\right)^2 = a^2\left(\frac{k - y_1}{h - x_1}\right)^2 - b^2$$

$$\Rightarrow \quad (hy_1 - kx_1)^2 = a^2(k - y_1)^2 - b^2(h - x_1)^2$$

Hence, locus of (h, k) is

$$(xy_1 - x_1y)^2 = a^2(y - y_1)^2 - b^2(x - x_1)^2$$

or $$(xy_1 - x_1y)^2 = -(b^2x^2 - a^2y^2) - (b^2x_1^2 - a^2y_1^2) - 2(a^2yy_1 - b^2xx_1)$$

or $$\left(\frac{xy_1 - x_1y}{ab}\right)^2 = -\left(\frac{x^2}{a^2} - \frac{y^2}{b^2}\right) - \left(\frac{x_1^2}{a^2} - \frac{y_1^2}{b^2}\right) + 2\left(\frac{xx_1}{a^2} - \frac{yy_1}{b^2}\right)$$

or $$-\left(\frac{xy_1 - x_1y}{ab}\right)^2 - \left(\frac{x^2}{a^2} - \frac{y^2}{b^2}\right) - \left(\frac{x_1^2}{a^2} - \frac{y_1^2}{b^2}\right) + 1 + \left(\frac{xx_1}{a^2} - \frac{yy_1}{b^2}\right)^2$$

$$= \left(\frac{xx_1}{a^2} - \frac{yy_1}{b^2}\right)^2 - 2\left(\frac{xx_1}{a^2} - \frac{yy_1}{b^2}\right) + 1$$

or $$\left(\frac{x^2}{a^2} - \frac{y^2}{b^2} - 1\right)\left(\frac{x_1^2}{a^2} - \frac{y_1^2}{b^2} - 1\right) = \left(\frac{xx_1}{a^2} - \frac{yy_1}{b^2} - 1\right)^2$$

or $$SS_1 = T^2$$

Aliter :

Let the hyperbola be $$\frac{x^2}{a^2} - \frac{y^2}{b^2} = 1 \quad \text{...(i)}$$

Let $P(x_1, y_1)$ be any point outside the hyperbola.

Let a chord of the hyperbola through the point $P(x_1, y_1)$ cut the hyperbola at Q and R. Let $R(h, k)$ be any arbitrary point on the line PQ (R inside or outside).

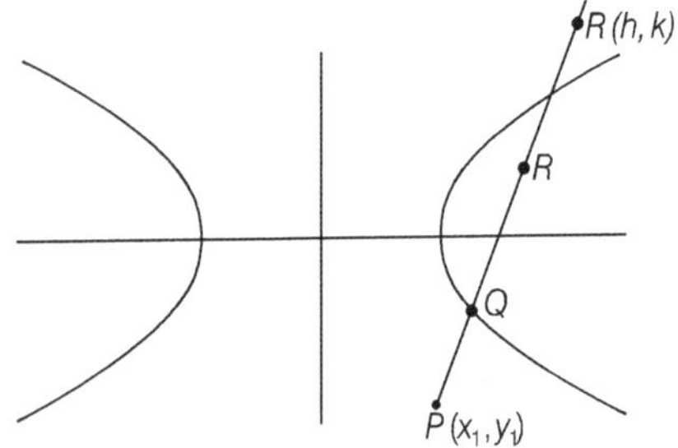

Let Q divides PR in the ratio $\lambda : 1$, then coordinates of Q are

$$\left(\frac{\lambda h + x_1}{\lambda + 1}, \frac{\lambda k + y_1}{\lambda + 1}\right) \quad (\because PQ:QR = \lambda:1)$$

Since, Q lies on hyperbola (i), then

$$\frac{1}{a^2}\left(\frac{\lambda h + x_1}{\lambda + 1}\right)^2 - \frac{1}{b^2}\left(\frac{\lambda k + y_1}{\lambda + 1}\right)^2 = 1$$

$$\Rightarrow \quad b^2(\lambda h + x_1)^2 - a^2(\lambda k + y_1)^2 = a^2 b^2 (\lambda + 1)^2$$

$$\Rightarrow \quad (b^2h^2 - a^2k^2 - a^2b^2)\lambda^2 + 2(b^2hx_1 - a^2ky_1 - a^2b^2)\lambda + (b^2x_1^2 - a^2y_1^2 - a^2b^2) = 0 \quad \text{...(ii)}$$

Let PR will become tangent to the hyperbola (i), then roots of Eq. (ii) are equal

$$4(b^2hx_1 - a^2ky_1 - a^2b^2)^2 - 4(b^2h^2 - a^2k^2 - a^2b^2) \times (b^2x_1^2 - a^2y_1^2 - a^2b^2) = 0$$

Dividing by $4a^4b^4$

$$\therefore \quad \left(\frac{hx_1}{a^2} - \frac{ky_1}{b^2} - 1\right)^2 = \left(\frac{h^2}{a^2} - \frac{k^2}{b^2} - 1\right)\left(\frac{x_1^2}{a^2} - \frac{y_1^2}{b^2} - 1\right)$$

Hence, locus of $R(h, k)$, i.e. equation of pair of tangents from $P(x_1, y_1)$ is

$$\left(\frac{xx_1}{a^2} - \frac{yy_1}{b^2} - 1\right)^2 = \left(\frac{x^2}{a^2} - \frac{y^2}{b^2} - 1\right)\left(\frac{x_1^2}{a^2} - \frac{y^2}{b^2} - 1\right)$$

i.e. $$T^2 = SS_1 \quad \text{or} \quad SS_1 = T^2$$

Remark

$S = 0$ is the equation of the curve, S_1 is obtained from S by replacing x by x_1 and y by y_1 and $T = 0$ is the equation of the tangent at (x_1, y_1) to $S = 0$.

Chord of Contact

Theorem : If the tangents from a point $P(x_1, y_1)$ to the hyperbola $\frac{x^2}{a^2} - \frac{y^2}{b^2} = 1$ touch the hyperbola at Q and R, then the equation of the chord of contact QR is

$$\frac{xx_1}{a^2} - \frac{yy_1}{b^2} = 1$$

Proof : Let $Q \equiv (x', y')$ and $R \equiv (x'', y'')$

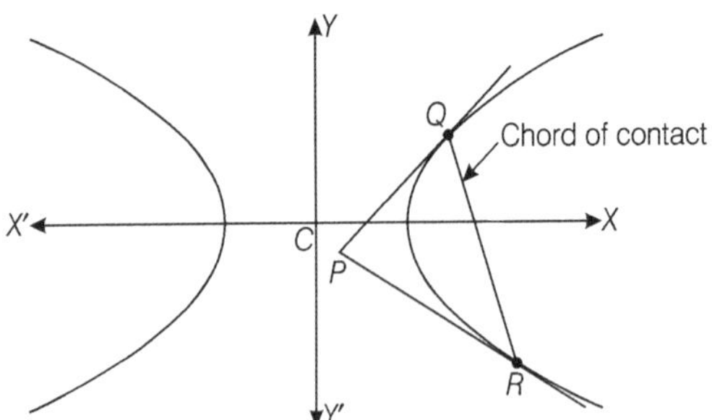

Now, equation of tangents PQ and PR are

$$\frac{xx'}{a^2} - \frac{yy'}{b^2} = 1 \quad \text{...(i)}$$

and $$\frac{xx''}{a^2} - \frac{yy''}{b^2} = 1 \quad \text{...(ii)}$$

Since, Eqs. (i) and (ii) pass through $P(x_1, y_1)$, then

$$\frac{x'x_1}{a^2} - \frac{y'y_1}{b^2} = 1 \quad \text{...(iii)}$$

and $$\frac{x''x_1}{a^2} - \frac{y''y_1}{b^2} = 1 \quad \text{...(iv)}$$

Hence, it is clear that $Q(x', y')$ and $R(x'', y'')$ lie on

$$\frac{xx_1}{a^2} - \frac{yy_1}{b^2} = 1 \quad \text{or} \quad T = 0$$

which is **chord of contact** QR.

Equation of the Chord Bisected at a Given Point

Theorem : The equation of the chord of the hyperbola

$$\frac{x^2}{a^2} - \frac{y^2}{b^2} = 1,$$

bisected at the point (x_1, y_1) is

$$\frac{xx_1}{a^2} - \frac{yy_1}{b^2} - 1 = \frac{x_1^2}{a^2} - \frac{y_1^2}{b^2} - 1$$

or $$T = S_1, \text{where } T = \frac{xx_1}{a^2} - \frac{yy_1}{b^2} - 1$$

and $$S_1 = \frac{x_1^2}{a^2} - \frac{y_1^2}{b^2} - 1.$$

Proof : Since equation of the hyperbola is

$$\frac{x^2}{a^2} - \frac{y^2}{b^2} = 1 \quad \text{...(i)}$$

Let QR be the chord of the hyperbola whose mid-point is $P(x_1, y_1)$. Since Q and R lie on the hyperbola (i).

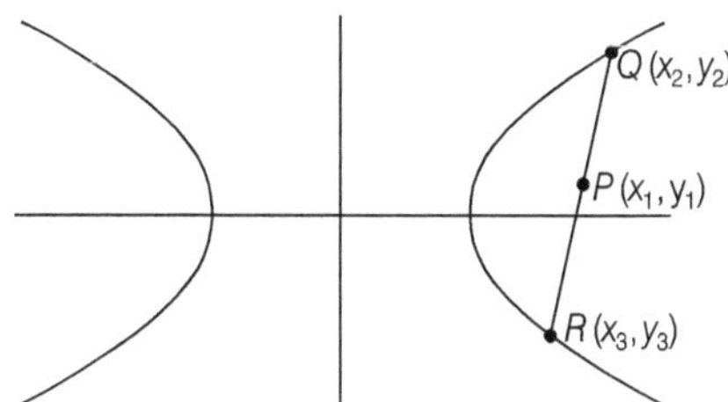

$$\therefore \quad \frac{x_2^2}{a^2} - \frac{y_2^2}{b^2} = 1 \qquad \text{...(ii)}$$

and
$$\frac{x_3^2}{a^2} - \frac{y_3^2}{b^2} = 1 \qquad \text{...(iii)}$$

Subtracting Eq. (iii) from Eq. (ii),

$$\frac{1}{a^2}(x_2^2 - x_3^2) - \frac{1}{b^2}(y_2^2 - y_3^2) = 0$$

$$\Rightarrow \quad \frac{(x_2 + x_3)(x_2 - x_3)}{a^2} - \frac{(y_2 + y_3)(y_2 - y_3)}{b^2} = 0$$

$$\Rightarrow \quad \frac{y_2 - y_3}{x_2 - x_3} = \frac{b^2(x_2 + x_3)}{a^2(y_2 + y_3)}$$

$$= \frac{b^2}{a^2}\frac{(2x_1)}{(2y_1)} \qquad [P \text{ is the mid-point of } QR]$$

$$= \frac{b^2 x_1}{a^2 y_1} \qquad \text{...(iv)}$$

$\therefore$ Equation of QR is

$$y - y_1 = \frac{y_2 - y_3}{x_2 - x_3}(x - x_1)$$

$$\Rightarrow \quad y - y_1 = \frac{b^2 x_1}{a^2 y_1}(x - x_1) \qquad \text{[from Eq. (iv)]}$$

$$\Rightarrow \quad \frac{yy_1}{b^2} - \frac{y_1^2}{b^2} = \frac{xx_1}{a^2} - \frac{x_1^2}{a^2}$$

$$\Rightarrow \quad \frac{xx_1}{a^2} - \frac{yy_1}{b^2} = \frac{x_1^2}{a^2} - \frac{y_1^2}{b^2}$$

$$\Rightarrow \quad \frac{xx_1}{a^2} - \frac{yy_1}{b^2} - 1 = \frac{x_1^2}{a^2} - \frac{y_1^2}{b^2} - 1$$

$$\Rightarrow \quad T = S_1$$

Example 25 Find the locus of the mid-points of the chords of the hyperbola $\frac{x^2}{a^2} - \frac{y^2}{b^2} = 1$ which subtend a right angle at the origin.

Sol. Let (h, k) be the mid-point of the chord of the hyperbola. Then its equation is

$$\frac{hx}{a^2} - \frac{ky}{b^2} - 1 = \frac{h^2}{a^2} - \frac{k^2}{b^2} - 1$$

or
$$\frac{hx}{a^2} - \frac{ky}{b^2} = \frac{h^2}{a^2} - \frac{k^2}{b^2} \qquad \text{...(i)}$$

The equation of the lines joining the origin to the points of intersection of the hyperbola and the chord (i) is obtained by making homogeneous hyperbola with the help of Eq. (i)

$$\therefore \quad \frac{x^2}{a^2} - \frac{y^2}{b^2} = \frac{\left(\frac{hx}{a^2} - \frac{ky}{b^2}\right)^2}{\left(\frac{h^2}{a^2} - \frac{k^2}{b^2}\right)^2}$$

$$\Rightarrow \quad \frac{1}{a^2}\left(\frac{h^2}{a^2} - \frac{k^2}{b^2}\right)^2 x^2 - \frac{1}{b^2}\left(\frac{h^2}{a^2} - \frac{k^2}{b^2}\right)^2 y^2$$

$$= \frac{h^2}{a^4}x^2 + \frac{k^2}{b^4}y^2 - \frac{2hk}{a^2b^2}xy \qquad \text{...(ii)}$$

The lines represented by Eq. (ii) will be at right angle if

Coefficient of x^2 + Coefficient of $y^2 = 0$

$$\Rightarrow \quad \frac{1}{a^2}\left(\frac{h^2}{a^2} - \frac{k^2}{b^2}\right)^2 - \frac{h^2}{a^4} - \frac{1}{b^2}\left(\frac{h^2}{a^2} - \frac{k^2}{b^2}\right)^2 - \frac{k^2}{b^4} = 0$$

$$\Rightarrow \quad \left(\frac{h^2}{a^2} - \frac{k^2}{b^2}\right)^2 \left(\frac{1}{a^2} - \frac{1}{b^2}\right) = \frac{h^2}{a^4} + \frac{k^2}{b^4}$$

Hence, the locus of (h, k) is

$$\left(\frac{x^2}{a^2} - \frac{y^2}{b^2}\right)^2 \left(\frac{1}{a^2} - \frac{1}{b^2}\right) = \frac{x^2}{a^4} + \frac{y^2}{b^4}$$

Example 26 From the points on the circle $x^2 + y^2 = a^2$, tangents are drawn to the hyperbola $x^2 - y^2 = a^2$; prove that the locus of the middle-points of the chords of contact is the curve $(x^2 - y^2)^2 = a^2(x^2 + y^2)$.

Sol. Since any point on the circle $x^2 + y^2 = a^2$ is $(a\cos\theta, a\sin\theta)$ chord of contact of this point w.r.t. hyperbola $x^2 - y^2 = a^2$ is

$$x(a\cos\theta) - y(a\sin\theta) = a^2$$

or
$$x\cos\theta - y\sin\theta = a \qquad \text{...(i)}$$

If its mid-point be (h, k), then it is same as

$$T = S_1$$

i.e.
$$hx - ky - a^2 = h^2 - k^2 - a^2$$

or
$$hx - ky = h^2 - k^2 \qquad \text{...(ii)}$$

On comparing Eqs. (i) and (ii), we get

$$\frac{\cos\theta}{h} = \frac{\sin\theta}{k} = \frac{a}{(h^2 - k^2)}$$

or $(h^2 - k^2)\cos\theta = ah$ ...(iii)

and $(h^2 - k^2)\sin\theta = ak$ ...(iv)

Squaring and adding Eqs. (iii) and (iv), we get

$$(h^2 - k^2)^2 = a^2h^2 + a^2k^2$$

$$\Rightarrow \quad (h^2 - k^2)^2 = a^2(h^2 + k^2)$$

Hence, the required locus is

$$(x^2 - y^2)^2 = a^2(x^2 + y^2).$$

Example 27 Prove that the locus of the middle-points of the chords of the hyperbola $\frac{x^2}{a^2} - \frac{y^2}{b^2} = 1$ which pass through a fixed point (α, β) is a hyperbola whose centre is $\left(\frac{\alpha}{2}, \frac{\beta}{2}\right)$.

Sol. Let the mid-point of the chord be (h, k). The equation of the chord whose mid-point is (h, k) is

$$\frac{hx}{a^2} - \frac{ky}{b^2} - 1 = \frac{h^2}{a^2} - \frac{k^2}{b^2} - 1 \text{ or } \frac{hx}{a^2} - \frac{ky}{b^2} = \frac{h^2}{a^2} - \frac{k^2}{b^2}$$

It passes through (α, β), then

$$\frac{\alpha h}{a^2} - \frac{\beta k}{b^2} = \frac{h^2}{a^2} - \frac{k^2}{b^2}$$

$\therefore$ locus of (h, k) is

$$\frac{x\alpha}{a^2} - \frac{y\beta}{b^2} = \frac{x^2}{a^2} - \frac{y^2}{b^2}$$

$$\Rightarrow \quad \frac{1}{a^2}(x^2 - \alpha x) - \frac{1}{b^2}(y^2 - \beta y) = 0$$

$$\Rightarrow \quad \frac{1}{a^2}\left\{\left(x - \frac{\alpha}{2}\right)^2 - \frac{\alpha^2}{4}\right\} - \frac{1}{b^2}\left\{\left(y - \frac{\beta}{2}\right)^2 - \frac{\beta^2}{4}\right\} = 0$$

or $$\frac{\left(x - \frac{\alpha}{2}\right)^2}{a^2} - \frac{\left(y - \frac{\beta}{2}\right)^2}{b^2} = \frac{1}{4}\left\{\frac{\alpha^2}{a^2} - \frac{\beta^2}{b^2}\right\} = \lambda \text{ (say)}$$

$$\therefore \quad \frac{\left(x - \frac{\alpha}{2}\right)^2}{a^2\lambda} - \frac{\left(y - \frac{\beta}{2}\right)^2}{b^2\lambda} = 1$$

The centre of this hyperbola is $\left(\frac{\alpha}{2}, \frac{\beta}{2}\right)$.

Exercise for Session 2

1. The tangents from $(1, 2\sqrt{2})$ to the hyperbola $16x^2 - 25y^2 = 400$ include between them an angle equal to

(a) $\frac{\pi}{6}$ (b) $\frac{\pi}{4}$ (c) $\frac{\pi}{3}$ (d) $\frac{\pi}{2}$

2. If $4x^2 + \lambda y^2 = 45$ and $x^2 - 4y^2 = 5$ cut orthogonally, then the value of λ is

(a) $\frac{1}{9}$ (b) $\frac{1}{3}$ (c) 9 (d) 18

3. If the tangent at the point $(2\sec\phi, 3\tan\phi)$ of the hyperbola $\frac{x^2}{4} - \frac{y^2}{9} = 1$ is parallel to $3x - y + 4 = 0$, then the value of ϕ is

(a) $\frac{\pi}{6}$ (b) $\frac{\pi}{4}$ (c) $\frac{\pi}{3}$ (d) $\frac{5\pi}{12}$

4. If the line $2x + \sqrt{6}y = 2$ touches the hyperbola $x^2 - 2y^2 = 4$, then the point of contact is

(a) $(-2, \sqrt{6})$ (b) $(-5, 2\sqrt{6})$ (c) $\left(\frac{1}{2}, \frac{1}{\sqrt{6}}\right)$ (d) $(4, -\sqrt{6})$

5. The equation of the chord of hyperbola $25x^2 - 16y^2 = 400$, whose mid-point is (5, 3), is

(a) $115x - 47y = 434$ (b) $125x - 48y = 481$
(c) $127x - 49y = 488$ (d) $155x - 67y = 574$

6. The value of m for which $y = mx + 6$ is a tangent to the hyperbola $\frac{x^2}{100} - \frac{y^2}{49} = 1$ is

(a) $\sqrt{\left(\frac{17}{20}\right)}$ (b) $-\sqrt{\left(\frac{17}{21}\right)}$ (c) $\sqrt{\left(\frac{20}{17}\right)}$ (d) $-\sqrt{\left(\frac{21}{17}\right)}$

7. P is a point on the hyperbola $\frac{x^2}{a^2} - \frac{y^2}{b^2} = 1$, N is the foot of the perpendicular from P on the transverse axis. The tangent to the hyperbola at P meets the transverse axis at T. If O is the centre of the hyperbola, then $OT \cdot ON$ is equal to

(a) a^2 (b) b^2 (c) e^2 (d) b^2/a

8. If $x = 9$ is the chord of contact of the hyperbola $x^2 - y^2 = 9$, then the equation of the corresponding pair of tangents, is

(a) $9x^2 - 8y^2 + 18x - 9 = 0$ (b) $9x^2 - 8y^2 - 18x + 9 = 0$

(c) $9x^2 - 8y^2 - 18x - 9 = 0$ (d) $9x^2 - 8y^2 + 18x + 9 = 0$

9. Let $P(a\sec\theta, b\tan\theta)$ and $Q(a\sec\phi, b\tan\phi)$, when $\theta + \phi = \frac{\pi}{2}$, be two points on the hyperbola $\frac{x^2}{a^2} - \frac{y^2}{b^2} = 1$. If (h, k) is the point of intersection of the normals at P and Q, then k is equal to

(a) $\left(\frac{a^2 + b^2}{a}\right)$ (b) $-\left(\frac{a^2 + b^2}{a}\right)$ (c) $\left(\frac{a^2 + b^2}{b}\right)$ (d) $-\left(\frac{a^2 + b^2}{b}\right)$

10. The tangent at a point P on the hyperbola $\frac{x^2}{a^2} - \frac{y^2}{b^2} = 1$ passes through the point $(0, -b)$ and the normal at P passes through $(2a\sqrt{2}, 0)$; then eccentricity of the hyperbola is

(a) $\frac{5}{4}$ (b) $\frac{3}{2}$ (c) $\sqrt{2}$ (d) $2\sqrt{2}$

11. A tangent to the hyperbola $\frac{x^2}{a^2} - \frac{y^2}{b^2} = 1$ cuts the ellipse $\frac{x^2}{a^2} + \frac{y^2}{b^2} = 1$ in points P and Q. Find the locus of the mid-point of PQ.

12. A line through the origin meets the circle $x^2 + y^2 = a^2$ at P and the hyperbola $x^2 - y^2 = a^2$ at Q. Prove that the locus of the point of intersection of tangent at P to the circle with the tangent at Q to the hyperbola is the curve.

13. Normals are drawn to the hyperbola $\frac{x^2}{a^2} - \frac{y^2}{b^2} = 1$ at the points $P(a\sec\theta_1, b\tan\theta_1)$ and $Q(a\sec\theta_2, b\tan\theta_2)$ meeting the conjugate axis at G_1 and G_2 respectively. If $\theta_1 + \theta_2 = \pi/2$, prove that

$$CG_1 \cdot CG_2 = \frac{a^2e^4}{(e^2 - 1)}$$

where C is the centre of the hyperbola and e is its eccentricity.

14. Chords of the hyperbola $x^2 - y^2 = a^2$ touch the parabola $y^2 = 4ax$. Prove that the locus of their middle-points is the curve $y^2(x - a) = x^3$.

Session 3

Diameter, Conjugate Diameters, Properties of Hyperbola, Intersection of Conjugate Diameters and Hyperbola, Director Circle, Asymptotes, Rectangular Hyperbola, The Rectangular Hyperbola $xy = c^2$, Reflection Property of a Hyperbola, Equation of a Hyperbola Referred to Two Perpendicular Lines

Diameter

The locus of the middle points of a system of parallel chords of a hyperbola is called a diameter and the point where the diameter intersects the hyperbola is called the vertex of the diameter.

Theorem : The equation of a diameter bisecting a system of parallel chords of slope m of the hyperbola $\frac{x^2}{a^2} - \frac{y^2}{b^2} = 1$ is

$$y = \frac{b^2}{a^2 m} x$$

Proof : Let $y = mx + c$ be a system of a parallel chords to $\frac{x^2}{a^2} - \frac{y^2}{b^2} = 1$ for different chords. As c varies, m remain constant.

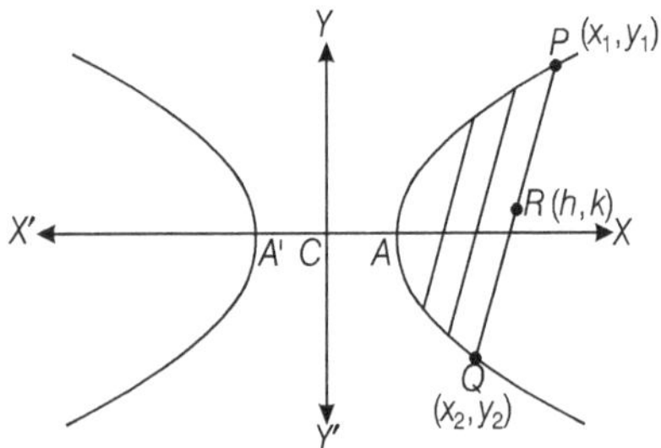

Let the extremities of any chord PQ of the set be $P(x_1, y_1)$ and $Q(x_2, y_2)$ and let its middle point be $R(h, k)$. Then solving equations

$$\frac{x^2}{a^2} - \frac{y^2}{b^2} = 1 \text{ and } y = mx + c$$

we get $$\frac{x^2}{a^2} - \frac{(mx + c)^2}{b^2} = 1$$

$$\Rightarrow \quad (a^2m^2 - b^2)x^2 + 2mca^2x + a^2(c^2 + b^2) = 0$$

Since, x_1 and x_2 be the roots of this equation, then

$$x_1 + x_2 = \frac{-2mca^2}{a^2m^2 - b^2} \quad \text{...(i)}$$

Since, (h, k) be the middle point of QR, then

$$h = \frac{x_1 + x_2}{2}$$

then from Eq. (i), $h = -\frac{mca^2}{a^2m^2 - b^2}$

but (h, k) lies on $y = mx + c$

$$\therefore \quad k = mh + c$$

or $$c = k - mh \quad \text{...(ii)}$$

From Eqs. (i) and (ii),

$$h = -\frac{ma^2(k - mh)}{a^2m^2 - b^2}$$

$$\Rightarrow \quad a^2m^2h - b^2h = -ma^2k + m^2a^2h$$

$$\Rightarrow \quad -b^2h = -ma^2k \text{ or } k = \frac{b^2h}{a^2m}$$

Hence, locus of $R(h, k)$ is $y = \frac{b^2x}{a^2m}$

which is the diameter of the hyperbola passing through $(0, 0)$.

Aliter :

Let (h, k) be the middle-point of the chord $y = mx + c$ of the hyperbola $\frac{x^2}{a^2} - \frac{y^2}{b^2} = 1$ then

$$T = S_1$$

$$\Rightarrow \quad \frac{xh}{a^2} - \frac{yk}{b^2} = \frac{h^2}{a^2} - \frac{k^2}{b^2}$$

$$\therefore \quad \text{Slope} = \frac{hb^2}{a^2k} = m$$

$$\Rightarrow \quad k = \frac{b^2h}{a^2m}$$

Hence, the locus of mid-point is $y = \frac{b^2x}{a^2m}$.

Conjugate Diameters

Two diameters are said to be conjugate when each bisects all chords parallel to the others.

If $y = mx, y = m_1x$ be conjugate diameters, then $mm_1 = \frac{b^2}{a^2}$.

Let $y = m_1x + c$ be a set of chords parallel to $y = m_1x$, then the diameter $y = \frac{b^2}{a^2m}x$ bisects them all. But being the conjugate diameter $y = mx$ also bisects them.

Hence, these two lines must be identical

$$\therefore \quad m = \frac{b^2}{a^2m_1} \Rightarrow mm_1 = \frac{b^2}{a^2}$$

Properties of Hyperbola

Prop. 1. *If a pair of diameters be conjugate with respect to a hyperbola, they are conjugate with respect to its conjugate hyperbola also.*

Let $y = mx$ and $y = m_1x$ be two conjugate diameters of the hyperbola $\frac{x^2}{a^2} - \frac{y^2}{b^2} = 1$, then

$$mm_1 = \frac{b^2}{a^2} \quad \text{...(i)}$$

Now conjugate hyperbola of $\frac{x^2}{a^2} - \frac{y^2}{b^2} = 1$ is

$$-\frac{x^2}{a^2} + \frac{y^2}{b^2} = 1$$

or

$$\frac{x^2}{-a^2} - \frac{y^2}{-b^2} = 1 \quad \text{...(ii)}$$

If $y = m_2x$ and $y = m_3x$ are the conjugate diameters of Eq. (ii), then

$$m_2m_3 = \frac{(-b^2)}{(-a^2)}$$

$$= \frac{b^2}{a^2} = mm_1 \quad \text{[from Eq. (i)]}$$

This proves the proposition.

Prop. 2. *The parallelogram formed by the tangents at the extremities of conjugate diameters of a hyperbola has its vertices lying on the asymptotes and is of constant area.*

Since, P and D lie on hyperbola $\frac{x^2}{a^2} - \frac{y^2}{b^2} = 1$

and its conjugate diameter $-\frac{x^2}{a^2} + \frac{y^2}{b^2} = 1$

then coordinates of P and D are $(a \sec \phi, b \tan\phi)$ and $(a \tan\phi, b \sec \phi)$ respectively.

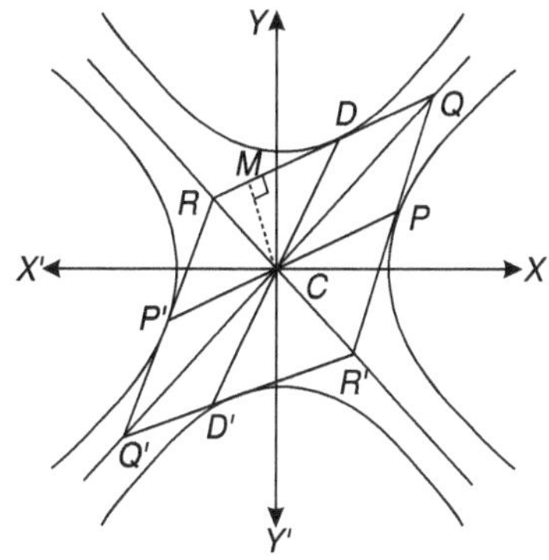

Then $D' \equiv (-a \tan\phi, -b \sec \phi)$

and $P' \equiv (-a \sec \phi, -b \tan\phi)$

Since, equations of asymptotes CQ and CR are $y = \frac{b}{a}x$ and $y = -\frac{b}{a}x$ respectively and the equations of tangents at P, P', D and D' are

$$\frac{x}{a}\sec \phi - \frac{y}{b}\tan\phi = 1 \quad \text{...(i)}$$

$$-\frac{x}{a}\sec \phi + \frac{y}{b}\tan\phi = 1 \quad \text{...(ii)}$$

$$-\frac{x}{a}\tan\phi + \frac{y}{b}\sec \phi = 1 \quad \text{...(iii)}$$

and

$$\frac{x}{a}\tan\phi - \frac{y}{b}\sec \phi = 1 \quad \text{...(iv)}$$

respectively.

Now, the lines (i) and (ii) are parallel and so are Eqs. (iii) and (iv).

Hence these tangents form a parallelogram. Solving Eqs. (i) and (iii), we get the coordinate of Q as $[a(\sec\phi+\tan\phi), b(\sec\phi+\tan\phi)]$ which clearly lies on the asymptote $y=\frac{b}{a}x$ similarly the other points of intersection lies on the asymptotes.

The equations of PCP' and DCD' are

$$y=\frac{b\tan\phi}{a\sec\phi}x \text{ or } bx\tan\phi-ay\sec\phi=0 \qquad \text{...(v)}$$

and $$y=\frac{b\sec\phi}{a\tan\phi}x \text{ or } bx\sec\phi-ay\tan\phi=0 \qquad \text{...(vi)}$$

Hence by symmetry.

Area of parallelogram $QRQ'R'=4$ (Area of parallelogram $QDCP$)

$$=4\cdot CP\times(\text{Perpendicular length from } C \text{ on } QD)$$

$$=4\cdot\sqrt{(a^2\sec^2\phi+b^2\tan^2\phi)}\times\frac{1}{\sqrt{\frac{\tan^2\phi}{a^2}+\frac{\sec^2\phi}{b^2}}}$$

$$=4ab=\text{ Constant.}$$

Prop. 3. *If the normal at P meets the transverse axis in G, then $SG=e\cdot SP$. Prove also that the tangent and normal bisect the angle between the focal distances of P.*

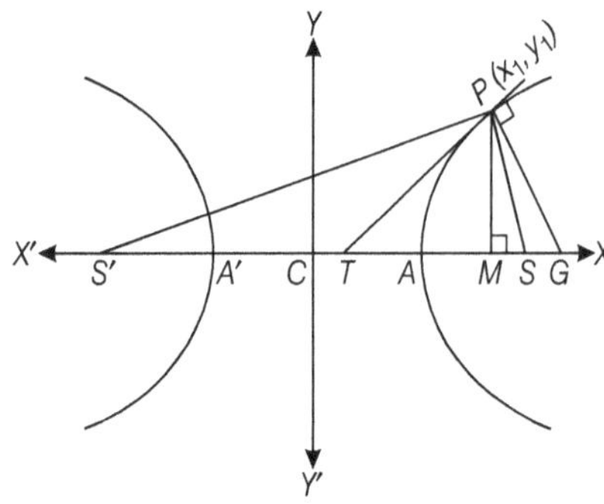

Let the coordinates of P be (x_1,y_1). The equation of normal at P on the hyperbola $\frac{x^2}{a^2}-\frac{y^2}{b^2}=1$ *is*

$$\frac{a^2x}{x_1}+\frac{b^2y}{y_1}=a^2+b^2 \qquad \text{... (i)}$$

The normal (i) meets the X-axis i.e. $y=0$ in Eq. (i), then coordinates of G are

$$\left(\frac{(a^2+b^2)}{a^2}x_1,0\right) \text{ or } (e^2x_1,0)$$

$\therefore$ $$CG=e^2x_1$$

Now $$SG=CG-CS$$

$$=e^2x_1-ae=e(ex_1-a)=e\cdot SP$$

Similarly, $$S'G=e\cdot S'P$$

$\therefore$ $$\frac{SG}{S'G}=\frac{SP}{S'P}$$

This relation shows that the normal PG is the external bisector of the angle SPS'. The tangent PT being perpendicular to PG is therefore the internal bisector of the angle SPS'.

Prop. 4. *If a pair of conjugate diameters meet the hyperbola in P, P' and its conjugate in D, D', then the asymptotes bisect PD, PD', P'D and P'D'.*

The coordinates of four points P, D, P', D' are $(a\sec\phi, b\tan\phi)$; $(a\tan\phi, b\sec\phi)$; $(-a\sec\phi, -b\tan\phi)$; $(-a\tan\phi, -b\sec\phi)$ respectively.

If (h,k) be the middle point of PD, then

$$h=\frac{a}{2}(\sec\phi+\tan\phi)$$

and $$k=\frac{b}{2}(\tan\phi+\sec\phi)$$

$\therefore$ $$\frac{h}{k}=\frac{a}{b}$$

$\therefore$ Locus of mid-point (h,k) is $y=\frac{b}{a}x$ which is equation of asymptote of hyperbola $\frac{x^2}{a^2}-\frac{y^2}{b^2}=1$.

Similarly other mid-points lie on the other asymptotes.

Intersection of Conjugate Diameters and Hyperbola

To prove that of a pair of conjugate diameters of a hyperbola, only one meets the curve in real points

Let $$y=mx \qquad \text{...(i)}$$

and $$y=m_1x \qquad \text{...(ii)}$$

be a pair of conjugate diameters of the hyperbola $\frac{x^2}{a^2}-\frac{y^2}{b^2}=1$, then

$$mm_1=\frac{b^2}{a^2} \qquad \text{...(iii)}$$

On solving Eq. (i) and the equation of hyperbola $\frac{x^2}{a^2}-\frac{y^2}{b^2}=1$, we get

$$\frac{x^2}{a^2} - \frac{m^2x^2}{b^2} = 1$$

or $$x^2 = \frac{a^2b^2}{b^2 - a^2m^2} \quad ...(iv)$$

Similarly Eq. (ii) meets the hyperbola at points whose abscissa are given by

$$x^2 = \frac{a^2b^2}{b^2 - a^2m_1^2} \quad ...(v)$$

The two values of x given by Eq. (iv) will be real if $b^2 - a^2m^2 > 0$ i.e. $m < \left(\frac{b}{a}\right)$

i.e. $$\frac{b^2}{a^2m_1} < \left(\frac{b}{a}\right) \qquad \left\{\because mm_1 = \frac{b^2}{a^2}\right\}$$

$\Rightarrow$ $$\frac{b}{a} < m_1 \text{ i.e. if } b^2 < a^2m_1^2$$

i.e. if $b^2 - a^2m_1^2 < 0$

Then from Eq. (v) the values of x are imaginary.

Hence, if Eq. (i) meets the hyperbola in real points then Eq. (ii) meets it in imaginary points and *vice-versa.*

Remark

If CD is the conjugate diameter of a diameter CP of the hyperbola $\frac{x^2}{a^2} - \frac{y^2}{b^2} = 1$, where P is $(a\sec\phi, b\tan\phi)$, then equation of CP, where C is $(0, 0)$ is

$$y - 0 = \frac{b\tan\phi - 0}{a\sec\phi - 0}(x - 0) \Rightarrow y = \frac{b}{a}\sin\phi . x$$

Comparing this with $y = mx$

$$m = \frac{b}{a}\sin\phi$$

$\because$ $$mm' = \frac{b^2}{a^2} \Rightarrow \frac{b}{a}\sin\phi \times m' = \frac{b^2}{a^2}$$

$\therefore$ $$m' = \left(\frac{b}{a}\right)\text{cosec }\phi$$

$\therefore$ Equation of conjugate diameter is $y = m'x = (b/a)\text{cosec }\phi . x$ on solving

$$y = (b/a)\text{cosec }\phi \cdot x \quad \text{and} \quad -\frac{x^2}{a^2} + \frac{y^2}{b^2} = 1.$$

Then we get coordinates of D

i.e. $D \equiv (a\tan\phi, b\sec\phi)$

Example 28 If a pair of conjugate diameters meets the hyperbola and its conjugate in P and D respectively, then prove that $CP^2 - CD^2 = a^2 - b^2$.

Sol. $\because$ Coordinates of P and D are $(a\sec\phi, b\tan\phi)$ and $(a\tan\phi, b\sec\phi)$ respectively.

Then $$(CP)^2 - (CD)^2 = a^2\sec^2\phi + b^2\tan^2\phi - a^2\tan^2\phi - b^2\sec^2\phi$$
$$= a^2(\sec^2\phi - \tan^2\phi) - b^2(\sec^2\phi - \tan^2\phi)$$
$$= a^2(1) - b^2(1) = a^2 - b^2$$

Example 29 For the hyperbola $x^2 - y^2 = a^2$, prove that the triangle CPD is isosceles and has constant area, where CP and CD are a pair of its conjugate diameters.

Sol. Since, CP and CD are the conjugate diameters of $x^2 - y^2 = a^2$, hence coordinates of P and D are $P \equiv (a\sec\phi, a\tan\phi)$, $D \equiv (a\tan\phi, a\sec\phi)$ respectively.

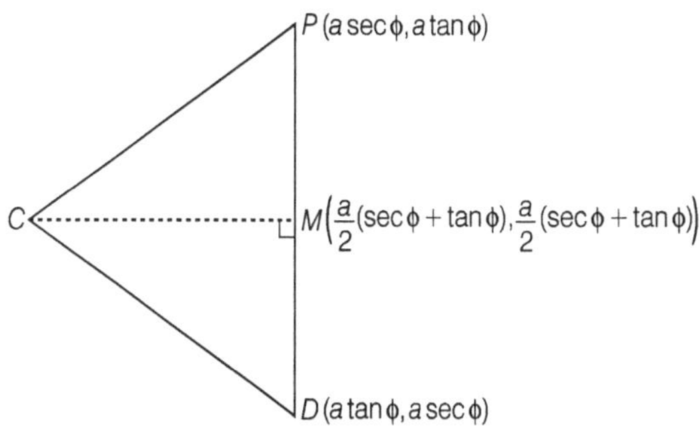

$\therefore$ $$CP = \sqrt{a^2(\sec^2\phi + \tan^2\phi)} = CD \qquad [\because C = 0(0, 0)]$$

Hence, ΔCPD is isosceles triangle.

Draw $\perp$ from C on PD, where M is the mid-point of PD

$\therefore$ $$M \equiv \left(\frac{a}{2}(\sec\phi + \tan\phi), \frac{a}{2}(\sec\phi + \tan\phi)\right)$$

$\therefore$ $$CM = \frac{|(\sec\phi + \tan\phi)|}{2}\sqrt{(a^2 + a^2)}$$

and $$PD = \sqrt{[a(\sec\phi - \tan\phi)]^2 + [a(\sec\phi - \tan\phi)]^2}$$
$$= |\sec\phi - \tan\phi)|\sqrt{(a^2 + a^2)}$$

$\therefore$ $$\text{Area of } \Delta PCD = \frac{1}{2} \cdot PD \cdot CM$$
$$= \frac{1}{4}(a^2 + a^2) = \frac{a^2}{2} = \text{constant}$$

Example 30 Find the condition for the lines $Ax^2 + 2Hxy + By^2 = 0$ to be conjugate diameters of $\frac{x^2}{a^2} - \frac{y^2}{b^2} = 1.$

Sol. Let the lines represented by

$$Ax^2 + 2Hxy + By^2 = 0$$

are $$y = mx \quad \text{and} \quad y = m_1x$$

$\therefore$ $$mm_1 = \frac{A}{B} \quad ...(i)$$

But $y = mx$ and $y = m_1x$ are the conjugate diameters of

$$\frac{x^2}{a^2} - \frac{y^2}{b^2} = 1$$

then $\qquad mm_1 = \frac{b^2}{a^2}$ ...(ii)

$\therefore$ From Eqs. (i) and (ii), $\frac{A}{B} = \frac{b^2}{a^2}$

or $\qquad a^2A = b^2B$

which is the required condition.

Example 31 If the lines $lx + my + n = 0$ passes through the extremities of a pair of conjugate diameters of the hyperbola $\frac{x^2}{a^2} - \frac{y^2}{b^2} = 1$, show that $a^2l^2 - b^2m^2 = 0$.

Sol. The extremities of a pair of conjugate diameters of $\frac{x^2}{a^2} - \frac{y^2}{b^2} = 1$ are $(a \sec \phi, b \tan \phi)$ and $(a \tan \phi, b \sec \phi)$ respectively.

According to the question, since extremities of a pair of conjugate diameters lie on $lx + my + n = 0$

$\therefore \qquad l(a \sec \phi) + m(b \tan \phi) + n = 0$ ...(i)

$\Rightarrow \qquad l(a \tan \phi) + m(b \sec \phi) + n = 0$ ...(ii)

then from Eq. (i), $al \sec \phi + bm \tan \phi = -n$

or $a^2l^2 \sec^2 \phi + b^2m^2 \tan^2 \phi + 2ablm \sec \phi \tan \phi = n^2$ ...(iii)

and from Eq. (ii), $al \tan \phi + bm \sec \phi = -n$

or $a^2l^2 \tan^2 \phi + b^2m^2 \sec^2 \phi + 2ablm \sec \phi \tan \phi = n^2$ ...(iv)

then subtracting Eq. (iv) from Eq. (iii),

$$a^2l^2(\sec^2\phi - \tan^2 \phi) + b^2m^2(\tan^2 \phi - \sec^2\phi) = 0$$

or $\qquad a^2l^2 - b^2m^2 = 0$

Director Circle

The locus of the point of intersection of the tangents to the hyperbola $\frac{x^2}{a^2} - \frac{y^2}{b^2} = 1$, which are perpendicular to each other is called director circle.

Let any tangent in terms of slope of hyperbola $\frac{x^2}{a^2} - \frac{y^2}{b^2} = 1$ is

P (h, k)
90°
A′ C A

$$y = mx + \sqrt{(a^2m^2 - b^2)}$$

It passes through (h, k)

$\therefore \qquad k = mh + \sqrt{(a^2m^2 - b^2)}$

or $\qquad (k - mh)^2 = a^2m^2 - b^2$

$\Rightarrow \qquad k^2 + m^2h^2 - 2mhk = a^2m^2 - b^2$

$\Rightarrow \qquad m^2(h^2 - a^2) - 2hkm + k^2 + b^2 = 0$

It is quadratic equation in m. Let slopes of two tangents are m_1 and m_2

$\therefore \qquad m_1m_2 = \frac{k^2 + b^2}{h^2 - a^2}$

$$-1 = \frac{k^2 + b^2}{h^2 - a^2} \quad (\because \text{tangents are perpendicular})$$

$\Rightarrow \qquad -h^2 + a^2 = k^2 + b^2$

or $\qquad h^2 + k^2 = a^2 - b^2$

Hence, locus of $P(h, k)$ is

$$x^2 + y^2 = a^2 - b^2 \qquad (a > b)$$

Aliter :

If $\quad$ tangents $y = mx + \sqrt{(a^2m^2 - b^2)}$ ...(i)

and $\qquad y = -\frac{x}{m} + \sqrt{\left\{a^2\left(-\frac{1}{m}\right)^2 - b^2\right\}}$ ...(ii)

touch the hyperbola and intersects at right angles

$\therefore$ From Eq. (i),

$$y - mx = \sqrt{(a^2m^2 - b^2)} \quad \text{...(iii)}$$

Eq. (ii) can be rewritten as

$$x + my = \sqrt{(a^2 - b^2m^2)} \quad \text{...(iv)}$$

Squaring and adding Eqs. (iii) and (iv), then

$$(y - mx)^2 + (x + my)^2 = a^2m^2 - b^2 + a^2 - b^2m^2$$

$$(1 + m^2)(x^2 + y^2) = (1 + m^2)(a^2 - b^2)$$

Hence, $x^2 + y^2 = a^2 - b^2$ is the **director circle** of the hyperbola.

Remarks

1. For director circle of $\frac{x^2}{a^2} - \frac{y^2}{b^2} = 1$, a must be greater than b.

   If $a < b$, then director circle $x^2 + y^2 = a^2 - b^2$ does not exist.

2. The equation of director circle of $-\frac{x^2}{a^2} + \frac{y^2}{b^2} = 1$ is $x^2 + y^2 = b^2 - a^2 \; (b > a)$.

   If $b < a$, then director circle does not exist.

Example 32 If any tangent to the hyperbola $\frac{x^2}{a^2} - \frac{y^2}{b^2} = 1$ with centre C, meets its director circle in P and Q, show that CP and CQ are conjugate semi-diameters of the hyperbola.

Sol. Since, equation of hyperbola is

$$\frac{x^2}{a^2} - \frac{y^2}{b^2} = 1 \quad \text{...(i)}$$

Equation of tangent at $(a \sec \phi, b \tan \phi)$ on Eq. (i) is

$$\frac{x}{a} \sec \phi - \frac{y}{b} \tan \phi = 1 \quad \text{...(ii)}$$

Equation of director circle of Eq. (i) is

$$x^2 + y^2 = a^2 - b^2 \quad \text{...(iii)}$$

Equation of lines joining the point of intersection of Eqs. (i) and (ii) to the origin is obtained by making Eq. (iii) homogeneous with the help of Eq. (ii).

$$\therefore \quad x^2 + y^2 = (a^2 - b^2)\left(\frac{x}{a} \sec \phi - \frac{y}{b} \tan \phi\right)^2$$

or

$$x^2\left(1 - \frac{(a^2 - b^2)\sec^2\phi}{a^2}\right) + y^2\left(1 - \frac{(a^2 - b^2)\tan^2\phi}{b^2}\right) + \frac{2(a^2 - b^2)\sec\phi \tan \phi}{ab} xy = 0 \quad \text{...(iv)}$$

Let m and m' represent the slopes of the lines given by Eq. (iv), then

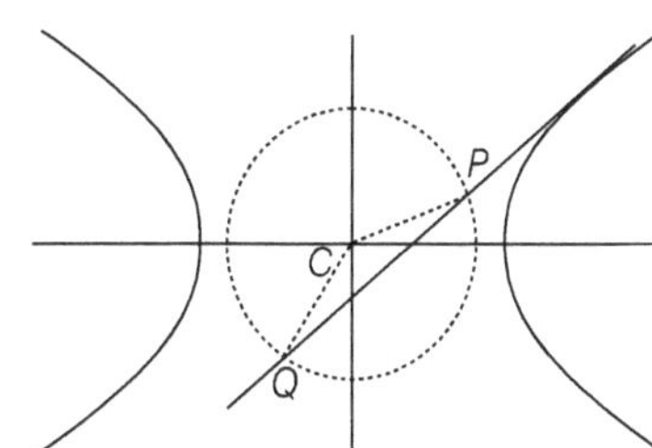

$$mm' = \frac{1 - \frac{(a^2 - b^2)\sec^2\phi}{a^2}}{1 - \frac{(a^2 - b^2)\tan^2\phi}{b^2}} = \frac{b^2}{a^2} \cdot \frac{a^2 - (a^2 - b^2)\sec^2\phi}{b^2 - (a^2 - b^2)\tan^2\phi}$$

$$= \frac{b^2}{a^2} \cdot \frac{b^2\sec^2\phi - a^2\tan^2\phi}{b^2\sec^2\phi - a^2\tan^2\phi} = \frac{b^2}{a^2}$$

Hence, the lines CP and CQ are conjugate semi-diameters of the hyperbola.

Asymptotes

An asymptotes of any hyperbola or a curve is a straight line which touches in it two points at infinity.

Asymptotes of hyperbola : *The equations of two asymptotes of the hyperbola* $\frac{x^2}{a^2} - \frac{y^2}{b^2} = 1$ *are* $y = \pm \frac{b}{a} x$ *or* $\frac{x}{a} \pm \frac{y}{b} = 0.$

Proof : Let $y = mx + c$ be an asymptote of the hyperbola

$$\frac{x^2}{a^2} - \frac{y^2}{b^2} = 1 \quad \text{...(i)}$$

Substituting the value of y in Eq. (i),

$$\frac{x^2}{a^2} - \frac{(mx + c)^2}{b^2} = 1$$

or

$$(a^2m^2 - b^2)x^2 + 2a^2mcx + a^2(b^2 + c^2) = 0 \quad \text{...(ii)}$$

If the line $y = mx + c$ is an asymptote to the given hyperbola, then it touches the hyperbola at infinity. So both roots of Eq. (ii) must be infinite.

$$\therefore \quad a^2m^2 - b^2 = 0$$

and

$$-2a^2mc = 0$$

then

$$m = \pm \frac{b}{a} \quad \text{and} \quad c = 0$$

Substituting the value of m and c in $y = mx + c$, we get

$$y = \pm \frac{b}{a} x \Rightarrow \frac{x}{a} \pm \frac{y}{b} = 0$$

Aliter :

The difference between the second degree curve and pair of asymptotes is constant.

$\because$ Given hyperbola is $\frac{x^2}{a^2} - \frac{y^2}{b^2} = 1$

$\therefore$ Pair of asymptotes is $\frac{x^2}{a^2} - \frac{y^2}{b^2} + \lambda = 0 \quad$ ... (i)

Eq. (i) represents a pair of lines, then $\Delta = 0$

$$\therefore \quad \frac{1}{a^2} \cdot \left(-\frac{1}{b^2}\right) \cdot \lambda + 0 - 0 - 0 - \lambda \cdot 0 = 0$$

$$\therefore \quad \lambda = 0$$

From Eq. (i), pair of asymptotes is $\frac{x^2}{a^2} - \frac{y^2}{b^2} = 0$

or

$$y = \pm \frac{b}{a} x \text{ or } \frac{x}{a} \pm \frac{y}{b} = 0$$

Remarks

1. If $b = a$, then $\frac{x^2}{a^2} - \frac{y^2}{b^2} = 1$ reduces to $x^2 - y^2 = a^2$. The asymptotes of rectangular hyperbola $x^2 - y^2 = a^2$ are $y = \pm x$ which are at right angles.
2. A hyperbola and its conjugate hyperbola have the same asymptotes.
3. The angle between the asymptotes of $\frac{x^2}{a^2} - \frac{y^2}{b^2} = 1$ is $2\tan^{-1}\left(\frac{b}{a}\right)$.

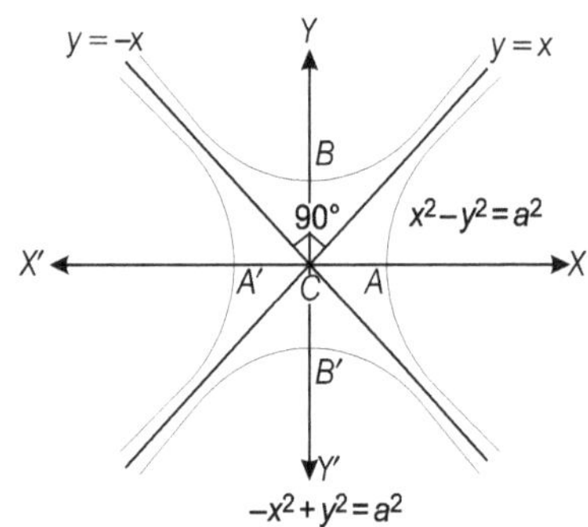

4. If the angle between the asymptotes of a hyperbola $\frac{x^2}{a^2}-\frac{y^2}{b^2}=1$ is 2θ, then $e=\sec\theta$.
5. The asymptotes pass through the centre of the hyperbola.
6. The bisectors of the angles between the asymptotes are the coordinate axes.
7. Let $H\equiv\frac{x^2}{a^2}-\frac{y^2}{b^2}-1=0$

$A\equiv\frac{x^2}{a^2}-\frac{y^2}{b^2}=0$ and $C\equiv\frac{x^2}{a^2}-\frac{y^2}{b^2}+1=0$

be the equation of the hyperbola, asymptotes and the conjugate hyperbola respectively, then clearly $C+H=2A$

Example 33 Find the asymptotes of the hyperbola $xy-3y-2x=0$.

Sol. Since equation of a hyperbola and its asymptotes differ in constant terms only,

$\therefore$ Pair of asymptotes is given by

$$xy-3y-2x+\lambda=0 \qquad \text{...(i)}$$

where, λ is any constant such that it represents two straight lines.

$$\therefore \quad abc+2fgh-af^2-bg^2-ch^2=0$$

$$\Rightarrow \quad 0+2\times-\frac{3}{2}\times-1\times\frac{1}{2}-0-0-\lambda\left(\frac{1}{2}\right)^2=0$$

$$\therefore \quad \lambda=6$$

From Eq. (i), the asymptotes of given hyperbola are given by

$$xy-3y-2x+6=0$$

or $\quad (y-2)(x-3)=0.$

$\therefore$ Asymptotes are $x-3=0$ and $y-2=0$.

Example 34 The asymptotes of a hyperbola having centre at the point (1, 2) are parallel to the lines $2x+3y=0$ and $3x+2y=0$. If the hyperbola passes through the point (5, 3), show that its equation is

$$(2x+3y-8)(3x+2y+7)=154.$$

Sol. Let the asymptotes be $2x+3y+\lambda=0$ and $3x+2y+\mu=0$.

Since asymptotes passes through (1, 2), then

$$\lambda=-8 \text{ and } \mu=-7$$

Thus, the equation of asymptotes are

$$2x+3y-8=0 \quad \text{and} \quad 3x+2y-7=0$$

Let the equation of hyperbola be

$$(2x+3y-8)(3x+2y-7)+v=0 \qquad \text{... (i)}$$

It passes through (5,3), then

$$(10+9-8)(15+6-7)+v=0$$

$$\Rightarrow \quad 11\times14+v=0$$

$$\therefore \quad \gamma=-154$$

Putting the value of v in Eq. (i), we obtain

$$(2x+3y-8)(3x+2y-7)-154=0$$

which is the equation of required hyperbola.

Example 35 Show that the tangent at any point of a hyperbola cuts off a triangle of constant area from the asymptotes and that the portion of it intercepted between the asymptotes is bisected at the point of contact.

Sol. Let $P(a\sec\phi, b\tan\phi)$ be any point on the hyperbola

$$\frac{x^2}{a^2}-\frac{y^2}{b^2}=1 \qquad \text{... (i)}$$

Asymptotes of Eq. (i) are

$$y=\pm\frac{b}{a}x$$

Equation of tangent of Eq. (i) at $P(a\sec\phi, b\tan\phi)$ is

$$\frac{x}{a}\sec\phi-\frac{y}{b}\tan\phi=1 \qquad \text{... (ii)}$$

Solving Eq. (ii) and $y=\frac{b}{a}x$

We get $\frac{x}{a}(\sec\phi-\tan\phi)=(\sec^2\phi-\tan^2\phi)$

$$\therefore \quad x=a(\sec\phi+\tan\phi)$$

and $\quad y=b(\sec\phi+\tan\phi)$

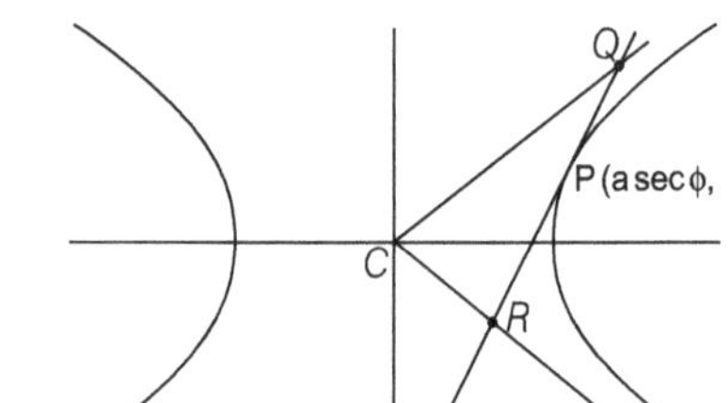

Let $Q\equiv[a(\sec\phi+\tan\phi), b(\sec\phi+\tan\phi)]$

Now solving Eq. (ii) and $y=-\frac{b}{a}x$

We get, $\quad \frac{x}{a}(\sec\phi+\tan\phi)=(\sec^2\phi-\tan^2\phi)$

or $\quad x=a(\sec\phi-\tan\phi)$

and $\quad y=-b(\sec\phi-\tan\phi)$

Let $R\equiv[a(\sec\phi-\tan\phi), -b(\sec\phi-\tan\phi)]$

Mid-point of QR is $(a\sec\phi, b\tan\phi)$ which is coordinate of P.

Area of $\Delta CQR=\frac{1}{2}|(x_1y_2-x_2y_1)|$

$$=\frac{1}{2}|-ab-ab|=ab=\text{constant}.$$

Rectangular Hyperbola

A hyperbola whose asymptotes include a right angle is said to be rectangular hyperbola.

OR

If the lengths of transverse and conjugate axes of any hyperbola be equal, it is called **rectangular or equilateral hyperbola**.

According to the first definition

$$2\tan^{-1}\left(\frac{b}{a}\right)=\frac{\pi}{2}$$

$$\Rightarrow \qquad \tan^{-1}\left(\frac{b}{a}\right)=\frac{\pi}{4} \Rightarrow \frac{b}{a}=1$$

$$a=b$$

then, $\frac{x^2}{a^2}-\frac{y^2}{b^2}=1$ becomes $x^2-y^2=a^2$

According to the second definition

When $a=b, \frac{x^2}{a^2}-\frac{y^2}{b^2}=1$ becomes

$$x^2-y^2=a^2$$

$$\text{Eccentricity, } e=\sqrt{\left(1+\frac{b^2}{a^2}\right)}=\sqrt{2}$$

Hence, $x^2-y^2=a^2$ is the general form of the equation of the rectangular hyperbola.

Remark

All the results of $\frac{x^2}{a^2}-\frac{y^2}{b^2}=1$ are applicable to the hyperbola $x^2-y^2=a^2$ after changing b by a.

The Rectangular Hyperbola $xy=c^2$

When the centre of any rectangular hyperbola be at the origin and its asymptotes coincide with the coordinate axes its, equation is $xy=c^2$.

Since, asymptotes coincides the coordinate axes.

Hence, asymptotes are $y=0$ and $x=0$.

$\therefore$ Combined equation of asymptotes is $xy=0$. Now equation of any hyperbola and its asymptotes differ in respect of constant terms only.

$\therefore$ Equation of rectangular hyperbola is $xy=c^2$ where c is any constant.

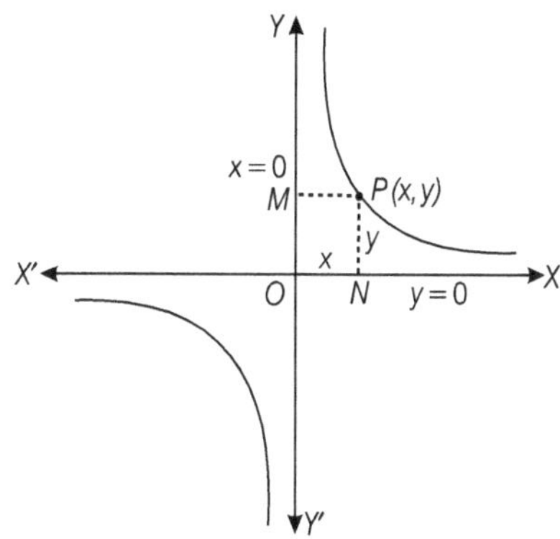

Second method (By rotation of axes) :

The equation of rectangular hyperbola is $x^2-y^2=a^2$ and its asymptotes are $x-y=0$ and $x+y=0$. Since, asymptotes are inclined at 45° and 135° to the X-axis respectively.

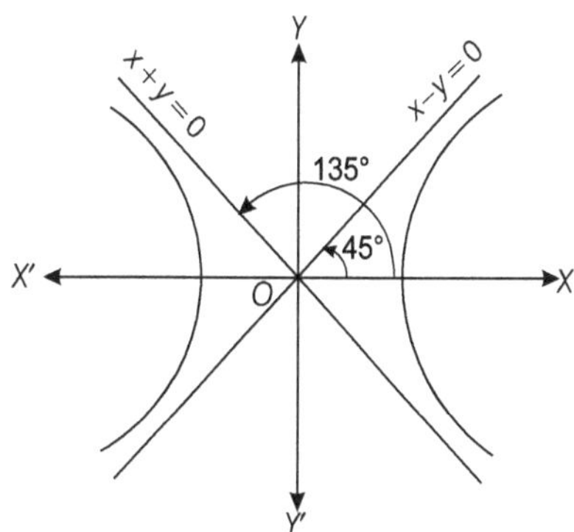

If we rotate the axes through $\theta=-45°$ without changing the origin. Thus, when we replace (x, y) by

$$[x\cos(-45°)-y\sin(-45°), x\sin(-45)° + y\cos(-45°)]$$

i.e. $\left(\frac{x+y}{\sqrt{2}}, \frac{-x+y}{\sqrt{2}}\right)$

then equation $x^2-y^2=a^2$ reduces to

$$\left(\frac{x+y}{\sqrt{2}}\right)^2-\left(\frac{-x+y}{\sqrt{2}}\right)^2=a^2$$

or $$\frac{1}{2}\{(x+y)^2-(-x+y)^2\}=a^2$$

$\Rightarrow$ $$\frac{1}{2}(2y)(2x)=a^2$$

or $$xy=\frac{a^2}{2}=\left(\frac{a}{\sqrt{2}}\right)^2=c^2 \quad \text{(say)}$$

or $$xy=c^2$$

Study of Hyperbola $xy = c^2$

(i) Vertices : $A(c,c)$ and $A'(-c,-c)$.

(ii) Transverse axis : $y = x$.

(iii) Conjugate axis : $y = -x$.

(iv) Foci : $S(c\sqrt{2},c\sqrt{2})$ and $S'(-c\sqrt{2},-c\sqrt{2})$.

(v) Length of latusrectum = Length of $AA' = 2\sqrt{2}c$.

(vi) Equation of auxiliary circle : $x^2 + y^2 = 2c^2$.

(vii) Equation of director circle $x^2 + y^2 = 0$.

(viii) Asymptotes : $x = 0, y = 0$.

Remarks

1. The equations of the asymptotes and the conjugate hyperbola of the rectangular hyperbola $xy = c^2$, where the axes are the asymptotes, are $xy = 0$ and $xy = -c^2$ respectively.
2. The equation of a rectangular hyperbola having coordinate axes as its asymptotes is $xy = c^2$. If the asymptotes of a rectangular hyperbola are $x = \alpha$, $y = \beta$ then its equation is $(x-\alpha)(y-\beta) = c^2$ or $xy - \alpha y - \beta x + \lambda = 0$.
3. Since $x = ct$, $y = \frac{c}{t}$ satisfies $xy = c^2$

   $\therefore (x, y) = \left(ct, \frac{c}{t}\right) (t \neq 0)$ is called a 't' point on the rectangular hyperbola. The set $\left\{x = ct, y = \frac{c}{t}\right\}$ represents its parametric equations with parameter 't'.

Properties of Rectangular Hyperbola $xy = c^2$

(i) Equation of the chord joining 't_1' and 't_2' is $x + yt_1t_2 - c(t_1 + t_2) = 0$.

(ii) Equation of tangent at (x_1, y_1) is $xy_1 + x_1y = 2c^2$.

(iii) Equation of tangent at 't' is $\frac{x}{t} + yt = 2c$.

(iv) Point of intersection of tangents at 't_1' and 't_2' is $\left(\frac{2ct_1t_2}{t_1 + t_2}, \frac{2c}{t_1 + t_2}\right)$.

(v) Equation of normal at (x_1, y_1) is $xx_1 - yy_1 = x_1^2 - y_1^2$.

(vi) Equation of normal at 't' is $xt^3 - yt - ct^4 + c = 0$.

(vii) Point of intersection of normals at 't_1' and 't_2' is.

$$\left(\frac{c\{t_1t_2(t_1^2 + t_1t_2 + t_2^2) - 1\}}{t_1t_2(t_1 + t_2)}, \frac{c\{t_1^3t_2^3 + (t_1^2 + t_1t_2 + t_2^2)\}}{t_1t_2(t_1 + t_2)}\right).$$

Example 36 If the normal at the point 't_1' to the rectangular hyperbola $xy = c^2$ meets it again at the point 't_2', prove that $t_1^3t_2 = -1$.

Sol. Since, the equation of normal at $\left(ct_1, \frac{c}{t_1}\right)$ to the hyperbola $xy = c^2$ is

$$xt_1^3 - yt_1 - ct_1^4 + c = 0$$

but this passes through $\left(ct_2, \frac{c}{t_2}\right)$, then

$$ct_2t_1^3 - \frac{c}{t_2}t_1 - ct_1^4 + c = 0$$

$\Rightarrow$ $t_2^2t_1^3 - t_1 - t_1^4t_2 + t_2 = 0$

$\Rightarrow$ $t_2t_1^3(t_2 - t_1) + (t_2 - t_1) = 0$

$\Rightarrow$ $(t_1^3t_2 + 1)(t_2 - t_1) = 0$

$\Rightarrow$ $t_1^3t_2 + 1 = 0$ $\quad [\because t_2 \neq t_1]$

$\therefore$ $t_1^3t_2 = -1$

Example 37 A triangle has its vertices on a rectangular hyperbola. Prove that the orthocentre of the triangle also lies on the same hyperbola.

Sol. Let "t_1", "t_2" and "t_3" are the vertices of the triangle ABC, described on the rectangular hyperbola $xy = c^2$.

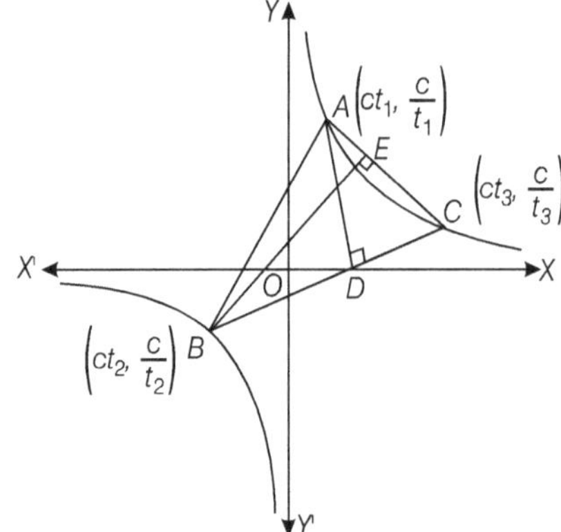

$\therefore$ Coordinates of A, B and C are $\left(ct_1, \frac{c}{t_1}\right)$, $\left(ct_2, \frac{c}{t_2}\right)$ and $\left(ct_3, \frac{c}{t_3}\right)$ respectively.

Now, slope of BC is $\dfrac{\frac{c}{t_3} - \frac{c}{t_2}}{ct_3 - ct_2} = -\dfrac{1}{t_2t_3}$

$\therefore$ Slope of AD is t_2t_3

Equation of altitude AD is

$$y - \frac{c}{t_1} = t_2t_3(x - ct_1)$$

or $$t_1 y - c = x\, t_1 t_2 t_3 - c t_1^2 t_2 t_3 \quad \text{...(i)}$$

Similarly equation of altitude BE is

$$t_2 y - c = x\, t_1 t_2 t_3 - c\, t_1 t_2^2 t_3 \quad \text{...(ii)}$$

Solving Eqs. (i) and (ii), we get the orthocentre

$\left(-\dfrac{c}{t_1 t_2 t_3}, -c\, t_1 t_2 t_3\right)$ which lies on $xy = c^2$.

Reflection Property of a Hyperbola

If an incoming light ray passing through one focus S strike convex side of the hyperbola then it will get reflected towards other focus S'.

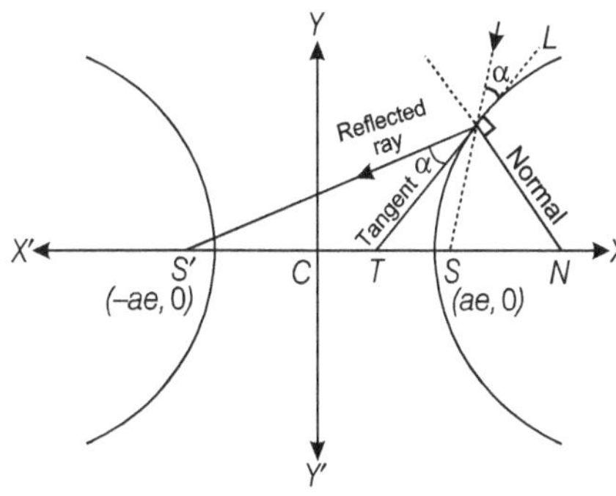

Example 38 A ray emanating from the point (5, 0) is incident on the hyperbola $9x^2 - 16y^2 = 144$ at the point P with abscissa 8. Find the equation of the reflected ray after first reflection and point P lies in first quadrant.

Sol. Given, hyperbola is $9x^2 - 16y^2 = 144$. This equation can be rewritten as

$$\frac{x^2}{16} - \frac{y^2}{9} = 1 \quad \text{...(i)}$$

Coordinates of foci are $(0, \pm\sqrt{16+9})$ i.e., $(0, \pm 5)$

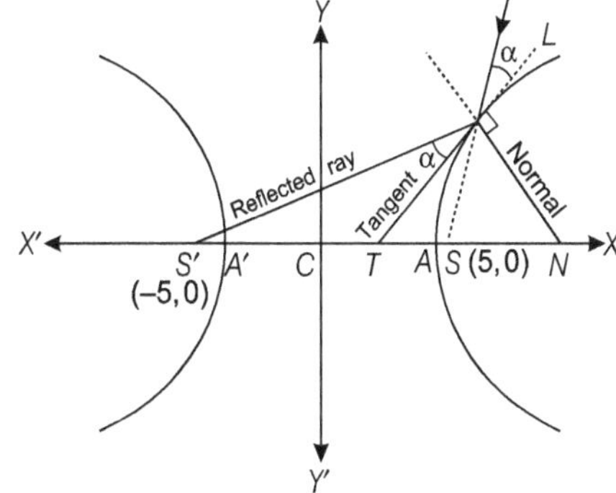

Since x-coordinate of P is 8. Let y-coordinate of P is α.

$\therefore$ $(8, \alpha)$ lies on Eq. (i)

$$\therefore \quad \frac{64}{16} - \frac{\alpha^2}{9} = 1$$

$$\Rightarrow \quad \alpha^2 = 27$$

$$\Rightarrow \quad \alpha = 3\sqrt{3} \qquad (\because P \text{ lies in first quadrant})$$

Hence coordinate of point P is $(8, 3\sqrt{3})$.

$\because$ Equation of reflected ray passing through $P(8, 3\sqrt{3})$ and $S'(-5, 0)$.

$\therefore$ Its equation is $y - 3\sqrt{3} = \dfrac{0 - 3\sqrt{3}}{-5-8}(x - 8)$

or $$13y - 39\sqrt{3} = 3\sqrt{3}x - 24\sqrt{3}$$

or $$3\sqrt{3}x - 13y + 15\sqrt{3} = 0.$$

Equation of a Hyperbola Referred to Two Perpendicular Lines

Let $P(x, y)$ be any point on the hyperbola $\dfrac{x^2}{a^2} - \dfrac{y^2}{b^2} = 1$, then

$$PM = y \text{ and } PN = x$$

$$\therefore \quad \frac{x^2}{a^2} - \frac{y^2}{b^2} = 1$$

$$\Rightarrow \quad \frac{(PN)^2}{a^2} - \frac{(PM)^2}{b^2} = 1$$

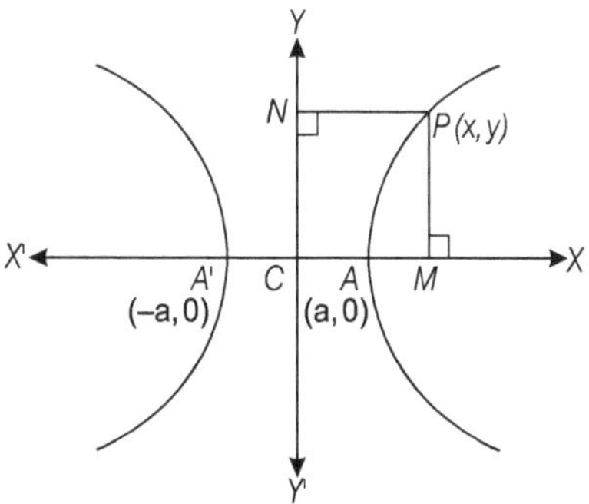

If perpendicular lines represented by

$$L_1 \equiv a_1 x + b_1 y + c_1 = 0$$

and $$L_2 \equiv b_1 x - a_1 y + c_2 = 0$$

then $$PN = p_1 = \left(\frac{a_1 x + b_1 y + c_1}{\sqrt{(a_1^2 + b_1^2)}}\right)$$

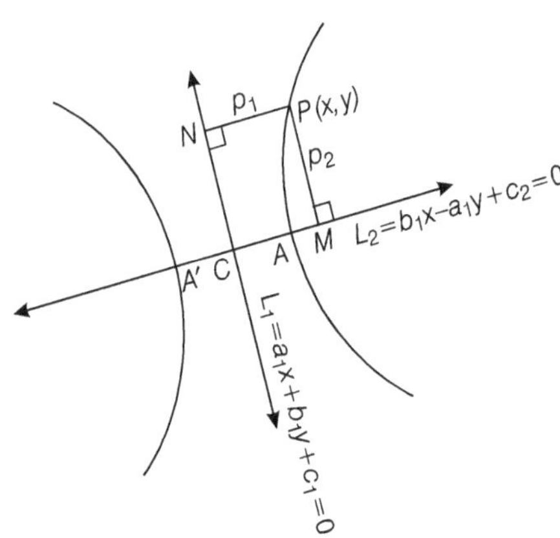

and $\quad PM = p_2 = \left(\dfrac{b_1x - a_1y + c_2}{\sqrt{(b_1^2 + a_1^2)}}\right)$

Now equation of hyperbola becomes

$$\frac{\left(\dfrac{a_1x + b_1y + c_1}{\sqrt{(a_1^2 + b_1^2)}}\right)^2}{a^2} - \frac{\left(\dfrac{b_1x - a_1y + c_2}{\sqrt{(b_1^2 + a_1^2)}}\right)^2}{b^2} = 1$$

Then the point P describes a hyperbola in the plane of the given lines such that :

(i) Centre : The centre of the hyperbola is the point of intersection of the lines $L_1 = 0$ and $L_2 = 0$.

(ii) Transverse axis : The transverse axis lies along $L_2 = 0$.

Conjugate axis : The conjugate axis lies along $L_1 = 0$.

(iii) Length of transverse and conjugate axes : The length of transverse and conjugate axes are $2a$ and $2b$ respectively.

(iv) Foci : The foci of the hyperbola is the point of intersection of the lines

$$\frac{a_1x + b_1y + c_1}{\sqrt{(a_1^2 + b_1^2)}} = \pm ae \text{ and } L_2 = 0.$$

(v) Directrix : The directrices of the hyperbola are

$$\frac{a_1x + b_1y + c_1}{\sqrt{(a_1^2 + b_1^2)}} = \pm \frac{a}{e}$$

(vi) Latusrectum : The latusrectum of the hyperbola is $\dfrac{2b^2}{a}$.

Example 39 The equations of the transverse and conjugate axes of a hyperbola are respectively $3x + 4y - 7 = 0$, $4x - 3y + 8 = 0$ and their respective lengths are 4 and 6. Find the equation of the hyperbola.

Sol. The equation of the required hyperbola is

$$\frac{\left(\dfrac{3x + 4y - 7}{\sqrt{(3^2 + 4^2)}}\right)^2}{\left(\dfrac{4}{2}\right)^2} - \frac{\left(\dfrac{4x - 3y + 8}{\sqrt{4^2 + (-3)^2}}\right)^2}{\left(\dfrac{6}{2}\right)^2} = 1$$

$$\Rightarrow \quad \frac{1}{100}(3x + 4y - 7)^2 - \frac{1}{225}(4x - 3y + 8)^2 = 1$$

$$\Rightarrow \quad 9(3x + 4y - 7)^2 - 4(4x - 3y + 8)^2 = 900$$

$$\Rightarrow \quad 9(9x^2 + 16y^2 + 49 + 24xy - 42x - 56y) - 4(16x^2 + 9y^2 + 64 - 24xy + 64x - 48y) = 900$$

$$\Rightarrow \quad 17x^2 + 312xy + 108y^2 - 634x - 312y - 715 = 0.$$

Exercise for Session 3

1. The diameter of $16x^2 - 9y^2 = 144$ which is conjugate to $x = 2y$ is

(a) $y = \dfrac{16}{9}x$ (b) $y = \dfrac{32}{9}x$ (c) $x = \dfrac{16}{9}y$ (d) $x = \dfrac{32}{9}y$

2. Tangents drawn from a point on the circle $x^2 + y^2 = 9$ to the hyperbola $\dfrac{x^2}{25} - \dfrac{y^2}{16} = 1$, then tangents are at angle

(a) $\dfrac{\pi}{6}$ (b) $\dfrac{\pi}{4}$ (c) $\dfrac{\pi}{3}$ (d) $\dfrac{\pi}{2}$

3. If $H \equiv \dfrac{x^2}{a^2} - \dfrac{y^2}{b^2} - 1 = 0$, $C \equiv \dfrac{x^2}{a^2} - \dfrac{y^2}{b^2} + 1 = 0$ and $A \equiv \dfrac{x^2}{a^2} - \dfrac{y^2}{b^2} = 0$ then H, A and C are in

(a) AP (b) GP (c) HP (d) AGP

4. The angle between the asymptotes of $\frac{x^2}{4} - \frac{y^2}{9} = 1$ is equal to

(a) $\tan^{-1}\left(\frac{2}{3}\right)$ (b) $\tan^{-1}\left(\frac{3}{2}\right)$ (c) $2\tan^{-1}\left(\frac{2}{3}\right)$ (d) $2\tan^{-1}\left(\frac{3}{2}\right)$

5. If e and e_1 are the eccentricities of the hyperbolas $xy = c^2$ and $x^2 - y^2 = a^2$, then $(e + e_1)^2$ is equal to

(a) 2 (b) 4 (c) 6 (d) 8

6. The product of the lengths of perpendiculars drawn from any point on the hyperbola $\frac{x^2}{2} - y^2 = 1$ to its asymptotes is

(a) $\frac{1}{2}$ (b) 2 (c) $\frac{2}{3}$ (d) $\frac{3}{2}$

7. The number of points on hyperbola $\frac{x^2}{a^2} - \frac{y^2}{b^2} = 3$ from which mutually perpendicular tangents can be drawn to the circle $x^2 + y^2 = a^2$ is/are

(a) 0 (b) 2 (c) 3 (d) 4

8. If the sum of the slopes of the normal from a point P to the hyperbola $xy = c^2$ is equal to $\lambda(\lambda \in R^+)$, then the locus of point P is

(a) $x^2 = \lambda c^2$ (b) $y^2 = \lambda c^2$ (c) $xy = \lambda c^2$ (d) None of these

9. If $S \equiv x^2 + 4xy + 3y^2 - 4x + 2y + 1 = 0$, then the value of λ for which $S + \lambda = 0$ represents its asymptotes is

(a) 20 (b) 18 (c) -16 (d) -22

10. A ray emanating from the point $(-\sqrt{41}, 0)$ is incident on the hyperbola $16x^2 - 25y^2 = 400$ at the point P with abscissa 10. Then the equation of the reflected ray after first reflection and point P lies in second quadrant is

(a) $4\sqrt{3}x - (10 - \sqrt{41})\,y + 4\sqrt{123} = 0$ (b) $4\sqrt{3}x + (10 - \sqrt{41})\,y - 4\sqrt{123} = 0$

(c) $4\sqrt{3}x + (10 - \sqrt{41})\,y + 4\sqrt{123} = 0$ (d) $4\sqrt{3}x - (10 - \sqrt{41})\,y - 4\sqrt{123} = 0$

11. A ray of light incident along the line $3x + (5 - 4\sqrt{2})y = 15$ gets reflected from the hyperbola $\frac{x^2}{16} - \frac{y^2}{9} = 1$, then its reflected ray goes along the line

(a) $x\sqrt{2} - y + 5 = 0$ (b) $y\sqrt{2} - x + 5 = 0$ (c) $y\sqrt{2} - x - 5 = 0$ (d) None of these

12. The equations of the transverse and conjugate axes of a hyperbola are $x + 2y - 3 = 0$ and $2x - y + 4 = 0$ respectively and their respective lengths are $\sqrt{2}$ and $\frac{2}{\sqrt{3}}$. The equation of the hyperbola is

(a) $2(x + 2y - 3)^2 - 3(2x - y + 4)^2 = 5$ (b) $2(2x - y + 4)^2 - 3(x + 2y - 3)^2 = 5$

(c) $2(x + 2y - 3)^2 - 3(2x - y + 4)^2 = 1$ (d) $2(2x - y + 4)^2 - 3(x + 2y - 3)^2 = 1$

13. Find the equation of that diameter which bisects the chord $7x + y - 2 = 0$ of the hyperbola $\frac{x^2}{3} - \frac{y^2}{7} = 1$.

14. Find the equation of the hyperbola which has $3x - 4y + 7 = 0$ and $4x + 3y + 1 = 0$ for its asymptotes and which passes through the origin.

15. The asymptotes of a hyperbola are parallel to lines $2x + 3y = 0$ and $3x + 2y = 0$. The hyperbola has its centre at $(1, 2)$ and it passes through $(5, 3)$, find its equation.

16. If the pair of straight lines $Ax^2 + 2Hxy + By^2 = 0$ be conjugate diameters of the hyperbola $\frac{x^2}{a^2} - \frac{y^2}{b^2} = 1$, then prove that $Aa^2 = Bb^2$.

17. A circle cuts the rectangular hyperbola $xy = 1$ in points $(x_r, y_r), r = 1, 2, 3, 4$ then prove that $x_1x_2x_3x_4 = y_1y_2y_3y_4 = 1$.

Shortcuts and Important Results to Remember

1. If P be any point and F_1 and F_2 are any other two points then :
   (a) If $|PF_1 - PF_2| < |F_1F_2|$, then the locus of P is a hyperbola.
   (b) If $|PF_1 - PF_2| = |F_1F_2|$, then the locus of P is a straight line.
   (c) If $|PF_1 - PF_2| > |F_1F_2|$, then the locus of P is an empty set.
2. The orthocentre of triangle inscribed in the hyperbola $xy = c^2$ lies on it.
3. Length of the chord of the rectangular hyperbola $xy = c^2$ whose middle-point is (h, k) is $2\sqrt{\left(\frac{(h^2 + k^2)(hk - c^2)}{hk}\right)}$.
4. The product of length of perpendicular drawn from any point on the hyperbola $\frac{x^2}{a^2} - \frac{y^2}{b^2} = 1$ to its asymptotes is $\frac{a^2b^2}{(a^2 + b^2)}$.
5. Asymptotes are the tangents from the centre of a hyperbola.
6. If the angle between the asymptotes is 2α, then eccentricity of the hyperbola is $\sec \alpha$.
7. If the tangent and normal to a rectangular hyperbola $xy = c^2$ at a point cuts off intercepts a_1 and a_2 on one axis and b_1, b_2 on the other axis, then $a_1a_2 + b_1b_2 = 0$.
8. The equation of common tangents to $\frac{x^2}{a^2} - \frac{y^2}{b^2} = 1$ and $-\frac{x^2}{a^2} + \frac{y^2}{b^2} = 1$ are $y = \pm x \pm \sqrt{(a^2 - b^2)}$.
9. The director circle of hyperbola $\frac{x^2}{a^2} - \frac{y^2}{b^2} = 1$ will be imaginary if $a < b$ and will become a circle, if $a > b$ (for $a = b$, point circle).
10. The ellipse $\frac{x^2}{a^2} + \frac{y^2}{b^2} = 1$ and the hyperbola $\frac{x^2}{a^2 - k^2} - \frac{y^2}{k^2 - b^2} = 1$ $(a > k > b)$ are confocal and therefore orthogonal.
11. If four normals can be drawn to a hyperbola from any point and if $\alpha, \beta, \gamma, \delta$ be eccentric angles of these four co-normal points, then $\alpha + \beta + \gamma + \delta =$ odd multiple of π.
12. If α, β, γ are the eccentric angles of three points on the hyperbola $\frac{x^2}{a^2} - \frac{y^2}{b^2} = 1$, the normals at which are concurrent, then $\sin(\alpha + \beta) + \sin(\beta + \gamma) + \sin(\gamma + \alpha) = 0$.
13. The locus of the foot of the perpendiculars drawn from the focus of the hyperbola $\frac{x^2}{a^2} - \frac{y^2}{b^2} = 1$ upon any tangent is its auxiliary circle i.e. $x^2 + y^2 = a^2$ and product of the perpendiculars is b^2.
14. The portion of tangent between the point of the contact and the directrix subtends a right angle at the corresponding focus.
15. The equation of the pair of asymptotes differ the hyperbola and the conjugate hyperbola by the same constant only.
16. The asymptotes pass through the centre of the hyperbola and the bisectors of the angles between the asymptotes are the axes of the hyperbola.
17. The asymptotes of a hyperbola are the diagonals of the rectangle formed by the lines drawn through the extremities of each axis parallel to the other axis.
18. Perpendicular from the foci on either asymptote meet it in the same points as the corresponding directrix and the common points of intersection lie on the auxiliary circle.
19. If from any point on the asymptote a straight line be drawn perpendicular to the transverse axis, the product of the segments of this line, intercepted between the point and the curve is always equal to the square of the semi conjugate axis.
20. The tangent at any point P on a hyperbola $\frac{x^2}{a^2} - \frac{y^2}{b^2} = 1$ with centre C, meets the asymptotes in Q and R and cuts off a ΔCQR of constant area equal to ab from the asymptotes and the portion of the tangent intercepted between the asymptotes is bisected at the point of the contact. This implies that locus of the centre of the circle circumscribing the ΔCQR in case of rectangular hyperbola is the hyperbola itself and for a standard hyperbola the locus would be the curve $4(a^2x^2 - b^2y^2) = (a^2 + b^2)^2$.
21. If a circle $x^2 + y^2 + 2gx + 2fy + c = 0$ intersects a rectangular hyperbola $xy = \lambda^2$ or $x^2 - y^2 = a^2$ at four points then the Arithmetic mean of the points of intersection lies on the middle of the line joining the centres of the circle and hyperbola.
22. The points (two) in which any tangent meets the tangents at the vertices and the foci of the hyperbola are concyclic i.e. S, P, S' and Q are lie on circle.

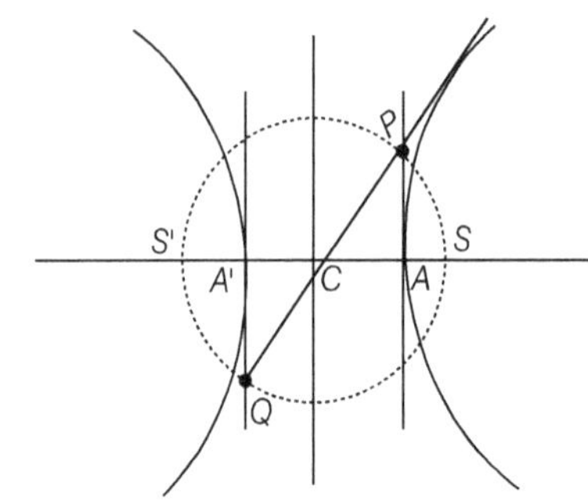

JEE Type Solved Examples :
Single Option Correct Type Questions

- This section contains 10 **multiple choice examples.** Each example has four choices (a), (b), (c) and (d) out of which **ONLY ONE** is correct.

Ex. 1 *If the eccentricity of the hyperbola $x^2 - y^2 \sec^2 \alpha = 5$ is $\sqrt{3}$ times the eccentricity of the ellipse $x^2 \sec^2 \alpha + y^2 = 25$, then a value of α is*

(a) $\frac{\pi}{6}$ (b) $\frac{\pi}{4}$

(c) $\frac{\pi}{3}$ (d) $\frac{\pi}{2}$

Sol. (b) For the hyperbola $\frac{x^2}{5} - \frac{y^2}{5\cos^2 \alpha} = 1$

we have, $e_1^2 = 1 + \frac{5\cos^2 \alpha}{5} = 1 + \cos^2 \alpha$ ... (i)

For the ellipse $\frac{x^2}{25\cos^2 \alpha} + \frac{y^2}{25} = 1$

we have, $e_2^2 = 1 - \frac{25\cos^2 \alpha}{25} = 1 - \cos^2 \alpha = \sin^2 \alpha$ ... (ii)

Given that, $e_1 = \sqrt{3}\, e_2$ or $e_1^2 = 3e_2^2$

$\Rightarrow$ $1 + \cos^2 \alpha = 3\sin^2 \alpha$ [from Eqs. (i) and (ii)]

$\Rightarrow$ $2 = 4\sin^2 \alpha$

or $\sin \alpha = \frac{1}{\sqrt{2}}$

$\Rightarrow$ $\alpha = \frac{\pi}{4}$

Ex. 2 *The asymptote of the hyperbola $\frac{x^2}{a^2} - \frac{y^2}{b^2} = 1$ form with any tangent to the hyperbola a triangle whose area is $a^2 \tan \lambda$ in magnitude, then its eccentricity is*

(a) $\sec \lambda$ (b) $\operatorname{cosec} \lambda$

(c) $\sec^2 \lambda$ (d) $\operatorname{cosec}^2 \lambda$

Sol. (a) Any tangent to the hyperbola $\frac{x^2}{a^2} - \frac{y^2}{b^2} = 1$ forms a triangle with the asymptotes which has constant area ab.

Given, $ab = a^2 \tan \lambda$

or $b = a \tan \lambda$

or $b^2 = a^2 \tan^2 \lambda$

or $a^2(e^2 - 1) = a^2 \tan^2 \lambda$

or $e^2 = 1 + \tan^2 \lambda = \sec^2 \lambda$

$\therefore$ $e = \sec \lambda$

Ex. 3 *The equation of the chord joining two points (x_1, y_1) and (x_2, y_2) on the rectangular hyperbola $xy = c^2$ is*

(a) $\frac{x}{x_1 + x_2} + \frac{y}{y_1 + y_2} = 1$ (b) $\frac{x}{x_1 - x_2} + \frac{y}{y_1 - y_2} = 1$

(c) $\frac{x}{y_1 + y_2} + \frac{y}{x_1 + x_2} = 1$ (d) $\frac{x}{y_1 - y_2} + \frac{y}{x_1 - x_2} = 1$

Sol. (a) The mid-point of the chord is $\left(\frac{x_1 + x_2}{2}, \frac{y_1 + y_2}{2}\right)$

$\therefore$ The equation of chord whose mid-point $\left(\frac{x_1 + x_2}{2}, \frac{y_1 + y_2}{2}\right)$ is $T = S_1$

or $\frac{1}{2}\left(x\left(\frac{y_1 + y_2}{2}\right) + y\left(\frac{x_1 + x_2}{2}\right)\right) - c^2$

$= \left(\frac{x_1 + x_2}{2}\right)\left(\frac{y_1 + y_2}{2}\right) - c^2$

$\Rightarrow$ $x(y_1 + y_2) + y(x_1 + x_2) = (x_1 + x_2)(y_1 + y_2)$

or $\frac{x}{x_1 + x_2} + \frac{y}{y_1 + y_2} = 1$

Ex. 4 *Area of quadrilateral formed with the foci of the hyperbola $\frac{x^2}{a^2} - \frac{y^2}{b^2} = 1$ and $\frac{x^2}{a^2} - \frac{y^2}{b^2} = -1$ is*

(a) $4(a^2 + b^2)$ (b) $2(a^2 + b^2)$

(c) $(a^2 + b^2)$ (d) $\frac{1}{2}(a^2 + b^2)$

Sol. (b) Required area $= 4 \times$ Area of $\Delta S_1 O S_3$

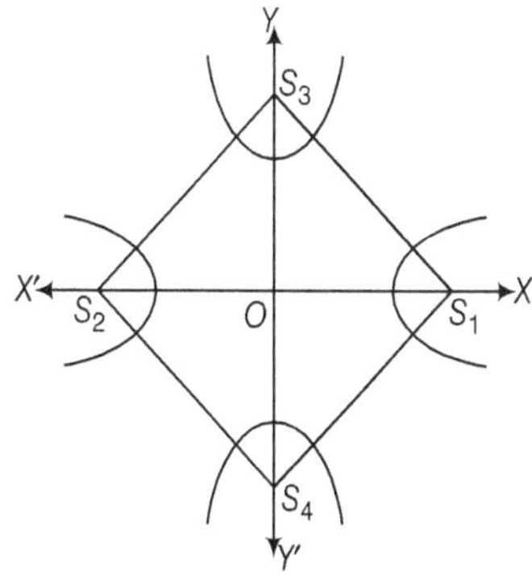

$= 4 \times \frac{1}{2} ae \times be_1 = (2ab)(ee_1)$ ...(i)

$\because$ $b^2 = a^2(e^2 - 1)$

$\therefore$ $e = \frac{\sqrt{(a^2 + b^2)}}{a}$ ...(ii)

and $a^2 = b^2(e_1^2 - 1)$

$$\therefore \quad e_1 = \frac{\sqrt{(a^2+b^2)}}{b} \quad \text{...(iii)}$$

Substituting the values of e and e_1 from Eqs. (ii) and (iii) in Eq. (i), then

$$\text{Required area} = 2ab \times \frac{\sqrt{(a^2+b^2)}}{a} \times \frac{\sqrt{(a^2+b^2)}}{b}$$

$$= 2(a^2+b^2)$$

Ex. 5 *Let $P(a\sec\theta, b\tan\theta)$ and $Q(a\sec\phi, b\tan\phi)$, where $\theta + \phi = \frac{\pi}{2}$, be two points on the hyperbola $\frac{x^2}{a^2} - \frac{y^2}{b^2} = 1$. If (h,k) is the point of intersection of normals at P and Q, then k is equal to*

(a) $\left(\frac{a^2+b^2}{a}\right)$ (b) $-\left(\frac{a^2+b^2}{a}\right)$

(c) $\left(\frac{a^2+b^2}{b}\right)$ (d) $-\left(\frac{a^2+b^2}{b}\right)$

Sol. (d) Equations of the normals at $P(\theta)$ and $Q(\phi)$ are

$$ax\cos\theta + by\cot\theta = a^2+b^2 \quad \text{... (i)}$$

and $$ax\cos\phi + by\cot\phi = a^2+b^2 \quad \text{... (ii)}$$

Now, dividing by $\cos\theta$ and $\cos\phi$ in Eqs. (i) and (ii) respectively, then

$$ax + by\,\text{cosec}\,\theta = (a^2+b^2)\sec\theta \quad \text{... (iii)}$$

and $$ax + by\,\text{cosec}\,\phi = (a^2+b^2)\sec\phi \quad \text{... (iv)}$$

Subtracting Eq. (iv) from Eq. (iii), we get

$$y = \left(\frac{a^2+b^2}{b}\right)\cdot\left(\frac{\sec\theta - \sec\phi}{\text{cosec}\,\theta - \text{cosec}\,\phi}\right)$$

$$\therefore \quad k = y$$

$$= \left(\frac{a^2+b^2}{b}\right)\cdot\left(\frac{\sec\theta - \sec\left(\frac{\pi}{2}-\theta\right)}{\text{cosec}\,\theta - \text{cosec}\left(\frac{\pi}{2}-\theta\right)}\right) \quad \left(\because \theta+\phi = \frac{\pi}{2}\right)$$

$$= \left(\frac{a^2+b^2}{b}\right)\cdot\left(\frac{\sec\theta - \text{cosec}\,\theta}{\text{cosec}\,\theta - \sec\theta}\right) = -\left(\frac{a^2+b^2}{b}\right)$$

Ex. 6 *Let the major axis of a standard ellipse equals the transverse axis of a standard hyperbola and their director circles have radius equal to 2R and R respectively. If e_1 and e_2 are the eccentricities of the ellipse and hyperbola, then the correct relation is*

(a) $4e_1^2 - e_2^2 = 6$ (b) $e_1^2 - 4e_2^2 = 2$

(c) $4e_2^2 - e_1^2 = 6$ (d) $e_2^2 - 4e_1^2 = 2$

Sol. (c) Let equation of ellipse is

$$\frac{x^2}{a^2} + \frac{y^2}{b^2} = 1 \; (a > b)$$

$\therefore$ Director circle is $x^2 + y^2 = a^2 + b^2$

and $$b^2 = a^2(1-e_1^2)$$

given $$a^2 + b^2 = (2R)^2$$

$$\Rightarrow \quad a^2 + a^2(1-e_1^2) = 4R^2$$

$$\Rightarrow \quad 2 - e_1^2 = \frac{4R^2}{a^2} \quad \text{... (i)}$$

and equation of hyperbola is $\frac{x^2}{a^2} - \frac{y^2}{b_1^2} = 1$

$\therefore$ Director circle is $x^2 + y^2 = a^2 - b_1^2$

and $$b_1^2 = a^2(e_2^2 - 1)$$

Given $$a^2 - b_1^2 = R^2$$

$$\Rightarrow \quad a^2 - a^2(e_2^2 - 1) = R^2$$

$$\Rightarrow \quad 2 - e_2^2 = \frac{R^2}{a^2} \quad \text{... (ii)}$$

Dividing Eq. (i) by Eq. (ii), then

$$\frac{2-e_1^2}{2-e_2^2} = 4 \Rightarrow 4e_2^2 - e_1^2 = 6$$

Ex. 7 *The tangent to the hyperbola $xy = c^2$ at point $P(t)$ intersects the X-axis at T and the Y-axis. at T′. The normal to the hyperbola at $P(t)$ intersects the X-axis at N and the Y-axis at N′. The areas of the triangles PNT and PN′T′ are Δ and Δ' respectively, then $\frac{1}{\Delta} + \frac{1}{\Delta'}$ is*

(a) equal to 1 (b) depends on t

(c) depends on c (d) equal to 2

Sol. (c) Equation of tangent at $P\left(ct, \frac{c}{t}\right)$ is $\frac{x}{t} + ty = 2c$

or $$\frac{x}{2ct} + \frac{y}{(2c/t)} = 1$$

$$\therefore \quad T \equiv (2ct, 0), T' \equiv \left(0, \frac{2c}{t}\right)$$

and equation of normal at $P\left(ct, \frac{c}{t}\right)$ is

$$xt^3 - yt - ct^4 + c = 0$$

or $$\frac{x}{\left(\frac{c(t^4-1)}{t^3}\right)} + \frac{y}{\left(\frac{c(t^4-1)}{-t}\right)} = 1$$

$$\therefore \quad N \equiv \left(\frac{c(t^4-1)}{t^3}, 0\right), N' \equiv \left(0, -\frac{c(t^4-1)}{t}\right)$$

$\because$ Area of triangle $PNT = \Delta$

$$\therefore \quad \Delta = \frac{1}{2}\begin{Vmatrix} ct - 2ct & \frac{c}{t} - 0 \\ \frac{c(t^4-1)}{t^3} - 2ct & 0 - 0 \end{Vmatrix}$$

$$=\frac{1}{2}\left|-\frac{c}{t}\left(\frac{c(t^4-1)}{t^3}-2ct\right)\right|=\frac{c^2}{2}\left(\frac{t^4+1}{t^4}\right)$$

and Area of $\Delta PN'T'=\Delta'$

$$\therefore \quad \Delta'=\frac{1}{2}\left|\begin{matrix} ct-0 & \frac{c}{t}-\frac{2c}{t} \\ 0-0 & -\frac{c(t^4-1)}{t}-\frac{2c}{t}\end{matrix}\right|$$

$$=\frac{1}{2}\left|ct\left(-\frac{c(t^4-1)}{t}-\frac{2c}{t}\right)\right|=\frac{c^2}{2}(t^4+1)$$

$$\therefore \quad \frac{1}{\Delta}+\frac{1}{\Delta'}=\frac{2t^4}{c^2(t^4+1)}+\frac{2}{c^2(t^4+1)}=\frac{2}{c^2}$$

Ex. 8 *Let any double ordinate PNP' of the hyperbola $\frac{x^2}{25}-\frac{y^2}{16}=1$ be produced both sides to meet the asymptotes is Q and Q', then $(PQ)(P'Q)$ is equal to*

(a) 9 (b) 16 (c) 25 (d) 41

Sol. (b) Let $Q\equiv(x_1,y_1)$

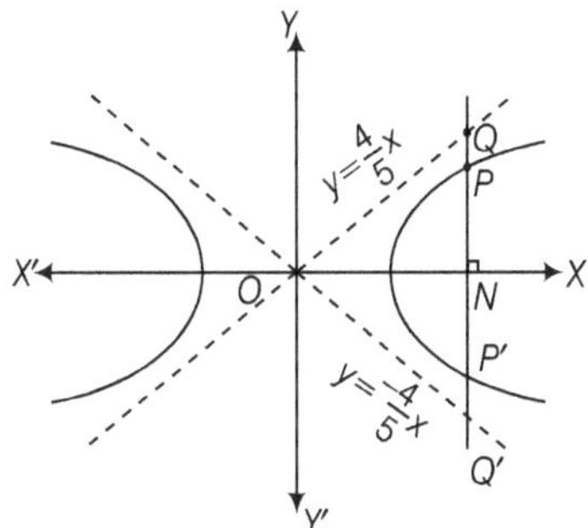

We have $\quad NP=\frac{4}{5}\sqrt{(x_1^2-25)}$

and Q is on $\quad y=\frac{4}{5}x$

$\therefore \quad NQ=\frac{4}{5}x_1$

Now, $\quad PQ=NQ-NP$

$$=\frac{4}{5}(x_1-\sqrt{(x_1^2-25)})$$

and $\quad P'Q=NP'+NQ=NP+NQ \quad (\because NP'=NP)$

$$=\frac{4}{5}(x_1+\sqrt{(x_1^2-25)})$$

$$\therefore \quad (PQ)(P'Q)=\frac{16}{25}(x_1^2-(x_1^2-25))$$

$$=\frac{16}{25}\times 25=16$$

Ex. 9 *The coordinates of a point on the hyperbola $\frac{x^2}{24}-\frac{y^2}{18}-1$. Which is nearest to the line $3x+2y+1=0$ are*

(a) (6, 3) (b) $(-6,-3)$
(c) $(6,-3)$ (d) $(-6,3)$

Sol. (d)

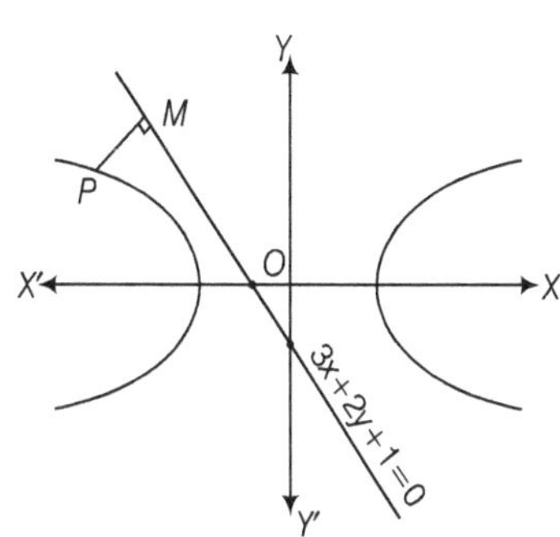

Let point P is nearest to the given line if the tangent at P is parallel to the given line.

Now, equation of tangent at $P(x_1,y_1)$ is

$$\frac{xx_1}{24}-\frac{yy_1}{18}=1$$

$\therefore$ Slope of tangent at $P(x_1,y_1)$ is

$$\frac{3}{4}\frac{x_1}{y_1}$$

which must be equal to $-\frac{3}{2}$

Therefore,

$$\frac{3}{4}\cdot\frac{x_1}{y_1}=-\frac{3}{2} \text{ or } x_1=-2y_1 \quad \text{...(i)}$$

Also, $P(x_1,y_1)$ lies on the curve

Hence, $$\frac{x_1^2}{24}-\frac{y_1^2}{18}=1 \quad \text{...(ii)}$$

Solving Eqs. (i) and (ii), we get two points $(6,-3)$ and $(-6,3)$ of which $(-6,3)$ is the nearest.

Aliter :

The equation of normal at $P(2\sqrt{6}\sec\theta, 3\sqrt{2}\tan\theta)$ is

$$(2\sqrt{6}\cos\theta)x+(3\sqrt{2}\cot\theta)y=42$$

Now, this line will be perpendicular to

$$3x+2y+1=0$$

then, $\quad (2\sqrt{6}\cos\theta)\times 3+(3\sqrt{2}\cot\theta)\times 2=0$

or $$\sin\theta=-\frac{1}{\sqrt{3}}$$

$$\therefore \quad \tan\theta=\frac{1}{\sqrt{2}} \text{ and } \sec\theta=-\frac{\sqrt{3}}{\sqrt{2}}$$

Hence, $\quad P\equiv(-6,3)$

Ex. 10 *For each positive integer n, consider the point P with abscissa n on the curve $y^2-x^2=1$. If d_n represents the shortest distance from the point P to the line $y=x$, then $\lim_{n\to\infty}(n.d_n)$ has the value equal to*

(a) $\frac{1}{2\sqrt{2}}$ (b) $\frac{1}{2}$
(c) $\frac{1}{\sqrt{2}}$ (d) 0

Sol. (a) Let $P \equiv (n, \sqrt{(n^2+1)})$

$\therefore \quad d_n = \left(\dfrac{\sqrt{(n^2+1)} - n}{\sqrt{2}}\right)$

or $\quad n \cdot d_n = \dfrac{n}{\sqrt{2}}(\sqrt{(n^2+1)} - n)$

or $\quad \lim\limits_{n\to\infty} (n.d_n) = \dfrac{1}{\sqrt{2}} \lim\limits_{n\to\infty} n(\sqrt{(n^2+1)} - n)$

$$= \frac{1}{\sqrt{2}} \lim_{n\to\infty} \frac{n(\sqrt{(n^2+1)} - n)(\sqrt{(n^2+1)} + n)}{(\sqrt{(n^2+1)} + n)}$$

$$= \frac{1}{\sqrt{2}} \lim_{n\to\infty} \frac{n(1)}{n\left(\sqrt{\left(1+\frac{1}{n^2}\right)}+1\right)}$$

$$= \frac{1}{\sqrt{2}} \lim_{n\to\infty} \left(\frac{1}{\sqrt{\left(1+\frac{1}{n^2}\right)}+1}\right)$$

$$= \frac{1}{\sqrt{2}} \cdot \left(\frac{1}{1+1}\right) = \frac{1}{2\sqrt{2}}$$

JEE Type Solved Examples :
More than One Correct Option Type Questions

- This section contains 5 **multiple choice examples.** Each example has four choices (a), (b), (c) and (d) out of which **MORE THAN ONE** may be correct.

Ex. 11 *If two tangents can be drawn to the different branches of hyperbola $\dfrac{x^2}{1} - \dfrac{y^2}{4} = 1$ from the point (α, α^2), then*

(a) $\alpha \in (-\infty, -2)$ (b) $\alpha \in (-2, 0)$
(c) $\alpha \in (0, 2)$ (d) $\alpha \in (2, \infty)$

Sol. (a, d) $\because (\alpha, \alpha^2)$ lie on the parabola $y = x^2$

$\therefore (\alpha, \alpha^2)$ must lie between the asymptotes of hyperbola

$\dfrac{x^2}{1} - \dfrac{y^2}{4} = 1$ in I and II quadrants.

$\because$ Asymptotes of $\dfrac{x^2}{1} - \dfrac{y^2}{4} = 1$ are $y = \pm 2x$

then $\quad 2\alpha < \alpha^2$ and $-2\alpha < \alpha^2$

$\Rightarrow \quad \alpha(\alpha - 2) > 0$ and $\alpha(\alpha + 2) > 0$

$\therefore \quad \alpha < 0$ or $\alpha > 2$ and $\alpha < -2$ or $\alpha > 0$

$\therefore \quad \alpha \in (-\infty, -2) \cup (2, \infty)$

Ex. 12 *If the ellipse $x^2 + \lambda^2 y^2 = \lambda^2 a^2; \lambda^2 > 1$ is confocal with the hyperbola $x^2 - y^2 = a^2$, then*

(a) ratio of eccentricities of ellipse and hyperbola is $1:\sqrt{3}$
(b) ratio of major axis of ellipse and transverse axis of hyperbola is $\sqrt{3}:1$
(c) The ellipse and hyperbola cuts each other orthogonally
(d) ratio of length of latusrectum of ellipse and hyperbola is $1:3$

Sol. (a, b, c) Given ellipse is $\dfrac{x^2}{\lambda^2 a^2} + \dfrac{y^2}{a^2} = 1$; $\lambda^2 a^2 > a^2$ and let e_1 and e_2 be the eccentricities of ellipse and hyperbola, then

$$a^2 = \lambda^2 a^2 (1 - e_1^2)$$

or $\quad e_1 = \sqrt{\left(1 - \dfrac{1}{\lambda^2}\right)}$

and $\quad e_2 = \sqrt{2}$

Now, $\quad \lambda a e_1 = a e_2$

$\Rightarrow \quad \lambda \sqrt{\left(1 - \dfrac{1}{\lambda^2}\right)} = \sqrt{2}$

$\Rightarrow \quad \lambda^2 - 1 = 2$ or $\lambda = \pm\sqrt{3}$

$\therefore \quad \lambda = \sqrt{3} \qquad (\because \lambda > 0)$

Alternate (a) : $\dfrac{e_1}{e_2} = \dfrac{1}{\lambda} = \dfrac{1}{\sqrt{3}}$

Alternate (b) : $= \dfrac{\text{Major axis of ellipse}}{\text{Transverse axis of hyperbola}}$

$$= \frac{2\lambda a}{2a} = \lambda = \sqrt{3}$$

Alternate (c) : Equations of tangents of ellipse and hyperbola at (x_1, y_1) are

$$\frac{xx_1}{\lambda^2 a^2} + \frac{yy_1}{a^2} = 1$$

and $\quad xx_1 - yy_1 = a^2$

i.e., $\quad$ slopes are $= -\dfrac{x_1}{\lambda^2 y_1}$ and $\dfrac{x_1}{y_1}$ (say m_1 and m_2)

According to alternate,

$$m_1 m_2 = -\frac{x_1}{\lambda^2 y_1} \times \frac{x_1}{y_1} = -\frac{x_1^2}{\lambda^2 y_1^2}$$

$$= -\frac{\dfrac{2a^2}{\lambda^2+1}}{\dfrac{a^2(\lambda^2-1)}{(\lambda^2+1)}} = -\frac{2}{\lambda^2 - 1} \qquad \left(\because \begin{array}{l} x_1^2 = \dfrac{2a^2\lambda^2}{\lambda^2+1} \\ \text{and } y_1^2 = \dfrac{a^2(\lambda^2-1)}{(\lambda^2+1)} \end{array}\right)$$

$$= -\frac{2}{3-1} = -1 \qquad (\because \lambda = \sqrt{3})$$

Alternate (d) : $= \dfrac{\text{Latus reaction of ellipse}}{\text{Latus reaction of hyperbola}}$

$$= \frac{\frac{2a^2}{\lambda a}}{\frac{2a^2}{a}} = \frac{1}{\lambda} = \frac{1}{\sqrt{3}}$$

● ***Ex. 13*** *If the circle $x^2 + y^2 = a^2$ intersects the hyperbola $xy = c^2$ at four points $P(x_1, y_1)$, $Q(x_2, y_2)$, $R(x_3, y_3)$ and $S(x_4, y_4)$, then*

(a) $\Sigma x_1 = 0$ (b) $\Sigma y_1 = 0$
(c) $\Pi x_1 = 0$ (d) $\Pi y_1 = 0$

Sol. (a, b, c, d) Solving $x^2 + y^2 = a^2$ and $xy = c^2$,

we have, $$x^2 + \frac{c^4}{x^2} = a^2$$

or $$x^4 - a^2x^2 + c^4 = 0$$

or $$\Sigma x_1 = 0 \text{ and } \Pi x_1 = c^4$$

Similarly, if we eliminate x, then

$$y^4 - a^2y^2 + c^4 = 0$$

or $$\Sigma y_1 = 0 \text{ and } \Pi y_1 = c^4$$

● ***Ex. 14*** *A straight line touches the rectangular hyperbola $9x^2 - 9y^2 = 8$ and the parabola $y^2 = 32x$, the equation of the line is*

(a) $9x + 3y - 8 = \infty$ (b) $9x - 3y + 8 = 0$
(c) $9x + 3y + 8 = 0$ (d) $9x - 3y - 8 = 0$

Sol. (b, c) Equation of tangent to the parabola $y^2 = 32x$ is

$$y = mx + \frac{8}{m} \qquad \text{... (i)}$$

Which is also touches the hyperbola $9x^2 - 9y^2 = 8$

i.e. $$x^2 - y^2 = \frac{8}{9}$$

So that, $$\left(\frac{8}{m}\right)^2 = \frac{8}{9} \times m^2 - \frac{8}{9}$$

$\Rightarrow$ $$\frac{8}{m^2} = \frac{m^2}{9} - \frac{1}{9}$$

$\Rightarrow$ $$m^4 - m^2 - 72 = 0$$

$\Rightarrow$ $$(m^2 - 9)(m^2 + 8) = 0$$

$\therefore$ $$m^2 - 9 = 0$$

but $$m^2 + 8 \neq 0$$

$\therefore$ $$m = \pm 3$$

Hence, from Eq. (i), the equation of tangents are

$$y = 3x + \frac{8}{3}$$

and $$y = -3x - \frac{8}{3}$$

or $$9x - 3y + 8 = 0$$

and $$9x + 3y + 8 = 0$$

● ***Ex. 15*** *The differential equation $\dfrac{dx}{dy} = \dfrac{3y}{2x}$ represents a family of hyperbolas (except when it represents a pair of lines) with eccentricity*

(a) $\sqrt{\frac{7}{3}}$ (b) $\sqrt{\frac{5}{3}}$
(c) $\sqrt{\frac{3}{2}}$ (d) $\sqrt{\frac{5}{2}}$

Sol. (b, d) $\because \dfrac{dx}{dy} = \dfrac{3y}{2x}$

or $$\int 2x\,dx = \int 3y\,dy$$

or $$x^2 = \frac{3y^2}{2} + c$$

or $$\frac{x^2}{3} - \frac{y^2}{2} = \frac{c}{3}$$

or $$\frac{x^2}{3} - \frac{y^2}{2} = c_1$$

Case I If $c_1 > 0$, then $e = \sqrt{\left(1 + \frac{2}{3}\right)} = \sqrt{\frac{5}{3}}$

Case II If $c_1 < 0$, then $e = \sqrt{\left(1 + \frac{3}{2}\right)} = \sqrt{\frac{5}{2}}$

JEE Type Solved Examples : Paragraph Based Questions

- This section contains 2 **solved paragraphs** based upon each of the paragraph 3 **multiple choice** questions have to be answered. Each of these questions has four choices (a), (b), (c) and (d) out of which **ONLY ONE** is correct.

Paragraph I

(Q. Nos. 16 to 18)

A conic C satisfies the differential equation. $(1+y^2)dx - xy\,dy = 0$ and passes through the point (1, 0). An ellipse E which is confocal with C having its eccentricity equal to $\sqrt{\left(\frac{2}{3}\right)}$.

16. Length of latusrectum of the conic C is

(a) 1 (b) 2

(c) 3 (d) 4

17. Equations of the ellipse E is

(a) $\frac{x^2}{3}+\frac{y^2}{1}=1$ (b) $\frac{x^2}{1}+\frac{y^2}{3}=1$

(c) $\frac{x^2}{4}+\frac{y^2}{9}=1$ (d) $\frac{x^2}{9}+\frac{y^2}{4}=1$

18. Locus of the point of intersection of the perpendicular tangents to the ellipse E, is

(a) $x^2+y^2=4$ (b) $x^2+y^2=8$

(c) $x^2+y^2=10$ (d) $x^2+y^2=13$

Sol. Given differential equation is $(1+y^2)\,dx - xy\,dy = 0$

$$\Rightarrow \quad \frac{dx}{x}-\frac{ydy}{(1+y^2)}=0 \text{ or } \frac{2dx}{x}-\frac{2ydy}{1+y^2}=0$$

On integrating, we have $2\ln x - \ln(1+y^2) = \ln c$

or $\quad \ln x^2 = \ln(c(1+y^2))$ or $x^2 = c(1+y^2)$

or $\quad \frac{x^2}{c}-\frac{y^2}{1}=1$ (Hyperbola)

It passes through (1, 0), then $\frac{1}{c}-0=1$

$\therefore \quad c=1$

$\therefore C$ is rectangular hyperbola $x^2-y^2=1$, having its eccentricity $=\sqrt{2}$ and its foci are $(\pm\sqrt{2}, 0)$.

If a is the length of semi major axis of ellipse E, then $ae=\sqrt{2}$

or $\quad a\sqrt{\frac{2}{3}}=\sqrt{2}$ or $a=\sqrt{3}$

Now, $\quad b^2 = a^2(1-e^2) = 3\left(1-\frac{2}{3}\right)=1$

16. (b) Length of latusrectum of the conic C is $\frac{2(1)^2}{1}=2$

17. (a) Equation of the ellipse E is

$$\frac{x^2}{a^2}+\frac{y^2}{b^2}=1 \text{ i.e, } \frac{x^2}{3}+\frac{y^2}{1}=1$$

18. (a) Required locus is the director circle of E which is $x^2+y^2=3+1$ or $x^2+y^2=4$

Paragraph II

(Q. Nos. 19 to 21)

For the hyperbola $\frac{x^2}{a^2}-\frac{y^2}{b^2}=1$, the normal at point P meets the transverse axis AA′ in G and the conjugate axis BB′ in g and CF be perpendicular to the normal from the centre.

19. The value of $\frac{PF.PG}{(CB)^2}$ is equal to

(a) 4 (b) 3

(c) 2 (d) 1

20. The value of $PF.Pg$ is equal to

(a) $(CA)^2$ (b) $(CF)^2$

(c) $(CB)^2$ (d) $CA.CB$

21. Locus of middle-point of G and g is a hyperbola of eccentricity

(a) $\frac{1}{\sqrt{(e^2-1)}}$ (b) $\frac{e}{\sqrt{(e^2-1)}}$

(c) $2\sqrt{(e^2-1)}$ (d) $\frac{e}{2}$

Sol. $C \equiv (0,0)$

$AA' = 2a$, $BB' = 2b$

$\therefore \quad CA = CA' = a$ and $CB = CB' = b$

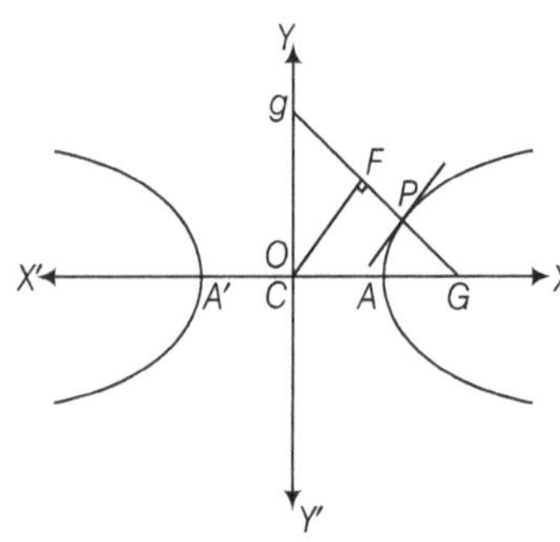

Let $\quad P \equiv (a\sec\theta, b\tan\theta)$

Equation of normals at P is

$$ax\cos\theta + by\cot\theta = a^2+b^2 \quad \text{... (i)}$$

$$\therefore \quad G \equiv \left(\frac{(a^2+b^2)}{a}\sec\theta, 0\right), g \equiv \left(0, \frac{(a^2+b^2)}{b}\tan\theta\right)$$

Equation of CF which is perpendicular to Eq. (i) and through origin is $bx\cot\theta - ay\cos\theta = 0$

$$\therefore \quad PF = \frac{ab}{\sqrt{(b^2\sec^2\theta + a^2\tan^2\theta)}}$$

and
$$PG = \sqrt{\left(a\sec\theta - \frac{a^2+b^2}{a}\sec\theta\right)^2 + (b\tan\theta - 0)^2}$$

$$= \frac{b}{a}\sqrt{(b^2\sec^2\theta + a^2\tan^2\theta)}$$

19. (d) $\because PF \cdot PG = \dfrac{ab}{\sqrt{(b^2\sec^2\theta + a^2\tan^2\theta)}} \cdot \dfrac{b}{a}\sqrt{(b^2\sec^2\theta + a^2\tan^2\theta)}$

$$= b^2 = (CB)^2$$

$$\therefore \quad \frac{PF \cdot PG}{(CB)^2} = 1$$

20. (a) $\because Pg = \sqrt{(a\sec\theta - 0)^2 + \left(b\tan\theta - \dfrac{(a^2+b^2)}{b}\tan\theta\right)^2}$

$$= \sqrt{\left(a^2\sec^2\theta + \frac{a^4}{b^2}\tan^2\theta\right)}$$

$$= \frac{a}{b}\sqrt{(b^2\sec^2\theta + a^2\tan^2\theta)}$$

$$\therefore \quad PF \cdot Pg = \frac{ab}{\sqrt{(b^2\sec^2\theta + a^2\tan^2\theta)}} \times \frac{a}{b}\sqrt{(b^2\sec^2\theta + a^2\tan^2\theta)}$$

$$= a^2 = (CA)^2$$

21. (b) $\because$ Mid-point of G and g is

$$\left(\frac{(a^2+b^2)}{2a}\sec\theta, \frac{(a^2+b^2)}{2b}\tan\theta\right)$$

$$\therefore \quad x = \left(\frac{a^2+b^2}{2a}\right)\sec\theta,\ y = \left(\frac{a^2+b^2}{2a}\right)\tan\theta$$

$$\therefore \quad (2ax)^2 - (2by)^2 = (a^2+b^2)^2$$

or
$$\frac{x^2}{\left(\dfrac{a^2+b^2}{2a}\right)^2} - \frac{y^2}{\left(\dfrac{a^2+b^2}{2b}\right)^2} = 1$$

$$\therefore \quad e_1 = \sqrt{\frac{\left(\dfrac{a^2+b^2}{2a}\right)^2 + \left(\dfrac{a^2+b^2}{2b}\right)^2}{\left(\dfrac{a^2+b^2}{2a}\right)^2}} = \sqrt{\left(\frac{\dfrac{1}{a^2}+\dfrac{1}{b^2}}{\dfrac{1}{a^2}}\right)}$$

$$= \sqrt{\frac{a^2+b^2}{2b^2}} = \sqrt{\frac{a^2+a^2(e^2-1)}{a^2(e^2-1)}} = \frac{e}{\sqrt{(e^2-1)}}$$

JEE Type Solved Examples :
Single Integer Answer Type Questions

- This section contains 2 **examples.** The answer to each example in **a single digit integer,** ranging from 0 to 9 (both inclusive).

• Ex. 22 *The equation of transverse axis of hyperbola (passing through origin) having asymptotes $3x - 4y - 1 = 0$ and $4x - 3y - 6 = 0$ is $ax + by - c = 0$, $a, b, c \in N$ and g.c.d $(a, b, c) = 1$, then the value of $a + b + c$ is*

Sol. (7) Since the equation of asymptotes are

$$3x - 4y - 1 = 0 \text{ and } 4x - 3y - 6 = 0$$

$\therefore$ Equation of transverse axis is given by

$$\frac{|(3x-4y-1)|}{\sqrt{(3)^2+(-4)^2}} = \frac{|4x-3y-6|}{\sqrt{(4)^2+(-3)^2}}$$

or $\quad |3x - 4y - 1| = |4x - 3y - 6|$

or $\quad (3x - 4y - 1) = \pm(4x - 3y - 6) \Rightarrow x + y - 5 = 0$

and $\quad x - y - 7 = 0$

$\therefore$ Transverse axis is given by $ax + by - c = 0$; $a, b, c \in N$

$\Rightarrow \quad ax + by - c \equiv x + y - 5 = 0$

$\Rightarrow \quad a = 1, b = 1, c = 5$

Hence, $\quad a + b + c = 1 + 1 + 5 = 7$

• Ex. 23 *If a variable line has its intercepts on the coordinate axes are e and e′, where $\frac{e}{2}$ and $\frac{e'}{2}$ are the eccentricities of a hyperbola and its conjugate hyperbola, then the line always touches the circle $x^2 + y^2 = r^2$, where r is*

Sol. (2) Since $\frac{e}{2}$ and $\frac{e'}{2}$ are the eccentricities of a hyperbola and its conjugate, we have

$$\left(\frac{e}{2}\right)^{-2} + \left(\frac{e'}{2}\right)^{-2} = 1 \text{ or } \frac{4}{e^2} + \frac{4}{(e')^2} = 1$$

or
$$4 = \frac{e^2e'^2}{e^2+e'^2} \quad \text{... (i)}$$

Equations of variable line is $\frac{x}{e} + \frac{y}{e'} = 1$

i.e. $\quad xe' + ye - ee' = 0.$

It is tangent to the circle $x^2 + y^2 = r^2$

$$\therefore \quad \frac{|0 - ee'|}{\sqrt{e^2+e'^2}} = r$$

$$\therefore \quad r = \frac{ee'}{\sqrt{(e^2+e'^2)}} = 2 \quad \text{[from Eq. (i)]}$$

JEE Type Solved Examples : Matching Type Questions

- This section contain **only one example.** This example has three statements (A, B and C) given in **Column I** and four statements (p, q, r, and s) in **Column II**. Any given statment in **Column I** can have correct matching with one or more statements (s) given in **Column II.**

Ex. 24 *Match the following.*

	Column I		Column II
(A)	The locus of the point of intersection of the lines $\sqrt{3}x-y-4\sqrt{3}t=0$ and $\sqrt{3}tx+ty-4\sqrt{3}=0$ (where t is a parameter) is a hyperbola whose eccentricity is	(p)	a natural number
(B)	If the product of the perpendicular distances from any point on the hyperbola $\frac{x^2}{a^2}-\frac{y^2}{b^2}=1$ of eccentricity $e=\sqrt{3}$ from its asymptotes is equal to 6, then the length of the transverse axis of the hyperbola is	(q)	a prime number
(C)	The area of the triangle that a tangent at a point of the hyperbola $\frac{x^2}{16}-\frac{y^2}{a}=1$ makes with its asymptotes is	(r)	a composite number
		(s)	a perfect number

Sol. (A) $\rightarrow$ (p, q); (B) $\rightarrow$ (p, r, s); (C)$\rightarrow$ (p, r)

(A) The given lines are

$$\sqrt{3}x-y-4\sqrt{3}t=0 \quad \text{... (i)}$$

and $$\sqrt{3}tx+ty-4\sqrt{3}=0 \quad \text{... (ii)}$$

Eliminate 't' from Eqs. (i) and (ii), then

$$\frac{\sqrt{3}x-y}{4\sqrt{3}}=\frac{4\sqrt{3}}{\sqrt{3}x+y}$$

$\Rightarrow$ $$3x^2-y^2=48$$

or $$\frac{x^2}{16}-\frac{y^2}{48}=1$$

or $$48=16(e^2-1)$$

$\Rightarrow$ $$e^2=4$$

$\therefore$ $$e=2$$

(B) Here, $e=\sqrt{3}$

$\therefore$ $$b^2=a^2(3-1)=2a^2 \quad \text{... (i)}$$

Now, hyperbola convert in the form

$$\frac{x^2}{a^2}-\frac{y^2}{2a^2}=1$$

Let $P(a\sec\theta, a\sqrt{2}\tan\theta)$ be any point on the hyperbola.

$\because$ Asymptotes of hyperbola are

$$\frac{x^2}{a^2}-\frac{y^2}{2a^2}=0$$

or $$2x^2-y^2=0$$

or $$x\sqrt{2}+y=0$$

and $$x\sqrt{2}-y=0$$

$\because$ Product of the perpendiculars from P on asymptotes $=6$

$\therefore$ $$\frac{|a\sqrt{2}\sec\theta+a\sqrt{2}\tan\theta|}{\sqrt{(2+1)}}\cdot\frac{|a\sqrt{2}\sec\theta-a\sqrt{2}\tan\theta|}{\sqrt{2+1}}=6$$

or $$\frac{2a^2}{3}=6$$

$\therefore$ $$a=3$$

Hence, length of transverse axis $=2a=6$

(C) Equation of tangent at $(a, 0)$ is $x=a$

Equation of asymptotes are $y=\pm\frac{b}{a}x$

$\therefore$ $$P\equiv(a,b), Q\equiv(a,-b)$$

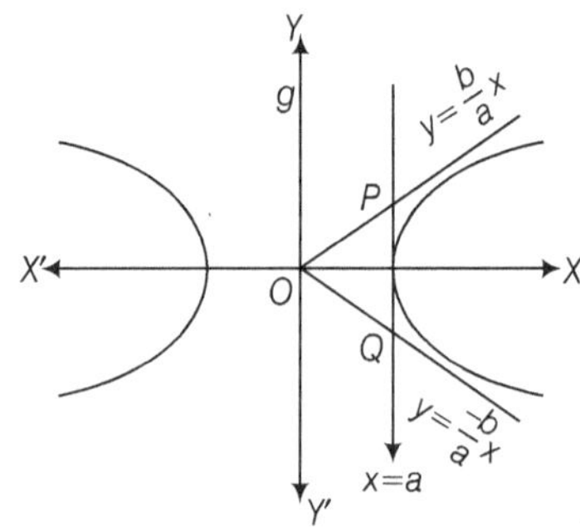

$\therefore$ Required area $=\frac{1}{2}\times a\times 2b$

$=ab$

$=(4)(3)=12$ (Here $a=4, b=3$)

JEE Type Solved Examples :

Statement I and II Type Questions

- **Directions** (Ex. Nos. 25 and 26) are Assertion-Reason type examples. Each of these examples contains two statements. **Statement I** (Assertion) and **Statement II** (Reason) Each of these also has four alternative choices, only one of which is the correct answer. You have to select the correct choice as given below :
  (a) Statement I is true, statement II is true; statement II is a correct explanation for statement I
  (b) Statement I is true, statement II is true; statement II is not a correct explanation for statement I
  (c) Statement I is true, statement II is false
  (d) Statement I is false, statement II is true

Ex. 25 **Statement I** *Director circle of hyperbola* $\frac{x^2}{a^2}-\frac{y^2}{b^2}+1=0$ *is defined only when* $b \geq a$

Statement II *Director circle of hyperbola* $\frac{x^2}{25}-\frac{y^2}{9}=1$ *is* $x^2+y^2=16$.

Sol. (b) Hyperbola $\frac{x^2}{a^2}-\frac{y^2}{b^2}+1=0$ can be re-written as

$$\frac{x^2}{(-a)^2}-\frac{y^2}{(-b^2)}=1$$

So, the director circle will be

$$x^2+y^2=(-a^2)-(-b^2)=b^2-a^2;$$

Which will be defined only where $b \geq a$ (i.e. $b^2-a^2 \geq 0$)

$\therefore$ Statement I is true and director circle of hyperbola $\frac{x^2}{25}-\frac{y^2}{9}=1$

is $\quad x^2+y^2=25-9=16$

$\therefore$ Statement II is true.

Hence, both statements are true but statement II is not a correct explanation of statement I.

Ex. 26 **Statement I** *If a circle* $S \equiv 0$ *intersect a hyperbola* $xy=4$ *at four points, three of them being (2, 2), (4, 1) and (6, 2/3), then the coordinates of the fourth point are* $\left(\frac{1}{4}, 16\right)$.

Statement II *If a circle* $S \equiv 0$ *intersects a hyperbola* $xy=c^2$ *at* t_1, t_2, t_3 *and* t_4, *then* $t_1 t_2 t_3 t_4=1$.

Sol. (d) Let circle $S \equiv x^2+y^2-a^2=0$

and given hyperbola $\quad xy=c^2$

Then, $\quad x^2+\frac{c^4}{x^2}=a^2$ or $x^4-a^2x^2+c^4=0$

If four intersecting points are

$\left(ct_1, \frac{c}{t_1}\right), \left(ct_2, \frac{c}{t_2}\right), \left(ct_3, \frac{c}{t_3}\right)$ and $\left(ct_4, \frac{c}{t_4}\right)$, then

$$(ct_1)(ct_2)(ct_3)(ct_4)=c^4$$

$\therefore \quad t_1 t_2 t_3 t_4=1$

$\therefore$ Statement II is true

For the point (2, 2); $t_1=1$

For the point (4, 1); $t_2=2$

For the point (6, 2/3); $t_3=3$

For the point $\left(\frac{1}{4}, 16\right)$; $t_4=\frac{1}{8}$

Now, $\quad t_1 t_2 t_3 t_4=\frac{3}{4} \neq 1$

$\therefore$ Statement I is false.

Subjective Type Questions

- In this section there are 11 **subjective examples.**

Ex. 27 *PP′ is a diameter of the rectangular hyperbola* $xy=c^2$. *Show that the intersection of the tangent of P with the straight line through P′ parallel to either asymptote is the locus* $xy+3c^2=0$.

Sol. The given rectangular hyperbola is

$$xy=c^2 \quad \text{...(i)}$$

Given that PP' is a diameter of Eq. (i). Therefore, if P is the point $(ct, c/t)$ then P' is $(-ct, -c/t)$. Equation of tangent at P is

$$x+yt^2=2ct \quad \text{...(ii)}$$

Asymptotes of Eq. (i) are $x=0, y=0$.

$\therefore$ The equation of the line through P' and parallel to the asymptote $y=0$ is

$$y=-c/t \quad \text{...(iii)}$$

Putting the value of t from Eq. (iii) in Eq. (ii), then

$$x+y \times \frac{c^2}{y^2}=2c \times -\frac{c}{y}$$

or $\quad xy+c^2=-2c^2$

or $\quad xy+3c^2=0$

which is the required locus of the point of intersection of Eqs. (ii) and (iii).

Again the equation of the line through P' and parallel to the asymptote $x = 0$ is

$$x = -ct \qquad \text{...(iv)}$$

Putting the value of t from Eq. (iv) in Eq. (ii), we get

$$x + y\left(\frac{x^2}{c^2}\right) = 2c \times -\frac{x}{c} \quad \text{or} \quad xy + 3c^2 = 0$$

which is the required locus of the point of intersection of Eqs. (ii) and (iv).

Ex. 28 *The tangent at a point P of a rectangular hyperbola meets the asymptotes at L and M and C is the centre of the hyperbola. Prove that*

$$PL = PM = CP.$$

Sol. Since hyperbola is

$$xy = c^2 \qquad \text{....(i)}$$

Let $P\left(ct, \frac{c}{t}\right)$ be any point on Eq. (i), then equation of tangent at P on Eq. (i) is

$$x + t^2 y = 2ct \qquad \text{...(ii)}$$

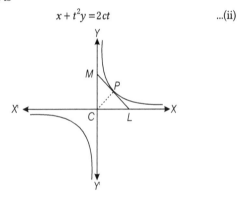

Since, asymptotes of $xy = c^2$ are $x = 0$ and $y = 0$

i.e. Y-axis and X-axis.

$\because$ Tangents meet X-axis at L and Y-axis at M.

$\therefore$ Coordinates of L and M are $(2ct, 0)$ and $\left(0, \frac{2c}{t}\right)$ respectively.

The middle-point of LM is $\left(\frac{2ct + 0}{2}, \frac{0 + \frac{2c}{t}}{2}\right)$ i.e. $\left(ct, \frac{c}{t}\right)$.

i.e. the point of P.

$$\therefore \quad PL = PM$$

$$\text{Also,} \quad CP = \sqrt{\left(c^2t^2 + \frac{c^2}{t^2}\right)}$$

$$\text{and} \quad ML = \sqrt{\left(4c^2t^2 + \frac{4c^2}{t^2}\right)} = 2CP$$

$$\therefore \quad CP = \frac{1}{2} ML = PL = PM$$

$$\text{Hence,} \quad PL = PM = CP.$$

Ex. 29 *Prove that the perpendicular focal chords of a rectangular hyperbola are equal.*

Sol. Let rectangular hyperbola is $x^2 - y^2 = a^2$.

Let equations of PQ and DE are

$$y = mx + c \qquad \text{...(i)}$$

$$\text{and} \quad y = m_1 x + c_1 \qquad \text{...(ii)}$$

respectively.

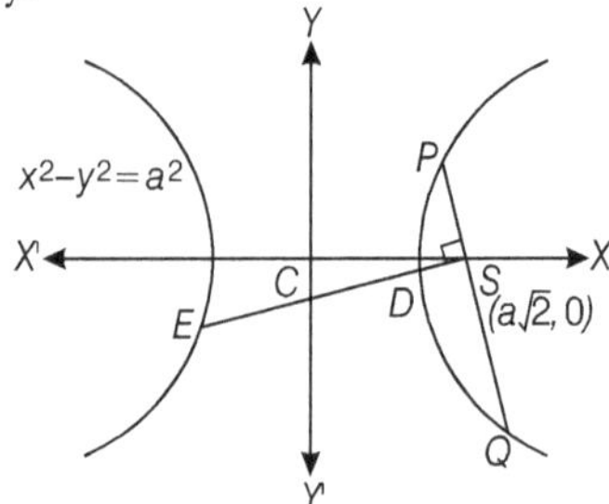

Be any two focal chords of any rectangular hyperbola $x^2 - y^2 = a^2$ through its focus. We have to prove $PQ = DE$.

Since, $PQ \perp DE$.

$$\therefore \quad mm_1 = -1 \qquad \text{...(iii)}$$

Also PQ passes through $S(a\sqrt{2}, 0)$ then from Eq. (i),

$$0 = ma\sqrt{2} + c$$

$$\text{or} \quad c^2 = 2a^2m^2 \qquad \text{...(iv)}$$

Let (x_1, y_1) and (x_2, y_2) be the coordinates of P and Q then

$$(PQ)^2 = (x_1 - x_2)^2 + (y_1 - y_2)^2 \qquad \text{...(v)}$$

Since, (x_1, y_1) and (x_2, y_2) lie on Eq. (i)

$$\therefore \quad y_1 = mx_1 + c \text{ and } y_2 = mx_2 + c$$

$$\therefore \quad (y_1 - y_2) = m(x_1 - x_2) \qquad \text{...(vi)}$$

From Eqs. (v) and (vi),

$$(PQ)^2 = (x_1 - x_2)^2 (1 + m^2) \qquad \text{...(vii)}$$

Now, solving $y = mx + c$ and $x^2 - y^2 = a^2$ then

$$x^2 - (mx + c)^2 = a^2$$

$$\text{or} \quad (m^2 - 1)x^2 + 2mcx + (a^2 + c^2) = 0$$

$$\therefore \quad x_1 + x_2 = \frac{2mc}{m^2 - 1} \quad \text{and} \quad x_1x_2 = \frac{a^2 + c^2}{m^2 - 1}$$

$$\Rightarrow \quad (x_1 - x_2)^2 = (x_1 + x_2)^2 - 4x_1x_2$$

$$= \frac{4m^2c^2}{(m^2 - 1)^2} - \frac{4(a^2 + c^2)}{(m^2 - 1)}$$

$$= \frac{4\{a^2 + c^2 - a^2m^2\}}{(m^2 - 1)^2}$$

$$= \frac{4a^2(m^2 + 1)}{(m^2 - 1)^2} \qquad [\because c^2 = 2a^2m^2]$$

$$\text{From Eq. (vii),} \quad (PQ)^2 = 4a^2\left(\frac{m^2 + 1}{m^2 - 1}\right)^2$$

$$\text{Similarly,} \quad (DE)^2 = 4a^2\left(\frac{m_1^2 + 1}{m_1^2 - 1}\right)^2$$

$$= 4a^2 \left(\frac{\left(-\frac{1}{m}\right)^2 + 1}{\left(-\frac{1}{m}\right)^2 - 1} \right)^2 \quad (\because mm_1 = -1)$$

$$= 4a^2 \left(\frac{m^2+1}{m^2-1} \right)^2$$

$$= (PQ)^2$$

Thus, $(PQ)^2 = (DE)^2 \Rightarrow PQ = DE.$

Hence, perpendicular focal chords of a rectangular hyperbola are equal.

Ex. 30 *The normals at three points P, Q, R on a rectangular hyperbola intersect at a point T on the curve. Prove that the centre of the hyperbola is the centroid of the triangle PQR.*

Sol. Equation of the normal at point $\left(ct, \frac{c}{t}\right)$ on $xy = c^2$ is

$$xt^3 - yt - ct^4 + c = 0$$

It will pass through the point (h, k)

$$\therefore \quad ht^3 - kt - ct^4 + c = 0 \quad \text{...(i)}$$

Also $T(h, k)$ lies on $xy = c^2$

$$\therefore \quad hk = c^2$$

Therefore, $h = cq$ and $k = \frac{c}{q}$

From, $cqt^3 - \frac{c}{q}t - ct^4 + c = 0$

or $qt^3 - \frac{t}{q} - t^4 + 1 = 0$

or $q^2t^3 - t - qt^4 + q = 0$

or $q(qt^3 + 1) - t(qt^3 + 1) = 0$

or $(q - t)(qt^3 + 1) = 0$

$$q \neq t$$

$$\therefore \quad qt^3 + 1 = 0$$

The three points other than T are given by

$$qt^3 + 1 = 0 \quad \text{...(ii)}$$

If coordinates of $P\left(ct_1, \frac{c}{t_1}\right), Q\left(ct_2, \frac{c}{t_2}\right)$ and $R\left(ct_3, \frac{c}{t_3}\right)$

then from Eq. (ii),

$$t_1 + t_2 + t_3 = 0 \quad \text{...(iii)}$$

$$t_1t_2 + t_2t_3 + t_3t_1 = 0 \quad \text{...(iv)}$$

and $$t_1t_2t_3 = -1 \quad \text{...(v)}$$

From Eq. (iii),

$$c(t_1 + t_2 + t_3) = 0$$

and from Eq. (iv),

$$t_1t_2t_3\left(\frac{1}{t_1} + \frac{1}{t_2} + \frac{1}{t_3}\right) = 0$$

or $$(-1)\left(\frac{1}{t_1} + \frac{1}{t_2} + \frac{1}{t_3}\right) = 0 \quad \text{[from Eq. (v)]}$$

$$\therefore \quad \frac{1}{t_1} + \frac{1}{t_2} + \frac{1}{t_3} = 0$$

or $$c\left(\frac{1}{t_1} + \frac{1}{t_2} + \frac{1}{t_3}\right) = 0$$

Hence, $c(t_1 + t_2 + t_3) = 0, c\left(\frac{1}{t_1} + \frac{1}{t_2} + \frac{1}{t_3}\right) = 0$

$\Rightarrow$ Centroid of ΔPQR is the origin.

Ex. 31 *Find the equation of the hyperbola whose asymptotes are $x + 2y + 3 = 0$ and $3x + 4y + 5 = 0$ and which passes through the point $(1, -1)$. Find also the equation of the conjugate hyperbola.*

Sol. Combined equation of asymptotes is

$$(x + 2y + 3)(3x + 4y + 5) = 0$$

or $$3x^2 + 10xy + 8y^2 + 14x + 22y + 15 = 0 \quad \text{...(i)}$$

Also, we know that the equation of the hyperbola differs from that of asymptotes by a constant.

Let the equation of the hyperbola be

$$3x^2 + 10xy + 8y^2 + 14x + 22y + \lambda = 0 \quad \text{...(ii)}$$

Since it passes through $(1, -1)$ then

$$3(1)^2 + 10(1)(-1) + 8(-1)^2 + 14(1) + 22(-1) + \lambda = 0$$

$$\Rightarrow \quad 3 - 10 + 8 + 14 - 22 + \lambda = 0$$

$$\therefore \quad \lambda = 7$$

From Eq. (ii), equation of hyperbola is

$$3x^2 + 10xy + 8y^2 + 14x + 22y + 7 = 0 \quad \text{...(iii)}$$

But we know that equation of conjugate hyperbola

= 2 (Combined equation of asymptotes) − (Equation of hyperbola)

$$\Rightarrow \quad 6x^2 + 20xy + 16y^2 + 28x + 44y + 30 - 3x^2 - 10xy - 8y^2 - 14x - 22y - 7 = 0$$

or $$3x^2 + 10xy + 8y^2 + 14x + 22y + 23 = 0.$$

Ex. 32 *A triangle is inscribed in $xy = c^2$ and two of its sides are parallel to $y = m_1x$ and $y = m_2x$ prove that the third side envelopes the hyperbola $4m_1m_2xy = c^2(m_1 + m_2)^2$.*

Sol. Let a triangle PQR be inscribed in $xy = c^2$.

Let the coordinates of the vertices of the triangle be

$$P\left(ct_1, \frac{c}{t_1}\right), Q\left(ct_2, \frac{c}{t_2}\right) \text{ and } R\left(ct_3, \frac{c}{t_3}\right)$$

Now, the equation of chord joining P and Q is

$$x + yt_1t_2 = c(t_1 + t_2) \quad \text{...(i)}$$

and the equation of chord joining Q and R is

$$x + yt_2t_3 = c(t_2 + t_3) \quad \text{...(ii)}$$

Let Eq. (i) be parallel to $y = m_1x$ and Eq. (ii) be parallel to $y = m_2x$.

$\therefore \quad m_1 = -\frac{1}{t_1 t_2}$ and $m_2 = -\frac{1}{t_2 t_3}$

$\therefore \quad \frac{m_1}{m_2} = \frac{t_3}{t_1}$ i.e. $t_3 = \left(\frac{m_1}{m_2}\right) t_1$ ...(iii)

Again the equation to the third side RP is

$$x + y t_3 t_1 = c(t_3 + t_1)$$

$$x + y\left(\frac{m_1}{m_2}\right) t_1^2 = c\left(\frac{m_1}{m_2} t_1 + t_1\right)$$

or $\quad y m_1 t_1^2 - c t_1 (m_1 + m_2) + x m_2 = 0$ ...(iv)

t_1 being a parameter. Since t_1 is real the envelope of Eq. (iv) is given by the discriminant of Eq. (iv) = 0

i.e. $\quad c^2 (m_1 + m_2)^2 - 4 y m_1 \cdot x m_2 = 0$

or $\quad 4 m_1 m_2 x y = c^2 (m_1 + m_2)^2.$

Ex. 33 *In both an ellipse and a hyperbola, prove that the focal distance of any point and the perpendicular from the centre upon the tangent at it meet on a circle whose centre is the focus and whose radius is the semi-transverse axis.*

Sol. Let the hyperbola be

$$\frac{x^2}{a^2} - \frac{y^2}{b^2} = 1 \quad \text{...(i)}$$

Let there be any point $P(a \sec \phi, b \tan \phi)$ on the hyperbola Eq. (i).

$\therefore$ Equation of tangent at 'P' is

$$\frac{x}{a} \sec \phi - \frac{y}{b} \tan \phi = 1 \quad \text{...(ii)}$$

Equation of focal chord SP is [if $S \equiv (-ae, 0)$]

$$y - 0 = \frac{b \tan \phi - 0}{a \sec \phi + ae}(x + ae)$$

$$\Rightarrow \quad y = \frac{b \sin \phi (x + ae)}{(a + ae \cos \phi)} \quad \text{...(iii)}$$

Equation of line passing through (0, 0) and perpendicular to Eq. (ii) is

$$y = -\frac{a}{b} \sin \phi \cdot x \quad \text{...(iv)}$$

Let Eqs. (iii) and (iv) are passing through (h, k), then

$$k = \frac{b(h + ae) \sin \phi}{(a + ae \cos \phi)} \quad \text{...(v)}$$

$$k = -\frac{a}{b} \sin \phi \cdot h \quad \text{...(vi)}$$

From Eq. (iv), $\sin \phi = -\frac{bk}{ah}$

and from Eq. (v), $\cos \phi = -\left\{\frac{a^2 h + (h + ae) b^2}{a^2 eh}\right\}$

$$= -\left\{\frac{(a^2 + b^2) h + aeb^2}{a^2 eh}\right\}$$

$$= -\left\{\frac{a^2 e^2 h + aeb^2}{a^2 eh}\right\} = -\left\{\frac{aeh + b^2}{ah}\right\}$$

$\therefore \quad \sin^2 \phi + \cos^2 \phi = 1$

$$\Rightarrow \quad \frac{b^2 k^2}{a^2 h^2} + \frac{(aeh + b^2)^2}{a^2 h^2} = 1$$

$\therefore$ Locus of (h, k) is

$$b^2 y^2 + (aex + b^2)^2 = a^2 x^2$$

$$\Rightarrow \quad b^2 y^2 + a^2 e^2 x^2 + b^4 + 2aeb^2 x = a^2 x^2$$

$$\Rightarrow \quad b^2 y^2 + (a^2 + b^2) x^2 + b^4 + 2aeb^2 x = a^2 x^2$$

$$\Rightarrow \quad y^2 b^2 + b^2 (x^2 + 2aex) + b^4 = 0$$

$$\Rightarrow \quad b^2 y^2 + b^2 \{(x + ae)^2 - a^2 e^2\} + b^4 = 0$$

$$\Rightarrow \quad b^2 y^2 + b^2 (x + ae)^2 - b^2 (a^2 + b^2) + b^4 = 0$$

$$\Rightarrow \quad b^2 y^2 + b^2 (x + ae)^2 - a^2 b^2 = 0$$

$$\Rightarrow \quad (x + ae)^2 + y^2 = a^2$$

Ex. 34 *Show that an infinite number of triangles can be inscribed in the rectangular hyperbola $xy = c^2$, whose sides all touch the parabola $y^2 = 4ax$.*

Sol. From any point $A\left(ct_1, \frac{c}{t_1}\right)$ on the rectangular hyperbola

$$xy = c^2. \quad \text{...(i)}$$

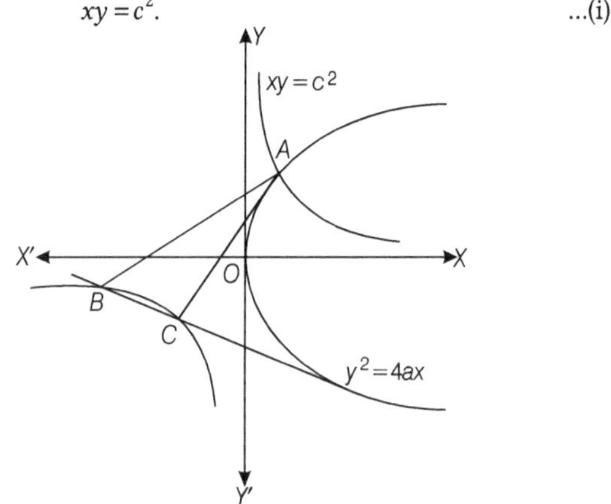

Tangent AB and AC are drawn to the parabola $y^2 = 4ax$,

then $\quad B \equiv \left(ct_2, \frac{c}{t_2}\right)$ and $C \equiv \left(ct_3, \frac{c}{t_3}\right)$.

Then ΔABC is inscribed in the rectangular hyperbola and its sides AB and AC touch the parabola.

$\because$ BC is also a tangent to it

Equations of chords AB, BC and CA are

$$AB \equiv x + y t_1 t_2 = c(t_1 + t_2)$$

$$BC \equiv x + y t_2 t_3 = c(t_2 + t_3)$$

$$CA \equiv x + y t_3 t_1 = c(t_3 + t_1)$$

$\because$ AB is tangent to parabola $y^2 = 4ax$, its equation

$$y = -\frac{1}{t_1 t_2} x + \frac{c(t_1 + t_2)}{t_1 t_2}$$

Touching condition $c = \frac{a}{m}$ or $cm = a$

$$\frac{c(t_1+t_2)}{t_1t_2}\cdot\left(\frac{-1}{t_1t_2}\right)=a$$

$\Rightarrow$ $$-at_1^2t_2^2=c(t_1+t_2)$$

$$(at_1^2)t_2^2+ct_2+ct_1=0$$

Similarly, $(at_2^2)t_3^2+ct_3+ct_1=0$

Hence, $(at_1^2)t^2+ct+ct_1=0$ ...(ii)

and t_2 and t_3 are the roots of Eq. (ii),

$\therefore$ $t_2+t_3=-\dfrac{c}{at_1^2}$ and $t_2t_3=\dfrac{c}{at_1}$

$\Rightarrow$ $c=at_1t_2t_3$

$\therefore$ $c(t_2+t_3)=-\dfrac{c^2}{at_1^2}=-\dfrac{(at_1t_2t_3)^2}{at_1^2}=-at_2^2t_3^2$

$\Rightarrow$ $-at_2t_3=\dfrac{c(t_2+t_3)}{t_2t_3}$ is the condition.

This proves BC to be also a tangent to the parabola. But any point A can be taken in infinite ways anywhere on the curve representing the rectangular hyperbola. Hence such triangles exist in infinite number.

Ex. 35 *A circle with centre $(3\alpha, 3\beta)$ and of variable radius cuts the rectangular hyperbola $x^2-y^2=9a^2$ at the points P, Q, R, S. Prove that the locus of the centroid of the triangle PQR is $(x-2\alpha)^2-(y-2\beta)^2=a^2$.*

Sol. The equation of the circle with centre $(3\alpha, 3\beta)$ is

$$x^2+y^2-6\alpha x-6\beta y+k=0 \quad \text{...(i)}$$

where k is variable.

Given hyperbola is $x^2-y^2=9a^2$ ...(ii)

Eliminating y from Eq. (i) with the help of Eq. (ii), we get

$$(x^2+x^2-9a^2-6\alpha x+k)^2=36\beta^2(x^2-9a^2)$$

$\Rightarrow$ $$4x^4-24\alpha x^3+\ldots=0$$

this is a biquadratic equation.

Let the abscissas of four points P, Q, R and S are x_1, x_2, x_3 and x_4, then

$$x_1+x_2+x_3+x_4=6\alpha \quad \text{...(iii)}$$

Similarly, $y_1+y_2+y_3+y_4=6\beta$ ...(iv)

If (x', y') be the centroid of the triangle PQR, then

$$x'=\frac{x_1+x_2+x_3}{3}=\frac{6\alpha-x_4}{3}$$

$\therefore$ $-3(x'-2\alpha)=x_4$

and $y'=\dfrac{y_1+y_2+y_3}{3}=\dfrac{6\beta-y_4}{3}$

$\therefore$ $-3(y'-2\beta)=y_4$

But $x_4^2-y_4^2=9a^2$

$\Rightarrow$ $9(x'-2\alpha)^2-9(y'-2\beta)^2=9a^2$

$\Rightarrow$ $(x'-2\alpha)^2-(y'-2\beta)^2=a^2$

Hence, locus of centroid (x', y') is $(x-2\alpha)^2-(y-2\beta)^2=a^2$.

Ex. 36 *If the normals at (x_i, y_i), $i=1, 2, 3, 4$ on the rectangular hyperbola, $xy=c^2$, meet at the point (α, β) show that*

(i) $\Sigma x_i=\alpha$ *(ii) $\Sigma y_i=\beta$* *(iii) $\Pi x_i=\Pi y_i=-c^4$*
(iv) $\Sigma x_i^2=\alpha^2$ *(v) $\Sigma y_i^2=\beta^2$*

Sol. Let $(x_i, y_i)=\left(ct_i, \dfrac{c}{t_i}\right)$, $i=1,2,3,4$ are the points on the rectangular hyperbola $xy=c^2$.

Equation of normal to the hyperbola

$$xy=c^2 \text{ at } \left(ct, \frac{c}{t}\right) \text{ is}$$

$$ct^4-t^3x+ty-c=0$$

It passes through (α, β), then

$$ct^4-t^3\alpha+t\beta-c=0$$

its biquadratic equation in t. Let the roots of this equation are t_1, t_2, t_3, t_4 then

$$\Sigma t_1=\frac{\alpha}{c},$$

$$\Sigma t_1t_2=0, \Sigma t_1t_2t_3=-\beta/c, t_1t_2t_3t_4=-1$$

Now, (i) $\Sigma x_i=c\,\Sigma t_1=\alpha$

(ii) $\Sigma y_i=c\left(\Sigma\dfrac{1}{t_1}\right)=c\left(\dfrac{\Sigma t_1t_2t_3}{t_1t_2t_3t_4}\right)=\beta$

(iii) $\Pi\, x_i=c^4\Pi\, t_i=-c^4$

and $\Pi\, y_i=c^4\left(\dfrac{1}{\Pi t_i}\right)=-c^4$

(iv) $\Sigma x_i^2=c^2(\Sigma t_1^2)=c^2\{(\Sigma t_1)^2-2\Sigma t_1t_2\}$

$=\alpha^2$

(v) $\Sigma y_i^2=(\Sigma y_1)^2-2\Sigma y_1y_2$

$$=\beta^2-2c^2\Sigma\left(\frac{1}{t_1t_2}\right)=\beta^2-2c^2\cdot\frac{\Sigma t_1t_2}{t_1t_2t_3t_4}=\beta^2$$

Ex. 37 *If a circle cuts a rectangular hyperbola $xy=c^2$ in A, B, C and D and the parameters of these four points be t_1, t_2, t_3 and t_4 respectively prove the following :*

(i) $t_1t_2t_3t_4=1$, find the value of $\Sigma\dfrac{1}{t_1}$.

(ii) If H be the orthocentre of the triangle ABC, then H and D are extremities of a diameter of the rectangular hyperbola.

(iii) The centre of mean position of the four points bisects the distance between the centres of the two curves.

(iv) The centre of the circle through A, B and C is

$$\left[\frac{c}{2}\left(t_1+t_2+t_3+\frac{1}{t_1t_2t_3}\right), \frac{c}{2}\left(\frac{1}{t_1}+\frac{1}{t_2}+\frac{1}{t_3}+t_1t_2t_3\right)\right].$$

Sol. (i) Let the equation of the circle is

$$x^2 + y^2 + 2gx + 2fy + k = 0 \qquad ...(i)$$

and the equation of the rectangular hyperbola is

$$xy = c^2 \qquad ...(ii)$$

Put $x = ct$ and $y = \frac{c}{t}$ in Eq. (i)

then, $$c^2t^2 + \frac{c^2}{t^2} + 2gct + \frac{2fc}{t} + k = 0$$

$$\Rightarrow \quad c^2t^4 + 2gct^3 + kt^2 + 2fct + c^2 = 0$$

this equation being fourth degree in t. Let roots be t_1, t_2, t_3, t_4 then

$$\Sigma t_1 = -\frac{2g}{c}, \Sigma t_1 t_2 = \frac{k}{c^2},$$

$$\Sigma t_1 t_2 t_3 = -\frac{2f}{c} \text{ and } t_1 t_2 t_3 t_4 = 1$$

$$\therefore \quad \Sigma \frac{1}{t_1} = \frac{\Sigma t_1 t_2 t_3}{t_1 t_2 t_3 t_4} = \frac{\frac{-2f}{c}}{1} = -\frac{-2f}{c}$$

(ii) Orthocentre of the ΔABC is $\left(\frac{-c}{t_1 t_2 t_3}, -ct_1 t_2 t_3\right)$

Hence orthocentre is $\left(\frac{-ct_4}{t_1 t_2 t_3 t_4}, \frac{-ct_1 t_2 t_3 t_4}{t_4}\right)$

i.e. $\left(-ct_4, \frac{-c}{t_4}\right)$

But D is $\left(ct_4, \frac{c}{t_4}\right)$.

Hence H and D are the extremities of a diagonal of rectangular hyperbola.

(iii) The centre of the mean position of the four points is

$$\left(\frac{c}{4}(t_1 + t_2 + t_3 + t_4), \frac{c}{4}\left(\frac{1}{t_1} + \frac{1}{t_2} + \frac{1}{t_3} + \frac{1}{t_4}\right)\right)$$

i.e. $$\left(\frac{c}{4}\Sigma t_1, \frac{c}{4}\Sigma\left(\frac{1}{t_1}\right)\right)$$

i.e. $$\left(-\frac{g}{2}, -\frac{f}{2}\right) \qquad \text{[from relation Eq. (i)]}$$

$\because$ Centres of the circle and rectangular hyperbola are $(-g, -f)$ and $(0, 0)$; mid point of centres of circle and rectangular hyperbola is $\left(\frac{-g}{2}, \frac{-f}{2}\right)$.

Hence the centre of the mean position of the four points bisects the distance between the centres of the two curves (circle and rectangular hyperbola).

(iv) Let the circle passing through ABC meet the hyperbola in fourth point D; then centre of circle is

$$(-g, -f), (-g, -f)$$

$$\Rightarrow \quad \left(\frac{c}{2}\left(\frac{-2g}{c}\right), \frac{c}{2}\left(\frac{-2f}{2}\right)\right) \qquad \text{[from Eq. (i) relation]}$$

$$\Rightarrow \quad \left(\frac{c}{2}(t_1 + t_2 + t_3 + t_4), \frac{c}{2}\left(\frac{1}{t_1} + \frac{1}{t_2} + \frac{1}{t_3} + \frac{1}{t_4}\right)\right)$$

But $\quad t_1 t_2 t_3 t_4 = 1$

$$\therefore \quad t_4 = \frac{1}{t_1 t_2 t_3}$$

Hence, centre of circle is

$$\left(\frac{c}{2}\left(t_1 + t_2 + t_3 + \frac{1}{t_1 t_2 t_3}\right), \frac{c}{2}\left(\frac{1}{t_1} + \frac{1}{t_2} + \frac{1}{t_3} + t_1 t_2 t_3\right)\right).$$

Hyperbola Exercise 1 :
Single Option Correct Type Questions

- This section contains **30 multiple choice questions.** Each question has four choices (a), (b), (c) and (d) out of which **ONLY ONE** is correct.

1. P is any point on the hyperbola $x^2 - y^2 = a^2$. If F_1 and F_2 are the foci of the hyperbola and $PF_1 \cdot PF_2 = \lambda(OP)^2$, where O is the origin, then λ is equal to

(a) 1 (b) $\sqrt{2}$ (c) 2 (d) 3

2. If the sum of the slopes of the normals from a point P to the hyperbola $xy = c^2$ is equal to $\lambda\,(\lambda \in R^+)$, then locus of point P is

(a) $x^2 - y^2 = \lambda c^2$ (b) $y^2 = \lambda c^2$
(c) $xy = \lambda c^2$ (d) $x^2 = \lambda c^2$

3. If $xy = \lambda^2 - 9$ be a rectangular hyperbola whose branches lie only in the second and fourth quadrant, then

(a) $|\lambda| \geq 3$ (b) $|\lambda| < 3$
(c) $\lambda \in R - \{-3, 3\}$ (d) None of these

4. If there are two points A and B on rectangular hyperbola $xy = c^2$ such that abscissa of A = ordinate of B, then the locus of point of intersection of tangents at A and B is

(a) $y^2 = x^2 + 2c^2$ (b) $y^2 = x^2 + \frac{c^2}{2}$
(c) $y = x$ (d) $y = 3x$

5. A series of hyperbola is drawn having a common transverse axis of length $2a$. Then the locus of a point P on each hyperbola, such that its distance from the transverse axis is equal to its distance from an asymptote, is

(a) $(x^2 - y^2)^2 = 4x^2(x^2 - a^2)$
(b) $(x^2 - y^2)^2 = x^2(x^2 - a^2)$
(c) $(x^2 - y^2)^2 = 4y^2(x^2 - a^2)$
(d) $(x^2 - y^2)^2 = y^2(x^2 - a^2)$

6. If a rectangular hyperbola $(x-1)(y-2) = 4$ cuts a circle $x^2 + y^2 + 2gx + 2fy + c = 0$ at points (3, 4) (5, 3), (2, 6) and (−1,0), then the value of $(g + f)$ is equal to

(a) −8 (b) −9 (c) 8 (d) 9

7. If $f(x) = ax^3 + bx^2 + cx + d, (a, b, c, d$ are rational numbers) and roots of $f(x) = 0$ are eccentricities of a parabola and a rectangular hyperbola, then $a + b + c + d$ equals

(a) −1 (b) 0 (c) 1 (d) data inadequate

8. From a point on the line $y = x + c, c$ (parameter), tangents are drawn to the hyperbola $\frac{x^2}{2} - \frac{y^2}{1} = 1$ such that chords of contact pass through a fixed point (x_1, y_1). Then, $\frac{x_1}{y_1}$ is equal to

(a) 2 (b) 3
(c) 4 (d) None of these

9. Two conics $\frac{x^2}{a^2} - \frac{y^2}{b^2} = 1$ and $x^2 = -\frac{a}{b}y$ intersect, if

(a) $0 < b \leq \frac{1}{2}$ (b) $0 < a < \frac{1}{2}$
(c) $a^2 < b^2$ (d) $a^2 > b^2$

10. The number of points outside the hyperbola $\frac{x^2}{9} - \frac{y^2}{16} = 1$ from where two perpendicular tangents can be drawn to the hyperbola are

(a) 0 (b) 1
(c) 2 (d) None of these

11. Let $A \equiv (-3, 4)$ and $B \equiv (2, -1)$ be two fixed points. A point C moves such that

$$\tan\left(\frac{1}{2}\angle ABC\right) : \tan\left(\frac{1}{2}\angle BAC\right) = 3:1$$

Thus, locus of C is a hyperbola, distance between whose foci is

(a) 5 (b) $5\sqrt{2}$ (c) $\frac{5}{2}$ (d) $\frac{5}{\sqrt{2}}$

12. A point P is taken on the right half of the hyperbola $\frac{x^2}{a^2} - \frac{y^2}{b^2} = 1$ having its foci as S_1 and S_2. If the internal angle bisector of the angle $\angle S_1PS_2$ cuts the x-axis at point $Q(\alpha, 0)$, then range of α is

(a) $[-a, a]$ (b) $[0, a]$
(c) $(0, a]$ (d) $[-a, 0)$

13. If angle between asymptotes of hyperbola $\frac{x^2}{a^2} - \frac{y^2}{b^2} = 1$ is 120° and product of perpendiculars drawn from foci upon its any tangent is 9, then locus of point of intersection of perpendicular tangents of the hyperbola can be

(a) $x^2 + y^2 = 3$ (b) $x^2 + y^2 = 6$
(c) $x^2 + y^2 = 9$ (d) $x^2 + y^2 = 18$

14. If $\alpha + \beta = 3\pi$, then the chord joining the points α and β for the hyperbola $\frac{x^2}{a^2} - \frac{y^2}{b^2} = 1$ passes through
(a) focus
(b) centre
(c) one of the end point of the transverse axis
(d) one of the end points of the conjugate axis

15. If the curves $\frac{x^2}{a^2} + \frac{y^2}{b^2} = 1 (a > b)$ and $x^2 - y^2 = c^2$ cut at right angles, then
(a) $a^2 + b^2 = 2c^2$ (b) $b^2 - a^2 = 2c^2$
(c) $a^2 - b^2 = 2c^2$ (d) $a^2b^2 = 2c^2$

16. If chords of the hyperbola $x^2 - y^2 = a^2$ touch the parabola $y^2 = 4ax$, then the locus of the middle points of these chords is the curve
(a) $y^2(x + a) = x^3$ (b) $y^2(x - a) = x^3$
(c) $y^2(x + 2a) = 3x^3$ (d) $y^2(x - 2a) = 2x^3$

17. An ellipse has eccentricity 1/2 and one focus at the point $P(1/2, 1)$. Its one directrix is the common tangent nearer to the point P, to the circle $x^2 + y^2 = 1$ and the hyperbola $x^2 - y^2 = 1$. The equation of the ellipse is standard form is
(a) $9x^2 + 12y^2 = 108$
(b) $9(x - 1/3)^2 + 12(y - 1)^2 = 1$
(c) $9(x - 1/3)^2 + 4(y - 1)^2 = 36$
(d) None of the above

18. The equation of the line passing through the centre of a rectangular hyperbola is $x - y - 1 = 0$.
If one of its asymptote is $3x - 4y - 6 = 0$, the equation of the other asymptote is
(a) $4x - 3y + 8 = 0$ (b) $4x + 3y + 17 = 0$
(c) $3x - 2y + 15 = 0$ (d) None of these

19. The condition that a straight line with slope m will be normal to parabola $y^2 = 4ax$ as well as a tangent to rectangular hyperbola $x^2 - y^2 = a^2$ is
(a) $m^6 - 4m^2 + 2m - 1 = 0$ (b) $m^4 + 3m^3 + 2m + 1 = 0$
(c) $m^6 - 2m = 0$ (d) $m^6 + 4m^4 + 3m^2 + 1 = 0$

20. The locus of the middle points of chords of hyperbola $3x^2 - 2y^2 + 4x - 6y = 0$ parallel to $y = 2x$ is
(a) $3x - 4y = 4$ (b) $3y - 4x + 4 = 0$
(c) $4x - 4y = 3$ (d) $3x - 4y = 2$

21. The coordinates of the centre of the hyperbola $x^2 + 3xy + 2y^2 + 2x + 3y + 2 = 0$ is
(a) $(-1, 0)$ (b) $(1, 0)$ (c) $(-1, 1)$ (d) $(1, -1)$

22. Let F_1, F_2 are foci of the hyperbola $\frac{x^2}{16} - \frac{y^2}{9} = 1$ and F_3, F_4 are the foci of its conjugate hyperbola.
If e_H and e_C are their eccentricities respectively, then the statement which holds true is
(a) their equations of their asymptotes are different
(b) $e_H > e_C$
(c) area of the quadrilateral formed by their foci is 50 sq units
(d) their auxiliary circles will have the same equation

23. Locus of the point of intersection of the tangents at the points with eccentric angles ϕ and $\frac{\pi}{2} - \phi$ on the hyperbola $\frac{x^2}{a^2} - \frac{y^2}{b^2} = 1$ is
(a) $x = a$ (b) $y = b$
(c) $x = ab$ (d) $y = ab$

24. Latusrectum of the conic satisfying the differential equation $xdy + ydx = 0$ and passing through the point $(2, 8)$ is
(a) $4\sqrt{2}$ (b) 8
(c) $8\sqrt{2}$ (d) 16

25. The points of the intersection of the curves whose parametric equations are $x = t^2 + 1, y = 2t$ and $x = 2s, y = \frac{2}{s}$ is given by
(a) $(1, -3)$ (b) $(2, 2)$
(c) $(-2, 4)$ (d) $(1, 2)$

26. If the tangent and normal to a rectangular hyperbola cut off intercepts x_1 and x_2 on one axis and y_1 and y_2 on the other axis, then
(a) $x_1y_1 + x_2y_2 = 0$ (b) $x_1y_2 + x_2y_1 = 0$
(c) $x_1x_2 + y_1y_2 = 0$ (d) None of these

27. The focus of rectangular hyperbola $(x - h)(y - k) = p^2$ is
(a) $(h - p, k - p)$
(b) $(h - p, k + p)$
(c) $(h + p, k - p)$
(d) None of the above

28. The equation of a hyperbola, conjugate to the hyperbola $x^2 + 3xy + 2y^2 + 2x + 3y = 0$ is
(a) $x^2 + 3xy + 2y^2 + 2x + 3y + 1 = 0$
(b) $x^2 + 3xy + 2y^2 + 2x + 3y + 2 = 0$
(c) $x^2 + 3xy + 2y^2 + 2x + 3y + 3 = 0$
(d) $x^2 + 3xy + 2y^2 + 2x + 3y + 4 = 0$

29. If the values of m for which the line $y = mx + 2\sqrt{5}$ touches the hyperbola $16x^2 - 9y^2 = 144$ are the roots of the equation $x^2 - (a+b)x - 4 = 0$, then the value of $a + b$ is

(a) -2 (b) 0
(c) 2 (d) 4

30. Let C be a curve which is the locus of the point of intersection of lines $x = 2 + m$ and $my = 4 - m$. A circle $s = (x-2)^2 + (y+1)^2 = 25$ intersects the curve C at four points P, Q, R and S. If O is the centre of the curve C, then $(OP)^2 + (OQ)^2 + (OR)^2 + (OS)^2$ is

(a) 25 (b) 50 (c) 100 (d) 200

Hyperbola Exercise 2 :
More than One Correct Option Type Questions

- This section contains **15 multiple choice questions.** Each question has four choices (a), (b), (c) and (d) out of which **MORE THAN ONE** may be correct.

31. Equation of common tangent to the parabola $y^2 = 8x$ and hyperbola $x^2 - \frac{y^2}{3} = 1$ is

(a) $2x - y + 1 = 0$ (b) $2x - y - 1 = 0$
(c) $2x + y + 1 = 0$ (d) $2x + y - 1 = 0$

32. If the foci of the ellipse $\frac{x^2}{k^2a^2} + \frac{y^2}{a^2} = 1$ and the hyperbola $\frac{x^2}{a^2} - \frac{y^2}{b^2} = 1$ coincide, then k is equal to

(a) $-\sqrt{2}$ (b) $\sqrt{2}$ (c) $-\sqrt{3}$ (d) $\sqrt{3}$

33. If $(a\sec\theta, b\tan\theta)$ and $(a\sec\phi, b\tan\phi)$ are the ends of a focal chord of $\frac{x^2}{a^2} - \frac{y^2}{b^2} = 1$, then $\tan\left(\frac{\theta}{2}\right)\tan\left(\frac{\phi}{2}\right)$ is equal to

(a) $\frac{e-1}{e+1}$ (b) $\frac{1-e}{1+e}$ (c) $\frac{1+e}{1-e}$ (d) $\frac{e+1}{e-1}$

34. If foci of $\frac{x^2}{a^2} - \frac{y^2}{b^2} = 1$ coincide with the foci of $\frac{x^2}{25} + \frac{y^2}{16} = 1$ and eccentricity of the hyperbola is 3, then

(a) $a^2 + b^2 = 9$
(b) there is no director circle to the hyperbola
(c) centre of the director circle is $(0, 0)$
(d) length of the latusrectum of the hyperbola = 16

35. The equation $16x^2 - 3y^2 - 32x - 12y - 44 = 0$ represents a hyperbola with

(a) length of the transverse axis = $2\sqrt{3}$
(b) length of the conjugate axis = 8
(c) centre at $(1, -2)$
(d) eccentricity = $\sqrt{19}$

36. If the line $ax + by + c = 0$ is normal to the hyperbola $xy = 1$, then

(a) $a > 0, b > 0$ (b) $a > 0, b < 0$
(c) $a < 0, b > 0$ (d) $a < 0, b < 0$

37. If $P(x_1, y_1), Q(x_2, y_2), R(x_3, y_3)$ and $S(x_4, y_4)$ are 4 concyclic points on the rectangular hyperbola $xy = c^2$, the coordinates of the orthocentre of the ΔPQR are

(a) $(x_4, -y_4)$ (b) (x_4, y_4)
(c) $(-x_4, -y_4)$ (d) $(-x_4, y_4)$

38. The line $y = x + 5$ touches

(a) the parabola $y^2 = 20x$
(b) the ellipse $9x^2 + 16y^2 = 144$
(c) the hyperbola $\frac{x^2}{29} - \frac{y^2}{4} = 1$
(d) the circle $x^2 + y^2 = 25$

39. The coordinates of a point common to a directrix and an asymptote of the hyperbola $x^2/25 - y^2/16 = 1$ are

(a) $(25/\sqrt{41}, 20/\sqrt{41})$ (b) $(-25/\sqrt{41}, -20/\sqrt{41})$
(c) $(25/3, 20/3)$ (d) $(-25/3, -20/3)$

40. If (5, 12) and (24, 7) are the foci of a hyperbola passing through the origin, then

(a) $e = \frac{\sqrt{386}}{12}$ (b) $e = \frac{\sqrt{386}}{13}$
(c) latusrectum = $\frac{121}{3}$ (d) latusrectum = $\frac{121}{6}$

41. For the hyperbola $\frac{x^2}{a^2} - \frac{y^2}{b^2} = 1$, let n be the number of points on the plane through which perpendicular tangents are drawn

(a) if $n = 1$, then $e = \sqrt{2}$
(b) if $n > 1$, then $0 < e < \sqrt{2}$
(c) if $n = 0$, then $e > \sqrt{2}$
(d) None of the above

42. Which of the following equations in parametric form can represent a hyperbola, where 't' is a parameter?

(a) $x = \frac{a}{2}\left(t + \frac{1}{t}\right)$ and $y = \frac{b}{2}\left(t - \frac{1}{t}\right)$

(b) $\frac{tx}{a} - \frac{y}{b} + t = 0$ and $\frac{x}{a} + \frac{ty}{b} - 1 = 0$

(c) $x = e^t + e^{-t}$ and $y = e^t - e^{-t}$

(d) $x^2 - 6 = 2\cos t$ and $y^2 + 2 = 4\cos^2\left(\frac{t}{2}\right)$

43. Equation of common tangent to the two hyperbolas $\frac{x^2}{a^2} - \frac{y^2}{b^2} = 1$ and $\frac{y^2}{a^2} - \frac{x^2}{b^2} = 1$ is

(a) $y = x + \sqrt{(a^2 - b^2)}$

(b) $y = x - \sqrt{(a^2 - b^2)}$

(c) $y = -x + \sqrt{(a^2 - b^2)}$

(d) $y = -x - \sqrt{(a^2 - b^2)}$

44. Given ellipse $\frac{x^2}{16} + \frac{y^2}{7} = 1$ and the hyperbola $\frac{x^2}{144} - \frac{y^2}{81} = \frac{1}{25}$, if the ordinate of one of the points of intersection is produced to cut an asymptote at P, then which of the following is true?

(a) They have the same foci

(b) Square of the ordinate of point of intersection is $\frac{63}{25}$

(c) Sum of the squares of coordinate of P is 16

(d) P lies on the auxiliary circle formed by ellipse

45. Solution of the differential equation $(1 - x^2)\frac{dy}{dx} + xy = ax$, where $a \in R$, is

(a) a conic which is an ellipse

(b) centre of the conic is $(0, a)$

(c) length of one of the principal axes is 1

(d) length of one of the principal axes is equal to 2

Hyperbola Exercise 3 : Paragraph Based Questions

- This section contains **5 paragraphs** based upon each of the paragraph 3 **multiple choice questions** have to be answered. Each of these questions has four choices (a), (b), (c) and (d) out of which **ONLY ONE** is correct.

Paragraph I

(Q. Nos. 46 to 48)

The graph of the conic $x^2 - (y-1)^2 = 1$ has one tangent line with positive slope that passes through the origin. The point of tangency being (a, b)`.

46. The value of $\sin^{-1}\left(\frac{a}{b}\right)$ is

(a) $\frac{5\pi}{12}$ (b) $\frac{\pi}{6}$ (c) $\frac{\pi}{4}$ (d) $\frac{\pi}{3}$

47. Length of the latusrectum of the conic is

(a) 1 (b) $\sqrt{2}$ (c) 2 (d) 4

48. If e be the eccentricity of the conic, then the value of $(1 + e^2 + e^4)$ is

(a) 3 (b) 7 (c) $\frac{7}{4}$ (d) 21

Paragraph II

(Q. Nos. 49 to 51)

A point P moves such that the sum of the slopes of the normals drawn from it to the hyperbola $xy = 4$ is equal to the sum of the ordinates of feet of normals. The locus of P is a curve C.

49. The equation of the curve C is

(a) $x^2 = 2y$ (b) $x^2 = 4y$

(c) $x^2 = 6y$ (d) $x^2 = 8y$

50. If the tangent to the curve C cuts the coordinate axes at A and B, then, the locus of the middle-point of AB is

(a) $x^2 + 2y = 0$ (b) $x^2 = y$

(c) $2x^2 + y = 0$ (d) $x^2 = 2y$

51. The area of the equilateral triangle inscribed in the curve C having one vertex as the vertex of curve C is

(a) $8\sqrt{3}$ sq units (b) $12\sqrt{3}$ sq units

(c) $27\sqrt{3}$ sq units (d) $48\sqrt{3}$ sq units

Paragraph III

(Q. Nos. 52 to 54)

Let $P(x, y)$ be a variable point such that

$$\left|\sqrt{(x-1)^2 + (y-2)^2} - \sqrt{(x-5)^2 + (y-5)^2}\right| = 4$$

which represents a hyperbola.

52. The eccentricity of the corresponding conjugate hyperbola is

(a) $\frac{5}{4}$ (b) $\frac{4}{3}$

(c) $\frac{5}{3}$ (d) $\frac{3}{2}$

53. Locus of point of intersection of two perpendicular tangents to the hyperbola is

(a) $(x-3)^2+(y-7/2)^2=\frac{1}{4}$

(b) $(x-3)^2+(y-7/2)^2=\frac{3}{4}$

(c) $(x-3)^2+(y-7/2)^2=\frac{5}{4}$

(d) $(x-3)^2+(y-7/2)^2=\frac{7}{4}$

54. If origin is shifted to point (3, 7/2) and axes are rotated in anticlockwise sense through an angle θ, so that the equation of hyperbola reduces to its standard form $\frac{x^2}{a^2}-\frac{y^2}{b^2}=1$, then θ equals

(a) $\tan^{-1}\left(\frac{4}{3}\right)$ (b) $\tan^{-1}\left(\frac{3}{4}\right)$

(c) $\tan^{-1}\left(\frac{5}{4}\right)$ (d) $\tan^{-1}\left(\frac{4}{5}\right)$

Paragraph IV

(Q. Nos. 55 to 57)

Let $P(\theta_1)$ and $Q(\theta_2)$ are the extremities of any focal chord of the hyperbola $\frac{x^2}{a^2}-\frac{y^2}{b^2}=1$ whose eccentricity is e. Let θ be the angle between its asymptotes. Tangents are drawn to the hyperbola at some arbitrary point R. These tangent meet the coordinate axes at the points A and B respectively. The rectangle OACB (O being the origin) is completed, then

55. Locus of point C is

(a) $\frac{b^2}{x^2}-\frac{a^2}{y^2}=1$ (b) $\frac{b^2}{x^2}+\frac{a^2}{y^2}=1$

(c) $\frac{a^2}{x^2}+\frac{b^2}{y^2}=1$ (d) $\frac{a^2}{x^2}-\frac{b^2}{y^2}=1$

56. If $\cos^2\left(\frac{\theta_1+\theta_2}{2}\right)=\lambda\cos^2\left(\frac{\theta_1-\theta_2}{2}\right)$, then λ is equal to

(a) $\left(\frac{a^2+b^2}{a^2}\right)$ (b) $\left(\frac{a^2+b^2}{b^2}\right)$

(c) $\left(\frac{a^2+b^2}{ab}\right)$ (d) $\left(\frac{a^2+b^2}{2ab}\right)$

57. The value of $\cos\left(\frac{\theta}{2}\right)$ is

(a) $\frac{1}{2e}$ (b) $\frac{1}{e}$

(c) $\frac{1}{e^2}$ (d) $\frac{1}{2e^2}$

Paragraph V

(Q. Nos. 58 to 60)

The vertices of ΔABC lie on a rectangular hyperbola such that the orthocentre of the triangle is (2, 3) and the asymptotes of the rectangular hyperbola are parallel to the coordinate axes. The two perpendicular tangents of the hyperbola intersect at the point (1, 1).

58. The equation of the asymptotes is

(a) $xy-1=y-x$ (b) $xy+1=x+y$

(c) $xy-1=x-y$ (d) $xy+1=-x-y$

59. The equation of the rectangular hyperbola is

(a) $xy-5=y-x$

(b) $xy-1=x+y$

(c) $xy=x+y+1$

(d) $xy-11=-x-y$

60. The number of real tangents that can be drawn from the point (1, 1) to the rectangular hyperbola is

(a) 0 (b) 2

(c) 3 (d) 4

Hyperbola Exercise 4 :
Single Integer Answer Type Questions

- This section contains **10 questions.** The answer to each question is **a single digit integer** ranging from 0 to 9 (both inclusive)

61. The ellipse $\frac{x^2}{a^2}+\frac{y^2}{b^2}=1$ and the hyperbola $\frac{x^2}{A^2}-\frac{y^2}{B^2}=1$ are given to be confocal and length of minor axis of the ellipse is same as the conjugate axis of the hyperbola. If e_1 and e_2 represents the eccentricities of ellipse and hyperbola respectively, then the value of $e_1^{-2}+e_2^{-2}$ is

62. If abscissa of orthocentre of a triangle inscribed in a rectangular hyperbola $xy=4$ is $\frac{1}{2}$, then the ordinate of orthocentre of triangle is

63. Normal drawn to the hyperbola $xy=2$ at the point $P(t_1)$ meets the hyperbola again at $Q(t_2)$, then minimum distance between the point P and Q is

64. The normal at P to a hyperbola of eccentricity $\frac{3}{2\sqrt{2}}$ intersects the transverse and conjugate axes at M and N respectively. The locus of mid-point of MN is a hyperbola, then its eccentricity

65. If radii of director circle of the ellipse $\frac{x^2}{a^2}+\frac{y^2}{b^2}=1$ and hyperbola $\frac{x^2}{a^2}-\frac{y^2}{b_1^2}=1$ are in the ratio 1 : 3 and $4e_1^2-e_2^2=\lambda$, where e_1 and e_2 are the eccentricities of ellipse and hyperbola respectively, then the value of λ is

66. The shortest distance between the curves $\frac{x^2}{a^2}-\frac{y^2}{b^2}=1$ and $4x^2+4y^2=a^2\ (b>a)$ is $f(a,b)$, then the value of $f(4,6)+f(2,3)$ is

67. ABC is a triangle such that $\angle ABC=2\angle BAC$. If AB is fixed and locus of C is a hyperbola, then the eccentricity of the hyperbola is

68. Point P lie on $2xy=1$. A triangle is constructed by P, S and S' (where S and S' are foci). The locus of ex-centre opposite S (S and P lie in first quadrant) is $(x+py)^2=(\sqrt{2}-1)^2(x-y)^2+q$, then the value of $p+q$ is

69. Chords of the circle $x^2+y^2=4$, touch the hyperbola $\frac{x^2}{4}-\frac{y^2}{16}=1$. The locus of their middle-points is the curve $(x^2+y^2)^2=\lambda x^2-16y^2$, then the value of λ is

70. Tangents are drawn from the point (α,β) to the hyperbola $3x^2-2y^2=6$ and are inclined at angles θ and ϕ to the X-axis. If $\tan\theta\,.\tan\phi=2$, then the value of $2\alpha^2-\beta^2$ is

Hyperbola Exercise 5 : Matching Type Questions

- This section contains 3 **questions.** Each question has four statements (A), (B), (C) and (D) given in **Column I** and four statements (p, q, r and s) in **Column II.** Any given statement in **Column I** can have correct matching with one or move statements (s) given in **Column II.**

71. Match the following.

	Column I		Column II
(A)	If λ be the length of the latusrectum of the hyperbola $16x^2 - 9y^2 + 32x + 36y - 164 = 0$, then 3λ is divisible by	(p)	4
(B)	If the chord $x\cos\alpha + y\sin\alpha = p$ of the hyperbola $\frac{x^2}{16} - \frac{y^2}{18} = 1$ subtends a right angle at the centre, a circle touches the given chord and concentric with hyperbola, then the diameter of circle is divisible by	(q)	6
(C)	For the hyperbola $xy = 8$ any tangent of it at P meets coordinate axes at Q and R, then the area of triangle CQR is divisible by (where 'C' is centre of the hyperbola)	(r)	8
(D)	For the hyperbola $x^2 - 3y^2 = 9$, acute angle between its asymptotes is $\frac{\pi\lambda}{24}$, then λ is divisible by	(s)	16

72. Match the following.

	Column I		Column II
A.	If the vertex of a hyperbola bisects the distance between its centre and the corresponding focus, then the ratio of the square of its conjugate axis to the square of its transverse axis is	(p)	A Natural number
B.	With one focus of the hyperbola $\frac{x^2}{9} - \frac{y^2}{16} = 1$ as the centre, a circle is drawn which is tangent to the hyperbola with no part of the circle being outside the hyperbola. The radius of the circle is	(q)	A Prime number
C.	If S_1 and S_2 are the foci of the hyperbola whose length of the transverse axis is 4 and that of the conjugate axis is 6, and S_3 and S_4 are the foci of the conjugate hyperbola, then the area of quadrilateral $S_1S_2S_3S_4$ is	(r)	A Composit e number
D.	If equation of hyperbola whose conjugate axis is 5 and distance between its foci is 13, is $ax^2 - by^2 = c$, where a and b are co-prime, then $\frac{3ab}{2c}$ is	(s)	A Perfect number

73. If e_1 and e_2 are the roots of the equation $x^2 - \lambda x + 2 = 0$

	Column I		Column II
A.	If e_1 and e_2 are the eccentricities of ellipse and hyperbola respectively, then the values of λ are	(p)	$2\sqrt{2}$
B.	If both e_1 and e_2 are the eccentricities of the hyperbolas, then the values of λ are	(q)	$2\sqrt{3}$
C.	If e_1 and e_2 are the eccentricities of the hyperbola and conjugate hyperbola, then the values of λ are	(r)	$2\sqrt{5}$
D.	If e_1 is the eccentricity of the hyperbola for which there exist infinite points from which perpendicular tangents can be drawn and e_2 is the eccentricity of the hyperbola in which no such points exist, then the values of λ are	(s)	$2\sqrt{6}$

Hyperbola Exercise 6 : Statement I and II Type Questions

- **Directions** (Q. Nos. 74 to 81) are Assertion-Reason type questions. Each of these questions contains two statements :
Statement I (Assertion) and **Statement II** (Reason)
Each of these questions also has four alternative choices, only one of which is the correct answer. You have to select the correct choice as given below :
  (a) Statement I is true, Statement II is true; Statement II is a correct explanation for Statement I
  (b) Statement I is true, Statement II is true; Statement II is not a correct explanation for Statement I
  (c) Statement I is true, Statement II is false
  (d) Statement I is false, Statement II is true

74. **Statement I** $\frac{5}{3}$ and $\frac{5}{4}$ are the eccentricities of two conjugate hyperbolas.

Statement II If e_1 and e_2 are the eccentricities of two conjugate hyperbolas, then $e_1e_2 > 1$.

75. **Statement I** A hyperbola and its conjugate hyperbola have the same asymptotes.

Statement II The difference between the second degree curve and pair of asymptotes is constant.

76. **Statement I** The equation of the director circle to the hyperbola $5x^2 - 4y^2 = 20$ is $x^2 + y^2 = 1$.

Statement II Director circle is the locus of the point of intersection of perpendicular tangents.

77. **Statement I** Two tangents are drawn from a point on the circle $x^2 + y^2 = 9$ to the hyperbola $\frac{x^2}{25} - \frac{y^2}{16} = 1$, then angle between tangents is $\pi/2$.

Statement II $x^2 + y^2 = 9$ is the director circle of $\frac{x^2}{25} - \frac{y^2}{16} = 1$.

78. **Statement I** If eccentricity of a hyperbola is 2, then eccentricity of its conjugate hyperbola is $2/\sqrt{3}$.

Statement II If e and e_1 are the eccentricities of two conjugate hyperbolas, then $ee_1 > 1$.

79. **Statement I** The line $4x - 5y = 0$ will not meet the hyperbola $16x^2 - 25y^2 = 400$.

Statement II The line $4x - 5y = 0$ is an asymptote to the hyperbola.

80. **Statement I** The point $(5, -3)$ inside the hyperbola $3y^2 - 5x^2 + 1 = 0$.

Statement II The point (x_1, y_1) inside the hyperbola $\frac{x^2}{a^2} - \frac{y^2}{b^2} = 1$, then $\frac{x_1^2}{a^2} - \frac{y_1^2}{b^2} - 1 < 0$.

81. **Statement I** A hyperbola whose asymptotes include $\pi/3$ is said to be equilateral hyperbola.

Statement II The eccentricity of an equilateral hyperbola is $\sqrt{2}$.

Hyperbola Exercise 7 : Subjective Type Questions

- In this section, there are **12 Subjective questions.**

82. Given the base of a triangle and the ratio of the tangent of half the base angles. Show that the vertex moves on a hyperbola whose foci are the extremities of the base.

83. A, B, C are three points on the rectangular hyperbola $xy = c^2$, find

(i) The area of the triangle ABC.

(ii) The area of the triangle formed by the tangents at A, B and C.

84. If a hyperbola be rectangular and its equation be $xy = c^2$, prove that the locus of the middle points of chords of constant length $2d$ is $(x^2 + y^2)(xy - c^2) = d^2xy$.

85. If four points be taken on a rectangular hyperbola such that the chord joining any two is perpendicular to the chord joining the other two, and if $\alpha, \beta, \gamma, \delta$ be the inclinations to either asymptote of the straight line joining these points to the centre, prove that $\tan\alpha \tan\beta \tan\gamma \tan\delta = 1$.

86. P and Q are two variable points on the rectangular hyperbola $xy = c^2$ such that tangent at Q passes through the foot of the ordinate of P. Show that the locus of the intersection of tangents at P and Q is a hyperbola with the same asymptotes as of the given hyperbola.

87. A circle cuts two perpendicular lines so that each intercept is of given length. Prove that the locus of the centre of the circle is a rectangular hyperbola.

88. (a) Prove that any line parallel to either of the asymptotes of a hyperbola shall meet it in one point at infinity.

(b) Prove that the asymptotes of a hyperbola are the diagonals of the rectangle formed by the lines drawn parallel to the axes at the vertices of the hyperbola [i.e. at $(\pm a, 0)$ and $(0, \pm b)$].

89. Let the tangent at a point P on the ellipse meet the major axis at B and the ordinate from *it* meet the major axis at A. If Q is a point on the line AP such that $AQ = AB$, prove that the locus of Q is a hyperbola. Find the asymptotes of this hyperbola.

90. From the point (x_1, y_1) and (x_2, y_2), tangents are drawn to the rectangular hyperbola $xy = c^2$. If the conic passing through the two given points and the four points of contact is a circle, then show that $x_1x_2 = y_1y_2$ and $x_1y_2 + x_2y_1 = 4c^2$.

91. A rectangular hyperbola passes through two fixed points and its asymptotes are in given directions. Prove that its vertices lie on an ellipse and hyperbola which intersect orthogonally.

92. Let normals are drawn from (α, β) to the hyperbola $xy = 1$, and $(x_i, y_i), i = 1, 2, 3, 4$ be the feet of the co-normal points. If the algebraic sum of the perpendicular distances drawn from $(x_i, y_i), i = 1, 2, 3, 4$ onto a variable line vanishes, show that the variable line passes through the point $(\alpha/4, \beta/4)$.

93. A series of hyperbolas is drawn having a common transverse axis of length $2a$. Prove that the locus of a point P on each hyperbola such that its distance from the transverse axis is equal to its distance from on asymptote, is the curve

$(x^2 - y^2)^2 = 4x^2(x^2 - a^2)$.

Hyperbola Exercise 8 :
Questions Asked in Previous 13 Year's Exams

- This section contains questions asked in **IIT-JEE, AIEEE, JEE Main & JEE Advanced** from year **2005** to **2017**.

94. The locus of a point $P(\alpha, \beta)$ moving under the condition that the line $y = \alpha x + \beta$ is a tangent to the hyperbola $\dfrac{x^2}{a^2} - \dfrac{y^2}{b^2} = 1$ is **[AIEEE 2005, 3M]**

(a) an ellipse
(b) a circle
(c) a parabola
(d) a hyperbola

95. Let a hyperbola passes through the focus of the ellipse $\dfrac{x^2}{25} + \dfrac{y^2}{16} = 1$. The transverse and conjugate axes of this hyperbola coincide with the major and minor axes of the given ellipse, also the product of eccentricities of given ellipse and hyperbola is 1, then **[IIT- JEE 2006, 5M]**

(a) the equation of hyperbola is $\dfrac{x^2}{9} - \dfrac{y^2}{16} = 1$
(b) the equations of hyperbola is $\dfrac{x^2}{9} - \dfrac{y^2}{25} = 1$
(c) focus of hyperbola is (5, 0)
(d) vertex of hyperbola is $(5\sqrt{3}, 0)$

96. A hyperbola, having the transverse axis of length $2\sin\theta$, is confocal with the ellipse $3x^2 + 4y^2 = 12$. Then, its equation is **[IIT- JEE 2007, 3M]**

(a) $x^2\operatorname{cosec}^2\theta - y^2\sec^2\theta = 1$
(b) $x^2\sec^2\theta - y^2\operatorname{cosec}^2\theta = 1$
(c) $x^2\sin^2\theta - y^2\cos^2\theta = 1$
(d) $x^2\cos^2\theta - y^2\sin^2\theta = 1$

97. Two branches of a hyperbola **[IIT- JEE 2007, 1.5M]**

(a) have a common tangent
(b) have a common normal
(c) do not have a common tangent
(d) do not have a common normal

98. For the hyperbola $\frac{x^2}{\cos^2\alpha} - \frac{y^2}{\sin^2\alpha} = 1$, which of the following remains constant when α varies **[AIEEE 2007, 3M]**

(a) abscissae of vertices (b) abscissae of foci
(c) eccentricity (d) directrix

99. Consider a branch of the hyperbola
$x^2 - 2y^2 - 2\sqrt{2}x - 4\sqrt{2}y - 6 = 0$
with vertex at the point A. Let B be one of the end points of its latusrectum. If C is the focus of the hyperbola nearest to the point A, then the area of the triangle ABC is **[IIT- JEE 2008, 3M]**

(a) $1-\sqrt{\frac{2}{3}}$ (b) $\sqrt{\frac{3}{2}}-1$ (c) $1+\sqrt{\frac{2}{3}}$ (d) $\sqrt{\frac{3}{2}}+1$

100. An ellipse intersects the hyperbola $2x^2 - 2y^2 = 1$ orthogonally. The eccentricity of the ellipse is reciprocal of that of the hyperbola. If the axes of the ellipse are along the coordinate axes, then **[IIT- JEE 2009, 4M]**

(a) equation of ellipse is $x^2 + 2y^2 = 2$
(b) the foci of ellipse are $(\pm 1, 0)$
(c) equation of ellipse is $x^2 + 2y^2 = 4$
(d) the foci of ellipse are $(\pm\sqrt{2}, 0)$

Paragraph

(Q. Nos. 100 and 102)

The circle $x^2 + y^2 - 8x = 0$ and hyperbola $\frac{x^2}{9} - \frac{y^2}{4} = 1$ intersect at the points A and B.

101. Equation of a common tangent with positive slope to the circle as well as to the hyperbola is

(a) $2x - \sqrt{5}y - 20 = 0$ (b) $2x - \sqrt{5}y + 4 = 0$
(c) $3x - 4y + 8 = 0$ (d) $4x - 3y + 4 = 0$

102. Equation of the circle with AB as its diameter is

(a) $x^2 + y^2 - 12x + 24 = 0$ (b) $x^2 + y^2 + 12x + 24 = 0$
(c) $x^2 + y^2 + 24x - 12 = 0$ (d) $x^2 + y^2 - 24x - 12 = 0$

[IIT- JEE 2010, 3 + 3M]

103. The line $2x + y = 1$ is tangent to the hyperbola $\frac{x^2}{a^2} - \frac{y^2}{b^2} = 1$. If this line passes through the point of intersection of the nearest directrix and the X-axis, then the eccentricity of the hyperbola is **[IIT- JEE 2010, 3M]**

104. Let $P(6, 3)$ be a point on the hyperbola $\frac{x^2}{a^2} - \frac{y^2}{b^2} = 1$. If the normal at the point P intersects the X-axis at $(9, 0)$, then the eccentricity of the hyperbola is **[IIT- JEE 2011, 3M]**

(a) $\sqrt{\frac{5}{2}}$ (b) $\sqrt{\frac{3}{2}}$
(c) $\sqrt{2}$ (d) $\sqrt{3}$

105. Let the eccentricity of the hyperbola $\frac{x^2}{a^2} - \frac{y^2}{b^2} = 1$ be reciprocal to that of the ellipse $x^2 + 4y^2 = 4$. If the hyperbola passes through a focus of the ellipse, then **[IIT- JEE 2011, 4M]**

(a) the equation of the hyperbola is $\frac{x^2}{3} - \frac{y^2}{2} = 1$
(b) a focus of the hyperbola is $(2, 0)$
(c) the eccentricity of the hyperbola is $\sqrt{\frac{5}{3}}$
(d) the equation of the hyperbola is $x^2 - 3y^2 = 3$

106. Tangents are drawn to the hyperbola $\frac{x^2}{9} - \frac{y^2}{4} = 1$, parallel to the straight line $2x - y = 1$. The points of contact of the tangents on the hyperbola are **[IIT- JEE 2012, 4M]**

(a) $\left(\frac{9}{2\sqrt{2}}, \frac{1}{\sqrt{2}}\right)$ (b) $\left(-\frac{9}{2\sqrt{2}}, -\frac{1}{\sqrt{2}}\right)$
(c) $(3\sqrt{3}, -2\sqrt{2})$ (d) $(-3\sqrt{3}, 2\sqrt{2})$

107. Consider the hyperbola $H: x^2 - y^2 = 1$ and a circle S with centre $N(x_2, 0)$. Suppose that H and S touch each other at a point $P(x_1, y_1)$ with $x_1 > 1$ and $y_1 > 0$. The common tangent to H and S at P intersects the X-axis at point M. If (l, m) is the centroid of the triangle PMN, then the correct expression(s) is(are) **[JEE (Advanced) 2015, 4M]**

(a) $\frac{dl}{dx_1} = 1 - \frac{1}{3x_1^2}$ for $x_1 > 1$ (b) $\frac{dm}{dx_1} = \frac{x_1}{3(\sqrt{(x_1^2 - 1)})}$ for $x_1 > 1$
(c) $\frac{dl}{dx_1} = 1 + \frac{1}{3x_1^2}$ for $x_1 > 1$ (d) $\frac{dm}{dy_1} = \frac{1}{3}$ for $y_1 > 0$

108. The eccentricity of the hyperbola whose length of the latusrectum is equal to 8 and the length of its conjugate axis is equal to half of the distance between its foci, is **[JEE (Main) 2016, 4M]**

(a) $\frac{2}{\sqrt{3}}$ (b) $\sqrt{3}$
(c) $\frac{4}{3}$ (d) $\frac{4}{\sqrt{3}}$

109. A hyperbola passes through the point $P(\sqrt{2}, \sqrt{3})$ and has foci at $(\pm 2, 0)$. Then the taught to this hyperbola at pals passes through the point **[JEE (Main) 2017, 4M]**

(a) $(-\sqrt{2}, -\sqrt{3})$ (b) $(3\sqrt{2}, 2\sqrt{3})$
(c) $(2\sqrt{2}, 3\sqrt{3})$ (d) $(\sqrt{3}, \sqrt{2})$

110. If $2x - y + 1 = 0$ is a tangent to the hyperbola $\frac{x^2}{a^2} - \frac{y^2}{16} = 1$, then which of the following cannot be sides of a right angled triangle? **[JEE Advanced 2017, 4M]**

(a) $2a, 8, 1$ (b) $a, 4, 1$
(c) $a, 4, 2$ (d) $2a, 4, 1$

▪ **Direction** (Q. No. 111 to 113) Matching the information given in the three columns of the following table.
Columns 1, 2 and 3 contain conics, equations of tangents to the conics and points of contact, respectively.

[JEE Advanced 2017, (3 + 3 + 3) M]

	Column 1		Column 2		Column 3
(I)	$x^2 + y^2 = a^2$	(i)	$my = m^2x + a$	(P)	$\left(\frac{a}{m^2}, \frac{2a}{m}\right)$
(II)	$x^2 + a^2y^2 = a^2$	(ii)	$y = mx + a\sqrt{m^2+1}$	(Q)	$\left(\frac{-ma}{\sqrt{m^2+1}}, \frac{a}{\sqrt{m^2+1}}\right)$
(III)	$y^2 = 4ax$	(iii)	$y = mx + \sqrt{a^2m^2-1}$	(R)	$\left(\frac{-a^2m}{\sqrt{a^2m^2+1}}, \frac{1}{\sqrt{a^2m^2+1}}\right)$
(IV)	$x^2 - a^2y^2 = a^2$	(iv)	$y = mx + \sqrt{a^2m^2+1}$	(S)	$\left(\frac{-a^2m}{\sqrt{a^2m^2-1}}, \frac{-1}{\sqrt{a^2m^2-1}}\right)$

111. The tangent to a suitable conic (Column 1) at $\left(\sqrt{3}, \frac{1}{2}\right)$ is found to be $\sqrt{3}x + 2y = 4$, then which of the following options is the only correct combination?

(a) (IV) (iii) (S)
(b) (II) (iv) (R)
(c) (IV) (iv) (S)
(d) (II) (iii) (R)

112. For $a = \sqrt{2}$, if a tangent is drawn to a suitable conic (Column 1) at the point of contact $(-1, 1)$, then which of the following options is the only correct combination for obtaining its equation?

(a) (III) (i) (P) (b) (I) (i) (P)
(c) (II) (ii) (Q) (d) (I) (ii) (Q)

113. If a tangent of a suitable conic (Column 1) is found to be $y = x + 8$ and its point of contact is (8, 16), then which of the following options is the only correct combination?

(a) (III) (i) (P) (b) (III) (ii) (Q)
(c) (II) (iv) (R) (d) (I) (ii) (Q)

Answers

Exercise for Session 1

1. (d) **2.** (b) **3.** (d) **4.** (a) **5.** (d)
6. (a) **7.** (a) **8.** (b) **9.** (c,d) **10.** (c)
11. (b) **12.** (c) **13.** $y^2 - x^2 = 5$
14. $8x^2 - y^2 - 64x + 10y + 71 = 0$
16. $(1, 2)$; $2\sqrt{\left(\frac{2}{5}\right)}$; $2\sqrt{5}$; $2\sqrt{3}$ **17.** 2 **18.** $\lambda = \pm 6$
19. $30x - 24y \pm \sqrt{(161)} = 0$; $\left(\pm \frac{15}{2\sqrt{161}}, \pm \frac{8}{3\sqrt{161}}\right)$

Exercise for Session 2

1. (d) **2.** (c) **3.** (a) **4.** (d) **5.** (b)
6. (a) **7.** (a) **8.** (b) **9.** (d) **10.** (c)
11. $\left(\frac{x^2}{a^2} + \frac{y^2}{b^2}\right)^2 = \frac{x^2}{a^2} - \frac{y^2}{b^2}$

Exercise for Session 3

1. (b) **2.** (d) **3.** (a) **4.** (d) **5.** (d)
6. (c) **7.** (a) **8.** (a) **9.** (d) **10.** (b)
11. (d) **12.** (b) **13.** $x + 3y = 0$
14. $12x^2 - 7xy - 12y^2 + 31x + 17y = 0$
15. $6x^2 + 13xy + 6y^2 - 38x - 37y - 98 = 0$

Chapter Exercises

1. (a) **2.** (d) **3.** (b) **4.** (c) **5.** (a) **6.** (a)
7. (b) **8.** (a) **9.** (b) **10.** (a) **11.** (b) **12.** (c)
13. (d) **14.** (b) **15.** (c) **16.** (b) **17.** (b) **18.** (b)
19. (d) **20.** (a) **21.** (a) **22.** (c) **23.** (b) **24.** (c)
25. (b) **26.** (c) **27.** (a) **28.** (b) **29.** (b) **30.** (c)
31. (a,c) **32.** (c,d) **33.** (b,c) **34.** (a,b,d) **35.** (a,b,c) **36.** (b,c)
37. (b,c) **38.** (a,b,c) **39.** (a,b) **40.** (a,d) **41.** (a,b,c) **42.** (a,c,d)
43. (a,b,c,d) **44.** (a,b,c,d) **45.** (a,b,d)
46. (c) **47.** (c) **48.** (b) **49.** (b) **50.** (c) **51.** (d)
52. (c) **53.** (d) **54.** (b) **55.** (d) **56.** (a) **57.** (b)
58. (b) **59.** (c) **60.** (b) **61.** (2) **62.** (8) **63.** (4)
64. (3) **65.** (7) **66.** (3) **67.** (2) **68.** (5) **69.** (4)
70. (7)
71. (A) → (p,r,s); (B) → (p,q,r); (C) → (p,r,s); (D) → (p,r)
72. (A) → (p,q); (B) → (p,q); (C) → (p,r); (D) → (p,r,s)
73. (A) → (q,r,s); (B) → (p); (C) → (p); (D) → (q,r,s)
74. (b) **75.** (a) **76.** (d) **77.** (a) **78.** (b) **79.** (a)
80. (c) **81.** (d)
83. (i) $\frac{c^2}{2t_1t_2t_3} |(t_1 - t_2)((t_2 - t_3)(t_3 - t_1)|$

(ii) $2c^2 \left| \frac{(t_1 - t_2)(t_2 - t_3)(t_3 - t_1)}{(t_1 + t_2)(t_2 + t_3)(t_3 + t_1)} \right|$

89. $x = 0$ and $x + y = 0$
94. (d) **95.** (a,c) **96.** (a) **97.** (b,c) **98.** (b) **99.** (b)
100. (a,b) **101.** (b) **102.** (a) **103.** (2) **104.** (b) **105.** (b,d)
106. (a,b) **107.** (a,b,d) **108.** (a) **109.** (c) **110.** (a,b,c)
111. (b) **112.** (d) **113.** (a)

Solutions

1. $\because PF_1 \cdot PF_2 = e\left(x_1 - \frac{a}{e}\right) \cdot e\left(x_1 + \frac{a}{e}\right)$

$= e^2 x_1^2 - a^2$

$= 2x_1^2 - a^2$ (for rectangular hyperbola $e = \sqrt{2}$)

$= x_1^2 + x_1^2 - a^2$ $(\because P(x_1, y_1),\ x_1^2 - y_1^2 = a^2)$

$= x_1^2 + y_1^2$

$= (OP)^2$

$\therefore \quad \lambda = 1$

2. Let the point of contact of normal from point $P(h, k)$, be $R(t)$ for the hyperbola $xy = c^2$

$\Rightarrow$ The equation of normal is

$ct^4 - xt^3 + yt - c = 0$ which gives

$ct^4 - ht^3 + kt - c = 0$ [$\because$ It passes through (h,k)]...(i)

$\Rightarrow \quad t_1^2 + t_2^2 + t_3^2 + t_4^2 = \lambda$ (given) ... (ii)

From Eq. (i),

$$\Sigma t_1 = \frac{h}{c},\ \Sigma t_1 t_2 = 0$$

$\therefore \quad (\Sigma t_1)^2 - 2\Sigma t_1 t_2 = t_1^2 + t_2^2 + t_3^2 + t_4^2$

$\Rightarrow \quad \left(\frac{h}{c}\right)^2 - 0 = \lambda$

or $\quad h^2 = \lambda c^2$

$\therefore$ Locus of P is $x^2 = \lambda c^2$

3. As branches lies in the second and fourth quadrant.

$\therefore$ We have $xy < 0$

$\Rightarrow \quad m^2 - 9 < 0 \Rightarrow |m| < 3$

4. Let A is (α, β), the B is (β, α)

$\because A$ and B an symmetrical about the line $y = x$.

So, tangents at A and B will be mirror images of each other about $y = x$. Thus, point of intersection will lie on $y = x$.

5. Let $P(h,k)$ be any point on any one member of hyperbola family, having equation $\frac{x^2}{a^2} - \frac{y^2}{b^2} = 1$; b is any arbitrary constant, then its asymptotes are given by $y = \pm \frac{b}{a}x$, then according to question

$$|k| = \frac{\left|\pm \frac{b}{a}h - k\right|}{\sqrt{\left(\frac{b^2}{a^2} + 1\right)}}$$

$\Rightarrow \quad k^2 = \left(\pm \frac{b}{a}h - k\right)^2 \left(\frac{a^2}{a^2 + b^2}\right)$

or $\quad k^2 = \frac{(\pm bh - ak)^2}{(a^2 + b^2)}$ ...(i)

Further (h,k) lies on hyperbola

$$\frac{h^2}{a^2} - \frac{k^2}{b^2} = 1 \Rightarrow b = \sqrt{\left(\frac{a^2k^2}{h^2 - a^2}\right)} \quad ...(ii)$$

From Eq. (i) and (ii), we get

$$(k^2 - h^2) = \pm 2h\sqrt{(h^2 - a^2)}$$

$\Rightarrow \quad (k^2 - h^2)^2 = 4h^2(h^2 - a^2)$

$\therefore$ Required locus is

$$(x^2 - y^2)^2 = 4x^2(x^2 - a^2)$$

6. We know that if a circle cuts a rectangular hyperbola, then arithmetic mean of points of intersections is the mid-point of centre of hyperbola and circle.

So, $\quad \frac{3 + 5 + 2 + (-1)}{4} = \frac{-g + 1}{2}$

and $\quad \frac{4 + 3 + 6 + 0}{4} = \frac{-f + 2}{2}$

$\therefore \quad g + f = -8$

7. We know that eccentricity of a parabola and rectangular hyperbola are 1 and $\sqrt{2}$ respectively. Also, irrational roots occur in conjugate pair, thus roots of $f(x) = 0$ are $1, \sqrt{2}$ and $-\sqrt{2}$

$\therefore \quad f(x) = (x - 1)(x - \sqrt{2})(x + \sqrt{2})$

$= x^3 - x^2 - 2x + 2$

$\therefore \quad a + b + c + d = 1 - 1 - 2 + 2 = 0$

8. Let the point be (α, β)

$\Rightarrow \quad \beta = \alpha + c$

Chord of contact of hyperbola $T = 0$.

$\therefore \quad \frac{x\alpha}{2} - \frac{y\beta}{1} = 1$

$\Rightarrow \quad \frac{x\alpha}{2} - y(\alpha + c) = 1$

$\Rightarrow \quad \left(\frac{x}{2} - y\right)\alpha - (yc + 1) = 0$

Since, this passes through point (x_1, y_1)

$\therefore \quad x_1 = 2y_1$ and $y_1 c + 1 = 0$

$\therefore \quad y_1 = \frac{x_1}{2}$

Hence, $\quad \frac{x_1}{y_1} = 2$

9. Eliminating x, we have

$$\frac{y^2}{b^2} + \frac{y}{ab} + 1 = 0$$

This equation has real and distinct roots

$\therefore \quad \frac{1}{a^2b^2} - \frac{4}{b^2} > 0$

i.e. $\quad \frac{1}{a^2} > 4$ or $a^2 < \frac{1}{4}$

$\Rightarrow a < \frac{1}{2}$ and hence the conics intersect if $0 < a < \frac{1}{2}$.

10. Points from where perpendicular tangents can be drawn to the give hyperbola lie on the director circle $x^2 + y^2 = 9 - 16 = -7$ which is an imaginary circle. Hence, no point exists.

11. $\because \dfrac{\tan\left(\frac{1}{2}\angle ABC\right)}{\tan\left(\frac{1}{2}\angle BAC\right)} = \dfrac{3}{1}$

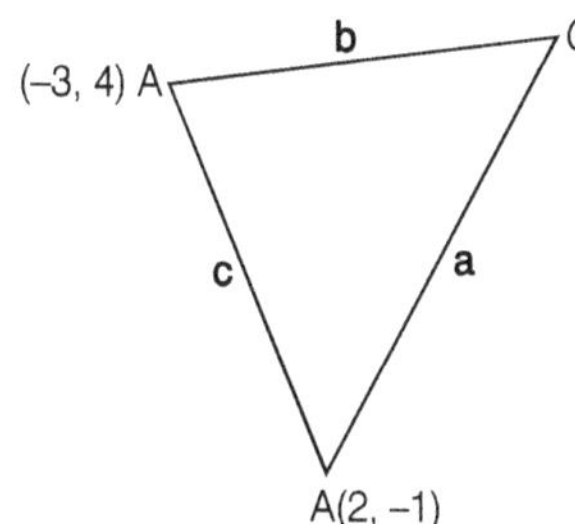

or $\quad \dfrac{\tan\left(\dfrac{B}{2}\right)}{\tan\left(\dfrac{A}{2}\right)} = 3$ or $\dfrac{\dfrac{\Delta}{s(s-b)}}{\dfrac{\Delta}{s(s-a)}} = 3$

or $\quad \dfrac{s-a}{s-b} = 3$

$\Rightarrow \quad s - a = 3s - 3b$

or $\quad 2s = 3b - a$

or $\quad a + b + c = 3b - a$

or $\quad b - a = \dfrac{c}{2}$

or $\quad AC - BC = \text{constant}$

$\therefore$ Locus of C is a hyperbola, whose foci are A and B.

$\therefore$ Distance between foci $= |AB| = 5\sqrt{2}$.

12.

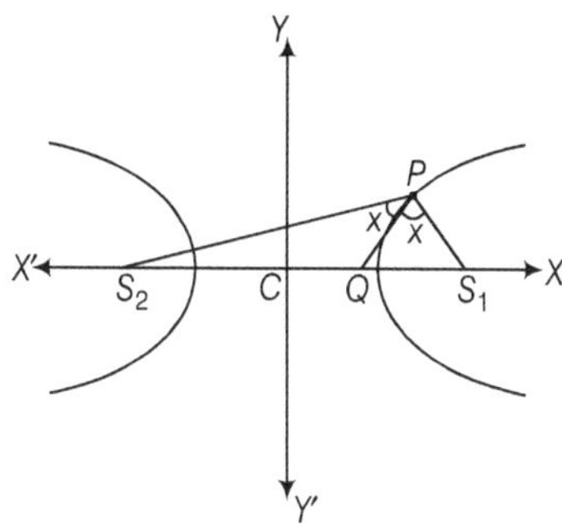

Let $\quad P \equiv (x_1, y_1)$

It is clear from figure

$$\alpha > 0 \quad \text{... (i)}$$

and $Q(\alpha, 0)$ out side on the hyperbola, then

$$\frac{x^2}{a^2} - \frac{y^2}{b^2} - 1 \le 0$$

$\Rightarrow \quad \dfrac{\alpha^2}{a^2} - 1 \le 0$

or $\quad \alpha^2 \le a^2$

$\therefore \quad -a \le \alpha \le a \quad \text{... (ii)}$

From Eqs. (i) and (ii), we get

$$0 < \alpha \le a$$

$$\alpha \in (0, a]$$

13. $\because$ Angle between asymptotes $= 2\tan^{-1}\left(\dfrac{b}{a}\right) = 120°$

or $\quad \tan^{-1}\left(\dfrac{b}{a}\right) = 60°$

or $\quad \dfrac{b}{a} = \sqrt{3}$

$\therefore \quad b = a\sqrt{3}$ or $b^2 = 3a^2$

$\Rightarrow \quad a^2 = 3 \quad (\because b^2 = 9)$

Required locus is director circle of the hyperbola and which is $x^2 + y^2 = a^2 - b^2 = 3 - 9 = -6$

which is not possible.

Now, angle between asymptotes $= 2\tan^{-1}\left(\dfrac{b}{a}\right) = 60°$.

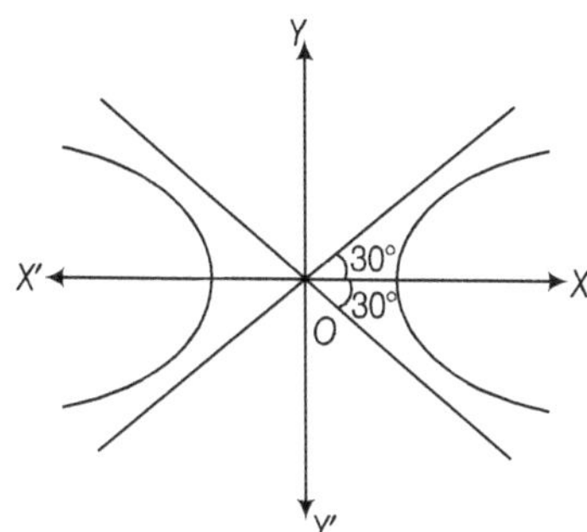

or $\quad \tan^{-1}\left(\dfrac{b}{a}\right) = 30°$

or $\quad \dfrac{b}{a} = \dfrac{1}{\sqrt{3}}$

or $\quad a^2 = 3b^2 = 27 \quad (\because b^2 = 9)$

$\therefore$ Required locus is

$$x^2 + y^2 = a^2 - b^2 = 27 - 9 = 18$$

14. Equation of chord joining α and β is

$$\frac{x}{a}\cos\left(\frac{\alpha-\beta}{2}\right) - \frac{y}{b}\sin\left(\frac{\alpha+\beta}{2}\right) = \cos\left(\frac{\alpha+\beta}{2}\right)$$

Put $\alpha + \beta = 3\pi$, then

$$\frac{x}{a}\cos\left(\frac{\alpha-\beta}{2}\right) + \frac{y}{b} = 0$$

It passes through the centre (0, 0).

15. Let $P(a\cos\theta, b\sin\theta)$ on the ellipse.

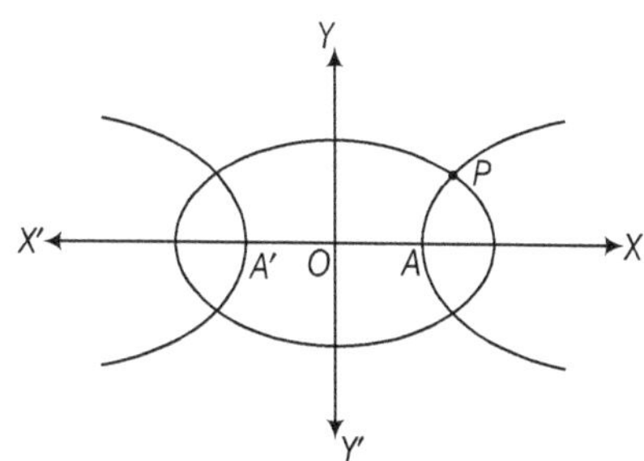

$\therefore$ Equation of tangent at P on ellipse is

$$\frac{x}{a}\cos\theta + \frac{y}{b}\sin\theta = 1 \quad \text{... (i)}$$

and equation of tangent at P on $x^2 - y^2 = c^2$ is

$$x(a\cos\theta) - y(b\sin\theta) = c^2 \quad \text{...(ii)}$$

Since, curves intersect at right angle, then

$$-\frac{b}{a}\cot\theta \times \frac{a}{b}\cot\theta = -1$$

$\therefore \quad \tan^2\theta = 1 \quad$ ... (iii)

Since, $P(a\cos\theta, b\sin\theta)$ also lies on hyperbola

$\therefore \quad (a\cos\theta)^2 - (b\sin\theta)^2 = c^2$

Dividing both sides by $\cos^2\theta$, then

or $\quad a^2 - b^2\tan^2\theta = c^2(1 + \tan^2\theta)$

$$a^2 - b^2 = 2c^2 \quad \text{[from Eq. (iii)]}$$

16. Let mid-point of the chord is (h,k).

$\therefore$ Equation of chord of $x^2 - y^2 = a^2$ is

$$T = S_1$$

$$hx - ky = h^2 - k^2$$

or $\quad y = \frac{h}{k}x - \frac{(h^2 - k^2)}{k}$

which is tangent of $y^2 = 4ax$

$\therefore \quad -\frac{(h^2 - k^2)}{k} = \frac{a}{\frac{h}{k}}$

or $\quad -(h^2 - k^2) = \frac{ak^2}{h}$

or $\quad -h^3 + hk^2 = ak^2$

or $\quad k^2(h - a) = h^3$

Hence, locus of mid-point is

$$y^2(x - a) = x^3$$

17. It is clear from the figure the common tangent to the circle $x^2 + y^2 = 1$ and hyperbola $x^2 - y^2 = 1$ is $x = 1$ (which is nearer to P (1/2, 1) and given one focus at P (1/2, 1), so the equation of the directrix is $x = 1$. Hence, the equation of the ellipse is

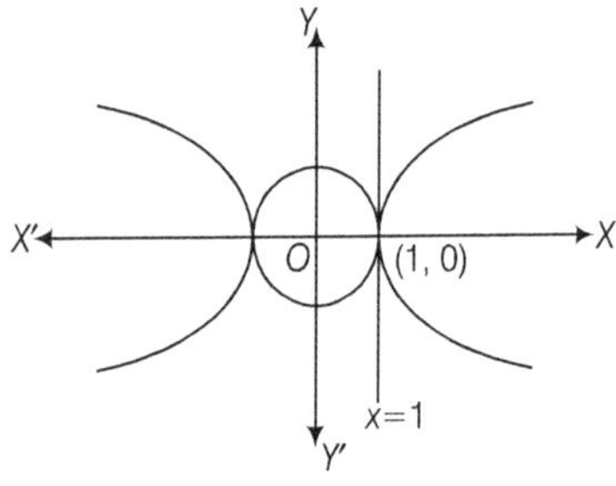

$$\sqrt{(x - 1/2)^2 + (y - 1)^2} = \frac{1}{2}|x - 1|$$

$\Rightarrow \quad 9(x - 1/3)^2 + 12(y - 1)^2 = 1$

18. Since, asymptotes of rectangular hyperbola are perpendicular to each other.

$\because$ Given asymptote is $3x - 4y - 6 = 0$

$\therefore$ Other asymptote is $4x + 3y + \lambda = 0 \quad$ ... (i)

Given, centre of hyperbola lies on $x - y - 1 = 0$

Since, asymptotes pass through the centre of hyperbola

$\therefore$ Centre is the point of intersection of $x - y - 1 = 0$ and $3x - 4y - 6 = 0$

$\therefore$ Centre is $(-2, -3)$, also $(-2, -3)$ lies on Eq. (i)

then $\quad -8 - 9 + \lambda = 0$

$\therefore \quad \lambda = 17$

Hence, other asymptote is

$$4x + 3y + 17 = 0 \quad \text{[from Eq. (i)]}$$

19. Equation of normal of $y^2 = 4ax$ is

$$y = mx - 2am - am^3$$

which is tangent of $x^2 - y^2 = a^2$

$\therefore \quad (-2am - am^3)^2 = a^2m^2 - a^2$

or $\quad 4m^2 + m^6 + 4m^4 = m^2 - 1$

or $\quad m^6 + 4m^4 + 3m^2 + 1 = 0$

20. Let the middle-point of the chord is (h,k)

$\therefore \quad T = S_1$

$$3xh - 2yk + 2(x + h) - 3(y + k) = 3h^2 - 2k^2 + 4h - 6k$$

Slope of this chord $= \frac{3h + 2}{2k + 3} = 2 \quad$ (given)

or $\quad 3h + 2 = 4k + 6$

$\Rightarrow \quad 3h - 4k = 4$

Hence, locus of middle-point is

$$3x - 4y = 4$$

21. Let $f(x, y) \equiv x^2 + 3xy + 2y^2 + 2x + 3y + 2 = 0$

$\therefore \frac{\partial f}{\partial x} = 2x + 3y + 2$ and $\frac{\partial f}{\partial y} = 3x + 4y + 3$

For centre, $\frac{\partial f}{\partial x} = 0$ and $\frac{\partial f}{\partial y} = 0$

$\therefore \quad 2x + 3y + 2 = 0$

$$3x + 4y + 3 = 0$$

After solving, we get

$$x = -1, y = 0$$

$\therefore$ Coordinates of centre are $(-1, 0)$.

22. $\because$ Hyperbola is $\frac{x^2}{16} - \frac{y^2}{9} = 1 \quad$ ... (i)

Foci are $(\pm 5, 0)$

$$F_1 \equiv (5, 0), F_2 \equiv (-5, 0)$$

Also, $\quad 4e_H = 5$

$\therefore \quad e_H = \frac{5}{4}$

Conjugate hyperbola of Eq. (i) is

$$-\frac{x^2}{16} + \frac{y^2}{9} = 1 \quad \text{... (ii)}$$

Foci are $(0, \pm 5)$

$$F_3 \equiv (0, 5), F_4 \equiv (0, -5)$$

Also, $\quad 3e_c = 5$

$\therefore \quad e_c = \frac{5}{3}$

Equation of asymptotes of Eqs. (i) and (ii) are same

$$y = \pm\frac{3}{4}x \text{ and } e_H < e_c$$

Auxiliary circle of Eq. (i) is $x^2 + y^2 = 7$ and Eq. (ii) is

$$x^2 + y^2 = -7$$

and area of quadrilateral formed by their foci $= 4 \times \frac{1}{2} \times 5 \times 5$

$= 50$ sq units

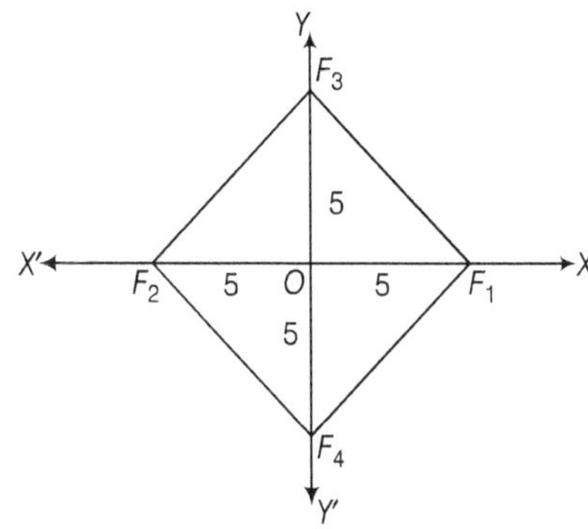

23. Point of intersection of tangents at $(a\sec\alpha, b\tan\alpha)$ and $(a\sec\beta, b\tan\beta)$ is

$$\left(\frac{a\cos\left(\frac{\alpha-\beta}{2}\right)}{\cos\left(\frac{\alpha+\beta}{2}\right)}, \frac{b\sin\left(\frac{\alpha+\beta}{2}\right)}{\cos\left(\frac{\alpha+\beta}{2}\right)}\right)$$

Here, $\alpha = \phi, \beta = \frac{\pi}{2} - \phi$

then, point of intersection is $\left(\frac{a\cos\left(\frac{\pi}{4}-\phi\right)}{\frac{1}{\sqrt{2}}}, b\right)$

$$x = a\sqrt{2}\cos\left(\frac{\pi}{4}-\phi\right)$$

and $y = b$

$\therefore$ Required locus is $y = b$

24. $xdy + ydx = 0$

$\Rightarrow d(xy) = 0$

$\therefore xy = c$

which pass through (2, 8), then $2 \times 8 = c$

$\therefore c = 16$

Equation of conic is $xy = 16$

$\therefore$Length of latusrectum $= 2\sqrt{2}\,(4) = 8\sqrt{2}$

25. $x = t^2 + 1, y = 2t$

$\Rightarrow x = \left(\frac{y}{2}\right)^2 + 1$

$\Rightarrow x = \frac{y^2}{4} + 1$

$\Rightarrow y^2 = 4(x-1)$ ... (i)

Also, $x = 2s, y = \frac{2}{s}$

$\therefore xy = 4$ ...(ii)

From Eqs. (i) and (ii),

$$\left(\frac{4}{x}\right)^2 = 4(x-1)$$

$\Rightarrow \frac{16}{x^2} = 4(x-1)$

$\Rightarrow 4 = x^3 - x^2$

$\Rightarrow x^3 - x^2 - 4 = 0$

$\Rightarrow (x-2)(x^2+x+2) = 0$

$\therefore x = 2, x^2 + x + 2 \neq 0$

From Eq. (ii),

$$y = \frac{4}{2} = 2$$

Point of intersection is (2, 2)

26. Let rectangular hyperbola $xy = c^2$

Equation of tangent at 't' is

$$\frac{x}{t} + yt = 2c$$

$\Rightarrow \frac{x}{2ct} + \frac{y}{\left(\frac{2c}{t}\right)} = 1$ ... (i)

and equation of normal at 't' is

$$xt^3 - yt - ct^4 + c = 0$$

$\Rightarrow xt^3 - ty = ct^4 - c$

$\Rightarrow \frac{x}{\left(\frac{ct^4-c}{t^3}\right)} + \frac{x}{\left(\frac{-ct^4+c}{t}\right)} = 1$ ... (ii)

From Eqs. (i) and (ii) it is clear that

$$x_1 = 2ct, x_2 = \left(\frac{ct^4-c}{t^3}\right)$$

and $y_1 = \frac{2c}{t}, y_2 = \left(\frac{-ct^4+c}{t}\right)$

$\therefore x_1x_2 + y_1y_2$

$$= \frac{2ct(ct^4-c)}{t^3} + \frac{2c}{t}\cdot\frac{(-ct^4+c)}{t}$$

$$= \frac{2c^2(t^4-1)}{t^2} + \frac{2c^2(t^4-1)}{t^2} = 0$$

27. $CS = p\sqrt{2}$

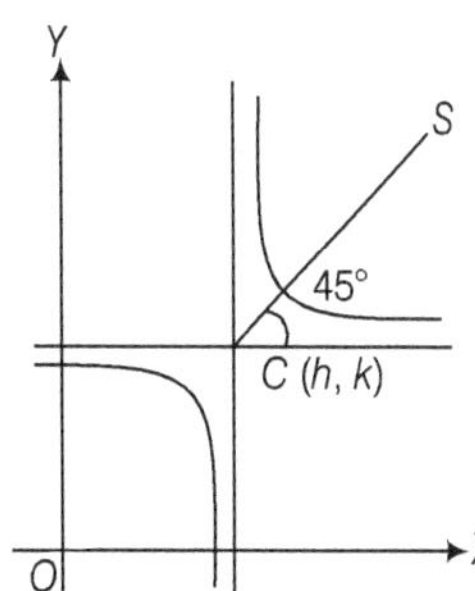

$\therefore$Coordinate of S is either

$$(h+p, k+p) \text{ or } (h-p, k-p)$$

28. $\because H : x^2 + 3xy + 2y^2 + 2x + 3y = 0$

Let pair of asymptotes is

$$x^2 + 3xy + 2y^2 + 2x + 3y + \lambda = 0$$

$\therefore \Delta = 0$

$$1\times2\times\lambda+2\times\frac{3}{2}\times1\times\frac{3}{2}-1\times\frac{9}{4}-2\times1-\lambda\times\frac{9}{4}=0$$

$$\Rightarrow \quad -\frac{\lambda}{4}+\frac{9}{2}-\frac{9}{4}-2=0$$

$$\Rightarrow \quad \frac{\lambda}{4}=\frac{9}{4}-2=\frac{1}{4}$$

$$\therefore \quad \lambda=1$$

$$A: x^2+3xy+2y^2+2x+3y+1=0$$

$$\because \quad H+C=2A$$

$$\therefore \quad C=2A-H$$

$$=x^2+3xy+2y^2+2x+3y+2$$

$\therefore$ Conjugate hyperbola is $x^2+3xy+2y^2+2x+3y+2=0$

29. The equation of the hyperbola is $\dfrac{x^2}{9}-\dfrac{y^2}{16}=1$

The equation of the tangent is

$$y=mx+\sqrt{(9m^2-16)}$$

or $\quad \sqrt{(9m^2-16)}=2\sqrt{5}$

or $\quad 9m^2-16=20$

or $\quad m^2=4$

$\therefore \quad m=\pm 2$

or $\quad a+b=$ sum of roots $=0$

30. $\because x-2=m$ and $y+1=\dfrac{4}{m}$

$\therefore \quad (x-2)(y+1)=4$

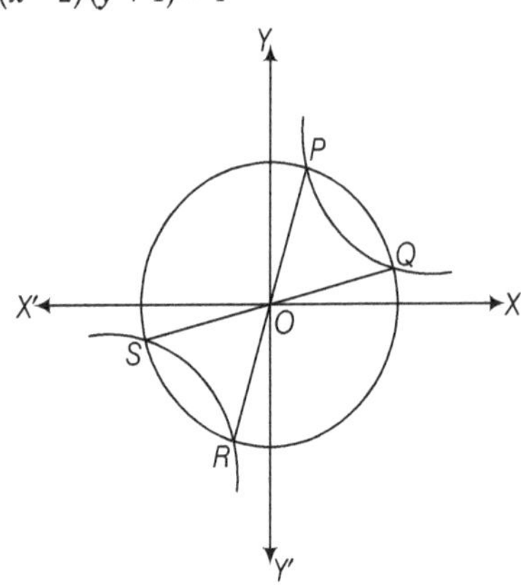

Let $\quad x-2=X, y+1=Y$

$\therefore \quad XY=4 \quad \ldots$ (i)

and $\quad s=(x-2)^2+(y+1)^2=25$

or $\quad X^2+Y^2=25$

Curve C and circle are concentric, therefore,

$$(OP)^2+(OQ)^2+(OR)^2+(OS)^2=4r^2$$

$$=4(5)^2$$

$$=100$$

31. Equation of any tangent to the parabola $y^2=8x$

is $\quad y=mx+\dfrac{2}{m} \quad \ldots$ (i)

which is also touches the hyperbola

$\dfrac{x^2}{1}-\dfrac{y^2}{3}=1$, then $\left(\dfrac{2}{m}\right)^2=1\times m^2-3$

or $\quad m^4-3m^2-4=0$

or $\quad (m^2-4)(m^2+1)=0$

$\therefore \quad m^2-4=0$

or $\quad m=\pm 2$

From Eq. (i), common tangents are

$$y=2x+1 \text{ and } y=-2x-1$$

i.e. $\quad 2x-y+1=0$ and $2x+y+1=0$

32. Foci of the ellipse $\dfrac{x^2}{k^2a^2}+\dfrac{y^2}{a^2}=1$ are $(\pm a\sqrt{(k^2-1)}, 0)$ and foci of the hyperbola $\dfrac{x^2}{a^2}-\dfrac{y^2}{b^2}=1$ are $(\pm ae, 0)$, $e>1$

$\because$ Foci are coincide, then

$$a\sqrt{(k^2-1)}=ae \quad \text{or} \quad \sqrt{(k^2-1)}>1$$

or $\quad k^2-1>1 \quad$ or $\quad k^2>2$

$\therefore \quad k<-\sqrt{2}$ or $\quad k>\sqrt{2}$

33. Equation of chord joining θ and ϕ is

$$\frac{x}{a}\cos\left(\frac{\theta-\phi}{2}\right)-\frac{y}{b}\sin\left(\frac{\theta+\phi}{2}\right)=\cos\left(\frac{\theta+\phi}{2}\right)$$

It passes through $(kae, 0)$, where $k=\pm 1$, then

$$\frac{\cos\left(\frac{\theta-\phi}{2}\right)}{\cos\left(\frac{\theta+\phi}{2}\right)}=\frac{1}{ke}$$

$$\Rightarrow \quad \frac{\cos\left(\frac{\theta-\phi}{2}\right)-\cos\left(\frac{\theta+\phi}{2}\right)}{\cos\left(\frac{\theta-\phi}{2}\right)+\cos\left(\frac{\theta+\phi}{2}\right)}=\frac{1-ke}{1+ke}$$

$$\therefore \quad \tan\left(\frac{\theta}{2}\right)\tan\left(\frac{\phi}{2}\right)=\frac{1-ke}{1+ke}$$

$$=\begin{cases}\dfrac{1-e}{1+e}, & \text{for } k=1\\[2mm] \dfrac{1+e}{1-e}, & \text{for } k=-1\end{cases}$$

34. $\because$ Foci of hyperbola are $(\pm 3a, 0)$ and foci of ellipse are $(\pm\sqrt{(25-16)}, 0)$ i.e. $(\pm 3, 0)$ according to question.

$$a=1$$

and $\quad b^2=a^2(e^2-1)=1(9-1)=8$

Now, hyperbola is $\dfrac{x^2}{1}-\dfrac{y^2}{8}=1$

Alternate (a) $a^2+b^2=1+8=9$

Alternate (b) Director circle is $x^2+y^2=1-8=-7$

i.e. there is no director circle.

Alternate (d) Length of latusrectum $=\dfrac{2b^2}{a}=\dfrac{2(8)}{1}=16$

35. $16x^2-3y^2-32x-12y-44=0$

$$\Rightarrow \quad 16(x^2-2x)-3(y^2+4y)-44=0$$

$$\Rightarrow 16\{(x-1)^2-1\}-3\{(y+2)^2-4\}-44=0$$

$$\Rightarrow \quad 16(x-1)^2-3(y+2)^2=48$$

$$\frac{(x-1)^2}{(\sqrt{3})^2}-\frac{(y+2)^2}{4^2}=1$$

Alternate (a) : Length of transverse axis

$$= 2 \times \sqrt{3} = 2\sqrt{3}$$

Alternate (b) : Length of conjugate axis

$$= 2 \times 4 = 8$$

Alternate (c) : Centre $x - 1 = 0$

and $\quad y + 2 = 0$, i.e. $(1, -2)$

Alternate (d) : $4^2 = (\sqrt{3})^2 (e^2 - 1)$

or $$e^2 - 1 = \frac{16}{3}$$

$\therefore$ $$e^2 = \frac{19}{3}$$

then $$e = \sqrt{\frac{19}{3}}$$

36. $xy = 1$

Equation of normal at 't' i.e. $\left(t, \frac{1}{t}\right)$

is $$xt^3 - yt - t^4 + 1 = 0$$

Slope is $$t^2 = -\frac{a}{b},$$

$$-\frac{a}{b} > 0 \Rightarrow \frac{a}{b} < 0$$

$\therefore$ $$a > 0, b < 0$$

or $$a < 0, b > 0$$

37. P, Q, R, S lies on the circle

$$x^2 + y^2 + 2gx + 2fy + c = 0 \quad \text{... (i)}$$

and also lies on

$$xy = c^2 \quad \text{... (ii)}$$

Solving Eqs. (i) and (ii), then

$$x^2 + \left(\frac{c^2}{x}\right)^2 + 2gx + \frac{2fc^2}{x} + c = 0$$

$$\Rightarrow \quad x^4 + 2gx^3 + cx^2 + 2fc^2x + c^4 = 0$$

$$\therefore \quad x_1x_2x_3x_4 = c^4 \quad \text{... (iii)}$$

and $$P \equiv (x_1, y_1) \equiv \left(x_1, \frac{c^2}{x_1}\right)$$

$$Q \equiv \left(x_2, \frac{c^2}{x_2}\right)$$

and $$R \equiv \left(x_3, \frac{c^2}{x_3}\right)$$

Let orthocentre $O \equiv (h, k)$

Then, slope of $QR \times$ slope of $OP = -1$

$$\left(\frac{\frac{c^2}{x_3} - \frac{c^2}{x_2}}{x_3 - x_2}\right) \times \left(\frac{k - \frac{c^2}{x_1}}{h - x_1}\right) = -1$$

$$\Rightarrow \quad -\frac{c^2}{x_2x_3} \times \left(\frac{k - \frac{c^2}{x_1}}{h - x_1}\right) = -1$$

$$\Rightarrow \quad k - \frac{c^2}{x_1} = \frac{hx_2x_3}{c^2} - \frac{x_1x_2x_3}{c^2} \quad \text{... (iv)}$$

Also, slope of $PQ \times$ slope of $OR = -1$

$$k - \frac{c^2}{x_3} = \frac{h\,x_1x_2}{c^2} - \frac{x_1x_2x_3}{c^2} \quad \text{...(v)}$$

From Eqs. (iii) and (iv),

$$\therefore \quad h = -\frac{c^4}{x_1x_2x_3} \text{ and } k = -\frac{x_1x_2x_3}{c^2}$$

From Eq. (iii),

$$h = -x_4 \text{ and } k = -\frac{c^2}{x_4}$$

$\therefore$ Orthocentre lies on $xy = c^2$

i.e. $\quad (x_4, y_4)$ and $(-x_4, -y_4)$

38. (c) $y = x + 5$

Comparing with $y = mx + c$

$\therefore \quad m = 1, c = 5$

Alternate (a) : Condition of tangency

$$c = \frac{a}{m}$$

$$5 = \frac{5}{1}$$

which is true.

Alternate (b) :

$$9x^2 + 16y^2 = 144$$

$$\Rightarrow \quad \frac{x^2}{16} + \frac{y^2}{9} = 1$$

$\because$ Condition of tangency

$$c^2 = a^2m^2 + b^2$$

$$\Rightarrow \quad 25 = 16 \times 1 + 9 = 25$$

Which is true

Alternate (c) :

$$\frac{x^2}{29} - \frac{y^2}{4} = 1$$

$\because$ Condition of tangency

$$c^2 = a^2m^2 - b^2$$

$$25 = 29 \times 1 - 4 = 25$$

Which is true.

Alternate (d) : Now length of perpendicular from centre (0, 0) to the line $y = x + 5$ is $\frac{|5|}{\sqrt{2}}$ i.e. $\frac{5}{\sqrt{2}} \neq$ radius (5).

39. Equation of the directrices of the given hyperbola $\frac{x^2}{25} - \frac{y^2}{16} = 1$ are

$$x = \pm \frac{5 \times 5}{\sqrt{(25 + 16)}} = \pm \frac{25}{\sqrt{41}} \quad \text{... (i)}$$

Equations of the asymptotes of the given hyperbola are

$$\frac{x^2}{15} - \frac{y^2}{16} = 0 \quad \text{...(ii)}$$

The points of intersection of Eqs. (i) and (ii) are

$(\pm 25/\sqrt{41}, \pm 20/\sqrt{41})$

40. $\because |SP - S'P| = 2a$

$$\Rightarrow \quad 2a = \sqrt{(24-0)^2 + (7-0)^2} - \sqrt{(5-0)^2 + (12-0)^2}$$

$$= 25 - 13 = 12$$

$$\therefore \quad a = 6$$

and $$2ae = \sqrt{(24-5)^2 + (7-12)^2} = \sqrt{(386)}$$

$$\therefore \quad e = \frac{\sqrt{386}}{12}$$

and $$b^2 = a^2(e^2 - 1) = 36\left(\frac{386}{144} - 1\right) = \frac{121}{2}$$

$$\therefore \quad \text{Latusrectum} = \frac{2b^2}{a} = \frac{121}{6}$$

41. The locus of the point of intersection of perpendicular tangents is director circle

$$x^2 + y^2 = a^2 - b^2$$

Now, $$e^2 = 1 + \frac{b^2}{a^2}$$

if $a^2 = b^2$, there is exactly one point (centre of the hyperbola)

i.e, $$e = \sqrt{2}$$

if $$a^2 > b^2 \text{ or } \frac{b^2}{a^2} < 1$$

i.e. $$e^2 < 2$$

or $0 < e < \sqrt{2}$, there are infinite (or more than one) points on the circle.

if $$a^2 < b^2 \text{ or } \frac{b^2}{a^2} > 1$$

i.e. $$e^2 > 2$$

or $e > \sqrt{2}$, there does not exist any point on the plane.

42. Alternate (a) :

$$\left(\frac{2x}{a}\right)^2 - \left(\frac{2y}{b}\right)^2 = \left(t + \frac{1}{t}\right)^2 - \left(t - \frac{1}{t}\right)^2 = 4$$

$$\Rightarrow \quad \frac{x^2}{a^2} - \frac{y^2}{b^2} = 1$$

Alternate (b) :

$$\because \quad \frac{tx}{a} - \frac{y}{b} + t = 0 \Rightarrow t = \frac{ay}{b(x+a)} \quad \text{... (i)}$$

and $$\frac{x}{a} + \frac{ty}{b} - 1 = 0 \Rightarrow t = \frac{(a-x)b}{ay} \quad \text{... (ii)}$$

From Eqs. (i) and (ii), we get

$$\frac{ay}{b(x+a)} = \frac{(a-x)b}{ay}$$

$$\Rightarrow \quad a^2y^2 = b^2(a^2 - x^2)$$

$$\Rightarrow \quad b^2x^2 + a^2y^2 = a^2b^2$$

or $$\frac{x^2}{a^2} + \frac{y^2}{b^2} = 1$$

Alternate (c) : $x^2 - y^2 = (e^t + e^{-t})^2 - (e^t - e^{-t})^2 = 4$

Alternate (d) : $\because x^2 - 6 = 2\cos t$

$$\Rightarrow \quad x^2 - 4 = 2(1 + \cos t) = 4\cos^2\left(\frac{t}{2}\right) \quad \text{... (i)}$$

and $$y^2 + 2 = 4\cos^2\left(\frac{t}{2}\right) \quad \text{... (ii)}$$

From Eqs. (i) and (ii), then

$$x^2 - 4 = y^2 + 2$$

or $$x^2 - y^2 = 6$$

43. Equation of any tangent to hyperbola is

$$y = mx \pm \sqrt{(a^2m^2 - b^2)} \quad \text{... (i)}$$

which is tangent of $-\dfrac{x^2}{b^2} + \dfrac{y^2}{a^2} = 1$

then $$a^2m^2 - b^2 = a^2 - b^2m^2$$

$$\Rightarrow \quad (a^2 + b^2)m^2 = (a^2 + b^2)$$

$$\therefore \quad m^2 = 1$$

or $$m = \pm 1$$

From Eq. (i), common tangent are

$$y = \pm x \pm \sqrt{(a^2 - b^2)}$$

44. Vertices and foci of ellipse $\dfrac{x^2}{16} + \dfrac{y^2}{7} = 1$ are $(\pm 4, 0)$ and $(\pm 3, 0)$ respectively.

Vertices and foci of the hyperbola $\dfrac{x^2}{\left(\frac{144}{25}\right)} - \dfrac{y^1}{\left(\frac{81}{25}\right)} = 1$

are $\left(\pm \dfrac{12}{5}, 0\right)$ and $(\pm 3, 0)$, respectively.

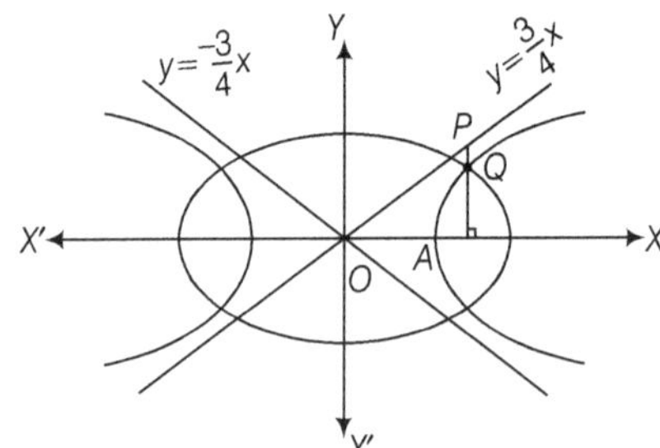

For point of intersection

$$7\left(1 - \frac{x^2}{16}\right) = 81\left(\frac{x^2}{144} - \frac{1}{25}\right)$$

$$\Rightarrow \quad x^2 = \frac{256}{25}$$

and $$y^2 = 7\left(1 - \frac{16}{25}\right) = \frac{63}{25}$$

= square of the ordinate of point of intersection

$$y^2 \text{ for } P = \frac{9}{16}x^2 = \frac{9}{16} \times \frac{256}{25} = \frac{144}{25}$$

$\therefore$Sum of the squares of coordinates of P is $x^2 + y^2 = 16$ which is auxiliary circle formed by ellipse.

45. $(1 - x^2)\dfrac{dy}{dx} + xy = ax$

or $$\frac{2dy}{(a-y)} = \frac{2x\,dx}{(1-x^2)}$$

$\Rightarrow \quad -2\ln(a-y) = -\ln(1-x^2) - \ln c$

or $\quad (a-y)^2 = c(1-x^2)$

$\Rightarrow \quad cx^2 + (y-a)^2 = c$

or $\quad \frac{x^2}{1} + \frac{(y-a)^2}{c} = 1$

for $c > 0$, ellipse and for $c < 0$, hyperbola centre of the conic is $(0, a)$ and length of one of the principal axes $= 2a = 2$

Sol. (Q. Nos. 46 to 48)

Give conic is

$$x^2 - y^2 + 2y - 2 = 0 \quad \text{... (i)}$$

Equation of tangent at (a,b) is

$$ax - by + (y+b) - 2 = 0$$

$\because$ Tangent line pass through (0, 0), then

$$b = 2$$

Also, (a, b) lies on Eq. (i), then

$$a^2 - b^2 + 2b - 2 = 0$$

or $\quad a^2 - 4 + 4 - 2 = 0$

$\Rightarrow \quad a^2 = 2$

$\therefore \quad a = \pm\sqrt{2}$

46. $\because$ Slope of tangent $= \frac{a}{b}$

$$= \frac{\sqrt{2}}{2} \quad \text{(for positive slope)}$$

$$= \frac{1}{\sqrt{2}}$$

$\therefore \quad \sin^{-1}\left(\frac{a}{b}\right) = \sin^{-1}\left(\frac{1}{\sqrt{2}}\right)$

$$= \frac{\pi}{4}$$

47. $\because$ Conic is $x^2 - (y-1)^2 = 1$

$\therefore$ Length of latusrectum $= \frac{2(1)^2}{1} = 2$

48. $\because$ Given curve is rectangular hyperbola

$\therefore \quad e = \sqrt{2}$

Thus, $\quad 1 + e^2 + e^4 = 1 + 2 + 4 = 7$

Sol. (Q. Nos. 49 to 51)

Any point on the hyperbola is $(2t, 2/t)$ normal at this point is

$$xt^3 - yt - 2t^4 + 2 = 0$$

If the normal passes through $P(h,k)$, then

$$2t^4 - ht^3 + kt - 2 = 0$$

The equation has roots t_1, t_2, t_3, t_4, then

$$\Sigma t_1 = \frac{h}{2}, \Sigma t_1 t_2 = 0,$$

$$\Sigma t_1 t_2 t_3 = -\frac{k}{2}, t_1 t_2 t_3 t_4 = -1$$

$\because$ Feet of normals are $\left(2t_1, \frac{2}{t_1}\right), \left(2t_2, \frac{2}{t_2}\right)$,

$$\left(2t_3, \frac{2}{t_3}\right) \text{ and } \left(2t_4, \frac{2}{t_4}\right)$$

$\because$ Sum of slopes of normals = Sum of ordinates of feet of normals

$\therefore \quad t_1^2 + t_2^2 + t_3^2 + t_4^2 = \frac{2}{t_1} + \frac{2}{t_2} + \frac{2}{t_3} + \frac{2}{t_4}$

$\Rightarrow \quad \Sigma t_1^2 = 2\Sigma\left(\frac{1}{t_1}\right)$

49. $(\Sigma t_1)^2 - 2\Sigma t_1 t_2 = 2\left(\frac{\Sigma t_1 t_2 t_3}{t_1 t_2 t_3 t_4}\right)$

$\Rightarrow \quad \left(\frac{h}{2}\right)^2 - 0 = 2\left(\frac{-k/2}{-1}\right)$ or $h^2 = 4k$

Hence, the locus of (h, k) is $x^2 = 4y$

50. $\because$ Curve C is $x^2 = 4y$

$\therefore$ Equation of tangent at $(2t, t^2)$ is $tx = y + t^2$

$\Rightarrow \quad A \equiv (t, 0)$ and $B \equiv (0, -t^2)$

Let mid-point of AB is (h, k).

$\therefore \quad 2h = t$ and $2k = -t^2$

$\Rightarrow \quad 2k = -(2h)^2$ or $2h^2 + k = 0$

$\therefore$ Required locus is $2x^2 + y = 0$

51.

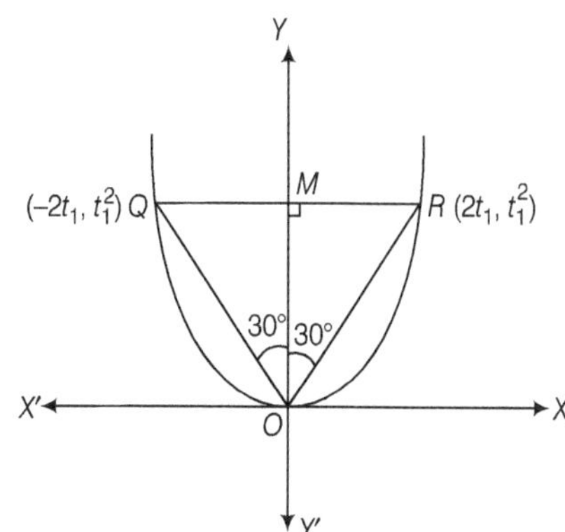

$\therefore \quad \tan 30° = \frac{2t_1}{t_1^2}$ or $\frac{1}{\sqrt{3}} = \frac{2}{t_1}$

$\therefore \quad t_1 = 2\sqrt{3}$

$\Rightarrow \quad QR = 4t_1 = 8\sqrt{3}$

Area of equilateral ΔOQR

$$= \frac{\sqrt{3}}{4}(8\sqrt{3})^2 = 48\sqrt{3} \text{ sq units}$$

Sol. (Q. Nos. 52 to 54)

$\because S_1(1,2)$ and S_2 (5, 5) are the foci

then $\quad S_1S_2 = 5 = 2ae \quad \text{... (i)}$

and $\quad |S'P - SP| = 2a$

Here, $\quad 2a = 4 \quad \text{... (ii)}$

From Eqs. (i) and (ii)

$$e = \frac{5}{4}$$

52. Let e' be the eccentricity of conjugate hyperbola.

$\therefore \quad \frac{1}{e^2} + \frac{1}{e'^2} = 1$

$\Rightarrow \quad \frac{16}{25} + \frac{1}{e'^2} = 1 \Rightarrow \frac{1}{e'^2} = \frac{9}{25}$

$\therefore \quad e' = \frac{5}{3}$

53. Locus of point of intersection of two mutually perpendicular tangents is the director circle given by

$$(x-h)^2+(y-k)^2=(a^2-b^2);$$

where (h, k) is the centre of hyperbola given by

$$(h,k)=\left(\frac{1+5}{2},\frac{2+5}{2}\right)\equiv\left(3,\frac{7}{2}\right)$$

$\therefore$ $$a^2=4, b^2=a^2(e^2-1)$$
$$=4\left(\frac{25}{16}-1\right)=\frac{9}{4}$$

$\therefore$ Required locus (director circle) is

$$(x-3)^2+\left(y-\frac{7}{2}\right)^2=4-\frac{9}{4}=\frac{7}{4}$$

54.

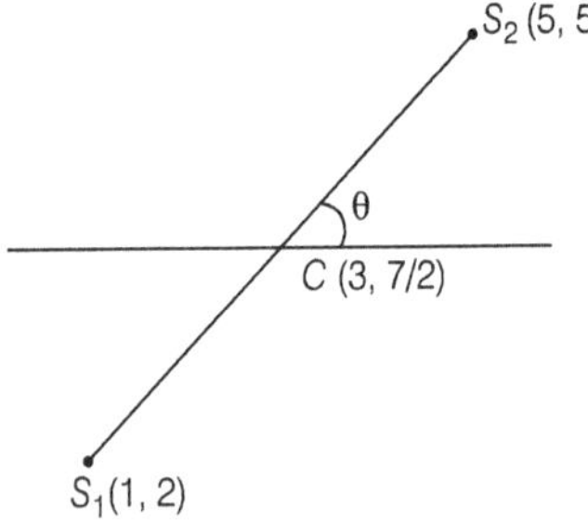

$\because \theta$ should be the angle between the transverse axis and X-axis, given by

$$\tan\theta=\frac{5-2}{5-1}=\frac{3}{4}$$

$\therefore$ $$\theta=\tan^{-1}\left(\frac{3}{4}\right)$$

Sol. (Q. Nos. 55 to 57)

$\because P(a\sec\theta_1, b\tan\theta_1)$ and $Q(a\sec\theta_2, b\tan\theta_2)$ are the extremities of focal chord, then

$$\tan\left(\frac{\theta_1}{2}\right)\tan\left(\frac{\theta_2}{2}\right)=\frac{1-e}{1+e} \text{ for focus } S(ae,0) \quad \text{...(i)}$$

and $$\theta=2\tan^{-1}\left(\frac{b}{a}\right) \quad \text{... (ii)}$$

Let $R\equiv(a\sec\phi, b\tan\phi)$

$\therefore$ Equation of tangent at R is

$$\frac{x}{a}\sec\phi-\frac{y}{b}\tan\phi=1$$

$\therefore$ $A\equiv(a\cos\phi, 0)$

and $B\equiv(0,-b\cot\phi)$

55. Let $C=(h,k)$

$\because OACB$ is rectangle

$\therefore$ Mid-point of OC = mid-point of AB

$$\Rightarrow \left(\frac{h}{2},\frac{k}{2}\right)\equiv\left(\frac{a\cos\phi}{2},\frac{-b\cot\phi}{2}\right)$$

or $$h=a\cos\phi \Rightarrow \sec\phi=\frac{a}{h} \quad \text{... (iii)}$$

and $$k=-b\cot\phi \Rightarrow \tan\phi=-\frac{b}{k} \quad \text{... (iv)}$$

From Eqs. (iii) and (iv), we get

$$\frac{a^2}{h^2}-\frac{b^2}{k^2}=1$$

Hence, required locus is

$$\frac{a^2}{x^2}-\frac{b^2}{y^2}=1$$

56. From Eq. (i)

$$1+\tan\left(\frac{\theta_1}{2}\right)\tan\left(\frac{\theta_2}{2}\right)=\frac{2}{1+e}$$

$$\Rightarrow \frac{\cos\left(\frac{\theta_1-\theta_2}{2}\right)}{\cos\left(\frac{\theta_1}{2}\right)\cos\left(\frac{\theta_2}{2}\right)}=\frac{2}{1+e} \quad \text{... (v)}$$

and $$1-\tan\left(\frac{\theta_1}{2}\right)\tan\left(\frac{\theta_2}{2}\right)=\frac{2e}{1+e}$$

$$\Rightarrow \frac{\cos\left(\frac{\theta_1+\theta_2}{2}\right)}{\cos\left(\frac{\theta_1}{2}\right)\cos\left(\frac{\theta_2}{2}\right)}=\frac{2e}{1+e} \quad \text{... (vi)}$$

From Eqs. (v) and (vi), we get

$$\frac{\cos\left(\frac{\theta_1+\theta_2}{2}\right)}{\cos\left(\frac{\theta_1-\theta_2}{2}\right)}=e \text{ or } \frac{\cos^2\left(\frac{\theta_1+\theta_2}{2}\right)}{\cos^2\left(\frac{\theta_1-\theta_2}{2}\right)}=e^2$$

or $$\lambda=e^2 \quad \text{(given)}$$
$$=\frac{a^2+b^2}{a^2}$$

57. From Eq. (ii),

$$\theta=2\tan^{-1}\left(\frac{b}{a}\right)$$

$\therefore$ $$\tan\left(\frac{\theta}{2}\right)=\frac{b}{a}$$

$$\Rightarrow \cos\left(\frac{\theta}{2}\right)=\frac{1}{\sec\left(\frac{\theta}{2}\right)}=\frac{1}{\sqrt{1+\tan^2\left(\frac{\theta}{2}\right)}}$$
$$=\frac{1}{\sqrt{\left(1+\frac{b^2}{a^2}\right)}}$$
$$=\frac{1}{\sqrt{1+e^2-1}}=\frac{1}{e}$$

Sol. (Q. Nos. 58 to 60)

58. $\because$ Perpendicular tangents intersect at the centre of rectangular hyperbola. Hence, centre of the hyperbola is (1, 1) and the equations of asymptotes are

$$x-1=0 \text{ and } y-1=0$$

$\therefore$ Pair of asymptotes is

$$(x-1)(y-1)=0$$

or $$xy-x-y+1=0$$

or $$xy+1=x+y$$

59. Let equation of the hyperbola be
$$xy - x - y + \lambda = 0$$
It passes through (2, 3), then
$$6 - 2 - 3 + \lambda = 0$$
$$\therefore \quad \lambda = -1$$
So, equation of hyperbola is
$$xy = x + y + 1$$

60. From the centre of the hyperbola, we can draw two real tangents to the rectangular hyperbola.

61. For ellipse (if $a > b$)
$$ae_1 = \sqrt{(a^2 - b^2)}$$
or
$$a^2e_1^2 = a^2 - b^2$$
and for hyperbola
$$Ae_2 = \sqrt{(A^2 + B^2)}$$
$$\Rightarrow \quad = \sqrt{(A^2 + b^2)} \quad [\because 2b = 2B \text{ (given)}]$$
or
$$A^2e_2^2 = A^2 + b^2$$
$$\Rightarrow \quad \frac{1}{e_1^2} + \frac{1}{e_2^2} = \frac{a^2}{(a^2 - b^2)} + \frac{A^2}{(A^2 + b^2)} \quad \text{... (i)}$$
Since, both the curves are confocal $\Rightarrow ae_1 = Ae_2$
or
$$a^2e_1^2 = A^2e_2^2$$
$$\Rightarrow \quad a^2 - b^2 = A^2 + b^2$$
or
$$A^2 = a^2 - 2b^2 \quad \text{... (ii)}$$
From Eqs. (i) and (ii), we get
$$\frac{1}{e_1^2} + \frac{1}{e_2^2} = \frac{a^2}{a^2 - b^2} + \frac{a^2 - 2b^2}{a^2 - b^2}$$
$$= \frac{2(a^2 - b^2)}{(a^2 - b^2)} = 2$$

62. Othrocentre of triangle formed by the points $\left(ct_1, \frac{c}{t_1}\right), \left(ct_2, \frac{c}{t_2}\right)$ and $\left(ct_3, \frac{c}{t_3}\right)$ on the rectangular hyperbola.
$$xy = c^2 \text{ is } \left(-\frac{c}{t_1t_2t_3}, -c\, t_1t_2t_3\right)$$
Here, $c = 2$ and $\frac{-c}{t_1t_2t_3} = \frac{1}{2}$ or $t_1t_2t_3 = -2c$

$\therefore$ Ordinate of orthocentre $= -c\, t_1t_2t_3$
$$= -c \times -2c$$
$$= 2c^2 = 2(2)^2$$
$$= 8$$

63. Since the normal drawn at $P(t_1)$ meets the hyperbola $xy = 2$ again at $Q(t_2)$, then
$$t_1^3 t_2 = -1 \quad \text{... (i)}$$
$$\because \quad P \equiv \left(\sqrt{2}t_1, \frac{\sqrt{2}}{t_1}\right) \text{ and } Q \equiv \left(\sqrt{2}\, t_2, \frac{\sqrt{2}}{t_2}\right)$$
$$\therefore \quad \text{Distance } PQ = \sqrt{(\sqrt{2}t_1 - \sqrt{2}t_2)^2 + \left(\frac{\sqrt{2}}{t_1} - \frac{\sqrt{2}}{t_2}\right)^2}$$
$$= \sqrt{2}\,|t_1 - t_2| \sqrt{\left(1 + \frac{1}{t_1^2t_2^2}\right)}$$
$$= \sqrt{2}\,\frac{(t_1^4 + 1)^{3/2}}{|t_1^3|} \quad \text{[from Eq. (i)]}$$
$$= \sqrt{2}\left(t_1^2 + \frac{1}{t_1^2}\right)^{3/2} \geq \sqrt{2}\,(2)^{3/2} = 4 \quad (\because AM \geq GM)$$
$\therefore$ Distance $PQ \geq 4$

Hence, minimum distance between the points P and Q is 4.

64. Let $P(a\sec\theta, b\tan\theta)$ be a point on the hyperbola $\frac{x^2}{a^2} - \frac{y^2}{b^2} = 1$ with eccentricity $e = \frac{3}{2\sqrt{2}}$
$$\therefore \quad a^2 = 8b^2 \quad (\because b^2 = a^2(e^2 - 1) \quad \text{...(i)}$$
$\because$ Equation of normal at P is
$$ax\cos\theta + by\cot\theta = a^2 + b^2$$
$$\therefore \quad M \equiv \left(\left(\frac{a^2 + b^2}{a}\right)\sec\theta, 0\right)$$
$$N \equiv \left(0, \left(\frac{a^2 + b^2}{b}\right)\tan\theta\right)$$
Let mid-point of MN is $R(h, k)$
$$\therefore \quad 2h = \left(\frac{a^2 + b^2}{a}\right)\sec\theta \quad \text{... (ii)}$$
and
$$2k = \left(\frac{a^2 + b^2}{b}\right)\tan\theta \quad \text{... (iii)}$$
From Eqs. (ii) and (iii), we get
$$4a^2h^2 - 4b^2k^2 = (a^2 + b^2)^2$$
$\therefore$ Locus of R is
$$\frac{x^2}{\left(\frac{a^2 + b^2}{2a}\right)^2} - \frac{y^2}{\left(\frac{a^2 + b^2}{2b}\right)^2} = 1$$
which have eccentricity
$$e_1 = \sqrt{\left(1 + \frac{a^2}{b^2}\right)} = \sqrt{(1 + 8)} = 3 \quad \text{[from Eq. (i)]}$$

65. Equations of director circle of ellipse
$$\frac{x^2}{a^2} + \frac{y^2}{b^2} = 1 \text{ is } x^2 + y^2 = a^2 + b^2$$
$$\therefore \quad \text{Radius } (r_1) = \sqrt{(a^2 + b^2)}$$
$$= \sqrt{a^2 + a^2(1 - e_1^2)}$$
$$= a\sqrt{(2 - e_1^2)} \quad \text{... (i)}$$
and director circle of hyperbola $\frac{x^2}{a^2} - \frac{y^2}{b_1^2} = 1$ is
$$x^2 + y^2 = a^2 - b_1^2$$
$$\therefore \quad \text{Radius } (r_2) = \sqrt{(a^2 - b_1^2)}$$
$$= \sqrt{a^2 - a^2(e_2^2 - 1)} = a\sqrt{(2 - e_2^2)} \quad \text{... (ii)}$$

Given, $\frac{r_1}{r_2} = \frac{1}{3}$

$\Rightarrow \quad \frac{a\sqrt{(2-e_1^2)}}{a\sqrt{(2-e_2^2)}} = \frac{1}{3}$ [from Eqs. (i) and (ii)]

$\Rightarrow \quad 9 - 9e_1^2 = 2 - e_2^2$

$\therefore \quad 9e_1^2 - e_2^2 = 7 = \lambda$

$\therefore \quad \lambda = 7$

66. $\because \frac{x^2}{a^2} - \frac{y^2}{b^2} = 1$ and $x^2 + y^2 = \frac{a^2}{4}$ having origin as their common centre.

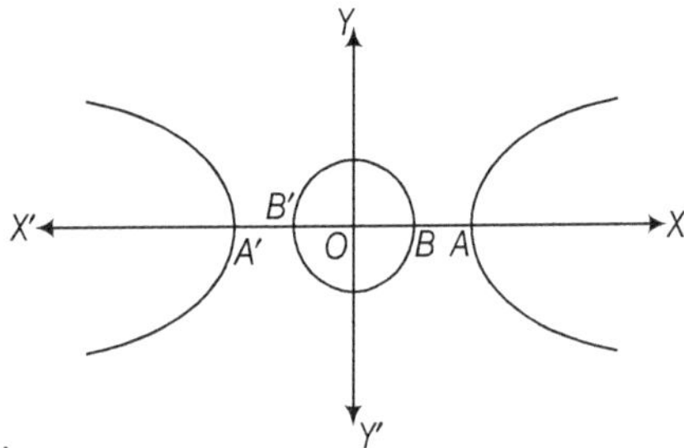

So, vertex is the nearest point. Hence, shortest distance = BA

$$= a - \frac{a}{2} = \frac{a}{2}$$

$\therefore \quad f(a, b) = \frac{a}{2}$

Hence, $f(4,6) + f(2,3) = \frac{4}{2} + \frac{2}{2} = 3$

67. Let $A \equiv (a, 0)$ and $B \equiv (-a, 0)$

If $C \equiv (x, y)$

$\therefore \quad \tan\theta = \frac{y}{a+x}$ ... (i)

and $\tan 2\theta = \frac{y}{a-x}$ ... (ii)

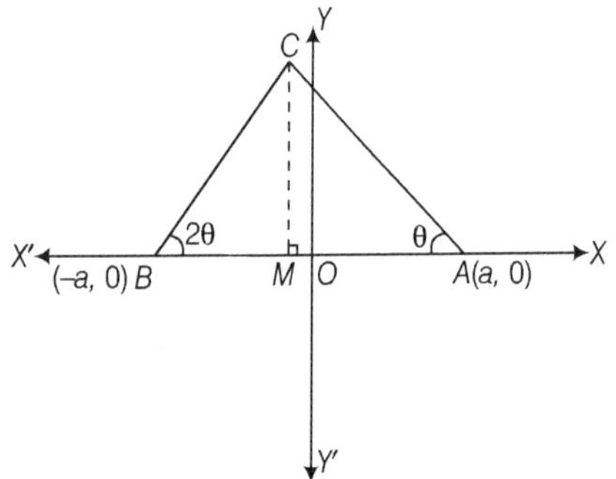

From Eq. (ii),

$$\frac{2\tan\theta}{1-\tan^2\theta} = \frac{y}{a-x}$$

$\Rightarrow \quad \frac{\frac{2y}{a+x}}{1 - \left(\frac{y}{a+x}\right)^2} = \frac{y}{a-x}$ [from Eq. (i)]

or $\quad \frac{2y(a+x)}{a^2 + x^2 + 2ax - y^2} = \frac{y}{a-x}$

$\Rightarrow \quad 2(a^2 - x^2) = a^2 + x^2 + 2ax - y^2$

or $\quad 3x^2 + 2ax - y^2 - a^2 = 0$

or $\quad 3\left(x + \frac{a}{3}\right)^2 - y^2 = \frac{2a^2}{3}$

or $\quad \frac{\left(x + \frac{a}{3}\right)^2}{\left(\frac{2a^2}{9}\right)} - \frac{y^2}{\left(\frac{2a^2}{3}\right)} = 1$

$\therefore \quad$ Eccentricity $(e) = \sqrt{\left(\frac{\frac{2a^2}{9} + \frac{2a^2}{3}}{\frac{2a^2}{9}}\right)} = 2$

68. Let $P\left(\frac{t}{\sqrt{2}}, \frac{1}{t\sqrt{2}}\right)$ be any point on $2xy = 1$ and $S \equiv (1, 1)$

and $\quad S' \equiv (-1, -1)$

Here $\quad t > 0$

Let $R(h, k)$ be the ex-centre of $\Delta PSS'$ opposite to vertex S.

$\Rightarrow \quad h = \frac{-a - c + \frac{tb}{\sqrt{2}}}{a + b - c}$

and $\quad k = \frac{-a - c + \frac{b}{t\sqrt{2}}}{a + b - c}$

Here, $\quad b = 2\sqrt{2}, a = ePM$

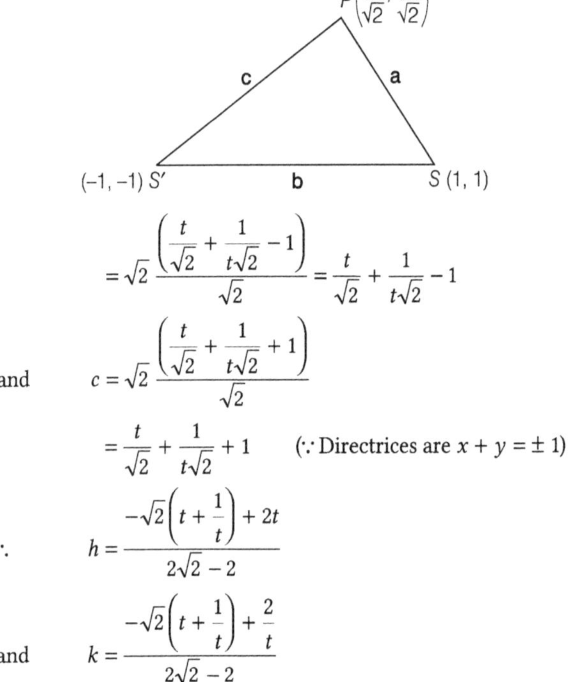

$$= \sqrt{2}\,\frac{\left(\frac{t}{\sqrt{2}} + \frac{1}{t\sqrt{2}} - 1\right)}{\sqrt{2}} = \frac{t}{\sqrt{2}} + \frac{1}{t\sqrt{2}} - 1$$

and $\quad c = \sqrt{2}\,\frac{\left(\frac{t}{\sqrt{2}} + \frac{1}{t\sqrt{2}} + 1\right)}{\sqrt{2}}$

$= \frac{t}{\sqrt{2}} + \frac{1}{t\sqrt{2}} + 1 \quad$ ($\because$ Directrices are $x + y = \pm 1$)

$\therefore \quad h = \frac{-\sqrt{2}\left(t + \frac{1}{t}\right) + 2t}{2\sqrt{2} - 2}$

and $\quad k = \frac{-\sqrt{2}\left(t + \frac{1}{t}\right) + \frac{2}{t}}{2\sqrt{2} - 2}$

$\therefore \quad h + k = -\left(t + \frac{1}{t}\right)$ ... (i) and $$h-k=\frac{t-\frac{1}{t}}{\sqrt{2}-1} \quad \text{... (ii)}$$

$\because$ $$\left(t+\frac{1}{t}\right)^2=\left(t-\frac{1}{t}\right)^2+4$$

$\Rightarrow$ $$(h+k)^2=(\sqrt{2}-1)^2(h-k)^2+4$$

$\therefore$ Locus of R is $(x+y)^2=(\sqrt{2}-1)^2(x-y)^2+4$

On comparing, we get $p=1$ and $q=4$

$\therefore$ $$p+q=5$$

69. Let $P(h,k)$ be the middle-point, then equation of chord whose mid-point $P(h,k)$ is

$$T=S_1$$

$\Rightarrow$ $$hx+ky-4=h^2+k^2-4$$

or $$y=-\frac{h}{k}x+\frac{(h^2+k^2)}{k}$$

It will touch the hyperbola $\frac{x^2}{4}-\frac{y^2}{16}=1$, then

$$\left(\frac{h^2+k^2}{k}\right)^2=4\times\frac{h^2}{k^2}-16$$

$\Rightarrow$ $$(h^2+k^2)^2=4h^2-16k^2$$

$\therefore$ Locus of $P(h,k)$ is

$$(x^2+y^2)^2=4x^2-16y^2$$

$\therefore$ $$\lambda=4$$

70. The given hyperbola is $\frac{x^2}{2}-\frac{y^2}{3}=1$

Equation of tangents is $y=mx\pm\sqrt{(2m^2-3)}$

$\because$ Tangents from the point (α,β) will be

$$(\beta-m\alpha)^2=2m^2-3$$

or $$m^2(\alpha^2-2)-2m\alpha\beta+\beta^2+3=0$$

$\because$ $$m_1m_2=\frac{\beta^2+3}{\alpha^2-2}\Rightarrow\tan\theta\tan\phi=\frac{\beta^2+3}{\alpha^2-2}$$

$\Rightarrow$ $$2=\frac{\beta^2+3}{\alpha^2-2}$$

or $$2\alpha^2-\beta^2=7$$

71. **(A)** $16x^2-9y^2+32x+36y-164=0$

$\Rightarrow$ $16(x^2+2x+1)-9(y^2-4y+4)-144=0$

or $$16(x+1)^2-9(y-2)^2=144$$

or $$\frac{(x+1)^2}{9}-\frac{(y-2)^2}{16}=1$$

$\therefore$ $\lambda=$ length latusrectum $=\frac{2\times16}{3}=\frac{32}{3}$

or $3\lambda=32$

(B) Making $\frac{x^2}{16}-\frac{y^2}{18}=1$ homogeneous with the help of $x\cos\alpha+y\sin\alpha=p$, then

$$\frac{x^2}{16}-\frac{y^2}{18}=\left(\frac{x\cos\alpha+y\sin\alpha}{p}\right)^2$$

Since, these lines are perpendicular to each other, then

$$\left(\frac{1}{16}-\frac{\cos^2\alpha}{p^2}\right)+\left(-\frac{1}{18}-\frac{\sin^2\alpha}{p^2}\right)=0$$

or $$\frac{1}{16}-\frac{1}{18}=\frac{1}{p^2}$$

or $$p=\pm12$$

$\therefore$ Radius of circle $=|p|=2$

Hence, diameter of the circle $=24$

(C) Any point on $xy=8$ is $P\left(\sqrt{8}\,t,\frac{\sqrt{8}}{t}\right)$

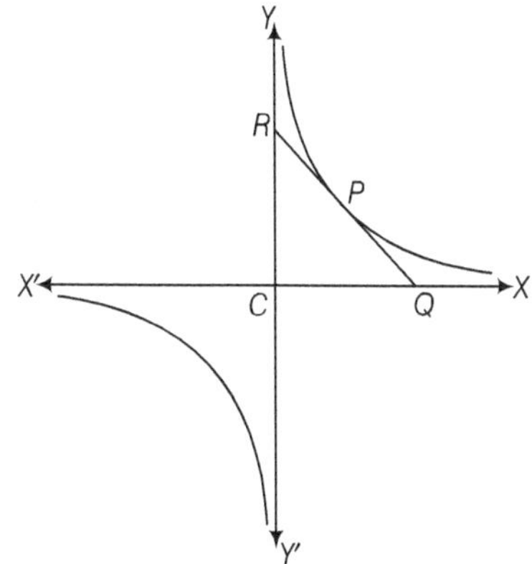

Equation of tangent at P

$$x\times\frac{\sqrt{8}}{t}+y\times\sqrt{8}\,t=16 \text{ or } \frac{x}{\left(\frac{16t}{\sqrt{8}}\right)}+\frac{x}{\left(\frac{16}{\sqrt{8}\,t}\right)}=1$$

$\therefore$ $$CQ=\frac{16t}{\sqrt{8}}\text{ and }CR=\frac{16}{\sqrt{8}t}$$

Hence, area of $\Delta CQR=\frac{1}{2}\times CQ\times CR$

$$=\frac{1}{2}\times\frac{16t}{\sqrt{8}}\times\frac{16}{\sqrt{8}t}=16$$

(D) Hyperbola is $x^2-3y^2=9$

or $$\frac{x^2}{9}-\frac{y^2}{3}=1$$

$\because$ Angle between asymptotes

$$=2\tan^{-1}\left(\frac{\sqrt{3}}{3}\right)=2\tan^{-1}\left(\frac{1}{\sqrt{3}}\right)$$

$$=2\times\frac{\pi}{6}=\frac{\pi\lambda}{24} \quad \text{(given)}$$

$\therefore$ $$\lambda=8$$

72. **(A)** Let the hyperbola be $\frac{x^2}{a^2}-\frac{y^2}{b^2}=1$

then $$2a=ae$$

$\Rightarrow$ $$e=2$$

$\therefore$ $$\frac{(2b)^2}{(2a)^2}=\frac{b^2}{a^2}=e^2-1=(2)^2-1=3$$

(B) Given hyperbola is

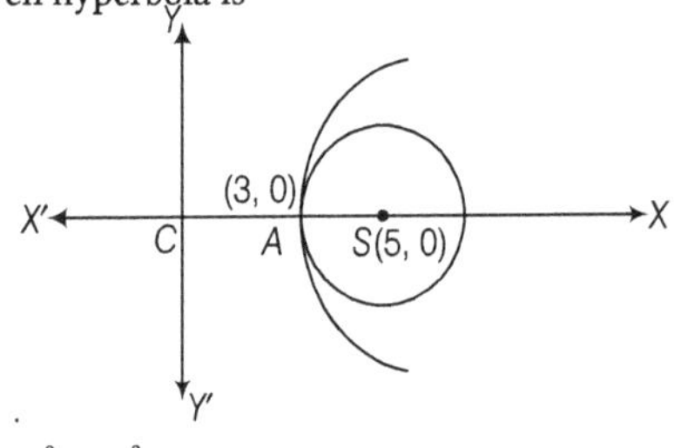

$$\frac{x^2}{9} - \frac{y^2}{16} = 1 \quad \text{... (i)}$$

or $\quad e^2 = 1 + \frac{16}{9} = \frac{25}{9}$

or $\quad e = \frac{5}{3}$

Hence, its foci are $(\pm 5, 0)$

The equation of the circle with (5, 0) as centre is

$$(x-5)^2 + (y-0)^2 = r^2 \quad \text{... (ii)}$$

Solving Eqs. (i) and (ii), we have

$$16x^2 - 9(r^2 - (x-5)^2) = 144$$

or $\quad 25x^2 - 90x - 9r^2 + 81 = 0$

Since, the circle touches the hyperbola, the above equation must have equal roots.

Hence, $\quad (90)^2 - 4(25)(81 - 9r^2) = 0$

or $\quad r = 0$

which is not possible.

Hence, the circle can not touch at two points. It can only be tangent at the vertex.

Hence, $\quad r = 5 - 3 = 2$

(C) Equation of hyperbola is

$$\frac{x^2}{2^2} - \frac{y^2}{3^2} = 1$$

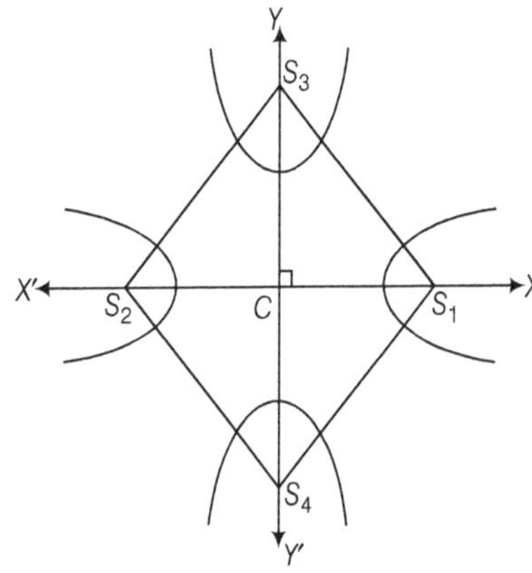

Its foci $(\pm\sqrt{(2^2+3^2)}, 0)$

or $S_1 \equiv (\sqrt{13}, 0)$ and $S_2 \equiv (-\sqrt{13}, 0)$

and equation of conjugate hyperbola is

$$-\frac{x^2}{2^2} + \frac{y^2}{3^2} = 1$$

Its foci $(0, \pm\sqrt{(3^2+2^2)})$

or $S_3 \equiv (0, \sqrt{13})$ and $S_4 \equiv (0, -\sqrt{13})$

Hence, area of quadrilateral $S_1S_2S_3S_4$

$$= 4 \times \text{Area of } \Delta S_1CS_3$$

$$= 4 \times \frac{1}{2} \times CS_1 \times CS_3$$

$$= 2 \times \sqrt{13} \times \sqrt{13} = 26$$

(D) Given hyperbola is

$$ax^2 - by^2 = c$$

or $\quad \dfrac{x^2}{(c/a)} - \dfrac{y^2}{(c/b)} = 1$

$\because \quad \sqrt{\dfrac{c}{b}} = \dfrac{5}{2} \quad \text{...(i)}$

and $\quad 2\sqrt{\left(\dfrac{c}{a} + \dfrac{c}{b}\right)} = 13 \quad \text{...(ii)}$

From Eqs. (i) and (ii)

$$2\sqrt{\left(\frac{c}{a} + \frac{25}{4}\right)} = 13$$

or $\quad \dfrac{c}{a} = \dfrac{169}{4} - \dfrac{25}{4} = 36 \quad \text{... (iii)}$

and $\quad \dfrac{c}{b} = \dfrac{25}{4} \quad \text{... (iv)}$

$\therefore \quad \dfrac{a}{b} = \dfrac{\frac{c}{b}}{\frac{c}{a}} = \dfrac{25}{144}$

$\because$ a and b are co-prime

$\therefore$ $a = 25, b = 144$

and from Eq. (iii), $c = 900$

Hence, $\quad \dfrac{3ab}{2c} = \dfrac{3 \times 25 \times 144}{2 \times 900} = 6$

73. Let $f(x) = x^2 - \lambda x + 2$

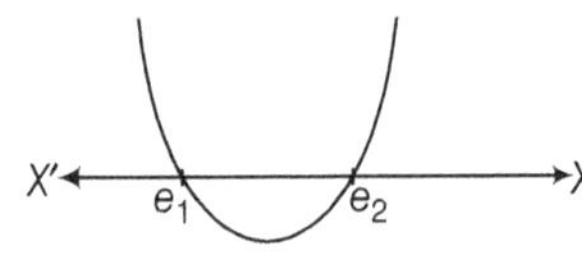

$\therefore \quad D = \lambda^2 - 8$

x-coordinate of vertex $= \dfrac{\lambda}{2}$ and $f(1) = 3 - \lambda$

(A) We must have

$$e_1 < 1 < e_2$$

then $\quad D > 0$ and $f(1) < 0$

$\Rightarrow \quad \lambda^2 > 8$ and $3 - \lambda < 0$

$\Rightarrow \quad \lambda \in (-\infty, -2\sqrt{2}) \cup (2\sqrt{2}, \infty)$ and $\lambda > 3$

$\therefore \quad \lambda > 3$

(B) $\because \quad e_1 > 1, e_2 > 1$

then $\quad D \geq 0$ and $f(1) > 0$ and $\dfrac{\lambda}{2} > 1$

$\Rightarrow \quad \lambda \in (-\infty, -2\sqrt{2})] \cup [2\sqrt{2}, \infty)$

and $\quad \lambda < 3$ and $\lambda > 2$

$\therefore \quad \lambda \in [2\sqrt{2}, 3)$

(C) We must have $\frac{1}{e_1^2} + \frac{1}{e_2^2} = 1$

or $\quad e_1^2 + e_2^2 = (e_1 e_2)^2$

$\Rightarrow \quad (e_1 + e_2)^2 - 2e_1 e_2 = (e_1 e_2)^2$

$\Rightarrow \quad \lambda^2 - 4 = (2)^2$ or $\lambda^2 = 8$

$\therefore \quad \lambda = \pm 2\sqrt{2}$

(D) We must have $e_1 < \sqrt{2} < e_2$

then $\quad D > 0$ and $f(\sqrt{2}) < 0$

$\Rightarrow \quad \lambda^2 > 8$ and $2 - \lambda\sqrt{2} + 2 < 0$

or $\quad \lambda \in (-\infty, -2\sqrt{2}) \cup (2\sqrt{2}, \infty)$

and $\quad \lambda > 2\sqrt{2}$

$\therefore \quad \lambda > 2\sqrt{2}$

74. Since, e_1 and e_2 are the eccentricities of two conjugate hyperbolas, so $e_1 > 1$ and $e_2 > 1$.

$\Rightarrow \quad e_2 e_2 > 1$

$\therefore$ Statement II is true.

As for e_1 and e_2 for hyperbola and its conjugate,

$$\frac{1}{e_1^2} + \frac{1}{e_2^2} = 1$$

Let $\quad e_1 = \frac{5}{3}$ and $e_2 = \frac{5}{4}$

Now, $\quad \frac{1}{e_1^2} + \frac{1}{e_2^2} = \frac{9}{25} + \frac{16}{15} = 1$

$\therefore$Statement I is true, but Statement II is not correct explanation of Statement I.

75. By definition, if $H(x, y) = 0$

then $\quad A_1(x, y) = H(x, y) + \lambda$

$\therefore$ Statement II is true

Since, $\quad C(x, y) = H(x, y) + 2$

$\quad = A_1(x, y) + (2 - \lambda)$

Since, for $A_1(x, y) = 0$, we have $\Delta = 0$ and also for $A_2(x, y)$, $\Delta = 0$, So $A_1 = A_2$

$\therefore$Statement I is true and Statement II is correct explanation of Statement I.

76. $\because$ Director circle is the locus of the point of intersection of perpendicular tangents.

$\therefore$ Statement II is true.

$\because$ Director circle of $5x^2 - 4y^2 = 20$

or $\quad \frac{x^2}{4} - \frac{y^2}{5} = 1$

is $\quad x^2 + y^2 = 4 - 5$ or $x^2 + y^2 = -1$

$\therefore$ Statement I is false.

77. Director circle of $\frac{x^2}{25} - \frac{y^2}{16} = 1$ is

$$x^2 + y^2 = 25 - 16 = 9$$

Hence, angle between tangents is $\pi/2$.

$\therefore$ Statement I and Statement II are true and Statement II is a correct explanation for Statement I.

78. The conjugate hyperbolas are

$$\frac{x^2}{a^2} - \frac{y^2}{b^2} = 1 \text{ and } \frac{y^2}{b^2} - \frac{x^2}{a^2} = 1$$

then $\quad e^2 = \frac{a^2 + b^2}{a^2}$ and $e_1^2 = \frac{a^2 + b^2}{b^2}$

$\therefore \quad \frac{1}{e^2} + \frac{1}{e_1^2} = 1$

$\because \quad \frac{1}{2^2} + \frac{1}{\left(\frac{2}{\sqrt{3}}\right)^2} = \frac{1}{4} + \frac{3}{4} = 1$ and $ee_1 = \frac{4}{\sqrt{3}} > 1$

$\therefore$ Statement I and Statement II are both true and Statement II is not a correct explanation of Statement I.

79. If we solve $4x - 5y = 0$

or $\quad y = \frac{4}{5}x$

and $\quad 16x^2 - 25y^2 = 400$

or $\quad \frac{x^2}{25} - \frac{y^2}{16} = 1$

we get, $0 = 1 \Rightarrow$ No solution

$\Rightarrow$ The line $y = \frac{4}{5}x$ does not meet but the line satisfies the condition of being a tangent.

$$c^2 - a^2m^2 + b^2 = 0 - 25 \times \frac{16}{25} + 16 = 0$$

$\Rightarrow$ It must touch the curve at infinity.

$\therefore$Statement I and Statement II are both true but Statement II is a correct explanation for Statement I.

80. The point (x_1, y_1) inside the hyperbola.

$\frac{x^2}{a^2} - \frac{y^2}{b^2} = 1$, then $\frac{x_1^2}{a^2} - \frac{y_1^2}{b^2} - 1 > 0$

$\therefore$ Statement II is false.

Also, $\quad 3y^2 - 5x^2 + 1 = 0$

or $\quad 5x^2 - 3y^2 - 1 = 0$

$\therefore$ Value of $5x^2 - 3y^2 - 1$ at $(5, -3)$ is

$\quad 5(5)^2 - 3(-3)^2 - 1$

$\quad = 125 - 27 - 1 = 97 > 0$

$\therefore$ Statement I is true.

81. If hyperbola is $\frac{x^2}{a^2} - \frac{y^2}{b^2} = 1$

$\therefore$Angle between asymptotes $= 2\tan^{-1}\left(\frac{b}{a}\right)$

For equilateral hyperbola $a = b$

then, angle between asymptotes

$$= 2\tan^{-1}(1) = 2 \cdot \frac{\pi}{4} = \frac{\pi}{2}$$

$\therefore$Statement I is false.

and eccentricity $e = \sqrt{\left(\frac{a^2 + b^2}{a^2}\right)} = \sqrt{\left(\frac{a^2 + a^2}{a^2}\right)} = \sqrt{2}$

$\therefore$Statement 2 is true.

82. BC = base of the triangle $= a$ (constant) and A is the vertex.

$$\frac{\tan(B/2)}{\tan(C/2)} = \frac{\sqrt{\frac{(s-c)(s-a)}{s(s-b)}}}{\sqrt{\frac{(s-a)(s-b)}{s(s-c)}}}$$

$$= \frac{s-c}{s-b} = \frac{2s-2c}{2s-2b}$$

$$= \frac{a+b-c}{a-b+c} = k \quad \text{(let)}$$

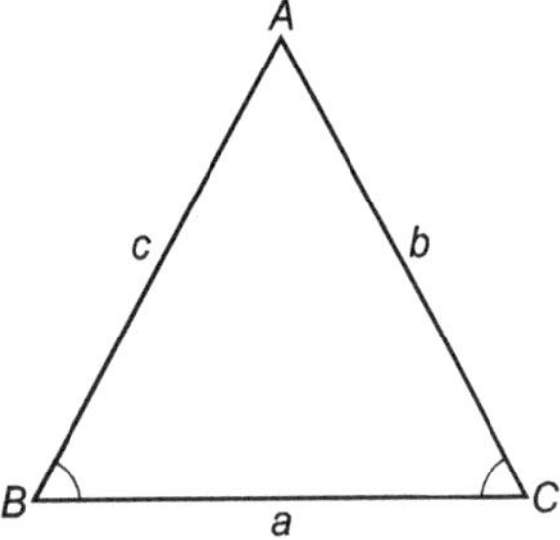

By componendo and dividendo

$$\Rightarrow \quad \frac{k-1}{k+1} = \frac{b-c}{a}$$

$$\Rightarrow \quad b-c = a\left(\frac{k-1}{k+1}\right) = \text{constant}$$

$$\Rightarrow \quad CA - BA = \text{constant}$$

By the focal property the locus of A is a hyperbola whose foci are B and C.

83. Let coordinates of A, B and C on the hyperbola $xy = c^2$ are $\left(ct_1, \frac{c}{t_1}\right), \left(ct_2, \frac{c}{t_2}\right)$ and $\left(ct_3, \frac{c}{t_3}\right)$ respectively.

(i) $\therefore$ Area of triangle $ABC = \frac{1}{2}\left|\begin{vmatrix} ct_1 & \frac{c}{t_1} \\ ct_2 & \frac{c}{t_2}\end{vmatrix} + \begin{vmatrix} ct_2 & \frac{c}{t_2} \\ ct_3 & \frac{c}{t_3}\end{vmatrix} + \begin{vmatrix} ct_3 & \frac{c}{t_3} \\ ct_1 & \frac{c}{t_1}\end{vmatrix}\right|$

$$= \frac{c^2}{2}\left|\frac{t_1}{t_2} - \frac{t_2}{t_1} + \frac{t_2}{t_3} - \frac{t_3}{t_2} + \frac{t_3}{t_1} - \frac{t_1}{t_3}\right|$$

$$= \frac{c^2}{2t_1t_2t_3}\left|t_2^2t_3 - t_2^2t_3 + t_1t_2^2 - t_3^2t_1 + t_2t_3^2 - t_1^2t_2\right|$$

$$= \frac{c^2}{2t_1t_2t_3}\left|(t_1-t_2)(t_2-t_3)(t_3-t_1)\right|$$

(ii) Equations of tangents at A, B, C are

$$x + yt_1^2 - 2ct_1 = 0$$

$$x + yt_2^2 - 2ct_2 = 0$$

and $$x + yt_3^2 - 2ct_3 = 0$$

$$\therefore \quad \text{Required area} = \frac{1}{2|C_1C_2C_3|}\begin{vmatrix} 1 & t_1^2 & -2ct_1 \\ 1 & t_2^2 & -2ct_2 \\ 1 & t_3^2 & -2ct_3\end{vmatrix}^2 \quad \text{... (i)}$$

where $C_1 = \begin{vmatrix} 1 & t_2^2 \\ 1 & t_3^2\end{vmatrix}$, $C_2 = -\begin{vmatrix} 1 & t_1^2 \\ 1 & t_3^2\end{vmatrix}$ and $C_3 = \begin{vmatrix} 1 & t_1^2 \\ 1 & t_2^2\end{vmatrix}$

$\therefore \quad C_1 = t_3^2 - t_2^2, C_2 = t_1^2 - t_3^2$ and $C_3 = t_2^2 - t_1^2$

From Eq. (i)

$$= \frac{1}{2|(t_3^2 - t_2^2)(t_1^2 - t_3^2)(t_2^2 - t_1^2)|} 4c^2 \cdot (t_1-t_2)^2(t_2-t_3)^2(t_3-t_1)^2$$

$$= 2c^2\left|\frac{(t_1-t_2)(t_2-t_3)(t_3-t_1)}{(t_1+t_2)(t_2+t_3)(t_3+t_1)}\right|$$

$\therefore$ Required area is, $2c^2\left|\frac{(t_1-t_2)(t_2-t_3)(t_3-t_1)}{(t_1+t_2)(t_2+t_3)(t_3+t_1)}\right|$

84. Let chord be PQ and coordinates of P and Q are $\left(ct_1, \frac{c}{t_1}\right)$ and $\left(ct_2, \frac{c}{t_2}\right)$ respectively.

Now let mid-point of PQ is $M(h, k)$

$$\therefore \quad h = \frac{1}{2}(ct_1 + ct_2)$$

$$\therefore \quad t_1 + t_2 = \frac{2h}{c} \text{ and } k = \frac{1}{2}\left\{\frac{c}{t_1} + \frac{c}{t_2}\right\}$$

$$\text{or} \quad \frac{2k}{c} = \frac{t_1+t_2}{t_1t_2}$$

$$\text{or} \quad \frac{2k}{c} = \frac{\frac{2h}{c}}{t_1t_2} \quad \left(\because t_1 + t_2 = \frac{2h}{c}\right)$$

$$\text{or} \quad t_1t_2 = \frac{h}{k}$$

$$\therefore \quad (t_1-t_2)^2 = (t_1+t_2)^2 - 4t_1t_2 = \frac{4h^2}{c^2} - \frac{4h}{k}$$

$$= \frac{4h}{c^2k}(hk - c^2) \quad \text{...(i)}$$

Since, $|PQ| = 2d$

$$\therefore \quad \sqrt{(ct_1 - ct_2)^2 + \left(\frac{c}{t_1} - \frac{c}{t_2}\right)^2} = 2d$$

$$\text{or} \quad c^2(t_1-t_2)^2\left\{1 + \frac{1}{t_1^2t_2^2}\right\} = (2d)^2$$

$$\text{or} \quad c^2 \times \frac{4h}{c^2k}(hk - c^2)\left\{1 + \frac{k^2}{h^2}\right\} = 4d^2 \quad \text{[from Eq. (i)]}$$

$$\text{or} \quad (h^2 + k^2)(hk - c^2) = d^2hk$$

Hence, locus of the middle-point of PQ is

$$(x^2 + y^2)(xy - c^2) = d^2xy.$$

85. Let the rectangular hyperbola is

$$xy = c^2 \quad \text{...(i)}$$

Since, the centre of hyperbola (i) is origin (0, 0) and equation of asymptotes are $x = 0$ and $y = 0$.

The equation of a line through (0, 0) and makes an angle θ with asymptote (X-axis) is $y = x\tan\theta$.

It will meet the hyperbola, where $x(x\tan\theta)=c^2$

i.e. $x=c\sqrt{\cot\theta}$

Putting $x=c\sqrt{\cot\theta}$ in (1)

then $y=c\sqrt{(\tan\theta)}$

$\therefore$ The four points are $(c\sqrt{\cot\theta}, c\sqrt{\tan\theta})$ where

$Q=\alpha,\beta,\gamma,\delta.$

The line joining the points α and β is perpendicular to the line joining the points γ and δ.

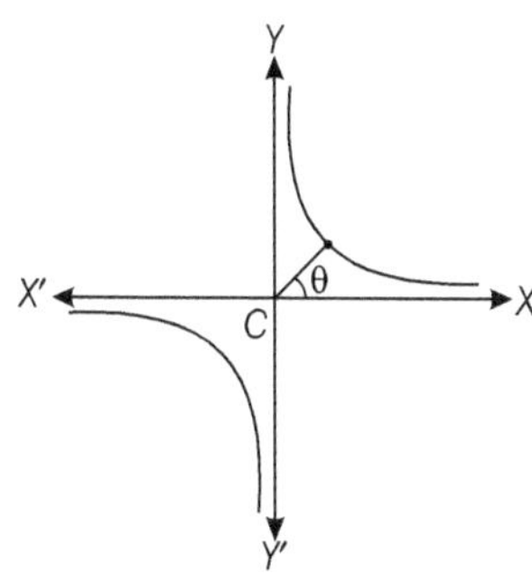

Therefore, the product of their slopes $=-1$

i.e. $$\frac{c\sqrt{\tan\beta}-c\sqrt{\tan\alpha}}{c\sqrt{\cot\beta}-c\sqrt{\cot\alpha}}\times\frac{c\sqrt{\tan\delta}-c\sqrt{\tan\gamma}}{c\sqrt{\cot\delta}-c\sqrt{\cot\gamma}}=-1$$

$$\Rightarrow \quad (-\sqrt{\tan\alpha}\sqrt{\tan\beta})\times(-\sqrt{\tan\gamma}\sqrt{\tan\delta})=-1$$

or $$\tan\alpha\tan\beta\tan\gamma\tan\delta=1$$

86. Let $P\left(ct_1, \frac{c}{t_1}\right)$ and $Q\left(ct_2, \frac{c}{t_2}\right)$ be any two points on $xy=c^2$.

Then tangents at P and Q are

$$x+yt_1^2=2ct_1 \quad \text{...(i)}$$

and $$x+yt_2^2=2ct_2 \quad \text{...(ii)}$$

On solving Eqs. (i) and (ii), the point of intersection, say (h,k), is given by

$$h=\frac{2ct_1t_2}{t_1+t_2} \text{ and } k=\frac{2c}{t_1+t_2} \quad \text{...(iii)}$$

The foot of the ordinate of P is $(ct_1, 0)$ and it lies on Eq. (ii) then

$$ct_1+0=2ct_2$$

$$\therefore \quad t_1=2t_2 \quad \text{...(iv)}$$

Then, from Eqs. (iii) and (iv),

$$h=\frac{2c\cdot 2t_2\cdot t_2}{2t_2+t_2} \text{ and } k=\frac{2c}{2t_2+t_2}$$

$$\therefore \quad h=\frac{4c}{3}t_2 \text{ and } k=\frac{2c}{3t_2}$$

$$\therefore \quad h\cdot k=\frac{4c}{3}t_2\times\frac{2c}{3t_2}$$

$$\therefore \quad hk=\frac{8}{9}c^2$$

$\therefore$ Locus of (h,k) is $xy=\frac{8}{9}c^2$, which is a rectangular hyperbola with the same asymptotes $x=0$ and $y=0$ as those of $xy=c^2$.

87. Take two given perpendicular straight lines as the coordinate axes and let the equation of variable circle be

$$x^2+y^2+2gx+2fy+c=0 \quad \text{...(i)}$$

Suppose circle (i) make an intercept of length a on X-axis and an intercept of length b on Y-axis.

$$\therefore \quad a=2\sqrt{(g^2-c)}$$

and $$b=2\sqrt{(f^2-c)}$$

Squaring and subtracting these, we get

$$4(g^2-c)-4(f^2-c)=a^2-b^2$$

or $$g^2-f^2=\frac{1}{4}(a^2-b^2)$$

or $$(-g)^2-(-f)^2=\frac{1}{4}(a^2-b^2)$$

Hence locus of the centre of circle $(-g,-f)$ is

$$x^2-y^2=\frac{1}{4}(a^2-b^2)$$

which is a rectangular hyperbola.

88. Let the hyperbola be

$$\frac{x^2}{a^2}-\frac{y^2}{b^2}=1 \quad \text{...(i)}$$

Its asymptotes are

$$\frac{x}{a}-\frac{y}{b}=0 \text{ and } \frac{x}{a}+\frac{y}{b}=0$$

(a) Let us take the asymptote

$$\frac{x}{a}-\frac{y}{b}=0 \Rightarrow y=\frac{b}{a}x \quad \text{...(ii)}$$

Any line parallel to Eq. (ii) is

$$y=\frac{b}{a}x+c \quad \text{...(iii)}$$

Eliminate y from Eqs. (i) and (iii), then

$$\frac{x^2}{a^2}-\frac{1}{b^2}\left(\frac{b}{a}x+c\right)^2=1$$

$$\Rightarrow \quad \frac{x^2}{a^2}-\frac{1}{b^2}\left(\frac{b^2x^2}{a^2}+c^2+\frac{2bc}{a}x\right)=1$$

$$\Rightarrow \quad 0\cdot x^2-\frac{2c}{ab}x-\frac{(c^2+b^2)}{b^2}=0$$

One root of its equation is infinite since coefficient of x^2 in it is zero. Also from Eq. (iii), when $y\to\infty$ as $x\to\infty$.

$\therefore$ Eqs. (i) and (iii) meet in one point at infinity.

(b) Lines through $(a,0)$; $(-a,0)$; $(0,b)$ and $(0,-b)$ are parallel to the principal axes, enclose a rectangle whose vertices are $A(a,b)$, $B(-a,b)$, $C(-a,-b)$ and $D(a,-b)$. Now equation of diagonal AC is

$$y-b=\frac{b-(-b)}{a-(-a)}(x-a)$$

$$\Rightarrow \quad y-b=\frac{b}{a}(x-a)$$

$$\Rightarrow \quad y=\frac{b}{a}x$$

$$\Rightarrow \quad \frac{x}{a}-\frac{y}{b}=0$$

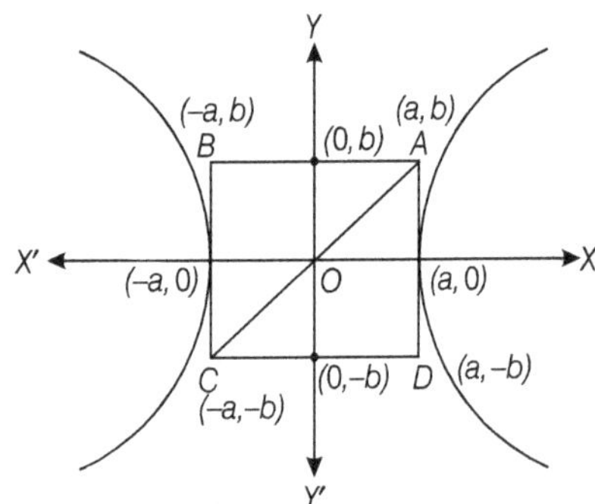

i.e. The diagonal AC is one of the asymptotes of the hyperbola $\frac{x^2}{a^2} - \frac{y^2}{b^2} = 1$. Similarly the diagonal BD is the other asymptote.

89. Let the equation of ellipse is

$$\frac{x^2}{a^2} + \frac{y^2}{b^2} = 1 \quad ...(i)$$

Tangent to Eq. (i) at $P(a\cos\phi, b\sin\phi)$ is

$$\frac{x}{a}\cos\phi + \frac{y}{b}\sin\phi = 1$$

Coordinate of point B is

$$B \equiv (a\sec\phi, 0) \text{ and } AB = a\{\sec\phi - \cos\phi\}$$

Let coordinate of Q be (x_1, y_1) then

$$x_1 = a\cos\phi \text{ and } y_1 = a(\sec\phi - \cos\phi)$$

So $\quad y_1 = a\left(\frac{a}{x_1} - \frac{x_1}{a}\right)$

$\Rightarrow \quad x_1y_1 = a^2 - x_1^2$

Hence, locus of Q is $xy = a^2 - x^2$ ...(ii)

which is clearly a hyperbola.

Since, the equation of a hyperbola and its asymptotes differ in constant terms only, asymptotes of Eq. (ii) are given by $x^2 + xy - a^2 + k = 0$, k is any constant.

It represents two straight lines. The required condition for this is

$$abc + 2fgh - af^2 - bg^2 - ch^2 = 0$$

then $\quad k = a^2$

$\therefore$ Asymptotes are

$$x = 0 \text{ and } x + y = 0$$

90. The given rectangular hyperbola is

$$xy = c^2 \quad ...(i)$$

Equations of chords of contact of (x_1, y_1) and (x_2, y_2) w.r.t., $xy = c^2$ are

$$xy_1 + x_1y = 2c^2 \quad ...(ii)$$

and $\quad xy_2 + x_2y = 2c^2 \quad ...(iii)$

The equation of the conic passing through Eq. (i) with Eqs. (ii) and (iii) is

$$(xy_1 + x_1y - 2c^2)(xy_2 + x_2y - 2c^2) + \lambda (xy - c^2) = 0 \quad ...(iv)$$

Now, Eq. (iv) represents a circle

$\therefore \quad$ coefficient of x^2 = coefficient of y^2

$\therefore \quad y_1y_2 = x_1x_2$

and coefficient of $xy = 0$

$\Rightarrow \quad x_1y_2 + x_2y_1 + \lambda = 0 \quad ...(v)$

Again the conic (iv) passes through (x_1, y_1) and (x_2, y_2) then

$$(2x_1y_1 - 2c^2)(x_1y_2 + x_2y_1 - 2c^2) + \lambda(x_1y_1 - c^2) = 0$$

or $\quad 2(x_1y_2 + x_2y_1 - 2c^2) + \lambda = 0 \quad (\because x_1y_1 \neq c^2)$ ...(vi)

and $\quad (x_2y_1 + y_2x_1 - 2c^2)(y_2x_2 + x_2y_2 - 2c^2) + \lambda(x_2y_2 - c^2) = 0$

$\Rightarrow \quad 2(x_2y_1 + x_1y_2 - 2c^2) + \lambda = 0 \quad (\because x_2y_2 \neq c^2)$ ... (vii)

From Eqs. (v) and (vi), we get

$$2(-\lambda - 2c^2) + \lambda = 0$$

$$-\lambda - 4c^2 = 0$$

$\therefore \quad \lambda = -4c^2$

Then from Eq. (v)

$$x_1y_2 + x_2y_1 = 4c^2$$

which is the other condition.

91. Let two perpendicular asymptotes of a rectangular hyperbola are CD and CE.

Let the coordinates of A, B and C are $(a, 0)$, $(0, b)$, (α, β). OX and OY are parallel to CD and CE.

Then equations of CD and CE are

$$y - \beta = 0 \text{ and } x - \alpha = 0$$

Thus combined equation of CD and CE is

$$(x - \alpha)(y - \beta) = 0$$

or $\quad xy - \alpha y - \beta x + \alpha\beta = 0$

is the equation of asymptotes of rectangular hyperbola.

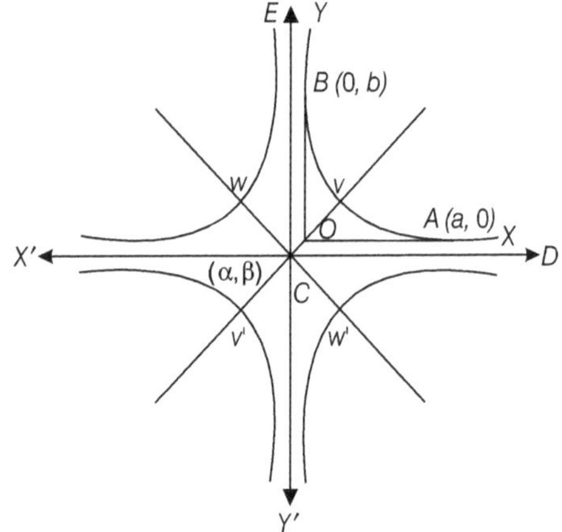

Hence, equation of rectangular hyperbola is

$$xy - \alpha y - \beta x + k = 0,$$

where k is any constant.

It passes through $A(a, 0)$ and $B(0, b)$

$\therefore \quad 0 - 0 - \beta a + k = 0$

and $\quad 0 - \alpha b - 0 + k = 0$

$\therefore \quad \beta = \frac{k}{a}$ and $\alpha = \frac{k}{b}$

Hence equation of rectangular hyperbola becomes

$$xy - k\left(\frac{x}{a} + \frac{y}{b} - 1\right) = 0 \quad ...(i)$$

Eq. (i) represents two sets of rectangular hyperbolas whose vertices lie on the straight lines VCV' and WCW' both passing through (α, β) inclined at 45° and 135° to OX.

Then $\alpha = \frac{k}{b}, \beta = \frac{k}{a}$ and their equations are

$$y - \beta = \pm (x - \alpha)$$

$$\Rightarrow \quad y - \frac{k}{a} = \pm \left(x - \frac{k}{b}\right)$$

or $\quad x + y = k\left(\frac{1}{a} + \frac{1}{b}\right)$

and $\quad x - y = k\left(\frac{1}{b} - \frac{1}{a}\right) \quad$ ...(ii)

or $\quad k = \frac{ab(x+y)}{(a+b)}$

and $\quad k = \frac{ab(x-y)}{(a-b)}$

Putting in Eq. (i) then

$$\frac{x^2}{a} + \frac{y^2}{b} - x - y = 0$$

and $\quad \frac{x^2}{b} - \frac{y^2}{a} - x + y = 0$

Differentiating these equations, we get

$$\frac{2x}{a} + \frac{2y}{b}\frac{dy}{dx} - 1 - \frac{dy}{dx} = 0$$

and $\quad \frac{2x}{b} - \frac{2y}{a}\frac{dy}{dx} - 1 + \frac{dy}{dx} = 0$

$\therefore$ Slopes of lines are

$$m_1 = \frac{dy}{dx} = \frac{b(a-2x)}{a(2y-b)}$$

and $\quad m_2 = \frac{dy}{dx} = \frac{a(2x-b)}{b(2y-a)}$

At (0, 0) $\quad m_1 = -1$ and $m_2 = 1$

$\therefore \quad m_1 m_2 = -1$

which shows that curves intersect orthogonally.

92. Equation of the normal to the hyperbola $xy = 1$ at t is

$$xt^3 - yt - t^4 + 1 = 0 \quad \text{...(i)}$$

$\because$ It passes through (α, β)

$\therefore \quad t^4 - \alpha t^3 + \beta t - 1 = 0$

If foot of the co-normal points are

$$\left(t_1, \frac{1}{t_1}\right), \left(t_2, \frac{1}{t_2}\right), \left(t_3, \frac{1}{t_3}\right) \text{ and } \left(t_4, \frac{1}{t_4}\right)$$

$\therefore \quad t_1 + t_2 + t_3 + t_4 = \alpha$

$\Rightarrow \quad x_1 + x_2 + x_3 + x_4 = \alpha$

and $\quad \frac{1}{t_1} + \frac{1}{t_2} + \frac{1}{t_3} + \frac{1}{t_4} = \beta$

$\Rightarrow \quad y_1 + y_2 + y_3 + y_4 = \beta$

Let the variable line be

$$px + qy + r = 0 \quad \text{...(ii)}$$

Since, algebraic sum of perpendicular distances from $(x_1, y_1), (x_2, y_2), (x_3, y_3)$ and (x_4, y_4) to Eq. (ii) is zero.

$$\left(\frac{px_1 + qy_1 + r}{\sqrt{(p^2+q^2)}}\right) + \left(\frac{px_2 + qy_2 + r}{\sqrt{p^2+q^2}}\right) + \left(\frac{px_3 + qy_3 + r}{\sqrt{(p^2+q^2)}}\right) + \left(\frac{px_4 + qy_4 + r}{\sqrt{(p^2+q^2)}}\right) = 0$$

$\Rightarrow \quad p(x_1 + x_2 + x_3 + x_4) + q(y_1 + y_2 + y_3 + y_4) + 4r = 0$

$\Rightarrow \quad p\left(\frac{x_1 + x_2 + x_3 + x_4}{4}\right) + q\left(\frac{y_1 + y_2 + y_3 + y_4}{4}\right) + r = 0$

$\Rightarrow \quad p \cdot \frac{\alpha}{4} + q \cdot \frac{\beta}{4} + r = 0$

$\therefore$ Eq. (ii) passes through $\left(\frac{\alpha}{4}, \frac{\beta}{4}\right)$.

93. Let the equation of hyperbola is

$$\frac{x^2}{a^2} - \frac{y^2}{b^2} = 1$$

whose asymptotes are

$$\frac{x}{a} + \frac{y}{b} = 0$$

and $\quad \frac{x}{a} - \frac{y}{b} = 0$

Let there be any point $P(h, k)$ on the hyperbola

$k =$ distance of P from transverse axis

$h =$ distance of P from any asymptotes

say $\left(\frac{x}{a} - \frac{y}{b} = 0\right)$

$\therefore \quad k = \frac{bh - ak}{\sqrt{(a^2+b^2)}}$

Squaring $(a^2 + b^2)k^2 = b^2h^2 + a^2k^2 - 2ab\,hk$

$\Rightarrow \quad b(h^2 - k^2) = 2ahk$

$\Rightarrow \quad (h^2 - k^2) = \frac{2ahk}{b}$

Squaring $\quad (h^2 - k^2)^2 = 4a^2h^2\left(\frac{k^2}{b^2}\right)$

$$= 4a^2h^2\left(\frac{h^2}{a^2} - 1\right) \quad \left\{\because \frac{h^2}{a^2} - \frac{k^2}{b^2} = 1\right\}$$

$\Rightarrow \quad (h^2 - k^2)^2 = 4h^2(h^2 - a^2)$

Hence locus of $P(h, k)$ is

$$(x^2 - y^2)^2 = 4x^2(x^2 - a^2).$$

94. Tangent to the hyperbola $\frac{x^2}{a^2} - \frac{y^2}{b^2} = 1$ is

$$y = mx \pm \sqrt{a^2m^2 - b^2}$$

Given that $y = \alpha x + \beta$ is the tangent of hyperbola

$\Rightarrow \quad m = \alpha$ and $a^2m^2 - b^2 = \beta^2$

$\therefore \quad a^2\alpha^2 - b^2 = \beta^2$

Locus is $a^2x^2 - y^2 = b^2$ which is hyperbola.

95. For the given ellipse $\frac{x^2}{25}+\frac{y^2}{16}=1$

$\Rightarrow \quad e=\sqrt{\left(1-\frac{16}{25}\right)}=\frac{3}{5}$

$\Rightarrow$ Eccentricity of hyperbola $=\frac{5}{3}$

Let the hyperbola be $\frac{x^2}{A^2}-\frac{y^2}{B^2}=1$ then

$$B^2=A^2\left(\frac{25}{9}-1\right)=\frac{16}{9}A^2$$

$\therefore \frac{x^2}{A^2}-\frac{9y^2}{16A^2}=1$, As it passes through focus of ellipse i.e. $(3,0)$

$\therefore$ We get $A^2=9 \Rightarrow B^2=16$

$\therefore$ Equation of hyperbola is $\frac{x^2}{9}-\frac{y^2}{16}=1$, focus of hyperbola is (5, 0), vertex of hyperbola is (3, 0).

96. The length of transverse axis $=2\sin\theta=2a$

$\Rightarrow \quad a=\sin\theta$

Also for ellipse $3x^2+4y^2=12$

or $\quad \frac{x^2}{4}+\frac{y^2}{3}=1, a^2=4, b^2=3$

$$e=\sqrt{1-\frac{b^2}{a^2}}=\sqrt{1-\frac{3}{4}}=\frac{1}{2}$$

$\therefore$ Focus of ellipse $=\left(2\times\frac{1}{2}, 0\right)\Rightarrow(1, 0)$

As hyperbola is confocal with ellipse, focus of hyperbola $=(1,0)$

$\Rightarrow \quad ae=1 \Rightarrow \sin\theta\times e=1$

$\Rightarrow \quad e=\operatorname{cosec}\theta$

$\therefore \quad b^2=a^2(e^2-1)$

$\quad =\sin^2\theta(\operatorname{cosec}^2\theta-1)=\cos^2\theta$

$\therefore$ Equation of hyperbola is

$$\frac{x^2}{\sin^2\theta}-\frac{y^2}{\cos^2\theta}=1$$

or, $\quad x^2\operatorname{cosec}^2\theta-y^2\sec^2\theta=1$

97. Two branches of hyperbola have no common tangent but have a common normal joining SS'.

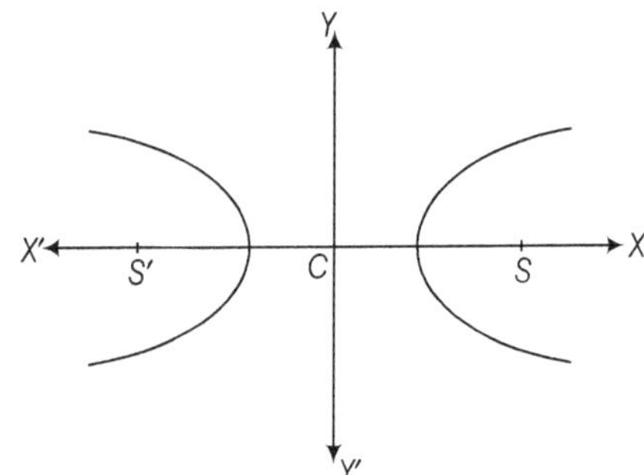

98. Given, equation of hyperbola is

$$\frac{x^2}{\cos^2\alpha}-\frac{y^2}{\sin^2\alpha}=1$$

Here, $a^2=\cos^2\alpha$ and $b^2=\sin^2\alpha$

$\because \quad b^2=a^2(e^2-1)$

$\therefore \quad \sin^2\alpha=\cos^2\alpha\,(e^2-1)$

or $\sin^2\alpha+\cos^2\alpha=\cos^2\alpha\,.\,e^2$

or $e^2=1+\tan^2\alpha=\sec^2\alpha \Rightarrow e=\sec\alpha$

$\therefore \quad ae=\cos\alpha\,.\,\frac{1}{\cos\alpha}=1$

Coordinates of foci are $(\pm ae, 0)$ i.e. $(\pm 1, 0)$

Hence, abscissae of foci remain constant, when α varies.

99. The given hyperbola is

$$x^2-2y^2-2\sqrt{2}x-4\sqrt{2}y-6=0$$

$\Rightarrow (x^2-2\sqrt{2}x+2)-2(y^2+2\sqrt{2}y+2)=6+2-4$

$\Rightarrow \quad (x-\sqrt{2})^2-2(y+\sqrt{2})^2=4$

$\Rightarrow \quad \frac{(x-\sqrt{2})^2}{2^2}-\frac{(y+\sqrt{2})^2}{(\sqrt{2})^2}=1$

$\therefore \quad a=2, b=\sqrt{2} \Rightarrow e=\sqrt{\left(1+\frac{2}{4}\right)}=\sqrt{\frac{3}{2}}$

Clearly, ΔABC is a right triangle.

$$B\left(ae, \frac{b^2}{a}\right)$$

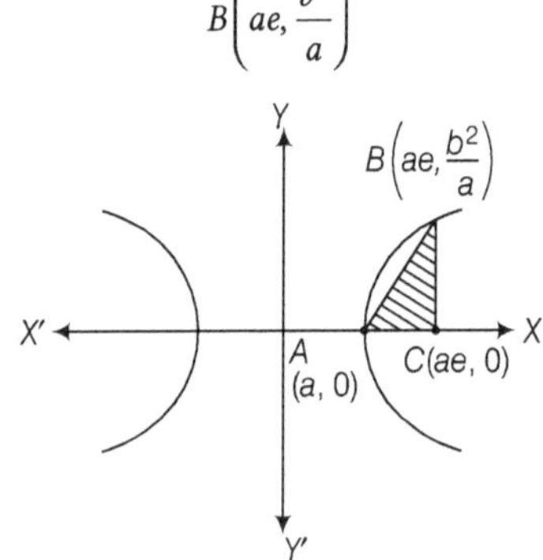

$\therefore$ Area of $(\Delta ABC)=\frac{1}{2}\times AC\times BC$

$$=\frac{1}{2}\times(ae-a)\times\frac{b^2}{a}$$

$$=\frac{1}{2}(e-1)\,b^2=\frac{1}{2}\left(\sqrt{\frac{3}{2}}-1\right).2$$

$$=\left(\sqrt{\frac{3}{2}}-1\right)$$

100. The given hyperbola is

$$x^2-y^2=\frac{1}{2} \quad \text{... (i)}$$

which is rectangular hyperbola

$\therefore \quad e=\sqrt{2}$

Let the ellipse be $\frac{x^2}{a^2}+\frac{y^2}{b^2}=1$

Its eccentricity $=\frac{1}{\sqrt{2}}$

$\therefore \quad b^2=a^2(1-e^2)=a^2\left(1-\frac{1}{2}\right)=\frac{a^2}{2}$

So, the equation of ellipse becomes

$$x^2 + 2y^2 = a^2 \quad \text{... (ii)}$$

Let the hyperbola (i) and ellipse (ii) intersect each other at $P(x_1, y_1)$.

$\therefore$(Slope of hyperbola (i) at (x_1, y_1)) $\times$ (Slope of ellipse (ii) at $(x_1, y_1)) = -1$

$$\Rightarrow \quad \frac{x_1}{y_1} \times \frac{-x_1}{2y_1} = -1$$

$$\text{or} \quad x_1^2 = 2y_1^2 \quad \text{... (iii)}$$

Also (x_1, y_1) lies on $x^2 - y^2 = \frac{1}{2}$

$$\therefore \quad x_1^2 - y_1^2 = \frac{1}{2} \quad \text{... (iv)}$$

From Eqs. (iii) and (iv), we get $y_1^2 = \frac{1}{2}$ and $x_1^2 = 1$

and (x_1, y_1) lies on ellipse $x^2 + 2y^2 = a^2$

$$\therefore \quad x_1^2 + 2y_1^2 = a^2$$

$$\Rightarrow \quad 1 + 1 = a^2 \text{ or } a^2 = 2$$

$\therefore$ Equation of ellipse is $x^2 + 2y^2 = 2$

whose foci $(\pm 1, 0)$.

Sol. (Q. Nos. 101 and 102)

The intersection points of given circle

$$x^2 + y^2 - 8x = 0 \quad \text{... (i)}$$

and hyperbola

$$4x^2 - 9y^2 = 36 \quad \text{... (ii)}$$

can be obtained by solving these equations substituting value of y^2 from Eq. (i) in Eq. (ii), we get

$$4x^2 - 9(8x - x^2) = 36$$

$$\Rightarrow \quad 13x^2 - 72x - 36 = 0$$

$$\Rightarrow \quad x = 6, -\frac{6}{13}$$

$$\Rightarrow \quad y^2 = 12, -\frac{660}{169} \quad \text{(not possible)}$$

$\therefore A(6, 2\sqrt{3})$ and $B(6, -2\sqrt{3})$ are points of intersection.

101. Equation of tangent to hyperbola having slope m is

$$y = mx + \sqrt{(9m^2 - 4)} \quad \text{... (i)}$$

Equation of tangent to circle is

$$y = m(x - 4) + \sqrt{(16m^2 + 16)} \quad \text{... (ii)}$$

Eqs. (i) and (ii) will be identical, then

$$m = \frac{2}{\sqrt{5}}$$

So, equation of common tangents

$$y = \frac{2x}{\sqrt{5}} + \sqrt{\left(\frac{36}{5} - 4\right)}$$

$$\Rightarrow \quad y = \frac{2x}{\sqrt{5}} + \frac{4}{\sqrt{5}}$$

or $2x - \sqrt{5}y + 4 = 0$

102. Equation of circle with AB as its diameter is

$$(x - 6)(x - 6) + (y - 2\sqrt{3})(y + 2\sqrt{3}) = 0$$

$$\Rightarrow \quad x^2 + y^2 - 12x + 24 = 0$$

103. $\because$ line $2x + y = 1$ is tangent to the hyperbola $\frac{x^2}{a^2} - \frac{y^2}{b^2} = 1$

$$\therefore \quad (1)^2 = a^2(-2)^2 - b^2$$

$$\Rightarrow \quad 4a^2 - b^2 = 1 \quad \text{... (i)}$$

Intersection point of nearest directrix $x = \frac{a}{e}$ and X-axis is $\left(\frac{a}{e}, 0\right)$

As, $2x + y = 1$ passes through $\left(\frac{a}{e}, 0\right)$

$$\therefore \quad \frac{2a}{e} + 0 = 1 \Rightarrow a = \frac{e}{2} \quad \text{... (ii)}$$

$$\text{and} \quad b^2 = a^2(e^2 - 1) = \frac{e^2}{4}(e^2 - 1) \quad \text{... (iii)}$$

Substituting the values of a and b from Eqs. (ii) and (iii) in Eq. (i), then

$$e^2 - \frac{e^2}{4}(e^2 - 1) = 1$$

$$\Rightarrow \quad (e^2 - 4)(e^2 - 1) = 0$$

$$\therefore \quad e^2 = 4, e^2 \neq 1 \quad (\because e > 1)$$

Hence, $e = 2$

104. Equation of normal at P (6, 3) is

$$\frac{a^2x}{6} + \frac{b^2y}{3} = a^2 + b^2$$

$\because$ Normal intersects the X-axis at (9, 0), then

$$\frac{9a^2}{6} + 0 = a^2 + b^2 \Rightarrow 3a^2 = 2a^2 + 2b^2$$

$$\text{or} \quad a^2 = 2b^2$$

$$\text{or} \quad a^2 = 2a^2(e^2 - 1)$$

$$\therefore \quad e^2 = \frac{3}{2}$$

Hence, $e = \sqrt{\frac{3}{2}}$

105. Given, ellipse is $x^2 + 4y^2 = 4$

$$\text{or} \quad \frac{x^2}{4} + \frac{y^2}{1} = 1$$

$$\therefore \quad e = \sqrt{\left(1 - \frac{1}{4}\right)} = \frac{\sqrt{3}}{2}$$

and foci are $(\pm\sqrt{3}, 0)$

$\therefore$ Eccentricity of hyperbola $= \frac{2}{\sqrt{3}} = e_1$

$$\text{and} \quad b^2 = a^2(e_1^2 - 1) = a^2\left(\frac{4}{3} - 1\right) = \frac{a^2}{3}$$

then equation of hyperbola becomes

$$x^2 - 3y^2 = a^2$$

which pass through $(\pm\sqrt{3}, 0)$

$$3 - 0 = a^2$$

$$\Rightarrow \quad a^2 = 3$$

$\therefore$Equation of hyperbola is

$$x^2 - 3y^2 = 3$$

and foci of hyperbola are $\left(\pm\sqrt{3} \times \frac{2}{\sqrt{3}}, 0\right)$ i.e., $(\pm 2, 0)$

106. Equation of tangent at (x_1, y_1) is

$$\frac{xx_1}{9} - \frac{yy_1}{4} = 1 \quad \dots \text{(i)}$$

Equation of line parallel to

$$2x - y = \lambda \quad \dots \text{(ii)}$$

$\because$ Line (ii) is tangent of $\frac{x^2}{9} - \frac{y^2}{4} = 1$, then

$$\lambda^2 = 9 \times 2^2 - 4$$

$$\therefore \quad \lambda = \pm 4\sqrt{2}$$

From Eq. (ii), Equation of tangent is

$$2x - y = \pm 4\sqrt{2} \quad \dots \text{(iii)}$$

Comparing Eqs. (i) and (iii), we get $\frac{x_1}{18} = \frac{y_1}{4} = \pm \frac{1}{4\sqrt{2}}$

or $\quad x_1 = \pm \frac{9}{2\sqrt{2}}$ and $y_1 = \pm \frac{1}{\sqrt{2}}$

Hence, points of contact of the tangents on the hyperbola are $\left(\frac{9}{2\sqrt{2}}, \frac{1}{\sqrt{2}}\right)$ and $\left(-\frac{9}{2\sqrt{2}}, -\frac{1}{\sqrt{2}}\right)$

107. $H : x^2 - y^2 = 1$

S : Circle with centre $N(x_2, 0)$

Common tangent to H and S at $P(x_1, y_1)$ is

$$xx_1 - yy_1 = 1 \Rightarrow m_1 = \frac{x_1}{y_1}$$

Also radius of circle S with centre $N(x_2, 0)$ through point of contact (x_1, y_1) is perpendicular to tangent.

$$\therefore \quad m_1 m_2 = -1 \Rightarrow \frac{x_1}{y_1} \times \frac{0 - y_1}{x_2 - x_1} = -1$$

$$\Rightarrow \quad x_1 = x_2 - x_1 \text{ or } x_2 = 2x_1$$

M is the point of intersection of tangent at P and X-axis

$$\therefore \quad M\left(\frac{1}{x_1}, 0\right)$$

$\because$ Centroid of ΔPMN is (ℓ, m)

$$\therefore \quad x_1 + \frac{1}{x_1} + x_2 = 3\ell \text{ and } y_1 = 3\text{ m}$$

Using $x_2 = 2x_1$,

$$\Rightarrow \quad \frac{1}{3}\left(3x_1 + \frac{1}{x_1}\right) = l \text{ and } \frac{y_1}{3} = m$$

$$\therefore \quad \frac{dl}{dx_1} = 1 - \frac{1}{3x_1^2}, \frac{dm}{dy_1} = \frac{1}{3}$$

Also, (x_1, y_1) lies on H,

$$\therefore \quad x_1^2 - y_1^2 = 1 \text{ or } y_1 = \sqrt{(x_1^2 - 1)}$$

$$\therefore \quad m = \frac{1}{3}\sqrt{(x_1^2 - 1)}$$

$$\therefore \quad \frac{dm}{dx_1} = \frac{x_1}{3\sqrt{(x_1^2 - 1)}}$$

108. $\because \frac{2b^2}{a} = 8$ and $2b = \frac{1}{2}(2ae)$

$$\Rightarrow \quad b^2 = 4a \text{ and } b = \frac{1}{2}ae \text{ or } b^2 = \frac{1}{4}a^2e^2$$

$$\Rightarrow \quad a^2(e^2 - 1) = \frac{1}{4}a^2e^2 \Rightarrow 4e^2 - 4 = e^2 \text{ or } e^2 = \frac{4}{3}$$

$$\therefore \quad e = \frac{2}{\sqrt{3}}$$

$$\Rightarrow b^2 = 4a \text{ and } b = \frac{1}{2}ae \text{ or } b^2 = \frac{1}{4}a^2e^2$$

109. Let Equation of hyperbola is $\frac{x^2}{a^2} - \frac{y^2}{b^2} = 1$

When it passes through $P(\sqrt{2}, \sqrt{3})$, then $\frac{2}{a^2} - \frac{3}{b^2} = 1$

$$\Rightarrow \quad 2b^2 - 3a^2 = a^2b^2 \quad \dots \text{(i)}$$

and $ae = 2 \Rightarrow a^2 + b^2 = 4 \quad \dots$(ii)

From Eqs. (i) and (ii), we get $2(4 - a^2) - 3a^2 = a^2(4 - a^2)$

$\Rightarrow a^2 - 9a^2 + 8 = 0 \Rightarrow (a^2 - 1)(a^2 - 8) = 0$

$\therefore \quad a^2 = 1 \quad (\because a^2 \neq 8)$

From Eq. (ii), $b^2 = 3$

$\therefore$ Equation of Hyperbola is $\frac{x^2}{1} - \frac{y^2}{3} = 1$

Equation of tangent at $P(\sqrt{2}, \sqrt{3})$ is $\frac{x\sqrt{2}}{1} - \frac{y\sqrt{3}}{3} = 1$

Which is passes through $(2\sqrt{2}, 3\sqrt{2})$

110. (a,b,c) $\because 2x - y + 1 = 0$ is a tangent of $\frac{x^2}{a^2} - \frac{y^2}{16} = 1$, then

$$(1)^2 = a^2(2)^2 - 16 \text{ or } (2a)^2 = (1)^2 + (4)^2$$

$\therefore$ $2a$, 4, 1 are the sides of a right angled triangle.

Sol. (Q. Nos. 111-113)

I. $x^2 + y^2 = a^2$

Equations of tangents in terms of slopes are

$$y = mx + a\sqrt{(m^2 + 1)} \text{ (ii)}$$

and points of contact in terms of slopes are

$$\left(\frac{-ma}{\sqrt{(m^2+1)}}, \frac{a}{\sqrt{(m^2+1)}}\right) \text{ (Q)}$$

$\therefore$ I (ii) (Q) (Ans. Q.No. 112) (Here, $a = \sqrt{2}, m = \pm 1$)

II. $x^2 + a^2y^2 = a^2$ or $\frac{x^2}{a^2} + \frac{y^2}{1^2} = 1$

Equations of tangents in terms of slopes are

$$y = mx + \sqrt{(a^2m^2 + 1)} \text{ (iv)}$$

and points of contact in terms of slopes are

$$\left(\frac{-a^2m}{\sqrt{(a^2m^2+1)}}, \frac{1}{\sqrt{(a^2m^2+1)}}\right) \text{ (R)}$$

$\therefore$ II (iv) (R) (Ans. Q.No. 111) (Here, $a = 2, m = \frac{-\sqrt{3}}{2}$)

III. $y^2 = 4ax$

Equation of tangent in terms of slopes are

$$y = mx + \frac{a}{m} \text{ or } my = m^2x + a \text{ (i)}$$

and points of contact in terms of slopes are

$$\left(\frac{a}{m^2}, \frac{2a}{m}\right) \text{ (P)}$$

$\therefore$ III (i) (P) (Ans. Q.No. 113) (Here, $a = 8, m = 1$)

Previous Years' Questions

JEE Main and Advanced (2021-18)

Coordinate System and Coordinates

1. Consider a triangle (Δ) whose two sides lie on the X-axis and the line $x+y+1=0$. If the orthocenter of triangle is (1, 1), then the equation of the circle passing through the vertices of the triangle (Δ) is **[JEE Advanced 2021]**

(a) $x^2+y^2-3x+y=0$ (b) $x^2+y^2+x+3y=0$
(c) $x^2+y^2+2y-1=0$ (d) $x^2+y^2+x+y=0$

2. A triangle ABC lying in the first quadrant has two vertices as $A(1, 2)$ and $B(3, 1)$. If $\angle BAC=90^\circ$, and ar $(\Delta ABC)=5\sqrt{5}$ sq units, then the abscissa of the vertex C is **[JEE Main 2020]**

(a) $2+\sqrt{5}$ (b) $1+2\sqrt{5}$
(c) $2\sqrt{5}-1$ (d) $1+\sqrt{5}$

3. Let $A(1,0)$, $B(6,2)$ and $C\left(\frac{3}{2},6\right)$ be the vertices of a triangle ABC. If P is a point inside the triangle ABC such that the triangles APC, APB and BPC have equal areas, then the length of the line segment PQ, where Q is the point $\left(-\frac{7}{6},-\frac{1}{3}\right)$, is **[JEE Main 2020]**

4. Let $O(0,0)$ and $A(0,1)$ be two fixed points, then the locus of a point P such that the perimeter of ΔAOP is 4, is **[JEE Main 2019]**

(a) $8x^2-9y^2+9y=18$ (b) $9x^2-8y^2+8y=16$
(c) $9x^2+8y^2-8y=16$ (d) $8x^2+9y^2-9y=18$

5. A triangle has a vertex at (1, 2) and the mid-points of the two sides through it are $(-1,1)$ and $(2,3)$. Then, the centroid of this triangle is **[JEE Main 2019]**

(a) $\left(1,\frac{7}{3}\right)$ (b) $\left(\frac{1}{3},2\right)$
(c) $\left(\frac{1}{3},1\right)$ (d) $\left(\frac{1}{3},\frac{5}{3}\right)$

6. Let S be the set of all triangles in the xy-plane, each having one vertex at the origin and the other two vertices lie on coordinate axes with integral coordinates. If each triangle in S has area 50 sq units, then the number of elements in the set S is **[JEE Main 2019]**

(a) 36 (b) 32 (c) 18 (d) 9

7. A point P moves on the line $2x-3y+4=0$. If $Q(1,4)$ and $R(3,-2)$ are fixed points, then the locus of the centroid of ΔPQR is a line **[JEE Main 2019]**

(a) with slope $\frac{2}{3}$ (b) with slope $\frac{3}{2}$
(c) parallel to Y-axis (d) parallel to X-axis

8. If the line $3x+4y-24=0$ intersects the X-axis at the point A and the Y-axis at the point B, then the incentre of the triangle OAB, where O is the origin, is **[JEE Main 2019]**

(a) (4, 3) (b) (3, 4)
(c) (4, 4) (d) (2, 2)

9. Let the orthocentre and centroid of a triangle be $A(-3,5)$ and $B(3,3)$, respectively. If C is the circumcentre of this triangle, then the radius of the circle having line segment AC as diameter, is **[JEE Main 2018]**

(a) $\sqrt{10}$ (b) $2\sqrt{10}$
(c) $3\sqrt{\frac{5}{2}}$ (d) $\frac{3\sqrt{5}}{2}$

Answers

1. (b) **2.** (b) **3.** (5) **4.** (c) **5.** (b) **6.** (a) **7.** (a) **8.** (d) **9.** (c)

The Straight lines

1. If p and q are the lengths of the perpendiculars from the origin on the lines,
$x\operatorname{cosec}\alpha-y\sec\alpha=k\cot 2\alpha$ and
$x\sin\alpha+y\cos\alpha=k\sin 2\alpha$
respetively, then k^2 is equal to **[JEE Main 2021]**

(a) $4p^2+q^2$ (b) $2p^2+q^2$
(c) p^2+2q^2 (d) p^2+4q^2

2. Let A be a fixed point (0, 6) and B be a moving point $(2t, 0)$. Let M be the mid-point of AB and the perpendicular bisector of AB meets the Y-axis at C. The locus of the mid-point P of MC is **[JEE Main 2021]**

(a) $3x^2 - 2y - 6 = 0$ (b) $3x^2 + 2y - 6 = 0$
(c) $2x^2 + 3y - 9 = 0$ (d) $2x^2 - 3y + 9 = 0$

3. Let ABC be a triangle with $A(-3,1)$ and $\angle ACB = \theta$, $0 < \theta < \frac{\pi}{2}$. If the equation of the median through B is $2x + y - 3 = 0$ and the equation of angle bisector of C is $7x - 4y - 1 = 0$, then $\tan\theta$ is equal to **[JEE Main 2021]**

(a) 1/2 (b) 3/4
(c) 4/3 (d) 2

4. Two sides of a parallelogram are along the lines $4x + 5y = 0$ and $7x + 2y = 0$. If the equation of one of the diagonals of the parallelogram is $11x + 7y = 9$, then other diagonal passes through the point **[JEE Main 2021]**

(a) (1, 2) (b) (2, 2)
(c) (2, 1) (d) (1, 3)

5. Consider a triangle having vertices $A(-2,3)$, $B(1,9)$ and $C(3,8)$. If a line L passing through the circumcentre of ΔABC, bisects line BC, and intersects Y-axis at point $\left(0, \frac{\alpha}{2}\right)$, then the value of real number α is **[JEE Main 2021]**

6. The number of integral values of m, so that the abscissa of point of intersection of lines $3x + 4y = 9$ and $y = mx + 1$ is also an integer, is **[JEE Main 2021]**

(a) 1 (b) 2
(c) 3 (d) 0

7. The equation of one of the straight lines which passes through the point $(1,3)$ and makes an angle $\tan^{-1}(\sqrt{2})$ with the straight line, $y + 1 = 3\sqrt{2}x$ is **[JEE Main 2021]**

(a) $4\sqrt{2}x + 5y - (15 + 4\sqrt{2}) = 0$
(b) $5\sqrt{2}x + 4y - (15 + 4\sqrt{2}) = 0$
(c) $4\sqrt{2}x + 5y - 4\sqrt{2} = 0$
(d) $4\sqrt{2}x - 5y - (5 + 4\sqrt{2}) = 0$

8. In a ΔPQR, the coordinates of the points P and Q are $(-2, 4)$ and $(4, -2)$, respectively. If the equation of the perpendicular bisector of PR is $2x - y + 2 = 0$, then the centre of the circumcircle of the ΔPQR is **[JEE Main 2021]**

(a) (–1, 0) (b) (–2, –2)
(c) (0, 2) (d) (1, 4)

9. Let $A(-1,1)$, $B(3,4)$ and $C(2,0)$ be given three points. A line $y = mx$, $m > 0$ intersects lines AC and BC at point P and Q, respectively. Let A_1 and A_2 be the areas of ΔABC and ΔPQC, respectively, such that $A_1 = 3A_2$, then the value of m is equal to **[JEE Main 2021]**

(a) $\frac{4}{15}$ (b) 1
(c) 2 (d) 3

10. The intersection of three lines $x - y = 0$, $x + 2y = 3$ and $2x + y = 6$ is a **[JEE Main 2021]**

(a) right angled triangle (b) equilateral triangle
(c) isosceles triangle (d) None of these

11. If the curve $x^2 + 2y^2 = 2$ intersects the line $x + y = 1$ at two points P and Q, then the angle subtended by the line segment PQ at the origin is **[JEE Main 2021]**

(a) $\frac{\pi}{2} + \tan^{-1}\left(\frac{1}{4}\right)$ (b) $\frac{\pi}{2} - \tan^{-1}\left(\frac{1}{4}\right)$
(c) $\frac{\pi}{2} + \tan^{-1}\left(\frac{1}{3}\right)$ (d) $\frac{\pi}{2} - \tan^{-1}\left(\frac{1}{3}\right)$

12. The image of the point (3, 5) in the line $x - y + 1 = 0$, lies on **[JEE Main 2021]**

(a) $(x-2)^2 + (y-2)^2 = 12$ (b) $(x-4)^2 + (y+2)^2 = 16$
(c) $(x-4)^2 + (y-4)^2 = 8$ (d) $(x-2)^2 + (y-4)^2 = 4$

13 A man is walking on a straight line. The arithmetic mean of the reciprocals of the intercepts of this line on the coordinate axes is $\frac{1}{4}$. Three stones A, B and C are placed at the points $(1,1)$, $(2, 2)$ and $(4, 4)$, respectively. Then, which of these stones is / are on the path of the man ? **[JEE Main 2021]**

(a) A only (b) B only
(d) All the three (c) C only

Question Stem for Question Nos. 14 and 15

Consider the lines L_1 and L_2 defined by

$$L_1 : x\sqrt{2} + y - 1 = 0 \text{ and } L_2 : x\sqrt{2} - y + 1 = 0$$

For a fixed constant λ, let C be the locus of a point P such that the product of the distance of P from L_1 and the distance of P from L_2 is λ^2. The line $y = 2x + 1$ meets C at two points R and S, where the distance between R and S is $\sqrt{270}$.

Let the perpendicular bisector of RS meet C at two distinct points R' and S'. Let D be the square of the distance between R' and S'. **[JEE Advanced 2021]**

14. The value of λ^2 is ....

15. The value of D is ....

16. The set of all possible values of θ in the interval $(0, \pi)$ for which the points $(1, 2)$ and $(\sin\theta, \cos\theta)$ lie on the same side of the line $x + y = 1$ is **[JEE Main 2020]**

(a) $\left(0, \frac{\pi}{2}\right)$ (b) $\left(\frac{\pi}{4}, \frac{3\pi}{4}\right)$
(c) $\left(0, \frac{3\pi}{4}\right)$ (d) $\left(0, \frac{\pi}{4}\right)$

17. If a ΔABC has vertices $A(-1,7)$, $B(-7,1)$ and $C(5,-5)$, then its orthocentre has coordinates **[JEE Main 2020]**

(a) $(3, -3)$ (b) $(-3, 3)$
(c) $\left(-\frac{3}{5}, \frac{3}{5}\right)$ (d) $\left(\frac{3}{5}, -\frac{3}{5}\right)$

18. If the perpendicular bisector of the line segment joining the points $P(1,4)$ and $Q(k,3)$ has y-intercept equal to -4, then a value of k is **[JEE Main 2020]**

(a) $\sqrt{15}$ (b) -4
(c) $\sqrt{14}$ (d) -2

19 If the line, $2x-y+3=0$ is at a distance $\frac{1}{\sqrt{5}}$ and $\frac{2}{\sqrt{5}}$ from the lines $4x-2y+\alpha=0$ and $6x-3y+\beta=0$, respectively, then the sum of all possible values of α and β is .... **[JEE Main 2020]**

20 A ray of light coming from the point $(2, 2\sqrt{3})$ is incident at an angle 30° on the line $x=1$ at the point A. The ray gets reflected on the line $x=1$ and meets X-axis at the point B. Then, the line AB passes through the point **[JEE Main 2020]**

(a) $\left(3, -\frac{1}{\sqrt{3}}\right)$ (b) $\left(4, -\frac{\sqrt{3}}{2}\right)$
(c) $(3, -\sqrt{3})$ (d) $(4, -\sqrt{3})$

21. Let L denote the line in the xy-plane with x and y intercepts as 3 and 1 respectively.

Then, the image of the point $(-1, -4)$ in this line is **[JEE Main 2020]**

(a) $\left(\frac{11}{5}, \frac{28}{5}\right)$ (b) $\left(\frac{29}{5}, \frac{8}{5}\right)$
(c) $\left(\frac{8}{5}, \frac{29}{5}\right)$ (d) $\left(\frac{29}{5}, \frac{11}{5}\right)$

22. The locus of the mid-points of the perpendiculars drawn from points on the line, $x=2y$ to the line $x=y$ is **[JEE Main 2020]**

(a) $5x-7y=0$ (b) $2x-3y=0$
(c) $3x-2y=0$ (d) $7x-5y=0$

23. Let two points be $A(1, -1)$ and $B(0, 2)$. If a point $P(x', y')$ be such that the area of $\Delta PAB = 5$ sq. units and it lies on the line, $3x+y-4\lambda=0$, then a value of λ is **[JEE Main 2020]**

(a) 1 (b) -3
(c) 3 (d) 4

24 The length of the perpendicular from the origin, on the normal to the curve, $x^2+2xy-3y^2=0$ at the point $(2, 2)$ is **[JEE Main 2020]**

(a) 2 (b) $2\sqrt{2}$
(c) $4\sqrt{2}$ (d) $\sqrt{2}$

25. Let C be the centroid of the triangle with vertices $(3, -1)$, $(1, 3)$ and $(2, 4)$. Let P be the point of intersection of the lines $x+3y-1=0$ and $3x-y+1=0$. Then the line passing through the points C and P also passes through the point **[JEE Main 2020]**

(a) $(-9, -7)$ (b) $(-9, -6)$
(c) $(7, 6)$ (d) $(9, 7)$

26. A point on the straight line, $3x+5y=15$ which is equidistant from the coordinate axes will lie only in **[JEE Main 2019]**

(a) IV quadrant (b) I quadrant
(c) I and II quadrants (d) I, II and IV quadrants

27. Suppose that the points (h, k), $(1, 2)$ and $(-3, 4)$ lie on the line L_1. If a line L_2 passing through the points (h, k) and $(4, 3)$ is perpendicular to L_1, then k/h equals **[JEE Main 2019]**

(a) $-\frac{1}{7}$ (b) $\frac{1}{3}$
(c) 3 (d) 0

28. Slope of a line passing through $P(2, 3)$ and intersecting the line, $x+y=7$ at a distance of 4 units from P, is **[JEE Main 2019]**

(a) $\frac{1-\sqrt{5}}{1+\sqrt{5}}$ (b) $\frac{\sqrt{7}-1}{\sqrt{7}+1}$
(c) $\frac{1-\sqrt{7}}{1+\sqrt{7}}$ (d) $\frac{\sqrt{5}-1}{\sqrt{5}+1}$

29. If the two lines $x+(a-1)y=1$ and $2x+a^2y=1$, $(a \in R-\{0, 1\})$ are perpendicular, then the distance of their point of intersection from the origin is **[JEE Main 2019]**

(a) $\frac{2}{5}$ (b) $\frac{\sqrt{2}}{5}$
(c) $\frac{2}{\sqrt{5}}$ (d) $\sqrt{\frac{2}{5}}$

30. Lines are drawn parallel to the line $4x-3y+2=0$, at a distance 3/5 from the origin. Then which one of the following points lies on any of these lines? **[JEE Main 2019]**

(a) $\left(-\frac{1}{4}, -\frac{2}{3}\right)$ (b) $\left(-\frac{1}{4}, \frac{2}{3}\right)$
(c) $\left(\frac{1}{4}, -\frac{1}{3}\right)$ (d) $\left(\frac{1}{4}, \frac{1}{3}\right)$

31. A straight line L at a distance of 4 units from the origin makes positive intercepts on the coordinate axes and the perpendicular from the origin to this line makes an angle of 60° with the line $x+y=0$. Then, an equation of the line L is **[JEE Main 2019]**

(a) $x+\sqrt{3}y=8$
(b) $(\sqrt{3}+1)x+(\sqrt{3}-1)y=8\sqrt{2}$
(c) $\sqrt{3}x+y=8$
(d) $(\sqrt{3}-1)x+(\sqrt{3}+1)y=8\sqrt{2}$

32. Consider the set of all lines $px+qy+r=0$ such that $3p+2q+4r=0$. Which one of the following statements is true? **[JEE Main 2019]**

(a) Each line passes through the origin.
(b) The lines are concurrent at the point $\left(\frac{3}{4}, \frac{1}{2}\right)$
(c) The lines are all parallel
(d) The lines are not concurrent

33. If the straight line, $2x-3y+17=0$ is perpendicular to the line passing through the points (7, 17) and (15, β), then β equals **[JEE Main 2019]**

(a) $\frac{35}{3}$ (b) -5
(c) $-\frac{35}{3}$ (d) 5

34. Let the equations of two sides of a triangle be $3x-2y+6=0$ and $4x+5y-20=0$. If the orthocentre of this triangle is at (1, 1) then the equation of its third side is **[JEE Main 2019]**

(a) $122y-26x-1675=0$ (b) $26x-122y-1675=0$
(c) $122y+26x+1675=0$ (d) $26x+61y+1675=0$

35. Two sides of a parallelogram are along the lines, $x+y=3$ and $x-y+3=0$. If its diagonals intersect at (2, 4), then one of its vertex is **[JEE Main 2019]**

(a) (3, 6) (b) (2, 6)
(c) (2, 1) (d) (3, 5)

36. Two vertices of a triangle are (0, 2) and (4, 3). If its orthocentre is at the origin, then its third vertex lies in which quadrant? **[JEE Main 2019]**

(a) Fourth (b) Third
(c) Second (d) First

37. If in a parallelogram $ABDC$, the coordinates of A, B and C are respectively (1, 2), (3, 4) and (2, 5), then the equation of the diagonal AD is **[JEE Main 2019]**

(a) $3x+5y-13=0$ (b) $3x-5y+7=0$
(c) $5x-3y+1=0$ (d) $5x+3y-11=0$

38. If a straight line passing through the point $P(-3,4)$ is such that its intercepted portion between the coordinate axes is bisected at P, then its equation is **[JEE Main 2019]**

(a) $x-y+7=0$ (b) $4x-3y+24=0$
(c) $3x-4y+25=0$ (d) $4x+3y=0$

39. A straight line through a fixed point (2, 3) intersects the coordinate axes at distinct points P and Q. If O is the origin and the rectangle $OPRQ$ is completed, then the locus of R is **[JEE Main 2018]**

(a) $3x+2y=6$ (b) $2x+3y=xy$
(c) $3x+2y=xy$ (d) $3x+2y=6xy$

Answers

1. (a)	**2.** (c)	**3.** (c)	**4.** (b)	**5.** (9)	**6.** (b)	**7.** (a)	**8.** (b)	**9.** (b)	**10.** (c)
11. (a)	**12.** (d)	**13.** (b)	**14.** (9)	**15.** (77.14)	**16.** (a)	**17.** (b)	**18.** (b)	**19.** (30.00)	**20.** (c)
21. (a)	**22.** (a)	**23.** (c)	**24.** (b)	**25.** (b)	**26.** (c)	**27.** (c)	**28.** (c)	**29.** (d)	**30.** (b)
31. (d)	**32.** (b)	**33.** (d)	**34.** (b)	**35.** (a)	**36.** (c)	**37.** (c)	**38.** (b)	**39.** (c)	

Circle

1. If the variable line $3x+4y=\alpha$ lies between the two circles $(x-1)^2+(y-1)^2=1$ and $(x-9)^2+(y-1)^2=4$, without intercepting a chord on either circle, then the sum of all the integral values of α is **[JEE Main 2021]**

2. Let B be the centre of the circle $x^2+y^2-2x+4y+1=0$. Let the tangents at two points P and Q on the circle intersect at the point $Az(3, 1)$. Then $8\left(\frac{\text{area}\,\Delta APQ}{\text{area}\,\Delta BPQ}\right)$ is equal to **[JEE Main 2021]**

3. Let the equation $x^2+y^2+px+(1-p)y+5=0$ represent circles of varying radius $r\in(0, 5]$. Then, the number of elements in the set $S=\{q:q=p^2$ and q is an integer$\}$ is **[JEE Main 2021]**

4. Two circles each of radius 5 units touch each other at the point (1, 2). If the equation of their common tangent is $4x+3y=10$ and $C_1(\alpha,\beta)$ and $C_2(\gamma,\delta)$, $C_1\neq C_2$ are their centres, then $|(\alpha+\beta)(\gamma+\delta)|$ is equal to **[JEE Main 2021]**

5. Let Z be the set of all integers,
$A=\{(x,y)\in Z\times Z:(x-2)^2+y^2\leq 4\}$,
$B=\{(x,y)\in Z\times Z:x^2+y^2\leq 4\}$ and
$C=\{(x,y)\in Z\times Z:(x-2)^2+(y-2)^2\leq 4\}$

If the total number of relation from $A\cap B$ to $A\cap B$ is 2^p, then the value of p is **[JEE Main 2021]**

(a) 16 (b) 25
(c) 49 (d) 9

6. The locus of a point, which moves such that the sum of squares of its distances from the points (0, 0), (1, 0), (0, 1)(1, 1) is 18 units, is a circle of diameter (d) Then, d^2 is equal to **[JEE Main 2021]**

7. A circle C touches the line $x=2y$ at the point (2,1) and intersects the circle $C_1:x^2+y^2+2y-5=0$ at two points P and Q such that PQ is a diameter of C_1. Then the diameter of C is **[JEE Main 2021]**

(a) $7\sqrt{5}$ (b) 15
(c) 285 (d) $4\sqrt{15}$

8. Two tangents are drawn from the point $P(-1,1)$ to the circle $x^2+y^2-2x-6y+6=0$. If these tangents touch the circle at points A and B, and if D is a point on the circle such that length of the segments AB and AD are equal, then the area of the $\Delta\, ABD$ is equal to **[JEE Main 2021]**

(a) 2 (b) $(3\sqrt{2}+2)$
(c) 4 (d) $3(\sqrt{2}-1)$

9. Let P and Q be two distinct points on a circle which has center at $C(2,3)$ and which passes through origin O. If OC is perpendicular to both the line segments CP and CQ, then the set $\{P,Q\}$ is equal to **[JEE Main 2021]**

(a) $\{(4, 0), (0, 6)\}$
(b) $\{(2+2\sqrt{2},3-\sqrt{3}),(2-2\sqrt{2},3+\sqrt{5})\}$
(c) $\{(2+2\sqrt{2},3+\sqrt{5}),(2-2\sqrt{2},3-\sqrt{5})\}$
(d) $\{(-1, 5), (5, 1)\}$

10. Let $A=\{(x,y)\in R\times R \mid 2x^2+2y^2-2x-2y=1\}$,

$B=\{(x, y)\in R\times R \mid 4x^2+4y^2-16y+7=0\}$

$C=\{(x,y)\in R\times R \mid x^2+y^2-4x-2y+5\le r^2\}$

Then the minimum value of $|r|$ such that $A\cup B\subseteq C$ is equal to **[JEE Main 2021]**

(a) $\frac{3+\sqrt{10}}{2}$ (b) $\frac{2+\sqrt{10}}{2}$
(c) $\frac{3+2\sqrt{5}}{2}$ (d) $1+\sqrt{5}$

11. Consider a circle C which touches the Y-axis at $(0, 6)$ and cuts off an intercept $6\sqrt{5}$ on the X-axis. Then the radius of the circle C is equal to **[JEE Main 2021]**

(a) $\sqrt{53}$ (b) 9
(c) 8 (d) $\sqrt{82}$

12. Let the circle $S: 36x^2+36y^2-108x+120y+C=0$ be such that it neither intersects nor touches the coordinate axes. If the point of intersection of the lines $x-2y=4$ and $2x-y=5$ lies inside the circle S, then **[JEE Main 2021]**

(a) $\frac{25}{9}<C<\frac{13}{3}$ (b) $100<C<165$
(c) $81<C<156$ (d) $100<C<156$

13. Let r_1 and r_2 be the radii of the largest and smallest circles, respectively, which pass through the point $(-4, 1)$ and having their centres on the circumference of the circle $x^2+y^2+2x+4y-4=0$. If $\frac{r_1}{r_2}=a+b\sqrt{2}$, then $a+b$ is equal to **[JEE Main 2021]**

(a) 3 (b) 11
(c) 5 (d) 7

14. Choose the correct statement about two circles whose equations are given below.

$x^2+y^2-10x-10y+41=0$
$x^2+y^2-22x-10y+137=0$ **[JEE Main 2021]**

(a) circles have same centre
(b) circles have no meeting point
(c) circles have only one meeting point
(d) circles have two meeting points

15. For the four circles M, N, O and P, following four equations are given

Circle $M: x^2+y^2=1$
Circle $N: x^2+y^2-2x=0$
Circle $O: x^2+y^2-2x-2y+1=0$
Circle $P: x^2+y^2-2y=0$

If the centre of circle M is joined with centre of the circle N, further centre of circle N is joined with centre of the circle O, centre of circle O is joined with the centre of circle P and lastly, centre of circle P is joined with centre of circle M, then these lines form the sides of a **[JEE Main 2021]**

(a) rhombus (b) square
(c) rectangle (d) parallelogram

16. Let $S_1\Rightarrow x^2+y^2=9$ and $S_2\Rightarrow(x-2)^2+y^2=1$. Then the locus of center of a variable circle S which touches S_1 internally and S_2 externally always passes through the points **[JEE Main 2021]**

(a) $(0, \pm\sqrt{3})$ (b) $\left(\frac{1}{2}, \pm\frac{\sqrt{5}}{2}\right)$
(c) $\left(2, \pm\frac{3}{2}\right)$ (d) $(1, \pm 2)$

17. The line $2x-y+1=0$ is a tangent to the circle at the point $(2, 5)$ and the centre of the circle lies on $x-2y=4$. Then, the radius of the circle is **[JEE Main 2021]**

(a) $3\sqrt{5}$ (b) $5\sqrt{3}$
(c) $5\sqrt{4}$ (d) $4\sqrt{5}$

18. Choose the incorrect statement about the two circles whose equations are given below

$x^2+y^2-10x-10y+41=0$ and $x^2+y^2-16x-10y+80=0$ **[JEE Main 2021]**

(a) Distance between two centres is the average of radii of both the circles.
(b) Both circles' centres lie inside region of one another.
(c) Both circles pass through the centre of each other.
(d) Circles have two intersection points.

19. The minimum distance between any two points P_1 and P_2 while considering point P_1 on one circle and point P_2 on the other circle for the given circles equations

$x^2+y^2-10x-10y+41=0\, x^2+y^2-24x-10y+160=0$ is .... **[JEE Main 2021]**

20. Let $ABCD$ be a square of side of unit length. Let a circle C_1 centred at A with unit radius is drawn. Another circle C_2, which touches C_1 and the lines AD and AB are tangent to it, is also drawn. Let a tangent line from the point C to the circle C_2 meet the side AB at E. If the length of EB is $\alpha+\sqrt{3}\beta$, where α, β are integers, then $\alpha+\beta$ is equal to .... **[JEE Main 2021]**

21. Let the lengths of intercepts on X-axis and Y-axis made by the circle $x^2+y^2+ax+2ay+c=0, (a<0)$ be $2\sqrt{2}$ and $2\sqrt{5}$, respectively. Then, the shortest distance from origin to a tangent to this circle which is perpendicular to the line $x+2y=0$, is equal to **[JEE Main 2021]**

(a) $\sqrt{11}$ (b) $\sqrt{7}$
(c) $\sqrt{6}$ (d) $\sqrt{10}$

22. If the locus of the mid-point of the line segment from the point (3, 2) to a point on the circle, $x^2+y^2=1$ is a circle of radius r, then r is equal to **[JEE Main 2021]**

(a) 1 (b) $\frac{1}{2}$
(c) $\frac{1}{3}$ (d) $\frac{1}{4}$

23. Let $A(1, 4)$ and $B(1, -5)$ be two points. Let P be a point on the circle $(x-1)^2+(y-1)^2=1$, such that $(PA)^2+(PB)^2$ have maximum value, then the points P, A and B lie on **[JEE Main 2021]**

(a) a straight line (b) a hyperbola
(c) an ellipse (d) a parabola

24. In the circle given below, let $OA = 1$ unit, $OB = 13$ unit and $PQ \perp OB$. Then, the area of the triangle PQB (in square units) is **[JEE Main 2021]**

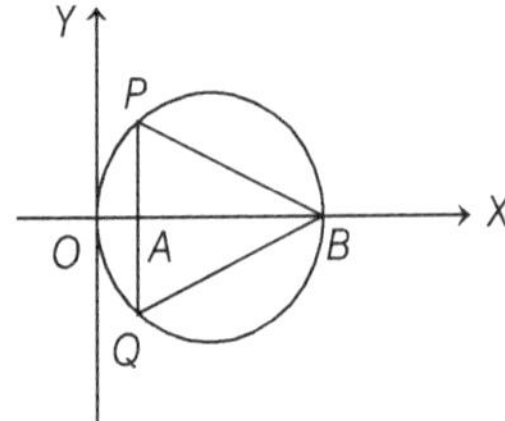

(a) $24\sqrt{2}$ (b) $24\sqrt{3}$
(c) $26\sqrt{3}$ (d) $26\sqrt{2}$

25. Let a point P be such that its distance from the point (5, 0) is thrice the distance of P from the point (– 5, 0). If the locus of the point P is a circle of radius r, then $4r^2$ is equal to .... **[JEE Main 2021]**

26. If one of the diameters of the circle $x^2+y^2-2x-6y+6=0$ is a chord of another circle 'C', whose centre is at (2, 1), then its radius is .... **[JEE Main 2021]**

27. For which of the following curves, the line $x+\sqrt{3}y=2\sqrt{3}$ is the tangent at the point $\left(\frac{3\sqrt{3}}{2}, \frac{1}{2}\right)$? **[JEE Main 2021]**

(a) $x^2+y^2=7$ (b) $y^2=\frac{1}{6\sqrt{3}}x$
(c) $2x^2-18y^2=9$ (d) $x^2+9y^2=9$

28. The number of integral values of k for which the line, $3x+4y=k$ intersects the circle, $x^2+y^2-2x-4y+4=0$ at two distinct points is...... **[JEE Main 2020]**

29. The diameter of the circle, whose centre lies on the line $x+y=2$ in the first quadrant and which touches both the lines $x=3$ and $y=2$, is .... **[JEE Main 2020]**

30. Let the latus rectum of the parabola $y^2=4x$ be the common chord to the circles C_1 and C_2 each of them having radius $2\sqrt{5}$. Then, the distance between the centres of the circles C_1 and C_2 is **[JEE Main 2020]**

(a) 8 (b) $4\sqrt{5}$
(c) $8\sqrt{5}$ (d) 12

31. Let PQ be a diameter of the circle $x^2+y^2=9$. If α and β are the lengths of the perpendiculars from P and Q on the straight line, $x+y=2$ respectively, then the maximum value of $\alpha\beta$ is .... **[JEE Main 2020]**

32. The circle passing through the intersection of the circles, $x^2+y^2-6x=0$ and $x^2+y^2-4y=0$, having its centre on the line, $2x-3y+12=0$, also passes through the point **[JEE Main 2020]**

(a) $(-1, 3)$ (b) $(-3, 1)$
(c) $(1, -3)$ (d) $(-3, 6)$

33. If the length of the chord of the circle, $x^2+y^2=r^2 (r>0)$ along the line, $y-2x=3$ is r, then r^2 is equal to **[JEE Main 2020]**

(a) $\frac{9}{5}$ (b) 12
(c) $\frac{24}{5}$ (d) $\frac{12}{5}$

34. Let the tangents drawn from the origin to the circle, $x^2+y^2-8x-4y+16=0$ touch it at the points A and B. The $(AB)^2$ is equal to **[JEE Main 2020]**

(a) $\frac{56}{5}$ (b) $\frac{52}{5}$
(c) $\frac{64}{5}$ (d) $\frac{32}{5}$

35. If a line, $y=mx+c$ is a tangent to the circle, $(x-3)^2+y^2=1$ and it is perpendicular to a line L_1, where L_1 is the tangent to the circle, $x^2+y^2=1$ at the point $\left(\frac{1}{\sqrt{2}}, \frac{1}{\sqrt{2}}\right)$; then **[JEE Main 2020]**

(a) $c^2+7c+6=0$
(b) $c^2-6c+7=0$
(c) $c^2-7c+6=0$
(d) $c^2+6c+7=0$

36. If the curves, $x^2-6x+y^2+8=0$ and $x^2-8y+y^2+16-k=0, (k>0)$ touch each other at a point, then the largest value of k is .... **[JEE Main 2020]**

37. Let O be the centre of the circle $x^2+y^2=r^2$, where $r>\frac{\sqrt{5}}{2}$. Suppose PQ is a chord of this circle and the equation of the line passing through P and Q is $2x+4y=5$. If the centre of the circumcircle of the triangle OPQ lies on the line $x+2y=4$, then the value of r is .... **[JEE Advanced 2020]**

38. The sum of the squares of the lengths of the chords intercepted on the circle, $x^2+y^2=16$, by the lines, $x+y=n, n\in N$, where N is the set of all natural numbers, is **[JEE Main 2019]**

(a) 320 (b) 105
(c) 160 (d) 210

39. The tangent and the normal lines at the point $(\sqrt{3},1)$ to the circle $x^2+y^2=4$ and the X-axis form a triangle. The area of this triangle (in square units) is **[JEE Main 2019]**

(a) $\frac{1}{3}$ (b) $\frac{4}{\sqrt{3}}$
(c) $\frac{2}{\sqrt{3}}$ (d) $\frac{1}{\sqrt{3}}$

40. If a tangent to the circle $x^2+y^2=1$ intersects the coordinate axes at distinct points P and Q, then the locus of the mid-point of PQ is **[JEE Main 2019]**

(a) $x^2+y^2-2x^2y^2=0$ (b) $x^2+y^2-2xy=0$
(c) $x^2+y^2-4x^2y^2=0$ (d) $x^2+y^2-16x^2y^2=0$

41. A rectangle is inscribed in a circle with a diameter lying along the line $3y=x+7$. If the two adjacent vertices of the rectangle are (-8, 5) and (6, 5), then the area of the rectangle (in sq units) is **[JEE Main 2019]**

(a) 72 (b) 84
(c) 98 (d) 56

42. The common tangent to the circles $x^2+y^2=4$ and $x^2+y^2+6x+8y-24=0$ also passes through the point **[JEE Main 2019]**

(a) $(6,-2)$ (b) $(4,-2)$
(c) $(-6,4)$ (d) $(-4,6)$

43. If the circles $x^2+y^2+5Kx+2y+K=0$ and $2(x^2+y^2)+2Kx+3y-1=0$, $(K\in R)$, intersect at the points P and Q, then the line $4x+5y-K=0$ passes through P and Q, for **[JEE Main 2019]**

(a) no values of K (b) exactly one value of K
(c) exactly two values of K (d) infinitely many values of K

44. The line $x=y$ touches a circle at the point (1, 1). If the circle also passes through the point $(1,-3)$, then its radius is **[JEE Main 2019]**

(a) $3\sqrt{2}$ (b) $2\sqrt{2}$
(c) 2 (d) 3

45. The locus of the centres of the circles, which touch the circle, $x^2+y^2=1$ externally, also touch the Y-axis and lie in the first quadrant, is **[JEE Main 2019]**

(a) $y=\sqrt{1+2x}, x\geq 0$ (b) $y=\sqrt{1+4x}, x\geq 0$
(c) $x=\sqrt{1+2y}, y\geq 0$ (d) $x=\sqrt{1+4y}, y\geq 0$

46. If the angle of intersection at a point where the two circles with radii 5 cm and 12 cm intersect is $90°$, then the length (in cm) of their common chord is **[JEE Main 2019]**

(a) $\frac{13}{5}$ (b) $\frac{120}{13}$
(c) $\frac{60}{13}$ (d) $\frac{13}{2}$

47. A circle touching the X-axis at (3, 0) and making a intercept of length 8 on the Y-axis passes through the point **[JEE Main 2019]**

(a) (3, 10) (b) (3, 5)
(c) (2, 3) (d) (1, 5)

48. Three circles of radii $a, b, c (a<b<c)$ touch each other externally. If they have X-axis as a common tangent, then **[JEE Main 2019]**

(a) a, b, c are in AP (b) $\frac{1}{\sqrt{a}}=\frac{1}{\sqrt{b}}+\frac{1}{\sqrt{c}}$
(c) $\sqrt{a}, \sqrt{b}, \sqrt{c}$ are in AP (d) $\frac{1}{\sqrt{b}}=\frac{1}{\sqrt{a}}+\frac{1}{\sqrt{c}}$

49. Equation of a common tangent to the circle, $x^2+y^2-6x=0$ and the parabola, $y^2=4x$, is **[JEE Main 2019]**

(a) $\sqrt{3}y=3x+1$ (b) $2\sqrt{3}y=12x+1$
(c) $\sqrt{3}y=x+3$ (d) $2\sqrt{3}y=-x-12$

50. If the circles $x^2+y^2-16x-20y+164=r^2$ and $(x-4)^2+(y-7)^2=36$ intersect at two distinct points, then **[JEE Main 2019]**

(a) $0<r<1$ (b) $r>11$
(c) $1<r<11$ (d) $r=11$

51. If a circle C passing through the point (4, 0) touches the circle $x^2+y^2+4x-6y=12$ externally at the point $(1,-1)$, then the radius of C is **[JEE Main 2019]**

(a) 5 (b) $2\sqrt{5}$
(c) $\sqrt{57}$ (d) 4

52. The straight line $x+2y=1$ meets the coordinate axes at A and B. A circle is drawn through A, B and the origin. Then, the sum of perpendicular distances from A and B on the tangent to the circle at the origin is **[JEE Main 2019]**

(a) $2\sqrt{5}$ (b) $\frac{\sqrt{5}}{4}$
(c) $4\sqrt{5}$ (d) $\frac{\sqrt{5}}{2}$

53. A square is inscribed in the circle $x^2+y^2-6x+8y-103=0$ with its sides parallel to the coordinate axes. Then, the distance of the vertex of this square which is nearest to the origin is **[JEE Main 2019]**

(a) 6 (b) 13
(c) $\sqrt{41}$ (d) $\sqrt{137}$

54. Two circles with equal radii are intersecting at the points (0, 1) and (0, –1). The tangent at the point (0,1) to one of the circles passes through the centre of the other circle. Then, the distance between the centres of these circles is **[JEE Main 2019]**

(a) $\sqrt{2}$ (b) $2\sqrt{2}$
(c) 1 (d) 2

55. A circle cuts a chord of length $4a$ on the X-axis and passes through a point on the Y-axis, distant $2b$ from the origin. Then, the locus of the centre of this circle, is **[JEE Main 2019]**

(a) a parabola (b) an ellipse
(c) a straight line (d) a hyperbola

56. Let C_1 and C_2 be the centres of the circles $x^2+y^2-2x-2y-2=0$ and $x^2+y^2-6x-6y+14=0$ respectively. If P and Q are the points of intersection of these circles, then the area (in sq units) of the quadrilateral PC_1QC_2 is **[JEE Main 2019]**

(a) 8 (b) 4
(c) 6 (d) 9

57. If a variable line, $3x+4y-\lambda=0$ is such that the two circles

$$x^2+y^2-2x-2y+1=0$$

and

$$x^2+y^2-18x-2y+78=0$$

are on its opposite sides, then the set of all values of λ is the interval **[JEE Main 2019]**

(a) [13, 23] (b) (2, 17)
(c) [12, 21] (d) (23, 31)

58. If a circle of radius R passes through the origin O and intersects the coordinate axes at A and B, then the locus of the foot of perpendicular from O on AB is **[JEE Main 2019]**

(a) $(x^2+y^2)^2 = 4R^2x^2y^2$
(b) $(x^2+y^2)^3 = 4R^2x^2y^2$
(c) $(x^2+y^2)(x+y) = R^2xy$
(d) $(x^2+y^2)^2 = 4Rx^2y^2$

59. A line $y=mx+1$ intersects the circle $(x-3)^2+(y+2)^2=25$ at the points P and Q. If the midpoint of the line segment PQ has x-coordinate $-\frac{3}{5}$, then which one of the following options is correct? **[JEE Advanced 2019]**

(a) $6 \le m < 8$ (b) $-3 \le m < -1$
(c) $4 \le m < 6$ (d) $2 \le m < 4$

60. Let the point B be the reflection of the point $A(2,3)$ with respect to the line $8x-6y-23=0$. Let Γ_A and Γ_B be circles of radii 2 and 1 with centres A and B respectively. Let T be a common tangent to the circles Γ_A and Γ_B such that both the circles are on the same side of T. If C is the point of intersection of T and the line passing through A and B, then the length of the line segment AC is .... **[JEE Advanced 2019]**

Paragraph (Q. Nos. 61-62)

Let S be the circle in the XY-plane defined by the equation $x^2+y^2=4$.

(There are two questions based on Paragraph "X", the question given below is one of them) **[JEE Advanced 2018]**

61. Let E_1E_2 and F_1F_2 be the chords of S passing through the point P_0 (1, 1) and parallel to the X-axis and the Y-axis, respectively. Let G_1G_2 be the chord of S passing through P_0 and having slope –1. Let the tangents to S at E_1 and E_2 meet at E_3, then tangents to S at F_1 and F_2 meet at F_3, and the tangents to S at G_1 and G_2 meet at G_3. Then, the points E_3, F_3 and G_3 lie on the curve

(a) $x+y=4$ (b) $(x-4)^2+(y-4)^2=16$
(c) $(x-4)(y-4)=4$ (d) $xy=4$

62. Let P be a point on the circle S with both coordinates being positive. Let the tangent to S at P intersect the coordinate axes at the points M and N. Then, the mid-point of the line segment MN must lie on the curve

(a) $(x+y)^2=3xy$ (b) $x^{2/3}+y^{2/3}=2^{4/3}$
(c) $x^2+y^2=2xy$ (d) $x^2+y^2=x^2y^2$

63. Let T be the line passing through the points $P(-2,7)$ and $Q(2,-5)$. Let F_1 be the set of all pairs of circles (S_1, S_2) such that T is tangent to S_1 at P and tangent to S_2 at Q, and also such that S_1 and S_2 touch each other at a point, say M. Let E_1 be the set representing the locus of M as the pair (S_1, S_2) varies in F_1. Let the set of all straight line segments joining a pair of distinct points of E_1 and passing through the point $R(1,1)$ be F_2. Let E_2 be the set of the mid-points of the line segments in the set F_2. Then, which of the following statement(s) is (are) TRUE? **[JEE Advanced 2018]**

(a) The point $(-2, 7)$ lies in E_1
(b) The point $\left(\frac{4}{5}, \frac{7}{5}\right)$ does NOT lie in E_2
(c) The point $\left(\frac{1}{2}, 1\right)$ lies in E_2
(d) The point $\left(0, \frac{3}{2}\right)$ does NOT lie in E_1

Answers

1. (165)	**2.** (18)	**3.** (61)	**4.** (40)	**5.** (b)	**6.** (16)	**7.** (a)	**8.** (c)	**9.** (d)	**10.** (c)
11. (b)	**12.** (d)	**13.** (c)	**14.** (c)	**15.** (b)	**16.** (c)	**17.** (a)	**18.** (b)	**19.** (1)	**20.** (1)
21. (c)	**22.** (b)	**23.** (a)	**24.** (b)	**25.** (56.25)	**26.** (3)	**27.** (d)	**28.** (9)	**29.** (3.00)	**30.** (a)
31. (7)	**32.** (d)	**33.** (d)	**34.** (c)	**35.** (d)	**36.** (36)	**37.** (2)	**38.** (d)	**39.** (c)	**40.** (c)
41. (b)	**42.** (a)	**43.** (a)	**44.** (b)	**45.** (a)	**46.** (b)	**47.** (a)	**48.** (b)	**49.** (c)	**50.** (c)
51. (a)	**52.** (d)	**53.** (c)	**54.** (d)	**55.** (a)	**56.** (b)	**57.** (c)	**58.** (b)	**59.** (d)	**60.** (10)
61. (a)	**62.** (d)	**63.** (a,d)							

Parabola

1. Consider the parabola with vertex $\left(\frac{1}{2}, \frac{3}{4}\right)$ and the directrix $y = \frac{1}{2}$. Let P be the point where the parabola meets the line $x = -\frac{1}{2}$. If the normal to the parabola at P intersects the parabola again at the point Q, then $(PQ)^2$ is equal to **[JEE Main 2021]**

(a) $\frac{75}{8}$ (b) $\frac{125}{16}$
(c) $\frac{25}{2}$ (d) $\frac{15}{2}$

2. The length of the latus rectum of a parabola, whose vertex and focus are on the positive X-axis at a distance R and $S(>R)$ respectively from the origin, is **[JEE Main 2021]**

(a) $4(S + R)$ (b) $2(S - R)$
(c) $4(S - R)$ (d) $2(S + R)$

3. A tangent line L is drawn at the point $(2, -4)$ on the parabola $y^2 = 8x$. If the line L is also tangent to the circle $x^2 + y^2 = a$, then a is equal to **[JEE Main 2021]**

4. A tangent and a normal are drawn at the point $P(2, -4)$ on the parabola $y^2 = 8x$, which meet the directrix of the parabola at the points A and B respectively. If $Q(a, b)$ is a point such that $AQBP$ is a square, then $2a + b$ is equal to **[JEE Main 2021]**

(a) -16 (b) -18
(c) -12 (d) -20

5. If two tangents drawn from a point P to the parabola $y^2 = 16(x - 3)$ are at right angles, then the locus of point P is **[JEE Main 2021]**

(a) $x + 3 = 0$ (b) $x + 1 = 0$
(c) $x + 2 = 0$ (d) $x + 4 = 0$

6. If a line along a chord of the circle $4x^2 + 4y^2 + 120x + 675 = 0$, passes through the point $(-30, 0)$ and is tangent to the parabola $y^2 = 30x$, then the length of this chord is **[JEE Main 2021]**

(a) 5 (b) 7
(c) $5\sqrt{3}$ (d) $3\sqrt{5}$

7. Let a parabola P be such that its vertex and focus lie on the positive X-axis at a distance 2 and 4 units from the origin, respectively. If tangents are drawn from $O(0, 0)$ to the parabola P which meet P at S and R, then the area (in sq. units) of ΔSOR is equal to **[JEE Main 2021]**

(a) $16\sqrt{2}$ (b) 16
(c) 32 (d) $8\sqrt{2}$

8. The equation of a circle is $\text{Re}(z^2) + 2[\text{Im}(z)]^2 + 2\text{Re}(z) = 0$. where, $z = x + iy$. A line which passes through the center of the given circle and the vertex of the parabola, $x^2 - 6x - y + 13 = 0$, has y-intercept equal to .... **[JEE Main 2021]**

9. Let the tangent to the parabola $S: y^2 = 2x$ at the point $P(2, 2)$ meet the X-axis at Q and normal at it meet the parabola S at the point R. Then, the area (in square units) of ΔPQR is equal to **[JEE Main 2021]**

(a) $\frac{25}{2}$ (b) $\frac{35}{2}$ (c) $\frac{15}{2}$ (d) 25

10. Let $y = mx + c, m > 0$ be the focal chord of $y^2 = -64x$, which is tangent to $(x + 10)^2 + y^2 = 4$. Then, the value of $4\sqrt{2}(m + c)$ is equal to .... **[JEE Main 2021]**

11. Let P be a variable point on the parabola $y = 4x^2 + 1$. Then, the locus of the mid point of the point P and the foot of the perpendicular drawn from the point P to the line $y = x$ is **[JEE Main 2021]**

(a) $(3x - y)^2 + (x - 3y) + 2 = 0$
(b) $2(3x - y)^2 + (x - 3y) + 2 = 0$
(c) $(3x - y)^2 + 2(x - 3y) + 2 = 0$
(d) $2(x - 3y)^2 + (3x - y) + 2 = 0$

12. If the point on the curve $y^2 = 6x$, nearest to the point $\left(3, \frac{3}{2}\right)$ is (α, β), then $2(\alpha + \beta)$ is equal to **[JEE Main 2021]**

13. If the three normals drawn to the parabola, $y^2 = 2x$ pass through the point $(a, 0), a \neq 0$, then a must be greater than **[JEE Main 2021]**

(a) $\frac{1}{2}$ (b) $-\frac{1}{2}$ (c) -1 (d) 1

14. Let C be the locus of the mirror image of a point on the parabola $y^2 = 4x$ with respect to the line $y = x$. Then, the equation of tangent to C at $P(2,1)$ is **[JEE Main 2021]**

(a) $x - y = 1$
(b) $2x + y = 5$
(c) $x + 3y = 5$
(d) $x + 2y = 5$

15. A line is a common tangent to the circle $(x-3)^2 + y^2 = 9$ and the parabola $y^2 = 4x$. If the two points of contact (a, b) and (c, d) are distinct and lie in the first quadrant, then $2(a+c)$ is equal to .... **[JEE Main 2021]**

16. A tangent is drawn to the parabola $y^2 = 6x$, which is perpendicular to the line $2x + y = 1$. Which of the following points does not lie on it? **[JEE Main 2021]**

(a) $(-6, 0)$
(b) $(4, 5)$
(c) $(5, 4)$
(d) $(0, 3)$

17. If the curve $y = ax^2 + bx + c$, $x \in R$, passes through the point $(1,2)$ and the tangent line to this curve at origin is $y = x$, then the possible values of a, b, c are **[JEE Main 2021]**

(a) $a = \frac{1}{2}, b = \frac{1}{2}, c = 1$
(b) $a = 1, b = 0, c = 1$
(c) $a = 1, b = 1, c = 0$
(d) $a = -1, b = 1, c = 1$

18. If P is a point on the parabola $y = x^2 + 4$ which is closest to the straight line $y = 4x - 1$, then the coordinates of P are **[JEE Main 2021]**

(a) $(3, 13)$
(b) $(1, 5)$
(c) $(-2, 8)$
(d) $(2, 8)$

19. The locus of the mid-point of the line segment joining the focus of the parabola $y^2 = 4ax$ to a moving point of the parabola, is another parabola whose directrix is **[JEE Main 2021]**

(a) $x = a$
(b) $x = -\frac{a}{2}$
(c) $x = 0$
(d) $x = \frac{a}{2}$

20. Let E denote the parabola $y^2 = 8x$. Let $P = (-2, 4)$, and let Q and Q' be two distinct points on E such that the lines PQ and PQ' are tangents to E. Let F be the focus of E. Then, which of the following statements is (are) TRUE ? **[JEE Advanced 2021]**

(a) The ΔPFQ is a right-angled triangle.
(b) The $\Delta QPQ'$ is a right-angled triangle.
(c) The distance between P and F is $5\sqrt{2}$.
(d) F lies on the line joining Q and Q'.

Question Stem for Question Nos. 21 and 22

Consider the region $R = \{(x, y) \in R \times R : x \geq 0$ and $y^2 \leq 4 - x\}$. Let F be the family of all circles that are contained in R and have centers on the X-axis. Let C be the circle that has largest radius among the circles in F. Let (α, β) be a point, where the circle C meets the curve $y^2 = 4 - x$. **[JEE Advanced 2021]**

21. The radius of the circle C is _____ .

22. The value of α is _____ .

23. The area (in sq. units) of an equilateral triangle inscribed in the parabola $y^2 = 8x$, with one of its vertices on the vertex of this parabola, is **[JEE Main 2020]**

(a) $64\sqrt{3}$
(b) $256\sqrt{3}$
(c) $192\sqrt{3}$
(d) $128\sqrt{3}$

24. Let P be a point on the parabola, $y^2 = 12x$ and N be the foot of the perpendicular drawn from P on the axis of the parabol(a) A line is now drawn through the mid-point M and PN, parallel to its axis which meets the parabola at Q. If the y-intercept of the line NQ is $\frac{4}{3}$, then **[JEE Main 2020]**

(a) $PN = 4$
(b) $MQ = \frac{1}{3}$
(c) $MQ = \frac{1}{4}$
(d) $PN = 3$

25. If the common tangent of the parabolas, $y^2 = 4x$ and $x^2 = 4y$ also touches the circle, $x^2 + y^2 = c^2$, then c is equal to **[JEE Main 2020]**

(a) $\frac{1}{\sqrt{2}}$
(b) $\frac{1}{4}$
(c) $\frac{1}{2}$
(d) $\frac{1}{2\sqrt{2}}$

26. If the lines $x + y = a$ and $x - y = b$ touch the curve $y = x^2 - 3x + 2$ at the points where the curve intersects the X-axis, then $\frac{a}{b}$ is equal to .... **[JEE Main 2020]**

27. Let L_1 be a tangent to the parabola $y^2 = 4(x+1)$ and L_2 be a tangent to the parabola $y^2 = 8(x+2)$ such that L_1 and L_2 intersect at right angles. Then, L_1 and L_2 meet on the straight line **[JEE Main 2020]**

(a) $x + 3 = 0$
(b) $2x + 1 = 0$
(c) $x + 2 = 0$
(d) $x + 2y = 0$

28. The centre of the circle passing through the point $(0, 1)$ and touching the parabola $y = x^2$ at the point $(2, 4)$ is **[JEE Main 2020]**

(a) $\left(\frac{-53}{10}, \frac{16}{5}\right)$
(b) $\left(\frac{6}{5}, \frac{53}{10}\right)$
(c) $\left(\frac{3}{10}, \frac{16}{5}\right)$
(d) $\left(-\frac{16}{5}, \frac{53}{10}\right)$

29. If $y = mx + 4$ is a tangent to both the parabolas, $y^2 = 4x$ and $x^2 = 2by$, then b is equal to **[JEE Main 2020]**

(a) -32 (b) -128 (c) -64 (d) 128

30. The locus of a point which divides the line segment joining the point $(0, -1)$ and a point on the parabola, $x^2 = 4y$, internally in the ratio $1 : 2$, is **[JEE Main 2020]**

(a) $4x^2 - 3y = 2$
(b) $x^2 - 3y = 2$
(c) $9x^2 - 12y = 8$
(d) $9x^2 - 3y = 2$

31. Let a line $y = mx (m > 0)$ intersect the parabola, $y^2 = x$ at a point P, other than the origin. Let the tangent to it at P meet the X-axis at the point Q. If area $(\Delta OPQ) = 4$ sq. units, then m is equal to .... **[JEE Main 2020]**

32. If one end of a focal chord AB of the parabola $y^2 = 8x$ is at $A\left(\frac{1}{2}, -2\right)$, then the equation of the tangent to it at B is **[JEE Main 2020]**

(a) $x - 2y + 8 = 0$ (b) $x + 2y + 8 = 0$
(c) $2x + y - 24 = 0$ (d) $2x - y - 24 = 0$

33. The shortest distance between the line $y = x$ and curve $y^2 = x - 2$ is **[JEE Main 2019]**

(a) 2 (b) $\frac{7}{8}$
(c) $\frac{7}{4\sqrt{2}}$ (d) $\frac{11}{4\sqrt{2}}$

34. The tangent to the parabola $y^2 = 4x$ at the point where it intersects the circle $x^2 + y^2 = 5$ in the first quadrant, passes through the point **[JEE Main 2019]**

(a) $\left(\frac{1}{4}, \frac{3}{4}\right)$ (b) $\left(\frac{3}{4}, \frac{7}{4}\right)$
(c) $\left(-\frac{1}{3}, \frac{4}{3}\right)$ (d) $\left(-\frac{1}{4}, \frac{1}{2}\right)$

35. If one end of a focal chord of the parabola, $y^2 = 16x$ is at (1, 4), then the length of this focal chord is **[JEE Main 2019]**

(a) 22 (b) 25 (c) 24 (d) 20

36. The area (in sq units) of the smaller of the two circles that touch the parabola, $y^2 = 4x$ at the point (1, 2) and the X-axis is **[JEE Main 2019]**

(a) $8\pi(3 - 2\sqrt{2})$ (b) $4\pi(3 + \sqrt{2})$
(c) $8\pi(2 - \sqrt{2})$ (d) $4\pi(2 - \sqrt{2})$

37. If the line $ax + y = c$, touches both the curves $x^2 + y^2 = 1$ and $y^2 = 4\sqrt{2}x$, then $|c|$ is equal to **[JEE Main 2019]**

(a) $\frac{1}{\sqrt{2}}$ (b) 2 (c) $\sqrt{2}$ (d) $\frac{1}{2}$

38. The tangents to the curve $y = (x - 2)^2 - 1$ at its points of intersection with the line $x - y = 3$, intersect at the point **[JEE Main 2019]**

(a) $\left(\frac{5}{2}, 1\right)$ (b) $\left(-\frac{5}{2}, -1\right)$
(c) $\left(\frac{5}{2}, -1\right)$ (d) $\left(-\frac{5}{2}, 1\right)$

39. Axis of a parabola lies along X-axis. If its vertex and focus are at distances 2 and 4 respectively from the origin, on the positive X-axis, then which of the following points does not lie on it? **[JEE Main 2019]**

(a) (4, −4) (b) $(6, 4\sqrt{2})$
(c) (8, 6) (d) $(5, 2\sqrt{6})$

40. Let $A(4, -4)$ and $B(9, 6)$ be points on the parabola, $y^2 = 4x$. Let C be chosen on the arc AOB of the parabola, where O is the origin, such that the area of ΔACB is maximum. Then, the area (in sq. units) of ΔACB, is **[JEE Main 2019]**

(a) $31\frac{1}{4}$ (b) 32
(c) $31\frac{3}{4}$ (d) $30\frac{1}{2}$

41. If the parabolas $y^2 = 4b(x - c)$ and $y^2 = 8ax$ have a common normal, then which one of the following is a valid choice for the ordered triad (a, b, c)? **[JEE Main 2019]**

(a) $\left(\frac{1}{2}, 2, 0\right)$ (b) (1, 1, 0)
(c) (1, 1, 3) (d) $\left(\frac{1}{2}, 2, 3\right)$

42. The shortest distance between the point $\left(\frac{3}{2}, 0\right)$ and the curve $y = \sqrt{x}, (x > 0)$, is **[JEE Main 2019]**

(a) $\frac{3}{2}$ (b) $\frac{5}{4}$
(c) $\frac{\sqrt{3}}{2}$ (d) $\frac{\sqrt{5}}{2}$

43. The length of the chord of the parabola $x^2 = 4y$ having equation $x - \sqrt{2}y + 4\sqrt{2} = 0$ is **[JEE Main 2019]**

(a) $8\sqrt{2}$ (b) $2\sqrt{11}$
(c) $3\sqrt{2}$ (d) $6\sqrt{3}$

44. Equation of a common tangent to the parabola $y^2 = 4x$ and the hyperbola $xy = 2$ is **[JEE Main 2019]**

(a) $x + 2y + 4 = 0$
(b) $x - 2y + 4 = 0$
(c) $4x + 2y + 1 = 0$
(d) $x + y + 1 = 0$

45. If the area of the triangle whose one vertex is at the vertex of the parabola, $y^2 + 4(x - a^2) = 0$ and the other two vertices are the points of intersection of the parabola and Y-axis, is 250 sq units, then a value of 'a' is **[JEE Main 2019]**

(a) $5\sqrt{5}$ (b) 5
(c) $5(2^{1/3})$ (d) $(10)^{2/3}$

46. Let $P(4, -4)$ and $Q(9, 6)$ be two points on the parabola, $y^2 = 4x$ and let X be any point on the arc POQ of this parabola, where O is the vertex of this parabola, such that the area of ΔPXQ is maximum. Then, this maximum area (in sq units) is **[JEE Main 2019]**

(a) $\frac{125}{2}$ (b) $\frac{75}{2}$
(c) $\frac{625}{4}$ (d) $\frac{125}{4}$

47. The maximum area (in sq. units) of a rectangle having its base on the X-axis and its other two vertices on the parabola, $y = 12 - x^2$ such that the rectangle lies inside the parabola, is **[JEE Main 2019]**

(a) 36 (b) $20\sqrt{2}$ (c) 32 (d) $18\sqrt{3}$

48. If the tangent at (1, 7) to the curve $x^2 = y - 6$ touches the circle $x^2 + y^2 + 16x + 12y + c = 0$, then the value of c is **[JEE Main 2018]**

(a) 195 (b) 185 (c) 85 (d) 95

49. Tangent and normal are drawn at $P(16, 16)$ on the parabola $y^2 = 16x$, which intersect the axis of the parabola at A and B, respectively. If C is the centre of the circle through the points P, A and B and $\angle CPB = \theta$, then a value of $\tan\theta$ is **[JEE Main 2018]**

(a) $\frac{1}{2}$ (b) 2

(c) 3 (d) $\frac{4}{3}$

Answers

1. (b)	**2.** (c)	**3.** (2)	**4.** (a)	**5.** (b)	**6.** (d)	**7.** (b)	**8.** (1)	**9.** (a)	**10.** (34)
11. (b)	**12.** (9)	**13.** (d)	**14.** (a)	**15.** (9)	**16.** (c)	**17.** (c)	**18.** (d)	**19.** (c)	**20.** (a,b,d)
21. (1.50)	**22.** (2.00)	**23.** (c)	**24.** (c)	**25.** (a)	**26.** (0.5)	**27.** (a)	**28.** (d)	**29.** (b)	**30.** (c)
31. (0.5)	**32.** (a)	**33.** (c)	**34.** (b)	**35.** (b)	**36.** (a)	**37.** (c)	**38.** (c)	**39.** (c)	**40.** (a)
41. (c)	**42.** (d)	**43.** (d)	**44.** (a)	**45.** (b)	**46.** (d)	**47.** (c)	**48.** (d)	**49.** (b)	

Ellipse

1. Let θ be the acute angle between the tangents to the ellipse $\frac{x^2}{9} + \frac{y^2}{1} = 1$ and the circle $x^2 + y^2 = 3$ at their point of intersection in the first quadrant. Then, $\tan\theta$ is equal to **[JEE Main 2021]**

(a) $\frac{5}{2\sqrt{3}}$ (b) $\frac{2}{\sqrt{3}}$

(c) $\frac{4}{\sqrt{3}}$ (d) 2

2. The line $12x\cos\theta + 5y\sin\theta = 60$ is tangent to which of the following curves? **[JEE Main 2021]**

(a) $x^2 + y^2 = 169$

(b) $144x^2 + 25y^2 = 3600$

(c) $25x^2 + 12y^2 = 3600$

(d) $x^2 + y^2 = 60$

3. The locus of mid-points of the line segments joining (– 3, –5) and the points on the ellipse $\frac{x^2}{4} + \frac{y^2}{9} = 1$ is **[JEE Main 2021]**

(a) $9x^2 + 4y^2 + 18x + 8y + 145 = 0$

(b) $36x^2 + 16y^2 + 90x + 56y + 145 = 0$

(c) $36x^2 + 16y^2 + 108x + 80y + 145 = 0$

(d) $36x^2 + 16y^2 + 72x + 32y + 145 = 0$

4. If the minimum area of the triangle formed by a tangent to the ellipse $\frac{x^2}{b^2} + \frac{y^2}{4a^2} = 1$ and the coordinate axis is kab, then k is equal to **[JEE Main 2021]**

5. If $x^2 + 9y^2 - 4x + 3 = 0$, $x, y \in R$, then x and y respectively lie in the intervals **[JEE Main 2021]**

(a) $\left[-\frac{1}{3}, \frac{1}{3}\right]$ and $\left[-\frac{1}{3}, \frac{1}{3}\right]$ (b) $\left[-\frac{1}{3}, \frac{1}{3}\right]$ and [1, 3]

(c) [1, 3] and [1, 3] (d) [1, 3] and $\left[-\frac{1}{3}, \frac{1}{3}\right]$

6. On the ellipse $\frac{x^2}{8} + \frac{y^2}{4} = 1$. Let P be a point in the second quadrant such that the tangent at P to the ellipse is perpendicular to the line $x + 2y = 0$. Let S and S' be the foci of the ellipse and e be its eccentricity. If A is the area of the $\Delta SPS'$ then, the value of $(5 - e^2) \cdot A$ is **[JEE Main 2021]**

(a) 6 (b) 12 (c) 14 (d) 24

7. A ray of light through (2, 1) is reflected at a point P on the Y-axis and then passes through the point (5, 3). If this reflected ray is the directrix of an ellipse with eccentricity $\frac{1}{3}$ and the distance of the nearer focus from this directrix is $\frac{8}{\sqrt{53}}$, then the equation of the other directrix can be **[JEE Main 2021]**

(a) $11x + 7y + 8 = 0$ or $11x + 7y - 15 = 0$

(b) $11x - 7y - 8 = 0$ or $11x + 7y + 15 = 0$

(c) $2x - 7y + 29 = 0$ or $2x - 7y - 7 = 0$

(d) $2x - 7y - 39 = 0$ or $2x - 7y - 7 = 0$

8. Let E be an ellipse whose axes are parallel to the co-ordinates axes, having its center at (3, – 4), one focus at (4, – 4) and one vertex at (5, – 4). If $mx - y = 4, m > 0$ is a tangent to the ellipse E, then the value of $5m^2$ is equal to .... **[JEE Main 2021]**

9. Let an ellipse $E \Rightarrow \frac{x^2}{a^2}+\frac{y^2}{b^2}=1, a^2>b^2$, passes through $\left(\sqrt{\frac{3}{2}},1\right)$ and has eccentricity $\frac{1}{\sqrt{3}}$. If a circle, centered at focus $F(\alpha,0), \alpha>0$, of E and radius $\frac{2}{\sqrt{3}}$, intersects E at two points P and Q, then PQ^2 is equal to **[JEE Main 2021]**

(a) $\frac{8}{3}$ (b) $\frac{4}{3}$
(c) $\frac{16}{3}$ (d) 3

10. If a tangent to the ellipse $x^2+4y^2=4$ meets the tangents at the extremities of its major axis at B and C, then the circle with BC as diameter passes through the point **[JEE Main 2021]**

(a) $(\sqrt{3}, 0)$ (b) $(\sqrt{2}, 0)$
(c) (1, 1) (d) (−1, 1)

11. Let $E_1 : \frac{x^2}{a^2}+\frac{y^2}{b^2}=1, a>b$. Let E_2 be another ellipse such that it touches the end points of major axis of E_1 and the foci of E_2 are the end points of minor axis of E_1. If E_1 and E_2 have same eccentricities, then its value is **[JEE Main 2021]**

(a) $\frac{-1+\sqrt{5}}{2}$ (b) $\frac{-1+\sqrt{8}}{2}$
(c) $\frac{-1+\sqrt{3}}{2}$ (d) $\frac{-1+\sqrt{6}}{2}$

12. Let T be the tangent to the ellipse $E : x^2+4y^2=5$ at the point $P(1,1)$. If the area of the region bounded by the tangent T, ellipse E, lines $x=1$ and $x=\sqrt{5}$ is $\alpha\sqrt{5}+\beta+\gamma\cos^{-1}\left(\frac{1}{\sqrt{5}}\right)$, then $|\alpha+\beta+\gamma|$ is equal to .... **[JEE Main 2021]**

13. Let a tangent be drawn to the ellipse $\frac{x^2}{27}+y^2=1$ at $(3\sqrt{3}\cos\theta, \sin\theta)$, where $\theta \in \left(0,\frac{\pi}{2}\right)$. Then the value of θ, such that the sum of intercepts on axes made by this tangent is minimum is equal to **[JEE Main 2021]**

(a) $\frac{\pi}{8}$ (b) $\frac{\pi}{4}$
(c) $\frac{\pi}{6}$ (d) $\frac{\pi}{3}$

14. Let L be a tangent line to the parabola $y^2=4x-20$ at (6,2). If L is also a tangent to the ellipse $\frac{x^2}{2}+\frac{y}{b}=1$, then the value of b is equal to **[JEE Main 2021]**

(a) 11 (b) 14
(c) 16 (d) 20

15. If the point of intersections of the ellipse $\frac{x^2}{16}+\frac{y^2}{b^2}=1$ and the circle $x^2+y^2=4b, b>4$, lie on the curve $y^2=3x^2$, then b is equal to **[JEE Main 2021]**

(a) 12 (b) 5
(c) 6 (d) 10

16. If the curves, $\frac{x^2}{a}+\frac{y^2}{b}=1$ and $\frac{x^2}{c}+\frac{y^2}{d}=1$, intersect each other at an angle of 90°, then which of the following relations is true? **[JEE Main 2021]**

(a) $a+b=c+d$ (b) $a-b=c-d$
(c) $a-c=b+d$ (d) $ab=\frac{c+d}{a+b}$

17. Let L be a common tangent line to the curves $4x^2+9y^2=36$ and $(2x)^2+(2y)^2=31$. Then, the square of the slope of the line L is ______. **[JEE Main 2021]**

18. Let E be the ellipse $\frac{x^2}{16}+\frac{y^2}{9}=1$. For any three distinct points P, Q and Q' on E, let $M(P,Q)$ be the mid-point of the line segment joining P and Q, and $M(P,Q')$ be the mid-point of the line segment joining P and Q'. Then, the maximum possible value of the distance between $M(P,Q)$ and $M(P,Q')$, as P, Q and Q' vary on E, is ___ . **[JEE Advanced 2021]**

19. Let $\frac{x^2}{a^2}+\frac{y^2}{b^2}=1 (a>b)$ be a given ellipse, length of whose latus rectum is 10. If its eccentricity is the maximum value of the function, $\phi(t)=\frac{5}{12}+t-t^2$, then a^2+b^2 is equal to **[JEE Main 2020]**

(a) 145 (b) 116
(c) 126 (d) 135

20. Let $x=4$ be a directrix to an ellipse whose centre is at origin and its eccentricity is $\frac{1}{2}$.
If $P(1,\beta), \beta>0$ is a point on this ellipse, then the equation of the normal to it at P is **[JEE Main 2020]**

(a) $8x-2y=5$ (b) $4x-3y=2$
(c) $7x-4y=1$ (d) $4x-2y=1$

21. If the point P on the curve, $4x^2+5y^2=20$ is farthest from the point $Q(0,-4)$, then PQ^2 is equal to **[JEE Main 2020]**

(a) 29 (b) 21
(c) 48 (d) 36

22. If the coordinates of two points A and B are $(\sqrt{7},0)$ and $(-\sqrt{7},0)$ respectively and P is any point on the conic, $9x^2+16y^2=144$, then $PA+PB$ is equal to **[JEE Main 2020]**

(a) 16 (b) 8
(c) 6 (d) 9

23. Which of the following points lies on the locus of the foot of perpendicular drawn upon any tangent to the ellipse, $\frac{x^2}{4}+\frac{y^2}{2}=1$ from any of its foci? **[JEE Main 2020]**

(a) $(-2, \sqrt{3})$ (b) $(-1, \sqrt{2})$
(c) $(-1, \sqrt{3})$ (d) $(1, 2)$

24. If the normal at an end of a latus rectum of an ellipse passes through an extremity of the minor axis, then the eccentricity e of the ellipse satisfies **[JEE Main 2020]**

(a) $e^4+2e^2-1=0$ (b) $e^2+e^2-1=0$
(c) $e^4+e^2-1=0$ (d) $e^2+2e-1=0$

25. If the distance between the foci of an ellipse is 6 and the distance between its directrices is 12, then the length of its latus rectum is **[JEE Main 2020]**

(a) $3\sqrt{2}$ (b) $\sqrt{3}$
(c) $2\sqrt{3}$ (d) $\frac{3}{\sqrt{2}}$

26. If $3x+4y=12\sqrt{2}$ is a tangent to the ellipse $\frac{x^2}{a^2}+\frac{y^2}{9}=1$ for some $a \in R$, then the distance between the foci of the ellipse is **[JEE Main 2020]**

(a) $2\sqrt{7}$ (b) 4
(c) $2\sqrt{2}$ (d) $2\sqrt{5}$

27. Let the line $y=mx$ and the ellipse $2x^2+y^2=1$ intersect at a point P in the first quadrant. If the normal to this ellipse at P meets the co-ordinate axes at $\left(-\frac{1}{3\sqrt{2}}, 0\right)$ and $(0, \beta)$, then β is equal to **[JEE Main 2020]**

(a) $\frac{2\sqrt{2}}{3}$ (b) $\frac{\sqrt{2}}{3}$
(c) $\frac{2}{\sqrt{3}}$ (d) $\frac{2}{3}$

28. If e_1 and e_2 are the eccentricities of the ellipse, $\frac{x^2}{18}+\frac{y^2}{4}=1$ and the hyperbola, $\frac{x^2}{9}-\frac{y^2}{4}=1$ respectively and (e_1, e_2) is a point on the ellipse, $15x^2+3y^2=k$, then k is equal to **[JEE Main 2020]**

(a) 14 (b) 15
(c) 17 (d) 16

29. The length of the minor axis (along y - axis) of an ellipse in the standard form is $\frac{4}{\sqrt{3}}$. If this ellipse touches the line, $x+6y=8$; then its eccentricity is **[JEE Main 2020]**

(a) $\sqrt{\frac{5}{6}}$ (b) $\frac{1}{2}\sqrt{\frac{11}{3}}$
(c) $\frac{1}{3}\sqrt{\frac{11}{3}}$ (d) $\frac{1}{2}\sqrt{\frac{5}{3}}$

30. Let a, b and λ be positive real numbers. Suppose P is an end point of the latus rectum of the parabola $y^2=4\lambda x$, and suppose the ellipse $\frac{x^2}{a^2}+\frac{y^2}{b^2}=1$ passes through the point P. If the tangents to the parabola and the ellipse at the point P are perpendicular to each other, then the eccentricity of the ellipse is **[JEE Advanced 2020]**

(a) $\frac{1}{\sqrt{2}}$ (b) $\frac{1}{2}$
(c) $\frac{1}{3}$ (d) $\frac{2}{5}$

31. If the tangents on the ellipse $4x^2+y^2=8$ at the points $(1, 2)$ and (a, b) are perpendicular to each other, then a^2 is equal to **[JEE Main 2019]**

(a) $\frac{128}{17}$ (b) $\frac{64}{17}$
(c) $\frac{4}{17}$ (d) $\frac{2}{17}$

32. In an ellipse, with centre at the origin, if the difference of the lengths of major axis and minor axis is 10 and one of the foci is at $(0, 5\sqrt{3})$, then the length of its latus rectum is **[JEE Main 2019]**

(a) 5 (b) 10
(c) 8 (d) 6

33. If the tangent to the parabola $y^2=x$ at a point $(\alpha, \beta), (\beta>0)$ is also a tangent to the ellipse, $x^2+2y^2=1$, then α is equal to **[JEE Main 2019]**

(a) $\sqrt{2}+1$ (b) $\sqrt{2}-1$
(c) $2\sqrt{2}+1$ (d) $2\sqrt{2}-1$

34. If the line $x-2y=12$ is tangent to the ellipse $\frac{x^2}{a^2}+\frac{y^2}{b^2}=1$ at the point $\left(3, \frac{-9}{2}\right)$, then the length of the latusrectum of the ellipse is **[JEE Main 2019]**

(a) $8\sqrt{3}$ (b) 9 (c) 5 (d) $12\sqrt{2}$

35. The tangent and normal to the ellipse $3x^2+5y^2=32$ at the point $P(2, 2)$ meets the X-axis at Q and R, respectively. Then, the area (in sq units) of the ΔPQR is **[JEE Main 2019]**

(a) $\frac{16}{3}$ (b) $\frac{14}{3}$ (c) $\frac{34}{15}$ (d) $\frac{68}{15}$

36. If the normal to the ellipse $3x^2+4y^2=12$ at a point P on it is parallel to the line, $2x+y=4$ and the tangent to the ellipse at P passes through $Q(4, 4)$ then PQ is equal to **[JEE Main 2019]**

(a) $\frac{5\sqrt{5}}{2}$ (b) $\frac{\sqrt{61}}{2}$
(c) $\frac{\sqrt{221}}{2}$ (d) $\frac{\sqrt{157}}{2}$

37. An ellipse, with foci at (0, 2) and (0, –2) and minor axis of length 4, passes through which of the following points? **[JEE Main 2019]**

(a) $(\sqrt{2}, 2)$ (b) $(2, \sqrt{2})$
(c) $(2, 2\sqrt{2})$ (d) $(1, 2\sqrt{2})$

38. If tangents are drawn to the ellipse $x^2+2y^2=2$ at all points on the ellipse other than its four vertices, then the mid-points of the tangents intercepted between the coordinate axes lie on the curve **[JEE Main 2019]**

(a) $\frac{x^2}{4}+\frac{y^2}{2}=1$ (b) $\frac{1}{4x^2}+\frac{1}{2y^2}=1$
(c) $\frac{x^2}{2}+\frac{y^2}{4}=1$ (d) $\frac{1}{2x^2}+\frac{1}{4y^2}=1$

39. Let the length of the latus rectum of an ellipse with its major axis along X-axis and centre at the origin, be 8. If the distance between the foci of this ellipse is equal to the length of its minor axis, then which one of the following points lies on it? **[JEE Main 2019]**

(a) $(4\sqrt{2}, 2\sqrt{3})$ (b) $(4\sqrt{3}, 2\sqrt{2})$
(c) $(4\sqrt{2}, 2\sqrt{2})$ (d) $(4\sqrt{3}, 2\sqrt{3})$

40. Let S and S' be the foci of an ellipse and B be any one of the extremities of its minor axis. If $\Delta S'BS$ is a right angled triangle with right angle at B and area $(\Delta S'BS) = 8$ sq units, then the length of a latus rectum of the ellipse is **[JEE Main 2019]**

(a) $2\sqrt{2}$ (b) $4\sqrt{2}$
(c) 2 (d) 4

41. Define the collections $\{E_1, E_2, E_3, \ldots\}$ of ellipses and $\{R_1, R_2, R_3, \ldots\}$ of rectangles as follows :

$$E_1 : \frac{x^2}{9}+\frac{y^2}{4}=1$$

R_1 : rectangle of largest area, with sides parallel to the axes, inscribed in E_1;

E_n : ellipse $\frac{x^2}{a_n^2}+\frac{y^2}{b_n^2}=1$ of the largest area inscribed in $R_{n-1}, n>1$;

R_n : rectangle of largest area, with sides parallel to the axes, inscribed in $E_n, n>1$.

Then which of the following options is/are correct? **[JEE Advanced 2019]**

(a) The eccentricities of E_{18} and E_{19} are NOT equal.

(b) The distance of a focus from the centre in E_9 is $\frac{\sqrt{5}}{32}$.

(c) $\sum_{n=1}^{N}$(area of R_n) < 24, for each positive integer N.

(d) The length of latusrectum of E_9 is $\frac{1}{6}$

42. Consider two straight lines, each of which is tangent to both the circle $x^2+y^2=(1/2)$ and the parabola $y^2=4x$. Let these lines intersect at the point Q. Consider the ellipse whose centre is at the origin $O(0, 0)$ and whose semi-major axis is OQ. If the length of the minor axis of this ellipse is $\sqrt{2}$, then which of the following statement(s) is (are) TRUE? **[JEE Main 2018]**

(a) For the ellipse, the eccentricity is $1/\sqrt{2}$ and the length of the latus rectum is 1

(b) For the ellipse, the eccentricity is 1/2 and the length of the latus rectum is 1/2

(c) The area of the region bounded by the ellipse between the lines $x=\frac{1}{\sqrt{2}}$ and $x=1$ is $\frac{1}{4\sqrt{2}}(\pi-2)$

(d) The area of the region bounded by the ellipse between the lines $x=\frac{1}{\sqrt{2}}$ and $x=1$ is $\frac{1}{16}(\pi-2)$

Answers

1. (b)	**2.** (b)	**3.** (c)	**4.** (2)	**5.** (d)	**6.** (a)	**7.** (c)	**8.** (3)	**9.** (c)	**10.** (a)
11. (a)	**12.** (1.25)	**13.** (c)	**14.** (b)	**15.** (a)	**16.** (b)	**17.** (3)	**18.** (4)	**19.** (c)	**20.** (d)
21. (d)	**22.** (b)	**23.** (c)	**24.** (c)	**25.** (a)	**26.** (a)	**27.** (b)	**28.** (d)	**29.** (b)	**30.** (a)
31. (d)	**32.** (a)	**33.** (a)	**34.** (b)	**35.** (d)	**36.** (a)	**37.** (a)	**38.** (d)	**39.** (b)	**40.** (d)
41. (c,d)	**42.** (a,c)								

Hyperbola

1. Let $A(\sec\theta, 2\tan\theta)$ and $B(\sec\phi, 2\tan\phi)$, where $\theta+\phi=\pi/2$, be two points on the hyperbola $2x^2-y^2=2$. If (α, β) is the point of the intersection of the normals to the hyperbola at A and B, then $(2\beta)^2$ is equal to **[JEE Main 2021]**

2. The point $P(-2\sqrt{6}, \sqrt{3})$ lies on the hyperbola $\frac{x^2}{a^2}-\frac{y^2}{b^2}=1$ having eccentricity $\sqrt{5}/2$. If the tangent and normal at P to the hyperbola intersect its conjugate axis at the point Q and R respectively, then QR is equal to **[JEE Main 2021]**

(a) $4\sqrt{3}$ (b) 6 (c) $6\sqrt{3}$ (d) $3\sqrt{6}$

3. The locus of the centroid of the triangle formed by any point P on the hyperbola $16x^2 - 9y^2 + 32x + 36y - 164 = 0$, and its foci is **[JEE Main 2021]**

(a) $16x^2 - 9y^2 + 32x - 36y - 36 = 0$
(b) $9x^2 - 16y^2 + 36x - 32y - 144 = 0$
(c) $16x^2 - 9y^2 + 32x - 36y - 144 = 0$
(d) $9x^2 - 16y^2 + 36x - 32y - 36 = 0$

4. Let a line $L: 2x + y = k, k > 0$ be a tangent to the hyperbola $x^2 - y^2 = 3$. If L is also a tangent to the parabola $y^2 = \alpha x$, then α is equal to **[JEE Main 2021]**

(a) 12 (b) −12
(c) 24 (d) −24

5. A square $ABCD$ has all its vertices on the curve $x^2 y^2 = 1$. The mid-points of its sides also lie on the same curve. Then, the square of area of $ABCD$ is .... **[JEE Main 2021]**

6. Consider a hyperbola $H: x^2 - 2y^2 = 4$. Let the tangent at a point $P(4, \sqrt{6})$ meet the x-axis at Q and latus rectum at $R(x_1, y_1), x_1 > 0$. If F is a focus of H which is nearer to the point P, then the area of ΔQFR is equal to **[JEE Main 2021]**

(a) $4\sqrt{6}$ (b) $\sqrt{6} - 1$
(c) $\frac{7}{\sqrt{6}} - 2$ (d) $4\sqrt{6} - 2$

7. The locus of the mid-points of the chord of the circle, $x^2 + y^2 = 25$ which is tangent to the hyperbola, $\frac{x^2}{9} - \frac{y^2}{16} = 1$ is **[JEE Main 2021]**

(a) $(x^2 + y^2)^2 - 16x^2 + 9y^2 = 0$
(b) $(x^2 + y^2)^2 - 9x^2 + 144y^2 = 0$
(c) $(x^2 + y^2)^2 - 9x^2 - 16y^2 = 0$
(d) $(x^2 + y^2)^2 - 9x^2 + 16y^2 = 0$

8. A hyperbola passes through the foci of the ellipse $\frac{x^2}{25} + \frac{y^2}{16} = 1$ and its transverse and conjugate axes coincide with major and minor axes of the ellipse, respectively. If the product of their eccentricities is one, then the equation of the hyperbola is **[JEE Main 2021]**

(a) $\frac{x^2}{9} - \frac{y^2}{16} = 1$ (b) $\frac{x^2}{9} - \frac{y^2}{4} = 1$
(c) $\frac{x^2}{9} - \frac{y^2}{25} = 1$ (d) $x^2 - y^2 = 9$

9. The locus of the point of intersection of the lines $(\sqrt{3})kx + ky - 4\sqrt{3} = 0$ and $\sqrt{3}x - y - 4(\sqrt{3})k = 0$ is a conic, whose eccentricity is .... **[JEE Main 2021]**

10. A line parallel to the straight line $2x - y = 0$ is tangent to the hyperbola $\frac{x^2}{4} - \frac{y^2}{2} = 1$ at the point (x_1, y_1). Then, $x_1^2 + 5y_1^2$ is equal to **[JEE Main 2020]**

(a) 10 (b) 5 (c) 6 (d) 8

11. For some $\theta \in \left(0, \frac{\pi}{2}\right)$, if the eccentric of the hyperbola, $x^2 - y^2 \sec^2\theta = 10$ is $\sqrt{5}$ times the eccentricity of the ellipse, $x^2 \sec^2\theta + y^2 = 5$, then the length of the latus rectum of the ellipse, is **[JEE Main 2020]**

(a) $2\sqrt{6}$ (b) $\sqrt{30}$
(c) $\frac{2\sqrt{5}}{3}$ (d) $\frac{4\sqrt{5}}{3}$

12 A hyperbola having the transverse axis of length $\sqrt{2}$ has the same foci as that of the ellipse $3x^2 + 4y^2 = 12$, then this hyperbola does not pass through which of the following points? **[JEE Main 2020]**

(a) $\left(\frac{1}{\sqrt{2}}, 0\right)$ (b) $\left(-\sqrt{\frac{3}{2}}, 1\right)$
(c) $\left(1, -\frac{1}{\sqrt{2}}\right)$ (d) $\left(\sqrt{\frac{3}{2}}, \frac{1}{\sqrt{2}}\right)$

13. Let e_1 and e_2 be the eccentricities of the ellipse, $\frac{x^2}{25} + \frac{y^2}{b^2} = 1 (b < 5)$ and the hyperbola, $\frac{x^2}{16} - \frac{y^2}{b^2} = 1$ respectively satisfying $e_1 e_2 = 1$. If α and β are the distances between the foci of the ellipse and the foci of the hyperbola respectively, then the ordered pair (α, β) is equal to **[JEE Main 2020]**

(a) (8, 12) (b) (8, 10)
(c) $\left(\frac{20}{3}, 12\right)$ (d) $\left(\frac{24}{5}, 10\right)$

14. Let $P(3, 3)$ be a point on the hyperbola, $\frac{x^2}{a^2} - \frac{y^2}{b^2} = 1$. If the normal to it at P intersects the X-axis at $(9, 0)$ and e is its eccentricity, then the ordered pair (a^2, e^2) is equal to **[JEE Main 2020]**

(a) $\left(\frac{9}{2}, 3\right)$ (b) $\left(\frac{3}{2}, 2\right)$
(c) $\left(\frac{9}{2}, 2\right)$ (d) (9, 3)

15. If the line $y = mx + c$ is a common tangent to the hyperbola $\frac{x^2}{100} - \frac{y^2}{64} = 1$ and the circle $x^2 + y^2 = 36$, then which one of the following is true? **[JEE Main 2020]**

(a) $c^2 = 369$ (b) $5m = 4$
(c) $4c^2 = 369$ (d) $8m + 5 = 0$

16. If a hyperbola passes through the point $P(10,16)$ and it has vertices at $(\pm 6,0)$, then the equation of the normal to it at P is **[JEE Main 2020]**

(a) $3x + 4y = 94$ (b) $x + 2y = 42$
(c) $2x + 5y = 100$ (d) $x + 3y = 58$

17. A circle touches the Y-axis at the point $(0, 4)$ and passes through the point $(2, 0)$. Which of the following lines is not a tangent to this circle? **[JEE Main 2020]**

(a) $4x-3y+17=0$
(b) $3x+4y-6=0$
(c) $4x+3y-8=0$
(d) $3x-4y-24=0$

18. Let a and b be positive real numbers such that $a>1$ and $b<a$. Let P be a point in the first quadrant that lies on the hyperbola $\dfrac{x^2}{a^2}-\dfrac{y^2}{b^2}=1$. Suppose the tangent to the hyperbola at P passes through the point $(1, 0)$, and suppose the normal to the hyperbola at P cuts off equal intercepts on the coordinate axes. Let Δ denote the area of the triangle formed by the tangent at P, the normal at P and the X-axis. If e denotes the eccentricity of the hyperbola, then which of the following statements is/are TRUE? **[JEE Advanced 2020]**

(a) $1<e<\sqrt{2}$ (b) $\sqrt{2}<e<2$
(c) $\Delta = a^4$ (d) $\Delta = b^4$

19. The equation of a common tangent to the curves, $y^2=16x$ and $xy=-4$, is **[JEE Main 2019]**

(a) $x-y+4=0$ (b) $x+y+4=0$
(c) $x-2y+16=0$ (d) $2x-y+2=0$

20. If the eccentricity of the standard hyperbola passing through the point $(4,6)$ is 2, then the equation of the tangent to the hyperbola at $(4,6)$ is **[JEE Main 2019]**

(a) $3x-2y=0$ (b) $x-2y+8=0$
(c) $2x-y-2=0$ (d) $2x-3y+10=0$

21. If the line $y=mx+7\sqrt{3}$ is normal to the hyperbola $\dfrac{x^2}{24}-\dfrac{y^2}{18}=1$, then a value of m is **[JEE Main 2019]**

(a) $\dfrac{3}{\sqrt{5}}$ (b) $\dfrac{\sqrt{15}}{2}$
(c) $\dfrac{2}{\sqrt{5}}$ (d) $\dfrac{\sqrt{5}}{2}$

22. If a directrix of a hyperbola centred at the origin and passing through the point $(4,-2\sqrt{3})$ is $5x=4\sqrt{5}$ and its eccentricity is e, then **[JEE Main 2019]**

(a) $4e^4-12e^2-27=0$
(b) $4e^4-24e^2+27=0$
(c) $4e^4+8e^2-35=0$
(d) $4e^4-24e^2+35=0$

23. If $5x+9=0$ is the directrix of the hyperbola $16x^2-9y^2=144$, then its corresponding focus is **[JEE Main 2019]**

(a) $\left(-\dfrac{5}{3},0\right)$ (b) $(-5, 0)$
(c) $\left(\dfrac{5}{3},0\right)$ (d) $(5, 0)$

24. Let P be the point of intersection of the common tangents to the parabola $y^2=12x$ and the hyperbola $8x^2-y^2=8$. If S and S' denotes the foci of the hyperbola where S lies on the positive X-axis then P divides SS' in a ratio **[JEE Main 2019]**

(a) $13:11$ (b) $14:13$
(c) $5:4$ (d) $2:1$

25. Let $0<\theta<\dfrac{\pi}{2}$. If the eccentricity of the hyperbola $\dfrac{x^2}{\cos^2\theta}-\dfrac{y^2}{\sin^2\theta}=1$ is greater than 2, then the length of its latus rectum lies in the interval **[JEE Main 2019]**

(a) $(1,\frac{3}{2}]$ (b) $(3,\infty)$
(c) $(\frac{3}{2},2]$ (d) $(2, 3]$

26. A hyperbola has its centre at the origin, passes through the point $(4, 2)$ and has transverse axis of length 4 along the X-axis. Then the eccentricity of the hyperbola is **[JEE Main 2019]**

(a) 2 (b) $\dfrac{2}{\sqrt{3}}$ (c) $\dfrac{3}{2}$ (d) $\sqrt{3}$

27. The equation of a tangent to the hyperbola $4x^2-5y^2=20$ parallel to the line $x-y=2$ is **[JEE Main 2019]**

(a) $x-y-3=0$ (b) $x-y+9=0$
(c) $x-y+1=0$ (d) $x-y+7=0$

28. Let $S=\left\{(x,y)\in R^2:\dfrac{y^2}{1+r}-\dfrac{x^2}{1-r}=1\right\}$, where $r\neq\pm1$. Then, S represents **[JEE Main 2019]**

(a) a hyperbola whose eccentricity is $\dfrac{2}{\sqrt{1-r}}$, when $0<r<1$.

(b) a hyperbola whose eccentricity is $\dfrac{2}{\sqrt{r+1}}$, when $0<r<1$.

(c) an ellipse whose eccentricity is $\sqrt{\dfrac{2}{r+1}}$, when $r>1$.

(d) an ellipse whose eccentricity is $\dfrac{1}{\sqrt{r+1}}$, when $r>1$.

29. If a hyperbola has length of its conjugate axis equal to 5 and the distance between its foci is 13, then the eccentricity of the hyperbola is **[JEE Main 2019]**

(a) $\dfrac{13}{12}$ (b) 2 (c) $\dfrac{13}{8}$ (d) $\dfrac{13}{6}$

30. If the vertices of a hyperbola be at $(-2, 0)$ and $(2, 0)$ and one of its foci be at $(-3, 0)$, then which one of the following points does not lie on this hyperbola? **[JEE Main 2019]**

(a) $(2\sqrt{6}, 5)$
(b) $(6, 5\sqrt{2})$
(c) $(4, \sqrt{15})$
(d) $(-6, 2\sqrt{10})$

31. Tangents are drawn to the hyperbola $4x^2 - y^2 = 36$ at the points P and Q. If these tangents intersect at the point $T(0, 3)$, then the area (in sq units) of ΔPTQ is **[JEE Main 2018]**

(a) $45\sqrt{5}$
(b) $54\sqrt{3}$
(c) $60\sqrt{3}$
(d) $36\sqrt{5}$

32. Let $H: \frac{x^2}{a^2} - \frac{y^2}{b^2} = 1$, where $a > b > 0$, be a hyperbola in the XY-plane whose conjugate axis LM subtends an angle of $60°$ at one of its vertices N. Let the area of the ΔLMN be $4\sqrt{3}$.

	List-I		List-II
P.	The length of the conjugate axis of H is	1.	8
Q.	The eccentricity of H is	2.	$\frac{4}{\sqrt{3}}$
R.	The distance between the foci of H is	3.	$\frac{2}{\sqrt{3}}$
S.	The length of the latus rectum of H is	4.	4

The correct option is

(a) P $\rightarrow$ 4; Q $\rightarrow$ 2; R $\rightarrow$ 1; S $\rightarrow$ 3
(b) P $\rightarrow$ 4; Q $\rightarrow$ 3; R $\rightarrow$ 1; S $\rightarrow$ 2
(c) P $\rightarrow$ 4; Q $\rightarrow$ 1; R $\rightarrow$ 3; S $\rightarrow$ 2
(d) P $\rightarrow$ 3; Q $\rightarrow$ 4; R $\rightarrow$ 2; S $\rightarrow$ 1

Answers

1. (*)	**2.** (c)	**3.** (a)	**4.** (d)	**5.** (80)	**6.** (c)	**7.** (d)	**8.** (a)	**9.** (2)	**10.** (c)
11. (d)	**12.** (d)	**13.** (b)	**14.** (a)	**15.** (c)	**16.** (c)	**17.** (c)	**18.** (a,d)	**19.** (a)	**20.** (c)
21. (c)	**22.** (d)	**23.** (b)	**24.** (c)	**25.** (b)	**26.** (b)	**27.** (c)	**28.** (c)	**29.** (a)	**30.** (b)
31. (a)	**32.** (b)								

For Solutions
Scan the QR Code

Lightning Source UK Ltd.
Milton Keynes UK
UKHW051810300922
409572UK00009B/1